$165.95 per copy (in United States)
Price is subject to change without prior notice.

0154

The 2014 *Open Shop Building Construction Cost Data,* 30th annual edition, and all of the RSMeans annual cost data books for 2014, are dedicated to the memory of our respected colleague and friend, Paula Reale-Camelio.

RSMeans
Open Shop
Building
Construction
Cost Data

30TH ANNUAL EDITION

2014

RSMeans
A division of Reed Construction Data, LLC
Construction Publishers & Consultants
700 Longwater Drive
Norwell, MA 02061
USA
1-800-334-3509
www.rsmeans.com

Printed in the United States of America
ISSN 0883-8127
ISBN 978-1-940238-14-2

The authors, editors, and engineers of RSMeans apply diligence and judgment in locating and using reliable sources for the information published. However, RSMeans makes no express or implied warranty or guarantee in connection with the content of the information contained herein, including the accuracy, correctness, value, sufficiency, or completeness of the data, methods, and other information contained herein. RSMeans makes no express or implied warranty of merchantability or fitness for a particular purpose. RSMeans shall have no liability to any customer or third party for any loss, expense, or damage, including consequential, incidental, special, or punitive damage, including lost profits or lost revenue, caused directly or indirectly by any error or omission, or arising out of, or in connection with, the information contained herein.

Senior Editor
Phillip R. Waier, PE *(1,13)**

Contributing Editors
Christopher Babbitt
Adrian C. Charest, PE *(26, 27, 28, 48)*
Gary W. Christensen
David G. Drain, PE *(33)*
Cheryl Elsmore
David Fiske
Robert Fortier, PE *(2, 31, 32, 34, 35, 46)*
Robert J. Kuchta *(8)*
Thomas Lane
Robert C. McNichols
Genevieve Medeiros
Melville J. Mossman, PE *(21, 22, 23)*
Jeannene D. Murphy
Marilyn Phelan, AIA *(9, 10, 11, 12)*
Stephen C. Plotner *(3, 5)*
Siobhan Soucie

Cover Design
Wendy McBay
Paul Robertson
Wayne Engebretson

Chief Operating Officer
Richard Remington

**Vice President,
Business Development**
Steven Ritchie

**Vice President,
Finance & Operations**
Renée Pinczes

Senior Director, Inside Sales
Derek F. Dean

Sales Manager
Reid Clanton

Director, Engineering
Bob Mewis, CCC *(4, 6, 7, 14, 41, 44)*

**Senior Director, Product
Management**
Jennifer Johnson

**Senior Product
Marketing Manager**
Andrea Sillah

**Senior Director,
Operations**
Rodney L. Sharples

Production Manager
Michael Kokernak

Production
Jill Goodman
Jonathan Forgit
Debbie Panarelli
Sara Rutan
Mary Lou Geary

Technical Support
Christopher Anderson
Gary L. Hoitt
Kathryn S. Rodriguez

** Numbers in italics are the divisional responsibilities for each editor.
Please contact the designated editor directly with any questions.*

This book is printed on 90% recycled paper using soy-based ink and is entirely recyclable.

Related RSMeans Products and Services

This book is aimed primarily at commercial and industrial projects or large multi-family housing projects costing $3,500,000 and up. For civil engineering structures such as bridges, dams, highways, or the like, please refer to *RSMeans Heavy Construction Cost Data*.

The engineers at RSMeans suggest the following products and services as companion information resources to *RSMeans Open Shop Building Construction Cost Data*:

Construction Cost Data Books

Light Commercial Cost Data 2014
Residential Cost Data 2014

Reference Books

Unit Price Estimating Methods
Building Security: Strategies & Costs
Designing & Building with the IBC
Estimating Building Costs
RSMeans Estimating Handbook
Green Building: Project Planning & Estimating
How to Estimate with RSMeans Data
Plan Reading & Material Takeoff
Project Scheduling & Management for Construction

Seminars and In-House Training

Unit Price Estimating
RSMeans Online® Training
RSMeans Data for Job Order Contracting (JOC)
Plan Reading & Material Takeoff
Scheduling & Project Management
Mechanical & Electrical Estimating

RSMeans Online Bookstore

Visit RSMeans at **www.rsmeans.com** for a one-stop portal for the most reliable and current resources available on the market. Here you can learn about our more than 20 annual cost data books, also available on CD and online versions, as well as our libary of reference books and RSMeans seminars.

RSMeans Electronic Data

Get the information found in RSMeans cost books electronically at **RSMeansOnline.com**.

RSMeans Business Solutions

Cost engineers and analysts conduct facility life cycle and benchmark research studies and predictive cost modeling, as well as offer consultation services for conceptual estimating, real property management, and job order contracting. Research studies are designed with the application of proprietary cost and project data from Reed Construction Data and RSMeans' extensive North American databases. Analysts offer building product manufacturers qualitative and quantitative market research, as well as time/motion studies for new products, and Web-based dashboards for market opportunity analysis. Clients are from both the public and private sectors, including federal, state, and municipal agencies; corporations; institutions; construction management firms; hospitals; and associations.

RSMeans for Job Order Contracting (JOC)

Best practice job order contracting (JOC) services support the owner in the development of their program. RSMeans develops all required contracting documents, works with stakeholders, and develops qualified and experienced contractor lists. RSMeans JOCWorks® software is the best of class in the functional tools that meet JOC specific requirements. RSMeans data is organized to meet JOC cost estimating requirements.

Construction Costs for Software Applications

More than 25 unit price and assemblies cost databases are available through a number of leading estimating and facilities management software providers (listed below). For more information see the "Other RSMeans Products" pages at the back of this publication.

RSMeansData™ is also available to federal, state, and local government agencies as multi-year, multi-seat licenses.

- 4Clicks-Solutions, LLC
- Assetworks
- Beck Technology
- BSD – Building Systems Design, Inc.
- CMS – Construction Management Software
- Corecon Technologies, Inc.
- CorVet Systems
- Hard Dollar Corporation
- Maxwell Systems
- MC^2
- MOCA Systems
- Parsons Corporation
- ProEst
- Refined Data
- Sage Timberline Office
- UDA Technologies, Inc.
- US Cost, Inc.
- VFA – Vanderweil Facility Advisers
- WinEstimator, Inc.
- R & K Solutions
- Tririga

Table of Contents

Foreword

Our Mission

Since 1942, RSMeans has been actively engaged in construction cost publishing and consulting throughout North America.

Today, more than 70 years after RSMeans began, our primary objective remains the same: to provide you, the construction and facilities professional, with the most current and comprehensive construction cost data possible.

Whether you are a contractor, owner, architect, engineer, facilities manager, or anyone else who needs a reliable construction cost estimate, you'll find this publication to be a highly useful and necessary tool.

With the constant flow of new construction methods and materials today, it's difficult to find the time to look at and evaluate all the different construction cost possibilities. In addition, because labor and material costs keep changing, last year's cost information is not a reliable basis for today's estimate or budget.

That's why so many construction professionals turn to RSMeans. We keep track of the costs for you, along with a wide range of other key information, from city cost indexes . . . to productivity rates . . . to crew composition . . . to contractor's overhead and profit rates.

RSMeans performs these functions by collecting data from all facets of the industry and organizing it in a format that is instantly accessible to you. From the preliminary budget to the detailed unit price estimate, you'll find the data in this book useful for all phases of construction cost determination.

The Staff, the Organization, and Our Services

When you purchase one of RSMeans' publications, you are, in effect, hiring the services of a full-time staff of construction and engineering professionals.

Our thoroughly experienced and highly qualified staff works daily at collecting, analyzing, and disseminating comprehensive cost information for your needs. These staff members have years of practical construction experience and engineering training prior to joining the firm. As a result, you can count on them not only for accurate cost figures, but also for additional background reference information that will help you create a realistic estimate.

The RSMeans organization is always prepared to help you solve construction problems through its variety of data solutions, including online, CD, and print book formats, as well as cost estimating expertise available via our business solutions, training, and seminars.

Besides a full array of construction cost estimating books, RSMeans also publishes a number of other reference works for the construction industry. Subjects include construction estimating and project and business management, special topics such as green building and job order contracting, and a library of facility management references.

In addition, you can access all of our construction cost data electronically in convenient CD format or on the web. Visit **RSMeansOnline.com** for more information on our 24/7 online cost data.

What's more, you can increase your knowledge and improve your construction estimating and management performance with an RSMeans construction seminar or in-house training program. These two-day seminar programs offer unparalleled opportunities for everyone in your organization to become updated on a wide variety of construction-related issues.

RSMeans is also a worldwide provider of construction cost management and analysis services for commercial and government owners.

In short, RSMeans can provide you with the tools and expertise for constructing accurate and dependable construction estimates and budgets in a variety of ways.

Robert Snow Means Established a Tradition of Quality That Continues Today

Robert Snow Means spent years building RSMeans, making certain he always delivered a quality product.

Today, at RSMeans, we do more than talk about the quality of our data and the usefulness of our books. We stand behind all of our data, from historical cost indexes to construction materials and techniques to current costs.

If you have any questions about our products or services, please call us toll-free at 1-800-334-3509. Our customer service representatives will be happy to assist you. You can also visit our website at **www.rsmeans.com**

How the Book is Built: An Overview

The Construction Specifications Institute (CSI) and Construction Specifications Canada (CSC) have produced the 2012 edition of MasterFormat®, a system of titles and numbers used extensively to organize construction information.

All unit price data in the RSMeans cost data books is now arranged in the 50-division MasterFormat® 2012 system.

A Powerful Construction Tool

You have in your hands one of the most powerful construction tools available today. A successful project is built on the foundation of an accurate and dependable estimate. This book will enable you to construct just such an estimate.

For the casual user the book is designed to be:

- quickly and easily understood so you can get right to your estimate.
- filled with valuable information so you can understand the necessary factors that go into the cost estimate.

For the regular user, the book is designed to be:

- a handy desk reference that can be quickly referred to for key costs.
- a comprehensive, fully reliable source of current construction costs and productivity rates so you'll be prepared to estimate any project.
- a source book for preliminary project cost, product selections, and alternate materials and methods.

To meet all of these requirements, we have organized the book into the following clearly defined sections.

Quick Start

See our "Quick Start" instructions on the following page to get started right away.

Estimating with RSMeans Unit Price Cost Data

Please refer to these steps for guidance on completing an estimate using RSMeans unit price cost data.

How to Use the Book: The Details

This section contains an in-depth explanation of how the book is arranged . . . and how you can use it to determine a reliable construction cost estimate. It includes information about how we develop our cost figures and how to completely prepare your estimate.

Unit Price Section

All cost data has been divided into the 50 divisions according to the MasterFormat system of classification and numbering. For a listing of these divisions and an outline of their subdivisions, see the Unit Price Section Table of Contents.

Estimating tips are included at the beginning of each division.

Reference Section

This section includes information on Equipment Rental Costs, Crew Listings, Historical Cost Indexes, City Cost Indexes, Location Factors, Reference Tables, Change Orders, Square Foot Costs, and a listing of Abbreviations.

Equipment Rental Costs: This section contains the average costs to rent and operate hundreds of pieces of construction equipment.

Crew Listings: This section lists all of the crews referenced in the book. For the purposes of this book, a crew is composed of more than one trade classification and/or the addition of power equipment to any trade classification. Power equipment is included in the cost of the crew. Costs are shown both with bare labor rates and with the installing contractor's overhead and profit added. For each, the total crew cost per eight-hour day and the composite cost per labor-hour are listed.

Historical Cost Indexes: These indexes provide you with data to adjust construction costs over time.

City Cost Indexes: All costs in this book are U.S. national averages. Costs vary because of the regional economy. You can adjust costs by CSI Division to over 700 locations throughout the U.S. and Canada by using the data in this section.

Location Factors: You can adjust total project costs to over 900 locations throughout the U.S. and Canada by using the data in this section.

Reference Tables: At the beginning of selected major classifications in the Unit Price section are reference numbers shown in a shaded box. These numbers refer you to related information in the Reference Section. In this section, you'll find reference tables, explanations, estimating information that support how we develop the unit price data, technical data, and estimating procedures.

Change Orders: This section includes information on the factors that influence the pricing of change orders.

Square Foot Costs: This section contains costs for 59 different building types that allow you to make a rough estimate for the overall cost of a project or its major components.

Abbreviations: A listing of abbreviations used throughout this book, along with the terms they represent, is included in this section.

Index

A comprehensive listing of all terms and subjects in this book will help you quickly find what you need when you are not sure where it occurs in MasterFormat.

The Scope of This Book

This book is designed to be as comprehensive and as easy to use as possible. To that end we have made certain assumptions and limited its scope in two key ways:

1. We have established material prices based on a national average.
2. We have computed labor costs based on a 30-city national average of union wage rates.

For a more detailed explanation of how the cost data is developed, see "How To Use the Book: The Details."

Project Size/Type

The material prices in RSMeans cost data books are "contractor's prices." They are the prices that contractors can expect to pay at the lumberyards, suppliers/distributers warehouses, etc. Small orders of speciality items would be higher than the costs shown, while very large orders, such as truckload lots, would be less. The variation would depend on the size, timing, and negotiating power of the contractor. The labor costs are primarily for new construction or major renovation rather than repairs or minor alterations.

With reasonable exercise of judgment, the figures can be used for any building work.

Absolute Essentials for a Quick Start

If you feel you are ready to use this book and don't think you will need the detailed instructions that begin on the following page, this Absolute Essentials for a Quick Start page is for you. These steps will allow you to get started estimating in a matter of minutes.

1 Scope

Think through the project that you will be estimating, and identify the many individual work tasks that will need to be covered in your estimate.

2 Quantify

Determine the number of units that will be required for each work task that you identified.

3 Pricing

Locate individual Unit Price line items that match the work tasks you identified. The Unit Price Section Table of Contents that begins on page 1 and the Index in the back of the book will help you find these line items.

4 Multiply

Multiply the Total Incl O&P cost for a Unit Price line item in the book by your quantity for that item. The price you calculate will be an estimate for a completed item of work performed by a subcontractor. Keep adding line items in this manner to build your estimate.

5 Project Overhead

Include project overhead items in your estimate. These items are needed to make the job run and are typically, but not always, provided by the General Contractor. They can be found in Division 1. An alternate method of estimating project overhead costs is to apply a percentage of the total project cost.

Include rented tools not included in crews, waste, rubbish handling, and cleanup.

6 Estimate Summary

Include General Contractor's markup on subcontractors, General Contractor's office overhead and profit, and sales tax on materials and equipment.

Adjust your estimate to the project's location by using the City Cost Indexes or Location Factors found in the Reference Section.

Editors' Note: We urge you to spend time reading and understanding the supporting material in the front of this book. An accurate estimate requires experience, knowledge, and careful calculation. The more you know about how we at RSMeans developed the data, the more accurate your estimate will be. In addition, it is important to take into consideration the reference material in the back of the book such as Equipment Listings, Crew Listings, City Cost Indexes, Location Factors, and Reference Tables.

Estimating with RSMeans Unit Price Cost Data

Following these steps will allow you to complete an accurate estimate using RSMeans Unit Price cost data.

1 Scope Out the Project

- Identify the individual work tasks that will need to be covered in your estimate.
- The Unit Price data in this book has been divided into 50 Divisions according to the CSI MasterFormat 2012—their titles are listed on the back cover of your book.
- Think through the project and identify those CSI Divisions needed in your estimate.
- The Unit Price Section Table of Contents on page 1 may also be helpful when scoping out your project.
- Experienced estimators find it helpful to begin with Division 2 and continue through completion. Division 1 can be estimated after the full project scope is known.

2 Quantify

- Determine the number of units required for each work task that you identified.
- Experienced estimators include an allowance for waste in their quantities. (Waste is not included in RSMeans Unit Price line items unless so stated.)

3 Price the Quantities

- Use the Unit Price Table of Contents, and the Index, to locate individual Unit Price line items for your estimate.
- Reference Numbers indicated within a Unit Price section refer to additional information that you may find useful.
- The crew indicates who is performing the work for that task. Crew codes are expanded in the Crew Listings in the Reference Section to include all trades and equipment that comprise the crew.

- The Daily Output is the amount of work the crew is expected to do in one day.
- The Labor-Hours value is the amount of time it will take for the crew to install one unit of work.
- The abbreviated Unit designation indicates the unit of measure upon which the crew, productivity, and prices are based.
- Bare Costs are shown for materials, labor, and equipment needed to complete the Unit Price line item. Bare costs do not include waste, project overhead, payroll insurance, payroll taxes, main office overhead, or profit.
- The Total Incl O&P cost is the billing rate or invoice amount of the installing contractor or subcontractor who performs the work for the Unit Price line item.

4 Multiply

- Multiply the total number of units needed for your project by the Total Incl O&P cost for each Unit Price line item.
- Be careful that your take off unit of measure matches the unit of measure in the Unit column.
- The price you calculate is an estimate for a completed item of work.
- Keep scoping individual tasks, determining the number of units required for those tasks, matching each task with individual Unit Price line items in the book, and multiply quantities by Total Incl O&P costs.
- An estimate completed in this manner is priced as if a subcontractor, or set of subcontractors, is performing the work. The estimate does not yet include Project Overhead or Estimate Summary components such as General Contractor markups on subcontracted work, General Contractor office overhead and profit, contingency, and location factor.

5 Project Overhead

- Include project overhead items from Division 1 – General Requirements.
- These items are needed to make the job run. They are typically, but not always, provided by the General Contractor. Items include, but are not limited to, field personnel, insurance, performance bond, permits, testing, temporary utilities, field office and storage facilities, temporary scaffolding and platforms, equipment mobilization and demobilization, temporary roads and sidewalks, winter protection, temporary barricades and fencing, temporary security, temporary signs, field engineering and layout, final cleaning and commissioning.
- Each item should be quantified, and matched to individual Unit Price line items in Division 1, and then priced and added to your estimate.
- An alternate method of estimating project overhead costs is to apply a percentage of the total project cost, usually 5% to 15% with an average of 10% (see General Conditions, page ix).
- Include other project related expenses in your estimate such as:
  - Rented equipment not itemized in the Crew Listings
  - Rubbish handling throughout the project (see 02 41 19.19)

6 Estimate Summary

- Include sales tax as required by laws of your state or county.
- Include the General Contractor's markup on self-performed work, usually 5% to 15% with an average of 10%.
- Include the General Contractor's markup on subcontracted work, usually 5% to 15% with an average of 10%.
- Include General Contractor's main office overhead and profit:
  - RSMeans gives general guidelines on the General Contractor's main office overhead (see section 01 31 13.60 and Reference Number R013113-50).
  - RSMeans gives no guidance on the General Contractor's profit.
  - Markups will depend on the size of the General Contractor's operations, his projected annual revenue, the level of risk he is taking on, and on the level of competition in the local area and for this project in particular.
- Include a contingency, usually 3% to 5%, if appropriate.
- Adjust your estimate to the project's location by using the City Cost Indexes or the Location Factors in the Reference Section:
  - Look at the rules on the pages for How to Use the City Cost Indexes to see how to apply the Indexes for your location.
  - When the proper Index or Factor has been identified for the project's location, convert it to a multiplier by dividing it by 100, and then multiply that multiplier by your estimated total cost. The original estimated total cost will now be adjusted up or down from the national average to a total that is appropriate for your location.

Editors' Notes:

1) *We urge you to spend time reading and understanding the supporting material in the front of this book. An accurate estimate requires experience, knowledge, and careful calculation. The more you know about how we at RSMeans developed the data, the more accurate your estimate will be. In addition, it is important to take into consideration the reference material in the back of the book such as Equipment Listings, Crew Listings, City Cost Indexes, Location Factors, and Reference Tables.*

2) *Contractors who are bidding or are involved in JOC, DOC, SABER, or IDIQ type contracts are cautioned that workers' compensation insurance, federal and state payroll taxes, waste, project supervision, project overhead, main office overhead, and profit are not included in bare costs. The coefficient or multiplier must cover these costs.*

How to Use the Book: The Details

What's Behind the Numbers? The Development of Cost Data

The staff at RSMeans continually monitors developments in the construction industry in order to ensure reliable, thorough, and up-to-date cost information. While overall construction costs may vary relative to general economic conditions, price fluctuations within the industry are dependent upon many factors. Individual price variations may, in fact, be opposite to overall economic trends. Therefore, costs are constantly tracked and complete updates are published yearly. Also, new items are frequently added in response to changes in materials and methods.

Costs—$ (U.S.)

All costs represent U.S. national averages and are given in U.S. dollars. The RSMeans City Cost Indexes can be used to adjust costs to a particular location. The City Cost Indexes for Canada can be used to adjust U.S. national averages to local costs in Canadian dollars. No exchange rate conversion is necessary.

G The processes or products identified by the green symbol in our publications have been determined to be environmentally responsible and/or resource-efficient solely by the RSMeans engineering staff. The inclusion of the green symbol does not represent compliance with any specific industry association or standard.

Material Costs

The RSMeans staff contacts manufacturers, dealers, distributors, and contractors all across the U.S. and Canada to determine national average material costs. If you have access to current material costs for your specific location, you may wish to make adjustments to reflect differences from the national average. Included within material costs are fasteners for a normal installation. RSMeans engineers use manufacturers' recommendations, written specifications, and/or standard construction practice for size and spacing of fasteners. Adjustments to material costs may be required for your specific application or location. The manufacturer's warranty is assumed. Extended warranties are not included in the material costs. Material costs do not include sales tax.

Labor Costs

Labor costs are based on the average of wage rates from 30 major U.S. cities. Rates are determined from labor union agreements or prevailing wages for construction trades for the current year. Rates, along with overhead and profit markups, are listed on the inside back cover of this book.

• If wage rates in your area vary from those used in this book, or if rate increases are expected within a given year, labor costs should be adjusted accordingly.

Labor costs reflect productivity based on actual working conditions. In addition to actual installation, these figures include time spent during a normal weekday on tasks such as, material receiving and handling, mobilization at site, site movement, breaks, and cleanup.

Productivity data is developed over an extended period so as not to be influenced by abnormal variations and reflects a typical average.

Equipment Costs

Equipment costs include not only rental, but also operating costs for equipment under normal use. The operating costs include parts and labor for routine servicing such as repair and replacement of pumps, filters, and worn lines. Normal operating expendables, such as fuel, lubricants, tires, and electricity (where applicable), are also included. Extraordinary operating expendables with highly variable wear patterns, such as diamond bits and blades, are excluded. These costs are included under materials. Equipment rental rates are obtained from industry sources throughout North America—contractors, suppliers, dealers, manufacturers, and distributors.

Rental rates can also be treated as reimbursement costs for contractor-owned equipment. Owned equipment costs include depreciation, loan payments, interest, taxes, insurance, storage and major repairs.

Equipment costs do not include operators' wages; nor do they include the cost to move equipment to a job site (mobilization) or from a job site (demobilization).

Equipment Cost/Day——The cost of power equipment required for each crew is included in the Crew Listings in the Reference Section (small tools that are considered as essential everyday tools are not listed out separately). The Crew Listings itemize specialized tools and heavy equipment along with labor trades. The daily cost of itemized equipment included in a crew is based on dividing the weekly bare rental rate by 5 (number of working days per week) and then adding the hourly operating cost times 8 (the number of hours per day). This Equipment Cost/Day is shown in the last column of the Equipment Rental Cost pages in the Reference Section.

Mobilization/Demobilization——The cost to move construction equipment from an equipment yard or rental company to the job site and back again is not included in equipment costs. Mobilization (to the site) and demobilization (from the site) costs can be found in the Unit Price Section. If a piece of equipment is already at the job site, it is not appropriate to utilize mob./demob. costs again in an estimate.

Overhead and Profit

Total Cost including O&P for the *Installing Contractor* is shown in the last column on the Unit Price and/or the Assemblies pages of this book. This figure is the sum of the bare material cost plus 10% for profit, the bare labor cost plus total overhead and profit, and the bare equipment cost plus 10% for profit. Details for the calculation of Overhead and Profit on labor are shown on the inside back cover and in the Reference Section of this book. (See "How RSMeans Data Works" for an example of this calculation.)

General Conditions

Cost data in this book is presented in two ways: Bare Costs and Total Cost including O&P (Overhead and Profit). General Conditions, or General Requirements, of the contract should also be added to the Total Cost including O&P when applicable. Costs for General Conditions are listed in Division 1 of the Unit Price Section and the Reference

Section of this book. General Conditions for the *Installing Contractor* may range from 0% to 10% of the Total Cost including O&P. For the *General* or *Prime Contractor*, costs for General Conditions may range from 5% to 15% of the Total Cost including O&P, with a figure of 10% as the most typical allowance. If applicable, the Assemblies and Models sections of this book use costs that include the installing contractor's overhead and profit (O&P).

Factors Affecting Costs

Costs can vary depending upon a number of variables. Here's how we have handled the main factors affecting costs.

Quality——The prices for materials and the workmanship upon which productivity is based represent sound construction work. They are also in line with U.S. government specifications.

Overtime——We have made no allowance for overtime. If you anticipate premium time or work beyond normal working hours, be sure to make an appropriate adjustment to your labor costs.

Productivity——The productivity, daily output, and labor-hour figures for each line item are based on working an eight-hour day in daylight hours in moderate temperatures. For work that extends beyond normal work hours or is performed under adverse conditions, productivity may decrease. (See "How RSMeans Data Works" for more on productivity.)

Size of Project——The size, scope of work, and type of construction project will have a significant impact on cost. Economies of scale can reduce costs for large projects. Unit costs can often run higher for small projects.

Location——Material prices in this book are for metropolitan areas. However, in dense urban areas, traffic and site storage limitations may increase costs. Beyond a 20-mile radius of large cities, extra trucking or transportation charges may also increase the material costs slightly. On the other hand, lower wage rates may be in effect. Be sure to consider both of these factors when preparing an estimate, particularly if the job site is located in a central city or remote rural location. In addition, highly specialized subcontract items may require travel and per-diem expenses for mechanics.

Other Factors——

- season of year
- contractor management
- weather conditions
- local union restrictions
- building code requirements
- availability of:
  - adequate energy
  - skilled labor
  - building materials
- owner's special requirements/restrictions
- safety requirements
- environmental considerations

Unpredictable Factors——General business conditions influence "in-place" costs of all items. Substitute materials and construction methods may have to be employed. These may affect the installed cost and/or life cycle costs. Such factors may be difficult to evaluate and cannot necessarily be predicted on the basis of the job's location in a particular section of the country. Thus, where these factors apply, you may find significant but unavoidable cost variations for which you will have to apply a measure of judgment to your estimate.

Rounding of Costs

In general, all unit prices in excess of $5.00 have been rounded to make them easier to use and still maintain adequate precision of the results. The rounding rules we have chosen are in the following table.

Prices from...	Rounded to the nearest...
$.01 to $5.00	$.01
$5.01 to $20.00	$.05
$20.01 to $100.00	$.50
$100.01 to $300.00	$1.00
$300.01 to $1,000.00	$5.00
$1,000.01 to $10,000.00	$25.00
$10,000.01 to $50,000.00	$100.00
$50,000.01 and above	$500.00

How Subcontracted Items Affect Costs

A considerable portion of all large construction jobs is usually subcontracted. In fact, the percentage done by subcontractors is constantly increasing and may run over 90%. Since the workers employed by these companies do nothing else but install their particular product, they soon become expert in that line. The result is, installation by these firms is accomplished so efficiently that the total in-place cost, even adding the general contractor's overhead and profit, is no more, and often less, than if the principal contractor had handled the installation himself/herself. Companies that deal with construction specialties are anxious to have their product perform well and, consequently, the installation will be the best possible.

Contingencies

The allowance for contingencies generally provides for unforeseen construction difficulties. On alterations or repair jobs, 20% is not too much. If drawings are final and only field contingencies are being considered, 2% or 3% is probably sufficient, and often nothing need be added. Contractually, changes in plans will be covered by extras. The contractor should consider inflationary price trends and possible material shortages during the course of the job. These escalation factors are dependent upon both economic conditions and the anticipated time between the estimate and actual construction. If drawings are not complete or approved, or a budget cost is wanted, it is wise to add 5% to 10%. Contingencies, then, are a matter of judgment. Additional allowances for contingencies are shown in Division 1.

Important Estimating Considerations

The "productivity," or daily output, of each craftsman includes mobilization and cleanup time, break time and plan layout time, as well as an allowance to carry stock from the storage trailer or location on the job site up to 200' into the building and to the first or second floor. If material has to be transported over greater distances or to higher floors, an additional allowance should be considered by the estimator. An allowance has also been included in the piping and fittings installation time for leak checking and minor tightening. Equipment installation time includes the following applicable items: positioning, leveling and securing the unit in place, connecting all associated piping, ducts, vents, etc., which shall have been estimated separately, connecting to an adjacent power source, filling/bleeding, startup, adjusting the controls up and down to ensure proper response, setting the integral controls/valves/ regulators/thermostats for proper operation (does not include external building type control systems, DDC systems, etc.), explaining/training owner's operator, and

warranty. A reasonable breakdown of the labor costs is as follows:

1. Movement into building, installation/setting of equipment — 35%
2. Connection to piping/duct/power, etc. — 25%
3. Filling/flushing/cleaning/touchup, etc. — 15%
4. Startup/running adjustments — 5%
5. Training owner's representative — 5%
6. Warranty/call back/service — 15%

Note that cranes or other lifting equipment are not included on any lines in the Mechanical divisions. For example, if a crane is required to lift a heavy piece of pipe into place high above a gym floor, or to put a rooftop unit on the roof of a four-story building, etc., it must be added. Due to the potential for extreme variation—from nothing additional required to a major crane or helicopter—we feel that including a nominal amount for "lifting contingency" would be useless and detract from the accuracy of the estimate. When using equipment rental from RSMeans, remember to include the cost of the operator(s).

Estimating Labor-Hours

The labor-hours expressed in this publication are based on Average Installation time, using an efficiency level of approximately 60%–65% (see item 7), which has been found reasonable and acceptable by many contractors. The book uses this national efficiency average to establish a consistent benchmark. For bid situations, adjustments to this efficiency level should be the responsibility of the contractor bidding the project. The unit labor-hour is divided in the following manner. A typical day for a journeyman might be:

1.	Study Plans	3%	14.4 min.
2.	Material Procurement	3%	14.4 min.
3.	Receiving and Storing	3%	14.4 min.
4.	Mobilization	5%	24.0 min.
5.	Site Movement	5%	24.0 min.
6.	Layout and Marking	8%	38.4 min.
7.	Actual Installation	64%	307.2 min.
8.	Cleanup	3%	14.4 min.
9.	Breaks, Nonproductive	6%	28.8 min.
		100%	480.0 min.

If any of the percentages expressed in this breakdown do not apply to the particular work or project situation, then that percentage or a portion of it may be deducted from or added to labor-hours.

Final Checklist

Estimating can be a straightforward process provided you remember the basics. Here's a checklist of some of the steps you should remember to complete before finalizing your estimate.

Did you remember to . . .

• factor in the City Cost Index for your locale?

• take into consideration which items have been marked up and by how much?

• mark up the entire estimate sufficiently for your purposes?

• read the background information on techniques and technical matters that could impact your project time span and cost?

• include all components of your project in the final estimate?

• double check your figures for accuracy?

• call RSMeans if you have any questions about your estimate or the data you've found in our publications? Remember, RSMeans stands behind its publications. If you have any questions about your estimate . . . about the costs you've used from our books . . . or even about the technical aspects of the job that may affect your estimate, feel free to call the RSMeans editors at 1-800-334-3509.

Free Quarterly Updates

Stay up-to-date throughout 2014 with RSMeans' free cost data updates four times a year. Sign up online to make sure you have access to the newest data. Every quarter we provide the city cost adjustment factors for hundreds of cities and key materials. Register at: **www.rsmeans2014updates.com**

Unit Cost Section

Table of Contents

Table of Contents (cont.)

Table of Contents (cont.)

How RSMeans Unit Price Data Works

All RSMeans unit price data is organized in the same way.

It is important to understand the structure, so that you can find information easily and use it correctly.

RSMeans **Line Numbers** consist of 12 characters, which identify a unique location in the database for each task. The first 6 or 8 digits conform to the Construction Specifications Institute MasterFormat® 2012. The remainder of the digits are a further breakdown by RSMeans in order to arrange items in understandable groups of similar tasks. Line numbers are consistent across all RSMeans publications, so a line number in any RSMeans product will always refer to the same unit of work.

RSMeans engineers have created **reference** information to assist you in your estimate. If there is information that applies to a section, it will be indicated at the start of the section. In this case, R033105-10 provides information on the proportionate quantities of formwork, reinforcing, and concrete used in cast-in-place concrete items such as footings, slabs, beams, and columns. The Reference Section is located in the back of the book on the pages with a gray edge.

RSMeans **Descriptions** are shown in a hierarchical structure to make them readable. In order to read a complete description, read up through the indents to the top of the section. Include everything that is above and to the left that is not contradicted by information below. For instance, the complete description for line 03 30 53.40 3550 is "Concrete in place, including forms (4 uses), Grade 60 rebar, concrete (Portland cement Type 1), placement and finishing unless otherwise indicated; Equipment pad (3000 psi), 4' x 4' x 6" thick."

When using **RSMeans data**, it is important to read through an entire section to ensure that you use the data that most closely matches your work. Note that sometimes there is additional information shown in the section that may improve your price. There are frequently lines that further describe, add to, or adjust data for specific situations.

03 30 Cast-In-Place Concrete

03 30 53 – Miscellaneous Cast-In-Place Concrete

03 30 53.40 Concrete In Place

0010	**CONCRETE IN PLACE**	R033105-10
0020	Including forms (4 uses), Grade 60 rebar, concrete (Portland cement	R033105-20
0050	Type I), placement and finishing unless otherwise indicated	R033105-50
0300	Beams (3500 psi), 5 kip per L.F., 10' span	R033105-65
0350	25' span	R033105-70
0500	Chimney foundations (5000 psi), over 5 C.Y.	R033105-85
0510	(3500 psi), under 5 C.Y.	
0700	Columns, square (4000 psi), 12" x 12", less than 2% reinforcing	
3540	Equipment pad (3000 psi), 3' x 3' x 6" thick	
3550	4' x 4' x 6" thick	
3560	5' x 5' x 8" thick	
3570	6' x 6' x 8" thick	
3580	8' x 8' x 10" thick	
3590	10' x 10' x 12" thick	
3800	Footings (3000 psi), spread under 1 C.Y.	

The data published in RSMeans print books represents a "national average" cost. This data should be modified to the project location using the **City Cost Indexes** or **Location Factors** tables found in the reference section (see pages 725–773). Use the location factors to adjust estimate totals if the project covers multiple trades. Use the city cost indexes (CCI) for single trade projects or projects where a more detailed analysis is required. All figures in the two tables are derived from the same research. The last row of data in the CCI, the weighted average, is the same as the numbers reported for each location in the location factor table.

Crews include labor or labor and equipment necessary to accomplish each task. In this case, Crew C-14H is used. RSMeans selects a crew to represent the workers and equipment that are typically used for that task. In this case, Crew C-14H consists of one carpenter foreman (outside), two carpenters, one rodman, one laborer, one cement finisher, and one gas engine vibrator. Details of all crews can be found in the reference section.

Crews

Crew No.	Bare Costs		Incl. Subs O&P		Cost Per Labor-Hour	
Crew C-14C	Hr.	Daily	Hr.	Daily	Bare Costs	Incl. O&P
1 Carpenter Foreman (outside)	$37.75	$302.00	$63.55	$508.40	$33.96	$57.13
6 Carpenters	35.75	1716.00	60.15	2887.20		
2 Rodmen (reinf.)	38.00	608.00	65.00	1040.00		
4 Laborers	28.20	902.40	47.45	1518.40		
1 Cement Finisher	34.35	274.80	55.60	444.80		
1 Gas Engine Vibrator		33.00		36.30	0.29	0.32
112 L.H., Daily Totals		$3836.20		$6435.10	$34.25	$57.46

The **Daily Output** is the amount of work that the crew can do in a normal 8-hour workday, including mobilization, layout, movement of materials, and cleanup. In this case, crew C-14H can install thirty 4' x 4' x 6" thick concrete pads in a day. Daily output is variable, based on many factors, including the size of the job, location, and environmental conditions. RSMeans data represents work done in daylight (or adequate lighting) and temperate conditions.

Bare Costs are the costs of materials, labor, and equipment that the installing contractor pays. They represent the cost, in U.S. dollars, for one unit of work. They do not include any markups for profit or labor burden.

Crew	Daily Output	Labor-Hours	Unit	Material	2014 Bare Costs Labor	Equipment	Total	Total Incl O&P
C-14A	15.62	12.804	C.Y.	315	455	47.50	817.50	1,175
"	18.55	10.782		335	385	40	760	1,050
C-14C	32.22	3.476		147	118	1.01	266.01	360
"	23.71	4.724		173	160	1.37	334.37	465
C-14A	11.96	16.722		355	595	62	1,012	1,475
C-14H	45	1.067	Ea.	44.50	37.50	.74	82.74	112
	30	1.600		66.50	56	1.10	123.60	168
	18	2.667		119	93.50	1.84	214.34	289
	14	3.429		160	120	2.37	282.37	380
	8	6		335	210	4.14	549.14	725
	5	9.600		575	335	6.60	916.60	1,200
C-14C	28	4	C.Y.	164	136	1.16	301.16	410

The **Total Incl O&P column** is the total cost, including overhead and profit, that the installing contractor will charge the customer. This represents the cost of materials plus 10% profit, the cost of labor plus labor burden and 10% profit, and the cost of equipment plus 10% profit. It does not include the general contractor's overhead and profit. Note: See the inside back cover for details of how RSMeans calculates labor burden.

The **Total column** represents the total bare cost for the installing contractor, in U.S. dollars. In this case, the sum of $66.50 for material + $56.00 for labor + $1.10 for equipment is $123.60.

The figure in the **Labor Hours** column is the amount of labor required to perform one unit of work—in this case the amount of labor required to construct one 4' x 4' equipment pad. This figure is calculated by dividing the number of hours of labor in the crew by the daily output (48 labor hours divided by 30 pads = 1.6 hours of labor per pad). Multiply 1.600 times 60 to see the value in minutes: 60 x 1.6 = 96 minutes. Note: the labor hour figure is not dependent on the crew size. A change in crew size will result in a corresponding change in daily output, but the labor hours per unit of work will not change.

All RSMeans unit cost data includes the typical **Unit of Measure** used for estimating that item. For concrete-in-place the typical unit is cubic yards (C.Y.) or each (Ea.). For installing broadloom carpet it is square yard, and for gypsum board it is square foot. The estimator needs to take special care that the unit in the data matches the unit in the take-off. Unit conversions may be found in the Reference Section.

Sample Estimate

This sample demonstrates the elements of an estimate, including a tally of the RSMeans data lines, and a summary of the markups on a contractor's work to arrive at a total cost to the owner. The RSMeans Location Factor is added at the bottom of the estimate to adjust the cost of the work to a specific location.

Work Performed: The body of the estimate shows the RSMeans data selected, including line number, a brief description of each item, its take-off unit and quantity, and the bare costs of materials, labor, and equipment. This estimate also includes a column titled "SubContract." This data is taken from the RSMeans column "Total Incl O&P," and represents the total that a subcontractor would charge a general contractor for the work, including the sub's markup for overhead and profit.

Division 1, General Requirements: This is the first division numerically, but the last division estimated. Division 1 includes project-wide needs provided by the general contractor. These requirements vary by project, but may include temporary facilities and utilities, security, testing, project cleanup, etc. For small projects a percentage can be used, typically between 5% and 15% of project cost. For large projects the costs may be itemized and priced individually.

Bonds: Bond costs should be added to the estimate. The figures here represent a typical performance bond, ensuring the owner that if the general contractor does not complete the obligations in the construction contract the bonding company will pay the cost for completion of the work.

Location Adjustment: RSMeans published data is based on national average costs. If necessary, adjust the total cost of the project using a location factor from the "Location Factor" table or the "City Cost Index" table. Use location factors if the work is general, covering multiple trades. If the work is by a single trade (e.g., masonry) use the more specific data found in the "City Cost Indexes."

This estimate is based on an interactive spreadsheet. A copy of this spreadsheet is located on the RSMeans website at **http://www.reedconstructiondata.com/rsmeans/extras/546011**. You are free to download it and adjust it to your methodology.

Project Name: Pre-Engineered Steel Building				Architect: As Shown	
Location:		**Anywhere, USA**			
Line Number	**Description**		**Qty**	**Unit**	**Material**
03 30 53.40 3940	Strip footing, 12" x 24", reinforced		34	C.Y.	$4,624.00
03 30 53.40 3950	Strip footing, 12" x 36", reinforced		15	C.Y.	$1,950.00
03 11 13.65 3000	Concrete slab edge forms		500	L.F.	$155.00
03 22 11.10 0200	Welded wire fabric reinforcing		150	C.S.F.	$2,580.00
03 31 13.35 0300	Ready mix concrete, 4000 psi for slab on grade		278	C.Y.	$28,912.00
03 31 13.70 4300	Place, strike off & consolidate concrete slab		278	C.Y.	$0.00
03 35 13.30 0250	Machine float & trowel concrete slab		15,000	S.F.	$0.00
03 15 16.20 0140	Cut control joints in concrete slab		950	L.F.	$57.00
03 39 23.13 0300	Sprayed concrete curing membrane		150	C.S.F.	$1,642.50
Division 03	**Subtotal**				**$39,920.50**
08 36 13.10 2650	Manual 10' x 10' steel sectional overhead door		8	Ea.	$8,800.00
08 36 13.10 2860	Insulation and steel back panel for OH door		800	S.F.	$3,760.00
Division 08	**Subtotal**				**$12,560.00**
13 34 19.50 1100	Pre-Engineered Steel Building, 100' x 150' x 24'		15,000	SF Flr.	$0.00
13 34 19.50 6050	Framing for PESB door opening, 3' x 7'		4	Opng.	$0.00
13 34 19.50 6100	Framing for PESB door opening, 10' x 10'		8	Opng.	$0.00
13 34 19.50 6200	Framing for PESB window opening, 4' x 3'		6	Opng.	$0.00
13 34 19.50 5750	PESB door, 3' x 7', single leaf		4	Opng.	$2,340.00
13 34 19.50 7750	PESB sliding window, 4' x 3' with screen		6	Opng.	$2,250.00
13 34 19.50 6550	PESB gutter, eave type, 26 ga., painted		300	L.F.	$2,010.00
13 34 19.50 8650	PESB roof vent, 12" wide x 10' long		15	Ea.	$540.00
13 34 19.50 6900	PESB insulation, vinyl faced, 4" thick		27,400	S.F.	$10,960.00
Division 13	**Subtotal**				**$18,100.00**
	Subtotal				$70,580.50
Division 01	**General Requirements @ 7%**				**4,940.64**
	Estimate Subtotal				$75,521.14
	Sales Tax @ 5%				3,776.06
	Subtotal A				79,297.19
	GC O & P				7,929.72
	Subtotal B				87,226.91
	Contingency @ 5%				
	Subtotal C				
	Bond @ $12/1000 +10% O&P				
	Subtotal D				
	Location Adjustment Factor				
	Grand Total				

This example shows the cost to construct a pre-engineered steel building. The foundation, doors, windows, and insulation will be installed by the general contractor. A subcontractor will install the structural steel, roofing, and siding.

		01/01/14	OPN	
Labor	Equipment	SubContract	Estimate Total	
$2,686.00	$23.12	$0.00		
$952.50	$8.10	$0.00		
$845.00	$0.00	$0.00		
$2,940.00	$0.00	$0.00		
$0.00	$0.00	$0.00		
$3,586.20	$166.80	$0.00		
$6,750.00	$450.00	$0.00		
$294.50	$95.00	$0.00		
$712.50	$0.00	$0.00		
$18,766.70	$743.02	$0.00	$59,430.22	Division 03
$2,560.00	$0.00	$0.00		
$0.00	$0.00	$0.00		
$2,560.00	$0.00	$0.00	$15,120.00	Division 08
$0.00	$0.00	$300,000.00		
$0.00	$0.00	$1,980.00		
$0.00	$0.00	$8,400.00		
$0.00	$0.00	$2,970.00		
$492.00	$0.00	$0.00		
$282.00	$65.70	$0.00		
$576.00	$0.00	$0.00		
$2,295.00	$0.00	$0.00		
$6,850.00	$0.00	$0.00		
$10,495.00	$65.70	$313,350.00	$342,010.70	Division 13
$31,821.70	$808.72	$313,350.00	$416,560.92	Subtotal
2,227.52	56.61	21,934.50		Gen. Requirements
$34,049.22	$865.33	$335,284.50	$416,560.92	Estimate Subtotal
	43.27	8,382.11		Sales tax
34,049.22	908.60	343,666.61		Subtotal
23,459.91	90.86	34,366.66		GC O & P
57,509.13	999.46	378,033.27	$523,768.77	Subtotal
			26,188.44	Contingency
			$549,957.21	Subtotal
			7,259.44	Bond
			$557,216.65	Subtotal
102.30			12,815.98	Location Adjustment
			$570,032.63	Grand Total

Sales Tax: If the work is subject to state or local sales taxes, the amount must be added to the estimate. Sales tax may be added to material costs, equipment costs, and subcontracted work. In this case, sales tax was added in all three categories. It was assumed that approximately half the subcontracted work would be material cost, so the tax was applied to 50% of the subcontract total.

GC O&P: This entry represents the general contractor's markup on material, labor, equipment, and subcontractor costs. RSMeans' standard markup on materials, equipment, and subcontracted work is 10%. In this estimate, the markup on the labor performed by the GC's workers uses "Skilled Workers Average" shown in Column F on the table "Installing Contractor's Overhead & Profit," which can be found on the inside-back cover of the book.

Contingency: A factor for contingency may be added to any estimate to represent the cost of unknowns that may occur between the time that the estimate is performed and the time the project is constructed. The amount of the allowance will depend on the stage of design at which the estimate is done, and the contractor's assessment of the risk involved. Refer to section 01 21 16.50 for contigency allowances.

Estimating Tips

01 20 00 Price and Payment Procedures

- Allowances that should be added to estimates to cover contingencies and job conditions that are not included in the national average material and labor costs are shown in section 01 21.

- When estimating historic preservation projects (depending on the condition of the existing structure and the owner's requirements), a 15%–20% contingency or allowance is recommended, regardless of the stage of the drawings.

01 30 00 Administrative Requirements

- Before determining a final cost estimate, it is a good practice to review all the items listed in Subdivisions 01 31 and 01 32 to make final adjustments for items that may need customizing to specific job conditions.

- Requirements for initial and periodic submittals can represent a significant cost to the General Requirements of a job. Thoroughly check the submittal specifications when estimating a project to determine any costs that should be included.

01 40 00 Quality Requirements

- All projects will require some degree of Quality Control. This cost is not included in the unit cost of construction listed in each division. Depending upon the terms of the contract, the various costs of inspection and testing can be the responsibility of either the owner or the contractor. Be sure to include the required costs in your estimate.

01 50 00 Temporary Facilities and Controls

- Barricades, access roads, safety nets, scaffolding, security, and many more requirements for the execution of a safe project are elements of direct cost. These costs can easily be overlooked when preparing an estimate. When looking through the major classifications of this subdivision, determine which items apply to each division in your estimate.

- Construction Equipment Rental Costs can be found in the Reference Section in section 01 54 33. Operators' wages are not included in equipment rental costs.

- Equipment mobilization and demobilization costs are not included in equipment rental costs and must be considered separately in section 01 54 36.50.

- The cost of small tools provided by the installing contractor for his workers is covered in the "Overhead" column on the "Installing Contractor's Overhead and Profit" table that lists labor trades, base rates and markups and, therefore, is included in the "Total Incl. O&P" cost of any Unit Price line item. For those users who are constrained by contract terms to use only bare costs, there are two line items in section 01 54 39.70 for small tools as a percentage of bare labor cost. If some of those users are further constrained by contract terms to refrain from using line items from Division 1, you are advised to cover the cost of small tools within your coefficient or multiplier.

01 70 00 Execution and Closeout Requirements

- When preparing an estimate, thoroughly read the specifications to determine the requirements for Contract Closeout. Final cleaning, record documentation, operation and maintenance data, warranties and bonds, and spare parts and maintenance materials can all be elements of cost for the completion of a contract. Do not overlook these in your estimate.

Reference Numbers

Reference numbers are shown in shaded boxes at the beginning of some major classifications. These numbers refer to related items in the Reference Section. The reference information may be an estimating procedure, an alternate pricing method, or technical information.

Note: Not all subdivisions listed here necessarily appear in this publication.

01 11 31 – Professional Consultants

01 11 31.10 Architectural Fees

			Crew	Daily Output	Labor-Hours	Unit	Material	2014 Bare Costs Labor	Equipment	Total	Total Incl O&P
0010	**ARCHITECTURAL FEES**	R011110-10									
0020	For new construction										
0060	Minimum					Project				4.90%	4.90%
0090	Maximum									16%	16%
0100	For alteration work, to $500,000, add to new construction fee									50%	50%
0150	Over $500,000, add to new construction fee									25%	25%
2000	For "Greening" of building	G								3%	3%

01 11 31.20 Construction Management Fees

			Crew	Daily Output	Labor-Hours	Unit	Material	2014 Bare Costs Labor	Equipment	Total	Total Incl O&P
0010	**CONSTRUCTION MANAGEMENT FEES**										
0020	$1,000,000 job, minimum					Project				4.50%	4.50%
0050	Maximum									7.50%	7.50%
0060	For work to $100,000									10%	10%
0070	To $250,000									9%	9%
0090	To $1,000,000									6%	6%
0100	To $5,000,000									5%	5%
0110	To $10,000,000									4%	4%
0300	$50,000,000 job, minimum									2.50%	2.50%
0350	Maximum									4%	4%

01 11 31.30 Engineering Fees

			Crew	Daily Output	Labor-Hours	Unit	Material	2014 Bare Costs Labor	Equipment	Total	Total Incl O&P
0010	**ENGINEERING FEES**	R011110-30									
0020	Educational planning consultant, minimum					Project				.50%	.50%
0100	Maximum					"				2.50%	2.50%
0200	Electrical, minimum					Contrct				4.10%	4.10%
0300	Maximum									10.10%	10.10%
0400	Elevator & conveying systems, minimum									2.50%	2.50%
0500	Maximum									5%	5%
0600	Food service & kitchen equipment, minimum									8%	8%
0700	Maximum									12%	12%
0800	Landscaping & site development, minimum									2.50%	2.50%
0900	Maximum									6%	6%
1000	Mechanical (plumbing & HVAC), minimum									4.10%	4.10%
1100	Maximum									10.10%	10.10%
1200	Structural, minimum					Project				1%	1%
1300	Maximum					"				2.50%	2.50%

01 11 31.50 Models

			Crew	Daily Output	Labor-Hours	Unit	Material	2014 Bare Costs Labor	Equipment	Total	Total Incl O&P
0010	**MODELS**										
0020	Cardboard & paper, 1 building, minimum					Ea.	735			735	810
0050	Maximum						1,675			1,675	1,850
0100	2 buildings, minimum						985			985	1,075
0150	Maximum						2,225			2,225	2,450
0200	Plexiglass and metal, basic layout					SF Flr.	.07			.07	.08
0210	Including equipment and personnel					"	.32			.32	.35
0300	Site plan layout, minimum					Ea.	1,400			1,400	1,550
0350	Maximum					"	2,350			2,350	2,600

01 11 31.75 Renderings

			Crew	Daily Output	Labor-Hours	Unit	Material	2014 Bare Costs Labor	Equipment	Total	Total Incl O&P
0010	**RENDERINGS** Color, matted, 20" x 30", eye level,										
0020	1 building, minimum					Ea.	2,050			2,050	2,275
0050	Average						2,875			2,875	3,175
0100	Maximum						4,625			4,625	5,100
1000	5 buildings, minimum						4,125			4,125	4,525
1100	Maximum						8,250			8,250	9,075
2000	Aerial perspective, color, 1 building, minimum						3,000			3,000	3,275

01 11 Summary of Work

01 11 31 – Professional Consultants

	01 11 31.75 Renderings	Crew	Daily Output	Labor-Hours	Unit	Material	2014 Bare Costs Labor	Equipment	Total	Total Incl O&P
2100	Maximum				Ea.	8,150			8,150	8,950
3000	5 buildings, minimum					5,875			5,875	6,450
3100	Maximum					11,700			11,700	12,900

01 21 Allowances

01 21 16 – Contingency Allowances

01 21 16.50 Contingencies

0010	**CONTINGENCIES**, Add to estimate									
0020	Conceptual stage				Project				20%	20%
0050	Schematic stage								15%	15%
0100	Preliminary working drawing stage (Design Dev.)								10%	10%
0150	Final working drawing stage								3%	3%

01 21 55 – Job Conditions Allowance

01 21 55.50 Job Conditions

0010	**JOB CONDITIONS** Modifications to applicable									
0020	cost summaries									
0100	Economic conditions, favorable, deduct				Project				2%	2%
0200	Unfavorable, add								5%	5%
0300	Hoisting conditions, favorable, deduct								2%	2%
0400	Unfavorable, add								5%	5%
0500	General Contractor management, experienced, deduct								2%	2%
0600	Inexperienced, add								10%	10%
0700	Labor availability, surplus, deduct								1%	1%
0800	Shortage, add								10%	10%
0900	Material storage area, available, deduct								1%	1%
1000	Not available, add								2%	2%
1100	Subcontractor availability, surplus, deduct								5%	5%
1200	Shortage, add								12%	12%
1300	Work space, available, deduct								2%	2%
1400	Not available, add								5%	5%

01 21 57 – Overtime Allowance

01 21 57.50 Overtime

0010	**OVERTIME** for early completion of projects or where	R012909-90								
0020	labor shortages exist, add to usual labor, up to				Costs		100%			

01 21 61 – Cost Indexes

01 21 61.10 Construction Cost Index

0010	**CONSTRUCTION COST INDEX** (Reference) over 930 zip code locations in									
0020	the U.S. and Canada, total bldg. cost, min. (Longview, TX)				%					73.50%
0050	Average									100%
0100	Maximum (New York, NY)									131.10%

01 21 61.20 Historical Cost Indexes

0010	**HISTORICAL COST INDEXES** (See Reference Section)									

01 21 61.30 Labor Index

0010	**LABOR INDEX** (Reference) For over 930 zip code locations in									
0020	the U.S. and Canada, minimum (Longview, TX)				%		40.50%			
0050	Average						100%			
0100	Maximum (New York, NY)						166.40%			

01 21 Allowances

01 21 61 – Cost Indexes

01 21 61.50 Material Index		Crew	Daily Output	Labor-Hours	Unit	Material	2014 Bare Costs Labor	Equipment	Total	Total Incl O&P
0010	**MATERIAL INDEX** (Reference) For over 930 zip code locations in									
0020	the U.S. and Canada, minimum (Vale, OR)				%	91.30%				
0040	Average					100%				
0060	Maximum (Ketchikan, AK)					132%				

01 21 63 – Taxes

01 21 63.10 Taxes

0010	**TAXES**	R012909-80								
0020	Sales tax, State, average				%	5.06%				
0050	Maximum	R012909-85				7.25%				
0200	Social Security, on first $115,800 of wages						7.65%			
0300	Unemployment, combined Federal and State, minimum						.60%			
0350	Average						7.80%			
0400	Maximum						13.50%			

01 31 Project Management and Coordination

01 31 13 – Project Coordination

01 31 13.20 Field Personnel

0010	**FIELD PERSONNEL**									
0020	Clerk, average				Week	335			335	565
0100	Field engineer, minimum					795			795	1,350
0120	Average					1,050			1,050	1,750
0140	Maximum					1,175			1,175	2,000
0160	General purpose laborer, average					1,125			1,125	1,900
0180	Project manager, minimum					1,475			1,475	2,500
0200	Average					1,700			1,700	2,875
0220	Maximum					1,950			1,950	3,275
0240	Superintendent, minimum					1,450			1,450	2,425
0260	Average					1,575			1,575	2,675
0280	Maximum					1,800			1,800	3,050
0290	Timekeeper, average					920			920	1,550

01 31 13.30 Insurance

0010	**INSURANCE**	R013113-40								
0020	Builders risk, standard, minimum				Job				.24%	.24%
0050	Maximum	R013113-50							.64%	.64%
0200	All-risk type, minimum								.25%	.25%
0250	Maximum	R013113-60							.62%	.62%
0400	Contractor's equipment floater, minimum				Value				.50%	.50%
0450	Maximum				"				1.50%	1.50%
0600	Public liability, average				Job				2.02%	2.02%
0800	Workers' compensation & employer's liability, average									
0850	by trade, carpentry, general				Payroll		15.38%			
0900	Clerical						.51%			
0950	Concrete						13.15%			
1000	Electrical						5.83%			
1050	Excavation						9.69%			
1100	Glazing						13.15%			
1150	Insulation						11.67%			
1200	Lathing						8.12%			
1250	Masonry						13.49%			
1300	Painting & decorating						11.54%			

01 31 13 – Project Coordination

01 31 13.30 Insurance

		Crew	Daily Output	Labor-Hours	Unit	Material	2014 Bare Costs Labor	Equipment	Total	Total Incl O&P
1350	Pile driving				Payroll		14.65%			
1400	Plastering						11.55%			
1450	Plumbing						7.08%			
1500	Roofing						31.29%			
1550	Sheet metal work (HVAC)						8.79%			
1600	Steel erection, structural						34.64%			
1650	Tile work, interior ceramic						8.54%			
1700	Waterproofing, brush or hand caulking						6.86%			
1800	Wrecking						29.21%			
2000	Range of 35 trades in 50 states, excl. wrecking, min.						2.48%			
2100	Average						14%			
2200	Maximum						150%			

01 31 13.40 Main Office Expense

		Crew	Daily Output	Labor-Hours	Unit	Material	2014 Bare Costs Labor	Equipment	Total	Total Incl O&P
0010	**MAIN OFFICE EXPENSE** Average for General Contractors R013113-50									
0020	As a percentage of their annual volume									
0125	Annual volume under 1 million dollars				% Vol.				17.50%	
0145	Up to 2.5 million dollars								8%	
0150	Up to 4.0 million dollars								6.80%	
0200	Up to 7.0 million dollars								5.60%	
0250	Up to 10 million dollars								5.10%	
0300	Over 10 million dollars								3.90%	

01 31 13.50 General Contractor's Mark-Up

		Crew	Daily Output	Labor-Hours	Unit	Material	2014 Bare Costs Labor	Equipment	Total	Total Incl O&P
0010	**GENERAL CONTRACTOR'S MARK-UP** on Change Orders									
0200	Extra work, by subcontractors, add				%				10%	10%
0250	By General Contractor, add								15%	15%
0400	Omitted work, by subcontractors, deduct all but								5%	5%
0450	By General Contractor, deduct all but								7.50%	7.50%
0600	Overtime work, by subcontractors, add								15%	15%
0650	By General Contractor, add								10%	10%

01 31 13.60 Installing Contractor's Main Office Overhead

		Crew	Daily Output	Labor-Hours	Unit	Material	2014 Bare Costs Labor	Equipment	Total	Total Incl O&P
0010	**INSTALLING CONTRACTOR'S MAIN OFFICE OVERHEAD** R013113-50									
0020	As percent of direct costs, minimum				%				5%	
0050	Average								25%	
0100	Maximum								30%	

01 31 13.80 Overhead and Profit

		Crew	Daily Output	Labor-Hours	Unit	Material	2014 Bare Costs Labor	Equipment	Total	Total Incl O&P
0010	**OVERHEAD & PROFIT** Allowance to add to items in this									
0020	book that do not include Subs O&P, average				%				25%	
0100	Allowance to add to items in this book that									
0110	do include Subs O&P, minimum				%				5%	5%
0150	Average								10%	10%
0200	Maximum								15%	15%
0300	Typical, by size of project, under $100,000								30%	
0350	$500,000 project								25%	
0400	$2,000,000 project								20%	
0450	Over $10,000,000 project								15%	

01 31 13.90 Performance Bond

		Crew	Daily Output	Labor-Hours	Unit	Material	2014 Bare Costs Labor	Equipment	Total	Total Incl O&P
0010	**PERFORMANCE BOND** R013113-80									
0020	For buildings, minimum				Job				.60%	.60%
0100	Maximum				"				2.50%	2.50%

01 32 Construction Progress Documentation

01 32 13 – Scheduling of work

01 32 13.50 Scheduling	Crew	Daily Output	Labor-Hours	Unit	Material	2014 Bare Costs Labor	Equipment	Total	Total Incl O&P
0010 **SCHEDULING**									
0020 Critical path, as % of architectural fee, minimum				%				.50%	.50%
0100 Maximum				"				1%	1%
0300 Computer-update, micro, no plots, minimum				Ea.				455	500
0400 Including plots, maximum				"				1,450	1,600
0600 Rule of thumb, CPM scheduling, small job ($10 Million)				Job				.05%	.05%
0650 Large job ($50 Million +)								.03%	.03%
0700 Including cost control, small job								.08%	.08%
0750 Large job								.04%	.04%

01 32 33 – Photographic Documentation

01 32 33.50 Photographs	Crew	Daily Output	Labor-Hours	Unit	Material	2014 Bare Costs Labor	Equipment	Total	Total Incl O&P
0010 **PHOTOGRAPHS**									
0020 8" x 10", 4 shots, 2 prints ea., std. mounting				Set	475			475	525
0100 Hinged linen mounts					530			530	580
0200 8" x 10", 4 shots, 2 prints each, in color					425			425	470
0300 For I.D. slugs, add to all above					5.30			5.30	5.85
0500 Aerial photos, initial fly-over, 6 shots, 1 print ea., 8" x 10"					865			865	950
0550 11" x 14" prints					980			980	1,075
0600 16" x 20" prints					1,175			1,175	1,300
0700 For full color prints, add					40%				
0750 Add for traffic control area					305			305	335
0900 For over 30 miles from airport, add per				Mile	5.55			5.55	6.15
1000 Vertical photography, 4 to 6 shots with									
1010 different scales, 1 print each				Set	1,150			1,150	1,275
1500 Time lapse equipment, camera and projector, buy				Ea.	2,650			2,650	2,925
1550 Rent per month				"	1,600			1,600	1,750
1700 Cameraman and film, including processing, B.&W.				Day	1,225			1,225	1,350
1720 Color				"	1,425			1,425	1,550

01 41 Regulatory Requirements

01 41 26 – Permit Requirements

01 41 26.50 Permits	Crew	Daily Output	Labor-Hours	Unit	Material	2014 Bare Costs Labor	Equipment	Total	Total Incl O&P
0010 **PERMITS**									
0020 Rule of thumb, most cities, minimum				Job				.50%	.50%
0100 Maximum				"				2%	2%

01 45 Quality Control

01 45 23 – Testing and Inspecting Services

01 45 23.50 Testing	Crew	Daily Output	Labor-Hours	Unit	Material	2014 Bare Costs Labor	Equipment	Total	Total Incl O&P
0010 **TESTING** and Inspecting Services									
0015 For concrete building costing $1,000,000, minimum				Project				4,725	5,200
0020 Maximum								38,000	41,800
0050 Steel building, minimum								4,725	5,200
0070 Maximum								14,800	16,300
0100 For building costing, $10,000,000, minimum								30,100	33,100
0150 Maximum								48,200	53,000
0200 Asphalt testing, compressive strength Marshall stability, set of 3				Ea.				145	165
0220 Density, set of 3								86	95
0250 Extraction, individual tests on sample								136	150

01 45 23.50 Testing		Crew	Daily Output	Labor-Hours	Unit	Material	2014 Bare Costs Labor	Equipment	Total	Total Incl O&P
0300	Penetration				Ea.				41	45
0350	Mix design, 5 specimens								182	200
0360	Additional specimen								36	40
0400	Specific gravity								41	45
0420	Swell test								64	70
0450	Water effect and cohesion, set of 6								182	200
0470	Water effect and plastic flow								64	70
0600	Concrete testing, aggregates, abrasion, ASTM C 131								136	150
0650	Absorption, ASTM C 127								42	46
0800	Petrographic analysis, ASTM C 295								775	850
0900	Specific gravity, ASTM C 127								50	55
1000	Sieve analysis, washed, ASTM C 136								59	65
1050	Unwashed								59	65
1200	Sulfate soundness								114	125
1300	Weight per cubic foot								36	40
1500	Cement, physical tests, ASTM C 150								320	350
1600	Chemical tests, ASTM C 150								245	270
1800	Compressive test, cylinder, delivered to lab, ASTM C 39								12	13
1900	Picked up by lab, minimum								14	15
1950	Average								18	20
2000	Maximum								27	30
2200	Compressive strength, cores (not incl. drilling), ASTM C 42								36	40
2250	Core drilling, 4" diameter (plus technician)				Inch				23	25
2260	Technician for core drilling				Hr.				45	50
2300	Patching core holes				Ea.				22	24
2400	Drying shrinkage at 28 days								236	260
2500	Flexural test beams, ASTM C 78								59	65
2600	Mix design, one batch mix								259	285
2650	Added trial batches								120	132
2800	Modulus of elasticity, ASTM C 469								164	180
2900	Tensile test, cylinders, ASTM C 496								45	50
3000	Water-Cement ratio curve, 3 batches								141	155
3100	4 batches								186	205
3300	Masonry testing, absorption, per 5 brick, ASTM C 67								45	50
3350	Chemical resistance, per 2 brick								50	55
3400	Compressive strength, per 5 brick, ASTM C 67								68	75
3420	Efflorescence, per 5 brick, ASTM C 67								68	75
3440	Imperviousness, per 5 brick								87	96
3470	Modulus of rupture, per 5 brick								86	95
3500	Moisture, block only								32	35
3550	Mortar, compressive strength, set of 3								23	25
4100	Reinforcing steel, bend test								55	61
4200	Tensile test, up to #8 bar								36	40
4220	#9 to #11 bar								41	45
4240	#14 bar and larger								64	70
4400	Soil testing, Atterberg limits, liquid and plastic limits								59	65
4510	Hydrometer analysis								109	120
4530	Specific gravity, ASTM D 354								44	48
4600	Sieve analysis, washed, ASTM D 422								55	60
4700	Unwashed, ASTM D 422								59	65
4710	Consolidation test (ASTM D2435), minimum								250	275
4715	Maximum								430	475
4720	Density and classification of undisturbed sample								73	80

15

01 45 Quality Control

01 45 23 – Testing and Inspecting Services

01 45 23.50 Testing		Crew	Daily Output	Labor-Hours	Unit	Material	2014 Bare Costs Labor	Equipment	Total	Total Incl O&P
4735	Soil density, nuclear method, ASTM D2922				Ea.				35	38.50
4740	Sand cone method ASTM D1556								27	30
4750	Moisture content, ASTM D 2216								9	10
4780	Permeability test, double ring infiltrometer								500	550
4800	Permeability, var. or constant head, undist., ASTM D 2434								227	250
4850	Recompacted								250	275
4900	Proctor compaction, 4" standard mold, ASTM D 698								123	135
4950	6" modified mold								68	75
5100	Shear tests, triaxial, minimum								410	450
5150	Maximum								545	600
5300	Direct shear, minimum, ASTM D 3080								320	350
5350	Maximum								410	450
5550	Technician for inspection, per day, earthwork								320	350
5650	Bolting								400	440
5750	Roofing								480	530
5790	Welding								480	530
5820	Non-destructive metal testing, dye penetrant				Day				310	340
5840	Magnetic particle								310	340
5860	Radiography								450	495
5880	Ultrasonic								310	340
6000	Welding certification, minimum				Ea.				91	100
6100	Maximum				"				250	275
7000	Underground storage tank									
7500	Volumetric tightness test ,<=12,000 gal.				Ea.				435	480
7510	<=30,000 gal.				"				615	675
7600	Vadose zone (soil gas) sampling, 10-40 samples, min.				Day				1,375	1,500
7610	Maximum				"				2,275	2,500
7700	Ground water monitoring incl. drilling 3 wells, min.				Total				4,550	5,000
7710	Maximum				"				6,375	7,000
8000	X-ray concrete slabs				Ea.				182	200
9000	Thermographic testing, for bldg envelope heat loss, average 2,000 S.F. [G]				"					500

01 51 Temporary Utilities

01 51 13 – Temporary Electricity

01 51 13.80 Temporary Utilities		Crew	Daily Output	Labor-Hours	Unit	Material	2014 Bare Costs Labor	Equipment	Total	Total Incl O&P
0010	**TEMPORARY UTILITIES**									
0101	Heat, incl. fuel and operation, per week, 12 hrs. per day	1 Clab	100	.080	CSF Flr	28	2.26		30.26	34.50
0201	24 hrs. per day	"	60	.133		53.50	3.76		57.26	65
0350	Lighting, incl. service lamps, wiring & outlets, minimum	1 Elec	34	.235		2.80	10.05		12.85	19.55
0360	Maximum	"	17	.471		5.85	20		25.85	39.50
0400	Power for temp lighting only, 6.6 KWH, per month								.92	1.01
0430	11.8 KWH, per month								1.65	1.82
0450	23.6 KWH, per month								3.30	3.63
0600	Power for job duration incl. elevator, etc., minimum								47	51.50
0650	Maximum								110	121
1000	Toilet, portable, see Equip. Rental 01 54 33 in Reference Section									

01 52 Construction Facilities

01 52 13 – Field Offices and Sheds

01 52 13.20 Office and Storage Space

		Crew	Daily Output	Labor-Hours	Unit	Material	2014 Bare Costs Labor	Equipment	Total	Total Incl O&P
0010	**OFFICE AND STORAGE SPACE**									
0020	Office trailer, furnished, no hookups, 20' x 8', buy	2 Skwk	1	16	Ea.	9,150	580		9,730	11,100
0250	Rent per month					169			169	185
0300	32' x 8', buy	2 Skwk	.70	22.857		14,000	830		14,830	16,800
0350	Rent per month					203			203	223
0400	50' x 10', buy	2 Skwk	.60	26.667		22,400	970		23,370	26,200
0450	Rent per month					305			305	335
0500	50' x 12', buy	2 Skwk	.50	32		27,000	1,150		28,150	31,700
0550	Rent per month					350			350	385
0700	For air conditioning, rent per month, add					48.50			48.50	53.50
0800	For delivery, add per mile				Mile	11			11	12.10
0890	Delivery each way				Ea.	200			200	220
0900	Bunk house trailer, 8' x 40' duplex dorm with kitchen, no hookups, buy	2 Carp	1	16		37,300	570		37,870	42,000
0910	9 man with kitchen and bath, no hookups, buy		1	16		38,000	570		38,570	42,800
0920	18 man sleeper with bath, no hookups, buy		1	16		49,000	570		49,570	55,000
1000	Portable buildings, prefab, on skids, economy, 8' x 8'		265	.060	S.F.	29.50	2.16		31.66	36
1100	Deluxe, 8' x 12'		150	.107	"	24	3.81		27.81	33
1200	Storage boxes, 20' x 8', buy	2 Skwk	1.80	8.889	Ea.	2,775	325		3,100	3,600
1250	Rent per month					78.50			78.50	86
1300	40' x 8', buy	2 Skwk	1.40	11.429		3,700	415		4,115	4,775
1350	Rent per month					99			99	109
5000	Air supported structures, see Section 13 31 13.13									

01 52 13.40 Field Office Expense

		Crew	Daily Output	Labor-Hours	Unit	Material	2014 Bare Costs Labor	Equipment	Total	Total Incl O&P
0010	**FIELD OFFICE EXPENSE**									
0100	Office equipment rental average				Month	200			200	220
0120	Office supplies, average				"	75			75	82.50
0125	Office trailer rental, see Section 01 52 13.20									
0140	Telephone bill; avg. bill/month incl. long dist.				Month	81			81	89
0160	Lights & HVAC				"	152			152	167

01 54 Construction Aids

01 54 09 – Protection Equipment

01 54 09.50 Personnel Protective Equipment

		Crew	Daily Output	Labor-Hours	Unit	Material	2014 Bare Costs Labor	Equipment	Total	Total Incl O&P
0010	**PERSONNEL PROTECTIVE EQUIPMENT**									
0015	Hazardous waste protection									
0020	Respirator mask only, full face, silicone				Ea.	335			335	370
0030	Half face, silicone					52.50			52.50	58
0040	Respirator cartridges, 2 req'd/mask, dust or asbestos					3.60			3.60	3.95
0050	Chemical vapor					2.78			2.78	3.06
0060	Combination vapor and dust					8.30			8.30	9.10
0100	Emergency escape breathing apparatus, 5 min					550			550	605
0110	10 min					665			665	730
0150	Self contained breathing apparatus with full face piece, 30 min					1,975			1,975	2,175
0160	60 min					3,700			3,700	4,075
0200	Encapsulating suits, limited use, level A					1,775			1,775	1,950
0210	Level B					375			375	415
0300	Over boots, latex				Pr.	7.50			7.50	8.25
0310	PVC					29			29	32
0320	Neoprene					37.50			37.50	41
0400	Gloves, nitrile/PVC					36			36	39.50
0410	Neoprene coated					37			37	41

01 54 09 – Protection Equipment

01 54 09.60 Safety Nets		Crew	Daily Output	Labor-Hours	Unit	Material	2014 Bare Costs Labor	Equipment	Total	Total Incl O&P
0010	**SAFETY NETS**									
0020	No supports, stock sizes, nylon, 3 1/2" mesh				S.F.	2.96			2.96	3.26
0100	Polypropylene, 6" mesh					1.59			1.59	1.75
0200	Small mesh debris nets, 1/4" mesh, stock sizes					.74			.74	.81
0220	Combined 3 1/2" mesh and 1/4" mesh, stock sizes					4.67			4.67	5.15
0300	Monthly rental, 4" mesh, stock sizes, 1st month					.50			.50	.55
0320	2nd month rental					.25			.25	.28
0340	Maximum rental/year					1.15			1.15	1.27

01 54 16 – Temporary Hoists

01 54 16.50 Weekly Forklift Crew

		Crew	Daily Output	Labor-Hours	Unit	Material	Labor	Equipment	Total	Total Incl O&P
0010	**WEEKLY FORKLIFT CREW**									
0100	All-terrain forklift, 45' lift, 35' reach, 9000 lb. capacity	A-3P	.20	40	Week		1,450	2,650	4,100	5,325

01 54 19 – Temporary Cranes

01 54 19.50 Daily Crane Crews

		Crew	Daily Output	Labor-Hours	Unit	Material	Labor	Equipment	Total	Total Incl O&P
0010	**DAILY CRANE CREWS** for small jobs, portal to portal									
0100	12-ton truck-mounted hydraulic crane	A-3H	1	8	Day		310	875	1,185	1,475
0200	25-ton	A-3I	1	8			310	1,000	1,310	1,625
0300	40-ton	A-3J	1	8			310	1,250	1,560	1,900
0400	55-ton	A-3K	1	16			580	1,650	2,230	2,775
0500	80-ton	A-3L	1	16			580	2,400	2,980	3,575
0600	100-ton	A-3M	1	16			580	2,375	2,955	3,575
0900	If crane is needed on a Saturday, Sunday or Holiday									
0910	At time-and-a-half, add				Day		50%			
0920	At double time, add				"		100%			

01 54 19.60 Monthly Tower Crane Crew

		Crew	Daily Output	Labor-Hours	Unit	Material	Labor	Equipment	Total	Total Incl O&P
0010	**MONTHLY TOWER CRANE CREW**, excludes concrete footing									
0100	Static tower crane, 130' high, 106' jib, 6200 lb. capacity	A-3N	.05	176	Month		6,800	24,200	31,000	37,900

01 54 23 – Temporary Scaffolding and Platforms

01 54 23.60 Pump Staging

			Crew	Daily Output	Labor-Hours	Unit	Material	Labor	Equipment	Total	Total Incl O&P
0010	**PUMP STAGING**, Aluminum	R015423-20									
0200	24' long pole section, buy					Ea.	355			355	390
0300	18' long pole section, buy						275			275	300
0400	12' long pole section, buy						185			185	204
0500	6' long pole section, buy						103			103	113
0600	6' long splice joint section, buy						72.50			72.50	80
0700	Pump jack, buy						148			148	163
0900	Foldable brace, buy						58			58	64
1000	Workbench/back safety rail support, buy						78			78	85.50
1100	Scaffolding planks/workbench, 14" wide x 24' long, buy						715			715	785
1200	Plank end safety rail, buy						291			291	320
1250	Safety net, 22' long, buy						355			355	390
1300	System in place, 50' working height, per use based on 50 uses		2 Carp	84.80	.189	C.S.F.	6.10	6.75		12.85	18.05
1400	100 uses			84.80	.189		3.06	6.75		9.81	14.70
1500	150 uses			84.80	.189		2.05	6.75		8.80	13.60

01 54 23.70 Scaffolding

			Crew	Daily Output	Labor-Hours	Unit	Material	Labor	Equipment	Total	Total Incl O&P
0010	**SCAFFOLDING**	R015423-10									
0015	Steel tube, regular, no plank, labor only to erect & dismantle										
0091	Building exterior, wall face, 1 to 5 stories, 6'-4" x 5' frames		3 Clab	8	3	C.S.F.		84.50		84.50	142
0201	6 to 12 stories		4 Clab	8	4			113		113	190
0310	13 to 20 stories		5 Carp	8	5			179		179	300

01 54 23.70 Scaffolding		Crew	Daily Output	Labor-Hours	Unit	Material	2014 Bare Costs Labor	Equipment	Total	Total Incl O&P
0461	Building interior, walls face area, up to 16' high	3 Clab	12	2	C.S.F.		56.50		56.50	95
0561	16' to 40' high		10	2.400	↓		67.50		67.50	114
0801	Building interior floor area, up to 30' high	↓	150	.160	C.C.F.		4.51		4.51	7.60
0901	Over 30' high	4 Clab	160	.200	"		5.65		5.65	9.50
0906	Complete system for face of walls, no plank, material only rent/mo				C.S.F.	35			35	38.50
0908	Interior spaces, no plank, material only rent/mo				C.C.F.	3.35			3.35	3.68
0910	Steel tubular, heavy duty shoring, buy									
0920	Frames 5' high 2' wide				Ea.	81.50			81.50	90
0925	5' high 4' wide					93			93	102
0930	6' high 2' wide					93.50			93.50	103
0935	6' high 4' wide				↓	109			109	120
0940	Accessories									
0945	Cross braces				Ea.	15.50			15.50	17.05
0950	U-head, 8" x 8"					19.10			19.10	21
0955	J-head, 4" x 8"					13.90			13.90	15.30
0960	Base plate, 8" x 8"					15.50			15.50	17.05
0965	Leveling jack				↓	33.50			33.50	36.50
1000	Steel tubular, regular, buy									
1100	Frames 3' high 5' wide				Ea.	72.50			72.50	80
1150	5' high 5' wide					86.50			86.50	95
1200	6'-4" high 5' wide					118			118	129
1350	7'-6" high 6' wide					158			158	173
1500	Accessories cross braces					15.50			15.50	17.05
1550	Guardrail post					16.40			16.40	18.05
1600	Guardrail 7' section					6.30			6.30	6.95
1650	Screw jacks & plates					21.50			21.50	24
1700	Sidearm brackets					25.50			25.50	28.50
1750	8" casters					31			31	34
1800	Plank 2" x 10" x 16'-0"					52			52	57.50
1900	Stairway section					276			276	305
1910	Stairway starter bar					32			32	35
1920	Stairway inside handrail					53			53	58
1930	Stairway outside handrail					81.50			81.50	90
1940	Walk-thru frame guardrail				↓	41.50			41.50	46
2000	Steel tubular, regular, rent/mo.									
2100	Frames 3' high 5' wide				Ea.	5			5	5.50
2150	5' high 5' wide					5			5	5.50
2200	6'-4" high 5' wide					5.15			5.15	5.65
2250	7'-6" high 6' wide					7			7	7.70
2500	Accessories, cross braces					1			1	1.10
2550	Guardrail post					1			1	1.10
2600	Guardrail 7' section					1			1	1.10
2650	Screw jacks & plates					2			2	2.20
2700	Sidearm brackets					2			2	2.20
2750	8" casters					8			8	8.80
2800	Outrigger for rolling tower					3			3	3.30
2850	Plank 2" x 10" x 16'-0"					6			6	6.60
2900	Stairway section					35.50			35.50	39
2940	Walk-thru frame guardrail				↓	2.50			2.50	2.75
3000	Steel tubular, heavy duty shoring, rent/mo.									
3250	5' high 2' & 4' wide				Ea.	5			5	5.50
3300	6' high 2' & 4' wide					5			5	5.50
3500	Accessories, cross braces				↓	1			1	1.10

01 54 23 – Temporary Scaffolding and Platforms

01 54 23.70 Scaffolding		Crew	Daily Output	Labor-Hours	Unit	Material	2014 Bare Costs Labor	Equipment	Total	Total Incl O&P
3600	U - head, 8" x 8"				Ea.	1			1	1.10
3650	J - head, 4" x 8"					1			1	1.10
3700	Base plate, 8" x 8"					1			1	1.10
3750	Leveling jack					2			2	2.20
5700	Planks, 2" x 10" x 16'-0", labor only to erect & remove to 50' H	3 Carp	72	.333			11.90		11.90	20
5800	Over 50' high	4 Carp	80	.400			14.30		14.30	24
6000	Heavy duty shoring for elevated slab forms to 8'-2" high, floor area									
6101	Labor only to erect & dismantle	4 Clab	16	2	C.S.F.		56.50		56.50	95
6110	Materials only, rent.mo				"	29.50			29.50	32.50
6500	To 14'-8" high									
6601	Labor only to erect & dismantle	4 Clab	10	3.200	C.S.F.		90		90	152
6610	Materials only, rent/mo				"	43			43	47.50

01 54 23.75 Scaffolding Specialties

		Crew	Daily Output	Labor-Hours	Unit	Material	Labor	Equipment	Total	Total Incl O&P
0010	**SCAFFOLDING SPECIALTIES**									
1200	Sidewalk bridge, heavy duty steel posts & beams, including									
1210	parapet protection & waterproofing (material cost is rent/month)									
1221	8' to 10' wide, 2 posts	3 Clab	15	1.600	L.F.	37	45		82	117
1231	3 posts	"	10	2.400	"	56.50	67.50		124	176
1500	Sidewalk bridge using tubular steel scaffold frames including									
1511	planking (material cost is rent/month)	3 Clab	45	.533	L.F.	5.60	15.05		20.65	31.50
1600	For 2 uses per month, deduct from all above					50%				
1700	For 1 use every 2 months, add to all above					100%				
1900	Catwalks, 20" wide, no guardrails, 7' span, buy				Ea.	133			133	146
2000	10' span, buy					186			186	205
3720	Putlog, standard, 8' span, with hangers, buy					66.50			66.50	73
3730	Rent per month					10			10	11
3750	12' span, buy					99			99	109
3755	Rent per month					15			15	16.50
3760	Trussed type, 16' span, buy					229			229	252
3770	Rent per month					20			20	22
3790	22' span, buy					274			274	300
3795	Rent per month					30			30	33
3800	Rolling ladders with handrails, 30" wide, buy, 2 step					231			231	254
4000	7 step					760			760	835
4050	10 step					1,050			1,050	1,150
4100	Rolling towers, buy, 5' wide, 7' long, 10' high					1,150			1,150	1,275
4200	For 5' high added sections, to buy, add					204			204	224
4300	Complete incl. wheels, railings, outriggers,									
4350	21' high, to buy				Ea.	1,975			1,975	2,175
4400	Rent/month = 5% of purchase cost				"	170			170	187
5000	Motorized work platform, mast climber									
5050	Base unit, 50' W, less than 100' tall, rent/mo				Ea.	3,100			3,100	3,400
5100	Less than 200' tall, rent/mo					3,900			3,900	4,300
5150	Less than 300' tall, rent/mo					4,575			4,575	5,050
5200	Less than 400' tall, rent/mo					5,200			5,200	5,700
5250	Set up and demob, per unit, less than 100' tall	B-68F	16.60	1.446	C.S.F.		53.50	19.55	73.05	112
5300	Less than 200' tall		25	.960			35.50	13	48.50	74.50
5350	Less than 300' tall		30	.800			29.50	10.80	40.30	62
5400	Less than 400' tall		33	.727			27	9.85	36.85	56.50
5500	Mobilization (price includes freight in and out) per unit				Ea.				1,100	1,225

01 54 Construction Aids

01 54 23 – Temporary Scaffolding and Platforms

01 54 23.80 Staging Aids

		Crew	Daily Output	Labor-Hours	Unit	Material	2014 Bare Costs Labor	Equipment	Total	Total Incl O&P
0010	**STAGING AIDS** and fall protection equipment									
0100	Sidewall staging bracket, tubular, buy				Ea.	51			51	56
0110	Cost each per day, based on 250 days use				Day	.20			.20	.22
0200	Guard post, buy				Ea.	48			48	53
0210	Cost each per day, based on 250 days use				Day	.19			.19	.21
0300	End guard chains, buy per pair				Pair	36			36	39.50
0310	Cost per set per day, based on 250 days use				Day	.20			.20	.22
1000	Roof shingling bracket, steel, buy				Ea.	8.90			8.90	9.80
1010	Cost each per day, based on 250 days use				Day	.04			.04	.04
1100	Wood bracket, buy				Ea.	16.80			16.80	18.50
1110	Cost each per day, based on 250 days use				Day	.07			.07	.07
2000	Ladder jack, aluminum, buy per pair				Pair	118			118	130
2010	Cost per pair per day, based on 250 days use				Day	.47			.47	.52
2100	Steel siderail jack, buy per pair				Pair	97.50			97.50	107
2110	Cost per pair per day, based on 250 days use				Day	.39			.39	.43
3000	Laminated wood plank, 2" x 10" x 16', buy				Ea.	52			52	57.50
3010	Cost each per day, based on 250 days use				Day	.21			.21	.23
3100	Aluminum scaffolding plank, 20" wide x 24' long, buy				Ea.	820			820	900
3110	Cost each per day, based on 250 days use				Day	3.28			3.28	3.60
4000	Nylon full body harness, lanyard and rope grab				Ea.	176			176	193
4010	Cost each per day, based on 250 days use				Day	.70			.70	.77
4100	Rope for safety line, 5/8" x 100' nylon, buy				Ea.	56			56	61.50
4110	Cost each per day, based on 250 days use				Day	.22			.22	.25
4200	Permanent U-Bolt roof anchor, buy				Ea.	30			30	33
4300	Temporary (one use) roof ridge anchor, buy				"	32			32	35.50
5000	Installation (setup and removal) of staging aids									
5010	Sidewall staging bracket	2 Carp	64	.250	Ea.		8.95		8.95	15.05
5020	Guard post with 2 wood rails	"	64	.250			8.95		8.95	15.05
5030	End guard chains, set	1 Carp	64	.125			4.47		4.47	7.50
5100	Roof shingling bracket		96	.083			2.98		2.98	5
5200	Ladder jack		64	.125			4.47		4.47	7.50
5300	Wood plank, 2" x 10" x 16'	2 Carp	80	.200			7.15		7.15	12.05
5310	Aluminum scaffold plank, 20" x 24'	"	40	.400			14.30		14.30	24
5410	Safety rope	1 Carp	40	.200			7.15		7.15	12.05
5420	Permanent U-Bolt roof anchor (install only)	2 Carp	40	.400			14.30		14.30	24
5430	Temporary roof ridge anchor (install only)	1 Carp	64	.125			4.47		4.47	7.50

01 54 26 – Temporary Swing Staging

01 54 26.50 Swing Staging

		Crew	Daily Output	Labor-Hours	Unit	Material	2014 Bare Costs Labor	Equipment	Total	Total Incl O&P
0010	**SWING STAGING**, 500 lb. cap., 2' wide to 24' long, hand operated									
0020	steel cable type, with 60' cables, buy				Ea.	4,900			4,900	5,375
0030	Rent per month				"	490			490	540
0600	Lightweight (not for masons) 24' long for 150' height,									
0610	manual type, buy				Ea.	10,200			10,200	11,200
0620	Rent per month					1,025			1,025	1,125
0700	Powered, electric or air, to 150' high, buy					25,600			25,600	28,200
0710	Rent per month					1,800			1,800	1,975
0780	To 300' high, buy					26,000			26,000	28,600
0800	Rent per month					1,825			1,825	2,000
1000	Bosun's chair or work basket 3' x 3.5', to 300' high, electric, buy					10,400			10,400	11,400
1010	Rent per month					730			730	800
2200	Move swing staging (setup and remove)	E-4	2	16	Move		620	71	691	1,250

01 54 Construction Aids

01 54 36 – Equipment Mobilization

01 54 36.50 Mobilization	Crew	Daily Output	Labor-Hours	Unit	Material	2014 Bare Costs Labor	Equipment	Total	Total Incl O&P
0010 **MOBILIZATION** (Use line item again for demobilization) R015433-10									
0015 Up to 25 mi. haul dist. (50 mi. RT for mob/demob crew)									
0020 Dozer, loader, backhoe, excav., grader, paver, roller, 70 to 150 H.P.	B-34N	4	2	Ea.		59.50	142	201.50	256
0100 Above 150 HP	B-34K	3	2.667			79	320	399	485
0300 Scraper, towed type (incl. tractor), 6 C.Y. capacity		3	2.667			79	320	399	485
0400 10 C.Y.		2.50	3.200			95	385	480	585
0600 Self-propelled scraper, 15 C.Y.		2.50	3.200			95	385	480	585
0700 24 C.Y.		2	4			119	480	599	730
0900 Shovel or dragline, 3/4 C.Y.		3.60	2.222			66	267	333	405
1000 1-1/2 C.Y.		3	2.667			79	320	399	485
1100 Small equipment, placed in rear of, or towed by pickup truck	A-3A	8	1			29	21	50	71
1150 Equip up to 70 HP, on flatbed trailer behind pickup truck	A-3D	4	2			57.50	70.50	128	174
2000 Crane, truck-mounted, up to 75 ton, (driver only, one-way)	1 Eqhv	7.20	1.111			43		43	71
2100 Crane, truck-mounted, over 75 ton	A-3E	2.50	6.400			219	67.50	286.50	440
2200 Crawler-mounted, up to 75 ton	A-3F	2	8			273	500	773	1,000
2300 Over 75 ton	A-3G	1.50	10.667			365	755	1,120	1,425
2500 For each additional 5 miles haul distance, add						10%	10%		
3000 For large pieces of equipment, allow for assembly/knockdown									
3001 For mob/demob of vibrofloatation equip, see Section 31 45 13.10									
3100 For mob/demob of micro-tunneling equip, see Section 33 05 23.19									
3200 For mob/demob of pile driving equip, see Section 31 62 19.10									
3300 For mob/demob of caisson drilling equip, see Section 31 63 26.13									

01 54 39 – Construction Equipment

01 54 39.70 Small Tools

0010 **SMALL TOOLS** R013113-50									
0020 As % of contractor's bare labor cost for project, minimum				Total		.50%			
0100 Maximum				"		2%			

01 55 Vehicular Access and Parking

01 55 23 – Temporary Roads

01 55 23.50 Roads and Sidewalks

	Crew	Daily Output	Labor-Hours	Unit	Material	Labor	Equipment	Total	Total Incl O&P
0010 **ROADS AND SIDEWALKS** Temporary									
0050 Roads, gravel fill, no surfacing, 4" gravel depth	B-14	715	.067	S.Y.	3.98	2.01	.51	6.50	8.30
0100 8" gravel depth	"	615	.078	"	7.95	2.33	.59	10.87	13.30
1001 Ramp, 3/4" plywood on 2" x 6" joists, 16" O.C.	2 Clab	300	.053	S.F.	1.44	1.50		2.94	4.11
1101 On 2" x 10" joists, 16" O.C.	"	275	.058	"	1.99	1.64		3.63	4.95

01 56 Temporary Barriers and Enclosures

01 56 13 – Temporary Air Barriers

01 56 13.60 Tarpaulins

				Unit	Material	Labor	Equipment	Total	Total Incl O&P
0010 **TARPAULINS**									
0020 Cotton duck, 10 oz. to 13.13 oz. per S.Y., 6'x8'				S.F.	.75			.75	.83
0050 30'x30'					.43			.43	.47
0100 Polyvinyl coated nylon, 14 oz. to 18 oz., minimum					1.30			1.30	1.43
0150 Maximum					1.19			1.19	1.31
0200 Reinforced polyethylene 3 mils thick, white					.03			.03	.03
0300 4 mils thick, white, clear or black					.09			.09	.10
0400 5.5 mils thick, clear					.17			.17	.19

01 56 Temporary Barriers and Enclosures

01 56 13 – Temporary Air Barriers

01 56 13.60 Tarpaulins

		Crew	Daily Output	Labor-Hours	Unit	Material	2014 Bare Costs Labor	Equipment	Total	Total Incl O&P
0500	White, fire retardant				S.F.	.41			.41	.45
0600	12 mils, oil resistant, fire retardant					.27			.27	.30
0700	8.5 mils, black					.57			.57	.63
0710	Woven polyethylene, 6 mils thick					.17			.17	.19
0730	Polyester reinforced w/integral fastening system 11 mils thick					.24			.24	.26
0740	Mylar polyester, non-reinforced, 7 mils thick					1.17			1.17	1.29

01 56 13.90 Winter Protection

		Crew	Daily Output	Labor-Hours	Unit	Material	2014 Bare Costs Labor	Equipment	Total	Total Incl O&P
0010	**WINTER PROTECTION**									
0100	Framing to close openings	2 Clab	500	.032	S.F.	.41	.90		1.31	1.97
0200	Tarpaulins hung over scaffolding, 8 uses, not incl. scaffolding		1500	.011		.25	.30		.55	.79
0250	Tarpaulin polyester reinf. w/integral fastening system 11 mils thick		1600	.010		.24	.28		.52	.73
0300	Prefab fiberglass panels, steel frame, 8 uses		1200	.013		2.20	.38		2.58	3.05

01 56 16 – Temporary Dust Barriers

01 56 16.10 Dust Barriers, Temporary

		Crew	Daily Output	Labor-Hours	Unit	Material	2014 Bare Costs Labor	Equipment	Total	Total Incl O&P
0010	**DUST BARRIERS, TEMPORARY**									
0020	Spring loaded telescoping pole & head, to 12', erect and dismantle	1 Clab	240	.033	Ea.		.94		.94	1.58
0025	Cost per day (based upon 250 days)				Day	.24			.24	.26
0030	To 21', erect and dismantle	1 Clab	240	.033	Ea.		.94		.94	1.58
0035	Cost per day (based upon 250 days)				Day	.38			.38	.42
0040	Accessories, caution tape reel, erect and dismantle	1 Clab	480	.017	Ea.		.47		.47	.79
0045	Cost per day (based upon 250 days)				Day	.36			.36	.40
0060	Foam rail and connector, erect and dismantle	1 Clab	240	.033	Ea.		.94		.94	1.58
0065	Cost per day (based upon 250 days)				Day	.10			.10	.11
0070	Caution tape	1 Clab	384	.021	C.L.F.	2.70	.59		3.29	3.96
0080	Zipper, standard duty		60	.133	Ea.	15.95	3.76		19.71	24
0090	Heavy duty		48	.167	"	18.90	4.70		23.60	29
0100	Polyethylene sheet, 4 mil		37	.216	Sq.	2.91	6.10		9.01	13.45
0110	6 mil		37	.216	"	3.98	6.10		10.08	14.65
1001	Dust partition, 6 mil polyethylene, 1" x 3" frame	2 Clab	2000	.008	S.F.	.35	.23		.58	.77
1081	2" x 4" frame	"	2000	.008	"	.32	.23		.55	.73

01 56 23 – Temporary Barricades

01 56 23.10 Barricades

		Crew	Daily Output	Labor-Hours	Unit	Material	2014 Bare Costs Labor	Equipment	Total	Total Incl O&P
0011	**BARRICADES**									
0030	5' high, 3 rail @ 2" x 8", fixed	2 Clab	20	.800	L.F.	5.75	22.50		28.25	44.50
0200	Precast barrier walls, 10' sections	B-6	240	.100	"	32.50	3.09	1.52	37.11	43
0300	Stock units, 6' high, 8' wide, plain, buy				Ea.	390			390	430
0350	With reflective tape, buy				"	405			405	445
0400	Break-a-way 3" PVC pipe barricade									
0410	with 3 ea. 1' x 4' reflectorized panels, buy				Ea.	128			128	141
0500	Plywood with steel legs, 24" wide					59			59	65
0600	Warning signal flag tree, 11' high, 2 flags, buy					238			238	262
0800	Traffic cones, PVC, 18" high					11			11	12.10
0850	28" high					18.60			18.60	20.50
1001	Guardrail, wooden, 3' high, 1" x 6" on 2" x 4" posts	2 Clab	200	.080	L.F.	1.29	2.26		3.55	5.20
1101	2" x 6" on 4" x 4" posts	"	165	.097		2.79	2.73		5.52	7.65
1200	Portable metal with base pads, buy					15.55			15.55	17.10
1251	Typical installation, assume 10 reuses	2 Clab	600	.027		2.55	.75		3.30	4.08
3000	Detour signs, set up and remove									
3010	Reflective aluminum, MUTCD, 24" x 24", post mounted	1 Clab	20	.400	Ea.	2.35	11.30		13.65	21.50

01 56 Temporary Barriers and Enclosures

01 56 26 – Temporary Fencing

01 56 26.50 Temporary Fencing		Crew	Daily Output	Labor-Hours	Unit	Material	2014 Bare Costs Labor	Equipment	Total	Total Incl O&P
0010	**TEMPORARY FENCING**									
0020	Chain link, 11 ga., 4' high	2 Clab	400	.040	L.F.	2.95	1.13		4.08	5.15
0100	6' high		300	.053		2.95	1.50		4.45	5.80
0200	Rented chain link, 6' high, to 1000' (up to 12 mo.)		400	.040		4.39	1.13		5.52	6.75
0250	Over 1000' (up to 12 mo.)		300	.053		4.29	1.50		5.79	7.25
0351	Plywood, painted, 2" x 4" frame, 4' high	3 Clab	135	.178		6.25	5		11.25	15.30
0401	4" x 4" frame, 8' high	"	110	.218		11.45	6.15		17.60	23
0501	Wire mesh on 4" x 4" posts, 4' high	2 Clab	100	.160		9.75	4.51		14.26	18.30
0551	8' high	"	80	.200		14.70	5.65		20.35	25.50

01 56 29 – Temporary Protective Walkways

01 56 29.50 Protection		Crew	Daily Output	Labor-Hours	Unit	Material	2014 Bare Costs Labor	Equipment	Total	Total Incl O&P
0010	**PROTECTION**									
0020	Stair tread, 2" x 12" planks, 1 use	1 Carp	75	.107	Tread	4.57	3.81		8.38	11.45
0100	Exterior plywood, 1/2" thick, 1 use		65	.123		1.79	4.40		6.19	9.35
0200	3/4" thick, 1 use		60	.133		2.64	4.77		7.41	10.90
2201	Sidewalks, 2" x 12" planks, 2 uses	1 Clab	350	.023	S.F.	.76	.64		1.40	1.92
2301	Exterior plywood, 2 uses, 1/2" thick		750	.011		.30	.30		.60	.84
2401	5/8" thick		650	.012		.37	.35		.72	.99
2501	3/4" thick		600	.013		.44	.38		.82	1.11

01 56 32 – Temporary Security

01 56 32.50 Watchman		Crew	Daily Output	Labor-Hours	Unit	Material	2014 Bare Costs Labor	Equipment	Total	Total Incl O&P
0010	**WATCHMAN**									
0020	Service, monthly basis, uniformed person, minimum				Hr.				25	27.50
0100	Maximum								45.50	50
0200	Person and command dog, minimum								31	34
0300	Maximum								54.50	60
0500	Sentry dog, leased, with job patrol (yard dog), 1 dog				Week				290	320
0600	2 dogs				"				390	430
0800	Purchase, trained sentry dog, minimum				Ea.				1,375	1,500
0900	Maximum				"				2,725	3,000

01 58 Project Identification

01 58 13 – Temporary Project Signage

01 58 13.50 Signs		Crew	Daily Output	Labor-Hours	Unit	Material	2014 Bare Costs Labor	Equipment	Total	Total Incl O&P
0010	**SIGNS**									
0020	High intensity reflectorized, no posts, buy				S.F.	31.50			31.50	34.50

01 71 Examination and Preparation

01 71 23 – Field Engineering

01 71 23.13 Construction Layout		Crew	Daily Output	Labor-Hours	Unit	Material	2014 Bare Costs Labor	Equipment	Total	Total Incl O&P
0010	**CONSTRUCTION LAYOUT**									
1100	Crew for layout of building, trenching or pipe laying, 2 person crew	A-6	1	16	Day		570	71.50	641.50	1,025
1200	3 person crew	A-7	1	24			925	71.50	996.50	1,625
1400	Crew for roadway layout, 4 person crew	A-8	1	32			1,200	71.50	1,271.50	2,075

01 71 Examination and Preparation

01 71 23 – Field Engineering

01 71 23.19 Surveyor Stakes		Crew	Daily Output	Labor-Hours	Unit	Material	2014 Bare Costs Labor	Equipment	Total	Total Incl O&P
0010	**SURVEYOR STAKES**									
0020	Hardwood, 1" x 1" x 48" long				C	66			66	72.50
0100	2" x 2" x 18" long					74			74	81.50
0150	2" x 2" x 24" long					130			130	143

01 74 Cleaning and Waste Management

01 74 13 – Progress Cleaning

01 74 13.20 Cleaning Up		Crew	Daily Output	Labor-Hours	Unit	Material	2014 Bare Costs Labor	Equipment	Total	Total Incl O&P
0010	**CLEANING UP**									
0020	After job completion, allow, minimum				Job				.30%	.30%
0040	Maximum				"				1%	1%
0050	Cleanup of floor area, continuous, per day, during const.	A-5	24	.750	M.S.F.	.81	21	2.81	24.62	39.50
0100	Final by GC at end of job	"	11.50	1.565	"	.86	44.50	5.85	51.21	82
0200	Rubbish removal, see Section 02 41 19.19									

01 76 Protecting Installed Construction

01 76 13 – Temporary Protection of Installed Construction

01 76 13.20 Temporary Protection		Crew	Daily Output	Labor-Hours	Unit	Material	2014 Bare Costs Labor	Equipment	Total	Total Incl O&P
0010	**TEMPORARY PROTECTION**									
0020	Flooring, 1/8" tempered hardboard, taped seams	2 Carp	1500	.011	S.F.	.39	.38		.77	1.07
0030	Peel away carpet protection	1 Clab	3200	.003	"	.11	.07		.18	.24

01 91 Commissioning

01 91 13 – General Commissioning Requirements

01 91 13.50 Building Commissioning		Crew	Daily Output	Labor-Hours	Unit	Material	2014 Bare Costs Labor	Equipment	Total	Total Incl O&P
0010	**BUILDING COMMISSIONING**									
0100	Basic building commissioning, minimum				%				.25%	.25%
0150	Maximum								.50%	.50%
0200	Enhanced building commissioning, minimum								.50%	.50%
0250	Maximum								1%	1%

Division Notes

		CREW	DAILY OUTPUT	LABOR-HOURS	UNIT	BARE COSTS				TOTAL INCL O&P
						MAT.	LABOR	EQUIP.	TOTAL	

Estimating Tips

02 30 00 Subsurface Investigation

In preparing estimates on structures involving earthwork or foundations, all information concerning soil characteristics should be obtained. Look particularly for hazardous waste, evidence of prior dumping of debris, and previous stream beds.

02 40 00 Demolition and Structure Moving

The costs shown for selective demolition do not include rubbish handling or disposal. These items should be estimated separately using RSMeans data or other sources.

- Historic preservation often requires that the contractor remove materials from the existing structure, rehab them, and replace them. The estimator must be aware of any related measures and precautions that must be taken when doing selective demolition and cutting and patching. Requirements may include special handling and storage, as well as security.

- In addition to Subdivision 02 41 00, you can find selective demolition items in each division. Example: Roofing demolition is in Division 7.

02 40 00 Building Deconstruction

This section provides costs for the careful dismantling and recycling of most of low-rise building materials.

02 50 00 Containment of Hazardous Waste

This section addresses on-site hazardous waste disposal costs.

02 80 00 Hazardous Material Disposal/ Remediation

This subdivision includes information on hazardous waste handling, asbestos remediation, lead remediation, and mold remediation. See reference R028213-20 and R028319-60 for further guidance in using these unit price lines.

02 90 00 Monitoring Chemical Sampling, Testing Analysis

This section provides costs for on-site sampling and testing hazardous waste.

Reference Numbers

Reference numbers are shown in shaded boxes at the beginning of some major classifications. These numbers refer to related items in the Reference Section. The reference information may be an estimating procedure, an alternate pricing method, or technical information.

Note: Not all subdivisions listed here necessarily appear in this publication.

Division 2 - Existing Conditions

02 21 Surveys

02 21 13 – Site Surveys

02 21 13.09 Topographical Surveys	Crew	Daily Output	Labor-Hours	Unit	Material	2014 Bare Costs Labor	2014 Bare Costs Equipment	Total	Total Incl O&P
0010 TOPOGRAPHICAL SURVEYS									
0020 Topographical surveying, conventional, minimum	A-7	3.30	7.273	Acre	19.20	280	21.50	320.70	515
0100 Maximum	A-8	.60	53.333	"	58.50	2,000	119	2,177.50	3,550

02 21 13.13 Boundary and Survey Markers

	Crew	Daily Output	Labor-Hours	Unit	Material	Labor	Equipment	Total	Total Incl O&P
0010 BOUNDARY AND SURVEY MARKERS									
0300 Lot location and lines, large quantities, minimum	A-7	2	12	Acre	34	460	35.50	529.50	850
0320 Average	"	1.25	19.200		54	740	57	851	1,375
0400 Small quantities, maximum	A-8	1	32	↓	71.50	1,200	71.50	1,343	2,150
0600 Monuments, 3' long	A-7	10	2.400	Ea.	34	92.50	7.15	133.65	200
0800 Property lines, perimeter, cleared land	"	1000	.024	L.F.	.04	.92	.07	1.03	1.67
0900 Wooded land	A-8	875	.037	"	.06	1.37	.08	1.51	2.46

02 21 13.16 Aerial Surveys

	Crew	Daily Output	Labor-Hours	Unit	Material	Labor	Equipment	Total	Total Incl O&P
0010 AERIAL SURVEYS									
1500 Aerial surveying, including ground control, minimum fee, 10 acres				Total					4,700
1510 100 acres									9,400
1550 From existing photography, deduct				↓					1,625
1600 2' contours, 10 acres				Acre					470
1850 100 acres									94
2000 1000 acres									90
2050 10,000 acres				↓					85

02 32 Geotechnical Investigations

02 32 13 – Subsurface Drilling and Sampling

02 32 13.10 Boring and Exploratory Drilling

	Crew	Daily Output	Labor-Hours	Unit	Material	Labor	Equipment	Total	Total Incl O&P
0010 BORING AND EXPLORATORY DRILLING									
0020 Borings, initial field stake out & determination of elevations	A-6	1	16	Day		570	71.50	641.50	1,025
0100 Drawings showing boring details				Total		335		335	425
0200 Report and recommendations from P.E.						775		775	970
0300 Mobilization and demobilization	B-55	4	4	↓		114	280	394	500
0350 For over 100 miles, per added mile		450	.036	Mile		1.01	2.49	3.50	4.44
0600 Auger holes in earth, no samples, 2-1/2" diameter		78.60	.204	L.F.		5.80	14.25	20.05	25.50
0650 4" diameter		67.50	.237			6.75	16.60	23.35	29.50
0800 Cased borings in earth, with samples, 2-1/2" diameter		55.50	.288		22	8.20	20	50.20	60
0850 4" diameter	↓	32.60	.491		33.50	14	34.50	82	98
1000 Drilling in rock, "BX" core, no sampling	B-56	34.90	.458			12.95	46	58.95	72.50
1050 With casing & sampling		31.70	.505		22	14.25	50.50	86.75	104
1200 "NX" core, no sampling		25.92	.617			17.40	62	79.40	97.50
1250 With casing and sampling	↓	25	.640	↓	26	18.05	64.50	108.55	130
1400 Borings, earth, drill rig and crew with truck mounted auger	B-55	1	16	Day		455	1,125	1,580	2,000
1450 Rock using crawler type drill	B-56	1	16	"		450	1,600	2,050	2,525
1500 For inner city borings add, minimum								10%	10%
1510 Maximum								20%	20%

02 32 19 – Exploratory Excavations

02 32 19.10 Test Pits

	Crew	Daily Output	Labor-Hours	Unit	Material	Labor	Equipment	Total	Total Incl O&P
0010 TEST PITS									
0020 Hand digging, light soil	1 Clab	4.50	1.778	C.Y.		50		50	84.50
0100 Heavy soil	"	2.50	3.200			90		90	152
0120 Loader-backhoe, light soil	B-11M	28	.571			18.80	14.20	33	47
0130 Heavy soil	"	20	.800	↓		26.50	19.90	46.40	66
1000 Subsurface exploration, mobilization				Mile				6.75	8.40

02 32 Geotechnical Investigations

02 32 19 – Exploratory Excavations

02 32 19.10 Test Pits	Crew	Daily Output	Labor-Hours	Unit	Material	2014 Bare Costs Labor	2014 Bare Costs Equipment	Total	Total Incl O&P
1010	Difficult access for rig, add				Hr.				260	320
1020	Auger borings, drill rig, incl. samples				L.F.				26.50	33
1030	Hand auger								31.50	40
1050	Drill and sample every 5', split spoon				↓				31.50	40
1060	Extra samples				Ea.				36	45.50

02 41 Demolition

02 41 13 – Selective Site Demolition

02 41 13.15 Hydrodemolition

		Crew	Daily Output	Labor-Hours	Unit	Material	Labor	Equipment	Total	Total Incl O&P
0010	**HYDRODEMOLITION** R024119-10									
0015	Hydrodemolition, concrete pavement, 4000 PSI, 2" depth	B-5	500	.080	S.F.		2.44	2.85	5.29	7.20
0120	4" depth		450	.089			2.71	3.17	5.88	8
0130	6" depth		400	.100			3.05	3.56	6.61	9
0410	6000 PSI, 2" depth		410	.098			2.97	3.48	6.45	8.80
0420	4" depth		350	.114			3.48	4.07	7.55	10.35
0430	6" depth		300	.133			4.07	4.75	8.82	12
0510	8000 PSI, 2" depth		330	.121			3.70	4.32	8.02	10.95
0520	4" depth		280	.143			4.36	5.10	9.46	12.90
0530	6" depth	↓	240	.167	↓		5.10	5.95	11.05	15.05

02 41 13.17 Demolish, Remove Pavement and Curb

		Crew	Daily Output	Labor-Hours	Unit	Material	Labor	Equipment	Total	Total Incl O&P
0010	**DEMOLISH, REMOVE PAVEMENT AND CURB** R024119-10									
5010	Pavement removal, bituminous roads, up to 3" thick	B-38	690	.035	S.Y.		1.07	.79	1.86	2.67
5050	4" to 6" thick		420	.057			1.76	1.30	3.06	4.38
5100	Bituminous driveways		640	.038			1.16	.85	2.01	2.88
5200	Concrete to 6" thick, hydraulic hammer, mesh reinforced		255	.094			2.91	2.14	5.05	7.20
5300	Rod reinforced		200	.120	↓		3.71	2.73	6.44	9.20
5400	Concrete, 7" to 24" thick, plain		33	.727	C.Y.		22.50	16.55	39.05	55.50
5500	Reinforced	↓	24	1	"		31	22.50	53.50	76.50
5600	With hand held air equipment, bituminous, to 6" thick	B-39	1900	.025	S.F.		.72	.12	.84	1.35
5700	Concrete to 6" thick, no reinforcing		1600	.030			.86	.15	1.01	1.60
5800	Mesh reinforced		1400	.034			.98	.17	1.15	1.83
5900	Rod reinforced	↓	765	.063	↓		1.79	.31	2.10	3.35
6000	Curbs, concrete, plain	B-6	360	.067	L.F.		2.06	1.01	3.07	4.56
6100	Reinforced		275	.087			2.69	1.33	4.02	5.95
6200	Granite		360	.067			2.06	1.01	3.07	4.56
6300	Bituminous	↓	528	.045	↓		1.40	.69	2.09	3.11

02 41 13.33 Minor Site Demolition

		Crew	Daily Output	Labor-Hours	Unit	Material	Labor	Equipment	Total	Total Incl O&P
0010	**MINOR SITE DEMOLITION** R024119-10									
0015	No hauling, abandon catch basin or manhole	B-6	7	3.429	Ea.		106	52	158	235
0020	Remove existing catch basin or manhole, masonry		4	6			185	91.50	276.50	410
0030	Catch basin or manhole frames and covers, stored		13	1.846			57	28	85	127
0040	Remove and reset	↓	7	3.429			106	52	158	235
0100	Roadside delineators, remove only	B-80	175	.137			3.96	4.33	8.29	11.40
0110	Remove and reset	"	100	.240	↓		6.95	7.60	14.55	20
0800	Guiderail, corrugated steel, remove only	B-80A	100	.240	L.F.		6.75	3.33	10.08	15.05
0850	Remove and reset	"	40	.600	"		16.90	8.35	25.25	37.50
0860	Guide posts, remove only	B-80B	120	.267	Ea.		8.05	2.07	10.12	15.80
0870	Remove and reset	B-55	50	.320			9.15	22.50	31.65	40
0901	Hydrants, fire, remove only	2 Skwk	4.70	3.404			124		124	209
0951	Remove and reset	"	1.40	11.429	↓		415		415	700

02 41 13.33 Minor Site Demolition

		Crew	Daily Output	Labor-Hours	Unit	Material	2014 Bare Costs Labor	Equipment	Total	Total Incl O&P
1000	Masonry walls, block, solid	B-5	1800	.022	C.F.		.68	.79	1.47	2.01
1200	Brick, solid		900	.044			1.36	1.58	2.94	4.01
1400	Stone, with mortar		900	.044			1.36	1.58	2.94	4.01
1500	Dry set		1500	.027			.81	.95	1.76	2.40
1600	Median barrier, precast concrete, remove and store	B-3	430	.112	L.F.		3.41	6	9.41	12.30
1610	Remove and reset	"	390	.123			3.77	6.60	10.37	13.55
2900	Pipe removal, sewer/water, no excavation, 12" diameter	B-6	175	.137			4.23	2.09	6.32	9.40
2930	15"-18" diameter	B-12Z	150	.160			5.05	10.90	15.95	20.50
2960	21"-24" diameter		120	.200			6.35	13.65	20	25.50
3000	27"-36" diameter		90	.267			8.45	18.20	26.65	34
3200	Steel, welded connections, 4" diameter	B-6	160	.150			4.63	2.28	6.91	10.25
3300	10" diameter	"	80	.300			9.25	4.57	13.82	20.50
3500	Railroad track removal, ties and track	B-13	330	.145			4.40	2.26	6.66	9.90
3600	Ballast	B-14	500	.096	C.Y.		2.87	.73	3.60	5.60
3700	Remove and re-install, ties & track using new bolts & spikes		50	.960	L.F.		28.50	7.30	35.80	56
3800	Turnouts using new bolts and spikes		1	48	Ea.		1,425	365	1,790	2,800
4000	Sidewalk removal, bituminous, 2" thick	B-6	350	.069	S.Y.		2.12	1.04	3.16	4.69
4010	2-1/2" thick		325	.074			2.28	1.12	3.40	5.05
4050	Brick, set in mortar		185	.130			4.01	1.97	5.98	8.85
4100	Concrete, plain, 4"		160	.150			4.63	2.28	6.91	10.25
4110	Plain, 5"		140	.171			5.30	2.61	7.91	11.70
4120	Plain, 6"		120	.200			6.20	3.04	9.24	13.70
4200	Mesh reinforced, concrete, 4"		150	.160			4.94	2.44	7.38	10.95
4210	5" thick		131	.183			5.65	2.79	8.44	12.50
4220	6" thick		112	.214			6.60	3.26	9.86	14.65
4300	Slab on grade removal, plain	B-5	45	.889	C.Y.		27	31.50	58.50	80.50
4310	Mesh reinforced		33	1.212			37	43	80	110
4320	Rod reinforced		25	1.600			49	57	106	145
4400	For congested sites or small quantities, add up to								200%	200%
4450	For disposal on site, add	B-11A	232	.069			2.27	5.70	7.97	10.10
4500	To 5 miles, add	B-34D	76	.105			3.12	9.90	13.02	16.10

02 41 13.60 Selective Demolition Fencing

		Crew	Daily Output	Labor-Hours	Unit	Material	Labor	Equipment	Total	Total Incl O&P
0010	**SELECTIVE DEMOLITION FENCING** R024119-10									
1600	Fencing, barbed wire, 3 strand	2 Clab	430	.037	L.F.		1.05		1.05	1.77
1650	5 strand	"	280	.057			1.61		1.61	2.71
1700	Chain link, posts & fabric, 8' to 10' high, remove only	B-6	445	.054			1.67	.82	2.49	3.69
1750	Remove and reset	"	70	.343			10.60	5.20	15.80	23.50

02 41 16.13 Building Demolition

		Crew	Daily Output	Labor-Hours	Unit	Material	Labor	Equipment	Total	Total Incl O&P
0010	**BUILDING DEMOLITION** Large urban projects, incl. 20 mi. haul R024119-10									
0011	No foundation or dump fees, C.F. is vol. of building standing									
0020	Steel	B-8	21500	.003	C.F.		.08	.15	.23	.31
0050	Concrete		15300	.004			.12	.22	.34	.43
0080	Masonry		20100	.003			.09	.17	.26	.33
0100	Mixture of types		20100	.003			.09	.17	.26	.33
0500	Small bldgs, or single bldgs, no salvage included, steel	B-3	14800	.003			.10	.17	.27	.36
0600	Concrete		11300	.004			.13	.23	.36	.47
0650	Masonry		14800	.003			.10	.17	.27	.36
0700	Wood		14800	.003			.10	.17	.27	.36
0750	For buildings with no interior walls, deduct								50%	50%
1000	Demoliton single family house, one story, wood 1600 S.F.	B-3	1	48	Ea.		1,475	2,575	4,050	5,275
1020	3200 S.F.		.50	96			2,925	5,150	8,075	10,600

02 41 Demolition

02 41 16 – Structure Demolition

02 41 16.13 Building Demolition

		Crew	Daily Output	Labor-Hours	Unit	Material	2014 Bare Costs Labor	Equipment	Total	Total Incl O&P
1200	Demoliton two family house, two story, wood 2400 S.F.	B-3	.67	71.964	Ea.		2,200	3,850	6,050	7,925
1220	4200 S.F.		.38	128			3,925	6,875	10,800	14,100
1300	Demoliton three family house, three story, wood 3200 S.F.		.50	96			2,925	5,150	8,075	10,600
1320	5400 S.F.	↓	.30	160	↓		4,900	8,575	13,475	17,600
5000	For buildings with no interior walls, deduct								50%	50%

02 41 16.15 Explosive/Implosive Demolition

		Crew	Daily Output	Labor-Hours	Unit	Material	2014 Bare Costs Labor	Equipment	Total	Total Incl O&P
0010	**EXPLOSIVE/IMPLOSIVE DEMOLITION** R024119-10									
0011	Large projects,									
0020	No disposal fee based on building volume, steel building	B-5B	16900	.003	C.F.		.09	.17	.26	.35
0100	Concrete building		16900	.003			.09	.17	.26	.35
0200	Masonry building	↓	16900	.003	↓		.09	.17	.26	.35
0400	Disposal of material, minimum	B-3	445	.108	C.Y.		3.30	5.80	9.10	11.85
0500	Maximum	"	365	.132	"		4.02	7.05	11.07	14.50

02 41 16.17 Building Demolition Footings and Foundations

		Crew	Daily Output	Labor-Hours	Unit	Material	2014 Bare Costs Labor	Equipment	Total	Total Incl O&P
0010	**BUILDING DEMOLITION FOOTINGS AND FOUNDATIONS** R024119-10									
0200	Floors, concrete slab on grade,									
0240	4" thick, plain concrete	B-9	500	.080	S.F.		2.29	.47	2.76	4.36
0280	Reinforced, wire mesh		470	.085			2.43	.50	2.93	4.65
0300	Rods		400	.100			2.86	.58	3.44	5.45
0400	6" thick, plain concrete		375	.107			3.05	.62	3.67	5.85
0420	Reinforced, wire mesh		340	.118			3.36	.69	4.05	6.40
0440	Rods	↓	300	.133	↓		3.81	.78	4.59	7.25
1000	Footings, concrete, 1' thick, 2' wide	B-5	300	.133	L.F.		4.07	4.75	8.82	12
1080	1'-6" thick, 2' wide		250	.160			4.88	5.70	10.58	14.45
1120	3' wide		200	.200			6.10	7.10	13.20	18.05
1140	2' thick, 3' wide	↓	175	.229			6.95	8.15	15.10	20.50
1200	Average reinforcing, add								10%	10%
1220	Heavy reinforcing, add				↓				20%	20%
2000	Walls, block, 4" thick	1 Clab	180	.044	S.F.		1.25		1.25	2.11
2040	6" thick		170	.047			1.33		1.33	2.23
2080	8" thick		150	.053			1.50		1.50	2.53
2100	12" thick	↓	150	.053			1.50		1.50	2.53
2200	For horizontal reinforcing, add								10%	10%
2220	For vertical reinforcing, add								20%	20%
2400	Concrete, plain concrete, 6" thick	B-9	160	.250			7.15	1.46	8.61	13.65
2420	8" thick		140	.286			8.15	1.67	9.82	15.60
2440	10" thick		120	.333			9.55	1.95	11.50	18.20
2500	12" thick	↓	100	.400			11.45	2.34	13.79	22
2600	For average reinforcing, add								10%	10%
2620	For heavy reinforcing, add								20%	20%
4000	For congested sites or small quantities, add up to				↓				200%	200%
4200	Add for disposal, on site	B-11A	232	.069	C.Y.		2.27	5.70	7.97	10.10
4250	To five miles	B-30	220	.109	"		3.53	11	14.53	17.95

02 41 19 – Selective Demolition

02 41 19.13 Selective Building Demolition

		Crew	Daily Output	Labor-Hours	Unit	Material	2014 Bare Costs Labor	Equipment	Total	Total Incl O&P
0010	**SELECTIVE BUILDING DEMOLITION**									
0020	Costs related to selective demolition of specific building components									
0025	are included under Common Work Results (XX 05)									
0030	in the component's appropriate division.									

31

02 41 19.16 Selective Demolition, Cutout

		Crew	Daily Output	Labor-Hours	Unit	Material	2014 Bare Costs Labor	2014 Bare Costs Equipment	Total	Total Incl O&P
0010	**SELECTIVE DEMOLITION, CUTOUT** R024119-10									
0020	Concrete, elev. slab, light reinforcement, under 6 C.F.	B-9	65	.615	C.F.		17.60	3.59	21.19	33.50
0050	Light reinforcing, over 6 C.F.		75	.533	"		15.25	3.11	18.36	29
0200	Slab on grade to 6" thick, not reinforced, under 8 S.F.		85	.471	S.F.		13.45	2.75	16.20	25.50
0250	8 – 16 S.F.		175	.229	"		6.55	1.33	7.88	12.45
0255	For over 16 S.F. see Line 02 41 16.17 0400									
0600	Walls, not reinforced, under 6 C.F.	B-9	60	.667	C.F.		19.05	3.89	22.94	36.50
0650	6 – 12 C.F.	"	80	.500	"		14.30	2.92	17.22	27
0655	For over 12 C.F. see Line 02 41 16.17 2500									
1000	Concrete, elevated slab, bar reinforced, under 6 C.F.	B-9	45	.889	C.F.		25.50	5.20	30.70	48.50
1050	Bar reinforced, over 6 C.F.		50	.800	"		23	4.67	27.67	43.50
1200	Slab on grade to 6" thick, bar reinforced, under 8 S.F.		75	.533	S.F.		15.25	3.11	18.36	29
1250	8 – 16 S.F.		150	.267	"		7.65	1.56	9.21	14.55
1255	For over 16 S.F. see Line 02 41 16.17 0440									
1400	Walls, bar reinforced, under 6 C.F.	B-9	50	.800	C.F.		23	4.67	27.67	43.50
1450	6 – 12 C.F.	"	70	.571	"		16.35	3.34	19.69	31
1455	For over 12 C.F. see Lines 02 41 16.17 2500 and 2600									
2000	Brick, to 4 S.F. opening, not including toothing									
2040	4" thick	B-9	30	1.333	Ea.		38	7.80	45.80	72.50
2060	8" thick		18	2.222			63.50	13	76.50	121
2080	12" thick		10	4			114	23.50	137.50	219
2400	Concrete block, to 4 S.F. opening, 2" thick		35	1.143			32.50	6.65	39.15	62.50
2420	4" thick		30	1.333			38	7.80	45.80	72.50
2440	8" thick		27	1.481			42.50	8.65	51.15	81
2460	12" thick		24	1.667			47.50	9.75	57.25	90.50
2600	Gypsum block, to 4 S.F. opening, 2" thick		80	.500			14.30	2.92	17.22	27
2620	4" thick		70	.571			16.35	3.34	19.69	31
2640	8" thick		55	.727			21	4.25	25.25	39.50
2800	Terra cotta, to 4 S.F. opening, 4" thick		70	.571			16.35	3.34	19.69	31
2840	8" thick		65	.615			17.60	3.59	21.19	33.50
2880	12" thick		50	.800			23	4.67	27.67	43.50
3000	Toothing masonry cutouts, brick, soft old mortar	1 Brhe	40	.200	V.L.F.		5.75		5.75	9.60
3100	Hard mortar		30	.267			7.70		7.70	12.80
3200	Block, soft old mortar		70	.114			3.30		3.30	5.50
3400	Hard mortar		50	.160			4.62		4.62	7.70
6000	Walls, interior, not including re-framing,									
6010	openings to 5 S.F.									
6100	Drywall to 5/8" thick	1 Clab	24	.333	Ea.		9.40		9.40	15.80
6200	Paneling to 3/4" thick		20	.400			11.30		11.30	19
6300	Plaster, on gypsum lath		20	.400			11.30		11.30	19
6340	On wire lath		14	.571			16.10		16.10	27
7000	Wood frame, not including re-framing, openings to 5 S.F.									
7200	Floors, sheathing and flooring to 2" thick	1 Clab	5	1.600	Ea.		45		45	76
7310	Roofs, sheathing to 1" thick, not including roofing		6	1.333			37.50		37.50	63.50
7410	Walls, sheathing to 1" thick, not including siding		7	1.143			32		32	54

02 41 19.18 Selective Demolition, Disposal Only

		Crew	Daily Output	Labor-Hours	Unit	Material	2014 Bare Costs Labor	2014 Bare Costs Equipment	Total	Total Incl O&P
0010	**SELECTIVE DEMOLITION, DISPOSAL ONLY** R024119-10									
0015	Urban bldg w/salvage value allowed									
0020	Including loading and 5 mile haul to dump									
0200	Steel frame	B-3	430	.112	C.Y.		3.41	6	9.41	12.30
0300	Concrete frame		365	.132			4.02	7.05	11.07	14.50
0400	Masonry construction		445	.108			3.30	5.80	9.10	11.85

02 41 Demolition

02 41 19 – Selective Demolition

02 41 19.18 Selective Demolition, Disposal Only	Crew	Daily Output	Labor-Hours	Unit	Material	2014 Bare Costs Labor	2014 Bare Costs Equipment	Total	Total Incl O&P
0500 Wood frame	B-3	247	.194	C.Y.		5.95	10.45	16.40	21.50

02 41 19.19 Selective Facility Services Demolition

	Crew	Daily Output	Labor-Hours	Unit	Material	2014 Bare Costs Labor	2014 Bare Costs Equipment	Total	Total Incl O&P
0010 **SELECTIVE FACILITY SERVICES DEMOLITION**, Rubbish Handling R024119-10									
0020 The following are to be added to the demolition prices									
0050 The following are components for a complete chute system									
0100 Top chute circular steel, 4' long, 18" diameter R024119-30	B-1C	15	1.600	Ea.	256	46	30.50	332.50	390
0102 23" diameter		15	1.600		277	46	30.50	353.50	415
0104 27" diameter		15	1.600		299	46	30.50	375.50	440
0106 30" diameter		15	1.600		320	46	30.50	396.50	460
0108 33" diameter		15	1.600		340	46	30.50	416.50	485
0110 36" diameter		15	1.600		365	46	30.50	441.50	510
0112 Regular chute, 18" diameter		15	1.600		192	46	30.50	268.50	320
0114 23" diameter		15	1.600		213	46	30.50	289.50	345
0116 27" diameter		15	1.600		234	46	30.50	310.50	370
0118 30" diameter		15	1.600		256	46	30.50	332.50	390
0120 33" diameter		15	1.600		277	46	30.50	353.50	415
0122 36" diameter		15	1.600		299	46	30.50	375.50	440
0124 Control door chute, 18" diameter		15	1.600		365	46	30.50	441.50	510
0126 23" diameter		15	1.600		385	46	30.50	461.50	530
0128 27" diameter		15	1.600		405	46	30.50	481.50	555
0130 30" diameter		15	1.600		425	46	30.50	501.50	580
0132 33" diameter		15	1.600		445	46	30.50	521.50	600
0134 36" diameter		15	1.600		470	46	30.50	546.50	625
0136 Chute liners, 14 ga., 18-30" diameter		15	1.600		215	46	30.50	291.50	345
0138 33-36" diameter		15	1.600		269	46	30.50	345.50	405
0140 17% thinner chute, 30" diameter		15	1.600		213	46	30.50	289.50	345
0142 33% thinner chute, 30" diameter		15	1.600		160	46	30.50	236.50	287
0144 Top chute cover	1 Clab	24	.333		147	9.40		156.40	178
0146 Door chute cover	"	24	.333		147	9.40		156.40	178
0148 Top chute trough	2 Clab	12	1.333		490	37.50		527.50	605
0150 Bolt down frame & counter weights, 250 lb.	B-1	4	6		4,075	173		4,248	4,775
0152 500 lb.		4	6		5,950	173		6,123	6,850
0154 750 lb.		4	6		8,750	173		8,923	9,925
0156 1000 lb.		2.67	8.989		9,775	260		10,035	11,200
0158 1500 lb.		2.67	8.989		12,500	260		12,760	14,200
0160 Chute warning light system, 5 stories	B-1C	4	6		8,625	173	114	8,912	9,900
0162 10 stories	"	2	12		13,700	345	228	14,273	15,900
0164 Dust control device for dumpsters	1 Clab	8	1		98	28		126	156
0166 Install or replace breakaway cord		8	1		26	28		54	76
0168 Install or replace warning sign		16	.500		11	14.10		25.10	35.50
0600 Dumpster, weekly rental, 1 dump/week, 6 C.Y. capacity (2 Tons)				Week	415			415	455
0700 10 C.Y. capacity (3 Tons)					480			480	530
0725 20 C.Y. capacity (5 Tons) R024119-20					565			565	625
0800 30 C.Y. capacity (7 Tons)					730			730	800
0840 40 C.Y. capacity (10 Tons)					775			775	850
2000 Load, haul, dump and return, 50' haul, hand carried	2 Clab	24	.667	C.Y.		18.80		18.80	31.50
2005 Wheeled		37	.432			12.20		12.20	20.50
2040 51' to 100' haul, hand carried		16.50	.970			27.50		27.50	46
2045 Wheeled		25	.640			18.05		18.05	30.50
2080 Over 100' haul, add per 100 L.F., hand carried		35.50	.451			12.70		12.70	21.50
2085 Wheeled		54	.296			8.35		8.35	14.05
2120 In elevators, per 10 floors, add		140	.114			3.22		3.22	5.40

02 41 19 – Selective Demolition

02 41 19.19 Selective Facility Services Demolition

		Crew	Daily Output	Labor-Hours	Unit	Material	2014 Bare Costs Labor	2014 Bare Costs Equipment	Total	Total Incl O&P
2130	Load, haul, dump and return, up to 50' haul, incl. up to 5 rsr stair, hand	2 Clab	23	.696	C.Y.		19.60		19.60	33
2135	Wheeled		35	.457			12.90		12.90	21.50
2140	6 – 10 riser stairs, hand carried		22	.727			20.50		20.50	34.50
2145	Wheeled		34	.471			13.25		13.25	22.50
2150	11 – 20 riser stairs, hand carried		20	.800			22.50		22.50	38
2155	Wheeled		31	.516			14.55		14.55	24.50
2160	21 – 40 riser stairs, hand carried		16	1			28		28	47.50
2165	Wheeled		24	.667			18.80		18.80	31.50
2170	100' haul, incl. 5 riser stair, hand carried		15	1.067			30		30	50.50
2175	Wheeled		23	.696			19.60		19.60	33
2180	6 – 10 riser stair, hand carried		14	1.143			32		32	54
2185	Wheeled		21	.762			21.50		21.50	36
2190	11 – 20 riser stair, hand carried		12	1.333			37.50		37.50	63.50
2195	Wheeled		18	.889			25		25	42
2200	21 – 40 riser stair, hand carried		8	2			56.50		56.50	95
2205	Wheeled		12	1.333			37.50		37.50	63.50
2210	Over 100' haul, add per 100 L.F., hand carried		35.50	.451			12.70		12.70	21.50
2215	Wheeled		54	.296			8.35		8.35	14.05
2220	For each additional flight of stairs, up to 5 risers, add		550	.029	Flight		.82		.82	1.38
2225	6 – 10 risers, add		275	.058			1.64		1.64	2.76
2230	11 – 20 risers, add		138	.116			3.27		3.27	5.50
2235	21 – 40 risers, add		69	.232			6.55		6.55	11
3000	Loading & trucking, including 2 mile haul, chute loaded	B-16	45	.711	C.Y.		20.50	15.40	35.90	51.50
3040	Hand loading truck, 50' haul	"	48	.667			19.35	14.40	33.75	48.50
3080	Machine loading truck	B-17	120	.267			8.15	6.50	14.65	21
5000	Haul, per mile, up to 8 C.Y. truck	B-34B	1165	.007			.20	.59	.79	.99
5100	Over 8 C.Y. truck	"	1550	.005			.15	.45	.60	.74

02 41 19.20 Selective Demolition, Dump Charges

					Unit	Material	Labor	Equipment	Total	Total Incl O&P
0010	**SELECTIVE DEMOLITION, DUMP CHARGES**	R024119-10								
0020	Dump charges, typical urban city, tipping fees only									
0100	Building construction materials				Ton	74			74	81
0200	Trees, brush, lumber					63			63	69.50
0300	Rubbish only					63			63	69.50
0500	Reclamation station, usual charge					74			74	81

02 41 19.21 Selective Demolition, Gutting

		Crew	Daily Output	Labor-Hours	Unit	Material	Labor	Equipment	Total	Total Incl O&P
0010	**SELECTIVE DEMOLITION, GUTTING**	R024119-10								
0020	Building interior, including disposal, dumpster fees not included									
0500	Residential building									
0560	Minimum	B-16	400	.080	SF Flr.		2.32	1.73	4.05	5.80
0580	Maximum	"	360	.089	"		2.58	1.92	4.50	6.45
0900	Commercial building									
1000	Minimum	B-16	350	.091	SF Flr.		2.66	1.98	4.64	6.65
1020	Maximum	"	250	.128	"		3.72	2.77	6.49	9.30

02 41 19.25 Selective Demolition, Saw Cutting

		Crew	Daily Output	Labor-Hours	Unit	Material	Labor	Equipment	Total	Total Incl O&P
0010	**SELECTIVE DEMOLITION, SAW CUTTING**	R024119-10								
0015	Asphalt, up to 3" deep	B-89	1050	.015	L.F.	.14	.49	.50	1.13	1.53
0020	Each additional inch of depth	"	1800	.009		.05	.29	.29	.63	.85
1200	Masonry walls, hydraulic saw, brick, per inch of depth	B-89B	300	.053		.05	1.74	3.03	4.82	6.25
1220	Block walls, solid, per inch of depth	"	250	.064		.05	2.08	3.64	5.77	7.50
2000	Brick or masonry w/hand held saw, per inch of depth	A-1	125	.064		.06	1.80	.67	2.53	3.85
5001	Wood sheathing, to 1" thick on walls	1 Clab	200	.040			1.13		1.13	1.90
5021	On roof	"	250	.032			.90		.90	1.52

02 41 Demolition

02 41 19 – Selective Demolition

02 41 19.27 Selective Demolition, Torch Cutting		Crew	Daily Output	Labor-Hours	Unit	Material	2014 Bare Costs Labor	Equipment	Total	Total Incl O&P
0010	**SELECTIVE DEMOLITION, TORCH CUTTING**	R024119-10								
0020	Steel, 1" thick plate		E-25	333	.024	L.F.	.76	.92	.03	1.71	2.62
0040	1" diameter bar		"	600	.013	Ea.	.13	.51	.02	.66	1.13
1000	Oxygen lance cutting, reinforced concrete walls										
1040	12" to 16" thick walls		1 Clab	10	.800	L.F.		22.50		22.50	38
1080	24" thick walls		"	6	1.333	"		37.50		37.50	63.50

02 42 Removal and Salvage of Construction Materials

02 42 10 – Building Deconstruction

02 42 10.10 Estimated Salvage Value or Savings			Daily Output	Labor-Hours	Unit	Material	2014 Bare Costs Labor	Equipment	Total	Total Incl O&P
0010	**ESTIMATED SALVAGE VALUE OR SAVINGS**									
0015	Excludes material handling, packaging, container costs and									
0020	transportation for salvage or disposal									
0050	All Items in Section 02 42 10.10 are credit deducts and not costs									
0100	Copper Wire Salvage Value	G			Lb.				1.60	1.60
0110	Disposal Savings	G							.04	.04
0200	Copper Pipe Salvage Value	G							2.50	2.50
0210	Disposal Savings	G							.05	.05
0300	Steel Pipe Salvage Value	G							.06	.06
0310	Disposal Savings	G							.03	.03
0400	Cast Iron Pipe Salvage Value	G							.03	.03
0410	Disposal Savings	G							.01	.01
0500	Steel Doors or Windows Salvage Value	G							.06	.06
0510	Aluminum	G							.55	.55
0520	Disposal Savings	G							.03	.03
0600	Aluminum Siding Salvage Value	G							.49	.49
0630	Disposal Savings	G							.03	.03
0640	Wood Siding (no lead or asbestos)	G			C.Y.				12	12
0800	Clean Concrete Disposal Savings	G			Ton				62	62
0850	Asphalt Shingles Disposal Savings	G			"				60	60
1000	Wood wall framing clean salvage value	G			M.B.F.				55	55
1010	Painted	G							44	44
1020	Floor framing	G							55	55
1030	Painted	G							44	44
1050	Roof framing	G							55	55
1060	Painted	G							44	44
1100	Wood beams salvage value	G							55	55
1200	Wood framing and beams disposal savings	G			Ton				66	66
1220	Wood sheating and sub-base flooring	G							72.50	72.50
1230	Wood wall paneling (1/4 inch thick)	G							66	66
1300	Wood panel 3/4-1 inch thick low salvage value	G			S.F.				.55	.55
1350	high salvage value	G			"				2.20	2.20
1400	Disposal savings	G			Ton				66	66
1500	Flooring tongue and groove 25/32 inch thick low salvage value	G			S.F.				.55	.55
1530	High salvage value	G			"				1.10	1.10
1560	Disposal savings	G			Ton				66	66
1600	Drywall or sheet rock salvage value	G							22	22
1650	Disposal savings	G							66	66

02 42 10.20 Deconstruction of Building Components		Crew	Daily Output	Labor-Hours	Unit	Material	2014 Bare Costs Labor	Equipment	Total	Total Incl O&P
0010	**DECONSTRUCTION OF BUILDING COMPONENTS**									
0012	Buildings one or two stories only									
0015	Excludes material handling, packaging, container costs and									
0020	transportation for salvage or disposal									
0050	Deconstruction of Plumbing Fixtures									
0100	Wall hung or countertop lavatory	G	2 Clab	16	1	Ea.		28		28	47.50
0110	Single or double compartment kitchen sink	G		14	1.143			32		32	54
0120	Wall hung urinal	G		14	1.143			32		32	54
0130	Floor mounted	G		8	2			56.50		56.50	95
0140	Floor mounted water closet	G		16	1			28		28	47.50
0150	Wall hung	G		14	1.143			32		32	54
0160	Water fountain, free standing	G		16	1			28		28	47.50
0170	Wall hung or deck mounted	G		12	1.333			37.50		37.50	63.50
0180	Bathtub, steel or fiberglass	G		10	1.600			45		45	76
0190	Cast iron	G		8	2			56.50		56.50	95
0200	Shower, single	G		6	2.667			75		75	127
0210	Group	G		7	2.286			64.50		64.50	108
0300	Deconstruction of Electrical Fixtures									
0310	Surface mount incandescent fixtures	G	2 Clab	48	.333	Ea.		9.40		9.40	15.80
0320	Fluorescent, 2 lamp	G		32	.500			14.10		14.10	23.50
0330	4 lamp	G		24	.667			18.80		18.80	31.50
0340	Strip Fluorescent, 1 lamp	G		40	.400			11.30		11.30	19
0350	2 lamp	G		32	.500			14.10		14.10	23.50
0400	Recessed drop-in fluorescent fixture, 2 lamp	G		27	.593			16.70		16.70	28
0410	4 lamp	G		18	.889			25		25	42
0500	Deconstruction of appliances									
0510	Cooking stoves	G	2 Clab	26	.615	Ea.		17.35		17.35	29
0520	Dishwashers	G	"	26	.615	"		17.35		17.35	29
0600	Deconstruction of millwork and trim									
0610	Cabinets, wood	G	2 Carp	40	.400	L.F.		14.30		14.30	24
0620	Countertops	G		100	.160	"		5.70		5.70	9.60
0630	Wall paneling, 1 inch thick	G		500	.032	S.F.		1.14		1.14	1.92
0640	Ceiling trim	G		500	.032	L.F.		1.14		1.14	1.92
0650	Wainscoting	G		500	.032	S.F.		1.14		1.14	1.92
0660	Base, 3/4" to 1" thick	G		600	.027	L.F.		.95		.95	1.60
0700	Deconstruction of doors and windows									
0710	Doors, wrap, interior, wood, single, no closers	G	2 Carp	21	.762	Ea.	4.25	27		31.25	50.50
0720	Double	G		13	1.231		8.50	44		52.50	83.50
0730	Solid core, single, exterior or interior	G		10	1.600		4.25	57		61.25	101
0740	Double	G		8	2		8.50	71.50		80	129
0810	Windows, wrap, wood, single									
0812	with no casement or cladding	G	2 Carp	21	.762	Ea.	4.25	27		31.25	50.50
0820	with casement and/or cladding	G	"	18	.889	"	4.25	32		36.25	58
0900	Deconstruction of interior finishes									
0910	Drywall for recycling	G	2 Clab	1775	.009	S.F.		.25		.25	.43
0920	Plaster wall, first floor	G		1775	.009			.25		.25	.43
0930	Second floor	G		1330	.012			.34		.34	.57
1000	Deconstruction of roofing and accessories									
1010	Built-up roofs	G	2 Clab	570	.028	S.F.		.79		.79	1.33
1020	Gutters, facia and rakes	G	"	1140	.014	L.F.		.40		.40	.67
2000	Deconstruction of wood components									
2010	Roof sheeting	G	2 Clab	570	.028	S.F.		.79		.79	1.33

02 42 Removal and Salvage of Construction Materials

02 42 10 – Building Deconstruction

02 42 10.20 Deconstruction of Building Components

		Crew	Daily Output	Labor-Hours	Unit	Material	2014 Bare Costs Labor	2014 Bare Costs Equipment	Total	Total Incl O&P
2020	Main roof framing	G 2 Clab	760	.021	L.F.		.59		.59	1
2030	Porch roof framing	G ↓	445	.036			1.01		1.01	1.71
2040	Beams 4" x 8"	G B-1	375	.064			1.85		1.85	3.11
2050	4" x 10"	G	300	.080			2.31		2.31	3.89
2055	4" x 12"	G	250	.096			2.77		2.77	4.66
2060	6" x 8"	G	250	.096			2.77		2.77	4.66
2065	6" x 10"	G	200	.120			3.46		3.46	5.85
2070	6" x 12"	G	170	.141			4.08		4.08	6.85
2075	8" x 12"	G	126	.190			5.50		5.50	9.25
2080	10" x 12"	G ↓	100	.240			6.95		6.95	11.65
2100	Ceiling joists	G 2 Clab	800	.020			.56		.56	.95
2150	Wall framing, interior	G	1230	.013	↓		.37		.37	.62
2160	Sub-floor	G	2000	.008	S.F.		.23		.23	.38
2170	Floor joists	G	2000	.008	L.F.		.23		.23	.38
2200	Wood siding (no lead or asbestos)	G	1300	.012	S.F.		.35		.35	.58
2300	Wall framing, exterior	G	1600	.010	L.F.		.28		.28	.47
2400	Stair risers	G	53	.302	Ea.		8.50		8.50	14.30
2500	Posts	G ↓	800	.020	L.F.		.56		.56	.95
3000	Deconstruction of exterior brick walls									
3010	Exterior brick walls, first floor	G 2 Clab	200	.080	S.F.		2.26		2.26	3.80
3020	Second floor	G ↓	64	.250	"		7.05		7.05	11.85
3030	Brick chimney	G ↓	100	.160	C.F.		4.51		4.51	7.60
4000	Deconstruction of concrete									
4010	Slab on grade, 4" thick, plain concrete	G B-9	500	.080	S.F.		2.29	.47	2.76	4.36
4020	Wire mesh reinforced	G	470	.085			2.43	.50	2.93	4.65
4030	Rod reinforced	G	400	.100			2.86	.58	3.44	5.45
4110	Foundation wall, 6" thick, plain concrete	G	160	.250			7.15	1.46	8.61	13.65
4120	8" thick	G	140	.286			8.15	1.67	9.82	15.60
4130	10" thick	G ↓	120	.333	↓		9.55	1.95	11.50	18.20
9000	Deconstruction process, support equipment as needed									
9010	Daily use, portal to portal, 12-ton truck-mounted hydraulic crane crew	G A-3H	1	8	Day		310	875	1,185	1,475
9020	Daily use, skid steer and operator	G A-3C	1	8			290	310	600	820
9030	Daily use, backhoe 48 H.P., operator and labor	G "	1	8	↓		290	310	600	820

02 42 10.30 Deconstruction Material Handling

		Crew	Daily Output	Labor-Hours	Unit	Material	2014 Bare Costs Labor	2014 Bare Costs Equipment	Total	Total Incl O&P
0010	**DECONSTRUCTION MATERIAL HANDLING**									
0012	Buildings one or two stories only									
0100	Clean and stack brick on pallet	G 2 Clab	1200	.013	Ea.		.38		.38	.63
0200	Haul 50' and load rough lumber up to 2" x 8" size	G	2000	.008	"		.23		.23	.38
0210	Lumber larger than 2" x 8"	G	3200	.005	B.F.		.14		.14	.24
0300	Finish wood for recycling stack and wrap per pallet	G	8	2	Ea.	34	56.50		90.50	133
0350	Light fixtures		6	2.667		61	75		136	195
0375	Windows		6	2.667		58	75		133	191
0400	Miscellaneous materials	↓	8	2	↓	17	56.50		73.50	114
1000	See Section 02 41 19.19 for bulk material handling									

02 43 Structure Moving

02 43 13 – Structure Relocation

02 43 13.13 Building Relocation		Crew	Daily Output	Labor-Hours	Unit	Material	2014 Bare Costs Labor	2014 Bare Costs Equipment	Total	Total Incl O&P
0010	**BUILDING RELOCATION**									
0011	One day move, up to 24' wide									
0020	Reset on new foundation, patch & hook-up, average move				Total					11,500
0040	Wood or steel frame bldg., based on ground floor area [G]	B-4	185	.259	S.F.		7.45	2.80	10.25	15.65
0060	Masonry bldg., based on ground floor area [G]	"	137	.350			10.10	3.78	13.88	21
0200	For 24' to 42' wide, add								15%	15%
0220	For each additional day on road, add [G]	B-4	1	48	Day		1,375	520	1,895	2,900
0240	Construct new basement, move building, 1 day									
0300	move, patch & hook-up, based on ground floor area [G]	B-3	155	.310	S.F.	10.25	9.45	16.60	36.30	45.50

02 56 Site containment

02 56 13 – Waste containment

02 56 13.10 Containment of Hazardous Waste

		Crew	Daily Output	Labor-Hours	Unit	Material	2014 Bare Costs Labor	2014 Bare Costs Equipment	Total	Total Incl O&P
0010	**CONTAINMENT OF HAZARDOUS WASTE**									
0020	OSHA hazard level C									
0030	OSHA Hazard level D decrease labor and equipment, deduct						-45%	-45%		
0035	OSHA Hazard level B increase labor and equipment, add						22%	22%		
0040	OSHA Hazard level A increase labor and equipment, add						71%	71%		
0100	Excavation of contaminated soil & waste									
0105	Includes one respirator filter and two disposable suits per work day									
0110	3/4 C.Y. excavator to 10 feet deep	B-12F	51	.314	B.C.Y.	2.55	10.50	13	26.05	34.50
0120	Labor crew to 6' deep	B-2	19	2.105		17.15	60		77.15	120
0130	6' - 12' deep	"	12	3.333		27	95.50		122.50	190
0200	Move contaminated soil/waste upto 150' on-site with 2.5 C.Y. loader	B-10T	300	.027	L.C.Y.	.43	1	1.74	3.17	4.06
0210	300'	"	186	.043	"	.70	1.62	2.81	5.13	6.55
0300	Secure burial cell construction									
0310	Various liner and cover materials									
0400	Very low density polyethylene (VLDPE)									
0410	50 mil top cover	B-47H	4000	.008	S.F.	.43	.29	.08	.80	1.06
0420	80 mil liner	"	4000	.008	"	.50	.29	.08	.87	1.14
0500	Chlorosulfunated polyethylene									
0510	36 mil hypalon top cover	B-47H	4000	.008	S.F.	1.53	.29	.08	1.90	2.27
0520	45 mil hypalon liner	"	4000	.008	"	1.63	.29	.08	2	2.38
0600	Polyvinyl chloride (PVC)									
0610	60 mil top cover	B-47H	4000	.008	S.F.	.80	.29	.08	1.17	1.46
0620	80 mil liner	"	4000	.008	"	.92	.29	.08	1.29	1.60
0700	Rough textured H.D. polyethylene (HDPE)									
0710	40 mil top cover	B-47H	4000	.008	S.F.	.41	.29	.08	.78	1.04
0720	60 mil top cover		4000	.008		.47	.29	.08	.84	1.10
0722	60 mil liner		4000	.008		.40	.29	.08	.77	1.03
0730	80 mil liner		3800	.008		.51	.31	.09	.91	1.18
1000	3/4" crushed stone, 6" deep ballast around liner	B-6	30	.800	L.C.Y.	28.50	24.50	12.20	65.20	86
1100	Hazardous waste, ballast cover with common borrow material	B-63	56	.714		12.35	20	3.11	35.46	51
1110	Mixture of common borrow & topsoil		56	.714		18.45	20	3.11	41.56	58
1120	Bank sand		56	.714		17.55	20	3.11	40.66	56.50
1130	Medium priced clay		44	.909		23	25.50	3.96	52.46	73
1140	Mixture of common borrow & medium priced clay		56	.714		17.75	20	3.11	40.86	57

02 58 Snow Control

02 58 13 – Snow Fencing

02 58 13.10 Snow Fencing System	Crew	Daily Output	Labor-Hours	Unit	Material	2014 Bare Costs Labor	Equipment	Total	Total Incl O&P
0010 **SNOW FENCING SYSTEM**									
7001 Snow fence on steel posts 10' O.C., 4' high	B-1	500	.048	L.F.	.96	1.39		2.35	3.39

02 65 Underground Storage Tank Removal

02 65 10 – Underground Tank and Contaminated Soil Removal

02 65 10.30 Removal of Underground Storage Tanks

		Crew	Daily Output	Labor-Hours	Unit	Material	2014 Bare Costs Labor	Equipment	Total	Total Incl O&P
0010	**REMOVAL OF UNDERGROUND STORAGE TANKS** R026510-20									
0011	Petroleum storage tanks, non-leaking									
0100	Excavate & load onto trailer									
0110	G 3000 gal. to 5000 gal. tank	B-14	4	12	Ea.		360	91.50	451.50	700
0120	G 6000 gal. to 8000 gal. tank	B-3A	3	13.333			400	345	745	1,050
0130	G 9000 gal. to 12000 gal. tank	"	2	20	↓		600	515	1,115	1,575
0190	Known leaking tank, add				%				100%	100%
0200	Remove sludge, water and remaining product from tank bottom									
0201	of tank with vacuum truck									
0300	G 3000 gal. to 5000 gal. tank	A-13	5	1.600	Ea.		58	154	212	266
0310	G 6000 gal. to 8000 gal. tank	↓	4	2			72.50	193	265.50	330
0320	G 9000 gal. to 12000 gal. tank	↓	3	2.667	↓		96.50	257	353.50	445
0390	Dispose of sludge off-site, average				Gal.				6.25	6.80
0400	Insert inert solid CO_2 "dry ice" into tank									
0401	G For cleaning/transporting tanks (1.5 lb./100 gal. cap)	1 Clab	500	.016	Lb.	1.08	.45		1.53	1.95
0403	G Insert solid carbon dioxide, 1.5 lb./100 gal.	"	400	.020	"	1.08	.56		1.64	2.14
0503	G Disconnect and remove piping	1 Plum	160	.050	L.F.		2.13		2.13	3.52
0603	G Transfer liquids, 10% of volume	"	1600	.005	Gal.		.21		.21	.35
0703	G Cut accessway into underground storage tank	1 Clab	5.33	1.501	Ea.		42.50		42.50	71
0813	G Remove sludge, wash and wipe tank, 500 gal.	1 Plum	8	1			42.50		42.50	70.50
0823	G 3,000 gal.		6.67	1.199			51		51	84.50
0833	G 5,000 gal.		6.15	1.301			55.50		55.50	91.50
0843	G 8,000 gal.		5.33	1.501			64		64	106
0853	G 10,000 gal.		4.57	1.751			74.50		74.50	123
0863	G 12,000 gal.	↓	4.21	1.900	↓		81		81	134
1020	Haul tank to certified salvage dump, 100 miles round trip									
1023	3000 gal. to 5000 gal. tank				Ea.				760	830
1026	6000 gal. to 8000 gal. tank								880	960
1029	9,000 gal. to 12,000 gal. tank				↓				1,050	1,150
1100	Disposal of contaminated soil to landfill									
1110	Minimum				C.Y.				145	160
1111	Maximum				"				400	440
1120	Disposal of contaminated soil to									
1121	bituminous concrete batch plant									
1130	Minimum				C.Y.				80	88
1131	Maximum				"				115	125
1203	G Excavate, pull, & load tank, backfill hole, 8,000 gal. +	B-12C	.50	32	Ea.		1,075	2,350	3,425	4,350
1213	G Haul tank to certified dump, 100 miles rt, 8,000 gal. +	B-34K	1	8			237	960	1,197	1,450
1223	G Excavate, pull, & load tank, backfill hole, 500 gal.	B-11C	1	16			525	365	890	1,275
1233	G Excavate, pull, & load tank, backfill hole, 3,000 – 5,000 gal.	B-11M	.50	32			1,050	795	1,845	2,625
1243	G Haul tank to certified dump, 100 miles rt, 500 gal.	B-34L	1	8			290	270	560	775
1253	G Haul tank to certified dump, 100 miles rt, 3,000 – 5,000 gal.	B-34M	1	8	↓		290	335	625	845
2010	Decontamination of soil on site incl poly tarp on top/bottom									
2011	Soil containment berm, and chemical treatment									
2020	G Minimum	B-11C	100	.160	C.Y.	7.80	5.25	3.65	16.70	21.50

02 65 Underground Storage Tank Removal

02 65 10 – Underground Tank and Contaminated Soil Removal

02 65 10.30 Removal of Underground Storage Tanks		Crew	Daily Output	Labor-Hours	Unit	Material	2014 Bare Costs Labor	Equipment	Total	Total Incl O&P
2021	Maximum	[G] B-11C	100	.160	C.Y.	10.10	5.25	3.65	19	24
2050	Disposal of decontaminated soil, minimum								135	150
2055	Maximum								400	440

02 81 Transportation and Disposal of Hazardous Materials

02 81 20 – Hazardous Waste Handling

02 81 20.10 Hazardous Waste Cleanup/Pickup/Disposal

		Crew	Daily Output	Labor-Hours	Unit	Material	Labor	Equipment	Total	Total Incl O&P
0010	**HAZARDOUS WASTE CLEANUP/PICKUP/DISPOSAL**									
0100	For contractor rental equipment, i.e., Dozer,									
0110	Front end loader, Dump truck, etc., see 01 54 33 Reference Section									
1000	Solid pickup									
1100	55 gal. drums				Ea.				240	265
1120	Bulk material, minimum				Ton				190	210
1130	Maximum				"				595	655
1200	Transportation to disposal site									
1220	Truckload = 80 drums or 25 C.Y. or 18 tons									
1260	Minimum				Mile				3.95	4.45
1270	Maximum				"				7.25	7.35
3000	Liquid pickup, vacuum truck, stainless steel tank									
3100	Minimum charge, 4 hours									
3110	1 compartment, 2200 gallon				Hr.				140	155
3120	2 compartment, 5000 gallon				"				200	225
3400	Transportation in 6900 gallon bulk truck				Mile				7.95	8.75
3410	In teflon lined truck				"				10.20	11.25
5000	Heavy sludge or dry vacuumable material				Hr.				140	160
6000	Dumpsite disposal charge, minimum				Ton				140	155
6020	Maximum				"				415	455

02 82 Asbestos Remediation

02 82 13 – Asbestos Abatement

02 82 13.39 Asbestos Remediation Plans and Methods

		Crew	Daily Output	Labor-Hours	Unit	Material	Labor	Equipment	Total	Total Incl O&P
0010	**ASBESTOS REMEDIATION PLANS AND METHODS**									
0100	Building Survey-Commercial Building				Ea.				2,200	2,400
0200	Asbestos Abatement Remediation Plan				"				1,350	1,475

02 82 13.41 Asbestos Abatement Equipment

		Crew	Daily Output	Labor-Hours	Unit	Material	Labor	Equipment	Total	Total Incl O&P
0010	**ASBESTOS ABATEMENT EQUIPMENT** R028213-20									
0011	Equipment and supplies, buy									
0200	Air filtration device, 2000 CFM				Ea.	940			940	1,025
0250	Large volume air sampling pump, minimum					340			340	375
0260	Maximum					330			330	360
0300	Airless sprayer unit, 2 gun					4,425			4,425	4,850
0350	Light stand, 500 watt					48			48	53
0400	Personal respirators									
0410	Negative pressure, 1/2 face, dual operation, min.				Ea.	26			26	28.50
0420	Maximum					29			29	31.50
0450	P.A.P.R., full face, minimum					122			122	134
0460	Maximum					162			162	178
0470	Supplied air, full face, incl. air line, minimum					165			165	182
0480	Maximum					395			395	435

02 82 Asbestos Remediation

02 82 13 – Asbestos Abatement

02 82 13.41 Asbestos Abatement Equipment	Crew	Daily Output	Labor-Hours	Unit	Material	2014 Bare Costs Labor	Equipment	Total	Total Incl O&P
0500	Personnel sampling pump				Ea.	222			222	244
1500	Power panel, 20 unit, incl. GFI					590			590	650
1600	Shower unit, including pump and filters					1,250			1,250	1,375
1700	Supplied air system (type C)					3,350			3,350	3,675
1750	Vacuum cleaner, HEPA, 16 gal., stainless steel, wet/dry					1,175			1,175	1,300
1760	55 gallon					1,225			1,225	1,350
1800	Vacuum loader, 9 – 18 ton/hr.					92,500			92,500	102,000
1900	Water atomizer unit, including 55 gal. drum					275			275	305
2000	Worker protection, whole body, foot, head cover & gloves, plastic					14.50			14.50	15.95
2500	Respirator, single use					24.50			24.50	27
2550	Cartridge for respirator					7.15			7.15	7.85
2570	Glove bag, 7 mil, 50" x 64"					16.25			16.25	17.90
2580	10 mil, 44" x 60"					5.65			5.65	6.20
3000	HEPA vacuum for work area, minimum					1,400			1,400	1,550
3050	Maximum					1,450			1,450	1,600
6000	Disposable polyethylene bags, 6 mil, 3 C.F.					1.65			1.65	1.82
6300	Disposable fiber drums, 3 C.F.					17.85			17.85	19.65
6400	Pressure sensitive caution labels, 3" x 5"					3.40			3.40	3.74
6450	11" x 17"					7.20			7.20	7.90
6500	Negative air machine, 1800 CFM					830			830	915

02 82 13.42 Preparation of Asbestos Containment Area

		Crew	Daily Output	Labor-Hours	Unit	Material	Labor	Equipment	Total	Total Incl O&P
0010	**PREPARATION OF ASBESTOS CONTAINMENT AREA**									
0100	Pre-cleaning, HEPA vacuum and wet wipe, flat surfaces	A-9	12000	.005	S.F.	.02	.20		.22	.37
0200	Protect carpeted area, 2 layers 6 mil poly on 3/4" plywood	"	1000	.064		2	2.43		4.43	6.30
0300	Separation barrier, 2" x 4" @ 16", 1/2" plywood ea. side, 8' high	2 Carp	400	.040		3.25	1.43		4.68	6
0310	12' high		320	.050		3.25	1.79		5.04	6.60
0320	16' high		200	.080		2.25	2.86		5.11	7.30
0400	Personnel decontam. chamber, 2" x 4" @ 16", 3/4" ply ea. side		280	.057		4.25	2.04		6.29	8.10
0450	Waste decontam. chamber, 2" x 4" studs @ 16", 3/4" ply ea. side		360	.044		4.25	1.59		5.84	7.35
0500	Cover surfaces with polyethylene sheeting									
0501	Including glue and tape									
0550	Floors, each layer, 6 mil	A-9	8000	.008	S.F.	.04	.30		.34	.56
0551	4 mil		9000	.007		.03	.27		.30	.49
0560	Walls, each layer, 6 mil		6000	.011		.04	.40		.44	.74
0561	4 mil		7000	.009		.03	.35		.38	.62
0570	For heights above 12', add						20%			
0575	For heights above 20', add						30%			
0580	For fire retardant poly, add					100%				
0590	For large open areas, deduct					10%	20%			
0600	Seal floor penetrations with foam firestop to 36 sq. in.	2 Carp	200	.080	Ea.	9.25	2.86		12.11	15
0610	36 sq. in. to 72 sq. in.		125	.128		18.50	4.58		23.08	28
0615	72 sq. in. to 144 sq. in.		80	.200		37	7.15		44.15	53
0620	Wall penetrations, to 36 square inches		180	.089		9.25	3.18		12.43	15.55
0630	36 sq. in. to 72 sq. in.		100	.160		18.50	5.70		24.20	30
0640	72 sq. in. to 144 sq. in.		60	.267		37	9.55		46.55	57
0800	Caulk seams with latex	1 Carp	230	.035	L.F.	.17	1.24		1.41	2.28
0900	Set up neg. air machine, 1-2k CFM/25 M.C.F. volume	1 Asbe	4.30	1.860	Ea.		70.50		70.50	119
0950	Set up and remove portable shower unit	2 Asbe	4	4	"		151		151	257

02 82 13.43 Bulk Asbestos Removal

		Crew	Daily Output	Labor-Hours	Unit	Material	Labor	Equipment	Total	Total Incl O&P
0010	**BULK ASBESTOS REMOVAL**									
0020	Includes disposable tools and 2 suits and 1 respirator filter/day/worker									
0100	Beams, W 10 x 19	A-9	235	.272	L.F.	1.23	10.30		11.53	18.85

02 82 13 – Asbestos Abatement

02 82 13.43 Bulk Asbestos Removal

		Crew	Daily Output	Labor-Hours	Unit	Material	2014 Bare Costs Labor	Equipment	Total	Total Incl O&P
0110	W 12 x 22	A-9	210	.305	L.F.	1.38	11.55		12.93	21
0120	W 14 x 26		180	.356		1.61	13.50		15.11	25
0130	W 16 x 31		160	.400		1.81	15.15		16.96	27.50
0140	W 18 x 40		140	.457		2.06	17.35		19.41	32
0150	W 24 x 55		110	.582		2.63	22		24.63	40.50
0160	W 30 x 108		85	.753		3.40	28.50		31.90	52
0170	W 36 x 150		72	.889		4.01	33.50		37.51	61.50
0200	Boiler insulation		480	.133	S.F.	.67	5.05		5.72	9.30
0210	With metal lath, add				%				50%	50%
0300	Boiler breeching or flue insulation	A-9	520	.123	S.F.	.56	4.67		5.23	8.50
0310	For active boiler, add				%				100%	100%
0400	Duct or AHU insulation	A-10B	440	.073	S.F.	.33	2.76		3.09	5.05
0500	Duct vibration isolation joints, up to 24 sq. in. duct	A-9	56	1.143	Ea.	5.15	43.50		48.65	79
0520	25 sq. in. to 48 sq. in. duct		48	1.333		6	50.50		56.50	92.50
0530	49 sq. in. to 76 sq. in. duct		40	1.600		7.25	60.50		67.75	111
0600	Pipe insulation, air cell type, up to 4" diameter pipe		900	.071	L.F.	.32	2.70		3.02	4.92
0610	4" to 8" diameter pipe		800	.080		.36	3.03		3.39	5.55
0620	10" to 12" diameter pipe		700	.091		.41	3.47		3.88	6.35
0630	14" to 16" diameter pipe		550	.116		.53	4.41		4.94	8.10
0650	Over 16" diameter pipe		650	.098	S.F.	.44	3.73		4.17	6.85
0700	With glove bag up to 3" diameter pipe		200	.320	L.F.	8.95	12.15		21.10	30.50
1000	Pipe fitting insulation up to 4" diameter pipe		320	.200	Ea.	.90	7.60		8.50	13.85
1100	6" to 8" diameter pipe		304	.211		.95	8		8.95	14.60
1110	10" to 12" diameter pipe		192	.333		1.51	12.65		14.16	23
1120	14" to 16" diameter pipe		128	.500		2.26	18.95		21.21	34.50
1130	Over 16" diameter pipe		176	.364	S.F.	1.64	13.80		15.44	25.50
1200	With glove bag, up to 8" diameter pipe		75	.853	L.F.	6.15	32.50		38.65	62
2000	Scrape foam fireproofing from flat surface		2400	.027	S.F.	.12	1.01		1.13	1.85
2100	Irregular surfaces		1200	.053		.24	2.02		2.26	3.69
3000	Remove cementitious material from flat surface		1800	.036		.16	1.35		1.51	2.47
3100	Irregular surface		1000	.064		.21	2.43		2.64	4.35
4000	Scrape acoustical coating/fireproofing, from ceiling		3200	.020		.09	.76		.85	1.39
5000	Remove VAT and mastic from floor by hand		2400	.027		.12	1.01		1.13	1.85
5100	By machine	A-11	4800	.013		.06	.51	.01	.58	.94
5150	For 2 layers, add				%				50%	50%
6000	Remove contaminated soil from crawl space by hand	A-9	400	.160	C.F.	.72	6.05		6.77	11.10
6100	With large production vacuum loader	A-12	700	.091	"	.41	3.47	1.10	4.98	7.55
7000	Radiator backing, not including radiator removal	A-9	1200	.053	S.F.	.24	2.02		2.26	3.69
8000	Cement-asbestos transite board and cement wall board	2 Asbe	1000	.016		.17	.61		.78	1.22
8100	Transite shingle siding	A-10B	750	.043		.28	1.62		1.90	3.06
8200	Shingle roofing	"	2000	.016		.08	.61		.69	1.12
8250	Built-up, no gravel, non-friable	B-2	1400	.029		.08	.82		.90	1.47
8260	Bituminous flashing	1 Rofc	300	.027		.08	.80		.88	1.57
8300	Asbestos millboard, flat board and VAT contaminated plywood	2 Asbe	1000	.016		.08	.61		.69	1.12
9000	For type B (supplied air) respirator equipment, add				%				10%	10%

02 82 13.44 Demolition In Asbestos Contaminated Area

		Crew	Daily Output	Labor-Hours	Unit	Material	2014 Bare Costs Labor	Equipment	Total	Total Incl O&P
0010	**DEMOLITION IN ASBESTOS CONTAMINATED AREA**									
0200	Ceiling, including suspension system, plaster and lath	A-9	2100	.030	S.F.	.14	1.16		1.30	2.11
0210	Finished plaster, leaving wire lath		585	.109		.49	4.15		4.64	7.60
0220	Suspended acoustical tile		3500	.018		.08	.69		.77	1.27
0230	Concealed tile grid system		3000	.021		.10	.81		.91	1.48
0240	Metal pan grid system		1500	.043		.19	1.62		1.81	2.95

02 82 Asbestos Remediation

02 82 13 – Asbestos Abatement

02 82 13.44 Demolition In Asbestos Contaminated Area	Crew	Daily Output	Labor-Hours	Unit	Material	2014 Bare Costs Labor	2014 Bare Costs Equipment	Total	Total Incl O&P
0250	Gypsum board	A-9	2500	.026	S.F.	.12	.97		1.09	1.78
0260	Lighting fixtures up to 2' x 4'	↓	72	.889	Ea.	4.01	33.50		37.51	61.50
0400	Partitions, non load bearing									
0410	Plaster, lath, and studs	A-9	690	.093	S.F.	1.02	3.52		4.54	7.05
0450	Gypsum board and studs	"	1390	.046	"	.21	1.75		1.96	3.19
9000	For type B (supplied air) respirator equipment, add				%				10%	10%

02 82 13.45 OSHA Testing

		Crew	Daily Output	Labor-Hours	Unit	Material	Labor	Equipment	Total	Total Incl O&P
0010	**OSHA TESTING**									
0100	Certified technician, minimum				Day				200	220
0110	Maximum								300	330
0120	Industrial hygienist, minimum								250	250
0130	Maximum				↓				400	440
0200	Asbestos sampling and PCM analysis, NIOSH 7400, minimum	1 Asbe	8	1	Ea.	2.90	38		40.90	67
0210	Maximum		4	2		3.20	75.50		78.70	132
1000	Cleaned area samples		8	1		2.75	38		40.75	67
1100	PCM air sample analysis, NIOSH 7400, minimum		8	1		31	38		69	98
1110	Maximum		4	2		3.35	75.50		78.85	132
1200	TEM air sample analysis, NIOSH 7402, minimum								80	106
1210	Maximum	↓			↓				360	450

02 82 13.46 Decontamination of Asbestos Containment Area

		Crew	Daily Output	Labor-Hours	Unit	Material	Labor	Equipment	Total	Total Incl O&P
0010	**DECONTAMINATION OF ASBESTOS CONTAINMENT AREA**									
0100	Spray exposed substrate with surfactant (bridging)									
0200	Flat surfaces	A-9	6000	.011	S.F.	.35	.40		.75	1.08
0250	Irregular surfaces		4000	.016	"	.30	.61		.91	1.36
0300	Pipes, beams, and columns		2000	.032	L.F.	.55	1.21		1.76	2.67
1000	Spray encapsulate polyethylene sheeting		8000	.008	S.F.	.33	.30		.63	.87
1100	Roll down polyethylene sheeting		8000	.008	"		.30		.30	.51
1500	Bag polyethylene sheeting		400	.160	Ea.	.79	6.05		6.84	11.15
2000	Fine clean exposed substrate, with nylon brush		2400	.027	S.F.		1.01		1.01	1.72
2500	Wet wipe substrate		4800	.013			.51		.51	.86
2600	Vacuum surfaces, fine brush	↓	6400	.010	↓		.38		.38	.64
3000	Structural demolition									
3100	Wood stud walls	A-9	2800	.023	S.F.		.87		.87	1.47
3500	Window manifolds, not incl. window replacement		4200	.015			.58		.58	.98
3600	Plywood carpet protection	↓	2000	.032	↓		1.21		1.21	2.06
4000	Remove custom decontamination facility	A-10A	8	3	Ea.	15.10	114		129.10	210
4100	Remove portable decontamination facility	3 Asbe	12	2	"	12.80	75.50		88.30	142
5000	HEPA vacuum, shampoo carpeting	A-9	4800	.013	S.F.	.07	.51		.58	.94
9000	Final cleaning of protected surfaces	A-10A	8000	.003	"		.11		.11	.19

02 82 13.47 Asbestos Waste Pkg., Handling, and Disp.

		Crew	Daily Output	Labor-Hours	Unit	Material	Labor	Equipment	Total	Total Incl O&P
0010	**ASBESTOS WASTE PACKAGING, HANDLING, AND DISPOSAL**									
0100	Collect and bag bulk material, 3 C.F. bags, by hand	A-9	400	.160	Ea.	1.65	6.05		7.70	12.10
0200	Large production vacuum loader	A-12	880	.073		.84	2.76	.88	4.48	6.55
1000	Double bag and decontaminate	A-9	960	.067		1.65	2.53		4.18	6.10
2000	Containerize bagged material in drums, per 3 C.F. drum	"	800	.080		17.85	3.03		20.88	25
3000	Cart bags 50' to dumpster	2 Asbe	400	.040	↓		1.51		1.51	2.57
5000	Disposal charges, not including haul, minimum				C.Y.				61	67
5020	Maximum				"				355	395
9000	For type B (supplied air) respirator equipment, add				%				10%	10%

02 82 13.48 Asbestos Encapsulation With Sealants

		Crew	Daily Output	Labor-Hours	Unit	Material	Labor	Equipment	Total	Total Incl O&P
0010	**ASBESTOS ENCAPSULATION WITH SEALANTS**									
0100	Ceilings and walls, minimum	A-9	21000	.003	S.F.	.30	.12		.42	.53

02 82 Asbestos Remediation

02 82 13 – Asbestos Abatement

02 82 13.48 Asbestos Encapsulation With Sealants		Crew	Daily Output	Labor-Hours	Unit	Material	2014 Bare Costs Labor	2014 Bare Costs Equipment	Total	Total Incl O&P
0110	Maximum	A-9	10600	.006	S.F.	.44	.23		.67	.87
0200	Columns and beams, minimum		13300	.005		.30	.18		.48	.64
0210	Maximum		5325	.012	↓	.50	.46		.96	1.32
0300	Pipes to 12" diameter including minor repairs, minimum		800	.080	L.F.	.42	3.03		3.45	5.60
0310	Maximum	↓	400	.160	"	1.10	6.05		7.15	11.50

02 83 Lead Remediation

02 83 19 – Lead-Based Paint Remediation

02 83 19.21 Lead Paint Remediation Plans and Methods

		Crew	Daily Output	Labor-Hours	Unit	Material	Labor	Equipment	Total	Total Incl O&P
0010	**LEAD PAINT REMEDIATION PLANS AND METHODS**									
0100	Building Survey-Commercial Building				Ea.				2,050	2,250
0200	Lead Abatement Remediation Plan								1,225	1,350
0300	Lead Paint Testing, AAS Analysis								51	56
0400	Lead Paint Testing, X-Ray Fluorescence				↓				51	56

02 83 19.23 Encapsulation of Lead-Based Paint

		Crew	Daily Output	Labor-Hours	Unit	Material	Labor	Equipment	Total	Total Incl O&P
0010	**ENCAPSULATION OF LEAD-BASED PAINT**									
0020	Interior, brushwork, trim, under 6"	1 Pord	240	.033	L.F.	2.25	1.04		3.29	4.19
0030	6" to 12" wide		180	.044		3	1.39		4.39	5.60
0040	Balustrades		300	.027		1.80	.83		2.63	3.35
0050	Pipe to 4" diameter		500	.016		1.10	.50		1.60	2.03
0060	To 8" diameter		375	.021		1.45	.67		2.12	2.70
0070	To 12" diameter		250	.032		2.15	1		3.15	4.01
0080	To 16" diameter		170	.047	↓	3.20	1.47		4.67	5.95
0090	Cabinets, ornate design		200	.040	S.F.	2.75	1.25		4	5.10
0100	Simple design	↓	250	.032	"	2.20	1		3.20	4.06
0110	Doors, 3' x 7', both sides, incl. frame & trim									
0120	Flush	1 Pord	6	1.333	Ea.	27.50	41.50		69	99
0130	French, 10 – 15 lite		3	2.667		5.55	83.50		89.05	143
0140	Panel		4	2		33.50	62.50		96	140
0150	Louvered	↓	2.75	2.909	↓	30.50	91		121.50	184
0160	Windows, per interior side, per 15 S.F.									
0170	1 to 6 lite	1 Pord	14	.571	Ea.	19	17.85		36.85	50.50
0180	7 to 10 lite		7.50	1.067		21	33.50		54.50	78.50
0190	12 lite		5.75	1.391		28.50	43.50		72	103
0200	Radiators		8	1	↓	67.50	31.50		99	126
0210	Grilles, vents		275	.029	S.F.	2	.91		2.91	3.70
0220	Walls, roller, drywall or plaster		1000	.008		.55	.25		.80	1.02
0230	With spunbonded reinforcing fabric		720	.011		.62	.35		.97	1.25
0240	Wood		800	.010		.68	.31		.99	1.26
0250	Ceilings, roller, drywall or plaster		900	.009		.62	.28		.90	1.14
0260	Wood		700	.011	↓	.76	.36		1.12	1.43
0270	Exterior, brushwork, gutters and downspouts		300	.027	L.F.	1.80	.83		2.63	3.35
0280	Columns		400	.020	S.F.	1.35	.63		1.98	2.52
0290	Spray, siding	↓	600	.013	"	.91	.42		1.33	1.69
0300	Miscellaneous									
0310	Electrical conduit, brushwork, to 2" diameter	1 Pord	500	.016	L.F.	1.10	.50		1.60	2.03
0320	Brick, block or concrete, spray		500	.016	S.F.	1.10	.50		1.60	2.03
0330	Steel, flat surfaces and tanks to 12"		500	.016		1.10	.50		1.60	2.03
0340	Beams, brushwork		400	.020		1.35	.63		1.98	2.52
0350	Trusses	↓	400	.020	↓	1.35	.63		1.98	2.52

02 83 Lead Remediation

02 83 19 – Lead-Based Paint Remediation

02 83 19.26 Removal of Lead-Based Paint

		Crew	Daily Output	Labor-Hours	Unit	Material	2014 Bare Costs Labor	Equipment	Total	Total Incl O&P
0010	**REMOVAL OF LEAD-BASED PAINT**	R028319-60								
0011	By chemicals, per application									
0050	Baseboard, to 6" wide	1 Pord	64	.125	L.F.	.71	3.91		4.62	7.25
0070	To 12" wide		32	.250	"	1.37	7.80		9.17	14.35
0200	Balustrades, one side		28	.286	S.F.	1.42	8.95		10.37	16.25
1400	Cabinets, simple design		32	.250		1.28	7.80		9.08	14.25
1420	Ornate design		25	.320		1.55	10		11.55	18.15
1600	Cornice, simple design		60	.133		1.47	4.17		5.64	8.45
1620	Ornate design		20	.400		5.25	12.50		17.75	26.50
2800	Doors, one side, flush		84	.095		1.84	2.98		4.82	6.90
2820	Two panel		80	.100		1.28	3.13		4.41	6.55
2840	Four panel		45	.178		1.37	5.55		6.92	10.65
2880	For trim, one side, add		64	.125	L.F.	.70	3.91		4.61	7.20
3000	Fence, picket, one side		30	.267	S.F.	1.28	8.35		9.63	15.10
3200	Grilles, one side, simple design		30	.267		1.30	8.35		9.65	15.15
3220	Ornate design		25	.320		1.40	10		11.40	18
3240	Handrails		90	.089	L.F.	1.30	2.78		4.08	6
4400	Pipes, to 4" diameter		90	.089		1.84	2.78		4.62	6.60
4420	To 8" diameter		50	.160		3.68	5		8.68	12.25
4440	To 12" diameter		36	.222		5.50	6.95		12.45	17.45
4460	To 16" diameter		20	.400		7.35	12.50		19.85	28.50
4500	For hangers, add		40	.200	Ea.	2.44	6.25		8.69	13
4800	Siding		90	.089	S.F.	1.22	2.78		4	5.90
5000	Trusses, open		55	.145	SF Face	1.92	4.55		6.47	9.60
6200	Windows, one side only, double hung, 1/1 light, 24" x 48" high		4	2	Ea.	23	62.50		85.50	128
6220	30" x 60" high		3	2.667		30.50	83.50		114	171
6240	36" x 72" high		2.50	3.200		36.50	100		136.50	204
6280	40" x 80" high		2	4		45.50	125		170.50	256
6400	Colonial window, 6/6 light, 24" x 48" high		2	4		45.50	125		170.50	256
6420	30" x 60" high		1.50	5.333		61	167		228	340
6440	36" x 72" high		1	8		91	250		341	510
6480	40" x 80" high		1	8		91	250		341	510
6600	8/8 light, 24" x 48" high		2	4		45.50	125		170.50	256
6620	40" x 80" high		1	8		91	250		341	510
6800	12/12 light, 24" x 48" high		1	8		91	250		341	510
6820	40" x 80" high		.75	10.667		122	335		457	685
6840	Window frame & trim items, included in pricing above									
7000	Hand scraping and HEPA vacuum, less than 4 S.F.	1 Pord	8	1	Ea.	1.65	31.50		33.15	53.50
8000	Collect and bag bulk material, 3 C.F. bags, by hand	"	30	.267	"	1.65	8.35		10	15.50

02 85 Mold Remediation

02 85 16 – Mold Remediation Preparation and Containment

02 85 16.40 Mold Remediation Plans and Methods

									Total	Total Incl O&P
0010	**MOLD REMEDIATION PLANS AND METHODS**									
0020	Initial inspection, areas to 2500 S.F.				Total				268	295
0030	Areas to 5000 S.F.								440	485
0032	Areas to 10000 S.F.								440	485
0040	Testing, air sample each								126	139
0050	Swab sample								115	127
0060	Tape sample								125	140

02 85 Mold Remediation

02 85 16 – Mold Remediation Preparation and Containment

02 85 16.40 Mold Remediation Plans and Methods

		Crew	Daily Output	Labor-Hours	Unit	Material	2014 Bare Costs Labor	Equipment	Total	Total Incl O&P
0070	Post remediation air test				Total				126	139
0080	Mold abatement plan, area to 2500 S.F.								1,225	1,325
0090	Areas to 5000 S.F.								1,625	1,775
0095	Areas to 10000 S.F.								2,550	2,800
0100	Packup & removal of contents, average 3 bedroom home, excl storage								8,150	8,975
0110	Average 5 bedroom home, excl storage				↓				15,300	16,800
0610	For personal protection equipment, see Section 02 82 13.41									

02 85 16.50 Preparation of Mold Containment Area

		Crew	Daily Output	Labor-Hours	Unit	Material	2014 Bare Costs Labor	Equipment	Total	Total Incl O&P
0010	**PREPARATION OF MOLD CONTAINMENT AREA**									
0100	Pre-cleaning, HEPA vacuum and wet wipe, flat surfaces	A-9	12000	.005	S.F.	.02	.20		.22	.37
0300	Separation barrier, 2" x 4" @ 16", 1/2" plywood ea. side, 8' high	2 Carp	400	.040		3.25	1.43		4.68	6
0310	12' high		320	.050		3.25	1.79		5.04	6.60
0320	16' high		200	.080		2.25	2.86		5.11	7.30
0400	Personnel decontam. chamber, 2" x 4" @ 16", 3/4" ply ea. side		280	.057		4.25	2.04		6.29	8.10
0450	Waste decontam. chamber, 2" x 4" studs @ 16", 3/4" ply each side	↓	360	.044	↓	4.25	1.59		5.84	7.35
0500	Cover surfaces with polyethylene sheeting									
0501	Including glue and tape									
0550	Floors, each layer, 6 mil	A-9	8000	.008	S.F.	.04	.30		.34	.56
0551	4 mil		9000	.007		.03	.27		.30	.49
0560	Walls, each layer, 6 mil		6000	.011		.04	.40		.44	.74
0561	4 mil	↓	7000	.009	↓	.03	.35		.38	.62
0570	For heights above 12', add						20%			
0575	For heights above 20', add						30%			
0580	For fire retardant poly, add					100%				
0590	For large open areas, deduct					10%	20%			
0600	Seal floor penetrations with foam firestop to 36 sq. in.	2 Carp	200	.080	Ea.	9.25	2.86		12.11	15
0610	36 sq. in. to 72 sq. in.		125	.128		18.50	4.58		23.08	28
0615	72 sq. in. to 144 sq. in.		80	.200		37	7.15		44.15	53
0620	Wall penetrations, to 36 square inches		180	.089		9.25	3.18		12.43	15.55
0630	36 sq. in. to 72 sq. in.		100	.160		18.50	5.70		24.20	30
0640	72 sq. in. to 144 sq. in.	↓	60	.267	↓	37	9.55		46.55	57
0800	Caulk seams with latex caulk	1 Carp	230	.035	L.F.	.17	1.24		1.41	2.28
0900	Set up neg. air machine, 1-2k CFM/25 M.C.F. volume	1 Asbe	4.30	1.860	Ea.		70.50		70.50	119

02 85 33 – Removal and Disposal of Materials with Mold

02 85 33.50 Demolition in Mold Contaminated Area

		Crew	Daily Output	Labor-Hours	Unit	Material	2014 Bare Costs Labor	Equipment	Total	Total Incl O&P
0010	**DEMOLITION IN MOLD CONTAMINATED AREA**									
0200	Ceiling, including suspension system, plaster and lath	A-9	2100	.030	S.F.	.14	1.16		1.30	2.11
0210	Finished plaster, leaving wire lath		585	.109		.49	4.15		4.64	7.60
0220	Suspended acoustical tile		3500	.018		.08	.69		.77	1.27
0230	Concealed tile grid system		3000	.021		.10	.81		.91	1.48
0240	Metal pan grid system		1500	.043		.19	1.62		1.81	2.95
0250	Gypsum board		2500	.026		.12	.97		1.09	1.78
0255	Plywood		2500	.026	↓	.12	.97		1.09	1.78
0260	Lighting fixtures up to 2' x 4'	↓	72	.889	Ea.	4.01	33.50		37.51	61.50
0400	Partitions, non load bearing									
0410	Plaster, lath, and studs	A-9	690	.093	S.F.	1.02	3.52		4.54	7.05
0450	Gypsum board and studs		1390	.046		.21	1.75		1.96	3.19
0465	Carpet & pad		1390	.046	↓	.21	1.75		1.96	3.19
0600	Pipe insulation, air cell type, up to 4" diameter pipe		900	.071	L.F.	.32	2.70		3.02	4.92
0610	4" to 8" diameter pipe		800	.080		.36	3.03		3.39	5.55
0620	10" to 12" diameter pipe		700	.091		.41	3.47		3.88	6.35
0630	14" to 16" diameter pipe	↓	550	.116	↓	.53	4.41		4.94	8.10

02 85 Mold Remediation

02 85 33 – Removal and Disposal of Materials with Mold

02 85 33.50 Demolition in Mold Contaminated Area	Crew	Daily Output	Labor-Hours	Unit	Material	2014 Bare Costs Labor	Equipment	Total	Total Incl O&P
0650 Over 16" diameter pipe	A-9	650	.098	S.F.	.44	3.73		4.17	6.85
9000 For type B (supplied air) respirator equipment, add				%				10%	10%

02 91 Chemical Sampling, Testing and Analysis

02 91 10 – Monitoring, Sampling, Testing and Analysis

02 91 10.10 Monitoring, Chemical Sampling, Testing and Analysis

	Crew	Daily Output	Labor-Hours	Unit	Material	2014 Bare Costs Labor	Equipment	Total	Total Incl O&P
0010 **MONITORING, CHEMICAL SAMPLING, TESTING AND ANALYSIS**									
0015 Field Sampling of waste									
0100 Field samples, sample collection, sludge	1 Skwk	32	.250	Ea.		9.10		9.10	15.35
0110 Contaminated soils	"	32	.250	"		9.10		9.10	15.35
0200 Vials and bottles									
0210 32 oz. clear wide mouth jar (case of 12)				Ea.	42			42	46
0220 32 oz. Boston round bottle (case of 12)					37			37	41
0230 32 oz. HDPE bottle (case of 12)					35.50			35.50	39
0300 Laboratory analytical services									
0310 Laboratory testing 13 metals				Ea.	182			182	200
0312 13 metals + mercury					215			215	237
0314 8 metals					156			156	172
0316 Mercury only					41			41	45
0318 Single metal (only Cs, Li, Sr, Ta)					42			42	46
0320 Single metal (excludes Hg, Cs, Li, Sr, Ta)					42			42	46
0400 Hydrocarbons standard					87			87	95.50
0410 Hydrocarbons fingerprint					157			157	173
0500 Radioactivity gross alpha					150			150	165
0510 Gross alpha & beta					150			150	165
0520 Radium 226					85			85	93.50
0530 Radium 228					125			125	138
0540 Radon					144			144	158
0550 Uranium					88			88	97
0600 Volatile organics without GC/MS					153			153	168
0610 Volatile organics including GC/MS					175			175	193
0630 Synthetic organic compounds					1,000			1,000	1,100
0640 Herbicides					210			210	231
0650 Pesticides					148			148	162
0660 PCB's					135			135	149

Division Notes

	CREW	DAILY OUTPUT	LABOR-HOURS	UNIT	BARE COSTS				TOTAL INCL O&P
					MAT.	LABOR	EQUIP.	TOTAL	

Estimating Tips

General

- Carefully check all the plans and specifications. Concrete often appears on drawings other than structural drawings, including mechanical and electrical drawings for equipment pads. The cost of cutting and patching is often difficult to estimate. See Subdivision 03 81 for Concrete Cutting, Subdivision 02 41 19.16 for Cutout Demolition, Subdivision 03 05 05.10 for Concrete Demolition, and Subdivision 02 41 19.19 for Rubbish Handling (handling, loading and hauling of debris).

- Always obtain concrete prices from suppliers near the job site. A volume discount can often be negotiated, depending upon competition in the area. Remember to add for waste, particularly for slabs and footings on grade.

03 10 00 Concrete Forming and Accessories

- A primary cost for concrete construction is forming. Most jobs today are constructed with prefabricated forms. The selection of the forms best suited for the job and the total square feet of forms required for efficient concrete forming and placing are key elements in estimating concrete construction. Enough forms must be available for erection to make efficient use of the concrete placing equipment and crew.

- Concrete accessories for forming and placing depend upon the systems used. Study the plans and specifications to ensure that all special accessory requirements have been included in the cost estimate, such as anchor bolts, inserts, and hangers.

- Included within costs for forms-in-place are all necessary bracing and shoring.

03 20 00 Concrete Reinforcing

- Ascertain that the reinforcing steel supplier has included all accessories, cutting, bending, and an allowance for lapping, splicing, and waste. A good rule of thumb is 10% for lapping, splicing, and waste. Also, 10% waste should be allowed for welded wire fabric.

- The unit price items in the subdivisions for Reinforcing In Place, Glass Fiber Reinforcing, and Welded Wire Fabric include the labor to install accessories such as beam and slab bolsters, high chairs, and bar ties and tie wire. The material cost for these accessories is not included; they may be obtained from the Accessories Division.

03 30 00 Cast-In-Place Concrete

- When estimating structural concrete, pay particular attention to requirements for concrete additives, curing methods, and surface treatments. Special consideration for climate, hot or cold, must be included in your estimate. Be sure to include requirements for concrete placing equipment, and concrete finishing.

- For accurate concrete estimating, the estimator must consider each of the following major components individually: forms, reinforcing steel, ready-mix concrete, placement of the concrete, and finishing of the top surface. For faster estimating, Subdivision 03 30 53.40 for Concrete-In-Place can be used; here, various items of concrete work are presented that include the costs of all five major components (unless specifically stated otherwise).

03 40 00 Precast Concrete
03 50 00 Cast Decks and Underlayment

- The cost of hauling precast concrete structural members is often an important factor. For this reason, it is important to get a quote from the nearest supplier. It may become economically feasible to set up precasting beds on the site if the hauling costs are prohibitive.

Reference Numbers

Reference numbers are shown in shaded boxes at the beginning of some major classifications. These numbers refer to related items in the Reference Section. The reference information may be an estimating procedure, an alternate pricing method, or technical information.

Note: Not all subdivisions listed here necessarily appear in this publication.

03 01 Maintenance of Concrete

03 01 30 – Maintenance of Cast-In-Place Concrete

03 01 30.62 Concrete Patching

03 01 30.62 Concrete Patching	Crew	Daily Output	Labor-Hours	Unit	Material	2014 Bare Costs Labor	2014 Bare Costs Equipment	Total	Total Incl O&P
0010 **CONCRETE PATCHING**									
0100 Floors, 1/4" thick, small areas, regular grout	1 Cefi	170	.047	S.F.	1.42	1.62		3.04	4.18
0150 Epoxy grout	"	100	.080	"	7.80	2.75		10.55	13
2000 Walls, including chipping, cleaning and epoxy grout									
2100 1/4" deep	1 Cefi	65	.123	S.F.	7.20	4.23		11.43	14.75
2150 1/2" deep		50	.160		14.40	5.50		19.90	25
2200 3/4" deep	↓	40	.200	↓	21.50	6.85		28.35	35

03 05 Common Work Results for Concrete

03 05 05 – Selective Concrete Demolition

03 05 05.10 Selective Demolition, Concrete

	Crew	Daily Output	Labor-Hours	Unit	Material	2014 Bare Costs Labor	2014 Bare Costs Equipment	Total	Total Incl O&P
0010 **SELECTIVE DEMOLITION, CONCRETE** R024119-10									
0012 Excludes saw cutting, torch cutting, loading or hauling									
0050 Break into small pieces, reinf. less than 1% of cross-sectional area	B-9	24	1.667	C.Y.		47.50	9.75	57.25	90.50
0060 Reinforcing 1% to 2% of cross-sectional area		16	2.500			71.50	14.60	86.10	136
0070 Reinforcing more than 2% of cross-sectional area	↓	8	5	↓		143	29	172	273
0150 Remove whole pieces, up to 2 tons per piece	E-18	36	1.111	Ea.		43	26.50	69.50	109
0160 2 – 5 tons per piece		30	1.333			51.50	32	83.50	131
0170 5 – 10 tons per piece		24	1.667			64.50	40	104.50	163
0180 10 – 15 tons per piece	↓	18	2.222			86	53.50	139.50	218
0250 Precast unit embedded in masonry, up to 1 C.F.	D-1	16	1			32		32	53.50
0260 1 – 2 C.F.		12	1.333			43		43	71.50
0270 2 – 5 C.F.		10	1.600			51.50		51.50	86
0280 5 – 10 C.F.	↓	8	2	↓		64.50		64.50	107
0990 For hydrodemolition see Section 02 41 13.15									

03 05 13 – Basic Concrete Materials

03 05 13.20 Concrete Admixtures and Surface Treatments

	Crew	Daily Output	Labor-Hours	Unit	Material	2014 Bare Costs Labor	2014 Bare Costs Equipment	Total	Total Incl O&P
0010 **CONCRETE ADMIXTURES AND SURFACE TREATMENTS**									
0040 Abrasives, aluminum oxide, over 20 tons				Lb.	1.82			1.82	2
0050 1 to 20 tons					1.95			1.95	2.14
0070 Under 1 ton					2.03			2.03	2.23
0100 Silicon carbide, black, over 20 tons					2.78			2.78	3.06
0110 1 to 20 tons					2.96			2.96	3.25
0120 Under 1 ton				↓	3.08			3.08	3.39
0200 Air entraining agent, .7 to 1.5 oz. per bag, 55 gallon drum				Gal.	13.35			13.35	14.65
0220 5 gallon pail					18.35			18.35	20
0300 Bonding agent, acrylic latex, 250 S.F. per gallon, 5 gallon pail					22			22	24.50
0320 Epoxy resin, 80 S.F. per gallon, 4 gallon case				↓	61.50			61.50	67.50
0400 Calcium chloride, 50 lb. bags, TL lots				Ton	770			770	845
0420 Less than truckload lots				Bag	23.50			23.50	25.50
0500 Carbon black, liquid, 2 to 8 lb. per bag of cement				Lb.	8.65			8.65	9.55
0600 Colored pigments, integral, 2 to 10 lb. per bag of cement, subtle colors					2.40			2.40	2.64
0610 Standard colors					3.25			3.25	3.58
0620 Premium colors				↓	5.40			5.40	5.95
0920 Dustproofing compound, 250 S.F./gal., 5 gallon pail				Gal.	6.20			6.20	6.80
1010 Epoxy based, 125 S.F./gal., 5 gallon pail				"	53			53	58
1100 Hardeners, metallic, 55 lb. bags, natural (grey)				Lb.	.66			.66	.73
1200 Colors					2.17			2.17	2.38
1300 Non-metallic, 55 lb. bags, natural grey					.41			.41	.45
1320 Colors				↓	.90			.90	.99

03 05 13 – Basic Concrete Materials

03 05 13.20 Concrete Admixtures and Surface Treatments	Crew	Daily Output	Labor-Hours	Unit	Material	2014 Bare Costs Labor	Equipment	Total	Total Incl O&P
1550	Release agent, for tilt slabs, 5 gallon pail				Gal.	16.20			16.20	17.80
1570	For forms, 5 gallon pail					13.35			13.35	14.70
1590	Concrete release agent for forms, 100% biodegradeable, zero VOC, 5 gal pail G					19.20			19.20	21
1595	55 gallon drum G					15.75			15.75	17.35
1600	Sealer, hardener and dustproofer, epoxy-based, 125 S.F./gal., 5 gallon unit					53			53	58
1620	3 gallon unit					58			58	64
1630	Sealer, solvent-based, 250 S.F./gal., 55 gallon drum					23.50			23.50	25.50
1640	5 gallon pail					29.50			29.50	32.50
1650	Sealer, water based, 350 S.F., 55 gallon drum					22			22	24.50
1660	5 gallon pail					25			25	27.50
1900	Set retarder, 100 S.F./gal., 1 gallon pail					22			22	24
2000	Waterproofing, integral 1 lb. per bag of cement				Lb.	2.02			2.02	2.22
2100	Powdered metallic, 40 lb. per 100 S.F., standard colors					2.40			2.40	2.64
2120	Premium colors					3.36			3.36	3.70
3000	For integral colored pigments, 2500 psi (5 bag mix)									
3100	Standard colors, 1.8 lb. per bag, add				C.Y.	21.50			21.50	24
3200	9.4 lb. per bag, add					113			113	124
3400	Premium colors, 1.8 lb. per bag, add					29.50			29.50	32
3500	7.5 lb. per bag, add					122			122	134
3700	Ultra premium colors, 1.8 lb. per bag, add					48.50			48.50	53.50
3800	7.5 lb. per bag, add					203			203	223
6000	Concrete ready mix additives, recycled coal fly ash, mixed at plant G				Ton	57			57	62.50
6010	Recycled blast furnace slag, mixed at plant G				"	87.50			87.50	96.50

03 05 13.25 Aggregate

		Crew	Daily Output	Labor-Hours	Unit	Material	2014 Bare Costs Labor	Equipment	Total	Total Incl O&P
0010	**AGGREGATE** R033105-20									
0100	Lightweight vermiculite or perlite, 4 C.F. bag, C.L. lots G				Bag	23.50			23.50	26
0150	L.C.L. lots R033105-40 G				"	26.50			26.50	29
0250	Sand & stone, loaded at pit, crushed bank gravel				Ton	21			21	23
0350	Sand, washed, for concrete R033105-50					17.40			17.40	19.15
0400	For plaster or brick					17.40			17.40	19.15
0450	Stone, 3/4" to 1-1/2"					16.85			16.85	18.50
0470	Round, river stone					26.50			26.50	29
0500	3/8" roofing stone & 1/2" pea stone					26			26	28.50
0550	For trucking 10-mile round trip, add to the above	B-34B	117	.068			2.03	5.90	7.93	9.90
0600	For trucking 30-mile round trip, add to the above	"	72	.111			3.29	9.60	12.89	16.10
0850	Sand & stone, loaded at pit, crushed bank gravel				C.Y.	29.50			29.50	32.50
0950	Sand, washed, for concrete					24			24	26.50
1000	For plaster or brick					24			24	26.50
1050	Stone, 3/4" to 1-1/2"					32			32	35.50
1055	Round, river stone					36			36	39.50
1100	3/8" roofing stone & 1/2" pea stone					24			24	26
1150	For trucking 10-mile round trip, add to the above	B-34B	78	.103			3.04	8.85	11.89	14.80
1200	For trucking 30-mile round trip, add to the above	"	48	.167			4.94	14.40	19.34	24
1310	Onyx chips, 50 lb. bags				Cwt.	33			33	36.50
1330	Quartz chips, 50 lb. bags					12.30			12.30	13.55
1410	White marble, 3/8" to 1/2", 50 lb. bags					8.25			8.25	9.10
1430	3/4", bulk				Ton	117			117	129

03 05 13.30 Cement

		Crew	Daily Output	Labor-Hours	Unit	Material	2014 Bare Costs Labor	Equipment	Total	Total Incl O&P
0010	**CEMENT** R033105-20									
0240	Portland, Type I/II, TL lots, 94 lb. bags				Bag	9.65			9.65	10.65
0250	LTL/LCL lots R033105-30				"	10.70			10.70	11.80
0300	Trucked in bulk, per Cwt.				Cwt.	8.30			8.30	9.10

03 05 13 – Basic Concrete Materials

03 05 13.30 Cement

		Crew	Daily Output	Labor-Hours	Unit	Material	2014 Bare Costs Labor	Equipment	Total	Total Incl O&P
0400	Type III, high early strength, TL lots, 94 lb. bags	R033105-40			Bag	12.55			12.55	13.80
0420	L.T.L. or L.C.L. lots					13.95			13.95	15.35
0500	White, type III, high early strength, T.L. or C.L. lots, bags	R033105-50				25			25	27.50
0520	L.T.L. or L.C.L. lots					28			28	30.50
0600	White, type I, T.L. or C.L. lots, bags					23			23	25
0620	L.T.L. or L.C.L. lots					24			24	26.50

03 05 13.80 Waterproofing and Dampproofing

		Crew	Daily Output	Labor-Hours	Unit	Material	2014 Bare Costs Labor	Equipment	Total	Total Incl O&P
0010	**WATERPROOFING AND DAMPPROOFING**									
0050	Integral waterproofing, add to cost of regular concrete				C.Y.	12.10			12.10	13.35

03 05 13.85 Winter Protection

		Crew	Daily Output	Labor-Hours	Unit	Material	2014 Bare Costs Labor	Equipment	Total	Total Incl O&P
0010	**WINTER PROTECTION**									
0012	For heated ready mix, add				C.Y.	4.50			4.50	4.95
0100	Temporary heat to protect concrete, 24 hours	2 Clab	50	.320	M.S.F.	535	9		544	600
0200	Temporary shelter for slab on grade, wood frame/polyethylene sheeting									
0201	Build or remove, light framing for short spans	2 Carp	10	1.600	M.S.F.	284	57		341	405
0210	Large framing for long spans	"	3	5.333	"	380	191		571	740
0500	Electrically heated pads, 110 volts, 15 watts per S.F., buy				S.F.	10.35			10.35	11.35
0600	20 watts per S.F., buy					13.75			13.75	15.10
0710	Electrically, heated pads, 15 watts/S.F., 20 uses					.52			.52	.57

03 11 Concrete Forming

03 11 13 – Structural Cast-In-Place Concrete Forming

03 11 13.20 Forms In Place, Beams and Girders

			Crew	Daily Output	Labor-Hours	Unit	Material	2014 Bare Costs Labor	Equipment	Total	Total Incl O&P
0010	**FORMS IN PLACE, BEAMS AND GIRDERS**	R031113-40									
0500	Exterior spandrel, job-built plywood, 12" wide, 1 use	R031113-60	C-2	225	.213	SFCA	2.98	6.80		9.78	14.75
0550	2 use			275	.175		1.57	5.55		7.12	11.10
0600	3 use			295	.163		1.19	5.20		6.39	10.05
0650	4 use			310	.155		.97	4.94		5.91	9.35
1000	18" wide, 1 use			250	.192		2.69	6.10		8.79	13.25
1050	2 use			275	.175		1.48	5.55		7.03	10.95
1100	3 use			305	.157		1.07	5		6.07	9.65
1150	4 use			315	.152		.88	4.86		5.74	9.15
1500	24" wide, 1 use			265	.181		2.47	5.75		8.22	12.45
1550	2 use			290	.166		1.40	5.30		6.70	10.45
1600	3 use			315	.152		.99	4.86		5.85	9.30
1650	4 use			325	.148		.80	4.71		5.51	8.85
2000	Interior beam, job-built plywood, 12" wide, 1 use			300	.160		3.54	5.10		8.64	12.50
2050	2 use			340	.141		1.70	4.50		6.20	9.45
2100	3 use			364	.132		1.42	4.20		5.62	8.65
2150	4 use			377	.127		1.15	4.06		5.21	8.10
2500	24" wide, 1 use			320	.150		2.52	4.78		7.30	10.80
2550	2 use			365	.132		1.42	4.19		5.61	8.60
2600	3 use			385	.125		1	3.97		4.97	7.80
2650	4 use			395	.122		.81	3.87		4.68	7.45
3000	Encasing steel beam, hung, job-built plywood, 1 use			325	.148		3.09	4.71		7.80	11.35
3050	2 use			390	.123		1.70	3.92		5.62	8.45
3100	3 use			415	.116		1.24	3.69		4.93	7.55
3150	4 use			430	.112		1	3.56		4.56	7.10
3500	Bottoms only, to 30" wide, job-built plywood, 1 use			230	.209		3.98	6.65		10.63	15.60
3550	2 use			265	.181		2.24	5.75		7.99	12.20

03 11 Concrete Forming

03 11 13 – Structural Cast-In-Place Concrete Forming

03 11 13.20 Forms In Place, Beams and Girders

		Crew	Daily Output	Labor-Hours	Unit	Material	2014 Bare Costs Labor	Equipment	Total	Total Incl O&P
3600	3 use	C-2	280	.171	SFCA	1.59	5.45		7.04	10.95
3650	4 use		290	.166		1.29	5.30		6.59	10.30
4000	Sides only, vertical, 36" high, job-built plywood, 1 use		335	.143		5.10	4.57		9.67	13.30
4050	2 use		405	.119		2.80	3.78		6.58	9.45
4100	3 use		430	.112		2.04	3.56		5.60	8.25
4150	4 use		445	.108		1.65	3.44		5.09	7.60
4500	Sloped sides, 36" high, 1 use		305	.157		4.92	5		9.92	13.85
4550	2 use		370	.130		2.74	4.14		6.88	9.95
4600	3 use		405	.119		1.97	3.78		5.75	8.50
4650	4 use		425	.113		1.60	3.60		5.20	7.80
5000	Upstanding beams, 36" high, 1 use		225	.213		6.25	6.80		13.05	18.30
5050	2 use		255	.188		3.47	6		9.47	13.90
5100	3 use		275	.175		2.51	5.55		8.06	12.10
5150	4 use		280	.171		2.04	5.45		7.49	11.45

03 11 13.25 Forms In Place, Columns

			Crew	Daily Output	Labor-Hours	Unit	Material	2014 Bare Costs Labor	Equipment	Total	Total Incl O&P
0010	**FORMS IN PLACE, COLUMNS**	R031113-40									
0500	Round fiberglass, 4 use per mo., rent, 12" diameter		C-1	160	.200	L.F.	8.15	6.35		14.50	19.60
0550	16" diameter	R031113-60		150	.213		9.70	6.75		16.45	22
0600	18" diameter			140	.229		10.85	7.25		18.10	24
0650	24" diameter			135	.237		13.50	7.50		21	27.50
0700	28" diameter			130	.246		15.10	7.80		22.90	29.50
0800	30" diameter			125	.256		15.75	8.10		23.85	31
0850	36" diameter			120	.267		21	8.45		29.45	37
1500	Round fiber tube, recycled paper, 1 use, 8" diameter	G		155	.206		1.66	6.55		8.21	12.85
1550	10" diameter	G		155	.206		2.24	6.55		8.79	13.45
1600	12" diameter	G		150	.213		2.60	6.75		9.35	14.20
1650	14" diameter	G		145	.221		3.77	7		10.77	15.90
1700	16" diameter	G		140	.229		4.52	7.25		11.77	17.15
1720	18" diameter	G		140	.229		5.30	7.25		12.55	18
1750	20" diameter	G		135	.237		7.30	7.50		14.80	20.50
1800	24" diameter	G		130	.246		9.30	7.80		17.10	23.50
1850	30" diameter	G		125	.256		13.60	8.10		21.70	28.50
1900	36" diameter	G		115	.278		17.05	8.80		25.85	33.50
1950	42" diameter	G		100	.320		42	10.15		52.15	63.50
2000	48" diameter	G		85	.376		48.50	11.90		60.40	73.50
2200	For seamless type, add						15%				
3000	Round, steel, 4 use per mo., rent, regular duty, 14" diameter	G	C-1	145	.221	L.F.	17.55	7		24.55	31
3050	16" diameter	G		125	.256		17.90	8.10		26	33.50
3100	Heavy duty, 20" diameter	G		105	.305		19.75	9.65		29.40	38
3150	24" diameter	G		85	.376		21.50	11.90		33.40	43.50
3200	30" diameter	G		70	.457		25	14.45		39.45	51.50
3250	36" diameter	G		60	.533		26.50	16.90		43.40	57.50
3300	48" diameter	G		50	.640		39.50	20.50		60	77.50
3350	60" diameter	G		45	.711		48.50	22.50		71	91.50
4500	For second and succeeding months, deduct						50%				
5000	Job-built plywood, 8" x 8" columns, 1 use		C-1	165	.194	SFCA	2.67	6.15		8.82	13.30
5050	2 use			195	.164		1.53	5.20		6.73	10.45
5100	3 use			210	.152		1.07	4.82		5.89	9.30
5150	4 use			215	.149		.88	4.71		5.59	8.90
5500	12" x 12" columns, 1 use			180	.178		2.56	5.65		8.21	12.30
5550	2 use			210	.152		1.41	4.82		6.23	9.65
5600	3 use			220	.145		1.02	4.60		5.62	8.90

03 11 13 – Structural Cast-In-Place Concrete Forming

03 11 13.25 Forms In Place, Columns

		Crew	Daily Output	Labor-Hours	Unit	Material	2014 Bare Costs Labor	Equipment	Total	Total Incl O&P
5650	4 use	C-1	225	.142	SFCA	.83	4.50		5.33	8.50
6000	16" x 16" columns, 1 use		185	.173		2.55	5.45		8	12
6050	2 use		215	.149		1.36	4.71		6.07	9.45
6100	3 use		230	.139		1.02	4.40		5.42	8.55
6150	4 use		235	.136		.83	4.31		5.14	8.15
6500	24" x 24" columns, 1 use		190	.168		2.87	5.35		8.22	12.15
6550	2 use		216	.148		1.58	4.69		6.27	9.65
6600	3 use		230	.139		1.15	4.40		5.55	8.65
6650	4 use		238	.134		.93	4.26		5.19	8.20
7000	36" x 36" columns, 1 use		200	.160		2.30	5.05		7.35	11.10
7050	2 use		230	.139		1.30	4.40		5.70	8.85
7100	3 use		245	.131		.92	4.13		5.05	7.95
7150	4 use		250	.128		.75	4.05		4.80	7.60
7400	Steel framed plywood, based on 50 uses of purchased									
7420	forms, and 4 uses of bracing lumber									
7500	8" x 8" column	C-1	340	.094	SFCA	2.11	2.98		5.09	7.30
7550	10" x 10"		350	.091		1.84	2.89		4.73	6.90
7600	12" x 12"		370	.086		1.56	2.74		4.30	6.35
7650	16" x 16"		400	.080		1.22	2.53		3.75	5.60
7700	20" x 20"		420	.076		1.08	2.41		3.49	5.25
7750	24" x 24"		440	.073		.78	2.30		3.08	4.73
7755	30" x 30"		440	.073		.99	2.30		3.29	4.97
7760	36" x 36"		460	.070		.87	2.20		3.07	4.67

03 11 13.30 Forms In Place, Culvert

			Crew	Daily Output	Labor-Hours	Unit	Material	2014 Bare Costs Labor	Equipment	Total	Total Incl O&P
0010	**FORMS IN PLACE, CULVERT**	R031113-40									
0015	5' to 8' square or rectangular, 1 use		C-1	170	.188	SFCA	3.98	5.95		9.93	14.40
0050	2 use	R031113-60		180	.178		2.39	5.65		8.04	12.15
0100	3 use			190	.168		1.86	5.35		7.21	11.05
0150	4 use			200	.160		1.59	5.05		6.64	10.30

03 11 13.35 Forms In Place, Elevated Slabs

			Crew	Daily Output	Labor-Hours	Unit	Material	2014 Bare Costs Labor	Equipment	Total	Total Incl O&P
0010	**FORMS IN PLACE, ELEVATED SLABS**	R031113-40									
1000	Flat plate, job-built plywood, to 15' high, 1 use	R031113-60	C-2	470	.102	S.F.	3.64	3.26		6.90	9.50
1050	2 use			520	.092		2	2.94		4.94	7.15
1100	3 use			545	.088		1.46	2.81		4.27	6.35
1150	4 use			560	.086		1.18	2.73		3.91	5.90
1500	15' to 20' high ceilings, 4 use			495	.097		1.25	3.09		4.34	6.55
1600	21' to 35' high ceilings, 4 use			450	.107		1.55	3.40		4.95	7.45
2000	Flat slab, drop panels, job-built plywood, to 15' high, 1 use			449	.107		4.20	3.41		7.61	10.35
2050	2 use			509	.094		2.31	3.01		5.32	7.60
2100	3 use			532	.090		1.68	2.88		4.56	6.70
2150	4 use			544	.088		1.37	2.81		4.18	6.25
2250	15' to 20' high ceilings, 4 use			480	.100		2.43	3.19		5.62	8
2350	20' to 35' high ceilings, 4 use			435	.110		2.73	3.52		6.25	8.95
3000	Floor slab hung from steel beams, 1 use			485	.099		2.72	3.16		5.88	8.30
3050	2 use			535	.090		2.09	2.86		4.95	7.10
3100	3 use			550	.087		1.87	2.78		4.65	6.75
3150	4 use			565	.085		1.77	2.71		4.48	6.50
3500	Floor slab, with 1-way joist pans, 1 use			415	.116		5.95	3.69		9.64	12.75
3550	2 use			445	.108		4.07	3.44		7.51	10.30
3600	3 use			475	.101		3.44	3.22		6.66	9.25
3650	4 use			500	.096		3.12	3.06		6.18	8.60
4500	With 2-way waffle domes, 1 use			405	.119		6.10	3.78		9.88	13.05

03 11 Concrete Forming

03 11 13 – Structural Cast-In-Place Concrete Forming

03 11 13.35 Forms In Place, Elevated Slabs

		Crew	Daily Output	Labor-Hours	Unit	Material	Labor	Equipment	Total	Total Incl O&P
4520	2 use	C-2	450	.107	S.F.	4.20	3.40		7.60	10.35
4530	3 use		460	.104		3.57	3.33		6.90	9.50
4550	4 use		470	.102		3.25	3.26		6.51	9.10
5000	Box out for slab openings, over 16" deep, 1 use		190	.253	SFCA	4.14	8.05		12.19	18.10
5050	2 use		240	.200	"	2.28	6.40		8.68	13.25
5500	Shallow slab box outs, to 10 S.F.		42	1.143	Ea.	10.50	36.50		47	73
5550	Over 10 S.F. (use perimeter)		600	.080	L.F.	1.41	2.55		3.96	5.85
6000	Bulkhead forms for slab, with keyway, 1 use, 2 piece		500	.096		1.95	3.06		5.01	7.30
6100	3 piece (see also edge forms)		460	.104		2.14	3.33		5.47	7.95
6200	Slab bulkhead form, 4-1/2" high, exp metal, w/keyway & stakes [G]	C-1	1200	.027		.88	.84		1.72	2.39
6210	5-1/2" high [G]		1100	.029		1.01	.92		1.93	2.66
6215	7-1/2" high [G]		960	.033		1.25	1.05		2.30	3.16
6220	9-1/2" high [G]		840	.038		1.36	1.21		2.57	3.53
6500	Curb forms, wood, 6" to 12" high, on elevated slabs, 1 use		180	.178	SFCA	1.51	5.65		7.16	11.15
6550	2 use		205	.156		.83	4.94		5.77	9.20
6600	3 use		220	.145		.60	4.60		5.20	8.40
6650	4 use		225	.142		.49	4.50		4.99	8.15
7000	Edge forms to 6" high, on elevated slab, 4 use		500	.064	L.F.	.18	2.03		2.21	3.61
7070	7" to 12" high, 1 use		162	.198	SFCA	1.14	6.25		7.39	11.80
7090	3 use		222	.144		.45	4.56		5.01	8.20
7101	4 use		350	.091		.18	2.89		3.07	5.05
7500	Depressed area forms to 12" high, 4 use		300	.107	L.F.	.92	3.38		4.30	6.70
7550	12" to 24" high, 4 use		175	.183		1.26	5.80		7.06	11.15
8000	Perimeter deck and rail for elevated slabs, straight		90	.356		12	11.25		23.25	32
8050	Curved		65	.492		16.45	15.60		32.05	44
8500	Void forms, round plastic, 8" high x 3" diameter [G]		450	.071	Ea.	2.08	2.25		4.33	6.10
8550	4" diameter [G]		425	.075		3.23	2.38		5.61	7.55
8600	6" diameter [G]		400	.080		5.05	2.53		7.58	9.80
8650	8" diameter [G]		375	.085		8.80	2.70		11.50	14.20

03 11 13.40 Forms In Place, Equipment Foundations

		Crew	Daily Output	Labor-Hours	Unit	Material	Labor	Equipment	Total	Total Incl O&P
0010	**FORMS IN PLACE, EQUIPMENT FOUNDATIONS** R031113-40									
0020	1 use	C-2	160	.300	SFCA	3.09	9.55		12.64	19.50
0050	2 use R031113-60		190	.253		1.70	8.05		9.75	15.40
0100	3 use		200	.240		1.24	7.65		8.89	14.25
0150	4 use		205	.234		1.01	7.45		8.46	13.65

03 11 13.45 Forms In Place, Footings

		Crew	Daily Output	Labor-Hours	Unit	Material	Labor	Equipment	Total	Total Incl O&P
0010	**FORMS IN PLACE, FOOTINGS** R031113-40									
0020	Continuous wall, plywood, 1 use	C-1	375	.085	SFCA	6.25	2.70		8.95	11.40
0050	2 use R031113-60		440	.073		3.42	2.30		5.72	7.65
0100	3 use		470	.068		2.49	2.16		4.65	6.35
0150	4 use		485	.066		2.03	2.09		4.12	5.75
0500	Dowel supports for footings or beams, 1 use		500	.064	L.F.	.84	2.03		2.87	4.33
1000	Integral starter wall, to 4" high, 1 use		400	.080		.84	2.53		3.37	5.20
1500	Keyway, 4 use, tapered wood, 2" x 4"	1 Carp	530	.015		.20	.54		.74	1.13
1550	2" x 6"		500	.016		.28	.57		.85	1.27
2000	Tapered plastic		530	.015		1.24	.54		1.78	2.27
2250	For keyway hung from supports, add		150	.053		.84	1.91		2.75	4.13
3000	Pile cap, square or rectangular, job-built plywood, 1 use	C-1	290	.110	SFCA	2.79	3.49		6.28	8.95
3050	2 use		346	.092		1.53	2.93		4.46	6.60
3100	3 use		371	.086		1.12	2.73		3.85	5.85
3150	4 use		383	.084		.91	2.64		3.55	5.45
4000	Triangular or hexagonal, 1 use		225	.142		3.26	4.50		7.76	11.20

03 11 Concrete Forming

03 11 13 – Structural Cast-In-Place Concrete Forming

03 11 13.45 Forms In Place, Footings

		Crew	Daily Output	Labor-Hours	Unit	Material	2014 Bare Costs Labor	2014 Bare Costs Equipment	Total	Total Incl O&P
4050	2 use	C-1	280	.114	SFCA	1.79	3.62		5.41	8.05
4100	3 use		305	.105		1.30	3.32		4.62	7.05
4150	4 use		315	.102		1.06	3.22		4.28	6.55
5000	Spread footings, job-built lumber, 1 use		305	.105		2	3.32		5.32	7.80
5050	2 use		371	.086		1.11	2.73		3.84	5.80
5100	3 use		401	.080		.80	2.53		3.33	5.15
5150	4 use		414	.077	↓	.65	2.45		3.10	4.83
6000	Supports for dowels, plinths or templates, 2' x 2' footing		25	1.280	Ea.	6.05	40.50		46.55	74.50
6050	4' x 4' footing		22	1.455		12.10	46		58.10	91
6100	8' x 8' footing		20	1.600		24	50.50		74.50	112
6150	12' x 12' footing		17	1.882	↓	34	59.50		93.50	137
7000	Plinths, job-built plywood, 1 use		250	.128	SFCA	3.53	4.05		7.58	10.70
7100	4 use	↓	270	.119	"	1.16	3.75		4.91	7.55

03 11 13.47 Forms In Place, Gas Station Forms

			Crew	Daily Output	Labor-Hours	Unit	Material	2014 Bare Costs Labor	2014 Bare Costs Equipment	Total	Total Incl O&P
0010	**FORMS IN PLACE, GAS STATION FORMS**										
0050	Curb fascia, with template, 12 ga. steel, left in place, 9" high	G	1 Carp	50	.160	L.F.	13.90	5.70		19.60	25
1000	Sign or light bases, 18" diameter, 9" high	G		9	.889	Ea.	87.50	32		119.50	150
1050	30" diameter, 13" high	G		8	1		139	36		175	213
2000	Island forms, 10' long, 9" high, 3'- 6" wide	G	C-1	10	3.200		390	101		491	595
2050	4' wide	G		9	3.556		400	113		513	630
2500	20' long, 9" high, 4' wide	G		6	5.333		645	169		814	995
2550	5' wide	G	↓	5	6.400	↓	670	203		873	1,075

03 11 13.50 Forms In Place, Grade Beam

			Crew	Daily Output	Labor-Hours	Unit	Material	2014 Bare Costs Labor	2014 Bare Costs Equipment	Total	Total Incl O&P
0010	**FORMS IN PLACE, GRADE BEAM**	R031113-40									
0020	Job-built plywood, 1 use		C-2	530	.091	SFCA	2.82	2.89		5.71	7.95
0050	2 use	R031113-60		580	.083		1.55	2.64		4.19	6.15
0100	3 use			600	.080		1.13	2.55		3.68	5.55
0150	4 use		↓	605	.079	↓	.92	2.53		3.45	5.25

03 11 13.55 Forms In Place, Mat Foundation

			Crew	Daily Output	Labor-Hours	Unit	Material	2014 Bare Costs Labor	2014 Bare Costs Equipment	Total	Total Incl O&P
0010	**FORMS IN PLACE, MAT FOUNDATION**	R031113-40									
0020	Job-built plywood, 1 use		C-2	290	.166	SFCA	2.89	5.30		8.19	12.10
0050	2 use	R031113-60		310	.155		1.10	4.94		6.04	9.50
0100	3 use			330	.145		.71	4.64		5.35	8.60
0120	4 use		↓	350	.137		.65	4.37		5.02	8.05

03 11 13.65 Forms In Place, Slab On Grade

			Crew	Daily Output	Labor-Hours	Unit	Material	2014 Bare Costs Labor	2014 Bare Costs Equipment	Total	Total Incl O&P
0010	**FORMS IN PLACE, SLAB ON GRADE**	R031113-40									
1000	Bulkhead forms w/keyway, wood, 6" high, 1 use		C-1	510	.063	L.F.	.93	1.99		2.92	4.36
1050	2 uses	R031113-60		400	.080		.51	2.53		3.04	4.82
1100	4 uses			350	.091		.30	2.89		3.19	5.20
1400	Bulkhead form for slab, 4-1/2" high, exp metal, incl keyway & stakes	G		1200	.027		.88	.84		1.72	2.39
1410	5-1/2" high	G		1100	.029		1.01	.92		1.93	2.66
1420	7-1/2" high	G		960	.033		1.25	1.05		2.30	3.16
1430	9-1/2" high	G		840	.038	↓	1.36	1.21		2.57	3.53
2000	Curb forms, wood, 6" to 12" high, on grade, 1 use			215	.149	SFCA	2.43	4.71		7.14	10.60
2050	2 use			250	.128		1.34	4.05		5.39	8.30
2100	3 use			265	.121		.97	3.82		4.79	7.50
2150	4 use			275	.116	↓	.79	3.68		4.47	7.05
3000	Edge forms, wood, 4 use, on grade, to 6" high			600	.053	L.F.	.31	1.69		2	3.18
3050	7" to 12" high			435	.074	SFCA	.77	2.33		3.10	4.76
3060	Over 12"			350	.091	"	.82	2.89		3.71	5.75
3500	For depressed slabs, 4 use, to 12" high			300	.107	L.F.	.67	3.38		4.05	6.45
3550	To 24" high		↓	175	.183	↓	.88	5.80		6.68	10.70

03 11 Concrete Forming

03 11 13 – Structural Cast-In-Place Concrete Forming

03 11 13.65 Forms In Place, Slab On Grade		Crew	Daily Output	Labor-Hours	Unit	Material	2014 Bare Costs Labor	Equipment	Total	Total Incl O&P
4000	For slab blockouts, to 12" high, 1 use	C-1	200	.160	L.F.	.71	5.05		5.76	9.35
4050	To 24" high, 1 use		120	.267		.90	8.45		9.35	15.20
4100	Plastic (extruded), to 6" high, multiple use, on grade	↓	800	.040	↓	8.20	1.27		9.47	11.15
5000	Screed, 24 ga. metal key joint, see Section 03 15 16.30									
5020	Wood, incl. wood stakes, 1" x 3"	C-1	900	.036	L.F.	.77	1.13		1.90	2.74
5050	2" x 4"		900	.036	"	.76	1.13		1.89	2.73
6000	Trench forms in floor, wood, 1 use		160	.200	SFCA	1.68	6.35		8.03	12.50
6050	2 use		175	.183		.92	5.80		6.72	10.75
6100	3 use		180	.178		.67	5.65		6.32	10.25
6150	4 use		185	.173	↓	.55	5.45		6	9.80
8760	Void form, corrugated fiberboard, 4" x 12", 4' long [G]		3000	.011	S.F.	3.01	.34		3.35	3.88
8770	6" x 12", 4' long	↓	3000	.011		3.59	.34		3.93	4.52
8780	1/4" thick hardboard protective cover for void form	2 Carp	1500	.011	↓	.57	.38		.95	1.27

03 11 13.85 Forms In Place, Walls		Crew	Daily Output	Labor-Hours	Unit	Material	2014 Bare Costs Labor	Equipment	Total	Total Incl O&P
0010	**FORMS IN PLACE, WALLS** R031113-10									
0100	Box out for wall openings, to 16" thick, to 10 S.F.	C-2	24	2	Ea.	25	64		89	135
0150	Over 10 S.F. (use perimeter) R031113-40	"	280	.171	L.F.	2.13	5.45		7.58	11.55
0250	Brick shelf, 4" w, add to wall forms, use wall area above shelf									
0260	1 use R031113-60	C-2	240	.200	SFCA	2.28	6.40		8.68	13.25
0300	2 use		275	.175		1.26	5.55		6.81	10.75
0350	4 use	↓	300	.160	↓	.91	5.10		6.01	9.60
0500	Bulkhead, wood with keyway, 1 use, 2 piece		265	.181	L.F.	1.90	5.75		7.65	11.85
0600	Bulkhead forms with keyway, 1 piece expanded metal, 8" wall [G]	C-1	1000	.032		1.25	1.01		2.26	3.09
0610	10" wall [G]		800	.040		1.36	1.27		2.63	3.63
0620	12" wall [G]	↓	525	.061	↓	1.63	1.93		3.56	5.05
0700	Buttress, to 8' high, 1 use	C-2	350	.137	SFCA	4.19	4.37		8.56	11.95
0750	2 use		430	.112		2.31	3.56		5.87	8.55
0800	3 use		460	.104		1.68	3.33		5.01	7.45
0850	4 use		480	.100	↓	1.38	3.19		4.57	6.85
1000	Corbel or haunch, to 12" wide, add to wall forms, 1 use		150	.320	L.F.	2.28	10.20		12.48	19.70
1050	2 use		170	.282		1.26	9		10.26	16.55
1100	3 use		175	.274		.91	8.75		9.66	15.75
1150	4 use	↓	180	.267	↓	.74	8.50		9.24	15.10
2000	Wall, job-built plywood, to 8' high, 1 use		370	.130	SFCA	2.64	4.14		6.78	9.85
2050	2 use		435	.110		1.67	3.52		5.19	7.80
2100	3 use		495	.097		1.21	3.09		4.30	6.55
2150	4 use		505	.095		.99	3.03		4.02	6.20
2400	8' to 16' high, 1 use		280	.171		2.91	5.45		8.36	12.40
2450	2 use		345	.139		1.24	4.44		5.68	8.80
2500	3 use		375	.128		.89	4.08		4.97	7.80
2550	4 use		395	.122		.73	3.87		4.60	7.35
2700	Over 16' high, 1 use		235	.204		2.51	6.50		9.01	13.70
2750	2 use		290	.166		1.38	5.30		6.68	10.40
2800	3 use		315	.152		1	4.86		5.86	9.30
2850	4 use		330	.145		.82	4.64		5.46	8.70
4000	Radial, smooth curved, job-built plywood, 1 use		245	.196		2.41	6.25		8.66	13.15
4050	2 use		300	.160		1.33	5.10		6.43	10.05
4100	3 use		325	.148		.96	4.71		5.67	9
4150	4 use		335	.143		.78	4.57		5.35	8.55
4200	Below grade, job-built plywood, 1 use		225	.213		2.48	6.80		9.28	14.15
4210	2 use		225	.213		1.36	6.80		8.16	12.95
4220	3 use	↓	225	.213	↓	1.13	6.80		7.93	12.70

03 11 Concrete Forming

03 11 13 – Structural Cast-In-Place Concrete Forming

03 11 13.85 Forms In Place, Walls

		Crew	Daily Output	Labor-Hours	Unit	Material	2014 Bare Costs Labor	Equipment	Total	Total Incl O&P
4230	4 use	C-2	225	.213	SFCA	.81	6.80		7.61	12.35
4300	Curved, 2' chords, job-built plywood, 1 use		290	.166		2	5.30		7.30	11.10
4350	2 use		355	.135		1.10	4.31		5.41	8.45
4400	3 use		385	.125		.80	3.97		4.77	7.60
4450	4 use		400	.120		.65	3.83		4.48	7.15
4500	Over 8' high, 1 use		290	.166		.88	5.30		6.18	9.85
4525	2 use		355	.135		.48	4.31		4.79	7.80
4550	3 use		385	.125		.35	3.97		4.32	7.10
4575	4 use		400	.120		.29	3.83		4.12	6.75
4600	Retaining wall, battered, job-built plyw'd, to 8' high, 1 use		300	.160		1.89	5.10		6.99	10.70
4650	2 use		355	.135		1.04	4.31		5.35	8.40
4700	3 use		375	.128		.76	4.08		4.84	7.70
4750	4 use		390	.123		.61	3.92		4.53	7.30
4900	Over 8' to 16' high, 1 use		240	.200		2.06	6.40		8.46	13
4950	2 use		295	.163		1.13	5.20		6.33	10
5000	3 use		305	.157		.82	5		5.82	9.35
5050	4 use		320	.150		.67	4.78		5.45	8.80
5500	For gang wall forming, 192 S.F. sections, deduct					10%	10%			
5550	384 S.F. sections, deduct					20%	20%			
7500	Lintel or sill forms, 1 use	1 Carp	30	.267		3.06	9.55		12.61	19.40
7520	2 use		34	.235		1.68	8.40		10.08	16
7540	3 use		36	.222		1.23	7.95		9.18	14.70
7560	4 use		37	.216		1	7.75		8.75	14.10
7800	Modular prefabricated plywood, based on 20 uses of purchased									
7820	forms, and 4 uses of bracing lumber									
7860	To 8' high	C-2	800	.060	SFCA	.85	1.91		2.76	4.16
8060	Over 8' to 16' high		600	.080		.90	2.55		3.45	5.30
8600	Pilasters, 1 use		270	.178		3.05	5.65		8.70	12.90
8620	2 use		330	.145		1.68	4.64		6.32	9.65
8640	3 use		370	.130		1.22	4.14		5.36	8.30
8660	4 use		385	.125		.99	3.97		4.96	7.80
9010	Steel framed plywood, based on 50 uses of purchased									
9020	forms, and 4 uses of bracing lumber									
9060	To 8' high	C-2	600	.080	SFCA	.68	2.55		3.23	5.05
9260	Over 8' to 16' high		450	.107		.68	3.40		4.08	6.50
9460	Over 16' to 20' high		400	.120		.68	3.83		4.51	7.20
9475	For elevated walls, add						10%			
9480	For battered walls, 1 side battered, add					10%	10%			
9485	For battered walls, 2 sides battered, add					15%	15%			

03 11 16 – Architectural Cast-in Place Concrete Forming

03 11 16.13 Concrete Form Liners

		Crew	Daily Output	Labor-Hours	Unit	Material	2014 Bare Costs Labor	Equipment	Total	Total Incl O&P
0010	**CONCRETE FORM LINERS**									
5750	Liners for forms (add to wall forms), ABS plastic									
5800	Aged wood, 4" wide, 1 use	1 Carp	256	.031	SFCA	3.30	1.12		4.42	5.50
5820	2 use		256	.031		1.82	1.12		2.94	3.88
5830	3 use		256	.031		1.32	1.12		2.44	3.33
5840	4 use		256	.031		1.07	1.12		2.19	3.06
5900	Fractured rope rib, 1 use		192	.042		4.79	1.49		6.28	7.75
5925	2 use		192	.042		2.63	1.49		4.12	5.40
5950	3 use		192	.042		1.92	1.49		3.41	4.62
6000	4 use		192	.042		1.56	1.49		3.05	4.22
6100	Ribbed, 3/4" deep x 1-1/2" O.C., 1 use		224	.036		4.79	1.28		6.07	7.40

03 11 Concrete Forming

03 11 16 – Architectural Cast-in Place Concrete Forming

03 11 16.13 Concrete Form Liners

		Crew	Daily Output	Labor-Hours	Unit	Material	2014 Bare Costs Labor	2014 Bare Costs Equipment	Total	Total Incl O&P
6125	2 use	1 Carp	224	.036	SFCA	2.63	1.28		3.91	5.05
6150	3 use		224	.036		1.92	1.28		3.20	4.26
6200	4 use		224	.036		1.56	1.28		2.84	3.86
6300	Rustic brick pattern, 1 use		224	.036		3.30	1.28		4.58	5.80
6325	2 use		224	.036		1.82	1.28		3.10	4.15
6350	3 use		224	.036		1.32	1.28		2.60	3.60
6400	4 use		224	.036		1.07	1.28		2.35	3.33
6500	3/8" striated, random, 1 use		224	.036		3.30	1.28		4.58	5.80
6525	2 use		224	.036		1.82	1.28		3.10	4.15
6550	3 use		224	.036		1.32	1.28		2.60	3.60
6600	4 use		224	.036		1.07	1.28		2.35	3.33
6850	Random vertical rustication, 1 use		384	.021		6.25	.74		6.99	8.15
6900	2 use		384	.021		3.45	.74		4.19	5.05
6925	3 use		384	.021		2.51	.74		3.25	4.01
6950	4 use		384	.021		2.04	.74		2.78	3.49
7050	Wood, beveled edge, 3/4" deep, 1 use		384	.021	L.F.	.16	.74		.90	1.43
7100	1" deep, 1 use		384	.021	"	.33	.74		1.07	1.61
7200	4" wide aged cedar, 1 use		256	.031	SFCA	3.30	1.12		4.42	5.50
7300	4" variable depth rough cedar		224	.036	"	4.79	1.28		6.07	7.40

03 11 19 – Insulating Concrete Forming

03 11 19.10 Insulating Forms, Left In Place

			Crew	Daily Output	Labor-Hours	Unit	Material	2014 Bare Costs Labor	2014 Bare Costs Equipment	Total	Total Incl O&P
0010	**INSULATING FORMS, LEFT IN PLACE**										
0020	S.F. is for exterior face, but includes forms for both faces (total R22)										
2000	4" wall, straight block, 16" x 48" (5.33 S.F.)	G	2 Carp	90	.178	Ea.	18.35	6.35		24.70	30.50
2010	90 corner block, exterior 16" x 38" x 22" (6.67 S.F.)	G		75	.213		21.50	7.65		29.15	37
2020	45 corner block, exterior 16" x 34" x 18" (5.78 S.F.)	G		75	.213		21.50	7.65		29.15	37
2100	6" wall, straight block, 16" x 48" (5.33 S.F.)	G		90	.178		18.85	6.35		25.20	31
2110	90 corner block, exterior 16" x 32" x 24" (6.22 S.F.)	G		75	.213		23.50	7.65		31.15	39
2120	45 corner block, exterior 16" x 26" x 18" (4.89 S.F.)	G		75	.213		21	7.65		28.65	36
2130	Brick ledge block, 16" x 48" (5.33 S.F.)	G		80	.200		24	7.15		31.15	38
2140	Taper top block, 16" x 48" (5.33 S.F.)	G		80	.200		22	7.15		29.15	36.50
2200	8" wall, straight block, 16" x 48" (5.33 S.F.)	G		90	.178		20	6.35		26.35	32.50
2210	90 corner block, exterior 16" x 34" x 26" (6.67 S.F.)	G		75	.213		26	7.65		33.65	41.50
2220	45 corner block, exterior 16" x 28" x 20" (5.33 S.F.)	G		75	.213		22	7.65		29.65	37
2230	Brick ledge block, 16" x 48" (5.33 S.F.)	G		80	.200		25	7.15		32.15	39.50
2240	Taper top block, 16" x 48" (5.33 S.F.)	G		80	.200		23	7.15		30.15	37.50

03 11 19.60 Roof Deck Form Boards

			Crew	Daily Output	Labor-Hours	Unit	Material	2014 Bare Costs Labor	2014 Bare Costs Equipment	Total	Total Incl O&P
0010	**ROOF DECK FORM BOARDS**	R051223-50									
0050	Includes bulb tee sub-purlins @ 32-5/8" O.C.										
0070	Non-asbestos fiber cement, 5/16" thick		C-13	2950	.008	S.F.	2.73	.31	.05	3.09	3.61
0100	Fiberglass, 1" thick			2700	.009		3.46	.33	.05	3.84	4.47
0500	Wood fiber, 1" thick	G		2700	.009		2.26	.33	.05	2.64	3.15

03 11 23 – Permanent Stair Forming

03 11 23.75 Forms In Place, Stairs

			Crew	Daily Output	Labor-Hours	Unit	Material	2014 Bare Costs Labor	2014 Bare Costs Equipment	Total	Total Incl O&P
0010	**FORMS IN PLACE, STAIRS**	R031113-40									
0015	(Slant length x width), 1 use		C-2	165	.291	S.F.	5.45	9.25		14.70	21.50
0050	2 use	R031113-60		170	.282		3.11	9		12.11	18.55
0100	3 use			180	.267		2.32	8.50		10.82	16.85
0150	4 use			190	.253		1.93	8.05		9.98	15.70
1000	Alternate pricing method (1.0 L.F./S.F.), 1 use			100	.480	LF Rsr	5.45	15.30		20.75	32
1050	2 use			105	.457		3.11	14.55		17.66	28

03 11 Concrete Forming

03 11 23 – Permanent Stair Forming

03 11 23.75 Forms In Place, Stairs

		Crew	Daily Output	Labor-Hours	Unit	Material	2014 Bare Costs Labor	Equipment	Total	Total Incl O&P
1100	3 use	C-2	110	.436	LF Rsr	2.32	13.90		16.22	26
1150	4 use		115	.417	↓	1.93	13.30		15.23	24.50
2000	Stairs, cast on sloping ground (length x width), 1 use		220	.218	S.F.	2.14	6.95		9.09	14.05
2025	2 use		232	.207		1.17	6.60		7.77	12.40
2050	3 use		244	.197		.85	6.25		7.10	11.50
2100	4 use	↓	256	.188	↓	.69	6		6.69	10.80

03 15 Concrete Accessories

03 15 05 – Concrete Forming Accessories

03 15 05.12 Chamfer Strips

		Crew	Daily Output	Labor-Hours	Unit	Material	2014 Bare Costs Labor	Equipment	Total	Total Incl O&P
0010	**CHAMFER STRIPS**									
2000	Polyvinyl chloride, 1/2" wide with leg	1 Carp	535	.015	L.F.	.38	.53		.91	1.32
2200	3/4" wide with leg		525	.015		.52	.54		1.06	1.49
2400	1" radius with leg		515	.016		.38	.56		.94	1.35
2800	2" radius with leg		500	.016		.66	.57		1.23	1.69
5000	Wood, 1/2" wide		535	.015		.13	.53		.66	1.04
5200	3/4" wide		525	.015		.16	.54		.70	1.10
5400	1" wide	↓	515	.016	↓	.33	.56		.89	1.29

03 15 05.15 Column Form Accessories

			Crew	Daily Output	Labor-Hours	Unit	Material	2014 Bare Costs Labor	Equipment	Total	Total Incl O&P
0010	**COLUMN FORM ACCESSORIES**										
1000	Column clamps, adjustable to 24" x 24", buy	G				Set	137			137	150
1100	Rent per month	G					13.70			13.70	15.05
1300	For sizes to 30" x 30", buy	G					150			150	165
1400	Rent per month	G					15			15	16.50
1600	For sizes to 36" x 36", buy	G					172			172	189
1700	Rent per month	G					17.20			17.20	18.90
2000	Bar type with wedges, 36" x 36", buy	G					112			112	123
2100	Rent per month	G					7.85			7.85	8.60
2300	48" x 48", buy	G					152			152	167
2400	Rent per month	G					10.65			10.65	11.70
3000	Scissor type with wedges, 36" x 36", buy	G					95			95	105
3100	Rent per month	G					9.50			9.50	10.45
3300	60" x 60", buy	G					135			135	149
3400	Rent per month	G					13.50			13.50	14.85
4000	Friction collars 2'-6" diam., buy	G					2,500			2,500	2,750
4100	Rent per month	G					175			175	193
4300	4'-0" diam., buy	G					3,050			3,050	3,350
4400	Rent per month	G				↓	214			214	235

03 15 05.30 Hangers

			Crew	Daily Output	Labor-Hours	Unit	Material	2014 Bare Costs Labor	Equipment	Total	Total Incl O&P
0010	**HANGERS**										
0020	Slab and beam form										
0500	Banding iron										
0550	3/4" x 22 ga., 14 L.F. per lb. or 1/2" x 14 ga., 7 L.F. per lb.	G				Lb.	1.34			1.34	1.47
1000	Fascia ties, coil type, to 24" long	G				C	405			405	445
1500	Frame ties to 8-1/8"	G					500			500	550
1550	8-1/8" to 10-1/8"	G					525			525	575
5000	Snap tie hanger, to 30" overall length, 3000#	G					405			405	445
5050	To 36" overall length	G					455			455	500
5100	To 48" overall length	G				↓	560			560	615
5500	Steel beam hanger										

03 15 Concrete Accessories

03 15 05 – Concrete Forming Accessories

		Crew	Daily Output	Labor-Hours	Unit	Material	2014 Bare Costs Labor	2014 Bare Costs Equipment	Total	Total Incl O&P
03 15 05.30 Hangers										
5600	Flange to 8-1/8"	G			C	500			500	550
5650	8-1/8" to 10-1/8"	G			"	525			525	575
5900	Coil threaded rods, continuous, 1/2" diameter	G			L.F.	1.32			1.32	1.45
6000	Tie hangers to 30" overall length, 4000#	G			C	455			455	505
6100	To 36" overall length	G				510			510	560
6500	Tie back hanger, up to 12-1/8" flange	G			↓	1,325			1,325	1,475
8500	Wire, black annealed, 15 gage	G			Cwt.	147			147	162
8600	16 ga				"	199			199	219
03 15 05.70 Shores										
0010	**SHORES**									
0020	Erect and strip, by hand, horizontal members									
0501	Aluminum joists and stringers	G	L-2	60	.267	Ea.		8.35		8.35	14.10
0602	Steel, adjustable beams	G		45	.356			11.15		11.15	18.75
0701	Wood joists			50	.320			10.05		10.05	16.90
0801	Wood stringers			30	.533			16.70		16.70	28
1001	Vertical members to 10' high	G		55	.291			9.10		9.10	15.35
1051	To 13' high	G		50	.320			10.05		10.05	16.90
1101	To 16' high	G		45	.356	↓		11.15		11.15	18.75
1501	Reshoring	G	↓	1400	.011	S.F.	.58	.36		.94	1.24
1600	Flying truss system	G	C-17D	9600	.009	SFCA		.32	.09	.41	.63
1760	Horizontal, aluminum joists, 6-1/4" high x 5' to 21' span, buy	G				L.F.	15.45			15.45	17
1770	Beams, 7-1/4" high x 4' to 30' span	G				"	18.10			18.10	19.90
1810	Horizontal, steel beam, W8x10, 7' span, buy	G				Ea.	54.50			54.50	60
1830	10' span	G					64.50			64.50	71
1920	15' span	G					111			111	122
1940	20' span	G				↓	156			156	172
1970	Steel stringer, W8x10, 4' to 16' span, buy	G				L.F.	6.45			6.45	7.10
3000	Rent for job duration, aluminum joist @ 2' O.C., per mo.	G				SF Flr.	.39			.39	.43
3050	Steel W8x10	G					.16			.16	.18
3060	Steel adjustable	G				↓	.16			.16	.18
3500	#1 post shore, steel, 5'-7" to 9'-6" high, 10000# cap., buy	G				Ea.	148			148	163
3550	#2 post shore, 7'-3" to 12'-10" high, 7800# capacity	G					171			171	188
3600	#3 post shore, 8'-10" to 16'-1" high, 3800# capacity	G				↓	187			187	206
5010	Frame shoring systems, steel, 12000#/leg, buy	G									
5040	Frame, 2' wide x 6' high	G				Ea.	93.50			93.50	103
5250	X-brace	G					15.50			15.50	17.05
5550	Base plate	G					15.50			15.50	17.05
5600	Screw jack	G					33.50			33.50	36.50
5650	U-head, 8" x 8"	G				↓	19.10			19.10	21
03 15 05.75 Sleeves and Chases										
0010	**SLEEVES AND CHASES**									
0100	Plastic, 1 use, 12" long, 2" diameter		1 Carp	100	.080	Ea.	2.44	2.86		5.30	7.50
0150	4" diameter			90	.089		6.65	3.18		9.83	12.65
0200	6" diameter			75	.107		14.25	3.81		18.06	22
0250	12" diameter		↓	60	.133	↓	46.50	4.77		51.27	59
03 15 05.80 Snap Ties										
0010	**SNAP TIES**, 8-1/4" L&W (Lumber and wedge)									
0100	2250 lb., w/flat washer, 8" wall	G				C	87			87	95.50
0150	10" wall	G					127			127	140
0200	12" wall	G					132			132	145
0250	16" wall	G					146			146	161
0300	18" wall	G				↓	151			151	166

03 15 Concrete Accessories

03 15 05 – Concrete Forming Accessories

03 15 05.80 Snap Ties

			Crew	Daily Output	Labor-Hours	Unit	Material	2014 Bare Costs Labor	Equipment	Total	Total Incl O&P
0500	With plastic cone, 8" wall	G				C	78			78	86
0550	10" wall	G					81			81	89
0600	12" wall	G					86			86	94.50
0650	16" wall	G					95			95	105
0700	18" wall	G					98			98	108
1000	3350 lb., w/flat washer, 8" wall	G					158			158	174
1150	12" wall	G					178			178	196
1200	16" wall	G					204			204	224
1250	18" wall	G					212			212	233
1500	With plastic cone, 8" wall	G					128			128	141
1600	12" wall	G					145			145	160
1650	16" wall	G					165			165	182
1700	18" wall	G					171			171	188

03 15 05.85 Stair Tread Inserts

		Crew	Daily Output	Labor-Hours	Unit	Material	2014 Bare Costs Labor	Equipment	Total	Total Incl O&P
0010	**STAIR TREAD INSERTS**									
0105	Cast nosing insert, abrasive surface, pre-drilled, includes screws									
0110	Aluminum, 3" wide x 3' long	1 Cefi	32	.250	Ea.	52.50	8.60		61.10	71.50
0120	4' long		31	.258		67	8.85		75.85	88
0130	5' long		30	.267		82.50	9.15		91.65	106
0135	Extruded nosing insert, black abrasive strips, continuous anchor									
0140	Aluminum, 3" wide x 3' long	1 Cefi	64	.125	Ea.	34	4.29		38.29	44.50
0150	4' long		60	.133		34	4.58		38.58	45
0160	5' long		56	.143		52.50	4.91		57.41	65.50
0165	Extruded nosing insert, black abrasive strips, pre-drilled, incl. screws									
0170	Aluminum, 3" wide x 3' long	1 Cefi	32	.250	Ea.	46.50	8.60		55.10	65
0180	4' long		31	.258		60.50	8.85		69.35	81
0190	5' long		30	.267		71	9.15		80.15	93

03 15 05.95 Wall and Foundation Form Accessories

			Crew	Daily Output	Labor-Hours	Unit	Material	2014 Bare Costs Labor	Equipment	Total	Total Incl O&P
0010	**WALL AND FOUNDATION FORM ACCESSORIES**										
2000	Footings, turnbuckle form aligner	G				Ea.	16.20			16.20	17.85
2050	Spreaders for footer, adjustable	G				"	23			23	25.50
3000	Form oil, up to 1200 S.F. per gallon coverage					Gal.	13.15			13.15	14.45
3050	Up to 800 S.F. per gallon					"	19.85			19.85	22
3500	Form patches, 1-3/4" diameter					C	26			26	28.50
3550	2-3/4" diameter					"	45			45	49.50
4000	Nail stakes, 3/4" diameter, 18" long	G				Ea.	3.08			3.08	3.39
4050	24" long	G					3.98			3.98	4.38
4200	30" long	G					5.10			5.10	5.60
4250	36" long	G					6.15			6.15	6.80

03 15 13 – Waterstops

03 15 13.50 Waterstops

		Crew	Daily Output	Labor-Hours	Unit	Material	2014 Bare Costs Labor	Equipment	Total	Total Incl O&P
0010	**WATERSTOPS**, PVC and Rubber									
0020	PVC, ribbed 3/16" thick, 4" wide	1 Carp	155	.052	L.F.	1.22	1.85		3.07	4.44
0050	6" wide		145	.055		2.16	1.97		4.13	5.70
0500	With center bulb, 6" wide, 3/16" thick		135	.059		1.88	2.12		4	5.65
0550	3/8" thick		130	.062		3.35	2.20		5.55	7.40
0600	9" wide x 3/8" thick		125	.064		5.45	2.29		7.74	9.85
0800	Dumbbell type, 6" wide, 3/16" thick		150	.053		1.87	1.91		3.78	5.25
0850	3/8" thick		145	.055		3.64	1.97		5.61	7.30
1000	9" wide, 3/8" thick, plain		130	.062		5.35	2.20		7.55	9.60
1050	Center bulb		130	.062		8.50	2.20		10.70	13.05
1250	Ribbed type, split, 3/16" thick, 6" wide		145	.055		1.84	1.97		3.81	5.35

03 15 13 – Waterstops

03 15 13.50 Waterstops

		Crew	Daily Output	Labor-Hours	Unit	Material	2014 Bare Costs Labor	Equipment	Total	Total Incl O&P
1300	3/8" thick	1 Carp	130	.062	L.F.	4.11	2.20		6.31	8.20
2000	Rubber, flat dumbbell, 3/8" thick, 6" wide		145	.055		10.10	1.97		12.07	14.40
2050	9" wide		135	.059		15.40	2.12		17.52	20.50
2500	Flat dumbbell split, 3/8" thick, 6" wide		145	.055		1.84	1.97		3.81	5.35
2550	9" wide		135	.059		4.11	2.12		6.23	8.10
3000	Center bulb, 1/4" thick, 6" wide		145	.055		9.95	1.97		11.92	14.25
3050	9" wide		135	.059		22	2.12		24.12	27.50
3500	Center bulb split, 3/8" thick, 6" wide		145	.055		14.10	1.97		16.07	18.80
3550	9" wide		135	.059		24.50	2.12		26.62	30
5000	Waterstop fittings, rubber, flat									
5010	Dumbbell or center bulb, 3/8" thick,									
5200	Field union, 6" wide	1 Carp	50	.160	Ea.	34	5.70		39.70	47
5250	9" wide		50	.160		45.50	5.70		51.20	59.50
5500	Flat cross, 6" wide		30	.267		42.50	9.55		52.05	63
5550	9" wide		30	.267		61.50	9.55		71.05	83.50
6000	Flat tee, 6" wide		30	.267		41.50	9.55		51.05	61.50
6050	9" wide		30	.267		56	9.55		65.55	78
6500	Flat ell, 6" wide		40	.200		40.50	7.15		47.65	56.50
6550	9" wide		40	.200		52	7.15		59.15	69
7000	Vertical tee, 6" wide		25	.320		30	11.45		41.45	52.50
7050	9" wide		25	.320		42.50	11.45		53.95	66.50
7500	Vertical ell, 6" wide		35	.229		28	8.15		36.15	45
7550	9" wide		35	.229		36	8.15		44.15	53.50

03 15 16 – Concrete Construction Joints

03 15 16.20 Control Joints, Saw Cut

		Crew	Daily Output	Labor-Hours	Unit	Material	2014 Bare Costs Labor	Equipment	Total	Total Incl O&P
0010	**CONTROL JOINTS, SAW CUT**									
0100	Sawcut control joints in green concrete									
0120	1" depth	C-27	2000	.008	L.F.	.04	.27	.09	.40	.58
0140	1-1/2" depth		1800	.009		.06	.31	.10	.47	.66
0160	2" depth		1600	.010		.07	.34	.11	.52	.76
0180	Sawcut joint reservoir in cured concrete									
0182	3/8" wide x 3/4" deep, with single saw blade	C-27	1000	.016	L.F.	.06	.55	.18	.79	1.14
0184	1/2" wide x 1" deep, with double saw blades		900	.018		.11	.61	.19	.91	1.32
0186	3/4" wide x 1-1/2" deep, with double saw blades		800	.020		.22	.69	.22	1.13	1.60
0190	Water blast joint to wash away laitance, 2 passes	C-29	2500	.003			.09	.03	.12	.18
0200	Air blast joint to blow out debris and air dry, 2 passes	C-28	2000	.004			.14	.01	.15	.23
0300	For backer rod, see Section 07 91 23.10									
0340	For joint sealant, see Sections 03 15 16.30 or 07 92 13.20									
0900	For replacement of joint sealant, see Section 07 01 90.81									

03 15 16.30 Expansion Joints

			Crew	Daily Output	Labor-Hours	Unit	Material	2014 Bare Costs Labor	Equipment	Total	Total Incl O&P
0010	**EXPANSION JOINTS**										
0020	Keyed, cold, 24 ga., incl. stakes, 3-1/2" high	G	1 Carp	200	.040	L.F.	.77	1.43		2.20	3.26
0050	4-1/2" high	G		200	.040		.88	1.43		2.31	3.38
0100	5-1/2" high	G		195	.041		1.01	1.47		2.48	3.58
0150	7-1/2" high	G		190	.042		1.25	1.51		2.76	3.91
0160	9-1/2" high	G		185	.043		1.36	1.55		2.91	4.10
0300	Poured asphalt, plain, 1/2" x 1"		1 Clab	450	.018		.76	.50		1.26	1.68
0350	1" x 2"			400	.020		3.02	.56		3.58	4.27
0500	Neoprene, liquid, cold applied, 1/2" x 1"			450	.018		2.88	.50		3.38	4.01
0550	1" x 2"			400	.020		11.50	.56		12.06	13.60
0700	Polyurethane, poured, 2 part, 1/2" x 1"			400	.020		1.33	.56		1.89	2.41
0750	1" x 2"			350	.023		5.30	.64		5.94	6.95

03 15 16 – Concrete Construction Joints

03 15 16.30 Expansion Joints

		Crew	Daily Output	Labor-Hours	Unit	Material	2014 Bare Costs Labor	2014 Bare Costs Equipment	Total	Total Incl O&P
0900	Rubberized asphalt, hot or cold applied, 1/2" x 1"	1 Clab	450	.018	L.F.	.40	.50		.90	1.28
0950	1" x 2"		400	.020		1.60	.56		2.16	2.71
1100	Hot applied, fuel resistant, 1/2" x 1"		450	.018		.60	.50		1.10	1.50
1150	1" x 2"		400	.020		2.40	.56		2.96	3.59
2000	Premolded, bituminous fiber, 1/2" x 6"	1 Carp	375	.021		.43	.76		1.19	1.75
2050	1" x 12"		300	.027		1.95	.95		2.90	3.75
2140	Concrete expansion joint, recycled paper and fiber, 1/2" x 6" Ⓖ		390	.021		.42	.73		1.15	1.69
2150	1/2" x 12" Ⓖ		360	.022		.83	.79		1.62	2.26
2250	Cork with resin binder, 1/2" x 6"		375	.021		.96	.76		1.72	2.34
2300	1" x 12"		300	.027		2.70	.95		3.65	4.57
2500	Neoprene sponge, closed cell, 1/2" x 6"		375	.021		2.37	.76		3.13	3.89
2550	1" x 12"		300	.027		8.25	.95		9.20	10.70
2750	Polyethylene foam, 1/2" x 6"		375	.021		.68	.76		1.44	2.03
2800	1" x 12"		300	.027		2.19	.95		3.14	4.01
3000	Polyethylene backer rod, 3/8" diameter		460	.017		.03	.62		.65	1.08
3050	3/4" diameter		460	.017		.06	.62		.68	1.11
3100	1" diameter		460	.017		.09	.62		.71	1.15
3500	Polyurethane foam, with polybutylene, 1/2" x 1/2"		475	.017		1.14	.60		1.74	2.26
3550	1" x 1"		450	.018		2.88	.64		3.52	4.24
3750	Polyurethane foam, regular, closed cell, 1/2" x 6"		375	.021		.84	.76		1.60	2.20
3800	1" x 12"		300	.027		3	.95		3.95	4.90
4000	Polyvinyl chloride foam, closed cell, 1/2" x 6"		375	.021		2.28	.76		3.04	3.79
4050	1" x 12"		300	.027		7.85	.95		8.80	10.25
4250	Rubber, gray sponge, 1/2" x 6"		375	.021		1.92	.76		2.68	3.39
4300	1" x 12"		300	.027		6.90	.95		7.85	9.20
4400	Redwood heartwood, 1" x 4"		400	.020		1.16	.72		1.88	2.48
4450	1" x 6"		375	.021		1.75	.76		2.51	3.21
5000	For installation in walls, add						75%			
5250	For installation in boxouts, add						25%			

03 15 19 – Cast-In Concrete Anchors

03 15 19.05 Anchor Bolt Accessories

		Crew	Daily Output	Labor-Hours	Unit	Material	2014 Bare Costs Labor	2014 Bare Costs Equipment	Total	Total Incl O&P
0010	**ANCHOR BOLT ACCESSORIES**									
0015	For anchor bolts set in fresh concrete, see Section 03 15 19.10									
8150	Anchor bolt sleeve, plastic, 1" diam. bolts	1 Carp	60	.133	Ea.	8.10	4.77		12.87	16.90
8500	1-1/2" diameter		28	.286		14.35	10.20		24.55	33
8600	2" diameter		24	.333		18.10	11.90		30	40
8650	3" diameter		20	.400		33	14.30		47.30	60.50

03 15 19.10 Anchor Bolts

		Crew	Daily Output	Labor-Hours	Unit	Material	2014 Bare Costs Labor	2014 Bare Costs Equipment	Total	Total Incl O&P
0010	**ANCHOR BOLTS**									
0015	Made from recycled materials									
0025	Single bolts installed in fresh concrete, no templates									
0030	Hooked w/nut and washer, 1/2" diameter, 8" long Ⓖ	1 Carp	132	.061	Ea.	1.49	2.17		3.66	5.30
0040	12" long Ⓖ		131	.061		1.66	2.18		3.84	5.50
0050	5/8" diameter, 8" long Ⓖ		129	.062		3.25	2.22		5.47	7.30
0060	12" long Ⓖ		127	.063		4	2.25		6.25	8.20
0070	3/4" diameter, 8" long Ⓖ		127	.063		4	2.25		6.25	8.20
0080	12" long Ⓖ		125	.064		5	2.29		7.29	9.35
0090	2-bolt pattern, including job-built 2-hole template, per set									
0100	J-type, incl. hex nut & washer, 1/2" diameter x 6" long Ⓖ	1 Carp	21	.381	Set	5.60	13.60		19.20	29
0110	12" long Ⓖ		21	.381		6.30	13.60		19.90	30
0120	18" long		21	.381		7.30	13.60		20.90	31
0130	3/4" diameter x 8" long Ⓖ		20	.400		10.95	14.30		25.25	36

03 15 19 – Cast-In Concrete Anchors

03 15 19.10 Anchor Bolts		Crew	Daily Output	Labor-Hours	Unit	Material	2014 Bare Costs Labor	Equipment	Total	Total Incl O&P
0140	12" long	G	1 Carp	20	.400	Set	12.95	14.30		27.25	38.50
0150	18" long	G		20	.400		15.95	14.30		30.25	41.50
0160	1" diameter x 12" long	G		19	.421		22	15.05		37.05	50
0170	18" long	G		19	.421		26	15.05		41.05	54
0180	24" long	G		19	.421		31	15.05		46.05	59.50
0190	36" long	G		18	.444		41.50	15.90		57.40	72
0200	1-1/2" diameter x 18" long	G		17	.471		65.50	16.80		82.30	101
0210	24" long	G		16	.500		77.50	17.90		95.40	116
0300	L-type, incl. hex nut & washer, 3/4" diameter x 12" long	G		20	.400		12.20	14.30		26.50	37.50
0310	18" long	G		20	.400		14.80	14.30		29.10	40.50
0320	24" long	G		20	.400		17.40	14.30		31.70	43
0330	30" long	G		20	.400		21.50	14.30		35.80	47.50
0340	36" long	G		20	.400		24	14.30		38.30	50.50
0350	1" diameter x 12" long	G		19	.421		18.90	15.05		33.95	46.50
0360	18" long	G		19	.421		23	15.05		38.05	50.50
0370	24" long	G		19	.421		27.50	15.05		42.55	55.50
0380	30" long	G		19	.421		32	15.05		47.05	60.50
0390	36" long	G		18	.444		36	15.90		51.90	66
0400	42" long	G		18	.444		43	15.90		58.90	74
0410	48" long	G		18	.444		48	15.90		63.90	79.50
0420	1-1/4" diameter x 18" long	G		18	.444		33	15.90		48.90	63
0430	24" long	G		18	.444		39	15.90		54.90	69
0440	30" long	G		17	.471		44.50	16.80		61.30	77.50
0450	36" long	G		17	.471		50	16.80		66.80	83.50
0460	42" long	G	2 Carp	32	.500		56.50	17.90		74.40	92
0470	48" long	G		32	.500		64	17.90		81.90	100
0480	54" long	G		31	.516		74.50	18.45		92.95	113
0490	60" long	G		31	.516		82	18.45		100.45	121
0500	1-1/2" diameter x 18" long	G		33	.485		48	17.35		65.35	81.50
0510	24" long	G		32	.500		55.50	17.90		73.40	91
0520	30" long	G		31	.516		62	18.45		80.45	99.50
0530	36" long	G		30	.533		71	19.05		90.05	110
0540	42" long	G		30	.533		80.50	19.05		99.55	121
0550	48" long	G		29	.552		90	19.70		109.70	132
0560	54" long	G		28	.571		109	20.50		129.50	155
0570	60" long	G		28	.571		119	20.50		139.50	166
0580	1-3/4" diameter x 18" long	G		31	.516		67.50	18.45		85.95	105
0590	24" long	G		30	.533		78.50	19.05		97.55	119
0600	30" long	G		29	.552		91	19.70		110.70	133
0610	36" long	G		28	.571		103	20.50		123.50	149
0620	42" long	G		27	.593		116	21		137	163
0630	48" long	G		26	.615		127	22		149	176
0640	54" long	G		26	.615		156	22		178	209
0650	60" long	G		25	.640		169	23		192	225
0660	2" diameter x 24" long	G		27	.593		105	21		126	151
0670	30" long	G		27	.593		117	21		138	165
0680	36" long	G		26	.615		129	22		151	179
0690	42" long	G		25	.640		143	23		166	197
0700	48" long	G		24	.667		164	24		188	221
0710	54" long	G		23	.696		195	25		220	256
0720	60" long	G		23	.696		209	25		234	272
0730	66" long	G		22	.727		224	26		250	290
0740	72" long	G		21	.762		245	27		272	315

03 15 19.10 Anchor Bolts		Crew	Daily Output	Labor-Hours	Unit	Material	2014 Bare Costs Labor	2014 Bare Costs Equipment	Total	Total Incl O&P
1000	4-bolt pattern, including job-built 4-hole template, per set									
1100	J-type, incl. hex nut & washer, 1/2" diameter x 6" long	G	1 Carp	19	.421	Set	8.25	15.05		23.30	34.50
1110	12" long	G		19	.421		9.60	15.05		24.65	36
1120	18" long	G		18	.444		11.60	15.90		27.50	39.50
1130	3/4" diameter x 8" long	G		17	.471		18.95	16.80		35.75	49.50
1140	12" long	G		17	.471		23	16.80		39.80	54
1150	18" long	G		17	.471		29	16.80		45.80	60.50
1160	1" diameter x 12" long	G		16	.500		41	17.90		58.90	75
1170	18" long	G		15	.533		49	19.05		68.05	86
1180	24" long	G		15	.533		59	19.05		78.05	97
1190	36" long	G		15	.533		80	19.05		99.05	120
1200	1-1/2" diameter x 18" long	G		13	.615		128	22		150	178
1210	24" long	G		12	.667		152	24		176	208
1300	L-type, incl. hex nut & washer, 3/4" diameter x 12" long	G		17	.471		21.50	16.80		38.30	52
1310	18" long	G		17	.471		26.50	16.80		43.30	58
1320	24" long	G		17	.471		32	16.80		48.80	63.50
1330	30" long	G		16	.500		39.50	17.90		57.40	73.50
1340	36" long	G		16	.500		45	17.90		62.90	79.50
1350	1" diameter x 12" long	G		16	.500		35	17.90		52.90	68.50
1360	18" long	G		15	.533		42.50	19.05		61.55	79
1370	24" long	G		15	.533		52	19.05		71.05	89
1380	30" long	G		15	.533		61	19.05		80.05	99
1390	36" long	G		15	.533		69	19.05		88.05	108
1400	42" long	G		14	.571		83.50	20.50		104	126
1410	48" long	G		14	.571		93	20.50		113.50	137
1420	1-1/4" diameter x 18" long	G		14	.571		63.50	20.50		84	104
1430	24" long	G		14	.571		74.50	20.50		95	117
1440	30" long	G		13	.615		86	22		108	132
1450	36" long	G		13	.615		97.50	22		119.50	144
1460	42" long	G	2 Carp	25	.640		110	23		133	160
1470	48" long	G		24	.667		125	24		149	177
1480	54" long	G		23	.696		146	25		171	203
1490	60" long	G		23	.696		161	25		186	219
1500	1-1/2" diameter x 18" long	G		25	.640		92.50	23		115.50	141
1510	24" long	G		24	.667		108	24		132	158
1520	30" long	G		23	.696		121	25		146	175
1530	36" long	G		22	.727		139	26		165	197
1540	42" long	G		22	.727		158	26		184	218
1550	48" long	G		21	.762		177	27		204	241
1560	54" long	G		20	.800		215	28.50		243.50	285
1570	60" long	G		20	.800		236	28.50		264.50	305
1580	1-3/4" diameter x 18" long	G		22	.727		132	26		158	189
1590	24" long	G		21	.762		154	27		181	215
1600	30" long	G		21	.762		179	27		206	243
1610	36" long	G		20	.800		204	28.50		232.50	272
1620	42" long	G		19	.842		228	30		258	300
1630	48" long	G		18	.889		251	32		283	330
1640	54" long	G		18	.889		310	32		342	395
1650	60" long	G		17	.941		335	33.50		368.50	425
1660	2" diameter x 24" long	G		19	.842		206	30		236	278
1670	30" long	G		18	.889		232	32		264	310
1680	36" long	G		18	.889		254	32		286	335
1690	42" long	G		17	.941		283	33.50		316.50	365

03 15 19 – Cast-In Concrete Anchors

		Crew	Daily Output	Labor-Hours	Unit	Material	2014 Bare Costs Labor	Equipment	Total	Total Incl O&P
03 15 19.10 Anchor Bolts										
1700	48" long	G 2 Carp	16	1	Set	325	36		361	420
1710	54" long	G	15	1.067		385	38		423	490
1720	60" long	G	15	1.067		415	38		453	520
1730	66" long	G	14	1.143		445	41		486	560
1740	72" long	G	14	1.143		485	41		526	605
1990	For galvanized, add				Ea.	75%				
03 15 19.20 Dovetail Anchor System										
0010	**DOVETAIL ANCHOR SYSTEM**									
0500	Dovetail anchor slot, galvanized, foam-filled, 26 ga.	G 1 Carp	425	.019	L.F.	.84	.67		1.51	2.05
0600	24 ga.	G	400	.020		1.56	.72		2.28	2.92
0625	22 ga.	G	400	.020		1.83	.72		2.55	3.21
0900	Stainless steel, foam-filled, 26 ga.	G	375	.021		1.34	.76		2.10	2.76
1200	Dovetail brick anchor, corrugated, galvanized, 3-1/2" long, 16 ga.	G 1 Bric	10.50	.762	C	29	27		56	77
1300	12 ga.	G	10.50	.762		41	27		68	90
1500	Seismic, galvanized, 3-1/2" long, 16 ga.	G	10.50	.762		42	27		69	91.50
1600	12 ga.	G	10.50	.762		40	27		67	89
2000	Dovetail cavity wall, corrugated, galvanized, 5-1/2" long, 16 ga.	G	10.50	.762		36.50	27		63.50	85
2100	12 ga.	G	10.50	.762		53	27		80	104
3000	Dovetail furring anchors, corrugated, galvanized, 1-1/2" long, 16 ga.	G	10.50	.762		14.70	27		41.70	61
3100	12 ga.	G	10.50	.762		25.50	27		52.50	73
6000	Dovetail stone panel anchors, galvanized, 1/8" x 1" wide, 3-1/2" long	G	10.50	.762		92	27		119	146
6100	1/4" x 1" wide	G	10.50	.762		104	27		131	160
03 15 19.30 Inserts										
0010	**INSERTS**									
1000	Inserts, slotted nut type for 3/4" bolts, 4" long	G 1 Carp	84	.095	Ea.	18.70	3.40		22.10	26.50
2100	6" long	G	84	.095		21	3.40		24.40	29
2150	8" long	G	84	.095		28	3.40		31.40	37
2200	Slotted, strap type, 4" long	G	84	.095		20	3.40		23.40	28
2250	6" long	G	84	.095		23	3.40		26.40	31
2300	8" long	G	84	.095		30	3.40		33.40	39
2350	Strap for slotted insert, 4" long	G	84	.095		11	3.40		14.40	17.85
4100	6" long	G	84	.095		11.95	3.40		15.35	18.90
4150	8" long	G	84	.095		14.90	3.40		18.30	22
4200	10" long	G	84	.095		18.15	3.40		21.55	25.50
7000	Loop ferrule type									
7100	1/4" diameter bolt	G 1 Carp	84	.095	Ea.	2.12	3.40		5.52	8.10
7350	7/8" diameter bolt	G "	84	.095	"	9.90	3.40		13.30	16.60
9000	Wedge type									
9100	For 3/4" diameter bolt	G 1 Carp	60	.133	Ea.	8.80	4.77		13.57	17.65
9800	Cut washers, black									
9900	3/4" bolt	G			Ea.	1.11			1.11	1.22
9950	For galvanized inserts, add					30%				
03 15 19.45 Machinery Anchors										
0010	**MACHINERY ANCHORS**, heavy duty, incl. sleeve, floating base nut,									
0020	lower stud & coupling nut, fiber plug, connecting stud, washer & nut.									
0030	For flush mounted embedment in poured concrete heavy equip. pads.									
0200	Stud & bolt, 1/2" diameter	G E-16	40	.400	Ea.	72.50	15.75	3.55	91.80	114
0300	5/8" diameter	G	35	.457		80.50	18	4.06	102.56	127
0500	3/4" diameter	G	30	.533		93	21	4.74	118.74	147
0600	7/8" diameter	G	25	.640		101	25	5.70	131.70	165
0800	1" diameter	G	20	.800		117	31.50	7.10	155.60	197
0900	1-1/4" diameter	G	15	1.067		141	42	9.45	192.45	245

03 21 05.10 Rebar Accessories		Crew	Daily Output	Labor-Hours	Unit	Material	2014 Bare Costs Labor	Equipment	Total	Total Incl O&P
0010	**REBAR ACCESSORIES**									
0030	Steel & plastic made from recycled materials									
0100	Beam bolsters (BB), lower, 1-1/2" high, plain steel	G				C.L.F.	28			28	31
0102	Galvanized	G					33.50			33.50	37
0104	Stainless tipped legs	G					455			455	500
0106	Plastic tipped legs	G					40			40	44
0108	Epoxy dipped	G					70			70	77
0110	2" high, plain	G					34			34	37.50
0120	Galvanized	G					41			41	45
0140	Stainless tipped legs	G					450			450	495
0160	Plastic tipped legs	G					47			47	51.50
0162	Epoxy dipped	G					79			79	87
0200	Upper (BBU), 1-1/2" high, plain steel	G					67			67	73.50
0210	3" high	G					76			76	83.50
0500	Slab bolsters, continuous (SB), 1" high, plain steel	G					28			28	31
0502	Galvanized	G					33.50			33.50	37
0504	Stainless tipped legs	G					455			455	500
0506	Plastic tipped legs	G					40			40	44
0510	2" high, plain steel	G					34			34	37.50
0515	Galvanized	G					41			41	45
0520	Stainless tipped legs	G					460			460	505
0525	Plastic tipped legs	G					47			47	51.50
0530	For bolsters with wire runners (SBR), add	G					37			37	40.50
0540	For bolsters with plates (SBP), add	G					88			88	97
0700	Bag ties, 16 ga., plain, 4" long	G				C	4			4	4.40
0710	5" long	G					5			5	5.50
0720	6" long	G					4			4	4.40
0730	7" long	G					5			5	5.50
1200	High chairs, individual (HC), 3" high, plain steel	G					56			56	61.50
1202	Galvanized	G					67			67	74
1204	Stainless tipped legs	G					480			480	530
1206	Plastic tipped legs	G					61			61	67
1210	5" high, plain	G					82			82	90
1212	Galvanized	G					98.50			98.50	108
1214	Stainless tipped legs	G					505			505	560
1216	Plastic tipped legs	G					90			90	99
1220	8" high, plain	G					121			121	133
1222	Galvanized	G					145			145	160
1224	Stainless tipped legs	G					545			545	600
1226	Plastic tipped legs	G					133			133	146
1230	12" high, plain	G					287			287	315
1232	Galvanized	G					345			345	380
1234	Stainless tipped legs	G					710			710	785
1236	Plastic tipped legs	G					315			315	345
1400	Individual high chairs, with plate (HCP), 5" high	G					171			171	188
1410	8" high	G					237			237	261
1500	Bar chair (BC), 1-1/2" high, plain steel	G					36			36	39.50
1520	Galvanized	G					41			41	45
1530	Stainless tipped legs	G					460			460	505
1540	Plastic tipped legs	G					39			39	43
1700	Continuous high chairs (CHC), legs 8" O.C., 4" high, plain steel	G				C.L.F.	49			49	54
1705	Galvanized	G					58.50			58.50	64.50
1710	Stainless tipped legs	G					475			475	520

03 21 05 – Reinforcing Steel Accessories

03 21 05.10 Rebar Accessories		Crew	Daily Output	Labor-Hours	Unit	Material	2014 Bare Costs Labor	Equipment	Total	Total Incl O&P
1715	Plastic tipped legs	G				C.L.F.	66			66	72.50
1718	Epoxy dipped	G					85			85	93.50
1720	6" high, plain	G					67			67	73.50
1725	Galvanized	G					80.50			80.50	88.50
1730	Stainless tipped legs	G					490			490	540
1735	Plastic tipped legs	G					90			90	99
1738	Epoxy dipped	G					116			116	128
1740	8" high, plain	G					75			75	82.50
1745	Galvanized	G					90			90	99
1750	Stainless tipped legs	G					500			500	550
1755	Plastic tipped legs	G					114			114	125
1758	Epoxy dipped	G					147			147	162
1900	For continuous bottom wire runners, add	G					50			50	55
1940	For continuous bottom plate, add	G					205			205	226
2200	Screed chair base, 1/2" coil thread diam., 2-1/2" high, plain steel	G				C	310			310	340
2210	Galvanized	G					370			370	405
2220	5-1/2" high, plain	G					370			370	410
2250	Galvanized	G					445			445	490
2300	3/4" coil thread diam., 2-1/2" high, plain steel	G					385			385	425
2310	Galvanized	G					465			465	510
2320	5-1/2" high, plain steel	G					475			475	525
2350	Galvanized	G					570			570	630
2400	Screed holder, 1/2" coil thread diam. for pipe screed, plain steel, 6" long	G					370			370	410
2420	12" long	G					570			570	630
2500	3/4" coil thread diam. for pipe screed, plain steel, 6" long	G					535			535	585
2520	12" long	G					855			855	940
2700	Screw anchor for bolts, plain steel, 3/4" diameter x 4" long	G					505			505	555
2720	1" diameter x 6" long	G					830			830	915
2740	1-1/2" diameter x 8" long	G					1,050			1,050	1,150
2800	Screw anchor eye bolts, 3/4" x 3" long	G					2,700			2,700	2,975
2820	1" x 3-1/2" long	G					3,625			3,625	3,975
2840	1-1/2" x 6" long	G					11,100			11,100	12,200
2900	Screw anchor bolts, 3/4" x 9" long	G					1,525			1,525	1,675
2920	1" x 12" long	G					2,925			2,925	3,200
3001	Slab lifting inserts, single pickup, galv, 3/4" diam., 5" high	G					1,475			1,475	1,625
3010	6" high	G					1,500			1,500	1,650
3030	7" high	G					1,525			1,525	1,675
3100	1" diameter, 5-1/2" high	G					1,550			1,550	1,700
3120	7" high	G					1,600			1,600	1,750
3200	Double pickup lifting inserts, 1" diameter, 5-1/2" high	G					3,000			3,000	3,300
3220	7" high	G					3,325			3,325	3,650
3330	1-1/2" diameter, 8" high	G					4,175			4,175	4,600
3800	Subgrade chairs, #4 bar head, 3-1/2" high	G					35			35	38.50
3850	12" high	G					41			41	45
3900	#6 bar head, 3-1/2" high	G					35			35	38.50
3950	12" high	G					41			41	45
4200	Subgrade stakes, no nail holes, 3/4" diameter, 12" long	G					275			275	305
4250	24" long	G					335			335	370
4300	7/8" diameter, 12" long	G					350			350	385
4350	24" long	G					585			585	645
4500	Tie wire, 16 ga. annealed steel	G				Cwt.	199			199	219

03 21 Reinforcement Bars

03 21 05 – Reinforcing Steel Accessories

03 21 05.75 Splicing Reinforcing Bars

		Crew	Daily Output	Labor-Hours	Unit	Material	2014 Bare Costs Labor	2014 Bare Costs Equipment	Total	Total Incl O&P
0010	**SPLICING REINFORCING BARS** R032110-70									
0020	Including holding bars in place while splicing									
0100	Standard, self-aligning type, taper threaded, #4 bars [G]	C-25	190	.168	Ea.	6.15	5.10		11.25	15.70
0105	#5 bars [G]		170	.188		7.50	5.70		13.20	18.25
0110	#6 bars [G]		150	.213		8.65	6.45		15.10	21
0120	#7 bars [G]		130	.246		10.10	7.45		17.55	24
0300	#8 bars [G]		115	.278		17.10	8.40		25.50	33.50
0305	#9 bars [G]	C-5	105	.457		18.70	16.10	7.10	41.90	55.50
0310	#10 bars [G]		95	.505		21	17.80	7.85	46.65	61.50
0320	#11 bars [G]		85	.565		22	19.85	8.80	50.65	67.50
0330	#14 bars [G]		65	.738		33	26	11.50	70.50	93
0340	#18 bars [G]		45	1.067		50.50	37.50	16.60	104.60	137
0500	Transition self-aligning, taper threaded, #18-14 [G]		45	1.067		52.50	37.50	16.60	106.60	139
0510	#18-11 [G]		45	1.067		53.50	37.50	16.60	107.60	140
0520	#14-11 [G]		65	.738		35	26	11.50	72.50	95
0540	#11-10 [G]		85	.565		24	19.85	8.80	52.65	69.50
0550	#10-9 [G]		95	.505		23	17.80	7.85	48.65	63.50
0560	#9-8 [G]	C-25	105	.305		21	9.20		30.20	39
0580	#8-7 [G]		115	.278		19.20	8.40		27.60	36
0590	#7-6 [G]		130	.246		12.10	7.45		19.55	26.50
0600	Position coupler for curved bars, taper threaded, #4 bars [G]		160	.200		28	6.05		34.05	41.50
0610	#5 bars [G]		145	.221		29.50	6.65		36.15	44
0620	#6 bars [G]		130	.246		35.50	7.45		42.95	52
0630	#7 bars [G]		110	.291		37.50	8.80		46.30	57
0640	#8 bars [G]		100	.320		39	9.65		48.65	60
0650	#9 bars [G]	C-5	90	.533		42.50	18.75	8.30	69.55	88
0660	#10 bars [G]		80	.600		46	21	9.30	76.30	97
0670	#11 bars [G]		70	.686		48	24	10.65	82.65	105
0680	#14 bars [G]		55	.873		60	30.50	13.55	104.05	133
0690	#18 bars [G]		40	1.200		86	42	18.65	146.65	187
0700	Transition position coupler for curved bars, taper threaded, #18-14 [G]		40	1.200		88	42	18.65	148.65	189
0710	#18-11 [G]		40	1.200		89	42	18.65	149.65	190
0720	#14-11 [G]		55	.873		62	30.50	13.55	106.05	135
0730	#11-10 [G]		70	.686		50	24	10.65	84.65	108
0740	#10-9 [G]		80	.600		48	21	9.30	78.30	99.50
0750	#9-8 [G]	C-25	90	.356		45	10.75		55.75	68.50
0760	#8-7 [G]		100	.320		41	9.65		50.65	62
0770	#7-6 [G]		110	.291		40	8.80		48.80	59.50
0800	Sleeve type w/grout filler, for precast concrete, #6 bars [G]		72	.444		22	13.45		35.45	48
0802	#7 bars [G]		64	.500		26.50	15.10		41.60	55.50
0805	#8 bars [G]		56	.571		31.50	17.25		48.75	65.50
0807	#9 bars [G]		48	.667		37.50	20		57.50	77
0810	#10 bars [G]	C-5	40	1.200		44.50	42	18.65	105.15	141
0900	#11 bars [G]		32	1.500		49	53	23.50	125.50	169
0920	#14 bars [G]		24	2		76.50	70.50	31	178	237
1000	Sleeve type w/ferrous filler, for critical structures, #6 bars [G]	C-25	72	.444		60.50	13.45		73.95	90.50
1210	#7 bars [G]		64	.500		61.50	15.10		76.60	94
1220	#8 bars [G]		56	.571		64.50	17.25		81.75	102
1230	#9 bars [G]	C-5	48	1		66.50	35	15.55	117.05	150
1240	#10 bars [G]		40	1.200		71	42	18.65	131.65	170
1250	#11 bars [G]		32	1.500		85.50	53	23.50	162	210
1260	#14 bars [G]		24	2		107	70.50	31	208.50	271

03 21 05 – Reinforcing Steel Accessories

03 21 05.75 Splicing Reinforcing Bars

		Crew	Daily Output	Labor-Hours	Unit	Material	2014 Bare Costs Labor	Equipment	Total	Total Incl O&P
1270	#18 bars	C-5	16	3	Ea.	109	106	46.50	261.50	350
2000	Weldable half coupler, taper threaded, #4 bars	E-16	120	.133		9.15	5.25	1.18	15.58	21.50
2100	#5 bars		112	.143		10.80	5.60	1.27	17.67	24
2200	#6 bars		104	.154		17.10	6.05	1.37	24.52	32
2300	#7 bars		96	.167		19.90	6.55	1.48	27.93	36
2400	#8 bars		88	.182		21	7.15	1.61	29.76	38.50
2500	#9 bars		80	.200		23	7.85	1.78	32.63	42
2600	#10 bars		72	.222		23.50	8.75	1.97	34.22	44.50
2700	#11 bars		64	.250		25	9.85	2.22	37.07	48.50
2800	#14 bars		56	.286		29	11.25	2.54	42.79	56.50
2900	#18 bars		48	.333		47	13.10	2.96	63.06	80

03 21 11 – Plain Steel Reinforcement Bars

03 21 11.60 Reinforcing In Place

			Crew	Daily Output	Labor-Hours	Unit	Material	2014 Bare Costs Labor	Equipment	Total	Total Incl O&P
0010	**REINFORCING IN PLACE**, 50-60 ton lots, A615 Grade 60	R032110-10									
0020	Includes labor, but not material cost, to install accessories										
0030	Made from recycled materials										
0100	Beams & Girders, #3 to #7		4 Rodm	1.60	20	Ton	1,000	760		1,760	2,400
0150	#8 to #18	R032110-20		2.70	11.852		1,000	450		1,450	1,875
0200	Columns, #3 to #7			1.50	21.333		1,000	810		1,810	2,475
0250	#8 to #18			2.30	13.913		1,000	530		1,530	2,000
0300	Spirals, hot rolled, 8" to 15" diameter			2.20	14.545		1,575	555		2,130	2,675
0320	15" to 24" diameter	R032110-40		2.20	14.545		1,500	555		2,055	2,600
0330	24" to 36" diameter			2.30	13.913		1,425	530		1,955	2,475
0340	36" to 48" diameter	R032110-50		2.40	13.333		1,350	505		1,855	2,375
0360	48" to 64" diameter			2.50	12.800		1,500	485		1,985	2,475
0380	64" to 84" diameter	R032110-70		2.60	12.308		1,575	470		2,045	2,525
0390	84" to 96" diameter			2.70	11.852		1,650	450		2,100	2,600
0400	Elevated slabs, #4 to #7	R032110-80		2.90	11.034		1,000	420		1,420	1,825
0500	Footings, #4 to #7			2.10	15.238		1,000	580		1,580	2,100
0550	#8 to #18			3.60	8.889		1,000	340		1,340	1,675
0600	Slab on grade, #3 to #7			2.30	13.913		1,000	530		1,530	2,000
0700	Walls, #3 to #7			3	10.667		1,000	405		1,405	1,800
0750	#8 to #18			4	8		1,000	305		1,305	1,625
0900	For other than 50 – 60 ton lots										
1000	Under 10 ton job, #3 to #7, add						25%	10%			
1010	#8 to #18, add						20%	10%			
1050	10 – 50 ton job, #3 to #7, add						10%				
1060	#8 to #18, add						5%				
1100	60 – 100 ton job, #3 to #7, deduct						5%				
1110	#8 to #18, deduct						10%				
1150	Over 100 ton job, #3 to #7, deduct						10%				
1160	#8 to #18, deduct						15%				
1200	Reinforcing in place, A615 Grade 75, add					Ton	92.50			92.50	102
1220	Grade 90, add						125			125	138
2000	Unloading & sorting, add to above		C-5	100	.480			16.90	7.45	24.35	36.50
2200	Crane cost for handling, 90 picks/day, up to 1.5 Tons/bundle, add to above			135	.356			12.50	5.55	18.05	27
2210	1.0 Ton/bundle			92	.522			18.35	8.10	26.45	40
2220	0.5 Ton/bundle			35	1.371			48.50	21.50	70	105
2400	Dowels, 2 feet long, deformed, #3		2 Rodm	520	.031	Ea.	.41	1.17		1.58	2.45
2410	#4			480	.033		.73	1.27		2	2.98
2420	#5			435	.037		1.15	1.40		2.55	3.65
2430	#6			360	.044		1.65	1.69		3.34	4.71

03 21 Reinforcement Bars

03 21 11 – Plain Steel Reinforcement Bars

03 21 11.60 Reinforcing In Place		Crew	Daily Output	Labor-Hours	Unit	Material	2014 Bare Costs Labor	Equipment	Total	Total Incl O&P
2450	Longer and heavier dowels, add G	2 Rodm	725	.022	Lb.	.55	.84		1.39	2.04
2500	Smooth dowels, 12" long, 1/4" or 3/8" diameter G		140	.114	Ea.	.72	4.34		5.06	8.25
2520	5/8" diameter G		125	.128		1.26	4.86		6.12	9.70
2530	3/4" diameter G		110	.145		1.57	5.55		7.12	11.15
2600	Dowel sleeves for CIP concrete, 2-part system									
2610	Sleeve base, plastic, for 5/8" smooth dowel sleeve, fasten to edge form	1 Rodm	200	.040	Ea.	.52	1.52		2.04	3.17
2615	Sleeve, plastic, 12" long, for 5/8" smooth dowel, snap onto base		400	.020		1.16	.76		1.92	2.58
2620	Sleeve base, for 3/4" smooth dowel sleeve		175	.046		.52	1.74		2.26	3.54
2625	Sleeve, 12" long, for 3/4" smooth dowel		350	.023		1.30	.87		2.17	2.92
2630	Sleeve base, for 1" smooth dowel sleeve		150	.053		.66	2.03		2.69	4.20
2635	Sleeve, 12" long, for 1" smooth dowel		300	.027		1.37	1.01		2.38	3.24
2700	Dowel caps, visual warning only, plastic, #3 to #8	2 Rodm	800	.020		.27	.76		1.03	1.60
2720	#8 to #18		750	.021		.68	.81		1.49	2.14
2750	Impalement protective, plastic, #4 to #9		800	.020		1.50	.76		2.26	2.95

03 21 13 – Galvanized Reinforcement Steel Bars

03 21 13.10 Galvanized Reinforcing

0010	**GALVANIZED REINFORCING**									
0150	Add to plain steel rebar pricing for galvanized rebar				Ton	460			460	505

03 21 16 – Epoxy-Coated Reinforcement Steel Bars

03 21 16.10 Epoxy-Coated Reinforcing

0010	**EPOXY-COATED REINFORCING**									
0100	Add to plain steel rebar pricing for epoxy-coated rebar				Ton	410			410	450

03 21 21 – Composite Reinforcement Bars

03 21 21.11 Glass Fiber-Reinforced Polymer Reinforcement Bars

0010	**GLASS FIBER-REINFORCED POLYMER REINFORCEMENT BARS**									
0020	Includes labor, but not material cost, to install accessories									
0050	#2 bar, .043 lb./L.F.	4 Rodm	9500	.003	L.F.	.36	.13		.49	.62
0100	#3 bar, .092 lb./L.F.		9300	.003		.49	.13		.62	.76
0150	#4 bar, .160 lb./L.F.		9100	.004		.71	.13		.84	1.01
0200	#5 bar, .258 lb./L.F.		8700	.004		1.09	.14		1.23	1.44
0250	#6 bar, .372 lb./L.F.		8300	.004		1.41	.15		1.56	1.80
0300	#7 bar, .497 lb./L.F.		7900	.004		1.84	.15		1.99	2.28
0350	#8 bar, .620 lb./L.F.		7400	.004		2.50	.16		2.66	3.03
0400	#9 bar, .800 lb./L.F.		6800	.005		3.16	.18		3.34	3.79
0450	#10 bar, 1.08 lb./L.F.		5800	.006		3.93	.21		4.14	4.68
0500	For Bends, add per bend				Ea.	1.48			1.48	1.63

03 22 Fabric and Grid Reinforcing

03 22 11 – Plain Welded Wire Fabric Reinforcing

03 22 11.10 Plain Welded Wire Fabric

0010	**PLAIN WELDED WIRE FABRIC** ASTM A185 R032205-30									
0020	Includes labor, but not material cost, to install accessories									
0030	Made from recycled materials									
0050	Sheets									
0100	6 x 6 - W1.4 x W1.4 (10 x 10) 21 lb. per C.S.F. G	2 Rodm	35	.457	C.S.F.	14.50	17.35		31.85	45.50
0200	6 x 6 - W2.1 x W2.1 (8 x 8) 30 lb. per C.S.F. G		31	.516		17.20	19.60		36.80	52.50
0300	6 x 6 - W2.9 x W2.9 (6 x 6) 42 lb. per C.S.F. G		29	.552		22.50	21		43.50	60.50
0400	6 x 6 - W4 x W4 (4 x 4) 58 lb. per C.S.F. G		27	.593		31.50	22.50		54	73
0500	4 x 4 - W1.4 x W1.4 (10 x 10) 31 lb. per C.S.F. G		31	.516		20	19.60		39.60	55.50

03 22 Fabric and Grid Reinforcing

03 22 11 – Plain Welded Wire Fabric Reinforcing

03 22 11.10 Plain Welded Wire Fabric

		Crew	Daily Output	Labor-Hours	Unit	Material	2014 Bare Costs Labor	Equipment	Total	Total Incl O&P
0600	4 x 4 - W2.1 x W2.1 (8 x 8) 44 lb. per C.S.F.	G 2 Rodm	29	.552	C.S.F.	25	21		46	63.50
0650	4 x 4 - W2.9 x W2.9 (6 x 6) 61 lb. per C.S.F.	G	27	.593		40.50	22.50		63	83
0700	4 x 4 - W4 x W4 (4 x 4) 85 lb. per C.S.F.	G ↓	25	.640	↓	50.50	24.50		75	97
0750	Rolls									
0800	2 x 2 - #14 galv., 21 lb./C.S.F., beam & column wrap	G 2 Rodm	6.50	2.462	C.S.F.	41.50	93.50		135	206
0900	2 x 2 - #12 galv. for gunite reinforcing	G "	6.50	2.462	"	62.50	93.50		156	229

03 22 13 – Galvanized Welded Wire Fabric Reinforcing

03 22 13.10 Galvanized Welded Wire Fabric

0010	**GALVANIZED WELDED WIRE FABRIC**									
0100	Add to plain welded wire pricing for galvanized welded wire				Lb.	.23			.23	.25

03 22 16 – Epoxy-Coated Welded Wire Fabric Reinforcing

03 22 16.10 Epoxy-Coated Welded Wire Fabric

0010	**EPOXY-COATED WELDED WIRE FABRIC**									
0100	Add to plain welded wire pricing for epoxy-coated welded wire				Lb.	.21			.21	.23

03 23 Stressed Tendon Reinforcing

03 23 05 – Prestressing Tendons

03 23 05.50 Prestressing Steel

			Crew	Daily Output	Labor-Hours	Unit	Material	2014 Bare Costs Labor	Equipment	Total	Total Incl O&P
0010	**PRESTRESSING STEEL**	R034136-90									
0100	Grouted strand, in beams, post-tensioned in field, 50' span, 100 kip	G	C-3	1200	.053	Lb.	2.62	1.83	.09	4.54	6.10
0150	300 kip	G		2700	.024		1.12	.81	.04	1.97	2.66
0300	100' span, 100 kip	G		1700	.038		2.62	1.29	.07	3.98	5.15
0350	300 kip	G		3200	.020		2.25	.69	.04	2.98	3.68
0500	200' span, 100 kip	G		2700	.024		2.62	.81	.04	3.47	4.31
0550	300 kip	G		3500	.018		2.25	.63	.03	2.91	3.58
0800	Grouted bars, in beams, 50' span, 42 kip	G		2600	.025		1.06	.85	.04	1.95	2.65
0850	143 kip	G		3200	.020		1.02	.69	.04	1.75	2.32
1000	75' span, 42 kip	G		3200	.020		1.08	.69	.04	1.81	2.38
1050	143 kip	G	↓	4200	.015		.90	.52	.03	1.45	1.91
1200	Ungrouted strand, in beams, 50' span, 100 kip	G	C-4	1275	.025		.61	.90	.02	1.53	2.24
1250	300 kip	G		1475	.022		.61	.78	.02	1.41	2.02
1400	100' span, 100 kip	G		1500	.021		.61	.77	.02	1.40	2
1450	300 kip	G		1650	.019		.61	.70	.02	1.33	1.88
1600	200' span, 100 kip	G		1500	.021		.61	.77	.02	1.40	2
1650	300 kip	G		1700	.019		.61	.68	.02	1.31	1.85
1800	Ungrouted bars, in beams, 50' span, 42 kip	G		1400	.023		.50	.82	.02	1.34	1.98
1850	143 kip	G		1700	.019		.50	.68	.02	1.20	1.73
2000	75' span, 42 kip	G		1800	.018		.50	.64	.02	1.16	1.66
2050	143 kip	G		2200	.015		.50	.52	.01	1.03	1.46
2220	Ungrouted single strand, 100' elevated slab, 25 kip	G		1200	.027		.61	.96	.03	1.60	2.34
2250	35 kip	G	↓	1475	.022	↓	.61	.78	.02	1.41	2.02
3000	Slabs on grade, 0.5-inch diam. non-bonded strands, HDPE sheathed,										
3050	attached dead-end anchors, loose stressing-end anchors										
3100	25' x 30' slab, strands @ 36" O.C., placing		2 Rodm	2940	.005	S.F.	.60	.21		.81	1.01
3105	Stressing		C-4A	3750	.004			.16	.01	.17	.29
3110	42" O.C., placing		2 Rodm	3200	.005		.53	.19		.72	.92
3115	Stressing		C-4A	4040	.004			.15	.01	.16	.27
3120	48" O.C., placing		2 Rodm	3510	.005		.47	.17		.64	.81
3125	Stressing		C-4A	4390	.004			.14	.01	.15	.25
3150	25' x 40' slab, strands @ 36" O.C., placing		2 Rodm	3370	.005	↓	.58	.18		.76	.95

03 23 05 – Prestressing Tendons

03 23 05.50 Prestressing Steel	Crew	Daily Output	Labor-Hours	Unit	Material	2014 Bare Costs Labor	Equipment	Total	Total Incl O&P
3155	Stressing	C-4A	4360	.004	S.F.		.14	.01	.15	.25
3160	42" O.C., placing	2 Rodm	3760	.004		.50	.16		.66	.83
3165	Stressing	C-4A	4820	.003			.13	.01	.14	.23
3170	48" O.C., placing	2 Rodm	4090	.004		.45	.15		.60	.74
3175	Stressing	C-4A	5190	.003			.12	.01	.13	.21
3200	30' x 30' slab, strands @ 36" O.C., placing	2 Rodm	3260	.005		.58	.19		.77	.96
3205	Stressing	C-4A	4190	.004			.15	.01	.16	.26
3210	42" O.C., placing	2 Rodm	3530	.005		.52	.17		.69	.87
3215	Stressing	C-4A	4500	.004			.14	.01	.15	.24
3220	48" O.C., placing	2 Rodm	3840	.004		.47	.16		.63	.78
3225	Stressing	C-4A	4850	.003			.13	.01	.14	.22
3230	30' x 40' slab, strands @ 36" O.C., placing	2 Rodm	3780	.004		.56	.16		.72	.90
3235	Stressing	C-4A	4920	.003			.12	.01	.13	.22
3240	42" O.C., placing	2 Rodm	4190	.004		.49	.15		.64	.79
3245	Stressing	C-4A	5410	.003			.11	.01	.12	.20
3250	48" O.C., placing	2 Rodm	4520	.004		.45	.13		.58	.72
3255	Stressing	C-4A	5790	.003			.10	.01	.11	.19
3260	30' x 50' slab, strands @ 36" O.C., placing	2 Rodm	4300	.004		.53	.14		.67	.83
3265	Stressing	C-4A	5650	.003			.11	.01	.12	.19
3270	42" O.C., placing	2 Rodm	4720	.003		.47	.13		.60	.74
3275	Stressing	C-4A	6150	.003			.10	.01	.11	.18
3280	48" O.C., placing	2 Rodm	5240	.003		.42	.12		.54	.66
3285	Stressing	C-4A	6760	.002			.09	.01	.10	.16

03 24 Fibrous Reinforcing

03 24 05 – Reinforcing Fibers

03 24 05.30 Synthetic Fibers

	03 24 05.30 Synthetic Fibers				Unit	Material	Labor	Equipment	Total	Total Incl O&P
0010	**SYNTHETIC FIBERS**									
0100	Synthetic fibers, add to concrete				Lb.	4.80			4.80	5.30
0110	1-1/2 lb. per C.Y.				C.Y.	7.40			7.40	8.15

03 24 05.70 Steel Fibers

	03 24 05.70 Steel Fibers				Unit	Material	Labor	Equipment	Total	Total Incl O&P
0010	**STEEL FIBERS**									
0140	ASTM A850, Type V, continuously deformed, 1-1/2" long x 0.045" diam.									
0150	Add to price of ready mix concrete	G			Lb.	1.25			1.25	1.38
0205	Alternate pricing, dosing at 5 lb. per C.Y., add to price of RMC	G			C.Y.	6.25			6.25	6.90
0210	10 lb. per C.Y.	G				12.50			12.50	13.75
0215	15 lb. per C.Y.	G				18.75			18.75	20.50
0220	20 lb. per C.Y.	G				25			25	27.50
0225	25 lb. per C.Y.	G				31.50			31.50	34.50
0230	30 lb. per C.Y.	G				37.50			37.50	41.50
0235	35 lb. per C.Y.	G				44			44	48
0240	40 lb. per C.Y.	G				50			50	55
0250	50 lb. per C.Y.	G				62.50			62.50	69
0275	75 lb. per C.Y.	G				94			94	103
0300	100 lb. per C.Y.	G				125			125	138

03 30 53 – Miscellaneous Cast-In-Place Concrete

03 30 53.40 Concrete In Place		Crew	Daily Output	Labor-Hours	Unit	Material	2014 Bare Costs Labor	Equipment	Total	Total Incl O&P
0010	**CONCRETE IN PLACE**	R033105-10								
0020	Including forms (4 uses), Grade 60 rebar, concrete (Portland cement	R033105-20								
0050	Type I), placement and finishing unless otherwise indicated	R033105-50								
0300	Beams (3500 psi), 5 kip per L.F., 10' span	R033105-65	C-14A	15.62	12.804	C.Y.	315	455	47.50	817.50	1,175
0350	25' span	R033105-70	"	18.55	10.782		335	385	40	760	1,050
0500	Chimney foundations (5000 psi), over 5 C.Y.	R033105-85	C-14C	32.22	3.476		147	118	1.01	266.01	360
0510	(3500 psi), under 5 C.Y.		"	23.71	4.724		173	160	1.37	334.37	465
0700	Columns, square (4000 psi), 12" x 12", less than 2% reinforcing		C-14A	11.96	16.722		355	595	62	1,012	1,475
0720	2% to 3% reinforcing reinforcing			10.13	19.743		565	705	73.50	1,343.50	1,875
0740	Over 3% reinforcing			9.03	22.148		850	790	82.50	1,722.50	2,350
0800	16" x 16", less than 2% reinforcing			16.22	12.330		282	440	46	768	1,100
0820	2% to 3% reinforcing reinforcing			12.57	15.911		480	565	59	1,104	1,550
0840	Over 3% reinforcing			10.25	19.512		745	695	72.50	1,512.50	2,075
0900	24" x 24", less than 2% reinforcing			23.66	8.453		238	300	31.50	569.50	800
0920	2% to 3% reinforcing reinforcing			17.71	11.293		425	400	42	867	1,200
0940	Over 3% reinforcing			14.15	14.134		680	505	52.50	1,237.50	1,650
1000	36" x 36", less than 2% reinforcing			33.69	5.936		210	211	22	443	610
1020	2% to 3% reinforcing reinforcing			23.32	8.576		375	305	32	712	965
1040	Over 3% reinforcing			17.82	11.223		635	400	42	1,077	1,425
1100	Columns, round (4000 psi), tied, 12" diameter, less than 2% reinforcing			20.97	9.537		305	340	35.50	680.50	950
1120	2% to 3% reinforcing reinforcing			15.27	13.098		515	465	48.50	1,028.50	1,400
1140	Over 3% reinforcing			12.11	16.515		785	590	61.50	1,436.50	1,925
1200	16" diameter, less than 2% reinforcing			31.49	6.351		280	226	23.50	529.50	715
1220	2% to 3% reinforcing reinforcing			19.12	10.460		490	370	39	899	1,200
1240	Over 3% reinforcing			13.77	14.524		740	515	54	1,309	1,750
1300	20" diameter, less than 2% reinforcing			41.04	4.873		283	174	18.15	475.15	620
1320	2% to 3% reinforcing reinforcing			24.05	8.316		475	296	31	802	1,050
1340	Over 3% reinforcing			17.01	11.758		740	420	43.50	1,203.50	1,575
1400	24" diameter, less than 2% reinforcing			51.85	3.857		264	137	14.35	415.35	540
1420	2% to 3% reinforcing reinforcing			27.06	7.391		475	263	27.50	765.50	995
1440	Over 3% reinforcing			18.29	10.935		725	390	40.50	1,155.50	1,500
1500	36" diameter, less than 2% reinforcing			75.04	2.665		265	95	9.90	369.90	460
1520	2% to 3% reinforcing reinforcing			37.49	5.335		450	190	19.85	659.85	835
1540	Over 3% reinforcing			22.84	8.757		705	310	32.50	1,047.50	1,325
1900	Elevated slab (4000 psi), flat slab with drops, 125 psf Sup. Load, 20' span		C-14B	38.45	5.410		256	192	19.30	467.30	630
1950	30' span			50.99	4.079		273	145	14.55	432.55	560
2100	Flat plate, 125 psf Sup. Load, 15' span			30.24	6.878		234	245	24.50	503.50	695
2150	25' span			49.60	4.194		245	149	14.95	408.95	535
2300	Waffle const., 30" domes, 125 psf Sup. Load, 20' span			37.07	5.611		254	200	20	474	635
2350	30' span			44.07	4.720		237	168	16.85	421.85	560
2500	One way joists, 30" pans, 125 psf Sup. Load, 15' span			27.38	7.597		299	270	27	596	815
2550	25' span			31.15	6.677		283	237	24	544	735
2700	One way beam & slab, 125 psf Sup. Load, 15' span			20.59	10.102		253	360	36	649	925
2750	25' span			28.36	7.334		241	261	26	528	735
2900	Two way beam & slab, 125 psf Sup. Load, 15' span			24.04	8.652		245	310	31	586	820
2950	25' span			35.87	5.799		212	206	20.50	438.50	600
3100	Elevated slabs, flat plate, including finish, not										
3110	including forms or reinforcing										
3150	Regular concrete (4000 psi), 4" slab		C-8	2613	.021	S.F.	1.39	.68	.27	2.34	2.95
3200	6" slab			2585	.022		2.03	.68	.27	2.98	3.66
3250	2-1/2" thick floor fill			2685	.021		.91	.66	.26	1.83	2.38
3300	Lightweight, 110# per C.F., 2-1/2" thick floor fill			2585	.022		1.24	.68	.27	2.19	2.79
3400	Cellular concrete, 1-5/8" fill, under 5000 S.F.			2000	.028		.84	.88	.36	2.08	2.79

03 30 53.40 Concrete In Place	Crew	Daily Output	Labor-Hours	Unit	Material	2014 Bare Costs Labor	Equipment	Total	Total Incl O&P
3450	Over 10,000 S.F.	C-8	2200	.025	S.F.	.80	.80	.32	1.92	2.58
3500	Add per floor for 3 to 6 stories high		31800	.002			.06	.02	.08	.11
3520	For 7 to 20 stories high		21200	.003			.08	.03	.11	.18
3540	Equipment pad (3000 psi), 3' x 3' x 6" thick	C-14H	45	1.067	Ea.	44.50	37.50	.74	82.74	112
3550	4' x 4' x 6" thick		30	1.600		66.50	56	1.10	123.60	168
3560	5' x 5' x 8" thick		18	2.667		119	93.50	1.84	214.34	289
3570	6' x 6' x 8" thick		14	3.429		160	120	2.37	282.37	380
3580	8' x 8' x 10" thick		8	6		335	210	4.14	549.14	725
3590	10' x 10' x 12" thick		5	9.600		575	335	6.60	916.60	1,200
3800	Footings (3000 psi), spread under 1 C.Y.	C-14C	28	4	C.Y.	164	136	1.16	301.16	410
3825	1 C.Y. to 5 C.Y.		43	2.605		198	88.50	.76	287.26	370
3850	Over 5 C.Y.		75	1.493		180	50.50	.43	230.93	284
3900	Footings, strip (3000 psi), 18" x 9", unreinforced	C-14L	40	2.400		120	80	.82	200.82	267
3920	18" x 9", reinforced	C-14C	35	3.200		144	109	.93	253.93	340
3925	20" x 10", unreinforced	C-14L	45	2.133		117	71	.73	188.73	248
3930	20" x 10", reinforced	C-14C	40	2.800		136	95	.81	231.81	310
3935	24" x 12", unreinforced	C-14L	55	1.745		116	58	.59	174.59	225
3940	24" x 12", reinforced	C-14C	48	2.333		136	79	.68	215.68	283
3945	36" x 12", unreinforced	C-14L	70	1.371		112	45.50	.47	157.97	200
3950	36" x 12", reinforced	C-14C	60	1.867		130	63.50	.54	194.04	251
4000	Foundation mat (3000 psi), under 10 C.Y.		38.67	2.896		204	98.50	.84	303.34	390
4050	Over 20 C.Y.		56.40	1.986		178	67.50	.58	246.08	310
4200	Wall, free-standing (3000 psi), 8" thick, 8' high	C-14D	45.83	4.364		152	155	16.25	323.25	445
4250	14' high		27.26	7.337		188	260	27.50	475.50	670
4260	12" thick, 8' high		64.32	3.109		142	110	11.55	263.55	355
4270	14' high		40.01	4.999		152	177	18.60	347.60	485
4300	15" thick, 8' high		80.02	2.499		137	88.50	9.30	234.80	310
4350	12' high		51.26	3.902		137	138	14.50	289.50	400
4500	18' high		48.85	4.094		155	145	15.25	315.25	430
4520	Handicap access ramp (4000 psi), railing both sides, 3' wide	C-14H	14.58	3.292	L.F.	315	115	2.27	432.27	545
4525	5' wide		12.22	3.928		330	137	2.71	469.71	595
4530	With 6" curb and rails both sides, 3' wide		8.55	5.614		325	196	3.87	524.87	695
4535	5' wide		7.31	6.566		330	230	4.53	564.53	755
4650	Slab on grade (3500 psi), not including finish, 4" thick	C-14E	60.75	1.449	C.Y.	120	50	.55	170.55	217
4700	6" thick	"	92	.957	"	115	33	.36	148.36	183
4701	Thickened slab edge (3500 psi), for slab on grade poured									
4702	monolithically with slab; depth is in addition to slab thickness;									
4703	formed vertical outside edge, earthen bottom and inside slope									
4705	8" deep x 8" wide bottom, unreinforced	C-14L	2190	.044	L.F.	3.33	1.46	.01	4.80	6.15
4710	8" x 8", reinforced	C-14C	1670	.067		5.70	2.28	.02	8	10.10
4715	12" deep x 12" wide bottom, unreinforced	C-14L	1800	.053		6.75	1.77	.02	8.54	10.45
4720	12" x 12", reinforced	C-14C	1310	.086		11.05	2.90	.02	13.97	17.05
4725	16" deep x 16" wide bottom, unreinforced	C-14L	1440	.067		11.40	2.22	.02	13.64	16.30
4730	16" x 16", reinforced	C-14C	1120	.100		16.50	3.40	.03	19.93	24
4735	20" deep x 20" wide bottom, unreinforced	C-14L	1150	.083		17.25	2.78	.03	20.06	23.50
4740	20" x 20", reinforced	C-14C	920	.122		24	4.13	.04	28.17	33
4745	24" deep x 24" wide bottom, unreinforced	C-14L	930	.103		24.50	3.44	.04	27.98	33
4750	24" x 24", reinforced	C-14C	740	.151		33	5.15	.04	38.19	44.50
4751	Slab on grade (3500 psi), incl. troweled finish, not incl. forms									
4760	or reinforcing, over 10,000 S.F., 4" thick	C-14F	3425	.021	S.F.	1.31	.68	.01	2	2.57
4820	6" thick		3350	.021		1.91	.70	.01	2.62	3.25
4840	8" thick		3184	.023		2.62	.74	.01	3.37	4.09
4900	12" thick		2734	.026		3.92	.86	.01	4.79	5.75

03 30 Cast-In-Place Concrete

03 30 53 – Miscellaneous Cast-In-Place Concrete

03 30 53.40 Concrete In Place

		Crew	Daily Output	Labor-Hours	Unit	Material	2014 Bare Costs Labor	Equipment	Total	Total Incl O&P
4950	15" thick	C-14F	2505	.029	S.F.	4.93	.93	.01	5.87	6.95
5000	Slab on grade (3000 psi), incl. broom finish, not incl. forms									
5001	or reinforcing, 4" thick	C-14G	2873	.019	S.F.	1.29	.62	.01	1.92	2.45
5010	6" thick		2590	.022		2.01	.69	.01	2.71	3.36
5020	8" thick	↓	2320	.024	↓	2.62	.77	.01	3.40	4.18
5200	Lift slab in place above the foundation, incl. forms, reinforcing,									
5210	concrete (4000 psi) and columns, over 20,000 S.F. per floor	C-14B	2113	.098	S.F.	6.80	3.50	.35	10.65	13.80
5250	10,000 S.F. to 20,000 S.F. per floor		1650	.126		7.45	4.48	.45	12.38	16.25
5300	Under 10,000 S.F. per floor	↓	1500	.139	↓	8.10	4.93	.50	13.53	17.80
5500	Lightweight, ready mix, including screed finish only,									
5510	not including forms or reinforcing									
5550	1:4 (2500 psi) for structural roof decks	C-14B	260	.800	C.Y.	138	28.50	2.86	169.36	203
5600	1:6 (3000 psi) for ground slab with radiant heat	C-14F	92	.783		140	25.50	.36	165.86	196
5650	1:3:2 (2000 psi) with sand aggregate, roof deck	C-14B	260	.800		135	28.50	2.86	166.36	200
5700	Ground slab (2000 psi)	C-14F	107	.673		135	22	.31	157.31	185
5900	Pile caps (3000 psi), incl. forms and reinf., sq. or rect., under 10 C.Y.	C-14C	54.14	2.069		165	70.50	.60	236.10	300
5950	Over 10 C.Y.		75	1.493		155	50.50	.43	205.93	256
6000	Triangular or hexagonal, under 10 C.Y.		53	2.113		121	72	.61	193.61	255
6050	Over 10 C.Y.	↓	85	1.318		137	45	.38	182.38	226
6200	Retaining walls (3000 psi), gravity, 4' high see Section 32 32	C-14D	66.20	3.021		137	107	11.25	255.25	340
6250	10' high		125	1.600		131	56.50	5.95	193.45	246
6300	Cantilever, level backfill loading, 8' high		70	2.857		147	101	10.65	258.65	345
6350	16' high	↓	91	2.198	↓	142	78	8.20	228.20	297
6800	Stairs (3500 psi), not including safety treads, free standing, 3'-6" wide	C-14H	83	.578	LF Nose	5.40	20	.40	25.80	40.50
6850	Cast on ground		125	.384	"	4.49	13.45	.27	18.21	27.50
7000	Stair landings, free standing		200	.240	S.F.	4.39	8.40	.17	12.96	19.10
7050	Cast on ground	↓	475	.101	"	3.45	3.53	.07	7.05	9.80

03 31 Structural Concrete

03 31 13 – Heavyweight Structural Concrete

03 31 13.25 Concrete, Hand Mix

		Crew	Daily Output	Labor-Hours	Unit	Material	2014 Bare Costs Labor	Equipment	Total	Total Incl O&P
0010	**CONCRETE, HAND MIX** for small quantities or remote areas									
0050	Includes bulk local aggregate, bulk sand, bagged Portland									
0060	cement (Type I) and water, using gas powered cement mixer									
0125	2500 psi	C-30	135	.059	C.F.	3.14	1.67	1.31	6.12	7.70
0130	3000 psi		135	.059		3.37	1.67	1.31	6.35	7.95
0135	3500 psi		135	.059		3.50	1.67	1.31	6.48	8.10
0140	4000 psi		135	.059		3.66	1.67	1.31	6.64	8.25
0145	4500 psi		135	.059		3.83	1.67	1.31	6.81	8.45
0150	5000 psi	↓	135	.059	↓	4.09	1.67	1.31	7.07	8.75
0300	Using pre-bagged dry mix and wheelbarrow (80-lb. bag = 0.6 C.F.)									
0340	4000 psi	1 Clab	48	.167	C.F.	6.25	4.70		10.95	14.80

03 31 13.30 Concrete, Volumetric Site-Mixed

		Crew	Daily Output	Labor-Hours	Unit	Material	2014 Bare Costs Labor	Equipment	Total	Total Incl O&P
0010	**CONCRETE, VOLUMETRIC SITE-MIXED**									
0015	Mixed on-site in volumetric truck									
0020	Includes local aggregate, sand, Portland cement (Type I) and water									
0025	Excludes all additives and treatments									
0100	3000 psi, 1 C.Y. mixed and discharged				C.Y.	159			159	175
0110	2 C.Y.					136			136	150
0120	3 C.Y.					122			122	134
0130	4 C.Y.				↓	114			114	125

03 31 13.30 Concrete, Volumetric Site-Mixed	Crew	Daily Output	Labor-Hours	Unit	Material	2014 Bare Costs Labor	Equipment	Total	Total Incl O&P
0140 5 C.Y.				C.Y.	106			106	116
0200 For truck holding/waiting time past first 2 on-site hours, add				Hr.	72			72	79
0210 For trip charge beyond first 20 miles, each way, add				Mile	2.25			2.25	2.48
0220 For each additional increase of 500 psi, add				Ea.	4.17			4.17	4.59

03 31 13.35 Heavyweight Concrete, Ready Mix

	Crew	Daily Output	Labor-Hours	Unit	Material	Labor	Equipment	Total	Total Incl O&P
0010 **HEAVYWEIGHT CONCRETE, READY MIX,** delivered R033105-10									
0012 Includes local aggregate, sand, Portland cement (Type I) and water									
0015 Excludes all additives and treatments R033105-20									
0020 2000 psi				C.Y.	93			93	102
0100 2500 psi R033105-30					95.50			95.50	105
0150 3000 psi					99			99	109
0200 3500 psi R033105-40					101			101	111
0300 4000 psi					104			104	114
0350 4500 psi R033105-50					107			107	117
0400 5000 psi					110			110	121
0411 6000 psi					113			113	124
0412 8000 psi					119			119	130
0413 10,000 psi					125			125	137
0414 12,000 psi					131			131	144
1000 For high early strength (Portland cement Type III), add					10%				
1010 For structural lightweight with regular sand, add					25%				
1300 For winter concrete (hot water), add					4.50			4.50	4.95
1400 For hot weather concrete (ice), add					7.65			7.65	8.40
1410 For mid-range water reducer, add					3.69			3.69	4.06
1420 For high-range water reducer/superplasticizer, add					5.70			5.70	6.30
1430 For retarder, add					3.06			3.06	3.37
1440 For non-Chloride accelerator, add					5.65			5.65	6.20
1450 For Chloride accelerator, per 1%, add					3.32			3.32	3.65
1460 For fiber reinforcing, synthetic (1 lb./C.Y.), add					6.95			6.95	7.60
1500 For Saturday delivery, add					4.93			4.93	5.40
1510 For truck holding/waiting time past 1st hour per load, add				Hr.	97			97	107
1520 For short load (less than 4 C.Y.), add per load				Ea.	77.50			77.50	85
2000 For all lightweight aggregate, add				C.Y.	45%				

03 31 13.70 Placing Concrete

	Crew	Daily Output	Labor-Hours	Unit	Material	Labor	Equipment	Total	Total Incl O&P
0010 **PLACING CONCRETE** R033105-70									
0020 Includes labor and equipment to place, level (strike off) and consolidate									
0050 Beams, elevated, small beams, pumped	C-20	60	1.067	C.Y.		32.50	12.95	45.45	68.50
0100 With crane and bucket	C-7	45	1.600			49	27.50	76.50	112
0200 Large beams, pumped	C-20	90	.711			21.50	8.65	30.15	45.50
0250 With crane and bucket	C-7	65	1.108			34	18.85	52.85	78
0400 Columns, square or round, 12" thick, pumped	C-20	60	1.067			32.50	12.95	45.45	68.50
0450 With crane and bucket	C-7	40	1.800			55.50	30.50	86	126
0600 18" thick, pumped	C-20	90	.711			21.50	8.65	30.15	45.50
0650 With crane and bucket	C-7	55	1.309			40.50	22.50	63	91.50
0800 24" thick, pumped	C-20	92	.696			21	8.45	29.45	45
0850 With crane and bucket	C-7	70	1.029			31.50	17.50	49	72.50
1000 36" thick, pumped	C-20	140	.457			13.90	5.55	19.45	29
1050 With crane and bucket	C-7	100	.720			22	12.25	34.25	50.50
1400 Elevated slabs, less than 6" thick, pumped	C-20	140	.457			13.90	5.55	19.45	29
1450 With crane and bucket	C-7	95	.758			23.50	12.90	36.40	53
1500 6" to 10" thick, pumped	C-20	160	.400			12.15	4.85	17	26
1550 With crane and bucket	C-7	110	.655			20	11.15	31.15	46

03 31 13.70 Placing Concrete	Crew	Daily Output	Labor-Hours	Unit	Material	2014 Bare Costs Labor	2014 Bare Costs Equipment	Total	Total Incl O&P
1600	Slabs over 10" thick, pumped	C-20	180	.356	C.Y.		10.80	4.31	15.11	23
1650	With crane and bucket	C-7	130	.554			17.05	9.45	26.50	39
1900	Footings, continuous, shallow, direct chute	C-6	120	.400			11.80	.55	12.35	20.50
1950	Pumped	C-20	150	.427			12.95	5.20	18.15	27
2000	With crane and bucket	C-7	90	.800			24.50	13.60	38.10	56
2100	Footings, continuous, deep, direct chute	C-6	140	.343			10.15	.47	10.62	17.45
2150	Pumped	C-20	160	.400			12.15	4.85	17	26
2200	With crane and bucket	C-7	110	.655			20	11.15	31.15	46
2400	Footings, spread, under 1 C.Y., direct chute	C-6	55	.873			26	1.20	27.20	44.50
2450	Pumped	C-20	65	.985			30	11.95	41.95	63
2500	With crane and bucket	C-7	45	1.600			49	27.50	76.50	112
2600	Over 5 C.Y., direct chute	C-6	120	.400			11.80	.55	12.35	20.50
2650	Pumped	C-20	150	.427			12.95	5.20	18.15	27
2700	With crane and bucket	C-7	100	.720			22	12.25	34.25	50.50
2900	Foundation mats, over 20 C.Y., direct chute	C-6	350	.137			4.05	.19	4.24	6.95
2950	Pumped	C-20	400	.160			4.86	1.94	6.80	10.25
3000	With crane and bucket	C-7	300	.240			7.40	4.09	11.49	16.80
3200	Grade beams, direct chute	C-6	150	.320			9.45	.44	9.89	16.30
3250	Pumped	C-20	180	.356			10.80	4.31	15.11	23
3300	With crane and bucket	C-7	120	.600			18.45	10.20	28.65	42.50
3500	High rise, for more than 5 stories, pumped, add per story	C-20	2100	.030			.93	.37	1.30	1.96
3510	With crane and bucket, add per story	C-7	2100	.034			1.05	.58	1.63	2.40
3700	Pile caps, under 5 C.Y., direct chute	C-6	90	.533			15.75	.74	16.49	27.50
3750	Pumped	C-20	110	.582			17.70	7.05	24.75	37.50
3800	With crane and bucket	C-7	80	.900			27.50	15.35	42.85	63
3850	Pile cap, 5 C.Y. to 10 C.Y., direct chute	C-6	175	.274			8.10	.38	8.48	13.95
3900	Pumped	C-20	200	.320			9.75	3.88	13.63	20.50
3950	With crane and bucket	C-7	150	.480			14.75	8.15	22.90	33.50
4000	Over 10 C.Y., direct chute	C-6	215	.223			6.60	.31	6.91	11.35
4050	Pumped	C-20	240	.267			8.10	3.23	11.33	17.10
4100	With crane and bucket	C-7	185	.389			11.95	6.65	18.60	27.50
4300	Slab on grade, up to 6" thick, direct chute	C-6	110	.436			12.90	.60	13.50	22
4350	Pumped	C-20	130	.492			14.95	5.95	20.90	31.50
4400	With crane and bucket	C-7	110	.655			20	11.15	31.15	46
4600	Over 6" thick, direct chute	C-6	165	.291			8.60	.40	9	14.80
4650	Pumped	C-20	185	.346			10.50	4.20	14.70	22
4700	With crane and bucket	C-7	145	.497			15.25	8.45	23.70	35
4900	Walls, 8" thick, direct chute	C-6	90	.533			15.75	.74	16.49	27.50
4950	Pumped	C-20	100	.640			19.45	7.75	27.20	41
5000	With crane and bucket	C-7	80	.900			27.50	15.35	42.85	63
5050	12" thick, direct chute	C-6	100	.480			14.20	.66	14.86	24
5100	Pumped	C-20	110	.582			17.70	7.05	24.75	37.50
5200	With crane and bucket	C-7	90	.800			24.50	13.60	38.10	56
5300	15" thick, direct chute	C-6	105	.457			13.50	.63	14.13	23
5350	Pumped	C-20	120	.533			16.20	6.45	22.65	34
5400	With crane and bucket	C-7	95	.758	▼		23.50	12.90	36.40	53
5600	Wheeled concrete dumping, add to placing costs above									
5610	Walking cart, 50' haul, add	C-18	32	.281	C.Y.		8	1.88	9.88	15.50
5620	150' haul, add		24	.375			10.65	2.51	13.16	20.50
5700	250' haul, add	▼	18	.500			14.20	3.35	17.55	27.50
5800	Riding cart, 50' haul, add	C-19	80	.113			3.20	1.26	4.46	6.80
5810	150' haul, add		60	.150			4.26	1.69	5.95	9
5900	250' haul, add	▼	45	.200	▼		5.70	2.25	7.95	12

79

03 31 Structural Concrete

03 31 13 – Heavyweight Structural Concrete

03 31 13.70 Placing Concrete

		Crew	Daily Output	Labor-Hours	Unit	Material	2014 Bare Costs Labor	2014 Bare Costs Equipment	Total	Total Incl O&P
6000	Concrete in-fill for pan-type metal stairs and landings. Manual placement									
6010	includes up to 50' horizontal haul from point of concrete discharge.									
6100	Stair pan treads, 2" deep									
6110	Flights in 1st floor level up/down from discharge point	C-8A	3200	.015	S.F.		.46		.46	.76
6120	2nd floor level		2500	.019			.59		.59	.97
6130	3rd floor level		2000	.024			.73		.73	1.22
6140	4th floor level	↓	1800	.027	↓		.82		.82	1.35
6200	Intermediate stair landings, pan-type 4" deep									
6210	Flights in 1st floor level up/down from discharge point	C-8A	2000	.024	S.F.		.73		.73	1.22
6220	2nd floor level		1500	.032			.98		.98	1.62
6230	3rd floor level		1200	.040			1.22		1.22	2.03
6240	4th floor level	↓	1000	.048	↓		1.47		1.47	2.44

03 35 Concrete Finishing

03 35 13 – High-Tolerance Concrete Floor Finishing

03 35 13.30 Finishing Floors, High Tolerance

		Crew	Daily Output	Labor-Hours	Unit	Material	2014 Bare Costs Labor	2014 Bare Costs Equipment	Total	Total Incl O&P
0010	**FINISHING FLOORS, HIGH TOLERANCE**									
0012	Finishing requires that concrete first be placed, struck off & consolidated									
0015	Basic finishing for various unspecified flatwork									
0100	Bull float only	C-10	4000	.006	S.F.		.19		.19	.32
0125	Bull float & manual float		2000	.012			.39		.39	.63
0150	Bull float, manual float, & broom finish, w/edging & joints		1850	.013			.42		.42	.69
0200	Bull float, manual float & manual steel trowel	↓	1265	.019	↓		.61		.61	1
0210	For specified Random Access Floors in ACI Classes 1, 2, 3 and 4 to achieve									
0215	Composite Overall Floor Flatness and Levelness values up to FF35/FL25									
0250	Bull float, machine float & machine trowel (walk-behind)	C-10C	1715	.014	S.F.		.45	.03	.48	.77
0300	Power screed, bull float, machine float & trowel (walk-behind)	C-10D	2400	.010			.32	.05	.37	.58
0350	Power screed, bull float, machine float & trowel (ride-on)	C-10E	4000	.006	↓		.19	.07	.26	.39
0352	For specified Random Access Floors in ACI Classes 5, 6, 7 and 8 to achieve									
0354	Composite Overall Floor Flatness and Levelness values up to FF50/FL50									
0356	Add for two-dimensional restraightening after power float	C-10	6000	.004	S.F.		.13		.13	.21
0358	For specified Random or Defined Access Floors in ACI Class 9 to achieve									
0360	Composite Overall Floor Flatness and Levelness values up to FF100/FL100									
0362	Add for two-dimensional restraightening after bull float & power float	C-10	3000	.008	S.F.		.26		.26	.42
0364	For specified Superflat Defined Access Floors in ACI Class 9 to achieve									
0366	Minimum Floor Flatness and Levelness values of FF100/FL100									
0368	Add for 2-dim'l restraightening after bull float, power float, power trowel	C-10	2000	.012	S.F.		.39		.39	.63

03 35 16 – Heavy-Duty Concrete Floor Finishing

03 35 16.30 Finishing Floors, Heavy-Duty

		Crew	Daily Output	Labor-Hours	Unit	Material	2014 Bare Costs Labor	2014 Bare Costs Equipment	Total	Total Incl O&P
0010	**FINISHING FLOORS, HEAVY-DUTY**									
1800	Floor abrasives, .25 psf, aluminum oxide	1 Cefi	850	.009	S.F.	.51	.32		.83	1.08
1850	Silicon carbide		850	.009		.77	.32		1.09	1.37
2000	Floor hardeners, metallic, light service, .50 psf, add		850	.009		.51	.32		.83	1.08
2050	Medium service, .75 psf		750	.011		.77	.37		1.14	1.43
2100	Heavy service, 1.0 psf		650	.012		1.02	.42		1.44	1.80
2150	Extra heavy, 1.5 psf		575	.014		1.53	.48		2.01	2.45
2300	Non-metallic, light service, .50 psf		850	.009		.20	.32		.52	.74
2350	Medium service, .75 psf		750	.011		.31	.37		.68	.93
2400	Heavy service, 1.00 psf		650	.012		.41	.42		.83	1.13
2450	Extra heavy, 1.50 psf	↓	575	.014	↓	.61	.48		1.09	1.44

03 35 Concrete Finishing

03 35 16 – Heavy-Duty Concrete Floor Finishing

03 35 16.30 Finishing Floors, Heavy-Duty

		Crew	Daily Output	Labor-Hours	Unit	Material	2014 Bare Costs Labor	Equipment	Total	Total Incl O&P
2800	Trap rock wearing surface for monolithic floors									
2810	2.0 psf	C-10B	1250	.032	S.F.	.02	.98	.23	1.23	1.89
3800	Dustproofing, solvent-based, 1 coat	1 Cefi	1900	.004		.18	.14		.32	.42
3850	2 coats		1300	.006		.63	.21		.84	1.04
4000	Epoxy-based, 1 coat		1500	.005		.14	.18		.32	.45
4050	2 coats		1500	.005		.28	.18		.46	.61

03 35 19 – Colored Concrete Finishing

03 35 19.30 Finishing Floors, Colored

		Crew	Daily Output	Labor-Hours	Unit	Material	2014 Bare Costs Labor	Equipment	Total	Total Incl O&P
0010	**FINISHING FLOORS, COLORED**									
3000	Floor coloring, dusted on (0.6 psf), add to above	1 Cefi	1300	.006	S.F.	.44	.21		.65	.82
3050	(1.0 psf), add to above	"	625	.013	"	.73	.44		1.17	1.52
3100	Colored powder only				Lb.	.73			.73	.81
3600	1/2" topping using 0.6 psf powdered color	C-10B	590	.068	S.F.	4.81	2.08	.48	7.37	9.25
3650	1/2" topping using 1.0 psf powdered color	"	590	.068	"	5.10	2.08	.48	7.66	9.55

03 35 23 – Exposed Aggregate Concrete Finishing

03 35 23.30 Finishing Floors, Exposed Aggregate

		Crew	Daily Output	Labor-Hours	Unit	Material	2014 Bare Costs Labor	Equipment	Total	Total Incl O&P
0010	**FINISHING FLOORS, EXPOSED AGGREGATE**									
1600	Exposed local aggregate finish, 3 lb. per S.F.	1 Cefi	625	.013	S.F.	.43	.44		.87	1.18
1650	4 lb. per S.F.	"	465	.017	"	.81	.59		1.40	1.85

03 35 29 – Tooled Concrete Finishing

03 35 29.30 Finishing Floors, Tooled

		Crew	Daily Output	Labor-Hours	Unit	Material	2014 Bare Costs Labor	Equipment	Total	Total Incl O&P
0010	**FINISHING FLOORS, TOOLED**									
4400	Stair finish, float	1 Cefi	275	.029	S.F.		1		1	1.62
4500	Steel trowel finish		200	.040			1.37		1.37	2.22
4600	Silicon carbide finish, .25 psf		150	.053		.51	1.83		2.34	3.53

03 35 29.60 Finishing Walls

		Crew	Daily Output	Labor-Hours	Unit	Material	2014 Bare Costs Labor	Equipment	Total	Total Incl O&P
0010	**FINISHING WALLS**									
0020	Break ties and patch voids	1 Cefi	540	.015	S.F.	.04	.51		.55	.86
0050	Burlap rub with grout		450	.018		.04	.61		.65	1.03
0100	Carborundum rub, dry		270	.030			1.02		1.02	1.65
0150	Wet rub		175	.046			1.57		1.57	2.54
0300	Bush hammer, green concrete	B-39	1000	.048			1.37	.23	1.60	2.57
0350	Cured concrete	"	650	.074			2.11	.36	2.47	3.95
0500	Acid etch	1 Cefi	575	.014		.14	.48		.62	.92
0600	Float finish, 1/16" thick	"	300	.027		.36	.92		1.28	1.87
0701	Sandblast, light penetration	E-11	1100	.029		.50	.93	.22	1.65	2.48
0751	Heavy penetration	"	375	.085		1	2.74	.63	4.37	6.75
0850	Grind form fins flush	1 Clab	700	.011	L.F.		.32		.32	.54

03 35 33 – Stamped Concrete Finishing

03 35 33.50 Slab Texture Stamping

		Crew	Daily Output	Labor-Hours	Unit	Material	2014 Bare Costs Labor	Equipment	Total	Total Incl O&P
0010	**SLAB TEXTURE STAMPING**									
0050	Stamping requires that concrete first be placed, struck off, consolidated,									
0060	bull floated and free of bleed water. Decorative stamping tasks include:									
0100	Step 1 - first application of dry shake colored hardener	1 Cefi	6400	.001	S.F.	.43	.04		.47	.54
0110	Step 2 - bull float		6400	.001			.04		.04	.07
0130	Step 3 - second application of dry shake colored hardener		6400	.001		.21	.04		.25	.30
0140	Step 4 - bull float, manual float & steel trowel	3 Cefi	1280	.019			.64		.64	1.04
0150	Step 5 - application of dry shake colored release agent	1 Cefi	6400	.001		.10	.04		.14	.18
0160	Step 6 - place, tamp & remove mats	3 Cefi	2400	.010		1.43	.34		1.77	2.14
0170	Step 7 - touch up edges, mat joints & simulated grout lines	1 Cefi	1280	.006			.21		.21	.35

03 35 Concrete Finishing

03 35 33 – Stamped Concrete Finishing

03 35 33.50 Slab Texture Stamping		Crew	Daily Output	Labor-Hours	Unit	Material	2014 Bare Costs		Total	Total Incl O&P
							Labor	Equipment		
0300	Alternate stamping estimating method includes all tasks above	4 Cefi	800	.040	S.F.	2.17	1.37		3.54	4.60
0400	Step 8 - pressure wash @ 3000 psi after 24 hours	1 Cefi	1600	.005			.17		.17	.28
0500	Step 9 - roll 2 coats cure/seal compound when dry	"	800	.010	↓	.59	.34		.93	1.21

03 35 43 – Polished Concrete Finishing

03 35 43.10 Polished Concrete Floors

		Crew	Daily Output	Labor-Hours	Unit	Material	2014 Bare Costs		Total	Total Incl O&P
							Labor	Equipment		
0010	**POLISHED CONCRETE FLOORS** R033543-10									
0015	Processing of cured concrete to include grinding, honing,									
0020	and polishing of interior floors with 22" segmented diamond									
0025	planetary floor grinder (2 passes in different directions per grit)									
0100	Removal of pre-existing coatings, dry, with carbide discs using									
0105	dry vacuum pick-up system, final hand sweeping									
0110	Glue, adhesive or tar	J-4	1.60	15	M.S.F.	24	485	124	633	955
0120	Paint, epoxy, 1 coat		3.60	6.667		24	215	55	294	440
0130	2 coats	↓	1.80	13.333	↓	24	430	110	564	850
0200	Grinding and edging, wet, including wet vac pick-up and auto									
0205	scrubbing between grit changes									
0210	40-grit diamond/metal matrix	J-4A	1.60	20	M.S.F.	31.50	625	256	912.50	1,350
0220	80-grit diamond/metal matrix		2	16		31.50	500	205	736.50	1,075
0230	120-grit diamond/metal matrix		2.40	13.333		31.50	415	171	617.50	910
0240	200-grit diamond/metal matrix	↓	2.80	11.429		31.50	355	146	532.50	785
0300	Spray on dye or stain (1 coat)	1 Cefi	16	.500		212	17.20		229.20	261
0400	Spray on densifier/hardener (2 coats)	"	8	1		340	34.50		374.50	430
0410	Auto scrubbing after 2nd coat, when dry	J-4B	16	.500	↓		14.10	13.25	27.35	38
0500	Honing and edging, wet, including wet vac pick-up and auto									
0505	scrubbing between grit changes									
0510	100-grit diamond/resin matrix	J-4A	2.80	11.429	M.S.F.	31.50	355	146	532.50	785
0520	200-grit diamond/resin matrix	"	2.80	11.429	"	31.50	355	146	532.50	785
0530	Dry, including dry vacuum pick-up system, final hand sweeping									
0540	400-grit diamond/resin matrix	J-4A	2.80	11.429	M.S.F.	31.50	355	146	532.50	785
0600	Polishing and edging, dry, including dry vac pick-up and hand									
0605	sweeping between grit changes									
0610	800-grit diamond/resin matrix	J-4A	2.80	11.429	M.S.F.	31.50	355	146	532.50	785
0620	1500-grit diamond/resin matrix		2.80	11.429		31.50	355	146	532.50	785
0630	3000-grit diamond/resin matrix	↓	2.80	11.429		31.50	355	146	532.50	785
0700	Auto scrubbing after final polishing step	J-4B	16	.500	↓		14.10	13.25	27.35	38

03 37 Specialty Placed Concrete

03 37 13 – Shotcrete

03 37 13.30 Gunite (Dry-Mix)

		Crew	Daily Output	Labor-Hours	Unit	Material	2014 Bare Costs		Total	Total Incl O&P
							Labor	Equipment		
0010	**GUNITE (DRY-MIX)**									
0020	Typical in place, 1" layers, no mesh included	C-16	2000	.028	S.F.	.32	.88	.20	1.40	2.04
0100	Mesh for gunite 2 x 2, #12	2 Rodm	800	.020		.63	.76		1.39	1.99
0150	#4 reinforcing bars @ 6" each way	"	500	.032		1.67	1.22		2.89	3.92
0300	Typical in place, including mesh, 2" thick, flat surfaces	C-16	1000	.056		1.26	1.77	.39	3.42	4.75
0350	Curved surfaces		500	.112		1.26	3.54	.79	5.59	8.10
0500	4" thick, flat surfaces		750	.075		1.90	2.36	.52	4.78	6.60
0550	Curved surfaces	↓	350	.160	↓	1.90	5.05	1.12	8.07	11.70
0901	Prepare old walls, no scaffolding, good condition	2 Clab	665	.024	S.Y.		.68		.68	1.14
0951	Poor condition	"	185	.086	"		2.44		2.44	4.10
1100	For high finish requirement or close tolerance, add				S.F.		50%			

03 37 Specialty Placed Concrete

03 37 13 - Shotcrete

03 37 13.30 Gunite (Dry-Mix)		Crew	Daily Output	Labor-Hours	Unit	Material	2014 Bare Costs Labor	Equipment	Total	Total Incl O&P
1150	Very high				S.F.		110%			

03 37 13.60 Shotcrete (Wet-Mix)		Crew	Daily Output	Labor-Hours	Unit	Material	Labor	Equipment	Total	Total Incl O&P
0010	**SHOTCRETE (WET-MIX)**									
0020	Wet mix, placed @ up to 12 C.Y. per hour, 3000 psi	C-8C	80	.600	C.Y.	103	18.70	5.70	127.40	150
0100	Up to 35 C.Y. per hour	C-8E	240	.200	"	92.50	6.20	2.23	100.93	115
1010	Fiber reinforced, 1" thick	C-8C	1740	.028	S.F.	.76	.86	.26	1.88	2.56
1020	2" thick		900	.053		1.53	1.66	.51	3.70	5
1030	3" thick		825	.058		2.29	1.81	.55	4.65	6.15
1040	4" thick		750	.064		3.06	1.99	.61	5.66	7.35

03 39 Concrete Curing

03 39 13 - Water Concrete Curing

03 39 13.50 Water Curing		Crew	Daily Output	Labor-Hours	Unit	Material	Labor	Equipment	Total	Total Incl O&P
0010	**WATER CURING**									
0015	With burlap, 4 uses assumed, 7.5 oz.	2 Clab	55	.291	C.S.F.	14.70	8.20		22.90	30
0100	10 oz.	"	55	.291	"	26.50	8.20		34.70	43
0400	Curing blankets, 1" to 2" thick, buy				S.F.	.19			.19	.21

03 39 23 - Membrane Concrete Curing

03 39 23.13 Chemical Compound Membrane Concrete Curing		Crew	Daily Output	Labor-Hours	Unit	Material	Labor	Equipment	Total	Total Incl O&P
0010	**CHEMICAL COMPOUND MEMBRANE CONCRETE CURING**									
0300	Sprayed membrane curing compound	2 Clab	95	.168	C.S.F.	10.95	4.75		15.70	20
0700	Curing compound, solvent based, 400 S.F./gal., 55 gallon lots				Gal.	23.50			23.50	25.50
0720	5 gallon lots					29.50			29.50	32.50
0800	Curing compound, water based, 250 S.F./gal., 55 gallon lots					22			22	24.50
0820	5 gallon lots					25			25	27.50

03 39 23.23 Sheet Membrane Concrete Curing		Crew	Daily Output	Labor-Hours	Unit	Material	Labor	Equipment	Total	Total Incl O&P
0010	**SHEET MEMBRANE CONCRETE CURING**									
0200	Curing blanket, burlap/poly, 2-ply	2 Clab	70	.229	C.S.F.	19.05	6.45		25.50	32

03 41 Precast Structural Concrete

03 41 13 - Precast Concrete Hollow Core Planks

03 41 13.50 Precast Slab Planks			Crew	Daily Output	Labor-Hours	Unit	Material	Labor	Equipment	Total	Total Incl O&P
0010	**PRECAST SLAB PLANKS**	R034105-30									
0020	Prestressed roof/floor members, grouted, solid, 4" thick		C-11	2400	.023	S.F.	5.85	.86	.77	7.48	8.75
0050	6" thick			2800	.020		6.30	.74	.66	7.70	8.85
0100	Hollow, 8" thick			3200	.018		7.10	.65	.57	8.32	9.50
0150	10" thick			3600	.016		7.30	.57	.51	8.38	9.55
0200	12" thick			4000	.014		7.90	.52	.46	8.88	10.05

03 41 16 - Precast Concrete Slabs

03 41 16.20 Precast Concrete Channel Slabs		Crew	Daily Output	Labor-Hours	Unit	Material	Labor	Equipment	Total	Total Incl O&P
0010	**PRECAST CONCRETE CHANNEL SLABS**									
0335	Lightweight concrete channel slab, long runs, 2-3/4" thick	C-12	1575	.030	S.F.	8	1.08	.42	9.50	11.05
0375	3-3/4" thick		1550	.031		8.30	1.09	.43	9.82	11.40
0475	4-3/4" thick		1525	.031		8.95	1.11	.43	10.49	12.20
1275	Short pieces, 2-3/4" thick		785	.061		12	2.16	.84	15	17.75
1375	3-3/4" thick		770	.062		12.45	2.20	.86	15.51	18.35
1475	4-3/4" thick		762	.063		13.45	2.22	.87	16.54	19.50

03 41 Precast Structural Concrete

03 41 16 – Precast Concrete Slabs

03 41 16.50 Precast Lightweight Concrete Plank	Crew	Daily Output	Labor-Hours	Unit	Material	2014 Bare Costs Labor	Equipment	Total	Total Incl O&P
0011 **PRECAST LIGHTWEIGHT CONCRETE PLANK**									
0020 Lightweight plank, nailable, T&G, 2" thick	C-11	2100	.027	S.F.	7.05	.98	.88	8.91	10.35
0150 For premium ceiling finish, add				"	10%				
0200 For sloping roofs, slope over 4 in 12, add						25%			
0250 Slope over 6 in 12, add						150%			

03 41 23 – Precast Concrete Stairs

03 41 23.50 Precast Stairs

	Crew	Daily Output	Labor-Hours	Unit	Material	2014 Bare Costs Labor	Equipment	Total	Total Incl O&P
0010 **PRECAST STAIRS**									
0020 Precast concrete treads on steel stringers, 3' wide	C-12	75	.640	Riser	134	22.50	8.85	165.35	195
0300 Front entrance, 5' wide with 48" platform, 2 risers		16	3	Flight	485	106	41.50	632.50	755
0350 5 risers		12	4		765	141	55	961	1,150
0500 6' wide, 2 risers		15	3.200		535	113	44	692	830
0550 5 risers		11	4.364		845	154	60.50	1,059.50	1,250
0700 7' wide, 2 risers		14	3.429		685	121	47.50	853.50	1,000
0751 5 risers	B-1	5	4.800		1,125	139		1,264	1,475
1200 Basement entrance stairwell, 6 steps, incl. steel bulkhead door	B-51	22	2.182		1,450	62.50	12.30	1,524.80	1,700
1250 14 steps	"	11	4.364		2,400	125	24.50	2,549.50	2,850

03 41 33 – Precast Structural Pretensioned Concrete

03 41 33.10 Precast Beams

	Crew	Daily Output	Labor-Hours	Unit	Material	2014 Bare Costs Labor	Equipment	Total	Total Incl O&P
0010 **PRECAST BEAMS** R034105-30									
0011 L-shaped, 20' span, 12" x 20"	C-11	32	1.750	Ea.	2,900	64.50	57.50	3,022	3,375
0060 18" x 36"		24	2.333		3,975	86	76.50	4,137.50	4,600
0100 24" x 44"		22	2.545		4,775	94	83.50	4,952.50	5,500
0150 30' span, 12" x 36"		24	2.333		5,375	86	76.50	5,537.50	6,150
0200 18" x 44"		20	2.800		6,550	103	92	6,745	7,475
0250 24" x 52"		16	3.500		7,850	129	115	8,094	9,000
0400 40' span, 12" x 52"		20	2.800		8,350	103	92	8,545	9,450
0450 18" x 52"		16	3.500		9,325	129	115	9,569	10,600
0500 24" x 52"		12	4.667		10,500	172	153	10,825	12,000
1200 Rectangular, 20' span, 12" x 20"		32	1.750		2,825	64.50	57.50	2,947	3,275
1250 18" x 36"		24	2.333		3,500	86	76.50	3,662.50	4,075
1300 24" x 44"		22	2.545		4,175	94	83.50	4,352.50	4,850
1400 30' span, 12" x 36"		24	2.333		4,700	86	76.50	4,862.50	5,400
1450 18" x 44"		20	2.800		5,675	103	92	5,870	6,500
1500 24" x 52"		16	3.500		6,850	129	115	7,094	7,875
1600 40' span, 12" x 52"		20	2.800		6,975	103	92	7,170	7,950
1650 18" x 52"		16	3.500		7,950	129	115	8,194	9,100
1700 24" x 52"		12	4.667		9,125	172	153	9,450	10,500
2000 "T" shaped, 20' span, 12" x 20"		32	1.750		3,325	64.50	57.50	3,447	3,825
2050 18" x 36"		24	2.333		4,450	86	76.50	4,612.50	5,125
2100 24" x 44"		22	2.545		5,350	94	83.50	5,527.50	6,125
2200 30' span, 12" x 36"		24	2.333		6,125	86	76.50	6,287.50	6,950
2250 18" x 44"		20	2.800		7,425	103	92	7,620	8,425
2300 24" x 52"		16	3.500		8,875	129	115	9,119	10,100
2500 40' span, 12" x 52"		20	2.800		10,100	103	92	10,295	11,400
2550 18" x 52"		16	3.500		10,700	129	115	10,944	12,100
2600 24" x 52"		12	4.667		11,800	172	153	12,125	13,500

03 41 33.15 Precast Columns

	Crew	Daily Output	Labor-Hours	Unit	Material	2014 Bare Costs Labor	Equipment	Total	Total Incl O&P
0010 **PRECAST COLUMNS** R034105-30									
0020 Rectangular to 12' high, 16" x 16"	C-11	120	.467	L.F.	166	17.25	15.30	198.55	229
0050 24" x 24"		96	.583		228	21.50	19.15	268.65	310

03 41 Precast Structural Concrete

03 41 33 – Precast Structural Pretensioned Concrete

03 41 33.15 Precast Columns	Crew	Daily Output	Labor-Hours	Unit	Material	2014 Bare Costs Labor	Equipment	Total	Total Incl O&P
0300	24' high, 28" x 28"	C-11	192	.292	L.F.	265	10.75	9.55	285.30	320
0350	36" x 36"	↓	144	.389	↓	355	14.35	12.75	382.10	430

03 41 33.25 Precast Joists	Crew	Daily Output	Labor-Hours	Unit	Material	2014 Bare Costs Labor	Equipment	Total	Total Incl O&P
0011	**PRECAST JOISTS**									
0020	40 psf L.L., 6" deep for 12' spans	C-11	700	.080	L.F.	23.50	2.95	2.63	29.08	33.50
0051	8" deep for 16' spans		670	.084		38.50	3.09	2.74	44.33	50.50
0101	10" deep for 20' spans		640	.088		67.50	3.23	2.87	73.60	83
0151	12" deep for 24' spans	↓	610	.092	↓	93	3.39	3.01	99.40	111

03 41 33.60 Precast Tees	Crew	Daily Output	Labor-Hours	Unit	Material	2014 Bare Costs Labor	Equipment	Total	Total Incl O&P
0010	**PRECAST TEES** R034105-30									
0020	Quad tee, short spans, roof	C-11	7200	.008	S.F.	7.65	.29	.26	8.20	9.15
0050	Floor		7200	.008		7.65	.29	.26	8.20	9.15
0200	Double tee, floor members, 60' span		8400	.007		9.10	.25	.22	9.57	10.65
0250	80' span		8000	.007		11.80	.26	.23	12.29	13.70
0300	Roof members, 30' span		4800	.012		7.65	.43	.38	8.46	9.55
0350	50' span		6400	.009		8.40	.32	.29	9.01	10.10
0400	Wall members, up to 55' high		3600	.016		11.35	.57	.51	12.43	14.05
0500	Single tee roof members, 40' span		3200	.018		11.30	.65	.57	12.52	14.10
0550	80' span		5120	.011		11.70	.40	.36	12.46	13.90
0600	100' span		6000	.009		17.15	.34	.31	17.80	19.75
0650	120' span	↓	6000	.009	↓	18.80	.34	.31	19.45	21.50
1000	Double tees, floor members									
1100	Lightweight, 20" x 8' wide, 45' span	C-11	20	2.800	Ea.	3,025	103	92	3,220	3,600
1150	24" x 8' wide, 50' span		18	3.111		3,350	115	102	3,567	4,000
1200	32" x 10' wide, 60' span		16	3.500		5,050	129	115	5,294	5,900
1250	Standard weight, 12" x 8' wide, 20' span		22	2.545		1,225	94	83.50	1,402.50	1,600
1300	16" x 8' wide, 25' span		20	2.800		1,525	103	92	1,720	1,950
1350	18" x 8' wide, 30' span		20	2.800		1,825	103	92	2,020	2,300
1400	20" x 8' wide, 45' span		18	3.111		2,750	115	102	2,967	3,325
1450	24" x 8' wide, 50' span		16	3.500		3,050	129	115	3,294	3,700
1500	32" x 10' wide, 60' span	↓	14	4	↓	4,575	148	131	4,854	5,450
2000	Roof members									
2050	Lightweight, 20" x 8' wide, 40' span	C-11	20	2.800	Ea.	2,700	103	92	2,895	3,225
2100	24" x 8' wide, 50' span		18	3.111		3,350	115	102	3,567	4,000
2150	32" x 10' wide, 60' span		16	3.500		5,050	129	115	5,294	5,900
2200	Standard weight, 12" x 8' wide, 30' span		22	2.545		1,825	94	83.50	2,002.50	2,275
2250	16" x 8' wide, 30' span		20	2.800		1,925	103	92	2,120	2,400
2300	18" x 8' wide, 30' span		20	2.800		2,025	103	92	2,220	2,500
2350	20" x 8' wide, 40' span		18	3.111		2,450	115	102	2,667	3,000
2400	24" x 8' wide, 50' span		16	3.500		3,050	129	115	3,294	3,700
2450	32" x 10' wide, 60' span	↓	14	4	↓	4,575	148	131	4,854	5,450

03 45 Precast Architectural Concrete

03 45 13 – Faced Architectural Precast Concrete

03 45 13.50 Precast Wall Panels		Crew	Daily Output	Labor-Hours	Unit	Material	2014 Bare Costs		Total	Total Incl O&P
							Labor	Equipment		
0010	**PRECAST WALL PANELS** R034513-10									
0050	Uninsulated, smooth gray									
0150	Low rise, 4' x 8' x 4" thick	C-11	320	.175	S.F.	20.50	6.45	5.75	32.70	40
0210	8' x 8', 4" thick		576	.097		20.50	3.59	3.19	27.28	32
0250	8' x 16' x 4" thick		1024	.055		20.50	2.02	1.79	24.31	28
0600	High rise, 4' x 8' x 4" thick		288	.194		20.50	7.20	6.40	34.10	42
0650	8' x 8' x 4" thick		512	.109		20.50	4.04	3.59	28.13	33.50
0700	8' x 16' x 4" thick		768	.073		20.50	2.69	2.39	25.58	29.50
0750	10' x 20', 6" thick		1400	.040		34.50	1.48	1.31	37.29	42
0800	Insulated panel, 2" polystyrene, add					1.05			1.05	1.16
0850	2" urethane, add					.79			.79	.87
1200	Finishes, white, add					2.68			2.68	2.95
1250	Exposed aggregate, add					2.10			2.10	2.31
1300	Granite faced, domestic, add					29.50			29.50	32.50
1350	Brick faced, modular, red, add					8.75			8.75	9.65
2200	Fiberglass reinforced cement with urethane core									
2210	R20, 8' x 8', 5" plain finish	E-2	750	.064	S.F.	21	2.48	2.04	25.52	30.50
2220	Exposed aggregate or brick finish	"	600	.080	"	32	3.10	2.55	37.65	43.50

03 47 Site-Cast Concrete

03 47 13 – Tilt-Up Concrete

03 47 13.50 Tilt-Up Wall Panels		Crew	Daily Output	Labor-Hours	Unit	Material	2014 Bare Costs		Total	Total Incl O&P
							Labor	Equipment		
0010	**TILT-UP WALL PANELS** R034713-20									
0015	Wall panel construction, walls only, 5-1/2" thick	C-14	1600	.085	S.F.	5.40	2.74	1.03	9.17	11.70
0100	7-1/2" thick		1550	.088		6.75	2.83	1.07	10.65	13.30
0500	Walls and columns, 5-1/2" thick walls, 12" x 12" columns		1565	.087		8.15	2.81	1.06	12.02	14.80
0550	7-1/2" thick wall, 12" x 12" columns		1370	.099		9.95	3.20	1.21	14.36	17.70
0800	Columns only, site precast, 12" x 12"		200	.680	L.F.	19.65	22	8.25	49.90	67.50
0850	16" x 16"		105	1.295	"	28.50	42	15.75	86.25	119

03 48 Precast Concrete Specialties

03 48 43 – Precast Concrete Trim

03 48 43.40 Precast Lintels		Crew	Daily Output	Labor-Hours	Unit	Material	2014 Bare Costs		Total	Total Incl O&P
							Labor	Equipment		
0010	**PRECAST LINTELS**, smooth gray, prestressed, stock units only									
0800	4" wide, 8" high, x 4' long	D-10	28	1.143	Ea.	23.50	40	17.20	80.70	112
0850	8' long		24	1.333		57	47	20	124	163
1000	6" wide, 8" high, x 4' long		26	1.231		33.50	43.50	18.50	95.50	130
1050	10' long		22	1.455		86	51	22	159	204
1200	8" wide, 8" high, x 4' long		24	1.333		42.50	47	20	109.50	147
1250	12' long		20	1.600		138	56.50	24	218.50	272
1275	For custom sizes, types, colors, or finishes of precast lintels, add					150%				

03 48 43.90 Precast Window Sills		Crew	Daily Output	Labor-Hours	Unit	Material	2014 Bare Costs		Total	Total Incl O&P
							Labor	Equipment		
0010	**PRECAST WINDOW SILLS**									
0600	Precast concrete, 4" tapers to 3", 9" wide	D-1	70	.229	L.F.	11.90	7.35		19.25	25.50
0650	11" wide		60	.267		15.55	8.60		24.15	31.50
0700	13" wide, 3 1/2" tapers to 2 1/2", 12" wall		50	.320		15.50	10.30		25.80	34

03 51 Cast Roof Decks

03 51 13 – Cementitious Wood Fiber Decks

03 51 13.50 Cementitious/Wood Fiber Planks		Crew	Daily Output	Labor-Hours	Unit	Material	2014 Bare Costs Labor	Equipment	Total	Total Incl O&P
0010	**CEMENTITIOUS/WOOD FIBER PLANKS**	R051223-50								
0050	Plank, beveled edge, 1" thick	2 Carp	1000	.016	S.F.	2.20	.57		2.77	3.38
0100	1-1/2" thick		975	.016		2.90	.59		3.49	4.18
0150	T & G, 2" thick		950	.017		2.40	.60		3	3.65
0200	2-1/2" thick		925	.017		2.70	.62		3.32	4.01
0250	3" thick	↓	900	.018		3	.64		3.64	4.37
1000	Bulb tee, sub-purlin and grout, 6' span, add	E-1	5000	.003		2.14	.12	.03	2.29	2.61
1100	8' span	"	4200	.004	↓	2.14	.15	.03	2.32	2.67

03 51 16 – Gypsum Concrete Roof Decks

03 51 16.50 Gypsum Roof Deck

		Crew	Daily Output	Labor-Hours	Unit	Material	Labor	Equipment	Total	Total Incl O&P
0010	**GYPSUM ROOF DECK**									
1000	Poured gypsum, 2" thick	C-8	6000	.009	S.F.	1.34	.29	.12	1.75	2.09
1100	3" thick	"	4800	.012	"	2.01	.37	.15	2.53	2.98

03 52 Lightweight Concrete Roof Insulation

03 52 16 – Lightweight Insulating Concrete

03 52 16.13 Lightweight Cellular Insulating Concrete

		Crew	Daily Output	Labor-Hours	Unit	Material	Labor	Equipment	Total	Total Incl O&P
0010	**LIGHTWEIGHT CELLULAR INSULATING CONCRETE**	R035216-10								
0020	Portland cement and foaming agent [G]	C-8	50	1.120	C.Y.	115	35.50	14.20	164.70	200

03 52 16.16 Lightweight Aggregate Insulating Concrete

		Crew	Daily Output	Labor-Hours	Unit	Material	Labor	Equipment	Total	Total Incl O&P
0010	**LIGHTWEIGHT AGGREGATE INSULATING CONCRETE**	R035216-10								
0100	Poured vermiculite or perlite, field mix,									
0110	1:6 field mix [G]	C-8	50	1.120	C.Y.	251	35.50	14.20	300.70	350
0200	Ready mix, 1:6 mix, roof fill, 2" thick [G]		10000	.006	S.F.	1.39	.18	.07	1.64	1.90
0250	3" thick [G]	↓	7700	.007		2.09	.23	.09	2.41	2.78
0401	Expanded volcanic glass rock, 1" thick [G]	L-2	1500	.011		.55	.33		.88	1.16
0451	3" thick [G]	"	1200	.013	↓	1.64	.42		2.06	2.51

03 53 Concrete Topping

03 53 16 – Iron-Aggregate Concrete Topping

03 53 16.50 Floor Topping

		Crew	Daily Output	Labor-Hours	Unit	Material	Labor	Equipment	Total	Total Incl O&P
0010	**FLOOR TOPPING**									
0400	Integral topping and finish, using 1:1:2 mix, 3/16" thick	C-10B	1000	.040	S.F.	.10	1.23	.28	1.61	2.45
0450	1/2" thick		950	.042		.26	1.29	.30	1.85	2.76
0500	3/4" thick		850	.047		.39	1.44	.33	2.16	3.19
0600	1" thick		750	.053		.52	1.64	.38	2.54	3.70
0800	Granolithic topping, laid after, 1:1:1-1/2 mix, 1/2" thick		590	.068		.29	2.08	.48	2.85	4.29
0820	3/4" thick		580	.069		.43	2.11	.49	3.03	4.52
0850	1" thick		575	.070		.58	2.13	.49	3.20	4.71
0950	2" thick		500	.080		1.16	2.45	.57	4.18	5.95
1200	Heavy duty, 1:1:2, 3/4" thick, preshrunk, gray, 20 M.S.F.		320	.125		.73	3.83	.89	5.45	8.15
1300	100 M.S.F.	↓	380	.105	↓	.39	3.23	.75	4.37	6.60

03 54 Cast Underlayment

03 54 13 – Gypsum Cement Underlayment

03 54 13.50 Poured Gypsum Underlayment

		Crew	Daily Output	Labor-Hours	Unit	Material	2014 Bare Costs Labor	Equipment	Total	Total Incl O&P
0010	**POURED GYPSUM UNDERLAYMENT**									
0400	Underlayment, gypsum based, self-leveling 2500 psi, pumped, 1/2" thick	C-8	24000	.002	S.F.	.33	.07	.03	.43	.52
0500	3/4" thick		20000	.003		.50	.09	.04	.63	.74
0600	1" thick		16000	.004		.67	.11	.04	.82	.97
1400	Hand placed, 1/2" thick	C-18	450	.020		.33	.57	.13	1.03	1.48
1500	3/4" thick	"	300	.030		.50	.85	.20	1.55	2.20

03 54 16 – Hydraulic Cement Underlayment

03 54 16.50 Cement Underlayment

		Crew	Daily Output	Labor-Hours	Unit	Material	2014 Bare Costs Labor	Equipment	Total	Total Incl O&P
0010	**CEMENT UNDERLAYMENT**									
2510	Underlayment, P.C based, self-leveling, 4100 psi, pumped, 1/4" thick	C-8	20000	.003	S.F.	1.49	.09	.04	1.62	1.83
2520	1/2" thick		19000	.003		2.99	.09	.04	3.12	3.48
2530	3/4" thick		18000	.003		4.48	.10	.04	4.62	5.15
2540	1" thick		17000	.003		6	.10	.04	6.14	6.80
2550	1-1/2" thick		15000	.004		8.95	.12	.05	9.12	10.10
2560	Hand placed, 1/2" thick	C-18	450	.020		2.99	.57	.13	3.69	4.40
2610	Topping, P.C based, self-leveling, 6100 psi, pumped, 1/4" thick	C-8	20000	.003		2.18	.09	.04	2.31	2.59
2620	1/2" thick		19000	.003		4.37	.09	.04	4.50	4.99
2630	3/4" thick		18000	.003		6.55	.10	.04	6.69	7.40
2660	1" thick		17000	.003		8.75	.10	.04	8.89	9.80
2670	1-1/2" thick		15000	.004		13.10	.12	.05	13.27	14.65
2680	Hand placed, 1/2" thick	C-18	450	.020		4.37	.57	.13	5.07	5.90

03 62 Non-Shrink Grouting

03 62 13 – Non-Metallic Non-Shrink Grouting

03 62 13.50 Grout, Non-Metallic Non-shrink

		Crew	Daily Output	Labor-Hours	Unit	Material	2014 Bare Costs Labor	Equipment	Total	Total Incl O&P
0010	**GROUT, NON-METALLIC NON-SHRINK**									
0300	Non-shrink, non-metallic, 1" deep	1 Cefi	35	.229	S.F.	6.15	7.85		14	19.45
0350	2" deep	"	25	.320	"	12.30	11		23.30	31.50

03 62 16 – Metallic Non-Shrink Grouting

03 62 16.50 Grout, Metallic Non-Shrink

		Crew	Daily Output	Labor-Hours	Unit	Material	2014 Bare Costs Labor	Equipment	Total	Total Incl O&P
0010	**GROUT, METALLIC NON-SHRINK**									
0020	Column & machine bases, non-shrink, metallic, 1" deep	1 Cefi	35	.229	S.F.	8.50	7.85		16.35	22
0050	2" deep	"	25	.320	"	16.95	11		27.95	36.50

03 63 Epoxy Grouting

03 63 05 – Grouting of Dowels and Fasteners

03 63 05.10 Epoxy Only

		Crew	Daily Output	Labor-Hours	Unit	Material	2014 Bare Costs Labor	Equipment	Total	Total Incl O&P
0010	**EPOXY ONLY**									
1500	Chemical anchoring, epoxy cartridge, excludes layout, drilling, fastener									
1530	For fastener 3/4" diam. x 6" embedment	2 Skwk	72	.222	Ea.	5.55	8.05		13.60	19.70
1535	1" diam. x 8" embedment		66	.242		8.30	8.80		17.10	24
1540	1-1/4" diam. x 10" embedment		60	.267		16.60	9.70		26.30	34.50
1545	1-3/4" diam. x 12" embedment		54	.296		27.50	10.75		38.25	48.50
1550	14" embedment		48	.333		33	12.10		45.10	57
1555	2" diam. x 12" embedment		42	.381		44.50	13.85		58.35	72
1560	18" embedment		32	.500		55.50	18.15		73.65	91.50

03 81 Concrete Cutting

03 81 13 – Flat Concrete Sawing

03 81 13.50 Concrete Floor/Slab Cutting

		Daily Output	Labor-Hours	Unit	Material	2014 Bare Costs Labor	Equipment	Total	Total Incl O&P
0010	**CONCRETE FLOOR/SLAB CUTTING**								
0050	Includes blade cost, layout and set-up time								
0300	Saw cut concrete slabs, plain, up to 3" deep	B-89 1060	.015	L.F.	.13	.49	.50	1.12	1.52
0320	Each additional inch of depth	3180	.005		.04	.16	.17	.37	.50
0400	Mesh reinforced, up to 3" deep	980	.016		.15	.53	.54	1.22	1.64
0420	Each additional inch of depth	2940	.005		.05	.18	.18	.41	.55
0500	Rod reinforced, up to 3" deep	800	.020		.19	.65	.66	1.50	2.01
0520	Each additional inch of depth	2400	.007		.06	.22	.22	.50	.67

03 81 13.75 Concrete Saw Blades

		Daily Output	Labor-Hours	Unit	Material	2014 Bare Costs Labor	Equipment	Total	Total Incl O&P
0010	**CONCRETE SAW BLADES**								
3000	Blades for saw cutting, included in cutting line items								
3020	Diamond, 12" diameter			Ea.	244			244	269
3040	18" diameter				445			445	490
3080	24" diameter				755			755	830
3120	30" diameter				1,100			1,100	1,200
3160	36" diameter				1,425			1,425	1,575
3200	42" diameter				2,700			2,700	2,975

03 81 16 – Track Mounted Concrete Wall Sawing

03 81 16.50 Concrete Wall Cutting

		Daily Output	Labor-Hours	Unit	Material	2014 Bare Costs Labor	Equipment	Total	Total Incl O&P
0010	**CONCRETE WALL CUTTING**								
0750	Includes blade cost, layout and set-up time								
0800	Concrete walls, hydraulic saw, plain, per inch of depth	B-89B 250	.064	L.F.	.04	2.08	3.64	5.76	7.50
0820	Rod reinforcing, per inch of depth	" 150	.107	"	.06	3.47	6.05	9.58	12.45

03 82 Concrete Boring

03 82 13 – Concrete Core Drilling

03 82 13.10 Core Drilling

		Daily Output	Labor-Hours	Unit	Material	2014 Bare Costs Labor	Equipment	Total	Total Incl O&P
0010	**CORE DRILLING**								
0015	Includes bit cost, layout and set-up time								
0020	Reinforced concrete slab, up to 6" thick								
0100	1" diameter core	B-89A 17	.941	Ea.	.18	30.50	6.85	37.53	58.50
0150	For each additional inch of slab thickness in same hole, add	1440	.011		.03	.36	.08	.47	.72
0200	2" diameter core	16.50	.970		.29	31.50	7.05	38.84	60.50
0250	For each additional inch of slab thickness in same hole, add	1080	.015		.05	.48	.11	.64	.98
0300	3" diameter core	16	1		.39	32.50	7.25	40.14	63
0350	For each additional inch of slab thickness in same hole, add	720	.022		.07	.72	.16	.95	1.46
0500	4" diameter core	15	1.067		.50	34.50	7.75	42.75	67
0550	For each additional inch of slab thickness in same hole, add	480	.033		.08	1.07	.24	1.39	2.17
0700	6" diameter core	14	1.143		.78	37	8.30	46.08	72
0750	For each additional inch of slab thickness in same hole, add	360	.044		.13	1.43	.32	1.88	2.92
0900	8" diameter core	13	1.231		1.08	39.50	8.95	49.53	78
0950	For each additional inch of slab thickness in same hole, add	288	.056		.18	1.79	.40	2.37	3.66
1100	10" diameter core	12	1.333		1.51	43	9.70	54.21	85
1150	For each additional inch of slab thickness in same hole, add	240	.067		.25	2.15	.48	2.88	4.44
1300	12" diameter core	11	1.455		1.79	47	10.55	59.34	92.50
1350	For each additional inch of slab thickness in same hole, add	206	.078		.30	2.50	.56	3.36	5.15
1500	14" diameter core	10	1.600		2.11	51.50	11.60	65.21	102
1550	For each additional inch of slab thickness in same hole, add	180	.089		.35	2.87	.65	3.87	5.95
1700	18" diameter core	9	1.778		2.84	57.50	12.90	73.24	114
1750	For each additional inch of slab thickness in same hole, add	144	.111		.47	3.58	.81	4.86	7.45

03 82 Concrete Boring

03 82 13 – Concrete Core Drilling

03 82 13.10 Core Drilling

		Crew	Daily Output	Labor-Hours	Unit	Material	2014 Bare Costs Labor	Equipment	Total	Total Incl O&P
1754	24" diameter core	B-89A	8	2	Ea.	3.99	64.50	14.50	82.99	129
1756	For each additional inch of slab thickness in same hole, add	↓	120	.133		.67	4.30	.97	5.94	9.05
1760	For horizontal holes, add to above				↓		20%	20%		
1770	Prestressed hollow core plank, 8" thick									
1780	1" diameter core	B-89A	17.50	.914	Ea.	.24	29.50	6.65	36.39	57
1790	For each additional inch of plank thickness in same hole, add		3840	.004		.03	.13	.03	.19	.29
1794	2" diameter core		17.25	.928		.38	30	6.75	37.13	58.50
1796	For each additional inch of plank thickness in same hole, add		2880	.006		.05	.18	.04	.27	.39
1800	3" diameter core		17	.941		.52	30.50	6.85	37.87	59
1810	For each additional inch of plank thickness in same hole, add		1920	.008		.07	.27	.06	.40	.59
1820	4" diameter core		16.50	.970		.66	31.50	7.05	39.21	61
1830	For each additional inch of plank thickness in same hole, add		1280	.013		.08	.40	.09	.57	.87
1840	6" diameter core		15.50	1.032		1.04	33.50	7.50	42.04	65.50
1850	For each additional inch of plank thickness in same hole, add		960	.017		.13	.54	.12	.79	1.18
1860	8" diameter core		15	1.067		1.44	34.50	7.75	43.69	68
1870	For each additional inch of plank thickness in same hole, add		768	.021		.18	.67	.15	1	1.50
1880	10" diameter core		14	1.143		2.01	37	8.30	47.31	73.50
1890	For each additional inch of plank thickness in same hole, add		640	.025		.25	.81	.18	1.24	1.84
1900	12" diameter core		13.50	1.185		2.39	38	8.60	48.99	76.50
1910	For each additional inch of plank thickness in same hole, add	↓	548	.029	↓	.30	.94	.21	1.45	2.15
3000	Bits for core drilling, included in drilling line items									
3010	Diamond, premium, 1" diameter				Ea.	72			72	79.50
3020	2" diameter					115			115	127
3030	3" diameter					157			157	173
3040	4" diameter					199			199	219
3060	6" diameter					315			315	345
3080	8" diameter					435			435	475
3110	10" diameter					605			605	665
3120	12" diameter					715			715	790
3140	14" diameter					845			845	930
3180	18" diameter					1,125			1,125	1,250
3240	24" diameter				↓	1,600			1,600	1,750

03 82 16 – Concrete Drilling

03 82 16.10 Concrete Impact Drilling

		Crew	Daily Output	Labor-Hours	Unit	Material	2014 Bare Costs Labor	Equipment	Total	Total Incl O&P
0010	**CONCRETE IMPACT DRILLING**									
0020	Includes bit cost, layout and set-up time, no anchors									
0050	Up to 4" deep in concrete/brick floors/walls									
0100	Holes, 1/4" diameter	1 Carp	75	.107	Ea.	.06	3.81		3.87	6.45
0150	For each additional inch of depth in same hole, add		430	.019		.02	.67		.69	1.14
0200	3/8" diameter		63	.127		.05	4.54		4.59	7.70
0250	For each additional inch of depth in same hole, add		340	.024		.01	.84		.85	1.43
0300	1/2" diameter		50	.160		.05	5.70		5.75	9.65
0350	For each additional inch of depth in same hole, add		250	.032		.01	1.14		1.15	1.93
0400	5/8" diameter		48	.167		.08	5.95		6.03	10.15
0450	For each additional inch of depth in same hole, add		240	.033		.02	1.19		1.21	2.02
0500	3/4" diameter		45	.178		.11	6.35		6.46	10.80
0550	For each additional inch of depth in same hole, add		220	.036		.03	1.30		1.33	2.22
0600	7/8" diameter		43	.186		.15	6.65		6.80	11.35
0650	For each additional inch of depth in same hole, add		210	.038		.04	1.36		1.40	2.33
0700	1" diameter		40	.200		.16	7.15		7.31	12.25
0750	For each additional inch of depth in same hole, add		190	.042		.04	1.51		1.55	2.57
0800	1-1/4" diameter	↓	38	.211		.23	7.55		7.78	12.90

03 82 Concrete Boring

03 82 16 – Concrete Drilling

03 82 16.10 Concrete Impact Drilling		Crew	Daily Output	Labor-Hours	Unit	Material	2014 Bare Costs Labor	Equipment	Total	Total Incl O&P
0850	For each additional inch of depth in same hole, add	1 Carp	180	.044	Ea.	.06	1.59		1.65	2.73
0900	1-1/2" diameter	↓	35	.229		.32	8.15		8.47	14.10
0950	For each additional inch of depth in same hole, add	↓	165	.048	↓	.08	1.73		1.81	3.01
1000	For ceiling installations, add						40%			

Division Notes

		CREW	DAILY OUTPUT	LABOR-HOURS	UNIT	BARE COSTS				TOTAL INCL O&P
						MAT.	LABOR	EQUIP.	TOTAL	

Estimating Tips

04 05 00 Common Work Results for Masonry

- The terms *mortar* and *grout* are often used interchangeably, and incorrectly. Mortar is used to bed masonry units, seal the entry of air and moisture, provide architectural appearance, and allow for size variations in the units. Grout is used primarily in reinforced masonry construction and is used to bond the masonry to the reinforcing steel. Common mortar types are M(2500 psi), S(1800 psi), N(750 psi), and O(350 psi), and conform to ASTM C270. Grout is either fine or coarse and conforms to ASTM C476, and in-place strengths generally exceed 2500 psi. Mortar and grout are different components of masonry construction and are placed by entirely different methods. An estimator should be aware of their unique uses and costs.

- Mortar is included in all assembled masonry line items. The mortar cost, part of the assembled masonry material cost, includes all ingredients, all labor, and all equipment required. Please see reference number R040513-10.

- Waste, specifically the loss/ droppings of mortar and the breakage of brick and block, is included in all masonry assemblies in this division. A factor of 25% is added for mortar and 3% for brick and concrete masonry units.

- Scaffolding or staging is not included in any of the Division 4 costs. Refer to Subdivision 01 54 23 for scaffolding and staging costs.

04 20 00 Unit Masonry

- The most common types of unit masonry are brick and concrete masonry. The major classifications of brick are building brick (ASTM C62), facing brick (ASTM C216), glazed brick, fire brick, and pavers. Many varieties of texture and appearance can exist within these classifications, and the estimator would be wise to check local custom and availability within the project area. For repair and remodeling jobs, matching the existing brick may be the most important criteria.

- Brick and concrete block are priced by the piece and then converted into a price per square foot of wall. Openings less than two square feet are generally ignored by the estimator because any savings in units used is offset by the cutting and trimming required.

- It is often difficult and expensive to find and purchase small lots of historic brick. Costs can vary widely. Many design issues affect costs, selection of mortar mix, and repairs or replacement of masonry materials. Cleaning techniques must be reflected in the estimate.

- All masonry walls, whether interior or exterior, require bracing. The cost of bracing walls during construction should be included by the estimator, and this bracing must remain in place until permanent bracing is complete. Permanent bracing of masonry walls is accomplished by masonry itself, in the form of pilasters or abutting wall corners, or by anchoring the walls to the structural frame. Accessories in the form of anchors, anchor slots, and ties are used, but their supply and installation can be by different trades. For instance, anchor slots on spandrel beams and columns are supplied and welded in place by the steel fabricator, but the ties from the slots into the masonry are installed by the bricklayer. Regardless of the installation method, the estimator must be certain that these accessories are accounted for in pricing.

Reference Numbers

Reference numbers are shown in shaded boxes at the beginning of some major classifications. These numbers refer to related items in the Reference Section. The reference information may be an estimating procedure, an alternate pricing method, or technical information.

Note: Not all subdivisions listed here necessarily appear in this publication.

04 01 20 – Maintenance of Unit Masonry

04 01 20.20 Pointing Masonry	Crew	Daily Output	Labor-Hours	Unit	Material	2014 Bare Costs Labor	Equipment	Total	Total Incl O&P
0010 **POINTING MASONRY**									
0300 Cut and repoint brick, hard mortar, running bond	1 Bric	80	.100	S.F.	.51	3.56		4.07	6.50
0320 Common bond		77	.104		.51	3.70		4.21	6.70
0360 Flemish bond		70	.114		.54	4.07		4.61	7.35
0400 English bond		65	.123		.54	4.38		4.92	7.90
0600 Soft old mortar, running bond		100	.080		.51	2.85		3.36	5.30
0620 Common bond		96	.083		.51	2.97		3.48	5.50
0640 Flemish bond		90	.089		.54	3.16		3.70	5.85
0680 English bond		82	.098		.54	3.47		4.01	6.40
0700 Stonework, hard mortar		140	.057	L.F.	.68	2.03		2.71	4.14
0720 Soft old mortar		160	.050	"	.68	1.78		2.46	3.71
1000 Repoint, mask and grout method, running bond		95	.084	S.F.	.68	3		3.68	5.75
1020 Common bond		90	.089		.68	3.16		3.84	6
1040 Flemish bond		86	.093		.72	3.31		4.03	6.30
1060 English bond		77	.104		.72	3.70		4.42	6.95
2000 Scrub coat, sand grout on walls, thin mix, brushed		120	.067		2.72	2.37		5.09	6.95
2020 Troweled		98	.082		3.79	2.91		6.70	9

04 01 20.30 Pointing CMU

	Crew	Daily Output	Labor-Hours	Unit	Material	Labor	Equipment	Total	Total Incl O&P
0010 **POINTING CMU**									
0300 Cut and repoint block, hard mortar, running bond	1 Bric	190	.042	S.F.	.21	1.50		1.71	2.73
0310 Stacked bond		200	.040		.21	1.42		1.63	2.60
0600 Soft old mortar, running bond		230	.035		.21	1.24		1.45	2.29
0610 Stacked bond		245	.033		.21	1.16		1.37	2.16

04 01 20.40 Sawing Masonry

	Crew	Daily Output	Labor-Hours	Unit	Material	Labor	Equipment	Total	Total Incl O&P
0010 **SAWING MASONRY**									
0050 Brick or block by hand, per inch depth	A-1	125	.064	L.F.	.06	1.80	.67	2.53	3.85

04 01 20.41 Unit Masonry Stabilization

	Crew	Daily Output	Labor-Hours	Unit	Material	Labor	Equipment	Total	Total Incl O&P
0010 **UNIT MASONRY STABILIZATION**									
0100 Structural repointing method									
0110 Cut / grind mortar joint	1 Bric	240	.033	L.F.		1.19		1.19	1.97
0120 Clean and mask joint		2500	.003		.13	.11		.24	.33
0130 Epoxy paste and 1/4" FRP rod		240	.033		1.07	1.19		2.26	3.15
0132 3/8" FRP rod		160	.050		1.63	1.78		3.41	4.75
0134 1/4" CFRP rod		240	.033		13.90	1.19		15.09	17.20
0136 3/8" CFRP rod		160	.050		17.50	1.78		19.28	22
0140 Remove masking		14400	.001			.02		.02	.03
0300 Structural fabric method									
0310 Primer	1 Bric	600	.013	S.F.	.46	.47		.93	1.29
0320 Apply filling/leveling paste		720	.011		.43	.40		.83	1.13
0330 Epoxy, glass fiber fabric		720	.011		5.65	.40		6.05	6.85
0340 Carbon fiber fabric		720	.011		15.45	.40		15.85	17.65

04 01 30 – Unit Masonry Cleaning

04 01 30.60 Brick Washing

	Crew	Daily Output	Labor-Hours	Unit	Material	Labor	Equipment	Total	Total Incl O&P
0010 **BRICK WASHING** R040130-10									
0012 Acid cleanser, smooth brick surface	1 Bric	560	.014	S.F.	.06	.51		.57	.92
0050 Rough brick		400	.020		.09	.71		.80	1.29
0060 Stone, acid wash		600	.013		.10	.47		.57	.90
1000 Muriatic acid, price per gallon in 5 gallon lots				Gal.	13			13	14.30

04 05 05 – Selective Masonry Demolition

04 05 05.10 Selective Demolition	Crew	Daily Output	Labor-Hours	Unit	Material	2014 Bare Costs Labor	Equipment	Total	Total Incl O&P
0010 **SELECTIVE DEMOLITION** R024119-10									
0200 Bond beams, 8" block with #4 bar	2 Clab	32	.500	L.F.		14.10		14.10	23.50
0300 Concrete block walls, unreinforced, 2" thick		1200	.013	S.F.		.38		.38	.63
0310 4" thick		1150	.014			.39		.39	.66
0320 6" thick		1100	.015			.41		.41	.69
0330 8" thick		1050	.015			.43		.43	.72
0340 10" thick		1000	.016			.45		.45	.76
0360 12" thick		950	.017			.47		.47	.80
0380 Reinforced alternate courses, 2" thick		1130	.014			.40		.40	.67
0390 4" thick		1080	.015			.42		.42	.70
0400 6" thick		1035	.015			.44		.44	.73
0410 8" thick		990	.016			.46		.46	.77
0420 10" thick		940	.017			.48		.48	.81
0430 12" thick		890	.018			.51		.51	.85
0440 Reinforced alternate courses & vertically 48" OC, 4" thick		900	.018			.50		.50	.84
0450 6" thick		850	.019			.53		.53	.89
0460 8" thick		800	.020			.56		.56	.95
0480 10" thick		750	.021			.60		.60	1.01
0490 12" thick		700	.023			.64		.64	1.08
1000 Chimney, 16" x 16", soft old mortar	1 Clab	55	.145	C.F.		4.10		4.10	6.90
1020 Hard mortar		40	.200			5.65		5.65	9.50
1030 16" x 20", soft old mortar		55	.145			4.10		4.10	6.90
1040 Hard mortar		40	.200			5.65		5.65	9.50
1050 16" x 24", soft old mortar		55	.145			4.10		4.10	6.90
1060 Hard mortar		40	.200			5.65		5.65	9.50
1080 20" x 20", soft old mortar		55	.145			4.10		4.10	6.90
1100 Hard mortar		40	.200			5.65		5.65	9.50
1110 20" x 24", soft old mortar		55	.145			4.10		4.10	6.90
1120 Hard mortar		40	.200			5.65		5.65	9.50
1140 20" x 32", soft old mortar		55	.145			4.10		4.10	6.90
1160 Hard mortar		40	.200			5.65		5.65	9.50
1200 48" x 48", soft old mortar		55	.145			4.10		4.10	6.90
1220 Hard mortar		40	.200			5.65		5.65	9.50
1250 Metal, high temp steel jacket, 24" diameter	E-2	130	.369	V.L.F.		14.30	11.75	26.05	39.50
1260 60" diameter	"	60	.800			31	25.50	56.50	86
1280 Flue lining, up to 12" x 12"	1 Clab	200	.040			1.13		1.13	1.90
1282 Up to 24" x 24"		150	.053			1.50		1.50	2.53
2000 Columns, 8" x 8", soft old mortar		48	.167			4.70		4.70	7.90
2020 Hard mortar		40	.200			5.65		5.65	9.50
2060 16" x 16", soft old mortar		16	.500			14.10		14.10	23.50
2100 Hard mortar		14	.571			16.10		16.10	27
2140 24" x 24", soft old mortar		8	1			28		28	47.50
2160 Hard mortar		6	1.333			37.50		37.50	63.50
2200 36" x 36", soft old mortar		4	2			56.50		56.50	95
2220 Hard mortar		3	2.667			75		75	127
2230 Alternate pricing method, soft old mortar		30	.267	C.F.		7.50		7.50	12.65
2240 Hard mortar		23	.348	"		9.80		9.80	16.50
3000 Copings, precast or masonry, to 8" wide									
3020 Soft old mortar	1 Clab	180	.044	L.F.		1.25		1.25	2.11
3040 Hard mortar	"	160	.050	"		1.41		1.41	2.37
3100 To 12" wide									
3120 Soft old mortar	1 Clab	160	.050	L.F.		1.41		1.41	2.37
3140 Hard mortar	"	140	.057	"		1.61		1.61	2.71

04 05 05 – Selective Masonry Demolition

04 05 05.10 Selective Demolition	Crew	Daily Output	Labor-Hours	Unit	Material	2014 Bare Costs Labor	2014 Bare Costs Equipment	Total	Total Incl O&P
4000	Fireplace, brick, 30" x 24" opening									
4020	Soft old mortar	1 Clab	2	4	Ea.		113		113	190
4040	Hard mortar		1.25	6.400			180		180	305
4100	Stone, soft old mortar		1.50	5.333			150		150	253
4120	Hard mortar		1	8			226		226	380
5000	Veneers, brick, soft old mortar		140	.057	S.F.		1.61		1.61	2.71
5020	Hard mortar		125	.064			1.80		1.80	3.04
5050	Glass block, up to 4" thick		500	.016			.45		.45	.76
5100	Granite and marble, 2" thick		180	.044			1.25		1.25	2.11
5120	4" thick		170	.047			1.33		1.33	2.23
5140	Stone, 4" thick		180	.044			1.25		1.25	2.11
5160	8" thick		175	.046			1.29		1.29	2.17
5400	Alternate pricing method, stone, 4" thick		60	.133	C.F.		3.76		3.76	6.35
5420	8" thick		85	.094	"		2.65		2.65	4.47

04 05 13 – Masonry Mortaring

04 05 13.10 Cement

04 05 13.10 Cement	Crew	Daily Output	Labor-Hours	Unit	Material	2014 Bare Costs Labor	2014 Bare Costs Equipment	Total	Total Incl O&P
0010	**CEMENT**									
0100	Masonry, 70 lb. bag, T.L. lots				Bag	11.05			11.05	12.15
0150	L.T.L. lots					11.70			11.70	12.90
0200	White, 70 lb. bag, T.L. lots					15.65			15.65	17.25
0250	L.T.L. lots					18.30			18.30	20

04 05 13.20 Lime

04 05 13.20 Lime	Crew	Daily Output	Labor-Hours	Unit	Material	2014 Bare Costs Labor	2014 Bare Costs Equipment	Total	Total Incl O&P
0010	**LIME**									
0020	Masons, hydrated, 50 lb. bag, T.L. lots				Bag	10.10			10.10	11.10
0050	L.T.L. lots					11.10			11.10	12.20
0200	Finish, double hydrated, 50 lb. bag, T.L. lots					8.65			8.65	9.55
0250	L.T.L. lots					9.55			9.55	10.50

04 05 13.23 Surface Bonding Masonry Mortaring

04 05 13.23 Surface Bonding Masonry Mortaring	Crew	Daily Output	Labor-Hours	Unit	Material	2014 Bare Costs Labor	2014 Bare Costs Equipment	Total	Total Incl O&P
0010	**SURFACE BONDING MASONRY MORTARING**									
0020	Gray or white colors, not incl. block work	1 Bric	540	.015	S.F.	.13	.53		.66	1.03

04 05 13.30 Mortar

04 05 13.30 Mortar	Crew	Daily Output	Labor-Hours	Unit	Material	2014 Bare Costs Labor	2014 Bare Costs Equipment	Total	Total Incl O&P
0010	**MORTAR** R040513-10									
0020	With masonry cement									
0100	Type M, 1:1:6 mix	1 Brhe	143	.056	C.F.	4.91	1.61		6.52	8.10
0200	Type N, 1:3 mix		143	.056		4.94	1.61		6.55	8.15
0300	Type O, 1:3 mix		143	.056		4.78	1.61		6.39	7.95
0400	Type PM, 1:1:6 mix, 2500 psi		143	.056		3.99	1.61		5.60	7.10
0500	Type S, 1/2:1:4 mix		143	.056		5.35	1.61		6.96	8.60
2000	With portland cement and lime									
2100	Type M, 1:1/4:3 mix	1 Brhe	143	.056	C.F.	8.45	1.61		10.06	12
2200	Type N, 1:1:6 mix, 750 psi		143	.056		6.60	1.61		8.21	9.95
2300	Type O, 1:2:9 mix (Pointing Mortar)		143	.056		7	1.61		8.61	10.40
2400	Type PL, 1:1/2:4 mix, 2500 psi		143	.056		3.99	1.61		5.60	7.10
2600	Type S, 1:1/2:4 mix, 1800 psi		143	.056		7.75	1.61		9.36	11.20
2650	Pre-mixed, type S or N					5.05			5.05	5.55
2700	Mortar for glass block	1 Brhe	143	.056		10.40	1.61		12.01	14.10
2900	Mortar for fire brick, dry mix, 10 lb. pail				Ea.	26			26	28.50

04 05 13.91 Masonry Restoration Mortaring

04 05 13.91 Masonry Restoration Mortaring	Crew	Daily Output	Labor-Hours	Unit	Material	2014 Bare Costs Labor	2014 Bare Costs Equipment	Total	Total Incl O&P
0010	**MASONRY RESTORATION MORTARING**									
0020	Masonry restoration mix				Lb.	.23			.23	.25
0050	White				"	.23			.23	.25

04 05 13 – Masonry Mortaring

04 05 13.93 Mortar Pigments

		Crew	Daily Output	Labor-Hours	Unit	Material	2014 Bare Costs Labor	2014 Bare Costs Equipment	Total	Total Incl O&P
0010	**MORTAR PIGMENTS**, 50 lb. bags (2 bags per M bricks)　R040513-10									
0020	Color admixture, range 2 to 10 lb. per bag of cement, light colors				Lb.	4.25			4.25	4.68
0050	Medium colors					6.20			6.20	6.80
0100	Dark colors					12.90			12.90	14.20

04 05 13.95 Sand

0010	**SAND**, screened and washed at pit									
0020	For mortar, per ton				Ton	17.40			17.40	19.15
0050	With 10 mile haul					32			32	35
0100	With 30 mile haul					52			52	57
0200	Screened and washed, at the pit				C.Y.	24			24	26.50
0250	With 10 mile haul					44			44	48.50
0300	With 30 mile haul					72			72	79.50

04 05 13.98 Mortar Admixtures

0010	**MORTAR ADMIXTURES**									
0020	Waterproofing admixture, per quart (1 qt. to 2 bags of masonry cement)				Qt.	3.50			3.50	3.85

04 05 16 – Masonry Grouting

04 05 16.30 Grouting

		Crew	Daily Output	Labor-Hours	Unit	Material	Labor	Equipment	Total	Total Incl O&P
0010	**GROUTING**　R040513-10									
0011	Bond beams & lintels, 8" deep, 6" thick, 0.15 C.F. per L.F.	D-4	1480	.027	L.F.	.66	.81	.09	1.56	2.18
0020	8" thick, 0.2 C.F. per L.F.		1400	.029		1.04	.86	.10	2	2.68
0050	10" thick, 0.25 C.F. per L.F.		1200	.033		1.09	1	.11	2.20	2.99
0060	12" thick, 0.3 C.F. per L.F.		1040	.038		1.31	1.16	.13	2.60	3.51
0200	Concrete block cores, solid, 4" thk., by hand, 0.067 C.F./S.F. of wall	D-8	1100	.036	S.F.	.29	1.20		1.49	2.31
0210	6" thick, pumped, 0.175 C.F. per S.F.	D-4	720	.056		.76	1.67	.19	2.62	3.84
0250	8" thick, pumped, 0.258 C.F. per S.F.		680	.059		1.13	1.77	.20	3.10	4.41
0300	10" thick, pumped, 0.340 C.F. per S.F.		660	.061		1.49	1.82	.20	3.51	4.89
0350	12" thick, pumped, 0.422 C.F. per S.F.		640	.063		1.84	1.88	.21	3.93	5.40
0500	Cavity walls, 2" space, pumped, 0.167 C.F./S.F. of wall		1700	.024		.73	.71	.08	1.52	2.07
0550	3" space, 0.250 C.F./S.F.		1200	.033		1.09	1	.11	2.20	2.99
0600	4" space, 0.333 C.F. per S.F.		1150	.035		1.46	1.05	.12	2.63	3.47
0700	6" space, 0.500 C.F. per S.F.		800	.050		2.19	1.50	.17	3.86	5.10
0800	Door frames, 3' x 7' opening, 2.5 C.F. per opening		60	.667	Opng.	10.95	20	2.25	33.20	48
0850	6' x 7' opening, 3.5 C.F. per opening		45	.889	"	15.30	26.50	3	44.80	64.50
2000	Grout, C476, for bond beams, lintels and CMU cores		350	.114	C.F.	4.37	3.44	.39	8.20	11

04 05 19 – Masonry Anchorage and Reinforcing

04 05 19.05 Anchor Bolts

		Crew	Daily Output	Labor-Hours	Unit	Material	Labor	Equipment	Total	Total Incl O&P
0010	**ANCHOR BOLTS**									
0015	Installed in fresh grout in CMU bond beams or filled cores, no templates									
0020	Hooked, with nut and washer, 1/2" diam., 8" long	1 Bric	132	.061	Ea.	1.49	2.16		3.65	5.25
0030	12" long		131	.061		1.66	2.17		3.83	5.45
0040	5/8" diameter, 8" long		129	.062		3.25	2.21		5.46	7.25
0050	12" long		127	.063		4	2.24		6.24	8.15
0060	3/4" diameter, 8" long		127	.063		4	2.24		6.24	8.15
0070	12" long		125	.064		5	2.28		7.28	9.30

04 05 19.16 Masonry Anchors

		Crew	Daily Output	Labor-Hours	Unit	Material	Labor	Equipment	Total	Total Incl O&P
0010	**MASONRY ANCHORS**									
0020	For brick veneer, galv., corrugated, 7/8" x 7", 22 Ga.	1 Bric	10.50	.762	C	13.45	27		40.45	60
0100	24 Ga.		10.50	.762		9.50	27		36.50	55.50
0150	16 Ga.		10.50	.762		26.50	27		53.50	74
0200	Buck anchors, galv., corrugated, 16 ga., 2" bend, 8" x 2"		10.50	.762		49	27		76	99

04 05 19 – Masonry Anchorage and Reinforcing

04 05 19.16 Masonry Anchors

		Crew	Daily Output	Labor-Hours	Unit	Material	2014 Bare Costs Labor	Equipment	Total	Total Incl O&P
0250	8" x 3"	1 Bric	10.50	.762	C	51	27		78	101
0660	Cavity wall, Z-type, galvanized, 6" long, 1/8" diam.		10.50	.762		23.50	27		50.50	71
0670	3/16" diameter		10.50	.762		27	27		54	74.50
0680	1/4" diameter		10.50	.762		40.50	27		67.50	89.50
0850	8" long, 3/16" diameter		10.50	.762		25	27		52	72.50
0855	1/4" diameter		10.50	.762		48.50	27		75.50	98.50
1000	Rectangular type, galvanized, 1/4" diameter, 2" x 6"		10.50	.762		70	27		97	122
1050	4" x 6"		10.50	.762		85	27		112	139
1100	3/16" diameter, 2" x 6"		10.50	.762		42	27		69	91.50
1150	4" x 6"		10.50	.762		48.50	27		75.50	98
1500	Rigid partition anchors, plain, 8" long, 1" x 1/8"		10.50	.762		235	27		262	305
1550	1" x 1/4"		10.50	.762		277	27		304	350
1580	1-1/2" x 1/8"		10.50	.762		259	27		286	330
1600	1-1/2" x 1/4"		10.50	.762		325	27		352	400
1650	2" x 1/8"		10.50	.762		305	27		332	380
1700	2" x 1/4"		10.50	.762		405	27		432	490

04 05 19.26 Masonry Reinforcing Bars

		Crew	Daily Output	Labor-Hours	Unit	Material	Labor	Equipment	Total	Total Incl O&P
0010	**MASONRY REINFORCING BARS** R040519-50									
0015	Steel bars A615, placed horiz., #3 & #4 bars	1 Bric	450	.018	Lb.	.50	.63		1.13	1.60
0020	#5 & #6 bars		800	.010		.50	.36		.86	1.14
0050	Placed vertical, #3 & #4 bars		350	.023		.50	.81		1.31	1.90
0060	#5 & #6 bars		650	.012		.50	.44		.94	1.28
0200	Joint reinforcing, regular truss, to 6" wide, mill std galvanized		30	.267	C.L.F.	21	9.50		30.50	39
0250	12" wide		20	.400		24.50	14.25		38.75	50.50
0400	Cavity truss with drip section, to 6" wide		30	.267		22.50	9.50		32	40.50
0450	12" wide		20	.400		26	14.25		40.25	52

04 05 23 – Masonry Accessories

04 05 23.13 Masonry Control and Expansion Joints

		Crew	Daily Output	Labor-Hours	Unit	Material	Labor	Equipment	Total	Total Incl O&P
0010	**MASONRY CONTROL AND EXPANSION JOINTS**									
0020	Rubber, for double wythe 8" minimum wall (Brick/CMU)	1 Bric	400	.020	L.F.	1.77	.71		2.48	3.14
0025	"T" shaped		320	.025		1.16	.89		2.05	2.76
0030	Cross-shaped for CMU units		280	.029		1.42	1.02		2.44	3.25
0050	PVC, for double wythe 8" minimum wall (Brick/CMU)		400	.020		1.27	.71		1.98	2.59
0120	"T" shaped		320	.025		.73	.89		1.62	2.28
0160	Cross-shaped for CMU units		280	.029		.92	1.02		1.94	2.70

04 05 23.19 Masonry Cavity Drainage, Weepholes, and Vents

		Crew	Daily Output	Labor-Hours	Unit	Material	Labor	Equipment	Total	Total Incl O&P
0010	**MASONRY CAVITY DRAINAGE, WEEPHOLES, AND VENTS**									
0020	Extruded aluminum, 4" deep, 2-3/8" x 8-1/8"	1 Bric	30	.267	Ea.	31.50	9.50		41	50.50
0050	5" x 8-1/8"		25	.320		41	11.40		52.40	64.50
0100	2-1/4" x 25"		25	.320		71.50	11.40		82.90	98
0150	5" x 16-1/2"		22	.364		62.50	12.95		75.45	90
0175	5" x 24"		22	.364		77.50	12.95		90.45	107
0200	6" x 16-1/2"		22	.364		83.50	12.95		96.45	114
0250	7-3/4" x 16-1/2"		20	.400		71	14.25		85.25	102
0400	For baked enamel finish, add					35%				
0500	For cast aluminum, painted, add					60%				
1000	Stainless steel ventilators, 6" x 6"	1 Bric	25	.320		188	11.40		199.40	225
1050	8" x 8"		24	.333		208	11.85		219.85	248
1100	12" x 12"		23	.348		228	12.40		240.40	271
1150	12" x 6"		24	.333		228	11.85		239.85	270
1200	Foundation block vent, galv., 1-1/4" thk, 8" high, 16" long, no damper		30	.267		16.20	9.50		25.70	33.50
1250	For damper, add					3.11			3.11	3.42

04 05 Common Work Results for Masonry

04 05 23 – Masonry Accessories

04 05 23.95 Wall Plugs	Crew	Daily Output	Labor-Hours	Unit	Material	2014 Bare Costs Labor	2014 Bare Costs Equipment	Total	Total Incl O&P
0010 **WALL PLUGS** (for nailing to brickwork)									
0020 25 ga., galvanized, plain	1 Bric	10.50	.762	C	26.50	27		53.50	74
0050 Wood filled	"	10.50	.762	"	63.50	27		90.50	115

04 21 Clay Unit Masonry

04 21 13 – Brick Masonry

04 21 13.13 Brick Veneer Masonry

	Crew	Daily Output	Labor-Hours	Unit	Material	2014 Bare Costs Labor	2014 Bare Costs Equipment	Total	Total Incl O&P
0010 **BRICK VENEER MASONRY**, T.L. lots, excl. scaff., grout & reinforcing R042110-20									
0015 Material costs incl. 3% brick and 25% mortar waste									
0020 Standard, select common, 4" x 2-2/3" x 8" (6.75/S.F.)	D-8	1.50	26.667	M	655	875		1,530	2,175
0050 Red, 4" x 2-2/3" x 8", running bond		1.50	26.667		595	875		1,470	2,100
0100 Full header every 6th course (7.88/S.F.) R042110-50		1.45	27.586		590	910		1,500	2,150
0150 English, full header every 2nd course (10.13/S.F.)		1.40	28.571		590	940		1,530	2,225
0200 Flemish, alternate header every course (9.00/S.F.)		1.40	28.571		590	940		1,530	2,225
0250 Flemish, alt. header every 6th course (7.13/S.F.)		1.45	27.586		590	910		1,500	2,150
0300 Full headers throughout (13.50/S.F.)		1.40	28.571		590	940		1,530	2,225
0350 Rowlock course (13.50/S.F.)		1.35	29.630		590	975		1,565	2,275
0400 Rowlock stretcher (4.50/S.F.)		1.40	28.571		600	940		1,540	2,225
0450 Soldier course (6.75/S.F.)		1.40	28.571		595	940		1,535	2,225
0500 Sailor course (4.50/S.F.)		1.30	30.769		600	1,000		1,600	2,325
0601 Buff or gray face, running bond, (6.75/S.F.)		1.50	26.667		595	875		1,470	2,100
0700 Glazed face, 4" x 2-2/3" x 8", running bond		1.40	28.571		1,775	940		2,715	3,525
0750 Full header every 6th course (7.88/S.F.)		1.35	29.630		1,700	975		2,675	3,475
1000 Jumbo, 6" x 4" x 12",(3.00/S.F.)		1.30	30.769		1,650	1,000		2,650	3,500
1051 Norman, 4" x 2-2/3" x 12" (4.50/S.F.)		1.45	27.586		1,150	910		2,060	2,775
1100 Norwegian, 4" x 3-1/5" x 12" (3.75/S.F.)		1.40	28.571		1,275	940		2,215	2,975
1150 Economy, 4" x 4" x 8" (4.50 per S.F.)		1.40	28.571		885	940		1,825	2,550
1201 Engineer, 4" x 3-1/5" x 8", (5.63/S.F.)		1.45	27.586		620	910		1,530	2,175
1251 Roman, 4" x 2" x 12", (6.00/S.F.)		1.50	26.667		1,300	875		2,175	2,900
1300 S.C.R. 6" x 2-2/3" x 12" (4.50/S.F.)		1.40	28.571		1,450	940		2,390	3,175
1350 Utility, 4" x 4" x 12" (3.00/S.F.)	↓	1.08	37.037		1,550	1,225		2,775	3,750
1360 For less than truck load lots, add				↓	15%				
1400 For battered walls, add						30%			
1450 For corbels, add						75%			
1500 For curved walls, add						30%			
1550 For pits and trenches, deduct						20%			
1999 Alternate method of figuring by square foot									
2000 Standard, sel. common, 4" x 2-2/3" x 8", (6.75/S.F.)	D-8	230	.174	S.F.	4.43	5.70		10.13	14.40
2020 Red, 4" x 2-2/3" x 8", running bond		220	.182		4	6		10	14.35
2050 Full header every 6th course (7.88/S.F.)		185	.216		4.66	7.10		11.76	16.95
2100 English, full header every 2nd course (10.13/S.F.)		140	.286		5.95	9.40		15.35	22
2150 Flemish, alternate header every course (9.00/S.F.)		150	.267		5.30	8.75		14.05	20.50
2200 Flemish, alt. header every 6th course (7.13/S.F.)		205	.195		4.22	6.40		10.62	15.35
2250 Full headers throughout (13.50/S.F.)		105	.381		7.95	12.55		20.50	30
2300 Rowlock course (13.50/S.F.)		100	.400		7.95	13.15		21.10	31
2350 Rowlock stretcher (4.50/S.F.)		310	.129		2.69	4.25		6.94	10
2400 Soldier course (6.75/S.F.)		200	.200		4	6.60		10.60	15.35
2450 Sailor course (4.50/S.F.)		290	.138		2.69	4.54		7.23	10.50
2600 Buff or gray face, running bond, (6.75/S.F.)		220	.182		4.23	6		10.23	14.60
2700 Glazed face brick, running bond		210	.190		11.40	6.25		17.65	23

04 21 13.13 Brick Veneer Masonry

		Crew	Daily Output	Labor-Hours	Unit	Material	2014 Bare Costs Labor	2014 Bare Costs Equipment	Total	Total Incl O&P
2750	Full header every 6th course (7.88/S.F.)	D-8	170	.235	S.F.	13.30	7.75		21.05	27.50
3000	Jumbo, 6" x 4" x 12" running bond (3.00/S.F.)		435	.092		4.51	3.03		7.54	10
3050	Norman, 4" x 2-2/3" x 12" running bond, (4.5/S.F.)		320	.125		5.80	4.11		9.91	13.25
3100	Norwegian, 4" x 3-1/5" x 12" (3.75/S.F.)		375	.107		4.66	3.51		8.17	10.95
3150	Economy, 4" x 4" x 8" (4.50/S.F.)		310	.129		3.95	4.25		8.20	11.40
3200	Engineer, 4" x 3-1/5" x 8" (5.63/S.F.)		260	.154		3.48	5.05		8.53	12.25
3250	Roman, 4" x 2" x 12" (6.00/S.F.)		250	.160		7.70	5.25		12.95	17.25
3300	SCR, 6" x 2-2/3" x 12" (4.50/S.F.)		310	.129		6.55	4.25		10.80	14.25
3350	Utility, 4" x 4" x 12" (3.00/S.F.)	↓	360	.111	↓	4.56	3.66		8.22	11.10
3360	For less than truck load lots, add				M	15%				
3370	For battered walls, add						30%			
3380	For corbels, add						75%			
3400	For cavity wall construction, add						15%			
3450	For stacked bond, add						10%			
3500	For interior veneer construction, add						15%			
3510	For pits and trenches, deduct						20%			
3550	For curved walls, add						30%			

04 21 13.14 Thin Brick Veneer

		Crew	Daily Output	Labor-Hours	Unit	Material	2014 Bare Costs Labor	2014 Bare Costs Equipment	Total	Total Incl O&P
0010	**THIN BRICK VENEER**									
0015	Material costs incl. 3% brick and 25% mortar waste									
0020	On & incl. metal panel support sys, modular, 2-2/3" x 5/8" x 8", red	D-7	92	.174	S.F.	8.75	5.10		13.85	17.90
0100	Closure, 4" x 5/8" x 8"		110	.145		8.75	4.27		13.02	16.55
0110	Norman, 2-2/3" x 5/8" x 12"		110	.145		8.95	4.27		13.22	16.75
0120	Utility, 4" x 5/8" x 12"		125	.128		8.95	3.76		12.71	15.90
0130	Emperor, 4" x 3/4" x 16"		175	.091		10.15	2.68		12.83	15.55
0140	Super emperor, 8" x 3/4" x 16"	↓	195	.082	↓	10.15	2.41		12.56	15.10
0150	For L shaped corners with 4" return, add				L.F.	9.25			9.25	10.20
0200	On masonry/plaster back-up, modular, 2-2/3" x 5/8" x 8", red	D-7	137	.117	S.F.	3.95	3.43		7.38	9.90
0210	Closure, 4" x 5/8" x 8"		165	.097		3.95	2.85		6.80	8.95
0220	Norman, 2-2/3" x 5/8" x 12"		165	.097		4.15	2.85		7	9.15
0230	Utility, 4" x 5/8" x 12"		185	.086		4.15	2.54		6.69	8.65
0240	Emperor, 4" x 3/4" x 16"		260	.062		5.35	1.81		7.16	8.80
0250	Super emperor, 8" x 3/4" x 16"	↓	285	.056	↓	5.35	1.65		7	8.55
0260	For L shaped corners with 4" return, add				L.F.	9.25			9.25	10.20
0270	For embedment into pre-cast concrete panels, add				S.F.	14.40			14.40	15.85

04 21 13.15 Chimney

		Crew	Daily Output	Labor-Hours	Unit	Material	2014 Bare Costs Labor	2014 Bare Costs Equipment	Total	Total Incl O&P
0010	**CHIMNEY**, excludes foundation, scaffolding, grout and reinforcing									
0100	Brick, 16" x 16", 8" flue	D-1	18.20	.879	V.L.F.	25	28.50		53.50	74.50
0150	16" x 20" with one 8" x 12" flue		16	1		38.50	32		70.50	96
0200	16" x 24" with two 8" x 8" flues		14	1.143		55.50	37		92.50	123
0250	20" x 20" with one 12" x 12" flue		13.70	1.168		50	37.50		87.50	117
0300	20" x 24" with two 8" x 12" flues		12	1.333		63	43		106	141
0350	20" x 32" with two 12" x 12" flues	↓	10	1.600	↓	87.50	51.50		139	183

04 21 13.18 Columns

		Crew	Daily Output	Labor-Hours	Unit	Material	2014 Bare Costs Labor	2014 Bare Costs Equipment	Total	Total Incl O&P
0010	**COLUMNS**, solid, excludes scaffolding, grout and reinforcing R042110-10									
0050	Brick, 8" x 8", 9 brick per V.L.F.	D-1	56	.286	V.L.F.	5.20	9.20		14.40	21
0100	12" x 8", 13.5 brick per V.L.F.		37	.432		7.80	13.95		21.75	31.50
0200	12" x 12", 20 brick per V.L.F.		25	.640		11.55	20.50		32.05	47
0300	16" x 12", 27 brick per V.L.F.		19	.842		15.60	27		42.60	62
0400	16" x 16", 36 brick per V.L.F.		14	1.143		21	37		58	84.50
0500	20" x 16", 45 brick per V.L.F.		11	1.455		26	47		73	107
0600	20" x 20", 56 brick per V.L.F.	↓	9	1.778	↓	32.50	57.50		90	131

04 21 13 – Brick Masonry

04 21 13.18 Columns

		Crew	Daily Output	Labor-Hours	Unit	Material	2014 Bare Costs Labor	2014 Bare Costs Equipment	Total	Total Incl O&P
0700	24" x 20", 68 brick per V.L.F.	D-1	7	2.286	V.L.F.	39	73.50		112.50	166
0800	24" x 24", 81 brick per V.L.F.		6	2.667		46.50	86		132.50	195
1000	36" x 36", 182 brick per V.L.F.	↓	3	5.333	↓	105	172		277	400

04 21 13.30 Oversized Brick

		Crew	Daily Output	Labor-Hours	Unit	Material	2014 Bare Costs Labor	2014 Bare Costs Equipment	Total	Total Incl O&P
0010	**OVERSIZED BRICK**, excludes scaffolding, grout and reinforcing									
0100	Veneer, 4" x 2.25" x 16"	D-8	387	.103	S.F.	5.05	3.40		8.45	11.20
0105	4" x 2.75" x 16"		412	.097		5.25	3.19		8.44	11.10
0110	4" x 4" x 16"		460	.087		5.90	2.86		8.76	11.25
0120	4" x 8" x 16"		533	.075		6	2.47		8.47	10.70
0125	Loadbearing, 6" x 4" x 16", grouted and reinforced		387	.103		14.10	3.40		17.50	21
0130	8" x 4" x 16", grouted and reinforced		327	.122		14.95	4.02		18.97	23
0135	6" x 8" x 16", grouted and reinforced		440	.091		13.40	2.99		16.39	19.75
0140	8" x 8" x 16", grouted and reinforced		400	.100		14.65	3.29		17.94	21.50
0145	Curtainwall/reinforced veneer, 6" x 4" x 16"		387	.103		18.35	3.40		21.75	25.50
0150	8" x 4" x 16"		327	.122		21.50	4.02		25.52	30
0155	6" x 8" x 16"		440	.091		18.15	2.99		21.14	25
0160	8" x 8" x 16"	↓	400	.100	↓	26	3.29		29.29	34
0200	For 1 to 3 slots in face, add					15%				
0210	For 4 to 7 slots in face, add					25%				
0220	For bond beams, add					20%				
0230	For bullnose shapes, add					20%				
0240	For open end knockout, add					10%				
0250	For white or gray color group, add					10%				
0260	For 135 degree corner, add					250%				

04 21 13.35 Common Building Brick

			Crew	Daily Output	Labor-Hours	Unit	Material	2014 Bare Costs Labor	2014 Bare Costs Equipment	Total	Total Incl O&P
0010	**COMMON BUILDING BRICK**, C62, TL lots, material only	R042110-20									
0020	Standard					M	490			490	540
0050	Select					"	550			550	605

04 21 13.40 Structural Brick

			Crew	Daily Output	Labor-Hours	Unit	Material	2014 Bare Costs Labor	2014 Bare Costs Equipment	Total	Total Incl O&P
0010	**STRUCTURAL BRICK** C652, Grade SW, incl. mortar, scaffolding not incl.										
0100	Standard unit, 4-5/8" x 2-3/4" x 9-5/8"		D-8	245	.163	S.F.	4.51	5.35		9.86	13.90
0120	Bond beam			225	.178		7	5.85		12.85	17.45
0140	V cut bond beam			225	.178		7.60	5.85		13.45	18.10
0160	Stretcher quoin, 5-5/8" x 2-3/4" x 9-5/8"			245	.163		7.40	5.35		12.75	17.10
0180	Corner quoin			245	.163		8.20	5.35		13.55	18
0200	Corner, 45 deg, 4-5/8" x 2-3/4" x 10-7/16"	↓		235	.170	↓	8.45	5.60		14.05	18.60

04 21 13.45 Face Brick

			Crew	Daily Output	Labor-Hours	Unit	Material	2014 Bare Costs Labor	2014 Bare Costs Equipment	Total	Total Incl O&P
0010	**FACE BRICK** Material Only, C216, TL lots	R042110-20									
0300	Standard modular, 4" x 2-2/3" x 8", minimum					M	490			490	540
0350	Maximum						695			695	760
0450	Economy, 4" x 4" x 8", minimum						765			765	840
0500	Maximum						990			990	1,100
0510	Economy, 4" x 4" x 12", minimum						1,200			1,200	1,325
0520	Maximum						1,575			1,575	1,725
0550	Jumbo, 6" x 4" x 12", minimum						1,375			1,375	1,500
0600	Maximum						1,825			1,825	2,000
0610	Jumbo, 8" x 4" x 12", minimum						1,375			1,375	1,500
0620	Maximum						1,825			1,825	2,000
0650	Norwegian, 4" x 3-1/5" x 12", minimum						1,125			1,125	1,225
0700	Maximum						1,450			1,450	1,600
0710	Norwegian, 6" x 3-1/5" x 12", minimum						1,475			1,475	1,600
0720	Maximum					↓	1,900			1,900	2,100

04 21 13 – Brick Masonry

04 21 13.45 Face Brick

	Crew	Daily Output	Labor-Hours	Unit	Material	2014 Bare Costs Labor	Equipment	Total	Total Incl O&P
0850	Standard glazed, plain colors, 4" x 2-2/3" x 8", minimum				M	1,550			1,550	1,725
0900	Maximum					2,025			2,025	2,225
1000	Deep trim shades, 4" x 2-2/3" x 8", minimum					1,975			1,975	2,150
1050	Maximum					2,200			2,200	2,425
1080	Jumbo utility, 4" x 4" x 12"					1,375			1,375	1,525
1120	4" x 8" x 8"					1,725			1,725	1,875
1140	4" x 8" x 16"					5,050			5,050	5,550
1260	Engineer, 4" x 3-1/5" x 8", minimum					515			515	565
1270	Maximum					715			715	785
1350	King, 4" x 2-3/4" x 10", minimum					465			465	515
1360	Maximum					575			575	630
1770	Standard modular, double glazed, 4" x 2-2/3" x 8"					2,325			2,325	2,550
1850	Jumbo, colored glazed ceramic, 6" x 4" x 12"					2,450			2,450	2,700
2050	Jumbo utility, glazed, 4" x 4" x 12"					4,600			4,600	5,050
2100	4" x 8" x 8"					5,400			5,400	5,950
2150	4" x 16" x 8"					6,325			6,325	6,950
2170	For less than truck load lots, add					15			15	16.50
2180	For buff or gray brick, add					16			16	17.60

04 21 26 – Glazed Structural Clay Tile Masonry

04 21 26.10 Structural Facing Tile

	Crew	Daily Output	Labor-Hours	Unit	Material	2014 Bare Costs Labor	Equipment	Total	Total Incl O&P
0010	**STRUCTURAL FACING TILE**, std. colors, excl. scaffolding, grout, reinforcing									
0020	6T series, 5-1/3" x 12", 2.3 pieces per S.F., glazed 1 side, 2" thick	D-8	225	.178	S.F.	8.80	5.85		14.65	19.45
0100	4" thick		220	.182		11.95	6		17.95	23
0150	Glazed 2 sides		195	.205		15.75	6.75		22.50	28.50
0250	6" thick		210	.190		17.85	6.25		24.10	30
0300	Glazed 2 sides		185	.216		21	7.10		28.10	35.50
0400	8" thick		180	.222		23.50	7.30		30.80	38
0500	Special shapes, group 1		400	.100	Ea.	7.55	3.29		10.84	13.80
0550	Group 2		375	.107		12.25	3.51		15.76	19.35
0600	Group 3		350	.114		15.75	3.76		19.51	23.50
0650	Group 4		325	.123		32.50	4.05		36.55	43
0700	Group 5		300	.133		39	4.39		43.39	50.50
0750	Group 6		275	.145		53	4.79		57.79	66
1000	Fire rated, 4" thick, 1 hr. rating		210	.190	S.F.	17.05	6.25		23.30	29
1300	Acoustic, 4" thick		210	.190	"	34	6.25		40.25	48
2000	8W series, 8" x 16", 1.125 pieces per S.F.									
2050	2" thick, glazed 1 side	D-8	360	.111	S.F.	10.25	3.66		13.91	17.35
2100	4" thick, glazed 1 side		345	.116		14.10	3.81		17.91	22
2150	Glazed 2 sides		325	.123		16.95	4.05		21	25.50
2200	6" thick, glazed 1 side		330	.121		24	3.99		27.99	33
2250	8" thick, glazed 1 side		310	.129		24	4.25		28.25	33.50
2500	Special shapes, group 1		300	.133	Ea.	14.60	4.39		18.99	23.50
2550	Group 2		280	.143		19.50	4.70		24.20	29.50
2600	Group 3		260	.154		20.50	5.05		25.55	31.50
2650	Group 4		250	.160		43	5.25		48.25	56
2700	Group 5		240	.167		38.50	5.50		44	51
2750	Group 6		230	.174		83	5.70		88.70	101
3000	4" thick, glazed 1 side		345	.116	S.F.	13.75	3.81		17.56	21.50
3100	Acoustic, 4" thick		345	.116	"	18	3.81		21.81	26
3120	4W series, 8" x 8", 2.25 pieces per S.F.									
3125	2" thick, glazed 1 side	D-8	360	.111	S.F.	9.45	3.66		13.11	16.50
3130	4" thick, glazed 1 side		345	.116		11.15	3.81		14.96	18.60

04 21 Clay Unit Masonry

04 21 26 – Glazed Structural Clay Tile Masonry

04 21 26.10 Structural Facing Tile		Crew	Daily Output	Labor-Hours	Unit	Material	2014 Bare Costs Labor	Equipment	Total	Total Incl O&P
3135	Glazed 2 sides	D-8	325	.123	S.F.	15.35	4.05		19.40	23.50
3140	6" thick, glazed 1 side		330	.121		15.85	3.99		19.84	24
3150	8" thick, glazed 1 side		310	.129	↓	23	4.25		27.25	32.50
3155	Special shapes, group I		300	.133	Ea.	7.40	4.39		11.79	15.45
3160	Group II	↓	280	.143	"	8.55	4.70		13.25	17.20
3200	For designer colors, add					25%				
3300	For epoxy mortar joints, add				S.F.	1.69			1.69	1.86

04 21 29 – Terra Cotta Masonry

04 21 29.10 Terra Cotta Masonry Components		Crew	Daily Output	Labor-Hours	Unit	Material	2014 Bare Costs Labor	Equipment	Total	Total Incl O&P
0010	**TERRA COTTA MASONRY COMPONENTS**									
0020	Coping, split type, not glazed, 9" wide	D-1	90	.178	L.F.	13.15	5.75		18.90	24
0100	13" wide		80	.200		18.35	6.45		24.80	31
0200	Coping, split type, glazed, 9" wide		90	.178		11.70	5.75		17.45	22.50
0250	13" wide	↓	80	.200	↓	15.45	6.45		21.90	28
0500	Partition or back-up blocks, scored, in C.L. lots									
0700	Non-load bearing 12" x 12", 3" thick, special order	D-8	550	.073	S.F.	16.85	2.39		19.24	22.50
0750	4" thick, standard		500	.080		5.35	2.63		7.98	10.25
0800	6" thick		450	.089		7.20	2.92		10.12	12.75
0850	8" thick		400	.100		9.05	3.29		12.34	15.45
1000	Load bearing, 12" x 12", 4" thick, in walls		500	.080		5.45	2.63		8.08	10.40
1050	In floors		750	.053		5.45	1.75		7.20	8.90
1200	6" thick, in walls		450	.089		7.35	2.92		10.27	12.95
1250	In floors		675	.059		7.35	1.95		9.30	11.35
1400	8" thick, in walls		400	.100		9.15	3.29		12.44	15.55
1450	In floors		575	.070		9.15	2.29		11.44	13.85
1600	10" thick, in walls, special order		350	.114		23	3.76		26.76	32
1650	In floors, special order		500	.080		23	2.63		25.63	30
1800	12" thick, in walls, special order		300	.133		23	4.39		27.39	33
1850	In floors, special order	↓	450	.089		23	2.92		25.92	30.50
2000	For reinforcing with steel rods, add to above					15%	5%			
2100	For smooth tile instead of scored, add					3.66			3.66	4.03
2200	For L.C.L. quantities, add				↓	10%	10%			

04 21 29.20 Terra Cotta Tile		Crew	Daily Output	Labor-Hours	Unit	Material	2014 Bare Costs Labor	Equipment	Total	Total Incl O&P
0010	**TERRA COTTA TILE**, on walls, dry set, 1/2" thick									
0100	Square, hexagonal or lattice shapes, unglazed	1 Tilf	135	.059	S.F.	4.62	1.94		6.56	8.25
0300	Glazed, plain colors		130	.062		7.10	2.02		9.12	11.05
0400	Intense colors	↓	125	.064	↓	8.30	2.10		10.40	12.55

04 22 Concrete Unit Masonry

04 22 10 – Concrete Masonry Units

04 22 10.11 Autoclave Aerated Concrete Block			Crew	Daily Output	Labor-Hours	Unit	Material	2014 Bare Costs Labor	Equipment	Total	Total Incl O&P
0010	**AUTOCLAVE AERATED CONCRETE BLOCK**, excl. scaffolding, grout & reinforcing										
0050	Solid, 4" x 8" x 24", incl. mortar	G	D-8	600	.067	S.F.	1.48	2.19		3.67	5.30
0060	6" x 8" x 24"	G		600	.067		2.23	2.19		4.42	6.10
0070	8" x 8" x 24"	G		575	.070		2.97	2.29		5.26	7.10
0080	10" x 8" x 24"	G		575	.070		3.63	2.29		5.92	7.80
0090	12" x 8" x 24"	G	↓	550	.073	↓	4.45	2.39		6.84	8.90

04 22 10 – Concrete Masonry Units

04 22 10.12 Chimney Block	Crew	Daily Output	Labor-Hours	Unit	Material	2014 Bare Costs Labor	Equipment	Total	Total Incl O&P
0010 **CHIMNEY BLOCK**, excludes scaffolding, grout and reinforcing									
0220 1 piece, with 8" x 8" flue, 16" x 16"	D-1	28	.571	V.L.F.	18.20	18.40		36.60	50.50
0230 2 piece, 16" x 16"		26	.615		22	19.85		41.85	57
0240 2 piece, with 8" x 12" flue, 16" x 20"		24	.667		31	21.50		52.50	70

04 22 10.14 Concrete Block, Back-Up	Crew	Daily Output	Labor-Hours	Unit	Material	2014 Bare Costs Labor	Equipment	Total	Total Incl O&P
0010 **CONCRETE BLOCK, BACK-UP**, C90, 2000 psi R042210-20									
0020 Normal weight, 8" x 16" units, tooled joint 1 side									
0050 Not-reinforced, 2000 psi, 2" thick	D-8	475	.084	S.F.	1.40	2.77		4.17	6.15
0200 4" thick		460	.087		1.66	2.86		4.52	6.60
0300 6" thick		440	.091		2.18	2.99		5.17	7.40
0350 8" thick		400	.100		2.45	3.29		5.74	8.20
0400 10" thick		330	.121		2.95	3.99		6.94	9.90
0450 12" thick	D-9	310	.155		3.76	4.99		8.75	12.45
1000 Reinforced, alternate courses, 4" thick	D-8	450	.089		1.82	2.92		4.74	6.85
1100 6" thick		430	.093		2.34	3.06		5.40	7.65
1150 8" thick		395	.101		2.62	3.33		5.95	8.45
1200 10" thick		320	.125		3.10	4.11		7.21	10.25
1250 12" thick	D-9	300	.160		3.92	5.15		9.07	12.90

04 22 10.16 Concrete Block, Bond Beam	Crew	Daily Output	Labor-Hours	Unit	Material	2014 Bare Costs Labor	Equipment	Total	Total Incl O&P
0010 **CONCRETE BLOCK, BOND BEAM**, C90, 2000 psi									
0020 Not including grout or reinforcing									
0125 Regular block, 6" thick	D-8	584	.068	L.F.	2.25	2.25		4.50	6.25
0130 8" high, 8" thick	"	565	.071		2.63	2.33		4.96	6.75
0150 12" thick	D-9	510	.094		3.91	3.03		6.94	9.35
0525 Lightweight, 6" thick	D-8	592	.068		2.67	2.22		4.89	6.65
0530 8" high, 8" thick	"	575	.070		3.22	2.29		5.51	7.35
0550 12" thick	D-9	520	.092		4.33	2.98		7.31	9.70
2000 Including grout and 2 #5 bars									
2100 Regular block, 8" high, 8" thick	D-8	300	.133	L.F.	4.72	4.39		9.11	12.50
2150 12" thick	D-9	250	.192		6.55	6.20		12.75	17.50
2500 Lightweight, 8" high, 8" thick	D-8	305	.131		5.30	4.31		9.61	13.05
2550 12" thick	D-9	255	.188		7	6.05		13.05	17.80

04 22 10.18 Concrete Block, Column	Crew	Daily Output	Labor-Hours	Unit	Material	2014 Bare Costs Labor	Equipment	Total	Total Incl O&P
0010 **CONCRETE BLOCK, COLUMN** or pilaster									
0050 Including vertical reinforcing (4-#4 bars) and grout									
0160 1 piece unit, 16" x 16"	D-1	26	.615	V.L.F.	15.85	19.85		35.70	50.50
0170 2 piece units, 16" x 20"		24	.667		20.50	21.50		42	58.50
0180 20" x 20"		22	.727		26	23.50		49.50	67.50
0190 22" x 24"		18	.889		38.50	28.50		67	90
0200 20" x 32"		14	1.143		45	37		82	111

04 22 10.19 Concrete Block, Insulation Inserts	Crew	Daily Output	Labor-Hours	Unit	Material	2014 Bare Costs Labor	Equipment	Total	Total Incl O&P
0010 **CONCRETE BLOCK, INSULATION INSERTS**									
0100 Styrofoam, plant installed, add to block prices									
0200 8" x 16" units, 6" thick				S.F.	1.20			1.20	1.32
0250 8" thick					1.35			1.35	1.49
0300 10" thick					1.50			1.50	1.65
0350 12" thick					1.65			1.65	1.82
0500 8" x 8" units, 8" thick					1.20			1.20	1.32
0550 12" thick					1.20			1.20	1.32

04 22 10.23 Concrete Block, Decorative	Crew	Daily Output	Labor-Hours	Unit	Material	2014 Bare Costs Labor	Equipment	Total	Total Incl O&P
0010 **CONCRETE BLOCK, DECORATIVE**, C90, 2000 psi									
0020 Embossed, simulated brick face									
0100 8" x 16" units, 4" thick	D-8	400	.100	S.F.	2.73	3.29		6.02	8.50
0200 8" thick		340	.118		3.92	3.87		7.79	10.75
0250 12" thick	↓	300	.133	↓	4.26	4.39		8.65	12
0400 Embossed both sides									
0500 8" thick	D-8	300	.133	S.F.	2.53	4.39		6.92	10.10
0550 12" thick	"	275	.145	"	3.67	4.79		8.46	12
1000 Fluted high strength									
1100 8" x 16" x 4" thick, flutes 1 side,	D-8	345	.116	S.F.	4.17	3.81		7.98	10.95
1150 Flutes 2 sides	↓	335	.119		4.73	3.93		8.66	11.75
1200 8" thick	↓	300	.133		5	4.39		9.39	12.80
1250 For special colors, add				↓	.46			.46	.51
1400 Deep grooved, smooth face									
1450 8" x 16" x 4" thick	D-8	345	.116	S.F.	2.59	3.81		6.40	9.20
1500 8" thick	"	300	.133	"	4.55	4.39		8.94	12.30
2000 Formblock, incl. inserts & reinforcing									
2100 8" x 16" x 8" thick	D-8	345	.116	S.F.	3.38	3.81		7.19	10.05
2150 12" thick	"	310	.129	"	4.42	4.25		8.67	11.90
2500 Ground face									
2600 8" x 16" x 4" thick	D-8	345	.116	S.F.	3.45	3.81		7.26	10.15
2650 6" thick		325	.123	↓	3.86	4.05		7.91	11
2700 8" thick	↓	300	.133		4.26	4.39		8.65	12
2750 12" thick	D-9	265	.181	↓	5.40	5.85		11.25	15.65
2900 For special colors, add, minimum					15%				
2950 For special colors, add, maximum					45%				
4000 Slump block									
4100 4" face height x 16" x 4" thick	D-1	165	.097	S.F.	3.68	3.13		6.81	9.25
4150 6" thick		160	.100		5.30	3.22		8.52	11.20
4200 8" thick		155	.103		5.35	3.33		8.68	11.45
4250 10" thick		140	.114		10.50	3.68		14.18	17.70
4300 12" thick		130	.123		11.05	3.97		15.02	18.75
4400 6" face height x 16" x 6" thick		155	.103		5.05	3.33		8.38	11.15
4450 8" thick		150	.107		7.45	3.44		10.89	13.90
4500 10" thick		130	.123		11	3.97		14.97	18.70
4550 12" thick	↓	120	.133	↓	11.25	4.30		15.55	19.55
5000 Split rib profile units, 1" deep ribs, 8 ribs									
5100 8" x 16" x 4" thick	D-8	345	.116	S.F.	3.62	3.81		7.43	10.35
5150 6" thick	↓	325	.123		4.17	4.05		8.22	11.35
5200 8" thick	↓	300	.133		4.83	4.39		9.22	12.60
5250 12" thick	D-9	275	.175		5.65	5.65		11.30	15.55
5400 For special deeper colors, 4" thick, add					1.23			1.23	1.35
5450 12" thick, add					1.27			1.27	1.39
5600 For white, 4" thick, add					1.23			1.23	1.35
5650 6" thick, add					1.25			1.25	1.38
5700 8" thick, add					1.28			1.28	1.40
5750 12" thick, add				↓	1.32			1.32	1.45
6000 Split face									
6100 8" x 16" x 4" thick	D-8	350	.114	S.F.	3.27	3.76		7.03	9.85
6150 6" thick		325	.123		3.79	4.05		7.84	10.90
6200 8" thick	↓	300	.133	↓	4.36	4.39		8.75	12.10
6250 12" thick	D-9	270	.178		5.25	5.75		11	15.30

04 22 10.23 Concrete Block, Decorative	Crew	Daily Output	Labor-Hours	Unit	Material	2014 Bare Costs Labor	2014 Bare Costs Equipment	Total	Total Incl O&P
6300	For scored, add				S.F.	.37			.37	.41
6400	For special deeper colors, 4" thick, add					.59			.59	.65
6450	6" thick, add					.70			.70	.77
6500	8" thick, add					.72			.72	.80
6550	12" thick, add					.75			.75	.82
6650	For white, 4" thick, add					1.22			1.22	1.34
6700	6" thick, add					1.23			1.23	1.35
6750	8" thick, add					1.24			1.24	1.37
6800	12" thick, add					1.27			1.27	1.39
7000	Scored ground face, 2 to 5 scores									
7100	8" x 16" x 4" thick	D-8	340	.118	S.F.	6.55	3.87		10.42	13.70
7150	6" thick		310	.129		7.30	4.25		11.55	15.10
7200	8" thick		290	.138		8.30	4.54		12.84	16.65
7250	12" thick	D-9	265	.181		12.55	5.85		18.40	23.50
8000	Hexagonal face profile units, 8" x 16" units									
8100	4" thick, hollow	D-8	340	.118	S.F.	3.45	3.87		7.32	10.25
8200	Solid		340	.118		4.42	3.87		8.29	11.30
8300	6" thick, hollow		310	.129		3.72	4.25		7.97	11.15
8350	8" thick, hollow		290	.138		4.12	4.54		8.66	12.10
8500	For stacked bond, add						26%			
8550	For high rise construction, add per story	D-8	67.80	.590	M.S.F.		19.40		19.40	32.50
8600	For scored block, add					10%				
8650	For honed or ground face, per face, add				Ea.	.98			.98	1.08
8700	For honed or ground end, per end, add				"	.98			.98	1.08
8750	For bullnose block, add					10%				
8800	For special color, add					13%				

04 22 10.24 Concrete Block, Exterior	Crew	Daily Output	Labor-Hours	Unit	Material	2014 Bare Costs Labor	2014 Bare Costs Equipment	Total	Total Incl O&P
0010	**CONCRETE BLOCK, EXTERIOR**, C90, 2000 psi									
0020	Reinforced alt courses, tooled joints 2 sides									
0100	Normal weight, 8" x 16" x 6" thick	D-8	395	.101	S.F.	2.27	3.33		5.60	8.05
0200	8" thick		360	.111		3.92	3.66		7.58	10.40
0250	10" thick		290	.138		4.08	4.54		8.62	12.05
0300	12" thick	D-9	250	.192		4.68	6.20		10.88	15.45
0500	Lightweight, 8" x 16" x 6" thick	D-8	450	.089		3	2.92		5.92	8.15
0600	8" thick		430	.093		3.82	3.06		6.88	9.30
0650	10" thick		395	.101		3.93	3.33		7.26	9.90
0700	12" thick	D-9	350	.137		4	4.42		8.42	11.75

04 22 10.26 Concrete Block Foundation Wall	Crew	Daily Output	Labor-Hours	Unit	Material	2014 Bare Costs Labor	2014 Bare Costs Equipment	Total	Total Incl O&P
0010	**CONCRETE BLOCK FOUNDATION WALL**, C90/C145									
0050	Normal-weight, cut joints, horiz joint reinf, no vert reinf.									
0200	Hollow, 8" x 16" x 6" thick	D-8	455	.088	S.F.	2.64	2.89		5.53	7.70
0250	8" thick		425	.094		2.93	3.10		6.03	8.40
0300	10" thick		350	.114		3.43	3.76		7.19	10
0350	12" thick	D-9	300	.160		4.25	5.15		9.40	13.30
0500	Solid, 8" x 16" block, 6" thick	D-8	440	.091		2.81	2.99		5.80	8.10
0550	8" thick	"	415	.096		4.12	3.17		7.29	9.85
0600	12" thick	D-9	350	.137		5.95	4.42		10.37	13.90

04 22 10.28 Concrete Block, High Strength	Crew	Daily Output	Labor-Hours	Unit	Material	2014 Bare Costs Labor	2014 Bare Costs Equipment	Total	Total Incl O&P
0010	**CONCRETE BLOCK, HIGH STRENGTH**									
0050	Hollow, reinforced alternate courses, 8" x 16" units									
0200	3500 psi, 4" thick	D-8	440	.091	S.F.	1.88	2.99		4.87	7.05
0250	6" thick		395	.101		2.20	3.33		5.53	7.95

04 22 Concrete Unit Masonry

04 22 10 – Concrete Masonry Units

04 22 10.28 Concrete Block, High Strength		Crew	Daily Output	Labor-Hours	Unit	Material	2014 Bare Costs Labor	Equipment	Total	Total Incl O&P
0300	8" thick	D-8	360	.111	S.F.	3.85	3.66		7.51	10.35
0350	12" thick	D-9	250	.192		4.57	6.20		10.77	15.35
0500	5000 psi, 4" thick	D-8	440	.091		1.95	2.99		4.94	7.15
0550	6" thick		395	.101		2.84	3.33		6.17	8.65
0600	8" thick		360	.111		4.04	3.66		7.70	10.55
0650	12" thick	D-9	300	.160		4.59	5.15		9.74	13.65
1000	For 75% solid block, add					30%				
1050	For 100% solid block, add					50%				

04 22 10.30 Concrete Block, Interlocking

		Crew	Daily Output	Labor-Hours	Unit	Material	Labor	Equipment	Total	Total Incl O&P
0010	**CONCRETE BLOCK, INTERLOCKING**									
0100	Not including grout or reinforcing									
0200	8" x 16" units, 2,000 psi, 8" thick	D-1	245	.065	S.F.	2.83	2.10		4.93	6.60
0300	12" thick		220	.073		4.20	2.34		6.54	8.50
0350	16" thick		185	.086		6.30	2.79		9.09	11.60
0400	Including grout & reinforcing, 8" thick	D-4	245	.163		7.60	4.91	.55	13.06	17.20
0450	12" thick		220	.182		9.20	5.45	.61	15.26	19.85
0500	16" thick		185	.216		11.50	6.50	.73	18.73	24.50

04 22 10.32 Concrete Block, Lintels

		Crew	Daily Output	Labor-Hours	Unit	Material	Labor	Equipment	Total	Total Incl O&P
0010	**CONCRETE BLOCK, LINTELS**, C90, normal weight									
0100	Including grout and horizontal reinforcing									
0200	8" x 8" x 8", 1 #4 bar	D-4	300	.133	L.F.	5.20	4.01	.45	9.66	12.95
0250	2 #4 bars		295	.136		5.45	4.08	.46	9.99	13.30
0400	8" x 16" x 8", 1 #4 bar		275	.145		3.65	4.37	.49	8.51	11.85
0450	2 #4 bars		270	.148		3.87	4.45	.50	8.82	12.25
1000	12" x 8" x 8", 1 #4 bar		275	.145		6.80	4.37	.49	11.66	15.35
1100	2 #4 bars		270	.148		7.05	4.45	.50	12	15.75
1150	2 #5 bars		270	.148		7.30	4.45	.50	12.25	16
1200	2 #6 bars		265	.151		7.60	4.54	.51	12.65	16.45
1500	12" x 16" x 8", 1 #4 bar		250	.160		7.40	4.81	.54	12.75	16.75
1600	2 #3 bars		245	.163		7.40	4.91	.55	12.86	16.95
1650	2 #4 bars		245	.163		7.60	4.91	.55	13.06	17.20
1700	2 #5 bars		240	.167		7.85	5	.56	13.41	17.60

04 22 10.33 Lintel Block

		Crew	Daily Output	Labor-Hours	Unit	Material	Labor	Equipment	Total	Total Incl O&P
0010	**LINTEL BLOCK**									
3481	Lintel block 6" x 8" x 8"	D-1	300	.053	Ea.	1.29	1.72		3.01	4.28
3501	6" x 16" x 8"		275	.058		2	1.88		3.88	5.30
3521	8" x 8" x 8"		275	.058		1.06	1.88		2.94	4.29
3561	8" x 16" x 8"		250	.064		1.84	2.06		3.90	5.45

04 22 10.34 Concrete Block, Partitions

		Crew	Daily Output	Labor-Hours	Unit	Material	Labor	Equipment	Total	Total Incl O&P
0010	**CONCRETE BLOCK, PARTITIONS**, excludes scaffolding R042210-20									
0100	Acoustical slotted block									
0200	4" thick, type A-1	D-8	315	.127	S.F.	3.87	4.18		8.05	11.20
0210	8" thick		275	.145		4.95	4.79		9.74	13.40
0250	8" thick, type Q		275	.145		8.65	4.79		13.44	17.45
0260	4" thick, type RSC		315	.127		6	4.18		10.18	13.55
0270	6" thick		295	.136		6	4.46		10.46	14
0280	8" thick		275	.145		6	4.79		10.79	14.55
0290	12" thick		250	.160		6	5.25		11.25	15.35
0300	8" thick, type RSR		275	.145		6	4.79		10.79	14.55
0400	8" thick, type RSC/RF		275	.145		6.70	4.79		11.49	15.35
0410	10" thick		260	.154		7.20	5.05		12.25	16.30
0420	12" thick		250	.160		7.75	5.25		13	17.25

04 22 Concrete Unit Masonry

04 22 10 – Concrete Masonry Units

04 22 10.34 Concrete Block, Partitions

		Crew	Daily Output	Labor-Hours	Unit	Material	2014 Bare Costs Labor	Equipment	Total	Total Incl O&P
0430	12" thick, type RSC/RF-4	D-8	250	.160	S.F.	9.35	5.25		14.60	19.05
0500	NRC .60 type R, 8" thick		265	.151		8.20	4.97		13.17	17.25
0600	NRC .65 type RR, 8" thick		265	.151		7.75	4.97		12.72	16.80
0700	NRC .65 type 4R-RF, 8" thick		265	.151		8.35	4.97		13.32	17.45
0710	NRC .70 type R, 12" thick	↓	245	.163	↓	8.80	5.35		14.15	18.65
1000	Lightweight block, tooled joints, 2 sides, hollow									
1100	Not reinforced, 8" x 16" x 4" thick	D-8	440	.091	S.F.	1.72	2.99		4.71	6.85
1150	6" thick		410	.098		2.45	3.21		5.66	8.05
1200	8" thick		385	.104		2.98	3.42		6.40	9
1250	10" thick	↓	370	.108		3.61	3.56		7.17	9.85
1300	12" thick	D-9	350	.137		3.81	4.42		8.23	11.55
2000	Not reinforced, 8" x 24" x 4" thick, hollow		460	.104		1.25	3.36		4.61	6.95
2100	6" thick		440	.109		1.75	3.52		5.27	7.80
2150	8" thick		415	.116		2.17	3.73		5.90	8.60
2200	10" thick		385	.125		2.63	4.02		6.65	9.60
2250	12" thick	↓	365	.132		2.80	4.24		7.04	10.15
2800	Solid, not reinforced, 8" x 16" x 2" thick	D-8	440	.091		1.33	2.99		4.32	6.45
2900	4" thick		420	.095		1.60	3.13		4.73	6.95
2950	6" thick		390	.103		2.86	3.37		6.23	8.75
3000	8" thick		365	.110		3.68	3.61		7.29	10.05
3050	10" thick	↓	350	.114		3.81	3.76		7.57	10.45
3100	12" thick	D-9	330	.145	↓	3.88	4.69		8.57	12.05
4000	Regular block, tooled joints, 2 sides, hollow									
4100	Not reinforced, 8" x 16" x 4" thick	D-8	430	.093	S.F.	1.58	3.06		4.64	6.85
4150	6" thick		400	.100		2.10	3.29		5.39	7.80
4200	8" thick		375	.107		2.37	3.51		5.88	8.45
4250	10" thick	↓	360	.111		2.86	3.66		6.52	9.25
4300	12" thick	D-9	340	.141		3.67	4.55		8.22	11.60
4500	Reinforced alternate courses, 8" x 16" x 4" thick	D-8	425	.094		1.73	3.10		4.83	7.05
4550	6" thick		395	.101		2.25	3.33		5.58	8.05
4600	8" thick		370	.108		2.53	3.56		6.09	8.70
4650	10" thick	↓	355	.113		3.70	3.71		7.41	10.20
4700	12" thick	D-9	335	.143		3.83	4.62		8.45	11.90
4900	Solid, not reinforced, 2" thick	D-8	435	.092		1.35	3.03		4.38	6.55
5000	3" thick		430	.093		1.44	3.06		4.50	6.70
5050	4" thick		415	.096		1.91	3.17		5.08	7.40
5100	6" thick		385	.104		2.26	3.42		5.68	8.20
5150	8" thick	↓	360	.111		3.56	3.66		7.22	10
5200	12" thick	D-9	325	.148		5.40	4.76		10.16	13.80
5500	Solid, reinforced alternate courses, 4" thick	D-8	420	.095		2.02	3.13		5.15	7.40
5550	6" thick		380	.105		2.40	3.46		5.86	8.40
5600	8" thick	↓	355	.113		3.70	3.71		7.41	10.20
5650	12" thick	D-9	320	.150	↓	4.20	4.83		9.03	12.65

04 22 10.38 Concrete Brick

		Crew	Daily Output	Labor-Hours	Unit	Material	2014 Bare Costs Labor	Equipment	Total	Total Incl O&P
0010	**CONCRETE BRICK,** C55, grade N, type 1									
0100	Regular, 4 x 2-1/4 x 8	D-8	660	.061	Ea.	.52	1.99		2.51	3.89
0125	Rusticated, 4 x 2-1/4 x 8		660	.061		.58	1.99		2.57	3.96
0150	Frog, 4 x 2-1/4 x 8		660	.061		.56	1.99		2.55	3.94
0200	Double, 4 x 4-7/8 x 8	↓	535	.075	↓	.91	2.46		3.37	5.10

04 22 Concrete Unit Masonry

04 22 10 – Concrete Masonry Units

04 22 10.42 Concrete Block, Screen Block	Crew	Daily Output	Labor-Hours	Unit	Material	2014 Bare Costs Labor	Equipment	Total	Total Incl O&P
0010 **CONCRETE BLOCK, SCREEN BLOCK**									
0200 8" x 16", 4" thick	D-8	330	.121	S.F.	2.22	3.99		6.21	9.10
0300 8" thick		270	.148		3.58	4.87		8.45	12.05
0350 12" x 12", 4" thick		290	.138		1.99	4.54		6.53	9.75
0500 8" thick	↓	250	.160	↓	2.59	5.25		7.84	11.60

04 22 10.44 Glazed Concrete Block

	Crew	Daily Output	Labor-Hours	Unit	Material	2014 Bare Costs Labor	Equipment	Total	Total Incl O&P
0010 **GLAZED CONCRETE BLOCK** C744									
0100 Single face, 8" x 16" units, 2" thick	D-8	360	.111	S.F.	9.55	3.66		13.21	16.60
0200 4" thick		345	.116		9.80	3.81		13.61	17.15
0250 6" thick		330	.121		10.60	3.99		14.59	18.30
0300 8" thick		310	.129		11.30	4.25		15.55	19.50
0350 10" thick	↓	295	.136		12.95	4.46		17.41	21.50
0400 12" thick	D-9	280	.171		13.80	5.55		19.35	24.50
0700 Double face, 8" x 16" units, 4" thick	D-8	340	.118		13.85	3.87		17.72	21.50
0750 6" thick		320	.125		16.85	4.11		20.96	25.50
0800 8" thick		300	.133	↓	17.65	4.39		22.04	27
1000 Jambs, bullnose or square, single face, 8" x 16", 2" thick		315	.127	Ea.	18.25	4.18		22.43	27
1050 4" thick		285	.140	"	21.50	4.62		26.12	31
1200 Caps, bullnose or square, 8" x 16", 2" thick		420	.095	L.F.	16.95	3.13		20.08	24
1250 4" thick		380	.105	"	18.45	3.46		21.91	26.50
1256 Corner, bullnose or square, 2" thick		280	.143	Ea.	19.80	4.70		24.50	30
1258 4" thick		270	.148		21.50	4.87		26.37	31.50
1260 6" thick		260	.154		26.50	5.05		31.55	38
1270 8" thick		250	.160		32.50	5.25		37.75	45
1280 10" thick		240	.167		33	5.50		38.50	45.50
1290 12" thick	↓	230	.174	↓	34.50	5.70		40.20	47.50
1500 Cove base, 8" x 16", 2" thick		315	.127	L.F.	8.55	4.18		12.73	16.35
1550 4" thick		285	.140		8.65	4.62		13.27	17.20
1600 6" thick		265	.151		9.25	4.97		14.22	18.45
1650 8" thick	↓	245	.163	↓	9.70	5.35		15.05	19.65

04 23 Glass Unit Masonry

04 23 13 – Vertical Glass Unit Masonry

04 23 13.10 Glass Block

	Crew	Daily Output	Labor-Hours	Unit	Material	2014 Bare Costs Labor	Equipment	Total	Total Incl O&P
0010 **GLASS BLOCK**									
0100 Plain, 4" thick, under 1,000 S.F., 6" x 6"	D-8	115	.348	S.F.	29	11.45		40.45	51
0150 8" x 8"		160	.250		16.65	8.25		24.90	32
0160 end block		160	.250		59	8.25		67.25	78.50
0170 90 deg corner		160	.250		53.50	8.25		61.75	72.50
0180 45 deg corner		160	.250		44	8.25		52.25	62
0200 12" x 12"		175	.229		23.50	7.50		31	38.50
0210 4" x 8"		160	.250		32	8.25		40.25	48.50
0220 6" x 8"		160	.250		22.50	8.25		30.75	38.50
0300 1,000 to 5,000 S.F., 6" x 6"		135	.296		28.50	9.75		38.25	47.50
0350 8" x 8"		190	.211		16.30	6.95		23.25	29.50
0400 12" x 12"		215	.186		23	6.10		29.10	35.50
0410 4" x 8"		215	.186		31	6.10		37.10	44.50
0420 6" x 8"		215	.186		22	6.10		28.10	34.50
0500 Over 5,000 S.F., 6" x 6"		145	.276		27.50	9.10		36.60	45.50
0550 8" x 8"	↓	215	.186	↓	15.80	6.10		21.90	27.50

04 23 Glass Unit Masonry

04 23 13 – Vertical Glass Unit Masonry

	04 23 13.10 Glass Block	Crew	Daily Output	Labor-Hours	Unit	Material	2014 Bare Costs Labor	Equipment	Total	Total Incl O&P
0600	12" x 12"	D-8	240	.167	S.F.	22.50	5.50		28	34
0610	4" x 8"		240	.167		30.50	5.50		36	42.50
0620	6" x 8"	↓	240	.167	↓	21.50	5.50		27	32.50
0700	For solar reflective blocks, add					100%				
1000	Thinline, plain, 3-1/8" thick, under 1,000 S.F., 6" x 6"	D-8	115	.348	S.F.	21	11.45		32.45	42
1050	8" x 8"		160	.250		11.85	8.25		20.10	26.50
1200	Over 5,000 S.F., 6" x 6"		145	.276		20	9.10		29.10	37
1250	8" x 8"		215	.186		11.30	6.10		17.40	22.50
1400	For cleaning block after installation (both sides), add	↓	1000	.040	↓	.16	1.32		1.48	2.37

04 24 Adobe Unit Masonry

04 24 16 – Manufactured Adobe Unit Masonry

04 24 16.06 Adobe Brick

	04 24 16.06 Adobe Brick		Crew	Daily Output	Labor-Hours	Unit	Material	2014 Bare Costs Labor	Equipment	Total	Total Incl O&P
0010	**ADOBE BRICK**, Semi-stabilized, with cement mortar										
0060	Brick, 10" x 4" x 14", 2.6/S.F.	G	D-8	560	.071	S.F.	4.17	2.35		6.52	8.50
0080	12" x 4" x 16", 2.3/S.F.	G		580	.069		6.85	2.27		9.12	11.35
0100	10" x 4" x 16", 2.3/S.F.	G		590	.068		6.30	2.23		8.53	10.65
0120	8" x 4" x 16", 2.3/S.F.	G		560	.071		4.82	2.35		7.17	9.20
0140	4" x 4" x 16", 2.3/S.F.	G		540	.074		4.75	2.44		7.19	9.30
0160	6" x 4" x 16", 2.3/S.F.	G		540	.074		4.39	2.44		6.83	8.90
0180	4" x 4" x 12", 3.0/S.F.	G		520	.077		5	2.53		7.53	9.70
0200	8" x 4" x 12", 3.0/S.F.	G	↓	520	.077	↓	3.98	2.53		6.51	8.60

04 25 Unit Masonry Panels

04 25 20 – Pre-Fabricated Masonry Panels

04 25 20.10 Brick and Epoxy Mortar Panels

	04 25 20.10 Brick and Epoxy Mortar Panels	Crew	Daily Output	Labor-Hours	Unit	Material	2014 Bare Costs Labor	Equipment	Total	Total Incl O&P
0010	**BRICK AND EPOXY MORTAR PANELS**									
0020	Prefabricated brick & epoxy mortar, 4" thick, minimum	C-11	775	.072	S.F.	5.45	2.67	2.37	10.49	13.10
0100	Maximum	"	500	.112		6.65	4.14	3.68	14.47	18.35
0200	For 2" concrete back-up, add					50%				
0300	For 1" urethane & 3" concrete back-up, add				↓	70%				

04 27 Multiple-Wythe Unit Masonry

04 27 10 – Multiple-Wythe Masonry

04 27 10.20 Cavity Walls

	04 27 10.20 Cavity Walls		Crew	Daily Output	Labor-Hours	Unit	Material	2014 Bare Costs Labor	Equipment	Total	Total Incl O&P
0010	**CAVITY WALLS**, brick and CMU, includes joint reinforcing and ties										
0200	4" face brick, 4" block		D-8	165	.242	S.F.	5.75	8		13.75	19.55
0400	6" block			145	.276		6.15	9.10		15.25	22
0600	8" block		↓	125	.320		6.30	10.55		16.85	24.50

04 27 10.30 Brick Walls

	04 27 10.30 Brick Walls		Crew	Daily Output	Labor-Hours	Unit	Material	2014 Bare Costs Labor	Equipment	Total	Total Incl O&P
0010	**BRICK WALLS**, including mortar, excludes scaffolding	R042110-20									
0020	Estimating by number of brick										
0140	Face brick, 4" thick wall, 6.75 brick/S.F.		D-8	1.45	27.586	M	585	910		1,495	2,150
0150	Common brick, 4" thick wall, 6.75 brick/S.F.			1.60	25		585	825		1,410	2,025
0204	8" thick, 13.50 bricks per S.F.			1.80	22.222		600	730		1,330	1,875
0250	12" thick, 20.25 bricks per S.F.			1.90	21.053		605	695		1,300	1,825
0304	16" thick, 27.00 bricks per S.F.		↓	2	20		610	660		1,270	1,775

04 27 Multiple-Wythe Unit Masonry

04 27 10 – Multiple-Wythe Masonry

04 27 10.30 Brick Walls

		Crew	Daily Output	Labor-Hours	Unit	Material	2014 Bare Costs Labor	Equipment	Total	Total Incl O&P
0500	Reinforced, face brick, 4" thick wall, 6.75 brick/S.F.	D-8	1.40	28.571	M	610	940		1,550	2,250
0520	Common brick, 4" thick wall, 6.75 brick/S.F.		1.55	25.806		610	850		1,460	2,100
0550	8" thick, 13.50 bricks per S.F.		1.75	22.857		625	750		1,375	1,950
0600	12" thick, 20.25 bricks per S.F.		1.85	21.622		630	710		1,340	1,875
0650	16" thick, 27.00 bricks per S.F.		1.95	20.513		635	675		1,310	1,825
0790	Alternate method of figuring by square foot									
0800	Face brick, 4" thick wall, 6.75 brick/S.F.	D-8	215	.186	S.F.	3.93	6.10		10.03	14.55
0850	Common brick, 4" thick wall, 6.75 brick/S.F.		240	.167		3.94	5.50		9.44	13.50
0900	8" thick, 13.50 bricks per S.F.		135	.296		8.10	9.75		17.85	25
1000	12" thick, 20.25 bricks per S.F.		95	.421		12.20	13.85		26.05	36.50
1050	16" thick, 27.00 bricks per S.F.		75	.533		16.50	17.55		34.05	47
1200	Reinforced, face brick, 4" thick wall, 6.75 brick/S.F.		210	.190		4.10	6.25		10.35	14.95
1220	Common brick, 4" thick wall, 6.75 brick/S.F.		235	.170		4.11	5.60		9.71	13.80
1250	8" thick, 13.50 bricks per S.F.		130	.308		8.45	10.10		18.55	26
1300	12" thick, 20.25 bricks per S.F.		90	.444		12.75	14.60		27.35	38.50
1350	16" thick, 27.00 bricks per S.F.		70	.571		17.20	18.80		36	50.50

04 27 10.40 Steps

		Crew	Daily Output	Labor-Hours	Unit	Material	2014 Bare Costs Labor	Equipment	Total	Total Incl O&P
0010	**STEPS**									
0012	Entry steps, select common brick	D-1	.30	53.333	M	550	1,725		2,275	3,450

04 41 Dry-Placed Stone

04 41 10 – Dry Placed Stone

04 41 10.10 Rough Stone Wall

			Crew	Daily Output	Labor-Hours	Unit	Material	2014 Bare Costs Labor	Equipment	Total	Total Incl O&P
0011	**ROUGH STONE WALL**, Dry										
0012	Dry laid (no mortar), under 18" thick	G	D-1	60	.267	C.F.	12.40	8.60		21	28
0100	Random fieldstone, under 18" thick	G	D-12	60	.533		12.40	17.20		29.60	42
0150	Over 18" thick	G	"	63	.508		14.85	16.35		31.20	43.50
0500	Field stone veneer	G	D-8	120	.333	S.F.	11.45	10.95		22.40	31
0510	Valley stone veneer	G		120	.333		11.45	10.95		22.40	31
0520	River stone veneer	G		120	.333		11.45	10.95		22.40	31
0600	Rubble stone walls, in mortar bed, up to 18" thick	G	D-11	75	.320	C.F.	14.95	10.65		25.60	34

04 43 Stone Masonry

04 43 10 – Masonry with Natural and Processed Stone

04 43 10.05 Ashlar Veneer

		Crew	Daily Output	Labor-Hours	Unit	Material	2014 Bare Costs Labor	Equipment	Total	Total Incl O&P
0011	**ASHLAR VENEER** 4" + or - thk, random or random rectangular									
0150	Sawn face, split joints, low priced stone	D-8	140	.286	S.F.	11.55	9.40		20.95	28.50
0200	Medium priced stone		130	.308		13.30	10.10		23.40	31.50
0300	High priced stone		120	.333		17.85	10.95		28.80	38
0600	Seam face, split joints, medium price stone		125	.320		20	10.55		30.55	39.50
0700	High price stone		120	.333		20.50	10.95		31.45	41
1000	Split or rock face, split joints, medium price stone		125	.320		14.70	10.55		25.25	33.50
1100	High price stone		120	.333		19.05	10.95		30	39.50

04 43 10.10 Bluestone

		Crew	Daily Output	Labor-Hours	Unit	Material	2014 Bare Costs Labor	Equipment	Total	Total Incl O&P
0010	**BLUESTONE**, cut to size									
0500	Sills, natural cleft, 10" wide to 6' long, 1-1/2" thick	D-11	70	.343	L.F.	13.35	11.45		24.80	33.50
0550	2" thick	"	63	.381		14.60	12.70		27.30	37
1000	Stair treads, natural cleft, 12" wide, 6' long, 1-1/2" thick	D-10	115	.278		12	9.80	4.19	25.99	34
1050	2" thick		105	.305		13	10.70	4.58	28.28	37

04 43 10 – Masonry with Natural and Processed Stone

04 43 10.10 Bluestone	Crew	Daily Output	Labor-Hours	Unit	Material	2014 Bare Costs Labor	Equipment	Total	Total Incl O&P
1100	Smooth finish, 1-1/2" thick	D-10	115	.278	L.F.	12	9.80	4.19	25.99	34
1150	2" thick		105	.305		13	10.70	4.58	28.28	37
1300	Thermal finish, 1-1/2" thick		115	.278		12	9.80	4.19	25.99	34
1350	2" thick		105	.305		13	10.70	4.58	28.28	37

04 43 10.45 Granite

		Crew	Daily Output	Labor-Hours	Unit	Material	Labor	Equipment	Total	Total Incl O&P
0010	**GRANITE**, cut to size									
0050	Veneer, polished face, 3/4" to 1-1/2" thick									
0150	Low price, gray, light gray, etc.	D-10	130	.246	S.F.	26.50	8.65	3.70	38.85	48
0180	Medium price, pink, brown, etc.		130	.246		29.50	8.65	3.70	41.85	51
0220	High price, red, black, etc.		130	.246		42	8.65	3.70	54.35	65
0300	1-1/2" to 2-1/2" thick, veneer									
0350	Low price, gray, light gray, etc.	D-10	130	.246	S.F.	28.50	8.65	3.70	40.85	50
0500	Medium price, pink, brown, etc.		130	.246		33.50	8.65	3.70	45.85	55.50
0550	High price, red, black, etc.		130	.246		52.50	8.65	3.70	64.85	76
0700	2-1/2" to 4" thick, veneer									
0750	Low price, gray, light gray, etc.	D-10	110	.291	S.F.	38.50	10.25	4.38	53.13	64.50
0850	Medium price, pink, brown, etc.		110	.291		44	10.25	4.38	58.63	70.50
0950	High price, red, black, etc.		110	.291		63	10.25	4.38	77.63	91.50
1000	For bush hammered finish, deduct					5%				
1050	Coarse rubbed finish, deduct					10%				
1100	Honed finish, deduct					5%				
1150	Thermal finish, deduct					18%				
2450	For radius under 5', add				L.F.	100%				
2500	Steps, copings, etc., finished on more than one surface									
2550	Minimum	D-10	50	.640	C.F.	91	22.50	9.65	123.15	148
2600	Maximum	"	50	.640	"	146	22.50	9.65	178.15	208
2800	Pavers, 4" x 4" x 4" blocks, split face and joints									
2850	Minimum	D-11	80	.300	S.F.	13.10	10		23.10	31
2900	Maximum	"	80	.300		29	10		39	48.50
4000	Soffits, 2" thick, minimum	D-13	35	1.371		37.50	47	13.75	98.25	135
4100	Maximum		35	1.371		91.50	47	13.75	152.25	193
4200	4" thick, minimum		35	1.371		63	47	13.75	123.75	163
4300	Maximum		35	1.371		119	47	13.75	179.75	224

04 43 10.50 Lightweight Natural Stone

			Crew	Daily Output	Labor-Hours	Unit	Material	Labor	Equipment	Total	Total Incl O&P
0011	**LIGHTWEIGHT NATURAL STONE** Lava type										
0100	Veneer, rubble face, sawed back, irregular shapes	G	D-10	130	.246	S.F.	6.25	8.65	3.70	18.60	25.50
0200	Sawed face and back, irregular shapes	G	"	130	.246	"	6.25	8.65	3.70	18.60	25.50

04 43 10.55 Limestone

		Crew	Daily Output	Labor-Hours	Unit	Material	Labor	Equipment	Total	Total Incl O&P
0010	**LIMESTONE**, cut to size									
0020	Veneer facing panels									
0500	Texture finish, light stick, 4-1/2" thick, 5' x 12'	D-4	300	.133	S.F.	47.50	4.01	.45	51.96	59.50
0750	5" thick, 5' x 14' panels	D-10	275	.116		51.50	4.09	1.75	57.34	65.50
1000	Sugarcube finish, 2" Thick, 3' x 5' panels		275	.116		35	4.09	1.75	40.84	47
1050	3" Thick, 4' x 9' panels		275	.116		38	4.09	1.75	43.84	50
1200	4" Thick, 5' x 11' panels		275	.116		40.50	4.09	1.75	46.34	53.50
1400	Sugarcube, textured finish, 4-1/2" thick, 5' x 12'		275	.116		44.50	4.09	1.75	50.34	57.50
1450	5" thick, 5' x 14' panels		275	.116		53	4.09	1.75	58.84	66.50
2000	Coping, sugarcube finish, top & 2 sides		30	1.067	C.F.	67.50	37.50	16.05	121.05	154
2100	Sills, lintels, jambs, trim, stops, sugarcube finish, average		20	1.600		67.50	56.50	24	148	194
2150	Detailed		20	1.600		67.50	56.50	24	148	194
2300	Steps, extra hard, 14" wide, 6" rise		50	.640	L.F.	25	22.50	9.65	57.15	75.50
3000	Quoins, plain finish, 6" x 12" x 12"	D-12	25	1.280	Ea.	37.50	41.50		79	110

04 43 Stone Masonry

04 43 10 – Masonry with Natural and Processed Stone

04 43 10.55 Limestone	Crew	Daily Output	Labor-Hours	Unit	Material	2014 Bare Costs Labor	Equipment	Total	Total Incl O&P
3050 6" x 16" x 24"	D-12	25	1.280	Ea.	50	41.50		91.50	124

04 43 10.60 Marble

	Crew	Daily Output	Labor-Hours	Unit	Material	Labor	Equipment	Total	Total Incl O&P
0011 **MARBLE**, ashlar, split face, 4" + or - thick, random									
0040 Lengths 1' to 4' & heights 2" to 7-1/2", average	D-8	175	.229	S.F.	14.25	7.50		21.75	28
0100 Base, polished, 3/4" or 7/8" thick, polished, 6" high	D-10	65	.492	L.F.	10.55	17.30	7.40	35.25	49
0300 Carvings or bas relief, from templates, average		80	.400	S.F.	144	14.10	6	164.10	188
0350 Maximum	↓	80	.400	"	335	14.10	6	355.10	400
0600 Columns, cornices, mouldings, etc.									
0650 Hand or special machine cut, average	D-10	35	.914	C.F.	133	32	13.75	178.75	215
0700 Maximum	"	35	.914	"	278	32	13.75	323.75	375
1000 Facing, polished finish, cut to size, 3/4" to 7/8" thick									
1050 Average	D-10	130	.246	S.F.	23.50	8.65	3.70	35.85	44
1100 Maximum		130	.246		33.50	8.65	3.70	45.85	55.50
1300 1-1/4" thick, average		125	.256		17.75	9	3.85	30.60	38.50
1350 Maximum		125	.256		40	9	3.85	52.85	63
1500 2" thick, average		120	.267		40	9.40	4.01	53.41	64
1550 Maximum	↓	120	.267	↓	62	9.40	4.01	75.41	88
1700 Rubbed finish, cut to size, 4" thick									
1740 Average	D-10	100	.320	S.F.	40	11.25	4.81	56.06	68
1780 Maximum	"	100	.320	"	69	11.25	4.81	85.06	100
2200 Window sills, 6" x 3/4" thick	D-1	85	.188	L.F.	10.45	6.05		16.50	21.50
2500 Flooring, polished tiles, 12" x 12" x 3/8" thick									
2510 Thin set, average	D-11	90	.267	S.F.	8.45	8.90		17.35	24
2600 Maximum		90	.267		86	8.90		94.90	109
2700 Mortar bed, average		65	.369		8.45	12.30		20.75	30
2740 Maximum	↓	65	.369	↓	90.50	12.30		102.80	120
2780 Travertine, 3/8" thick, average	D-10	130	.246		9.25	8.65	3.70	21.60	28.50
2790 Maximum	"	130	.246		25.50	8.65	3.70	37.85	46.50
2800 Patio tile, non-slip, 1/2" thick, flame finish	D-11	75	.320	↓	11	10.65		21.65	30
2900 Shower or toilet partitions, 7/8" thick partitions									
3050 3/4" or 1-1/4" thick stiles, polished 2 sides, average	D-11	75	.320	S.F.	45.50	10.65		56.15	68
3201 Soffits, add to above prices				"	20%	100%			
3210 Stairs, risers, 7/8" thick x 6" high	D-10	115	.278	L.F.	15.25	9.80	4.19	29.24	37.50
3360 Treads, 12" wide x 1-1/4" thick	"	115	.278	"	42.50	9.80	4.19	56.49	67.50
3500 Thresholds, 3' long, 7/8" thick, 4" to 5" wide, plain	D-12	24	1.333	Ea.	31.50	43		74.50	106
3550 Beveled		24	1.333	"	67.50	43		110.50	146
3700 Window stools, polished, 7/8" thick, 5" wide	↓	85	.376	L.F.	20.50	12.15		32.65	42.50

04 43 10.75 Sandstone or Brownstone

	Crew	Daily Output	Labor-Hours	Unit	Material	Labor	Equipment	Total	Total Incl O&P
0011 **SANDSTONE OR BROWNSTONE**									
0100 Sawed face veneer, 2-1/2" thick, to 2' x 4' panels	D-10	130	.246	S.F.	19	8.65	3.70	31.35	39.50
0150 4" thick, to 3'-6" x 8'panels		100	.320		19	11.25	4.81	35.06	45
0300 Split face, random sizes	↓	100	.320	↓	13.65	11.25	4.81	29.71	39
0350 Cut stone trim (limestone)									
0360 Ribbon stone, 4" thick, 5' pieces	D-8	120	.333	Ea.	172	10.95		182.95	207
0370 Cove stone, 4" thick, 5' pieces		105	.381		173	12.55		185.55	211
0380 Cornice stone, 10" to 12" wide		90	.444		214	14.60		228.60	260
0390 Band stone, 4" thick, 5' pieces		145	.276		110	9.10		119.10	136
0410 Window and door trim, 3" to 4" wide		160	.250		93.50	8.25		101.75	117
0420 Key stone, 18" long	↓	60	.667	↓	98.50	22		120.50	145

04 43 10.80 Slate		Crew	Daily Output	Labor-Hours	Unit	Material	2014 Bare Costs Labor	Equipment	Total	Total Incl O&P
0010	**SLATE**									
0040	Pennsylvania - blue gray to black									
0050	Vermont - unfading green, mottled green & purple, gray & purple									
0100	Virginia - blue black									
0200	Exterior paving, natural cleft, 1" thick									
0250	6" x 6" Pennsylvania	D-12	100	.320	S.F.	6.75	10.30		17.05	24.50
0300	Vermont		100	.320		11.25	10.30		21.55	29.50
0350	Virginia		100	.320		14.10	10.30		24.40	32.50
0500	24" x 24", Pennsylvania		120	.267		13	8.60		21.60	28.50
0550	Vermont		120	.267		28	8.60		36.60	45
0600	Virginia		120	.267		20.50	8.60		29.10	37
0700	18" x 30" Pennsylvania		120	.267		14.75	8.60		23.35	30.50
0750	Vermont		120	.267		28	8.60		36.60	45
0800	Virginia		120	.267		18.20	8.60		26.80	34.50
1000	Interior flooring, natural cleft, 1/2" thick									
1100	6" x 6" Pennsylvania	D-12	100	.320	S.F.	4	10.30		14.30	21.50
1150	Vermont		100	.320		9.90	10.30		20.20	28
1200	Virginia		100	.320		11.15	10.30		21.45	29.50
1300	24" x 24" Pennsylvania		120	.267		7.75	8.60		16.35	23
1350	Vermont		120	.267		22.50	8.60		31.10	39.50
1400	Virginia		120	.267		14.75	8.60		23.35	30.50
1500	18" x 24" Pennsylvania		120	.267		7.75	8.60		16.35	23
1550	Vermont		120	.267		18	8.60		26.60	34
1600	Virginia		120	.267		14.95	8.60		23.55	31
2000	Facing panels, 1-1/4" thick, to 4' x 4' panels									
2100	Natural cleft finish, Pennsylvania	D-10	180	.178	S.F.	34	6.25	2.67	42.92	50.50
2110	Vermont		180	.178		27	6.25	2.67	35.92	43.50
2120	Virginia		180	.178		33	6.25	2.67	41.92	50
2150	Sand rubbed finish, surface, add					10.15			10.15	11.20
2200	Honed finish, add					7.35			7.35	8.10
2500	Ribbon, natural cleft finish, 1" thick, to 9 S.F.	D-10	80	.400		13.10	14.10	6	33.20	44.50
2550	Sand rubbed finish		80	.400		17.75	14.10	6	37.85	49.50
2600	Honed finish		80	.400		16.50	14.10	6	36.60	48.50
2700	1-1/2" thick		78	.410		17.05	14.45	6.15	37.65	49.50
2750	Sand rubbed finish		78	.410		22.50	14.45	6.15	43.10	56
2800	Honed finish		78	.410		21.50	14.45	6.15	42.10	54.50
2850	2" thick		76	.421		20.50	14.80	6.35	41.65	54
2900	Sand rubbed finish		76	.421		28.50	14.80	6.35	49.65	62.50
2950	Honed finish		76	.421		26	14.80	6.35	47.15	60
3100	Stair landings, 1" thick, black, clear	D-1	65	.246		20	7.95		27.95	35
3200	Ribbon	"	65	.246		22	7.95		29.95	37
3500	Stair treads, sand finish, 1" thick x 12" wide									
3550	Under 3 L.F.	D-10	85	.376	L.F.	22	13.25	5.65	40.90	52.50
3600	3 L.F. to 6 L.F.	"	120	.267	"	24	9.40	4.01	37.41	46
3700	Ribbon, sand finish, 1" thick x 12" wide									
3750	To 6 L.F.	D-10	120	.267	L.F.	20	9.40	4.01	33.41	42
4000	Stools or sills, sand finish, 1" thick, 6" wide	D-12	160	.200		11.50	6.45		17.95	23.50
4100	Honed finish		160	.200		11	6.45		17.45	23
4200	10" wide		90	.356		17.75	11.45		29.20	38.50
4250	Honed finish		90	.356		16.50	11.45		27.95	37
4400	2" thick, 6" wide		140	.229		18.50	7.35		25.85	33
4450	Honed finish		140	.229		17.60	7.35		24.95	31.50

04 43 Stone Masonry

04 43 10 - Masonry with Natural and Processed Stone

04 43 10.80 Slate

		Crew	Daily Output	Labor-Hours	Unit	Material	2014 Bare Costs Labor	Equipment	Total	Total Incl O&P
4600	10" wide	D-12	90	.356	L.F.	29	11.45		40.45	51
4650	Honed finish	↓	90	.356		27.50	11.45		38.95	49.50
4800	For lengths over 3', add				↓	25%				

04 43 10.85 Window Sill

		Crew	Daily Output	Labor-Hours	Unit	Material	2014 Bare Costs Labor	Equipment	Total	Total Incl O&P
0010	**WINDOW SILL**									
0020	Bluestone, thermal top, 10" wide, 1-1/2" thick	D-1	85	.188	S.F.	9.25	6.05		15.30	20.50
0050	2" thick		75	.213	"	8.85	6.90		15.75	21
0100	Cut stone, 5" x 8" plain		48	.333	L.F.	11.90	10.75		22.65	31
0200	Face brick on edge, brick, 8" wide		80	.200		5.30	6.45		11.75	16.55
0400	Marble, 9" wide, 1" thick		85	.188		8.50	6.05		14.55	19.45
0900	Slate, colored, unfading, honed, 12" wide, 1" thick		85	.188		8.50	6.05		14.55	19.45
0950	2" thick	↓	70	.229	↓	8.50	7.35		15.85	21.50

04 51 Flue Liner Masonry

04 51 10 - Clay Flue Lining

04 51 10.10 Flue Lining

		Crew	Daily Output	Labor-Hours	Unit	Material	2014 Bare Costs Labor	Equipment	Total	Total Incl O&P
0010	**FLUE LINING**, including mortar									
0020	Clay, 8" x 8"	D-1	125	.128	V.L.F.	5.30	4.13		9.43	12.65
0100	8" x 12"		103	.155		7.85	5		12.85	17
0200	12" x 12"		93	.172		10.20	5.55		15.75	20.50
0300	12" x 18"		84	.190		20	6.15		26.15	32
0400	18" x 18"		75	.213		26	6.90		32.90	40.50
0500	20" x 20"		66	.242		40	7.80		47.80	57
0600	24" x 24"		56	.286		51.50	9.20		60.70	72
1000	Round, 18" diameter		66	.242		37	7.80		44.80	53.50
1100	24" diameter	↓	47	.340	↓	72	10.95		82.95	97.50

04 54 Refractory Brick Masonry

04 54 10 - Refractory Brick Work

04 54 10.10 Fire Brick

		Crew	Daily Output	Labor-Hours	Unit	Material	2014 Bare Costs Labor	Equipment	Total	Total Incl O&P
0010	**FIRE BRICK**									
0012	Low duty, 2000°F, 9" x 2-1/2" x 4-1/2"	D-1	.60	26.667	M	1,375	860		2,235	2,950
0050	High duty, 3000°F	"	.60	26.667	"	1,800	860		2,660	3,400

04 54 10.20 Fire Clay

		Crew	Daily Output	Labor-Hours	Unit	Material	2014 Bare Costs Labor	Equipment	Total	Total Incl O&P
0010	**FIRE CLAY**									
0020	Gray, high duty, 100 lb. bag				Bag	30			30	33
0050	100 lb. drum, premixed (400 brick per drum)				Drum	41			41	45

04 57 Masonry Fireplaces

04 57 10 – Brick or Stone Fireplaces

04 57 10.10 Fireplace

		Crew	Daily Output	Labor-Hours	Unit	Material	2014 Bare Costs Labor	2014 Bare Costs Equipment	Total	Total Incl O&P
0010	**FIREPLACE**									
0100	Brick fireplace, not incl. foundations or chimneys									
0110	30" x 29" opening, incl. chamber, plain brickwork	D-1	.40	40	Ea.	550	1,300		1,850	2,750
0200	Fireplace box only (110 brick)	"	2	8	"	157	258		415	600
0300	For elaborate brickwork and details, add					35%	35%			
0400	For hearth, brick & stone, add	D-1	2	8	Ea.	205	258		463	655
0410	For steel, damper, cleanouts, add		4	4		19.40	129		148.40	237
0600	Plain brickwork, incl. metal circulator		.50	32		985	1,025		2,010	2,800
0800	Face brick only, standard size, 8" x 2-2/3" x 4"		.30	53.333	M	550	1,725		2,275	3,450

04 71 Manufactured Brick Masonry

04 71 10 – Simulated or Manufactured Brick

04 71 10.10 Simulated Brick

		Crew	Daily Output	Labor-Hours	Unit	Material	2014 Bare Costs Labor	2014 Bare Costs Equipment	Total	Total Incl O&P
0010	**SIMULATED BRICK**									
0020	Aluminum, baked on colors	1 Carp	200	.040	S.F.	3.92	1.43		5.35	6.70
0050	Fiberglass panels		200	.040		8.05	1.43		9.48	11.25
0100	Urethane pieces cemented in mastic		150	.053		8.25	1.91		10.16	12.25
0150	Vinyl siding panels		200	.040		9.70	1.43		11.13	13.10
0160	Cement base, brick, incl. mastic	D-1	100	.160		9.65	5.15		14.80	19.20
0170	Corner		50	.320	V.L.F.	20.50	10.30		30.80	39.50
0180	Stone face, incl. mastic		100	.160	S.F.	8.90	5.15		14.05	18.40
0190	Corner		50	.320	V.L.F.	20.50	10.30		30.80	39.50

04 72 Cast Stone Masonry

04 72 10 – Cast Stone Masonry Features

04 72 10.10 Coping

		Crew	Daily Output	Labor-Hours	Unit	Material	2014 Bare Costs Labor	2014 Bare Costs Equipment	Total	Total Incl O&P
0010	**COPING**, stock units									
0050	Precast concrete, 10" wide, 4" tapers to 3-1/2", 8" wall	D-1	75	.213	L.F.	17.10	6.90		24	30.50
0100	12" wide, 3-1/2" tapers to 3", 10" wall		70	.229		18.45	7.35		25.80	33
0110	14" wide, 4" tapers to 3-1/2", 12" wall		65	.246		20.50	7.95		28.45	35.50
0150	16" wide, 4" tapers to 3-1/2", 14" wall		60	.267		22	8.60		30.60	39
0250	Precast concrete corners		40	.400	Ea.	29	12.90		41.90	53
0300	Limestone for 12" wall, 4" thick		90	.178	L.F.	14.70	5.75		20.45	25.50
0350	6" thick		80	.200		22	6.45		28.45	35.50
0500	Marble, to 4" thick, no wash, 9" wide		90	.178		13.70	5.75		19.45	24.50
0550	12" wide		80	.200		15.70	6.45		22.15	28
0700	Terra cotta, 9" wide		90	.178		6.15	5.75		11.90	16.30
0750	12" wide		80	.200		8.40	6.45		14.85	20
0800	Aluminum, for 12" wall		80	.200		8.90	6.45		15.35	20.50

04 72 20 – Cultured Stone Veneer

04 72 20.10 Cultured Stone Veneer Components

		Crew	Daily Output	Labor-Hours	Unit	Material	2014 Bare Costs Labor	2014 Bare Costs Equipment	Total	Total Incl O&P
0010	**CULTURED STONE VENEER COMPONENTS**									
0110	On wood frame and sheathing substrate, random sized cobbles, corner stones	D-8	70	.571	V.L.F.	9.10	18.80		27.90	41.50
0120	Field stones		140	.286	S.F.	6.65	9.40		16.05	23
0130	Random sized flats, corner stones		70	.571	V.L.F.	9.35	18.80		28.15	42
0140	Field stones		140	.286	S.F.	7.55	9.40		16.95	24
0150	Horizontal lined ledgestones, corner stones		75	.533	V.L.F.	9.30	17.55		26.85	39
0160	Field stones		150	.267	S.F.	6.85	8.75		15.60	22
0170	Random shaped flats, corner stones		65	.615	V.L.F.	9.30	20.50		29.80	43.50

04 72 Cast Stone Masonry

04 72 20 – Cultured Stone Veneer

04 72 20.10 Cultured Stone Veneer Components	Crew	Daily Output	Labor-Hours	Unit	Material	2014 Bare Costs Labor	2014 Bare Costs Equipment	Total	Total Incl O&P
0180	Field stones	D-8	150	.267	S.F.	6.85	8.75		15.60	22
0190	Random shaped/textured face, corner stones		65	.615	V.L.F.	9.10	20.50		29.60	43.50
0200	Field stones		130	.308	S.F.	6.85	10.10		16.95	24.50
0210	Random shaped river rock, corner stones		65	.615	V.L.F.	9.10	20.50		29.60	43.50
0220	Field stones		130	.308	S.F.	6.85	10.10		16.95	24.50
0240	On concrete or CMU substrate, random sized cobbles, corner stones		70	.571	V.L.F.	8.45	18.80		27.25	41
0250	Field stones		140	.286	S.F.	6.30	9.40		15.70	22.50
0260	Random sized flats, corner stones		70	.571	V.L.F.	8.70	18.80		27.50	41
0270	Field stones		140	.286	S.F.	7.20	9.40		16.60	23.50
0280	Horizontal lined ledgestones, corner stones		75	.533	V.L.F.	8.60	17.55		26.15	38.50
0290	Field stones		150	.267	S.F.	6.50	8.75		15.25	22
0300	Random shaped flats, corner stones		70	.571	V.L.F.	8.60	18.80		27.40	41
0310	Field stones		140	.286	S.F.	6.50	9.40		15.90	23
0320	Random shaped/textured face, corner stones		65	.615	V.L.F.	8.45	20.50		28.95	43
0330	Field stones		130	.308	S.F.	6.55	10.10		16.65	24
0340	Random shaped river rock, corner stones		65	.615	V.L.F.	8.45	20.50		28.95	43
0350	Field stones	▼	130	.308	S.F.	6.55	10.10		16.65	24
0360	Cultured stone veneer, #15 felt weather resistant barrier	1 Clab	3700	.002	Sq.	5.40	.06		5.46	6.05
0370	Expanded metal lath, diamond, 2.5 lb./S.Y., galvanized	1 Lath	85	.094	S.Y.	3.05	2.98		6.03	8.15
0390	Water table or window sill, 18" long	1 Bric	80	.100	Ea.	9.50	3.56		13.06	16.40

04 73 Manufactured Stone Masonry

04 73 20 – Simulated or Manufactured Stone

04 73 20.10 Simulated Stone

		Crew	Daily Output	Labor-Hours	Unit	Material	Labor	Equipment	Total	Total Incl O&P
0010	**SIMULATED STONE**									
0100	Insulated fiberglass panels, 5/8" ply backer	L-4	200	.080	S.F.	10.55	2.53		13.08	15.85

Division Notes

	CREW	DAILY OUTPUT	LABOR-HOURS	UNIT	BARE COSTS				TOTAL INCL O&P
					MAT.	LABOR	EQUIP.	TOTAL	

Estimating Tips

05 05 00 Common Work Results for Metals

- Nuts, bolts, washers, connection angles, and plates can add a significant amount to both the tonnage of a structural steel job and the estimated cost. As a rule of thumb, add 10% to the total weight to account for these accessories.

- Type 2 steel construction, commonly referred to as "simple construction," consists generally of field-bolted connections with lateral bracing supplied by other elements of the building, such as masonry walls or x-bracing. The estimator should be aware, however, that shop connections may be accomplished by welding or bolting. The method may be particular to the fabrication shop and may have an impact on the estimated cost.

05 10 00 Structural Steel

- Steel items can be obtained from two sources: a fabrication shop or a metals service center. Fabrication shops can fabricate items under more controlled conditions than can crews in the field. They are also more efficient and can produce items more economically. Metal service centers serve as a source of long mill shapes to both fabrication shops and contractors.

- Most line items in this structural steel subdivision, and most items in 05 50 00 Metal Fabrications, are indicated as being shop fabricated. The bare material cost for these shop fabricated items is the "Invoice Cost" from the shop and includes the mill base price of steel plus mill extras, transportation to the shop, shop drawings and detailing where warranted, shop fabrication and handling, sandblasting and a shop coat of primer paint, all necessary structural bolts, and delivery to the job site. The bare labor cost and bare equipment cost for these shop fabricated items is for field installation or erection.

- Line items in Subdivision 05 12 23.40 Lightweight Framing, and other items scattered in Division 5, are indicated as being field fabricated. The bare material cost for these field fabricated items is the "Invoice Cost" from the metals service center and includes the mill base price of steel plus mill extras, transportation to the metals service center, material handling, and delivery of long lengths of mill shapes to the job site. Material costs for structural bolts and welding rods should be added to the estimate. The bare labor cost and bare equipment cost for these items is for both field fabrication and field installation or erection, and include time for cutting, welding and drilling in the fabricated metal items. Drilling into concrete and fasteners to fasten field fabricated items to other work are not included and should be added to the estimate.

05 20 00 Steel Joist Framing

- In any given project the total weight of open web steel joists is determined by the loads to be supported and the design. However, economies can be realized in minimizing the amount of labor used to place the joists. This is done by maximizing the joist spacing, and therefore minimizing the number of joists required to be installed on the job. Certain spacings and locations may be required by the design, but in other cases maximizing the spacing and keeping it as uniform as possible will keep the costs down.

05 30 00 Steel Decking

- The takeoff and estimating of metal deck involves more than simply the area of the floor or roof and the type of deck specified or shown on the drawings. Many different sizes and types of openings may exist. Small openings for individual pipes or conduits may be drilled after the floor/roof is installed, but larger openings may require special deck lengths as well as reinforcing or structural support. The estimator should determine who will be supplying this reinforcing. Additionally, some deck terminations are part of the deck package, such as screed angles and pour stops, and others will be part of the steel contract, such as angles attached to structural members and cast-in-place angles and plates. The estimator must ensure that all pieces are accounted for in the complete estimate.

05 50 00 Metal Fabrications

- The most economical steel stairs are those that use common materials, standard details, and most importantly, a uniform and relatively simple method of field assembly. Commonly available A36 channels and plates are very good choices for the main stringers of the stairs, as are angles and tees for the carrier members. Risers and treads are usually made by specialty shops, and it is most economical to use a typical detail in as many places as possible. The stairs should be pre-assembled and shipped directly to the site. The field connections should be simple and straightforward to be accomplished efficiently, and with minimum equipment and labor.

Reference Numbers

Reference numbers are shown in shaded boxes at the beginning of some major classifications. These numbers refer to related items in the Reference Section. The reference information may be an estimating procedure, an alternate pricing method, or technical information. *Note:* Not all subdivisions listed here necessarily appear in this publication.

05 01 Maintenance of Metals

05 01 10 – Maintenance of Structural Metal Framing

05 01 10.51 Cleaning of Structural Metal Framing	Crew	Daily Output	Labor-Hours	Unit	Material	2014 Bare Costs Labor	Equipment	Total	Total Incl O&P
0010 **CLEANING OF STRUCTURAL METAL FRAMING**									
6125 Steel surface treatments, PDCA guidelines									
6171 Wire brush, hand (SSPC-SP2)	1 Pord	400	.020	S.F.	.02	.63		.65	1.06
6181 Power tool (SSPC-SP3)		700	.011		.09	.36		.45	.68
6215 Pressure washing, up to 5000 psi, 5000-15,000 S.F./day		10000	.001			.03		.03	.04
6220 Steam cleaning, 600 psi @ 300 F, 1250 – 2500 S.F./day		2000	.004			.13		.13	.21
6225 Water blasting, up to 25,000 psi, 1750 – 3500 S.F./day		2500	.003			.10		.10	.16
6230 Brush-off blast (SSPC-SP7)	E-11	1750	.018		.17	.59	.14	.90	1.39
6235 Com'l blast (SSPC-SP6), loose scale, fine pwder rust, 2.0#/S.F. sand		1200	.027		.33	.86	.20	1.39	2.14
6240 Tight mill scale, little/no rust, 3.0#/S.F. sand		1000	.032		.50	1.03	.24	1.77	2.67
6245 Exist coat blistered/pitted, 4.0#/S.F. sand		875	.037		.67	1.17	.27	2.11	3.16
6250 Exist coat badly pitted/nodules, 6.7#/S.F. sand		825	.039		1.12	1.25	.29	2.66	3.80
6255 Near white blast (SSPC-SP10), loose scale, fine rust, 5.6#/S.F. sand		450	.071		.94	2.28	.53	3.75	5.75
6260 Tight mill scale, little/no rust, 6.9#/S.F. sand		325	.098		1.16	3.16	.73	5.05	7.75
6265 Exist coat blistered/pitted, 9.0#/S.F. sand		225	.142		1.51	4.57	1.05	7.13	11.05
6270 Exist coat badly pitted/nodules, 11.3#/S.F. sand		150	.213		1.89	6.85	1.58	10.32	16.15

05 05 Common Work Results for Metals

05 05 05 – Selective Metals Demolition

05 05 05.10 Selective Demolition, Metals

		Crew	Daily Output	Labor-Hours	Unit	Material	2014 Bare Costs Labor	Equipment	Total	Total Incl O&P
0010	**SELECTIVE DEMOLITION, METALS** R024119-10									
0015	Excludes shores, bracing, cutting, loading, hauling, dumping									
0020	Remove nuts only up to 3/4" diameter	1 Sswk	480	.017	Ea.		.64		.64	1.22
0030	7/8" to 1-1/4" diameter		240	.033			1.28		1.28	2.43
0040	1-3/8" to 2" diameter		160	.050			1.92		1.92	3.65
0060	Unbolt and remove structural bolts up to 3/4" diameter		240	.033			1.28		1.28	2.43
0070	7/8" to 2" diameter		160	.050			1.92		1.92	3.65
0140	Light weight framing members, remove whole or cut up, up to 20 lb.		240	.033			1.28		1.28	2.43
0150	21 – 40 lb.	2 Sswk	210	.076			2.92		2.92	5.55
0160	41 – 80 lb.	3 Sswk	180	.133			5.10		5.10	9.75
0170	81 – 120 lb.	4 Sswk	150	.213			8.20		8.20	15.60
0230	Structural members, remove whole or cut up, up to 500 lb.	E-19	48	.500			19.15	20	39.15	57
0240	1/4 – 2 tons	E-18	36	1.111			43	26.50	69.50	109
0250	2 – 5 tons	E-24	30	1.067			40.50	25	65.50	103
0260	5 – 10 tons	E-20	24	2.667			101	49	150	241
0270	10 – 15 tons	E-2	18	2.667			103	85	188	287
0340	Fabricated item, remove whole or cut up, up to 20 lb.	1 Sswk	96	.083			3.20		3.20	6.10
0350	21 – 40 lb.	2 Sswk	84	.190			7.30		7.30	13.90
0360	41 – 80 lb.	3 Sswk	72	.333			12.80		12.80	24.50
0370	81 – 120 lb.	4 Sswk	60	.533			20.50		20.50	39
0380	121 – 500 lb.	E-19	48	.500			19.15	20	39.15	57
0390	501 – 1000 lb.	"	36	.667			25.50	26.50	52	76
0500	Steel roof decking, uncovered, bare	B-2	5000	.008	S.F.		.23		.23	.39

05 05 13 – Shop-Applied Coatings for Metal

05 05 13.50 Paints and Protective Coatings

		Crew	Daily Output	Labor-Hours	Unit	Material	2014 Bare Costs Labor	Equipment	Total	Total Incl O&P
0010	**PAINTS AND PROTECTIVE COATINGS**									
5900	Galvanizing structural steel in shop, under 1 ton R050516-30				Ton	550			550	605
5950	1 ton to 20 tons					505			505	555
6000	Over 20 tons					460			460	505

05 05 19 – Post-Installed Concrete Anchors

05 05 19.10 Chemical Anchors		Crew	Daily Output	Labor-Hours	Unit	Material	2014 Bare Costs Labor	Equipment	Total	Total Incl O&P
0010	**CHEMICAL ANCHORS**									
0020	Includes layout & drilling									
1430	Chemical anchor, w/rod & epoxy cartridge, 3/4" diam. x 9-1/2" long	B-89A	27	.593	Ea.	9.75	19.10	4.30	33.15	47.50
1435	1" diameter x 11-3/4" long		24	.667		16.70	21.50	4.84	43.04	60
1440	1-1/4" diameter x 14" long		21	.762		36	24.50	5.55	66.05	87.50
1445	1-3/4" diameter x 15" long		20	.800		64.50	26	5.80	96.30	121
1450	18" long		17	.941		77.50	30.50	6.85	114.85	144
1455	2" diameter x 18" long		16	1		102	32.50	7.25	141.75	175
1460	24" long		15	1.067		132	34.50	7.75	174.25	213

05 05 19.20 Expansion Anchors			Crew	Daily Output	Labor-Hours	Unit	Material	2014 Bare Costs Labor	Equipment	Total	Total Incl O&P
0010	**EXPANSION ANCHORS**										
0100	Anchors for concrete, brick or stone, no layout and drilling										
0200	Expansion shields, zinc, 1/4" diameter, 1-5/16" long, single	G	1 Carp	90	.089	Ea.	.48	3.18		3.66	5.90
0300	1-3/8" long, double	G		85	.094		.59	3.36		3.95	6.30
0400	3/8" diameter, 1-1/2" long, single	G		85	.094		.81	3.36		4.17	6.55
0500	2" long, double	G		80	.100		1.32	3.58		4.90	7.45
0600	1/2" diameter, 2-1/16" long, single	G		80	.100		1.62	3.58		5.20	7.80
0700	2-1/2" long, double	G		75	.107		2.10	3.81		5.91	8.70
0800	5/8" diameter, 2-5/8" long, single	G		75	.107		2.85	3.81		6.66	9.55
0900	2-3/4" long, double	G		70	.114		2.99	4.09		7.08	10.15
1000	3/4" diameter, 2-3/4" long, single	G		70	.114		3.25	4.09		7.34	10.45
1100	3-15/16" long, double	G		65	.123		5.80	4.40		10.20	13.80
2100	Hollow wall anchors for gypsum wall board, plaster or tile										
2300	1/8" diameter, short	G	1 Carp	160	.050	Ea.	.23	1.79		2.02	3.26
2400	Long	G		150	.053		.23	1.91		2.14	3.46
2500	3/16" diameter, short	G		150	.053		.40	1.91		2.31	3.65
2600	Long	G		140	.057		.58	2.04		2.62	4.08
2700	1/4" diameter, short	G		140	.057		.62	2.04		2.66	4.12
2800	Long	G		130	.062		.61	2.20		2.81	4.37
3000	Toggle bolts, bright steel, 1/8" diameter, 2" long	G		85	.094		.19	3.36		3.55	5.85
3100	4" long	G		80	.100		.25	3.58		3.83	6.30
3200	3/16" diameter, 3" long	G		80	.100		.26	3.58		3.84	6.30
3300	6" long	G		75	.107		.35	3.81		4.16	6.80
3400	1/4" diameter, 3" long	G		75	.107		.34	3.81		4.15	6.75
3500	6" long	G		70	.114		.50	4.09		4.59	7.40
3600	3/8" diameter, 3" long	G		70	.114		.82	4.09		4.91	7.75
3700	6" long	G		60	.133		1.24	4.77		6.01	9.35
3800	1/2" diameter, 4" long	G		60	.133		1.84	4.77		6.61	10
3900	6" long	G		50	.160		2.40	5.70		8.10	12.25
4000	Nailing anchors										
4100	Nylon nailing anchor, 1/4" diameter, 1" long		1 Carp	3.20	2.500	C	16.35	89.50		105.85	168
4200	1-1/2" long			2.80	2.857		21	102		123	196
4300	2" long			2.40	3.333		25.50	119		144.50	229
4400	Metal nailing anchor, 1/4" diameter, 1" long	G		3.20	2.500		17.60	89.50		107.10	169
4500	1-1/2" long	G		2.80	2.857		22.50	102		124.50	197
4600	2" long	G		2.40	3.333		28	119		147	232
5000	Screw anchors for concrete, masonry,										
5100	stone & tile, no layout or drilling included										
5700	Lag screw shields, 1/4" diameter, short	G	1 Carp	90	.089	Ea.	.37	3.18		3.55	5.75
5800	Long	G		85	.094		.41	3.36		3.77	6.10
5900	3/8" diameter, short	G		85	.094		.65	3.36		4.01	6.35
6000	Long	G		80	.100		.78	3.58		4.36	6.85

05 05 Common Work Results for Metals

05 05 19 – Post-Installed Concrete Anchors

05 05 19.20 Expansion Anchors		Crew	Daily Output	Labor-Hours	Unit	Material	2014 Bare Costs Labor	Equipment	Total	Total Incl O&P
6100	1/2" diameter, short	G 1 Carp	80	.100	Ea.	1.05	3.58		4.63	7.15
6200	Long	G	75	.107		1.18	3.81		4.99	7.70
6300	5/8" diameter, short	G	70	.114		1.81	4.09		5.90	8.85
6400	Long	G	65	.123		2	4.40		6.40	9.60
6600	Lead, #6 & #8, 3/4" long	G	260	.031		.18	1.10		1.28	2.05
6700	#10 - #14, 1-1/2" long	G	200	.040		.29	1.43		1.72	2.73
6800	#16 & #18, 1-1/2" long	G	160	.050		.39	1.79		2.18	3.44
6900	Plastic, #6 & #8, 3/4" long		260	.031		.04	1.10		1.14	1.89
7000	#8 & #10, 7/8" long		240	.033		.04	1.19		1.23	2.04
7100	#10 & #12, 1" long		220	.036		.05	1.30		1.35	2.25
7200	#14 & #16, 1-1/2" long		160	.050		.07	1.79		1.86	3.09
8000	Wedge anchors, not including layout or drilling									
8050	Carbon steel, 1/4" diameter, 1-3/4" long	G 1 Carp	150	.053	Ea.	.40	1.91		2.31	3.65
8100	3-1/4" long	G	140	.057		.53	2.04		2.57	4.02
8150	3/8" diameter, 2-1/4" long	G	145	.055		.49	1.97		2.46	3.86
8200	5" long	G	140	.057		.86	2.04		2.90	4.39
8250	1/2" diameter, 2-3/4" long	G	140	.057		.97	2.04		3.01	4.51
8300	7" long	G	125	.064		1.66	2.29		3.95	5.70
8350	5/8" diameter, 3-1/2" long	G	130	.062		1.69	2.20		3.89	5.55
8400	8-1/2" long	G	115	.070		3.60	2.49		6.09	8.15
8450	3/4" diameter, 4-1/4" long	G	115	.070		2.81	2.49		5.30	7.25
8500	10" long	G	95	.084		6.40	3.01		9.41	12.10
8550	1" diameter, 6" long	G	100	.080		9.05	2.86		11.91	14.75
8575	9" long	G	85	.094		11.75	3.36		15.11	18.60
8600	12" long	G	75	.107		12.70	3.81		16.51	20.50
8650	1-1/4" diameter, 9" long	G	70	.114		24	4.09		28.09	33
8700	12" long	G	60	.133		30.50	4.77		35.27	41.50
8750	For type 303 stainless steel, add					350%				
8800	For type 316 stainless steel, add					450%				
8950	Self-drilling concrete screw, hex washer head, 3/16" diam. x 1-3/4" long	G 1 Carp	300	.027	Ea.	.20	.95		1.15	1.82
8960	2-1/4" long	G	250	.032		.23	1.14		1.37	2.17
8970	Phillips flat head, 3/16" diam. x 1-3/4" long	G	300	.027		.20	.95		1.15	1.82
8980	2-1/4" long	G	250	.032		.23	1.14		1.37	2.17

05 05 21 – Fastening Methods for Metal

05 05 21.10 Cutting Steel

		Crew	Daily Output	Labor-Hours	Unit	Material	Labor	Equipment	Total	Total Incl O&P
0010	**CUTTING STEEL**									
0020	Hand burning, incl. preparation, torch cutting & grinding, no staging									
0050	Steel to 1/4" thick	E-25	400	.020	L.F.	.17	.77	.03	.97	1.68
0100	1/2" thick		320	.025		.32	.96	.04	1.32	2.22
0150	3/4" thick		260	.031		.53	1.18	.04	1.75	2.88
0200	1" thick		200	.040		.76	1.53	.06	2.35	3.81

05 05 21.15 Drilling Steel

		Crew	Daily Output	Labor-Hours	Unit	Material	Labor	Equipment	Total	Total Incl O&P
0010	**DRILLING STEEL**									
1910	Drilling & layout for steel, up to 1/4" deep, no anchor									
1920	Holes, 1/4" diameter	1 Sswk	112	.071	Ea.	.08	2.74		2.82	5.30
1925	For each additional 1/4" depth, add		336	.024		.08	.91		.99	1.83
1930	3/8" diameter		104	.077		.09	2.95		3.04	5.70
1935	For each additional 1/4" depth, add		312	.026		.09	.98		1.07	1.97
1940	1/2" diameter		96	.083		.09	3.20		3.29	6.20
1945	For each additional 1/4" depth, add		288	.028		.09	1.07		1.16	2.13
1950	5/8" diameter		88	.091		.13	3.49		3.62	6.80
1955	For each additional 1/4" depth, add		264	.030		.13	1.16		1.29	2.36

05 05 Common Work Results for Metals

05 05 21 – Fastening Methods for Metal

05 05 21.15 Drilling Steel

		Crew	Daily Output	Labor-Hours	Unit	Material	2014 Bare Costs Labor	2014 Bare Costs Equipment	Total	Total Incl O&P
1960	3/4" diameter	1 Sswk	80	.100	Ea.	.17	3.84		4.01	7.50
1965	For each additional 1/4" depth, add		240	.033		.17	1.28		1.45	2.61
1970	7/8" diameter		72	.111		.22	4.26		4.48	8.35
1975	For each additional 1/4" depth, add		216	.037		.22	1.42		1.64	2.95
1980	1" diameter		64	.125		.23	4.79		5.02	9.40
1985	For each additional 1/4" depth, add	↓	192	.042		.23	1.60		1.83	3.29
1990	For drilling up, add				↓		40%			

05 05 21.90 Welding Steel

			Crew	Daily Output	Labor-Hours	Unit	Material	2014 Bare Costs Labor	2014 Bare Costs Equipment	Total	Total Incl O&P
0010	**WELDING STEEL**, Structural	R050521-20									
0020	Field welding, 1/8" E6011, cost per welder, no operating engineer		E-14	8	1	Hr.	4.33	38.50	17.75	60.58	97.50
0200	With 1/2 operating engineer		E-13	8	1.500		4.33	58.50	17.75	80.58	131
0300	With 1 operating engineer		E-12	8	2	↓	4.33	76.50	17.75	98.58	161
0500	With no operating engineer, 2# weld rod per ton		E-14	8	1	Ton	4.33	38.50	17.75	60.58	97.50
0600	8# E6011 per ton		"	2	4		17.30	153	71	241.30	390
0800	With one operating engineer per welder, 2# E6011 per ton		E-12	8	2		4.33	76.50	17.75	98.58	161
0900	8# E6011 per ton		"	2	8	↓	17.30	305	71	393.30	645
1200	Continuous fillet, down welding										
1300	Single pass, 1/8" thick, 0.1#/L.F.		E-14	150	.053	L.F.	.22	2.05	.95	3.22	5.20
1400	3/16" thick, 0.2#/L.F.			75	.107		.43	4.09	1.89	6.41	10.35
1500	1/4" thick, 0.3#/L.F.			50	.160		.65	6.15	2.84	9.64	15.55
1610	5/16" thick, 0.4#/L.F.			38	.211		.87	8.05	3.74	12.66	20.50
1800	3 passes, 3/8" thick, 0.5#/L.F.			30	.267		1.08	10.25	4.73	16.06	26
2010	4 passes, 1/2" thick, 0.7#/L.F.			22	.364		1.52	13.95	6.45	21.92	35.50
2200	5 to 6 passes, 3/4" thick, 1.3#/L.F.			12	.667		2.81	25.50	11.85	40.16	64.50
2400	8 to 11 passes, 1" thick, 2.4#/L.F.		↓	6	1.333		5.20	51	23.50	79.70	129
2600	For vertical joint welding, add							20%			
2700	Overhead joint welding, add							300%			
2900	For semi-automatic welding, obstructed joints, deduct							5%			
3000	Exposed joints, deduct					↓		15%			
4000	Cleaning and welding plates, bars, or rods										
4010	to existing beams, columns, or trusses		E-14	12	.667	L.F.	1.08	25.50	11.85	38.43	62.50

05 05 23 – Metal Fastenings

05 05 23.10 Bolts and Hex Nuts

			Crew	Daily Output	Labor-Hours	Unit	Material	2014 Bare Costs Labor	2014 Bare Costs Equipment	Total	Total Incl O&P
0010	**BOLTS & HEX NUTS**, Steel, A307										
0100	1/4" diameter, 1/2" long	G	1 Sswk	140	.057	Ea.	.06	2.19		2.25	4.24
0200	1" long	G		140	.057		.07	2.19		2.26	4.25
0300	2" long	G		130	.062		.10	2.36		2.46	4.61
0400	3" long	G		130	.062		.15	2.36		2.51	4.67
0500	4" long	G		120	.067		.17	2.56		2.73	5.05
0600	3/8" diameter, 1" long	G		130	.062		.14	2.36		2.50	4.66
0700	2" long	G		130	.062		.18	2.36		2.54	4.70
0800	3" long	G		120	.067		.24	2.56		2.80	5.15
0900	4" long	G		120	.067		.30	2.56		2.86	5.20
1000	5" long	G		115	.070		.38	2.67		3.05	5.50
1100	1/2" diameter, 1-1/2" long	G		120	.067		.40	2.56		2.96	5.30
1200	2" long	G		120	.067		.46	2.56		3.02	5.40
1300	4" long	G		115	.070		.75	2.67		3.42	5.95
1400	6" long	G		110	.073		1.05	2.79		3.84	6.45
1500	8" long	G		105	.076		1.38	2.92		4.30	7.05
1600	5/8" diameter, 1-1/2" long	G		120	.067		.98	2.56		3.54	5.95
1700	2" long	G		120	.067		1.09	2.56		3.65	6.05
1800	4" long	G		115	.070		1.59	2.67		4.26	6.85

05 05 23 – Metal Fastenings

05 05 23.10 Bolts and Hex Nuts		Crew	Daily Output	Labor-Hours	Unit	Material	2014 Bare Costs Labor	2014 Bare Costs Equipment	Total	Total Incl O&P
1900	6" long	G	1 Sswk	110	.073	Ea.	2.05	2.79		4.84	7.55
2000	8" long	G		105	.076		3.06	2.92		5.98	8.90
2100	10" long	G		100	.080		3.87	3.07		6.94	10.10
2200	3/4" diameter, 2" long	G		120	.067		1.15	2.56		3.71	6.15
2300	4" long	G		110	.073		1.65	2.79		4.44	7.10
2400	6" long	G		105	.076		2.12	2.92		5.04	7.90
2500	8" long	G		95	.084		3.20	3.23		6.43	9.65
2600	10" long	G		85	.094		4.20	3.61		7.81	11.50
2700	12" long	G		80	.100		4.92	3.84		8.76	12.70
2800	1" diameter, 3" long	G		105	.076		2.69	2.92		5.61	8.50
2900	6" long	G		90	.089		3.94	3.41		7.35	10.85
3000	12" long	G		75	.107		7.10	4.09		11.19	15.60
3100	For galvanized, add						75%				
3200	For stainless, add						350%				

05 05 23.25 High Strength Bolts		Crew	Daily Output	Labor-Hours	Unit	Material	2014 Bare Costs Labor	2014 Bare Costs Equipment	Total	Total Incl O&P
0010	**HIGH STRENGTH BOLTS** R050523-10										
0020	A325 Type 1, structural steel, bolt-nut-washer set										
0100	1/2" diameter x 1-1/2" long	G	1 Sswk	130	.062	Ea.	.97	2.36		3.33	5.55
0120	2" long	G		125	.064		1.05	2.45		3.50	5.85
0150	3" long	G		120	.067		1.46	2.56		4.02	6.50
0170	5/8" diameter x 1-1/2" long	G		125	.064		1.67	2.45		4.12	6.50
0180	2" long	G		120	.067		1.79	2.56		4.35	6.85
0190	3" long	G		115	.070		2.20	2.67		4.87	7.50
0200	3/4" diameter x 2" long	G		120	.067		2.70	2.56		5.26	7.85
0220	3" long	G		115	.070		3.23	2.67		5.90	8.65
0250	4" long	G		110	.073		3.95	2.79		6.74	9.65
0300	6" long	G		105	.076		5.10	2.92		8.02	11.15
0350	8" long	G		95	.084		10.05	3.23		13.28	17.20
0360	7/8" diameter x 2" long	G		115	.070		3.70	2.67		6.37	9.15
0365	3" long	G		110	.073		4.36	2.79		7.15	10.10
0370	4" long	G		105	.076		5.25	2.92		8.17	11.35
0380	6" long	G		100	.080		6.65	3.07		9.72	13.20
0390	8" long	G		90	.089		10.55	3.41		13.96	18.10
0400	1" diameter x 2" long	G		105	.076		4.55	2.92		7.47	10.55
0420	3" long	G		100	.080		5.15	3.07		8.22	11.50
0450	4" long	G		95	.084		5.85	3.23		9.08	12.55
0500	6" long	G		90	.089		7.75	3.41		11.16	15
0550	8" long	G		85	.094		13.45	3.61		17.06	21.50
0600	1-1/4" diameter x 3" long	G		85	.094		10.60	3.61		14.21	18.55
0650	4" long	G		80	.100		11.55	3.84		15.39	20
0700	6" long	G		75	.107		15	4.09		19.09	24.50
0750	8" long	G		70	.114		19.15	4.38		23.53	29.50
1020	A490, bolt-nut-washer set										
1170	5/8" diameter x 1-1/2" long	G	1 Sswk	125	.064	Ea.	4.48	2.45		6.93	9.60
1180	2" long	G		120	.067		5.35	2.56		7.91	10.70
1190	3" long	G		115	.070		6.55	2.67		9.22	12.30
1200	3/4" diameter x 2" long	G		120	.067		3.84	2.56		6.40	9.10
1220	3" long	G		115	.070		4.54	2.67		7.21	10.10
1250	4" long	G		110	.073		5.30	2.79		8.09	11.10
1300	6" long	G		105	.076		7.75	2.92		10.67	14.10
1350	8" long	G		95	.084		13.20	3.23		16.43	20.50
1360	7/8" diameter x 2" long	G		115	.070		5.80	2.67		8.47	11.45

05 05 23 – Metal Fastenings

05 05 23.25 High Strength Bolts

			Crew	Daily Output	Labor-Hours	Unit	Material	Labor	2014 Bare Costs Equipment	Total	Total Incl O&P
1365	3" long	G	1 Sswk	110	.073	Ea.	6.80	2.79		9.59	12.80
1370	4" long	G		105	.076		8.45	2.92		11.37	14.85
1380	6" long	G		100	.080		11.90	3.07		14.97	18.95
1390	8" long	G		90	.089		17.35	3.41		20.76	25.50
1400	1" diameter x 2" long	G		105	.076		7.65	2.92		10.57	13.95
1420	3" long	G		100	.080		9.30	3.07		12.37	16.05
1450	4" long	G		95	.084		10.70	3.23		13.93	17.95
1500	6" long	G		90	.089		14.35	3.41		17.76	22.50
1550	8" long	G		85	.094		23	3.61		26.61	32
1600	1-1/4" diameter x 3" long	G		85	.094		37.50	3.61		41.11	48
1650	4" long	G		80	.100		43	3.84		46.84	55
1700	6" long	G		75	.107		60.50	4.09		64.59	74.50
1750	8" long	G		70	.114		79	4.38		83.38	95.50

05 05 23.30 Lag Screws

			Crew	Daily Output	Labor-Hours	Unit	Material	Labor	Equipment	Total	Total Incl O&P
0010	**LAG SCREWS**										
0020	Steel, 1/4" diameter, 2" long	G	1 Carp	200	.040	Ea.	.09	1.43		1.52	2.51
0100	3/8" diameter, 3" long	G		150	.053		.29	1.91		2.20	3.53
0200	1/2" diameter, 3" long	G		130	.062		.63	2.20		2.83	4.39
0300	5/8" diameter, 3" long	G		120	.067		1.13	2.38		3.51	5.25

05 05 23.35 Machine Screws

			Crew	Daily Output	Labor-Hours	Unit	Material	Labor	Equipment	Total	Total Incl O&P
0010	**MACHINE SCREWS**										
0020	Steel, round head, #8 x 1" long	G	1 Carp	4.80	1.667	C	3.79	59.50		63.29	104
0110	#8 x 2" long	G		2.40	3.333		6.10	119		125.10	208
0200	#10 x 1" long	G		4	2		6	71.50		77.50	127
0300	#10 x 2" long	G		2	4		8.50	143		151.50	250

05 05 23.50 Powder Actuated Tools and Fasteners

			Crew	Daily Output	Labor-Hours	Unit	Material	Labor	Equipment	Total	Total Incl O&P
0010	**POWDER ACTUATED TOOLS & FASTENERS**										
0020	Stud driver, .22 caliber, single shot					Ea.	147			147	161
0100	.27 caliber, semi automatic, strip					"	435			435	475
0300	Powder load, single shot, .22 cal, power level 2, brown					C	5.30			5.30	5.80
0400	Strip, .27 cal, power level 4, red						7.60			7.60	8.35
0600	Drive pin, .300 x 3/4" long	G	1 Carp	4.80	1.667		4.86	59.50		64.36	105
0700	.300 x 3" long with washer	G	"	4	2		12.50	71.50		84	134

05 05 23.55 Rivets

			Crew	Daily Output	Labor-Hours	Unit	Material	Labor	Equipment	Total	Total Incl O&P
0010	**RIVETS**										
0100	Aluminum rivet & mandrel, 1/2" grip length x 1/8" diameter	G	1 Carp	4.80	1.667	C	7.65	59.50		67.15	108
0200	3/16" diameter	G		4	2		11.40	71.50		82.90	133
0300	Aluminum rivet, steel mandrel, 1/8" diameter	G		4.80	1.667		10.25	59.50		69.75	111
0400	3/16" diameter	G		4	2		16.45	71.50		87.95	138
0500	Copper rivet, steel mandrel, 1/8" diameter	G		4.80	1.667		9.10	59.50		68.60	110
0800	Stainless rivet & mandrel, 1/8" diameter	G		4.80	1.667		26	59.50		85.50	129
0900	3/16" diameter	G		4	2		36	71.50		107.50	160
1000	Stainless rivet, steel mandrel, 1/8" diameter	G		4.80	1.667		15.65	59.50		75.15	117
1100	3/16" diameter	G		4	2		25.50	71.50		97	148
1200	Steel rivet and mandrel, 1/8" diameter	G		4.80	1.667		7.40	59.50		66.90	108
1300	3/16" diameter	G		4	2		12	71.50		83.50	133
1400	Hand riveting tool, standard					Ea.	71.50			71.50	78.50
1500	Deluxe						380			380	420
1600	Power riveting tool, standard						570			570	625
1700	Deluxe						3,600			3,600	3,950

05 05 23.70 Structural Blind Bolts

		Crew	Daily Output	Labor-Hours	Unit	Material	2014 Bare Costs Labor	2014 Bare Costs Equipment	Total	Total Incl O&P
0010	**STRUCTURAL BLIND BOLTS**									
0100	1/4" diameter x 1/4" grip [G]	1 Sswk	240	.033	Ea.	1.24	1.28		2.52	3.79
0150	1/2" grip [G]		216	.037		1.33	1.42		2.75	4.17
0200	3/8" diameter x 1/2" grip [G]		232	.034		1.75	1.32		3.07	4.45
0250	3/4" grip [G]		208	.038		1.84	1.47		3.31	4.83
0300	1/2" diameter x 1/2" grip [G]		224	.036		3.99	1.37		5.36	7
0350	3/4" grip [G]		200	.040		5.60	1.53		7.13	9.05
0400	5/8" diameter x 3/4" grip [G]		216	.037		8.25	1.42		9.67	11.80
0450	1" grip [G]		192	.042		9.50	1.60		11.10	13.50

05 05 23.80 Vibration and Bearing Pads

		Crew	Daily Output	Labor-Hours	Unit	Material	2014 Bare Costs Labor	2014 Bare Costs Equipment	Total	Total Incl O&P
0010	**VIBRATION & BEARING PADS**									
0300	Laminated synthetic rubber impregnated cotton duck, 1/2" thick	2 Sswk	24	.667	S.F.	69	25.50		94.50	125
0400	1" thick		20	.800		135	30.50		165.50	208
0600	Neoprene bearing pads, 1/2" thick		24	.667		26.50	25.50		52	77.50
0700	1" thick		20	.800		52.50	30.50		83	117
0900	Fabric reinforced neoprene, 5000 psi, 1/2" thick		24	.667		11.50	25.50		37	61
1000	1" thick		20	.800		23	30.50		53.50	84
1200	Felt surfaced vinyl pads, cork and sisal, 5/8" thick		24	.667		29	25.50		54.50	80.50
1300	1" thick		20	.800		52.50	30.50		83	116
1500	Teflon bonded to 10 ga. carbon steel, 1/32" layer		24	.667		51.50	25.50		77	105
1600	3/32" layer		24	.667		77	25.50		102.50	133
1800	Bonded to 10 ga. stainless steel, 1/32" layer		24	.667		91	25.50		116.50	149
1900	3/32" layer		24	.667		120	25.50		145.50	181
2100	Circular machine leveling pad & stud				Kip	6.45			6.45	7.10

05 05 23.85 Weld Shear Connectors

		Crew	Daily Output	Labor-Hours	Unit	Material	2014 Bare Costs Labor	2014 Bare Costs Equipment	Total	Total Incl O&P
0010	**WELD SHEAR CONNECTORS**									
0020	3/4" diameter, 3-3/16" long [G]	E-10	960	.025	Ea.	.53	.98	.49	2	2.99
0030	3-3/8" long [G]		950	.025		.56	.99	.50	2.05	3.04
0200	3-7/8" long [G]		945	.025		.60	.99	.50	2.09	3.10
0300	4-3/16" long [G]		935	.026		.63	1	.51	2.14	3.16
0500	4-7/8" long [G]		930	.026		.70	1.01	.51	2.22	3.25
0600	5-3/16" long [G]		920	.026		.73	1.02	.52	2.27	3.31
0800	5-3/8" long [G]		910	.026		.74	1.03	.52	2.29	3.34
0900	6-3/16" long [G]		905	.027		.81	1.03	.52	2.36	3.44
1000	7-3/16" long [G]		895	.027		1	1.05	.53	2.58	3.67
1100	8-3/16" long [G]		890	.027		1.10	1.05	.53	2.68	3.80
1500	7/8" diameter, 3-11/16" long [G]		920	.026		.86	1.02	.52	2.40	3.46
1600	4-3/16" long [G]		910	.026		.93	1.03	.52	2.48	3.55
1700	5-3/16" long [G]		905	.027		1.05	1.03	.52	2.60	3.71
1800	6-3/16" long [G]		895	.027		1.17	1.05	.53	2.75	3.86
1900	7-3/16" long [G]		890	.027		1.30	1.05	.53	2.88	4.02
2000	8-3/16" long [G]		880	.027		1.42	1.06	.54	3.02	4.19

05 05 23.87 Weld Studs

		Crew	Daily Output	Labor-Hours	Unit	Material	2014 Bare Costs Labor	2014 Bare Costs Equipment	Total	Total Incl O&P
0010	**WELD STUDS**									
0020	1/4" diameter, 2-11/16" long [G]	E-10	1120	.021	Ea.	.35	.84	.42	1.61	2.45
0100	4-1/8" long [G]		1080	.022		.33	.87	.44	1.64	2.49
0200	3/8" diameter, 4-1/8" long [G]		1080	.022		.38	.87	.44	1.69	2.55
0300	6-1/8" long [G]		1040	.023		.49	.90	.46	1.85	2.76
0400	1/2" diameter, 2-1/8" long [G]		1040	.023		.35	.90	.46	1.71	2.61
0500	3-1/8" long [G]		1025	.023		.43	.91	.46	1.80	2.72
0600	4-1/8" long [G]		1010	.024		.50	.93	.47	1.90	2.84

05 05 Common Work Results for Metals

05 05 23 – Metal Fastenings

05 05 23.87 Weld Studs

		Crew	Daily Output	Labor-Hours	Unit	Material	2014 Bare Costs Labor	Equipment	Total	Total Incl O&P
0700	5-5/16" long	G E-10	990	.024	Ea.	.62	.95	.48	2.05	3.01
0800	6-1/8" long	G	975	.025		.67	.96	.49	2.12	3.11
0900	8-1/8" long	G	960	.025		.95	.98	.49	2.42	3.44
1000	5/8" diameter, 2-11/16" long	G	1000	.024		.61	.94	.48	2.03	2.98
1010	4-3/16" long	G	990	.024		.76	.95	.48	2.19	3.17
1100	6-9/16" long	G	975	.025		.99	.96	.49	2.44	3.46
1200	8-3/16" long	G	960	.025		1.33	.98	.49	2.80	3.86

05 05 23.90 Welding Rod

		Crew	Daily Output	Labor-Hours	Unit	Material	2014 Bare Costs Labor	Equipment	Total	Total Incl O&P
0010	**WELDING ROD**									
0020	Steel, type 6011, 1/8" diam., less than 500#				Lb.	2.16			2.16	2.38
0100	500# to 2,000#					1.95			1.95	2.15
0200	2,000# to 5,000#					1.83			1.83	2.02
0300	5/32" diameter, less than 500#					2.20			2.20	2.42
0310	500# to 2,000#					1.98			1.98	2.18
0320	2,000# to 5,000#					1.86			1.86	2.05
0400	3/16" diam., less than 500#					2.46			2.46	2.71
0500	500# to 2,000#					2.22			2.22	2.44
0600	2,000# to 5,000#					2.09			2.09	2.30
0620	Steel, type 6010, 1/8" diam., less than 500#					2.22			2.22	2.44
0630	500# to 2,000#					2			2	2.20
0640	2,000# to 5,000#					1.88			1.88	2.07
0650	Steel, type 7018 Low Hydrogen, 1/8" diam., less than 500#					2.15			2.15	2.37
0660	500# to 2,000#					1.94			1.94	2.13
0670	2,000# to 5,000#					1.82			1.82	2.01
0700	Steel, type 7024 Jet Weld, 1/8" diam., less than 500#					2.43			2.43	2.67
0710	500# to 2,000#					2.19			2.19	2.41
0720	2,000# to 5,000#					2.06			2.06	2.26
1550	Aluminum, type 4043 TIG, 1/8" diam., less than 10#					5.10			5.10	5.65
1560	10# to 60#					4.61			4.61	5.05
1570	Over 60#					4.33			4.33	4.77
1600	Aluminum, type 5356 TIG, 1/8" diam., less than 10#					5.45			5.45	6
1610	10# to 60#					4.90			4.90	5.40
1620	Over 60#					4.61			4.61	5.05
1900	Cast iron, type 8 Nickel, 1/8" diam., less than 500#					22			22	24
1910	500# to 1,000#					19.75			19.75	21.50
1920	Over 1,000#					18.55			18.55	20.50
2000	Stainless steel, type 316/316L, 1/8" diam., less than 500#					7.10			7.10	7.85
2100	500# to 1000#					6.40			6.40	7.05
2220	Over 1000#					6.05			6.05	6.65

05 12 Structural Steel Framing

05 12 23 – Structural Steel for Buildings

05 12 23.05 Canopy Framing

		Crew	Daily Output	Labor-Hours	Unit	Material	2014 Bare Costs Labor	Equipment	Total	Total Incl O&P
0010	**CANOPY FRAMING**									
0020	6" and 8" members, shop fabricated	G E-4	3000	.011	Lb.	1.59	.41	.05	2.05	2.59

05 12 23.10 Ceiling Supports

		Crew	Daily Output	Labor-Hours	Unit	Material	2014 Bare Costs Labor	Equipment	Total	Total Incl O&P
0010	**CEILING SUPPORTS**									
1000	Entrance door/folding partition supports, shop fabricated	G E-4	60	.533	L.F.	26.50	20.50	2.37	49.37	71
1100	Linear accelerator door supports	G	14	2.286		121	89	10.15	220.15	315
1200	Lintels or shelf angles, hung, exterior hot dipped galv.	G	267	.120		18.10	4.66	.53	23.29	29.50

05 12 23 – Structural Steel for Buildings

05 12 23.10 Ceiling Supports

		Crew	Daily Output	Labor-Hours	Unit	Material	2014 Bare Costs Labor	Equipment	Total	Total Incl O&P
1250	Two coats primer paint instead of galv.	G E-4	267	.120	L.F.	15.65	4.66	.53	20.84	26.50
1400	Monitor support, ceiling hung, expansion bolted	G	4	8	Ea.	420	310	35.50	765.50	1,100
1450	Hung from pre-set inserts	G	6	5.333		450	207	23.50	680.50	915
1600	Motor supports for overhead doors	G	4	8		214	310	35.50	559.50	865
1700	Partition support for heavy folding partitions, without pocket	G	24	1.333	L.F.	60.50	52	5.90	118.40	172
1750	Supports at pocket only	G	12	2.667		121	104	11.85	236.85	345
2000	Rolling grilles & fire door supports	G	34	.941		51.50	36.50	4.18	92.18	131
2100	Spider-leg light supports, expansion bolted to ceiling slab	G	8	4	Ea.	172	155	17.75	344.75	505
2150	Hung from pre-set inserts	G	12	2.667	"	186	104	11.85	301.85	415
2400	Toilet partition support	G	36	.889	L.F.	60.50	34.50	3.95	98.95	137
2500	X-ray travel gantry support	G	12	2.667	"	207	104	11.85	322.85	435

05 12 23.15 Columns, Lightweight

		Crew	Daily Output	Labor-Hours	Unit	Material	2014 Bare Costs Labor	Equipment	Total	Total Incl O&P
0010	**COLUMNS, LIGHTWEIGHT**									
1000	Lightweight units (lally), 3-1/2" diameter	E-2	780	.062	L.F.	8.25	2.38	1.96	12.59	15.70
1050	4" diameter	"	900	.053	"	10.15	2.07	1.70	13.92	16.85
5800	Adjustable jack post, 8' maximum height, 2-3/4" diameter	G			Ea.	52			52	57
5850	4" diameter	G			"	83			83	91.50

05 12 23.17 Columns, Structural

		Crew	Daily Output	Labor-Hours	Unit	Material	2014 Bare Costs Labor	Equipment	Total	Total Incl O&P
0010	**COLUMNS, STRUCTURAL** R051223-10									
0015	Made from recycled materials									
0020	Shop fab'd for 100-ton, 1-2 story project, bolted connections									
0800	Steel, concrete filled, extra strong pipe, 3-1/2" diameter	E-2	660	.073	L.F.	43.50	2.82	2.32	48.64	56
0830	4" diameter		780	.062		48.50	2.38	1.96	52.84	60
0890	5" diameter		1020	.047		58	1.82	1.50	61.32	69
0930	6" diameter		1200	.040		77	1.55	1.27	79.82	89
0940	8" diameter		1100	.044		77	1.69	1.39	80.08	89
1100	For galvanizing, add				Lb.	.25			.25	.28
1300	For web ties, angles, etc., add per added lb.	1 Sswk	945	.008		1.33	.32		1.65	2.08
1500	Steel pipe, extra strong, no concrete, 3" to 5" diameter	G E-2	16000	.003		1.33	.12	.10	1.55	1.79
1600	6" to 12" diameter	G	14000	.003		1.33	.13	.11	1.57	1.83
1700	Steel pipe, extra strong, no concrete, 3" diameter x 12'-0"	G	60	.800	Ea.	163	31	25.50	219.50	265
1750	4" diameter x 12'-0"	G	58	.828		238	32	26.50	296.50	350
1800	6" diameter x 12'-0"	G	54	.889		455	34.50	28.50	518	595
1850	8" diameter x 14'-0"	G	50	.960		805	37	30.50	872.50	990
1900	10" diameter x 16'-0"	G	48	1		1,150	38.50	32	1,220.50	1,375
1950	12" diameter x 18'-0"	G	45	1.067		1,550	41.50	34	1,625.50	1,850
3300	Structural tubing, square, A500GrB, 4" to 6" square, light section	G	11270	.004	Lb.	1.33	.17	.14	1.64	1.92
3600	Heavy section	G	32000	.002	"	1.33	.06	.05	1.44	1.62
4000	Concrete filled, add				L.F.	4.16			4.16	4.57
4500	Structural tubing, square, 4" x 4" x 1/4" x 12'-0"	G E-2	58	.828	Ea.	219	32	26.50	277.50	330
4550	6" x 6" x 1/4" x 12'-0"	G	54	.889		360	34.50	28.50	423	490
4600	8" x 8" x 3/8" x 14'-0"	G	50	.960		775	37	30.50	842.50	960
4650	10" x 10" x 1/2" x 16'-0"	G	48	1		1,450	38.50	32	1,520.50	1,675
5100	Structural tubing, rect., 5" to 6" wide, light section	G	8000	.006	Lb.	1.33	.23	.19	1.75	2.10
5200	Heavy section	G	12000	.004		1.33	.16	.13	1.62	1.89
5300	7" to 10" wide, light section	G	15000	.003		1.33	.12	.10	1.55	1.80
5400	Heavy section	G	18000	.003		1.33	.10	.09	1.52	1.74
5500	Structural tubing, rect., 5" x 3" x 1/4" x 12'-0"	G	58	.828	Ea.	212	32	26.50	270.50	320
5550	6" x 4" x 5/16" x 12'-0"	G	54	.889		330	34.50	28.50	393	460
5600	8" x 4" x 3/8" x 12'-0"	G	54	.889		485	34.50	28.50	548	625
5650	10" x 6" x 3/8" x 14'-0"	G	50	.960		775	37	30.50	842.50	960
5700	12" x 8" x 1/2" x 16'-0"	G	48	1		1,425	38.50	32	1,495.50	1,675

05 12 Structural Steel Framing

05 12 23 – Structural Steel for Buildings

05 12 23.17 Columns, Structural

		Crew	Daily Output	Labor-Hours	Unit	Material	2014 Bare Costs Labor	Equipment	Total	Total Incl O&P
6800	W Shape, A992 steel, 2 tier, W8 x 24 [G]	E-2	1080	.044	L.F.	35	1.72	1.42	38.14	43.50
6850	W8 x 31 [G]		1080	.044		45	1.72	1.42	48.14	54.50
6900	W8 x 48 [G]		1032	.047		70	1.80	1.48	73.28	82
6950	W8 x 67 [G]		984	.049		97.50	1.89	1.55	100.94	112
7000	W10 x 45 [G]		1032	.047		65.50	1.80	1.48	68.78	77
7050	W10 x 68 [G]		984	.049		99	1.89	1.55	102.44	114
7100	W10 x 112 [G]		960	.050		163	1.94	1.59	166.53	185
7150	W12 x 50 [G]		1032	.047		73	1.80	1.48	76.28	85
7200	W12 x 87 [G]		984	.049		127	1.89	1.55	130.44	144
7250	W12 x 120 [G]		960	.050		175	1.94	1.59	178.53	197
7300	W12 x 190 [G]		912	.053		277	2.04	1.68	280.72	310
7350	W14 x 74 [G]		984	.049		108	1.89	1.55	111.44	124
7400	W14 x 120 [G]		960	.050		175	1.94	1.59	178.53	197
7450	W14 x 176 [G]		912	.053		257	2.04	1.68	260.72	288
8090	For projects 75 to 99 tons, add				All	10%				
8092	50 to 74 tons, add					20%				
8094	25 to 49 tons, add					30%	10%			
8096	10 to 24 tons, add					50%	25%			
8098	2 to 9 tons, add					75%	50%			
8099	Less than 2 tons, add					100%	100%			

05 12 23.20 Curb Edging

		Crew	Daily Output	Labor-Hours	Unit	Material	2014 Bare Costs Labor	Equipment	Total	Total Incl O&P
0010	**CURB EDGING**									
0030	Steel angle w/anchors, shop fabricated, on forms, 1" x 1", 0.8#/L.F. [G]	2 Carp	175	.091	L.F.	1.67	3.27		4.94	7.35
0101	2" x 2" angles, 3.92#/L.F. [G]		165	.097		6.65	3.47		10.12	13.15
0201	3" x 3" angles, 6.1#/L.F. [G]		150	.107		13	3.81		16.81	20.50
0301	4" x 4" angles, 8.2#/L.F. [G]		140	.114		13.85	4.09		17.94	22
1002	6" x 4" angles, 12.3#/L.F. [G]		125	.128		20.50	4.58		25.08	30
1051	Steel channels with anchors, on forms, 3" channel, 5#/L.F. [G]		145	.110		8.35	3.94		12.29	15.85
1101	4" channel, 5.4#/L.F. [G]		135	.119		9	4.24		13.24	17.05
1201	6" channel, 8.2#/L.F. [G]		130	.123		13.85	4.40		18.25	22.50
1301	8" channel, 11.5#/L.F. [G]		115	.139		19.10	4.97		24.07	29.50
1401	10" channel, 15.3#/L.F. [G]		90	.178		25	6.35		31.35	38
1501	12" channel, 20.7#/L.F. [G]		70	.229		33.50	8.15		41.65	51
2000	For curved edging, add					35%	10%			

05 12 23.40 Lightweight Framing

		Crew	Daily Output	Labor-Hours	Unit	Material	2014 Bare Costs Labor	Equipment	Total	Total Incl O&P
0010	**LIGHTWEIGHT FRAMING** R051223-35									
0015	Made from recycled materials									
0200	For load-bearing steel studs see Section 05 41 13.30									
0400	Angle framing, field fabricated, 4" and larger R051223-45 [G]	E-3	440	.055	Lb.	.77	2.13	.32	3.22	5.25
0450	Less than 4" angles [G]		265	.091	"	.80	3.53	.54	4.87	8.20
0460	1/2" x 1/2" x 1/8" [G]		200	.120	L.F.	.16	4.68	.71	5.55	9.85
0462	3/4" x 3/4" x 1/8" [G]		160	.150		.45	5.85	.89	7.19	12.60
0464	1" x 1" x 1/8" [G]		135	.178		.64	6.95	1.05	8.64	15.05
0466	1-1/4" x 1-1/4" x 3/16" [G]		115	.209		1.18	8.15	1.24	10.57	18.15
0468	1-1/2" x 1-1/2" x 3/16" [G]		100	.240		1.43	9.35	1.42	12.20	21
0470	2" x 2" x 1/4" [G]		90	.267		2.54	10.40	1.58	14.52	24.50
0472	2-1/2" x 2-1/2" x 1/4" [G]		72	.333		3.26	13	1.97	18.23	31
0474	3" x 2" x 3/8" [G]		65	.369		4.69	14.40	2.19	21.28	35
0476	3" x 3" x 3/8" [G]		57	.421		5.70	16.45	2.49	24.64	40.50
0600	Channel framing, field fabricated, 8" and larger [G]		500	.048	Lb.	.80	1.87	.28	2.95	4.75
0650	Less than 8" channels [G]		335	.072	"	.80	2.80	.42	4.02	6.65
0660	C2 x 1.78 [G]		115	.209	L.F.	1.42	8.15	1.24	10.81	18.40

05 12 Structural Steel Framing

05 12 23 – Structural Steel for Buildings

05 12 23.40 Lightweight Framing		Crew	Daily Output	Labor-Hours	Unit	Material	2014 Bare Costs Labor	Equipment	Total	Total Incl O&P
0662	C3 x 4.1	G	E-3	80	.300	L.F.	3.26	11.70	1.78	16.74	28
0664	C4 x 5.4	G		66	.364		4.29	14.20	2.15	20.64	34
0666	C5 x 6.7	G		57	.421		5.35	16.45	2.49	24.29	40
0668	C6 x 8.2	G		55	.436		6.30	17.05	2.58	25.93	42.50
0670	C7 x 9.8	G		40	.600		7.80	23.50	3.55	34.85	57
0672	C8 x 11.5	G		36	.667		9.15	26	3.95	39.10	64
0710	Structural bar tee, field fabricated, 3/4" x 3/4" x 1/8"	G		160	.150		.45	5.85	.89	7.19	12.60
0712	1" x 1" x 1/8"	G		135	.178		.64	6.95	1.05	8.64	15.05
0714	1-1/2" x 1-1/2" x 1/4"	G		114	.211		1.86	8.20	1.25	11.31	19.05
0716	2" x 2" x 1/4"	G		89	.270		2.54	10.50	1.60	14.64	24.50
0718	2-1/2" x 2-1/2" x 3/8"	G		72	.333		4.69	13	1.97	19.66	32.50
0720	3" x 3" x 3/8"	G		57	.421		5.70	16.45	2.49	24.64	40.50
0730	Structural zee, field fabricated, 1-1/4" x 1-3/4" x 1-3/4"	G		114	.211		.60	8.20	1.25	10.05	17.70
0732	2-11/16" x 3" x 2-11/16"	G		114	.211		1.42	8.20	1.25	10.87	18.60
0734	3-1/16" x 4" x 3-1/16"	G		133	.180		2.14	7.05	1.07	10.26	16.90
0736	3-1/4" x 5" x 3-1/4"	G		133	.180		2.92	7.05	1.07	11.04	17.80
0738	3-1/2" x 6" x 3-1/2"	G		160	.150		4.40	5.85	.89	11.14	16.95
0740	Junior beam, field fabricated, 3"	G		80	.300		4.53	11.70	1.78	18.01	29.50
0742	4"	G		72	.333		6.10	13	1.97	21.07	34
0744	5"	G		67	.358		7.95	14	2.12	24.07	37.50
0746	6"	G		62	.387		9.95	15.10	2.29	27.34	42.50
0748	7"	G		57	.421		12.15	16.45	2.49	31.09	47.50
0750	8"	G		53	.453		14.65	17.65	2.68	34.98	52.50
1000	Continuous slotted channel framing system, shop fab, simple framing	G	2 Sswk	2400	.007	Lb.	4.11	.26		4.37	5
1200	Complex framing	G	"	1600	.010		4.64	.38		5.02	5.85
1300	Cross bracing, rods, shop fabricated, 3/4" diameter	G	E-3	700	.034		1.59	1.34	.20	3.13	4.52
1310	7/8" diameter	G		850	.028		1.59	1.10	.17	2.86	4.03
1320	1" diameter	G		1000	.024		1.59	.94	.14	2.67	3.69
1330	Angle, 5" x 5" x 3/8"	G		2800	.009		1.59	.33	.05	1.97	2.45
1350	Hanging lintels, shop fabricated	G		850	.028		1.59	1.10	.17	2.86	4.03
1380	Roof frames, shop fabricated, 3'-0" square, 5' span	G	E-2	4200	.011		1.59	.44	.36	2.39	2.98
1400	Tie rod, not upset, 1-1/2" to 4" diameter, with turnbuckle	G	2 Sswk	800	.020		1.72	.77		2.49	3.35
1420	No turnbuckle	G		700	.023		1.66	.88		2.54	3.49
1500	Upset, 1-3/4" to 4" diameter, with turnbuckle	G		800	.020		1.72	.77		2.49	3.35
1520	No turnbuckle	G		700	.023		1.66	.88		2.54	3.49

05 12 23.45 Lintels

			Crew	Daily Output	Labor-Hours	Unit	Material	2014 Bare Costs Labor	Equipment	Total	Total Incl O&P
0010	**LINTELS**										
0015	Made from recycled materials										
0020	Plain steel angles, shop fabricated, under 500 lb.	G	1 Bric	550	.015	Lb.	1.02	.52		1.54	1.98
0100	500 to 1000 lb.	G		640	.013		.99	.45		1.44	1.83
0200	1,000 to 2,000 lb.	G		640	.013		.97	.45		1.42	1.80
0300	2,000 to 4,000 lb.	G		640	.013		.94	.45		1.39	1.77
0500	For built-up angles and plates, add to above	G					.33			.33	.36
0700	For engineering, add to above						.13			.13	.15
0900	For galvanizing, add to above, under 500 lb.						.30			.30	.33
0950	500 to 2,000 lb.						.28			.28	.30
1000	Over 2,000 lb.						.25			.25	.28
2000	Steel angles, 3-1/2" x 3", 1/4" thick, 2'-6" long	G	1 Bric	47	.170	Ea.	14.30	6.05		20.35	26
2100	4'-6" long	G		26	.308		26	10.95		36.95	47
2600	4" x 3-1/2", 1/4" thick, 5'-0" long	G		21	.381		33	13.55		46.55	58.50
2700	9'-0" long	G		12	.667		59	23.50		82.50	105

05 12 Structural Steel Framing

05 12 23 – Structural Steel for Buildings

05 12 23.60 Pipe Support Framing

		Crew	Daily Output	Labor-Hours	Unit	Material	2014 Bare Costs Labor	Equipment	Total	Total Incl O&P
0010	**PIPE SUPPORT FRAMING**									
0020	Under 10#/L.F., shop fabricated	G E-4	3900	.008	Lb.	1.78	.32	.04	2.14	2.60
0200	10.1 to 15#/L.F.	G	4300	.007		1.75	.29	.03	2.07	2.51
0400	15.1 to 20#/L.F.	G	4800	.007		1.72	.26	.03	2.01	2.41
0600	Over 20#/L.F.	G	5400	.006		1.70	.23	.03	1.96	2.34

05 12 23.65 Plates

			Crew	Daily Output	Labor-Hours	Unit	Material	2014 Bare Costs Labor	Equipment	Total	Total Incl O&P
0010	**PLATES**	R051223-80									
0015	Made from recycled materials										
0020	For connections & stiffener plates, shop fabricated										
0050	1/8" thick (5.1 lb./S.F.)		G				S.F.	6.75			6.75	7.45
0100	1/4" thick (10.2 lb./S.F.)		G					13.50			13.50	14.85
0300	3/8" thick (15.3 lb./S.F.)		G					20.50			20.50	22.50
0400	1/2" thick (20.4 lb./S.F.)		G					27			27	29.50
0450	3/4" thick (30.6 lb./S.F.)		G					40.50			40.50	44.50
0500	1" thick (40.8 lb./S.F.)		G					54			54	59.50
2000	Steel plate, warehouse prices, no shop fabrication											
2100	1/4" thick (10.2 lb./S.F.)		G				S.F.	8.05			8.05	8.85

05 12 23.70 Stressed Skin Steel Roof and Ceiling System

			Crew	Daily Output	Labor-Hours	Unit	Material	2014 Bare Costs Labor	Equipment	Total	Total Incl O&P
0010	**STRESSED SKIN STEEL ROOF & CEILING SYSTEM**											
0020	Double panel flat roof, spans to 100'		G E-2	1150	.042	S.F.	10.60	1.62	1.33	13.55	16.10
0100	Double panel convex roof, spans to 200'		G	960	.050		17.25	1.94	1.59	20.78	24.50
0200	Double panel arched roof, spans to 300'		G	760	.063		26.50	2.45	2.01	30.96	36

05 12 23.75 Structural Steel Members

			Crew	Daily Output	Labor-Hours	Unit	Material	2014 Bare Costs Labor	Equipment	Total	Total Incl O&P
0010	**STRUCTURAL STEEL MEMBERS**	R051223-10									
0015	Made from recycled materials										
0020	Shop fab'd for 100-ton, 1-2 story project, bolted connections										
0100	Beam or girder, W 6 x 9		G E-2	600	.080	L.F.	13.10	3.10	2.55	18.75	23
0120	x 15		G	600	.080		22	3.10	2.55	27.65	32.50
0140	x 20		G	600	.080		29	3.10	2.55	34.65	40.50
0300	W 8 x 10		G	600	.080		14.60	3.10	2.55	20.25	24.50
0320	x 15		G	600	.080		22	3.10	2.55	27.65	32.50
0350	x 21		G	600	.080		30.50	3.10	2.55	36.15	42
0360	x 24		G	550	.087		35	3.38	2.78	41.16	48
0370	x 28		G	550	.087		41	3.38	2.78	47.16	54.50
0500	x 31		G	550	.087		45	3.38	2.78	51.16	59
0520	x 35		G	550	.087		51	3.38	2.78	57.16	65.50
0540	x 48		G	550	.087		70	3.38	2.78	76.16	86.50
0600	W 10 x 12		G	600	.080		17.50	3.10	2.55	23.15	28
0620	x 15		G	600	.080		22	3.10	2.55	27.65	32.50
0700	x 22		G	600	.080		32	3.10	2.55	37.65	44
0720	x 26		G	600	.080		38	3.10	2.55	43.65	50
0740	x 33		G	550	.087		48	3.38	2.78	54.16	62.50
0900	x 49		G	550	.087		71.50	3.38	2.78	77.66	88
1100	W 12 x 16		G	880	.055		23.50	2.11	1.74	27.35	31.50
1300	x 22		G	880	.055		32	2.11	1.74	35.85	41.50
1500	x 26		G	880	.055		38	2.11	1.74	41.85	47.50
1520	x 35		G	810	.059		51	2.30	1.89	55.19	62.50
1560	x 50		G	750	.064		73	2.48	2.04	77.52	87
1580	x 58		G	750	.064		84.50	2.48	2.04	89.02	100
1700	x 72		G	640	.075		105	2.91	2.39	110.30	123
1740	x 87		G	640	.075		127	2.91	2.39	132.30	147

05 12 23.75 Structural Steel Members		Crew	Daily Output	Labor-Hours	Unit	Material	2014 Bare Costs Labor	Equipment	Total	Total Incl O&P
1900	W 14 x 26	G	E-2	990	.048	L.F.	38	1.88	1.54	41.42	46.50
2100	x 30	G		900	.053		43.50	2.07	1.70	47.27	53.50
2300	x 34	G		810	.059		49.50	2.30	1.89	53.69	61
2320	x 43	G		810	.059		62.50	2.30	1.89	66.69	75.50
2340	x 53	G		800	.060		77.50	2.32	1.91	81.73	91.50
2360	x 74	G		760	.063		108	2.45	2.01	112.46	126
2380	x 90	G		740	.065		131	2.51	2.07	135.58	151
2500	x 120	G		720	.067		175	2.58	2.12	179.70	199
2700	W 16 x 26	G		1000	.048		38	1.86	1.53	41.39	46.50
2900	x 31	G		900	.053		45	2.07	1.70	48.77	55
3100	x 40	G		800	.060		58.50	2.32	1.91	62.73	70.50
3120	x 50	G		800	.060		73	2.32	1.91	77.23	86.50
3140	x 67	G		760	.063		97.50	2.45	2.01	101.96	114
3300	W 18 x 35	G	E-5	960	.075		51	2.90	1.74	55.64	63.50
3500	x 40	G		960	.075		58.50	2.90	1.74	63.14	71.50
3520	x 46	G		960	.075		67	2.90	1.74	71.64	81.50
3700	x 50	G		912	.079		73	3.05	1.83	77.88	87.50
3900	x 55	G		912	.079		80	3.05	1.83	84.88	95.50
3920	x 65	G		900	.080		94.50	3.09	1.86	99.45	112
3940	x 76	G		900	.080		111	3.09	1.86	115.95	130
3960	x 86	G		900	.080		125	3.09	1.86	129.95	146
3980	x 106	G		900	.080		155	3.09	1.86	159.95	178
4100	W 21 x 44	G		1064	.068		64	2.61	1.57	68.18	77
4300	x 50	G		1064	.068		73	2.61	1.57	77.18	86.50
4500	x 62	G		1036	.070		90.50	2.68	1.61	94.79	106
4700	x 68	G		1036	.070		99	2.68	1.61	103.29	116
4720	x 83	G		1000	.072		121	2.78	1.67	125.45	140
4740	x 93	G		1000	.072		136	2.78	1.67	140.45	156
4760	x 101	G		1000	.072		147	2.78	1.67	151.45	169
4780	x 122	G		1000	.072		178	2.78	1.67	182.45	203
4900	W 24 x 55	G		1110	.065		80	2.50	1.51	84.01	94.50
5100	x 62	G		1110	.065		90.50	2.50	1.51	94.51	106
5300	x 68	G		1110	.065		99	2.50	1.51	103.01	115
5500	x 76	G		1110	.065		111	2.50	1.51	115.01	128
5700	x 84	G		1080	.067		122	2.57	1.55	126.12	142
5720	x 94	G		1080	.067		137	2.57	1.55	141.12	158
5740	x 104	G		1050	.069		152	2.65	1.59	156.24	174
5760	x 117	G		1050	.069		171	2.65	1.59	175.24	195
5780	x 146	G		1050	.069		213	2.65	1.59	217.24	241
5800	W 27 x 84	G		1190	.061		122	2.34	1.40	125.74	141
5900	x 94	G		1190	.061		137	2.34	1.40	140.74	157
5920	x 114	G		1150	.063		166	2.42	1.45	169.87	189
5940	x 146	G		1150	.063		213	2.42	1.45	216.87	240
5960	x 161	G		1150	.063		235	2.42	1.45	238.87	264
6100	W 30 x 99	G		1200	.060		144	2.32	1.39	147.71	165
6300	x 108	G		1200	.060		157	2.32	1.39	160.71	179
6500	x 116	G		1160	.062		169	2.40	1.44	172.84	192
6520	x 132	G		1160	.062		192	2.40	1.44	195.84	218
6540	x 148	G		1160	.062		216	2.40	1.44	219.84	243
6560	x 173	G		1120	.064		252	2.48	1.49	255.97	283
6580	x 191	G		1120	.064		278	2.48	1.49	281.97	310
6700	W 33 x 118	G		1176	.061		172	2.36	1.42	175.78	195
6900	x 130	G		1134	.063		189	2.45	1.47	192.92	214

05 12 Structural Steel Framing

05 12 23 – Structural Steel for Buildings

05 12 23.75 Structural Steel Members

			Crew	Daily Output	Labor-Hours	Unit	Material	2014 Bare Costs Labor	2014 Bare Costs Equipment	Total	Total Incl O&P
7100	x 141	G	E-5	1134	.063	L.F.	206	2.45	1.47	209.92	232
7120	x 169	G		1100	.065		246	2.53	1.52	250.05	277
7140	x 201	G		1100	.065		293	2.53	1.52	297.05	325
7300	W 36 x 135	G		1170	.062		197	2.38	1.43	200.81	222
7500	x 150	G		1170	.062		219	2.38	1.43	222.81	246
7600	x 170	G		1150	.063		248	2.42	1.45	251.87	279
7700	x 194	G		1125	.064		283	2.47	1.49	286.96	315
7900	x 231	G		1125	.064		335	2.47	1.49	338.96	375
7920	x 262	G		1035	.070		380	2.69	1.61	384.30	425
8100	x 302	G		1035	.070		440	2.69	1.61	444.30	490
8490	For projects 75 to 99 tons, add						10%				
8492	50 to 74 tons, add						20%				
8494	25 to 49 tons, add						30%	10%			
8496	10 to 24 tons, add						50%	25%			
8498	2 to 9 tons, add						75%	50%			
8499	Less than 2 tons, add						100%	100%			

05 12 23.77 Structural Steel Projects

			Crew	Daily Output	Labor-Hours	Unit	Material	2014 Bare Costs Labor	2014 Bare Costs Equipment	Total	Total Incl O&P
0010	**STRUCTURAL STEEL PROJECTS** R050516-30										
0015	Made from recycled materials										
0020	Shop fab'd for 100-ton, 1-2 story project, bolted connections										
0201	Apartments, nursing homes, etc., 1 to 2 stories R050523-10	G	E-2	6.45	7.442	Ton	2,650	288	237	3,175	3,725
0302	3 to 6 stories	G	"	6.30	7.619		2,700	295	243	3,238	3,800
0402	7 to 15 stories R051223-10	G	E-5	8.74	8.238		2,750	320	191	3,261	3,825
0500	Over 15 stories	G	E-6	13.90	8.633		2,850	330	134	3,314	3,925
0701	Offices, hospitals, etc., steel bearing, 1 to 2 stories R051223-20	G	E-2	6.45	7.442		2,650	288	237	3,175	3,725
0801	3 to 6 stories	G	"	6.30	7.619		2,700	295	243	3,238	3,800
0901	7 to 15 stories R051223-25	G	E-5	8.74	8.238		2,750	320	191	3,261	3,825
1000	Over 15 stories	G	E-6	13.90	8.633		2,850	330	134	3,314	3,925
1100	For multi-story masonry wall bearing construction, add R051223-30							30%			
1301	Industrial bldgs., 1 story, beams & girders, steel bearing	G	E-2	8.06	5.955		2,650	231	190	3,071	3,575
1401	Masonry bearing	G	"	6.25	7.680		2,650	298	245	3,193	3,750
1500	Industrial bldgs., 1 story, under 10 tons,										
1510	steel from warehouse, trucked	G	E-2	7.50	6.400	Ton	3,175	248	204	3,627	4,175
1601	1 story with roof trusses, steel bearing	G		6.63	7.240		3,125	280	231	3,636	4,225
1701	Masonry bearing	G		6	8		3,125	310	255	3,690	4,300
1901	Monumental structures, banks, stores, etc., simple connections	G	E-5	8	9		2,650	345	209	3,204	3,800
2000	Moment/composite connections	G	E-6	9	13.333		4,400	510	207	5,117	6,050
2201	Churches, simple connections	G	E-2	7.25	6.621		2,475	256	211	2,942	3,400
2300	Moment/composite connections	G	E-5	5.20	13.846		3,275	535	320	4,130	4,975
2800	Power stations, fossil fuels, simple connections	G	E-6	11	10.909		2,650	420	170	3,240	3,900
2900	Moment/composite connections	G		5.70	21.053		3,975	810	325	5,110	6,225
2950	Nuclear fuels, non-safety steel, simple connections	G		7	17.143		2,650	660	266	3,576	4,450
3000	Moment/composite connections	G		5.50	21.818		3,975	835	340	5,150	6,325
3040	Safety steel, simple connections	G		2.50	48		3,875	1,850	745	6,470	8,525
3070	Moment/composite connections	G		1.50	80		5,100	3,075	1,250	9,425	12,700
3101	Roof trusses, simple connections	G	E-2	8.13	5.904		3,700	229	188	4,117	4,700
3200	Moment/composite connections	G	E-5	8.30	8.675		4,500	335	201	5,036	5,800
3211	Schools, simple connections	G	E-2	9	5.333		2,650	207	170	3,027	3,500
3220	Moment/composite connections	G	E-5	8.30	8.675		3,875	335	201	4,411	5,100
3400	Welded construction, simple commercial bldgs., 1 to 2 stories	G	E-7	7.60	9.474		2,700	365	239	3,304	3,925
3501	7 to 15 stories	G	E-8	6.38	13.793		3,125	530	330	3,985	4,800
3701	Welded rigid frame, 1 story, simple connections	G	E-2	9.88	4.858		2,750	188	155	3,093	3,550

05 12 23.77 Structural Steel Projects		Crew	Daily Output	Labor-Hours	Unit	Material	2014 Bare Costs Labor	Equipment	Total	Total Incl O&P
3800	Moment/composite connections	G E-7	5.50	13.091	Ton	3,575	505	330	4,410	5,250
3810	Fabrication shop costs (incl in project bare material cost, above)									
3820	Mini mill base price, Grade A992	G			Ton	770			770	845
3830	Mill extras plus delivery to warehouse					275			275	305
3835	Delivery from warehouse to fabrication shop					85			85	93.50
3840	Shop extra for shop drawings and detailing					295			295	325
3850	Shop fabricating and handling					950			950	1,050
3860	Shop sandblasting and primer coat of paint					155			155	171
3870	Shop delivery to the job site					120			120	132
3880	Total material cost, shop fabricated, primed, delivered					2,650			2,650	2,925
3900	High strength steel mill spec extras:									
3950	A529, A572 (50 ksi) and A36: same as A992 steel (no extra)									
4000	Add to A992 price for A572 (60, 65 ksi)	G			Ton	80			80	88
4100	A242 and A588 Weathering	G			"	80			80	88
4200	Mill size extras for W-Shapes: 0 to 30 plf: no extra charge									
4210	Member sizes 31 to 65 plf, deduct	G			Ton	.01			.01	.01
4220	Member sizes 66 to 100 plf, deduct	G				5.65			5.65	6.25
4230	Member sizes 101 to 387 plf, add	G				55.50			55.50	61
4300	Column base plates, light, up to 150 lb.	G	2 Sswk	2000	.008	Lb.	1.46	.31		1.77	2.18
4400	Heavy, over 150 lb.	G	E-2	7500	.006	"	1.52	.25	.20	1.97	2.36
4600	Castellated beams, light sections, to 50#/L.F., simple connections	G		10.70	4.486	Ton	2,775	174	143	3,092	3,525
4700	Moment/composite connections	G		7	6.857		3,050	266	218	3,534	4,075
4900	Heavy sections, over 50 plf, simple connections	G		11.70	4.103		2,925	159	131	3,215	3,650
5000	Moment/composite connections	G		7.80	6.154		3,175	238	196	3,609	4,150
5390	For projects 75 to 99 tons, add						10%			
5392	50 to 74 tons, add						20%			
5394	25 to 49 tons, add						30%	10%		
5396	10 to 24 tons, add						50%	25%		
5398	2 to 9 tons, add						75%	50%		
5399	Less than 2 tons, add						100%	100%		

0010	**STRUCTURAL STEEL SECONDARY MEMBERS**									
0015	Made from recycled materials									
0020	Shop fabricated for 20-ton girt/purlin framing package, materials only									
0100	Girts/purlins, C/Z-shapes, includes clips and bolts									
0110	6" x 2-1/2" x 2-1/2", 16 ga., 3.0 lb./L.F.					L.F.	3.58			3.58	3.94
0115	14 ga., 3.5 lb./L.F.						4.17			4.17	4.59
0120	8" x 2-3/4" x 2-3/4", 16 ga., 3.4 lb./L.F.						4.05			4.05	4.46
0125	14 ga., 4.1 lb./L.F.						4.89			4.89	5.40
0130	12 ga., 5.6 lb./L.F.						6.70			6.70	7.35
0135	10" x 3-1/2" x 3-1/2", 14 ga., 4.7 lb./L.F.						5.60			5.60	6.15
0140	12 ga., 6.7 lb./L.F.						8			8	8.80
0145	12" x 3-1/2" x 3-1/2", 14 ga., 5.3 lb./L.F.						6.30			6.30	6.95
0150	12 ga., 7.4 lb./L.F.						8.80			8.80	9.70
0200	Eave struts, C-shape, includes clips and bolts									
0210	6" x 4" x 3", 16 ga., 3.1 lb./L.F.					L.F.	3.70			3.70	4.07
0215	14 ga., 3.9 lb./L.F.						4.65			4.65	5.10
0220	8" x 4" x 3", 16 ga., 3.5 lb./L.F.						4.17			4.17	4.59
0225	14 ga., 4.4 lb./L.F.						5.25			5.25	5.75
0230	12 ga., 6.2 lb./L.F.						7.40			7.40	8.15
0235	10" x 5" x 3", 14 ga., 5.2 lb./L.F.						6.20			6.20	6.80
0240	12 ga., 7.3 lb./L.F.						8.70			8.70	9.60

05 12 23 – Structural Steel for Buildings

05 12 23.78 Structural Steel Secondary Members	Crew	Daily Output	Labor-Hours	Unit	Material	2014 Bare Costs Labor	Equipment	Total	Total Incl O&P
0245 12" x 5" x 4", 14 ga., 6.0 lb./L.F.				L.F.	7.15			7.15	7.85
0250 12 ga., 8.4 lb./L.F.				↓	10			10	11
0300 Rake/base angle, excludes concrete drilling and expansion anchors									
0310 2" x 2", 14 ga., 1.0 lb./L.F.	2 Sswk	640	.025	L.F.	1.19	.96		2.15	3.14
0315 3" x 2", 14 ga., 1.3 lb./L.F.		535	.030		1.55	1.15		2.70	3.89
0320 3" x 3", 14 ga., 1.6 lb./L.F.		500	.032		1.91	1.23		3.14	4.44
0325 4" x 3", 14 ga., 1.8 lb./L.F.	↓	480	.033	↓	2.15	1.28		3.43	4.79
0600 Installation of secondary members, erection only									
0610 Girts, purlins, eave struts, 16 ga., 6" deep	E-18	100	.400	Ea.		15.45	9.60	25.05	39
0615 8" deep		80	.500			19.30	12	31.30	49
0620 14 ga., 6" deep		80	.500			19.30	12	31.30	49
0625 8" deep		65	.615			24	14.80	38.80	60.50
0630 10" deep		55	.727			28	17.45	45.45	71
0635 12" deep		50	.800			31	19.20	50.20	78.50
0640 12 ga., 8" deep		50	.800			31	19.20	50.20	78.50
0645 10" deep		45	.889			34.50	21.50	56	87
0650 12" deep	↓	40	1	↓		38.50	24	62.50	98
0900 For less than 20-ton job lots									
0905 For 15 to 19 tons, add					10%				
0910 For 10 to 14 tons, add					25%				
0915 For 5 to 9 tons, add					50%	50%	50%		
0920 For 1 to 4 tons, add					75%	75%	75%		
0925 For less than 1 ton, add					100%	100%	100%		

05 12 23.80 Subpurlins

	Crew	Daily Output	Labor-Hours	Unit	Material	Labor	Equipment	Total	Total Incl O&P
0010 **SUBPURLINS** R051223-50									
0015 Made from recycled materials									
0020 Bulb tees, shop fabricated, painted, 32-5/8" O.C., 40 psf L.L.									
0200 Type 218, max 10'-2" span, 3.19 plf, 2-1/8" high x 2-1/8" wide [G]	E-1	3100	.005	S.F.	1.66	.20	.05	1.91	2.25
1420 For 24-5/8" spacing, add					33%	33%			
1430 For 48-5/8" spacing, deduct				↓	33%	33%			

05 14 Structural Aluminum Framing

05 14 23 – Non-Exposed Structural Aluminum Framing

05 14 23.05 Aluminum Shapes

	Crew	Daily Output	Labor-Hours	Unit	Material	Labor	Equipment	Total	Total Incl O&P
0010 **ALUMINUM SHAPES**									
0015 Made from recycled materials									
0020 Structural shapes, 1" to 10" members, under 1 ton [G]	E-2	4000	.012	Lb.	4.18	.46	.38	5.02	5.90
0050 1 to 5 tons [G]		4300	.011		3.83	.43	.36	4.62	5.40
0100 Over 5 tons [G]		4600	.010		3.65	.40	.33	4.38	5.15
0300 Extrusions, over 5 tons, stock shapes [G]		1330	.036		3.48	1.40	1.15	6.03	7.70
0400 Custom shapes [G]	↓	1330	.036	↓	3.61	1.40	1.15	6.16	7.85

05 15 Wire Rope Assemblies

05 15 16 - Steel Wire Rope Assemblies

05 15 16.05 Accessories for Steel Wire Rope		Crew	Daily Output	Labor-Hours	Unit	Material	2014 Bare Costs Labor	Equipment	Total	Total Incl O&P
0010	**ACCESSORIES FOR STEEL WIRE ROPE**									
0015	Made from recycled materials									
1500	Thimbles, heavy duty, 1/4"	G	E-17	160	.100	Ea.	.51	3.94		4.45	8.05
1510	1/2"	G		160	.100		2.23	3.94		6.17	9.95
1520	3/4"	G		105	.152		5.05	6		11.05	16.95
1530	1"	G		52	.308		10.15	12.10		22.25	34
1540	1-1/4"	G		38	.421		15.60	16.55		32.15	48.50
1550	1-1/2"	G		13	1.231		44	48.50		92.50	141
1560	1-3/4"	G		8	2		90.50	78.50		169	250
1570	2"	G		6	2.667		132	105		237	345
1580	2-1/4"	G		4	4		178	157		335	495
1600	Clips, 1/4" diameter	G		160	.100		2.64	3.94		6.58	10.40
1610	3/8" diameter	G		160	.100		2.90	3.94		6.84	10.70
1620	1/2" diameter	G		160	.100		4.66	3.94		8.60	12.60
1630	3/4" diameter	G		102	.157		7.55	6.15		13.70	20
1640	1" diameter	G		64	.250		12.60	9.85		22.45	32.50
1650	1-1/4" diameter	G		35	.457		20.50	18		38.50	57
1670	1-1/2" diameter	G		26	.615		28	24		52	76.50
1680	1-3/4" diameter	G		16	1		65	39.50		104.50	147
1690	2" diameter	G		12	1.333		72	52.50		124.50	180
1700	2-1/4" diameter	G		10	1.600		106	63		169	237
1800	Sockets, open swage, 1/4" diameter	G		160	.100		45.50	3.94		49.44	57.50
1810	1/2" diameter	G		77	.208		65.50	8.20		73.70	88
1820	3/4" diameter	G		19	.842		102	33		135	175
1830	1" diameter	G		9	1.778		183	70		253	335
1840	1-1/4" diameter	G		5	3.200		254	126		380	520
1850	1-1/2" diameter	G		3	5.333		555	210		765	1,000
1860	1-3/4" diameter	G		3	5.333		985	210		1,195	1,475
1870	2" diameter	G		1.50	10.667		1,500	420		1,920	2,450
1900	Closed swage, 1/4" diameter	G		160	.100		27	3.94		30.94	37
1910	1/2" diameter	G		104	.154		46.50	6.05		52.55	62.50
1920	3/4" diameter	G		32	.500		69.50	19.70		89.20	114
1930	1" diameter	G		15	1.067		122	42		164	214
1940	1-1/4" diameter	G		7	2.286		183	90		273	375
1950	1-1/2" diameter	G		4	4		330	157		487	665
1960	1-3/4" diameter	G		3	5.333		490	210		700	940
1970	2" diameter	G		2	8		955	315		1,270	1,650
2000	Open spelter, galv., 1/4" diameter	G		160	.100		58	3.94		61.94	71.50
2010	1/2" diameter	G		70	.229		60.50	9		69.50	83.50
2020	3/4" diameter	G		26	.615		90.50	24		114.50	146
2030	1" diameter	G		10	1.600		252	63		315	395
2040	1-1/4" diameter	G		5	3.200		360	126		486	635
2050	1-1/2" diameter	G		4	4		765	157		922	1,150
2060	1-3/4" diameter	G		2	8		1,325	315		1,640	2,075
2070	2" diameter	G		1.20	13.333		1,525	525		2,050	2,700
2080	2-1/2" diameter	G		1	16		2,825	630		3,455	4,300
2100	Closed spelter, galv., 1/4" diameter	G		160	.100		48.50	3.94		52.44	60.50
2110	1/2" diameter	G		88	.182		51.50	7.15		58.65	70.50
2120	3/4" diameter	G		30	.533		78.50	21		99.50	126
2130	1" diameter	G		13	1.231		167	48.50		215.50	276
2140	1-1/4" diameter	G		7	2.286		267	90		357	465
2150	1-1/2" diameter	G		6	2.667		575	105		680	830
2160	1-3/4" diameter	G		2.80	5.714		765	225		990	1,275

05 15 Wire Rope Assemblies

05 15 16 – Steel Wire Rope Assemblies

			Crew	Daily Output	Labor-Hours	Unit	Material	2014 Bare Costs Labor	Equipment	Total	Total Incl O&P
05 15 16.05	**Accessories for Steel Wire Rope**										
2170	2" diameter	G	E-17	2	8	Ea.	945	315		1,260	1,650
2200	Jaw & jaw turnbuckles, 1/4" x 4"	G		160	.100		16.35	3.94		20.29	25.50
2250	1/2" x 6"	G		96	.167		20.50	6.55		27.05	35
2260	1/2" x 9"	G		77	.208		27.50	8.20		35.70	46
2270	1/2" x 12"	G		66	.242		31	9.55		40.55	52
2300	3/4" x 6"	G		38	.421		40.50	16.55		57.05	76
2310	3/4" x 9"	G		30	.533		45	21		66	89.50
2320	3/4" x 12"	G		28	.571		57.50	22.50		80	107
2330	3/4" x 18"	G		23	.696		69	27.50		96.50	128
2350	1" x 6"	G		17	.941		78.50	37		115.50	157
2360	1" x 12"	G		13	1.231		86	48.50		134.50	188
2370	1" x 18"	G		10	1.600		129	63		192	262
2380	1" x 24"	G		9	1.778		142	70		212	289
2400	1-1/4" x 12"	G		7	2.286		145	90		235	330
2410	1-1/4" x 18"	G		6.50	2.462		179	97		276	380
2420	1-1/4" x 24"	G		5.60	2.857		241	112		353	480
2450	1-1/2" x 12"	G		5.20	3.077		425	121		546	695
2460	1-1/2" x 18"	G		4	4		450	157		607	800
2470	1-1/2" x 24"	G		3.20	5		610	197		807	1,050
2500	1-3/4" x 18"	G		3.20	5		920	197		1,117	1,375
2510	1-3/4" x 24"	G		2.80	5.714		1,050	225		1,275	1,575
2550	2" x 24"	G		1.60	10		1,425	395		1,820	2,300
05 15 16.50	**Steel Wire Rope**										
0010	**STEEL WIRE ROPE**										
0015	Made from recycled materials										
0020	6 x 19, bright, fiber core, 5000' rolls, 1/2" diameter	G				L.F.	.88			.88	.96
0050	Steel core	G					1.15			1.15	1.27
0100	Fiber core, 1" diameter	G					2.95			2.95	3.25
0150	Steel core	G					3.37			3.37	3.70
0300	6 x 19, galvanized, fiber core, 1/2" diameter	G					1.29			1.29	1.42
0350	Steel core	G					1.48			1.48	1.62
0400	Fiber core, 1" diameter	G					3.78			3.78	4.16
0450	Steel core	G					3.96			3.96	4.36
0500	6 x 7, bright, IPS, fiber core, <500 L.F. w/acc., 1/4" diameter	G	E-17	6400	.003		1.47	.10		1.57	1.81
0510	1/2" diameter	G		2100	.008		3.59	.30		3.89	4.52
0520	3/4" diameter	G		960	.017		6.50	.66		7.16	8.40
0550	6 x 19, bright, IPS, IWRC, <500 L.F. w/acc., 1/4" diameter	G		5760	.003		.97	.11		1.08	1.27
0560	1/2" diameter	G		1730	.009		1.57	.36		1.93	2.41
0570	3/4" diameter	G		770	.021		2.72	.82		3.54	4.55
0580	1" diameter	G		420	.038		4.61	1.50		6.11	7.90
0590	1-1/4" diameter	G		290	.055		7.65	2.17		9.82	12.55
0600	1-1/2" diameter	G		192	.083		9.40	3.28		12.68	16.60
0610	1-3/4" diameter	G	E-18	240	.167		15	6.45	4	25.45	33
0620	2" diameter	G		160	.250		19.20	9.65	6	34.85	45.50
0630	2-1/4" diameter	G		160	.250		25.50	9.65	6	41.15	53
0650	6 x 37, bright, IPS, IWRC, <500 L.F. w/acc., 1/4" diameter	G	E-17	6400	.003		1.15	.10		1.25	1.46
0660	1/2" diameter	G		1730	.009		1.96	.36		2.32	2.84
0670	3/4" diameter	G		770	.021		3.16	.82		3.98	5.05
0680	1" diameter	G		430	.037		5	1.46		6.46	8.30
0690	1-1/4" diameter	G		290	.055		7.60	2.17		9.77	12.50
0700	1-1/2" diameter	G		190	.084		10.85	3.31		14.16	18.25
0710	1-3/4" diameter	G	E-18	260	.154		17.20	5.95	3.69	26.84	34

05 15 Wire Rope Assemblies

05 15 16 – Steel Wire Rope Assemblies

05 15 16.50 Steel Wire Rope		Crew	Daily Output	Labor-Hours	Unit	Material	2014 Bare Costs Labor	Equipment	Total	Total Incl O&P
0720	2" diameter	G	E-18	200	.200	L.F.	22.50	7.70	4.80	35	44
0730	2-1/4" diameter	G	↓	160	.250		29.50	9.65	6	45.15	57
0800	6 x 19 & 6 x 37, swaged, 1/2" diameter	G	E-17	1220	.013		2.43	.52		2.95	3.65
0810	9/16" diameter	G		1120	.014		2.83	.56		3.39	4.18
0820	5/8" diameter	G		930	.017		3.35	.68		4.03	4.98
0830	3/4" diameter	G		640	.025		4.27	.98		5.25	6.55
0840	7/8" diameter	G		480	.033		5.40	1.31		6.71	8.45
0850	1" diameter	G		350	.046		6.55	1.80		8.35	10.70
0860	1-1/8" diameter	G		288	.056		8.10	2.19		10.29	13.05
0870	1-1/4" diameter	G		230	.070		9.80	2.74		12.54	15.95
0880	1-3/8" diameter	G	↓	192	.083		11.30	3.28		14.58	18.70
0890	1-1/2" diameter	G	E-18	300	.133	↓	13.75	5.15	3.20	22.10	28

05 15 16.60 Galvanized Steel Wire Rope and Accessories

		Crew	Daily Output	Labor-Hours	Unit	Material	Labor	Equipment	Total	Total Incl O&P
0010	**GALVANIZED STEEL WIRE ROPE & ACCESSORIES**									
0015	Made from recycled materials									
3000	Aircraft cable, galvanized, 7 x 7 x 1/8"	G	E-17	5000	.003	L.F.	.17	.13		.30	.43
3100	Clamps, 1/8"	G	"	125	.128	Ea.	1.89	5.05		6.94	11.70

05 15 16.70 Temporary Cable Safety Railing

		Crew	Daily Output	Labor-Hours	Unit	Material	Labor	Equipment	Total	Total Incl O&P
0010	**TEMPORARY CABLE SAFETY RAILING**, Each 100' strand incl.									
0020	2 eyebolts, 1 turnbuckle, 100' cable, 2 thimbles, 6 clips									
0025	Made from recycled materials									
0100	One strand using 1/4" cable & accessories	G	2 Sswk	4	4	C.L.F.	205	153		358	515
0200	1/2" cable & accessories	G	"	2	8	"	430	305		735	1,050

05 21 Steel Joist Framing

05 21 13 – Deep Longspan Steel Joist Framing

05 21 13.50 Deep Longspan Joists		Crew	Daily Output	Labor-Hours	Unit	Material	Labor	Equipment	Total	Total Incl O&P
0010	**DEEP LONGSPAN JOISTS**									
3010	DLH series, 40-ton job lots, bolted cross bridging, shop primer									
3015	Made from recycled materials									
3040	Spans to 144' (shipped in 2 pieces)	G	E-7	13	5.538	Ton	1,925	214	139	2,278	2,675
3200	52DLH11, 26 lb./L.F.	G		2000	.036	L.F.	24	1.39	.91	26.30	30
3220	52DLH16, 45 lb./L.F.	G		2000	.036		43.50	1.39	.91	45.80	51
3240	56DLH11, 26 lb./L.F.	G		2000	.036		25	1.39	.91	27.30	31
3260	56DLH16, 46 lb./L.F.	G		2000	.036		44.50	1.39	.91	46.80	52.50
3280	60DLH12, 29 lb./L.F.	G		2000	.036		28	1.39	.91	30.30	34.50
3300	60DLH17, 52 lb./L.F.	G		2000	.036		50	1.39	.91	52.30	58.50
3320	64DLH12, 31 lb./L.F.	G		2200	.033		30	1.26	.82	32.08	36.50
3340	64DLH17, 52 lb./L.F.	G		2200	.033		50	1.26	.82	52.08	58.50
3360	68DLH13, 37 lb./L.F.	G		2200	.033		35.50	1.26	.82	37.58	43
3380	68DLH18, 61 lb./L.F.	G		2200	.033		59	1.26	.82	61.08	68
3400	72DLH14, 41 lb./L.F.	G		2200	.033		39.50	1.26	.82	41.58	47
3420	72DLH19, 70 lb./L.F.	G	↓	2200	.033	↓	67.50	1.26	.82	69.58	78
3500	For less than 40-ton job lots									
3502	For 30 to 39 tons, add						10%			
3504	20 to 29 tons, add						20%			
3506	10 to 19 tons, add						30%			
3507	5 to 9 tons, add						50%	25%		
3508	1 to 4 tons, add						75%	50%		
3509	Less than 1 ton, add						100%	100%		

05 21 Steel Joist Framing

05 21 13 – Deep Longspan Steel Joist Framing

05 21 13.50 Deep Longspan Joists

		Crew	Daily Output	Labor-Hours	Unit	Material	2014 Bare Costs Labor	Equipment	Total	Total Incl O&P
4010	SLH series, 40-ton job lots, bolted cross bridging, shop primer									
4040	Spans to 200' (shipped in 3 pieces)	G	E-7	13	5.538	Ton	1,975	214	139	2,328	2,725
4200	80SLH15, 40 lb./L.F.	G		1500	.048	L.F.	39.50	1.85	1.21	42.56	48.50
4220	80SLH20, 75 lb./L.F.	G		1500	.048		74.50	1.85	1.21	77.56	87
4240	88SLH16, 46 lb./L.F.	G		1500	.048		45.50	1.85	1.21	48.56	55
4260	88SLH21, 89 lb./L.F.	G		1500	.048		88.50	1.85	1.21	91.56	102
4280	96SLH17, 52 lb./L.F.	G		1500	.048		51.50	1.85	1.21	54.56	61.50
4300	96SLH22, 102 lb./L.F.	G		1500	.048		101	1.85	1.21	104.06	116
4320	104SLH18, 59 lb./L.F.	G		1800	.040		58.50	1.54	1.01	61.05	68.50
4340	104SLH23, 109 lb./L.F.	G		1800	.040		108	1.54	1.01	110.55	123
4360	112SLH19, 67 lb./L.F.	G		1800	.040		66.50	1.54	1.01	69.05	77
4380	112SLH24, 131 lb./L.F.	G		1800	.040		130	1.54	1.01	132.55	147
4400	120SLH20, 77 lb./L.F.	G		1800	.040		76.50	1.54	1.01	79.05	88
4420	120SLH25, 152 lb./L.F.	G		1800	.040		151	1.54	1.01	153.55	170
6100	For less than 40-ton job lots										
6102	For 30 to 39 tons, add						10%				
6104	20 to 29 tons, add						20%				
6106	10 to 19 tons, add						30%				
6107	5 to 9 tons, add						50%	25%			
6108	1 to 4 tons, add						75%	50%			
6109	Less than 1 ton, add						100%	100%			

05 21 16 – Longspan Steel Joist Framing

05 21 16.50 Longspan Joists

		Crew	Daily Output	Labor-Hours	Unit	Material	2014 Bare Costs Labor	Equipment	Total	Total Incl O&P
0010	**LONGSPAN JOISTS**										
2000	LH series, 40-ton job lots, bolted cross bridging, shop primer										
2015	Made from recycled materials										
2040	Longspan joists, LH series, up to 96'	G	E-7	13	5.538	Ton	1,825	214	139	2,178	2,575
2200	18LH04, 12 lb./L.F.	G		1400	.051	L.F.	11	1.99	1.30	14.29	17.25
2220	18LH08, 19 lb./L.F.	G		1400	.051		17.40	1.99	1.30	20.69	24.50
2240	20LH04, 12 lb./L.F.	G		1400	.051		11	1.99	1.30	14.29	17.25
2260	20LH08, 19 lb./L.F.	G		1400	.051		17.40	1.99	1.30	20.69	24.50
2280	24LH05, 13 lb./L.F.	G		1400	.051		11.90	1.99	1.30	15.19	18.25
2300	24LH10, 23 lb./L.F.	G		1400	.051		21	1.99	1.30	24.29	28
2320	28LH06, 16 lb./L.F.	G		1800	.040		14.65	1.54	1.01	17.20	20
2340	28LH11, 25 lb./L.F.	G		1800	.040		23	1.54	1.01	25.55	29
2360	32LH08, 17 lb./L.F.	G		1800	.040		15.60	1.54	1.01	18.15	21
2380	32LH13, 30 lb./L.F.	G		1800	.040		27.50	1.54	1.01	30.05	34.50
2400	36LH09, 21 lb./L.F.	G		1800	.040		19.25	1.54	1.01	21.80	25
2420	36LH14, 36 lb./L.F.	G		1800	.040		33	1.54	1.01	35.55	40.50
2440	40LH10, 21 lb./L.F.	G		2200	.033		19.25	1.26	.82	21.33	24.50
2460	40LH15, 36 lb./L.F.	G		2200	.033		33	1.26	.82	35.08	40
2480	44LH11, 22 lb./L.F.	G		2200	.033		20	1.26	.82	22.08	25.50
2500	44LH16, 42 lb./L.F.	G		2200	.033		38.50	1.26	.82	40.58	46
2520	48LH11, 22 lb./L.F.	G		2200	.033		20	1.26	.82	22.08	25.50
2540	48LH16, 42 lb./L.F.	G		2200	.033		38.50	1.26	.82	40.58	46
2600	For less than 40-ton job lots										
2602	For 30 to 39 tons, add						10%				
2604	20 to 29 tons, add						20%				
2606	10 to 19 tons, add						30%				
2607	5 to 9 tons, add						50%	25%			
2608	1 to 4 tons, add						75%	50%			
2609	Less than 1 ton, add						100%	100%			

05 21 Steel Joist Framing

05 21 16 – Longspan Steel Joist Framing

05 21 16.50 Longspan Joists		Crew	Daily Output	Labor-Hours	Unit	Material	2014 Bare Costs		Total	Total Incl O&P
							Labor	Equipment		
6000	For welded cross bridging, add						30%			

05 21 19 – Open Web Steel Joist Framing

05 21 19.10 Open Web Joists

			Crew	Daily Output	Labor-Hours	Unit	Material	Labor	Equipment	Total	Total Incl O&P
0010	**OPEN WEB JOISTS**										
0015	Made from recycled materials										
0050	K series, 40-ton lots, horiz. bridging, spans to 30', shop primer	G	E-7	12	6	Ton	1,650	232	151	2,033	2,425
0130	8K1, 5.1 lb./L.F.	G		1200	.060	L.F.	4.22	2.32	1.51	8.05	10.65
0140	10K1, 5.0 lb./L.F.	G		1200	.060		4.14	2.32	1.51	7.97	10.55
0160	12K3, 5.7 lb./L.F.	G		1500	.048		4.72	1.85	1.21	7.78	10
0180	14K3, 6.0 lb./L.F.	G		1500	.048		4.97	1.85	1.21	8.03	10.25
0200	16K3, 6.3 lb./L.F.	G		1800	.040		5.20	1.54	1.01	7.75	9.75
0220	16K6, 8.1 lb./L.F.	G		1800	.040		6.70	1.54	1.01	9.25	11.40
0240	18K5, 7.7 lb./L.F.	G		2000	.036		6.40	1.39	.91	8.70	10.60
0260	18K9, 10.2 lb./L.F.	G		2000	.036		8.45	1.39	.91	10.75	12.90
0440	K series, 30' to 50' spans	G		17	4.235	Ton	1,625	164	107	1,896	2,225
0500	20K5, 8.2 lb./L.F.	G		2000	.036	L.F.	6.65	1.39	.91	8.95	10.95
0520	20K9, 10.8 lb./L.F.	G		2000	.036		8.80	1.39	.91	11.10	13.25
0540	22K5, 8.8 lb./L.F.	G		2000	.036		7.15	1.39	.91	9.45	11.45
0560	22K9, 11.3 lb./L.F.	G		2000	.036		9.20	1.39	.91	11.50	13.70
0580	24K6, 9.7 lb./L.F.	G		2200	.033		7.90	1.26	.82	9.98	11.95
0600	24K10, 13.1 lb./L.F.	G		2200	.033		10.65	1.26	.82	12.73	15
0620	26K6, 10.6 lb./L.F.	G		2200	.033		8.60	1.26	.82	10.68	12.75
0640	26K10, 13.8 lb./L.F.	G		2200	.033		11.20	1.26	.82	13.28	15.65
0660	28K8, 12.7 lb./L.F.	G		2400	.030		10.30	1.16	.76	12.22	14.35
0680	28K12, 17.1 lb./L.F.	G		2400	.030		13.90	1.16	.76	15.82	18.30
0700	30K8, 13.2 lb./L.F.	G		2400	.030		10.75	1.16	.76	12.67	14.80
0720	30K12, 17.6 lb./L.F.	G		2400	.030		14.30	1.16	.76	16.22	18.75
0800	For less than 40-ton job lots										
0802	For 30 to 39 tons, add						10%				
0804	20 to 29 tons, add						20%				
0806	10 to 19 tons, add						30%				
0807	5 to 9 tons, add						50%	25%			
0808	1 to 4 tons, add						75%	50%			
0809	Less than 1 ton, add						100%	100%			
1010	CS series, 40-ton job lots, horizontal bridging, shop primer										
1040	Spans to 30'	G	E-7	12	6	Ton	1,700	232	151	2,083	2,475
1100	10CS2, 7.5 lb./L.F.	G		1200	.060	L.F.	6.40	2.32	1.51	10.23	13
1120	12CS2, 8.0 lb./L.F.	G		1500	.048		6.80	1.85	1.21	9.86	12.30
1140	14CS2, 8.0 lb./L.F.	G		1500	.048		6.80	1.85	1.21	9.86	12.30
1160	16CS2, 8.5 lb./L.F.	G		1800	.040		7.25	1.54	1.01	9.80	11.95
1180	16CS4, 14.5 lb./L.F.	G		1800	.040		12.35	1.54	1.01	14.90	17.55
1200	18CS2, 9.0 lb./L.F.	G		2000	.036		7.65	1.39	.91	9.95	12
1220	18CS4, 15.0 lb./L.F.	G		2000	.036		12.75	1.39	.91	15.05	17.65
1240	20CS2, 9.5 lb./L.F.	G		2000	.036		8.10	1.39	.91	10.40	12.50
1260	20CS4, 16.5 lb./L.F.	G		2000	.036		14.05	1.39	.91	16.35	19.05
1280	22CS2, 10.0 lb./L.F.	G		2000	.036		8.50	1.39	.91	10.80	12.95
1300	22CS4, 16.5 lb./L.F.	G		2000	.036		14.05	1.39	.91	16.35	19.05
1320	24CS2, 10.0 lb./L.F.	G		2200	.033		8.50	1.26	.82	10.58	12.65
1340	24CS4, 16.5 lb./L.F.	G		2200	.033		14.05	1.26	.82	16.13	18.75
1360	26CS2, 10.0 lb./L.F.	G		2200	.033		8.50	1.26	.82	10.58	12.65
1380	26CS4, 16.5 lb./L.F.	G		2200	.033		14.05	1.26	.82	16.13	18.75
1400	28CS2, 10.5 lb./L.F.	G		2400	.030		8.95	1.16	.76	10.87	12.80

05 21 Steel Joist Framing

05 21 19 – Open Web Steel Joist Framing

05 21 19.10 Open Web Joists

		Crew	Daily Output	Labor-Hours	Unit	Material	2014 Bare Costs Labor	Equipment	Total	Total Incl O&P
1420	28CS4, 16.5 lb./L.F.	E-7 [G]	2400	.030	L.F.	14.05	1.16	.76	15.97	18.45
1440	30CS2, 11.0 lb./L.F.	[G]	2400	.030		9.35	1.16	.76	11.27	13.30
1460	30CS4, 16.5 lb./L.F.	[G]	2400	.030		14.05	1.16	.76	15.97	18.45
1500	For less than 40-ton job lots									
1502	For 30 to 39 tons, add					10%				
1504	20 to 29 tons, add					20%				
1506	10 to 19 tons, add					30%				
1507	5 to 9 tons, add					50%	25%			
1508	1 to 4 tons, add					75%	50%			
1509	Less than 1 ton, add					100%	100%			
6200	For shop prime paint other than mfrs. standard, add					20%				
6300	For bottom chord extensions, add per chord	[G]			Ea.	36			36	39.50
6400	Individual steel bearing plate, 6" x 6" x 1/4" with J-hook	[G] 1 Bric	160	.050	"	7.95	1.78		9.73	11.70

05 21 23 – Steel Joist Girder Framing

05 21 23.50 Joist Girders

		Crew	Daily Output	Labor-Hours	Unit	Material	2014 Bare Costs Labor	Equipment	Total	Total Incl O&P
0010	**JOIST GIRDERS**									
0015	Made from recycled materials									
7020	Joist girders, 40-ton job lots, shop primer	[G] E-5	13	5.538	Ton	1,650	214	129	1,993	2,375
7100	For less than 40-ton job lots									
7102	For 30 to 39 tons, add					10%				
7104	20 to 29 tons, add					20%				
7106	10 to 19 tons, add					30%				
7107	5 to 9 tons, add					50%	25%			
7108	1 to 4 tons, add					75%	50%			
7109	Less than 1 ton, add					100%	100%			
8000	Trusses, 40-ton job lots, shop fabricated WT chords, shop primer	[G] E-5	11	6.545	Ton	5,425	253	152	5,830	6,600
8100	For less than 40-ton job lots									
8102	For 30 to 39 tons, add					10%				
8104	20 to 29 tons, add					20%				
8106	10 to 19 tons, add					30%				
8107	5 to 9 tons, add					50%	25%			
8108	1 to 4 tons, add					75%	50%			
8109	Less than 1 ton, add					100%	100%			

05 31 Steel Decking

05 31 13 – Steel Floor Decking

05 31 13.50 Floor Decking

		Crew	Daily Output	Labor-Hours	Unit	Material	2014 Bare Costs Labor	Equipment	Total	Total Incl O&P
0010	**FLOOR DECKING**	R053100-10								
0015	Made from recycled materials									
5100	Non-cellular composite decking, galvanized, 1-1/2" deep, 16 ga.	[G] E-4	3500	.009	S.F.	3.31	.36	.04	3.71	4.36
5120	18 ga.	[G]	3650	.009		2.68	.34	.04	3.06	3.64
5140	20 ga.	[G]	3800	.008		2.13	.33	.04	2.50	3.01
5200	2" deep, 22 ga.	[G]	3860	.008		1.86	.32	.04	2.22	2.70
5300	20 ga.	[G]	3600	.009		2.05	.35	.04	2.44	2.96
5400	18 ga.	[G]	3380	.009		2.62	.37	.04	3.03	3.63
5500	16 ga.	[G]	3200	.010		3.27	.39	.04	3.70	4.39
5700	3" deep, 22 ga.	[G]	3200	.010		2.03	.39	.04	2.46	3.02
5800	20 ga.	[G]	3000	.011		2.26	.41	.05	2.72	3.32
5900	18 ga.	[G]	2850	.011		2.79	.44	.05	3.28	3.95
6000	16 ga.	[G]	2700	.012		3.72	.46	.05	4.23	5.05

05 31 Steel Decking

05 31 23 – Steel Roof Decking

05 31 23.50 Roof Decking		Crew	Daily Output	Labor-Hours	Unit	Material	2014 Bare Costs Labor	Equipment	Total	Total Incl O&P
0010	**ROOF DECKING**									
0015	Made from recycled materials									
2100	Open type, 1-1/2" deep, Type B, wide rib, galv., 22 ga., under 50 sq.	G E-4	4500	.007	S.F.	1.97	.28	.03	2.28	2.73
2200	50-500 squares	G	4900	.007		1.53	.25	.03	1.81	2.19
2400	Over 500 squares	G	5100	.006		1.42	.24	.03	1.69	2.05
2600	20 ga., under 50 squares	G	3865	.008		2.30	.32	.04	2.66	3.19
2650	50-500 squares	G	4170	.008		1.84	.30	.03	2.17	2.64
2700	Over 500 squares	G	4300	.007		1.66	.29	.03	1.98	2.42
2900	18 ga., under 50 squares	G	3800	.008		2.97	.33	.04	3.34	3.93
2950	50-500 squares	G	4100	.008		2.38	.30	.03	2.71	3.24
3000	Over 500 squares	G	4300	.007		2.14	.29	.03	2.46	2.95
3050	16 ga., under 50 squares	G	3700	.009		4	.34	.04	4.38	5.10
3060	50-500 squares	G	4000	.008		3.20	.31	.04	3.55	4.15
3100	Over 500 squares	G	4200	.008		2.88	.30	.03	3.21	3.77
3200	3" deep, Type N, 22 ga., under 50 squares	G	3600	.009		2.90	.35	.04	3.29	3.89
3250	50-500 squares	G	3800	.008		2.32	.33	.04	2.69	3.21
3260	over 500 squares	G	4000	.008		2.09	.31	.04	2.44	2.92
3300	20 ga., under 50 squares	G	3400	.009		3.13	.37	.04	3.54	4.19
3350	50-500 squares	G	3600	.009		2.50	.35	.04	2.89	3.45
3360	over 500 squares	G	3800	.008		2.25	.33	.04	2.62	3.14
3400	18 ga., under 50 squares	G	3200	.010		4.04	.39	.04	4.47	5.25
3450	50-500 squares	G	3400	.009		3.23	.37	.04	3.64	4.31
3460	over 500 squares	G	3600	.009		2.91	.35	.04	3.30	3.90
3500	16 ga., under 50 squares	G	3000	.011		5.35	.41	.05	5.81	6.75
3550	50-500 squares	G	3200	.010		4.27	.39	.04	4.70	5.50
3560	over 500 squares	G	3400	.009		3.85	.37	.04	4.26	4.98
3700	4-1/2" deep, Type J, 20 ga., over 50 squares	G	2700	.012		3.50	.46	.05	4.01	4.79
3800	18 ga.	G	2460	.013		4.62	.51	.06	5.19	6.10
3900	16 ga.	G	2350	.014		6	.53	.06	6.59	7.70
4100	6" deep, Type H, 18 ga., over 50 squares	G	2000	.016		5.55	.62	.07	6.24	7.35
4200	16 ga.	G	1930	.017		6.90	.64	.07	7.61	8.90
4300	14 ga.	G	1860	.017		8.90	.67	.08	9.65	11.15
4500	7-1/2" deep, Type H, 18 ga., over 50 squares	G	1690	.019		6.55	.74	.08	7.37	8.75
4600	16 ga.	G	1590	.020		8.20	.78	.09	9.07	10.60
4700	14 ga.	G	1490	.021		10.20	.83	.10	11.13	12.95
4800	For painted instead of galvanized, deduct					5%				
5000	For acoustical perforated with fiberglass insulation, add				S.F.	25%				
5100	For type F intermediate rib instead of type B wide rib, add	G				25%				
5150	For type A narrow rib instead of type B wide rib, add	G				25%				

05 31 33 – Steel Form Decking

05 31 33.50 Form Decking		Crew	Daily Output	Labor-Hours	Unit	Material	2014 Bare Costs Labor	Equipment	Total	Total Incl O&P
0010	**FORM DECKING**									
0015	Made from recycled materials									
6100	Slab form, steel, 28 ga., 9/16" deep, Type UFS, uncoated	G E-4	4000	.008	S.F.	1.49	.31	.04	1.84	2.27
6200	Galvanized	G	4000	.008		1.32	.31	.04	1.67	2.08
6220	24 ga., 1" deep, Type UF1X, uncoated	G	3900	.008		1.43	.32	.04	1.79	2.22
6240	Galvanized	G	3900	.008		1.68	.32	.04	2.04	2.50
6300	24 ga., 1-5/16" deep, Type UFX, uncoated	G	3800	.008		1.52	.33	.04	1.89	2.33
6400	Galvanized	G	3800	.008		1.79	.33	.04	2.16	2.63
6500	22 ga., 1-5/16" deep, uncoated	G	3700	.009		1.92	.34	.04	2.30	2.79
6600	Galvanized	G	3700	.009		1.96	.34	.04	2.34	2.84
6700	22 ga., 2" deep, uncoated	G	3600	.009		2.50	.35	.04	2.89	3.45

05 31 Steel Decking

05 31 33 – Steel Form Decking

05 31 33.50 Form Decking		Crew	Daily Output	Labor-Hours	Unit	Material	2014 Bare Costs Labor	Equipment	Total	Total Incl O&P
6800	Galvanized	G E-4	3600	.009	S.F.	2.45	.35	.04	2.84	3.40
7000	Sheet metal edge closure form, 12" wide with 2 bends, galvanized									
7100	18 ga.	G E-14	360	.022	L.F.	4.04	.85	.39	5.28	6.50
7200	16 ga.	G "	360	.022	"	5.45	.85	.39	6.69	8.05

05 35 Raceway Decking Assemblies

05 35 13 – Steel Cellular Decking

05 35 13.50 Cellular Decking		Crew	Daily Output	Labor-Hours	Unit	Material	2014 Bare Costs Labor	Equipment	Total	Total Incl O&P
0010	**CELLULAR DECKING**									
0015	Made from recycled materials									
0200	Cellular units, galv, 1-1/2" deep, Type BC, 20-20 ga., over 15 squares	G E-4	1460	.022	S.F.	7.75	.85	.10	8.70	10.30
0250	18-20 ga.	G	1420	.023		8.85	.88	.10	9.83	11.50
0300	18-18 ga.	G	1390	.023		9.05	.89	.10	10.04	11.75
0320	16-18 ga.	G	1360	.024		10.80	.91	.10	11.81	13.70
0340	16-16 ga.	G	1330	.024		12	.93	.11	13.04	15.10
0400	3" deep, Type NC, galvanized, 20-20 ga.	G	1375	.023		8.55	.90	.10	9.55	11.25
0500	18-20 ga.	G	1350	.024		10.35	.92	.11	11.38	13.20
0600	18-18 ga.	G	1290	.025		10.30	.96	.11	11.37	13.25
0700	16-18 ga.	G	1230	.026		11.60	1.01	.12	12.73	14.80
0800	16-16 ga.	G	1150	.028		12.65	1.08	.12	13.85	16.10
1000	4-1/2" deep, Type JC, galvanized, 18-20 ga.	G	1100	.029		11.90	1.13	.13	13.16	15.40
1100	18-18 ga.	G	1040	.031		11.85	1.20	.14	13.19	15.45
1200	16-18 ga.	G	980	.033		13.35	1.27	.15	14.77	17.25
1300	16-16 ga.	G	935	.034		14.55	1.33	.15	16.03	18.70
1500	For acoustical deck, add					15%				
1700	For cells used for ventilation, add					15%				
1900	For multi-story or congested site, add						50%			
8000	Metal deck and trench, 2" thick, 20 ga., combination									
8010	60% cellular, 40% non-cellular, inserts and trench	G R-4	1100	.036	S.F.	15.55	1.44	.13	17.12	19.90

05 41 Structural Metal Stud Framing

05 41 13 – Load-Bearing Metal Stud Framing

05 41 13.05 Bracing		Crew	Daily Output	Labor-Hours	Unit	Material	2014 Bare Costs Labor	Equipment	Total	Total Incl O&P
0010	**BRACING**, shear wall X-bracing, per 10' x 10' bay, one face									
0015	Made of recycled materials									
0120	Metal strap, 20 ga. x 4" wide	G 2 Carp	18	.889	Ea.	17.55	32		49.55	73
0130	6" wide	G	18	.889		29.50	32		61.50	85.50
0160	18 ga. x 4" wide	G	16	1		30.50	36		66.50	93.50
0170	6" wide	G	16	1		45	36		81	110
0410	Continuous strap bracing, per horizontal row on both faces									
0420	Metal strap, 20 ga. x 2" wide, studs 12" O.C.	G 1 Carp	7	1.143	C.L.F.	53	41		94	127
0430	16" O.C.	G	8	1		53	36		89	118
0440	24" O.C.	G	10	.800		53	28.50		81.50	106
0450	18 ga. x 2" wide, studs 12" O.C.	G	6	1.333		75	47.50		122.50	163
0460	16" O.C.	G	7	1.143		75	41		116	151
0470	24" O.C.	G	8	1		75	36		111	143

05 41 13 – Load-Bearing Metal Stud Framing

05 41 13.10 Bridging

		Crew	Daily Output	Labor-Hours	Unit	Material	Labor	2014 Bare Costs Equipment	Total	Total Incl O&P
0010	**BRIDGING**, solid between studs w/1-1/4" leg track, per stud bay									
0015	Made from recycled materials									
0200	Studs 12" O.C., 18 ga. x 2-1/2" wide [G]	1 Carp	125	.064	Ea.	.89	2.29		3.18	4.83
0210	3-5/8" wide [G]		120	.067		1.07	2.38		3.45	5.20
0220	4" wide [G]		120	.067		1.13	2.38		3.51	5.25
0230	6" wide [G]		115	.070		1.48	2.49		3.97	5.80
0240	8" wide [G]		110	.073		1.84	2.60		4.44	6.40
0300	16 ga. x 2-1/2" wide [G]		115	.070		1.13	2.49		3.62	5.45
0310	3-5/8" wide [G]		110	.073		1.38	2.60		3.98	5.90
0320	4" wide [G]		110	.073		1.47	2.60		4.07	6
0330	6" wide [G]		105	.076		1.87	2.72		4.59	6.65
0340	8" wide [G]		100	.080		2.34	2.86		5.20	7.40
1200	Studs 16" O.C., 18 ga. x 2-1/2" wide [G]		125	.064		1.14	2.29		3.43	5.10
1210	3-5/8" wide [G]		120	.067		1.37	2.38		3.75	5.50
1220	4" wide [G]		120	.067		1.45	2.38		3.83	5.60
1230	6" wide [G]		115	.070		1.90	2.49		4.39	6.25
1240	8" wide [G]		110	.073		2.36	2.60		4.96	6.95
1300	16 ga. x 2-1/2" wide [G]		115	.070		1.45	2.49		3.94	5.80
1310	3-5/8" wide [G]		110	.073		1.77	2.60		4.37	6.30
1320	4" wide [G]		110	.073		1.88	2.60		4.48	6.45
1330	6" wide [G]		105	.076		2.39	2.72		5.11	7.20
1340	8" wide [G]		100	.080		3	2.86		5.86	8.10
2200	Studs 24" O.C., 18 ga. x 2-1/2" wide [G]		125	.064		1.65	2.29		3.94	5.65
2210	3-5/8" wide [G]		120	.067		1.98	2.38		4.36	6.20
2220	4" wide [G]		120	.067		2.10	2.38		4.48	6.30
2230	6" wide [G]		115	.070		2.75	2.49		5.24	7.20
2240	8" wide [G]		110	.073		3.41	2.60		6.01	8.10
2300	16 ga. x 2-1/2" wide [G]		115	.070		2.10	2.49		4.59	6.50
2310	3-5/8" wide [G]		110	.073		2.55	2.60		5.15	7.20
2320	4" wide [G]		110	.073		2.72	2.60		5.32	7.35
2330	6" wide [G]		105	.076		3.46	2.72		6.18	8.40
2340	8" wide [G]		100	.080		4.34	2.86		7.20	9.60
3000	Continuous bridging, per row									
3100	16 ga. x 1-1/2" channel thru studs 12" O.C. [G]	1 Carp	6	1.333	C.L.F.	48	47.50		95.50	133
3110	16" O.C. [G]		7	1.143		48	41		89	122
3120	24" O.C. [G]		8.80	.909		48	32.50		80.50	108
4100	2" x 2" angle x 18 ga., studs 12" O.C. [G]		7	1.143		75	41		116	151
4110	16" O.C. [G]		9	.889		75	32		107	136
4120	24" O.C. [G]		12	.667		75	24		99	123
4200	16 ga., studs 12" O.C. [G]		5	1.600		94.50	57		151.50	200
4210	16" O.C. [G]		7	1.143		94.50	41		135.50	173
4220	24" O.C. [G]		10	.800		94.50	28.50		123	152

05 41 13.25 Framing, Boxed Headers/Beams

		Crew	Daily Output	Labor-Hours	Unit	Material	Labor	2014 Bare Costs Equipment	Total	Total Incl O&P
0010	**FRAMING, BOXED HEADERS/BEAMS**									
0015	Made from recycled materials									
0200	Double, 18 ga. x 6" deep [G]	2 Carp	220	.073	L.F.	5.10	2.60		7.70	9.95
0210	8" deep [G]		210	.076		5.65	2.72		8.37	10.80
0220	10" deep [G]		200	.080		6.90	2.86		9.76	12.40
0230	12" deep [G]		190	.084		7.55	3.01		10.56	13.35
0300	16 ga. x 8" deep [G]		180	.089		6.50	3.18		9.68	12.50
0310	10" deep [G]		170	.094		7.90	3.36		11.26	14.30
0320	12" deep [G]		160	.100		8.60	3.58		12.18	15.45

05 41 13 – Load-Bearing Metal Stud Framing

05 41 13.25 Framing, Boxed Headers/Beams		Crew	Daily Output	Labor-Hours	Unit	Material	2014 Bare Costs Labor	Equipment	Total	Total Incl O&P
0400	14 ga. x 10" deep	G 2 Carp	140	.114	L.F.	9.10	4.09		13.19	16.85
0410	12" deep	G	130	.123		10	4.40		14.40	18.35
1210	Triple, 18 ga. x 8" deep	G	170	.094		8.20	3.36		11.56	14.65
1220	10" deep	G	165	.097		9.85	3.47		13.32	16.70
1230	12" deep	G	160	.100		10.85	3.58		14.43	17.90
1300	16 ga. x 8" deep	G	145	.110		9.50	3.94		13.44	17.05
1310	10" deep	G	140	.114		11.35	4.09		15.44	19.30
1320	12" deep	G	135	.119		12.40	4.24		16.64	21
1400	14 ga. x 10" deep	G	115	.139		12.40	4.97		17.37	22
1410	12" deep	G	110	.145		13.70	5.20		18.90	24

05 41 13.30 Framing, Stud Walls

		Crew	Daily Output	Labor-Hours	Unit	Material	2014 Bare Costs Labor	Equipment	Total	Total Incl O&P
0010	**FRAMING, STUD WALLS** w/top & bottom track, no openings,									
0020	Headers, beams, bridging or bracing									
0025	Made from recycled materials									
4100	8' high walls, 18 ga. x 2-1/2" wide, studs 12" O.C.	G 2 Carp	54	.296	L.F.	8.50	10.60		19.10	27
4110	16" O.C.	G	77	.208		6.80	7.45		14.25	19.95
4120	24" O.C.	G	107	.150		5.10	5.35		10.45	14.60
4130	3-5/8" wide, studs 12" O.C.	G	53	.302		10.05	10.80		20.85	29
4140	16" O.C.	G	76	.211		8.05	7.55		15.60	21.50
4150	24" O.C.	G	105	.152		6.05	5.45		11.50	15.80
4160	4" wide, studs 12" O.C.	G	52	.308		10.55	11		21.55	30
4170	16" O.C.	G	74	.216		8.45	7.75		16.20	22.50
4180	24" O.C.	G	103	.155		6.35	5.55		11.90	16.35
4190	6" wide, studs 12" O.C.	G	51	.314		13.40	11.20		24.60	33.50
4200	16" O.C.	G	73	.219		10.75	7.85		18.60	25
4210	24" O.C.	G	101	.158		8.10	5.65		13.75	18.45
4220	8" wide, studs 12" O.C.	G	50	.320		16.30	11.45		27.75	37
4230	16" O.C.	G	72	.222		13.10	7.95		21.05	28
4240	24" O.C.	G	100	.160		9.90	5.70		15.60	20.50
4300	16 ga. x 2-1/2" wide, studs 12" O.C.	G	47	.340		10.10	12.15		22.25	31.50
4310	16" O.C.	G	68	.235		8	8.40		16.40	23
4320	24" O.C.	G	94	.170		5.90	6.10		12	16.75
4330	3-5/8" wide, studs 12" O.C.	G	46	.348		12.05	12.45		24.50	34.50
4340	16" O.C.	G	66	.242		9.55	8.65		18.20	25
4350	24" O.C.	G	92	.174		7.05	6.20		13.25	18.20
4360	4" wide, studs 12" O.C.	G	45	.356		12.65	12.70		25.35	35.50
4370	16" O.C.	G	65	.246		10	8.80		18.80	26
4380	24" O.C.	G	90	.178		7.40	6.35		13.75	18.85
4390	6" wide, studs 12" O.C.	G	44	.364		15.80	13		28.80	39.50
4400	16" O.C.	G	64	.250		12.55	8.95		21.50	29
4410	24" O.C.	G	88	.182		9.30	6.50		15.80	21
4420	8" wide, studs 12" O.C.	G	43	.372		19.50	13.30		32.80	44
4430	16" O.C.	G	63	.254		15.50	9.10		24.60	32.50
4440	24" O.C.	G	86	.186		11.50	6.65		18.15	24
5100	10' high walls, 18 ga. x 2-1/2" wide, studs 12" O.C.	G	54	.296		10.20	10.60		20.80	29
5110	16" O.C.	G	77	.208		8.05	7.45		15.50	21.50
5120	24" O.C.	G	107	.150		5.95	5.35		11.30	15.55
5130	3-5/8" wide, studs 12" O.C.	G	53	.302		12.05	10.80		22.85	31.50
5140	16" O.C.	G	76	.211		9.55	7.55		17.10	23
5150	24" O.C.	G	105	.152		7.05	5.45		12.50	16.90
5160	4" wide, studs 12" O.C.	G	52	.308		12.65	11		23.65	32.50
5170	16" O.C.	G	74	.216		10.05	7.75		17.80	24

05 41 13.30 Framing, Stud Walls		Crew	Daily Output	Labor-Hours	Unit	Material	2014 Bare Costs Labor	Equipment	Total	Total Incl O&P
5180	24" O.C.	G	2 Carp	103	.155	L.F.	7.40	5.55		12.95	17.50
5190	6" wide, studs 12" O.C.	G		51	.314		16	11.20		27.20	36.50
5200	16" O.C.	G		73	.219		12.70	7.85		20.55	27
5210	24" O.C.	G		101	.158		9.40	5.65		15.05	19.90
5220	8" wide, studs 12" O.C.	G		50	.320		19.50	11.45		30.95	41
5230	16" O.C.	G		72	.222		15.50	7.95		23.45	30.50
5240	24" O.C.	G		100	.160		11.50	5.70		17.20	22.50
5300	16 ga. x 2-1/2" wide, studs 12" O.C.	G		47	.340		12.20	12.15		24.35	34
5310	16" O.C.	G		68	.235		9.55	8.40		17.95	24.50
5320	24" O.C.	G		94	.170		6.95	6.10		13.05	17.90
5330	3-5/8" wide, studs 12" O.C.	G		46	.348		14.55	12.45		27	37
5340	16" O.C.	G		66	.242		11.40	8.65		20.05	27
5350	24" O.C.	G		92	.174		8.30	6.20		14.50	19.55
5360	4" wide, studs 12" O.C.	G		45	.356		15.25	12.70		27.95	38.50
5370	16" O.C.	G		65	.246		12	8.80		20.80	28
5380	24" O.C.	G		90	.178		8.70	6.35		15.05	20.50
5390	6" wide, studs 12" O.C.	G		44	.364		19	13		32	43
5400	16" O.C.	G		64	.250		14.95	8.95		23.90	31.50
5410	24" O.C.	G		88	.182		10.90	6.50		17.40	23
5420	8" wide, studs 12" O.C.	G		43	.372		23.50	13.30		36.80	48.50
5430	16" O.C.	G		63	.254		18.50	9.10		27.60	36
5440	24" O.C.	G		86	.186		13.50	6.65		20.15	26
6190	12' high walls, 18 ga. x 6" wide, studs 12" O.C.	G		41	.390		18.65	13.95		32.60	44
6200	16" O.C.	G		58	.276		14.70	9.85		24.55	33
6210	24" O.C.	G		81	.198		10.75	7.05		17.80	23.50
6220	8" wide, studs 12" O.C.	G		40	.400		22.50	14.30		36.80	49
6230	16" O.C.	G		57	.281		17.90	10.05		27.95	36.50
6240	24" O.C.	G		80	.200		13.10	7.15		20.25	26.50
6390	16 ga. x 6" wide, studs 12" O.C.	G		35	.457		22.50	16.35		38.85	52
6400	16" O.C.	G		51	.314		17.40	11.20		28.60	38
6410	24" O.C.	G		70	.229		12.55	8.15		20.70	27.50
6420	8" wide, studs 12" O.C.	G		34	.471		27.50	16.80		44.30	59
6430	16" O.C.	G		50	.320		21.50	11.45		32.95	43
6440	24" O.C.	G		69	.232		15.50	8.30		23.80	31
6530	14 ga. x 3-5/8" wide, studs 12" O.C.	G		34	.471		21	16.80		37.80	52
6540	16" O.C.	G		48	.333		16.55	11.90		28.45	38.50
6550	24" O.C.	G		65	.246		11.90	8.80		20.70	28
6560	4" wide, studs 12" O.C.	G		33	.485		22.50	17.35		39.85	53.50
6570	16" O.C.	G		47	.340		17.55	12.15		29.70	40
6580	24" O.C.	G		64	.250		12.65	8.95		21.60	29
6730	12 ga. x 3-5/8" wide, studs 12" O.C.	G		31	.516		29.50	18.45		47.95	63.50
6740	16" O.C.	G		43	.372		23	13.30		36.30	47.50
6750	24" O.C.	G		59	.271		16.05	9.70		25.75	34
6760	4" wide, studs 12" O.C.	G		30	.533		31.50	19.05		50.55	66.50
6770	16" O.C.	G		42	.381		24.50	13.60		38.10	49.50
6780	24" O.C.	G		58	.276		17.15	9.85		27	35.50
7390	16' high walls, 16 ga. x 6" wide, studs 12" O.C.	G		33	.485		28.50	17.35		45.85	60.50
7400	16" O.C.	G		48	.333		22.50	11.90		34.40	44.50
7410	24" O.C.	G		67	.239		15.80	8.55		24.35	31.50
7420	8" wide, studs 12" O.C.	G		32	.500		35.50	17.90		53.40	69
7430	16" O.C.	G		47	.340		27.50	12.15		39.65	51
7440	24" O.C.	G		66	.242		19.50	8.65		28.15	36
7560	14 ga. x 4" wide, studs 12" O.C.	G		31	.516		29	18.45		47.45	63

05 41 Structural Metal Stud Framing

05 41 13 – Load-Bearing Metal Stud Framing

05 41 13.30 Framing, Stud Walls

		Crew	Daily Output	Labor-Hours	Unit	Material	2014 Bare Costs Labor	Equipment	Total	Total Incl O&P
7570	16" O.C.	G 2 Carp	45	.356	L.F.	22.50	12.70		35.20	46
7580	24" O.C.	G	61	.262		15.90	9.40		25.30	33.50
7590	6" wide, studs 12" O.C.	G	30	.533		36.50	19.05		55.55	72
7600	16" O.C.	G	44	.364		28.50	13		41.50	53
7610	24" O.C.	G	60	.267		20	9.55		29.55	38
7760	12 ga. x 4" wide, studs 12" O.C.	G	29	.552		41	19.70		60.70	78
7770	16" O.C.	G	40	.400		31.50	14.30		45.80	58.50
7780	24" O.C.	G	55	.291		22	10.40		32.40	41.50
7790	6" wide, studs 12" O.C.	G	28	.571		51.50	20.50		72	91.50
7800	16" O.C.	G	39	.410		39.50	14.65		54.15	68
7810	24" O.C.	G	54	.296		27.50	10.60		38.10	48.50
8590	20' high walls, 14 ga. x 6" wide, studs 12" O.C.	G	29	.552		45	19.70		64.70	82
8600	16" O.C.	G	42	.381		34.50	13.60		48.10	61
8610	24" O.C.	G	57	.281		24	10.05		34.05	43.50
8620	8" wide, studs 12" O.C.	G	28	.571		48.50	20.50		69	88
8630	16" O.C.	G	41	.390		37.50	13.95		51.45	64.50
8640	24" O.C.	G	56	.286		26.50	10.20		36.70	46
8790	12 ga. x 6" wide, studs 12" O.C.	G	27	.593		64	21		85	106
8800	16" O.C.	G	37	.432		48.50	15.45		63.95	79.50
8810	24" O.C.	G	51	.314		33.50	11.20		44.70	56
8820	8" wide, studs 12" O.C.	G	26	.615		77.50	22		99.50	122
8830	16" O.C.	G	36	.444		59	15.90		74.90	91.50
8840	24" O.C.	G	50	.320		41	11.45		52.45	64.50

05 42 Cold-Formed Metal Joist Framing

05 42 13 – Cold-Formed Metal Floor Joist Framing

05 42 13.05 Bracing

		Crew	Daily Output	Labor-Hours	Unit	Material	2014 Bare Costs Labor	Equipment	Total	Total Incl O&P
0010	**BRACING**, continuous, per row, top & bottom									
0015	Made from recycled materials									
0120	Flat strap, 20 ga. x 2" wide, joists at 12" O.C.	G 1 Carp	4.67	1.713	C.L.F.	55	61		116	164
0130	16" O.C.	G	5.33	1.501		53.50	53.50		107	149
0140	24" O.C.	G	6.66	1.201		51.50	43		94.50	129
0150	18 ga. x 2" wide, joists at 12" O.C.	G	4	2		74	71.50		145.50	202
0160	16" O.C.	G	4.67	1.713		73	61		134	183
0170	24" O.C.	G	5.33	1.501		71.50	53.50		125	169

05 42 13.10 Bridging

		Crew	Daily Output	Labor-Hours	Unit	Material	2014 Bare Costs Labor	Equipment	Total	Total Incl O&P
0010	**BRIDGING**, solid between joists w/1-1/4" leg track, per joist bay									
0015	Made from recycled materials									
0230	Joists 12" O.C., 18 ga. track x 6" wide	G 1 Carp	80	.100	Ea.	1.48	3.58		5.06	7.65
0240	8" wide	G	75	.107		1.84	3.81		5.65	8.40
0250	10" wide	G	70	.114		2.29	4.09		6.38	9.35
0260	12" wide	G	65	.123		2.60	4.40		7	10.25
0330	16 ga. track x 6" wide	G	70	.114		1.87	4.09		5.96	8.90
0340	8" wide	G	65	.123		2.34	4.40		6.74	10
0350	10" wide	G	60	.133		2.91	4.77		7.68	11.20
0360	12" wide	G	55	.145		3.35	5.20		8.55	12.45
0440	14 ga. track x 8" wide	G	60	.133		2.93	4.77		7.70	11.25
0450	10" wide	G	55	.145		3.64	5.20		8.84	12.75
0460	12" wide	G	50	.160		4.20	5.70		9.90	14.20
0550	12 ga. track x 10" wide	G	45	.178		5.35	6.35		11.70	16.55
0560	12" wide	G	40	.200		5.45	7.15		12.60	18.05

05 42 13 – Cold-Formed Metal Floor Joist Framing

05 42 13.10 Bridging

05 42 13.10 Bridging		Crew	Daily Output	Labor-Hours	Unit	Material	2014 Bare Costs Labor	Equipment	Total	Total Incl O&P
1230	16" O.C., 18 ga. track x 6" wide	G 1 Carp	80	.100	Ea.	1.90	3.58		5.48	8.10
1240	8" wide	G	75	.107		2.36	3.81		6.17	9
1250	10" wide	G	70	.114		2.94	4.09		7.03	10.10
1260	12" wide	G	65	.123		3.33	4.40		7.73	11.05
1330	16 ga. track x 6" wide	G	70	.114		2.39	4.09		6.48	9.50
1340	8" wide	G	65	.123		3	4.40		7.40	10.70
1350	10" wide	G	60	.133		3.73	4.77		8.50	12.10
1360	12" wide	G	55	.145		4.29	5.20		9.49	13.45
1440	14 ga. track x 8" wide	G	60	.133		3.76	4.77		8.53	12.15
1450	10" wide	G	55	.145		4.67	5.20		9.87	13.90
1460	12" wide	G	50	.160		5.40	5.70		11.10	15.50
1550	12 ga. track x 10" wide	G	45	.178		6.85	6.35		13.20	18.20
1560	12" wide	G	40	.200		7	7.15		14.15	19.75
2230	24" O.C., 18 ga. track x 6" wide	G	80	.100		2.75	3.58		6.33	9
2240	8" wide	G	75	.107		3.41	3.81		7.22	10.15
2250	10" wide	G	70	.114		4.25	4.09		8.34	11.50
2260	12" wide	G	65	.123		4.82	4.40		9.22	12.70
2330	16 ga. track x 6" wide	G	70	.114		3.46	4.09		7.55	10.65
2340	8" wide	G	65	.123		4.34	4.40		8.74	12.20
2350	10" wide	G	60	.133		5.40	4.77		10.17	13.95
2360	12" wide	G	55	.145		6.20	5.20		11.40	15.60
2440	14 ga. track x 8" wide	G	60	.133		5.45	4.77		10.22	14
2450	10" wide	G	55	.145		6.75	5.20		11.95	16.20
2460	12" wide	G	50	.160		7.80	5.70		13.50	18.15
2550	12 ga. track x 10" wide	G	45	.178		9.90	6.35		16.25	21.50
2560	12" wide	G	40	.200		10.10	7.15		17.25	23

05 42 13.25 Framing, Band Joist

05 42 13.25 Framing, Band Joist		Crew	Daily Output	Labor-Hours	Unit	Material	2014 Bare Costs Labor	Equipment	Total	Total Incl O&P
0010	**FRAMING, BAND JOIST** (track) fastened to bearing wall									
0015	Made from recycled materials									
0220	18 ga. track x 6" deep	G 2 Carp	1000	.016	L.F.	1.21	.57		1.78	2.29
0230	8" deep	G	920	.017		1.50	.62		2.12	2.70
0240	10" deep	G	860	.019		1.87	.67		2.54	3.18
0320	16 ga. track x 6" deep	G	900	.018		1.52	.64		2.16	2.74
0330	8" deep	G	840	.019		1.91	.68		2.59	3.25
0340	10" deep	G	780	.021		2.37	.73		3.10	3.84
0350	12" deep	G	740	.022		2.73	.77		3.50	4.30
0430	14 ga. track x 8" deep	G	750	.021		2.39	.76		3.15	3.91
0440	10" deep	G	720	.022		2.97	.79		3.76	4.61
0450	12" deep	G	700	.023		3.42	.82		4.24	5.15
0540	12 ga. track x 10" deep	G	670	.024		4.35	.85		5.20	6.20
0550	12" deep	G	650	.025		4.45	.88		5.33	6.40

05 42 13.30 Framing, Boxed Headers/Beams

05 42 13.30 Framing, Boxed Headers/Beams		Crew	Daily Output	Labor-Hours	Unit	Material	2014 Bare Costs Labor	Equipment	Total	Total Incl O&P
0010	**FRAMING, BOXED HEADERS/BEAMS**									
0015	Made from recycled materials									
0200	Double, 18 ga. x 6" deep	G 2 Carp	220	.073	L.F.	5.10	2.60		7.70	9.95
0210	8" deep	G	210	.076		5.65	2.72		8.37	10.80
0220	10" deep	G	200	.080		6.90	2.86		9.76	12.40
0230	12" deep	G	190	.084		7.55	3.01		10.56	13.35
0300	16 ga. x 8" deep	G	180	.089		6.50	3.18		9.68	12.50
0310	10" deep	G	170	.094		7.90	3.36		11.26	14.30
0320	12" deep	G	160	.100		8.60	3.58		12.18	15.45
0400	14 ga. x 10" deep	G	140	.114		9.10	4.09		13.19	16.85

05 42 Cold-Formed Metal Joist Framing

05 42 13 – Cold-Formed Metal Floor Joist Framing

05 42 13.30 Framing, Boxed Headers/Beams

		Crew	Daily Output	Labor-Hours	Unit	Material	2014 Bare Costs Labor	Equipment	Total	Total Incl O&P
0410	12" deep	G	2 Carp	130	.123	L.F.	10	4.40		14.40	18.35
0500	12 ga. x 10" deep	G		110	.145		12	5.20		17.20	22
0510	12" deep	G		100	.160		13.25	5.70		18.95	24
1210	Triple, 18 ga. x 8" deep	G		170	.094		8.20	3.36		11.56	14.65
1220	10" deep	G		165	.097		9.85	3.47		13.32	16.70
1230	12" deep	G		160	.100		10.85	3.58		14.43	17.90
1300	16 ga. x 8" deep	G		145	.110		9.50	3.94		13.44	17.05
1310	10" deep	G		140	.114		11.35	4.09		15.44	19.30
1320	12" deep	G		135	.119		12.40	4.24		16.64	21
1400	14 ga. x 10" deep	G		115	.139		13.15	4.97		18.12	23
1410	12" deep	G		110	.145		14.50	5.20		19.70	24.50
1500	12 ga. x 10" deep	G		90	.178		17.50	6.35		23.85	30
1510	12" deep	G		85	.188		19.40	6.75		26.15	33

05 42 13.40 Framing, Joists

		Crew	Daily Output	Labor-Hours	Unit	Material	2014 Bare Costs Labor	Equipment	Total	Total Incl O&P
0010	**FRAMING, JOISTS**, no band joists (track), web stiffeners, headers,										
0020	Beams, bridging or bracing										
0025	Made from recycled materials										
0030	Joists (2" flange) and fasteners, materials only										
0220	18 ga. x 6" deep	G				L.F.	1.58			1.58	1.73
0230	8" deep	G					1.86			1.86	2.04
0240	10" deep	G					2.18			2.18	2.40
0320	16 ga. x 6" deep	G					1.93			1.93	2.13
0330	8" deep	G					2.31			2.31	2.54
0340	10" deep	G					2.70			2.70	2.97
0350	12" deep	G					3.07			3.07	3.37
0430	14 ga. x 8" deep	G					2.90			2.90	3.19
0440	10" deep	G					3.34			3.34	3.67
0450	12" deep	G					3.80			3.80	4.18
0540	12 ga. x 10" deep	G					4.86			4.86	5.35
0550	12" deep	G					5.50			5.50	6.10
1010	Installation of joists to band joists, beams & headers, labor only										
1220	18 ga. x 6" deep		2 Carp	110	.145	Ea.		5.20		5.20	8.75
1230	8" deep			90	.178			6.35		6.35	10.70
1240	10" deep			80	.200			7.15		7.15	12.05
1320	16 ga. x 6" deep			95	.168			6		6	10.15
1330	8" deep			70	.229			8.15		8.15	13.75
1340	10" deep			60	.267			9.55		9.55	16.05
1350	12" deep			55	.291			10.40		10.40	17.50
1430	14 ga. x 8" deep			65	.246			8.80		8.80	14.80
1440	10" deep			45	.356			12.70		12.70	21.50
1450	12" deep			35	.457			16.35		16.35	27.50
1540	12 ga. x 10" deep			40	.400			14.30		14.30	24
1550	12" deep			30	.533			19.05		19.05	32

05 42 13.45 Framing, Web Stiffeners

		Crew	Daily Output	Labor-Hours	Unit	Material	2014 Bare Costs Labor	Equipment	Total	Total Incl O&P
0010	**FRAMING, WEB STIFFENERS** at joist bearing, fabricated from										
0020	Stud piece (1-5/8" flange) to stiffen joist (2" flange)										
0025	Made from recycled materials										
2120	For 6" deep joist, with 18 ga. x 2-1/2" stud	G	1 Carp	120	.067	Ea.	.85	2.38		3.23	4.95
2130	3-5/8" stud	G		110	.073		1	2.60		3.60	5.45
2140	4" stud	G		105	.076		1.05	2.72		3.77	5.75
2150	6" stud	G		100	.080		1.32	2.86		4.18	6.25
2160	8" stud	G		95	.084		1.60	3.01		4.61	6.80

05 42 13.45 Framing, Web Stiffeners	Crew	Daily Output	Labor-Hours	Unit	Material	2014 Bare Costs Labor	Equipment	Total	Total Incl O&P
2220	8" deep joist, with 2-1/2" stud	G	1 Carp	120	.067	Ea.	1.14	2.38		3.52	5.25
2230	3-5/8" stud	G		110	.073		1.34	2.60		3.94	5.85
2240	4" stud	G		105	.076		1.41	2.72		4.13	6.15
2250	6" stud	G		100	.080		1.77	2.86		4.63	6.75
2260	8" stud	G		95	.084		2.14	3.01		5.15	7.40
2320	10" deep joist, with 2-1/2" stud	G		110	.073		1.41	2.60		4.01	5.90
2330	3-5/8" stud	G		100	.080		1.66	2.86		4.52	6.65
2340	4" stud	G		95	.084		1.74	3.01		4.75	6.95
2350	6" stud	G		90	.089		2.19	3.18		5.37	7.75
2360	8" stud	G		85	.094		2.66	3.36		6.02	8.55
2420	12" deep joist, with 2-1/2" stud	G		110	.073		1.70	2.60		4.30	6.25
2430	3-5/8" stud	G		100	.080		2	2.86		4.86	7
2440	4" stud	G		95	.084		2.10	3.01		5.11	7.35
2450	6" stud	G		90	.089		2.64	3.18		5.82	8.25
2460	8" stud	G		85	.094		3.20	3.36		6.56	9.15
3130	For 6" deep joist, with 16 ga. x 3-5/8" stud	G		100	.080		1.25	2.86		4.11	6.20
3140	4" stud	G		95	.084		1.31	3.01		4.32	6.50
3150	6" stud	G		90	.089		1.62	3.18		4.80	7.15
3160	8" stud	G		85	.094		2	3.36		5.36	7.85
3230	8" deep joist, with 3-5/8" stud	G		100	.080		1.68	2.86		4.54	6.65
3240	4" stud	G		95	.084		1.76	3.01		4.77	7
3250	6" stud	G		90	.089		2.17	3.18		5.35	7.75
3260	8" stud	G		85	.094		2.68	3.36		6.04	8.60
3330	10" deep joist, with 3-5/8" stud	G		85	.094		2.08	3.36		5.44	7.95
3340	4" stud	G		80	.100		2.17	3.58		5.75	8.40
3350	6" stud	G		75	.107		2.69	3.81		6.50	9.35
3360	8" stud	G		70	.114		3.32	4.09		7.41	10.50
3430	12" deep joist, with 3-5/8" stud	G		85	.094		2.50	3.36		5.86	8.40
3440	4" stud	G		80	.100		2.62	3.58		6.20	8.90
3450	6" stud	G		75	.107		3.24	3.81		7.05	9.95
3460	8" stud	G		70	.114		4	4.09		8.09	11.25
4230	For 8" deep joist, with 14 ga. x 3-5/8" stud	G		90	.089		2.08	3.18		5.26	7.65
4240	4" stud	G		85	.094		2.20	3.36		5.56	8.05
4250	6" stud	G		80	.100		2.76	3.58		6.34	9.05
4260	8" stud	G		75	.107		2.95	3.81		6.76	9.65
4330	10" deep joist, with 3-5/8" stud	G		75	.107		2.57	3.81		6.38	9.25
4340	4" stud	G		70	.114		2.72	4.09		6.81	9.85
4350	6" stud	G		65	.123		3.42	4.40		7.82	11.15
4360	8" stud	G		60	.133		3.65	4.77		8.42	12
4430	12" deep joist, with 3-5/8" stud	G		75	.107		3.10	3.81		6.91	9.80
4440	4" stud	G		70	.114		3.28	4.09		7.37	10.45
4450	6" stud	G		65	.123		4.12	4.40		8.52	11.95
4460	8" stud	G		60	.133		4.40	4.77		9.17	12.85
5330	For 10" deep joist, with 12 ga. x 3-5/8" stud	G		65	.123		3.72	4.40		8.12	11.50
5340	4" stud	G		60	.133		3.97	4.77		8.74	12.35
5350	6" stud	G		55	.145		5	5.20		10.20	14.25
5360	8" stud	G		50	.160		6.05	5.70		11.75	16.25
5430	12" deep joist, with 3-5/8" stud	G		65	.123		4.48	4.40		8.88	12.35
5440	4" stud	G		60	.133		4.78	4.77		9.55	13.25
5450	6" stud	G		55	.145		6	5.20		11.20	15.35
5460	8" stud	G		50	.160		7.30	5.70		13	17.60

05 42 Cold-Formed Metal Joist Framing

05 42 23 – Cold-Formed Metal Roof Joist Framing

05 42 23.05 Framing, Bracing

		Crew	Daily Output	Labor-Hours	Unit	Material	2014 Bare Costs Labor	Equipment	Total	Total Incl O&P
0010	**FRAMING, BRACING**									
0015	Made from recycled materials									
0020	Continuous bracing, per row									
0100	16 ga. x 1-1/2" channel thru rafters/trusses @ 16" O.C.	G	1 Carp	4.50	1.778	C.L.F.	48	63.50	111.50	160
0120	24" O.C.	G		6	1.333		48	47.50	95.50	133
0300	2" x 2" angle x 18 ga., rafters/trusses @ 16" O.C.	G		6	1.333		75	47.50	122.50	163
0320	24" O.C.	G		8	1		75	36	111	143
0400	16 ga., rafters/trusses @ 16" O.C.	G		4.50	1.778		94.50	63.50	158	211
0420	24" O.C.	G		6.50	1.231		94.50	44	138.50	178

05 42 23.10 Framing, Bridging

		Crew	Daily Output	Labor-Hours	Unit	Material	2014 Bare Costs Labor	Equipment	Total	Total Incl O&P
0010	**FRAMING, BRIDGING**									
0015	Made from recycled materials									
0020	Solid, between rafters w/1-1/4" leg track, per rafter bay									
1200	Rafters 16" O.C., 18 ga. x 4" deep	G	1 Carp	60	.133	Ea.	1.45	4.77	6.22	9.60
1210	6" deep	G		57	.140		1.90	5	6.90	10.55
1220	8" deep	G		55	.145		2.36	5.20	7.56	11.35
1230	10" deep	G		52	.154		2.94	5.50	8.44	12.50
1240	12" deep	G		50	.160		3.33	5.70	9.03	13.25
2200	24" O.C., 18 ga. x 4" deep	G		60	.133		2.10	4.77	6.87	10.30
2210	6" deep	G		57	.140		2.75	5	7.75	11.45
2220	8" deep	G		55	.145		3.41	5.20	8.61	12.50
2230	10" deep	G		52	.154		4.25	5.50	9.75	13.90
2240	12" deep	G		50	.160		4.82	5.70	10.52	14.90

05 42 23.50 Framing, Parapets

		Crew	Daily Output	Labor-Hours	Unit	Material	2014 Bare Costs Labor	Equipment	Total	Total Incl O&P
0010	**FRAMING, PARAPETS**									
0015	Made from recycled materials									
0100	3' high installed on 1st story, 18 ga. x 4" wide studs, 12" O.C.	G	2 Carp	100	.160	L.F.	5.30	5.70	11	15.45
0110	16" O.C.	G		150	.107		4.52	3.81	8.33	11.35
0120	24" O.C.	G		200	.080		3.73	2.86	6.59	8.90
0200	6" wide studs, 12" O.C.	G		100	.160		6.80	5.70	12.50	17.05
0210	16" O.C.	G		150	.107		5.80	3.81	9.61	12.75
0220	24" O.C.	G		200	.080		4.80	2.86	7.66	10.10
1100	Installed on 2nd story, 18 ga. x 4" wide studs, 12" O.C.	G		95	.168		5.30	6	11.30	16
1110	16" O.C.	G		145	.110		4.52	3.94	8.46	11.60
1120	24" O.C.	G		190	.084		3.73	3.01	6.74	9.15
1200	6" wide studs, 12" O.C.	G		95	.168		6.80	6	12.80	17.60
1210	16" O.C.	G		145	.110		5.80	3.94	9.74	13
1220	24" O.C.	G		190	.084		4.80	3.01	7.81	10.35
2100	Installed on gable, 18 ga. x 4" wide studs, 12" O.C.	G		85	.188		5.30	6.75	12.05	17.15
2110	16" O.C.	G		130	.123		4.52	4.40	8.92	12.35
2120	24" O.C.	G		170	.094		3.73	3.36	7.09	9.75
2200	6" wide studs, 12" O.C.	G		85	.188		6.80	6.75	13.55	18.75
2210	16" O.C.	G		130	.123		5.80	4.40	10.20	13.75
2220	24" O.C.	G		170	.094		4.80	3.36	8.16	10.95

05 42 23.60 Framing, Roof Rafters

		Crew	Daily Output	Labor-Hours	Unit	Material	2014 Bare Costs Labor	Equipment	Total	Total Incl O&P
0010	**FRAMING, ROOF RAFTERS**									
0015	Made from recycled materials									
0100	Boxed ridge beam, double, 18 ga. x 6" deep	G	2 Carp	160	.100	L.F.	5.10	3.58	8.68	11.60
0110	8" deep	G		150	.107		5.65	3.81	9.46	12.60
0120	10" deep	G		140	.114		6.90	4.09	10.99	14.45
0130	12" deep	G		130	.123		7.55	4.40	11.95	15.70

05 42 23 – Cold-Formed Metal Roof Joist Framing

05 42 23.60 Framing, Roof Rafters		Crew	Daily Output	Labor-Hours	Unit	Material	2014 Bare Costs Labor	Equipment	Total	Total Incl O&P
0200	16 ga. x 6" deep	2 Carp	150	.107	L.F.	5.80	3.81		9.61	12.75
0210	8" deep		140	.114		6.50	4.09		10.59	14
0220	10" deep		130	.123		7.90	4.40		12.30	16.05
0230	12" deep		120	.133		8.60	4.77		13.37	17.45
1100	Rafters, 2" flange, material only, 18 ga. x 6" deep					1.58			1.58	1.73
1110	8" deep					1.86			1.86	2.04
1120	10" deep					2.18			2.18	2.40
1130	12" deep					2.52			2.52	2.77
1200	16 ga. x 6" deep					1.93			1.93	2.13
1210	8" deep					2.31			2.31	2.54
1220	10" deep					2.70			2.70	2.97
1230	12" deep					3.07			3.07	3.37
2100	Installation only, ordinary rafter to 4:12 pitch, 18 ga. x 6" deep	2 Carp	35	.457	Ea.		16.35		16.35	27.50
2110	8" deep		30	.533			19.05		19.05	32
2120	10" deep		25	.640			23		23	38.50
2130	12" deep		20	.800			28.50		28.50	48
2200	16 ga. x 6" deep		30	.533			19.05		19.05	32
2210	8" deep		25	.640			23		23	38.50
2220	10" deep		20	.800			28.50		28.50	48
2230	12" deep		15	1.067			38		38	64
8100	Add to labor, ordinary rafters on steep roofs						25%			
8110	Dormers & complex roofs						50%			
8200	Hip & valley rafters to 4:12 pitch						25%			
8210	Steep roofs						50%			
8220	Dormers & complex roofs						75%			
8300	Hip & valley jack rafters to 4:12 pitch						50%			
8310	Steep roofs						75%			
8320	Dormers & complex roofs						100%			

05 42 23.70 Framing, Soffits and Canopies

05 42 23.70 Framing, Soffits and Canopies		Crew	Daily Output	Labor-Hours	Unit	Material	2014 Bare Costs Labor	Equipment	Total	Total Incl O&P
0010	**FRAMING, SOFFITS & CANOPIES**									
0015	Made from recycled materials									
0130	Continuous ledger track @ wall, studs @ 16" O.C., 18 ga. x 4" wide	2 Carp	535	.030	L.F.	.97	1.07		2.04	2.86
0140	6" wide		500	.032		1.27	1.14		2.41	3.31
0150	8" wide		465	.034		1.57	1.23		2.80	3.80
0160	10" wide		430	.037		1.96	1.33		3.29	4.39
0230	Studs @ 24" O.C., 18 ga. x 4" wide		800	.020		.92	.72		1.64	2.22
0240	6" wide		750	.021		1.21	.76		1.97	2.61
0250	8" wide		700	.023		1.50	.82		2.32	3.03
0260	10" wide		650	.025		1.87	.88		2.75	3.54
1000	Horizontal soffit and canopy members, material only									
1030	1-5/8" flange studs, 18 ga. x 4" deep				L.F.	1.26			1.26	1.39
1040	6" deep					1.58			1.58	1.74
1050	8" deep					1.92			1.92	2.11
1140	2" flange joists, 18 ga. x 6" deep					1.80			1.80	1.98
1150	8" deep					2.12			2.12	2.34
1160	10" deep					2.50			2.50	2.75
4030	Installation only, 18 ga., 1-5/8" flange x 4" deep	2 Carp	130	.123	Ea.		4.40		4.40	7.40
4040	6" deep		110	.145			5.20		5.20	8.75
4050	8" deep		90	.178			6.35		6.35	10.70
4140	2" flange, 18 ga. x 6" deep		110	.145			5.20		5.20	8.75
4150	8" deep		90	.178			6.35		6.35	10.70
4160	10" deep		80	.200			7.15		7.15	12.05

05 42 Cold-Formed Metal Joist Framing

05 42 23 – Cold-Formed Metal Roof Joist Framing

05 42 23.70 Framing, Soffits and Canopies		Crew	Daily Output	Labor-Hours	Unit	Material	2014 Bare Costs Labor	Equipment	Total	Total Incl O&P
6010	Clips to attach facia to rafter tails, 2" x 2" x 18 ga. angle	G 1 Carp	120	.067	Ea.	.88	2.38		3.26	4.98
6020	16 ga. angle	G "	100	.080	↓	1.12	2.86		3.98	6.05

05 44 Cold-Formed Metal Trusses

05 44 13 – Cold-Formed Metal Roof Trusses

05 44 13.60 Framing, Roof Trusses

		Crew	Daily Output	Labor-Hours	Unit	Material	2014 Bare Costs Labor	Equipment	Total	Total Incl O&P
0010	**FRAMING, ROOF TRUSSES**									
0015	Made from recycled materials									
0020	Fabrication of trusses on ground, Fink (W) or King Post, to 4:12 pitch									
0120	18 ga. x 4" chords, 16' span	G 2 Carp	12	1.333	Ea.	59	47.50		106.50	145
0130	20' span	G	11	1.455		73.50	52		125.50	169
0140	24' span	G	11	1.455		88	52		140	185
0150	28' span	G	10	1.600		103	57		160	209
0160	32' span	G	10	1.600		118	57		175	225
0250	6" chords, 28' span	G	9	1.778		129	63.50		192.50	249
0260	32' span	G	9	1.778		148	63.50		211.50	270
0270	36' span	G	8	2		166	71.50		237.50	305
0280	40' span	G	8	2		185	71.50		256.50	325
1120	5:12 to 8:12 pitch, 18 ga. x 4" chords, 16' span	G	10	1.600		67	57		124	170
1130	20' span	G	9	1.778		84	63.50		147.50	200
1140	24' span	G	9	1.778		101	63.50		164.50	218
1150	28' span	G	8	2		118	71.50		189.50	249
1160	32' span	G	8	2		134	71.50		205.50	268
1250	6" chords, 28' span	G	7	2.286		148	81.50		229.50	300
1260	32' span	G	7	2.286		169	81.50		250.50	325
1270	36' span	G	6	2.667		190	95.50		285.50	370
1280	40' span	G	6	2.667		211	95.50		306.50	390
2120	9:12 to 12:12 pitch, 18 ga. x 4" chords, 16' span	G	8	2		84	71.50		155.50	213
2130	20' span	G	7	2.286		105	81.50		186.50	253
2140	24' span	G	7	2.286		126	81.50		207.50	276
2150	28' span	G	6	2.667		147	95.50		242.50	320
2160	32' span	G	6	2.667		168	95.50		263.50	345
2250	6" chords, 28' span	G	5	3.200		185	114		299	395
2260	32' span	G	5	3.200		211	114		325	425
2270	36' span	G	4	4		238	143		381	500
2280	40' span	G	4	4		264	143		407	530
5120	Erection only of roof trusses, to 4:12 pitch, 16' span	F-6	48	.833			28	13.80	41.80	61.50
5130	20' span		46	.870			29	14.40	43.40	64.50
5140	24' span		44	.909			30.50	15.05	45.55	67.50
5150	28' span		42	.952			31.50	15.80	47.30	70.50
5160	32' span		40	1			33.50	16.60	50.10	74.50
5170	36' span		38	1.053			35	17.45	52.45	78
5180	40' span		36	1.111			37	18.40	55.40	82.50
5220	5:12 to 8:12 pitch, 16' span		42	.952			31.50	15.80	47.30	70.50
5230	20' span		40	1			33.50	16.60	50.10	74.50
5240	24' span		38	1.053			35	17.45	52.45	78
5250	28' span		36	1.111			37	18.40	55.40	82.50
5260	32' span		34	1.176			39	19.50	58.50	87
5270	36' span		32	1.250			41.50	20.50	62	93
5280	40' span		30	1.333			44.50	22	66.50	99
5320	9:12 to 12:12 pitch, 16' span		36	1.111	↓		37	18.40	55.40	82.50

153

05 44 Cold-Formed Metal Trusses

05 44 13 – Cold-Formed Metal Roof Trusses

05 44 13.60 Framing, Roof Trusses		Crew	Daily Output	Labor-Hours	Unit	Material	2014 Bare Costs Labor	2014 Bare Costs Equipment	Total	Total Incl O&P
5330	20' span	F-6	34	1.176	Ea.	39	19.50		58.50	87
5340	24' span		32	1.250		41.50	20.50		62	93
5350	28' span		30	1.333		44.50	22		66.50	99
5360	32' span		28	1.429		47.50	23.50		71	106
5370	36' span		26	1.538		51.50	25.50		77	114
5380	40' span		24	1.667		55.50	27.50		83	124

05 51 Metal Stairs

05 51 13 – Metal Pan Stairs

05 51 13.50 Pan Stairs

			Crew	Daily Output	Labor-Hours	Unit	Material	Labor	Equipment	Total	Total Incl O&P
0010	**PAN STAIRS**, shop fabricated, steel stringers										
0015	Made from recycled materials										
0200	Cement fill metal pan, picket rail, 3'-6" wide	G	E-4	35	.914	Riser	500	35.50	4.06	539.56	620
0300	4'-0" wide	G		30	1.067		560	41.50	4.74	606.24	700
0350	Wall rail, both sides, 3'-6" wide	G		53	.604		380	23.50	2.68	406.18	465
1500	Landing, steel pan, conventional	G		160	.200	S.F.	66	7.75	.89	74.64	89
1600	Pre-erected	G		255	.125	"	118	4.88	.56	123.44	140
1700	Pre-erected, steel pan tread, 3'-6" wide, 2 line pipe rail	G	E-2	87	.552	Riser	550	21.50	17.55	589.05	665

05 51 16 – Metal Floor Plate Stairs

05 51 16.50 Floor Plate Stairs

			Crew	Daily Output	Labor-Hours	Unit	Material	Labor	Equipment	Total	Total Incl O&P
0010	**FLOOR PLATE STAIRS**, shop fabricated, steel stringers										
0015	Made from recycled materials										
0400	Cast iron tread and pipe rail, 3'-6" wide	G	E-4	35	.914	Riser	535	35.50	4.06	574.56	655
0500	Checkered plate tread, industrial, 3'-6" wide	G		28	1.143		330	44.50	5.05	379.55	450
0550	Circular, for tanks, 3'-0" wide	G		33	.970		370	37.50	4.31	411.81	480
0600	For isolated stairs, add						100%				
0800	Custom steel stairs, 3'-6" wide, economy	G	E-4	35	.914		500	35.50	4.06	539.56	620
0810	Medium priced	G		30	1.067		660	41.50	4.74	706.24	815
0900	Deluxe	G		20	1.600		825	62	7.10	894.10	1,025
1100	For 4' wide stairs, add						5%	5%			
1300	For 5' wide stairs, add						10%	10%			

05 51 19 – Metal Grating Stairs

05 51 19.50 Grating Stairs

			Crew	Daily Output	Labor-Hours	Unit	Material	Labor	Equipment	Total	Total Incl O&P
0010	**GRATING STAIRS**, shop fabricated, steel stringers, safety nosing on treads										
0015	Made from recycled materials										
0020	Grating tread and pipe railing, 3'-6" wide	G	E-4	35	.914	Riser	330	35.50	4.06	369.56	430
0100	4'-0" wide	G	"	30	1.067	"	430	41.50	4.74	476.24	560

05 51 23 – Metal Fire Escapes

05 51 23.25 Fire Escapes

			Crew	Daily Output	Labor-Hours	Unit	Material	Labor	Equipment	Total	Total Incl O&P
0010	**FIRE ESCAPES**, shop fabricated										
0200	2' wide balcony, 1" x 1/4" bars 1-1/2" O.C., with railing	G	2 Sswk	10	1.600	L.F.	58.50	61.50		120	182
0400	1st story cantilevered stair, standard, with railing	G		.50	32	Ea.	2,425	1,225		3,650	5,025
0500	Cable counterweighted, with railing	G		.40	40	"	2,250	1,525		3,775	5,400
0700	36" x 40" platform & fixed stair, with railing	G		.40	40	Flight	1,075	1,525		2,600	4,100
0900	For 3'-6" wide escapes, add to above						100%	150%			

05 51 Metal Stairs

05 51 23 – Metal Fire Escapes

05 51 23.50 Fire Escape Stairs		Crew	Daily Output	Labor-Hours	Unit	Material	2014 Bare Costs Labor	Equipment	Total	Total Incl O&P
0010	**FIRE ESCAPE STAIRS**, portable									
0100	Portable ladder					Ea.	128			128	141

05 51 33 – Metal Ladders

05 51 33.13 Vertical Metal Ladders

0010	**VERTICAL METAL LADDERS**, shop fabricated									
0015	Made from recycled materials									
0020	Steel, 20" wide, bolted to concrete, with cage	G	E-4	50	.640	V.L.F.	64	25	2.84	91.84	121
0100	Without cage	G		85	.376		37	14.65	1.67	53.32	70.50
0300	Aluminum, bolted to concrete, with cage	G		50	.640		115	25	2.84	142.84	177
0400	Without cage	G		85	.376		49.50	14.65	1.67	65.82	84.50

05 51 33.16 Inclined Metal Ladders

0010	**INCLINED METAL LADDERS**, shop fabricated									
0015	Made from recycled materials									
3900	Industrial ships ladder, steel, 24" W, grating treads, 2 line pipe rail	G	E-4	30	1.067	Riser	193	41.50	4.74	239.24	296
4000	Aluminum	G	"	30	1.067	"	270	41.50	4.74	316.24	380

05 51 33.23 Alternating Tread Ladders

0010	**ALTERNATING TREAD LADDERS**, shop fabricated									
0015	Made from recycled materials									
1350	Alternating tread stair, 56/68°, steel, standard paint color	G	2 Sswk	50	.320	V.L.F.	266	12.25		278.25	315
1360	Non-standard paint color	G		50	.320		300	12.25		312.25	355
1370	Galvanized steel	G		50	.320		310	12.25		322.25	365
1380	Stainless steel	G		50	.320		445	12.25		457.25	515
1390	68°, aluminum	G		50	.320		325	12.25		337.25	385

05 52 Metal Railings

05 52 13 – Pipe and Tube Railings

05 52 13.50 Railings, Pipe

0010	**RAILINGS, PIPE**, shop fab'd, 3'-6" high, posts @ 5' O.C.									
0015	Made from recycled materials									
0020	Aluminum, 2 rail, satin finish, 1-1/4" diameter	G	E-4	160	.200	L.F.	36	7.75	.89	44.64	55.50
0030	Clear anodized	G		160	.200		44	7.75	.89	52.64	64.50
0040	Dark anodized	G		160	.200		49	7.75	.89	57.64	70
0080	1-1/2" diameter, satin finish	G		160	.200		42.50	7.75	.89	51.14	62.50
0090	Clear anodized	G		160	.200		47.50	7.75	.89	56.14	68
0100	Dark anodized	G		160	.200		52.50	7.75	.89	61.14	73.50
0140	Aluminum, 3 rail, 1-1/4" diam., satin finish	G		137	.234		54.50	9.05	1.04	64.59	78
0150	Clear anodized	G		137	.234		67.50	9.05	1.04	77.59	93
0160	Dark anodized	G		137	.234		75	9.05	1.04	85.09	101
0200	1-1/2" diameter, satin finish	G		137	.234		64.50	9.05	1.04	74.59	89.50
0210	Clear anodized	G		137	.234		74	9.05	1.04	84.09	99.50
0220	Dark anodized	G		137	.234		80.50	9.05	1.04	90.59	107
0500	Steel, 2 rail, on stairs, primed, 1-1/4" diameter	G		160	.200		25	7.75	.89	33.64	43.50
0520	1-1/2" diameter	G		160	.200		27	7.75	.89	35.64	46
0540	Galvanized, 1-1/4" diameter	G		160	.200		34	7.75	.89	42.64	53.50
0560	1-1/2" diameter	G		160	.200		38.50	7.75	.89	47.14	58
0580	Steel, 3 rail, primed, 1-1/4" diameter	G		137	.234		37.50	9.05	1.04	47.59	59.50
0600	1-1/2" diameter	G		137	.234		39	9.05	1.04	49.09	61.50
0620	Galvanized, 1-1/4" diameter	G		137	.234		52.50	9.05	1.04	62.59	76
0640	1-1/2" diameter	G		137	.234		60.50	9.05	1.04	70.59	85

05 52 Metal Railings

05 52 13 – Pipe and Tube Railings

05 52 13.50 Railings, Pipe

			Crew	Daily Output	Labor-Hours	Unit	Material	Labor	Equipment	Total	Total Incl O&P
								2014 Bare Costs			
0700	Stainless steel, 2 rail, 1-1/4" diam. #4 finish	G	E-4	137	.234	L.F.	110	9.05	1.04	120.09	139
0720	High polish	G		137	.234		178	9.05	1.04	188.09	214
0740	Mirror polish	G		137	.234		223	9.05	1.04	233.09	263
0760	Stainless steel, 3 rail, 1-1/2" diam., #4 finish	G		120	.267		166	10.35	1.18	177.53	204
0770	High polish	G		120	.267		275	10.35	1.18	286.53	325
0780	Mirror finish	G		120	.267		335	10.35	1.18	346.53	390
0900	Wall rail, alum. pipe, 1-1/4" diam., satin finish	G		213	.150		20	5.85	.67	26.52	34
0905	Clear anodized	G		213	.150		25	5.85	.67	31.52	39.50
0910	Dark anodized	G		213	.150		29.50	5.85	.67	36.02	44.50
0915	1-1/2" diameter, satin finish	G		213	.150		22.50	5.85	.67	29.02	37
0920	Clear anodized	G		213	.150		28	5.85	.67	34.52	43
0925	Dark anodized	G		213	.150		35	5.85	.67	41.52	50.50
0930	Steel pipe, 1-1/4" diameter, primed	G		213	.150		15	5.85	.67	21.52	28.50
0935	Galvanized	G		213	.150		22	5.85	.67	28.52	36
0940	1-1/2" diameter	G		176	.182		15.50	7.05	.81	23.36	31.50
0945	Galvanized	G		213	.150		22	5.85	.67	28.52	36
0955	Stainless steel pipe, 1-1/2" diam., #4 finish	G		107	.299		88	11.60	1.33	100.93	120
0960	High polish	G		107	.299		179	11.60	1.33	191.93	220
0965	Mirror polish	G		107	.299		212	11.60	1.33	224.93	256
2000	2-line pipe rail (1-1/2" T&B) with 1/2" pickets @ 4-1/2" O.C.,											
2005	attached handrail on brackets											
2010	42" high aluminum, satin finish, straight & level	G	E-4	120	.267	L.F.	198	10.35	1.18	209.53	239
2050	42" high steel, primed, straight & level	G	"	120	.267		127	10.35	1.18	138.53	161
4000	For curved and level rails, add							10%	10%			
4100	For sloped rails for stairs, add							30%	30%			

05 52 16 – Industrial Railings

05 52 16.50 Railings, Industrial

			Crew	Daily Output	Labor-Hours	Unit	Material	Labor	Equipment	Total	Total Incl O&P
0010	**RAILINGS, INDUSTRIAL,** shop fab'd, 3'-6" high, posts @ 5' O.C.											
0020	2 rail, 3'-6" high, 1-1/2" pipe	G	E-4	255	.125	L.F.	27	4.88	.56	32.44	40
0100	2" angle rail	G	"	255	.125		25	4.88	.56	30.44	37.50
0200	For 4" high kick plate, 10 ga., add	G						5.65			5.65	6.20
0300	1/4" thick, add	G						7.40			7.40	8.15
0500	For curved level rails, add							10%	10%			
0550	For sloped rails for stairs, add							30%	30%			

05 53 Metal Gratings

05 53 13 – Bar Gratings

05 53 13.10 Floor Grating, Aluminum

			Crew	Daily Output	Labor-Hours	Unit	Material	Labor	Equipment	Total	Total Incl O&P
0010	**FLOOR GRATING, ALUMINUM,** field fabricated from panels											
0015	Made from recycled materials											
0110	Bearing bars @ 1-3/16" O.C., cross bars @ 4" O.C.,											
0111	Up to 300 S.F., 1" x 1/8" bar	G	E-4	900	.036	S.F.	16.90	1.38	.16	18.44	21.50
0112	Over 300 S.F.	G		850	.038		15.35	1.46	.17	16.98	19.85
0113	1-1/4" x 1/8" bar, up to 300 S.F.	G		800	.040		17.55	1.55	.18	19.28	22.50
0114	Over 300 S.F.	G		1000	.032		15.95	1.24	.14	17.33	20
0122	1-1/4" x 3/16" bar, up to 300 S.F.	G		750	.043		27	1.66	.19	28.85	33
0124	Over 300 S.F.	G		1000	.032		24.50	1.24	.14	25.88	29.50
0132	1-1/2" x 3/16" bar, up to 300 S.F.	G		700	.046		31	1.78	.20	32.98	37.50
0134	Over 300 S.F.	G		1000	.032		28.50	1.24	.14	29.88	33.50
0136	1-3/4" x 3/16" bar, up to 300 S.F.	G		500	.064		34.50	2.49	.28	37.27	43

05 53 Metal Gratings

05 53 13 – Bar Gratings

05 53 13.10 Floor Grating, Aluminum

		Crew	Daily Output	Labor-Hours	Unit	Material	2014 Bare Costs Labor	2014 Bare Costs Equipment	Total	Total Incl O&P
0138	Over 300 S.F.	E-4	1000	.032	S.F.	31.50	1.24	.14	32.88	37
0146	2-1/4" x 3/16" bar, up to 300 S.F.		600	.053		44	2.07	.24	46.31	52
0148	Over 300 S.F.		1000	.032		40	1.24	.14	41.38	46.50
0162	Cross bars @ 2" O.C., 1" x 1/8", up to 300 S.F.		600	.053		29.50	2.07	.24	31.81	36.50
0164	Over 300 S.F.		1000	.032		27	1.24	.14	28.38	32
0172	1-1/4" x 3/16" bar, up to 300 S.F.		600	.053		48.50	2.07	.24	50.81	57
0174	Over 300 S.F.		1000	.032		44	1.24	.14	45.38	51
0182	1-1/2" x 3/16" bar, up to 300 S.F.		600	.053		55.50	2.07	.24	57.81	65
0184	Over 300 S.F.		1000	.032		50.50	1.24	.14	51.88	58
0186	1-3/4" x 3/16" bar, up to 300 S.F.		600	.053		60	2.07	.24	62.31	70
0188	Over 300 S.F.		1000	.032		54.50	1.24	.14	55.88	62.50
0200	For straight cuts, add				L.F.	4.30			4.30	4.73
0300	For curved cuts, add					5.30			5.30	5.85
0400	For straight banding, add					5.50			5.50	6.05
0500	For curved banding, add					6.60			6.60	7.25
0600	For aluminum checkered plate nosings, add					7.15			7.15	7.85
0700	For straight toe plate, add					10.80			10.80	11.90
0800	For curved toe plate, add					12.60			12.60	13.85
1000	For cast aluminum abrasive nosings, add					10.50			10.50	11.55
1200	Expanded aluminum, .65# per S.F.	E-4	1050	.030	S.F.	11.90	1.18	.14	13.22	15.50
1400	Extruded I bars are 10% less than 3/16" bars									
1600	Heavy duty, all extruded plank, 3/4" deep, 1.8# per S.F.	E-4	1100	.029	S.F.	26	1.13	.13	27.26	31
1700	1-1/4" deep, 2.9# per S.F.		1000	.032		28	1.24	.14	29.38	33.50
1800	1-3/4" deep, 4.2# per S.F.		925	.035		39.50	1.34	.15	40.99	46
1900	2-1/4" deep, 5.0# per S.F.		875	.037		60.50	1.42	.16	62.08	69.50
2100	For safety serrated surface, add					15%				

05 53 13.70 Floor Grating, Steel

		Crew	Daily Output	Labor-Hours	Unit	Material	2014 Bare Costs Labor	2014 Bare Costs Equipment	Total	Total Incl O&P
0010	**FLOOR GRATING, STEEL**, field fabricated from panels									
0015	Made from recycled materials									
0300	Platforms, to 12' high, rectangular	E-4	3150	.010	Lb.	3.21	.39	.05	3.65	4.33
0400	Circular	"	2300	.014	"	4.01	.54	.06	4.61	5.50
0410	Painted bearing bars @ 1-3/16"									
0412	Cross bars @ 4" O.C., 3/4" x 1/8" bar, up to 300 S.F.	E-2	500	.096	S.F.	7.70	3.72	3.06	14.48	18.80
0414	Over 300 S.F.		750	.064		7	2.48	2.04	11.52	14.55
0422	1-1/4" x 3/16", up to 300 S.F.		400	.120		11.85	4.65	3.82	20.32	26
0424	Over 300 S.F.		600	.080		10.80	3.10	2.55	16.45	20.50
0432	1-1/2" x 3/16", up to 300 S.F.		400	.120		13.60	4.65	3.82	22.07	28
0434	Over 300 S.F.		600	.080		12.35	3.10	2.55	18	22
0436	1-3/4" x 3/16", up to 300 S.F.		400	.120		17.80	4.65	3.82	26.27	32.50
0438	Over 300 S.F.		600	.080		16.15	3.10	2.55	21.80	26.50
0452	2-1/4" x 3/16", up to 300 S.F.		300	.160		22	6.20	5.10	33.30	41.50
0454	Over 300 S.F.		450	.107		20	4.13	3.40	27.53	33.50
0462	Cross bars @ 2" O.C., 3/4" x 1/8", up to 300 S.F.		500	.096		15.15	3.72	3.06	21.93	27
0464	Over 300 S.F.		750	.064		12.60	2.48	2.04	17.12	20.50
0472	1-1/4" x 3/16", up to 300 S.F.		400	.120		19.80	4.65	3.82	28.27	35
0474	Over 300 S.F.		600	.080		16.50	3.10	2.55	22.15	27
0482	1-1/2" x 3/16", up to 300 S.F.		400	.120		22.50	4.65	3.82	30.97	37.50
0484	Over 300 S.F.		600	.080		18.60	3.10	2.55	24.25	29
0486	1-3/4" x 3/16", up to 300 S.F.		400	.120		33.50	4.65	3.82	41.97	50
0488	Over 300 S.F.		600	.080		28	3.10	2.55	33.65	39.50
0502	2-1/4" x 3/16", up to 300 S.F.		300	.160		33	6.20	5.10	44.30	53
0504	Over 300 S.F.		450	.107		27.50	4.13	3.40	35.03	41.50

05 53 Metal Gratings

05 53 13 – Bar Gratings

05 53 13.70 Floor Grating, Steel		Crew	Daily Output	Labor-Hours	Unit	Material	2014 Bare Costs Labor	Equipment	Total	Total Incl O&P
0690	For galvanized grating, add				S.F.	25%				
0800	For straight cuts, add				L.F.	6.15			6.15	6.75
0900	For curved cuts, add					7.80			7.80	8.60
1000	For straight banding, add	G				6.60			6.60	7.25
1100	For curved banding, add	G				8.70			8.70	9.55
1200	For checkered plate nosings, add	G				7.65			7.65	8.40
1300	For straight toe or kick plate, add	G				13.70			13.70	15.05
1400	For curved toe or kick plate, add	G				15.50			15.50	17.05
1500	For abrasive nosings, add	G				10.15			10.15	11.15
1510	For stair treads, see Section 05 55 13.50									
1600	For safety serrated surface, bearing bars @ 1-3/16" O.C., add					15%				
1700	Bearing bars @ 15/16" O.C., add					25%				
2000	Stainless steel gratings, close spaced, 1" x 1/8" bars, up to 300 S.F.	G	E-4	450	.071	S.F.	73	2.76	.32	76.08	86
2100	Standard spacing, 3/4" x 1/8" bars	G		500	.064		84	2.49	.28	86.77	97
2200	1-1/4" x 3/16" bars	G		400	.080		80	3.11	.36	83.47	94.50
2400	Expanded steel grating, at ground, 3.0# per S.F.	G		900	.036		8.05	1.38	.16	9.59	11.70
2500	3.14# per S.F.	G		900	.036		7.15	1.38	.16	8.69	10.70
2600	4.0# per S.F.	G		850	.038		8.60	1.46	.17	10.23	12.45
2650	4.27# per S.F.	G		850	.038		9.30	1.46	.17	10.93	13.20
2700	5.0# per S.F.	G		800	.040		13.80	1.55	.18	15.53	18.30
2800	6.25# per S.F.	G		750	.043		17.80	1.66	.19	19.65	23
2900	7.0# per S.F.	G		700	.046		19.65	1.78	.20	21.63	25
3100	For flattened expanded steel grating, add					8%				
3300	For elevated installation above 15', add						15%			

05 53 16 – Plank Gratings

05 53 16.50 Grating Planks

		Crew	Daily Output	Labor-Hours	Unit	Material	2014 Bare Costs Labor	Equipment	Total	Total Incl O&P
0010	**GRATING PLANKS**, field fabricated from planks									
0020	Aluminum, 9-1/2" wide, 14 ga., 2" rib	G	E-4	950	.034	L.F.	25.50	1.31	.15	26.96	31
0200	Galvanized steel, 9-1/2" wide, 14 ga., 2-1/2" rib	G		950	.034		16.80	1.31	.15	18.26	21
0300	4" rib	G		950	.034		18.50	1.31	.15	19.96	23
0500	12 ga., 2-1/2" rib	G		950	.034		16.55	1.31	.15	18.01	21
0600	3" rib	G		950	.034		22.50	1.31	.15	23.96	27
0800	Stainless steel, type 304, 16 ga., 2" rib	G		950	.034		39	1.31	.15	40.46	45.50
0900	Type 316	G		950	.034		57	1.31	.15	58.46	65.50

05 53 19 – Floor Grating Frame

05 53 19.30 Grating Frame

		Crew	Daily Output	Labor-Hours	Unit	Material	2014 Bare Costs Labor	Equipment	Total	Total Incl O&P
0010	**GRATING FRAME**, field fabricated									
0021	Aluminum, for gratings 1" to 1-1/2" deep	G	1 Carp	70	.114	L.F.	3.72	4.09		7.81	10.95
0100	For each corner, add	G				Ea.	5.60			5.60	6.15

05 54 Metal Floor Plates

05 54 13 – Floor Plates

05 54 13.20 Checkered Plates

		Crew	Daily Output	Labor-Hours	Unit	Material	2014 Bare Costs Labor	Equipment	Total	Total Incl O&P
0010	**CHECKERED PLATES**, steel, field fabricated									
0015	Made from recycled materials									
0020	1/4" & 3/8", 2000 to 5000 S.F., bolted	G	E-4	2900	.011	Lb.	.87	.43	.05	1.35	1.83
0100	Welded	G		4400	.007	"	.83	.28	.03	1.14	1.49
0300	Pit or trench cover and frame, 1/4" plate, 2' to 3' wide	G		100	.320	S.F.	11.05	12.45	1.42	24.92	37
0400	For galvanizing, add	G				Lb.	.29			.29	.32
0500	Platforms, 1/4" plate, no handrails included, rectangular	G	E-4	4200	.008		3.21	.30	.03	3.54	4.13
0600	Circular	G	"	2500	.013		4.01	.50	.06	4.57	5.40

05 54 13.70 Trench Covers

		Crew	Daily Output	Labor-Hours	Unit	Material	2014 Bare Costs Labor	Equipment	Total	Total Incl O&P
0010	**TRENCH COVERS**, field fabricated									
0021	Cast iron grating with bar stops and angle frame, to 18" wide	G	1 Carp	20	.400	L.F.	235	14.30		249.30	282
0101	Frame only (both sides of trench), 1" grating	G		45	.178		1.38	6.35		7.73	12.20
0151	2" grating	G		35	.229		3.27	8.15		11.42	17.35
0200	Aluminum, stock units, including frames and									
0211	3/8" plain cover plate, 4" opening	G	2 Carp	100	.160	L.F.	22.50	5.70		28.20	34
0301	6" opening	G		90	.178		27	6.35		33.35	40
0401	10" opening	G		85	.188		36	6.75		42.75	51
0501	16" opening	G		80	.200		50	7.15		57.15	67
0700	Add per inch for additional widths to 24"	G					2.06			2.06	2.27
0900	For custom fabrication, add						50%				
1100	For 1/4" plain cover plate, deduct						12%				
1500	For cover recessed for tile, 1/4" thick, deduct						12%				
1600	3/8" thick, add						5%				
1800	For checkered plate cover, 1/4" thick, deduct						12%				
1900	3/8" thick, add						2%				
2100	For slotted or round holes in cover, 1/4" thick, add						3%				
2200	3/8" thick, add						4%				
2300	For abrasive cover, add						12%				

05 55 Metal Stair Treads and Nosings

05 55 13 – Metal Stair Treads

05 55 13.50 Stair Treads

		Crew	Daily Output	Labor-Hours	Unit	Material	2014 Bare Costs Labor	Equipment	Total	Total Incl O&P
0010	**STAIR TREADS**, stringers and bolts not included									
3000	Diamond plate treads, steel, 1/8" thick									
3005	Open riser, black enamel									
3010	9" deep x 36" long	G	2 Sswk	48	.333	Ea.	91.50	12.80		104.30	125
3020	42" long	G		48	.333		96.50	12.80		109.30	131
3030	48" long	G		48	.333		101	12.80		113.80	136
3040	11" deep x 36" long	G		44	.364		96.50	13.95		110.45	133
3050	42" long	G		44	.364		102	13.95		115.95	139
3060	48" long	G		44	.364		108	13.95		121.95	146
3110	Galvanized, 9" deep x 36" long	G		48	.333		144	12.80		156.80	184
3120	42" long	G		48	.333		154	12.80		166.80	194
3130	48" long	G		48	.333		163	12.80		175.80	204
3140	11" deep x 36" long	G		44	.364		149	13.95		162.95	191
3150	42" long	G		44	.364		163	13.95		176.95	206
3160	48" long	G		44	.364		169	13.95		182.95	213
3200	Closed riser, black enamel									
3210	12" deep x 36" long	G	2 Sswk	40	.400	Ea.	110	15.35		125.35	150
3220	42" long	G		40	.400		119	15.35		134.35	160
3230	48" long	G		40	.400		126	15.35		141.35	167

05 55 13 – Metal Stair Treads

05 55 13.50 Stair Treads		Crew	Daily Output	Labor-Hours	Unit	Material	2014 Bare Costs Labor	Equipment	Total	Total Incl O&P
3240	Galvanized, 12" deep x 36" long	G 2 Sswk	40	.400	Ea.	173	15.35		188.35	220
3250	42" long	G	40	.400		189	15.35		204.35	237
3260	48" long	G	40	.400		198	15.35		213.35	247
4000	Bar grating treads									
4005	Steel, 1-1/4" x 3/16" bars, anti-skid nosing, black enamel									
4010	8-5/8" deep x 30" long	G 2 Sswk	48	.333	Ea.	54	12.80		66.80	84
4020	36" long	G	48	.333		63.50	12.80		76.30	94
4030	48" long	G	48	.333		97.50	12.80		110.30	132
4040	10-15/16" deep x 36" long	G	44	.364		70	13.95		83.95	104
4050	48" long	G	44	.364		100	13.95		113.95	137
4060	Galvanized, 8-5/8" deep x 30" long	G	48	.333		62	12.80		74.80	93
4070	36" long	G	48	.333		73.50	12.80		86.30	106
4080	48" long	G	48	.333		108	12.80		120.80	144
4090	10-15/16" deep x 36" long	G	44	.364		86.50	13.95		100.45	122
4100	48" long	G	44	.364		112	13.95		125.95	150
4200	Aluminum, 1-1/4" x 3/16" bars, serrated, with nosing									
4210	7-5/8" deep x 18" long	G 2 Sswk	52	.308	Ea.	50	11.80		61.80	77.50
4220	24" long	G	52	.308		59	11.80		70.80	87.50
4230	30" long	G	52	.308		68.50	11.80		80.30	97.50
4240	36" long	G	52	.308		177	11.80		188.80	218
4250	8-13/16" deep x 18" long	G	48	.333		67	12.80		79.80	98.50
4260	24" long	G	48	.333		99.50	12.80		112.30	134
4270	30" long	G	48	.333		115	12.80		127.80	151
4280	36" long	G	48	.333		194	12.80		206.80	239
4290	10" deep x 18" long	G	44	.364		130	13.95		143.95	170
4300	30" long	G	44	.364		173	13.95		186.95	217
4310	36" long	G	44	.364		210	13.95		223.95	258
5000	Channel grating treads									
5005	Steel, 14 ga., 2-12" thick, galvanized									
5010	9" deep x 36" long	G 2 Sswk	48	.333	Ea.	103	12.80		115.80	138
5020	48" long	G "	48	.333	"	139	12.80		151.80	177

05 55 19 – Metal Stair Tread Covers

05 55 19.50 Stair Tread Covers for Renovation

		Crew	Daily Output	Labor-Hours	Unit	Material	2014 Bare Costs Labor	Equipment	Total	Total Incl O&P
0010	**STAIR TREAD COVERS FOR RENOVATION**									
0205	Extruded tread cover with nosing, pre-drilled, includes screws									
0210	Aluminum with black abrasive strips, 9" wide x 3' long	1 Carp	24	.333	Ea.	106	11.90		117.90	136
0220	4' long		22	.364		140	13		153	175
0230	5' long		20	.400		174	14.30		188.30	215
0240	11" wide x 3' long		24	.333		136	11.90		147.90	170
0250	4' long		22	.364		175	13		188	215
0260	5' long		20	.400		225	14.30		239.30	272
0305	Black abrasive strips with yellow front strips									
0310	Aluminum, 9" wide x 3' long	1 Carp	24	.333	Ea.	114	11.90		125.90	145
0320	4' long		22	.364		152	13		165	189
0330	5' long		20	.400		193	14.30		207.30	236
0340	11" wide x 3' long		24	.333		146	11.90		157.90	180
0350	4' long		22	.364		188	13		201	229
0360	5' long		20	.400		242	14.30		256.30	291
0405	Black abrasive strips with photoluminescent front strips									
0410	Aluminum, 9" wide x 3' long	1 Carp	24	.333	Ea.	151	11.90		162.90	186
0420	4' long		22	.364		172	13		185	211
0430	5' long		20	.400		215	14.30		229.30	260

05 55 Metal Stair Treads and Nosings

05 55 19 – Metal Stair Tread Covers

05 55 19.50 Stair Tread Covers for Renovation		Crew	Daily Output	Labor-Hours	Unit	Material	2014 Bare Costs Labor	Equipment	Total	Total Incl O&P
0440	11" wide x 3' long	1 Carp	24	.333	Ea.	153	11.90		164.90	188
0450	4' long		22	.364		204	13		217	246
0460	5' long		20	.400		255	14.30		269.30	305

05 56 Metal Castings

05 56 13 – Metal Construction Castings

05 56 13.50 Construction Castings

			Crew	Daily Output	Labor-Hours	Unit	Material	Labor	Equipment	Total	Total Incl O&P
0010	**CONSTRUCTION CASTINGS**										
0020	Manhole covers and frames, see Section 33 44 13.13										
0101	Column bases, cast iron, 16" x 16", approx. 65 lb.	G	2 Carp	23	.696	Ea.	153	25		178	210
0201	32" x 32", approx. 256 lb.	G	"	11.50	1.391		570	49.50		619.50	715
0400	Cast aluminum for wood columns, 8" x 8"	G	1 Carp	32	.250		45.50	8.95		54.45	65
0500	12" x 12"	G	"	32	.250		99	8.95		107.95	124
0601	Miscellaneous C.I. castings, light sections	G	2 Carp	1600	.010	Lb.	2.38	.36		2.74	3.22
1101	Heavy sections	G		2100	.008		1.15	.27		1.42	1.73
1301	Special low volume items	G		1600	.010		4.13	.36		4.49	5.15
1500	For ductile iron, add						100%				

05 58 Formed Metal Fabrications

05 58 13 – Column Covers

05 58 13.05 Column Covers

			Crew	Daily Output	Labor-Hours	Unit	Material	Labor	Equipment	Total	Total Incl O&P
0010	**COLUMN COVERS**										
0015	Made from recycled materials										
0020	Excludes structural steel, light ga. metal framing, misc. metals, sealants										
0100	Round covers, 2 halves with 2 vertical joints for backer rod and sealant										
0110	Up to 12' high, no horizontal joints										
0120	12" diameter, 0.125" aluminum, anodized/painted finish	G	2 Sswk	32	.500	V.L.F.	31.50	19.20		50.70	71
0130	Type 304 stainless steel, 16 gauge, #4 brushed finish	G		32	.500		47	19.20		66.20	88
0140	Type 316 stainless steel, 16 gauge, #4 brushed finish	G		32	.500		54	19.20		73.20	96
0150	18" diameter, aluminum	G		32	.500		47	19.20		66.20	88
0160	Type 304 stainless steel	G		32	.500		70.50	19.20		89.70	114
0170	Type 316 stainless steel	G		32	.500		81.50	19.20		100.70	126
0180	24" diameter, aluminum	G		32	.500		62.50	19.20		81.70	106
0190	Type 304 stainless steel	G		32	.500		94	19.20		113.20	140
0200	Type 316 stainless steel	G		32	.500		108	19.20		127.20	156
0210	30" diameter, aluminum	G		30	.533		78.50	20.50		99	125
0220	Type 304 stainless steel	G		30	.533		117	20.50		137.50	168
0230	Type 316 stainless steel	G		30	.533		135	20.50		155.50	188
0240	36" diameter, aluminum	G		30	.533		94	20.50		114.50	142
0250	Type 304 stainless steel	G		30	.533		141	20.50		161.50	194
0260	Type 316 stainless steel	G		30	.533		163	20.50		183.50	218
0400	Up to 24' high, 2 stacked sections with 1 horizontal joint										
0410	18" diameter, aluminum	G	2 Sswk	28	.571	V.L.F.	49.50	22		71.50	96
0450	Type 304 stainless steel	G		28	.571		74	22		96	123
0460	Type 316 stainless steel	G		28	.571		85.50	22		107.50	136
0470	24" diameter, aluminum	G		28	.571		66	22		88	114
0480	Type 304 stainless steel	G		28	.571		98.50	22		120.50	150
0490	Type 316 stainless steel	G		28	.571		114	22		136	167
0500	30" diameter, aluminum	G		24	.667		82	25.50		107.50	139

05 58 Formed Metal Fabrications

05 58 13 – Column Covers

05 58 13.05 Column Covers

		Crew	Daily Output	Labor-Hours	Unit	Material	2014 Bare Costs Labor	Equipment	Total	Total Incl O&P
0510	Type 304 stainless steel	G 2 Sswk	24	.667	V.L.F.	123	25.50		148.50	184
0520	Type 316 stainless steel	G	24	.667		142	25.50		167.50	205
0530	36" diameter, aluminum	G	24	.667		98.50	25.50		124	158
0540	Type 304 stainless steel	G	24	.667		148	25.50		173.50	212
0550	Type 316 stainless steel	G	24	.667		171	25.50		196.50	237

05 58 21 – Formed Chain

05 58 21.05 Alloy Steel Chain

		Crew	Daily Output	Labor-Hours	Unit	Material	2014 Bare Costs Labor	Equipment	Total	Total Incl O&P
0010	**ALLOY STEEL CHAIN**, Grade 80, for lifting	G								
0015	Self-colored, cut lengths, 1/4"	G E-17	4	4	C.L.F.	725	157		882	1,100
0020	3/8"	G	2	8		920	315		1,235	1,625
0030	1/2"	G	1.20	13.333		1,475	525		2,000	2,625
0040	5/8"	G	.72	22.222		2,375	875		3,250	4,300
0050	3/4"	G E-18	.48	83.333		3,125	3,225	2,000	8,350	11,600
0060	7/8"	G	.40	100		5,525	3,850	2,400	11,775	15,900
0070	1"	G	.35	114		7,100	4,425	2,750	14,275	19,100
0080	1-1/4"	G	.24	166		13,400	6,425	4,000	23,825	31,000
0110	Hook, Grade 80, Clevis slip, 1/4"	G			Ea.	26			26	28.50
0120	3/8"	G				30.50			30.50	33.50
0130	1/2"	G				49			49	54
0140	5/8"	G				72			72	79.50
0150	3/4"	G				105			105	116
0160	Hook, Grade 80, eye/sling w/hammerlock coupling, 15 Ton	G				335			335	365
0170	22 Ton	G				905			905	995
0180	37 Ton	G				2,650			2,650	2,925

05 58 23 – Formed Metal Guards

05 58 23.90 Window Guards

		Crew	Daily Output	Labor-Hours	Unit	Material	2014 Bare Costs Labor	Equipment	Total	Total Incl O&P
0010	**WINDOW GUARDS**, shop fabricated	G								
0015	Expanded metal, steel angle frame, permanent	G E-4	350	.091	S.F.	23	3.55	.41	26.96	32
0025	Steel bars, 1/2" x 1/2", spaced 5" O.C.	G "	290	.110	"	15.90	4.29	.49	20.68	26
0030	Hinge mounted, add	G			Opng.	46			46	50.50
0040	Removable type, add	G			"	29			29	32
0050	For galvanized guards, add				S.F.	35%				
0070	For pivoted or projected type, add					105%	40%			
0100	Mild steel, stock units, economy	G E-4	405	.079		6.25	3.07	.35	9.67	13.15
0200	Deluxe	G	405	.079		12.70	3.07	.35	16.12	20
0400	Woven wire, stock units, 3/8" channel frame, 3' x 5' opening	G	40	.800	Opng.	169	31	3.55	203.55	249
0500	4' x 6' opening	G	38	.842		270	32.50	3.74	306.24	365
0800	Basket guards for above, add	G				233			233	256
1000	Swinging guards for above, add	G				79.50			79.50	87.50

05 58 25 – Formed Lamp Posts

05 58 25.40 Lamp Posts

		Crew	Daily Output	Labor-Hours	Unit	Material	2014 Bare Costs Labor	Equipment	Total	Total Incl O&P
0010	**LAMP POSTS**									
0020	Aluminum, 7' high, stock units, post only	G 1 Carp	16	.500	Ea.	82	17.90		99.90	120
0100	Mild steel, plain	G "	16	.500	"	71	17.90		88.90	108

05 71 Decorative Metal Stairs

05 71 13 – Fabricated Metal Spiral Stairs

05 71 13.50 Spiral Stairs

05 71 13.50 Spiral Stairs		Crew	Daily Output	Labor-Hours	Unit	Material	2014 Bare Costs Labor	2014 Bare Costs Equipment	Total	Total Incl O&P
0010	**SPIRAL STAIRS**									
1805	Shop fabricated, custom ordered									
1810	Aluminum, 5'-0" diameter, plain units	G	E-4	45	.711	Riser	575	27.50	3.16	605.66	690
1820	Fancy units	G		45	.711		1,100	27.50	3.16	1,130.66	1,250
1900	Cast iron, 4'-0" diameter, plain units	G		45	.711		540	27.50	3.16	570.66	650
1920	Fancy Units	G		25	1.280		735	49.50	5.70	790.20	910
2000	Steel, industrial checkered plate, 4' diameter	G		45	.711		540	27.50	3.16	570.66	650
2200	6' diameter	G		40	.800		650	31	3.55	684.55	780
3100	Spiral stair kits, 12 stacking risers to fit exact floor height										
3110	Steel, flat metal treads, primed, 3'-6" diameter	G	2 Carp	1.60	10	Flight	1,275	360		1,635	2,000
3120	4'-0" diameter	G		1.45	11.034		1,450	395		1,845	2,275
3130	4'-6" diameter	G		1.35	11.852		1,600	425		2,025	2,500
3140	5'-0" diameter	G		1.25	12.800		1,750	460		2,210	2,700
3210	Galvanized, 3'-6" diameter	G		1.60	10		1,525	360		1,885	2,275
3220	4'-0" diameter	G		1.45	11.034		1,750	395		2,145	2,600
3230	4'-6" diameter	G		1.35	11.852		1,925	425		2,350	2,850
3240	5'-0" diameter	G		1.25	12.800		2,100	460		2,560	3,075
3310	Checkered plate tread, primed, 3'-6" diameter	G		1.45	11.034		1,500	395		1,895	2,325
3320	4'-0" diameter	G		1.35	11.852		1,700	425		2,125	2,600
3330	4'-6" diameter	G		1.25	12.800		1,850	460		2,310	2,825
3340	5'-0" diameter	G		1.15	13.913		2,025	495		2,520	3,050
3410	Galvanized, 3'-6" diameter	G		1.45	11.034		1,800	395		2,195	2,675
3420	4'-0" diameter	G		1.35	11.852		2,050	425		2,475	2,975
3430	4'-6" diameter	G		1.25	12.800		2,225	460		2,685	3,225
3440	5'-0" diameter	G		1.15	13.913		2,425	495		2,920	3,500
3510	Red oak covers on flat metal treads, 3'-6" diameter			1.35	11.852		2,600	425		3,025	3,600
3520	4'-0" diameter			1.25	12.800		2,875	460		3,335	3,950
3530	4'-6" diameter			1.15	13.913		3,100	495		3,595	4,225
3540	5'-0" diameter			1.05	15.238		3,375	545		3,920	4,650

05 73 Decorative Metal Railings

05 73 16 – Wire Rope Decorative Metal Railings

05 73 16.10 Cable Railings

		Crew	Daily Output	Labor-Hours	Unit	Material	Labor	Equipment	Total	Total Incl O&P
0010	**CABLE RAILINGS**, with 316 stainless steel 1 x 19 cable, 3/16" diameter									
0015	Made from recycled materials										
0100	1-3/4" diameter stainless steel posts x 42" high, cables 4" OC	G	2 Sswk	25	.640	L.F.	34	24.50		58.50	84.50

05 73 23 – Ornamental Railings

05 73 23.50 Railings, Ornamental

		Crew	Daily Output	Labor-Hours	Unit	Material	Labor	Equipment	Total	Total Incl O&P
0010	**RAILINGS, ORNAMENTAL**, 3'-6" high, posts @ 6' O.C.									
0020	Bronze or stainless, hand forged, plain	G	2 Sswk	24	.667	L.F.	118	25.50		143.50	179
0100	Fancy	G		18	.889		195	34		229	280
0200	Aluminum, panelized, plain	G		24	.667		12.65	25.50		38.15	62.50
0300	Fancy	G		18	.889		28.50	34		62.50	96
0400	Wrought iron, hand forged, plain	G		24	.667		79	25.50		104.50	136
0500	Fancy	G		18	.889		139	34		173	218
0550	Steel, panelized, plain	G		24	.667		19.75	25.50		45.25	70
0560	Fancy	G		18	.889		28	34		62	95.50
0600	Composite metal/wood/glass, plain			18	.889		119	34		153	196
0700	Fancy			12	1.333		238	51		289	360

05 75 13.10 Aluminum Columns		Crew	Daily Output	Labor-Hours	Unit	Material	2014 Bare Costs Labor	Equipment	Total	Total Incl O&P
0010	**ALUMINUM COLUMNS**									
0015	Made from recycled materials									
0020	Aluminum, extruded, stock units, no cap or base, 6" diameter	G	E-4	240	.133	L.F.	10.85	5.20	.59	16.64	22.50
0100	8" diameter	G		170	.188		14.25	7.30	.84	22.39	30.50
0200	10" diameter	G		150	.213		19.20	8.30	.95	28.45	38
0300	12" diameter	G		140	.229		36	8.90	1.01	45.91	58
0400	15" diameter	G		120	.267		48	10.35	1.18	59.53	73.50
0410	Caps and bases, plain, 6" diameter	G				Set	22.50			22.50	25
0420	8" diameter	G					29.50			29.50	32.50
0430	10" diameter	G					41			41	45.50
0440	12" diameter	G					59.50			59.50	65
0450	15" diameter	G					110			110	121
0460	Caps, ornamental, plain	G					340			340	370
0470	Fancy	G					1,675			1,675	1,850
0500	For square columns, add to column prices above					L.F.	50%				
0700	Residential, flat, 8' high, plain	G	E-4	20	1.600	Ea.	97.50	62	7.10	166.60	233
0720	Fancy	G		20	1.600		190	62	7.10	259.10	335
0740	Corner type, plain	G		20	1.600		168	62	7.10	237.10	310
0760	Fancy	G		20	1.600		330	62	7.10	399.10	490

05 75 13.20 Columns, Ornamental

05 75 13.20 Columns, Ornamental			Crew	Daily Output	Labor-Hours	Unit	Material	Labor	Equipment	Total	Total Incl O&P
0010	**COLUMNS, ORNAMENTAL**, shop fabricated	R051223-10									
6400	Mild steel, flat, 9" wide, stock units, painted, plain	G	E-4	160	.200	V.L.F.	9.15	7.75	.89	17.79	26
6450	Fancy	G		160	.200		17.75	7.75	.89	26.39	35.50
6500	Corner columns, painted, plain	G		160	.200		15.75	7.75	.89	24.39	33
6550	Fancy	G		160	.200		31	7.75	.89	39.64	50.50

Estimating Tips

06 05 00 Common Work Results for Wood, Plastics, and Composites

- Common to any wood-framed structure are the accessory connector items such as screws, nails, adhesives, hangers, connector plates, straps, angles, and hold-downs. For typical wood-framed buildings, such as residential projects, the aggregate total for these items can be significant, especially in areas where seismic loading is a concern. For floor and wall framing, the material cost is based on 10 to 25 lbs. per MBF. Hold-downs, hangers, and other connectors should be taken off by the piece.

Included with material costs are fasteners for a normal installation. RSMeans engineers use manufacturer's recommendations, written specifications, and/or standard construction practice for size and spacing of fasteners. Prices for various fasteners are shown for informational purposes only. Adjustments should be made if unusual fastening conditions exist.

06 10 00 Carpentry

- Lumber is a traded commodity and therefore sensitive to supply and demand in the marketplace. Even in "budgetary" estimating of wood-framed projects, it is advisable to call local suppliers for the latest market pricing.

- Common quantity units for wood-framed projects are "thousand board feet" (MBF). A board foot is a volume of wood, 1" x 1' x 1', or 144 cubic inches. Board-foot quantities are generally calculated using nominal material dimensions—dressed sizes are ignored. Board foot per lineal foot of any stick of lumber can be calculated by dividing the nominal cross-sectional area by 12. As an example, 2,000 lineal feet of 2 x 12 equates to 4 MBF by dividing the nominal area, 2 x 12, by 12, which equals 2, and multiplying by 2,000 to give 4,000 board feet. This simple rule applies to all nominal dimensioned lumber.

- Waste is an issue of concern at the quantity takeoff for any area of construction. Framing lumber is sold in even foot lengths, i.e., 10', 12', 14', 16', and depending on spans, wall heights, and the grade of lumber, waste is inevitable. A rule of thumb for lumber waste is 5%–10% depending on material quality and the complexity of the framing.

- Wood in various forms and shapes is used in many projects, even where the main structural framing is steel, concrete, or masonry. Plywood as a back-up partition material and 2x boards used as blocking and cant strips around roof edges are two common examples. The estimator should ensure that the costs of all wood materials are included in the final estimate.

06 20 00 Finish Carpentry

- It is necessary to consider the grade of workmanship when estimating labor costs for erecting millwork and interior finish. In practice, there are three grades: premium, custom, and economy. The RSMeans daily output for base and case moldings is in the range of 200 to 250 L.F. per carpenter per day. This is appropriate for most average custom-grade projects. For premium projects, an adjustment to productivity of 25%–50% should be made, depending on the complexity of the job.

Reference Numbers

Reference numbers are shown in shaded boxes at the beginning of some major classifications. These numbers refer to related items in the Reference Section. The reference information may be an estimating procedure, an alternate pricing method, or technical information.

Note: Not all subdivisions listed here necessarily appear in this publication.

06 05 05.10 Selective Demolition Wood Framing	Crew	Daily Output	Labor-Hours	Unit	Material	2014 Bare Costs Labor	Equipment	Total	Total Incl O&P
0010 SELECTIVE DEMOLITION WOOD FRAMING R024119-10									
0100 Timber connector, nailed, small	1 Clab	96	.083	Ea.		2.35		2.35	3.95
0110 Medium		60	.133			3.76		3.76	6.35
0120 Large		48	.167			4.70		4.70	7.90
0130 Bolted, small		48	.167			4.70		4.70	7.90
0140 Medium		32	.250			7.05		7.05	11.85
0150 Large		24	.333			9.40		9.40	15.80
2958 Beams, 2" x 6"	2 Clab	1100	.015	L.F.		.41		.41	.69
2960 2" x 8"		825	.019			.55		.55	.92
2965 2" x 10"		665	.024			.68		.68	1.14
2970 2" x 12"		550	.029			.82		.82	1.38
2972 2" x 14"		470	.034			.96		.96	1.62
2975 4" x 8"	B-1	413	.058			1.68		1.68	2.82
2980 4" x 10"		330	.073			2.10		2.10	3.53
2985 4" x 12"		275	.087			2.52		2.52	4.24
3000 6" x 8"		275	.087			2.52		2.52	4.24
3040 6" x 10"		220	.109			3.15		3.15	5.30
3080 6" x 12"		185	.130			3.75		3.75	6.30
3120 8" x 12"		140	.171			4.95		4.95	8.35
3160 10" x 12"		110	.218			6.30		6.30	10.60
3162 Alternate pricing method		1.10	21.818	M.B.F.		630		630	1,050
3170 Blocking, in 16" OC wall framing, 2" x 4"	1 Clab	600	.013	L.F.		.38		.38	.63
3172 2" x 6"		400	.020			.56		.56	.95
3174 In 24" OC wall framing, 2" x 4"		600	.013			.38		.38	.63
3176 2" x 6"		400	.020			.56		.56	.95
3178 Alt method, wood blocking removal from wood framing		.40	20	M.B.F.		565		565	950
3179 Wood blocking removal from steel framing		.36	22.222	"		625		625	1,050
3180 Bracing, let in, 1" x 3", studs 16" OC		1050	.008	L.F.		.21		.21	.36
3181 Studs 24" OC		1080	.007			.21		.21	.35
3182 1" x 4", studs 16" OC		1050	.008			.21		.21	.36
3183 Studs 24" OC		1080	.007			.21		.21	.35
3184 1" x 6", studs 16" OC		1050	.008			.21		.21	.36
3185 Studs 24" OC		1080	.007			.21		.21	.35
3186 2" x 3", studs 16" OC		800	.010			.28		.28	.47
3187 Studs 24" OC		830	.010			.27		.27	.46
3188 2" x 4", studs 16" OC		800	.010			.28		.28	.47
3189 Studs 24" OC		830	.010			.27		.27	.46
3190 2" x 6", studs 16" OC		800	.010			.28		.28	.47
3191 Studs 24" OC		830	.010			.27		.27	.46
3192 2" x 8", studs 16" OC		800	.010			.28		.28	.47
3193 Studs 24" OC		830	.010			.27		.27	.46
3194 "T" shaped metal bracing, studs at 16" OC		1060	.008			.21		.21	.36
3195 Studs at 24" OC		1200	.007			.19		.19	.32
3196 Metal straps, studs at 16" OC		1200	.007			.19		.19	.32
3197 Studs at 24" OC		1240	.006			.18		.18	.31
3200 Columns, round, 8' to 14' tall		40	.200	Ea.		5.65		5.65	9.50
3202 Dimensional lumber sizes	2 Clab	1.10	14.545	M.B.F.		410		410	690
3250 Blocking, between joists	1 Clab	320	.025	Ea.		.71		.71	1.19
3252 Bridging, metal strap, between joists		320	.025	Pr.		.71		.71	1.19
3254 Wood, between joists		320	.025	"		.71		.71	1.19
3260 Door buck, studs, header & access., 8' high 2" x 4" wall, 3' wide		32	.250	Ea.		7.05		7.05	11.85
3261 4' wide		32	.250			7.05		7.05	11.85
3262 5' wide		32	.250			7.05		7.05	11.85

06 05 05 – Selective Wood and Plastics Demolition

06 05 05.10 Selective Demolition Wood Framing		Crew	Daily Output	Labor-Hours	Unit	Material	2014 Bare Costs Labor	Equipment	Total	Total Incl O&P
3263	6' wide	1 Clab	32	.250	Ea.		7.05		7.05	11.85
3264	8' wide		30	.267			7.50		7.50	12.65
3265	10' wide		30	.267			7.50		7.50	12.65
3266	12' wide		30	.267			7.50		7.50	12.65
3267	2" x 6" wall, 3' wide		32	.250			7.05		7.05	11.85
3268	4' wide		32	.250			7.05		7.05	11.85
3269	5' wide		32	.250			7.05		7.05	11.85
3270	6' wide		32	.250			7.05		7.05	11.85
3271	8' wide		30	.267			7.50		7.50	12.65
3272	10' wide		30	.267			7.50		7.50	12.65
3273	12' wide		30	.267			7.50		7.50	12.65
3274	Window buck, studs, header & access, 8' high 2" x 4" wall, 2' wide		24	.333			9.40		9.40	15.80
3275	3' wide		24	.333			9.40		9.40	15.80
3276	4' wide		24	.333			9.40		9.40	15.80
3277	5' wide		24	.333			9.40		9.40	15.80
3278	6' wide		24	.333			9.40		9.40	15.80
3279	7' wide		24	.333			9.40		9.40	15.80
3280	8' wide		22	.364			10.25		10.25	17.25
3281	10' wide		22	.364			10.25		10.25	17.25
3282	12' wide		22	.364			10.25		10.25	17.25
3283	2" x 6" wall, 2' wide		24	.333			9.40		9.40	15.80
3284	3' wide		24	.333			9.40		9.40	15.80
3285	4' wide		24	.333			9.40		9.40	15.80
3286	5' wide		24	.333			9.40		9.40	15.80
3287	6' wide		24	.333			9.40		9.40	15.80
3288	7' wide		24	.333			9.40		9.40	15.80
3289	8' wide		22	.364			10.25		10.25	17.25
3290	10' wide		22	.364			10.25		10.25	17.25
3291	12' wide		22	.364			10.25		10.25	17.25
3360	Deck or porch decking		825	.010	L.F.		.27		.27	.46
3400	Fascia boards, 1" x 6"		500	.016			.45		.45	.76
3440	1" x 8"		450	.018			.50		.50	.84
3480	1" x 10"		400	.020			.56		.56	.95
3490	2" x 6"		450	.018			.50		.50	.84
3500	2" x 8"		400	.020			.56		.56	.95
3510	2" x 10"		350	.023			.64		.64	1.08
3610	Furring, on wood walls or ceiling		4000	.002	S.F.		.06		.06	.09
3620	On masonry or concrete walls or ceiling		1200	.007	"		.19		.19	.32
3800	Headers over openings, 2 @ 2" x 6"		110	.073	L.F.		2.05		2.05	3.45
3840	2 @ 2" x 8"		100	.080			2.26		2.26	3.80
3880	2 @ 2" x 10"		90	.089			2.51		2.51	4.22
3885	Alternate pricing method		.26	30.651	M.B.F.		865		865	1,450
3920	Joists, 1" x 4"		1250	.006	L.F.		.18		.18	.30
3930	1" x 6"		1135	.007			.20		.20	.33
3940	1" x 8"		1000	.008			.23		.23	.38
3950	1" x 10"		895	.009			.25		.25	.42
3960	1" x 12"		765	.010			.30		.30	.50
4200	2" x 4"	2 Clab	1000	.016			.45		.45	.76
4230	2" x 6"		970	.016			.47		.47	.78
4240	2" x 8"		940	.017			.48		.48	.81
4250	2" x 10"		910	.018			.50		.50	.83
4280	2" x 12"		880	.018			.51		.51	.86
4281	2" x 14"		850	.019			.53		.53	.89

06 05 05.10 Selective Demolition Wood Framing	Crew	Daily Output	Labor-Hours	Unit	Material	2014 Bare Costs Labor	Equipment	Total	Total Incl O&P
4282	Composite joists, 9-1/2"	2 Clab	960	.017	L.F.		.47		.47	.79
4283	11-7/8"		930	.017			.49		.49	.82
4284	14"		897	.018			.50		.50	.85
4285	16"		865	.019			.52		.52	.88
4290	Wood joists, alternate pricing method		1.50	10.667	M.B.F.		300		300	505
4500	Open web joist, 12" deep		500	.032	L.F.		.90		.90	1.52
4505	14" deep		475	.034			.95		.95	1.60
4510	16" deep		450	.036			1		1	1.69
4520	18" deep		425	.038			1.06		1.06	1.79
4530	24" deep		400	.040			1.13		1.13	1.90
4550	Ledger strips, 1" x 2"	1 Clab	1200	.007			.19		.19	.32
4560	1" x 3"		1200	.007			.19		.19	.32
4570	1" x 4"		1200	.007			.19		.19	.32
4580	2" x 2"		1100	.007			.21		.21	.35
4590	2" x 4"		1000	.008			.23		.23	.38
4600	2" x 6"		1000	.008			.23		.23	.38
4601	2" x 8" or 2" x 10"		800	.010			.28		.28	.47
4602	4" x 6"		600	.013			.38		.38	.63
4604	4" x 8"		450	.018			.50		.50	.84
5400	Posts, 4" x 4"	2 Clab	800	.020			.56		.56	.95
5405	4" x 6"		550	.029			.82		.82	1.38
5410	4" x 8"		440	.036			1.03		1.03	1.73
5425	4" x 10"		390	.041			1.16		1.16	1.95
5430	4" x 12"		350	.046			1.29		1.29	2.17
5440	6" x 6"		400	.040			1.13		1.13	1.90
5445	6" x 8"		350	.046			1.29		1.29	2.17
5450	6" x 10"		320	.050			1.41		1.41	2.37
5455	6" x 12"		290	.055			1.56		1.56	2.62
5480	8" x 8"		300	.053			1.50		1.50	2.53
5500	10" x 10"		240	.067			1.88		1.88	3.16
5660	Tongue and groove floor planks		2	8	M.B.F.		226		226	380
5682	Rafters, ordinary, 16" OC, 2" x 4"		880	.018	S.F.		.51		.51	.86
5683	2" x 6"		840	.019			.54		.54	.90
5684	2" x 8"		820	.020			.55		.55	.93
5685	2" x 10"		820	.020			.55		.55	.93
5686	2" x 12"		810	.020			.56		.56	.94
5687	24" OC, 2" x 4"		1170	.014			.39		.39	.65
5688	2" x 6"		1117	.014			.40		.40	.68
5689	2" x 8"		1091	.015			.41		.41	.70
5690	2" x 10"		1091	.015			.41		.41	.70
5691	2" x 12"		1077	.015			.42		.42	.71
5795	Rafters, ordinary, 2" x 4" (alternate method)		862	.019	L.F.		.52		.52	.88
5800	2" x 6" (alternate method)		850	.019			.53		.53	.89
5840	2" x 8" (alternate method)		837	.019			.54		.54	.91
5855	2" x 10" (alternate method)		825	.019			.55		.55	.92
5865	2" x 12" (alternate method)		812	.020			.56		.56	.93
5870	Sill plate, 2" x 4"	1 Clab	1170	.007			.19		.19	.32
5871	2" x 6"		780	.010			.29		.29	.49
5872	2" x 8"		586	.014			.38		.38	.65
5873	Alternate pricing method		.78	10.256	M.B.F.		289		289	485
5885	Ridge board, 1" x 4"	2 Clab	900	.018	L.F.		.50		.50	.84
5886	1" x 6"		875	.018			.52		.52	.87
5887	1" x 8"		850	.019			.53		.53	.89

06 05 05.10 Selective Demolition Wood Framing		Crew	Daily Output	Labor-Hours	Unit	Material	2014 Bare Costs Labor	Equipment	Total	Total Incl O&P
5888	1" x 10"	2 Clab	825	.019	L.F.		.55		.55	.92
5889	1" x 12"		800	.020			.56		.56	.95
5890	2" x 4"		900	.018			.50		.50	.84
5892	2" x 6"		875	.018			.52		.52	.87
5894	2" x 8"		850	.019			.53		.53	.89
5896	2" x 10"		825	.019			.55		.55	.92
5898	2" x 12"		800	.020			.56		.56	.95
6050	Rafter tie, 1" x 4"		1250	.013			.36		.36	.61
6052	1" x 6"		1135	.014			.40		.40	.67
6054	2" x 4"		1000	.016			.45		.45	.76
6056	2" x 6"		970	.016			.47		.47	.78
6070	Sleepers, on concrete, 1" x 2"	1 Clab	4700	.002			.05		.05	.08
6075	1" x 3"		4000	.002			.06		.06	.09
6080	2" x 4"		3000	.003			.08		.08	.13
6085	2" x 6"		2600	.003			.09		.09	.15
6086	Sheathing from roof, 5/16"	2 Clab	1600	.010	S.F.		.28		.28	.47
6088	3/8"		1525	.010			.30		.30	.50
6090	1/2"		1400	.011			.32		.32	.54
6092	5/8"		1300	.012			.35		.35	.58
6094	3/4"		1200	.013			.38		.38	.63
6096	Board sheathing from roof		1400	.011			.32		.32	.54
6100	Sheathing, from walls, 1/4"		1200	.013			.38		.38	.63
6110	5/16"		1175	.014			.38		.38	.65
6120	3/8"		1150	.014			.39		.39	.66
6130	1/2"		1125	.014			.40		.40	.67
6140	5/8"		1100	.015			.41		.41	.69
6150	3/4"		1075	.015			.42		.42	.71
6152	Board sheathing from walls		1500	.011			.30		.30	.51
6158	Subfloor, with boards		1050	.015			.43		.43	.72
6160	Plywood, 1/2" thick		768	.021			.59		.59	.99
6162	5/8" thick		760	.021			.59		.59	1
6164	3/4" thick		750	.021			.60		.60	1.01
6165	1-1/8" thick		720	.022			.63		.63	1.05
6166	Underlayment, particle board, 3/8" thick	1 Clab	780	.010			.29		.29	.49
6168	1/2" thick		768	.010			.29		.29	.49
6170	5/8" thick		760	.011			.30		.30	.50
6172	3/4" thick		750	.011			.30		.30	.51
6200	Stairs and stringers, minimum	2 Clab	40	.400	Riser		11.30		11.30	19
6240	Maximum	"	26	.615	"		17.35		17.35	29
6300	Components, tread	1 Clab	110	.073	Ea.		2.05		2.05	3.45
6320	Riser		80	.100	"		2.82		2.82	4.75
6390	Stringer, 2" x 10"		260	.031	L.F.		.87		.87	1.46
6400	2" x 12"		260	.031			.87		.87	1.46
6410	3" x 10"		250	.032			.90		.90	1.52
6420	3" x 12"		250	.032			.90		.90	1.52
6590	Wood studs, 2" x 3"	2 Clab	3076	.005			.15		.15	.25
6600	2" x 4"		2000	.008			.23		.23	.38
6640	2" x 6"		1600	.010			.28		.28	.47
6720	Wall framing, including studs, plates and blocking, 2" x 4"	1 Clab	600	.013	S.F.		.38		.38	.63
6740	2" x 6"		480	.017	"		.47		.47	.79
6750	Headers, 2" x 4"		1125	.007	L.F.		.20		.20	.34
6755	2" x 6"		1125	.007			.20		.20	.34
6760	2" x 8"		1050	.008			.21		.21	.36

06 05 05 – Selective Wood and Plastics Demolition

06 05 05.10 Selective Demolition Wood Framing		Crew	Daily Output	Labor-Hours	Unit	Material	2014 Bare Costs Labor	Equipment	Total	Total Incl O&P
6765	2" x 10"	1 Clab	1050	.008	L.F.		.21		.21	.36
6770	2" x 12"		1000	.008			.23		.23	.38
6780	4" x 10"		525	.015			.43		.43	.72
6785	4" x 12"		500	.016			.45		.45	.76
6790	6" x 8"		560	.014			.40		.40	.68
6795	6" x 10"		525	.015			.43		.43	.72
6797	6" x 12"		500	.016			.45		.45	.76
7000	Trusses									
7050	12' span	2 Clab	74	.216	Ea.		6.10		6.10	10.25
7150	24' span	F-3	66	.606			19.90	10.05	29.95	44.50
7200	26' span		64	.625			20.50	10.35	30.85	46
7250	28' span		62	.645			21	10.70	31.70	47.50
7300	30' span		58	.690			22.50	11.45	33.95	50.50
7350	32' span		56	.714			23.50	11.85	35.35	52.50
7400	34' span		54	.741			24.50	12.30	36.80	54.50
7450	36' span		52	.769			25	12.75	37.75	56.50
8000	Soffit, T & G wood	1 Clab	520	.015	S.F.		.43		.43	.73
8010	Hardboard, vinyl or aluminum	"	640	.013			.35		.35	.59
8030	Plywood	2 Carp	315	.051			1.82		1.82	3.06
9500	See Section 02 41 19.19 for rubbish handling									

06 05 05.20 Selective Demolition Millwork and Trim

06 05 05.20 Selective Demolition Millwork and Trim		Crew	Daily Output	Labor-Hours	Unit	Material	2014 Bare Costs Labor	Equipment	Total	Total Incl O&P
0010	**SELECTIVE DEMOLITION MILLWORK AND TRIM** R024119-10									
1000	Cabinets, wood, base cabinets, per L.F.	2 Clab	80	.200	L.F.		5.65		5.65	9.50
1020	Wall cabinets, per L.F.	"	80	.200	"		5.65		5.65	9.50
1060	Remove and reset, base cabinets	2 Carp	18	.889	Ea.		32		32	53.50
1070	Wall cabinets	"	20	.800	"		28.50		28.50	48
1100	Steel, painted, base cabinets	2 Clab	60	.267	L.F.		7.50		7.50	12.65
1120	Wall cabinets		60	.267	"		7.50		7.50	12.65
1200	Casework, large area		320	.050	S.F.		1.41		1.41	2.37
1220	Selective		200	.080	"		2.26		2.26	3.80
1500	Counter top, minimum		200	.080	L.F.		2.26		2.26	3.80
1510	Maximum		120	.133			3.76		3.76	6.35
1550	Remove and reset, minimum	2 Carp	50	.320			11.45		11.45	19.25
1560	Maximum	"	40	.400			14.30		14.30	24
2000	Paneling, 4' x 8' sheets	2 Clab	2000	.008	S.F.		.23		.23	.38
2100	Boards, 1" x 4"		700	.023			.64		.64	1.08
2120	1" x 6"		750	.021			.60		.60	1.01
2140	1" x 8"		800	.020			.56		.56	.95
3000	Trim, baseboard, to 6" wide		1200	.013	L.F.		.38		.38	.63
3040	Greater than 6" and up to 12" wide		1000	.016			.45		.45	.76
3080	Remove and reset, minimum	2 Carp	400	.040			1.43		1.43	2.41
3090	Maximum	"	300	.053			1.91		1.91	3.21
3100	Ceiling trim	2 Clab	1000	.016			.45		.45	.76
3120	Chair rail		1200	.013			.38		.38	.63
3140	Railings with balusters		240	.067			1.88		1.88	3.16
3160	Wainscoting		700	.023	S.F.		.64		.64	1.08

06 05 23 – Wood, Plastic, and Composite Fastenings

06 05 23.10 Nails

06 05 23.10 Nails		Crew	Daily Output	Labor-Hours	Unit	Material	2014 Bare Costs Labor	Equipment	Total	Total Incl O&P
0010	**NAILS**, material only, based upon 50# box purchase									
0020	Copper nails, plain				Lb.	9.65			9.65	10.60
0400	Stainless steel, plain					9.25			9.25	10.15
0500	Box, 3d to 20d, bright					1.28			1.28	1.41

06 05 23 – Wood, Plastic, and Composite Fastenings

06 05 23.10 Nails

		Crew	Daily Output	Labor-Hours	Unit	Material	2014 Bare Costs Labor	Equipment	Total	Total Incl O&P
0520	Galvanized				Lb.	1.76			1.76	1.94
0600	Common, 3d to 60d, plain					1.10			1.10	1.21
0700	Galvanized					1.97			1.97	2.17
0800	Aluminum					5.85			5.85	6.45
1000	Annular or spiral thread, 4d to 60d, plain					2.56			2.56	2.82
1200	Galvanized					3.03			3.03	3.33
1400	Drywall nails, plain					1.37			1.37	1.51
1600	Galvanized					2			2	2.20
1800	Finish nails, 4d to 10d, plain					1.25			1.25	1.38
2000	Galvanized					1.86			1.86	2.05
2100	Aluminum					5.85			5.85	6.45
2300	Flooring nails, hardened steel, 2d to 10d, plain					2.63			2.63	2.89
2400	Galvanized					4.04			4.04	4.44
2500	Gypsum lath nails, 1-1/8", 13 ga. flathead, blued					2			2	2.20
2600	Masonry nails, hardened steel, 3/4" to 3" long, plain					1.71			1.71	1.88
2700	Galvanized					3.79			3.79	4.17
2900	Roofing nails, threaded, galvanized					1.76			1.76	1.94
3100	Aluminum					4.85			4.85	5.35
3300	Compressed lead head, threaded, galvanized					2.49			2.49	2.74
3600	Siding nails, plain shank, galvanized					2.02			2.02	2.22
3800	Aluminum					5.85			5.85	6.45
5000	Add to prices above for cement coating					.11			.11	.12
5200	Zinc or tin plating					.14			.14	.15
5500	Vinyl coated sinkers, 8d to 16d					2.50			2.50	2.75

06 05 23.40 Sheet Metal Screws

		Crew	Daily Output	Labor-Hours	Unit	Material	2014 Bare Costs Labor	Equipment	Total	Total Incl O&P
0010	**SHEET METAL SCREWS**									
0020	Steel, standard, #8 x 3/4", plain				C	3.20			3.20	3.52
0100	Galvanized					3.20			3.20	3.52
0300	#10 x 1", plain					4.40			4.40	4.84
0400	Galvanized					4.40			4.40	4.84
0600	With washers, #14 x 1", plain					9.65			9.65	10.60
0700	Galvanized					9.65			9.65	10.60
0900	#14 x 2", plain					15			15	16.50
1000	Galvanized					15			15	16.50
1500	Self-drilling, with washers, (pinch point) #8 x 3/4", plain					7.30			7.30	8
1600	Galvanized					7.30			7.30	8
1800	#10 x 3/4", plain					7.80			7.80	8.55
1900	Galvanized					7.80			7.80	8.55
3000	Stainless steel w/aluminum or neoprene washers, #14 x 1", plain					8.10			8.10	8.95
3100	#14 x 2", plain					10			10	11

06 05 23.50 Wood Screws

		Crew	Daily Output	Labor-Hours	Unit	Material	2014 Bare Costs Labor	Equipment	Total	Total Incl O&P
0010	**WOOD SCREWS**									
0020	#8 x 1" long, steel				C	2.70			2.70	2.97
0100	Brass					12.20			12.20	13.40
0200	#8, 2" long, steel					4.16			4.16	4.58
0300	Brass					22			22	24
0400	#10, 1" long, steel					3.30			3.30	3.63
0500	Brass					15.60			15.60	17.15
0600	#10, 2" long, steel					5.30			5.30	5.85
0700	Brass					27			27	29.50
0800	#10, 3" long, steel					8.85			8.85	9.75
1000	#12, 2" long, steel					7.30			7.30	8.05

06 05 23.50 Wood Screws

		Crew	Daily Output	Labor-Hours	Unit	Material	2014 Bare Costs Labor	2014 Bare Costs Equipment	Total	Total Incl O&P
1100	Brass				C	34.50			34.50	38
1500	#12, 3" long, steel					11.15			11.15	12.30
2000	#12, 4" long, steel					18.75			18.75	20.50

06 05 23.60 Timber Connectors

		Crew	Daily Output	Labor-Hours	Unit	Material	2014 Bare Costs Labor	2014 Bare Costs Equipment	Total	Total Incl O&P
0010	**TIMBER CONNECTORS**									
0020	Add up cost of each part for total cost of connection									
0100	Connector plates, steel, with bolts, straight	2 Carp	75	.213	Ea.	30.50	7.65		38.15	46.50
0110	Tee, 7 ga.		50	.320		35	11.45		46.45	58
0120	T- Strap, 14 ga., 12" x 8" x 2"		50	.320		35	11.45		46.45	58
0150	Anchor plates, 7 ga., 9" x 7"		75	.213		30.50	7.65		38.15	46.50
0200	Bolts, machine, sq. hd. with nut & washer, 1/2" diameter, 4" long	1 Carp	140	.057		.75	2.04		2.79	4.27
0300	7-1/2" long		130	.062		1.37	2.20		3.57	5.20
0500	3/4" diameter, 7-1/2" long		130	.062		3.20	2.20		5.40	7.20
0610	Machine bolts, w/nut, washer, 3/4" diam., 15" L, HD's & beam hangers		95	.084		5.95	3.01		8.96	11.60
0800	Drilling bolt holes in timber, 1/2" diameter		450	.018	Inch		.64		.64	1.07
0900	1" diameter		350	.023	"		.82		.82	1.38
1100	Framing anchor, angle, 3" x 3" x 1-1/2", 12 ga		175	.046	Ea.	2.61	1.63		4.24	5.60
1150	Framing anchors, 18 ga., 4-1/2" x 2-3/4"		175	.046		2.61	1.63		4.24	5.60
1160	Framing anchors, 18 ga., 4-1/2" x 3"		175	.046		2.61	1.63		4.24	5.60
1170	Clip anchors plates, 18 ga., 12" x 1-1/8"		175	.046		2.61	1.63		4.24	5.60
1250	Holdowns, 3 ga. base, 10 ga. body		8	1		25	36		61	87.50
1260	Holdowns, 7 ga. 11-1/16" x 3-1/4"		8	1		25	36		61	87.50
1270	Holdowns, 7 ga. 14-3/8" x 3-1/8"		8	1		25	36		61	87.50
1275	Holdowns, 12 ga. 8" x 2-1/2"		8	1		25	36		61	87.50
1300	Joist and beam hangers, 18 ga. galv., for 2" x 4" joist		175	.046		.73	1.63		2.36	3.55
1400	2" x 6" to 2" x 10" joist		165	.048		1.39	1.73		3.12	4.45
1600	16 ga. galv., 3" x 6" to 3" x 10" joist		160	.050		2.96	1.79		4.75	6.25
1700	3" x 10" to 3" x 14" joist		160	.050		4.92	1.79		6.71	8.40
1800	4" x 6" to 4" x 10" joist		155	.052		3.07	1.85		4.92	6.50
1900	4" x 10" to 4" x 14" joist		155	.052		5	1.85		6.85	8.60
2000	Two-2" x 6" to two-2" x 10" joists		150	.053		4.19	1.91		6.10	7.80
2100	Two-2" x 10" to two-2" x 14" joists		150	.053		4.68	1.91		6.59	8.35
2300	3/16" thick, 6" x 8" joist		145	.055		65	1.97		66.97	75
2400	6" x 10" joist		140	.057		67.50	2.04		69.54	78
2500	6" x 12" joist		135	.059		70.50	2.12		72.62	81
2700	1/4" thick, 6" x 14" joist		130	.062		73	2.20		75.20	84
2900	Plywood clips, extruded aluminum H clip, for 3/4" panels					.24			.24	.26
3000	Galvanized 18 ga. back-up clip					.18			.18	.20
3200	Post framing, 16 ga. galv. for 4" x 4" base, 2 piece	1 Carp	130	.062		16.40	2.20		18.60	22
3300	Cap		130	.062		23	2.20		25.20	28.50
3500	Rafter anchors, 18 ga. galv., 1-1/2" wide, 5-1/4" long		145	.055		.49	1.97		2.46	3.86
3600	10-3/4" long		145	.055		1.46	1.97		3.43	4.93
3800	Shear plates, 2-5/8" diameter		120	.067		2.38	2.38		4.76	6.65
3900	4" diameter		115	.070		5.65	2.49		8.14	10.40
4000	Sill anchors, embedded in concrete or block, 25-1/2" long		115	.070		12.70	2.49		15.19	18.15
4100	Spike grids, 3" x 6"		120	.067		.96	2.38		3.34	5.05
4400	Split rings, 2-1/2" diameter		120	.067		1.96	2.38		4.34	6.15
4500	4" diameter		110	.073		2.97	2.60		5.57	7.65
4550	Tie plate, 20 ga., 7" x 3 1/8"		110	.073		2.97	2.60		5.57	7.65
4560	Tie plate, 20 ga., 5" x 4 1/8"		110	.073		2.97	2.60		5.57	7.65
4575	Twist straps, 18 ga., 12" x 1 1/4"		110	.073		2.97	2.60		5.57	7.65
4580	Twist straps, 18 ga., 16" x 1 1/4"		110	.073		2.97	2.60		5.57	7.65

06 05 23.60 Timber Connectors		Crew	Daily Output	Labor-Hours	Unit	Material	2014 Bare Costs Labor	Equipment	Total	Total Incl O&P
4600	Strap ties, 20 ga., 2 -1/16" wide, 12 13/16" long	1 Carp	180	.044	Ea.	.94	1.59		2.53	3.70
4700	Strap ties, 16 ga., 1-3/8" wide, 12" long		180	.044		.94	1.59		2.53	3.70
4800	21-5/8" x 1-1/4"		160	.050		2.96	1.79		4.75	6.25
5000	Toothed rings, 2-5/8" or 4" diameter		90	.089		1.78	3.18		4.96	7.30
5200	Truss plates, nailed, 20 ga., up to 32' span		17	.471	Truss Ea.	12.90	16.80		29.70	42.50
5400	Washers, 2" x 2" x 1/8"					.40			.40	.44
5500	3" x 3" x 3/16"				"	1.06			1.06	1.17
6000	Angles and gussets, painted									
6012	7 ga., 3-1/4" x 3-1/4" x 2-1/2" long	1 Carp	1.90	4.211	C	1,100	151		1,251	1,475
6014	3-1/4" x 3-1/4" x 5" long		1.90	4.211		2,150	151		2,301	2,625
6016	3-1/4" x 3-1/4" x 7-1/2" long		1.85	4.324		4,075	155		4,230	4,725
6018	5-3/4" x 5-3/4" x 2-1/2" long		1.85	4.324		2,625	155		2,780	3,150
6020	5-3/4" x 5-3/4" x 5" long		1.85	4.324		4,175	155		4,330	4,850
6022	5-3/4" x 5-3/4" x 7-1/2" long		1.80	4.444		6,175	159		6,334	7,075
6024	3 ga., 4-1/4" x 4-1/4" x 3" long		1.85	4.324		2,800	155		2,955	3,325
6026	4-1/4" x 4-1/4" x 6" long		1.85	4.324		6,000	155		6,155	6,850
6028	4-1/4" x 4-1/4" x 9" long		1.80	4.444		6,750	159		6,909	7,700
6030	7-1/4" x 7-1/4" x 3" long		1.80	4.444		4,825	159		4,984	5,600
6032	7-1/4" x 7-1/4" x 6" long		1.80	4.444		6,525	159		6,684	7,450
6034	7-1/4" x 7-1/4" x 9" long		1.75	4.571		14,600	163		14,763	16,400
6036	Gussets									
6038	7 ga., 8-1/8" x 8-1/8" x 2-3/4" long	1 Carp	1.80	4.444	C	4,625	159		4,784	5,350
6040	3 ga., 9-3/4" x 9-3/4" x 3-1/4" long	"	1.80	4.444	"	6,400	159		6,559	7,325
6101	Beam hangers, polymer painted									
6102	Bolted, 3 ga., (W x H x L)									
6104	3-1/4" x 9" x 12" top flange	1 Carp	1	8	C	19,600	286		19,886	22,100
6106	5-1/4" x 9" x 12" top flange		1	8		20,500	286		20,786	23,000
6108	5-1/4" x 11" x 11-3/4" top flange		1	8		23,200	286		23,486	26,100
6110	6-7/8" x 9" x 12" top flange		1	8		21,200	286		21,486	23,800
6112	6-7/8" x 11" x 13-1/2" top flange		1	8		24,400	286		24,686	27,400
6114	8-7/8" x 11" x 15-1/2" top flange		1	8		26,100	286		26,386	29,200
6116	Nailed, 3 ga., (W x H x L)									
6118	3-1/4" x 10-1/2" x 10" top flange	1 Carp	1.80	4.444	C	20,500	159		20,659	22,800
6120	3-1/4" x 10-1/2" x 12" top flange		1.80	4.444		20,500	159		20,659	22,800
6122	5-1/4" x 9-1/2" x 10" top flange		1.80	4.444		20,900	159		21,059	23,300
6124	5-1/4" x 9-1/2" x 12" top flange		1.80	4.444		20,900	159		21,059	23,300
6128	6-7/8" x 8-1/2" x 12" top flange		1.80	4.444		21,400	159		21,559	23,800
6134	Saddle hangers, glu-lam (W x H x L)									
6136	3-1/4" x 10-1/2" x 5-1/4" x 6" saddle	1 Carp	.50	16	C	15,300	570		15,870	17,800
6138	3-1/4" x 10-1/2" x 6-7/8" x 6" saddle		.50	16		16,100	570		16,670	18,700
6140	3-1/4" x 10-1/2" x 8-7/8" x 6" saddle		.50	16		16,900	570		17,470	19,600
6142	3-1/4" x 19-1/2" x 5-1/4" x 10-1/8" saddle		.40	20		15,300	715		16,015	18,000
6144	3-1/4" x 19-1/2" x 6-7/8" x 10-1/8" saddle		.40	20		16,100	715		16,815	18,900
6146	3-1/4" x 19-1/2" x 8-7/8" x 10-1/8" saddle		.40	20		16,900	715		17,615	19,800
6148	5-1/4" x 9-1/2" x 5-1/4" x 12" saddle		.50	16		18,300	570		18,870	21,100
6150	5-1/4" x 9-1/2" x 6-7/8" x 9" saddle		.50	16		20,000	570		20,570	23,000
6152	5-1/4" x 10-1/2" x spec x 12" saddle		.50	16		21,800	570		22,370	24,900
6154	5-1/4" x 18" x 5-1/4" x 12-1/8" saddle		.40	20		18,300	715		19,015	21,300
6156	5-1/4" x 18" x 6-7/8" x 12-1/8" saddle		.40	20		20,000	715		20,715	23,200
6158	5-1/4" x 18" x spec x 12-1/8" saddle		.40	20		21,800	715		22,515	25,100
6160	6-7/8" x 8-1/2" x 6-7/8" x 12" saddle		.50	16		21,800	570		22,370	25,000
6162	6-7/8" x 8-1/2" x 8-7/8" x 12" saddle		.50	16		22,600	570		23,170	25,800
6164	6-7/8" x 10-1/2" x spec x 12" saddle		.50	16		21,800	570		22,370	25,000

06 05 23.60 Timber Connectors		Crew	Daily Output	Labor-Hours	Unit	Material	2014 Bare Costs Labor	Equipment	Total	Total Incl O&P
6166	6-7/8" x 18" x 6-7/8" x 13-3/4" saddle	1 Carp	.40	20	C	21,800	715		22,515	25,200
6168	6-7/8" x 18" x 8-7/8" x 13-3/4" saddle		.40	20		22,600	715		23,315	26,000
6170	6-7/8" x 18" x spec x 13-3/4" saddle		.40	20		24,400	715		25,115	28,000
6172	8-7/8" x 18" x spec x 15-3/4" saddle		.40	20		38,000	715		38,715	43,000
6201	Beam and purlin hangers, galvanized, 12 ga.									
6202	Purlin or joist size, 3" x 8"	1 Carp	1.70	4.706	C	2,025	168		2,193	2,500
6204	3" x 10"		1.70	4.706		2,175	168		2,343	2,675
6206	3" x 12"		1.65	4.848		2,500	173		2,673	3,050
6208	3" x 14"		1.65	4.848		2,675	173		2,848	3,225
6210	3" x 16"		1.65	4.848		2,825	173		2,998	3,400
6212	4" x 8"		1.65	4.848		2,025	173		2,198	2,550
6214	4" x 10"		1.65	4.848		2,200	173		2,373	2,725
6216	4" x 12"		1.60	5		2,600	179		2,779	3,150
6218	4" x 14"		1.60	5		2,750	179		2,929	3,325
6220	4" x 16"		1.60	5		2,925	179		3,104	3,525
6222	6" x 8"		1.60	5		2,625	179		2,804	3,175
6224	6" x 10"		1.55	5.161		2,675	185		2,860	3,250
6226	6" x 12"		1.55	5.161		4,575	185		4,760	5,350
6228	6" x 14"		1.50	5.333		4,850	191		5,041	5,675
6230	6" x 16"		1.50	5.333		5,125	191		5,316	5,975
6250	Beam seats									
6252	Beam size, 5-1/4" wide									
6254	5" x 7" x 1/4"	1 Carp	1.80	4.444	C	7,725	159		7,884	8,750
6256	6" x 7" x 3/8"		1.80	4.444		8,650	159		8,809	9,800
6258	7" x 7" x 3/8"		1.80	4.444		9,250	159		9,409	10,500
6260	8" x 7" x 3/8"		1.80	4.444		10,900	159		11,059	12,300
6262	Beam size, 6-7/8" wide									
6264	5" x 9" x 1/4"	1 Carp	1.80	4.444	C	9,225	159		9,384	10,400
6266	6" x 9" x 3/8"		1.80	4.444		12,000	159		12,159	13,500
6268	7" x 9" x 3/8"		1.80	4.444		12,200	159		12,359	13,700
6270	8" x 9" x 3/8"		1.80	4.444		14,400	159		14,559	16,200
6272	Special beams, over 6-7/8" wide									
6274	5" x 10" x 3/8"	1 Carp	1.80	4.444	C	12,500	159		12,659	14,000
6276	6" x 10" x 3/8"		1.80	4.444		14,600	159		14,759	16,300
6278	7" x 10" x 3/8"		1.80	4.444		15,200	159		15,359	17,000
6280	8" x 10" x 3/8"		1.75	4.571		16,300	163		16,463	18,200
6282	5-1/4" x 12" x 5/16"		1.75	4.571		12,600	163		12,763	14,200
6284	6-1/2" x 12" x 3/8"		1.75	4.571		20,900	163		21,063	23,300
6286	5-1/4" x 16" x 5/16"		1.70	4.706		18,600	168		18,768	20,700
6288	6-1/2" x 16" x 3/8"		1.70	4.706		24,200	168		24,368	27,000
6290	5-1/4" x 20" x 5/16"		1.70	4.706		21,800	168		21,968	24,300
6292	6-1/2" x 20" x 3/8"		1.65	4.848		28,500	173		28,673	31,700
6300	Column bases									
6302	4 x 4, 16 ga.	1 Carp	1.80	4.444	C	780	159		939	1,125
6306	7 ga.		1.80	4.444		2,850	159		3,009	3,425
6308	4 x 6, 16 ga.		1.80	4.444		1,825	159		1,984	2,275
6312	7 ga.		1.80	4.444		2,975	159		3,134	3,550
6314	6 x 6, 16 ga.		1.75	4.571		2,050	163		2,213	2,550
6318	7 ga.		1.75	4.571		4,075	163		4,238	4,750
6320	6 x 8, 7 ga.		1.70	4.706		3,175	168		3,343	3,750
6322	6 x 10, 7 ga.		1.70	4.706		3,400	168		3,568	4,000
6324	6 x 12, 7 ga.		1.70	4.706		3,675	168		3,843	4,325
6326	8 x 8, 7 ga.		1.65	4.848		6,200	173		6,373	7,125

06 05 23 – Wood, Plastic, and Composite Fastenings

06 05 23.60 Timber Connectors		Crew	Daily Output	Labor-Hours	Unit	Material	2014 Bare Costs Labor	Equipment	Total	Total Incl O&P
6330	8 x 10, 7 ga.	1 Carp	1.65	4.848	C	7,425	173		7,598	8,475
6332	8 x 12, 7 ga.		1.60	5		8,075	179		8,254	9,175
6334	10 x 10, 3 ga.		1.60	5		8,225	179		8,404	9,350
6336	10 x 12, 3 ga.		1.60	5		9,475	179		9,654	10,700
6338	12 x 12, 3 ga.		1.55	5.161		10,300	185		10,485	11,600
6350	Column caps, painted, 3 ga.									
6352	3-1/4" x 3-5/8"	1 Carp	1.80	4.444	C	10,400	159		10,559	11,800
6354	3-1/4" x 5-1/2"		1.80	4.444		10,400	159		10,559	11,800
6356	3-5/8" x 3-5/8"		1.80	4.444		8,550	159		8,709	9,675
6358	3-5/8" x 5-1/2"		1.80	4.444		8,550	159		8,709	9,675
6360	5-1/4" x 5-1/2"		1.75	4.571		11,200	163		11,363	12,600
6362	5-1/4" x 7-1/2"		1.75	4.571		11,200	163		11,363	12,600
6364	5-1/2" x 3-5/8"		1.75	4.571		12,100	163		12,263	13,600
6366	5-1/2" x 5-1/2"		1.75	4.571		12,100	163		12,263	13,600
6368	5-1/2" x 7-1/2"		1.70	4.706		12,100	168		12,268	13,600
6370	6-7/8" x 5-1/2"		1.70	4.706		12,600	168		12,768	14,100
6372	6-7/8" x 6-7/8"		1.70	4.706		12,600	168		12,768	14,100
6374	6-7/8" x 7-1/2"		1.70	4.706		12,600	168		12,768	14,100
6376	7-1/2" x 5-1/2"		1.65	4.848		13,100	173		13,273	14,800
6378	7-1/2" x 7-1/2"		1.65	4.848		13,100	173		13,273	14,800
6380	8-7/8" x 5-1/2"		1.60	5		13,900	179		14,079	15,600
6382	8-7/8" x 7-1/2"		1.60	5		13,900	179		14,079	15,600
6384	9-1/2" x 5-1/2"		1.60	5		18,800	179		18,979	20,900
6400	Floor tie anchors, polymer paint									
6402	10 ga., 3" x 37-1/2"	1 Carp	1.80	4.444	C	5,000	159		5,159	5,775
6404	3-1/2" x 45-1/2"		1.75	4.571		5,250	163		5,413	6,050
6406	3 ga., 3-1/2" x 56"		1.70	4.706		9,250	168		9,418	10,500
6410	Girder hangers									
6412	6" wall thickness, 4" x 6"	1 Carp	1.80	4.444	C	2,800	159		2,959	3,375
6414	4" x 8"		1.80	4.444		3,150	159		3,309	3,725
6416	8" wall thickness, 4" x 6"		1.80	4.444		3,250	159		3,409	3,850
6418	4" x 8"		1.80	4.444		3,250	159		3,409	3,850
6420	Hinge connections, polymer painted									
6422	3/4" thick top plate									
6424	5-1/4" x 12" w/5" x 5" top	1 Carp	1	8	C	35,900	286		36,186	40,000
6426	5-1/4" x 15" w/6" x 6" top		.80	10		38,100	360		38,460	42,500
6428	5-1/4" x 18" w/7" x 7" top		.70	11.429		40,100	410		40,510	44,800
6430	5-1/4" x 26" w/9" x 9" top		.60	13.333		42,700	475		43,175	47,700
6432	1" thick top plate									
6434	6-7/8" x 14" w/5" x 5" top	1 Carp	.80	10	C	43,700	360		44,060	48,700
6436	6-7/8" x 17" w/6" x 6" top		.80	10		48,600	360		48,960	54,000
6438	6-7/8" x 21" w/7" x 7" top		.70	11.429		53,000	410		53,410	* 59,000
6440	6-7/8" x 31" w/9" x 9" top		.60	13.333		58,000	475		58,475	65,000
6442	1-1/4" thick top plate									
6444	8-7/8" x 16" w/5" x 5" top	1 Carp	.60	13.333	C	54,500	475		54,975	61,000
6446	8-7/8" x 21" w/6" x 6" top		.50	16		60,000	570		60,570	67,000
6448	8-7/8" x 26" w/7" x 7" top		.40	20		68,000	715		68,715	75,500
6450	8-7/8" x 39" w/9" x 9" top		.30	26.667		84,500	955		85,455	94,500
6460	Holddowns									
6462	Embedded along edge									
6464	26" long, 12 ga.	1 Carp	.90	8.889	C	1,375	320		1,695	2,025
6466	35" long, 12 ga.		.85	9.412		1,800	335		2,135	2,575
6468	35" long, 10 ga.		.85	9.412		1,450	335		1,785	2,150

06 05 23.60 Timber Connectors		Crew	Daily Output	Labor-Hours	Unit	Material	2014 Bare Costs Labor	Equipment	Total	Total Incl O&P
6470	Embedded away from edge									
6472	Medium duty, 12 ga.									
6474	18-1/2" long	1 Carp	.95	8.421	C	825	300		1,125	1,400
6476	23-3/4" long		.90	8.889		965	320		1,285	1,575
6478	28" long		.85	9.412		985	335		1,320	1,650
6480	35" long		.85	9.412		1,350	335		1,685	2,050
6482	Heavy duty, 10 ga.									
6484	28" long	1 Carp	.85	9.412	C	1,750	335		2,085	2,525
6486	35" long	"	.85	9.412	"	1,925	335		2,260	2,675
6490	Surface mounted (W x H)									
6492	2-1/2" x 5-3/4", 7 ga.	1 Carp	1	8	C	2,000	286		2,286	2,675
6494	2-1/2" x 8", 12 ga.		1	8		1,225	286		1,511	1,825
6496	2-7/8" x 6-3/8", 7 ga.		1	8		4,425	286		4,711	5,350
6498	2-7/8" x 12-1/2", 3 ga.		1	8		4,550	286		4,836	5,475
6500	3-3/16" x 9-3/8", 10 ga.		1	8		3,025	286		3,311	3,825
6502	3-1/2" x 11-5/8", 3 ga.		1	8		5,525	286		5,811	6,575
6504	3-1/2" x 14-3/4", 3 ga.		1	8		7,000	286		7,286	8,175
6506	3-1/2" x 16-1/2", 3 ga.		1	8		8,450	286		8,736	9,775
6508	3-1/2" x 20-1/2", 3 ga.		.90	8.889		8,650	320		8,970	10,100
6510	3-1/2" x 24-1/2", 3 ga.		.90	8.889		10,900	320		11,220	12,500
6512	4-1/4" x 20-3/4", 3 ga.		.90	8.889		7,450	320		7,770	8,725
6520	Joist hangers									
6522	Sloped, field adjustable, 18 ga.									
6524	2" x 6"	1 Carp	1.65	4.848	C	545	173		718	890
6526	2" x 8"		1.65	4.848		980	173		1,153	1,375
6528	2" x 10" and up		1.65	4.848		1,625	173		1,798	2,100
6530	3" x 10" and up		1.60	5		1,225	179		1,404	1,650
6532	4" x 10" and up		1.55	5.161		1,475	185		1,660	1,925
6536	Skewed 45°, 16 ga.									
6538	2" x 4"	1 Carp	1.75	4.571	C	870	163		1,033	1,225
6540	2" x 6" or 2" x 8"		1.65	4.848		885	173		1,058	1,275
6542	2" x 10" or 2" x 12"		1.65	4.848		1,025	173		1,198	1,425
6544	2" x 14" or 2" x 16"		1.60	5		1,825	179		2,004	2,300
6546	(2) 2" x 6" or (2) 2" x 8"		1.60	5		1,650	179		1,829	2,100
6548	(2) 2" x 10" or (2) 2" x 12"		1.55	5.161		1,750	185		1,935	2,250
6550	(2) 2" x 14" or (2) 2" x 16"		1.50	5.333		2,775	191		2,966	3,375
6552	4" x 6" or 4" x 8"		1.60	5		1,375	179		1,554	1,800
6554	4" x 10" or 4" x 12"		1.55	5.161		1,600	185		1,785	2,075
6556	4" x 14" or 4" x 16"		1.55	5.161		2,475	185		2,660	3,025
6560	Skewed 45°, 14 ga.									
6562	(2) 2" x 6" or (2) 2" x 8"	1 Carp	1.60	5	C	1,900	179		2,079	2,375
6564	(2) 2" x 10" or (2) 2" x 12"		1.55	5.161		2,625	185		2,810	3,175
6566	(2) 2" x 14" or (2) 2" x 16"		1.50	5.333		3,850	191		4,041	4,550
6568	4" x 6" or 4" x 8"		1.60	5		2,250	179		2,429	2,775
6570	4" x 10" or 4" x 12"		1.55	5.161		2,375	185		2,560	2,900
6572	4" x 14" or 4" x 16"		1.55	5.161		3,175	185		3,360	3,800
6590	Joist hangers, heavy duty 12 ga., galvanized									
6592	2" x 4"	1 Carp	1.75	4.571	C	1,275	163		1,438	1,675
6594	2" x 6"		1.65	4.848		1,400	173		1,573	1,825
6595	2" x 6", 16 ga.		1.65	4.848		1,325	173		1,498	1,750
6596	2" x 8"		1.65	4.848		2,100	173		2,273	2,625
6597	2" x 8", 16 ga.		1.65	4.848		2,000	173		2,173	2,500
6598	2" x 10"		1.65	4.848		2,175	173		2,348	2,675

06 05 23.60 Timber Connectors	Crew	Daily Output	Labor-Hours	Unit	Material	2014 Bare Costs Labor	Equipment	Total	Total Incl O&P
6600	2" x 12"	1 Carp	1.65	4.848	C	2,675	173		2,848	3,225
6602	2" x 14"		1.65	4.848		2,775	173		2,948	3,350
6604	2" x 16"		1.65	4.848		2,925	173		3,098	3,525
6606	3" x 4"		1.65	4.848		1,775	173		1,948	2,250
6608	3" x 6"		1.65	4.848		2,375	173		2,548	2,900
6610	3" x 8"		1.65	4.848		2,400	173		2,573	2,950
6612	3" x 10"		1.60	5		2,775	179		2,954	3,375
6614	3" x 12"		1.60	5		3,350	179		3,529	3,975
6616	3" x 14"		1.60	5		3,900	179		4,079	4,600
6618	3" x 16"		1.60	5		4,300	179		4,479	5,050
6620	(2) 2" x 4"		1.75	4.571		2,075	163		2,238	2,550
6622	(2) 2" x 6"		1.60	5		2,500	179		2,679	3,050
6624	(2) 2" x 8"		1.60	5		2,550	179		2,729	3,100
6626	(2) 2" x 10"		1.55	5.161		2,750	185		2,935	3,325
6628	(2) 2" x 12"		1.55	5.161		3,525	185		3,710	4,175
6630	(2) 2" x 14"		1.50	5.333		3,550	191		3,741	4,250
6632	(2) 2" x 16"		1.50	5.333		3,600	191		3,791	4,275
6634	4" x 4"		1.65	4.848		1,500	173		1,673	1,950
6636	4" x 6"		1.60	5		1,650	179		1,829	2,125
6638	4" x 8"		1.60	5		1,900	179		2,079	2,400
6640	4" x 10"		1.55	5.161		2,350	185		2,535	2,875
6642	4" x 12"		1.55	5.161		2,500	185		2,685	3,050
6644	4" x 14"		1.55	5.161		2,975	185		3,160	3,575
6646	4" x 16"		1.55	5.161		3,275	185		3,460	3,900
6648	(3) 2" x 10"		1.50	5.333		3,625	191		3,816	4,300
6650	(3) 2" x 12"		1.50	5.333		4,025	191		4,216	4,775
6652	(3) 2" x 14"		1.45	5.517		4,325	197		4,522	5,075
6654	(3) 2" x 16"		1.45	5.517		4,400	197		4,597	5,175
6656	6" x 6"		1.60	5		1,950	179		2,129	2,450
6658	6" x 8"		1.60	5		2,000	179		2,179	2,500
6660	6" x 10"		1.55	5.161		2,400	185		2,585	2,925
6662	6" x 12"		1.55	5.161		2,725	185		2,910	3,300
6664	6" x 14"		1.50	5.333		3,425	191		3,616	4,075
6666	6" x 16"		1.50	5.333		4,025	191		4,216	4,750
6690	Knee braces, galvanized, 12 ga.									
6692	Beam depth, 10" x 15" x 5' long	1 Carp	1.80	4.444	C	5,225	159		5,384	6,025
6694	15" x 22-1/2" x 7' long		1.70	4.706		6,000	168		6,168	6,875
6696	22-1/2" x 28-1/2" x 8' long		1.60	5		6,450	179		6,629	7,400
6698	28-1/2" x 36" x 10' long		1.55	5.161		6,725	185		6,910	7,700
6700	36" x 42" x 12' long		1.50	5.333		7,425	191		7,616	8,475
6710	Mudsill anchors									
6714	2" x 4" or 3" x 4"	1 Carp	115	.070	C	1,350	2.49		1,352.49	1,475
6716	2" x 6" or 3" x 6"		115	.070		1,350	2.49		1,352.49	1,475
6718	Block wall, 13-1/4" long		115	.070		85	2.49		87.49	97.50
6720	21-1/4" long		115	.070		126	2.49		128.49	143
6730	Post bases, 12 ga. galvanized									
6732	Adjustable, 3-9/16" x 3-9/16"	1 Carp	1.30	6.154	C	1,075	220		1,295	1,550
6734	3-9/16" x 5-1/2"		1.30	6.154		2,025	220		2,245	2,600
6736	4" x 4"		1.30	6.154		930	220		1,150	1,400
6738	4" x 6"		1.30	6.154		2,700	220		2,920	3,350
6740	5-1/2" x 5-1/2"		1.30	6.154		3,325	220		3,545	4,025
6742	6" x 6"		1.30	6.154		3,325	220		3,545	4,025
6744	Elevated, 3-9/16" x 3-1/4"		1.30	6.154		1,150	220		1,370	1,650

06 05 23.60 Timber Connectors		Crew	Daily Output	Labor-Hours	Unit	Material	2014 Bare Costs Labor	Equipment	Total	Total Incl O&P
6746	5-1/2" x 3-5/16"	1 Carp	1.30	6.154	C	1,650	220		1,870	2,175
6748	5-1/2" x 5"		1.30	6.154		2,475	220		2,695	3,075
6750	Regular, 3-9/16" x 3-3/8"		1.30	6.154		885	220		1,105	1,350
6752	4" x 3-3/8"		1.30	6.154		1,250	220		1,470	1,750
6754	18 ga., 5-1/4" x 3-1/8"		1.30	6.154		1,300	220		1,520	1,800
6755	5-1/2" x 3-3/8"		1.30	6.154		1,300	220		1,520	1,800
6756	5-1/2" x 5-3/8"		1.30	6.154		1,875	220		2,095	2,425
6758	6" x 3-3/8"		1.30	6.154		2,250	220		2,470	2,850
6760	6" x 5-3/8"		1.30	6.154		2,500	220		2,720	3,150
6762	Post combination cap/bases									
6764	3-9/16" x 3-9/16"	1 Carp	1.20	6.667	C	460	238		698	910
6766	3-9/16" x 5-1/2"		1.20	6.667		1,050	238		1,288	1,550
6768	4" x 4"		1.20	6.667		2,075	238		2,313	2,700
6770	5-1/2" x 5-1/2"		1.20	6.667		1,150	238		1,388	1,675
6772	6" x 6"		1.20	6.667		4,175	238		4,413	5,000
6774	7-1/2" x 7-1/2"		1.20	6.667		4,575	238		4,813	5,425
6776	8" x 8"		1.20	6.667		4,725	238		4,963	5,600
6790	Post-beam connection caps									
6792	Beam size 3-9/16"									
6794	12 ga. post, 4" x 4"	1 Carp	1	8	C	2,900	286		3,186	3,650
6796	4" x 6"		1	8		3,850	286		4,136	4,725
6798	4" x 8"		1	8		5,700	286		5,986	6,750
6800	16 ga. post, 4" x 4"		1	8		1,200	286		1,486	1,775
6802	4" x 6"		1	8		2,000	286		2,286	2,675
6804	4" x 8"		1	8		3,350	286		3,636	4,175
6805	18 ga. post, 2-7/8" x 3"		1	8		3,350	286		3,636	4,175
6806	Beam size 5-1/2"									
6808	12 ga. post, 6" x 4"	1 Carp	1	8	C	3,450	286		3,736	4,275
6810	6" x 6"		1	8		5,450	286		5,736	6,475
6812	6" x 8"		1	8		3,750	286		4,036	4,600
6816	16 ga. post, 6" x 4"		1	8		1,875	286		2,161	2,550
6818	6" x 6"		1	8		2,000	286		2,286	2,675
6820	Beam size 7-1/2"									
6822	12 ga. post, 8" x 4"	1 Carp	1	8	C	4,775	286		5,061	5,750
6824	8" x 6"		1	8		5,025	286		5,311	6,000
6826	8" x 8"		1	8		7,550	286		7,836	8,775
6840	Purlin anchors, embedded									
6842	Heavy duty, 10 ga.									
6844	Straight, 28" long	1 Carp	1.60	5	C	1,450	179		1,629	1,875
6846	35" long		1.50	5.333		1,775	191		1,966	2,275
6848	Twisted, 28" long		1.60	5		1,450	179		1,629	1,875
6850	35" long		1.50	5.333		1,775	191		1,966	2,275
6852	Regular duty, 12 ga.									
6854	Straight, 18-1/2" long	1 Carp	1.80	4.444	C	825	159		984	1,175
6856	23-3/4" long		1.70	4.706		1,025	168		1,193	1,425
6858	29" long		1.60	5		1,050	179		1,229	1,475
6860	35" long		1.50	5.333		1,450	191		1,641	1,925
6862	Twisted, 18" long		1.80	4.444		825	159		984	1,175
6866	28" long		1.60	5		980	179		1,159	1,375
6868	35" long		1.50	5.333		1,450	191		1,641	1,925
6870	Straight, plastic coated									
6872	23-1/2" long	1 Carp	1.60	5	C	2,025	179		2,204	2,525
6874	26-7/8" long		1.60	5		2,375	179		2,554	2,900

06 05 23 – Wood, Plastic, and Composite Fastenings

06 05 23.60 Timber Connectors		Crew	Daily Output	Labor-Hours	Unit	Material	Labor	Equipment	Total	Total Incl O&P
6876	32-1/2" long	1 Carp	1.50	5.333	C	2,525	191		2,716	3,100
6878	35-7/8" long	↓	1.50	5.333	↓	2,625	191		2,816	3,225
6890	Purlin hangers, painted									
6892	12 ga., 2" x 6"	1 Carp	1.80	4.444	C	1,850	159		2,009	2,325
6894	2" x 8"		1.80	4.444		2,025	159		2,184	2,500
6896	2" x 10"		1.80	4.444		2,175	159		2,334	2,675
6898	2" x 12"		1.75	4.571		2,350	163		2,513	2,850
6900	2" x 14"		1.75	4.571		2,500	163		2,663	3,025
6902	2" x 16"		1.75	4.571		2,650	163		2,813	3,200
6904	3" x 6"		1.70	4.706		1,875	168		2,043	2,325
6906	3" x 8"		1.70	4.706		2,025	168		2,193	2,500
6908	3" x 10"		1.70	4.706		2,175	168		2,343	2,675
6910	3" x 12"		1.65	4.848		2,500	173		2,673	3,050
6912	3" x 14"		1.65	4.848		2,675	173		2,848	3,225
6914	3" x 16"		1.65	4.848		2,825	173		2,998	3,400
6916	4" x 6"		1.65	4.848		1,875	173		2,048	2,375
6918	4" x 8"		1.65	4.848		2,025	173		2,198	2,550
6920	4" x 10"		1.65	4.848		2,200	173		2,373	2,725
6922	4" x 12"		1.60	5		2,600	179		2,779	3,150
6924	4" x 14"		1.60	5		2,750	179		2,929	3,325
6926	4" x 16"		1.60	5		2,925	179		3,104	3,525
6928	6" x 6"		1.60	5		2,475	179		2,654	3,025
6930	6" x 8"		1.60	5		2,625	179		2,804	3,175
6932	6" x 10"		1.55	5.161		2,675	185		2,860	3,250
6934	double 2" x 6"		1.70	4.706		2,025	168		2,193	2,500
6936	double 2" x 8"		1.70	4.706		2,175	168		2,343	2,675
6938	double 2" x 10"		1.70	4.706		2,350	168		2,518	2,850
6940	double 2" x 12"		1.65	4.848		2,500	173		2,673	3,050
6942	double 2" x 14"		1.65	4.848		2,675	173		2,848	3,225
6944	double 2" x 16"		1.65	4.848		2,825	173		2,998	3,400
6960	11 ga., 4" x 6"		1.65	4.848		3,700	173		3,873	4,375
6962	4" x 8"		1.65	4.848		3,975	173		4,148	4,675
6964	4" x 10"		1.65	4.848		4,250	173		4,423	4,975
6966	6" x 6"		1.60	5		3,750	179		3,929	4,425
6968	6" x 8"		1.60	5		4,025	179		4,204	4,725
6970	6" x 10"		1.55	5.161		4,300	185		4,485	5,025
6972	6" x 12"		1.55	5.161		4,575	185		4,760	5,350
6974	6" x 14"		1.55	5.161		4,850	185		5,035	5,650
6976	6" x 16"		1.50	5.333		5,125	191		5,316	5,975
6978	7 ga., 8" x 6"		1.60	5		4,075	179		4,254	4,775
6980	8" x 8"		1.60	5		4,350	179		4,529	5,075
6982	8" x 10"		1.55	5.161		4,625	185		4,810	5,400
6984	8" x 12"		1.55	5.161		4,900	185		5,085	5,700
6986	8" x 14"		1.50	5.333		5,175	191		5,366	6,025
6988	8" x 16"	↓	1.50	5.333	↓	5,450	191		5,641	6,325
7000	Strap connectors, galvanized									
7002	12 ga., 2-1/16" x 36"	1 Carp	1.55	5.161	C	1,175	185		1,360	1,600
7004	2-1/16" x 47"		1.50	5.333		1,650	191		1,841	2,125
7005	10 ga., 2-1/16" x 72"		1.50	5.333		1,725	191		1,916	2,225
7006	7 ga., 2-1/16" x 34"		1.55	5.161		2,925	185		3,110	3,525
7008	2-1/16" x 45"		1.50	5.333		3,825	191		4,016	4,525
7010	3 ga., 3" x 32"		1.55	5.161		4,925	185		5,110	5,725
7012	3" x 41"		1.55	5.161		5,125	185		5,310	5,950

06 05 23 – Wood, Plastic, and Composite Fastenings

06 05 23.60 Timber Connectors		Crew	Daily Output	Labor-Hours	Unit	Material	2014 Bare Costs Labor	Equipment	Total	Total Incl O&P
7014	3" x 50"	1 Carp	1.50	5.333	C	7,825	191		8,016	8,925
7016	3" x 59"		1.50	5.333		9,525	191		9,716	10,800
7018	3-1/2" x 68"	↓	1.45	5.517	↓	9,675	197		9,872	10,900
7030	Tension ties									
7032	19-1/8" long, 16 ga., 3/4" anchor bolt	1 Carp	1.80	4.444	C	1,350	159		1,509	1,775
7034	20" long, 12 ga., 1/2" anchor bolt		1.80	4.444		1,750	159		1,909	2,200
7036	20" long, 12 ga., 3/4" anchor bolt		1.80	4.444		1,750	159		1,909	2,200
7038	27-3/4" long, 12 ga., 3/4" anchor bolt	↓	1.75	4.571	↓	3,100	163		3,263	3,700
7050	Truss connectors, galvanized									
7052	Adjustable hanger									
7054	18 ga., 2" x 6"	1 Carp	1.65	4.848	C	530	173		703	875
7056	4" x 6"		1.65	4.848		700	173		873	1,050
7058	16 ga., 4" x 10"		1.60	5		1,025	179		1,204	1,425
7060	(2) 2" x 10"	↓	1.60	5	↓	1,025	179		1,204	1,425
7062	Connectors to plate									
7064	16 ga., 2" x 4" plate	1 Carp	1.80	4.444	C	525	159		684	840
7066	2" x 6" plate	"	1.80	4.444	"	675	159		834	1,000
7068	Hip jack connector									
7070	14 ga.	1 Carp	1.50	5.333	C	2,750	191		2,941	3,350

06 05 23.70 Rough Hardware

0010	ROUGH HARDWARE, average percent of carpentry material									
0020	Minimum				Job	.50%				
0200	Maximum					1.50%				
0210	In seismic or hurricane areas, up to				↓	10%				

06 05 23.80 Metal Bracing

0010	METAL BRACING									
0302	Let-in, "T" shaped, 22 ga. galv. steel, studs at 16" O.C.	1 Carp	580	.014	L.F.	.81	.49		1.30	1.72
0402	Studs at 24" O.C.		600	.013		.81	.48		1.29	1.69
0502	16 ga. galv. steel straps, studs at 16" O.C.		600	.013		1.05	.48		1.53	1.96
0602	Studs at 24" O.C.	↓	620	.013	↓	1.05	.46		1.51	1.94

06 11 Wood Framing

06 11 10 – Framing with Dimensional, Engineered or Composite Lumber

06 11 10.01 Forest Stewardship Council Certification

0010	FOREST STEWARDSHIP COUNCIL CERTIFICATION									
0020	For Forest Stewardship Council (FSC) cert dimension lumber, add G					65%				

06 11 10.02 Blocking

0010	BLOCKING									
2600	Miscellaneous, to wood construction									
2620	2" x 4"	1 Carp	.17	47.059	M.B.F.	570	1,675		2,245	3,450
2625	Pneumatic nailed		.21	38.095		575	1,350		1,925	2,925
2660	2" x 8"		.27	29.630		645	1,050		1,695	2,475
2665	Pneumatic nailed	↓	.33	24.242	↓	650	865		1,515	2,175
2720	To steel construction									
2740	2" x 4"	1 Carp	.14	57.143	M.B.F.	570	2,050		2,620	4,050
2780	2" x 8"	"	.21	38.095	"	645	1,350		1,995	3,000

06 11 10.04 Wood Bracing

0010	WOOD BRACING									
0012	Let-in, with 1" x 6" boards, studs @ 16" O.C.	1 Carp	150	.053	L.F.	.80	1.91		2.71	4.09
0202	Studs @ 24" O.C.	"	230	.035	"	.80	1.24		2.04	2.97

06 11 Wood Framing

06 11 10 – Framing with Dimensional, Engineered or Composite Lumber

06 11 10.06 Bridging

		Crew	Daily Output	Labor-Hours	Unit	Material	2014 Bare Costs Labor	Equipment	Total	Total Incl O&P
0010	**BRIDGING**									
0012	Wood, for joists 16" O.C., 1" x 3"	1 Carp	130	.062	Pr.	.62	2.20		2.82	4.38
0017	Pneumatic nailed		170	.047		.68	1.68		2.36	3.58
0102	2" x 3" bridging		130	.062		.64	2.20		2.84	4.40
0107	Pneumatic nailed		170	.047		.66	1.68		2.34	3.56
0302	Steel, galvanized, 18 ga., for 2" x 10" joists at 12" O.C.		130	.062		.90	2.20		3.10	4.69
0352	16" O.C.		135	.059		.93	2.12		3.05	4.58
0402	24" O.C.		140	.057		1.90	2.04		3.94	5.55
0602	For 2" x 14" joists at 16" O.C.		130	.062		1.40	2.20		3.60	5.25
0902	Compression type, 16" O.C., 2" x 8" joists		200	.040		.93	1.43		2.36	3.43
1002	2" x 12" joists		200	.040		.93	1.43		2.36	3.43

06 11 10.10 Beam and Girder Framing

			Crew	Daily Output	Labor-Hours	Unit	Material	2014 Bare Costs Labor	Equipment	Total	Total Incl O&P
0010	**BEAM AND GIRDER FRAMING**	R061110-30									
3500	Single, 2" x 6"		2 Carp	.70	22.857	M.B.F.	570	815		1,385	2,000
3505	Pneumatic nailed			.81	19.704		575	705		1,280	1,800
3520	2" x 8"			.86	18.605		645	665		1,310	1,825
3525	Pneumatic nailed			1	16.048		650	575		1,225	1,675
3540	2" x 10"			1	16		680	570		1,250	1,700
3545	Pneumatic nailed			1.16	13.793		685	495		1,180	1,575
3560	2" x 12"			1.10	14.545		770	520		1,290	1,725
3565	Pneumatic nailed			1.28	12.539		775	450		1,225	1,600
3580	2" x 14"			1.17	13.675		770	490		1,260	1,675
3585	Pneumatic nailed			1.36	11.791		775	420		1,195	1,575
3600	3" x 8"			1.10	14.545		1,275	520		1,795	2,275
3620	3" x 10"			1.25	12.800		1,275	460		1,735	2,200
3640	3" x 12"			1.35	11.852		1,275	425		1,700	2,150
3660	3" x 14"			1.40	11.429		1,275	410		1,685	2,100
3680	4" x 8"		F-3	2.66	15.038		1,300	495	249	2,044	2,550
3700	4" x 10"			3.16	12.658		1,275	415	210	1,900	2,325
3720	4" x 12"			3.60	11.111		1,275	365	184	1,824	2,225
3740	4" x 14"			3.96	10.101		1,450	330	167	1,947	2,350
4000	Double, 2" x 6"		2 Carp	1.25	12.800		570	460		1,030	1,400
4005	Pneumatic nailed			1.45	11.034		575	395		970	1,300
4020	2" x 8"			1.60	10		645	360		1,005	1,300
4025	Pneumatic nailed			1.86	8.621		650	310		960	1,225
4040	2" x 10"			1.92	8.333		680	298		978	1,250
4045	Pneumatic nailed			2.23	7.185		685	257		942	1,175
4060	2" x 12"			2.20	7.273		770	260		1,030	1,275
4065	Pneumatic nailed			2.55	6.275		775	224		999	1,225
4080	2" x 14"			2.45	6.531		770	233		1,003	1,250
4085	Pneumatic nailed			2.84	5.634		775	201		976	1,200
5000	Triple, 2" x 6"			1.65	9.697		570	345		915	1,200
5005	Pneumatic nailed			1.91	8.377		575	299		874	1,150
5020	2" x 8"			2.10	7.619		645	272		917	1,175
5025	Pneumatic nailed			2.44	6.568		650	235		885	1,100
5040	2" x 10"			2.50	6.400		680	229		909	1,125
5045	Pneumatic nailed			2.90	5.517		685	197		882	1,075
5060	2" x 12"			2.85	5.614		770	201		971	1,200
5065	Pneumatic nailed			3.31	4.840		775	173		948	1,150
5080	2" x 14"			3.15	5.079		770	182		952	1,150
5085	Pneumatic nailed			3.35	4.770		775	171		946	1,150

06 11 Wood Framing

06 11 10 – Framing with Dimensional, Engineered or Composite Lumber

06 11 10.12 Ceiling Framing

		Crew	Daily Output	Labor-Hours	Unit	Material	2014 Bare Costs Labor	2014 Bare Costs Equipment	Total	Total Incl O&P
0010	**CEILING FRAMING**									
6400	Suspended, 2" x 3"	2 Carp	.50	32	M.B.F.	745	1,150		1,895	2,750
6450	2" x 4"		.59	27.119		570	970		1,540	2,250
6500	2" x 6"		.80	20		570	715		1,285	1,825
6550	2" x 8"		.86	18.605		645	665		1,310	1,825

06 11 10.14 Posts and Columns

		Crew	Daily Output	Labor-Hours	Unit	Material	2014 Bare Costs Labor	2014 Bare Costs Equipment	Total	Total Incl O&P
0010	**POSTS AND COLUMNS**									
0400	4" x 4"	2 Carp	.52	30.769	M.B.F.	1,300	1,100		2,400	3,275
0420	4" x 6"		.55	29.091		1,300	1,050		2,350	3,175
0440	4" x 8"		.59	27.119		1,325	970		2,295	3,075
0460	6" x 6"		.65	24.615		1,600	880		2,480	3,225
0480	6" x 8"		.70	22.857		1,600	815		2,415	3,125
0500	6" x 10"		.75	21.333		1,600	765		2,365	3,025

06 11 10.18 Joist Framing

		Crew	Daily Output	Labor-Hours	Unit	Material	2014 Bare Costs Labor	2014 Bare Costs Equipment	Total	Total Incl O&P
0010	**JOIST FRAMING** R061110-30									
2650	Joists, 2" x 4"	2 Carp	.83	19.277	M.B.F.	570	690		1,260	1,775
2655	Pneumatic nailed		.96	16.667		575	595		1,170	1,625
2680	2" x 6"		1.25	12.800		570	460		1,030	1,400
2685	Pneumatic nailed		1.44	11.111		575	395		970	1,300
2700	2" x 8"		1.46	10.959		645	390		1,035	1,375
2705	Pneumatic nailed		1.68	9.524		650	340		990	1,300
2720	2" x 10"		1.49	10.738		680	385		1,065	1,400
2725	Pneumatic nailed		1.71	9.357		685	335		1,020	1,325
2740	2" x 12"		1.75	9.143		770	325		1,095	1,400
2745	Pneumatic nailed		2.01	7.960		775	285		1,060	1,325
2760	2" x 14"		1.79	8.939		770	320		1,090	1,400
2765	Pneumatic nailed		2.06	7.767		775	278		1,053	1,325
2780	3" x 6"		1.39	11.511		940	410		1,350	1,725
2790	3" x 8"		1.90	8.421		1,275	300		1,575	1,900
2800	3" x 10"		1.95	8.205		1,275	293		1,568	1,925
2820	3" x 12"		1.80	8.889		1,275	320		1,595	1,950
2840	4" x 6"		1.60	10		1,300	360		1,660	2,025
2860	4" x 10"		2	8		1,275	286		1,561	1,875
2880	4" x 12"		1.80	8.889		1,275	320		1,595	1,925
3000	Composite wood joist 9-1/2" deep		.90	17.778	M.L.F.	1,725	635		2,360	2,975
3010	11-1/2" deep		.88	18.182		1,950	650		2,600	3,250
3020	14" deep		.82	19.512		2,325	700		3,025	3,725
3030	16" deep		.78	20.513		3,425	735		4,160	5,000
4000	Open web joist 12" deep		.88	18.182		3,100	650		3,750	4,500
4002	Per linear foot		880	.018	L.F.	3.10	.65		3.75	4.50
4004	Treated, per linear foot		880	.018	"	3.97	.65		4.62	5.45
4010	14" deep		.82	19.512	M.L.F.	3,275	700		3,975	4,775
4012	Per linear foot		820	.020	L.F.	3.27	.70		3.97	4.77
4014	Treated, per linear foot		820	.020	"	4.28	.70		4.98	5.90
4020	16" deep		.78	20.513	M.L.F.	3,650	735		4,385	5,250
4022	Per linear foot		780	.021	L.F.	3.66	.73		4.39	5.25
4024	Treated, per linear foot		780	.021	"	4.81	.73		5.54	6.55
4030	18" deep		.74	21.622	M.L.F.	4,000	775		4,775	5,700
4032	Per linear foot		740	.022	L.F.	3.99	.77		4.76	5.70
4034	Treated, per linear foot		740	.022	"	5.30	.77		6.07	7.10
6000	Composite rim joist, 1-1/4" x 9-1/2"		.90	17.778	M.L.F.	1,875	635		2,510	3,125
6010	1-1/4" x 11-1/2"		.88	18.182		2,300	650		2,950	3,625

06 11 10 – Framing with Dimensional, Engineered or Composite Lumber

06 11 10.18 Joist Framing

		Crew	Daily Output	Labor-Hours	Unit	Material	2014 Bare Costs Labor	2014 Bare Costs Equipment	Total	Total Incl O&P
6020	1-1/4" x 14-1/2"	2 Carp	.82	19.512	M.L.F.	2,775	700		3,475	4,225
6030	1-1/4" x 16-1/2"	↓	.78	20.513	↓	3,300	735		4,035	4,850

06 11 10.24 Miscellaneous Framing

		Crew	Daily Output	Labor-Hours	Unit	Material	Labor	Equipment	Total	Total Incl O&P
0010	**MISCELLANEOUS FRAMING**									
8500	Firestops, 2" x 4"	2 Carp	.51	31.373	M.B.F.	570	1,125		1,695	2,500
8505	Pneumatic nailed		.62	25.806		575	925		1,500	2,175
8520	2" x 6"		.60	26.667		570	955		1,525	2,225
8525	Pneumatic nailed		.73	21.858		575	780		1,355	1,950
8540	2" x 8"		.60	26.667		645	955		1,600	2,300
8560	2" x 12"		.70	22.857		770	815		1,585	2,225
8600	Nailers, treated, wood construction, 2" x 4"		.53	30.189		735	1,075		1,810	2,625
8605	Pneumatic nailed		.64	25.157		745	900		1,645	2,350
8620	2" x 6"		.75	21.333		760	765		1,525	2,100
8625	Pneumatic nailed		.90	17.778		765	635		1,400	1,925
8640	2" x 8"		.93	17.204		760	615		1,375	1,850
8645	Pneumatic nailed		1.12	14.337		765	515		1,280	1,700
8660	Steel construction, 2" x 4"		.50	32		740	1,150		1,890	2,725
8680	2" x 6"		.70	22.857		760	815		1,575	2,200
8700	2" x 8"		.87	18.391		760	655		1,415	1,925
8760	Rough bucks, treated, for doors or windows, 2" x 6"		.40	40		760	1,425		2,185	3,225
8765	Pneumatic nailed		.48	33.333		765	1,200		1,965	2,850
8780	2" x 8"		.51	31.373		760	1,125		1,885	2,700
8785	Pneumatic nailed		.61	26.144		765	935		1,700	2,425
8800	Stair stringers, 2" x 10"		.22	72.727		680	2,600		3,280	5,125
8820	2" x 12"		.26	61.538		770	2,200		2,970	4,550
8840	3" x 10"		.31	51.613		1,275	1,850		3,125	4,525
8860	3" x 12"	↓	.38	42.105	↓	1,275	1,500		2,775	3,950

06 11 10.26 Partitions

		Crew	Daily Output	Labor-Hours	Unit	Material	Labor	Equipment	Total	Total Incl O&P
0010	**PARTITIONS**									
0020	Single bottom and double top plate, no waste, std. & better lumber									
0180	2" x 4" studs, 8' high, studs 12" O.C.	2 Carp	80	.200	L.F.	4.17	7.15		11.32	16.65
0185	12" O.C., pneumatic nailed		96	.167		4.22	5.95		10.17	14.70
0200	16" O.C.		100	.160		3.41	5.70		9.11	13.35
0205	16" O.C., pneumatic nailed		120	.133		3.45	4.77		8.22	11.80
0300	24" O.C.		125	.128		2.65	4.58		7.23	10.60
0305	24" O.C., pneumatic nailed		150	.107		2.68	3.81		6.49	9.35
0380	10' high, studs 12" O.C.		80	.200		4.93	7.15		12.08	17.45
0385	12" O.C., pneumatic nailed		96	.167		4.98	5.95		10.93	15.55
0400	16" O.C.		100	.160		3.98	5.70		9.68	14
0405	16" O.C., pneumatic nailed		120	.133		4.03	4.77		8.80	12.45
0500	24" O.C.		125	.128		3.03	4.58		7.61	11.05
0505	24" O.C., pneumatic nailed		150	.107		3.07	3.81		6.88	9.75
0580	12' high, studs 12" O.C.		65	.246		5.70	8.80		14.50	21
0585	12" O.C., pneumatic nailed		78	.205		5.75	7.35		13.10	18.70
0600	16" O.C.		80	.200		4.55	7.15		11.70	17.05
0605	16" O.C., pneumatic nailed		96	.167		4.60	5.95		10.55	15.10
0700	24" O.C.		100	.160		3.41	5.70		9.11	13.35
0705	24" O.C., pneumatic nailed		120	.133		3.45	4.77		8.22	11.80
0780	2" x 6" studs, 8' high, studs 12" O.C.		70	.229		6.25	8.15		14.40	20.50
0785	12" O.C., pneumatic nailed		84	.190		6.35	6.80		13.15	18.40
0800	16" O.C.		90	.178		5.10	6.35		11.45	16.35
0805	16" O.C., pneumatic nailed		108	.148		5.20	5.30		10.50	14.60

06 11 Wood Framing

06 11 10 – Framing with Dimensional, Engineered or Composite Lumber

06 11 10.26 Partitions

		Crew	Daily Output	Labor-Hours	Unit	Material	2014 Bare Costs Labor	Equipment	Total	Total Incl O&P
0900	24" O.C.	2 Carp	115	.139	L.F.	3.98	4.97		8.95	12.75
0905	24" O.C., pneumatic nailed		138	.116		4.03	4.14		8.17	11.40
0980	10' high, studs 12" O.C.		70	.229		7.40	8.15		15.55	22
0985	12" O.C., pneumatic nailed		84	.190		7.50	6.80		14.30	19.70
1000	16" O.C.		90	.178		5.95	6.35		12.30	17.25
1005	16" O.C., pneumatic nailed		108	.148		6.05	5.30		11.35	15.55
1100	24" O.C.		115	.139		4.55	4.97		9.52	13.35
1105	24" O.C., pneumatic nailed		138	.116		4.60	4.14		8.74	12
1180	12' high, studs 12" O.C.		55	.291		8.55	10.40		18.95	27
1185	12" O.C., pneumatic nailed		66	.242		8.65	8.65		17.30	24
1200	16" O.C.		70	.229		6.85	8.15		15	21.50
1205	16" O.C., pneumatic nailed		84	.190		6.90	6.80		13.70	19.05
1300	24" O.C.		90	.178		5.10	6.35		11.45	16.35
1305	24" O.C., pneumatic nailed		108	.148		5.20	5.30		10.50	14.60
1400	For horizontal blocking, 2" x 4", add		600	.027		.38	.95		1.33	2.02
1500	2" x 6", add		600	.027		.57	.95		1.52	2.23
1600	For openings, add		250	.064			2.29		2.29	3.85
1700	Headers for above openings, material only, add				M.B.F.	645			645	710

06 11 10.28 Porch or Deck Framing

		Crew	Daily Output	Labor-Hours	Unit	Material	2014 Bare Costs Labor	Equipment	Total	Total Incl O&P
0010	**PORCH OR DECK FRAMING**									
0100	Treated lumber, posts or columns, 4" x 4"	2 Carp	390	.041	L.F.	1.22	1.47		2.69	3.81
0110	4" x 6"		275	.058		1.77	2.08		3.85	5.45
0120	4" x 8"		220	.073		3.07	2.60		5.67	7.75
0130	Girder, single, 4" x 4"		675	.024		1.22	.85		2.07	2.77
0140	4" x 6"		600	.027		1.77	.95		2.72	3.54
0150	4" x 8"		525	.030		3.07	1.09		4.16	5.20
0160	Double, 2" x 4"		625	.026		1.01	.92		1.93	2.65
0170	2" x 6"		600	.027		1.56	.95		2.51	3.32
0180	2" x 8"		575	.028		2.08	.99		3.07	3.96
0190	2" x 10"		550	.029		2.72	1.04		3.76	4.74
0200	2" x 12"		525	.030		4.07	1.09		5.16	6.30
0210	Triple, 2" x 4"		575	.028		1.51	.99		2.50	3.33
0220	2" x 6"		550	.029		2.34	1.04		3.38	4.32
0230	2" x 8"		525	.030		3.12	1.09		4.21	5.25
0240	2" x 10"		500	.032		4.08	1.14		5.22	6.40
0250	2" x 12"		475	.034		6.10	1.20		7.30	8.75
0260	Ledger, bolted 4' O.C., 2" x 4"		400	.040		.64	1.43		2.07	3.12
0270	2" x 6"		395	.041		.91	1.45		2.36	3.44
0280	2" x 8"		390	.041		1.16	1.47		2.63	3.74
0290	2" x 10"		385	.042		1.47	1.49		2.96	4.12
0300	2" x 12"		380	.042		2.13	1.51		3.64	4.88
0310	Joists, 2" x 4"		1250	.013		.50	.46		.96	1.32
0320	2" x 6"		1250	.013		.78	.46		1.24	1.62
0330	2" x 8"		1100	.015		1.04	.52		1.56	2.02
0340	2" x 10"		900	.018		1.36	.64		2	2.56
0350	2" x 12"		875	.018		1.63	.65		2.28	2.89
0360	Railings and trim , 1" x 4"	1 Carp	300	.027		.47	.95		1.42	2.12
0370	2" x 2"		300	.027		.33	.95		1.28	1.97
0380	2" x 4"		300	.027		.50	.95		1.45	2.15
0390	2" x 6"		300	.027		.77	.95		1.72	2.44
0400	Decking, 1" x 4"		275	.029	S.F.	1.95	1.04		2.99	3.90
0410	2" x 4"		300	.027		1.67	.95		2.62	3.44

06 11 10.28 Porch or Deck Framing

		Crew	Daily Output	Labor-Hours	Unit	Material	2014 Bare Costs Labor	2014 Bare Costs Equipment	Total	Total Incl O&P
0420	2" x 6"	1 Carp	320	.025	S.F.	1.65	.89		2.54	3.32
0430	5/4" x 6"	↓	320	.025	↓	2.04	.89		2.93	3.74
0440	Balusters, square, 2" x 2"	2 Carp	660	.024	L.F.	.34	.87		1.21	1.83
0450	Turned, 2" x 2"		420	.038		.45	1.36		1.81	2.78
0460	Stair stringer, 2" x 10"		130	.123		1.36	4.40		5.76	8.90
0470	2" x 12"		130	.123		1.63	4.40		6.03	9.20
0480	Stair treads, 1" x 4"		140	.114		1.96	4.09		6.05	9
0490	2" x 4"		140	.114		.50	4.09		4.59	7.40
0500	2" x 6"		160	.100		.75	3.58		4.33	6.85
0510	5/4" x 6"		160	.100	↓	.95	3.58		4.53	7.05
0520	Turned handrail post, 4" x 4"		64	.250	Ea.	31	8.95		39.95	49
0530	Lattice panel, 4' x 8', 1/2"		1600	.010	S.F.	.80	.36		1.16	1.48
0535	3/4"		1600	.010	"	1.20	.36		1.56	1.92
0540	Cedar, posts or columns, 4" x 4"		390	.041	L.F.	3.80	1.47		5.27	6.65
0550	4" x 6"		275	.058		5.90	2.08		7.98	9.95
0560	4" x 8"		220	.073		10	2.60		12.60	15.35
0800	Decking, 1" x 4"		550	.029		1.81	1.04		2.85	3.74
0810	2" x 4"		600	.027		3.63	.95		4.58	5.60
0820	2" x 6"		640	.025		6.60	.89		7.49	8.75
0830	5/4" x 6"		640	.025		4.45	.89		5.34	6.40
0840	Railings and trim, 1" x 4"		600	.027		1.81	.95		2.76	3.59
0860	2" x 4"		600	.027		3.63	.95		4.58	5.60
0870	2" x 6"		600	.027		6.60	.95		7.55	8.85
0920	Stair treads, 1" x 4"		140	.114		1.81	4.09		5.90	8.85
0930	2" x 4"		140	.114		3.63	4.09		7.72	10.85
0940	2" x 6"		160	.100		6.60	3.58		10.18	13.25
0950	5/4" x 6"		160	.100		4.45	3.58		8.03	10.90
0980	Redwood, posts or columns, 4" x 4"		390	.041		6.45	1.47		7.92	9.50
0990	4" x 6"		275	.058		11.20	2.08		13.28	15.80
1000	4" x 8"	↓	220	.073	↓	20.50	2.60		23.10	27
1240	Redwood decking, 1" x 4"	1 Carp	275	.029	S.F.	3.97	1.04		5.01	6.10
1260	2" x 6"		340	.024		7.50	.84		8.34	9.65
1270	5/4" x 6"	↓	320	.025	↓	4.77	.89		5.66	6.75
1280	Railings and trim, 1" x 4"	2 Carp	600	.027	L.F.	1.17	.95		2.12	2.89
1310	2" x 6"		600	.027		7.50	.95		8.45	9.85
1420	Alternative decking, wood/plastic composite, 5/4" x 6" [G]		640	.025		3.04	.89		3.93	4.84
1440	1" x 4" square edge fir		550	.029		1.97	1.04		3.01	3.92
1450	1" x 4" tongue and groove fir		450	.036		1.31	1.27		2.58	3.58
1460	1" x 4" mahogany		550	.029		1.81	1.04		2.85	3.74
1462	5/4" x 6" PVC	↓	550	.029	↓	3.62	1.04		4.66	5.75
1465	Framing, porch or deck, alt deck fastening, screws, add	1 Carp	240	.033	S.F.		1.19		1.19	2
1470	Accessories, joist hangers, 2" x 4"		160	.050	Ea.	.73	1.79		2.52	3.81
1480	2" x 6" through 2" x 12"	↓	150	.053		1.39	1.91		3.30	4.74
1530	Post footing, incl excav, backfill, tube form & concrete, 4' deep, 8" dia	F-7	12	2.667		11.60	85.50		97.10	156
1540	10" diameter		11	2.909		16.90	93		109.90	176
1550	12" diameter	↓	10	3.200	↓	22.50	102		124.50	197

06 11 10.30 Roof Framing

		Crew	Daily Output	Labor-Hours	Unit	Material	2014 Bare Costs Labor	2014 Bare Costs Equipment	Total	Total Incl O&P
0010	**ROOF FRAMING**									
6070	Fascia boards, 2" x 8"	2 Carp	.30	53.333	M.B.F.	645	1,900		2,545	3,900
6080	2" x 10"		.30	53.333		680	1,900		2,580	3,950
7000	Rafters, to 4 in 12 pitch, 2" x 6"		1	16		570	570		1,140	1,575
7060	2" x 8"	↓	1.26	12.698	↓	645	455		1,100	1,475

06 11 Wood Framing

06 11 10 – Framing with Dimensional, Engineered or Composite Lumber

06 11 10.30 Roof Framing

		Crew	Daily Output	Labor-Hours	Unit	Material	2014 Bare Costs Labor	Equipment	Total	Total Incl O&P
7300	Hip and valley rafters, 2" x 6"	2 Carp	.76	21.053	M.B.F.	570	755		1,325	1,900
7360	2" x 8"		.96	16.667		645	595		1,240	1,700
7540	Hip and valley jacks, 2" x 6"		.60	26.667		570	955		1,525	2,225
7600	2" x 8"		.65	24.615		645	880		1,525	2,175
7780	For slopes steeper than 4 in 12, add						30%			
7790	For dormers or complex roofs, add						50%			
7800	Rafter tie, 1" x 4", #3	2 Carp	.27	59.259	M.B.F.	1,400	2,125		3,525	5,125
7820	Ridge board, #2 or better, 1" x 6"		.30	53.333		1,600	1,900		3,500	4,975
7840	1" x 8"		.37	43.243		1,800	1,550		3,350	4,575
7860	1" x 10"		.42	38.095		1,875	1,350		3,225	4,350
7880	2" x 6"		.50	32		570	1,150		1,720	2,550
7900	2" x 8"		.60	26.667		645	955		1,600	2,300
7920	2" x 10"		.66	24.242		680	865		1,545	2,200
7940	Roof cants, split, 4" x 4"		.86	18.605		1,275	665		1,940	2,525
7960	6" x 6"		1.80	8.889		1,575	320		1,895	2,275
7980	Roof curbs, untreated, 2" x 6"		.52	30.769		570	1,100		1,670	2,475
8000	2" x 12"		.80	20		770	715		1,485	2,050

06 11 10.32 Sill and Ledger Framing

		Crew	Daily Output	Labor-Hours	Unit	Material	2014 Bare Costs Labor	Equipment	Total	Total Incl O&P
0010	**SILL AND LEDGER FRAMING**									
4482	Ledgers, nailed, 2" x 4"	2 Carp	.50	32	M.B.F.	570	1,150		1,720	2,550
4484	2" x 6"		.60	26.667		570	955		1,525	2,225
4486	Bolted, not including bolts, 3" x 8"		.65	24.615		1,275	880		2,155	2,875
4488	3" x 12"		.70	22.857		1,275	815		2,090	2,775
4490	Mud sills, redwood, construction grade, 2" x 4"		.59	27.119		3,400	970		4,370	5,350
4492	2" x 6"		.78	20.513		3,400	735		4,135	4,975
4500	Sills, 2" x 4"		.40	40		560	1,425		1,985	3,025
4520	2" x 6"		.55	29.091		560	1,050		1,610	2,375
4540	2" x 8"		.67	23.881		635	855		1,490	2,125
4600	Treated, 2" x 4"		.36	44.444		725	1,600		2,325	3,475
4620	2" x 6"		.50	32		750	1,150		1,900	2,750
4640	2" x 8"		.60	26.667		750	955		1,705	2,425
4700	4" x 4"		.60	26.667		885	955		1,840	2,575
4720	4" x 6"		.70	22.857		855	815		1,670	2,325
4740	4" x 8"		.80	20		1,125	715		1,840	2,425
4760	4" x 10"		.87	18.391		1,400	655		2,055	2,625

06 11 10.34 Sleepers

		Crew	Daily Output	Labor-Hours	Unit	Material	2014 Bare Costs Labor	Equipment	Total	Total Incl O&P
0010	**SLEEPERS**									
0300	On concrete, treated, 1" x 2"	2 Carp	.39	41.026	M.B.F.	1,600	1,475		3,075	4,250
0320	1" x 3"		.50	32		1,800	1,150		2,950	3,925
0340	2" x 4"		.99	16.162		860	580		1,440	1,925
0360	2" x 6"		1.30	12.308		885	440		1,325	1,700

06 11 10.36 Soffit and Canopy Framing

		Crew	Daily Output	Labor-Hours	Unit	Material	2014 Bare Costs Labor	Equipment	Total	Total Incl O&P
0010	**SOFFIT AND CANOPY FRAMING**									
1300	Canopy or soffit framing, 1" x 4"	2 Carp	.30	53.333	M.B.F.	1,400	1,900		3,300	4,750
1340	1" x 8"		.50	32		1,800	1,150		2,950	3,900
1360	2" x 4"		.41	39.024		570	1,400		1,970	2,975
1400	2" x 8"		.67	23.881		645	855		1,500	2,125
1420	3" x 4"		.50	32		1,075	1,150		2,225	3,100
1460	3" x 8"		.60	26.667		1,275	955		2,230	3,000

06 11 Wood Framing

06 11 10 – Framing with Dimensional, Engineered or Composite Lumber

06 11 10.38 Treated Lumber Framing Material

		Crew	Daily Output	Labor-Hours	Unit	Material	2014 Bare Costs Labor	Equipment	Total	Total Incl O&P
0010	**TREATED LUMBER FRAMING MATERIAL**									
0100	2" x 4"				M.B.F.	725			725	800
0110	2" x 6"					750			750	825
0120	2" x 8"					750			750	825
0130	2" x 10"					785			785	865
0140	2" x 12"					990			990	1,075
0200	4" x 4"					885			885	975
0210	4" x 6"					855			855	940
0220	4" x 8"					1,125			1,125	1,225

06 11 10.40 Wall Framing

		Crew	Daily Output	Labor-Hours	Unit	Material	2014 Bare Costs Labor	Equipment	Total	Total Incl O&P
0010	**WALL FRAMING** R061110-30									
5860	Headers over openings, 2" x 6"	2 Carp	.36	44.444	M.B.F.	570	1,600		2,170	3,300
5865	2" x 6", pneumatic nailed		.43	37.209		575	1,325		1,900	2,875
5880	2" x 8"		.45	35.556		645	1,275		1,920	2,850
5885	2" x 8", pneumatic nailed		.54	29.630		650	1,050		1,700	2,500
5900	2" x 10"		.53	30.189		680	1,075		1,755	2,575
5905	2" x 10", pneumatic nailed		.67	23.881		685	855		1,540	2,175
5920	2" x 12"		.60	26.667		770	955		1,725	2,450
5925	2" x 12", pneumatic nailed		.72	22.222		775	795		1,570	2,175
5940	4" x 12"		.76	21.053		1,275	755		2,030	2,675
5945	4" x 12", pneumatic nailed		.92	17.391		1,300	620		1,920	2,475
5960	6" x 12"		.84	19.048		1,600	680		2,280	2,900
5965	6" x 12", pneumatic nailed		1.01	15.873		1,600	565		2,165	2,700
6000	Plates, untreated, 2" x 3"		.43	37.209		745	1,325		2,070	3,075
6005	2" x 3", pneumatic nailed		.52	30.769		750	1,100		1,850	2,675
6020	2" x 4"		.53	30.189		570	1,075		1,645	2,450
6025	2" x 4", pneumatic nailed		.67	23.881		575	855		1,430	2,050
6040	2" x 6"		.75	21.333		570	765		1,335	1,900
6045	2" x 6", pneumatic nailed		.90	17.778		575	635		1,210	1,700
6120	Studs, 8' high wall, 2" x 3"		.60	26.667		745	955		1,700	2,425
6125	2" x 3", pneumatic nailed		.72	22.222		750	795		1,545	2,150
6140	2" x 4"		.92	17.391		570	620		1,190	1,675
6145	2" x 4", pneumatic nailed		1.10	14.493		575	520		1,095	1,500
6160	2" x 6"		1	16		570	570		1,140	1,575
6165	2" x 6", pneumatic nailed		1.20	13.333		575	475		1,050	1,425
6180	3" x 4"		.80	20		1,075	715		1,790	2,375
6185	3" x 4", pneumatic nailed		.96	16.667		1,075	595		1,670	2,175
8200	For 12' high walls, deduct						5%			
8220	For stub wall, 6' high, add						20%			
8240	3' high, add						40%			
8250	For second story & above, add						5%			
8300	For dormer & gable, add						15%			

06 11 10.42 Furring

		Crew	Daily Output	Labor-Hours	Unit	Material	2014 Bare Costs Labor	Equipment	Total	Total Incl O&P
0010	**FURRING**									
0012	Wood strips, 1" x 2", on walls, on wood	1 Carp	550	.015	L.F.	.24	.52		.76	1.14
0015	On wood, pneumatic nailed		710	.011		.24	.40		.64	.94
0300	On masonry		495	.016		.26	.58		.84	1.26
0400	On concrete		260	.031		.26	1.10		1.36	2.14
0600	1" x 3", on walls, on wood		550	.015		.38	.52		.90	1.30
0605	On wood, pneumatic nailed		710	.011		.39	.40		.79	1.10
0700	On masonry		495	.016		.42	.58		1	1.43
0800	On concrete		260	.031		.42	1.10		1.52	2.31

06 11 Wood Framing

06 11 10 – Framing with Dimensional, Engineered or Composite Lumber

06 11 10.42 Furring

		Crew	Daily Output	Labor-Hours	Unit	Material	2014 Bare Costs Labor	2014 Bare Costs Equipment	Total	Total Incl O&P
0850	On ceilings, on wood	1 Carp	350	.023	L.F.	.38	.82		1.20	1.80
0855	On wood, pneumatic nailed		450	.018		.39	.64		1.03	1.49
0900	On masonry		320	.025		.42	.89		1.31	1.96
0950	On concrete		210	.038		.42	1.36		1.78	2.75

06 11 10.44 Grounds

		Crew	Daily Output	Labor-Hours	Unit	Material	2014 Bare Costs Labor	2014 Bare Costs Equipment	Total	Total Incl O&P
0010	**GROUNDS**									
0020	For casework, 1" x 2" wood strips, on wood	1 Carp	330	.024	L.F.	.24	.87		1.11	1.72
0100	On masonry		285	.028		.26	1		1.26	1.98
0200	On concrete		250	.032		.26	1.14		1.40	2.21
0400	For plaster, 3/4" deep, on wood		450	.018		.24	.64		.88	1.33
0500	On masonry		225	.036		.26	1.27		1.53	2.43
0600	On concrete		175	.046		.26	1.63		1.89	3.04
0700	On metal lath		200	.040		.26	1.43		1.69	2.70

06 12 Structural Panels

06 12 10 – Structural Insulated Panels

06 12 10.10 OSB Faced Panels

			Crew	Daily Output	Labor-Hours	Unit	Material	2014 Bare Costs Labor	2014 Bare Costs Equipment	Total	Total Incl O&P
0010	**OSB FACED PANELS**										
0100	Structural insul. panels, 7/16" OSB both faces, EPS insul, 3-5/8" T	G	F-3	2075	.019	S.F.	3.06	.63	.32	4.01	4.78
0110	5-5/8" thick	G		1725	.023		3.43	.76	.38	4.57	5.45
0120	7-3/8" thick	G		1425	.028		3.73	.92	.47	5.12	6.15
0130	9-3/8" thick	G		1125	.036		4.08	1.17	.59	5.84	7.10
0140	7/16" OSB one face, EPS insul, 3-5/8" thick	G		2175	.018		3.25	.60	.30	4.15	4.93
0150	5-5/8" thick	G		1825	.022		3.72	.72	.36	4.80	5.70
0160	7-3/8" thick	G		1525	.026		4.15	.86	.43	5.44	6.50
0170	9-3/8" thick	G		1225	.033		4.62	1.07	.54	6.23	7.50
0190	7/16" OSB - 1/2" GWB faces , EPS insul, 3-5/8" T	G		2075	.019		3.22	.63	.32	4.17	4.95
0200	5-5/8" thick	G		1725	.023		3.69	.76	.38	4.83	5.75
0210	7-3/8" thick	G		1425	.028		4.11	.92	.47	5.50	6.60
0220	9-3/8" thick	G		1125	.036		4.82	1.17	.59	6.58	7.90
0240	7/16" OSB - 1/2" MRGWB faces , EPS insul, 3-5/8" T	G		2075	.019		3.22	.63	.32	4.17	4.95
0250	5-5/8" thick	G		1725	.023		3.69	.76	.38	4.83	5.75
0260	7-3/8" thick	G		1425	.028		4.11	.92	.47	5.50	6.60
0270	9-3/8" thick	G		1125	.036		4.82	1.17	.59	6.58	7.90
0300	For 1/2" GWB added to OSB skin, add	G					.68			.68	.75
0310	For 1/2" MRGWB added to OSB skin, add	G					.68			.68	.75
0320	For one T1-11 skin, add to OSB-OSB	G					1.55			1.55	1.71
0330	For one 19/32" CDX skin, add to OSB-OSB	G					.79			.79	.87
0500	Structural insulated panel, 7/16" OSB both sides, straw core										
0510	4-3/8" T, walls (w/sill, splines, plates)	G	F-6	2400	.017	S.F.	7.40	.56	.28	8.24	9.35
0520	Floors (w/splines)	G		2400	.017		7.40	.56	.28	8.24	9.35
0530	Roof (w/splines)	G		2400	.017		7.40	.56	.28	8.24	9.35
0550	7-7/8" T, walls (w/sill, splines, plates)	G		2400	.017		11.20	.56	.28	12.04	13.55
0560	Floors (w/splines)	G		2400	.017		11.20	.56	.28	12.04	13.55
0570	Roof (w/splines)	G		2400	.017		11.20	.56	.28	12.04	13.55

06 12 19 – Composite Shearwall Panels

06 12 19.10 Steel and Wood Composite Shearwall Panels

		Crew	Daily Output	Labor-Hours	Unit	Material	2014 Bare Costs Labor	2014 Bare Costs Equipment	Total	Total Incl O&P
0010	**STEEL & WOOD COMPOSITE SHEARWALL PANELS**									
0020	Anchor bolts, 36" long (must be placed in wet concrete)	1 Carp	150	.053	Ea.	35	1.91		36.91	41.50
0030	On concrete, 2 x 4 & 2 x 6 walls, 7' - 10' high, 360 lb. shear, 12" wide	2 Carp	8	2		465	71.50		536.50	630

06 12 Structural Panels

06 12 19 – Composite Shearwall Panels

06 12 19.10 Steel and Wood Composite Shearwall Panels	Crew	Daily Output	Labor-Hours	Unit	Material	2014 Bare Costs Labor	Equipment	Total	Total Incl O&P
0040	715 lb. shear, 15" wide	2 Carp	8	2	Ea.	560	71.50		631.50	735
0050	1860 lb. shear, 18" wide		8	2		580	71.50		651.50	755
0060	2780 lb. shear, 21" wide		8	2		685	71.50		756.50	875
0070	3790 lb. shear, 24" wide		8	2		790	71.50		861.50	985
0080	2 x 6 walls, 11' to 13' high, 1180 lb. shear, 18" wide		6	2.667		705	95.50		800.50	935
0090	1555 lb. shear, 21" wide		6	2.667		890	95.50		985.50	1,150
0100	2280 lb. shear, 24" wide		6	2.667		995	95.50		1,090.50	1,250
0110	For installing above on wood floor frame, add									
0120	Coupler nuts, threaded rods, bolts, shear transfer plate kit	1 Carp	16	.500	Ea.	70	17.90		87.90	107
0130	Framing anchors, angle (2 required)	"	96	.083	"	2.61	2.98		5.59	7.85
0140	For blocking see Section 06 11 10.02									
0150	For installing above, first floor to second floor, wood floor frame, add									
0160	Add stack option to first floor wall panel				Ea.	77			77	84.50
0170	Threaded rods, bolts, shear transfer plate kit	1 Carp	16	.500		84	17.90		101.90	123
0180	Framing anchors, angle (2 required)	"	96	.083		2.61	2.98		5.59	7.85
0190	For blocking see 06 11 10.02									
0200	For installing stacked panels, balloon framing									
0210	Add stack option to first floor wall panel				Ea.	77			77	84.50
0220	Threaded rods, bolts kit	1 Carp	16	.500	"	49	17.90		66.90	84

06 13 Heavy Timber Construction

06 13 23 – Heavy Timber Framing

06 13 23.10 Heavy Framing	Crew	Daily Output	Labor-Hours	Unit	Material	2014 Bare Costs Labor	Equipment	Total	Total Incl O&P
0010	**HEAVY FRAMING**									
0020	Beams, single 6" x 10"	2 Carp	1.10	14.545	M.B.F.	1,600	520		2,120	2,625
0100	Single 8" x 16"		1.20	13.333		2,000	475		2,475	3,000
0200	Built from 2" lumber, multiple 2" x 14"		.90	17.778		760	635		1,395	1,925
0210	Built from 3" lumber, multiple 3" x 6"		.70	22.857		930	815		1,745	2,400
0220	Multiple 3" x 8"		.80	20		1,275	715		1,990	2,600
0230	Multiple 3" x 10"		.90	17.778		1,275	635		1,910	2,475
0240	Multiple 3" x 12"		1	16		1,275	570		1,845	2,350
0250	Built from 4" lumber, multiple 4" x 6"		.80	20		1,300	715		2,015	2,625
0260	Multiple 4" x 8"		.90	17.778		1,300	635		1,935	2,500
0270	Multiple 4" x 10"		1	16		1,275	570		1,845	2,350
0280	Multiple 4" x 12"		1.10	14.545		1,275	520		1,795	2,275
0290	Columns, structural grade, 1500f, 4" x 4"		.60	26.667		1,275	955		2,230	3,000
0300	6" x 6"		.65	24.615		1,400	880		2,280	3,025
0400	8" x 8"		.70	22.857		1,350	815		2,165	2,850
0500	10" x 10"		.75	21.333		1,450	765		2,215	2,875
0600	12" x 12"		.80	20		1,525	715		2,240	2,875
0800	Floor planks, 2" thick, T & G, 2" x 6"		1.05	15.238		1,600	545		2,145	2,675
0900	2" x 10"		1.10	14.545		1,600	520		2,120	2,625
1100	3" thick, 3" x 6"		1.05	15.238		1,600	545		2,145	2,675
1200	3" x 10"		1.10	14.545		1,600	520		2,120	2,625
1400	Girders, structural grade, 12" x 12"		.80	20		1,525	715		2,240	2,875
1500	10" x 16"		1	16		2,400	570		2,970	3,600
2300	Roof purlins, 4" thick, structural grade		1.05	15.238		1,300	545		1,845	2,350

06 15 Wood Decking

06 15 16 – Wood Roof Decking

06 15 16.10 Solid Wood Roof Decking

		Crew	Daily Output	Labor-Hours	Unit	Material	2014 Bare Costs Labor	Equipment	Total	Total Incl O&P
0010	**SOLID WOOD ROOF DECKING**									
0350	Cedar planks, 2" thick	2 Carp	350	.046	S.F.	5.35	1.63		6.98	8.60
0400	3" thick		320	.050		8	1.79		9.79	11.80
0500	4" thick		250	.064		10.65	2.29		12.94	15.60
0550	6" thick		200	.080		16	2.86		18.86	22.50
0650	Douglas fir, 2" thick		350	.046		2.69	1.63		4.32	5.70
0700	3" thick		320	.050		4.04	1.79		5.83	7.45
0800	4" thick		250	.064		5.40	2.29		7.69	9.75
0850	6" thick		200	.080		8.05	2.86		10.91	13.70
0950	Hemlock, 2" thick		350	.046		2.74	1.63		4.37	5.75
1000	3" thick		320	.050		4.11	1.79		5.90	7.55
1100	4" thick		250	.064		5.50	2.29		7.79	9.85
1150	6" thick		200	.080		8.20	2.86		11.06	13.85
1250	Western white spruce, 2" thick		350	.046		1.75	1.63		3.38	4.67
1300	3" thick		320	.050		2.62	1.79		4.41	5.90
1400	4" thick		250	.064		3.50	2.29		5.79	7.70
1450	6" thick		200	.080		5.25	2.86		8.11	10.55

06 15 23 – Laminated Wood Decking

06 15 23.10 Laminated Roof Deck

		Crew	Daily Output	Labor-Hours	Unit	Material	2014 Bare Costs Labor	Equipment	Total	Total Incl O&P
0010	**LAMINATED ROOF DECK**									
0020	Pine or hemlock, 3" thick	2 Carp	425	.038	S.F.	6.30	1.35		7.65	9.20
0100	4" thick		325	.049		8.70	1.76		10.46	12.50
0300	Cedar, 3" thick		425	.038		6.85	1.35		8.20	9.80
0400	4" thick		325	.049		9.15	1.76		10.91	13.05
0600	Fir, 3" thick		425	.038		6.30	1.35		7.65	9.20
0700	4" thick		325	.049		8.70	1.76		10.46	12.50

06 16 Sheathing

06 16 13 – Insulating Sheathing

06 16 13.10 Insulating Sheathing

			Crew	Daily Output	Labor-Hours	Unit	Material	2014 Bare Costs Labor	Equipment	Total	Total Incl O&P
0010	**INSULATING SHEATHING**										
0020	Expanded polystyrene, 1#/C.F. density, 3/4" thick R2.89	G	2 Carp	1400	.011	S.F.	.32	.41		.73	1.05
0030	1" thick R3.85	G		1300	.012		.38	.44		.82	1.16
0040	2" thick R7.69	G		1200	.013		.62	.48		1.10	1.49
0050	Extruded polystyrene, 15 PSI compressive strength, 1" thick, R5	G		1300	.012		.67	.44		1.11	1.48
0060	2" thick, R10	G		1200	.013		.83	.48		1.31	1.72
0070	Polyisocyanurate, 2#/C.F. density, 3/4" thick	G		1400	.011		.58	.41		.99	1.33
0080	1" thick	G		1300	.012		.64	.44		1.08	1.45
0090	1-1/2" thick	G		1250	.013		.77	.46		1.23	1.62
0100	2" thick	G		1200	.013		.93	.48		1.41	1.83

06 16 23 – Subflooring

06 16 23.10 Subfloor

			Crew	Daily Output	Labor-Hours	Unit	Material	2014 Bare Costs Labor	Equipment	Total	Total Incl O&P
0010	**SUBFLOOR**	R061636-20									
0011	Plywood, CDX, 1/2" thick		2 Carp	1500	.011	SF Flr.	.60	.38		.98	1.29
0015	Pneumatic nailed			1860	.009		.60	.31		.91	1.17
0100	5/8" thick			1350	.012		.74	.42		1.16	1.53
0105	Pneumatic nailed			1674	.010		.74	.34		1.08	1.40
0200	3/4" thick			1250	.013		.88	.46		1.34	1.74
0205	Pneumatic nailed			1550	.010		.88	.37		1.25	1.59
0300	1-1/8" thick, 2-4-1 including underlayment			1050	.015		2.23	.54		2.77	3.37

06 16 Sheathing

06 16 23 – Subflooring

06 16 23.10 Subfloor

		Crew	Daily Output	Labor-Hours	Unit	Material	2014 Bare Costs Labor	Equipment	Total	Total Incl O&P
0440	With boards, 1" x 6", S4S, laid regular	2 Carp	900	.018	SF Flr.	1.74	.64		2.38	2.99
0450	1" x 8", laid regular		1000	.016		1.90	.57		2.47	3.05
0460	Laid diagonal		850	.019		1.90	.67		2.57	3.22
0500	1" x 10", laid regular		1100	.015		1.95	.52		2.47	3.02
0600	Laid diagonal		900	.018		1.95	.64		2.59	3.21
8990	Subfloor adhesive, 3/8" bead	1 Carp	2300	.003	L.F.	.12	.12		.24	.34

06 16 26 – Underlayment

06 16 26.10 Wood Product Underlayment

			Crew	Daily Output	Labor-Hours	Unit	Material	2014 Bare Costs Labor	Equipment	Total	Total Incl O&P
0010	**WOOD PRODUCT UNDERLAYMENT**	R061636-20									
0015	Plywood, underlayment grade, 1/4" thick		2 Carp	1500	.011	S.F.	.84	.38		1.22	1.56
0018	Pneumatic nailed			1860	.009		.84	.31		1.15	1.44
0030	3/8" thick			1500	.011		.93	.38		1.31	1.66
0070	Pneumatic nailed			1860	.009		.93	.31		1.24	1.54
0100	1/2" thick			1450	.011		1.06	.39		1.45	1.83
0105	Pneumatic nailed			1798	.009		1.06	.32		1.38	1.71
0200	5/8" thick			1400	.011		1.18	.41		1.59	1.99
0205	Pneumatic nailed			1736	.009		1.18	.33		1.51	1.85
0300	3/4" thick			1300	.012		1.40	.44		1.84	2.28
0305	Pneumatic nailed			1612	.010		1.40	.36		1.76	2.14
0500	Particle board, 3/8" thick	G		1500	.011		.40	.38		.78	1.08
0505	Pneumatic nailed	G		1860	.009		.40	.31		.71	.96
0600	1/2" thick	G		1450	.011		.42	.39		.81	1.12
0605	Pneumatic nailed	G		1798	.009		.42	.32		.74	1
0800	5/8" thick	G		1400	.011		.52	.41		.93	1.26
0805	Pneumatic nailed	G		1736	.009		.52	.33		.85	1.12
0900	3/4" thick	G		1300	.012		.62	.44		1.06	1.42
0905	Pneumatic nailed	G		1612	.010		.62	.36		.98	1.28
0955	Particleboard, 100% recycled straw/wheat, 4' x 8' x 1/4"	G		1450	.011		.29	.39		.68	.98
0960	4' x 8' x 3/8"	G		1450	.011		.42	.39		.81	1.12
0965	4' x 8' x 1/2"	G		1350	.012		.59	.42		1.01	1.36
0970	4' x 8' x 5/8"	G		1300	.012		.71	.44		1.15	1.52
0975	4' x 8' x 3/4"	G		1250	.013		.81	.46		1.27	1.66
0980	4' x 8' x 1"	G		1150	.014		1.08	.50		1.58	2.03
0985	4' x 8' x 1-1/4"	G		1100	.015		1.24	.52		1.76	2.24
1100	Hardboard, underlayment grade, 4' x 4', .215" thick	G		1500	.011		.57	.38		.95	1.27

06 16 33 – Wood Board Sheathing

06 16 33.10 Board Sheathing

		Crew	Daily Output	Labor-Hours	Unit	Material	2014 Bare Costs Labor	Equipment	Total	Total Incl O&P
0009	**BOARD SHEATHING**									
0010	Roof, 1" x 6" boards, laid horizontal	2 Carp	725	.022	S.F.	1.74	.79		2.53	3.25
0020	On steep roof		520	.031		1.74	1.10		2.84	3.77
0040	On dormers, hips, & valleys		480	.033		1.74	1.19		2.93	3.92
0050	Laid diagonal		650	.025		1.74	.88		2.62	3.40
0070	1" x 8" boards, laid horizontal		875	.018		1.90	.65		2.55	3.19
0080	On steep roof		635	.025		1.90	.90		2.80	3.61
0090	On dormers, hips, & valleys		580	.028		1.95	.99		2.94	3.80
0100	Laid diagonal		725	.022		1.90	.79		2.69	3.42
0110	Skip sheathing, 1" x 4", 7" OC	1 Carp	1200	.007		.58	.24		.82	1.04
0120	1" x 6", 9" OC	"	1450	.006		.80	.20		1	1.21
0200	Walls, 1" x 6" boards, laid regular	2 Carp	650	.025		1.74	.88		2.62	3.40
0210	Laid diagonal		585	.027		1.74	.98		2.72	3.57
0220	1" x 8" boards, laid regular		765	.021		1.90	.75		2.65	3.35
0230	Laid diagonal		650	.025		1.90	.88		2.78	3.57

06 16 36 – Wood Panel Product Sheathing

06 16 36.10 Sheathing		Crew	Daily Output	Labor-Hours	Unit	Material	2014 Bare Costs Labor	Equipment	Total	Total Incl O&P
0010	**SHEATHING**	R061110-30								
0012	Plywood on roofs, CDX									
0030	5/16" thick	2 Carp	1600	.010	S.F.	.55	.36		.91	1.21
0035	Pneumatic nailed	R061636-20	1952	.008		.55	.29		.84	1.10
0050	3/8" thick		1525	.010		.50	.38		.88	1.18
0055	Pneumatic nailed		1860	.009		.50	.31		.81	1.07
0100	1/2" thick		1400	.011		.60	.41		1.01	1.34
0105	Pneumatic nailed		1708	.009		.60	.34		.94	1.21
0200	5/8" thick		1300	.012		.74	.44		1.18	1.56
0205	Pneumatic nailed		1586	.010		.74	.36		1.10	1.43
0300	3/4" thick		1200	.013		.88	.48		1.36	1.77
0305	Pneumatic nailed		1464	.011		.88	.39		1.27	1.63
0500	Plywood on walls, with exterior CDX, 3/8" thick		1200	.013		.50	.48		.98	1.35
0505	Pneumatic nailed		1488	.011		.50	.38		.88	1.20
0600	1/2" thick		1125	.014		.60	.51		1.11	1.51
0605	Pneumatic nailed		1395	.011		.60	.41		1.01	1.34
0700	5/8" thick		1050	.015		.74	.54		1.28	1.74
0705	Pneumatic nailed		1302	.012		.74	.44		1.18	1.56
0800	3/4" thick		975	.016		.88	.59		1.47	1.96
0805	Pneumatic nailed		1209	.013		.88	.47		1.35	1.77
1000	For shear wall construction, add						20%			
1200	For structural 1 exterior plywood, add				S.F.	10%				
3000	Wood fiber, regular, no vapor barrier, 1/2" thick	2 Carp	1200	.013		.60	.48		1.08	1.46
3100	5/8" thick		1200	.013		.76	.48		1.24	1.64
3300	No vapor barrier, in colors, 1/2" thick		1200	.013		.73	.48		1.21	1.60
3400	5/8" thick		1200	.013		.77	.48		1.25	1.65
3600	With vapor barrier one side, white, 1/2" thick		1200	.013		.59	.48		1.07	1.45
3700	Vapor barrier 2 sides, 1/2" thick		1200	.013		.82	.48		1.30	1.70
3800	Asphalt impregnated, 25/32" thick		1200	.013		.32	.48		.80	1.15
3850	Intermediate, 1/2" thick		1200	.013		.24	.48		.72	1.06
4500	Oriented strand board, on roof, 7/16" thick Ⓖ		1460	.011		.50	.39		.89	1.21
4505	Pneumatic nailed Ⓖ		1780	.009		.50	.32		.82	1.09
4550	1/2" thick Ⓖ		1400	.011		.50	.41		.91	1.24
4555	Pneumatic nailed Ⓖ		1736	.009		.50	.33		.83	1.10
4600	5/8" thick Ⓖ		1300	.012		.69	.44		1.13	1.50
4605	Pneumatic nailed Ⓖ		1586	.010		.69	.36		1.05	1.37
4610	On walls, 7/16" thick		1200	.013		.50	.48		.98	1.35
4615	Pneumatic nailed		1488	.011		.50	.38		.88	1.20
4620	1/2" thick		1195	.013		.50	.48		.98	1.36
4625	Pneumatic nailed		1325	.012		.50	.43		.93	1.28
4630	5/8" thick		1050	.015		.69	.54		1.23	1.68
4635	Pneumatic nailed		1302	.012		.69	.44		1.13	1.50
4700	Oriented strand board, factory laminated W.R. barrier, on roof, 1/2" thick Ⓖ		1400	.011		.62	.41		1.03	1.37
4705	Pneumatic nailed Ⓖ		1736	.009		.62	.33		.95	1.23
4720	5/8" thick Ⓖ		1300	.012		.77	.44		1.21	1.59
4725	Pneumatic nailed Ⓖ		1586	.010		.77	.36		1.13	1.46
4730	5/8" thick, T&G Ⓖ		1150	.014		.78	.50		1.28	1.70
4735	Pneumatic nailed, T&G Ⓖ		1400	.011		.78	.41		1.19	1.55
4740	On walls, 7/16" thick Ⓖ		1200	.013		.56	.48		1.04	1.42
4745	Pneumatic nailed Ⓖ		1488	.011		.56	.38		.94	1.27
4750	1/2" thick Ⓖ		1195	.013		.62	.48		1.10	1.49
4755	Pneumatic nailed Ⓖ		1325	.012		.62	.43		1.05	1.41

06 16 Sheathing

06 16 36 – Wood Panel Product Sheathing

	06 16 36.10 Sheathing	Crew	Daily Output	Labor-Hours	Unit	Material	2014 Bare Costs Labor	Equipment	Total	Total Incl O&P
4800	Joint sealant tape, 3-1/2"	2 Carp	7600	.002	L.F.	.28	.08		.36	.44
4810	Joint sealant tape, 6"	↓	7600	.002	"	.44	.08		.52	.61

06 16 43 – Gypsum Sheathing

06 16 43.10 Gypsum Sheathing

		Crew	Daily Output	Labor-Hours	Unit	Material	Labor	Equipment	Total	Total Incl O&P
0010	**GYPSUM SHEATHING**									
0020	Gypsum, weatherproof, 1/2" thick	2 Carp	1125	.014	S.F.	.44	.51		.95	1.34
0040	With embedded glass mats	"	1100	.015	"	.77	.52		1.29	1.73

06 17 Shop-Fabricated Structural Wood

06 17 33 – Wood I-Joists

06 17 33.10 Wood and Composite I-Joists

		Crew	Daily Output	Labor-Hours	Unit	Material	Labor	Equipment	Total	Total Incl O&P
0010	**WOOD AND COMPOSITE I-JOISTS**									
0100	Plywood webs, incl. bridging & blocking, panels 24" O.C.									
1200	15' to 24' span, 50 psf live load	F-5	2400	.013	SF Flr.	1.95	.42		2.37	2.84
1300	55 psf live load		2250	.014		2.21	.45		2.66	3.18
1400	24' to 30' span, 45 psf live load		2600	.012		2.61	.39		3	3.53
1500	55 psf live load	↓	2400	.013	↓	3.89	.42		4.31	4.98

06 17 53 – Shop-Fabricated Wood Trusses

06 17 53.10 Roof Trusses

		Crew	Daily Output	Labor-Hours	Unit	Material	Labor	Equipment	Total	Total Incl O&P
0010	**ROOF TRUSSES**									
0100	Fink (W) or King post type, 2'-0" O.C.									
0200	Metal plate connected, 4 in 12 slope									
0210	24' to 29' span	F-3	3000	.013	SF Flr.	1.71	.44	.22	2.37	2.85
0300	30' to 43' span		3000	.013		2.18	.44	.22	2.84	3.37
0400	44' to 60' span	↓	3000	.013	↓	2.36	.44	.22	3.02	3.56
0700	Glued and nailed, add					50%				

06 18 Glued-Laminated Construction

06 18 13 – Glued-Laminated Beams

06 18 13.20 Laminated Framing

		Crew	Daily Output	Labor-Hours	Unit	Material	Labor	Equipment	Total	Total Incl O&P
0010	**LAMINATED FRAMING**									
0020	30 lb., short term live load, 15 lb. dead load									
0200	Straight roof beams, 20' clear span, beams 8' O.C.	F-3	2560	.016	SF Flr.	1.91	.51	.26	2.68	3.24
0300	Beams 16' O.C.		3200	.013		1.38	.41	.21	2	2.44
0500	40' clear span, beams 8' O.C.		3200	.013		3.65	.41	.21	4.27	4.94
0600	Beams 16' O.C.	↓	3840	.010		2.99	.34	.17	3.50	4.05
0800	60' clear span, beams 8' O.C.	F-4	2880	.014		6.30	.46	.39	7.15	8.10
0900	Beams 16' O.C.	"	3840	.010		4.68	.34	.30	5.32	6.05
1100	Tudor arches, 30' to 40' clear span, frames 8' O.C.	F-3	1680	.024		8.20	.78	.39	9.37	10.75
1200	Frames 16' O.C.	"	2240	.018		6.40	.59	.30	7.29	8.35
1400	50' to 60' clear span, frames 8' O.C.	F-4	2200	.018		8.85	.60	.52	9.97	11.25
1500	Frames 16' O.C.		2640	.015		7.50	.50	.43	8.43	9.55
1700	Radial arches, 60' clear span, frames 8' O.C.		1920	.021		8.25	.68	.59	9.52	10.90
1800	Frames 16' O.C.		2880	.014		6.35	.46	.39	7.20	8.20
2000	100' clear span, frames 8' O.C.		1600	.025		8.55	.82	.71	10.08	11.55
2100	Frames 16' O.C.		2400	.017		7.50	.55	.47	8.52	9.70
2300	120' clear span, frames 8' O.C.		1440	.028		11.35	.91	.79	13.05	14.90
2400	Frames 16' O.C.	↓	1920	.021	↓	10.35	.68	.59	11.62	13.20

06 18 13.20 Laminated Framing	Crew	Daily Output	Labor-Hours	Unit	Material	2014 Bare Costs Labor	2014 Bare Costs Equipment	Total	Total Incl O&P
2600 Bowstring trusses, 20' O.C., 40' clear span	F-3	2400	.017	SF Flr.	5.10	.55	.28	5.93	6.85
2700 60' clear span	F-4	3600	.011		4.60	.36	.32	5.28	6
2800 100' clear span		4000	.010		6.50	.33	.28	7.11	8
2900 120' clear span		3600	.011		7	.36	.32	7.68	8.65
3000 For less than 1000 B.F., add					20%				
3050 For over 5000 B.F., deduct					10%				
3100 For premium appearance, add to S.F. prices					5%				
3300 For industrial type, deduct					15%				
3500 For stain and varnish, add					5%				
3900 For 3/4" laminations, add to straight					25%				
4100 Add to curved					15%				
4300 Alternate pricing method: (use nominal footage of									
4310 components). Straight beams, camber less than 6"	F-3	3.50	11.429	M.B.F.	2,825	375	189	3,389	3,975
4400 Columns, including hardware		2	20		3,050	655	330	4,035	4,825
4600 Curved members, radius over 32'		2.50	16		3,125	525	265	3,915	4,600
4700 Radius 10' to 32'		3	13.333		3,075	435	221	3,731	4,375
4900 For complicated shapes, add maximum					100%				
5100 For pressure treating, add to straight					35%				
5200 Add to curved					45%				
6000 Laminated veneer members, southern pine or western species									
6050 1-3/4" wide x 5-1/2" deep	2 Carp	480	.033	L.F.	2.94	1.19		4.13	5.25
6100 9-1/2" deep		480	.033		4.35	1.19		5.54	6.80
6150 14" deep		450	.036		6.75	1.27		8.02	9.55
6200 18" deep		450	.036		9.50	1.27		10.77	12.60
6300 Parallel strand members, southern pine or western species									
6350 1-3/4" wide x 9-1/4" deep	2 Carp	480	.033	L.F.	4.35	1.19		5.54	6.80
6400 11-1/4" deep		450	.036		4.93	1.27		6.20	7.55
6450 14" deep		400	.040		6.75	1.43		8.18	9.80
6500 3-1/2" wide x 9-1/4" deep		480	.033		15.15	1.19		16.34	18.65
6550 11-1/4" deep		450	.036		18.10	1.27		19.37	22
6600 14" deep		400	.040		22.50	1.43		23.93	27
6650 7" wide x 9-1/4" deep		450	.036		30.50	1.27		31.77	35.50
6700 11-1/4" deep		420	.038		38	1.36		39.36	44
6750 14" deep		400	.040		44.50	1.43		45.93	51.50
8000 Straight beams									
8102 20' span									
8104 3-1/8" x 9"	F-3	30	1.333	Ea.	133	43.50	22	198.50	244
8106 X 10-1/2"		30	1.333		155	43.50	22	220.50	268
8108 X 12"		30	1.333		177	43.50	22	242.50	293
8110 X 13-1/2"		30	1.333		199	43.50	22	264.50	315
8112 X 15"		29	1.379		221	45	23	289	345
8114 5-1/8" x 10-1/2"		30	1.333		254	43.50	22	319.50	375
8116 X 12"		30	1.333		290	43.50	22	355.50	420
8118 X 13-1/2"		30	1.333		325	43.50	22	390.50	460
8120 X 15"		29	1.379		365	45	23	433	500
8122 X 16-1/2"		29	1.379		400	45	23	468	540
8124 X 18"		29	1.379		435	45	23	503	580
8126 X 19-1/2"		29	1.379		470	45	23	538	620
8128 X 21"		28	1.429		510	47	23.50	580.50	665
8130 X 22-1/2"		28	1.429		545	47	23.50	615.50	705
8132 X 24"		28	1.429		580	47	23.50	650.50	745
8134 6-3/4" x 12"		29	1.379		380	45	23	448	520
8136 X 13-1/2"		29	1.379		430	45	23	498	575

06 18 13 – Glued-Laminated Beams

06 18 13.20 Laminated Framing	Crew	Daily Output	Labor-Hours	Unit	Material	2014 Bare Costs Labor	Equipment	Total	Total Incl O&P
8138	X 15"	F-3	29	1.379	Ea.	480	45	23	548	625
8140	X 16-1/2"		28	1.429		525	47	23.50	595.50	685
8142	X 18"		28	1.429		575	47	23.50	645.50	735
8144	X 19-1/2"		28	1.429		620	47	23.50	690.50	790
8146	X 21"		27	1.481		670	48.50	24.50	743	845
8148	X 22-1/2"		27	1.481		715	48.50	24.50	788	900
8150	X 24"		27	1.481		765	48.50	24.50	838	950
8152	X 25-1/2"		27	1.481		810	48.50	24.50	883	1,000
8154	X 27"		26	1.538		860	50.50	25.50	936	1,050
8156	X 28-1/2"		26	1.538		910	50.50	25.50	986	1,125
8158	X 30"		26	1.538		955	50.50	25.50	1,031	1,175
8200	30' span									
8250	3-1/8" x 9"	F-3	30	1.333	Ea.	199	43.50	22	264.50	315
8252	X 10-1/2"		30	1.333		232	43.50	22	297.50	355
8254	X 12"		30	1.333		266	43.50	22	331.50	390
8256	X 13-1/2"		30	1.333		299	43.50	22	364.50	430
8258	X 15"		29	1.379		330	45	23	398	465
8260	5-1/8" x 10-1/2"		30	1.333		380	43.50	22	445.50	520
8262	X 12"		30	1.333		435	43.50	22	500.50	580
8264	X 13-1/2"		30	1.333		490	43.50	22	555.50	640
8266	X 15"		29	1.379		545	45	23	613	700
8268	X 16-1/2"		29	1.379		600	45	23	668	760
8270	X 18"		29	1.379		655	45	23	723	820
8272	X 19-1/2"		29	1.379		710	45	23	778	880
8274	X 21"		28	1.429		760	47	23.50	830.50	945
8276	X 22-1/2"		28	1.429		815	47	23.50	885.50	1,000
8278	X 24"		28	1.429		870	47	23.50	940.50	1,075
8280	6-3/4" x 12"		29	1.379		575	45	23	643	730
8282	X 13-1/2"		29	1.379		645	45	23	713	810
8284	X 15"		29	1.379		715	45	23	783	890
8286	X 16-1/2"		28	1.429		790	47	23.50	860.50	970
8288	X 18"		28	1.429		860	47	23.50	930.50	1,050
8290	X 19-1/2"		28	1.429		930	47	23.50	1,000.50	1,125
8292	X 21"		27	1.481		1,000	48.50	24.50	1,073	1,200
8294	X 22-1/2"		27	1.481		1,075	48.50	24.50	1,148	1,275
8296	X 24"		27	1.481		1,150	48.50	24.50	1,223	1,350
8298	X 25-1/2"		27	1.481		1,225	48.50	24.50	1,298	1,450
8300	X 27"		26	1.538		1,300	50.50	25.50	1,376	1,550
8302	X 28-1/2"		26	1.538		1,350	50.50	25.50	1,426	1,625
8304	X 30"		26	1.538		1,425	50.50	25.50	1,501	1,700
8400	40' span									
8402	3-1/8" x 9"	F-3	30	1.333	Ea.	266	43.50	22	331.50	390
8404	X 10-1/2"		30	1.333		310	43.50	22	375.50	440
8406	X 12"		30	1.333		355	43.50	22	420.50	490
8408	X 13-1/2"		30	1.333		400	43.50	22	465.50	540
8410	X 15"		29	1.379		445	45	23	513	585
8412	5-1/8" x 10-1/2"		30	1.333		510	43.50	22	575.50	660
8414	X 12"		30	1.333		580	43.50	22	645.50	740
8416	X 13-1/2"		30	1.333		655	43.50	22	720.50	820
8418	X 15"		29	1.379		725	45	23	793	900
8420	X 16-1/2"		29	1.379		800	45	23	868	980
8422	X 18"		29	1.379		870	45	23	938	1,050
8424	X 19-1/2"		29	1.379		945	45	23	1,013	1,150

06 18 Glued-Laminated Construction

06 18 13 – Glued-Laminated Beams

06 18 13.20 Laminated Framing		Crew	Daily Output	Labor-Hours	Unit	Material	2014 Bare Costs		Total	Total Incl O&P
							Labor	Equipment		
8426	X 21"	F-3	28	1.429	Ea.	1,025	47	23.50	1,095.50	1,225
8428	X 22-1/2"		28	1.429		1,100	47	23.50	1,170.50	1,300
8430	X 24"		28	1.429		1,150	47	23.50	1,220.50	1,375
8432	6-3/4" x 12"		29	1.379		765	45	23	833	940
8434	X 13-1/2"		29	1.379		860	45	23	928	1,050
8436	X 15"		29	1.379		955	45	23	1,023	1,150
8438	X 16-1/2"		28	1.429		1,050	47	23.50	1,120.50	1,250
8440	X 18"		28	1.429		1,150	47	23.50	1,220.50	1,350
8442	X 19-1/2"		28	1.429		1,250	47	23.50	1,320.50	1,475
8444	X 21"		27	1.481		1,350	48.50	24.50	1,423	1,575
8446	X 22-1/2"		27	1.481		1,425	48.50	24.50	1,498	1,675
8448	X 24"		27	1.481		1,525	48.50	24.50	1,598	1,775
8450	X 25-1/2"		27	1.481		1,625	48.50	24.50	1,698	1,875
8452	X 27"		26	1.538		1,725	50.50	25.50	1,801	2,025
8454	X 28-1/2"		26	1.538		1,825	50.50	25.50	1,901	2,125
8456	X 30"		26	1.538		1,900	50.50	25.50	1,976	2,225

06 22 Millwork

06 22 13 – Standard Pattern Wood Trim

06 22 13.15 Moldings, Base

		Crew	Daily Output	Labor-Hours	Unit	Material	Labor	Equipment	Total	Total Incl O&P
0010	**MOLDINGS, BASE**									
5100	Classic profile, 5/8" x 5-1/2", finger jointed and primed	1 Carp	250	.032	L.F.	1.39	1.14		2.53	3.45
5105	Poplar		240	.033		1.47	1.19		2.66	3.62
5110	Red oak		220	.036		2.15	1.30		3.45	4.55
5115	Maple		220	.036		3.40	1.30		4.70	5.95
5120	Cherry		220	.036		4.04	1.30		5.34	6.65
5125	3/4 x 7-1/2", finger jointed and primed		250	.032		1.76	1.14		2.90	3.85
5130	Poplar		240	.033		2.34	1.19		3.53	4.57
5135	Red oak		220	.036		3.12	1.30		4.42	5.60
5140	Maple		220	.036		4.52	1.30		5.82	7.15
5145	Cherry		220	.036		5.40	1.30		6.70	8.15
5150	Modern profile, 5/8" x 3-1/2", finger jointed and primed		250	.032		.93	1.14		2.07	2.94
5155	Poplar		240	.033		.93	1.19		2.12	3.02
5160	Red oak		220	.036		1.47	1.30		2.77	3.81
5165	Maple		220	.036		2.38	1.30		3.68	4.81
5170	Cherry		220	.036		2.57	1.30		3.87	5
5175	Ogee profile, 7/16" x 3", finger jointed and primed		250	.032		.56	1.14		1.70	2.53
5180	Poplar		240	.033		.61	1.19		1.80	2.67
5185	Red oak		220	.036		.82	1.30		2.12	3.09
5200	9/16" x 3-1/2", finger jointed and primed		250	.032		.62	1.14		1.76	2.60
5205	Pine		240	.033		1.44	1.19		2.63	3.58
5210	Red oak		220	.036		2.32	1.30		3.62	4.74
5215	9/16" x 4-1/2", red oak		220	.036		3.47	1.30		4.77	6
5220	5/8" x 3-1/2", finger jointed and primed		250	.032		.85	1.14		1.99	2.85
5225	Poplar		240	.033		.93	1.19		2.12	3.02
5230	Red oak		220	.036		1.47	1.30		2.77	3.81
5235	Maple		220	.036		2.38	1.30		3.68	4.81
5240	Cherry		220	.036		2.57	1.30		3.87	5
5245	5/8" x 4", finger jointed and primed		250	.032		1.10	1.14		2.24	3.13
5250	Poplar		240	.033		1.20	1.19		2.39	3.32
5255	Red oak		220	.036		1.65	1.30		2.95	4

06 22 Millwork

06 22 13 – Standard Pattern Wood Trim

06 22 13.15 Moldings, Base

		Crew	Daily Output	Labor-Hours	Unit	Material	2014 Bare Costs Labor	Equipment	Total	Total Incl O&P
5260	Maple	1 Carp	220	.036	L.F.	2.66	1.30		3.96	5.10
5265	Cherry		220	.036		2.79	1.30		4.09	5.25
5270	Rectangular profile, oak, 3/8" x 1-1/4"		260	.031		1.25	1.10		2.35	3.23
5275	1/2" x 2-1/2"		255	.031		1.91	1.12		3.03	3.99
5280	1/2" x 3-1/2"		250	.032		2.31	1.14		3.45	4.46
5285	1" x 6"		240	.033		3.64	1.19		4.83	6
5290	1" x 8"		240	.033		5.10	1.19		6.29	7.60
5295	Pine, 3/8" x 1-3/4"		260	.031		.62	1.10		1.72	2.53
5300	7/16" x 2-1/2"		255	.031		.90	1.12		2.02	2.88
5305	1" x 6"		240	.033		.88	1.19		2.07	2.97
5310	1" x 8"		240	.033		1.18	1.19		2.37	3.30
5315	Shoe, 1/2" x 3/4", primed		260	.031		.46	1.10		1.56	2.35
5320	Pine		240	.033		.37	1.19		1.56	2.41
5325	Poplar		240	.033		.36	1.19		1.55	2.39
5330	Red oak		220	.036		.47	1.30		1.77	2.71
5335	Maple		220	.036		.66	1.30		1.96	2.91
5340	Cherry		220	.036		.74	1.30		2.04	3
5345	11/16" x 1-1/2", pine		240	.033		.80	1.19		1.99	2.88
5350	Caps, 11/16" x 1-3/8", pine		240	.033		.84	1.19		2.03	2.92
5355	3/4" x 1-3/4", finger jointed and primed		260	.031		.67	1.10		1.77	2.59
5360	Poplar		240	.033		.94	1.19		2.13	3.03
5365	Red oak		220	.036		1.08	1.30		2.38	3.38
5370	Maple		220	.036		1.48	1.30		2.78	3.82
5375	Cherry		220	.036		3.12	1.30		4.42	5.60
5380	Combination base & shoe, 9/16" x 3-1/2" & 1/2" x 3/4", pine		125	.064		1.81	2.29		4.10	5.85
5385	Three piece oak, 6" high		80	.100		5.20	3.58		8.78	11.70
5390	Including 3/4" x 1" base shoe		70	.114		5.50	4.09		9.59	12.90
5395	Flooring cant strip, 3/4" x 3/4", pre-finished pine		260	.031		.47	1.10		1.57	2.37
5400	For pre-finished, stain and clear coat, add					.50			.50	.55
5405	Clear coat only, add					.40			.40	.44

06 22 13.30 Moldings, Casings

		Crew	Daily Output	Labor-Hours	Unit	Material	2014 Bare Costs Labor	Equipment	Total	Total Incl O&P
0010	**MOLDINGS, CASINGS**									
0085	Apron, 9/16" x 2-1/2", pine	1 Carp	250	.032	L.F.	1.58	1.14		2.72	3.66
0090	5/8" x 2-1/2", pine		250	.032		1.64	1.14		2.78	3.72
0110	5/8" x 3-1/2", pine		220	.036		2.45	1.30		3.75	4.88
0300	Band, 11/16" x 1-1/8", pine		270	.030		1	1.06		2.06	2.88
0310	11/16" x 1-1/2", finger jointed and primed		270	.030		.67	1.06		1.73	2.52
0320	Pine		270	.030		1.24	1.06		2.30	3.14
0330	11/16" x 1-3/4", finger jointed and primed		270	.030		.75	1.06		1.81	2.60
0350	Pine		270	.030		1.25	1.06		2.31	3.15
0355	Beaded, 3/4" x 3-1/2", finger jointed and primed		220	.036		1.04	1.30		2.34	3.33
0360	Poplar		220	.036		1.04	1.30		2.34	3.33
0365	Red oak		220	.036		1.47	1.30		2.77	3.81
0370	Maple		220	.036		2.38	1.30		3.68	4.81
0375	Cherry		220	.036		2.88	1.30		4.18	5.35
0380	3/4" x 4", finger jointed and primed		220	.036		1.10	1.30		2.40	3.40
0385	Poplar		220	.036		1.34	1.30		2.64	3.66
0390	Red oak		220	.036		1.80	1.30		3.10	4.17
0395	Maple		220	.036		2.48	1.30		3.78	4.92
0400	Cherry		220	.036		3.13	1.30		4.43	5.65
0405	3/4" x 5-1/2", finger jointed and primed		200	.040		1.07	1.43		2.50	3.59
0410	Poplar		200	.040		1.80	1.43		3.23	4.39

06 22 13 – Standard Pattern Wood Trim

06 22 13.30 Moldings, Casings		Crew	Daily Output	Labor-Hours	Unit	Material	2014 Bare Costs Labor	Equipment	Total	Total Incl O&P
0415	Red oak	1 Carp	200	.040	L.F.	2.53	1.43		3.96	5.20
0420	Maple		200	.040		3.49	1.43		4.92	6.25
0425	Cherry		200	.040		4.02	1.43		5.45	6.85
0430	Classic profile, 3/4" x 2-3/4", finger jointed and primed		250	.032		.73	1.14		1.87	2.72
0435	Poplar		250	.032		.93	1.14		2.07	2.94
0440	Red oak		250	.032		1.30	1.14		2.44	3.35
0445	Maple		250	.032		1.95	1.14		3.09	4.06
0450	Cherry		250	.032		2.21	1.14		3.35	4.35
0455	Fluted, 3/4" x 3-1/2", poplar		220	.036		1.04	1.30		2.34	3.33
0460	Red oak		220	.036		1.47	1.30		2.77	3.81
0465	Maple		220	.036		2.38	1.30		3.68	4.81
0470	Cherry		220	.036		2.88	1.30		4.18	5.35
0475	3/4" x 4", poplar		220	.036		1.34	1.30		2.64	3.66
0480	Red oak		220	.036		1.80	1.30		3.10	4.17
0485	Maple		220	.036		2.48	1.30		3.78	4.92
0490	Cherry		220	.036		3.13	1.30		4.43	5.65
0495	3/4" x 5-1/2", poplar		200	.040		1.80	1.43		3.23	4.39
0500	Red oak		200	.040		2.53	1.43		3.96	5.20
0505	Maple		200	.040		3.49	1.43		4.92	6.25
0510	Cherry		200	.040		4.02	1.43		5.45	6.85
0515	3/4" x 7-1/2", poplar		190	.042		1.27	1.51		2.78	3.92
0520	Red oak		190	.042		3.50	1.51		5.01	6.40
0525	Maple		190	.042		5.30	1.51		6.81	8.35
0530	Cherry		190	.042		6.30	1.51		7.81	9.50
0535	3/4" x 9-1/2", poplar		180	.044		3.85	1.59		5.44	6.90
0540	Red oak		180	.044		5.85	1.59		7.44	9.10
0545	Maple		180	.044		8.40	1.59		9.99	11.90
0550	Cherry		180	.044		9.15	1.59		10.74	12.70
0555	Modern profile, 9/16" x 2-1/4", poplar		250	.032		.53	1.14		1.67	2.50
0560	Red oak		250	.032		.69	1.14		1.83	2.68
0565	11/16" x 2-1/2", finger jointed & primed		250	.032		.72	1.14		1.86	2.71
0570	Pine		250	.032		1.55	1.14		2.69	3.62
0575	3/4" x 2-1/2", poplar		250	.032		.82	1.14		1.96	2.82
0580	Red oak		250	.032		1.06	1.14		2.20	3.08
0585	Maple		250	.032		1.68	1.14		2.82	3.77
0590	Cherry		250	.032		2.12	1.14		3.26	4.25
0595	Mullion, 5/16" x 2", pine		270	.030		.99	1.06		2.05	2.87
0600	9/16" x 2-1/2", fingerjointed and primed		250	.032		.83	1.14		1.97	2.83
0605	Pine		250	.032		1.64	1.14		2.78	3.72
0610	Red oak		250	.032		2.80	1.14		3.94	5
0615	1-1/16" x 3-3/4", red oak		220	.036		6.85	1.30		8.15	9.70
0620	Ogee, 7/16" x 2-1/2", poplar		250	.032		.51	1.14		1.65	2.48
0625	Red oak		250	.032		.67	1.14		1.81	2.66
0630	9/16" x 2-1/4", finger jointed and primed		250	.032		.47	1.14		1.61	2.44
0635	Poplar		250	.032		.53	1.14		1.67	2.50
0640	Red oak		250	.032		.69	1.14		1.83	2.68
0645	11/16" x 2-1/2", finger jointed and primed		250	.032		.67	1.14		1.81	2.66
0700	Pine		250	.032		1.52	1.14		2.66	3.59
0701	Red oak		250	.032		2.59	1.14		3.73	4.77
0730	11/16" x 3-1/2", finger jointed and primed		220	.036		2.12	1.30		3.42	4.52
0750	Pine		220	.036		2.18	1.30		3.48	4.59
0755	3/4" x 2-1/2", finger jointed and primed		250	.032		.67	1.14		1.81	2.66
0760	Poplar		250	.032		.82	1.14		1.96	2.82

06 22 Millwork

06 22 13 – Standard Pattern Wood Trim

06 22 13.30 Moldings, Casings

		Crew	Daily Output	Labor-Hours	Unit	Material	2014 Bare Costs Labor	Equipment	Total	Total Incl O&P
0765	Red oak	1 Carp	250	.032	L.F.	1.06	1.14		2.20	3.08
0770	Maple		250	.032		1.68	1.14		2.82	3.77
0775	Cherry		250	.032		2.12	1.14		3.26	4.25
0780	3/4" x 3-1/2", finger jointed and primed		220	.036		.85	1.30		2.15	3.12
0785	Poplar		220	.036		1.04	1.30		2.34	3.33
0790	Red oak		220	.036		1.47	1.30		2.77	3.81
0795	Maple		220	.036		2.38	1.30		3.68	4.81
0800	Cherry		220	.036		2.88	1.30		4.18	5.35
4700	Square profile, 1" x 1", teak		215	.037		2.01	1.33		3.34	4.45
4800	Rectangular profile, 1" x 3", teak		200	.040		6	1.43		7.43	9

06 22 13.35 Moldings, Ceilings

		Crew	Daily Output	Labor-Hours	Unit	Material	2014 Bare Costs Labor	Equipment	Total	Total Incl O&P
0010	**MOLDINGS, CEILINGS**									
0600	Bed, 9/16" x 1-3/4", pine	1 Carp	270	.030	L.F.	1.20	1.06		2.26	3.10
0650	9/16" x 2", pine		270	.030		1.43	1.06		2.49	3.35
0710	9/16" x 1-3/4", oak		270	.030		1.96	1.06		3.02	3.93
1200	Cornice, 9/16" x 1-3/4", pine		270	.030		1.21	1.06		2.27	3.11
1300	9/16" x 2-1/4", pine		265	.030		1.47	1.08		2.55	3.43
1350	Cove, 1/2" x 2-1/4", poplar		265	.030		.92	1.08		2	2.83
1360	Red oak		265	.030		1.18	1.08		2.26	3.11
1370	Hard maple		265	.030		1.69	1.08		2.77	3.68
1380	Cherry		265	.030		2.07	1.08		3.15	4.09
2400	9/16" x 1-3/4", pine		270	.030		1.12	1.06		2.18	3.01
2500	11/16" x 2-3/4", pine		265	.030		2.21	1.08		3.29	4.25
2510	Crown, 5/8" x 5/8", poplar		300	.027		.41	.95		1.36	2.05
2520	Red oak		300	.027		.46	.95		1.41	2.10
2530	Hard maple		300	.027		.66	.95		1.61	2.32
2540	Cherry		300	.027		.70	.95		1.65	2.37
2600	9/16" x 3-5/8", pine		250	.032		2.70	1.14		3.84	4.89
2700	11/16" x 4-1/4", pine		250	.032		4.55	1.14		5.69	6.90
2705	Oak		250	.032		6.30	1.14		7.44	8.85
2710	3/4" x 1-3/4", poplar		270	.030		.65	1.06		1.71	2.49
2720	Red oak		270	.030		.91	1.06		1.97	2.78
2730	Hard maple		270	.030		1.26	1.06		2.32	3.16
2740	Cherry		270	.030		1.55	1.06		2.61	3.48
2750	3/4" x 2", poplar		270	.030		.85	1.06		1.91	2.71
2760	Red oak		270	.030		1.10	1.06		2.16	2.99
2770	Hard maple		270	.030		1.52	1.06		2.58	3.45
2780	Cherry		270	.030		1.70	1.06		2.76	3.65
2790	3/4" x 2-3/4", poplar		265	.030		.92	1.08		2	2.83
2800	Red oak		265	.030		1.36	1.08		2.44	3.31
2810	Hard maple		265	.030		1.89	1.08		2.97	3.90
2820	Cherry		265	.030		2.18	1.08		3.26	4.21
2830	3/4" x 3-1/2", poplar		250	.032		1.18	1.14		2.32	3.21
2840	Red oak		250	.032		1.70	1.14		2.84	3.79
2850	Hard maple		250	.032		2.32	1.14		3.46	4.47
2860	Cherry		250	.032		2.72	1.14		3.86	4.91
2870	FJP poplar		250	.032		.84	1.14		1.98	2.84
2880	3/4" x 5", poplar		245	.033		1.75	1.17		2.92	3.88
2890	Red oak		245	.033		2.47	1.17		3.64	4.67
2900	Hard maple		245	.033		3.40	1.17		4.57	5.70
2910	Cherry		245	.033		3.92	1.17		5.09	6.25
2920	FJP poplar		245	.033		1.19	1.17		2.36	3.27

06 22 13.35 Moldings, Ceilings

		Crew	Daily Output	Labor-Hours	Unit	Material	2014 Bare Costs Labor	Equipment	Total	Total Incl O&P
2930	3/4" x 6-1/4", poplar	1 Carp	240	.033	L.F.	2.09	1.19		3.28	4.29
2940	Red oak		240	.033		3	1.19		4.19	5.30
2950	Hard maple		240	.033		4.11	1.19		5.30	6.50
2960	Cherry		240	.033		4.87	1.19		6.06	7.35
2970	7/8" x 8-3/4", poplar		220	.036		3.24	1.30		4.54	5.75
2980	Red oak		220	.036		4.71	1.30		6.01	7.40
2990	Hard maple		220	.036		6.80	1.30		8.10	9.70
3000	Cherry		220	.036		7.80	1.30		9.10	10.75
3010	1" x 7-1/4", poplar		220	.036		3.43	1.30		4.73	5.95
3020	Red oak		220	.036		5.10	1.30		6.40	7.80
3030	Hard maple		220	.036		7.40	1.30		8.70	10.30
3040	Cherry		220	.036		8.60	1.30		9.90	11.70
3050	1-1/16" x 4-1/4", poplar		250	.032		2.08	1.14		3.22	4.20
3060	Red oak		250	.032		2.33	1.14		3.47	4.48
3070	Hard maple		250	.032		3.22	1.14		4.36	5.45
3080	Cherry		250	.032		4.60	1.14		5.74	6.95
3090	Dentil crown, 3/4" x 5", poplar		250	.032		1.75	1.14		2.89	3.84
3100	Red oak		250	.032		2.47	1.14		3.61	4.63
3110	Hard maple		250	.032		3.30	1.14		4.44	5.55
3120	Cherry		250	.032		3.92	1.14		5.06	6.25
3130	Dentil piece for above, 1/2" x 1/2", poplar		300	.027		2.48	.95		3.43	4.32
3140	Red oak		300	.027		2.72	.95		3.67	4.59
3150	Hard maple		300	.027		3.23	.95		4.18	5.15
3160	Cherry		300	.027		3.52	.95		4.47	5.45

06 22 13.40 Moldings, Exterior

		Crew	Daily Output	Labor-Hours	Unit	Material	2014 Bare Costs Labor	Equipment	Total	Total Incl O&P
0010	**MOLDINGS, EXTERIOR**									
0100	Band board, cedar, rough sawn, 1" x 2"	1 Carp	300	.027	L.F.	.54	.95		1.49	2.20
0110	1" x 3"		300	.027		.81	.95		1.76	2.49
0120	1" x 4"		250	.032		1.07	1.14		2.21	3.10
0130	1" x 6"		250	.032		1.61	1.14		2.75	3.69
0140	1" x 8"		225	.036		2.15	1.27		3.42	4.51
0150	1" x 10"		225	.036		2.67	1.27		3.94	5.10
0160	1" x 12"		200	.040		3.21	1.43		4.64	5.95
0240	STK, 1" x 2"		300	.027		.43	.95		1.38	2.08
0250	1" x 3"		300	.027		.48	.95		1.43	2.12
0260	1" x 4"		250	.032		.62	1.14		1.76	2.60
0270	1" x 6"		250	.032		.96	1.14		2.10	2.97
0280	1" x 8"		225	.036		1.41	1.27		2.68	3.69
0290	1" x 10"		225	.036		2.08	1.27		3.35	4.43
0300	1" x 12"		200	.040		3.21	1.43		4.64	5.95
0310	Pine, #2, 1" x 2"		300	.027		.25	.95		1.20	1.88
0320	1" x 3"		300	.027		.40	.95		1.35	2.04
0330	1" x 4"		250	.032		.49	1.14		1.63	2.46
0340	1" x 6"		250	.032		.83	1.14		1.97	2.83
0350	1" x 8"		225	.036		1.22	1.27		2.49	3.48
0360	1" x 10"		225	.036		1.59	1.27		2.86	3.89
0370	1" x 12"		200	.040		2.05	1.43		3.48	4.66
0380	D & better, 1" x 2"		300	.027		.41	.95		1.36	2.06
0390	1" x 3"		300	.027		.61	.95		1.56	2.28
0400	1" x 4"		250	.032		.82	1.14		1.96	2.82
0410	1" x 6"		250	.032		1.12	1.14		2.26	3.15
0420	1" x 8"		225	.036		1.62	1.27		2.89	3.92

06 22 Millwork

06 22 13 – Standard Pattern Wood Trim

06 22 13.40 Moldings, Exterior	Crew	Daily Output	Labor-Hours	Unit	Material	2014 Bare Costs Labor	Equipment	Total	Total Incl O&P
0430	1" x 10"	1 Carp	225	.036	L.F.	2.03	1.27		3.30	4.38
0440	1" x 12"		200	.040		2.63	1.43		4.06	5.30
0450	Redwood, clear all heart, 1" x 2"		300	.027		.63	.95		1.58	2.30
0460	1" x 3"		300	.027		.94	.95		1.89	2.64
0470	1" x 4"		250	.032		1.19	1.14		2.33	3.23
0480	1" x 6"		252	.032		1.78	1.14		2.92	3.87
0490	1" x 8"		225	.036		2.36	1.27		3.63	4.73
0500	1" x 10"		225	.036		3.96	1.27		5.23	6.50
0510	1" x 12"		200	.040		4.75	1.43		6.18	7.65
0530	Corner board, cedar, rough sawn, 1" x 2"		225	.036		.54	1.27		1.81	2.74
0540	1" x 3"		225	.036		.81	1.27		2.08	3.03
0550	1" x 4"		200	.040		1.07	1.43		2.50	3.59
0560	1" x 6"		200	.040		1.61	1.43		3.04	4.18
0570	1" x 8"		200	.040		2.15	1.43		3.58	4.78
0580	1" x 10"		175	.046		2.67	1.63		4.30	5.70
0590	1" x 12"		175	.046		3.21	1.63		4.84	6.30
0670	STK, 1" x 2"		225	.036		.43	1.27		1.70	2.62
0680	1" x 3"		225	.036		.48	1.27		1.75	2.66
0690	1" x 4"		200	.040		.60	1.43		2.03	3.07
0700	1" x 6"		200	.040		.96	1.43		2.39	3.46
0710	1" x 8"		200	.040		1.41	1.43		2.84	3.96
0720	1" x 10"		175	.046		2.08	1.63		3.71	5.05
0730	1" x 12"		175	.046		3.21	1.63		4.84	6.30
0740	Pine, #2, 1" x 2"		225	.036		.25	1.27		1.52	2.42
0750	1" x 3"		225	.036		.40	1.27		1.67	2.58
0760	1" x 4"		200	.040		.49	1.43		1.92	2.95
0770	1" x 6"		200	.040		.83	1.43		2.26	3.32
0780	1" x 8"		200	.040		1.22	1.43		2.65	3.75
0790	1" x 10"		175	.046		1.59	1.63		3.22	4.50
0800	1" x 12"		175	.046		2.05	1.63		3.68	5
0810	D & better, 1" x 2"		225	.036		.41	1.27		1.68	2.60
0820	1" x 3"		225	.036		.61	1.27		1.88	2.82
0830	1" x 4"		200	.040		.82	1.43		2.25	3.31
0840	1" x 6"		200	.040		1.12	1.43		2.55	3.64
0850	1" x 8"		200	.040		1.62	1.43		3.05	4.19
0860	1" x 10"		175	.046		2.03	1.63		3.66	4.99
0870	1" x 12"		175	.046		2.63	1.63		4.26	5.65
0880	Redwood, clear all heart, 1" x 2"		225	.036		.63	1.27		1.90	2.84
0890	1" x 3"		225	.036		.94	1.27		2.21	3.18
0900	1" x 4"		200	.040		1.19	1.43		2.62	3.72
0910	1" x 6"		200	.040		1.78	1.43		3.21	4.37
0920	1" x 8"		200	.040		2.36	1.43		3.79	5
0930	1" x 10"		175	.046		3.96	1.63		5.59	7.10
0940	1" x 12"		175	.046		4.75	1.63		6.38	8
0950	Cornice board, cedar, rough sawn, 1" x 2"		330	.024		.54	.87		1.41	2.06
0960	1" x 3"		290	.028		.81	.99		1.80	2.55
0970	1" x 4"		250	.032		1.07	1.14		2.21	3.10
0980	1" x 6"		250	.032		1.61	1.14		2.75	3.69
0990	1" x 8"		200	.040		2.15	1.43		3.58	4.78
1000	1" x 10"		180	.044		2.67	1.59		4.26	5.60
1010	1" x 12"		180	.044		3.21	1.59		4.80	6.20
1020	STK, 1" x 2"		330	.024		.43	.87		1.30	1.94
1030	1" x 3"		290	.028		.48	.99		1.47	2.18

06 22 13 – Standard Pattern Wood Trim

06 22 13.40 Moldings, Exterior		Crew	Daily Output	Labor-Hours	Unit	Material	2014 Bare Costs Labor	Equipment	Total	Total Incl O&P
1040	1" x 4"	1 Carp	250	.032	L.F.	.62	1.14		1.76	2.60
1050	1" x 6"		250	.032		.96	1.14		2.10	2.97
1060	1" x 8"		200	.040		1.41	1.43		2.84	3.96
1070	1" x 10"		180	.044		2.08	1.59		3.67	4.96
1080	1" x 12"		180	.044		3.21	1.59		4.80	6.20
1500	Pine, #2, 1" x 2"		330	.024		.25	.87		1.12	1.74
1510	1" x 3"		290	.028		.27	.99		1.26	1.96
1600	1" x 4"		250	.032		.49	1.14		1.63	2.46
1700	1" x 6"		250	.032		.83	1.14		1.97	2.83
1800	1" x 8"		200	.040		1.22	1.43		2.65	3.75
1900	1" x 10"		180	.044		1.59	1.59		3.18	4.42
2000	1" x 12"		180	.044		2.05	1.59		3.64	4.92
2020	D & better, 1" x 2"		330	.024		.41	.87		1.28	1.92
2030	1" x 3"		290	.028		.61	.99		1.60	2.34
2040	1" x 4"		250	.032		.82	1.14		1.96	2.82
2050	1" x 6"		250	.032		1.12	1.14		2.26	3.15
2060	1" x 8"		200	.040		1.62	1.43		3.05	4.19
2070	1" x 10"		180	.044		2.03	1.59		3.62	4.91
2080	1" x 12"		180	.044		2.63	1.59		4.22	5.55
2090	Redwood, clear all heart, 1" x 2"		330	.024		.63	.87		1.50	2.16
2100	1" x 3"		290	.028		.94	.99		1.93	2.70
2110	1" x 4"		250	.032		1.19	1.14		2.33	3.23
2120	1" x 6"		250	.032		1.78	1.14		2.92	3.88
2130	1" x 8"		200	.040		2.36	1.43		3.79	5
2140	1" x 10"		180	.044		3.96	1.59		5.55	7.05
2150	1" x 12"		180	.044		4.75	1.59		6.34	7.90
2160	3 piece, 1" x 2", 1" x 4", 1" x 6", rough sawn cedar		80	.100		3.24	3.58		6.82	9.55
2180	STK cedar		80	.100		2.01	3.58		5.59	8.20
2200	#2 pine		80	.100		1.57	3.58		5.15	7.75
2210	D & better pine		80	.100		2.35	3.58		5.93	8.60
2220	Clear all heart redwood		80	.100		3.60	3.58		7.18	9.95
2230	1" x 8", 1" x 10", 1" x 12", rough sawn cedar		65	.123		8	4.40		12.40	16.20
2240	STK cedar		65	.123		6.65	4.40		11.05	14.75
2300	#2 pine		65	.123		4.83	4.40		9.23	12.70
2320	D & better pine		65	.123		6.25	4.40		10.65	14.30
2330	Clear all heart redwood		65	.123		11.05	4.40		15.45	19.55
2340	Door/window casing, cedar, rough sawn, 1" x 2"		275	.029		.54	1.04		1.58	2.35
2350	1" x 3"		275	.029		.81	1.04		1.85	2.64
2360	1" x 4"		250	.032		1.07	1.14		2.21	3.10
2370	1" x 6"		250	.032		1.61	1.14		2.75	3.69
2380	1" x 8"		230	.035		2.15	1.24		3.39	4.46
2390	1" x 10"		230	.035		2.67	1.24		3.91	5.05
2395	1" x 12"		210	.038		3.21	1.36		4.57	5.80
2410	STK, 1" x 2"		275	.029		.43	1.04		1.47	2.23
2420	1" x 3"		275	.029		.48	1.04		1.52	2.27
2430	1" x 4"		250	.032		.62	1.14		1.76	2.60
2440	1" x 6"		250	.032		.96	1.14		2.10	2.97
2450	1" x 8"		230	.035		1.41	1.24		2.65	3.64
2460	1" x 10"		230	.035		2.08	1.24		3.32	4.38
2470	1" x 12"		210	.038		3.21	1.36		4.57	5.80
2550	Pine, #2, 1" x 2"		275	.029		.25	1.04		1.29	2.03
2560	1" x 3"		275	.029		.40	1.04		1.44	2.19
2570	1" x 4"		250	.032		.49	1.14		1.63	2.46

06 22 13 – Standard Pattern Wood Trim

06 22 13.40 Moldings, Exterior		Crew	Daily Output	Labor-Hours	Unit	Material	2014 Bare Costs Labor	Equipment	Total	Total Incl O&P
2580	1" x 6"	1 Carp	250	.032	L.F.	.83	1.14		1.97	2.83
2590	1" x 8"		230	.035		1.22	1.24		2.46	3.43
2600	1" x 10"		230	.035		1.59	1.24		2.83	3.84
2610	1" x 12"		210	.038		2.05	1.36		3.41	4.54
2620	Pine, D & better, 1" x 2"		275	.029		.41	1.04		1.45	2.21
2630	1" x 3"		275	.029		.61	1.04		1.65	2.43
2640	1" x 4"		250	.032		.82	1.14		1.96	2.82
2650	1" x 6"		250	.032		1.12	1.14		2.26	3.15
2660	1" x 8"		230	.035		1.62	1.24		2.86	3.87
2670	1" x 10"		230	.035		2.03	1.24		3.27	4.33
2680	1" x 12"		210	.038		2.63	1.36		3.99	5.20
2690	Redwood, clear all heart, 1" x 2"		275	.029		.63	1.04		1.67	2.45
2695	1" x 3"		275	.029		.94	1.04		1.98	2.79
2710	1" x 4"		250	.032		1.19	1.14		2.33	3.23
2715	1" x 6"		250	.032		1.78	1.14		2.92	3.88
2730	1" x 8"		230	.035		2.36	1.24		3.60	4.68
2740	1" x 10"		230	.035		3.96	1.24		5.20	6.45
2750	1" x 12"		210	.038		4.75	1.36		6.11	7.55
3500	Bellyband, 11/16" x 4-1/4"		250	.032		3.23	1.14		4.37	5.45
3610	Brickmold, pine, 1-1/4" x 2"		200	.040		2.50	1.43		3.93	5.15
3620	FJP, 1-1/4" x 2"		200	.040		1.06	1.43		2.49	3.58
5100	Fascia, cedar, rough sawn, 1" x 2"		275	.029		.54	1.04		1.58	2.35
5110	1" x 3"		275	.029		.81	1.04		1.85	2.64
5120	1" x 4"		250	.032		1.07	1.14		2.21	3.10
5200	1" x 6"		250	.032		1.61	1.14		2.75	3.69
5300	1" x 8"		230	.035		2.15	1.24		3.39	4.46
5310	1" x 10"		230	.035		2.67	1.24		3.91	5.05
5320	1" x 12"		210	.038		3.21	1.36		4.57	5.80
5400	2" x 4"		220	.036		1.05	1.30		2.35	3.35
5500	2" x 6"		220	.036		1.58	1.30		2.88	3.93
5600	2" x 8"		200	.040		2.11	1.43		3.54	4.73
5700	2" x 10"		180	.044		2.62	1.59		4.21	5.55
5800	2" x 12"		170	.047		6.25	1.68		7.93	9.75
6120	STK, 1" x 2"		275	.029		.43	1.04		1.47	2.23
6130	1" x 3"		275	.029		.48	1.04		1.52	2.27
6140	1" x 4"		250	.032		.62	1.14		1.76	2.60
6150	1" x 6"		250	.032		.96	1.14		2.10	2.97
6160	1" x 8"		230	.035		1.41	1.24		2.65	3.64
6170	1" x 10"		230	.035		2.08	1.24		3.32	4.38
6180	1" x 12"		210	.038		3.21	1.36		4.57	5.80
6185	2" x 2"		260	.031		.56	1.10		1.66	2.47
6190	Pine, #2, 1" x 2"		275	.029		.25	1.04		1.29	2.03
6200	1" x 3"		275	.029		.40	1.04		1.44	2.19
6210	1" x 4"		250	.032		.49	1.14		1.63	2.46
6220	1" x 6"		250	.032		.83	1.14		1.97	2.83
6230	1" x 8"		230	.035		1.22	1.24		2.46	3.43
6240	1" x 10"		230	.035		1.59	1.24		2.83	3.84
6250	1" x 12"		210	.038		2.05	1.36		3.41	4.54
6260	D & better, 1" x 2"		275	.029		.41	1.04		1.45	2.21
6270	1" x 3"		275	.029		.61	1.04		1.65	2.43
6280	1" x 4"		250	.032		.82	1.14		1.96	2.82
6290	1" x 6"		250	.032		1.12	1.14		2.26	3.15
6300	1" x 8"		230	.035		1.62	1.24		2.86	3.87

06 22 13.40 Moldings, Exterior		Crew	Daily Output	Labor-Hours	Unit	Material	2014 Bare Costs Labor	Equipment	Total	Total Incl O&P
6310	1" x 10"	1 Carp	230	.035	L.F.	2.03	1.24		3.27	4.33
6312	1" x 12"		210	.038		2.63	1.36		3.99	5.20
6330	Southern yellow, 1-1/4" x 5"		240	.033		2.27	1.19		3.46	4.49
6340	1-1/4" x 6"		240	.033		2.52	1.19		3.71	4.77
6350	1-1/4" x 8"		215	.037		3.43	1.33		4.76	6
6360	1-1/4" x 12"		190	.042		5.05	1.51		6.56	8.10
6370	Redwood, clear all heart, 1" x 2"		275	.029		.63	1.04		1.67	2.45
6380	1" x 3"		275	.029		1.19	1.04		2.23	3.06
6390	1" x 4"		250	.032		1.19	1.14		2.33	3.23
6400	1" x 6"		250	.032		1.78	1.14		2.92	3.88
6410	1" x 8"		230	.035		2.36	1.24		3.60	4.68
6420	1" x 10"		230	.035		3.96	1.24		5.20	6.45
6430	1" x 12"		210	.038		4.75	1.36		6.11	7.55
6440	1-1/4" x 5"		240	.033		1.86	1.19		3.05	4.04
6450	1-1/4" x 6"		240	.033		2.22	1.19		3.41	4.44
6460	1-1/4" x 8"		215	.037		3.53	1.33		4.86	6.10
6470	1-1/4" x 12"		190	.042		7.10	1.51		8.61	10.40
6580	Frieze, cedar, rough sawn, 1" x 2"		275	.029		.54	1.04		1.58	2.35
6590	1" x 3"		275	.029		.81	1.04		1.85	2.64
6600	1" x 4"		250	.032		1.07	1.14		2.21	3.10
6610	1" x 6"		250	.032		1.61	1.14		2.75	3.69
6620	1" x 8"		250	.032		2.15	1.14		3.29	4.29
6630	1" x 10"		225	.036		2.67	1.27		3.94	5.10
6640	1" x 12"		200	.040		3.18	1.43		4.61	5.90
6650	STK, 1" x 2"		275	.029		.43	1.04		1.47	2.23
6660	1" x 3"		275	.029		.48	1.04		1.52	2.27
6670	1" x 4"		250	.032		.62	1.14		1.76	2.60
6680	1" x 6"		250	.032		.96	1.14		2.10	2.97
6690	1" x 8"		250	.032		1.41	1.14		2.55	3.47
6700	1" x 10"		225	.036		2.08	1.27		3.35	4.43
6710	1" x 12"		200	.040		3.21	1.43		4.64	5.95
6790	Pine, #2, 1" x 2"		275	.029		.25	1.04		1.29	2.03
6800	1" x 3"		275	.029		.40	1.04		1.44	2.19
6810	1" x 4"		250	.032		.49	1.14		1.63	2.46
6820	1" x 6"		250	.032		.83	1.14		1.97	2.83
6830	1" x 8"		250	.032		1.22	1.14		2.36	3.26
6840	1" x 10"		225	.036		1.59	1.27		2.86	3.89
6850	1" x 12"		200	.040		2.05	1.43		3.48	4.66
6860	D & better, 1" x 2"		275	.029		.41	1.04		1.45	2.21
6870	1" x 3"		275	.029		.61	1.04		1.65	2.43
6880	1" x 4"		250	.032		.82	1.14		1.96	2.82
6890	1" x 6"		250	.032		1.12	1.14		2.26	3.15
6900	1" x 8"		250	.032		1.62	1.14		2.76	3.70
6910	1" x 10"		225	.036		2.03	1.27		3.30	4.38
6920	1" x 12"		200	.040		2.63	1.43		4.06	5.30
6930	Redwood, clear all heart, 1" x 2"		275	.029		.63	1.04		1.67	2.45
6940	1" x 3"		275	.029		.94	1.04		1.98	2.79
6950	1" x 4"		250	.032		1.19	1.14		2.33	3.23
6960	1" x 6"		250	.032		1.78	1.14		2.92	3.88
6970	1" x 8"		250	.032		2.36	1.14		3.50	4.51
6980	1" x 10"		225	.036		3.96	1.27		5.23	6.50
6990	1" x 12"		200	.040		4.75	1.43		6.18	7.65
7000	Grounds, 1" x 1", cedar, rough sawn		300	.027		.28	.95		1.23	1.90

06 22 13 – Standard Pattern Wood Trim

06 22 13.40 Moldings, Exterior		Crew	Daily Output	Labor-Hours	Unit	Material	2014 Bare Costs Labor	Equipment	Total	Total Incl O&P
7010	STK	1 Carp	300	.027	L.F.	.27	.95		1.22	1.89
7020	Pine, #2		300	.027		.16	.95		1.11	1.77
7030	D & better		300	.027		.25	.95		1.20	1.88
7050	Redwood		300	.027		.39	.95		1.34	2.02
7060	Rake/verge board, cedar, rough sawn, 1" x 2"		225	.036		.54	1.27		1.81	2.74
7070	1" x 3"		225	.036		.81	1.27		2.08	3.03
7080	1" x 4"		200	.040		1.07	1.43		2.50	3.59
7090	1" x 6"		200	.040		1.61	1.43		3.04	4.18
7100	1" x 8"		190	.042		2.15	1.51		3.66	4.90
7110	1" x 10"		190	.042		2.67	1.51		4.18	5.45
7120	1" x 12"		180	.044		3.21	1.59		4.80	6.20
7130	STK, 1" x 2"		225	.036		.43	1.27		1.70	2.62
7140	1" x 3"		225	.036		.48	1.27		1.75	2.66
7150	1" x 4"		200	.040		.62	1.43		2.05	3.09
7160	1" x 6"		200	.040		.96	1.43		2.39	3.46
7170	1" x 8"		190	.042		1.41	1.51		2.92	4.08
7180	1" x 10"		190	.042		2.08	1.51		3.59	4.82
7190	1" x 12"		180	.044		3.21	1.59		4.80	6.20
7200	Pine, #2, 1" x 2"		225	.036		.25	1.27		1.52	2.42
7210	1" x 3"		225	.036		.40	1.27		1.67	2.58
7220	1" x 4"		200	.040		.49	1.43		1.92	2.95
7230	1" x 6"		200	.040		.83	1.43		2.26	3.32
7240	1" x 8"		190	.042		1.22	1.51		2.73	3.87
7250	1" x 10"		190	.042		1.59	1.51		3.10	4.28
7260	1" x 12"		180	.044		2.05	1.59		3.64	4.92
7340	D & better, 1" x 2"		225	.036		.41	1.27		1.68	2.60
7350	1" x 3"		225	.036		.61	1.27		1.88	2.82
7360	1" x 4"		200	.040		.82	1.43		2.25	3.31
7370	1" x 6"		200	.040		1.12	1.43		2.55	3.64
7380	1" x 8"		190	.042		1.62	1.51		3.13	4.31
7390	1" x 10"		190	.042		2.03	1.51		3.54	4.77
7400	1" x 12"		180	.044		2.63	1.59		4.22	5.55
7410	Redwood, clear all heart, 1" x 2"		225	.036		.63	1.27		1.90	2.84
7420	1" x 3"		225	.036		.94	1.27		2.21	3.18
7430	1" x 4"		200	.040		1.19	1.43		2.62	3.72
7440	1" x 6"		200	.040		1.78	1.43		3.21	4.37
7450	1" x 8"		190	.042		2.36	1.51		3.87	5.10
7460	1" x 10"		190	.042		3.96	1.51		5.47	6.90
7470	1" x 12"		180	.044		4.75	1.59		6.34	7.90
7480	2" x 4"		200	.040		2.29	1.43		3.72	4.93
7490	2" x 6"		182	.044		3.43	1.57		5	6.40
7500	2" x 8"		165	.048		4.56	1.73		6.29	7.90
7630	Soffit, cedar, rough sawn, 1" x 2"	2 Carp	440	.036		.54	1.30		1.84	2.79
7640	1" x 3"		440	.036		.81	1.30		2.11	3.08
7650	1" x 4"		420	.038		1.07	1.36		2.43	3.47
7660	1" x 6"		420	.038		1.61	1.36		2.97	4.06
7670	1" x 8"		420	.038		2.15	1.36		3.51	4.66
7680	1" x 10"		400	.040		2.67	1.43		4.10	5.35
7690	1" x 12"		400	.040		3.21	1.43		4.64	5.95
7700	STK, 1" x 2"		440	.036		.43	1.30		1.73	2.67
7710	1" x 3"		440	.036		.48	1.30		1.78	2.71
7720	1" x 4"		420	.038		.62	1.36		1.98	2.97
7730	1" x 6"		420	.038		.96	1.36		2.32	3.34

06 22 13.40 Moldings, Exterior

		Crew	Daily Output	Labor-Hours	Unit	Material	2014 Bare Costs Labor	Equipment	Total	Total Incl O&P
7740	1" x 8"	2 Carp	420	.038	L.F.	1.41	1.36		2.77	3.84
7750	1" x 10"		400	.040		2.08	1.43		3.51	4.70
7760	1" x 12"		400	.040		3.21	1.43		4.64	5.95
7770	Pine, #2, 1" x 2"		440	.036		.25	1.30		1.55	2.47
7780	1" x 3"		440	.036		.40	1.30		1.70	2.63
7790	1" x 4"		420	.038		.49	1.36		1.85	2.83
7800	1" x 6"		420	.038		.83	1.36		2.19	3.20
7810	1" x 8"		420	.038		1.22	1.36		2.58	3.63
7820	1" x 10"		400	.040		1.59	1.43		3.02	4.16
7830	1" x 12"		400	.040		2.05	1.43		3.48	4.66
7840	D & better, 1" x 2"		440	.036		.41	1.30		1.71	2.65
7850	1" x 3"		440	.036		.61	1.30		1.91	2.87
7860	1" x 4"		420	.038		.82	1.36		2.18	3.19
7870	1" x 6"		420	.038		1.12	1.36		2.48	3.52
7880	1" x 8"		420	.038		1.62	1.36		2.98	4.07
7890	1" x 10"		400	.040		2.03	1.43		3.46	4.65
7900	1" x 12"		400	.040		2.63	1.43		4.06	5.30
7910	Redwood, clear all heart, 1" x 2"		440	.036		.63	1.30		1.93	2.89
7920	1" x 3"		440	.036		.94	1.30		2.24	3.23
7930	1" x 4"		420	.038		1.19	1.36		2.55	3.60
7940	1" x 6"		420	.038		1.78	1.36		3.14	4.25
7950	1" x 8"		420	.038		2.36	1.36		3.72	4.88
7960	1" x 10"		400	.040		3.96	1.43		5.39	6.75
7970	1" x 12"		400	.040		4.75	1.43		6.18	7.65
8050	Trim, crown molding, pine, 11/16" x 4-1/4"	1 Carp	250	.032		4.54	1.14		5.68	6.90
8060	Back band, 11/16" x 1-1/16"		250	.032		.99	1.14		2.13	3.01
8070	Insect screen frame stock, 1-1/16" x 1-3/4"		395	.020		2.39	.72		3.11	3.85
8080	Dentils, 2-1/2" x 2-1/2" x 4", 6" O.C.		30	.267		1.22	9.55		10.77	17.40
8100	Fluted, 5-1/2"		165	.048		4.52	1.73		6.25	7.90
8110	Stucco bead, 1-3/8" x 1-5/8"		250	.032		2.50	1.14		3.64	4.67

06 22 13.45 Moldings, Trim

		Crew	Daily Output	Labor-Hours	Unit	Material	2014 Bare Costs Labor	Equipment	Total	Total Incl O&P
0010	**MOLDINGS, TRIM**									
0200	Astragal, stock pine, 11/16" x 1-3/4"	1 Carp	255	.031	L.F.	1.42	1.12		2.54	3.45
0250	1-5/16" x 2-3/16"		240	.033		2.10	1.19		3.29	4.31
0800	Chair rail, stock pine, 5/8" x 2-1/2"		270	.030		1.68	1.06		2.74	3.63
0900	5/8" x 3-1/2"		240	.033		2.65	1.19		3.84	4.92
1000	Closet pole, stock pine, 1-1/8" diameter		200	.040		1.22	1.43		2.65	3.75
1100	Fir, 1-5/8" diameter		200	.040		2.36	1.43		3.79	5
3300	Half round, stock pine, 1/4" x 1/2"		270	.030		.31	1.06		1.37	2.12
3350	1/2" x 1"		255	.031		.74	1.12		1.86	2.70
3400	Handrail, fir, single piece, stock, hardware not included									
3450	1-1/2" x 1-3/4"	1 Carp	80	.100	L.F.	2.50	3.58		6.08	8.75
3470	Pine, 1-1/2" x 1-3/4"		80	.100		2.38	3.58		5.96	8.60
3500	1-1/2" x 2-1/2"		76	.105		2.67	3.76		6.43	9.30
3600	Lattice, stock pine, 1/4" x 1-1/8"		270	.030		.51	1.06		1.57	2.34
3700	1/4" x 1-3/4"		250	.032		.92	1.14		2.06	2.93
3800	Miscellaneous, custom, pine, 1" x 1"		270	.030		.38	1.06		1.44	2.20
3850	1" x 2"		265	.030		.76	1.08		1.84	2.66
3900	1" x 3"		240	.033		1.14	1.19		2.33	3.25
4100	Birch or oak, nominal 1" x 1"		240	.033		.45	1.19		1.64	2.49
4200	Nominal 1" x 3"		215	.037		1.34	1.33		2.67	3.71
4400	Walnut, nominal 1" x 1"		215	.037		.54	1.33		1.87	2.84

06 22 Millwork

06 22 13 – Standard Pattern Wood Trim

06 22 13.45 Moldings, Trim

06 22 13.45 Moldings, Trim		Crew	Daily Output	Labor-Hours	Unit	Material	2014 Bare Costs Labor	Equipment	Total	Total Incl O&P
4500	Nominal 1" x 3"	1 Carp	200	.040	L.F.	1.63	1.43		3.06	4.20
4700	Teak, nominal 1" x 1"		215	.037		2.54	1.33		3.87	5.05
4800	Nominal 1" x 3"		200	.040		7.60	1.43		9.03	10.75
4900	Quarter round, stock pine, 1/4" x 1/4"		275	.029		.31	1.04		1.35	2.09
4950	3/4" x 3/4"		255	.031		.71	1.12		1.83	2.67
5600	Wainscot moldings, 1-1/8" x 9/16", 2' high, minimum		76	.105	S.F.	12.35	3.76		16.11	19.95
5700	Maximum		65	.123	"	15.65	4.40		20.05	24.50

06 22 13.50 Moldings, Window and Door

06 22 13.50 Moldings, Window and Door		Crew	Daily Output	Labor-Hours	Unit	Material	2014 Bare Costs Labor	Equipment	Total	Total Incl O&P
0010	**MOLDINGS, WINDOW AND DOOR**									
2800	Door moldings, stock, decorative, 1-1/8" wide, plain	1 Carp	17	.471	Set	51.50	16.80		68.30	85
2900	Detailed		17	.471	"	87.50	16.80		104.30	125
2960	Clear pine door jamb, no stops, 11/16" x 4-9/16"		240	.033	L.F.	5.15	1.19		6.34	7.70
3150	Door trim set, 1 head and 2 sides, pine, 2-1/2 wide		12	.667	Opng.	25.50	24		49.50	68
3170	3-1/2" wide		11	.727	"	37	26		63	84.50
3250	Glass beads, stock pine, 3/8" x 1/2"		275	.029	L.F.	.37	1.04		1.41	2.16
3270	3/8" x 7/8"		270	.030		.50	1.06		1.56	2.33
4850	Parting bead, stock pine, 3/8" x 3/4"		275	.029		.45	1.04		1.49	2.25
4870	1/2" x 3/4"		255	.031		.57	1.12		1.69	2.52
5000	Stool caps, stock pine, 11/16" x 3-1/2"		200	.040		2.65	1.43		4.08	5.35
5100	1-1/16" x 3-1/4"		150	.053		4.15	1.91		6.06	7.80
5300	Threshold, oak, 3' long, inside, 5/8" x 3-5/8"		32	.250	Ea.	6.40	8.95		15.35	22
5400	Outside, 1-1/2" x 7-5/8"		16	.500	"	38	17.90		55.90	72
5900	Window trim sets, including casings, header, stops,									
5910	stool and apron, 2-1/2" wide, minimum	1 Carp	13	.615	Opng.	37	22		59	77.50
5950	Average		10	.800		43.50	28.50		72	96
6000	Maximum		6	1.333		62.50	47.50		110	149

06 22 13.60 Moldings, Soffits

06 22 13.60 Moldings, Soffits		Crew	Daily Output	Labor-Hours	Unit	Material	2014 Bare Costs Labor	Equipment	Total	Total Incl O&P
0010	**MOLDINGS, SOFFITS**									
0200	Soffits, pine, 1" x 4"	2 Carp	420	.038	L.F.	.47	1.36		1.83	2.80
0210	1" x 6"		420	.038		.80	1.36		2.16	3.17
0220	1" x 8"		420	.038		1.19	1.36		2.55	3.60
0230	1" x 10"		400	.040		1.55	1.43		2.98	4.11
0240	1" x 12"		400	.040		2.01	1.43		3.44	4.62
0250	STK cedar, 1" x 4"		420	.038		.59	1.36		1.95	2.94
0260	1" x 6"		420	.038		.93	1.36		2.29	3.31
0270	1" x 8"		420	.038		1.38	1.36		2.74	3.81
0280	1" x 10"		400	.040		2.04	1.43		3.47	4.65
0290	1" x 12"		400	.040		3.17	1.43		4.60	5.90
1000	Exterior AC plywood, 1/4" thick		400	.040	S.F.	.62	1.43		2.05	3.09
1050	3/8" thick		400	.040		.93	1.43		2.36	3.43
1100	1/2" thick		400	.040		1.06	1.43		2.49	3.58
1150	Polyvinyl chloride, white, solid	1 Carp	230	.035		2.04	1.24		3.28	4.33
1160	Perforated	"	230	.035		2.04	1.24		3.28	4.33
1170	Accessories, "J" channel 5/8"	2 Carp	700	.023	L.F.	.43	.82		1.25	1.85

06 25 13 – Prefinished Hardboard Paneling

06 25 13.10 Paneling, Hardboard		Crew	Daily Output	Labor-Hours	Unit	Material	2014 Bare Costs Labor	Equipment	Total	Total Incl O&P
0010	**PANELING, HARDBOARD**									
0050	Not incl. furring or trim, hardboard, tempered, 1/8" thick [G]	2 Carp	500	.032	S.F.	.39	1.14		1.53	2.35
0100	1/4" thick [G]		500	.032		.63	1.14		1.77	2.61
0300	Tempered pegboard, 1/8" thick [G]		500	.032		.40	1.14		1.54	2.36
0400	1/4" thick [G]		500	.032		.65	1.14		1.79	2.64
0600	Untempered hardboard, natural finish, 1/8" thick [G]		500	.032		.41	1.14		1.55	2.37
0700	1/4" thick [G]		500	.032		.50	1.14		1.64	2.47
0900	Untempered pegboard, 1/8" thick [G]		500	.032		.42	1.14		1.56	2.38
1000	1/4" thick [G]		500	.032		.46	1.14		1.60	2.43
1200	Plastic faced hardboard, 1/8" thick [G]		500	.032		.63	1.14		1.77	2.61
1300	1/4" thick [G]		500	.032		.86	1.14		2	2.87
1500	Plastic faced pegboard, 1/8" thick [G]		500	.032		.64	1.14		1.78	2.62
1600	1/4" thick [G]		500	.032		.82	1.14		1.96	2.82
1800	Wood grained, plain or grooved, 1/4" thick, minimum [G]		500	.032		.66	1.14		1.80	2.65
1900	Maximum [G]		425	.038		1.35	1.35		2.70	3.75
2100	Moldings for hardboard, wood or aluminum, minimum		500	.032	L.F.	.39	1.14		1.53	2.35
2200	Maximum		425	.038	"	1.29	1.35		2.64	3.68

06 25 16 – Prefinished Plywood Paneling

06 25 16.10 Paneling, Plywood

06 25 16.10 Paneling, Plywood		Crew	Daily Output	Labor-Hours	Unit	Material	2014 Bare Costs Labor	Equipment	Total	Total Incl O&P
0010	**PANELING, PLYWOOD** R061636-20									
2400	Plywood, prefinished, 1/4" thick, 4' x 8' sheets									
2410	with vertical grooves. Birch faced, minimum	2 Carp	500	.032	S.F.	.41	1.14		1.55	2.37
2420	Average		420	.038		.83	1.36		2.19	3.20
2430	Maximum		350	.046		1.25	1.63		2.88	4.13
2600	Mahogany, African		400	.040		2.90	1.43		4.33	5.60
2700	Philippine (Lauan)		500	.032		.60	1.14		1.74	2.58
2900	Oak or Cherry, minimum		500	.032		.34	1.14		1.48	2.29
3000	Maximum		400	.040		2.06	1.43		3.49	4.68
3200	Rosewood		320	.050		2.90	1.79		4.69	6.20
3400	Teak		400	.040		2.90	1.43		4.33	5.60
3600	Chestnut		375	.043		4.87	1.53		6.40	7.90
3800	Pecan		400	.040		2.10	1.43		3.53	4.72
3900	Walnut, minimum		500	.032		2.06	1.14		3.20	4.19
3950	Maximum		400	.040		5.30	1.43		6.73	8.25
4000	Plywood, prefinished, 3/4" thick, stock grades, minimum		320	.050		1.56	1.79		3.35	4.73
4100	Maximum		224	.071		4.68	2.55		7.23	9.45
4300	Architectural grade, minimum		224	.071		4.68	2.55		7.23	9.45
4400	Maximum		160	.100		4.68	3.58		8.26	11.15
4600	Plywood, "A" face, birch, VC, 1/2" thick, natural		450	.036		2.18	1.27		3.45	4.54
4700	Select		450	.036		2.18	1.27		3.45	4.54
4900	Veneer core, 3/4" thick, natural		320	.050		2.03	1.79		3.82	5.25
5000	Select		320	.050		2.27	1.79		4.06	5.50
5200	Lumber core, 3/4" thick, natural		320	.050		3.05	1.79		4.84	6.35
5500	Plywood, knotty pine, 1/4" thick, A2 grade		450	.036		1.67	1.27		2.94	3.98
5600	A3 grade		450	.036		2.10	1.27		3.37	4.45
5800	3/4" thick, veneer core, A2 grade		320	.050		2.15	1.79		3.94	5.40
5900	A3 grade		320	.050		2.42	1.79		4.21	5.65
6100	Aromatic cedar, 1/4" thick, plywood		400	.040		2.12	1.43		3.55	4.74
6200	1/4" thick, particle board		400	.040		1.03	1.43		2.46	3.54

06 25 Prefinished Paneling

06 25 26 – Panel System

06 25 26.10 Panel Systems

		Crew	Daily Output	Labor-Hours	Unit	Material	2014 Bare Costs Labor	Equipment	Total	Total Incl O&P
0010	**PANEL SYSTEMS**									
0100	Raised panel, eng. wood core w/wood veneer, std., paint grade	2 Carp	300	.053	S.F.	10.35	1.91		12.26	14.60
0110	Oak veneer		300	.053		24	1.91		25.91	29
0120	Maple veneer		300	.053		30	1.91		31.91	36
0130	Cherry veneer		300	.053		34.50	1.91		36.41	40.50
0300	Class I fire rated, paint grade		300	.053		12	1.91		13.91	16.40
0310	Oak veneer		300	.053		28	1.91		29.91	33.50
0320	Maple veneer		300	.053		37.50	1.91		39.41	44
0330	Cherry veneer		300	.053		45	1.91		46.91	52.50
0510	Beadboard, 5/8" MDF, standard, primed		300	.053		7.85	1.91		9.76	11.80
0520	Oak veneer, unfinished		300	.053		12.40	1.91		14.31	16.85
0530	Maple veneer, unfinished		300	.053		13.55	1.91		15.46	18.10
0610	Rustic paneling, 5/8" MDF, standard, maple veneer, unfinished	↓	300	.053	↓	13.60	1.91		15.51	18.15

06 26 Board Paneling

06 26 13 – Profile Board Paneling

06 26 13.10 Paneling, Boards

		Crew	Daily Output	Labor-Hours	Unit	Material	2014 Bare Costs Labor	Equipment	Total	Total Incl O&P
0010	**PANELING, BOARDS**									
6400	Wood board paneling, 3/4" thick, knotty pine	2 Carp	300	.053	S.F.	1.91	1.91		3.82	5.30
6500	Rough sawn cedar		300	.053		3.09	1.91		5	6.60
6700	Redwood, clear, 1" x 4" boards		300	.053		4.96	1.91		6.87	8.65
6900	Aromatic cedar, closet lining, boards	↓	275	.058	↓	2.02	2.08		4.10	5.70

06 43 Wood Stairs and Railings

06 43 13 – Wood Stairs

06 43 13.20 Prefabricated Wood Stairs

		Crew	Daily Output	Labor-Hours	Unit	Material	2014 Bare Costs Labor	Equipment	Total	Total Incl O&P
0010	**PREFABRICATED WOOD STAIRS**									
0100	Box stairs, prefabricated, 3'-0" wide									
0110	Oak treads, up to 14 risers	2 Carp	39	.410	Riser	92.50	14.65		107.15	127
0600	With pine treads for carpet, up to 14 risers	"	39	.410	"	59.50	14.65		74.15	90
1100	For 4' wide stairs, add				Flight	25%				
1550	Stairs, prefabricated stair handrail with balusters	1 Carp	30	.267	L.F.	74	9.55		83.55	97.50
1700	Basement stairs, prefabricated, pine treads									
1710	Pine risers, 3' wide, up to 14 risers	2 Carp	52	.308	Riser	59.50	11		70.50	84
4000	Residential, wood, oak treads, prefabricated		1.50	10.667	Flight	1,200	380		1,580	1,975
4200	Built in place	↓	.44	36.364	"	1,900	1,300		3,200	4,275
4400	Spiral, oak, 4'-6" diameter, unfinished, prefabricated,									
4500	incl. railing, 9' high	2 Carp	1.50	10.667	Flight	3,625	380		4,005	4,625

06 43 13.40 Wood Stair Parts

		Crew	Daily Output	Labor-Hours	Unit	Material	2014 Bare Costs Labor	Equipment	Total	Total Incl O&P
0010	**WOOD STAIR PARTS**									
0020	Pin top balusters, 1-1/4", oak, 34"	1 Carp	96	.083	Ea.	7.80	2.98		10.78	13.60
0030	38"		96	.083		9.85	2.98		12.83	15.85
0040	42"		96	.083		12.10	2.98		15.08	18.30
0050	Poplar, 34"		96	.083		3.05	2.98		6.03	8.35
0060	38"		96	.083		3.88	2.98		6.86	9.25
0070	42"		96	.083		8.85	2.98		11.83	14.70
0080	Maple, 34"		96	.083		4.90	2.98		7.88	10.40
0090	38"		96	.083	↓	5.60	2.98		8.58	11.20

06 43 13.40 Wood Stair Parts		Crew	Daily Output	Labor-Hours	Unit	Material	2014 Bare Costs Labor	2014 Bare Costs Equipment	Total	Total Incl O&P
0100	42"	1 Carp	96	.083	Ea.	6.50	2.98		9.48	12.15
0130	Primed, 34"		96	.083		3	2.98		5.98	8.30
0140	38"		96	.083		3.62	2.98		6.60	9
0150	42"		96	.083		4.42	2.98		7.40	9.85
0180	Box top balusters, 1-1/4", oak, 34"		60	.133		10.85	4.77		15.62	19.95
0190	38"		60	.133		12.50	4.77		17.27	22
0200	42"		60	.133		12.95	4.77		17.72	22.50
0210	Poplar, 34"		60	.133		8.65	4.77		13.42	17.50
0220	38"		60	.133		9.50	4.77		14.27	18.45
0230	42"		60	.133		10	4.77		14.77	19
0240	Maple, 34"		60	.133		11.90	4.77		16.67	21
0250	38"		60	.133		13.80	4.77		18.57	23
0260	42"		60	.133		14.20	4.77		18.97	23.50
0290	Primed, 34"		60	.133		7	4.77		11.77	15.70
0300	38"		60	.133		8	4.77		12.77	16.80
0310	42"		60	.133		8.35	4.77		13.12	17.20
0340	Square balusters, cut from lineal stock, pine, 1-1/16" x 1-1/16"		180	.044	L.F.	1.49	1.59		3.08	4.31
0350	1-5/16" x 1-5/16"		180	.044		2	1.59		3.59	4.87
0360	1-5/8" x 1-5/8"		180	.044		3.29	1.59		4.88	6.30
0370	Turned newel, oak, 3-1/2" square, 48" high		8	1	Ea.	94.50	36		130.50	164
0380	62" high		8	1		138	36		174	212
0390	Poplar, 3-1/2" square, 48" high		8	1		55	36		91	121
0400	62" high		8	1		75	36		111	143
0410	Maple, 3-1/2" square, 48" high		8	1		66	36		102	133
0420	62" high		8	1		93	36		129	162
0430	Square newel, oak, 3-1/2" square, 48" high		8	1		50	36		86	115
0440	58" high		8	1		70	36		106	137
0450	Poplar, 3-1/2" square, 48" high		8	1		35	36		71	98.50
0460	58" high		8	1		39	36		75	103
0470	Maple, 3" square, 48" high		8	1		50	36		86	115
0480	58" high		8	1		62	36		98	128
0490	Railings, oak, minimum		96	.083	L.F.	9.50	2.98		12.48	15.45
0500	Average		96	.083		12.90	2.98		15.88	19.15
0510	Maximum		96	.083		13.50	2.98		16.48	19.85
0520	Maple, minimum		96	.083		15	2.98		17.98	21.50
0530	Average		96	.083		15.25	2.98		18.23	22
0540	Maximum		96	.083		15.50	2.98		18.48	22
0550	Oak, for bending rail, minimum		48	.167		22	5.95		27.95	34
0560	Average		48	.167		25	5.95		30.95	37.50
0570	Maximum		48	.167		28	5.95		33.95	41
0580	Maple, for bending rail, minimum		48	.167		25	5.95		30.95	37
0590	Average		48	.167		27	5.95		32.95	40
0600	Maximum		48	.167		29.50	5.95		35.45	42.50
0610	Risers, oak, 3/4" x 8", 36" long		80	.100	Ea.	18	3.58		21.58	26
0620	42" long		80	.100		21	3.58		24.58	29
0630	48" long		80	.100		24	3.58		27.58	32.50
0640	54" long		80	.100		27	3.58		30.58	35.50
0650	60" long		80	.100		30	3.58		33.58	39
0660	72" long		80	.100		36	3.58		39.58	45.50
0670	Poplar, 3/4" x 8", 36" long		80	.100		12	3.58		15.58	19.20
0680	42" long		80	.100		14	3.58		17.58	21.50
0690	48" long		80	.100		16	3.58		19.58	23.50
0700	54" long		80	.100		18	3.58		21.58	26

06 43 Wood Stairs and Railings

06 43 13 – Wood Stairs

06 43 13.40 Wood Stair Parts

		Crew	Daily Output	Labor-Hours	Unit	Material	2014 Bare Costs Labor	Equipment	Total	Total Incl O&P
0710	60" long	1 Carp	80	.100	Ea.	20	3.58		23.58	28
0720	72" long		80	.100		24	3.58		27.58	32.50
0730	Pine, 1" x 8", 36" long		80	.100		3.57	3.58		7.15	9.95
0740	42" long		80	.100		4.17	3.58		7.75	10.60
0750	48" long		80	.100		4.76	3.58		8.34	11.25
0760	54" long		80	.100		5.35	3.58		8.93	11.90
0770	60" long		80	.100		5.95	3.58		9.53	12.55
0780	72" long		80	.100		7.15	3.58		10.73	13.85
0790	Treads, oak, no returns, 1-1/32" x 11-1/2" x 36" long		32	.250		29	8.95		37.95	47
0800	42" long		32	.250		34	8.95		42.95	52
0810	48" long		32	.250		38.50	8.95		47.45	57.50
0820	54" long		32	.250		43.50	8.95		52.45	63
0830	60" long		32	.250		48.50	8.95		57.45	68
0840	72" long		32	.250		58	8.95		66.95	79
0850	Mitred return one end, 1-1/32" x 11-1/2" x 36" long		24	.333		52	11.90		63.90	77
0860	42" long		24	.333		60.50	11.90		72.40	86.50
0870	48" long		24	.333		69.50	11.90		81.40	96.50
0880	54" long		24	.333		78	11.90		89.90	106
0890	60" long		24	.333		86.50	11.90		98.40	116
0900	72" long		24	.333		104	11.90		115.90	134
0910	Mitred return two ends, 1-1/32" x 11-1/2" x 36" long		12	.667		53	24		77	98.50
0920	42" long		12	.667		62	24		86	108
0930	48" long		12	.667		70.50	24		94.50	118
0940	54" long		12	.667		79.50	24		103.50	128
0950	60" long		12	.667		88.50	24		112.50	137
0960	72" long		12	.667		106	24		130	157
0970	Starting step, oak, 48", bullnose		8	1		195	36		231	275
0980	Double end bullnose		8	1	↓	345	36		381	440
1030	Skirt board, pine, 1" x 10"		55	.145	L.F.	1.55	5.20		6.75	10.45
1040	1" x 12"		52	.154	"	2.01	5.50		7.51	11.45
1050	Oak landing tread, 1-1/16" thick		54	.148	S.F.	9	5.30		14.30	18.80
1060	Oak cove molding		96	.083	L.F.	1.45	2.98		4.43	6.60
1070	Oak stringer molding		96	.083	"	3.25	2.98		6.23	8.60
1090	Rail bolt, 5/16" x 3-1/2"		48	.167	Ea.	2.75	5.95		8.70	13.10
1100	5/16" x 4-1/2"		48	.167		2.75	5.95		8.70	13.10
1120	Newel post anchor		16	.500		9.75	17.90		27.65	41
1130	Tapered plug, 1/2"		240	.033		1	1.19		2.19	3.10
1140	1"		240	.033	↓	.99	1.19		2.18	3.09

06 43 16 – Wood Railings

06 43 16.10 Wood Handrails and Railings

		Crew	Daily Output	Labor-Hours	Unit	Material	2014 Bare Costs Labor	Equipment	Total	Total Incl O&P
0010	**WOOD HANDRAILS AND RAILINGS**									
0020	Custom design, architectural grade, hardwood, minimum	1 Carp	38	.211	L.F.	10	7.55		17.55	23.50
0100	Maximum		30	.267		62.50	9.55		72.05	85
0300	Stock interior railing with spindles 4" O.C., 4' long		40	.200		41	7.15		48.15	57
0400	8' long	↓	48	.167	↓	41	5.95		46.95	55

06 44 Ornamental Woodwork

06 44 19 – Wood Grilles

06 44 19.10 Grilles

		Crew	Daily Output	Labor-Hours	Unit	Material	2014 Bare Costs Labor	2014 Bare Costs Equipment	Total	Total Incl O&P
0010	**GRILLES** and panels, hardwood, sanded									
0020	2' x 4' to 4' x 8', custom designs, unfinished, minimum	1 Carp	38	.211	S.F.	61	7.55		68.55	79.50
0050	Average		30	.267		67.50	9.55		77.05	90.50
0100	Maximum		19	.421		70.50	15.05		85.55	103

06 44 33 – Wood Mantels

06 44 33.10 Fireplace Mantels

		Crew	Daily Output	Labor-Hours	Unit	Material	2014 Bare Costs Labor	2014 Bare Costs Equipment	Total	Total Incl O&P
0010	**FIREPLACE MANTELS**									
0015	6" molding, 6' x 3'-6" opening, minimum	1 Carp	5	1.600	Opng.	248	57		305	370
0100	Maximum		5	1.600		445	57		502	585
0300	Prefabricated pine, colonial type, stock, deluxe		2	4		1,500	143		1,643	1,900
0400	Economy		3	2.667		690	95.50		785.50	920

06 44 33.20 Fireplace Mantel Beam

		Crew	Daily Output	Labor-Hours	Unit	Material	2014 Bare Costs Labor	2014 Bare Costs Equipment	Total	Total Incl O&P
0010	**FIREPLACE MANTEL BEAM**									
0020	Rough texture wood, 4" x 8"	1 Carp	36	.222	L.F.	8.30	7.95		16.25	22.50
0100	4" x 10"		35	.229	"	10.90	8.15		19.05	26
0300	Laminated hardwood, 2-1/4" x 10-1/2" wide, 6' long		5	1.600	Ea.	110	57		167	217
0400	8' long		5	1.600	"	150	57		207	261
0600	Brackets for above, rough sawn		12	.667	Pr.	10	24		34	51
0700	Laminated		12	.667	"	15	24		39	56.50

06 44 39 – Wood Posts and Columns

06 44 39.10 Decorative Beams

		Crew	Daily Output	Labor-Hours	Unit	Material	2014 Bare Costs Labor	2014 Bare Costs Equipment	Total	Total Incl O&P
0010	**DECORATIVE BEAMS**									
0020	Rough sawn cedar, non-load bearing, 4" x 4"	2 Carp	180	.089	L.F.	1.20	3.18		4.38	6.65
0100	4" x 6"		170	.094		1.79	3.36		5.15	7.60
0200	4" x 8"		160	.100		2.39	3.58		5.97	8.65
0300	4" x 10"		150	.107		3.63	3.81		7.44	10.40
0400	4" x 12"		140	.114		4.61	4.09		8.70	11.90
0500	8" x 8"		130	.123		4.78	4.40		9.18	12.65

06 44 39.20 Columns

		Crew	Daily Output	Labor-Hours	Unit	Material	2014 Bare Costs Labor	2014 Bare Costs Equipment	Total	Total Incl O&P
0010	**COLUMNS**									
0050	Aluminum, round colonial, 6" diameter	2 Carp	80	.200	V.L.F.	18.60	7.15		25.75	32.50
0100	8" diameter		62.25	.257		21.50	9.20		30.70	39
0200	10" diameter		55	.291		25.50	10.40		35.90	45.50
0250	Fir, stock units, hollow round, 6" diameter		80	.200		20	7.15		27.15	34
0300	8" diameter		80	.200		25	7.15		32.15	39
0350	10" diameter		70	.229		32.50	8.15		40.65	50
0360	12" diameter		65	.246		38.50	8.80		47.30	57
0400	Solid turned, to 8' high, 3-1/2" diameter		80	.200		9.10	7.15		16.25	22
0500	4-1/2" diameter		75	.213		13.60	7.65		21.25	28
0600	5-1/2" diameter		70	.229		17.75	8.15		25.90	33.50
0800	Square columns, built-up, 5" x 5"		65	.246		15.50	8.80		24.30	32
0900	Solid, 3-1/2" x 3-1/2"		130	.123		9.10	4.40		13.50	17.45
1600	Hemlock, tapered, T & G, 12" diam., 10' high		100	.160		36.50	5.70		42.20	50
1700	16' high		65	.246		71.50	8.80		80.30	94
1900	10' high, 14" diameter		100	.160		112	5.70		117.70	133
2000	18' high		65	.246		91	8.80		99.80	115
2200	18" diameter, 12' high		65	.246		163	8.80		171.80	195
2300	20' high		50	.320		115	11.45		126.45	145
2500	20" diameter, 14' high		40	.400		184	14.30		198.30	226
2600	20' high		35	.457		172	16.35		188.35	217
2800	For flat pilasters, deduct					33%				

06 44 Ornamental Woodwork

06 44 39 – Wood Posts and Columns

06 44 39.20 Columns

		Crew	Daily Output	Labor-Hours	Unit	Material	2014 Bare Costs Labor	Equipment	Total	Total Incl O&P
3000	For splitting into halves, add				Ea.	105			105	116
4000	Rough sawn cedar posts, 4" x 4"	2 Carp	250	.064	V.L.F.	3.33	2.29		5.62	7.50
4100	4" x 6"		235	.068		7.25	2.43		9.68	12.05
4200	6" x 6"		220	.073		11.70	2.60		14.30	17.20
4300	8" x 8"		200	.080		20.50	2.86		23.36	27.50

06 48 Wood Frames

06 48 13 – Exterior Wood Door Frames

06 48 13.10 Exterior Wood Door Frames and Accessories

		Crew	Daily Output	Labor-Hours	Unit	Material	2014 Bare Costs Labor	Equipment	Total	Total Incl O&P
0010	**EXTERIOR WOOD DOOR FRAMES AND ACCESSORIES**									
0400	Exterior frame, incl. ext. trim, pine, 5/4 x 4-9/16" deep	2 Carp	375	.043	L.F.	6.60	1.53		8.13	9.85
0420	5-3/16" deep		375	.043		7.80	1.53		9.33	11.15
0440	6-9/16" deep		375	.043		7.90	1.53		9.43	11.25
0600	Oak, 5/4 x 4-9/16" deep		350	.046		16.90	1.63		18.53	21.50
0620	5-3/16" deep		350	.046		18.55	1.63		20.18	23.50
0640	6-9/16" deep		350	.046		20	1.63		21.63	25
1000	Sills, 8/4 x 8" deep, oak, no horns		100	.160		6.40	5.70		12.10	16.60
1020	2" horns		100	.160		17.10	5.70		22.80	28.50
1040	3" horns		100	.160		17.10	5.70		22.80	28.50
1100	8/4 x 10" deep, oak, no horns		90	.178		6	6.35		12.35	17.30
1120	2" horns		90	.178		22.50	6.35		28.85	35
1140	3" horns		90	.178		22.50	6.35		28.85	35
2000	Exterior, colonial, frame & trim, 3' opng., in-swing, minimum		22	.727	Ea.	355	26		381	435
2010	Average		21	.762		580	27		607	680
2020	Maximum		20	.800		1,200	28.50		1,228.50	1,375
2100	5'-4" opening, in-swing, minimum		17	.941		420	33.50		453.50	520
2120	Maximum		15	1.067		1,200	38		1,238	1,400
2140	Out-swing, minimum		17	.941		420	33.50		453.50	520
2160	Maximum		15	1.067		1,200	38		1,238	1,400
2400	6'-0" opening, in-swing, minimum		16	1		420	36		456	525
2420	Maximum		10	1.600		1,200	57		1,257	1,425
2460	Out-swing, minimum		16	1		420	36		456	525
2480	Maximum		10	1.600		1,200	57		1,257	1,425
2600	For two sidelights, add, minimum		30	.533	Opng.	67	19.05		86.05	106
2620	Maximum		20	.800	"	845	28.50		873.50	975
2700	Custom birch frame, 3'-0" opening		16	1	Ea.	230	36		266	315
2750	6'-0" opening		16	1		350	36		386	445
2900	Exterior, modern, plain trim, 3' opng., in-swing, minimum		26	.615		45	22		67	86.50
2920	Average		24	.667		53.50	24		77.50	98.50
2940	Maximum		22	.727		61.50	26		87.50	112

06 48 16 – Interior Wood Door Frames

06 48 16.10 Interior Wood Door Jamb and Frames

		Crew	Daily Output	Labor-Hours	Unit	Material	2014 Bare Costs Labor	Equipment	Total	Total Incl O&P
0010	**INTERIOR WOOD DOOR JAMB AND FRAMES**									
3000	Interior frame, pine, 11/16" x 3-5/8" deep	2 Carp	375	.043	L.F.	6.10	1.53		7.63	9.25
3020	4-9/16" deep		375	.043		6.25	1.53		7.78	9.40
3200	Oak, 11/16" x 3-5/8" deep		350	.046		9	1.63		10.63	12.65
3220	4-9/16" deep		350	.046		9	1.63		10.63	12.65
3240	5-3/16" deep		350	.046		12.75	1.63		14.38	16.80
3400	Walnut, 11/16" x 3-5/8" deep		350	.046		8.25	1.63		9.88	11.85
3420	4-9/16" deep		350	.046		9	1.63		10.63	12.65

06 48 Wood Frames

06 48 16 – Interior Wood Door Frames

06 48 16.10 Interior Wood Door Jamb and Frames	Crew	Daily Output	Labor-Hours	Unit	Material	2014 Bare Costs Labor	2014 Bare Costs Equipment	Total	Total Incl O&P
3440	5-3/16" deep	2 Carp	350	.046	L.F.	9	1.63		10.63	12.65
3600	Pocket door frame		16	1	Ea.	82	36		118	150
3800	Threshold, oak, 5/8" x 3-5/8" deep		200	.080	L.F.	3.56	2.86		6.42	8.75
3820	4-5/8" deep		190	.084		4.13	3.01		7.14	9.60
3840	5-5/8" deep		180	.089		6.50	3.18		9.68	12.50

06 49 Wood Screens and Exterior Wood Shutters

06 49 19 – Exterior Wood Shutters

06 49 19.10 Shutters, Exterior

		Crew	Daily Output	Labor-Hours	Unit	Material	2014 Bare Costs Labor	2014 Bare Costs Equipment	Total	Total Incl O&P
0010	**SHUTTERS, EXTERIOR**									
0012	Aluminum, louvered, 1'-4" wide, 3'-0" long	1 Carp	10	.800	Pr.	75	28.50		103.50	131
0400	6'-8" long		9	.889		150	32		182	220
1000	Pine, louvered, primed, each 1'-2" wide, 3'-3" long		10	.800		215	28.50		243.50	285
1100	4'-7" long		10	.800		282	28.50		310.50	360
1500	Each 1'-6" wide, 3'-3" long		10	.800		262	28.50		290.50	335
1600	4'-7" long		10	.800		350	28.50		378.50	435
1620	Cedar, louvered, 1'-2" wide, 5'-7" long		10	.800		335	28.50		363.50	415
1630	Each 1'-4" wide, 2'-2" long		10	.800		176	28.50		204.50	242
1670	4'-3" long		10	.800		296	28.50		324.50	375
1690	5'-11" long		10	.800		390	28.50		418.50	480
1700	Door blinds, 6'-9" long, each 1'-3" wide		9	.889		415	32		447	515
1710	1'-6" wide		9	.889		490	32		522	595
1720	Cedar, solid raised panel, each 1'-4" wide, 3'-3" long		10	.800		335	28.50		363.50	415
1740	4'-3" long		10	.800		415	28.50		443.50	505
1770	5'-11" long		10	.800		550	28.50		578.50	655
1800	Door blinds, 6'-9" long, each 1'-3" wide		9	.889		415	32		447	515
1900	1'-6" wide		9	.889		490	32		522	595
2500	Polystyrene, solid raised panel, each 1'-4" wide, 3'-3" long		10	.800		72	28.50		100.50	127
2700	4'-7" long		10	.800		109	28.50		137.50	168
4500	Polystyrene, louvered, each 1'-2" wide, 3'-3" long		10	.800		65	28.50		93.50	120
4750	5'-3" long		10	.800		102	28.50		130.50	160
6000	Vinyl, louvered, each 1'-2" x 4'-7" long		10	.800		88	28.50		116.50	145
6200	Each 1'-4" x 6'-8" long		9	.889		126	32		158	193

06 51 Structural Plastic Shapes and Plates

06 51 13 – Plastic Lumber

06 51 13.10 Recycled Plastic Lumber

			Crew	Daily Output	Labor-Hours	Unit	Material	2014 Bare Costs Labor	2014 Bare Costs Equipment	Total	Total Incl O&P
0010	**RECYCLED PLASTIC LUMBER**										
4000	Sheeting, recycled plastic, black or white, 4' x 8' x 1/8"	G	2 Carp	1100	.015	S.F.	1.58	.52		2.10	2.62
4010	4' x 8' x 3/16"	G		1100	.015		2.27	.52		2.79	3.38
4020	4' x 8' x 1/4"	G		950	.017		2.36	.60		2.96	3.61
4030	4' x 8' x 3/8"	G		950	.017		3.67	.60		4.27	5.05
4040	4' x 8' x 1/2"	G		900	.018		4.85	.64		5.49	6.40
4050	4' x 8' x 5/8"	G		900	.018		6.55	.64		7.19	8.25
4060	4' x 8' x 3/4"	G		850	.019		8.25	.67		8.92	10.25
4070	Add for colors	G				Ea.	5%				
8500	100% recycled plastic, var colors, NLB, 2" x 2"	G				L.F.	1.76			1.76	1.94
8510	2" x 4"	G					3.67			3.67	4.04
8520	2" x 6"	G					5.75			5.75	6.35

06 51 Structural Plastic Shapes and Plates

06 51 13 – Plastic Lumber

06 51 13.10 Recycled Plastic Lumber

		Crew	Daily Output	Labor-Hours	Unit	Material	2014 Bare Costs Labor	Equipment	Total	Total Incl O&P
8530	2" x 8"	G			L.F.	7.90			7.90	8.70
8540	2" x 10"	G				11.50			11.50	12.65
8550	5/4" x 4"	G				4.26			4.26	4.69
8560	5/4" x 6"	G				5.05			5.05	5.55
8570	1" x 6"	G				2.86			2.86	3.15
8580	1/2" x 8"	G				3.41			3.41	3.75
8590	2" x 10" T & G	G				11.50			11.50	12.65
8600	3" x 10" T & G	G				13.65			13.65	15
8610	Add for premium colors	G				20%				

06 52 Plastic Structural Assemblies

06 52 10 – Fiberglass Structural Assemblies

06 52 10.10 Castings, Fiberglass

		Crew	Daily Output	Labor-Hours	Unit	Material	2014 Bare Costs Labor	Equipment	Total	Total Incl O&P
0010	**CASTINGS, FIBERGLASS**									
0100	Angle, 1" x 1" x 1/8" thick	2 Sswk	240	.067	L.F.	2.25	2.56		4.81	7.35
0120	3" x 3" x 1/4" thick		200	.080		7.30	3.07		10.37	13.85
0140	4" x 4" x 1/4" thick		200	.080		9.15	3.07		12.22	15.90
0160	4" x 4" x 3/8" thick		200	.080		13.60	3.07		16.67	21
0180	6" x 6" x 1/2" thick		160	.100		33	3.84		36.84	44
1000	Flat sheet, 1/8" thick		140	.114	S.F.	6.60	4.38		10.98	15.60
1020	1/4" thick		120	.133		11.85	5.10		16.95	23
1040	3/8" thick		100	.160		17.40	6.15		23.55	31
1060	1/2" thick		80	.200		21	7.65		28.65	37.50
2000	Handrail, 42" high, 2" diam. rails pickets 5' O.C.		32	.500	L.F.	53.50	19.20		72.70	95.50
3000	Round bar, 1/4" diam.		240	.067		.46	2.56		3.02	5.40
3020	1/2" diam.		200	.080		1.32	3.07		4.39	7.30
3040	3/4" diam.		200	.080		3.58	3.07		6.65	9.80
3060	1" diam.		160	.100		6.10	3.84		9.94	14
3080	1-1/4" diam.		160	.100		11.30	3.84		15.14	19.70
3100	1-1/2" diam.		140	.114		15.50	4.38		19.88	25.50
3500	Round tube, 1" diam. x 1/8" thick		240	.067		2.40	2.56		4.96	7.50
3520	2" diam. x 1/4" thick		200	.080		8.35	3.07		11.42	15
3540	3" diam. x 1/4" thick		160	.100		10.60	3.84		14.44	18.95
4000	Square bar, 1/2" square		240	.067		4.18	2.56		6.74	9.45
4020	1" square		200	.080		5.70	3.07		8.77	12.15
4040	1-1/2" square		160	.100		10.95	3.84		14.79	19.35
4500	Square tube, 1" x 1" x 1/8" thick		240	.067		2.77	2.56		5.33	7.90
4520	2" x 2" x 1/8" thick		200	.080		5.70	3.07		8.77	12.15
4540	3" x 3" x 1/4" thick		160	.100		16	3.84		19.84	25
5000	Threaded rod, 3/8" diam.		320	.050		4.11	1.92		6.03	8.15
5020	1/2" diam.		320	.050		4.75	1.92		6.67	8.90
5040	5/8" diam.		280	.057		5.20	2.19		7.39	9.90
5060	3/4" diam.		280	.057		6	2.19		8.19	10.75
6000	Wide flange beam, 4" x 4" x 1/4" thick		120	.133		12.35	5.10		17.45	23.50
6020	6" x 6" x 1/4" thick		100	.160		20.50	6.15		26.65	34
6040	8" x 8" x 3/8" thick		80	.200		36	7.65		43.65	54

06 52 10.20 Fiberglass Stair Treads

		Crew	Daily Output	Labor-Hours	Unit	Material	2014 Bare Costs Labor	Equipment	Total	Total Incl O&P
0010	**FIBERGLASS STAIR TREADS**									
0100	24" wide	2 Sswk	52	.308	Ea.	29.50	11.80		41.30	55
0140	30" wide		52	.308		36.50	11.80		48.30	63
0180	36" wide		52	.308		44	11.80		55.80	71

06 52 Plastic Structural Assemblies

06 52 10 – Fiberglass Structural Assemblies

06 52 10.20 Fiberglass Stair Treads	Crew	Daily Output	Labor-Hours	Unit	Material	2014 Bare Costs Labor	Equipment	Total	Total Incl O&P
0220	42" wide	2 Sswk	52	.308	Ea.	51.50	11.80		63.30	79

06 52 10.30 Fiberglass Grating

		Crew	Daily Output	Labor-Hours	Unit	Material	Labor	Equipment	Total	Total Incl O&P
0010	**FIBERGLASS GRATING**									
0100	Molded, green (for mod. corrosive environment)									
0140	1" x 4" mesh, 1" thick	2 Sswk	400	.040	S.F.	10.65	1.53		12.18	14.60
0180	1-1/2" square mesh, 1" thick		400	.040		18.65	1.53		20.18	23.50
0220	1-1/4" thick		400	.040		11.90	1.53		13.43	16
0260	1-1/2" thick		400	.040		26	1.53		27.53	32
0300	2" square mesh, 2" thick		320	.050		24.50	1.92		26.42	30.50
1000	Orange (for highly corrosive environment)									
1040	1" x 4" mesh, 1" thick	2 Sswk	400	.040	S.F.	14.75	1.53		16.28	19.10
1080	1-1/2" square mesh, 1" thick		400	.040		19.55	1.53		21.08	24.50
1120	1-1/4" thick		400	.040		20.50	1.53		22.03	25.50
1160	1-1/2" thick		400	.040		22	1.53		23.53	27
1200	2" square mesh, 2" thick		320	.050		26	1.92		27.92	32.50
3000	Pultruded, green (for mod. corrosive environment)									
3040	1" O.C. bar spacing, 1" thick	2 Sswk	400	.040	S.F.	17.30	1.53		18.83	22
3080	1-1/2" thick		320	.050		18.30	1.92		20.22	23.50
3120	1-1/2" O.C. bar spacing, 1" thick		400	.040		14.20	1.53		15.73	18.50
3160	1-1/2" thick		400	.040		16.80	1.53		18.33	21.50
4000	Grating support legs, fixed height, no base				Ea.	45.50			45.50	50
4040	With base					41			41	45
4080	Adjustable to 60"					62			62	68.50

06 52 10.40 Fiberglass Floor Grating

		Crew	Daily Output	Labor-Hours	Unit	Material	Labor	Equipment	Total	Total Incl O&P
0010	**FIBERGLASS FLOOR GRATING**									
0101	Reinforced polyester, fire retardant, 1" x 4" grid, 1" thick	2 Carp	255	.063	S.F.	14.95	2.24		17.19	20
0201	1-1/2" x 6" mesh, 1-1/2" thick		250	.064		17.50	2.29		19.79	23
0301	With grit surface, 1-1/2" x 6" grid, 1-1/2" thick		250	.064		17.85	2.29		20.14	23.50

06 63 Plastic Railings

06 63 10 – Plastic (PVC) Railings

06 63 10.10 Plastic Railings

		Crew	Daily Output	Labor-Hours	Unit	Material	Labor	Equipment	Total	Total Incl O&P
0010	**PLASTIC RAILINGS**									
0100	Horizontal PVC handrail with balusters, 3-1/2" wide, 36" high	1 Carp	96	.083	L.F.	25	2.98		27.98	32.50
0150	42" high		96	.083		28	2.98		30.98	36
0200	Angled PVC handrail with balusters, 3-1/2" wide, 36" high		72	.111		28.50	3.97		32.47	37.50
0250	42" high		72	.111		31.50	3.97		35.47	41.50
0300	Post sleeve for 4 x 4 post		96	.083		14	2.98		16.98	20.50
0400	Post cap for 4 x 4 post, flat profile		48	.167	Ea.	13.90	5.95		19.85	25.50
0450	Newel post style profile		48	.167		23.50	5.95		29.45	36
0500	Raised corbeled profile		48	.167		28.50	5.95		34.45	41
0550	Post base trim for 4 x 4 post		96	.083		18.25	2.98		21.23	25

06 65 10.10 PVC Trim, Exterior

		Crew	Daily Output	Labor-Hours	Unit	Material	2014 Bare Costs Labor	Equipment	Total	Total Incl O&P
0010	**PVC TRIM, EXTERIOR**									
0100	Cornerboards, 5/4" x 6" x 6"	1 Carp	240	.033	L.F.	8.90	1.19		10.09	11.80
0110	Door/window casing, 1" x 4"		200	.040		1.35	1.43		2.78	3.90
0120	1" x 6"		200	.040		2.12	1.43		3.55	4.74
0130	1" x 8"		195	.041		2.80	1.47		4.27	5.55
0140	1" x 10"		195	.041		3.55	1.47		5.02	6.40
0150	1" x 12"		190	.042		4.34	1.51		5.85	7.30
0160	5/4" x 4"		195	.041		1.72	1.47		3.19	4.36
0170	5/4" x 6"		195	.041		2.72	1.47		4.19	5.45
0180	5/4" x 8"		190	.042		3.57	1.51		5.08	6.45
0190	5/4" x 10"		190	.042		4.57	1.51		6.08	7.60
0200	5/4" x 12"		185	.043		5	1.55		6.55	8.10
0210	Fascia, 1" x 4"		250	.032		1.35	1.14		2.49	3.41
0220	1" x 6"		250	.032		2.12	1.14		3.26	4.25
0230	1" x 8"		225	.036		2.80	1.27		4.07	5.20
0240	1" x 10"		225	.036		3.55	1.27		4.82	6.05
0250	1" x 12"		200	.040		4.34	1.43		5.77	7.20
0260	5/4" x 4"		240	.033		1.72	1.19		2.91	3.89
0270	5/4" x 6"		240	.033		2.72	1.19		3.91	4.99
0280	5/4" x 8"		215	.037		3.57	1.33		4.90	6.15
0290	5/4" x 10"		215	.037		4.57	1.33		5.90	7.30
0300	5/4" x 12"		190	.042		5	1.51		6.51	8.05
0310	Frieze, 1" x 4"		250	.032		1.35	1.14		2.49	3.41
0320	1" x 6"		250	.032		2.12	1.14		3.26	4.25
0330	1" x 8"		225	.036		2.80	1.27		4.07	5.20
0340	1" x 10"		225	.036		3.55	1.27		4.82	6.05
0350	1" x 12"		200	.040		4.34	1.43		5.77	7.20
0360	5/4" x 4"		240	.033		1.72	1.19		2.91	3.89
0370	5/4" x 6"		240	.033		2.72	1.19		3.91	4.99
0380	5/4" x 8"		215	.037		3.57	1.33		4.90	6.15
0390	5/4" x 10"		215	.037		4.57	1.33		5.90	7.30
0400	5/4" x 12"		190	.042		5	1.51		6.51	8.05
0410	Rake, 1" x 4"		200	.040		1.35	1.43		2.78	3.90
0420	1" x 6"		200	.040		2.12	1.43		3.55	4.74
0430	1" x 8"		190	.042		2.80	1.51		4.31	5.60
0440	1" x 10"		190	.042		3.55	1.51		5.06	6.45
0450	1" x 12"		180	.044		4.34	1.59		5.93	7.45
0460	5/4" x 4"		195	.041		1.72	1.47		3.19	4.36
0470	5/4" x 6"		195	.041		2.72	1.47		4.19	5.45
0480	5/4" x 8"		185	.043		3.57	1.55		5.12	6.55
0490	5/4" x 10"		185	.043		4.57	1.55		6.12	7.65
0500	5/4" x 12"		175	.046		5	1.63		6.63	8.25
0510	Rake trim, 1" x 4"		225	.036		1.35	1.27		2.62	3.63
0520	1" x 6"		225	.036		2.12	1.27		3.39	4.47
0560	5/4" x 4"		220	.036		1.72	1.30		3.02	4.08
0570	5/4" x 6"		220	.036		2.72	1.30		4.02	5.20
0610	Soffit, 1" x 4"	2 Carp	420	.038		1.35	1.36		2.71	3.78
0620	1" x 6"		420	.038		2.12	1.36		3.48	4.62
0630	1" x 8"		420	.038		2.80	1.36		4.16	5.35
0640	1" x 10"		400	.040		3.55	1.43		4.98	6.30
0650	1" x 12"		400	.040		4.34	1.43		5.77	7.20
0660	5/4" x 4"		410	.039		1.72	1.40		3.12	4.24
0670	5/4" x 6"		410	.039		2.72	1.40		4.12	5.35

06 65 Plastic Simulated Wood Trim

06 65 10 – PVC Trim

06 65 10.10 PVC Trim, Exterior		Crew	Daily Output	Labor-Hours	Unit	Material	2014 Bare Costs Labor	Equipment	Total	Total Incl O&P
0680	5/4" x 8"	2 Carp	410	.039	L.F.	3.57	1.40		4.97	6.30
0690	5/4" x 10"		390	.041		4.57	1.47		6.04	7.50
0700	5/4" x 12"		390	.041		5	1.47		6.47	7.95

Estimating Tips

07 10 00 Dampproofing and Waterproofing

- Be sure of the job specifications before pricing this subdivision. The difference in cost between waterproofing and dampproofing can be great. Waterproofing will hold back standing water. Dampproofing prevents the transmission of water vapor. Also included in this section are vapor retarding membranes.

07 20 00 Thermal Protection

- Insulation and fireproofing products are measured by area, thickness, volume or R-value. Specifications may give only what the specific R-value should be in a certain situation. The estimator may need to choose the type of insulation to meet that R-value.

07 30 00 Steep Slope Roofing
07 40 00 Roofing and Siding Panels

- Many roofing and siding products are bought and sold by the square. One square is equal to an area that measures 100 square feet.

This simple change in unit of measure could create a large error if the estimator is not observant. Accessories necessary for a complete installation must be figured into any calculations for both material and labor.

07 50 00 Membrane Roofing
07 60 00 Flashing and Sheet Metal
07 70 00 Roofing and Wall Specialties and Accessories

- The items in these subdivisions compose a roofing system. No one component completes the installation, and all must be estimated. Built-up or single-ply membrane roofing systems are made up of many products and installation trades. Wood blocking at roof perimeters or penetrations, parapet coverings, reglets, roof drains, gutters, downspouts, sheet metal flashing, skylights, smoke vents, and roof hatches all need to be considered along with the roofing material. Several different installation trades will need to work together on the roofing system. Inherent difficulties in the scheduling and coordination of various trades must be accounted for when estimating labor costs.

07 90 00 Joint Protection

- To complete the weather-tight shell, the sealants and caulkings must be estimated. Where different materials meet—at expansion joints, at flashing penetrations, and at hundreds of other locations throughout a construction project—they provide another line of defense against water penetration. Often, an entire system is based on the proper location and placement of caulking or sealants. The detailed drawings that are included as part of a set of architectural plans show typical locations for these materials. When caulking or sealants are shown at typical locations, this means the estimator must include them for all the locations where this detail is applicable. Be careful to keep different types of sealants separate, and remember to consider backer rods and primers if necessary.

Reference Numbers

Reference numbers are shown in shaded boxes at the beginning of some major classifications. These numbers refer to related items in the Reference Section. The reference information may be an estimating procedure, an alternate pricing method, or technical information.

Note: Not all subdivisions listed here necessarily appear in this publication.

07 01 Operation and Maint. of Thermal and Moisture Protection

07 01 50 – Maintenance of Membrane Roofing

07 01 50.10 Roof Coatings

		Crew	Daily Output	Labor-Hours	Unit	Material	2014 Bare Costs Labor	Equipment	Total	Total Incl O&P
0010	**ROOF COATINGS**									
0012	Asphalt, brush grade, material only				Gal.	9.15			9.15	10.10
0200	Asphalt base, fibered aluminum coating G					7.65			7.65	8.40
0300	Asphalt primer, 5 gallon				↓	7.60			7.60	8.35
0600	Coal tar pitch, 200 lb. barrels				Ton	1,525			1,525	1,700
0700	Tar roof cement, 5 gal. lots				Gal.	11.55			11.55	12.70
0800	Glass fibered roof & patching cement, 5 gallon				"	7.65			7.65	8.40
0900	Reinforcing glass membrane, 450 S.F./roll				Ea.	59.50			59.50	65.50
1000	Neoprene roof coating, 5 gal., 2 gal./sq.				Gal.	30.50			30.50	33.50
1100	Roof patch & flashing cement, 5 gallon					8.30			8.30	9.10
1200	Roof resaturant, glass fibered, 3 gal./sq.				↓	8.85			8.85	9.75

07 01 90 – Maintenance of Joint Protection

07 01 90.81 Joint Sealant Replacement

		Crew	Daily Output	Labor-Hours	Unit	Material	2014 Bare Costs Labor	Equipment	Total	Total Incl O&P
0010	**JOINT SEALANT REPLACEMENT**									
0050	Control joints in concrete floors/slabs									
0100	Option 1 for joints with hard dry sealant									
0110	Step 1: Sawcut to remove 95% of old sealant									
0112	1/4" wide x 1/2" deep, with single saw blade	C-27	4800	.003	L.F.	.02	.11	.04	.17	.25
0114	3/8" wide x 3/4" deep, with single saw blade		4000	.004		.03	.14	.04	.21	.30
0116	1/2" wide x 1" deep, with double saw blades		3600	.004		.06	.15	.05	.26	.37
0118	3/4" wide x 1-1/2" deep, with double saw blades	↓	3200	.005		.13	.17	.05	.35	.48
0120	Step 2: Water blast joint faces and edges	C-29	2500	.003			.09	.03	.12	.18
0130	Step 3: Air blast joint faces and edges	C-28	2000	.004			.14	.01	.15	.23
0140	Step 4: Sand blast joint faces and edges	E-11	2000	.016			.51	.12	.63	1.06
0150	Step 5: Air blast joint faces and edges	C-28	2000	.004	↓		.14	.01	.15	.23
0200	Option 2 for joints with soft pliable sealant									
0210	Step 1: Plow joint with rectangular blade	B-62	2600	.009	L.F.		.29	.07	.36	.55
0220	Step 2: Sawcut to re-face joint faces									
0222	1/4" wide x 1/2" deep, with single saw blade	C-27	2400	.007	L.F.	.02	.23	.07	.32	.47
0224	3/8" wide x 3/4" deep, with single saw blade		2000	.008		.04	.27	.09	.40	.59
0226	1/2" wide x 1" deep, with double saw blades		1800	.009		.08	.31	.10	.49	.69
0228	3/4" wide x 1-1/2" deep, with double saw blades	↓	1600	.010		.17	.34	.11	.62	.86
0230	Step 3: Water blast joint faces and edges	C-29	2500	.003			.09	.03	.12	.18
0240	Step 4: Air blast joint faces and edges	C-28	2000	.004			.14	.01	.15	.23
0250	Step 5: Sand blast joint faces and edges	E-11	2000	.016			.51	.12	.63	1.06
0260	Step 6: Air blast joint faces and edges	C-28	2000	.004	↓		.14	.01	.15	.23
0290	For saw cutting new control joints, see Section 03 15 16.20									
8910	For backer rod, see Section 07 91 23.10									
8920	For joint sealant, see Sections 03 15 16.30 or 07 92 13.20									

07 05 Common Work Results for Thermal and Moisture Protection

07 05 05 – Selective Demolition

07 05 05.10 Selective Demo., Thermal and Moist. Protection

			Crew	Daily Output	Labor-Hours	Unit	Material	2014 Bare Costs Labor	Equipment	Total	Total Incl O&P
0010	**SELECTIVE DEMO., THERMAL AND MOISTURE PROTECTION**										
0020	Caulking/sealant, to 1" x 1" joint	R024119-10	1 Clab	600	.013	L.F.		.38		.38	.63
0120	Downspouts, including hangers			350	.023	"		.64		.64	1.08
0220	Flashing, sheet metal			290	.028	S.F.		.78		.78	1.31
0420	Gutters, aluminum or wood, edge hung			240	.033	L.F.		.94		.94	1.58
0520	Built-in			100	.080	"		2.26		2.26	3.80
0620	Insulation, air/vapor barrier		↓	3500	.002	S.F.		.06		.06	.11

07 05 05 – Selective Demolition

07 05 05.10 Selective Demo., Thermal and Moist. Protection	Crew	Daily Output	Labor-Hours	Unit	Material	2014 Bare Costs Labor	Equipment	Total	Total Incl O&P
0670	Batts or blankets	1 Clab	1400	.006	C.F.		.16		.16	.27
0720	Foamed or sprayed in place	2 Clab	1000	.016	B.F.		.45		.45	.76
0770	Loose fitting	1 Clab	3000	.003	C.F.		.08		.08	.13
0870	Rigid board		3450	.002	B.F.		.07		.07	.11
1120	Roll roofing, cold adhesive		12	.667	Sq.		18.80		18.80	31.50
1170	Roof accessories, adjustable metal chimney flashing		9	.889	Ea.		25		25	42
1325	Plumbing vent flashing		32	.250	"		7.05		7.05	11.85
1375	Ridge vent strip, aluminum		310	.026	L.F.		.73		.73	1.22
1620	Skylight to 10 S.F.		8	1	Ea.		28		28	47.50
2120	Roof edge, aluminum soffit and fascia		570	.014	L.F.		.40		.40	.67
2170	Concrete coping, up to 12" wide	2 Clab	160	.100			2.82		2.82	4.75
2220	Drip edge	1 Clab	1000	.008			.23		.23	.38
2270	Gravel stop		950	.008			.24		.24	.40
2370	Sheet metal coping, up to 12" wide		240	.033			.94		.94	1.58
2470	Roof insulation board, over 2" thick	B-2	7800	.005	B.F.		.15		.15	.25
2520	Up to 2" thick	"	3900	.010	S.F.		.29		.29	.49
2620	Roof ventilation, louvered gable vent	1 Clab	16	.500	Ea.		14.10		14.10	23.50
2670	Remove, roof hatch	G-3	15	2.133			73		73	123
2675	Rafter vents	1 Clab	960	.008			.23		.23	.40
2720	Soffit vent and/or fascia vent		575	.014	L.F.		.39		.39	.66
2775	Soffit vent strip, aluminum, 3" to 4" wide		160	.050			1.41		1.41	2.37
2820	Roofing accessories, shingle moulding, to 1" x 4"		1600	.005			.14		.14	.24
2870	Cant strip	B-2	2000	.020			.57		.57	.96
2920	Concrete block walkway	1 Clab	230	.035			.98		.98	1.65
3070	Roofing, felt paper, 15#		70	.114	Sq.		3.22		3.22	5.40
3125	#30 felt		30	.267	"		7.50		7.50	12.65
3170	Asphalt shingles, 1 layer	B-2	3500	.011	S.F.		.33		.33	.55
3180	2 layers		1750	.023	"		.65		.65	1.10
3370	Modified bitumen		26	1.538	Sq.		44		44	74
3420	Built-up, no gravel, 3 ply		25	1.600			46		46	77
3470	4 ply		21	1.905			54.50		54.50	91.50
3620	5 ply		1600	.025	S.F.		.72		.72	1.20
3720	5 ply, with gravel		890	.045			1.29		1.29	2.16
3725	Gravel removal, minimum		5000	.008			.23		.23	.39
3730	Maximum		2000	.020			.57		.57	.96
3870	Fiberglass sheet		1200	.033			.95		.95	1.60
4120	Slate shingles		1900	.021			.60		.60	1.01
4170	Ridge shingles, clay or slate		2000	.020	L.F.		.57		.57	.96
4320	Single ply membrane, attached at seams		52	.769	Sq.		22		22	37
4370	Ballasted		75	.533			15.25		15.25	25.50
4420	Fully adhered		39	1.026			29.50		29.50	49.50
4550	Roof hatch, 2'-6" x 3'-0"	1 Clab	10	.800	Ea.		22.50		22.50	38
4670	Wood shingles	B-2	2200	.018	S.F.		.52		.52	.88
4820	Sheet metal roofing	"	2150	.019			.53		.53	.90
4970	Siding, horizontal wood clapboards	1 Clab	380	.021			.59		.59	1
5025	Exterior insulation finish system	"	120	.067			1.88		1.88	3.16
5070	Tempered hardboard, remove and reset	1 Carp	380	.021			.75		.75	1.27
5120	Tempered hardboard sheet siding	"	375	.021			.76		.76	1.28
5170	Metal, corner strips	1 Clab	850	.009	L.F.		.27		.27	.45
5225	Horizontal strips		444	.018	S.F.		.51		.51	.86
5320	Vertical strips		400	.020			.56		.56	.95
5520	Wood shingles		350	.023			.64		.64	1.08
5620	Stucco siding		360	.022			.63		.63	1.05

07 05 Common Work Results for Thermal and Moisture Protection

07 05 05 – Selective Demolition

07 05 05.10 Selective Demo., Thermal and Moist. Protection	Crew	Daily Output	Labor-Hours	Unit	Material	2014 Bare Costs Labor	Equipment	Total	Total Incl O&P
5670	Textured plywood	1 Clab	725	.011	S.F.		.31		.31	.52
5720	Vinyl siding		510	.016	↓		.44		.44	.74
5770	Corner strips		900	.009	L.F.		.25		.25	.42
5870	Wood, boards, vertical	↓	400	.020	S.F.		.56		.56	.95
5920	Waterproofing, protection/drain board	2 Clab	3900	.004	B.F.		.12		.12	.19
5970	Over 1/2" thick		1750	.009	S.F.		.26		.26	.43
6020	To 1/2" thick	↓	2000	.008	"		.23		.23	.38

07 11 Dampproofing

07 11 13 – Bituminous Dampproofing

07 11 13.10 Bituminous Asphalt Coating

		Crew	Daily Output	Labor-Hours	Unit	Material	2014 Bare Costs Labor	Equipment	Total	Total Incl O&P
0010	**BITUMINOUS ASPHALT COATING**									
0030	Brushed on, below grade, 1 coat	1 Rofc	665	.012	S.F.	.23	.36		.59	.92
0100	2 coat		500	.016		.46	.48		.94	1.39
0300	Sprayed on, below grade, 1 coat		830	.010		.23	.29		.52	.79
0400	2 coat	↓	500	.016	↓	.45	.48		.93	1.38
0500	Asphalt coating, with fibers				Gal.	7.65			7.65	8.40
0600	Troweled on, asphalt with fibers, 1/16" thick	1 Rofc	500	.016	S.F.	.33	.48		.81	1.26
0700	1/8" thick		400	.020		.59	.60		1.19	1.76
1000	1/2" thick	↓	350	.023	↓	1.91	.69		2.60	3.37

07 11 16 – Cementitious Dampproofing

07 11 16.20 Cementitious Parging

		Crew	Daily Output	Labor-Hours	Unit	Material	2014 Bare Costs Labor	Equipment	Total	Total Incl O&P
0010	**CEMENTITIOUS PARGING**									
0020	Portland cement, 2 coats, 1/2" thick	D-1	250	.064	S.F.	.30	2.06		2.36	3.76
0100	Waterproofed Portland cement, 1/2" thick, 2 coats	"	250	.064	"	3.73	2.06		5.79	7.55

07 12 Built-up Bituminous Waterproofing

07 12 13 – Built-Up Asphalt Waterproofing

07 12 13.20 Membrane Waterproofing

		Crew	Daily Output	Labor-Hours	Unit	Material	2014 Bare Costs Labor	Equipment	Total	Total Incl O&P
0010	**MEMBRANE WATERPROOFING**									
0012	On slabs, 1 ply, felt, mopped	G-1	3000	.019	S.F.	.41	.53	.18	1.12	1.62
0100	On slabs, 1 ply, glass fiber fabric, mopped		2100	.027		.46	.75	.26	1.47	2.18
0300	On slabs, 2 ply, felt, mopped		2500	.022		.83	.63	.22	1.68	2.32
0400	On slabs, 2 ply, glass fiber fabric, mopped		1650	.034		1.01	.96	.34	2.31	3.25
0600	On slabs, 3 ply, felt, mopped		2100	.027		1.24	.75	.26	2.25	3.04
0700	On slabs, 3 ply, glass fiber fabric, mopped	↓	1550	.036		1.37	1.02	.36	2.75	3.77
0710	Asphaltic hardboard protection board, 1/8" thick	2 Rofc	500	.032		.62	.96		1.58	2.46
1000	1/4" EPS membrane protection board		3500	.005		.33	.14		.47	.61
1050	3/8" thick		3500	.005		.36	.14		.50	.65
1060	1/2" thick		3500	.005	↓	.39	.14		.53	.68
1070	Fiberglass fabric, black, 20/10 mesh	↓	116	.138	Sq.	14.70	4.16		18.86	24

07 13 Sheet Waterproofing

07 13 53 – Elastomeric Sheet Waterproofing

07 13 53.10 Elastomeric Sheet Waterproofing and Access.	Crew	Daily Output	Labor-Hours	Unit	Material	2014 Bare Costs Labor	Equipment	Total	Total Incl O&P
0010 **ELASTOMERIC SHEET WATERPROOFING AND ACCESS.**									
0090 EPDM, plain, 45 mils thick	2 Rofc	580	.028	S.F.	1.40	.83		2.23	3.07
0100 60 mils thick		570	.028		1.52	.85		2.37	3.23
0300 Nylon reinforced sheets, 45 mils thick		580	.028		1.58	.83		2.41	3.27
0400 60 mils thick	▼	570	.028	▼	1.67	.85		2.52	3.39
0600 Vulcanizing splicing tape for above, 2" wide				C.L.F.	75			75	82.50
0700 4" wide				"	144			144	158
0900 Adhesive, bonding, 60 S.F. per gal.				Gal.	31.50			31.50	35
1000 Splicing, 75 S.F. per gal.				"	37			37	40.50
1200 Neoprene sheets, plain, 45 mils thick	2 Rofc	580	.028	S.F.	1.76	.83		2.59	3.47
1300 60 mils thick		570	.028		2.23	.85		3.08	4.01
1500 Nylon reinforced, 45 mils thick		580	.028		2	.83		2.83	3.73
1600 60 mils thick		570	.028		3.03	.85		3.88	4.89
1800 120 mils thick	▼	500	.032	▼	6.05	.96		7.01	8.45
1900 Adhesive, splicing, 150 S.F. per gal. per coat				Gal.	37			37	40.50
2100 Fiberglass reinforced, fluid applied, 1/8" thick	2 Rofc	500	.032	S.F.	1.63	.96		2.59	3.57
2200 Polyethylene and rubberized asphalt sheets, 60 mils thick		550	.029		.76	.88		1.64	2.46
2400 Polyvinyl chloride sheets, plain, 10 mils thick		580	.028		.14	.83		.97	1.68
2500 20 mils thick		570	.028		.18	.85		1.03	1.76
2700 30 mils thick	▼	560	.029	▼	.25	.86		1.11	1.87
3000 Adhesives, trowel grade, 40-100 S.F. per gal.				Gal.	23			23	25.50
3100 Brush grade, 100-250 S.F. per gal.				"	20.50			20.50	23
3300 Bitumen modified polyurethane, fluid applied, 55 mils thick	2 Rofc	665	.024	S.F.	.89	.73		1.62	2.32

07 16 Cementitious and Reactive Waterproofing

07 16 16 – Crystalline Waterproofing

07 16 16.20 Cementitious Waterproofing	Crew	Daily Output	Labor-Hours	Unit	Material	2014 Bare Costs Labor	Equipment	Total	Total Incl O&P
0010 **CEMENTITIOUS WATERPROOFING**									
0020 1/8" application, sprayed on	G-2A	1000	.024	S.F.	.60	.65	.74	1.99	2.63
0050 4 coat cementitious metallic slurry	1 Cefi	1.20	6.667	C.S.F.	30.50	229		259.50	405

07 17 Bentonite Waterproofing

07 17 13 – Bentonite Panel Waterproofing

07 17 13.10 Bentonite	Crew	Daily Output	Labor-Hours	Unit	Material	2014 Bare Costs Labor	Equipment	Total	Total Incl O&P
0010 **BENTONITE**									
0020 Panels, 4' x 4', 3/16" thick	1 Rofc	625	.013	S.F.	1.46	.39		1.85	2.32
0100 Rolls, 3/8" thick, with geotextile fabric both sides	"	550	.015	"	1.50	.44		1.94	2.46
0300 Granular bentonite, 50 lb. bags (.625 C.F.)				Bag	15.10			15.10	16.60
0400 3/8" thick, troweled on	1 Rofc	475	.017	S.F.	.75	.51		1.26	1.77
0500 Drain board, expanded polystyrene, 1-1/2" thick	1 Rohe	1600	.005		.36	.11		.47	.61
0510 2" thick		1600	.005		.48	.11		.59	.74
0520 3" thick		1600	.005		.72	.11		.83	1
0530 4" thick		1600	.005		.96	.11		1.07	1.27
0600 With filter fabric, 1-1/2" thick		1600	.005		.42	.11		.53	.68
0625 2" thick		1600	.005		.54	.11		.65	.81
0650 3" thick		1600	.005		.78	.11		.89	1.07
0675 4" thick	▼	1600	.005	▼	1.02	.11		1.13	1.34

07 19 Water Repellents

07 19 19 – Silicone Water Repellents

07 19 19.10 Silicone Based Water Repellents		Crew	Daily Output	Labor-Hours	Unit	Material	2014 Bare Costs Labor	Equipment	Total	Total Incl O&P
0010	**SILICONE BASED WATER REPELLENTS**									
0020	Water base liquid, roller applied	2 Rofc	7000	.002	S.F.	.49	.07		.56	.67
0200	Silicone or stearate, sprayed on CMU, 1 coat	1 Rofc	4000	.002		.35	.06		.41	.50
0300	2 coats	"	3000	.003	↓	.71	.08		.79	.93

07 21 Thermal Insulation

07 21 13 – Board Insulation

07 21 13.10 Rigid Insulation

07 21 13.10 Rigid Insulation			Crew	Daily Output	Labor-Hours	Unit	Material	2014 Bare Costs Labor	Equipment	Total	Total Incl O&P
0010	**RIGID INSULATION**, for walls										
0040	Fiberglass, 1.5#/C.F., unfaced, 1" thick, R4.1	G	1 Carp	1000	.008	S.F.	.27	.29		.56	.78
0060	1-1/2" thick, R6.2	G		1000	.008		.40	.29		.69	.92
0080	2" thick, R8.3	G		1000	.008		.45	.29		.74	.98
0120	3" thick, R12.4	G		800	.010		.56	.36		.92	1.22
0370	3#/C.F., unfaced, 1" thick, R4.3	G		1000	.008		.52	.29		.81	1.05
0390	1-1/2" thick, R6.5	G		1000	.008		.78	.29		1.07	1.34
0400	2" thick, R8.7	G		890	.009		1.05	.32		1.37	1.70
0420	2-1/2" thick, R10.9	G		800	.010		1.10	.36		1.46	1.81
0440	3" thick, R13	G		800	.010		1.59	.36		1.95	2.35
0520	Foil faced, 1" thick, R4.3	G		1000	.008		.90	.29		1.19	1.47
0540	1-1/2" thick, R6.5	G		1000	.008		1.35	.29		1.64	1.97
0560	2" thick, R8.7	G		890	.009		1.69	.32		2.01	2.40
0580	2-1/2" thick, R10.9	G		800	.010		1.98	.36		2.34	2.78
0600	3" thick, R13	G	↓	800	.010	↓	2.18	.36		2.54	3
1600	Isocyanurate, 4' x 8' sheet, foil faced, both sides										
1610	1/2" thick	G	1 Carp	800	.010	S.F.	.29	.36		.65	.92
1620	5/8" thick	G		800	.010		.32	.36		.68	.95
1630	3/4" thick	G		800	.010		.33	.36		.69	.96
1640	1" thick	G		800	.010		.51	.36		.87	1.16
1650	1-1/2" thick	G		730	.011		.63	.39		1.02	1.35
1660	2" thick	G		730	.011		.79	.39		1.18	1.53
1670	3" thick	G		730	.011		1.78	.39		2.17	2.62
1680	4" thick	G		730	.011		2	.39		2.39	2.86
1700	Perlite, 1" thick, R2.77	G		800	.010		.36	.36		.72	1
1750	2" thick, R5.55	G		730	.011		.72	.39		1.11	1.45
1900	Extruded polystyrene, 25 PSI compressive strength, 1" thick, R5	G		800	.010		.52	.36		.88	1.17
1940	2" thick R10	G		730	.011		1.05	.39		1.44	1.82
1960	3" thick, R15	G		730	.011		1.49	.39		1.88	2.30
2100	Expanded polystyrene, 1" thick, R3.85	G		800	.010		.24	.36		.60	.86
2120	2" thick, R7.69	G		730	.011		.48	.39		.87	1.19
2140	3" thick, R11.49	G	↓	730	.011	↓	.72	.39		1.11	1.45

07 21 13.13 Foam Board Insulation

07 21 13.13 Foam Board Insulation			Crew	Daily Output	Labor-Hours	Unit	Material	2014 Bare Costs Labor	Equipment	Total	Total Incl O&P
0010	**FOAM BOARD INSULATION**										
0600	Polystyrene, expanded, 1" thick, R4	G	1 Carp	680	.012	S.F.	.24	.42		.66	.97
0700	2" thick, R8	G	"	675	.012	"	.48	.42		.90	1.24

07 21 16 – Blanket Insulation

07 21 16.10 Blanket Insulation for Floors/Ceilings

07 21 16.10 Blanket Insulation for Floors/Ceilings			Crew	Daily Output	Labor-Hours	Unit	Material	2014 Bare Costs Labor	Equipment	Total	Total Incl O&P
0010	**BLANKET INSULATION FOR FLOORS/CEILINGS**										
0020	Including spring type wire fasteners										
2000	Fiberglass, blankets or batts, paper or foil backing										
2100	3-1/2" thick, R13	G	1 Carp	700	.011	S.F.	.37	.41		.78	1.10

07 21 Thermal Insulation

07 21 16 – Blanket Insulation

07 21 16.10 Blanket Insulation for Floors/Ceilings

		Crew	Daily Output	Labor-Hours	Unit	Material	2014 Bare Costs Labor	Equipment	Total	Total Incl O&P
2150	6-1/4" thick, R19	G 1 Carp	600	.013	S.F.	.48	.48		.96	1.33
2210	9-1/2" thick, R30	G	500	.016		.70	.57		1.27	1.73
2220	12" thick, R38	G	475	.017		.89	.60		1.49	1.99
3000	Unfaced, 3-1/2" thick, R13	G	600	.013		.32	.48		.80	1.15
3010	6-1/4" thick, R19	G	500	.016		.37	.57		.94	1.37
3020	9-1/2" thick, R30	G	450	.018		.60	.64		1.24	1.73
3030	12" thick, R38	G	425	.019		.75	.67		1.42	1.96

07 21 16.20 Blanket Insulation for Walls

		Crew	Daily Output	Labor-Hours	Unit	Material	2014 Bare Costs Labor	Equipment	Total	Total Incl O&P
0010	**BLANKET INSULATION FOR WALLS**									
0020	Kraft faced fiberglass, 3-1/2" thick, R11, 15" wide	G 1 Carp	1350	.006	S.F.	.26	.21		.47	.65
0030	23" wide	G	1600	.005		.26	.18		.44	.59
0060	R13, 11" wide	G	1150	.007		.31	.25		.56	.76
0080	15" wide	G	1350	.006		.31	.21		.52	.70
0100	23" wide	G	1600	.005		.31	.18		.49	.64
0110	R15, 11" wide	G	1150	.007		.51	.25		.76	.98
0120	15" wide	G	1350	.006		.51	.21		.72	.92
0130	23" wide	G	1600	.005		.51	.18		.69	.86
0140	6" thick, R19, 11" wide	G	1150	.007		.42	.25		.67	.88
0160	15" wide	G	1350	.006		.42	.21		.63	.82
0180	23" wide	G	1600	.005		.42	.18		.60	.76
0182	R21, 11" wide	G	1150	.007		.60	.25		.85	1.08
0184	15" wide	G	1350	.006		.60	.21		.81	1.02
0186	23" wide	G	1600	.005		.60	.18		.78	.96
0188	9" thick, R30, 11" wide	G	985	.008		.70	.29		.99	1.26
0200	15" wide	G	1150	.007		.70	.25		.95	1.19
0220	23" wide	G	1350	.006		.70	.21		.91	1.13
0230	12" thick, R38, 11" wide	G	985	.008		.89	.29		1.18	1.47
0240	15" wide	G	1150	.007		.89	.25		1.14	1.40
0260	23" wide	G	1350	.006		.89	.21		1.10	1.34
0410	Foil faced fiberglass, 3-1/2" thick, R13, 11" wide	G	1150	.007		.44	.25		.69	.90
0420	15" wide	G	1350	.006		.44	.21		.65	.84
0440	23" wide	G	1600	.005		.44	.18		.62	.78
0442	R15, 11" wide	G	1150	.007		.48	.25		.73	.95
0444	15" wide	G	1350	.006		.48	.21		.69	.89
0446	23" wide	G	1600	.005		.48	.18		.66	.83
0448	6" thick, R19, 11" wide	G	1150	.007		.57	.25		.82	1.05
0460	15" wide	G	1350	.006		.57	.21		.78	.99
0480	23" wide	G	1600	.005		.57	.18		.75	.93
0482	R21, 11" wide	G	1150	.007		.60	.25		.85	1.08
0484	15" wide	G	1350	.006		.60	.21		.81	1.02
0486	23" wide	G	1600	.005		.60	.18		.78	.96
0488	9" thick, R30, 11" wide	G	985	.008		.89	.29		1.18	1.47
0500	15" wide	G	1150	.007		.89	.25		1.14	1.40
0550	23" wide	G	1350	.006		.89	.21		1.10	1.34
0560	12" thick, R38, 11" wide	G	985	.008		1.03	.29		1.32	1.62
0570	15" wide	G	1150	.007		1.03	.25		1.28	1.55
0580	23" wide	G	1350	.006		1.03	.21		1.24	1.49
0620	Unfaced fiberglass, 3-1/2" thick, R13, 11" wide	G	1150	.007		.32	.25		.57	.77
0820	15" wide	G	1350	.006		.32	.21		.53	.71
0830	23" wide	G	1600	.005		.32	.18		.50	.65
0832	R15, 11" wide	G	1150	.007		.46	.25		.71	.93
0836	23" wide	G	1600	.005		.46	.18		.64	.81

07 21 16 – Blanket Insulation

07 21 16.20 Blanket Insulation for Walls		Crew	Daily Output	Labor-Hours	Unit	Material	2014 Bare Costs Labor	Equipment	Total	Total Incl O&P
0838	6" thick, R19, 11" wide	G	1 Carp	1150	.007	S.F.	.37	.25		.62	.83
0860	15" wide	G		1150	.007		.37	.25		.62	.83
0880	23" wide	G		1350	.006		.37	.21		.58	.77
0882	R21, 11" wide	G		1150	.007		.50	.25		.75	.97
0886	15" wide	G		1350	.006		.50	.21		.71	.91
0888	23" wide	G		1600	.005		.50	.18		.68	.85
0890	9" thick, R30, 11" wide	G		985	.008		.60	.29		.89	1.15
0900	15" wide	G		1150	.007		.60	.25		.85	1.08
0920	23" wide	G		1350	.006		.60	.21		.81	1.02
0930	12" thick, R38, 11" wide	G		985	.008		.75	.29		1.04	1.32
0940	15" wide	G		1000	.008		.75	.29		1.04	1.31
0960	23" wide	G		1150	.007		.75	.25		1	1.25
1300	Wall or ceiling insulation, mineral wool batts										
1320	3-1/2" thick, R15	G	1 Carp	1600	.005	S.F.	.60	.18		.78	.96
1340	5-1/2" thick, R23	G		1600	.005		.94	.18		1.12	1.34
1380	7-1/4" thick, R30	G		1350	.006		1.24	.21		1.45	1.73
1850	Friction fit wire insulation supports, 16" O.C.			960	.008	Ea.	.06	.30		.36	.57

07 21 19 – Foamed In Place Insulation

07 21 19.10 Masonry Foamed In Place Insulation

		Crew	Daily Output	Labor-Hours	Unit	Material	Labor	Equipment	Total	Total Incl O&P
0010	**MASONRY FOAMED IN PLACE INSULATION**										
0100	Amino-plast foam, injected into block core, 6" block	G	G-2A	6000	.004	Ea.	.15	.11	.12	.38	.50
0110	8" block	G		5000	.005		.19	.13	.15	.47	.59
0120	10" block	G		4000	.006		.23	.16	.19	.58	.75
0130	12" block	G		3000	.008		.31	.22	.25	.78	1
0140	Injected into cavity wall	G		13000	.002	B.F.	.05	.05	.06	.16	.21
0150	Preparation, drill holes into mortar joint every 4 VLF, 5/8" dia		1 Clab	960	.008	Ea.		.23		.23	.40
0160	7/8" dia			680	.012			.33		.33	.56
0170	Patch drilled holes, 5/8" diameter			1800	.004		.03	.13		.16	.24
0180	7/8" diameter			1200	.007		.04	.19		.23	.37

07 21 23 – Loose-Fill Insulation

07 21 23.10 Poured Loose-Fill Insulation

		Crew	Daily Output	Labor-Hours	Unit	Material	Labor	Equipment	Total	Total Incl O&P
0010	**POURED LOOSE-FILL INSULATION**										
0020	Cellulose fiber, R3.8 per inch	G	1 Carp	200	.040	C.F.	.69	1.43		2.12	3.17
0021	4" thick	G		1000	.008	S.F.	.17	.29		.46	.66
0022	6" thick	G		800	.010	"	.28	.36		.64	.91
0080	Fiberglass wool, R4 per inch	G		200	.040	C.F.	.53	1.43		1.96	3
0081	4" thick	G		600	.013	S.F.	.18	.48		.66	1
0082	6" thick	G		400	.020	"	.26	.72		.98	1.48
0100	Mineral wool, R3 per inch	G		200	.040	C.F.	.39	1.43		1.82	2.84
0101	4" thick	G		600	.013	S.F.	.13	.48		.61	.94
0102	6" thick	G		400	.020	"	.20	.72		.92	1.41
0300	Polystyrene, R4 per inch	G		200	.040	C.F.	2.50	1.43		3.93	5.15
0301	4" thick	G		600	.013	S.F.	.83	.48		1.31	1.71
0302	6" thick	G		400	.020	"	1.25	.72		1.97	2.58
0400	Perlite, R2.78 per inch	G		200	.040	C.F.	5.40	1.43		6.83	8.35
0401	4" thick	G		1000	.008	S.F.	1.80	.29		2.09	2.46
0402	6" thick	G		800	.010	"	2.70	.36		3.06	3.57

07 21 23.20 Masonry Loose-Fill Insulation

		Crew	Daily Output	Labor-Hours	Unit	Material	Labor	Equipment	Total	Total Incl O&P
0010	**MASONRY LOOSE-FILL INSULATION**, vermiculite or perlite										
0100	In cores of concrete block, 4" thick wall, .115 C.F./S.F.	G	D-1	4800	.003	S.F.	.62	.11		.73	.86
0200	6" thick wall, .175 C.F./S.F.	G		3000	.005		.95	.17		1.12	1.33

07 21 Thermal Insulation

07 21 23 – Loose-Fill Insulation

07 21 23.20 Masonry Loose-Fill Insulation

		Crew	Daily Output	Labor-Hours	Unit	Material	2014 Bare Costs Labor	Equipment	Total	Total Incl O&P
0300	8" thick wall, .258 C.F./S.F.	G	D-1	2400	.007	S.F.	1.39	.22		1.61	1.89
0400	10" thick wall, .340 C.F./S.F.	G		1850	.009		1.84	.28		2.12	2.48
0500	12" thick wall, .422 C.F./S.F.	G		1200	.013		2.28	.43		2.71	3.22
0550	For sand fill, deduct from above	G					70%				
0600	Poured cavity wall, vermiculite or perlite, water repellant	G	D-1	250	.064	C.F.	5.40	2.06		7.46	9.40
0700	Foamed in place, urethane in 2-5/8" cavity	G	G-2A	1035	.023	S.F.	1.38	.62	.72	2.72	3.43
0800	For each 1" added thickness, add	G	"	2372	.010	"	.53	.27	.31	1.11	1.41

07 21 26 – Blown Insulation

07 21 26.10 Blown Insulation

		Crew	Daily Output	Labor-Hours	Unit	Material	2014 Bare Costs Labor	Equipment	Total	Total Incl O&P
0010	**BLOWN INSULATION** Ceilings, with open access										
0020	Cellulose, 3-1/2" thick, R13	G	G-4	5000	.005	S.F.	.24	.14	.09	.47	.58
0030	5-3/16" thick, R19	G		3800	.006		.35	.18	.11	.64	.82
0050	6-1/2" thick, R22	G		3000	.008		.45	.23	.14	.82	1.05
0100	8-11/16" thick, R30	G		2600	.009		.61	.27	.16	1.04	1.30
0120	10-7/8" thick, R38	G		1800	.013		.78	.38	.24	1.40	1.76
1000	Fiberglass, 5.5" thick, R11	G		3800	.006		.18	.18	.11	.47	.63
1050	6" thick, R12	G		3000	.008		.26	.23	.14	.63	.83
1100	8.8" thick, R19	G		2200	.011		.32	.32	.19	.83	1.09
1200	10" thick, R22	G		1800	.013		.37	.38	.24	.99	1.32
1300	11.5" thick, R26	G		1500	.016		.44	.46	.29	1.19	1.58
1350	13" thick, R30	G		1400	.017		.52	.49	.31	1.32	1.74
1450	16" thick, R38	G		1145	.021		.66	.61	.37	1.64	2.16
1500	20" thick, R49	G		920	.026		.87	.75	.46	2.08	2.74

07 21 27 – Reflective Insulation

07 21 27.10 Reflective Insulation Options

		Crew	Daily Output	Labor-Hours	Unit	Material	2014 Bare Costs Labor	Equipment	Total	Total Incl O&P
0010	**REFLECTIVE INSULATION OPTIONS**										
0020	Aluminum foil on reinforced scrim	G	1 Carp	19	.421	C.S.F.	14.20	15.05		29.25	41
0100	Reinforced with woven polyolefin	G		19	.421		22	15.05		37.05	49.50
0500	With single bubble air space, R8.8	G		15	.533		26	19.05		45.05	60.50
0600	With double bubble air space, R9.8	G		15	.533		29	19.05		48.05	63.50

07 21 29 – Sprayed Insulation

07 21 29.10 Sprayed-On Insulation

		Crew	Daily Output	Labor-Hours	Unit	Material	2014 Bare Costs Labor	Equipment	Total	Total Incl O&P
0010	**SPRAYED-ON INSULATION**										
0020	Fibrous/cementitious, finished wall, 1" thick, R3.7	G	G-2	2050	.012	S.F.	.29	.35	.07	.71	.97
0100	Attic, 5.2" thick, R19	G		1550	.015	"	.51	.46	.09	1.06	1.43
0200	Fiberglass, R4 per inch, vertical	G		1600	.015	B.F.	.18	.45	.08	.71	1.02
0210	Horizontal	G		1200	.020	"	.18	.60	.11	.89	1.30
0300	Closed cell, spray polyurethane foam, 2 pounds per cubic foot density										
0310	1" thick	G	G-2A	6000	.004	S.F.	.53	.11	.12	.76	.91
0320	2" thick	G		3000	.008		1.05	.22	.25	1.52	1.82
0330	3" thick	G		2000	.012		1.58	.32	.37	2.27	2.72
0335	3-1/2" thick	G		1715	.014		1.84	.38	.43	2.65	3.17
0340	4" thick	G		1500	.016		2.10	.43	.49	3.02	3.62
0350	5" thick	G		1200	.020		2.63	.54	.62	3.79	4.53
0355	5-1/2" thick	G		1090	.022		2.89	.59	.68	4.16	4.99
0360	6" thick	G		1000	.024		3.15	.65	.74	4.54	5.45

07 22 16.10 Roof Deck Insulation		Crew	Daily Output	Labor-Hours	Unit	Material	2014 Bare Costs Labor	Equipment	Total	Total Incl O&P
0010	**ROOF DECK INSULATION**, fastening excluded									
0020	Fiberboard low density, 1/2" thick R1.39	G	1 Rofc	1300	.006	S.F.	.30	.19		.49	.67
0030	1" thick R2.78	G		1040	.008		.52	.23		.75	1
0080	1 1/2" thick R4.17	G		1040	.008		.80	.23		1.03	1.31
0100	2" thick R5.56	G		1040	.008		1.06	.23		1.29	1.60
0110	Fiberboard high density, 1/2" thick R1.3	G		1300	.006		.29	.19		.48	.66
0120	1" thick R2.5	G		1040	.008		.60	.23		.83	1.09
0130	1-1/2" thick R3.8	G		1040	.008		.89	.23		1.12	1.41
0200	Fiberglass, 3/4" thick R2.78	G		1300	.006		.61	.19		.80	1.01
0400	15/16" thick R3.70	G		1300	.006		.81	.19		1	1.23
0460	1-1/16" thick R4.17	G		1300	.006		1.01	.19		1.20	1.45
0600	1-5/16" thick R5.26	G		1300	.006		1.37	.19		1.56	1.85
0650	2-1/16" thick R8.33	G		1040	.008		1.45	.23		1.68	2.03
0700	2-7/16" thick R10	G		1040	.008		1.68	.23		1.91	2.28
1650	Perlite, 1/2" thick R1.32	G		1365	.006		.31	.18		.49	.67
1655	3/4" thick R2.08	G		1040	.008		.35	.23		.58	.82
1660	1" thick R2.78	G		1040	.008		.49	.23		.72	.97
1670	1-1/2" thick R4.17	G		1040	.008		.72	.23		.95	1.22
1680	2" thick R5.56	G		910	.009		.99	.27		1.26	1.58
1685	2-1/2" thick R6.67	G		910	.009		1.30	.27		1.57	1.92
1690	Tapered for drainage	G		1040	.008	B.F.	1.01	.23		1.24	1.54
1700	Polyisocyanurate, 2#/C.F. density, 3/4" thick	G		1950	.004	S.F.	.44	.12		.56	.71
1705	1" thick	G		1820	.004		.50	.13		.63	.79
1715	1-1/2" thick	G		1625	.005		.63	.15		.78	.96
1725	2" thick	G		1430	.006		.79	.17		.96	1.18
1735	2-1/2" thick	G		1365	.006		1.01	.18		1.19	1.44
1745	3" thick	G		1300	.006		1.22	.19		1.41	1.68
1755	3-1/2" thick	G		1300	.006		1.95	.19		2.14	2.49
1765	Tapered for drainage	G		1820	.004	B.F.	.57	.13		.70	.87
1900	Extruded Polystyrene										
1910	15 PSI compressive strength, 1" thick, R5	G	1 Rofc	1950	.004	S.F.	.53	.12		.65	.81
1920	2" thick, R10	G		1625	.005		.69	.15		.84	1.03
1930	3" thick R15	G		1300	.006		1.38	.19		1.57	1.86
1932	4" thick R20	G		1300	.006		1.86	.19		2.05	2.38
1934	Tapered for drainage	G		1950	.004	B.F.	.56	.12		.68	.85
1940	25 PSI compressive strength, 1" thick R5	G		1950	.004	S.F.	.66	.12		.78	.96
1942	2" thick R10	G		1625	.005		1.25	.15		1.40	1.65
1944	3" thick R15	G		1300	.006		1.91	.19		2.10	2.45
1946	4" thick R20	G		1300	.006		2.64	.19		2.83	3.24
1948	Tapered for drainage	G		1950	.004	B.F.	.58	.12		.70	.87
1950	40 psi compressive strength, 1" thick R5	G		1950	.004	S.F.	.51	.12		.63	.79
1952	2" thick R10	G		1625	.005		.97	.15		1.12	1.34
1954	3" thick R15	G		1300	.006		1.40	.19		1.59	1.88
1956	4" thick R20	G		1300	.006		1.84	.19		2.03	2.36
1958	Tapered for drainage	G		1820	.004	B.F.	.73	.13		.86	1.04
1960	60 PSI compressive strength, 1" thick R5	G		1885	.004	S.F.	.71	.13		.84	1.02
1962	2" thick R10	G		1560	.005		1.35	.15		1.50	1.77
1964	3" thick R15	G		1270	.006		2.20	.19		2.39	2.77
1966	4" thick R20	G		1235	.006		2.73	.20		2.93	3.37
1968	Tapered for drainage	G		1820	.004	B.F.	.93	.13		1.06	1.26
2010	Expanded polystyrene, 1#/C.F. density, 3/4" thick R2.89	G		1950	.004	S.F.	.18	.12		.30	.43
2020	1" thick R3.85	G		1950	.004		.24	.12		.36	.49
2100	2" thick R7.69	G		1625	.005		.48	.15		.63	.80

07 22 Roof and Deck Insulation

07 22 16 – Roof Board Insulation

07 22 16.10 Roof Deck Insulation		Crew	Daily Output	Labor-Hours	Unit	Material	2014 Bare Costs Labor	Equipment	Total	Total Incl O&P
2110	3" thick R11.49	G 1 Rofc	1625	.005	S.F.	.72	.15		.87	1.06
2120	4" thick R15.38	G	1625	.005		.96	.15		1.11	1.33
2130	5" thick R19.23	G	1495	.005		1.20	.16		1.36	1.62
2140	6" thick R23.26	G	1495	.005		1.44	.16		1.60	1.88
2150	Tapered for drainage	G	1950	.004	B.F.	.51	.12		.63	.79
2400	Composites with 2" EPS									
2410	1" fiberboard	G 1 Rofc	1325	.006	S.F.	1.33	.18		1.51	1.80
2420	7/16" oriented strand board	G	1040	.008		1.07	.23		1.30	1.61
2430	1/2" plywood	G	1040	.008		1.32	.23		1.55	1.88
2440	1" perlite	G	1040	.008		1.09	.23		1.32	1.63
2450	Composites with 1-1/2" polyisocyanurate									
2460	1" fiberboard	G 1 Rofc	1040	.008	S.F.	1.13	.23		1.36	1.67
2470	1" perlite	G	1105	.007		1.01	.22		1.23	1.51
2480	7/16" oriented strand board	G	1040	.008		.89	.23		1.12	1.41
3000	Fastening alternatives, coated screws, 2"		3744	.002	Ea.	.05	.06		.11	.18
3010	4"		3120	.003		.10	.08		.18	.25
3020	6"		2675	.003		.17	.09		.26	.36
3030	8"		2340	.003		.25	.10		.35	.47
3040	10"		1872	.004		.43	.13		.56	.71
3050	Pre-drill and drive wedge spike, 2-1/2"		1248	.006		.37	.19		.56	.77
3060	3-1/2"		1101	.007		.48	.22		.70	.93
3070	4-1/2"		936	.009		.60	.26		.86	1.14
3075	3" galvanized deck plates		7488	.001		.07	.03		.10	.14
3080	Spot mop asphalt	G-1	295	.190	Sq.	5.50	5.35	1.88	12.73	17.95
3090	Full mop asphalt	"	192	.292		11	8.25	2.88	22.13	30.50
3100	Low-rise polyurethane adhesive	G-2A	100	.240		.18	6.45	7.40	14.03	19.90

07 24 Exterior Insulation and Finish Systems

07 24 13 – Polymer-Based Exterior Insulation and Finish System

07 24 13.10 Exterior Insulation and Finish Systems

		Crew	Daily Output	Labor-Hours	Unit	Material	2014 Bare Costs Labor	Equipment	Total	Total Incl O&P
0010	**EXTERIOR INSULATION AND FINISH SYSTEMS**									
0095	Field applied, 1" EPS insulation	G J-1	390	.103	S.F.	1.92	3.20	.37	5.49	7.75
0100	With 1/2" cement board sheathing	G	268	.149		2.65	4.66	.54	7.85	11.15
0105	2" EPS insulation	G	390	.103		2.16	3.20	.37	5.73	8.05
0110	With 1/2" cement board sheathing	G	268	.149		2.89	4.66	.54	8.09	11.40
0115	3" EPS insulation	G	390	.103		2.40	3.20	.37	5.97	8.30
0120	With 1/2" cement board sheathing	G	268	.149		3.13	4.66	.54	8.33	11.70
0125	4" EPS insulation	G	390	.103		2.64	3.20	.37	6.21	8.55
0130	With 1/2" cement board sheathing	G	268	.149		4.11	4.66	.54	9.31	12.75
0140	Premium finish add		1265	.032		.31	.99	.11	1.41	2.08
0150	Heavy duty reinforcement add		914	.044		.81	1.37	.16	2.34	3.31
0160	2.5#/S.Y. metal lath substrate add	1 Lath	75	.107	S.Y.	3.05	3.38		6.43	8.80
0170	3.4#/S.Y. metal lath substrate add	"	75	.107	"	3.80	3.38		7.18	9.65
0180	Color or texture change,	J-1	1265	.032	S.F.	.75	.99	.11	1.85	2.57
0190	With substrate leveling base coat	1 Plas	530	.015		.75	.49		1.24	1.64
0210	With substrate sealing base coat	1 Pord	1224	.007		.08	.20		.28	.43
0370	V groove shape in panel face				L.F.	.60			.60	.66
0380	U groove shape in panel face				"	.79			.79	.87
0440	For higher than one story, add						25%			

07 25 Weather Barriers

07 25 10 – Weather Barriers or Wraps

07 25 10.10 Weather Barriers		Crew	Daily Output	Labor-Hours	Unit	Material	2014 Bare Costs Labor	Equipment	Total	Total Incl O&P
0010	**WEATHER BARRIERS**									
0400	Asphalt felt paper, 15#	1 Carp	37	.216	Sq.	5.40	7.75		13.15	18.95
0401	Per square foot	"	3700	.002	S.F.	.05	.08		.13	.19
0450	Housewrap, exterior, spun bonded polypropylene									
0470	Small roll	1 Carp	3800	.002	S.F.	.14	.08		.22	.29
0480	Large roll	"	4000	.002	"	.14	.07		.21	.27
2100	Asphalt felt roof deck vapor barrier, class 1 metal decks	1 Rofc	37	.216	Sq.	22	6.50		28.50	36
2200	For all other decks	"	37	.216		16.40	6.50		22.90	30
2800	Asphalt felt, 50% recycled content, 15 lb., 4 sq. per roll	1 Carp	36	.222		5.40	7.95		13.35	19.30
2810	30 lb., 2 sq. per roll	"	36	.222		10.80	7.95		18.75	25.50
3000	Building wrap, spunbonded polyethylene	2 Carp	8000	.002	S.F.	.14	.07		.21	.27

07 26 Vapor Retarders

07 26 10 – Above-Grade Vapor Retarders

07 26 10.10 Vapor Retarders			Crew	Daily Output	Labor-Hours	Unit	Material	2014 Bare Costs Labor	Equipment	Total	Total Incl O&P
0010	**VAPOR RETARDERS**										
0020	Aluminum and kraft laminated, foil 1 side	G	1 Carp	37	.216	Sq.	11.25	7.75		19	25.50
0100	Foil 2 sides	G		37	.216		12.50	7.75		20.25	27
0600	Polyethylene vapor barrier, standard, .002" thick	G		37	.216		1.50	7.75		9.25	14.65
0700	.004" thick	G		37	.216		2.91	7.75		10.66	16.20
0900	.006" thick	G		37	.216		3.98	7.75		11.73	17.40
1200	.010" thick	G		37	.216		8.85	7.75		16.60	23
1300	Clear reinforced, fire retardant, .008" thick	G		37	.216		10.50	7.75		18.25	24.50
1350	Cross laminated type, .003" thick	G		37	.216		7.45	7.75		15.20	21
1400	.004" thick	G		37	.216		7.80	7.75		15.55	21.50
1800	Reinf. waterproof, .002" polyethylene backing, 1 side			37	.216		5.95	7.75		13.70	19.50
1900	2 sides			37	.216		7.80	7.75		15.55	21.50
2400	Waterproofed kraft with sisal or fiberglass fibers, minimum			37	.216		12.50	7.75		20.25	27
2500	Maximum			37	.216		13.50	7.75		21.25	28

07 27 Air Barriers

07 27 26 – Fluid-Applied Membrane Air Barriers

07 27 26.10 Fluid Applied Membrane Air Barrier		Crew	Daily Output	Labor-Hours	Unit	Material	2014 Bare Costs Labor	Equipment	Total	Total Incl O&P
0010	**FLUID APPLIED MEMBRANE AIR BARRIER**									
0100	Spray applied vapor barrier, 25 S.F./gallon	1 Pord	1375	.006	S.F.	.01	.18		.19	.32

07 31 Shingles and Shakes

07 31 13 – Asphalt Shingles

07 31 13.10 Asphalt Roof Shingles		Crew	Daily Output	Labor-Hours	Unit	Material	2014 Bare Costs Labor	Equipment	Total	Total Incl O&P
0010	**ASPHALT ROOF SHINGLES**									
0100	Standard strip shingles									
0150	Inorganic, class A, 210-235 lb./sq.	1 Rofc	5.50	1.455	Sq.	81	44		125	170
0155	Pneumatic nailed		7	1.143		81	34.50		115.50	153
0200	235-240 lb./sq.		5	1.600		96	48		144	195
0205	Pneumatic nailed		6.25	1.280		96	38.50		134.50	177
0250	Standard, laminated multi-layered shingles									
0300	Class A, 240-260 lb./sq.	1 Rofc	4.50	1.778	Sq.	106	53.50		159.50	215

07 31 Shingles and Shakes

07 31 13 – Asphalt Shingles

07 31 13.10 Asphalt Roof Shingles

		Crew	Daily Output	Labor-Hours	Unit	Material	2014 Bare Costs Labor	2014 Bare Costs Equipment	Total	Total Incl O&P
0305	Pneumatic nailed	1 Rofc	5.63	1.422	Sq.	106	43		149	195
0350	Class A, 260-300 lb./square, 4 bundles/square		4	2		106	60.50		166.50	227
0355	Pneumatic nailed	↓	5	1.600	↓	106	48		154	205
0400	Premium, laminated multi-layered shingles									
0450	Class A, 260-300 lb., 4 bundles/sq.	1 Rofc	3.50	2.286	Sq.	165	69		234	310
0455	Pneumatic nailed		4.37	1.831		165	55		220	283
0500	Class A, 300-385 lb./square, 5 bundles/square		3	2.667		219	80.50		299.50	390
0505	Pneumatic nailed		3.75	2.133		219	64.50		283.50	360
0800	#15 felt underlayment		64	.125		5.40	3.77		9.17	12.90
0825	#30 felt underlayment		58	.138		10.80	4.16		14.96	19.55
0850	Self adhering polyethylene and rubberized asphalt underlayment		22	.364	↓	77	10.95		87.95	105
0900	Ridge shingles		330	.024	L.F.	2	.73		2.73	3.55
0905	Pneumatic nailed	↓	412.50	.019	"	2	.58		2.58	3.28
1000	For steep roofs (7 to 12 pitch or greater), add						50%			

07 31 16 – Metal Shingles

07 31 16.10 Aluminum Shingles

		Crew	Daily Output	Labor-Hours	Unit	Material	2014 Bare Costs Labor	2014 Bare Costs Equipment	Total	Total Incl O&P
0010	**ALUMINUM SHINGLES**									
0020	Mill finish, .019 thick	1 Carp	5	1.600	Sq.	221	57		278	340
0100	.020" thick	"	5	1.600		222	57		279	340
0300	For colors, add				↓	20			20	22
0600	Ridge cap, .024" thick	1 Carp	170	.047	L.F.	3.60	1.68		5.28	6.80
0700	End wall flashing, .024" thick		170	.047		1.99	1.68		3.67	5
0900	Valley section, .024" thick		170	.047		3.43	1.68		5.11	6.60
1000	Starter strip, .024" thick		400	.020		1.58	.72		2.30	2.94
1200	Side wall flashing, .024" thick		170	.047		1.99	1.68		3.67	5
1500	Gable flashing, .024" thick	↓	400	.020	↓	1.58	.72		2.30	2.94

07 31 16.20 Steel Shingles

		Crew	Daily Output	Labor-Hours	Unit	Material	2014 Bare Costs Labor	2014 Bare Costs Equipment	Total	Total Incl O&P
0010	**STEEL SHINGLES**									
0012	Galvanized, 26 ga.	1 Rots	2.20	3.636	Sq.	335	110		445	570
0200	24 ga.	"	2.20	3.636		335	110		445	570
0300	For colored galvanized shingles, add				↓	55			55	60.50

07 31 26 – Slate Shingles

07 31 26.10 Slate Roof Shingles

			Crew	Daily Output	Labor-Hours	Unit	Material	2014 Bare Costs Labor	2014 Bare Costs Equipment	Total	Total Incl O&P
0010	**SLATE ROOF SHINGLES**	R073126-20									
0100	Buckingham Virginia black, 3/16" - 1/4" thick	G	1 Rots	1.75	4.571	Sq.	475	139		614	780
0900	Pennsylvania black, Bangor, #1 clear	G		1.75	4.571		490	139		629	795
1200	Vermont, unfading, green, mottled green	G		1.75	4.571		480	139		619	780
1300	Semi-weathering green & gray	G		1.75	4.571		350	139		489	635
1400	Purple	G		1.75	4.571		425	139		564	720
1500	Black or gray	G		1.75	4.571		460	139		599	760
1600	Red	G		1.75	4.571		1,175	139		1,314	1,525
1700	Variegated purple			1.75	4.571	↓	415	139		554	710
2700	Ridge shingles, slate		↓	200	.040	L.F.	9.30	1.21		10.51	12.45

07 31 29 – Wood Shingles and Shakes

07 31 29.13 Wood Shingles

		Crew	Daily Output	Labor-Hours	Unit	Material	2014 Bare Costs Labor	2014 Bare Costs Equipment	Total	Total Incl O&P
0010	**WOOD SHINGLES**									
0012	16" No. 1 red cedar shingles, 5" exposure, on roof	1 Carp	2.50	3.200	Sq.	264	114		378	485
0015	Pneumatic nailed		3.25	2.462		264	88		352	440
0200	7-1/2" exposure, on walls		2.05	3.902		176	140		316	430
0205	Pneumatic nailed		2.67	2.996		176	107		283	375
0300	18" No. 1 red cedar perfections, 5-1/2" exposure, on roof	↓	2.75	2.909	↓	227	104		331	425

07 31 Shingles and Shakes

07 31 29 – Wood Shingles and Shakes

07 31 29.13 Wood Shingles

		Crew	Daily Output	Labor-Hours	Unit	Material	2014 Bare Costs Labor	Equipment	Total	Total Incl O&P
0305	Pneumatic nailed	1 Carp	3.57	2.241	Sq.	227	80		307	385
0500	7-1/2" exposure, on walls		2.25	3.556		167	127		294	400
0505	Pneumatic nailed		2.92	2.740		167	98		265	350
0600	Resquared, and rebutted, 5-1/2" exposure, on roof		3	2.667		280	95.50		375.50	470
0605	Pneumatic nailed		3.90	2.051		280	73.50		353.50	435
0900	7-1/2" exposure, on walls		2.45	3.265		206	117		323	425
0905	Pneumatic nailed		3.18	2.516		206	90		296	380
1000	Add to above for fire retardant shingles					55			55	60.50
1060	Preformed ridge shingles	1 Carp	400	.020	L.F.	4.50	.72		5.22	6.15
2000	White cedar shingles, 16" long, extras, 5" exposure, on roof		2.40	3.333	Sq.	173	119		292	390
2005	Pneumatic nailed		3.12	2.564		173	91.50		264.50	345
2050	5" exposure on walls		2	4		173	143		316	430
2055	Pneumatic nailed		2.60	3.077		173	110		283	375
2100	7-1/2" exposure, on walls		2	4		123	143		266	375
2105	Pneumatic nailed		2.60	3.077		123	110		233	320
2150	"B" grade, 5" exposure on walls		2	4		150	143		293	405
2155	Pneumatic nailed		2.60	3.077		150	110		260	350
2300	For 15# organic felt underlayment on roof, 1 layer, add		64	.125		5.40	4.47		9.87	13.45
2400	2 layers, add		32	.250		10.80	8.95		19.75	27
2600	For steep roofs (7/12 pitch or greater), add to above						50%			
2700	Panelized systems, No.1 cedar shingles on 5/16" CDX plywood									
2800	On walls, 8' strips, 7" or 14" exposure	2 Carp	700	.023	S.F.	6	.82		6.82	8
3500	On roofs, 8' strips, 7" or 14" exposure	1 Carp	3	2.667	Sq.	600	95.50		695.50	820
3505	Pneumatic nailed	"	4	2	"	600	71.50		671.50	780

07 31 29.16 Wood Shakes

		Crew	Daily Output	Labor-Hours	Unit	Material	2014 Bare Costs Labor	Equipment	Total	Total Incl O&P
0010	**WOOD SHAKES**									
1100	Hand-split red cedar shakes, 1/2" thick x 24" long, 10" exp. on roof	1 Carp	2.50	3.200	Sq.	253	114		367	470
1105	Pneumatic nailed		3.25	2.462		253	88		341	425
1110	3/4" thick x 24" long, 10" exp. on roof		2.25	3.556		253	127		380	490
1115	Pneumatic nailed		2.92	2.740		253	98		351	445
1200	1/2" thick, 18" long, 8-1/2" exp. on roof		2	4		179	143		322	440
1205	Pneumatic nailed		2.60	3.077		179	110		289	380
1210	3/4" thick x 18" long, 8 1/2" exp. on roof		1.80	4.444		179	159		338	465
1215	Pneumatic nailed		2.34	3.419		179	122		301	405
1255	10" exp. on walls		2	4		173	143		316	430
1260	10" exposure on walls, pneumatic nailed		2.60	3.077		173	110		283	375
1700	Add to above for fire retardant shakes, 24" long					55			55	60.50
1800	18" long					55			55	60.50
1810	Ridge shakes	1 Carp	350	.023	L.F.	4.50	.82		5.32	6.35

07 32 Roof Tiles

07 32 13 – Clay Roof Tiles

07 32 13.10 Clay Tiles

		Crew	Daily Output	Labor-Hours	Unit	Material	2014 Bare Costs Labor	Equipment	Total	Total Incl O&P
0010	**CLAY TILES**, including accessories									
0300	Flat shingle, interlocking, 15", 166 pcs/sq, fireflashed blend	3 Rots	6	4	Sq.	510	121		631	785
0500	Terra cotta red		6	4		510	121		631	785
0600	Roman pan and top, 18", 102 pcs/sq, fireflashed blend		5.50	4.364		560	132		692	860
0640	Terra cotta red	1 Rots	2.40	3.333		560	101		661	800
1100	Barrel mission tile, 18", 166 pcs/sq, fireflashed blend	3 Rots	5.50	4.364		405	132		537	690
1140	Terra cotta red		5.50	4.364		405	132		537	690
1700	Scalloped edge flat shingle, 14", 145 pcs/sq, fireflashed blend		6	4		1,125	121		1,246	1,475

07 32 Roof Tiles

07 32 13 – Clay Roof Tiles

07 32 13.10 Clay Tiles		Crew	Daily Output	Labor-Hours	Unit	Material	2014 Bare Costs Labor	Equipment	Total	Total Incl O&P
1800	Terra cotta red	3 Rots	6	4	Sq.	1,125	121		1,246	1,475
3010	#15 felt underlayment	1 Rofc	64	.125		5.40	3.77		9.17	12.90
3020	#30 felt underlayment		58	.138		10.80	4.16		14.96	19.55
3040	Polyethylene and rubberized asph. underlayment		22	.364		77	10.95		87.95	105

07 32 16 – Concrete Roof Tiles

07 32 16.10 Concrete Tiles		Crew	Daily Output	Labor-Hours	Unit	Material	2014 Bare Costs Labor	Equipment	Total	Total Incl O&P
0010	**CONCRETE TILES**									
0020	Corrugated, 13" x 16-1/2", 90 per sq., 950 lb. per sq.									
0050	Earthtone colors, nailed to wood deck	1 Rots	1.35	5.926	Sq.	104	180		284	445
0150	Blues		1.35	5.926		104	180		284	445
0200	Greens		1.35	5.926		108	180		288	450
0250	Premium colors		1.35	5.926		108	180		288	450
0500	Shakes, 13" x 16-1/2", 90 per sq., 950 lb. per sq.									
0600	All colors, nailed to wood deck	1 Rots	1.50	5.333	Sq.	88.50	162		250.50	395
1500	Accessory pieces, ridge & hip, 10" x 16-1/2", 8 lb. each	"	120	.067	Ea.	3.88	2.02		5.90	8
1700	Rake, 6-1/2" x 16-3/4", 9 lb. each					3.88			3.88	4.27
1800	Mansard hip, 10" x 16-1/2", 9.2 lb. each					3.88			3.88	4.27
1900	Hip starter, 10" x 16-1/2", 10.5 lb. each					12.20			12.20	13.40
2000	3 or 4 way apex, 10" each side, 11.5 lb. each					14.10			14.10	15.50

07 32 19 – Metal Roof Tiles

07 32 19.10 Metal Roof Tiles		Crew	Daily Output	Labor-Hours	Unit	Material	2014 Bare Costs Labor	Equipment	Total	Total Incl O&P
0010	**METAL ROOF TILES**									
0020	Accessories included, .032" thick aluminum, mission tile	1 Carp	2.50	3.200	Sq.	815	114		929	1,075
0200	Spanish tiles	"	3	2.667	"	560	95.50		655.50	775

07 33 Natural Roof Coverings

07 33 63 – Vegetated Roofing

07 33 63.10 Green Roof Systems			Crew	Daily Output	Labor-Hours	Unit	Material	2014 Bare Costs Labor	Equipment	Total	Total Incl O&P
0010	**GREEN ROOF SYSTEMS**										
0020	Soil mixture for green roof 30% sand, 55% gravel, 15% soil										
0100	.Hoist and spread soil mixture 4 inch depth up to five stories tall roof	G	B-13B	4000	.014	S.F.	.25	.43	.28	.96	1.30
0150	6 inch depth	G		2667	.021		.37	.65	.43	1.45	1.96
0200	8 inch depth	G		2000	.028		.50	.86	.57	1.93	2.62
0250	10 inch depth	G		1600	.035		.62	1.08	.71	2.41	3.26
0300	12 inch depth	G		1335	.042		.75	1.29	.85	2.89	3.92
0310	Alt. man-made soil mix, hoist & spread, 4" deep up to 5 stories tall roof	G		4000	.014		1.80	.43	.28	2.51	3.01
0350	Mobilization 55 ton crane to site	G	1 Eqhv	3.60	2.222	Ea.		86		86	142
0355	Hoisting cost to five stories per day (Avg. 28 picks per day)	G	B-13B	1	56	Day		1,725	1,125	2,850	4,125
0360	Mobilization or demobilization, 100 ton crane to site driver & escort	G	A-3E	2.50	6.400	Ea.		219	67.50	286.50	440
0365	Hoisting cost six to ten stories per day (Avg. 21 picks per day)	G	B-13C	1	56	Day		1,725	1,700	3,425	4,750
0370	Hoist and spread soil mixture 4 inch depth six to ten stories tall roof	G		4000	.014	S.F.	.25	.43	.43	1.11	1.46
0375	6 inch depth	G		2667	.021		.37	.65	.64	1.66	2.19
0380	8 inch depth	G		2000	.028		.50	.86	.85	2.21	2.93
0385	10 inch depth	G		1600	.035		.62	1.08	1.06	2.76	3.65
0390	12 inch depth	G		1335	.042		.75	1.29	1.28	3.32	4.38
0400	Green roof edging treated lumber 4" x 4" no hoisting included	G	2 Carp	400	.040	L.F.	1.22	1.43		2.65	3.75
0410	4" x 6"	G		400	.040		1.77	1.43		3.20	4.35
0420	4" x 8"	G		360	.044		3.07	1.59		4.66	6.05
0430	4" x 6" double stacked	G		300	.053		3.53	1.91		5.44	7.10
0500	Green roof edging redwood lumber 4" x 4" no hoisting included	G		400	.040		6.45	1.43		7.88	9.45

233

07 33 Natural Roof Coverings

07 33 63 – Vegetated Roofing

07 33 63.10 Green Roof Systems		Crew	Daily Output	Labor-Hours	Unit	Material	2014 Bare Costs Labor	Equipment	Total	Total Incl O&P
0510	4" x 6"	G	2 Carp	400	.040	L.F.	11.20	1.43		12.63	14.70
0520	4" x 8"	G		360	.044		20.50	1.59		22.09	25
0530	4" x 6" double stacked	G	↓	300	.053	↓	22.50	1.91		24.41	27.50
0550	Components, not including membrane or insulation:										
0560	Fluid applied rubber membrane, reinforced, 215 mil thick	G	G-5	350	.114	S.F.	.26	3.14	.57	3.97	6.70
0570	Root barrier	G	2 Rofc	775	.021		.55	.62		1.17	1.76
0580	Moisture retention barrier and reservoir	G	"	900	.018		2.20	.54		2.74	3.41
0600	Planting sedum, light soil, potted, 2-1/4" diameter, two per S.F.	G	1 Clab	420	.019		5.20	.54		5.74	6.60
0610	one per S.F.	G	"	840	.010		2.60	.27		2.87	3.31
0630	Planting sedum mat per S.F. including shipping (4000 S.F. min)	G	4 Clab	4000	.008		6.25	.23		6.48	7.25
0640	Installation sedum mat system (no soil required) per S.F. (4000 S.F. min)	G	"	4000	.008	↓	8.70	.23		8.93	9.95
0645	Note: pricing of sedum mats shipped in full truck loads (4000-5000 S.F.)										

07 41 Roof Panels

07 41 13 – Metal Roof Panels

07 41 13.10 Aluminum Roof Panels

		Crew	Daily Output	Labor-Hours	Unit	Material	Labor	Equipment	Total	Total Incl O&P
0010	**ALUMINUM ROOF PANELS**										
0020	Corrugated or ribbed, .0155" thick, natural	G-3	1200	.027	S.F.	.99	.92		1.91	2.62
0300	Painted		1200	.027		1.44	.92		2.36	3.11
0400	Corrugated, .018" thick, on steel frame, natural finish		1200	.027		1.30	.92		2.22	2.96
0600	Painted		1200	.027		1.60	.92		2.52	3.29
0700	Corrugated, on steel frame, natural, .024" thick		1200	.027		1.85	.92		2.77	3.57
0800	Painted		1200	.027		2.25	.92		3.17	4.01
0900	.032" thick, natural		1200	.027		2.39	.92		3.31	4.16
1200	Painted		1200	.027		3.06	.92		3.98	4.90
1300	V-Beam, on steel frame construction, .032" thick, natural		1200	.027		2.53	.92		3.45	4.31
1500	Painted		1200	.027		3.10	.92		4.02	4.94
1600	.040" thick, natural		1200	.027		3.07	.92		3.99	4.91
1800	Painted		1200	.027		3.70	.92		4.62	5.60
1900	.050" thick, natural		1200	.027		3.69	.92		4.61	5.60
2100	Painted		1200	.027		4.45	.92		5.37	6.45
2200	For roofing on wood frame, deduct		4600	.007	↓	.08	.24		.32	.49
2400	Ridge cap, .032" thick, natural	↓	800	.040	L.F.	2.91	1.37		4.28	5.50

07 41 13.20 Steel Roofing Panels

		Crew	Daily Output	Labor-Hours	Unit	Material	Labor	Equipment	Total	Total Incl O&P
0010	**STEEL ROOFING PANELS**										
0012	Corrugated or ribbed, on steel framing, 30 ga. galv	G-3	1100	.029	S.F.	1.67	1		2.67	3.51
0100	28 ga.		1050	.030		1.79	1.05		2.84	3.72
0300	26 ga.		1000	.032		1.85	1.10		2.95	3.88
0400	24 ga.		950	.034		2.90	1.16		4.06	5.10
0600	Colored, 28 ga.		1050	.030		1.67	1.05		2.72	3.59
0700	26 ga.		1000	.032		1.98	1.10		3.08	4.02
0710	Flat profile, 1-3/4" standing seams, 10" wide, standard finish, 26 ga.		1000	.032		3.75	1.10		4.85	5.95
0715	24 ga.		950	.034		4.35	1.16		5.51	6.70
0720	22 ga.		900	.036		5.35	1.22		6.57	7.95
0725	Zinc aluminum alloy finish, 26 ga.		1000	.032		2.94	1.10		4.04	5.05
0730	24 ga.		950	.034		3.51	1.16		4.67	5.80
0735	22 ga.		900	.036		4.02	1.22		5.24	6.45
0740	12" wide, standard finish, 26 ga.		1000	.032		3.74	1.10		4.84	5.95
0745	24 ga.		950	.034		4.91	1.16		6.07	7.35
0750	Zinc aluminum alloy finish, 26 ga.		1000	.032		4.26	1.10		5.36	6.55
0755	24 ga.	↓	950	.034	↓	3.50	1.16		4.66	5.80

07 41 Roof Panels

07 41 13 – Metal Roof Panels

07 41 13.20 Steel Roofing Panels

		Crew	Daily Output	Labor-Hours	Unit	Material	2014 Bare Costs Labor	Equipment	Total	Total Incl O&P
0840	Flat profile, 1" x 3/8" batten, 12" wide, standard finish, 26 ga.	G-3	1000	.032	S.F.	3.30	1.10		4.40	5.45
0845	24 ga.		950	.034		3.87	1.16		5.03	6.20
0850	22 ga.		900	.036		4.63	1.22		5.85	7.15
0855	Zinc aluminum alloy finish, 26 ga.		1000	.032		3.16	1.10		4.26	5.30
0860	24 ga.		950	.034		3.53	1.16		4.69	5.80
0865	22 ga.		900	.036		4.08	1.22		5.30	6.55
0870	16-1/2" wide, standard finish, 24 ga.		950	.034		3.81	1.16		4.97	6.10
0875	22 ga.		900	.036		4.27	1.22		5.49	6.75
0880	Zinc aluminum alloy finish, 24 ga.		950	.034		3.33	1.16		4.49	5.60
0885	22 ga.		900	.036		3.71	1.22		4.93	6.10
0890	Flat profile, 2" x 2" batten, 12" wide, standard finish, 26 ga.		1000	.032		3.79	1.10		4.89	6
0895	24 ga.		950	.034		4.53	1.16		5.69	6.90
0900	22 ga.		900	.036		5.55	1.22		6.77	8.15
0905	Zinc aluminum alloy finish, 26 ga.		1000	.032		3.53	1.10		4.63	5.70
0910	24 ga.		950	.034		4.03	1.16		5.19	6.35
0915	22 ga.		900	.036		4.69	1.22		5.91	7.20
0920	16-1/2" wide, standard finish, 24 ga.		950	.034		4.16	1.16		5.32	6.50
0925	22 ga.		900	.036		4.87	1.22		6.09	7.40
0930	Zinc aluminum alloy finish, 24 ga.		950	.034		3.77	1.16		4.93	6.10
0935	22 ga.		900	.036		4.29	1.22		5.51	6.75
1200	Ridge, galvanized, 10" wide	G	800	.040	L.F.	3.05	1.37		4.42	5.65
1203	14" wide	G	2 Shee	.051		3.66	2.05		5.71	7.45
1205	18" wide	G	" 308	.052		4.27	2.10		6.37	8.20
1210	20" wide	G	G-3 750	.043		4.32	1.46		5.78	7.20

07 41 33 – Plastic Roof Panels

07 41 33.10 Fiberglass Panels

		Crew	Daily Output	Labor-Hours	Unit	Material	2014 Bare Costs Labor	Equipment	Total	Total Incl O&P
0010	**FIBERGLASS PANELS**									
0012	Corrugated panels, roofing, 8 oz. per S.F.	G-3	1000	.032	S.F.	2.08	1.10		3.18	4.13
0100	12 oz. per S.F.		1000	.032		3.55	1.10		4.65	5.75
0300	Corrugated siding, 6 oz. per S.F.		880	.036		1.75	1.25		3	4.02
0400	8 oz. per S.F.		880	.036		2.08	1.25		3.33	4.38
0500	Fire retardant		880	.036		3.51	1.25		4.76	5.95
0600	12 oz. siding, textured		880	.036		3.60	1.25		4.85	6.05
0700	Fire retardant		880	.036		4.20	1.25		5.45	6.70
0900	Flat panels, 6 oz. per S.F., clear or colors		880	.036		2.20	1.25		3.45	4.51
1100	Fire retardant, class A		880	.036		3.30	1.25		4.55	5.70
1300	8 oz. per S.F., clear or colors		880	.036		2.42	1.25		3.67	4.75
1700	Sandwich panels, fiberglass, 1-9/16" thick, panels to 20 S.F.		180	.178		35	6.10		41.10	48.50
1900	As above, but 2-3/4" thick, panels to 100 S.F.		265	.121		25	4.15		29.15	34.50

07 42 Wall Panels

07 42 13 – Metal Wall Panels

07 42 13.10 Mansard Panels

		Crew	Daily Output	Labor-Hours	Unit	Material	2014 Bare Costs Labor	Equipment	Total	Total Incl O&P
0010	**MANSARD PANELS**									
0600	Aluminum, stock units, straight surfaces	1 Shee	115	.070	S.F.	3.79	2.81		6.60	8.85
0700	Concave or convex surfaces		75	.107	"	2	4.31		6.31	9.40
0800	For framing, to 5' high, add		115	.070	L.F.	3.50	2.81		6.31	8.55
0900	Soffits, to 1' wide		125	.064	S.F.	2.14	2.59		4.73	6.65

07 42 13 – Metal Wall Panels

07 42 13.20 Aluminum Siding Panels	Crew	Daily Output	Labor-Hours	Unit	Material	2014 Bare Costs Labor	Equipment	Total	Total Incl O&P
0010 **ALUMINUM SIDING PANELS**									
0012 Corrugated, on steel framing, .019 thick, natural finish	G-3	775	.041	S.F.	1.52	1.42		2.94	4.04
0100 Painted		775	.041		1.63	1.42		3.05	4.16
0400 Farm type, .021" thick on steel frame, natural		775	.041		1.53	1.42		2.95	4.05
0600 Painted		775	.041		1.63	1.42		3.05	4.16
0700 Industrial type, corrugated, on steel, .024" thick, mill		775	.041		2.12	1.42		3.54	4.70
0900 Painted		775	.041		2.28	1.42		3.70	4.88
1000 .032" thick, mill		775	.041		2.44	1.42		3.86	5.05
1200 Painted		775	.041		2.97	1.42		4.39	5.65
1300 V-Beam, on steel frame, .032" thick, mill		775	.041		2.75	1.42		4.17	5.40
1500 Painted		775	.041		3.15	1.42		4.57	5.85
1600 .040" thick, mill		775	.041		3.34	1.42		4.76	6.05
1800 Painted		775	.041		3.91	1.42		5.33	6.65
1900 .050" thick, mill		775	.041		3.95	1.42		5.37	6.70
2100 Painted		775	.041		4.71	1.42		6.13	7.55
2200 Ribbed, 3" profile, on steel frame, .032" thick, natural		775	.041		2.37	1.42		3.79	4.98
2400 Painted		775	.041		3.01	1.42		4.43	5.70
2500 .040" thick, natural		775	.041		2.72	1.42		4.14	5.35
2700 Painted		775	.041		3.17	1.42		4.59	5.85
2750 .050" thick, natural		775	.041		3.13	1.42		4.55	5.80
2760 Painted		775	.041		3.60	1.42		5.02	6.35
3300 For siding on wood frame, deduct from above		2800	.011		.09	.39		.48	.76
3400 Screw fasteners, aluminum, self tapping, neoprene washer, 1"				M	206			206	226
3600 Stitch screws, self tapping, with neoprene washer, 5/8"				"	154			154	170
3630 Flashing, sidewall, .032" thick	G-3	800	.040	L.F.	2.85	1.37		4.22	5.45
3650 End wall, .040" thick		800	.040		3.33	1.37		4.70	5.95
3670 Closure strips, corrugated, .032" thick		800	.040		.85	1.37		2.22	3.24
3680 Ribbed, 4" or 8", .032" thick		800	.040		.85	1.37		2.22	3.24
3690 V-beam, .040" thick		800	.040		1.14	1.37		2.51	3.55
3800 Horizontal, colored clapboard, 8" wide, plain	2 Carp	515	.031	S.F.	2.36	1.11		3.47	4.47
3810 Insulated		515	.031		2.57	1.11		3.68	4.70
4000 Vertical board & batten, colored, non-insulated		515	.031		1.83	1.11		2.94	3.88
4200 For simulated wood design, add					.11			.11	.12
4300 Corners for above, outside	2 Carp	515	.031	V.L.F.	3.23	1.11		4.34	5.40
4500 Inside corners	"	515	.031	"	1.55	1.11		2.66	3.58

07 42 13.30 Steel Siding

	Crew	Daily Output	Labor-Hours	Unit	Material	2014 Bare Costs Labor	Equipment	Total	Total Incl O&P
0010 **STEEL SIDING**									
0020 Beveled, vinyl coated, 8" wide	1 Carp	265	.030	S.F.	1.91	1.08		2.99	3.92
0050 10" wide	"	275	.029		2.04	1.04		3.08	3.99
0080 Galv, corrugated or ribbed, on steel frame, 30 ga.	G-3	800	.040		1.31	1.37		2.68	3.74
0100 28 ga.		795	.040		1.38	1.38		2.76	3.83
0300 26 ga.		790	.041		1.91	1.39		3.30	4.43
0400 24 ga.		785	.041		1.94	1.40		3.34	4.47
0600 22 ga.		770	.042		2.24	1.43		3.67	4.85
0700 Colored, corrugated/ribbed, on steel frame, 10 yr. finish, 28 ga.		800	.040		2.04	1.37		3.41	4.54
0900 26 ga.		795	.040		2.13	1.38		3.51	4.65
1000 24 ga.		790	.041		2.49	1.39		3.88	5.05
1020 20 ga.		785	.041		3.15	1.40		4.55	5.80
1200 Factory sandwich panel, 26 ga., 1" insulation, galvanized		380	.084		5.25	2.89		8.14	10.60
1300 Colored 1 side		380	.084		6.40	2.89		9.29	11.90
1500 Galvanized 2 sides		380	.084		7.95	2.89		10.84	13.60
1600 Colored 2 sides		380	.084		8.25	2.89		11.14	13.90

07 42 Wall Panels

07 42 13 – Metal Wall Panels

07 42 13.30 Steel Siding		Crew	Daily Output	Labor-Hours	Unit	Material	2014 Bare Costs Labor	Equipment	Total	Total Incl O&P
1800	Acrylic paint face, regular paint liner	G-3	380	.084	S.F.	6.20	2.89		9.09	11.65
1900	For 2" thick polystyrene, add					.96			.96	1.06
2000	22 ga., galv, 2" insulation, baked enamel exterior	G-3	360	.089		12.15	3.05		15.20	18.50
2100	Polyvinylidene exterior finish	"	360	.089		12.80	3.05		15.85	19.20

07 44 Faced Panels

07 44 73 – Metal Faced Panels

07 44 73.10 Metal Faced Panels and Accessories		Crew	Daily Output	Labor-Hours	Unit	Material	2014 Bare Costs Labor	Equipment	Total	Total Incl O&P
0010	**METAL FACED PANELS AND ACCESSORIES**									
0400	Textured aluminum, 4' x 8' x 5/16" plywood backing, single face	2 Shee	375	.043	S.F.	4.07	1.73		5.80	7.35
0600	Double face		375	.043		5.25	1.73		6.98	8.70
0700	4' x 10' x 5/16" plywood backing, single face		375	.043		4.26	1.73		5.99	7.55
0900	Double face		375	.043		5.80	1.73		7.53	9.30
1000	4' x 12' x 5/16" plywood backing, single face		375	.043		4.26	1.73		5.99	7.55
1300	Smooth aluminum, 1/4" plywood panel, fluoropolymer finish, double face		375	.043		6.05	1.73		7.78	9.55
1350	Clear anodized finish, double face		375	.043		10.05	1.73		11.78	13.95
1400	Double face textured aluminum, structural panel, 1" EPS insulation		375	.043		5.70	1.73		7.43	9.15
1500	Accessories, outside corner	1 Shee	175	.046	L.F.	1.90	1.85		3.75	5.15
1600	Inside corner		175	.046		1.34	1.85		3.19	4.55
1800	Batten mounting clip		200	.040		.49	1.62		2.11	3.24
1900	Low profile batten		480	.017		.61	.67		1.28	1.79
2100	High profile batten		480	.017		1.41	.67		2.08	2.67
2200	Water table		200	.040		2.12	1.62		3.74	5.05
2400	Horizontal joint connector		200	.040		1.67	1.62		3.29	4.54
2500	Corner cap		200	.040		1.84	1.62		3.46	4.72
2700	H - moulding		480	.017		1.25	.67		1.92	2.50

07 46 Siding

07 46 23 – Wood Siding

07 46 23.10 Wood Board Siding		Crew	Daily Output	Labor-Hours	Unit	Material	2014 Bare Costs Labor	Equipment	Total	Total Incl O&P
0010	**WOOD BOARD SIDING**									
3200	Wood, cedar bevel, A grade, 1/2" x 6"	1 Carp	295	.027	S.F.	4.14	.97		5.11	6.20
3300	1/2" x 8"		330	.024		5.90	.87		6.77	7.95
3500	3/4" x 10", clear grade		375	.021		6.30	.76		7.06	8.20
3600	"B" grade		375	.021		3.79	.76		4.55	5.45
3800	Cedar, rough sawn, 1" x 4", A grade, natural		220	.036		6.35	1.30		7.65	9.20
3900	Stained		220	.036		6.50	1.30		7.80	9.35
4100	1" x 12", board & batten, #3 & Btr., natural		420	.019		4.35	.68		5.03	5.95
4200	Stained		420	.019		4.67	.68		5.35	6.30
4400	1" x 8" channel siding, #3 & Btr., natural		330	.024		4.43	.87		5.30	6.35
4500	Stained		330	.024		4.78	.87		5.65	6.70
4700	Redwood, clear, beveled, vertical grain, 1/2" x 4"		220	.036		4.11	1.30		5.41	6.70
4800	1/2" x 8"		330	.024		4.89	.87		5.76	6.85
5000	3/4" x 10"		375	.021		4.50	.76		5.26	6.25
5200	Channel siding, 1" x 10", B grade		375	.021		4.12	.76		4.88	5.80
5250	Redwood, T&G boards, B grade, 1" x 4"		220	.036		2.54	1.30		3.84	4.98
5270	1" x 8"		330	.024		4.10	.87		4.97	5.95
5400	White pine, rough sawn, 1" x 8", natural		330	.024		2.19	.87		3.06	3.87
5500	Stained		330	.024		2.19	.87		3.06	3.87

07 46 29 – Plywood Siding

07 46 29.10 Plywood Siding Options	Crew	Daily Output	Labor-Hours	Unit	Material	2014 Bare Costs Labor	Equipment	Total	Total Incl O&P
0010 **PLYWOOD SIDING OPTIONS**									
0900 Plywood, medium density overlaid, 3/8" thick	2 Carp	750	.021	S.F.	1.15	.76		1.91	2.55
1000 1/2" thick		700	.023		1.36	.82		2.18	2.88
1100 3/4" thick		650	.025		1.74	.88		2.62	3.39
1600 Texture 1-11, cedar, 5/8" thick, natural		675	.024		2.43	.85		3.28	4.10
1700 Factory stained		675	.024		2.69	.85		3.54	4.39
1900 Texture 1-11, fir, 5/8" thick, natural		675	.024		1.57	.85		2.42	3.16
2000 Factory stained		675	.024		1.80	.85		2.65	3.41
2050 Texture 1-11, S.Y.P., 5/8" thick, natural		675	.024		1.19	.85		2.04	2.74
2100 Factory stained		675	.024		1.24	.85		2.09	2.79
2200 Rough sawn cedar, 3/8" thick, natural		675	.024		1.20	.85		2.05	2.75
2300 Factory stained		675	.024		1.46	.85		2.31	3.04
2500 Rough sawn fir, 3/8" thick, natural		675	.024		.82	.85		1.67	2.33
2600 Factory stained		675	.024		1.04	.85		1.89	2.57
2800 Redwood, textured siding, 5/8" thick		675	.024		1.92	.85		2.77	3.54
3000 Polyvinyl chloride coated, 3/8" thick		750	.021		1.11	.76		1.87	2.50

07 46 33 – Plastic Siding

07 46 33.10 Vinyl Siding

	Crew	Daily Output	Labor-Hours	Unit	Material	2014 Bare Costs Labor	Equipment	Total	Total Incl O&P
0010 **VINYL SIDING**									
3995 Clapboard profile, woodgrain texture, .048 thick, double 4	2 Carp	495	.032	S.F.	.97	1.16		2.13	3.01
4000 Double 5		550	.029		.97	1.04		2.01	2.82
4005 Single 8		495	.032		1.08	1.16		2.24	3.13
4010 Single 10		550	.029		1.30	1.04		2.34	3.18
4015 .044 thick, double 4		495	.032		.95	1.16		2.11	2.99
4020 Double 5		550	.029		.95	1.04		1.99	2.80
4025 .042 thick, double 4		495	.032		.90	1.16		2.06	2.94
4030 Double 5		550	.029		.90	1.04		1.94	2.75
4035 Cross sawn texture, .040 thick, double 4		495	.032		.64	1.16		1.80	2.65
4040 Double 5		550	.029		.64	1.04		1.68	2.46
4045 Smooth texture, .042 thick, double 4		495	.032		.72	1.16		1.88	2.74
4050 Double 5		550	.029		.72	1.04		1.76	2.55
4055 Single 8		495	.032		.72	1.16		1.88	2.74
4060 Cedar texture, .044 thick, double 4		495	.032		.95	1.16		2.11	2.99
4065 Double 6		600	.027		.96	.95		1.91	2.66
4070 Dutch lap profile, woodgrain texture, .048 thick, double 5		550	.029		.97	1.04		2.01	2.82
4075 .044 thick, double 4.5		525	.030		.95	1.09		2.04	2.88
4080 .042 thick, double 4.5		525	.030		.80	1.09		1.89	2.72
4085 .040 thick, double 4.5		525	.030		.64	1.09		1.73	2.54
4100 Shake profile, 10" wide		400	.040		3.26	1.43		4.69	6
4105 Vertical pattern, .046 thick, double 5		550	.029		1.29	1.04		2.33	3.17
4110 .044 thick, triple 3		550	.029		1.47	1.04		2.51	3.37
4115 .040 thick, triple 4		550	.029		1.47	1.04		2.51	3.37
4120 .040 thick, triple 2.66		550	.029		1.62	1.04		2.66	3.54
4125 Insulation, fan folded extruded polystyrene, 1/4"		2000	.008		.27	.29		.56	.78
4130 3/8"		2000	.008		.30	.29		.59	.81
4135 Accessories, J channel, 5/8" pocket		700	.023	L.F.	.44	.82		1.26	1.86
4140 3/4" pocket		695	.023		.46	.82		1.28	1.88
4145 1-1/4" pocket		680	.024		.70	.84		1.54	2.19
4150 Flexible, 3/4" pocket		600	.027		2.20	.95		3.15	4.02
4155 Under sill finish trim		500	.032		.49	1.14		1.63	2.46
4160 Vinyl starter strip		700	.023		.50	.82		1.32	1.93
4165 Aluminum starter strip		700	.023		.26	.82		1.08	1.66

07 46 Siding

07 46 33 – Plastic Siding

07 46 33.10 Vinyl Siding

		Crew	Daily Output	Labor-Hours	Unit	Material	2014 Bare Costs Labor	2014 Bare Costs Equipment	Total	Total Incl O&P
4170	Window casing, 2-1/2" wide, 3/4" pocket	2 Carp	510	.031	L.F.	1.46	1.12		2.58	3.49
4175	Outside corner, woodgrain finish, 4" face, 3/4" pocket		700	.023		1.82	.82		2.64	3.39
4180	5/8" pocket		700	.023		1.82	.82		2.64	3.39
4185	Smooth finish, 4" face, 3/4" pocket		700	.023		1.82	.82		2.64	3.39
4190	7/8" pocket		690	.023		1.82	.83		2.65	3.40
4195	1-1/4" pocket		700	.023		1.28	.82		2.10	2.79
4200	Soffit and fascia, 1' overhang, solid		120	.133		4	4.77		8.77	12.40
4205	Vented		120	.133		4	4.77		8.77	12.40
4207	18" overhang, solid		110	.145		4.65	5.20		9.85	13.85
4208	Vented		110	.145		4.65	5.20		9.85	13.85
4210	2' overhang, solid		100	.160		5.30	5.70		11	15.40
4215	Vented		100	.160		5.30	5.70		11	15.40
4217	3' overhang, solid		100	.160		6.55	5.70		12.25	16.85
4218	Vented		100	.160		6.55	5.70		12.25	16.85
4220	Colors for siding and soffits, add				S.F.	.14			.14	.15
4225	Colors for accessories and trim, add				L.F.	.29			.29	.32

07 46 33.20 Polypropylene Siding

		Crew	Daily Output	Labor-Hours	Unit	Material	2014 Bare Costs Labor	2014 Bare Costs Equipment	Total	Total Incl O&P
0010	**POLYPROPYLENE SIDING**									
4090	Shingle profile, random grooves, double 7	2 Carp	400	.040	S.F.	2.87	1.43		4.30	5.55
4092	Cornerpost for above	1 Carp	365	.022	L.F.	11.15	.78		11.93	13.55
4095	Triple 5	2 Carp	400	.040	S.F.	2.87	1.43		4.30	5.55
4097	Cornerpost for above	1 Carp	365	.022	L.F.	10.50	.78		11.28	12.80
5000	Staggered butt, double 7"	2 Carp	400	.040	S.F.	3.26	1.43		4.69	6
5002	Cornerpost for above	1 Carp	365	.022	L.F.	11.30	.78		12.08	13.75
5010	Half round, double 6-1/4"	2 Carp	360	.044	S.F.	3.25	1.59		4.84	6.25
5020	Shake profile, staggered butt, double 9"	"	510	.031	"	3.25	1.12		4.37	5.45
5022	Cornerpost for above	1 Carp	365	.022	L.F.	8.35	.78		9.13	10.45
5030	Straight butt, double 7"	2 Carp	400	.040	S.F.	3.25	1.43		4.68	6
5032	Cornerpost for above	1 Carp	365	.022	L.F.	11.20	.78		11.98	13.60
6000	Accessories, J channel, 5/8" pocket	2 Carp	700	.023		.44	.82		1.26	1.86
6010	3/4" pocket		695	.023		.46	.82		1.28	1.88
6020	1-1/4" pocket		680	.024		.70	.84		1.54	2.19
6030	Aluminum starter strip		700	.023		.26	.82		1.08	1.66

07 46 46 – Fiber Cement Siding

07 46 46.10 Fiber Cement Siding

		Crew	Daily Output	Labor-Hours	Unit	Material	2014 Bare Costs Labor	2014 Bare Costs Equipment	Total	Total Incl O&P
0010	**FIBER CEMENT SIDING**									
0020	Lap siding, 5/16" thick, 6" wide, 4-3/4" exposure, smooth texture	2 Carp	415	.039	S.F.	1.21	1.38		2.59	3.65
0025	Woodgrain texture		415	.039		1.21	1.38		2.59	3.65
0030	7-1/2" wide, 6-1/4" exposure, smooth texture		425	.038		1.42	1.35		2.77	3.82
0035	Woodgrain texture		425	.038		1.42	1.35		2.77	3.82
0040	8" wide, 6-3/4" exposure, smooth texture		425	.038		1.55	1.35		2.90	3.96
0045	Roughsawn texture		425	.038		1.55	1.35		2.90	3.96
0050	9-1/2" wide, 8-1/4" exposure, smooth texture		440	.036		1.54	1.30		2.84	3.89
0055	Woodgrain texture		440	.036		1.54	1.30		2.84	3.89
0060	12" wide, 10-3/8" exposure, smooth texture		455	.035		1.34	1.26		2.60	3.58
0065	Woodgrain texture		455	.035		1.34	1.26		2.60	3.58
0070	Panel siding, 5/16" thick, smooth texture		750	.021		1.31	.76		2.07	2.72
0075	Stucco texture		750	.021		1.31	.76		2.07	2.72
0080	Grooved woodgrain texture		750	.021		1.31	.76		2.07	2.72
0085	V - grooved woodgrain texture		750	.021		1.31	.76		2.07	2.72
0088	Shingle siding, 48" x 15-1/4" panels, 7" exposure		700	.023		4	.82		4.82	5.80
0090	Wood starter strip		400	.040	L.F.	.42	1.43		1.85	2.87

07 46 Siding

07 46 73 – Soffit

07 46 73.10 Soffit Options	Crew	Daily Output	Labor-Hours	Unit	Material	2014 Bare Costs Labor	Equipment	Total	Total Incl O&P
0010 **SOFFIT OPTIONS**									
0012 Aluminum, residential, .020" thick	1 Carp	210	.038	S.F.	1.87	1.36		3.23	4.35
0100 Baked enamel on steel, 16 or 18 ga.		105	.076		5.80	2.72		8.52	11
0300 Polyvinyl chloride, white, solid		230	.035		2.04	1.24		3.28	4.33
0400 Perforated		230	.035		2.04	1.24		3.28	4.33
0500 For colors, add					.12			.12	.13

07 51 Built-Up Bituminous Roofing

07 51 13 – Built-Up Asphalt Roofing

07 51 13.10 Built-Up Roofing Components

	Crew	Daily Output	Labor-Hours	Unit	Material	2014 Bare Costs Labor	Equipment	Total	Total Incl O&P
0010 **BUILT-UP ROOFING COMPONENTS**									
0012 Asphalt saturated felt, #30, 2 square per roll	1 Rofc	58	.138	Sq.	10.80	4.16		14.96	19.55
0200 #15, 4 sq. per roll, plain or perforated, not mopped		58	.138		5.40	4.16		9.56	13.60
0300 Roll roofing, smooth, #65		15	.533		9.65	16.10		25.75	40
0500 #90		12	.667		35	20		55	75.50
0520 Mineralized		12	.667		35	20		55	75.50
0540 D.C. (Double coverage), 19" selvage edge		10	.800		52	24		76	102
0580 Adhesive (lap cement)				Gal.	8.50			8.50	9.35
0800 Steep, flat or dead level asphalt, 10 ton lots, packaged				Ton	915			915	1,000

07 51 13.13 Cold-Applied Built-Up Asphalt Roofing

	Crew	Daily Output	Labor-Hours	Unit	Material	2014 Bare Costs Labor	Equipment	Total	Total Incl O&P
0010 **COLD-APPLIED BUILT-UP ASPHALT ROOFING**									
0020 3 ply system, installation only (components listed below)	G-5	50	.800	Sq.		22	3.98	25.98	45
0100 Spunbond poly. fabric, 1.35 oz./S.Y., 36"W, 10.8 sq./roll				Ea.	134			134	147
0500 Base & finish coat, 3 gal./sq., 5 gal./can				Gal.	7.75			7.75	8.50
0600 Coating, ceramic granules, 1/2 sq./bag				Ea.	21.50			21.50	23.50
0700 Aluminum, 2 gal./sq.				Gal.	11.80			11.80	13
0800 Emulsion, fibered or non-fibered, 4 gal./sq.				"	6.35			6.35	6.95

07 51 13.20 Built-Up Roofing Systems

	Crew	Daily Output	Labor-Hours	Unit	Material	2014 Bare Costs Labor	Equipment	Total	Total Incl O&P
0010 **BUILT-UP ROOFING SYSTEMS** R075113-20									
0120 Asphalt flood coat with gravel/slag surfacing, not including									
0140 Insulation, flashing or wood nailers									
0200 Asphalt base sheet, 3 plies #15 asphalt felt, mopped	G-1	22	2.545	Sq.	98.50	72	25	195.50	269
0350 On nailable decks		21	2.667		101	75.50	26.50	203	279
0500 4 plies #15 asphalt felt, mopped		20	2.800		134	79	27.50	240.50	325
0550 On nailable decks		19	2.947		119	83	29	231	315
0700 Coated glass base sheet, 2 plies glass (type IV), mopped		22	2.545		106	72	25	203	277
0850 3 plies glass, mopped		20	2.800		129	79	27.50	235.50	320
0950 On nailable decks		19	2.947		121	83	29	233	320
1100 4 plies glass fiber felt (type IV), mopped		20	2.800		159	79	27.50	265.50	350
1150 On nailable decks		19	2.947		143	83	29	255	345
1200 Coated & saturated base sheet, 3 plies #15 asph. felt, mopped		20	2.800		111	79	27.50	217.50	299
1250 On nailable decks		19	2.947		103	83	29	215	298
1300 4 plies #15 asphalt felt, mopped		22	2.545		129	72	25	226	300
2000 Asphalt flood coat, smooth surface									
2200 Asphalt base sheet & 3 plies #15 asphalt felt, mopped	G-1	24	2.333	Sq.	104	66	23	193	261
2400 On nailable decks		23	2.435		96	69	24	189	260
2600 4 plies #15 asphalt felt, mopped		24	2.333		122	66	23	211	281
2700 On nailable decks		23	2.435		114	69	24	207	280
2900 Coated glass fiber base sheet, mopped, and 2 plies of									
2910 glass fiber felt (type IV)	G-1	25	2.240	Sq.	102	63.50	22	187.50	254

07 51 Built-Up Bituminous Roofing

07 51 13 – Built-Up Asphalt Roofing

07 51 13.20 Built-Up Roofing Systems

		Crew	Daily Output	Labor-Hours	Unit	Material	2014 Bare Costs Labor	Equipment	Total	Total Incl O&P
3100	On nailable decks	G-1	24	2.333	Sq.	96	66	23	185	253
3200	3 plies, mopped		23	2.435		124	69	24	217	291
3300	On nailable decks		22	2.545		117	72	25	214	288
3800	4 plies glass fiber felt (type IV), mopped		23	2.435		147	69	24	240	315
3900	On nailable decks		22	2.545		139	72	25	236	315
4000	Coated & saturated base sheet, 3 plies #15 asph. felt, mopped		24	2.333		106	66	23	195	264
4200	On nailable decks		23	2.435		98.50	69	24	191.50	262
4300	4 plies #15 organic felt, mopped	↓	22	2.545	↓	125	72	25	222	297
4500	Coal tar pitch with gravel/slag surfacing									
4600	4 plies #15 tarred felt, mopped	G-1	21	2.667	Sq.	234	75.50	26.50	336	425
4800	3 plies glass fiber felt (type IV), mopped	"	19	2.947	"	193	83	29	305	395
5000	Coated glass fiber base sheet, and 2 plies of									
5010	glass fiber felt, (type IV), mopped	G-1	19	2.947	Sq.	196	83	29	308	400
5300	On nailable decks		18	3.111		170	88	31	289	385
5600	4 plies glass fiber felt (type IV), mopped		21	2.667		264	75.50	26.50	366	460
5800	On nailable decks	↓	20	2.800	↓	238	79	27.50	344.50	440

07 51 13.30 Cants

		Crew	Daily Output	Labor-Hours	Unit	Material	2014 Bare Costs Labor	Equipment	Total	Total Incl O&P
0010	**CANTS**									
0012	Lumber, treated, 4" x 4" cut diagonally	1 Rofc	325	.025	L.F.	1.75	.74		2.49	3.30
0300	Mineral or fiber, trapezoidal, 1" x 4" x 48"		325	.025		.24	.74		.98	1.63
0400	1-1/2" x 5-5/8" x 48"	↓	325	.025	↓	.42	.74		1.16	1.83

07 51 13.40 Felts

		Crew	Daily Output	Labor-Hours	Unit	Material	2014 Bare Costs Labor	Equipment	Total	Total Incl O&P
0010	**FELTS**									
0012	Glass fibered roofing felt, #15, not mopped	1 Rofc	58	.138	Sq.	9.65	4.16		13.81	18.25
0300	Base sheet, #80, channel vented		58	.138		42.50	4.16		46.66	54.50
0400	#70, coated		58	.138		17.20	4.16		21.36	26.50
0500	Cap, #87, mineral surfaced		58	.138		80	4.16		84.16	95.50
0600	Flashing membrane, #65		16	.500		9.65	15.10		24.75	38.50
0800	Coal tar fibered, #15, no mopping		58	.138		18.10	4.16		22.26	27.50
0900	Asphalt felt, #15, 4 sq. per roll, no mopping		58	.138		5.40	4.16		9.56	13.60
1100	#30, 2 sq. per roll		58	.138		10.80	4.16		14.96	19.55
1200	Double coated, #33		58	.138		11	4.16		15.16	19.75
1400	#40, base sheet		58	.138		9.65	4.16		13.81	18.25
1450	Coated and saturated		58	.138		12	4.16		16.16	21
1500	Tarred felt, organic, #15, 4 sq. rolls		58	.138		13.95	4.16		18.11	23
1550	#30, 2 sq. roll	↓	58	.138		28	4.16		32.16	38
1700	Add for mopping above felts, per ply, asphalt, 24 lb. per sq.	G-1	192	.292		11	8.25	2.88	22.13	30.50
1800	Coal tar mopping, 30 lb. per sq.		186	.301		23	8.50	2.98	34.48	44.50
1900	Flood coat, with asphalt, 60 lb. per sq.		60	.933		27.50	26.50	9.25	63.25	89
2000	With coal tar, 75 lb. per sq.	↓	56	1	↓	57.50	28	9.90	95.40	126

07 51 13.50 Walkways for Built-Up Roofs

		Crew	Daily Output	Labor-Hours	Unit	Material	2014 Bare Costs Labor	Equipment	Total	Total Incl O&P
0010	**WALKWAYS FOR BUILT-UP ROOFS**									
0020	Asphalt impregnated, 3' x 6' x 1/2" thick	1 Rofc	400	.020	S.F.	1.56	.60		2.16	2.82
0100	3' x 3' x 3/4" thick	"	400	.020		4.48	.60		5.08	6.05
0300	Concrete patio blocks, 2" thick, natural	1 Clab	115	.070		3.37	1.96		5.33	7
0400	Colors	"	115	.070	↓	3.73	1.96		5.69	7.40

07 52 Modified Bituminous Membrane Roofing

07 52 13 – Atactic-Polypropylene-Modified Bituminous Membrane Roofing

07 52 13.10 APP Modified Bituminous Membrane

07 52 13.10 APP Modified Bituminous Membrane		Crew	Daily Output	Labor-Hours	Unit	Material	2014 Bare Costs Labor	Equipment	Total	Total Incl O&P
0010	**APP MODIFIED BITUMINOUS MEMBRANE**	R075213-30								
0020	Base sheet, #15 glass fiber felt, nailed to deck	1 Rofc	58	.138	Sq.	10.65	4.16		14.81	19.35
0030	Spot mopped to deck	G-1	295	.190		15.15	5.35	1.88	22.38	28.50
0040	Fully mopped to deck	"	192	.292		20.50	8.25	2.88	31.63	41
0050	#15 organic felt, nailed to deck	1 Rofc	58	.138		6.40	4.16		10.56	14.70
0060	Spot mopped to deck	G-1	295	.190		10.90	5.35	1.88	18.13	24
0070	Fully mopped to deck	"	192	.292		16.40	8.25	2.88	27.53	36.50
2100	APP mod., smooth surf. cap sheet, poly. reinf., torched, 160 mils	G-5	2100	.019	S.F.	.68	.52	.09	1.29	1.81
2150	170 mils		2100	.019		.70	.52	.09	1.31	1.83
2200	Granule surface cap sheet, poly. reinf., torched, 180 mils		2000	.020		.89	.55	.10	1.54	2.10
2250	Smooth surface flashing, torched, 160 mils		1260	.032		.68	.87	.16	1.71	2.53
2300	170 mils		1260	.032		.70	.87	.16	1.73	2.55
2350	Granule surface flashing, torched, 180 mils		1260	.032		.89	.87	.16	1.92	2.76
2400	Fibrated aluminum coating	1 Rofc	3800	.002		.08	.06		.14	.20

07 52 16 – Styrene-Butadiene-Styrene Modified Bituminous Membrane Roofing

07 52 16.10 SBS Modified Bituminous Membrane

07 52 16.10 SBS Modified Bituminous Membrane		Crew	Daily Output	Labor-Hours	Unit	Material	2014 Bare Costs Labor	Equipment	Total	Total Incl O&P
0010	**SBS MODIFIED BITUMINOUS MEMBRANE**									
0080	SBS modified, granule surf cap sheet, polyester reinf., mopped									
0600	150 mils	G-1	2000	.028	S.F.	.65	.79	.28	1.72	2.48
1100	160 mils		2000	.028		.71	.79	.28	1.78	2.54
1500	Glass fiber reinforced, mopped, 160 mils		2000	.028		.71	.79	.28	1.78	2.54
1600	Smooth surface cap sheet, mopped, 145 mils		2100	.027		.78	.75	.26	1.79	2.54
1700	Smooth surface flashing, 145 mils		1260	.044		.78	1.26	.44	2.48	3.65
1800	150 mils		1260	.044		.49	1.26	.44	2.19	3.33
1900	Granular surface flashing, 150 mils		1260	.044		.65	1.26	.44	2.35	3.51
2000	160 mils		1260	.044		.71	1.26	.44	2.41	3.57

07 53 Elastomeric Membrane Roofing

07 53 16 – Chlorosulfonate-Polyethylene Roofing

07 53 16.10 Chlorosulfonated Polyethylene Roofing

07 53 16.10 Chlorosulfonated Polyethylene Roofing		Crew	Daily Output	Labor-Hours	Unit	Material	2014 Bare Costs Labor	Equipment	Total	Total Incl O&P
0010	**CHLOROSULFONATED POLYETHYLENE ROOFING**									
0800	Chlorosulfonated polyethylene (CSPE)									
0900	45 mils, heat welded seams, plate attachment	G-5	35	1.143	Sq.	310	31.50	5.70	347.20	405
1100	Heat welded seams, plate attachment and ballasted		26	1.538		320	42.50	7.65	370.15	435
1200	60 mils, heat welded seams, plate attachment		35	1.143		410	31.50	5.70	447.20	515
1300	Heat welded seams, plate attachment and ballasted		26	1.538		415	42.50	7.65	465.15	545

07 53 23 – Ethylene-Propylene-Diene-Monomer Roofing

07 53 23.20 Ethylene-Propylene-Diene-Monomer Roofing

07 53 23.20 Ethylene-Propylene-Diene-Monomer Roofing		Crew	Daily Output	Labor-Hours	Unit	Material	2014 Bare Costs Labor	Equipment	Total	Total Incl O&P
0010	**ETHYLENE-PROPYLENE-DIENE-MONOMER ROOFING (EPDM)**									
3500	Ethylene-propylene-diene-monomer (EPDM), 45 mils, 0.28 psf									
3600	Loose-laid & ballasted with stone (10 psf)	G-5	51	.784	Sq.	83	21.50	3.91	108.41	135
3700	Mechanically attached		35	1.143		78.50	31.50	5.70	115.70	150
3800	Fully adhered with adhesive		26	1.538		111	42.50	7.65	161.15	208
4500	60 mils, 0.40 psf									
4600	Loose-laid & ballasted with stone (10 psf)	G-5	51	.784	Sq.	97.50	21.50	3.91	122.91	152
4700	Mechanically attached		35	1.143		92	31.50	5.70	129.20	165
4800	Fully adhered with adhesive		26	1.538		124	42.50	7.65	174.15	223
4810	45 mil, .28 psf, membrane only					50			50	55
4820	60 mil, .40 psf, membrane only					62.50			62.50	69
4850	Seam tape for membrane, 3" x 100' roll				Ea.	39.50			39.50	43.50

07 53 Elastomeric Membrane Roofing

07 53 23 – Ethylene-Propylene-Diene-Monomer Roofing

07 53 23.20 Ethylene-Propylene-Diene-Monomer Roofing	Crew	Daily Output	Labor-Hours	Unit	Material	2014 Bare Costs Labor	Equipment	Total	Total Incl O&P
4900	Batten strips, 10' sections				Ea.	3.43			3.43	3.77
4910	Cover tape for batten strips, 6" x 100' roll				↓	186			186	205
4930	Plate anchors				M	75			75	82.50
4970	Adhesive for fully adhered systems, 60 S.F./gal.				Gal.	19.70			19.70	21.50

07 53 29 – Polyisobutylene Roofing

07 53 29.10 Polyisobutylene Roofing

	07 53 29.10 Polyisobutylene Roofing	Crew	Daily Output	Labor-Hours	Unit	Material	Labor	Equipment	Total	Total Incl O&P
0010	**POLYISOBUTYLENE ROOFING**									
7500	Polyisobutylene (PIB), 100 mils, 0.57 psf									
7600	Loose-laid & ballasted with stone/gravel (10 psf)	G-5	51	.784	Sq.	200	21.50	3.91	225.41	264
7700	Partially adhered with adhesive		35	1.143		240	31.50	5.70	277.20	330
7800	Hot asphalt attachment		35	1.143		230	31.50	5.70	267.20	315
7900	Fully adhered with contact cement	↓	26	1.538	↓	250	42.50	7.65	300.15	360

07 54 Thermoplastic Membrane Roofing

07 54 19 – Polyvinyl-Chloride Roofing

07 54 19.10 Polyvinyl-Chloride Roofing (PVC)

	07 54 19.10 Polyvinyl-Chloride Roofing (PVC)	Crew	Daily Output	Labor-Hours	Unit	Material	Labor	Equipment	Total	Total Incl O&P
0010	**POLYVINYL-CHLORIDE ROOFING (PVC)**									
8200	Heat welded seams									
8700	Reinforced, 48 mils, 0.33 psf									
8750	Loose-laid & ballasted with stone/gravel (12 psf)	G-5	51	.784	Sq.	117	21.50	3.91	142.41	172
8800	Mechanically attached		35	1.143		111	31.50	5.70	148.20	186
8850	Fully adhered with adhesive	↓	26	1.538	↓	153	42.50	7.65	203.15	254
8860	Reinforced, 60 mils, .40 psf									
8870	Loose-laid & ballasted with stone/gravel (12 psf)	G-5	51	.784	Sq.	118	21.50	3.91	143.41	174
8880	Mechanically attached		35	1.143		112	31.50	5.70	149.20	188
8890	Fully adhered with adhesive	↓	26	1.538	↓	154	42.50	7.65	204.15	256

07 54 23 – Thermoplastic-Polyolefin Roofing

07 54 23.10 Thermoplastic Polyolefin Roofing (T.P.O)

	07 54 23.10 Thermoplastic Polyolefin Roofing (T.P.O.)	Crew	Daily Output	Labor-Hours	Unit	Material	Labor	Equipment	Total	Total Incl O&P
0010	**THERMOPLASTIC POLYOLEFIN ROOFING (T.P.O.)**									
0100	45 mils, loose laid & ballasted with stone(1/2 ton/sq.)	G-5	51	.784	Sq.	86	21.50	3.91	111.41	138
0120	Fully adhered		25	1.600		78	44	7.95	129.95	175
0140	Mechanically attached		34	1.176		77	32.50	5.85	115.35	151
0160	Self adhered		35	1.143		87	31.50	5.70	124.20	160
0180	60 mil membrane, heat welded seams, ballasted		50	.800		98.50	22	3.98	124.48	154
0200	Fully adhered		25	1.600		90	44	7.95	141.95	189
0220	Mechanically attached		34	1.176		93.50	32.50	5.85	131.85	169
0240	Self adhered	↓	35	1.143	↓	107	31.50	5.70	144.20	182

07 55 Protected Membrane Roofing

07 55 10 – Protected Membrane Roofing Components

07 55 10.10 Protected Membrane Roofing Components	Crew	Daily Output	Labor-Hours	Unit	Material	2014 Bare Costs Labor	Equipment	Total	Total Incl O&P
0010 **PROTECTED MEMBRANE ROOFING COMPONENTS**									
0100 Choose roofing membrane from 07 50									
0120 Then choose roof deck insulation from 07 22									
0130 Filter fabric	2 Rofc	10000	.002	S.F.	.12	.05		.17	.23
0140 Ballast, 3/8" - 1/2" in place	G-1	36	1.556	Ton	17.10	44	15.40	76.50	117
0150 3/4" - 1-1/2" in place	"	36	1.556	"	17.10	44	15.40	76.50	117
0200 2" concrete blocks, natural	1 Clab	115	.070	S.F.	3.37	1.96		5.33	7
0210 Colors	"	115	.070	"	3.73	1.96		5.69	7.40

07 56 Fluid-Applied Roofing

07 56 10 – Fluid-Applied Roofing Elastomers

07 56 10.10 Elastomeric Roofing

	Crew	Daily Output	Labor-Hours	Unit	Material	2014 Bare Costs Labor	Equipment	Total	Total Incl O&P
0010 **ELASTOMERIC ROOFING**									
0110 Acrylic rubber, fluid applied, 20 mils thick	G-5	2000	.020	S.F.	1.90	.55	.10	2.55	3.21
0120 50 mils, reinforced		1200	.033		2.90	.92	.17	3.99	5.05
0130 For walking surface, add		900	.044		.96	1.22	.22	2.40	3.55
0300 Neoprene, fluid applied, 20 mil thick, not-reinforced	G-1	1135	.049		1.30	1.39	.49	3.18	4.54
0600 Non-woven polyester, reinforced		960	.058		1.42	1.65	.58	3.65	5.20
0700 5 coat neoprene deck, 60 mil thick, under 10,000 S.F.		325	.172		4.32	4.87	1.70	10.89	15.55
0900 Over 10,000 S.F.		625	.090		4.32	2.53	.89	7.74	10.40

07 57 Coated Foamed Roofing

07 57 13 – Sprayed Polyurethane Foam Roofing

07 57 13.10 Sprayed Polyurethane Foam Roofing (S.P.F.)

	Crew	Daily Output	Labor-Hours	Unit	Material	2014 Bare Costs Labor	Equipment	Total	Total Incl O&P
0010 **SPRAYED POLYURETHANE FOAM ROOFING (S.P.F.)**									
0100 Primer for metal substrate (when required)	G-2A	3000	.008	S.F.	.42	.22	.25	.89	1.12
0200 Primer for non-metal substrate (when required)		3000	.008		.16	.22	.25	.63	.84
0300 Closed cell spray, polyurethane foam, 3 lb. per C.F. density, 1", R6.7		15000	.002		.66	.04	.05	.75	.86
0400 2", R13.4		13125	.002		1.32	.05	.06	1.43	1.60
0500 3", R18.6		11485	.002		1.98	.06	.06	2.10	2.35
0550 4", R24.8		10080	.002		2.64	.06	.07	2.77	3.10
0700 Spray-on silicone coating		2500	.010		.95	.26	.30	1.51	1.83
0800 Warranty 5-20 year manufacturer's									.15
0900 Warranty 20 year, no dollar limit									.20

07 58 Roll Roofing

07 58 10 – Asphalt Roll Roofing

07 58 10.10 Roll Roofing

	Crew	Daily Output	Labor-Hours	Unit	Material	2014 Bare Costs Labor	Equipment	Total	Total Incl O&P
0010 **ROLL ROOFING**									
0100 Asphalt, mineral surface									
0200 1 ply #15 organic felt, 1 ply mineral surfaced									
0300 Selvage roofing, lap 19", nailed & mopped	G-1	27	2.074	Sq.	74	58.50	20.50	153	212
0400 3 plies glass fiber felt (type IV), 1 ply mineral surfaced									
0500 Selvage roofing, lapped 19", mopped	G-1	25	2.240	Sq.	125	63.50	22	210.50	280
0600 Coated glass fiber base sheet, 2 plies of glass fiber									
0700 Felt (type IV), 1 ply mineral surfaced selvage									
0800 Roofing, lapped 19", mopped	G-1	25	2.240	Sq.	133	63.50	22	218.50	288

07 58 Roll Roofing

07 58 10 – Asphalt Roll Roofing

07 58 10.10 Roll Roofing	Crew	Daily Output	Labor-Hours	Unit	Material	2014 Bare Costs Labor	Equipment	Total	Total Incl O&P
0900 On nailable decks	G-1	24	2.333	Sq.	122	66	23	211	281
1000 3 plies glass fiber felt (type III), 1 ply mineral surfaced									
1100 Selvage roofing, lapped 19", mopped	G-1	25	2.240	Sq.	125	63.50	22	210.50	280

07 61 Sheet Metal Roofing

07 61 13 – Standing Seam Sheet Metal Roofing

07 61 13.10 Standing Seam Sheet Metal Roofing, Field Fab.

	Crew	Daily Output	Labor-Hours	Unit	Material	2014 Bare Costs Labor	Equipment	Total	Total Incl O&P
0010 **STANDING SEAM SHEET METAL ROOFING, FIELD FABRICATED**									
0400 Copper standing seam roofing, over 10 squares, 16 oz., 125 lb. per sq.	1 Shee	1.30	6.154	Sq.	870	249		1,119	1,375
0600 18 oz., 140 lb. per sq.		1.20	6.667		975	270		1,245	1,525
0700 20 oz., 150 lb. per sq.		1.10	7.273		1,225	294		1,519	1,850
1200 For abnormal conditions or small areas, add					25%	100%			
1300 For lead-coated copper, add					25%				

07 61 16 – Batten Seam Sheet Metal Roofing

07 61 16.10 Batten Seam Sheet Metal Roofing, Field Fabricated

	Crew	Daily Output	Labor-Hours	Unit	Material	2014 Bare Costs Labor	Equipment	Total	Total Incl O&P
0010 **BATTEN SEAM SHEET METAL ROOFING, FIELD FABRICATED**									
0012 Copper batten seam roofing, over 10 sq., 16 oz., 130 lb. per sq.	1 Shee	1.10	7.273	Sq.	1,100	294		1,394	1,700
0020 Lead batten seam roofing, 5 lb. per S.F.		1.20	6.667		1,350	270		1,620	1,950
0100 Zinc/copper alloy batten seam roofing, .020 thick		1.20	6.667		1,150	270		1,420	1,725
0200 Copper roofing, batten seam, over 10 sq., 18 oz., 145 lb. per sq.		1	8		1,225	325		1,550	1,900
0300 20 oz., 160 lb. per sq.		1	8		1,550	325		1,875	2,275
0500 Stainless steel batten seam roofing, type 304, 28 ga.		1.20	6.667		555	270		825	1,050
0600 26 ga.		1.15	6.957		515	281		796	1,025
0800 Zinc, copper alloy roofing, batten seam, .027" thick		1.15	6.957		1,450	281		1,731	2,075
0900 .032" thick		1.10	7.273		1,850	294		2,144	2,550
1000 .040" thick		1.05	7.619		2,325	310		2,635	3,075

07 61 19 – Flat Seam Sheet Metal Roofing

07 61 19.10 Flat Seam Sheet Metal Roofing, Field Fabricated

	Crew	Daily Output	Labor-Hours	Unit	Material	2014 Bare Costs Labor	Equipment	Total	Total Incl O&P
0010 **FLAT SEAM SHEET METAL ROOFING, FIELD FABRICATED**									
0900 Copper flat seam roofing, over 10 squares, 16 oz., 115 lb./sq.	1 Shee	1.20	6.667	Sq.	805	270		1,075	1,350
0950 18 oz., 130 lb./sq.		1.15	6.957		905	281		1,186	1,475
1000 20 oz., 145 lb./sq.		1.10	7.273		1,150	294		1,444	1,750
1008 Zinc flat seam roofing, .020" thick		1.20	6.667		990	270		1,260	1,550
1010 .027" thick		1.15	6.957		1,250	281		1,531	1,850
1020 .032" thick		1.12	7.143		1,575	289		1,864	2,225
1030 .040" thick		1.05	7.619		1,975	310		2,285	2,700
1100 Lead flat seam roofing, 5 lb. per S.F.		1.30	6.154		1,150	249		1,399	1,700

07 65 Flexible Flashing

07 65 10 - Sheet Metal Flashing

07 65 10.10 Sheet Metal Flashing and Counter Flashing

07 65 10.10 Sheet Metal Flashing and Counter Flashing	Crew	Daily Output	Labor-Hours	Unit	Material	2014 Bare Costs Labor	Equipment	Total	Total Incl O&P
0010 **SHEET METAL FLASHING AND COUNTER FLASHING**									
0011 Including up to 4 bends									
0020 Aluminum, mill finish, .013" thick	1 Rofc	145	.055	S.F.	.79	1.66		2.45	3.93
0030 .016" thick		145	.055		.91	1.66		2.57	4.06
0060 .019" thick		145	.055		1.15	1.66		2.81	4.33
0100 .032" thick		145	.055		1.35	1.66		3.01	4.55
0200 .040" thick		145	.055		2.31	1.66		3.97	5.60
0300 .050" thick		145	.055		2.43	1.66		4.09	5.75
0325 Mill finish 5" x 7" step flashing, .016" thick		1920	.004	Ea.	.15	.13		.28	.40
0350 Mill finish 12" x 12" step flashing, .016" thick		1600	.005	"	.50	.15		.65	.83
0400 Painted finish, add				S.F.	.29			.29	.32
1000 Mastic-coated 2 sides, .005" thick	1 Rofc	330	.024		1.82	.73		2.55	3.35
1100 .016" thick		330	.024		2.01	.73		2.74	3.56
1600 Copper, 16 oz., sheets, under 1000 lb.		115	.070		6.95	2.10		9.05	11.50
1700 Over 4000 lb.		155	.052		6.95	1.56		8.51	10.50
1900 20 oz. sheets, under 1000 lb.		110	.073		9.85	2.19		12.04	14.90
2000 Over 4000 lb.		145	.055		9.35	1.66		11.01	13.35
2200 24 oz. sheets, under 1000 lb.		105	.076		12.10	2.30		14.40	17.60
2300 Over 4000 lb.		135	.059		11.50	1.79		13.29	15.95
2500 32 oz. sheets, under 1000 lb.		100	.080		16.15	2.41		18.56	22
2600 Over 4000 lb.		130	.062		15.35	1.86		17.21	20.50
2700 W shape for valleys, 16 oz., 24" wide		100	.080	L.F.	14	2.41		16.41	19.85
5800 Lead, 2.5 lb. per S.F., up to 12" wide		135	.059	S.F.	4.99	1.79		6.78	8.80
5900 Over 12" wide		135	.059		3.99	1.79		5.78	7.70
8900 Stainless steel sheets, 32 ga., .010" thick		155	.052		3	1.56		4.56	6.15
9000 28 ga., .015" thick		155	.052		3.99	1.56		5.55	7.25
9100 26 ga., .018" thick		155	.052		4.25	1.56		5.81	7.55
9200 24 ga., .025" thick		155	.052		4.75	1.56		6.31	8.10
9290 For mechanically keyed flashing, add					40%				
9320 Steel sheets, galvanized, 20 ga.	1 Rofc	130	.062	S.F.	1.25	1.86		3.11	4.80
9322 22 ga.		135	.059		1.21	1.79		3	4.62
9324 24 ga.		140	.057		.92	1.72		2.64	4.18
9326 26 ga.		145	.055		.80	1.66		2.46	3.94
9328 28 ga.		155	.052		.69	1.56		2.25	3.63
9340 30 ga.		160	.050		.58	1.51		2.09	3.42
9400 Terne coated stainless steel, .015" thick, 28 ga		155	.052		7.35	1.56		8.91	10.95
9500 .018" thick, 26 ga		155	.052		8.30	1.56		9.86	11.95
9600 Zinc and copper alloy (brass), .020" thick		155	.052		8.55	1.56		10.11	12.25
9700 .027" thick		155	.052		10.70	1.56		12.26	14.60
9800 .032" thick		155	.052		13.65	1.56		15.21	17.90
9900 .040" thick		155	.052		17.10	1.56		18.66	21.50

07 65 12 - Fabric and Mastic Flashings

07 65 12.10 Fabric and Mastic Flashing and Counter Flashing

07 65 12.10 Fabric and Mastic Flashing and Counter Flashing	Crew	Daily Output	Labor-Hours	Unit	Material	2014 Bare Costs Labor	Equipment	Total	Total Incl O&P
0010 **FABRIC AND MASTIC FLASHING AND COUNTER FLASHING**									
1300 Asphalt flashing cement, 5 gallon				Gal.	8.45			8.45	9.30
4900 Fabric, asphalt-saturated cotton, specification grade	1 Rofc	35	.229	S.Y.	2.96	6.90		9.86	15.95
5000 Utility grade		35	.229		1.42	6.90		8.32	14.25
5300 Close-mesh fabric, saturated, 17 oz. per S.Y.		35	.229		2.15	6.90		9.05	15.05
5500 Fiberglass, resin-coated		35	.229		.97	6.90		7.87	13.75
8500 Shower pan, bituminous membrane, 7 oz.		155	.052	S.F.	1.62	1.56		3.18	4.65

07 65 Flexible Flashing

07 65 13 – Laminated Sheet Flashing

07 65 13.10 Laminated Sheet Flashing

		Crew	Daily Output	Labor-Hours	Unit	Material	2014 Bare Costs Labor	2014 Bare Costs Equipment	Total	Total Incl O&P
0010	**LAMINATED SHEET FLASHING**, Including up to 4 bends									
0500	Aluminum, fabric-backed 2 sides, .004" thick	1 Rofc	330	.024	S.F.	1.54	.73		2.27	3.04
0700	.005" thick		330	.024		1.82	.73		2.55	3.35
0750	Mastic-backed, self adhesive		460	.017		3.51	.52		4.03	4.83
0800	Mastic-coated 2 sides, .004" thick		330	.024		1.54	.73		2.27	3.04
2800	Copper, paperbacked 1 side, 2 oz.		330	.024		1.67	.73		2.40	3.19
2900	3 oz.		330	.024		1.97	.73		2.70	3.52
3100	Paperbacked 2 sides, 2 oz.		330	.024		1.72	.73		2.45	3.24
3150	3 oz.		330	.024		2.07	.73		2.80	3.63
3200	5 oz.		330	.024		2.69	.73		3.42	4.31
3250	7 oz.		330	.024		4.81	.73		5.54	6.65
3400	Mastic-backed 2 sides, copper, 2 oz.		330	.024		1.65	.73		2.38	3.17
3500	3 oz.		330	.024		2	.73		2.73	3.55
3700	5 oz.		330	.024		3	.73		3.73	4.65
3800	Fabric-backed 2 sides, copper, 2 oz.		330	.024		1.93	.73		2.66	3.47
4000	3 oz.		330	.024		2.19	.73		2.92	3.76
4100	5 oz.		330	.024		3.13	.73		3.86	4.79
4300	Copper-clad stainless steel, .015" thick, under 500 lb.		115	.070		5.80	2.10		7.90	10.25
4400	Over 2000 lb.		155	.052		5.55	1.56		7.11	8.95
4600	.018" thick, under 500 lb.		100	.080		6.55	2.41		8.96	11.65
4700	Over 2000 lb.		145	.055		6.20	1.66		7.86	9.90
8550	Shower pan, 3 ply copper and fabric, 3 oz.		155	.052		3.13	1.56		4.69	6.30
8600	7 oz.		155	.052		3.99	1.56		5.55	7.25
9300	Stainless steel, paperbacked 2 sides, .005" thick		330	.024		3.62	.73		4.35	5.35

07 65 19 – Plastic Sheet Flashing

07 65 19.10 Plastic Sheet Flashing and Counter Flashing

		Crew	Daily Output	Labor-Hours	Unit	Material	2014 Bare Costs Labor	2014 Bare Costs Equipment	Total	Total Incl O&P
0010	**PLASTIC SHEET FLASHING AND COUNTER FLASHING**									
7300	Polyvinyl chloride, black, .010" thick	1 Rofc	285	.028	S.F.	.21	.85		1.06	1.79
7400	.020" thick		285	.028		.28	.85		1.13	1.87
7600	.030" thick		285	.028		.35	.85		1.20	1.95
7700	.056" thick		285	.028		.85	.85		1.70	2.50
7900	Black or white for exposed roofs, .060" thick		285	.028		1.80	.85		2.65	3.54
8060	PVC tape, 5" x 45 mils, for joint covers, 100 L.F./roll				Ea.	170			170	187
8850	Polyvinyl chloride, .030" thick	1 Rofc	160	.050	S.F.	1.30	1.51		2.81	4.21

07 65 23 – Rubber Sheet Flashing

07 65 23.10 Rubber Sheet Flashing and Counterflashing

		Crew	Daily Output	Labor-Hours	Unit	Material	2014 Bare Costs Labor	2014 Bare Costs Equipment	Total	Total Incl O&P
0010	**RUBBER SHEET FLASHING AND COUNTERFLASHING**									
4810	EPDM 90 mils, 1" diameter pipe flashing	1 Rofc	32	.250	Ea.	19.45	7.55		27	35.50
4820	2" diameter		30	.267		19.45	8.05		27.50	36.50
4830	3" diameter		28	.286		21	8.60		29.60	39
4840	4" diameter		24	.333		24	10.05		34.05	45
4850	6" diameter		22	.364		24	10.95		34.95	46.50
8100	Rubber, butyl, 1/32" thick		285	.028	S.F.	1.92	.85		2.77	3.67
8200	1/16" thick		285	.028		2.60	.85		3.45	4.42
8300	Neoprene, cured, 1/16" thick		285	.028		2.23	.85		3.08	4.01
8400	1/8" thick		285	.028		6.05	.85		6.90	8.20

07 71 Roof Specialties

07 71 19 – Manufactured Gravel Stops and Fasciae

07 71 19.10 Gravel Stop

		Crew	Daily Output	Labor-Hours	Unit	Material	2014 Bare Costs Labor	Equipment	Total	Total Incl O&P
0010	**GRAVEL STOP**									
0020	Aluminum, .050" thick, 4" face height, mill finish	1 Shee	145	.055	L.F.	6	2.23		8.23	10.30
0080	Duranodic finish		145	.055		6.50	2.23		8.73	10.85
0100	Painted		145	.055		6.85	2.23		9.08	11.20
0300	6" face height		135	.059		6.45	2.40		8.85	11.10
0350	Duranodic finish		135	.059		6.95	2.40		9.35	11.65
0400	Painted		135	.059		8.10	2.40		10.50	12.90
0600	8" face height		125	.064		7.30	2.59		9.89	12.30
0650	Duranodic finish		125	.064		8	2.59		10.59	13.10
0700	Painted		125	.064		8.15	2.59		10.74	13.25
0900	12" face height, .080 thick, 2 piece		100	.080		10.15	3.24		13.39	16.60
0950	Duranodic finish		100	.080		10.05	3.24		13.29	16.45
1000	Painted		100	.080		11.90	3.24		15.14	18.50
1200	Copper, 16 oz., 3" face height		145	.055		39.50	2.23		41.73	46.50
1300	6" face height		135	.059		39.50	2.40		41.90	47
1350	Galv steel, 24 ga., 4" leg, plain, with continuous cleat, 4" face		145	.055		6	2.23		8.23	10.30
1360	6" face height		145	.055		6	2.23		8.23	10.30
1500	Polyvinyl chloride, 6" face height		135	.059		4.90	2.40		7.30	9.40
1600	9" face height		125	.064		5.80	2.59		8.39	10.65
1800	Stainless steel, 24 ga., 6" face height		135	.059		9.85	2.40		12.25	14.80
1900	12" face height		100	.080		19.70	3.24		22.94	27
2100	20 ga., 6" face height		135	.059		11.90	2.40		14.30	17.05
2200	12" face height		100	.080		24	3.24		27.24	31.50

07 71 19.30 Fascia

		Crew	Daily Output	Labor-Hours	Unit	Material	2014 Bare Costs Labor	Equipment	Total	Total Incl O&P
0010	**FASCIA**									
0100	Aluminum, reverse board and batten, .032" thick, colored, no furring incl	1 Shee	145	.055	S.F.	6.25	2.23		8.48	10.60
0300	Steel, galv and enameled, stock, no furring, long panels		145	.055		3.91	2.23		6.14	8
0600	Short panels		115	.070		5.30	2.81		8.11	10.55

07 71 23 – Manufactured Gutters and Downspouts

07 71 23.10 Downspouts

		Crew	Daily Output	Labor-Hours	Unit	Material	2014 Bare Costs Labor	Equipment	Total	Total Incl O&P
0010	**DOWNSPOUTS**									
0020	Aluminum 2" x 3", .020" thick, embossed	1 Shee	190	.042	L.F.	.97	1.70		2.67	3.91
0100	Enameled		190	.042		1.32	1.70		3.02	4.29
0300	Enameled, .024" thick, 2" x 3"		180	.044		2.05	1.80		3.85	5.25
0400	3" x 4"		140	.057		2.88	2.31		5.19	7
0600	Round, corrugated aluminum, 3" diameter, .020" thick		190	.042		1.57	1.70		3.27	4.57
0700	4" diameter, .025" thick		140	.057		2.33	2.31		4.64	6.40
0900	Wire strainer, round, 2" diameter		155	.052	Ea.	3.92	2.09		6.01	7.80
1000	4" diameter		155	.052		7.20	2.09		9.29	11.45
1200	Rectangular, perforated, 2" x 3"		145	.055		2.30	2.23		4.53	6.25
1300	3" x 4"		145	.055		3.32	2.23		5.55	7.35
1500	Copper, round, 16 oz., stock, 2" diameter		190	.042	L.F.	8.55	1.70		10.25	12.25
1600	3" diameter		190	.042		8.45	1.70		10.15	12.10
1800	4" diameter		145	.055		10.55	2.23		12.78	15.30
1900	5" diameter		130	.062		18.20	2.49		20.69	24
2100	Rectangular, corrugated copper, stock, 2" x 3"		190	.042		8.80	1.70		10.50	12.50
2200	3" x 4"		145	.055		12.20	2.23		14.43	17.15
2400	Rectangular, plain copper, stock, 2" x 3"		190	.042		13.30	1.70		15	17.50
2500	3" x 4"		145	.055		16.90	2.23		19.13	22.50
2700	Wire strainers, rectangular, 2" x 3"		145	.055	Ea.	13.50	2.23		15.73	18.55
2800	3" x 4"		145	.055		14.65	2.23		16.88	19.85
3000	Round, 2" diameter		145	.055		5.95	2.23		8.18	10.20

07 71 23 – Manufactured Gutters and Downspouts

07 71 23.10 Downspouts		Crew	Daily Output	Labor-Hours	Unit	Material	Labor	2014 Bare Costs Equipment	Total	Total Incl O&P
3100	3" diameter	1 Shee	145	.055	Ea.	5.95	2.23		8.18	10.20
3300	4" diameter		145	.055		8	2.23		10.23	12.50
3400	5" diameter		115	.070	↓	19.80	2.81		22.61	26.50
3600	Lead-coated copper, round, stock, 2" diameter		190	.042	L.F.	25	1.70		26.70	30.50
3700	3" diameter		190	.042		21.50	1.70		23.20	26.50
3900	4" diameter		145	.055		22.50	2.23		24.73	28
4000	5" diameter, corrugated		130	.062		24	2.49		26.49	30.50
4200	6" diameter, corrugated		105	.076		30	3.08		33.08	38
4300	Rectangular, corrugated, stock, 2" x 3"		190	.042		15	1.70		16.70	19.35
4500	Plain, stock, 2" x 3"		190	.042		24	1.70		25.70	29.50
4600	3" x 4"		145	.055		33	2.23		35.23	40
4800	Steel, galvanized, round, corrugated, 2" or 3" diameter, 28 ga.		190	.042		2.08	1.70		3.78	5.15
4900	4" diameter, 28 ga.		145	.055		2.61	2.23		4.84	6.60
5100	5" diameter, 26 ga.		130	.062		3.46	2.49		5.95	7.95
5400	6" diameter, 28 ga.		105	.076		4.20	3.08		7.28	9.75
5500	26 ga.		105	.076		5.80	3.08		8.88	11.55
5700	Rectangular, corrugated, 28 ga., 2" x 3"		190	.042		1.94	1.70		3.64	4.97
5800	3" x 4"		145	.055		1.82	2.23		4.05	5.70
6000	Rectangular, plain, 28 ga., galvanized, 2" x 3"		190	.042		3.03	1.70		4.73	6.15
6100	3" x 4"		145	.055		3.06	2.23		5.29	7.10
6300	Epoxy painted, 24 ga., corrugated, 2" x 3"		190	.042		2.20	1.70		3.90	5.25
6400	3" x 4"		145	.055	↓	2.75	2.23		4.98	6.75
6600	Wire strainers, rectangular, 2" x 3"		145	.055	Ea.	15.90	2.23		18.13	21
6700	3" x 4"		145	.055		16.60	2.23		18.83	22
6900	Round strainers, 2" or 3" diameter		145	.055		3.86	2.23		6.09	7.95
7000	4" diameter		145	.055	↓	5.80	2.23		8.03	10.05
7800	Stainless steel tubing, schedule 5, 2" x 3" or 3" diameter		190	.042	L.F.	38.50	1.70		40.20	45.50
7900	3" x 4" or 4" diameter		145	.055		49	2.23		51.23	57.50
8100	4" x 5" or 5" diameter		135	.059		101	2.40		103.40	115
8200	Vinyl, rectangular, 2" x 3"		210	.038		2.08	1.54		3.62	4.86
8300	Round, 2-1/2"	↓	220	.036	↓	1.31	1.47		2.78	3.89

07 71 23.20 Downspout Elbows

		Crew	Daily Output	Labor-Hours	Unit	Material	Labor	2014 Bare Costs Equipment	Total	Total Incl O&P
0010	**DOWNSPOUT ELBOWS**									
0020	Aluminum, 2" x 3", embossed	1 Shee	100	.080	Ea.	.95	3.24		4.19	6.45
0100	Enameled		100	.080		1.75	3.24		4.99	7.35
0200	3" x 4", .025" thick, embossed		100	.080		3.50	3.24		6.74	9.25
0300	Enameled		100	.080		3.75	3.24		6.99	9.55
0400	Round corrugated, 3", embossed, .020" thick		100	.080		2.74	3.24		5.98	8.40
0500	4", .025" thick		100	.080		5.80	3.24		9.04	11.75
0600	Copper, 16 oz. round, 2" diameter		100	.080		9.45	3.24		12.69	15.80
0700	3" diameter		100	.080		9	3.24		12.24	15.30
0800	4" diameter		100	.080		13.15	3.24		16.39	19.90
1000	2" x 3" corrugated		100	.080		9	3.24		12.24	15.30
1100	3" x 4" corrugated		100	.080		13.65	3.24		16.89	20.50
1300	Vinyl, 2-1/2" diameter, 45° or 75°		100	.080		3.88	3.24		7.12	9.65
1400	Tee Y junction	↓	75	.107	↓	12.90	4.31		17.21	21.50

07 71 23.30 Gutters

		Crew	Daily Output	Labor-Hours	Unit	Material	Labor	2014 Bare Costs Equipment	Total	Total Incl O&P
0010	**GUTTERS**									
0012	Aluminum, stock units, 5" K type, .027" thick, plain	1 Shee	125	.064	L.F.	2.61	2.59		5.20	7.20
0100	Enameled		125	.064		2.60	2.59		5.19	7.15
0300	5" K type type, .032" thick, plain		125	.064		3.20	2.59		5.79	7.85
0400	Enameled		125	.064	↓	3	2.59		5.59	7.60

07 71 23 – Manufactured Gutters and Downspouts

07 71 23.30 Gutters	Crew	Daily Output	Labor-Hours	Unit	Material	2014 Bare Costs Labor	Equipment	Total	Total Incl O&P
0700	Copper, half round, 16 oz., stock units, 4" wide	1 Shee	125	.064	L.F.	10.50	2.59		13.09	15.85
0900	5" wide		125	.064		7.70	2.59		10.29	12.75
1000	6" wide		118	.068		14	2.74		16.74	19.95
1200	K type, 16 oz., stock, 5" wide		125	.064		12.60	2.59		15.19	18.15
1300	6" wide		125	.064		8.80	2.59		11.39	14
1500	Lead coated copper, half round, stock, 4" wide		125	.064		13.80	2.59		16.39	19.50
1600	6" wide		118	.068		22	2.74		24.74	29
1800	K type, stock, 5" wide		125	.064		18.90	2.59		21.49	25.50
1900	6" wide		125	.064		18.40	2.59		20.99	24.50
2100	Copper clad stainless steel, K type, 5" wide		125	.064		7	2.59		9.59	12
2200	6" wide		125	.064		8.90	2.59		11.49	14.10
2400	Steel, galv, half round or box, 28 ga., 5" wide, plain		125	.064		2.18	2.59		4.77	6.70
2500	Enameled		125	.064		2.13	2.59		4.72	6.65
2700	26 ga., stock, 5" wide		125	.064		2.18	2.59		4.77	6.70
2800	6" wide		125	.064		2.67	2.59		5.26	7.25
3000	Vinyl, O.G., 4" wide	1 Carp	115	.070		1.19	2.49		3.68	5.50
3100	5" wide		115	.070		1.55	2.49		4.04	5.90
3200	4" half round, stock units		115	.070		1.28	2.49		3.77	5.60
3250	Joint connectors				Ea.	2.88			2.88	3.17
3300	Wood, clear treated cedar, fir or hemlock, 3" x 4"	1 Carp	100	.080	L.F.	12.40	2.86		15.26	18.45
3400	4" x 5"	"	100	.080	"	19.45	2.86		22.31	26.50
5000	Accessories, end cap, K type, aluminum 5"	1 Shee	625	.013	Ea.	.66	.52		1.18	1.59
5010	6"		625	.013		1.44	.52		1.96	2.44
5020	Copper, 5"		625	.013		3.89	.52		4.41	5.15
5030	6"		625	.013		3.54	.52		4.06	4.75
5040	Lead coated copper, 5"		625	.013		12.50	.52		13.02	14.60
5050	6"		625	.013		13.35	.52		13.87	15.55
5060	Copper clad stainless steel, 5"		625	.013		3	.52		3.52	4.16
5070	6"		625	.013		3.60	.52		4.12	4.82
5080	Galvanized steel, 5"		625	.013		1.28	.52		1.80	2.27
5090	6"		625	.013		2.18	.52		2.70	3.26
5100	Vinyl, 4"	1 Carp	625	.013		5.80	.46		6.26	7.15
5110	5"	"	625	.013		6.10	.46		6.56	7.45
5120	Half round, copper, 4"	1 Shee	625	.013		4.40	.52		4.92	5.70
5130	5"		625	.013		4.72	.52		5.24	6.05
5140	6"		625	.013		5.15	.52		5.67	6.50
5150	Lead coated copper, 5"		625	.013		14.15	.52		14.67	16.40
5160	6"		625	.013		21	.52		21.52	24.50
5170	Copper clad stainless steel, 5"		625	.013		4.50	.52		5.02	5.80
5180	6"		625	.013		4.50	.52		5.02	5.80
5190	Galvanized steel, 5"		625	.013		2.25	.52		2.77	3.34
5200	6"		625	.013		2.80	.52		3.32	3.94
5210	Outlet, aluminum, 2" x 3"		420	.019		.62	.77		1.39	1.96
5220	3" x 4"		420	.019		1.05	.77		1.82	2.44
5230	2-3/8" round		420	.019		.56	.77		1.33	1.90
5240	Copper, 2" x 3"		420	.019		6.50	.77		7.27	8.45
5250	3" x 4"		420	.019		7.85	.77		8.62	9.95
5260	2-3/8" round		420	.019		4.55	.77		5.32	6.30
5270	Lead coated copper, 2" x 3"		420	.019		25.50	.77		26.27	29.50
5280	3" x 4"		420	.019		28.50	.77		29.27	33
5290	2-3/8" round		420	.019		25.50	.77		26.27	29.50
5300	Copper clad stainless steel, 2" x 3"		420	.019		6.50	.77		7.27	8.45
5310	3" x 4"		420	.019		7.85	.77		8.62	9.95

07 71 Roof Specialties

07 71 23 – Manufactured Gutters and Downspouts

07 71 23.30 Gutters

		Crew	Daily Output	Labor-Hours	Unit	Material	2014 Bare Costs Labor	Equipment	Total	Total Incl O&P
5320	2-3/8" round	1 Shee	420	.019	Ea.	4.55	.77		5.32	6.30
5330	Galvanized steel, 2" x 3"		420	.019		3.18	.77		3.95	4.78
5340	3" x 4"		420	.019		4.90	.77		5.67	6.70
5350	2-3/8" round		420	.019		3.98	.77		4.75	5.65
5360	K type mitres, aluminum		65	.123		3	4.98		7.98	11.60
5370	Copper		65	.123		17.40	4.98		22.38	27.50
5380	Lead coated copper		65	.123		54.50	4.98		59.48	68.50
5390	Copper clad stainless steel		65	.123		27.50	4.98		32.48	39
5400	Galvanized steel		65	.123		22.50	4.98		27.48	33.50
5420	Half round mitres, copper		65	.123		63.50	4.98		68.48	78.50
5430	Lead coated copper		65	.123		89.50	4.98		94.48	107
5440	Copper clad stainless steel		65	.123		56	4.98		60.98	70.50
5450	Galvanized steel		65	.123		25.50	4.98		30.48	36.50
5460	Vinyl mitres and outlets		65	.123		9.75	4.98		14.73	19.05
5470	Sealant		940	.009	L.F.	.01	.34		.35	.58
5480	Soldering		96	.083	"	.20	3.37		3.57	5.80

07 71 23.35 Gutter Guard

		Crew	Daily Output	Labor-Hours	Unit	Material	2014 Bare Costs Labor	Equipment	Total	Total Incl O&P
0010	**GUTTER GUARD**									
0020	6" wide strip, aluminum mesh	1 Carp	500	.016	L.F.	2.17	.57		2.74	3.35
0100	Vinyl mesh	"	500	.016	"	2.25	.57		2.82	3.44

07 71 26 – Reglets

07 71 26.10 Reglets and Accessories

		Crew	Daily Output	Labor-Hours	Unit	Material	2014 Bare Costs Labor	Equipment	Total	Total Incl O&P
0010	**REGLETS AND ACCESSORIES**									
0020	Aluminum, .025" thick, in concrete parapet	1 Carp	225	.036	L.F.	1.84	1.27		3.11	4.16
0300	16 oz.		225	.036		5.85	1.27		7.12	8.55
0400	Galvanized steel, 24 ga.		225	.036		1.28	1.27		2.55	3.55
0600	Stainless steel, .020" thick		225	.036		3.64	1.27		4.91	6.15
0900	Counter flashing for above, 12" wide, .032" aluminum	1 Shee	150	.053		2.29	2.16		4.45	6.10
1200	16 oz.		150	.053		5.45	2.16		7.61	9.60
1300	Galvanized steel, .020" thick		150	.053		1.29	2.16		3.45	5
1500	Stainless steel, .020" thick		150	.053		5.70	2.16		7.86	9.85

07 71 29 – Manufactured Roof Expansion Joints

07 71 29.10 Expansion Joints

		Crew	Daily Output	Labor-Hours	Unit	Material	2014 Bare Costs Labor	Equipment	Total	Total Incl O&P
0010	**EXPANSION JOINTS**									
0300	Butyl or neoprene center with foam insulation, metal flanges									
0400	Aluminum, .032" thick for openings to 2-1/2"	1 Rofc	165	.048	L.F.	18.40	1.46		19.86	22.50
0600	For joint openings to 3-1/2"		165	.048		18.40	1.46		19.86	22.50
0610	For joint openings to 5"		165	.048		18.90	1.46		20.36	23.50
0620	For joint openings to 8"		165	.048		21	1.46		22.46	25.50
0700	Copper, 16 oz. for openings to 2-1/2"		165	.048		28.50	1.46		29.96	33.50
0900	For joint openings to 3-1/2"		165	.048		28.50	1.46		29.96	33.50
0910	For joint openings to 5"		165	.048		29	1.46		30.46	34.50
0920	For joint openings to 8"		165	.048		31	1.46		32.46	36.50
1000	Galvanized steel, 26 ga. for openings to 2-1/2"		165	.048		14.85	1.46		16.31	19.05
1200	For joint openings to 3-1/2"		165	.048		14.85	1.46		16.31	19.05
1210	For joint openings to 5"		165	.048		16	1.46		17.46	20.50
1220	For joint openings to 8"		165	.048		19.85	1.46		21.31	24.50
1300	Lead-coated copper, 16 oz. for openings to 2-1/2"		165	.048		35	1.46		36.46	41
1500	For joint openings to 3-1/2"		165	.048		40	1.46		41.46	46.50
1600	Stainless steel, .018", for openings to 2-1/2"		165	.048		20	1.46		21.46	24.50
1800	For joint openings to 3-1/2"		165	.048		17.90	1.46		19.36	22.50

07 71 Roof Specialties

07 71 29 – Manufactured Roof Expansion Joints

07 71 29.10 Expansion Joints

		Crew	Daily Output	Labor-Hours	Unit	Material	2014 Bare Costs Labor	Equipment	Total	Total Incl O&P
1810	For joint openings to 5"	1 Rofc	165	.048	L.F.	18.60	1.46		20.06	23
1820	For joint openings to 8"		165	.048		22	1.46		23.46	26.50
1900	Neoprene, double-seal type with thick center, 4-1/2" wide		125	.064		15	1.93		16.93	20
1950	Polyethylene bellows, with galv steel flat flanges		100	.080		6	2.41		8.41	11.05
1960	With galvanized angle flanges		100	.080		6.50	2.41		8.91	11.60
2000	Roof joint with extruded aluminum cover, 2"	1 Shee	115	.070		38	2.81		40.81	46.50
2100	Roof joint, plastic curbs, foam center, standard	1 Rofc	100	.080		15	2.41		17.41	21
2200	Large		100	.080		19	2.41		21.41	25.50
2300	Transitions, regular, minimum		10	.800	Ea.	120	24		144	177
2350	Maximum		4	2		150	60.50		210.50	277
2400	Large, minimum		9	.889		175	27		202	243
2450	Maximum		3	2.667		185	80.50		265.50	350
2500	Roof to wall joint with extruded aluminum cover	1 Shee	115	.070	L.F.	32	2.81		34.81	39.50
2700	Wall joint, closed cell foam on PVC cover, 9" wide	1 Rofc	125	.064		5	1.93		6.93	9.05
2800	12" wide	"	115	.070		6	2.10		8.10	10.45

07 71 43 – Drip Edge

07 71 43.10 Drip Edge, Rake Edge, Ice Belts

		Crew	Daily Output	Labor-Hours	Unit	Material	2014 Bare Costs Labor	Equipment	Total	Total Incl O&P
0010	**DRIP EDGE, RAKE EDGE, ICE BELTS**									
0020	Aluminum, .016" thick, 5" wide, mill finish	1 Carp	400	.020	L.F.	.40	.72		1.12	1.64
0100	White finish		400	.020		.41	.72		1.13	1.65
0200	8" wide, mill finish		400	.020		.69	.72		1.41	1.96
0300	Ice belt, 28" wide, mill finish		100	.080		3.85	2.86		6.71	9.05
0310	Vented, mill finish		400	.020		2.86	.72		3.58	4.35
0320	Painted finish		400	.020		2.90	.72		3.62	4.39
0400	Galvanized, 5" wide		400	.020		.53	.72		1.25	1.78
0500	8" wide, mill finish		400	.020		.69	.72		1.41	1.96
0510	Rake edge, aluminum, 1-1/2" x 1-1/2"		400	.020		.30	.72		1.02	1.53
0520	3-1/2" x 1-1/2"		400	.020		.41	.72		1.13	1.65

07 72 Roof Accessories

07 72 23 – Relief Vents

07 72 23.10 Roof Vents

		Crew	Daily Output	Labor-Hours	Unit	Material	2014 Bare Costs Labor	Equipment	Total	Total Incl O&P
0010	**ROOF VENTS**									
0020	Mushroom shape, for built-up roofs, aluminum	1 Rofc	30	.267	Ea.	108	8.05		116.05	134
0100	PVC, 6" high	"	30	.267	"	28.50	8.05		36.55	46.50

07 72 26 – Ridge Vents

07 72 26.10 Ridge Vents and Accessories

		Crew	Daily Output	Labor-Hours	Unit	Material	2014 Bare Costs Labor	Equipment	Total	Total Incl O&P
0010	**RIDGE VENTS AND ACCESSORIES**									
0100	Aluminum strips, mill finish	1 Rofc	160	.050	L.F.	2.75	1.51		4.26	5.80
0150	Painted finish		160	.050	"	4.05	1.51		5.56	7.25
0200	Connectors		48	.167	Ea.	4.65	5.05		9.70	14.35
0300	End caps		48	.167	"	1.98	5.05		7.03	11.45
0400	Galvanized strips		160	.050	L.F.	3.58	1.51		5.09	6.70
0430	Molded polyethylene, shingles not included		160	.050	"	2.74	1.51		4.25	5.80
0440	End plugs		48	.167	Ea.	1.98	5.05		7.03	11.45
0450	Flexible roll, shingles not included		160	.050	L.F.	2.38	1.51		3.89	5.40
2300	Ridge vent strip, mill finish	1 Shee	155	.052	"	2.98	2.09		5.07	6.75

07 72 Roof Accessories

07 72 33 – Roof Hatches

07 72 33.10 Roof Hatch Options

		Crew	Daily Output	Labor- Hours	Unit	Material	2014 Bare Costs Labor	Equipment	Total	Total Incl O&P
0010	**ROOF HATCH OPTIONS**									
0500	2'-6" x 3', aluminum curb and cover	G-3	10	3.200	Ea.	1,075	110		1,185	1,350
0520	Galvanized steel curb and aluminum cover		10	3.200		640	110		750	890
0540	Galvanized steel curb and cover		10	3.200		635	110		745	880
0600	2'-6" x 4'-6", aluminum curb and cover		9	3.556		915	122		1,037	1,200
0800	Galvanized steel curb and aluminum cover		9	3.556		885	122		1,007	1,175
0900	Galvanized steel curb and cover		9	3.556		890	122		1,012	1,175
1100	4' x 4' aluminum curb and cover		8	4		1,800	137		1,937	2,200
1120	Galvanized steel curb and aluminum cover		8	4		1,725	137		1,862	2,125
1140	Galvanized steel curb and cover		8	4		1,700	137		1,837	2,100
1200	2'-6" x 8'-0", aluminum curb and cover		6.60	4.848		1,800	166		1,966	2,250
1400	Galvanized steel curb and aluminum cover		6.60	4.848		1,800	166		1,966	2,250
1500	Galvanized steel curb and cover	↓	6.60	4.848		1,425	166		1,591	1,850
1800	For plexiglass panels, 2'-6" x 3'-0", add to above				↓	440			440	485

07 72 36 – Smoke Vents

07 72 36.10 Smoke Hatches

					Unit	Material	Labor			
0010	**SMOKE HATCHES**									
0200	For 3'-0" long, add to roof hatches from Section 07 72 33.10				Ea.	25%	5%			
0250	For 4'-0" long, add to roof hatches from Section 07 72 33.10					20%	5%			
0300	For 8'-0" long, add to roof hatches from Section 07 72 33.10				↓	10%	5%			

07 72 36.20 Smoke Vent Options

		Crew	Daily Output	Labor- Hours	Unit	Material	Labor	Equipment	Total	Total Incl O&P
0010	**SMOKE VENT OPTIONS**									
0100	4' x 4' aluminum cover and frame	G-3	13	2.462	Ea.	2,050	84.50		2,134.50	2,400
0200	Galvanized steel cover and frame		13	2.462		1,800	84.50		1,884.50	2,125
0300	4' x 8' aluminum cover and frame		8	4		2,800	137		2,937	3,300
0400	Galvanized steel cover and frame	↓	8	4	↓	2,375	137		2,512	2,850

07 72 53 – Snow Guards

07 72 53.10 Snow Guard Options

		Crew	Daily Output	Labor- Hours	Unit	Material	Labor	Equipment	Total	Total Incl O&P
0010	**SNOW GUARD OPTIONS**									
0100	Slate & asphalt shingle roofs, fastened with nails	1 Rofc	160	.050	Ea.	12.55	1.51		14.06	16.60
0200	Standing seam metal roofs, fastened with set screws		48	.167		16.95	5.05		22	28
0300	Surface mount for metal roofs, fastened with solder		48	.167	↓	6.05	5.05		11.10	15.90
0400	Double rail pipe type, including pipe	↓	130	.062	L.F.	32	1.86		33.86	38.50

07 72 73 – Pitch Pockets

07 72 73.10 Pitch Pockets, Variable Sizes

		Crew	Daily Output	Labor- Hours	Unit	Material	Labor	Equipment	Total	Total Incl O&P
0010	**PITCH POCKETS, VARIABLE SIZES**									
0100	Adjustable, 4" to 7", welded corners, 4" deep	1 Rofc	48	.167	Ea.	15.75	5.05		20.80	26.50
0200	Side extenders, 6"	"	240	.033	"	2.15	1		3.15	4.22

07 72 80 – Vents

07 72 80.30 Vent Options

		Crew	Daily Output	Labor- Hours	Unit	Material	Labor	Equipment	Total	Total Incl O&P
0010	**VENT OPTIONS**									
0020	Plastic, for insulated decks, 1 per M.S.F., minimum	1 Rofc	40	.200	Ea.	19.15	6.05		25.20	32
0100	Maximum		20	.400		36	12.05		48.05	61.50
0300	Aluminum	↓	30	.267		19.50	8.05		27.55	36.50
0800	Polystyrene baffles, 12" wide for 16" O.C. rafter spacing	1 Carp	90	.089		.40	3.18		3.58	5.80
0900	For 24" O.C. rafter spacing	"	110	.073	↓	.75	2.60		3.35	5.20

07 76 Roof Pavers

07 76 16 – Roof Decking Pavers

07 76 16.10 Roof Pavers and Supports	Crew	Daily Output	Labor-Hours	Unit	Material	2014 Bare Costs Labor	Equipment	Total	Total Incl O&P
0010 **ROOF PAVERS AND SUPPORTS**									
1000 Roof decking pavers, concrete blocks, 2" thick, natural	1 Clab	115	.070	S.F.	3.37	1.96		5.33	7
1100 Colors		115	.070	"	3.73	1.96		5.69	7.40
1200 Support pedestal, bottom cap		960	.008	Ea.	2.99	.23		3.22	3.69
1300 Top cap		960	.008		4.79	.23		5.02	5.65
1400 Leveling shims, 1/16"		1920	.004		1.19	.12		1.31	1.51
1500 1/8"		1920	.004		1.19	.12		1.31	1.51
1600 Buffer pad		960	.008		2.49	.23		2.72	3.14
1700 PVC legs (4" SDR 35)		2880	.003	Inch	.12	.08		.20	.26
2000 Alternate pricing method, system in place		101	.079	S.F.	7	2.23		9.23	11.45

07 81 Applied Fireproofing

07 81 16 – Cementitious Fireproofing

07 81 16.10 Sprayed Cementitious Fireproofing

	Crew	Daily Output	Labor-Hours	Unit	Material	2014 Bare Costs Labor	Equipment	Total	Total Incl O&P
0010 **SPRAYED CEMENTITIOUS FIREPROOFING**									
0050 Not including canvas protection, normal density									
0100 Per 1" thick, on flat plate steel	G-2	3000	.008	S.F.	.53	.24	.05	.82	1.03
0200 Flat decking		2400	.010		.53	.30	.06	.89	1.14
0400 Beams		1500	.016		.53	.48	.09	1.10	1.47
0500 Corrugated or fluted decks		1250	.019		.79	.58	.11	1.48	1.94
0700 Columns, 1-1/8" thick		1100	.022		.59	.65	.12	1.36	1.86
0800 2-3/16" thick		700	.034		1.20	1.03	.19	2.42	3.23
0900 For canvas protection, add		5000	.005		.07	.14	.03	.24	.35
1500 Intumescent epoxy fireproofing on wire mesh, 3/16" thick									
1550 1 hour rating, exterior use	G-2	136	.176	S.F.	7.30	5.30	.99	13.59	17.90
1600 Magnesium oxychloride, 35# to 40# density, 1/4" thick		3000	.008		1.53	.24	.05	1.82	2.13
1650 1/2" thick		2000	.012		3.09	.36	.07	3.52	4.07
1700 60# to 70# density, 1/4" thick		3000	.008		2.04	.24	.05	2.33	2.69
1750 1/2" thick		2000	.012		4.10	.36	.07	4.53	5.20
2000 Vermiculite cement, troweled or sprayed, 1/4" thick		3000	.008		1.39	.24	.05	1.68	1.98
2050 1/2" thick		2000	.012		2.77	.36	.07	3.20	3.72

07 84 Firestopping

07 84 13 – Penetration Firestopping

07 84 13.10 Firestopping

		Crew	Daily Output	Labor-Hours	Unit	Material	2014 Bare Costs Labor	Equipment	Total	Total Incl O&P
0010 **FIRESTOPPING**	R078413-30									
0100 Metallic piping, non insulated										
0110 Through walls, 2" diameter		1 Carp	16	.500	Ea.	15.90	17.90		33.80	47.50
0120 4" diameter			14	.571		24.50	20.50		45	61
0130 6" diameter			12	.667		32.50	24		56.50	76
0140 12" diameter			10	.800		57.50	28.50		86	112
0150 Through floors, 2" diameter			32	.250		9.65	8.95		18.60	25.50
0160 4" diameter			28	.286		13.85	10.20		24.05	32.50
0170 6" diameter			24	.333		18.20	11.90		30.10	40
0180 12" diameter			20	.400		31	14.30		45.30	58
0190 Metallic piping, insulated										
0200 Through walls, 2" diameter		1 Carp	16	.500	Ea.	22.50	17.90		40.40	55
0210 4" diameter			14	.571		31	20.50		51.50	68.50
0220 6" diameter			12	.667		39	24		63	83

07 84 13 – Penetration Firestopping

07 84 13.10 Firestopping		Crew	Daily Output	Labor- Hours	Unit	Material	2014 Bare Costs Labor	2014 Bare Costs Equipment	Total	Total Incl O&P
0230	12" diameter	1 Carp	10	.800	Ea.	64	28.50		92.50	119
0240	Through floors, 2" diameter		32	.250		16.30	8.95		25.25	33
0250	4" diameter		28	.286		20.50	10.20		30.70	39.50
0260	6" diameter		24	.333		25	11.90		36.90	47.50
0270	12" diameter		20	.400		31	14.30		45.30	58
0280	Non metallic piping, non insulated									
0290	Through walls, 2" diameter	1 Carp	12	.667	Ea.	65.50	24		89.50	112
0300	4" diameter		10	.800		82	28.50		110.50	139
0310	6" diameter		8	1		114	36		150	186
0330	Through floors, 2" diameter		16	.500		51.50	17.90		69.40	86.50
0340	4" diameter		6	1.333		63.50	47.50		111	150
0350	6" diameter		6	1.333		76.50	47.50		124	164
0370	Ductwork, insulated & non insulated, round									
0380	Through walls, 6" diameter	1 Carp	12	.667	Ea.	33.50	24		57.50	76.50
0390	12" diameter		10	.800		66	28.50		94.50	121
0400	18" diameter		8	1		108	36		144	179
0410	Through floors, 6" diameter		16	.500		18.20	17.90		36.10	50
0420	12" diameter		14	.571		33.50	20.50		54	71
0430	18" diameter		12	.667		57.50	24		81.50	104
0440	Ductwork, insulated & non insulated, rectangular									
0450	With stiffener/closure angle, through walls, 6" x 12"	1 Carp	8	1	Ea.	27.50	36		63.50	90.50
0460	12" x 24"		6	1.333		36.50	47.50		84	120
0470	24" x 48"		4	2		105	71.50		176.50	235
0480	With stiffener/closure angle, through floors, 6" x 12"		10	.800		14.95	28.50		43.45	64.50
0490	12" x 24"		8	1		27	36		63	89.50
0500	24" x 48"		6	1.333		52.50	47.50		100	138
0510	Multi trade openings									
0520	Through walls, 6" x 12"	1 Carp	2	4	Ea.	57.50	143		200.50	305
0530	12" x 24"	"	1	8		234	286		520	735
0540	24" x 48"	2 Carp	1	16		935	570		1,505	1,975
0550	48" x 96"	"	.75	21.333		3,750	765		4,515	5,400
0560	Through floors, 6" x 12"	1 Carp	2	4		57.50	143		200.50	305
0570	12" x 24"	"	1	8		234	286		520	735
0580	24" x 48"	2 Carp	.75	21.333		935	765		1,700	2,300
0590	48" x 96"	"	.50	32		3,750	1,150		4,900	6,050
0600	Structural penetrations, through walls									
0610	Steel beams, W8 x 10	1 Carp	8	1	Ea.	36.50	36		72.50	100
0620	W12 x 14		6	1.333		57.50	47.50		105	144
0630	W21 x 44		5	1.600		116	57		173	224
0640	W36 x 135		3	2.667		282	95.50		377.50	470
0650	Bar joists, 18" deep		6	1.333		53.50	47.50		101	139
0660	24" deep		6	1.333		66	47.50		113.50	153
0670	36" deep		5	1.600		99.50	57		156.50	205
0680	48" deep		4	2		116	71.50		187.50	248
0690	Construction joints, floor slab at exterior wall									
0700	Precast, brick, block or drywall exterior									
0710	2" wide joint	1 Carp	125	.064	L.F.	8.30	2.29		10.59	12.95
0720	4" wide joint	"	75	.107	"	16.55	3.81		20.36	24.50
0730	Metal panel, glass or curtain wall exterior									
0740	2" wide joint	1 Carp	40	.200	L.F.	19.60	7.15		26.75	33.50
0750	4" wide joint	"	25	.320	"	27	11.45		38.45	49
0760	Floor slab to drywall partition									
0770	Flat joint	1 Carp	100	.080	L.F.	8.15	2.86		11.01	13.75

07 84 Firestopping

07 84 13 – Penetration Firestopping

07 84 13.10 Firestopping		Crew	Daily Output	Labor-Hours	Unit	Material	2014 Bare Costs Labor	Equipment	Total	Total Incl O&P
0780	Fluted joint	1 Carp	50	.160	L.F.	16.55	5.70		22.25	28
0790	Etched fluted joint	↓	75	.107	↓	10.75	3.81		14.56	18.25
0800	Floor slab to concrete/masonry partition									
0810	Flat joint	1 Carp	75	.107	L.F.	18.20	3.81		22.01	26.50
0820	Fluted joint	"	50	.160	"	21.50	5.70		27.20	33
0830	Concrete/CMU wall joints									
0840	1" wide	1 Carp	100	.080	L.F.	9.95	2.86		12.81	15.70
0850	2" wide		75	.107		18.20	3.81		22.01	26.50
0860	4" wide	↓	50	.160	↓	34.50	5.70		40.20	47.50
0870	Concrete/CMU floor joints									
0880	1" wide	1 Carp	200	.040	L.F.	4.99	1.43		6.42	7.90
0890	2" wide		150	.053		9.10	1.91		11.01	13.20
0900	4" wide	↓	100	.080	↓	17.40	2.86		20.26	24

07 91 Preformed Joint Seals

07 91 13 – Compression Seals

07 91 13.10 Compression Seals

		Crew	Daily Output	Labor-Hours	Unit	Material	Labor	Equipment	Total	Total Incl O&P
0010	**COMPRESSION SEALS**									
4900	O-ring type cord, 1/4"	1 Bric	472	.017	L.F.	.48	.60		1.08	1.53
4910	1/2"		440	.018		1.79	.65		2.44	3.05
4920	3/4"		424	.019		3.62	.67		4.29	5.10
4930	1"		408	.020		6.95	.70		7.65	8.80
4940	1-1/4"		384	.021		13.75	.74		14.49	16.35
4950	1-1/2"		368	.022		17.40	.77		18.17	20.50
4960	1-3/4"		352	.023		36.50	.81		37.31	41.50
4970	2"	↓	344	.023	↓	64.50	.83		65.33	72

07 91 16 – Joint Gaskets

07 91 16.10 Joint Gaskets

		Crew	Daily Output	Labor-Hours	Unit	Material	Labor	Equipment	Total	Total Incl O&P
0010	**JOINT GASKETS**									
4400	Joint gaskets, neoprene, closed cell w/adh, 1/8" x 3/8"	1 Bric	240	.033	L.F.	.28	1.19		1.47	2.28
4500	1/4" x 3/4"		215	.037		.59	1.32		1.91	2.85
4700	1/2" x 1"		200	.040		1.30	1.42		2.72	3.80
4800	3/4" x 1-1/2"	↓	165	.048	↓	1.45	1.73		3.18	4.47

07 91 23 – Backer Rods

07 91 23.10 Backer Rods

		Crew	Daily Output	Labor-Hours	Unit	Material	Labor	Equipment	Total	Total Incl O&P
0010	**BACKER RODS**									
0030	Backer rod, polyethylene, 1/4" diameter	1 Bric	4.60	1.739	C.L.F.	2.43	62		64.43	106
0050	1/2" diameter		4.60	1.739		3.66	62		65.66	107
0070	3/4" diameter		4.60	1.739		5.55	62		67.55	109
0090	1" diameter	↓	4.60	1.739	↓	8.80	62		70.80	113

07 91 26 – Joint Fillers

07 91 26.10 Joint Fillers

		Crew	Daily Output	Labor-Hours	Unit	Material	Labor	Equipment	Total	Total Incl O&P
0010	**JOINT FILLERS**									
4360	Butyl rubber filler, 1/4" x 1/4"	1 Bric	290	.028	L.F.	.23	.98		1.21	1.88
4365	1/2" x 1/2"		250	.032		.92	1.14		2.06	2.91
4370	1/2" x 3/4"		210	.038		1.38	1.36		2.74	3.78
4375	3/4" x 3/4"		230	.035		2.08	1.24		3.32	4.34
4380	1" x 1"	↓	180	.044	↓	2.77	1.58		4.35	5.70
4390	For coloring, add					12%				

07 91 Preformed Joint Seals

07 91 26 – Joint Fillers

07 91 26.10 Joint Fillers

		Crew	Daily Output	Labor-Hours	Unit	Material	2014 Bare Costs Labor	Equipment	Total	Total Incl O&P
4980	Polyethylene joint backing, 1/4" x 2"	1 Bric	2.08	3.846	C.L.F.	12	137		149	241
4990	1/4" x 6"		1.28	6.250	"	28	223		251	400
5600	Silicone, room temp vulcanizing foam seal, 1/4" x 1/2"		1312	.006	L.F.	.33	.22		.55	.73
5610	1/2" x 1/2"		656	.012		.67	.43		1.10	1.46
5620	1/2" x 3/4"		442	.018		1	.64		1.64	2.17
5630	3/4" x 3/4"		328	.024		1.50	.87		2.37	3.10
5640	1/8" x 1"		1312	.006		.33	.22		.55	.73
5650	1/8" x 3"		442	.018		1	.64		1.64	2.17
5670	1/4" x 3"		295	.027		2.01	.97		2.98	3.82
5680	1/4" x 6"		148	.054		4.01	1.92		5.93	7.60
5690	1/2" x 6"		82	.098		8	3.47		11.47	14.60
5700	1/2" x 9"		52.50	.152		12.05	5.40		17.45	22.50
5710	1/2" x 12"		33	.242		16.05	8.65		24.70	32

07 92 Joint Sealants

07 92 13 – Elastomeric Joint Sealants

07 92 13.20 Caulking and Sealant Options

		Crew	Daily Output	Labor-Hours	Unit	Material	2014 Bare Costs Labor	Equipment	Total	Total Incl O&P
0010	**CAULKING AND SEALANT OPTIONS**									
0050	Latex acrylic based, bulk				Gal.	29.50			29.50	32.50
0055	Bulk in place 1/4" x 1/4" bead	1 Bric	300	.027	L.F.	.09	.95		1.04	1.68
0060	1/4" x 3/8"		294	.027		.16	.97		1.13	1.78
0065	1/4" x 1/2"		288	.028		.21	.99		1.20	1.88
0075	3/8" x 3/8"		284	.028		.23	1		1.23	1.92
0080	3/8" x 1/2"		280	.029		.31	1.02		1.33	2.03
0085	3/8" x 5/8"		276	.029		.39	1.03		1.42	2.15
0095	3/8" x 3/4"		272	.029		.46	1.05		1.51	2.25
0100	1/2" x 1/2"		275	.029		.41	1.04		1.45	2.18
0105	1/2" x 5/8"		269	.030		.52	1.06		1.58	2.33
0110	1/2" x 3/4"		263	.030		.62	1.08		1.70	2.48
0115	1/2" x 7/8"		256	.031		.72	1.11		1.83	2.65
0120	1/2" x 1"		250	.032		.83	1.14		1.97	2.81
0125	3/4" x 3/4"		244	.033		.93	1.17		2.10	2.97
0130	3/4" x 1"		225	.036		1.24	1.27		2.51	3.48
0135	1" x 1"		200	.040		1.66	1.42		3.08	4.19
0190	Cartridges				Gal.	26.50			26.50	29
0200	11 fl. oz. cartridge				Ea.	2.28			2.28	2.51
0500	1/4" x 1/2"	1 Bric	288	.028	L.F.	.19	.99		1.18	1.85
0600	1/2" x 1/2"		275	.029		.37	1.04		1.41	2.13
0800	3/4" x 3/4"		244	.033		.84	1.17		2.01	2.86
0900	3/4" x 1"		225	.036		1.12	1.27		2.39	3.34
1000	1" x 1"		200	.040		1.40	1.42		2.82	3.91
1400	Butyl based, bulk				Gal.	34			34	37.50
1500	Cartridges				"	38.50			38.50	42.50
1700	1/4" x 1/2", 154 L.F./gal.	1 Bric	288	.028	L.F.	.22	.99		1.21	1.89
1800	1/2" x 1/2", 77 L.F./gal.	"	275	.029	"	.44	1.04		1.48	2.21
2300	Polysulfide compounds, 1 component, bulk				Gal.	61			61	67
2600	1 or 2 component, in place, 1/4" x 1/4", 308 L.F./gal.	1 Bric	300	.027	L.F.	.20	.95		1.15	1.80
2700	1/2" x 1/4", 154 L.F./gal.		288	.028		.40	.99		1.39	2.09
2900	3/4" x 3/8", 68 L.F./gal.		272	.029		.90	1.05		1.95	2.73
3000	1" x 1/2", 38 L.F./gal.		250	.032		1.61	1.14		2.75	3.67
3200	Polyurethane, 1 or 2 component				Gal.	51			51	56

07 92 Joint Sealants

07 92 13 – Elastomeric Joint Sealants

07 92 13.20 Caulking and Sealant Options		Crew	Daily Output	Labor-Hours	Unit	Material	2014 Bare Costs Labor	Equipment	Total	Total Incl O&P
3500	Bulk, in place, 1/4" x 1/4"	1 Bric	300	.027	L.F.	.17	.95		1.12	1.76
3655	1/2" x 1/4"		288	.028		.33	.99		1.32	2.01
3800	3/4" x 3/8"		272	.029		.75	1.05		1.80	2.57
3900	1" x 1/2"		250	.032		1.33	1.14		2.47	3.36
4100	Silicone rubber, bulk				Gal.	45.50			45.50	50
4200	Cartridges				"	45			45	49.50

07 92 16 – Rigid Joint Sealants

07 92 16.10 Rigid Joint Sealants

		Crew	Daily Output	Labor-Hours	Unit	Material	Labor	Equipment	Total	Total Incl O&P
0010	**RIGID JOINT SEALANTS**									
5800	Tapes, sealant, PVC foam adhesive, 1/16" x 1/4"				C.L.F.	6			6	6.60
5900	1/16" x 1/2"					8			8	8.80
5950	1/16" x 1"					15			15	16.50
6000	1/8" x 1/2"					9			9	9.90

07 92 19 – Acoustical Joint Sealants

07 92 19.10 Acoustical Sealant

		Crew	Daily Output	Labor-Hours	Unit	Material	Labor	Equipment	Total	Total Incl O&P
0010	**ACOUSTICAL SEALANT**									
0020	Acoustical sealant, elastomeric, cartridges				Ea.	8.50			8.50	9.35
0025	In place, 1/4" x 1/4"	1 Bric	300	.027	L.F.	.35	.95		1.30	1.96
0030	1/4" x 1/2"		288	.028		.69	.99		1.68	2.41
0035	1/2" x 1/2"		275	.029		1.39	1.04		2.43	3.24
0040	1/2" x 3/4"		263	.030		2.08	1.08		3.16	4.09
0045	3/4" x 3/4"		244	.033		3.12	1.17		4.29	5.35
0050	1" x 1"		200	.040		5.55	1.42		6.97	8.45

07 95 Expansion Control

07 95 13 – Expansion Joint Cover Assemblies

07 95 13.50 Expansion Joint Assemblies

		Crew	Daily Output	Labor-Hours	Unit	Material	Labor	Equipment	Total	Total Incl O&P
0010	**EXPANSION JOINT ASSEMBLIES**									
0201	Floor cover assemblies, 1" space, aluminum	1 Carp	38	.211	L.F.	21.50	7.55		29.05	36.50
0301	Bronze or stainless		38	.211		51	7.55		58.55	68.50
0501	2" space, aluminum		38	.211		26.50	7.55		34.05	41.50
0601	Bronze or stainless		38	.211		55	7.55		62.55	73
0801	Wall and ceiling assemblies, 1" space, aluminum		38	.211		12.90	7.55		20.45	27
0901	Bronze or stainless		38	.211		48	7.55		55.55	65
1101	2" space, aluminum		38	.211		22	7.55		29.55	36.50
1201	Bronze or stainless		38	.211		59	7.55		66.55	77
1401	Floor to wall assemblies, 1" space, aluminum		38	.211		19.70	7.55		27.25	34
1501	Bronze or stainless		38	.211		58	7.55		65.55	76
1701	Gym floor angle covers, aluminum, 3" x 3" angle		46	.174		17.05	6.20		23.25	29
1801	3" x 4" angle		46	.174		23.50	6.20		29.70	36.50
2001	Roof closures, aluminum, 1" space, flat roof, low profile		57	.140		39.50	5		44.50	52
2101	High profile		57	.140		56.50	5		61.50	71
2302	Roof to wall, 1" space, low profile		57	.140		22	5		27	32.50
2401	High profile		57	.140		28.50	5		33.50	39.50

Estimating Tips

08 10 00 Doors and Frames

All exterior doors should be addressed for their energy conservation (insulation and seals).

- Most metal doors and frames look alike, but there may be significant differences among them. When estimating these items, be sure to choose the line item that most closely compares to the specification or door schedule requirements regarding:
  - type of metal
  - metal gauge
  - door core material
  - fire rating
  - finish
- Wood and plastic doors vary considerably in price. The primary determinant is the veneer material. Lauan, birch, and oak are the most common veneers. Other variables include the following:
  - hollow or solid core
  - fire rating
  - flush or raised panel
  - finish
- Door pricing includes bore for cylindrical lockset and mortise for hinges.

08 30 00 Specialty Doors and Frames

- There are many varieties of special doors, and they are usually priced per each. Add frames, hardware, or operators required for a complete installation.

08 40 00 Entrances, Storefronts, and Curtain Walls

- Glazed curtain walls consist of the metal tube framing and the glazing material. The cost data in this subdivision is presented for the metal tube framing alone or the composite wall. If your estimate requires a detailed takeoff of the framing, be sure to add the glazing cost.

08 50 00 Windows

- Most metal windows are delivered preglazed. However, some metal windows are priced without glass. Refer to 08 80 00 Glazing for glass pricing. The grade C indicates commercial grade windows, usually ASTM C-35.
- All wood windows and vinyl are priced preglazed. The glazing is insulating glass. Some wood windows may have single pane float glass. Add the cost of screens and grills if required, and not already included.

08 70 00 Hardware

- Hardware costs add considerably to the cost of a door. The most efficient method to determine the hardware requirements for a project is to review the door and hardware schedule together.

- Door hinges are priced by the pair, with most doors requiring 1-1/2 pairs per door. The hinge prices do not include installation labor because it is included in door installation. Hinges are classified according to the frequency of use, base material, and finish.

08 80 00 Glazing

- Different openings require different types of glass. The most common types are:
  - float
  - tempered
  - insulating
  - impact-resistant
  - ballistic-resistant
- Most exterior windows are glazed with insulating glass. Entrance doors and window walls, where the glass is less than 18" from the floor, are generally glazed with tempered glass. Interior windows and some residential windows are glazed with float glass.
- Coastal communities require the use of impact-resistant glass, dependant on wind speed.
- The insulation or 'u' value is a strong consideration, along with solar heat gain, to determine total energy efficiency.

Reference Numbers

Reference numbers are shown in shaded boxes at the beginning of some major classifications. These numbers refer to related items in the Reference Section. The reference information may be an estimating procedure, an alternate pricing method, or technical information.

Note: Not all subdivisions listed here necessarily appear in this publication.

08 05 05 – Selective Windows and Doors Demolition

08 05 05.10 Selective Demolition Doors

	08 05 05.10 Selective Demolition Doors	Crew	Daily Output	Labor-Hours	Unit	Material	2014 Bare Costs Labor	2014 Bare Costs Equipment	Total	Total Incl O&P
0010	**SELECTIVE DEMOLITION DOORS** R024119-10									
0200	Doors, exterior, 1-3/4" thick, single, 3' x 7' high	1 Clab	16	.500	Ea.		14.10		14.10	23.50
0210	3' x 8' high		10	.800			22.50		22.50	38
0215	Double, 3' x 8' high		6	1.333			37.50		37.50	63.50
0220	Double, 6' x 7' high		12	.667			18.80		18.80	31.50
0500	Interior, 1-3/8" thick, single, 3' x 7' high		20	.400			11.30		11.30	19
0520	Double, 6' x 7' high		16	.500			14.10		14.10	23.50
0700	Bi-folding, 3' x 6'-8" high		20	.400			11.30		11.30	19
0720	6' x 6'-8" high		18	.444			12.55		12.55	21
0900	Bi-passing, 3' x 6'-8" high		16	.500			14.10		14.10	23.50
0940	6' x 6'-8" high		14	.571			16.10		16.10	27
1500	Remove and reset, minimum	1 Carp	8	1			36		36	60
1520	Maximum		6	1.333			47.50		47.50	80
2000	Frames, including trim, metal		8	1			36		36	60
2200	Wood	2 Carp	32	.500			17.90		17.90	30
2201	Alternate pricing method	1 Carp	200	.040	L.F.		1.43		1.43	2.41
3001	Special doors, counter doors	2 Clab	6	2.667	Ea.		75		75	127
3101	Double acting		10	1.600			45		45	76
3201	Floor door (trap type)		8	2			56.50		56.50	95
3301	Glass, sliding, including frames		12	1.333			37.50		37.50	63.50
3400	Overhead, commercial, 12' x 12' high	2 Carp	4	4			143		143	241
3441	20' x 16' high	2 Clab	3	5.333			150		150	253
3500	Residential, 9' x 7' high	2 Carp	8	2			71.50		71.50	120
3540	16' x 7' high	"	7	2.286			81.50		81.50	137
3601	Remove and reset, minimum	1 Clab	2	4			113		113	190
3621	Maximum	"	1.25	6.400			180		180	305
3701	Roll-up grille	2 Clab	5	3.200			90		90	152
3801	Revolving door		2	8			226		226	380
3902	Cafe/bar swing door		8	2			56.50		56.50	95
6600	Demo flexible transparent strip entrance	3 Shee	115	.209	SF Surf		8.45		8.45	14.10
7100	Remove double swing pneumatic doors, openers and sensors	2 Skwk	.50	32	Opng.		1,150		1,150	1,950
7110	Remove automatic operators, industrial, sliding doors, to 12' wide	"	.40	40	"		1,450		1,450	2,450

08 05 05.20 Selective Demolition of Windows

	08 05 05.20 Selective Demolition of Windows	Crew	Daily Output	Labor-Hours	Unit	Material	2014 Bare Costs Labor	2014 Bare Costs Equipment	Total	Total Incl O&P
0010	**SELECTIVE DEMOLITION OF WINDOWS** R024119-10									
0200	Aluminum, including trim, to 12 S.F.	1 Clab	16	.500	Ea.		14.10		14.10	23.50
0240	To 25 S.F.		11	.727			20.50		20.50	34.50
0280	To 50 S.F.		5	1.600			45		45	76
0320	Storm windows/screens, to 12 S.F.		27	.296			8.35		8.35	14.05
0360	To 25 S.F.		21	.381			10.75		10.75	18.10
0400	To 50 S.F.		16	.500			14.10		14.10	23.50
0600	Glass, minimum		200	.040	S.F.		1.13		1.13	1.90
0620	Maximum		150	.053	"		1.50		1.50	2.53
1000	Steel, including trim, to 12 S.F.		13	.615	Ea.		17.35		17.35	29
1020	To 25 S.F.		9	.889			25		25	42
1040	To 50 S.F.		4	2			56.50		56.50	95
2000	Wood, including trim, to 12 S.F.		22	.364			10.25		10.25	17.25
2020	To 25 S.F.		18	.444			12.55		12.55	21
2060	To 50 S.F.		13	.615			17.35		17.35	29
2065	To 180 S.F.		8	1			28		28	47.50
4410	Remove skylight, plstc domes, flush/curb mtd	G-3	395	.081	S.F.		2.78		2.78	4.65
5020	Remove and reset window, minimum	1 Carp	6	1.333	Ea.		47.50		47.50	80
5040	Average		4	2			71.50		71.50	120

08 05 Common Work Results for Openings

08 05 05 – Selective Windows and Doors Demolition

08 05 05.20 Selective Demolition of Windows	Crew	Daily Output	Labor-Hours	Unit	Material	2014 Bare Costs Labor	Equipment	Total	Total Incl O&P
5080	Maximum	1 Carp	2	4	Ea.		143		143	241

08 11 Metal Doors and Frames

08 11 16 – Aluminum Doors and Frames

08 11 16.10 Entrance Doors

		Crew	Daily Output	Labor-Hours	Unit	Material	2014 Bare Costs Labor	Equipment	Total	Total Incl O&P
0010	**ENTRANCE DOORS** and frame, Aluminum, narrow stile									
0011	Including standard hardware, clear finish, no glass									
0012	Top and bottom offset pivots, 1/4" beveled glass stops, threshold									
0013	Dead bolt lock with inside thumb screw, standard push pull									
0020	3'-0" x 7'-0" opening	2 Sswk	2	8	Ea.	885	305		1,190	1,550
0025	Anodizing aluminum entr. door & frame, add					98.50			98.50	109
0030	3'-6" x 7'-0" opening	2 Sswk	2	8		810	305		1,115	1,475
0100	3'-0" x 10'-0" opening, 3' high transom		1.80	8.889		1,275	340		1,615	2,075
0200	3'-6" x 10'-0" opening, 3' high transom		1.80	8.889		1,350	340		1,690	2,125
0280	5'-0" x 7'-0" opening		2	8		1,425	305		1,730	2,150
0300	6'-0" x 7'-0" opening		1.30	12.308		1,200	470		1,670	2,225
0301	6'-0" x 7'-0" opening		1.30	12.308	Pr.	1,200	470		1,670	2,225
0400	6'-0" x 10'-0" opening, 3' high transom		1.10	14.545		1,625	560		2,185	2,850
0420	7'-0" x 7'-0" opening		1	16		1,350	615		1,965	2,675
0520	3'-0" x 7'-0" opening, wide stile		2	8	Ea.	1,000	305		1,305	1,675
0540	3'-6" x 7'-0" opening		2	8		1,200	305		1,505	1,900
0560	5'-0" x 7'-0" opening		2	8		1,525	305		1,830	2,250
0580	6'-0" x 7'-0" opening		1.30	12.308	Pr.	1,575	470		2,045	2,650
0600	7'-0" x 7'-0" opening		1	16	"	1,725	615		2,340	3,050
1200	For non-standard size, add				Leaf	80%				
1250	For installation of non-standard size, add						20%			
1300	Light bronze finish, add				Leaf	36%				
1400	Dark bronze finish, add					25%				
1500	For black finish, add					40%				
1600	Concealed panic device, add					940			940	1,025
1700	Electric striker release, add				Opng.	260			260	286
1800	Floor check, add				Leaf	650			650	710
1900	Concealed closer, add				"	520			520	570

08 11 63 – Metal Screen and Storm Doors and Frames

08 11 63.23 Aluminum Screen and Storm Doors and Frames

		Crew	Daily Output	Labor-Hours	Unit	Material	2014 Bare Costs Labor	Equipment	Total	Total Incl O&P
0010	**ALUMINUM SCREEN AND STORM DOORS AND FRAMES**									
0020	Combination storm and screen									
0420	Clear anodic coating, 2'-8" wide	2 Carp	14	1.143	Ea.	165	41		206	251
0440	3'-0" wide	"	14	1.143	"	163	41		204	248
0500	For 7' door height, add					8%				
1020	Mill finish, 2'-8" wide	2 Carp	14	1.143	Ea.	235	41		276	330
1040	3'-0" wide	"	14	1.143		258	41		299	355
1100	For 7'-0" door, add					8%				
1520	White painted, 2'-8" wide	2 Carp	14	1.143		286	41		327	385
1540	3'-0" wide	"	14	1.143		305	41		346	405
1600	For 7'-0" door, add					8%				
2000	Wood door & screen, see Section 08 14 33.20									

08 11 Metal Doors and Frames

08 11 74 – Sliding Metal Grilles

08 11 74.10 Rolling Grille Supports		Crew	Daily Output	Labor-Hours	Unit	Material	2014 Bare Costs Labor	Equipment	Total	Total Incl O&P
0010	**ROLLING GRILLE SUPPORTS**									
0020	Rolling grille supports, overhead framed	E-4	36	.889	L.F.	30	34.50	3.95	68.45	103

08 12 Metal Frames

08 12 13 – Hollow Metal Frames

08 12 13.13 Standard Hollow Metal Frames

			Crew	Daily Output	Labor-Hours	Unit	Material	2014 Bare Costs Labor	Equipment	Total	Total Incl O&P
0010	**STANDARD HOLLOW METAL FRAMES**										
0020	16 ga., up to 5-3/4" jamb depth										
0025	3'-0" x 6'-8" single	G	2 Carp	16	1	Ea.	145	36		181	220
0028	3'-6" wide, single	G		16	1		152	36		188	227
0030	4'-0" wide, single	G		16	1		151	36		187	226
0040	6'-0" wide, double	G		14	1.143		204	41		245	293
0045	8'-0" wide, double	G		14	1.143		213	41		254	305
0100	3'-0" x 7'-0" single	G		16	1		150	36		186	225
0110	3'-6" wide, single	G		16	1		157	36		193	233
0112	4'-0" wide, single	G		16	1		157	36		193	233
0140	6'-0" wide, double	G		14	1.143		194	41		235	283
0145	8'-0" wide, double	G		14	1.143		229	41		270	320
1000	16 ga., up to 4-7/8" deep, 3'-0" x 7'-0" single	G		16	1		166	36		202	243
1140	6'-0" wide, double	G		14	1.143		188	41		229	276
1200	16 ga., 8-3/4" deep, 3'-0" x 7'-0" single	G		16	1		199	36		235	279
1240	6'-0" wide, double	G		14	1.143		234	41		275	325
2800	14 ga., up to 3-7/8" deep, 3'-0" x 7'-0" single	G		16	1		181	36		217	259
2840	6'-0" wide, double	G		14	1.143		217	41		258	305
3000	14 ga., up to 5-3/4" deep, 3'-0" x 6'-8" single	G		16	1		155	36		191	231
3002	3'-6" wide, single	G		16	1		196	36		232	275
3005	4'-0" wide, single	G		16	1		196	36		232	275
3600	up to 5-3/4" jamb depth, 4'-0" x 7'-0" single	G		15	1.067		185	38		223	267
3620	6'-0" wide, double	G		12	1.333		235	47.50		282.50	340
3640	8'-0" wide, double	G		12	1.333		246	47.50		293.50	350
3700	8'-0" high, 4'-0" wide, single	G		15	1.067		235	38		273	325
3740	8'-0" wide, double	G		12	1.333		290	47.50		337.50	400
4000	6-3/4" deep, 4'-0" x 7'-0" single	G		15	1.067		220	38		258	305
4020	6'-0" wide, double	G		12	1.333		275	47.50		322.50	380
4040	8'-0", wide double	G		12	1.333		282	47.50		329.50	390
4100	8'-0" high, 4'-0" wide, single	G		15	1.067		276	38		314	370
4140	8'-0" wide, double	G		12	1.333		320	47.50		367.50	435
4400	8-3/4" deep, 4'-0" x 7'-0" , single	G		15	1.067		252	38		290	340
4440	8'-0" wide, double	G		12	1.333		315	47.50		362.50	425
4500	4'-0" x 8'-0" , single	G		15	1.067		283	38		321	375
4540	8'-0" wide, double	G		12	1.333		350	47.50		397.50	465
4900	For welded frames, add						63			63	69.50
5400	14 ga., "B" label, up to 5-3/4" deep, 4'-0" x 7'-0" single	G	2 Carp	15	1.067		208	38		246	293
5440	8'-0" wide, double	G		12	1.333		271	47.50		318.50	380
5800	6-3/4" deep, 7'-0" high, 4'-0" wide, single	G		15	1.067		218	38		256	305
5840	8'-0" wide, double	G		12	1.333		385	47.50		432.50	505
6200	8-3/4" deep, 4'-0" x 7'-0" single	G		15	1.067		289	38		327	385
6240	8'-0" wide, double	G		12	1.333		365	47.50		412.50	480
6300	For "A" label use same price as "B" label										
6400	For baked enamel finish, add						30%	15%			

08 12 Metal Frames

08 12 13 – Hollow Metal Frames

08 12 13.13 Standard Hollow Metal Frames

		Crew	Daily Output	Labor-Hours	Unit	Material	2014 Bare Costs Labor	2014 Bare Costs Equipment	Total	Total Incl O&P
6500	For galvanizing, add					20%				
6600	For hospital stop, add				Ea.	295			295	325
6620	For hospital stop, stainless steel add				"	380			380	420
7900	Transom lite frames, fixed, add	2 Carp	155	.103	S.F.	54	3.69		57.69	65.50
8000	Movable, add	"	130	.123	"	68	4.40		72.40	82.50

08 12 13.25 Channel Metal Frames

			Crew	Daily Output	Labor-Hours	Unit	Material	2014 Bare Costs Labor	2014 Bare Costs Equipment	Total	Total Incl O&P
0010	**CHANNEL METAL FRAMES**										
0020	Steel channels with anchors and bar stops										
0100	6" channel @ 8.2#/L.F., 3' x 7' door, weighs 150#	G	E-4	13	2.462	Ea.	239	95.50	10.95	345.45	455
0200	8" channel @ 11.5#/L.F., 6' x 8' door, weighs 275#	G		9	3.556		435	138	15.80	588.80	760
0300	8' x 12' door, weighs 400#	G		6.50	4.923		635	191	22	848	1,100
0400	10" channel @ 15.3#/L.F., 10' x 10' door, weighs 500#	G		6	5.333		795	207	23.50	1,025.50	1,300
0500	12' x 12' door, weighs 600#	G		5.50	5.818		955	226	26	1,207	1,500
0600	12" channel @ 20.7#/L.F., 12' x 12' door, weighs 825#	G		4.50	7.111		1,300	276	31.50	1,607.50	2,000
0700	12' x 16' door, weighs 1000#	G		4	8		1,600	310	35.50	1,945.50	2,375
0800	For frames without bar stops, light sections, deduct						15%				
0900	Heavy sections, deduct						10%				

08 13 Metal Doors

08 13 13 – Hollow Metal Doors

08 13 13.13 Standard Hollow Metal Doors

			Crew	Daily Output	Labor-Hours	Unit	Material	2014 Bare Costs Labor	2014 Bare Costs Equipment	Total	Total Incl O&P
0010	**STANDARD HOLLOW METAL DOORS** R081313-20										
0015	Flush, full panel, hollow core										
0017	When noted doors are prepared but do not include glass or louvers										
0020	1-3/8" thick, 20 ga., 2'-0" x 6'-8"	G	2 Carp	20	.800	Ea.	335	28.50		363.50	420
0040	2'-8" x 6'-8"	G		18	.889		350	32		382	440
0060	3'-0" x 6'-8"	G		17	.941		350	33.50		383.50	440
0100	3'-0" x 7'-0"	G		17	.941		360	33.50		393.50	450
0120	For vision lite, add						94.50			94.50	104
0140	For narrow lite, add						102			102	112
0320	Half glass, 20 ga., 2'-0" x 6'-8"	G	2 Carp	20	.800		490	28.50		518.50	590
0340	2'-8" x 6'-8"	G		18	.889		515	32		547	620
0360	3'-0" x 6'-8"	G		17	.941		510	33.50		543.50	615
0400	3'-0" x 7'-0"	G		17	.941		625	33.50		658.50	740
0410	1-3/8" thick, 18 ga., 2'-0" x 6'-8"	G		20	.800		400	28.50		428.50	490
0420	3'-0" x 6'-8"	G		17	.941		405	33.50		438.50	500
0425	3'-0" x 7'-0"	G		17	.941		415	33.50		448.50	515
0450	For vision lite, add						94.50			94.50	104
0452	For narrow lite, add						102			102	112
0460	Half glass, 18 ga., 2'-0" x 6'-8"	G	2 Carp	20	.800		555	28.50		583.50	665
0465	2'-8" x 6'-8"	G		18	.889		575	32		607	690
0470	3'-0" x 6'-8"	G		17	.941		565	33.50		598.50	675
0475	3'-0" x 7'-0"	G		17	.941		565	33.50		598.50	680
0500	Hollow core, 1-3/4" thick, full panel, 20 ga., 2'-8" x 6'-8"	G		18	.889		420	32		452	515
0520	3'-0" x 6'-8"	G		17	.941		420	33.50		453.50	515
0640	3'-0" x 7'-0"	G		17	.941		435	33.50		468.50	535
0680	4'-0" x 7'-0"	G		15	1.067		630	38		668	760
0700	4'-0" x 8'-0"	G		13	1.231		735	44		779	885
1000	18 ga., 2'-8" x 6'-8"	G		17	.941		490	33.50		523.50	595
1020	3'-0" x 6'-8"	G		16	1		475	36		511	585
1120	3'-0" x 7'-0"	G		17	.941		515	33.50		548.50	620

08 13 13 – Hollow Metal Doors

08 13 13.13 Standard Hollow Metal Doors		Crew	Daily Output	Labor-Hours	Unit	Material	2014 Bare Costs Labor	2014 Bare Costs Equipment	Total	Total Incl O&P
1180	4'-0" x 7'-0"	G 2 Carp	14	1.143	Ea.	630	41		671	765
1200	4'-0" x 8'-0"	G	17	.941		735	33.50		768.50	865
1212	For vision lite, add					94.50			94.50	104
1214	For narrow lite, add					102			102	112
1230	Half glass, 20 ga., 2'-8" x 6'-8"	G 2 Carp	20	.800		575	28.50		603.50	685
1240	3'-0" x 6'-8"	G	18	.889		575	32		607	690
1260	3'-0" x 7'-0"	G	18	.889		595	32		627	705
1280	Embossed panel, 1-3/4" thick, poly core, 20 ga., 3'-0" x 7'-0"	G	18	.889		415	32		447	510
1290	Half glass, 1-3/4" thick, poly core, 20 ga., 3'-0" x 7'-0"	G	18	.889		610	32		642	725
1320	18 ga., 2'-8" x 6'-8"	G	18	.889		640	32		672	760
1340	3'-0" x 6'-8"	G	17	.941		635	33.50		668.50	750
1360	3'-0" x 7'-0"	G	17	.941		645	33.50		678.50	765
1380	4'-0" x 7'-0"	G	15	1.067		785	38		823	930
1400	4'-0" x 8'-0"	G	14	1.143		890	41		931	1,050
1500	Flush full panel, 16 ga., steel hollow core									
1520	2'-0" x 6'-8"	G 2 Carp	20	.800	Ea.	555	28.50		583.50	660
1530	2'-8" x 6'-8"	G	20	.800		555	28.50		583.50	665
1540	3'-0" x 6'-8"	G	20	.800		550	28.50		578.50	655
1560	2'-8" x 7'-0"	G	18	.889		575	32		607	685
1570	3'-0" x 7'-0"	G	18	.889		560	32		592	670
1580	3'-6" x 7'-0"	G	18	.889		655	32		687	775
1590	4'-0" x 7'-0"	G	18	.889		725	32		757	850
1600	2'-8" x 8'-0"	G	18	.889		700	32		732	825
1620	3'-0" x 8'-0"	G	18	.889		720	32		752	845
1630	3'-6" x 8'-0"	G	18	.889		800	32		832	935
1640	4'-0" x 8'-0"	G	18	.889		850	32		882	985
1650	1-13/16", 14 Ga., 2'-8" x 7'-0"	G	10	1.600		1,125	57		1,182	1,350
1670	3'-0" x 7'-0"	G	10	1.600		1,075	57		1,132	1,300
1690	3'-6" x 7'-0"	G	10	1.600		1,200	57		1,257	1,400
1700	4'-0" x 7'-0"	G	10	1.600		1,250	57		1,307	1,475
1720	Insulated, 1-3/4" thick, full panel, 18 ga., 3'-0" x 6'-8"	G	15	1.067		475	38		513	590
1740	2'-8" x 7'-0"	G	16	1		505	36		541	615
1760	3'-0" x 7'-0"	G	15	1.067		490	38		528	605
1800	4'-0" x 8'-0"	G	13	1.231		740	44		784	885
1820	Half glass, 18 ga., 3'-0" x 6'-8"	G	16	1		635	36		671	755
1840	2'-8" x 7'-0"	G	17	.941		660	33.50		693.50	780
1860	3'-0" x 7'-0"	G	16	1		685	36		721	815
1900	4'-0" x 8'-0"	G	14	1.143		670	41		711	805
2000	For vision lite, add					94.50			94.50	104
2010	For narrow lite, add					102			102	112
8100	For bottom louver, add					281			281	310
8110	For baked enamel finish, add					30%	15%			
8120	For galvanizing, add					20%				

08 13 13.15 Metal Fire Doors

0010	**METAL FIRE DOORS**	R081313-20								
0015	Steel, flush, "B" label, 90 minute									
0020	Full panel, 20 ga., 2'-0" x 6'-8"	2 Carp	20	.800	Ea.	420	28.50		448.50	510
0040	2'-8" x 6'-8"		18	.889		435	32		467	535
0060	3'-0" x 6'-8"		17	.941		435	33.50		468.50	535
0080	3'-0" x 7'-0"		17	.941		455	33.50		488.50	555
0140	18 ga., 3'-0" x 6'-8"		16	1		495	36		531	605
0160	2'-8" x 7'-0"		17	.941		520	33.50		553.50	625

08 13 Metal Doors

08 13 13 – Hollow Metal Doors

08 13 13.15 Metal Fire Doors

		Crew	Daily Output	Labor-Hours	Unit	Material	2014 Bare Costs Labor	Equipment	Total	Total Incl O&P
0180	3'-0" x 7'-0"	2 Carp	16	1	Ea.	505	36		541	615
0200	4'-0" x 7'-0"	↓	15	1.067	↓	650	38		688	780
0220	For "A" label, 3 hour, 18 ga., use same price as "B" label									
0240	For vision lite, add				Ea.	156			156	172
0300	Full panel, 16 ga., 2'-0" x 6'-8"	2 Carp	20	.800		545	28.50		573.50	650
0310	2'-8" x 6'-8"		18	.889		545	32		577	655
0320	3'-0" x 6'-8"		17	.941		540	33.50		573.50	650
0350	2'-8" x 7'-0"		17	.941		565	33.50		598.50	675
0360	3'-0" x 7'-0"		16	1		545	36		581	660
0370	4'-0" x 7'-0"		15	1.067		705	38		743	845
0520	Flush, "B" label 90 min., egress core, 20 ga., 2'-0" x 6'-8"		18	.889		655	32		687	775
0540	2'-8" x 6'-8"		17	.941		665	33.50		698.50	785
0560	3'-0" x 6'-8"		16	1		665	36		701	790
0580	3'-0" x 7'-0"		16	1		685	36		721	810
0640	Flush, "A" label 3 hour, egress core, 18 ga., 3'-0" x 6'-8"		15	1.067		720	38		758	860
0660	2'-8" x 7'-0"		16	1		750	36		786	880
0680	3'-0" x 7'-0"		15	1.067		740	38		778	880
0700	4'-0" x 7'-0"	↓	14	1.143	↓	885	41		926	1,050

08 13 13.20 Residential Steel Doors

			Crew	Daily Output	Labor-Hours	Unit	Material	2014 Bare Costs Labor	Equipment	Total	Total Incl O&P
0010	**RESIDENTIAL STEEL DOORS**										
0020	Prehung, insulated, exterior										
0030	Embossed, full panel, 2'-8" x 6'-8"	G	2 Carp	17	.941	Ea.	305	33.50		338.50	390
0040	3'-0" x 6'-8"	G		15	1.067		247	38		285	335
0060	3'-0" x 7'-0"	G		15	1.067		330	38		368	430
0070	5'-4" x 6'-8", double	G		8	2		625	71.50		696.50	805
0220	Half glass, 2'-8" x 6'-8"	G		17	.941		320	33.50		353.50	405
0240	3'-0" x 6'-8"	G		16	1		320	36		356	410
0260	3'-0" x 7'-0"	G		16	1		370	36		406	465
0270	5'-4" x 6'-8", double	G		8	2		650	71.50		721.50	835
1320	Flush face, full panel, 2'-8" x 6'-8"	G		16	1		264	36		300	350
1340	3'-0" x 6'-8"	G		15	1.067		264	38		302	355
1360	3'-0" x 7'-0"	G		15	1.067		296	38		334	390
1380	5'-4" x 6'-8", double	G		8	2		560	71.50		631.50	735
1420	Half glass, 2'-8" x 6'-8"	G		17	.941		325	33.50		358.50	410
1440	3'-0" x 6'-8"	G		16	1		325	36		361	415
1460	3'-0" x 7'-0"	G		16	1		360	36		396	455
1480	5'-4" x 6'-8", double	G	↓	8	2		640	71.50		711.50	825
1500	Sidelight, full lite, 1'-0" x 6'-8" with grille	G					252			252	277
1510	1'-0" x 6'-8", low e	G					268			268	295
1520	1'-0" x 6'-8", half lite	G					280			280	310
1530	1'-0" x 6'-8", half lite, low e	G					284			284	310
2300	Interior, residential, closet, bi-fold, 2'-0" x 6'-8"	G	2 Carp	16	1		161	36		197	237
2330	3'-0" wide	G		16	1		200	36		236	280
2360	4'-0" wide	G		15	1.067		260	38		298	350
2400	5'-0" wide	G		14	1.143		315	41		356	420
2420	6'-0" wide	G	↓	13	1.231	↓	335	44		379	445

08 13 13.25 Doors Hollow Metal

			Crew	Daily Output	Labor-Hours	Unit	Material	2014 Bare Costs Labor	Equipment	Total	Total Incl O&P
0010	**DOORS HOLLOW METAL**										
0500	Exterior, commercial, flush, 20 ga., 1-3/4" x 7'-0" x 2'-6" wide	G	2 Carp	15	1.067	Ea.	395	38		433	495
0530	2'-8" wide	G		15	1.067		435	38		473	540
0560	3'-0" wide	G		14	1.143		435	41		476	545
1000	18 ga., 1-3/4" x 7'-0" x 2'-6" wide	G	↓	15	1.067		495	38		533	610

08 13 Metal Doors

08 13 13 – Hollow Metal Doors

08 13 13.25 Doors Hollow Metal		Crew	Daily Output	Labor-Hours	Unit	Material	2014 Bare Costs Labor	Equipment	Total	Total Incl O&P
1030	2'-8" wide	G	2 Carp	15	1.067	Ea.	500	38		538	615
1060	3'-0" wide	G		14	1.143		485	41		526	605
1500	16 ga., 1-3/4 x 7'-0" x 2'-6" wide	G		15	1.067		560	38		598	680
1530	2'-8" wide	G		15	1.067		565	38		603	690
1560	3'-0" wide	G		14	1.143		555	41		596	680
1590	3'-6" wide	G		14	1.143		645	41		686	780
2900	Fire door, "A" label, 18 gauge, 1-3/4 x 2'-6" x 7'-0"	G		15	1.067		645	38		683	775
2930	2'-8" wide	G		15	1.067		665	38		703	795
2960	3'-0" wide	G		14	1.143		640	41		681	775
2990	3'-6" wide	G		14	1.143		735	41		776	875
3100	"B" label, 2'-6" wide	G		15	1.067		585	38		623	710
3130	2'-8" wide	G		15	1.067		590	38		628	715
3160	3'-0" wide	G		14	1.143		580	41		621	710

08 13 16 – Aluminum Doors

08 13 16.10 Commercial Aluminum Doors

		Crew	Daily Output	Labor-Hours	Unit	Material	Labor	Equipment	Total	Total Incl O&P
0010	**COMMERCIAL ALUMINUM DOORS**, flush, no glazing									
5000	Flush panel doors, pair of 2'-6" x 7'-0"	2 Sswk	2	8	Pr.	1,425	305		1,730	2,150
5050	3'-0" x 7'-0", single		2.50	6.400	Ea.	805	245		1,050	1,350
5100	Pair of 3'-0" x 7'-0"		2	8	Pr.	1,525	305		1,830	2,250
5150	3'-6" x 7'-0", single		2.50	6.400	Ea.	965	245		1,210	1,525

08 13 73 – Sliding Metal Doors

08 13 73.10 Steel Sliding Doors

		Crew	Daily Output	Labor-Hours	Unit	Material	Labor	Equipment	Total	Total Incl O&P
0010	**STEEL SLIDING DOORS**									
0020	Up to 50' x 18', electric, standard duty, minimum	L-5	360	.156	S.F.	29.50	6	2.07	37.57	46
0100	Maximum		340	.165		46	6.35	2.19	54.54	65
0500	Heavy duty, minimum		297	.189		37.50	7.30	2.51	47.31	57.50
0600	Maximum		277	.202		93.50	7.80	2.69	103.99	121

08 14 Wood Doors

08 14 13 – Carved Wood Doors

08 14 13.10 Types of Wood Doors, Carved

		Crew	Daily Output	Labor-Hours	Unit	Material	Labor	Equipment	Total	Total Incl O&P
0010	**TYPES OF WOOD DOORS, CARVED**									
3000	Solid wood, 1-3/4" thick stile and rail									
3020	Mahogany, 3'-0" x 7'-0", minimum	2 Carp	14	1.143	Ea.	1,075	41		1,116	1,250
3030	Maximum		10	1.600		1,800	57		1,857	2,075
3040	3'-6" x 8'-0", minimum		10	1.600		1,500	57		1,557	1,750
3050	Maximum		8	2		2,500	71.50		2,571.50	2,875
3100	Pine, 3'-0" x 7'-0", minimum		14	1.143		490	41		531	605
3110	Maximum		10	1.600		825	57		882	1,000
3120	3'-6" x 8'-0", minimum		10	1.600		900	57		957	1,075
3130	Maximum		8	2		1,825	71.50		1,896.50	2,150
3200	Red oak, 3'-0" x 7'-0", minimum		14	1.143		1,725	41		1,766	1,975
3210	Maximum		10	1.600		2,300	57		2,357	2,625
3220	3'-6" x 8'-0", minimum		10	1.600		2,600	57		2,657	2,950
3230	Maximum		8	2		3,300	71.50		3,371.50	3,750
4000	Hand carved door, mahogany									
4020	3'-0" x 7'-0", minimum	2 Carp	14	1.143	Ea.	1,750	41		1,791	2,000
4030	Maximum		11	1.455		3,700	52		3,752	4,175
4040	3'-6" x 8'-0", minimum		10	1.600		3,000	57		3,057	3,400
4050	Maximum		8	2		3,700	71.50		3,771.50	4,200

08 14 Wood Doors

08 14 13 – Carved Wood Doors

08 14 13.10 Types of Wood Doors, Carved

		Crew	Daily Output	Labor-Hours	Unit	Material	2014 Bare Costs Labor	2014 Bare Costs Equipment	Total	Total Incl O&P
4200	Rose wood, 3'-0" x 7'-0", minimum	2 Carp	14	1.143	Ea.	5,200	41		5,241	5,800
4210	Maximum		11	1.455		13,700	52		13,752	15,200
4220	3'-6" x 8'-0", minimum		10	1.600		5,900	57		5,957	6,600
4225	Maximum		10	1.600		8,900	57		8,957	9,900
4400	For custom finish, add					475			475	525
4600	Side light, mahogany, 7'-0" x 1'-6" wide, minimum	2 Carp	18	.889		1,100	32		1,132	1,250
4610	Maximum		14	1.143		2,625	41		2,666	2,975
4620	8'-0" x 1'-6" wide, minimum		14	1.143		1,800	41		1,841	2,050
4630	Maximum		10	1.600		2,100	57		2,157	2,400
4640	Side light, oak, 7'-0" x 1'-6" wide, minimum		18	.889		1,200	32		1,232	1,375
4650	Maximum		14	1.143		2,100	41		2,141	2,375
4660	8'-0" x 1'-6" wide, minimum		14	1.143		1,100	41		1,141	1,275
4670	Maximum		10	1.600		2,100	57		2,157	2,400

08 14 16 – Flush Wood Doors

08 14 16.09 Smooth Wood Doors

		Crew	Daily Output	Labor-Hours	Unit	Material	2014 Bare Costs Labor	2014 Bare Costs Equipment	Total	Total Incl O&P
0010	**SMOOTH WOOD DOORS**									
0015	Flush, interior, hollow core									
0025	Lauan face, 1-3/8", 3'-0" x 6'-8"	2 Carp	17	.941	Ea.	54.50	33.50		88	117
0030	4'-0" x 6'-8"		16	1		126	36		162	199
0080	1-3/4", 2'-0" x 6'-8"		17	.941		39	33.50		72.50	99
0140	Birch face, 1-3/8", 2'-6" x 6'-8"		17	.941		85	33.50		118.50	150
0180	3'-0" x 6'-8"		17	.941		95.50	33.50		129	162
0200	4'-0" x 6'-8"		16	1		158	36		194	234
0202	1-3/4", 2'-0" x 6'-8"		17	.941		50.50	33.50		84	112
0220	Oak face, 1-3/8", 2'-0" x 6'-8"		17	.941		104	33.50		137.50	171
0280	3'-0" x 6'-8"		17	.941		115	33.50		148.50	184
0300	4'-0" x 6'-8"		16	1		139	36		175	213
0305	1-3/4", 2'-6" x 6'-8"		17	.941		110	33.50		143.50	178
0310	3'-0" x 7'-0"		16	1		211	36		247	292
0320	Walnut face, 1-3/8", 2'-0" x 6'-8"		17	.941		182	33.50		215.50	258
0340	2'-6" x 6'-8"		17	.941		189	33.50		222.50	265
0380	3'-0" x 6'-8"		17	.941		197	33.50		230.50	273
0400	4'-0" x 6'-8"		16	1		216	36		252	298
0430	For 7'-0" high, add					26			26	28.50
0440	For 8'-0" high, add					36			36	39.50
0480	For prefinishing, clear, add					42			42	46
0500	For prefinishing, stain, add					52			52	57
1320	M.D. overlay on hardboard, 1-3/8", 2'-0" x 6'-8"	2 Carp	17	.941		115	33.50		148.50	184
1340	2'-6" x 6'-8"		17	.941		115	33.50		148.50	184
1380	3'-0" x 6'-8"		17	.941		126	33.50		159.50	196
1400	4'-0" x 6'-8"		16	1		178	36		214	256
1420	For 7'-0" high, add					15.75			15.75	17.35
1440	For 8'-0" high, add					31.50			31.50	34.50
1720	H.P. plastic laminate, 1-3/8", 2'-0" x 6'-8"	2 Carp	16	1		260	36		296	345
1740	2'-6" x 6'-8"		16	1		260	36		296	345
1780	3'-0" x 6'-8"		15	1.067		290	38		328	385
1800	4'-0" x 6'-8"		14	1.143		385	41		426	490
1820	For 7'-0" high, add					15.75			15.75	17.35
1840	For 8'-0" high, add					31.50			31.50	34.50
2020	Particle core, lauan face, 1-3/8", 2'-6" x 6'-8"	2 Carp	15	1.067		92	38		130	165
2040	3'-0" x 6'-8"		14	1.143		94	41		135	172
2080	3'-0" x 7'-0"		13	1.231		98.50	44		142.50	182

08 14 16.09 Smooth Wood Doors		Crew	Daily Output	Labor-Hours	Unit	Material	2014 Bare Costs Labor	Equipment	Total	Total Incl O&P
2085	4'-0" x 7'-0"	2 Carp	12	1.333	Ea.	123	47.50		170.50	215
2110	1-3/4", 3'-0" x 7'-0"		13	1.231		123	44		167	209
2120	Birch face, 1-3/8", 2'-6" x 6'-8"		15	1.067		103	38		141	177
2140	3'-0" x 6'-8"		14	1.143		113	41		154	193
2180	3'-0" x 7'-0"		13	1.231		123	44		167	209
2200	4'-0" x 7'-0"		12	1.333		139	47.50		186.50	233
2205	1-3/4", 3'-0" x 7'-0"		13	1.231		123	44		167	209
2220	Oak face, 1-3/8", 2'-6" x 6'-8"		15	1.067		116	38		154	192
2240	3'-0" x 6'-8"		14	1.143		128	41		169	210
2280	3'-0" x 7'-0"		13	1.231		133	44		177	220
2300	4'-0" x 7'-0"		12	1.333		156	47.50		203.50	252
2305	1-3/4" 3'-0" x 7'-0"		13	1.231		190	44		234	283
2320	Walnut face, 1-3/8", 2'-0" x 6'-8"		15	1.067		123	38		161	199
2340	2'-6" x 6'-8"		14	1.143		139	41		180	222
2380	3'-0" x 6'-8"		13	1.231		156	44		200	246
2400	4'-0" x 6'-8"		12	1.333		206	47.50		253.50	305
2440	For 8'-0" high, add					41			41	45
2460	For 8'-0" high walnut, add					36			36	39.50
2480	For solid wood core, add					40			40	44
2720	For prefinishing, clear, add					36			36	39.50
2740	For prefinishing, stain, add					53			53	58.50
3320	M.D. overlay on hardboard, 1-3/8", 2'-6" x 6'-8"	2 Carp	14	1.143		106	41		147	186
3340	3'-0" x 6'-8"		13	1.231		115	44		159	201
3380	3'-0" x 7'-0"		12	1.333		117	47.50		164.50	209
3400	4'-0" x 7'-0"		10	1.600		155	57		212	267
3440	For 8'-0" height, add					37			37	40.50
3460	For solid wood core, add					42			42	46
3720	H.P. plastic laminate, 1-3/8", 2'-6" x 6'-8"	2 Carp	13	1.231		160	44		204	250
3740	3'-0" x 6'-8"		12	1.333		185	47.50		232.50	284
3780	3'-0" x 7'-0"		11	1.455		190	52		242	297
3800	4'-0" x 7'-0"		8	2		225	71.50		296.50	370
3840	For 8'-0" height, add					37			37	40.50
3860	For solid wood core, add					42			42	46
4000	Exterior, flush, solid core, birch, 1-3/4" x 2'-6" x 7'-0"	2 Carp	15	1.067		173	38		211	254
4020	2'-8" wide		15	1.067		159	38		197	239
4040	3'-0" wide		14	1.143		209	41		250	299
4100	Oak faced 1-3/4" x 2'-6" x 7'-0"		15	1.067		215	38		253	300
4120	2'-8" wide		15	1.067		225	38		263	310
4140	3'-0" wide		14	1.143		230	41		271	320
4180	3'-6" wide	1 Carp	17	.471		365	16.80		381.80	430
4200	Walnut faced, 1-3/4" x 2'-6" x 7'-0"	2 Carp	15	1.067		310	38		348	405
4220	2'-8" wide		15	1.067		315	38		353	410
4240	3'-0" wide		14	1.143		320	41		361	420
4300	For 6'-8" high door, deduct from 7'-0" door					16.80			16.80	18.50

08 14 16.20 Wood Fire Doors

		Crew	Daily Output	Labor-Hours	Unit	Material	2014 Bare Costs Labor	Equipment	Total	Total Incl O&P
0010	**WOOD FIRE DOORS**									
0020	Particle core, 7 face plys, "B" label,									
0040	1 hour, birch face, 1-3/4" x 2'-6" x 6'-8"	2 Carp	14	1.143	Ea.	420	41		461	530
0080	3'-0" x 6'-8"		13	1.231		400	44		444	515
0090	3'-0" x 7'-0"		12	1.333		435	47.50		482.50	560
0100	4'-0" x 7'-0"		12	1.333		540	47.50		587.50	675
0140	Oak face, 2'-6" x 6'-8"		14	1.143		450	41		491	565

08 14 Wood Doors

08 14 16 – Flush Wood Doors

08 14 16.20 Wood Fire Doors

		Crew	Daily Output	Labor-Hours	Unit	Material	2014 Bare Costs Labor	Equipment	Total	Total Incl O&P
0180	3'-0" x 6'-8"	2 Carp	13	1.231	Ea.	455	44		499	575
0190	3'-0" x 7'-0"		12	1.333		460	47.50		507.50	585
0200	4'-0" x 7'-0"		12	1.333		590	47.50		637.50	730
0240	Walnut face, 2'-6" x 6'-8"		14	1.143		470	41		511	585
0280	3'-0" x 6'-8"		13	1.231		490	44		534	615
0290	3'-0" x 7'-0"		12	1.333		510	47.50		557.50	640
0300	4'-0" x 7'-0"		12	1.333		630	47.50		677.50	775
0440	M.D. overlay on hardboard, 2'-6" x 6'-8"		15	1.067		315	38		353	410
0480	3'-0" x 6'-8"		14	1.143		375	41		416	485
0490	3'-0" x 7'-0"		13	1.231		395	44		439	510
0500	4'-0" x 7'-0"		12	1.333		415	47.50		462.50	535
0740	90 minutes, birch face, 1-3/4" x 2'-6" x 6'-8"		14	1.143		325	41		366	425
0780	3'-0" x 6'-8"		13	1.231		320	44		364	425
0790	3'-0" x 7'-0"		12	1.333		385	47.50		432.50	505
0800	4'-0" x 7'-0"		12	1.333		540	47.50		587.50	670
0840	Oak face, 2'-6" x 6'-8"		14	1.143		430	41		471	545
0880	3'-0" x 6'-8"		13	1.231		440	44		484	560
0890	3'-0" x 7'-0"		12	1.333		455	47.50		502.50	580
0900	4'-0" x 7'-0"		12	1.333		590	47.50		637.50	730
0940	Walnut face, 2'-6" x 6'-8"		14	1.143		400	41		441	510
0980	3'-0" x 6'-8"		13	1.231		410	44		454	525
0990	3'-0" x 7'-0"		12	1.333		470	47.50		517.50	595
1000	4'-0" x 7'-0"		12	1.333		620	47.50		667.50	760
1140	M.D. overlay on hardboard, 2'-6" x 6'-8"		15	1.067		355	38		393	455
1180	3'-0" x 6'-8"		14	1.143		375	41		416	485
1190	3'-0" x 7'-0"		13	1.231		405	44		449	520
1200	4'-0" x 7'-0"		12	1.333		455	47.50		502.50	580
1240	For 8'-0" height, add					75			75	82.50
1260	For 8'-0" height walnut, add					90			90	99
2200	Custom architectural "B" label, flush, 1-3/4" thick, birch,									
2210	Solid core									
2220	2'-6" x 7'-0"	2 Carp	15	1.067	Ea.	305	38		343	400
2260	3'-0" x 7'-0"		14	1.143		315	41		356	415
2300	4'-0" x 7'-0"		13	1.231		400	44		444	515
2420	4'-0" x 8'-0"		11	1.455		430	52		482	565
2480	For oak veneer, add					50%				
2500	For walnut veneer, add					75%				

08 14 23 – Clad Wood Doors

08 14 23.13 Metal-Faced Wood Doors

		Crew	Daily Output	Labor-Hours	Unit	Material	Labor	Equipment	Total	Total Incl O&P
0010	**METAL-FACED WOOD DOORS**									
0020	Interior, flush type, 3' x 7'	2 Carp	4.30	3.721	Opng.	390	133		523	655

08 14 23.20 Tin Clad Wood Doors

		Crew	Daily Output	Labor-Hours	Unit	Material	Labor	Equipment	Total	Total Incl O&P
0010	**TIN CLAD WOOD DOORS**									
0020	3 ply, 6' x 7', double sliding, doors only	2 Carp	1	16	Opng.	2,000	570		2,570	3,150
1000	For electric operator, add	1 Elec	2	4	"	3,250	171		3,421	3,850

08 14 33 – Stile and Rail Wood Doors

08 14 33.10 Wood Doors Paneled

		Crew	Daily Output	Labor-Hours	Unit	Material	Labor	Equipment	Total	Total Incl O&P
0010	**WOOD DOORS PANELED**									
0020	Interior, six panel, hollow core, 1-3/8" thick									
0040	Molded hardboard, 2'-0" x 6'-8"	2 Carp	17	.941	Ea.	62	33.50		95.50	125
0060	2'-6" x 6'-8"		17	.941		64	33.50		97.50	127

08 14 Wood Doors

08 14 33 – Stile and Rail Wood Doors

08 14 33.10 Wood Doors Paneled

		Crew	Daily Output	Labor-Hours	Unit	Material	2014 Bare Costs Labor	2014 Bare Costs Equipment	Total	Total Incl O&P
0070	2'-8" x 6'-8"	2 Carp	17	.941	Ea.	67	33.50		100.50	130
0080	3'-0" x 6'-8"		17	.941		72	33.50		105.50	136
0140	Embossed print, molded hardboard, 2'-0" x 6'-8"		17	.941		64	33.50		97.50	127
0160	2'-6" x 6'-8"		17	.941		64	33.50		97.50	127
0180	3'-0" x 6'-8"		17	.941		72	33.50		105.50	136
0540	Six panel, solid, 1-3/8" thick, pine, 2'-0" x 6'-8"		15	1.067		155	38		193	235
0560	2'-6" x 6'-8"		14	1.143		170	41		211	256
0580	3'-0" x 6'-8"		13	1.231		145	44		189	234
1020	Two panel, bored rail, solid, 1-3/8" thick, pine, 1'-6" x 6'-8"		16	1		270	36		306	355
1040	2'-0" x 6'-8"		15	1.067		355	38		393	455
1060	2'-6" x 6'-8"		14	1.143		400	41		441	510
1340	Two panel, solid, 1-3/8" thick, fir, 2'-0" x 6'-8"		15	1.067		160	38		198	240
1360	2'-6" x 6'-8"		14	1.143		210	41		251	300
1380	3'-0" x 6'-8"		13	1.231		415	44		459	530
1740	Five panel, solid, 1-3/8" thick, fir, 2'-0" x 6'-8"		15	1.067		280	38		318	375
1760	2'-6" x 6'-8"		14	1.143		420	41		461	530
1780	3'-0" x 6'-8"		13	1.231		420	44		464	535

08 14 33.20 Wood Doors Residential

		Crew	Daily Output	Labor-Hours	Unit	Material	2014 Bare Costs Labor	2014 Bare Costs Equipment	Total	Total Incl O&P
0010	**WOOD DOORS RESIDENTIAL**									
0200	Exterior, combination storm & screen, pine									
0260	2'-8" wide	2 Carp	10	1.600	Ea.	300	57		357	425
0280	3'-0" wide		9	1.778		310	63.50		373.50	445
0300	7'-1" x 3'-0" wide		9	1.778		335	63.50		398.50	475
0400	Full lite, 6'-9" x 2'-6" wide		11	1.455		320	52		372	440
0420	2'-8" wide		10	1.600		320	57		377	445
0440	3'-0" wide		9	1.778		325	63.50		388.50	460
0500	7'-1" x 3'-0" wide		9	1.778		355	63.50		418.50	495
0700	Dutch door, pine, 1-3/4" x 2'-8" x 6'-8", minimum		12	1.333		790	47.50		837.50	945
0720	Maximum		10	1.600		900	57		957	1,075
0800	3'-0" wide, minimum		12	1.333		790	47.50		837.50	945
0820	Maximum		10	1.600		900	57		957	1,075
1000	Entrance door, colonial, 1-3/4" x 6'-8" x 2'-8" wide		16	1		500	36		536	605
1020	6 panel pine, 3'-0" wide		15	1.067		445	38		483	555
1100	8 panel pine, 2'-8" wide		16	1		575	36		611	695
1120	3'-0" wide		15	1.067		570	38		608	690
1200	For tempered safety glass lites, (min of 2) add					76.50			76.50	84.50
1300	Flush, birch, solid core, 1-3/4" x 6'-8" x 2'-8" wide	2 Carp	16	1		113	36		149	185
1320	3'-0" wide		15	1.067		119	38		157	194
1350	7'-0" x 2'-8" wide		16	1		121	36		157	194
1360	3'-0" wide		15	1.067		143	38		181	221
1380	For tempered safety glass lites, add					103			103	113
2700	Interior, closet, bi-fold, w/hardware, no frame or trim incl.									
2720	Flush, birch, 6'-6" or 6'-8" x 2'-6" wide	2 Carp	13	1.231	Ea.	67.50	44		111.50	149
2740	3'-0" wide		13	1.231		71.50	44		115.50	153
2760	4'-0" wide		12	1.333		109	47.50		156.50	200
2780	5'-0" wide		11	1.455		105	52		157	204
2800	6'-0" wide		10	1.600		128	57		185	237
3000	Raised panel pine, 6'-6" or 6'-8" x 2'-6" wide		13	1.231		198	44		242	292
3020	3'-0" wide		13	1.231		278	44		322	380
3040	4'-0" wide		12	1.333		305	47.50		352.50	415
3060	5'-0" wide		11	1.455		365	52		417	490
3080	6'-0" wide		10	1.600		400	57		457	535

08 14 33 – Stile and Rail Wood Doors

08 14 33.20 Wood Doors Residential	Crew	Daily Output	Labor-Hours	Unit	Material	2014 Bare Costs Labor	Equipment	Total	Total Incl O&P
3200	Louvered, pine 6'-6" or 6'-8" x 2'-6" wide	2 Carp	13	1.231	Ea.	144	44		188	232
3220	3'-0" wide		13	1.231		208	44		252	300
3240	4'-0" wide		12	1.333		235	47.50		282.50	340
3260	5'-0" wide		11	1.455		262	52		314	375
3280	6'-0" wide		10	1.600		289	57		346	415
4400	Bi-passing closet, incl. hardware and frame, no trim incl.									
4420	Flush, lauan, 6'-8" x 4'-0" wide	2 Carp	12	1.333	Opng.	176	47.50		223.50	274
4440	5'-0" wide		11	1.455		187	52		239	293
4460	6'-0" wide		10	1.600		209	57		266	325
4600	Flush, birch, 6'-8" x 4'-0" wide		12	1.333		223	47.50		270.50	325
4620	5'-0" wide		11	1.455		212	52		264	320
4640	6'-0" wide		10	1.600		260	57		317	380
4800	Louvered, pine, 6'-8" x 4'-0" wide		12	1.333		410	47.50		457.50	530
4820	5'-0" wide		11	1.455		395	52		447	525
4840	6'-0" wide		10	1.600		530	57		587	680
5000	Paneled, pine, 6'-8" x 4'-0" wide		12	1.333		510	47.50		557.50	645
5020	5'-0" wide		11	1.455		410	52		462	540
5040	6'-0" wide		10	1.600		610	57		667	765
5042	8'-0" wide		12	1.333		1,025	47.50		1,072.50	1,200
6100	Folding accordion, closet, including track and frame									
6120	Vinyl, 2 layer, stock	2 Carp	10	1.600	Ea.	66	57		123	169
6200	Rigid PVC	"	10	1.600	"	55	57		112	157
7310	Passage doors, flush, no frame included									
7320	Hardboard, hollow core, 1-3/8" x 6'-8" x 1'-6" wide	2 Carp	18	.889	Ea.	40.50	32		72.50	98
7330	2'-0" wide		18	.889		43	32		75	101
7340	2'-6" wide		18	.889		47.50	32		79.50	106
7350	2'-8" wide		18	.889		49	32		81	108
7360	3'-0" wide		17	.941		52	33.50		85.50	114
7420	Lauan, hollow core, 1-3/8" x 6'-8" x 1'-6" wide		18	.889		34	32		66	91
7440	2'-0" wide		18	.889		35	32		67	92
7450	2'-4" wide		18	.889		38.50	32		70.50	96
7460	2'-6" wide		18	.889		38.50	32		70.50	96
7480	2'-8" wide		18	.889		40	32		72	97.50
7500	3'-0" wide		17	.941		42.50	33.50		76	103
7700	Birch, hollow core, 1-3/8" x 6'-8" x 1'-6" wide		18	.889		41	32		73	98.50
7720	2'-0" wide		18	.889		42.50	32		74.50	100
7740	2'-6" wide		18	.889		50	32		82	109
7760	2'-8" wide		18	.889		50.50	32		82.50	109
7780	3'-0" wide		17	.941		52	33.50		85.50	114
8000	Pine louvered, 1-3/8" x 6'-8" x 1'-6" wide		19	.842		120	30		150	183
8020	2'-0" wide		18	.889		131	32		163	198
8040	2'-6" wide		18	.889		150	32		182	219
8060	2'-8" wide		18	.889		161	32		193	231
8080	3'-0" wide		17	.941		175	33.50		208.50	249
8300	Pine paneled, 1-3/8" x 6'-8" x 1'-6" wide		19	.842		128	30		158	192
8320	2'-0" wide		18	.889		153	32		185	222
8330	2'-4" wide		18	.889		182	32		214	254
8340	2'-6" wide		18	.889		182	32		214	254
8360	2'-8" wide		18	.889		185	32		217	258
8380	3'-0" wide		17	.941		204	33.50		237.50	281

08 14 Wood Doors

08 14 40 – Interior Cafe Doors

08 14 40.10 Cafe Style Doors		Crew	Daily Output	Labor-Hours	Unit	Material	2014 Bare Costs Labor	Equipment	Total	Total Incl O&P
0010	**CAFE STYLE DOORS**									
6520	Interior cafe doors, 2'-6" opening, stock, panel pine	2 Carp	16	1	Ea.	218	36		254	299
6540	3'-0" opening	"	16	1	"	240	36		276	325
6550	Louvered pine									
6560	2'-6" opening	2 Carp	16	1	Ea.	180	36		216	258
8000	3'-0" opening		16	1		193	36		229	272
8010	2'-6" opening, hardwood		16	1		264	36		300	350
8020	3'-0" opening		16	1		281	36		317	370

08 16 Composite Doors

08 16 13 – Fiberglass Doors

08 16 13.10 Entrance Doors, Fiberous Glass			Crew	Daily Output	Labor-Hours	Unit	Material	2014 Bare Costs Labor	Equipment	Total	Total Incl O&P
0010	**ENTRANCE DOORS, FIBEROUS GLASS**										
0020	Exterior, fiberglass, door, 2'-8" wide x 6'-8" high	G	2 Carp	15	1.067	Ea.	259	38		297	350
0040	3'-0" wide x 6'-8" high	G		15	1.067		259	38		297	350
0060	3'-0" wide x 7'-0" high	G		15	1.067		460	38		498	570
0080	3'-0" wide x 6'-8" high, with two lites	G		15	1.067		294	38		332	390
0100	3'-0" wide x 8'-0" high, with two lites	G		15	1.067		495	38		533	610
0110	Half glass, 3'-0" wide x 6'-8" high	G		15	1.067		435	38		473	545
0120	3'-0" wide x 6'-8" high, low e	G		15	1.067		465	38		503	575
0130	3'-0" wide x 8'-0" high	G		15	1.067		580	38		618	705
0140	3'-0" wide x 8'-0" high, low e	G		15	1.067		640	38		678	765
0150	Side lights, 1'-0" wide x 6'-8" high	G					251			251	276
0160	1'-0" wide x 6'-8" high, low e	G					256			256	281
0180	1'-0" wide x 6'-8" high, full glass	G					285			285	315
0190	1'-0" wide x 6'-8" high, low e	G					300			300	330

08 16 14 – French Doors

08 16 14.10 Exterior Doors With Glass Lites		Crew	Daily Output	Labor-Hours	Unit	Material	2014 Bare Costs Labor	Equipment	Total	Total Incl O&P
0010	**EXTERIOR DOORS WITH GLASS LITES**									
0020	French, Fir, 1-3/4", 3'-0"wide x 6'-8" high	2 Carp	12	1.333	Ea.	600	47.50		647.50	740
0025	Double		12	1.333		1,200	47.50		1,247.50	1,400
0030	Maple, 1-3/4", 3'-0"wide x 6'-8" high		12	1.333		675	47.50		722.50	825
0035	Double		12	1.333		1,350	47.50		1,397.50	1,550
0040	Cherry, 1-3/4", 3'-0"wide x 6'-8" high		12	1.333		790	47.50		837.50	945
0045	Double		12	1.333		1,575	47.50		1,622.50	1,800
0100	Mahogany, 1-3/4", 3'-0"wide x 8'-0" high		10	1.600		800	57		857	975
0105	Double		10	1.600		1,600	57		1,657	1,850
0110	Fir, 1-3/4", 3'-0"wide x 8'-0" high		10	1.600		1,200	57		1,257	1,425
0115	Double		10	1.600		2,400	57		2,457	2,750
0120	Oak, 1-3/4", 3'-0"wide x 8'-0" high		10	1.600		1,825	57		1,882	2,100
0125	Double		10	1.600		3,650	57		3,707	4,100

08 17 13 – Integrated Metal Door Opening Assemblies

08 17 13.20 Stainless Steel Doors and Frames		Crew	Daily Output	Labor-Hours	Unit	Material	2014 Bare Costs Labor	Equipment	Total	Total Incl O&P
0010	**STAINLESS STEEL DOORS AND FRAMES**									
0020	Stainless Steel(304) prehung 24 g 2'-6" x 6'-8" door w/16 g frame [G]	2 Carp	6	2.667	Ea.	1,775	95.50		1,870.50	2,100
0025	2'-8" x 6'-8" [G]		6	2.667		1,825	95.50		1,920.50	2,150
0030	3'-0" x 6'-8" [G]		6	2.667		1,825	95.50		1,920.50	2,150
0040	3'-0" x 7'-0" [G]		6	2.667		1,850	95.50		1,945.50	2,175
0050	4'-0" x 7'-0" [G]		5	3.200		2,375	114		2,489	2,825
0100	Stainless Steel(316) prehung 24 g 2'-6" x 6'-8" door w/16 g frame [G]		6	2.667		2,700	95.50		2,795.50	3,125
0110	2'-8" x 6'-8" [G]		6	2.667		2,725	95.50		2,820.50	3,125
0120	3'-0" x 6'-8" [G]		6	2.667		2,500	95.50		2,595.50	2,900
0150	3'-0" x 7'-0" [G]		6	2.667		2,675	95.50		2,770.50	3,100
0160	4'-0" x 7'-0" [G]		6	2.667		3,300	95.50		3,395.50	3,775
0300	Stainless Steel(304) prehung 18 g 2'-6" x 6'-8" door w/16 g frame [G]		6	2.667		3,075	95.50		3,170.50	3,525
0310	2'-8" x 6'-8" [G]		6	2.667		3,100	95.50		3,195.50	3,550
0320	3'-0" x 6'-8" [G]		6	2.667		3,150	95.50		3,245.50	3,625
0350	3'-0" x 7'-0" [G]		6	2.667		3,200	95.50		3,295.50	3,675
0360	4'-0" x 7'-0" [G]		5	3.200		3,400	114		3,514	3,925
0500	Stainless steel, prehung door, foam core, 14 ga, 3'-0" x 7'-0" [G]		5	3.200		3,400	114		3,514	3,950
0600	Stainless steel, prehung double door, foam core, 14 ga, 3'-0" x 7'-0" [G]		4	4		6,700	143		6,843	7,625

08 17 23 – Integrated Wood Door Opening Assemblies

08 17 23.10 Pre-Hung Doors

		Crew	Daily Output	Labor-Hours	Unit	Material	Labor	Equipment	Total	Total Incl O&P
0010	**PRE-HUNG DOORS**									
0300	Exterior, wood, comb. storm & screen, 6'-9" x 2'-6" wide	2 Carp	15	1.067	Ea.	296	38		334	390
0320	2'-8" wide		15	1.067		296	38		334	390
0340	3'-0" wide		15	1.067		305	38		343	400
0360	For 7'-0" high door, add					30			30	33
1600	Entrance door, flush, birch, solid core									
1620	4-5/8" solid jamb, 1-3/4" x 6'-8" x 2'-8" wide	2 Carp	16	1	Ea.	289	36		325	380
1640	3'-0" wide	"	16	1		375	36		411	475
1680	For 7'-0" high door, add					25			25	27.50
2000	Entrance door, colonial, 6 panel pine									
2020	4-5/8" solid jamb, 1-3/4" x 6'-8" x 2'-8" wide	2 Carp	16	1	Ea.	640	36		676	765
2040	3'-0" wide	"	16	1		675	36		711	800
2060	For 7'-0" high door, add					54			54	59
2200	For 5-5/8" solid jamb, add					41.50			41.50	46
4000	Interior, passage door, 4-5/8" solid jamb									
4400	Lauan, flush, solid core, 1-3/8" x 6'-8" x 2'-6" wide	2 Carp	17	.941	Ea.	186	33.50		219.50	262
4420	2'-8" wide		17	.941		186	33.50		219.50	262
4440	3'-0" wide		16	1		201	36		237	281
4600	Hollow core, 1-3/8" x 6'-8" x 2'-6" wide		17	.941		125	33.50		158.50	195
4620	2'-8" wide		17	.941		125	33.50		158.50	194
4640	3'-0" wide		16	1		140	36		176	214
4700	For 7'-0" high door, add					35.50			35.50	39
5000	Birch, flush, solid core, 1-3/8" x 6'-8" x 2'-6" wide	2 Carp	17	.941		259	33.50		292.50	340
5020	2'-8" wide		17	.941		201	33.50		234.50	278
5040	3'-0" wide		16	1		288	36		324	375
5200	Hollow core, 1-3/8" x 6'-8" x 2'-6" wide		17	.941		210	33.50		243.50	288
5220	2'-8" wide		17	.941		252	33.50		285.50	335
5240	3'-0" wide		16	1		216	36		252	298
5280	For 7'-0" high door, add					30.50			30.50	33.50
5500	Hardboard paneled, 1-3/8" x 6'-8" x 2'-6" wide	2 Carp	17	.941		145	33.50		178.50	216
5520	2'-8" wide		17	.941		153	33.50		186.50	225
5540	3'-0" wide		16	1		150	36		186	225

08 17 Integrated Door Opening Assemblies

08 17 23 – Integrated Wood Door Opening Assemblies

08 17 23.10 Pre-Hung Doors

08 17 23.10 Pre-Hung Doors		Crew	Daily Output	Labor-Hours	Unit	Material	2014 Bare Costs		Total	Total Incl O&P
							Labor	Equipment		
6000	Pine paneled, 1-3/8" x 6'-8" x 2'-6" wide	2 Carp	17	.941	Ea.	255	33.50		288.50	340
6020	2'-8" wide		17	.941		274	33.50		307.50	355
6040	3'-0" wide	▼	16	1		282	36		318	370
6500	For 5-5/8" solid jamb, add					25			25	27.50
6520	For split jamb, deduct				▼	24			24	26.50

08 31 Access Doors and Panels

08 31 13 – Access Doors and Frames

08 31 13.10 Types of Framed Access Doors

08 31 13.10 Types of Framed Access Doors		Crew	Daily Output	Labor-Hours	Unit	Material	2014 Bare Costs		Total	Total Incl O&P
							Labor	Equipment		
0010	**TYPES OF FRAMED ACCESS DOORS**									
1000	Fire rated door with lock									
1100	Metal, 12" x 12"	1 Carp	10	.800	Ea.	165	28.50		193.50	230
1150	18" x 18"		9	.889		220	32		252	296
1200	24" x 24"		9	.889		325	32		357	415
1250	24" x 36"		8	1		335	36		371	425
1300	24" x 48"		8	1		430	36		466	535
1350	36" x 36"		7.50	1.067		495	38		533	610
1400	48" x 48"		7.50	1.067		635	38		673	760
1600	Stainless steel, 12" x 12"		10	.800		282	28.50		310.50	360
1650	18" x 18"		9	.889		410	32		442	505
1700	24" x 24"		9	.889		500	32		532	605
1750	24" x 36"	▼	8	1	▼	640	36		676	765
2000	Flush door for finishing									
2100	Metal 8" x 8"	1 Carp	10	.800	Ea.	38	28.50		66.50	90
2150	12" x 12"	"	10	.800	"	42	28.50		70.50	94
3000	Recessed door for acoustic tile									
3100	Metal, 12" x 12"	1 Carp	4.50	1.778	Ea.	82	63.50		145.50	197
3150	12" x 24"		4.50	1.778		95	63.50		158.50	212
3200	24" x 24"		4	2		125	71.50		196.50	258
3250	24" x 36"	▼	4	2	▼	175	71.50		246.50	315
4000	Recessed door for drywall									
4100	Metal 12" x 12"	1 Carp	6	1.333	Ea.	80	47.50		127.50	168
4150	12" x 24"		5.50	1.455		114	52		166	213
4200	24" x 36"	▼	5	1.600	▼	182	57		239	296
6000	Standard door									
6100	Metal, 8" x 8"	1 Carp	10	.800	Ea.	45	28.50		73.50	97.50
6150	12" x 12"		10	.800		50	28.50		78.50	103
6200	18" x 18"		9	.889		70	32		102	131
6250	24" x 24"		9	.889		85	32		117	147
6300	24" x 36"		8	1		125	36		161	198
6350	36" x 36"		8	1		145	36		181	220
6500	Stainless steel, 8" x 8"		10	.800		85	28.50		113.50	142
6550	12" x 12"		10	.800		110	28.50		138.50	169
6600	18" x 18"		9	.889		205	32		237	280
6650	24" x 24"	▼	9	.889	▼	265	32		297	345

08 31 13.20 Bulkhead/Cellar Doors

08 31 13.20 Bulkhead/Cellar Doors		Crew	Daily Output	Labor-Hours	Unit	Material	2014 Bare Costs		Total	Total Incl O&P
							Labor	Equipment		
0010	**BULKHEAD/CELLAR DOORS**									
0020	Steel, not incl. sides, 44" x 62"	1 Carp	5.50	1.455	Ea.	560	52		612	705
0100	52" x 73"		5.10	1.569		790	56		846	965
0500	With sides and foundation plates, 57" x 45" x 24"		4.70	1.702		810	61		871	990
0600	42" x 49" x 51"	▼	4.30	1.860		915	66.50		981.50	1,100

08 31 Access Doors and Panels

08 31 13 – Access Doors and Frames

08 31 13.30 Commercial Floor Doors		Crew	Daily Output	Labor-Hours	Unit	Material	2014 Bare Costs Labor	2014 Bare Costs Equipment	Total	Total Incl O&P
0010	**COMMERCIAL FLOOR DOORS**									
0021	Aluminum tile, steel frame, one leaf, 2' x 2' opng.	L-4	3.50	4.571	Opng.	800	144		944	1,125
0051	3'-6" x 3'-6" opening		3.50	4.571		1,600	144		1,744	2,000
0501	Double leaf, 4' x 4' opening		3	5.333		1,750	169		1,919	2,200
0551	5' x 5' opening		3	5.333		3,100	169		3,269	3,675

08 31 13.35 Industrial Floor Doors		Crew	Daily Output	Labor-Hours	Unit	Material	Labor	Equipment	Total	Total Incl O&P
0010	**INDUSTRIAL FLOOR DOORS**									
0021	Steel 300 psf L.L., single leaf, 2' x 2', 175#	L-4	6	2.667	Opng.	760	84.50		844.50	975
0051	3' x 3' opening, 300#		5.50	2.909		1,075	92		1,167	1,325
0301	Double leaf, 4' x 4' opening, 455#		5	3.200		1,900	101		2,001	2,275
0351	5' x 5' opening, 645#		4.50	3.556		2,750	112		2,862	3,225
1001	Aluminum, 300 psf L.L., single leaf, 2' x 2', 60#		6	2.667		750	84.50		834.50	965
1051	3' x 3' opening, 100#		5.50	2.909		1,300	92		1,392	1,575
1501	Double leaf, 4' x 4' opening, 160#		5	3.200		2,100	101		2,201	2,475
1551	5' x 5' opening, 235#		4.50	3.556		2,800	112		2,912	3,275
2001	Aluminum, 150 psf L.L., single leaf, 2' x 2', 60#		6	2.667		700	84.50		784.50	910
2051	3' x 3' opening, 95#		5.50	2.909		1,000	92		1,092	1,250
2501	Double leaf, 4' x 4' opening, 150#		5	3.200		1,450	101		1,551	1,775
2551	5' x 5' opening, 230#		4.50	3.556		1,950	112		2,062	2,325

08 31 13.40 Kennel Doors		Crew	Daily Output	Labor-Hours	Unit	Material	Labor	Equipment	Total	Total Incl O&P
0010	**KENNEL DOORS**									
0020	2 way, swinging type, 13" x 19" opening	2 Carp	11	1.455	Opng.	90	52		142	187
0100	17" x 29" opening		11	1.455		110	52		162	209
0200	9" x 9" opening, electronic with accessories		11	1.455		144	52		196	246

08 32 Sliding Glass Doors

08 32 13 – Sliding Aluminum-Framed Glass Doors

08 32 13.10 Sliding Aluminum Doors		Crew	Daily Output	Labor-Hours	Unit	Material	Labor	Equipment	Total	Total Incl O&P
0010	**SLIDING ALUMINUM DOORS**									
0350	Aluminum, 5/8" tempered insulated glass, 6' wide									
0400	Premium	2 Carp	4	4	Ea.	1,575	143		1,718	1,975
0450	Economy		4	4		905	143		1,048	1,225
0500	8' wide, premium		3	5.333		1,650	191		1,841	2,150
0550	Economy		3	5.333		1,425	191		1,616	1,875
0600	12' wide, premium		2.50	6.400		2,975	229		3,204	3,650
0650	Economy		2.50	6.400		1,525	229		1,754	2,050
4000	Aluminum, baked on enamel, temp glass, 6'-8" x 10'-0" wide		4	4		1,050	143		1,193	1,425
4020	Insulating glass, 6'-8" x 6'-0" wide		4	4		920	143		1,063	1,275
4040	8'-0" wide		3	5.333		1,075	191		1,266	1,500
4060	10'-0" wide		2	8		1,325	286		1,611	1,925
4080	Anodized, temp glass, 6'-8" x 6'-0" wide		4	4		455	143		598	740
4100	8'-0" wide		3	5.333		575	191		766	955
4120	10'-0" wide		2	8		645	286		931	1,200

08 32 19 – Sliding Wood-Framed Glass Doors

08 32 19.15 Sliding Glass Vinyl-Clad Wood Doors			Crew	Daily Output	Labor-Hours	Unit	Material	Labor	Equipment	Total	Total Incl O&P
0010	**SLIDING GLASS VINYL-CLAD WOOD DOORS**										
0020	Glass, sliding vinyl clad, insul. glass, 6'-0" x 6'-8"	G	2 Carp	4	4	Opng.	1,500	143		1,643	1,925
0025	6'-0" x 6'-10" high	G		4	4		1,650	143		1,793	2,075
0100	8'-0" x 6'-10" high	G		4	4		2,025	143		2,168	2,475

08 32 Sliding Glass Doors

08 32 19 – Sliding Wood-Framed Glass Doors

08 32 19.15 Sliding Glass Vinyl-Clad Wood Doors		Crew	Daily Output	Labor-Hours	Unit	Material	2014 Bare Costs Labor	Equipment	Total	Total Incl O&P
0500	4 leaf, 9'-0" x 6'-10" high	G 2 Carp	3	5.333	Opng.	3,250	191		3,441	3,900
0600	12'-0" x 6'-10" high	G ↓	3	5.333	↓	3,875	191		4,066	4,600

08 33 Coiling Doors and Grilles

08 33 13 – Coiling Counter Doors

08 33 13.10 Counter Doors, Coiling Type

		Crew	Daily Output	Labor-Hours	Unit	Material	2014 Bare Costs Labor	Equipment	Total	Total Incl O&P
0010	**COUNTER DOORS, COILING TYPE**									
0020	Manual, incl. frame and hardware, galv. stl., 4' roll-up, 6' long	2 Carp	2	8	Opng.	1,200	286		1,486	1,800
0300	Galvanized steel, UL label		1.80	8.889		1,225	320		1,545	1,875
0600	Stainless steel, 4' high roll-up, 6' long		2	8		2,150	286		2,436	2,825
0700	10' long		1.80	8.889		2,500	320		2,820	3,275
2000	Aluminum, 4' high, 4' long		2.20	7.273		1,475	260		1,735	2,050
2020	6' long		2	8		1,775	286		2,061	2,425
2040	8' long		1.90	8.421		2,000	300		2,300	2,700
2060	10' long		1.80	8.889		2,050	320		2,370	2,775
2080	14' long		1.40	11.429		2,625	410		3,035	3,550
2100	6' high, 4' long		2	8		1,800	286		2,086	2,450
2120	6' long		1.60	10		1,625	360		1,985	2,400
2140	10' long	↓	1.40	11.429	↓	2,150	410		2,560	3,025

08 33 16 – Coiling Counter Grilles

08 33 16.10 Coiling Grilles

		Crew	Daily Output	Labor-Hours	Unit	Material	2014 Bare Costs Labor	Equipment	Total	Total Incl O&P
0010	**COILING GRILLES**									
2021	Aluminum, manual operated, mill finish	L-4	82	.195	S.F.	28	6.15		34.15	41
2041	Bronze anodized		82	.195	"	44.50	6.15		50.65	59.50
2061	Steel, manual operated, 10' x 10' high		1	16	Opng.	2,500	505		3,005	3,600
2081	15' x 8' high	↓	.80	20	"	2,900	630		3,530	4,250
3000	For safety edge bottom bar, electric, add				L.F.	49			49	54
3101	For motor operation, add	L-4	5	3.200	Opng.	1,250	101		1,351	1,550

08 33 23 – Overhead Coiling Doors

08 33 23.10 Coiling Service Doors

		Crew	Daily Output	Labor-Hours	Unit	Material	2014 Bare Costs Labor	Equipment	Total	Total Incl O&P
0010	**COILING SERVICE DOORS** Steel, manual, 20 ga., incl. hardware									
0051	8' x 8' high	L-4	1.60	10	Ea.	1,125	315		1,440	1,750
0101	10' x 10' high		1.40	11.429		1,850	360		2,210	2,650
0201	20' x 10' high		1	16		3,075	505		3,580	4,225
0301	12' x 12' high		1.20	13.333		1,875	420		2,295	2,775
0401	20' x 12' high		.90	17.778		2,125	560		2,685	3,300
0501	14' x 14' high		.80	20		3,050	630		3,680	4,425
0601	20' x 16' high		.60	26.667		3,550	845		4,395	5,325
0701	10' x 20' high		.50	32		2,500	1,000		3,500	4,450
1001	12' x 12', crank operated, crank on door side		.80	20		1,700	630		2,330	2,950
1101	Crank thru wall	↓	.70	22.857		1,975	720		2,695	3,400
1300	For vision panel, add				↓	345			345	380
1400	For 22 ga., deduct				S.F.	1.36			1.36	1.50
1600	3' x 7' pass door within rolling steel door, new construction				Ea.	1,825			1,825	2,025
1701	Existing construction	L-4	2	8		1,950	253		2,203	2,575
2001	Class A fire doors, manual, 20 ga., 8' x 8' high		1.40	11.429		1,525	360		1,885	2,275
2101	10' x 10' high		1.10	14.545		2,075	460		2,535	3,075
2201	20' x 10' high		.80	20		4,250	630		4,880	5,750
2301	12' x 12' high		1	16		3,275	505		3,780	4,450
2401	20' x 12' high	↓	.80	20	↓	4,600	630		5,230	6,125

08 33 Coiling Doors and Grilles

08 33 23 – Overhead Coiling Doors

08 33 23.10 Coiling Service Doors

		Crew	Daily Output	Labor-Hours	Unit	Material	2014 Bare Costs Labor	Equipment	Total	Total Incl O&P
2501	14' x 14' high	L-4	.60	26.667	Ea.	3,575	845		4,420	5,375
2601	20' x 16' high		.50	32		5,675	1,000		6,675	7,950
2701	10' x 20' high	↓	.40	40	↓	4,450	1,275		5,725	7,025
3000	For 18 ga. doors, add				S.F.	1.55			1.55	1.71
3300	For enamel finish, add				"	1.80			1.80	1.98
3600	For safety edge bottom bar, pneumatic, add				L.F.	21.50			21.50	24
3700	Electric, add					41			41	45
4000	For weatherstripping, extruded rubber, jambs, add					13.70			13.70	15.05
4100	Hood, add					8.45			8.45	9.30
4200	Sill, add				↓	4.86			4.86	5.35
4501	Motor operators, to 14' x 14' opening	L-4	5	3.200	Ea.	1,075	101		1,176	1,375
4601	Over 14' x 14', jack shaft type	"	5	3.200		1,050	101		1,151	1,325
4700	For fire door, additional fusible link, add				↓	27			27	29.50

08 34 Special Function Doors

08 34 13 – Cold Storage Doors

08 34 13.10 Doors for Cold Area Storage

		Crew	Daily Output	Labor-Hours	Unit	Material	2014 Bare Costs Labor	Equipment	Total	Total Incl O&P
0010	**DOORS FOR COLD AREA STORAGE**									
0020	Single, 20 ga. galvanized steel									
0300	Horizontal sliding, 5' x 7', manual operation, 3.5" thick	2 Carp	2	8	Ea.	3,225	286		3,511	4,025
0400	4" thick		2	8		3,250	286		3,536	4,050
0500	6" thick		2	8		3,425	286		3,711	4,250
0800	5' x 7', power operation, 2" thick		1.90	8.421		5,600	300		5,900	6,650
0900	4" thick		1.90	8.421		5,700	300		6,000	6,775
1000	6" thick		1.90	8.421		6,500	300		6,800	7,650
1300	9' x 10', manual operation, 2" insulation		1.70	9.412		4,550	335		4,885	5,575
1400	4" insulation		1.70	9.412		4,675	335		5,010	5,725
1500	6" insulation		1.70	9.412		5,575	335		5,910	6,725
1800	Power operation, 2" insulation		1.60	10		7,675	360		8,035	9,050
1900	4" insulation		1.60	10		7,900	360		8,260	9,275
2000	6" insulation	↓	1.70	9.412	↓	8,850	335		9,185	10,300
2300	For stainless steel face, add					25%				
3001	Hinged, lightweight, 3' x 7'-0", galvanized, 2" thick	2 Carp	2	8	Ea.	1,425	286		1,711	2,025
3051	4" thick		1.90	8.421		1,775	300		2,075	2,450
3301	Aluminum doors, 3' x 7'-0", 4" thick		1.90	8.421		1,350	300		1,650	1,975
3351	6" thick		1.40	11.429		2,350	410		2,760	3,250
3601	Stainless steel, 3' x 7'-0", 4" thick		1.90	8.421		1,725	300		2,025	2,400
3651	6" thick		1.40	11.429		2,950	410		3,360	3,900
3901	Painted, 3' x 7'-0", 4" thick		1.90	8.421		1,275	300		1,575	1,900
3951	6" thick	↓	1.40	11.429	↓	2,350	410		2,760	3,250
5000	Bi-parting, electric operated									
5011	6' x 8' opening, galv. faces, 4" thick for cooler	2 Carp	.80	20	Opng.	7,225	715		7,940	9,125
5051	For freezer		.80	20		7,950	715		8,665	9,950
5301	For door buck framing and door protection, add		2.50	6.400		640	229		869	1,100
6001	Galvanized batten door, galvanized hinges, 4' x 7'		2	8		1,825	286		2,111	2,500
6051	6' x 8'		1.80	8.889		2,475	320		2,795	3,250
6501	Fire door, 3 hr., 6' x 8', single slide		.80	20		8,275	715		8,990	10,300
6551	Double, bi-parting	↓	.70	22.857	↓	12,200	815		13,015	14,800

08 34 Special Function Doors

08 34 16 – Hangar Doors

08 34 16.10 Aircraft Hangar Doors

08 34 16.10 Aircraft Hangar Doors	Crew	Daily Output	Labor-Hours	Unit	Material	2014 Bare Costs Labor	Equipment	Total	Total Incl O&P
0010 **AIRCRAFT HANGAR DOORS**									
0020 Bi-fold, ovhd., 20 psf wind load, incl. elec. oper.									
0101 12' high x 40'	L-4	240	.067	S.F.	16.40	2.11		18.51	21.50
0201 16' high x 60'		230	.070		19.70	2.20		21.90	25
0301 20' high x 80'		220	.073		21.50	2.30		23.80	27.50

08 34 36 – Darkroom Doors

08 34 36.10 Various Types of Darkroom Doors

08 34 36.10 Various Types of Darkroom Doors	Crew	Daily Output	Labor-Hours	Unit	Material	2014 Bare Costs Labor	Equipment	Total	Total Incl O&P
0010 **VARIOUS TYPES OF DARKROOM DOORS**									
0015 Revolving, standard, 2 way, 36" diameter	2 Carp	3.10	5.161	Opng.	2,525	185		2,710	3,075
0020 41" diameter		3.10	5.161		2,825	185		3,010	3,425
0050 3 way, 51" diameter		1.40	11.429		3,675	410		4,085	4,725
1001 4 way, 49" diameter		1.40	11.429		3,775	410		4,185	4,825
2000 Hinged safety, 2 way, 41" diameter		2.30	6.957		3,300	249		3,549	4,050
2500 3 way, 51" diameter		1.40	11.429		3,650	410		4,060	4,700
3000 Pop out safety, 2 way, 41" diameter		3.10	5.161		3,925	185		4,110	4,600
4000 3 way, 51" diameter		1.40	11.429		4,775	410		5,185	5,925
5000 Wheelchair-type, pop out, 51" diameter		1.40	11.429		5,675	410		6,085	6,925
9300 For complete darkrooms, see Section 13 21 53.50									

08 34 53 – Security Doors and Frames

08 34 53.20 Steel Door

08 34 53.20 Steel Door	Crew	Daily Output	Labor-Hours	Unit	Material	2014 Bare Costs Labor	Equipment	Total	Total Incl O&P
0010 **STEEL DOOR** with ballistic core and welded frame both 14 ga.									
0050 Flush, UL 752 Level 3, 1-3/4", 3'-0" x 6'-8"	2 Carp	1.50	10.667	Opng.	2,300	380		2,680	3,175
0055 1-3/4", 3'-6" x 6'-8"		1.50	10.667		2,400	380		2,780	3,300
0060 1-3/4", 4'-0" x 6'-8"		1.20	13.333		2,625	475		3,100	3,675
0100 UL 752 Level 8, 1-3/4", 3'-0" x 6'-8"		1.50	10.667		10,100	380		10,480	11,700
0105 1-3/4", 3'-6" x 6'-8"		1.50	10.667		10,200	380		10,580	11,800
0110 1-3/4", 4'-0" x 6'-8"		1.20	13.333		11,600	475		12,075	13,600
0120 UL 752 Level 3, 1-3/4", 3'-0" x 7'-0"		1.50	10.667		2,325	380		2,705	3,225
0125 1-3/4", 3'-6" x 7'-0"		1.50	10.667		2,450	380		2,830	3,325
0130 1-3/4", 4'-0" x 7'-0"		1.20	13.333		2,650	475		3,125	3,725
0150 UL 752 Level 8, 1-3/4", 3'-0" x 7'-0"		1.50	10.667		10,200	380		10,580	11,800
0155 1-3/4", 3'-6" x 7'-0"		1.50	10.667		10,200	380		10,580	11,800
0160 1-3/4", 4'-0" x 7'-0"		1.20	13.333		11,700	475		12,175	13,700
1000 Safe Room sliding door and hardware, 1-3/4", 3'-0" x 7'-0" UL 752 Level 3		.50	32		23,300	1,150		24,450	27,500
1050 Safe Room swinging door and hardware, 1-3/4", 3'-0" x 7'-0" UL 752 Level 3		.50	32		27,800	1,150		28,950	32,500

08 34 53.30 Wood Ballistic Doors

08 34 53.30 Wood Ballistic Doors	Crew	Daily Output	Labor-Hours	Unit	Material	2014 Bare Costs Labor	Equipment	Total	Total Incl O&P
0010 **WOOD BALLISTIC DOORS** with frames and hardware									
0050 Wood, 1-3/4", 3'-0" x 7'-0" UL 752 Level 3	2 Carp	1.50	10.667	Opng.	2,225	380		2,605	3,100

08 34 59 – Vault Doors and Day Gates

08 34 59.10 Secure Storage Doors

08 34 59.10 Secure Storage Doors	Crew	Daily Output	Labor-Hours	Unit	Material	2014 Bare Costs Labor	Equipment	Total	Total Incl O&P
0010 **SECURE STORAGE DOORS**									
0020 Door and frame, 32" x 78", clear opening									
0101 1 hour test, weighs 750 lb.	L-4	1.50	10.667	Opng.	6,600	335		6,935	7,825
0201 2 hour test, 32" door, weighs 950 lb.		1.30	12.308		8,125	390		8,515	9,575
0251 40" door, weighs 1130 lb.		1	16		9,200	505		9,705	11,000
0301 4 hour test, 32" door, weighs 1025 lb.		1.20	13.333		8,550	420		8,970	10,100
0351 40" door, weighs 1140 lb.		.90	17.778		9,900	560		10,460	11,900
0500 For stainless steel front, including frame, add to above					2,100			2,100	2,300
0550 Back, add					2,000			2,000	2,200
0600 For time lock, two movement, add	1 Elec	2	4	Ea.	2,250	171		2,421	2,750

08 34 Special Function Doors

08 34 59 – Vault Doors and Day Gates

08 34 59.10 Secure Storage Doors

		Crew	Daily Output	Labor-Hours	Unit	Material	2014 Bare Costs Labor	Equipment	Total	Total Incl O&P
0650	Three movement, add	1 Elec	2	4	Ea.	2,200	171		2,371	2,700
0801	Day gate, painted, wire mesh, 32" wide	L-4	1.50	10.667		1,900	335		2,235	2,650
0851	40" wide		1.40	11.429		2,100	360		2,460	2,900
0901	Aluminum, 32" wide		1.50	10.667		3,150	335		3,485	4,050
0951	40" wide		1.40	11.429		3,350	360		3,710	4,300
2051	Security vault door, class I	E-24	.19	166	Opng.	15,700	6,375	3,875	25,950	33,300
2101	Class II		.19	166		18,600	6,375	3,875	28,850	36,500
2151	Class III		.13	250		23,500	9,550	5,825	38,875	49,800

08 34 63 – Detention Doors and Frames

08 34 63.13 Steel Detention Doors and Frames

		Crew	Daily Output	Labor-Hours	Unit	Material	2014 Bare Costs Labor	Equipment	Total	Total Incl O&P
0010	**STEEL DETENTION DOORS AND FRAMES**									
0500	Rolling cell door, bar front, 7/8" bars, 4" O.C., 7' H, 5' W, with hardware [G]	E-4	2	16	Ea.	5,275	620	71	5,966	7,050
0550	Actuator for rolling cell door, bar front	2 Skwk	2	8		4,200	290		4,490	5,125
1000	Doors & frames, 3' x 7', complete, with hardware, single plate	E-4	4	8		4,600	310	35.50	4,945.50	5,675
1650	Double plate	"	4	8		5,600	310	35.50	5,945.50	6,775

08 34 73 – Sound Control Door Assemblies

08 34 73.10 Acoustical Doors

		Crew	Daily Output	Labor-Hours	Unit	Material	2014 Bare Costs Labor	Equipment	Total	Total Incl O&P
0010	**ACOUSTICAL DOORS**									
0020	Including framed seals, 3' x 7', wood, 40 STC rating	2 Carp	1.50	10.667	Ea.	1,300	380		1,680	2,075
0100	Steel, 41 STC rating		1.50	10.667		3,200	380		3,580	4,175
0200	45 STC rating		1.50	10.667		3,600	380		3,980	4,600
0300	48 STC rating		1.50	10.667		4,200	380		4,580	5,275
0400	52 STC rating		1.50	10.667		4,800	380		5,180	5,925

08 36 Panel Doors

08 36 13 – Sectional Doors

08 36 13.10 Overhead Commercial Doors

		Crew	Daily Output	Labor-Hours	Unit	Material	2014 Bare Costs Labor	Equipment	Total	Total Incl O&P
0010	**OVERHEAD COMMERCIAL DOORS**									
1000	Stock, sectional, heavy duty, wood, 1-3/4" thick, 8' x 8' high	2 Carp	2	8	Ea.	1,025	286		1,311	1,600
1100	10' x 10' high		1.80	8.889		1,475	320		1,795	2,150
1200	12' x 12' high		1.50	10.667		2,025	380		2,405	2,875
1300	Chain hoist, 14' x 14' high		1.30	12.308		3,250	440		3,690	4,300
1400	12' x 16' high		1	16		3,225	570		3,795	4,475
1500	20' x 8' high		1.30	12.270		2,825	440		3,265	3,850
1600	20' x 16' high		.65	24.615		5,325	880		6,205	7,325
1800	Center mullion openings, 8' high		4	4		1,225	143		1,368	1,600
1900	20' high		2	8		2,050	286		2,336	2,725
2100	For medium duty custom door, deduct					5%	5%			
2150	For medium duty stock doors, deduct					10%	5%			
2300	Fiberglass and aluminum, heavy duty, sectional, 12' x 12' high	2 Carp	1.50	10.667	Ea.	2,700	380		3,080	3,625
2450	Chain hoist, 20' x 20' high		.50	32		6,675	1,150		7,825	9,275
2600	Steel, 24 ga. sectional, manual, 8' x 8' high		2	8		810	286		1,096	1,375
2650	10' x 10' high		1.80	8.889		1,100	320		1,420	1,725
2700	12' x 12' high		1.50	10.667		1,325	380		1,705	2,100
2800	Chain hoist, 20' x 14' high		.70	22.857		3,700	815		4,515	5,450
2850	For 1-1/4" rigid insulation and 26 ga. galv.									
2860	back panel, add				S.F.	4.70			4.70	5.15
2900	For electric trolley operator, 1/3 H.P., to 12' x 12', add	1 Carp	2	4	Ea.	935	143		1,078	1,275
2950	Over 12' x 12', 1/2 H.P., add		1	8		1,100	286		1,386	1,700
2980	Overhead, for row of clear lites add		1	8		110	286		396	600

08 36 Panel Doors

08 36 13 – Sectional Doors

08 36 13.20 Residential Garage Doors		Crew	Daily Output	Labor-Hours	Unit	Material	2014 Bare Costs Labor	Equipment	Total	Total Incl O&P
0010	**RESIDENTIAL GARAGE DOORS**									
0051	Hinged, wood, custom, double door, 9' x 7'	2 Carp	3	5.333	Ea.	715	191		906	1,100
0071	16' x 7'		2	8		1,100	286		1,386	1,675
0201	Overhead, sectional, incl. hardware, fiberglass, 9' x 7', standard		8	2		930	71.50		1,001.50	1,150
0221	Deluxe		8	2		1,150	71.50		1,221.50	1,375
0301	16' x 7', standard		6	2.667		1,575	95.50		1,670.50	1,875
0321	Deluxe		6	2.667		2,150	95.50		2,245.50	2,500
0501	Hardboard, 9' x 7', standard		8	2		590	71.50		661.50	770
0521	Deluxe		8	2		815	71.50		886.50	1,025
0601	16' x 7', standard		6	2.667		1,225	95.50		1,320.50	1,500
0621	Deluxe		6	2.667		1,425	95.50		1,520.50	1,725
0701	Metal, 9' x 7', standard		8	2		685	71.50		756.50	875
0721	Deluxe		8	2		910	71.50		981.50	1,125
0801	16' x 7', standard		6	2.667		870	95.50		965.50	1,125
0821	Deluxe		6	2.667		1,400	95.50		1,495.50	1,700
0901	Wood, 9' x 7', standard		8	2		920	71.50		991.50	1,125
0921	Deluxe		8	2		2,150	71.50		2,221.50	2,475
1001	16' x 7', standard		6	2.667		1,625	95.50		1,720.50	1,950
1021	Deluxe		6	2.667		3,025	95.50		3,120.50	3,475
1800	Door hardware, sectional	1 Carp	4	2		330	71.50		401.50	485
1810	Door tracks only		4	2		163	71.50		234.50	299
1820	One side only		7	1.143		112	41		153	192
3001	Swing-up, including hardware, fiberglass, 9' x 7', standard	2 Carp	8	2		1,000	71.50		1,071.50	1,225
3021	Deluxe		8	2		1,100	71.50		1,171.50	1,325
3101	16' x 7' standard		6	2.667		1,250	95.50		1,345.50	1,525
3121	Deluxe		6	2.667		1,600	95.50		1,695.50	1,900
3201	Hardboard, 9' x 7', standard		8	2		550	71.50		621.50	725
3221	Deluxe		8	2		650	71.50		721.50	835
3301	16' x 7', standard		6	2.667		670	95.50		765.50	895
3321	Deluxe		6	2.667		850	95.50		945.50	1,100
3401	Metal, 9' x 7', standard		8	2		600	71.50		671.50	780
3421	Deluxe		8	2		965	71.50		1,036.50	1,175
3501	16' x 7', standard		6	2.667		800	95.50		895.50	1,050
3522	Deluxe		6	2.667		1,100	95.50		1,195.50	1,350
3601	Wood, 9' x 7', standard		8	2		700	71.50		771.50	890
3621	Deluxe		8	2		1,125	71.50		1,196.50	1,350
3701	16' x 7', standard		6	2.667		900	95.50		995.50	1,150
3721	Deluxe		6	2.667		2,100	95.50		2,195.50	2,450
3900	Door hardware only, swing up	1 Carp	4	2		168	71.50		239.50	305
3920	One side only		7	1.143		90	41		131	168
4000	For electric operator, economy, add		8	1		425	36		461	530
4100	Deluxe, including remote control		8	1		610	36		646	735
4500	For transmitter/receiver control, add to operator				Total	110			110	121
4600	Transmitters, additional				"	60			60	66

08 36 19 – Multi-Leaf Vertical Lift Doors

08 36 19.10 Sectional Vertical Lift Doors

		Crew	Daily Output	Labor-Hours	Unit	Material	Labor	Equipment	Total	Total Incl O&P
0010	**SECTIONAL VERTICAL LIFT DOORS**									
0020	Motorized, 14 ga. steel, incl. frame and control panel									
0050	16' x 16' high	L-10	.50	48	Ea.	21,500	1,875	1,325	24,700	28,600
0100	10' x 20' high		1.30	18.462		31,900	720	510	33,130	37,000
0120	15' x 20' high		1.30	18.462		39,500	720	510	40,730	45,300
0140	20' x 20' high		1	24		45,900	940	665	47,505	53,000

08 36 Panel Doors

08 36 19 – Multi-Leaf Vertical Lift Doors

08 36 19.10 Sectional Vertical Lift Doors		Crew	Daily Output	Labor-Hours	Unit	Material	2014 Bare Costs Labor	Equipment	Total	Total Incl O&P
0160	25' x 20' high	L-10	1	24	Ea.	52,500	940	665	54,105	60,500
0170	32' x 24' high		.75	32		46,400	1,250	885	48,535	54,000
0180	20' x 25' high		1	24		54,000	940	665	55,605	62,000
0200	25' x 25' high		.70	34.286		61,000	1,350	945	63,295	70,500
0220	25' x 30' high		.70	34.286		68,000	1,350	945	70,295	78,000
0240	30' x 30' high		.70	34.286		79,000	1,350	945	81,295	90,500
0260	35' x 30' high	▼	.70	34.286	▼	89,000	1,350	945	91,295	101,500

08 36 23 – Telescoping Vertical Lift Doors

08 36 23.10 Telescoping Steel Doors

		Crew	Daily Output	Labor-Hours	Unit	Material	Labor	Equipment	Total	Total Incl O&P
0010	**TELESCOPING STEEL DOORS**									
1000	Overhead, .03" thick, electric operated, 10' x 10'	E-3	.80	30	Ea.	14,700	1,175	178	16,053	18,600
2000	20' x 10'		.60	40		18,800	1,550	237	20,587	23,900
3000	20' x 16'	▼	.40	60	▼	19,000	2,350	355	21,705	25,700

08 38 Traffic Doors

08 38 13 – Flexible Strip Doors

08 38 13.10 Flexible Transparent Strip Doors

		Crew	Daily Output	Labor-Hours	Unit	Material	Labor	Equipment	Total	Total Incl O&P
0010	**FLEXIBLE TRANSPARENT STRIP DOORS**									
0100	12" strip width, 2/3 overlap	3 Shee	135	.178	SF Surf	7.60	7.20		14.80	20.50
0200	Full overlap		115	.209		9.60	8.45		18.05	24.50
0220	8" strip width, 1/2 overlap		140	.171		6.20	6.95		13.15	18.35
0240	Full overlap	▼	120	.200	▼	7.80	8.10		15.90	22
0300	Add for suspension system, header mount				L.F.	9.10			9.10	10
0400	Wall mount				"	9.40			9.40	10.35

08 38 19 – Rigid Traffic Doors

08 38 19.20 Double Acting Swing Doors

		Crew	Daily Output	Labor-Hours	Unit	Material	Labor	Equipment	Total	Total Incl O&P
0010	**DOUBLE ACTING SWING DOORS**									
1000	.063" aluminum, 7'-0" high, 4'-0" wide	2 Carp	4.20	3.810	Pr.	2,100	136		2,236	2,525
1050	6'-8" wide	"	4	4	"	2,400	143		2,543	2,900
2000	Solid core wood, 3/4" thick, metal frame, stainless steel									
2010	base plate, 7' high opening, 4' wide	2 Carp	4	4	Pr.	2,600	143		2,743	3,100
2050	7' wide	"	3.80	4.211	"	2,800	151		2,951	3,325

08 38 19.30 Shock Absorbing Doors

		Crew	Daily Output	Labor-Hours	Unit	Material	Labor	Equipment	Total	Total Incl O&P
0010	**SHOCK ABSORBING DOORS**									
0021	Rigid, no frame, insulated, 1-13/16" thick, 5' x 7'	L-4	1.90	8.421	Opng.	1,400	266		1,666	2,000
0101	8' x 8'		1.80	8.889		2,000	281		2,281	2,675
0501	Flexible, frame not incl., 5' x 7' opening, economy		2	8		1,750	253		2,003	2,350
0601	Deluxe		1.90	8.421		2,625	266		2,891	3,325
1001	8' x 8' opening, economy		2	8		2,750	253		3,003	3,450
1101	Deluxe	▼	1.90	8.421	▼	3,500	266		3,766	4,300

08 41 13 – Aluminum-Framed Entrances and Storefronts

08 41 13.20 Tube Framing

		Crew	Daily Output	Labor-Hours	Unit	Material	2014 Bare Costs Labor	Equipment	Total	Total Incl O&P
0010	**TUBE FRAMING**, For window walls and store fronts, aluminum stock									
0050	Plain tube frame, mill finish, 1-3/4" x 1-3/4"	2 Glaz	103	.155	L.F.	9.75	5.40		15.15	19.70
0150	1-3/4" x 4"		98	.163		13.20	5.70		18.90	24
0200	1-3/4" x 4-1/2"		95	.168		14.85	5.85		20.70	26
0250	2" x 6"		89	.180		22.50	6.25		28.75	35
0350	4" x 4"		87	.184		25.50	6.40		31.90	38.50
0400	4-1/2" x 4-1/2"		85	.188		28	6.55		34.55	41.50
0450	Glass bead		240	.067		2.93	2.32		5.25	7.05
1000	Flush tube frame, mill finish, 1/4" glass, 1-3/4" x 4", open header		80	.200		12.65	6.95		19.60	25.50
1050	Open sill		82	.195		10.30	6.80		17.10	22.50
1100	Closed back header		83	.193		18.20	6.70		24.90	31
1150	Closed back sill		85	.188		17.35	6.55		23.90	30
1160	Tube fmg., spandrel cover both sides, alum 1" wide	1 Sswk	85	.094	S.F.	97	3.61		100.61	114
1170	Tube fmg., spandrel cover both sides, alum 2" wide	"	85	.094	"	37.50	3.61		41.11	48.50
1200	Vertical mullion, one piece	2 Glaz	75	.213	L.F.	19.05	7.40		26.45	33.50
1250	Two piece		73	.219		20	7.65		27.65	34.50
1300	90° or 180° vertical corner post		75	.213		31	7.40		38.40	46.50
1400	1-3/4" x 4-1/2", open header		80	.200		15.40	6.95		22.35	28.50
1450	Open sill		82	.195		12.90	6.80		19.70	25.50
1500	Closed back header		83	.193		18.35	6.70		25.05	31
1550	Closed back sill		85	.188		18.15	6.55		24.70	31
1600	Vertical mullion, one piece		75	.213		20.50	7.40		27.90	35
1650	Two piece		73	.219		21.50	7.65		29.15	36
1700	90° or 180° vertical corner post		75	.213		22	7.40		29.40	36.50
2000	Flush tube frame, mil fin.,ins. glass w/thml brk, 2" x 4-1/2", open header		75	.213		16	7.40		23.40	30
2050	Open sill		77	.208		13.45	7.25		20.70	27
2100	Closed back header		78	.205		15	7.15		22.15	28.50
2150	Closed back sill		80	.200		16.15	6.95		23.10	29.50
2200	Vertical mullion, one piece		70	.229		16.70	7.95		24.65	31.50
2250	Two piece		68	.235		18	8.20		26.20	33.50
2300	90° or 180° vertical corner post		70	.229		17.20	7.95		25.15	32
5000	Flush tube frame, mill fin., thermal brk., 2-1/4" x 4-1/2", open header		74	.216		16.60	7.50		24.10	31
5050	Open sill		75	.213		14.80	7.40		22.20	28.50
5100	Vertical mullion, one piece		69	.232		17.15	8.05		25.20	32.50
5150	Two piece		67	.239		21	8.30		29.30	37
5200	90° or 180° vertical corner post		69	.232		18.50	8.05		26.55	34
6980	Door stop (snap in)		380	.042		3.35	1.47		4.82	6.10
7000	For joints, 90°, clip type, add				Ea.	25			25	27.50
7050	Screw spline joint, add					23.50			23.50	26
7100	For joint other than 90°, add					49			49	54
8000	For bronze anodized aluminum, add					15%				
8020	For black finish, add					30%				
8050	For stainless steel materials, add					350%				
8100	For monumental grade, add					53%				
8150	For steel stiffener, add	2 Glaz	200	.080	L.F.	11.25	2.78		14.03	17
8200	For 2 to 5 stories, add per story				Story		8%			

08 41 19 – Stainless-Steel-Framed Entrances and Storefronts

08 41 19.10 Stainless-Steel and Glass Entrance Unit

		Crew	Daily Output	Labor-Hours	Unit	Material	2014 Bare Costs Labor	Equipment	Total	Total Incl O&P
0010	**STAINLESS-STEEL AND GLASS ENTRANCE UNIT**, narrow stiles									
0021	3' x 7' opening, including hardware, minimum	L-4	1.60	10	Opng.	6,600	315		6,915	7,775
0051	Average		1.40	11.429		7,050	360		7,410	8,350
0101	Maximum		1.20	13.333		7,600	420		8,020	9,050

08 41 Entrances and Storefronts

08 41 19 – Stainless-Steel-Framed Entrances and Storefronts

08 41 19.10 Stainless-Steel and Glass Entrance Unit	Crew	Daily Output	Labor-Hours	Unit	Material	2014 Bare Costs Labor	Equipment	Total	Total Incl O&P
1000	For solid bronze entrance units, statuary finish, add				Opng.	64%				
1100	Without statuary finish, add				↓	45%				
2001	Balanced doors, 3' x 7', economy	L-4	.90	17.778	Ea.	8,950	560		9,510	10,800
2101	Premium	"	.70	22.857	"	15,300	720		16,020	18,000

08 41 26 – All-Glass Entrances and Storefronts

08 41 26.10 Window Walls Aluminum, Stock

		Crew	Daily Output	Labor-Hours	Unit	Material	Labor	Equipment	Total	Total Incl O&P
0010	**WINDOW WALLS ALUMINUM, STOCK**, including glazing									
0020	Minimum	H-2	160	.150	S.F.	44.50	4.89		49.39	57
0050	Average		140	.171		61.50	5.60		67.10	77
0100	Maximum	↓	110	.218	↓	168	7.10		175.10	197
0500	For translucent sandwich wall systems, see Section 07 41 33.10									
0850	Cost of the above walls depends on material,									
0860	finish, repetition, and size of units.									
0870	The larger the opening, the lower the S.F. cost									
1200	Double glazed acoustical window wall for airports,									
1220	including 1" thick glass with 2" x 4-1/2" tube frame	H-2	40	.600	S.F.	115	19.55		134.55	160

08 42 Entrances

08 42 26 – All-Glass Entrances

08 42 26.10 Swinging Glass Doors

		Crew	Daily Output	Labor-Hours	Unit	Material	Labor	Equipment	Total	Total Incl O&P
0010	**SWINGING GLASS DOORS**									
0020	Including hardware, 1/2" thick, tempered, 3' x 7' opening	2 Glaz	2	8	Opng.	2,200	278		2,478	2,850
0100	6' x 7' opening	"	1.40	11.429	"	4,300	400		4,700	5,375

08 42 29 – Automatic Entrances

08 42 29.23 Sliding Automatic Entrances

		Crew	Daily Output	Labor-Hours	Unit	Material	Labor	Equipment	Total	Total Incl O&P
0010	**SLIDING AUTOMATIC ENTRANCES** 12' x 7'-6" opng., 5' x 7' door, 2 way traffic									
0020	Mat or electronic activated, panic pushout, incl. operator & hardware,									
0030	not including glass or glazing	2 Glaz	.70	22.857	Opng.	8,200	795		8,995	10,400

08 42 33 – Revolving Door Entrances

08 42 33.10 Circular Rotating Entrance Doors

		Crew	Daily Output	Labor-Hours	Unit	Material	Labor	Equipment	Total	Total Incl O&P
0010	**CIRCULAR ROTATING ENTRANCE DOORS**, Aluminum									
0021	6'-10" to 7' high, stock units, minimum	L-4	.38	42.105	Opng.	20,400	1,325		21,725	24,700
0051	Average		.30	53.333		24,600	1,675		26,275	29,900
0101	Maximum		.23	69.565		42,000	2,200		44,200	49,900
1001	Stainless steel		.15	106		40,000	3,375		43,375	49,700
1101	Solid bronze	↓	.07	228		47,100	7,225		54,325	64,000
1500	For automatic controls, add	2 Elec	2	8	↓	15,100	340		15,440	17,200

08 42 36 – Balanced Door Entrances

08 42 36.10 Balanced Entrance Doors

		Crew	Daily Output	Labor-Hours	Unit	Material	Labor	Equipment	Total	Total Incl O&P
0010	**BALANCED ENTRANCE DOORS**									
0021	Hardware & frame, alum. & glass, 3' x 7', econ.	L-4	.90	17.778	Ea.	6,600	560		7,160	8,225
0151	Premium	"	.70	22.857	"	7,925	720		8,645	9,950

08 43 Storefronts

08 43 13 – Aluminum-Framed Storefronts

08 43 13.10 Aluminum-Framed Entrance Doors and Frames

08 43 13.10 Aluminum-Framed Entrance Doors and Frames	Crew	Daily Output	Labor-Hours	Unit	Material	2014 Bare Costs Labor	Equipment	Total	Total Incl O&P
0010 **ALUMINUM-FRAMED ENTRANCE DOORS AND FRAMES**									
0015 Standard hardware and glass stops but no glass									
0020 Entrance door, 3' x 7' opening, clear anodized finish	2 Sswk	7	2.286	Opng.	495	87.50		582.50	710
0040 Bronze finish		7	2.286		520	87.50		607.50	735
0060 Black finish		7	2.286		575	87.50		662.50	795
0220 Bronze finish		7	2.286		625	87.50		712.50	855
0240 Black finish		7	2.286		700	87.50		787.50	935
0500 6' x 7' opening, clear finish		6	2.667		815	102		917	1,100
0520 Bronze finish		6	2.667		890	102		992	1,175
0540 Black finish		6	2.667		970	102		1,072	1,275
1000 With 3' high transom above, 3' x 7' opening, clear finish		5.50	2.909		490	112		602	755
1050 Bronze finish		5.50	2.909		510	112		622	775
1100 Black finish		5.50	2.909		535	112		647	800
1501 With 3' high transoms, 6' x 10' opening, clear finish		5.50	2.909		595	112		707	870
1550 Bronze finish		5.50	2.909		615	112		727	890
1600 Black finish		5.50	2.909		675	112		787	960

08 43 13.20 Storefront Systems

08 43 13.20 Storefront Systems	Crew	Daily Output	Labor-Hours	Unit	Material	2014 Bare Costs Labor	Equipment	Total	Total Incl O&P
0010 **STOREFRONT SYSTEMS**, aluminum frame clear 3/8" plate glass									
0020 incl. 3' x 7' door with hardware (400 sq. ft. max. wall)									
0500 Wall height to 12' high, commercial grade	2 Glaz	150	.107	S.F.	21	3.71		24.71	29
0600 Institutional grade		130	.123		26	4.28		30.28	35.50
0700 Monumental grade		115	.139		39	4.84		43.84	51
1000 6' x 7' door with hardware, commercial grade		135	.119		21	4.12		25.12	30
1100 Institutional grade		115	.139		29	4.84		33.84	40
1200 Monumental grade		100	.160		53	5.55		58.55	68
1500 For bronze anodized finish, add					15%				
1600 For black anodized finish, add					36%				
1700 For stainless steel framing, add to monumental					78%				

08 43 29 – Sliding Storefronts

08 43 29.10 Sliding Panels

08 43 29.10 Sliding Panels	Crew	Daily Output	Labor-Hours	Unit	Material	2014 Bare Costs Labor	Equipment	Total	Total Incl O&P
0010 **SLIDING PANELS**									
0020 Mall fronts, aluminum & glass, 15' x 9' high	2 Glaz	1.30	12.308	Opng.	3,375	430		3,805	4,400
0100 24' x 9' high		.70	22.857		4,800	795		5,595	6,600
0200 48' x 9' high, with fixed panels		.90	17.778		8,950	620		9,570	10,900
0500 For bronze finish, add					17%				

08 44 Curtain Wall and Glazed Assemblies

08 44 13 – Glazed Aluminum Curtain Walls

08 44 13.10 Glazed Curtain Walls

08 44 13.10 Glazed Curtain Walls	Crew	Daily Output	Labor-Hours	Unit	Material	2014 Bare Costs Labor	Equipment	Total	Total Incl O&P
0010 **GLAZED CURTAIN WALLS**, aluminum, stock, including glazing									
0020 Minimum	H-1	205	.156	S.F.	35	5.70		40.70	48.50
0050 Average, single glazed		195	.164		51	6		57	67
0150 Average, double glazed		180	.178		65.50	6.50		72	84
0200 Maximum		160	.200		176	7.30		183.30	206

08 45 Translucent Wall and Roof Assemblies

08 45 10 – Translucent Roof Assemblies

08 45 10.10 Skyroofs

		Crew	Daily Output	Labor-Hours	Unit	Material	2014 Bare Costs Labor	2014 Bare Costs Equipment	Total	Total Incl O&P
0010	**SKYROOFS**, Translucent panels, 2-3/4" thick									
0020	Under 5000 S.F.	G-3	395	.081	SF Hor.	35	2.78		37.78	43
0100	Over 5000 S.F.		465	.069		32.50	2.36		34.86	40
0300	Continuous vaulted, semi-circular, to 8' wide, double glazed [G]		145	.221		54	7.60		61.60	72
0400	Single glazed		160	.200		37	6.85		43.85	52
0600	To 20' wide, single glazed		175	.183		48	6.30		54.30	63
0700	Over 20' wide, single glazed		200	.160		47	5.50		52.50	60.50
0900	Motorized opening type, single glazed, 1/3 opening		145	.221		46.50	7.60		54.10	64
1000	Full opening	↓	130	.246	↓	53	8.45		61.45	72.50
1200	Pyramid type units, self-supporting, to 30' clear opening,									
1300	square or circular, single glazed, minimum	G-3	200	.160	SF Hor.	28.50	5.50		34	40.50
1310	Average		165	.194		38.50	6.65		45.15	53.50
1400	Maximum		130	.246		56	8.45		64.45	76
1500	Grid type, 4' to 10' modules, single glass glazed, minimum		200	.160		37.50	5.50		43	50.50
1550	Maximum		128	.250		58	8.60		66.60	78
1600	Preformed acrylic, minimum		300	.107		49.50	3.66		53.16	60
1650	Maximum	↓	175	.183	↓	62	6.30		68.30	79
1800	Skyroofs, dome type, self-supporting, to 100' clear opening, circular									
1900	Rise to span ratio = 0.20									
1920	Minimum	G-3	197	.162	SF Hor.	16.10	5.60		21.70	27
1950	Maximum		113	.283		53.50	9.70		63.20	75.50
2100	Rise to span ratio = 0.33, minimum		169	.189		32	6.50		38.50	46.50
2150	Maximum		101	.317		63	10.90		73.90	87.50
2200	Rise to span ratio = 0.50, minimum		148	.216		48	7.40		55.40	65.50
2250	Maximum		87	.368		70	12.65		82.65	98
2400	Ridge units, continuous, to 8' wide, double [G]		130	.246		122	8.45		130.45	148
2500	Single [G]		200	.160		84.50	5.50		90	102
2700	Ridge and furrow units, over 4' O.C., double, minimum [G]		200	.160		26.50	5.50		32	38
2750	Maximum [G]		120	.267		52	9.15		61.15	72.50
2800	Single, minimum		214	.150		22.50	5.15		27.65	33.50
2850	Maximum		153	.209	↓	47.50	7.20		54.70	64.50
3000	Rolling roof, translucent panels, flat roof, minimum		253	.126	S.F.	20.50	4.34		24.84	30
3030	Maximum [G]		160	.200		40.50	6.85		47.35	56.50
3100	Lean-to skyroof, long span, double, minimum [G]		197	.162		27	5.60		32.60	39.50
3150	Maximum [G]		101	.317		54.50	10.90		65.40	78
3300	Single, minimum		321	.100		21	3.42		24.42	29
3350	Maximum	↓	160	.200	↓	34	6.85		40.85	49

08 51 Metal Windows

08 51 13 – Aluminum Windows

08 51 13.10 Aluminum Sash

		Crew	Daily Output	Labor-Hours	Unit	Material	2014 Bare Costs Labor	2014 Bare Costs Equipment	Total	Total Incl O&P
0010	**ALUMINUM SASH**									
0021	Stock, grade C, glaze & trim not incl., casement	L-4	200	.080	S.F.	38.50	2.53		41.03	47
0051	Double hung		200	.080		39	2.53		41.53	47.50
0101	Fixed casement		200	.080		17.25	2.53		19.78	23.50
0151	Picture window		200	.080		18.30	2.53		20.83	24.50
0201	Projected window		200	.080		35	2.53		37.53	43
0251	Single hung		200	.080		16.30	2.53		18.83	22
0301	Sliding		200	.080	↓	21	2.53		23.53	28
1001	Mullions for above, tubular	↓	240	.067	L.F.	6.10	2.11		8.21	10.25
2000	Custom aluminum sash, grade HC, glazing not included	2 Sswk	140	.114	S.F.	39.50	4.38		43.88	51.50

285

08 51 Metal Windows

08 51 13 – Aluminum Windows

08 51 13.20 Aluminum Windows

	08 51 13.20 Aluminum Windows	Crew	Daily Output	Labor-Hours	Unit	Material	2014 Bare Costs Labor	Equipment	Total	Total Incl O&P
0010	**ALUMINUM WINDOWS**, incl. frame and glazing, commercial grade									
1001	Stock units, casement, 3'-1" x 3'-2" opening	L-4	10	1.600	Ea.	370	50.50		420.50	490
1050	Add for storms					119			119	131
1601	Projected, with screen, 3'-1" x 3'-2" opening	L-4	10	1.600		350	50.50		400.50	470
1700	Add for storms					116			116	128
2001	4'-5" x 5'-3" opening	L-4	8	2		395	63		458	540
2100	Add for storms					124			124	136
2501	Enamel finish windows, 3'-1" x 3'-2"	L-4	10	1.600		355	50.50		405.50	475
2601	4'-5" x 5'-3"		8	2		400	63		463	545
3001	Single hung, 2' x 3' opening, enameled, standard glazed		10	1.600		205	50.50		255.50	310
3101	Insulating glass		10	1.600		249	50.50		299.50	360
3301	2'-8" x 6'-8" opening, standard glazed		8	2		360	63		423	505
3401	Insulating glass		8	2		465	63		528	620
3701	3'-4" x 5'-0" opening, standard glazed		9	1.778		296	56		352	420
3801	Insulating glass		9	1.778		330	56		386	455
3891	Awning type, 3' x 3' opening standard glass		14	1.143		420	36		456	520
3901	Insulating glass		14	1.143		445	36		481	550
3911	3' x 4' opening, standard glass		10	1.600		490	50.50		540.50	625
3921	Insulating glass		10	1.600		565	50.50		615.50	705
3931	3' x 5'-4" opening, standard glass		10	1.600		590	50.50		640.50	735
3941	Insulating glass		10	1.600		695	50.50		745.50	850
3951	4' x 5'-4" opening, standard glass		9	1.778		650	56		706	810
3961	Insulating glass		9	1.778		775	56		831	950
4001	Sliding aluminum, 3' x 2' opening, standard glazed		10	1.600		217	50.50		267.50	325
4101	Insulating glass		10	1.600		232	50.50		282.50	340
4301	5' x 3' opening, standard glazed		9	1.778		330	56		386	460
4401	Insulating glass		9	1.778		385	56		441	520
4601	8' x 4' opening, standard glazed		6	2.667		350	84.50		434.50	525
4701	Insulating glass		6	2.667		565	84.50		649.50	760
5001	9' x 5' opening, standard glazed		4	4		530	126		656	800
5101	Insulating glass		4	4		850	126		976	1,150
5501	Sliding, with thermal barrier and screen, 6' x 4', 2 track		8	2		725	63		788	900
5701	4 track	▼	8	2		910	63		973	1,100
6000	For above units with bronze finish, add					15%				
6200	For installation in concrete openings, add				▼	8%				

08 51 23 – Steel Windows

08 51 23.10 Steel Sash

	08 51 23.10 Steel Sash	Crew	Daily Output	Labor-Hours	Unit	Material	2014 Bare Costs Labor	Equipment	Total	Total Incl O&P
0010	**STEEL SASH** Custom units, glazing and trim not included R085123-10									
0103	Casement, 100% vented	L-4	200	.080	S.F.	65	2.53		67.53	76
0201	50% vented		200	.080		53.50	2.53		56.03	63
0301	Fixed		200	.080		28.50	2.53		31.03	36
1001	Projected, commercial, 40% vented		200	.080		51	2.53		53.53	60.50
1101	Intermediate, 50% vented		200	.080		58	2.53		60.53	68.50
1501	Industrial, horizontally pivoted		200	.080		53	2.53		55.53	62.50
1601	Fixed		200	.080		31	2.53		33.53	38.50
2001	Industrial security sash, 50% vented		200	.080		57	2.53		59.53	67.50
2101	Fixed		200	.080		46.50	2.53		49.03	56
2501	Picture window		200	.080		30	2.53		32.53	37.50
3001	Double hung		200	.080	▼	58.50	2.53		61.03	68.50
5001	Mullions for above, open interior face		240	.067	L.F.	10.25	2.11		12.36	14.85
5101	With interior cover	▼	240	.067	"	17.05	2.11		19.16	22.50

08 51 Metal Windows

08 51 23 – Steel Windows

08 51 23.20 Steel Windows		Crew	Daily Output	Labor-Hours	Unit	Material	2014 Bare Costs Labor	Equipment	Total	Total Incl O&P
0010	**STEEL WINDOWS** Stock, including frame, trim and insul. glass R085123-10									
0020	See Section 13 34 19.50									
1001	Custom units, double hung, 2'-8" x 4'-6" opening	L-4	12	1.333	Ea.	705	42		747	850
1101	2'-4" x 3'-9" opening		12	1.333		585	42		627	710
1501	Commercial projected, 3'-9" x 5'-5" opening		10	1.600		1,225	50.50		1,275.50	1,425
1601	6'-9" x 4'-1" opening		7	2.286		1,625	72		1,697	1,900
2001	Intermediate projected, 2'-9" 4'-1" opening		12	1.333		685	42		727	825
2101	4'-1" x 5'-5" opening		10	1.600		1,400	50.50		1,450.50	1,625

08 51 66 – Metal Window Screens

08 51 66.10 Screens		Crew	Daily Output	Labor-Hours	Unit	Material	2014 Bare Costs Labor	Equipment	Total	Total Incl O&P
0010	**SCREENS**									
0021	For metal sash, aluminum or bronze mesh, flat screen	L-4	1200	.013	S.F.	4.24	.42		4.66	5.35
0500	Wicket screen, inside window	2 Sswk	1000	.016		6.55	.61		7.16	8.35
0800	Security screen, aluminum frame with stainless steel cloth	"	1200	.013		23.50	.51		24.01	27
0901	Steel grate, painted, on steel frame	L-4	1600	.010		15	.32		15.32	17.05
1001	Screens for solar louvers	"	160	.100		27	3.16		30.16	35
4000	See Section 05 58 23.90									

08 52 Wood Windows

08 52 10 – Plain Wood Windows

08 52 10.20 Awning Window

08 52 10.20 Awning Window		Crew	Daily Output	Labor-Hours	Unit	Material	2014 Bare Costs Labor	Equipment	Total	Total Incl O&P
0010	**AWNING WINDOW**, Including frame, screens and grilles									
0100	34" x 22", insulated glass	1 Carp	10	.800	Ea.	270	28.50		298.50	345
0200	Low E glass		10	.800		271	28.50		299.50	345
0300	40" x 28", insulated glass		9	.889		315	32		347	400
0400	Low E Glass		9	.889		340	32		372	430
0500	48" x 36", insulated glass		8	1		465	36		501	575
0600	Low E glass		8	1		490	36		526	600
4000	Impact windows, minimum, add					60%				
4010	Impact windows, maximum, add					160%				

08 52 10.40 Casement Window

08 52 10.40 Casement Window			Crew	Daily Output	Labor-Hours	Unit	Material	2014 Bare Costs Labor	Equipment	Total	Total Incl O&P
0010	**CASEMENT WINDOW**, including frame, screen and grilles										
0100	2'-0" x 3'-0" H, dbl. insulated glass	G	1 Carp	10	.800	Ea.	268	28.50		296.50	345
0150	Low E glass	G		10	.800		259	28.50		287.50	335
0200	2'-0" x 4'-6" high, double insulated glass	G		9	.889		360	32		392	450
0250	Low E glass	G		9	.889		370	32		402	460
0260	Casement 4'-2" x 4'-2" double insulated glass	G		11	.727		875	26		901	1,000
0270	4'-0" x 4'-0" Low E glass	G		11	.727		535	26		561	635
0290	6'-4" x 5'-7" Low E glass	G		9	.889		1,125	32		1,157	1,275
0300	2'-4" x 6'-0" high, double insulated glass	G		8	1		430	36		466	535
0350	Low E glass	G		8	1		475	36		511	585
0522	Vinyl clad, premium, double insulated glass, 2'-0" x 3'-0"	G		10	.800		271	28.50		299.50	345
0524	2'-0" x 4'-0"	G		9	.889		315	32		347	405
0525	2'-0" x 5'-0"	G		8	1		360	36		396	460
0528	2'-0" x 6'-0"	G		8	1		380	36		416	480
0600	3'-0" x 5'-0"	G		8	1		665	36		701	790
0700	4'-0" x 3'-0"	G		8	1		730	36		766	865
0710	4'-0" x 4'-0"	G		8	1		625	36		661	745
0720	4'-8" x 4'-0"	G		8	1		690	36		726	820
0730	4'-8" x 5'-0"	G		6	1.333		790	47.50		837.50	945

08 52 10.40 Casement Window

			Crew	Daily Output	Labor-Hours	Unit	Material	2014 Bare Costs Labor	Equipment	Total	Total Incl O&P
0740	4'-8" x 6'-0"	G	1 Carp	6	1.333	Ea.	880	47.50		927.50	1,050
0750	6'-0" x 4'-0"	G		6	1.333		805	47.50		852.50	965
0800	6'-0" x 5'-0"	G		6	1.333		895	47.50		942.50	1,075
0900	5'-6" x 5'-6"	G	2 Carp	15	1.067		1,425	38		1,463	1,650
2000	Bay, casement units, 8' x 5', w/screens, dbl. insul. glass			2.50	6.400	Opng.	1,600	229		1,829	2,125
2100	Low E glass			2.50	6.400	"	1,675	229		1,904	2,225
8190	For installation, add per leaf					Ea.		15%			
8200	For multiple leaf units, deduct for stationary sash										
8220	2' high					Ea.	23			23	25.50
8240	4'-6" high						26			26	28.50
8260	6' high						34.50			34.50	38
8300	Impact windows, minimum, add						60%				
8310	Impact windows, maximum, add						160%				

08 52 10.50 Double Hung

			Crew	Daily Output	Labor-Hours	Unit	Material	2014 Bare Costs Labor	Equipment	Total	Total Incl O&P
0010	**DOUBLE HUNG**, Including frame, screens and grilles	R085216-10									
0100	2'-0" x 3'-0" high, low E insul. glass	G	1 Carp	10	.800	Ea.	210	28.50		238.50	279
0200	3'-0" x 4'-0" high, double insulated glass	G		9	.889		279	32		311	360
0300	4'-0" x 4'-6" high, low E insulated glass	G		8	1		320	36		356	415
8000	Impact windows, minimum, add						60%				
8010	Impact windows, maximum, add						160%				

08 52 10.55 Picture Window

			Crew	Daily Output	Labor-Hours	Unit	Material	2014 Bare Costs Labor	Equipment	Total	Total Incl O&P
0010	**PICTURE WINDOW**, Including frame and grilles										
0100	3'-6" x 4'-0" high, dbl. insulated glass		2 Carp	12	1.333	Ea.	420	47.50		467.50	545
0150	Low E glass			12	1.333		435	47.50		482.50	555
0200	4'-0" x 4'-6" high, double insulated glass			11	1.455		550	52		602	695
0250	Low E glass			11	1.455		530	52		582	675
0300	5'-0" x 4'-0" high, double insulated glass			11	1.455		580	52		632	730
0350	Low E glass			11	1.455		605	52		657	755
0400	6'-0" x 4'-6" high, double insulated glass			10	1.600		625	57		682	785
0450	Low E glass			10	1.600		635	57		692	795

08 52 10.65 Wood Sash

			Crew	Daily Output	Labor-Hours	Unit	Material	2014 Bare Costs Labor	Equipment	Total	Total Incl O&P
0010	**WOOD SASH**, Including glazing but not trim										
0050	Custom, 5'-0" x 4'-0", 1" dbl. glazed, 3/16" thick lites		2 Carp	3.20	5	Ea.	230	179		409	555
0100	1/4" thick lites			5	3.200		245	114		359	460
0200	1" thick, triple glazed			5	3.200		415	114		529	645
0300	7'-0" x 4'-6" high, 1" double glazed, 3/16" thick lites			4.30	3.721		420	133		553	685
0400	1/4" thick lites			4.30	3.721		475	133		608	745
0500	1" thick, triple glazed			4.30	3.721		540	133		673	820
0600	8'-6" x 5'-0" high, 1" double glazed, 3/16" thick lites			3.50	4.571		565	163		728	900
0700	1/4" thick lites			3.50	4.571		620	163		783	955
0800	1" thick, triple glazed			3.50	4.571		625	163		788	960
0900	Window frames only, based on perimeter length					L.F.	4.02			4.02	4.42
1200	Window sill, stock, per lineal foot						8.50			8.50	9.35
1250	Casing, stock						3.30			3.30	3.63

08 52 10.70 Sliding Windows

			Crew	Daily Output	Labor-Hours	Unit	Material	2014 Bare Costs Labor	Equipment	Total	Total Incl O&P
0010	**SLIDING WINDOWS**										
0100	3'-0" x 3'-0" high, double insulated	G	1 Carp	10	.800	Ea.	284	28.50		312.50	360
0120	Low E glass	G		10	.800		310	28.50		338.50	390
0200	4'-0" x 3'-6" high, double insulated	G		9	.889		355	32		387	445
0220	Low E glass	G		9	.889		360	32		392	455
0300	6'-0" x 5'-0" high, double insulated	G		8	1		490	36		526	595
0320	Low E glass	G		8	1		530	36		566	640

08 52 Wood Windows

08 52 13 – Metal-Clad Wood Windows

08 52 13.10 Awning Windows, Metal-Clad		Crew	Daily Output	Labor-Hours	Unit	Material	2014 Bare Costs Labor	Equipment	Total	Total Incl O&P
0010	**AWNING WINDOWS, METAL-CLAD**									
2000	Metal clad, awning deluxe, double insulated glass, 34" x 22"	1 Carp	9	.889	Ea.	247	32		279	325
2050	36" x 25"		9	.889		272	32		304	355
2100	40" x 22"		9	.889		291	32		323	375
2150	40" x 30"		9	.889		340	32		372	430
2200	48" x 28"		8	1		345	36		381	440
2250	60" x 36"		8	1		370	36		406	470

08 52 13.20 Casement Windows, Metal-Clad			Crew	Daily Output	Labor-Hours	Unit	Material	2014 Bare Costs Labor	Equipment	Total	Total Incl O&P
0010	**CASEMENT WINDOWS, METAL-CLAD**										
0100	Metal clad, deluxe, dbl. insul. glass, 2'-0" x 3'-0" high	G	1 Carp	10	.800	Ea.	279	28.50		307.50	355
0120	2'-0" x 4'-0" high	G		9	.889		315	32		347	400
0130	2'-0" x 5'-0" high	G		8	1		325	36		361	420
0140	2'-0" x 6'-0" high	G		8	1		365	36		401	460
0310	9'-0" x 4'-0", 4 panels		2 Carp	8	2		1,550	71.50		1,621.50	1,825
0320	10'-0" x 5'-0", 5 panels			7	2.286		2,100	81.50		2,181.50	2,450
0330	12'-0" x 6'-0", 6 panels			6	2.667		2,700	95.50		2,795.50	3,100

08 52 13.30 Double-Hung Windows, Metal-clad			Crew	Daily Output	Labor-Hours	Unit	Material	2014 Bare Costs Labor	Equipment	Total	Total Incl O&P
0010	**DOUBLE-HUNG WINDOWS, METAL-CLAD**										
0100	Metal clad, deluxe, dbl. insul. glass, 2'-6" x 3'-0" high	G	1 Carp	10	.800	Ea.	272	28.50		300.50	345
0120	3'-0" x 3'-6" high	G		10	.800		315	28.50		343.50	395
0140	3'-0" x 4'-0" high	G		9	.889		325	32		357	415
0160	3'-0" x 4'-6" high	G		9	.889		345	32		377	435
0180	3'-0" x 5'-0" high	G		8	1		370	36		406	470
0200	3'-6" x 6'-0" high	G		8	1		450	36		486	555

08 52 13.35 Picture and Sliding Windows Metal-Clad			Crew	Daily Output	Labor-Hours	Unit	Material	2014 Bare Costs Labor	Equipment	Total	Total Incl O&P
0010	**PICTURE AND SLIDING WINDOWS METAL-CLAD**										
2000	Metal clad, dlx picture, dbl. insul. glass, 4'-0" x 4'-0" high		2 Carp	12	1.333	Ea.	375	47.50		422.50	490
2100	4'-0" x 6'-0" high			11	1.455		545	52		597	690
2200	5'-0" x 6'-0" high			10	1.600		610	57		667	765
2300	6'-0" x 6'-0" high			10	1.600		695	57		752	860
2400	Metal clad, dlx sliding, double insulated glass, 3'-0" x 3'-0" high	G	1 Carp	10	.800		330	28.50		358.50	410
2420	4'-0" x 3'-6" high	G		9	.889		400	32		432	495
2440	5'-0" x 4'-0" high	G		9	.889		480	32		512	580
2460	6'-0" x 5'-0" high	G		8	1		725	36		761	855

08 52 13.40 Bow and Bay Windows, Metal-Clad		Crew	Daily Output	Labor-Hours	Unit	Material	2014 Bare Costs Labor	Equipment	Total	Total Incl O&P
0010	**BOW AND BAY WINDOWS, METAL-CLAD**									
0100	Metal clad, deluxe, dbl. insul. glass, 8'-0" x 5'-0" high, 4 panels	2 Carp	10	1.600	Ea.	1,675	57		1,732	1,925
0120	10'-0" x 5'-0" high, 5 panels		8	2		1,800	71.50		1,871.50	2,100
0140	10'-0" x 6'-0" high, 5 panels		7	2.286		2,100	81.50		2,181.50	2,450
0160	12'-0" x 6'-0" high, 6 panels		6	2.667		2,925	95.50		3,020.50	3,375
0400	Double hung, bldrs. model, bay, 8' x 4' high, dbl. insulated glass		10	1.600		1,325	57		1,382	1,550
0440	Low E glass		10	1.600		1,425	57		1,482	1,675
0480	Low E glass		6	2.667		1,500	95.50		1,595.50	1,800
0500	Metal clad, deluxe, dbl. insul. glass, 7'-0" x 4'-0" high		10	1.600		1,275	57		1,332	1,500
0520	8'-0" x 4'-0" high		8	2		1,300	71.50		1,371.50	1,575
0540	8'-0" x 5'-0" high		7	2.286		1,350	81.50		1,431.50	1,625
0560	9'-0" x 5'-0" high		6	2.667		1,450	95.50		1,545.50	1,725

08 52 16 – Plastic-Clad Wood Windows

08 52 16.10 Bow Window

08 52 16.10 Bow Window	Crew	Daily Output	Labor-Hours	Unit	Material	2014 Bare Costs Labor	Equipment	Total	Total Incl O&P
0010	**BOW WINDOW** Including frames, screens, and grilles									
0020	End panels operable									
1001	Bow type, casement, wood, bldrs mdl., 8' x 5' dbl. insltd glass, 4 panel	2 Carp	10	1.600	Ea.	1,500	57		1,557	1,750
1050	Low E glass		10	1.600		1,325	57		1,382	1,550
1100	10'-0" x 5'-0", double insulated glass, 6 panels		6	2.667		1,350	95.50		1,445.50	1,650
1200	Low E glass, 6 panels		6	2.667		1,450	95.50		1,545.50	1,750
1300	Vinyl clad, bldrs. model, double insulated glass, 6'-0" x 4'-0", 3 panel		10	1.600		1,025	57		1,082	1,225
1340	9'-0" x 4'-0", 4 panel		8	2		1,350	71.50		1,421.50	1,625
1380	10'-0" x 6'-0", 5 panels		7	2.286		2,250	81.50		2,331.50	2,600
1420	12'-0" x 6'-0", 6 panels		6	2.667		2,925	95.50		3,020.50	3,375
1601	Metal clad, bldrs model, 6'-0" x 4'-0" dbl. insltd glass, 3 panels		10	1.600		1,200	57		1,257	1,425
2000	Bay window, 8' x 5', dbl. insul glass		10	1.600		1,875	57		1,932	2,175
2050	Low E glass		10	1.600		2,275	57		2,332	2,600
2100	12'-0" x 6'-0", double insulated glass, 6 panels		6	2.667		2,350	95.50		2,445.50	2,725
2200	Low E glass		6	2.667		2,375	95.50		2,470.50	2,775
2280	6'-0" x 4'-0"		11	1.455		1,250	52		1,302	1,475
2300	Vinyl clad, premium, double insulated glass, 8'-0" x 5'-0"		10	1.600		1,750	57		1,807	2,025
2340	10'-0" x 5'-0"		8	2		2,300	71.50		2,371.50	2,650
2380	10'-0" x 6'-0"		7	2.286		2,625	81.50		2,706.50	3,000
2420	12'-0" x 6'-0"		6	2.667		3,200	95.50		3,295.50	3,675
3101	9'-0" x 5'-0" high, 4 panels, double insulated glass		6	2.667		1,425	95.50		1,520.50	1,725
3300	Vinyl clad, premium, double insulated glass, 7'-0" x 4'-6"		10	1.600		1,375	57		1,432	1,600
3340	8'-0" x 4'-6"		8	2		1,400	71.50		1,471.50	1,650
3380	8'-0" x 5'-0"		7	2.286		1,450	81.50		1,531.50	1,725
3420	9'-0" x 5'-0"		6	2.667		1,500	95.50		1,595.50	1,800

08 52 16.15 Awning Window Vinyl-Clad

08 52 16.15 Awning Window Vinyl-Clad	Crew	Daily Output	Labor-Hours	Unit	Material	Labor	Equipment	Total	Total Incl O&P
0010	**AWNING WINDOW VINYL-CLAD** Including frames, screens, and grilles									
0240	Vinyl clad, 34" x 22"	1 Carp	10	.800	Ea.	264	28.50		292.50	340
0280	36" x 28"		9	.889		305	32		337	390
0300	36" x 36"		9	.889		340	32		372	430
0340	40" x 22"		10	.800		288	28.50		316.50	365
0360	48" x 28"		8	1		370	36		406	465
0380	60" x 36"		8	1		500	36		536	610

08 52 16.30 Palladian Windows

08 52 16.30 Palladian Windows	Crew	Daily Output	Labor-Hours	Unit	Material	Labor	Equipment	Total	Total Incl O&P
0010	**PALLADIAN WINDOWS**									
0020	Vinyl clad, double insulated glass, including frame and grilles									
0040	3'-2" x 2'-6" high	2 Carp	11	1.455	Ea.	1,250	52		1,302	1,475
0060	3'-2" x 4'-10"		11	1.455		1,750	52		1,802	2,000
0080	3'-2" x 6'-4"		10	1.600		1,700	57		1,757	1,975
0100	4'-0" x 4'-0"		10	1.600		1,525	57		1,582	1,775
0120	4'-0" x 5'-4"	3 Carp	10	2.400		1,875	86		1,961	2,200
0140	4'-0" x 6'-0"		9	2.667		1,950	95.50		2,045.50	2,300
0160	4'-0" x 7'-4"		9	2.667		2,125	95.50		2,220.50	2,475
0180	5'-5" x 4'-10"		9	2.667		2,275	95.50		2,370.50	2,650
0200	5'-5" x 6'-10"		9	2.667		2,575	95.50		2,670.50	3,000
0220	5'-5" x 7'-9"		9	2.667		2,800	95.50		2,895.50	3,225
0240	6'-0" x 7'-11"		8	3		3,475	107		3,582	4,000
0260	8'-0" x 6'-0"		8	3		3,075	107		3,182	3,550

08 52 Wood Windows

08 52 16 – Plastic-Clad Wood Windows

08 52 16.35 Double-Hung Window

		Crew	Daily Output	Labor-Hours	Unit	Material	2014 Bare Costs Labor	2014 Bare Costs Equipment	Total	Total Incl O&P
0010	**DOUBLE-HUNG WINDOW** Including frames, screens, and grilles									
0300	Vinyl clad, premium, double insulated glass, 2'-6" x 3'-0"	G 1 Carp	10	.800	Ea.	310	28.50		338.50	390
0305	2'-6" x 4'-0"	G	10	.800		360	28.50		388.50	445
0400	3'-0" x 3'-6"	G	10	.800		335	28.50		363.50	420
0500	3'-0" x 4'-0"	G	9	.889		395	32		427	490
0600	3'-0" x 4'-6"	G	9	.889		410	32		442	505
0700	3'-0" x 5'-0"	G	8	1		445	36		481	545
0790	3'-4" x 5'-0"	G	8	1		455	36		491	560
0800	3'-6" x 6'-0"	G	8	1		490	36		526	600
0820	4'-0" x 5'-0"	G	7	1.143		560	41		601	685
0830	4'-0" x 6'-0"	G	7	1.143		700	41		741	835

08 52 16.40 Transom Windows

		Crew	Daily Output	Labor-Hours	Unit	Material	2014 Bare Costs Labor	2014 Bare Costs Equipment	Total	Total Incl O&P
0010	**TRANSOM WINDOWS**									
1000	Vinyl clad, premium, dbl. insul. glass, 4'-0" x 4'-0"	2 Carp	12	1.333	Ea.	495	47.50		542.50	625
1100	4'-0" x 6'-0"		11	1.455		935	52		987	1,125
1200	5'-0" x 6'-0"		10	1.600		1,050	57		1,107	1,250
1300	6'-0" x 6'-0"		10	1.600		1,050	57		1,107	1,250

08 52 16.70 Vinyl Clad, Premium, Dbl. Insulated Glass

		Crew	Daily Output	Labor-Hours	Unit	Material	2014 Bare Costs Labor	2014 Bare Costs Equipment	Total	Total Incl O&P
0010	**VINYL CLAD, PREMIUM, DBL. INSULATED GLASS**									
1000	Sliding, 3'-0" x 3'-0"	G 1 Carp	10	.800	Ea.	605	28.50		633.50	715
1050	4'-0" x 3'-6"	G	9	.889		685	32		717	810
1100	5'-0" x 4'-0"	G	9	.889		900	32		932	1,050
1150	6'-0" x 5'-0"	G	8	1		1,125	36		1,161	1,300

08 52 50 – Window Accessories

08 52 50.10 Window Grille or Muntin

		Crew	Daily Output	Labor-Hours	Unit	Material	2014 Bare Costs Labor	2014 Bare Costs Equipment	Total	Total Incl O&P
0010	**WINDOW GRILLE OR MUNTIN**, snap in type									
0020	Standard pattern interior grilles									
2000	Wood, awning window, glass size 28" x 16" high	1 Carp	30	.267	Ea.	28	9.55		37.55	47
2060	44" x 24" high		32	.250		40	8.95		48.95	59
2100	Casement, glass size, 20" x 36" high		30	.267		32	9.55		41.55	51
2180	20" x 56" high		32	.250		43	8.95		51.95	62.50
2200	Double hung, glass size, 16" x 24" high		24	.333	Set	51	11.90		62.90	76.50
2280	32" x 32" high		34	.235	"	131	8.40		139.40	158
2500	Picture, glass size, 48" x 48" high		30	.267	Ea.	120	9.55		129.55	148
2580	60" x 68" high		28	.286	"	183	10.20		193.20	219
2600	Sliding, glass size, 14" x 36" high		24	.333	Set	35.50	11.90		47.40	59
2680	36" x 36" high		22	.364	"	43.50	13		56.50	69.50

08 52 66 – Wood Window Screens

08 52 66.10 Wood Screens

		Crew	Daily Output	Labor-Hours	Unit	Material	2014 Bare Costs Labor	2014 Bare Costs Equipment	Total	Total Incl O&P
0010	**WOOD SCREENS**									
0021	Over 3 S.F., 3/4" frames	2 Carp	375	.043	S.F.	4.89	1.53		6.42	7.95
0101	1-1/8" frames	"	375	.043	"	8.15	1.53		9.68	11.55

08 52 69 – Wood Storm Windows

08 52 69.10 Storm Windows

		Crew	Daily Output	Labor-Hours	Unit	Material	2014 Bare Costs Labor	2014 Bare Costs Equipment	Total	Total Incl O&P
0010	**STORM WINDOWS**, aluminum residential									
0300	Basement, mill finish, incl. fiberglass screen									
0320	1'-10" x 1'-0" high	G 2 Carp	30	.533	Ea.	35	19.05		54.05	70.50
0340	2'-9" x 1'-6" high	G "	30	.533	"	38	19.05		57.05	74
1600	Double-hung, combination, storm & screen									
2000	Clear anodic coating, 2'-0" x 3'-5" high	G 2 Carp	30	.533	Ea.	86	19.05		105.05	127

08 52 Wood Windows

08 52 69 – Wood Storm Windows

08 52 69.10 Storm Windows		Crew	Daily Output	Labor-Hours	Unit	Material	2014 Bare Costs Labor	Equipment	Total	Total Incl O&P
2020	2'-6" x 5'-0" high	G 2 Carp	28	.571	Ea.	114	20.50		134.50	160
2040	4'-0" x 6'-0" high	G	25	.640		126	23		149	178
2400	White painted, 2'-0" x 3'-5" high	G	30	.533		85	19.05		104.05	126
2420	2'-6" x 5'-0" high	G	28	.571		92	20.50		112.50	136
2440	4'-0" x 6'-0" high	G	25	.640		100	23		123	149
2600	Mill finish, 2'-0" x 3'-5" high	G	30	.533		77	19.05		96.05	117
2620	2'-6" x 5'-0" high	G	28	.571		86	20.50		106.50	129
2640	4'-0" x 6'-8" high	G	25	.640		100	23		123	149

08 53 Plastic Windows

08 53 13 – Vinyl Windows

08 53 13.20 Vinyl Single Hung Windows

		Crew	Daily Output	Labor-Hours	Unit	Material	2014 Bare Costs Labor	Equipment	Total	Total Incl O&P
0010	**VINYL SINGLE HUNG WINDOWS**, insulated glass									
0100	Grids, low E, J fin, ext. jambs, 21" x 53"	G 2 Carp	18	.889	Ea.	198	32		230	272
0110	21" x 57"	G	17	.941		200	33.50		233.50	277
0120	21" x 65"	G	16	1		205	36		241	286
0130	25" x 41"	G	20	.800		190	28.50		218.50	257
0140	25" x 49"	G	18	.889		200	32		232	274
0150	25" x 57"	G	17	.941		205	33.50		238.50	283
0160	25" x 65"	G	16	1		240	36		276	325
0170	29" x 41"	G	18	.889		195	32		227	269
0180	29" x 53"	G	18	.889		205	32		237	280
0190	29" x 57"	G	17	.941		210	33.50		243.50	288
0200	29" x 65"	G	16	1		215	36		251	297
0210	33" x 41"	G	20	.800		200	28.50		228.50	268
0220	33" x 53"	G	18	.889		215	32		247	291
0230	33" x 57"	G	17	.941		215	33.50		248.50	294
0240	33" x 65"	G	16	1		220	36		256	300
0250	37" x 41"	G	20	.800		225	28.50		253.50	296
0260	37" x 53"	G	18	.889		235	32		267	315
0270	37" x 57"	G	17	.941		240	33.50		273.50	320
0280	37" x 65"	G	16	1		256	36		292	340

08 53 13.30 Vinyl Double Hung Windows

		Crew	Daily Output	Labor-Hours	Unit	Material	2014 Bare Costs Labor	Equipment	Total	Total Incl O&P
0010	**VINYL DOUBLE HUNG WINDOWS**, insulated glass									
0100	Grids, low E, J fin, ext. jambs, 21" x 53"	G 2 Carp	18	.889	Ea.	215	32		247	291
0102	21" x 37"	G	18	.889		200	32		232	274
0104	21" x 41"	G	18	.889		205	32		237	280
0106	21" x 49"	G	18	.889		221	32		253	297
0110	21" x 57"	G	17	.941		222	33.50		255.50	300
0120	21" x 65"	G	16	1		230	36		266	315
0128	25" x 37"	G	20	.800		210	28.50		238.50	279
0130	25" x 41"	G	20	.800		215	28.50		243.50	285
0140	25" x 49"	G	18	.889		220	32		252	296
0145	25" x 53"	G	18	.889		225	32		257	300
0150	25" x 57"	G	17	.941		225	33.50		258.50	305
0160	25" x 65"	G	16	1		235	36		271	320
0162	25" x 69"	G	16	1		242	36		278	325
0164	25" x 77"	G	16	1		260	36		296	345
0168	29" x 37"	G	18	.889		215	32		247	291
0170	29" x 41"	G	18	.889		218	32		250	294
0172	29" x 49"	G	18	.889		225	32		257	300

08 53 13 – Vinyl Windows

08 53 13.30 Vinyl Double Hung Windows		Crew	Daily Output	Labor-Hours	Unit	Material	2014 Bare Costs Labor	Equipment	Total	Total Incl O&P
0180	29" x 53"	G	2 Carp	18	.889	Ea.	230	32		262	305
0190	29" x 57"	G		17	.941		232	33.50		265.50	310
0200	29" x 65"	G		16	1		240	36		276	325
0202	29" x 69"	G		16	1		247	36		283	330
0205	29" x 77"	G		16	1		267	36		303	355
0208	33" x 37"	G		20	.800		220	28.50		248.50	290
0210	33" x 41"	G		20	.800		222	28.50		250.50	292
0215	33" x 49"	G		20	.800		230	28.50		258.50	300
0220	33" x 53"	G		18	.889		235	32		267	315
0230	33" x 57"	G		17	.941		238	33.50		271.50	320
0240	33" x 65"	G		16	1		242	36		278	325
0242	33" x 69"	G		16	1		257	36		293	345
0246	33" x 77"	G		16	1		263	36		299	350
0250	37" x 41"	G		20	.800		242	28.50		270.50	315
0255	37" x 49"	G		20	.800		250	28.50		278.50	325
0260	37" x 53"	G		18	.889		257	32		289	335
0270	37" x 57"	G		17	.941		262	33.50		295.50	345
0280	37" x 65"	G		16	1		280	36		316	370
0282	37" x 69"	G		16	1		287	36		323	375
0286	37" x 77"	G		16	1		295	36		331	385
0300	Solid vinyl, average quality, double insulated glass, 2'-0" x 3'-0"	G	1 Carp	10	.800		291	28.50		319.50	370
0310	3'-0" x 4'-0"	G		9	.889		205	32		237	279
0320	4'-0" x 4'-6"	G		8	1		335	36		371	425
0330	Premium, double insulated glass, 2'-6" x 3'-0"	G		10	.800		260	28.50		288.50	335
0340	3'-0" x 3'-6"	G		9	.889		283	32		315	365
0350	3'-0" x 4'-0"	G		9	.889		310	32		342	395
0360	3'-0" x 4'-6"	G		9	.889		320	32		352	405
0370	3'-0" x 5'-0"	G		8	1		340	36		376	430
0380	3'-6" x 6'-0"	G		8	1		360	36		396	460

08 53 13.40 Vinyl Casement Windows		Crew	Daily Output	Labor-Hours	Unit	Material	2014 Bare Costs Labor	Equipment	Total	Total Incl O&P
0010	**VINYL CASEMENT WINDOWS**, insulated glass										
0015	Grids, low E, J fin, extension jambs, screens										
0100	One lite, 21" x 41"	G	2 Carp	20	.800	Ea.	271	28.50		299.50	345
0110	21" x 47"	G		20	.800		294	28.50		322.50	375
0120	21" x 53"	G		20	.800		315	28.50		343.50	400
0128	24" x 35"	G		19	.842		263	30		293	340
0130	24" x 41"	G		19	.842		283	30		313	360
0140	24" x 47"	G		19	.842		305	30		335	385
0150	24" x 53"	G		19	.842		325	30		355	410
0158	28" x 35"	G		19	.842		278	30		308	355
0160	28" x 41"	G		19	.842		298	30		328	380
0170	28" x 47"	G		19	.842		320	30		350	400
0180	28" x 53"	G		19	.842		350	30		380	435
0184	28" x 59"	G		19	.842		350	30		380	435
0188	Two lites, 33" x 35"	G		18	.889		435	32		467	535
0190	33" x 41"	G		18	.889		460	32		492	560
0200	33" x 47"	G		18	.889		495	32		527	600
0210	33" x 53"	G		18	.889		525	32		557	635
0212	33" x 59"	G		18	.889		555	32		587	665
0215	33" x 72"	G		18	.889		570	32		602	685
0220	41" x 41"	G		18	.889		455	32		487	555
0230	41" x 47"	G		18	.889		530	32		562	640

08 53 Plastic Windows

08 53 13 – Vinyl Windows

08 53 13.40 Vinyl Casement Windows

			Crew	Daily Output	Labor-Hours	Unit	Material	2014 Bare Costs Labor	Equipment	Total	Total Incl O&P
0240	41" x 53"	G	2 Carp	17	.941	Ea.	565	33.50		598.50	675
0242	41" x 59"	G		17	.941		590	33.50		623.50	705
0246	41" x 72"	G		17	.941		615	33.50		648.50	735
0250	47" x 41"	G		17	.941		505	33.50		538.50	610
0260	47" x 47"	G		17	.941		535	33.50		568.50	645
0270	47" x 53"	G		17	.941		565	33.50		598.50	675
0272	47" x 59"	G		17	.941		615	33.50		648.50	735
0280	56" x 41"	G		15	1.067		540	38		578	660
0290	56" x 47"	G		15	1.067		565	38		603	685
0300	56" x 53"	G		15	1.067		615	38		653	740
0302	56" x 59"	G		15	1.067		640	38		678	770
0310	56" x 72"	G		15	1.067		690	38		728	825
0340	Solid vinyl, premium, double insulated glass, 2'-0" x 3'-0" high	G	1 Carp	10	.800		263	28.50		291.50	335
0360	2'-0" x 4'-0" high	G		9	.889		293	32		325	375
0380	2'-0" x 5'-0" high	G		8	1		325	36		361	415

08 53 13.50 Vinyl Picture Windows

			Crew	Daily Output	Labor-Hours	Unit	Material	2014 Bare Costs Labor	Equipment	Total	Total Incl O&P
0010	**VINYL PICTURE WINDOWS**, insulated glass										
0100	Grids, low E, J fin, ext. jambs, 33" x 47"		2 Carp	12	1.333	Ea.	250	47.50		297.50	355
0110	35" x 71"			12	1.333		335	47.50		382.50	450
0120	41" x 47"			12	1.333		270	47.50		317.50	375
0130	41" x 71"			12	1.333		350	47.50		397.50	465
0140	47" x 47"			12	1.333		305	47.50		352.50	415
0150	47" x 71"			11	1.455		380	52		432	510
0160	53" x 47"			11	1.455		330	52		382	455
0170	53" x 71"			11	1.455		345	52		397	470
0180	59" x 47"			11	1.455		370	52		422	495
0190	59" x 71"			11	1.455		380	52		432	510
0200	71" x 47"			10	1.600		390	57		447	525
0210	71" x 71"			10	1.600		405	57		462	540

08 54 Composite Windows

08 54 13 – Fiberglass Windows

08 54 13.10 Fiberglass Single Hung Windows

			Crew	Daily Output	Labor-Hours	Unit	Material	2014 Bare Costs Labor	Equipment	Total	Total Incl O&P
0010	**FIBERGLASS SINGLE HUNG WINDOWS**										
0100	Grids, low E, 18" x 24"	G	2 Carp	18	.889	Ea.	335	32		367	425
0110	18" x 40"	G		17	.941		340	33.50		373.50	430
0130	24" x 40"	G		20	.800		360	28.50		388.50	445
0230	36" x 36"	G		17	.941		370	33.50		403.50	460
0250	36" x 48"	G		20	.800		405	28.50		433.50	495
0260	36" x 60"	G		18	.889		445	32		477	545
0280	36" x 72"	G		16	1		470	36		506	575
0290	48" x 40"	G		16	1		470	36		506	575

08 56 Special Function Windows

08 56 46 – Radio-Frequency-Interference Shielding Windows

08 56 46.10 Radio-Frequency-interference Mesh	Crew	Daily Output	Labor-Hours	Unit	Material	2014 Bare Costs Labor	Equipment	Total	Total Incl O&P
0010 **RADIO-FREQUENCY-INTERFERENCE MESH**									
0100　16 mesh copper 0.011" wire				S.F.	4.05			4.05	4.46
0150　22 mesh copper 0.015" wire					5.85			5.85	6.45
0200　100 mesh copper 0.022" wire					7.50			7.50	8.25
0250　100 mesh stainless steel 0.0012" wire					13.20			13.20	14.50

08 56 63 – Detention Windows

08 56 63.13 Visitor Cubicle Windows

	Crew	Daily Output	Labor-Hours	Unit	Material	2014 Bare Costs Labor	Equipment	Total	Total Incl O&P
0010 **VISITOR CUBICLE WINDOWS**									
4000　Visitor cubicle, vision panel, no intercom	E-4	2	16	Ea.	3,200	620	71	3,891	4,775

08 62 Unit Skylights

08 62 13 – Domed Unit Skylights

08 62 13.20 Skylights

		Crew	Daily Output	Labor-Hours	Unit	Material	2014 Bare Costs Labor	Equipment	Total	Total Incl O&P
0010 **SKYLIGHTS**, flush or curb mounted										
2025　22-1/2" x 46-1/2"		1 Carp	8	1	Ea.	395	36		431	495
2050　46-1/2" x 46-1/2"		"	8	1	"	695	36		731	825
2120　Ventilating insulated plexiglass dome with										
2130　　curb mounting, 36" x 36"	G	G-3	12	2.667	Ea.	480	91.50		571.50	685
2150　　52" x 52"	G		12	2.667		660	91.50		751.50	880
2160　　28" x 52"	G		10	3.200		485	110		595	720
2170　　36" x 52"	G		10	3.200		540	110		650	780
2180　For electric opening system, add	G					310			310	340
2300　Insulated safety glass with aluminum frame	G	G-3	160	.200	S.F.	92	6.85		98.85	113

08 71 Door Hardware

08 71 13 – Automatic Door Operators

08 71 13.10 Automatic Openers Commercial

	Crew	Daily Output	Labor-Hours	Unit	Material	2014 Bare Costs Labor	Equipment	Total	Total Incl O&P
0010 **AUTOMATIC OPENERS COMMERCIAL**									
0020　Pneumatic, incl opener, motion sens, control box, tubing, compressor									
0050　　For single swing door, per opening	2 Skwk	.80	20	Ea.	4,550	725		5,275	6,225
0100　　　Pair, per opening		.50	32	Opng.	7,375	1,150		8,525	10,100
1000　　For single sliding door, per opening		.60	26.667		4,975	970		5,945	7,100
1300　　　Bi-parting pair		.50	32		7,475	1,150		8,625	10,200
1420　Electronic door opener incl motion sens, 12 V control box, motor									
1450　　For single swing door, per opening	2 Skwk	.80	20	Opng.	3,550	725		4,275	5,150
1500　　　Pair, per opening		.50	32		6,500	1,150		7,650	9,100
1600　　For single sliding door, per opening		.60	26.667		4,300	970		5,270	6,350
1700　　　Bi-parting pair		.50	32		5,250	1,150		6,400	7,725
1750　Handicap actuator buttons, 2, including 12 V DC wiring, add	1 Carp	1.50	5.333	Pr.	470	191		661	835

08 71 13.20 Automatic Openers Industrial

	Crew	Daily Output	Labor-Hours	Unit	Material	2014 Bare Costs Labor	Equipment	Total	Total Incl O&P
0010 **AUTOMATIC OPENERS INDUSTRIAL**									
0015　Sliding doors up to 6' wide	2 Skwk	.60	26.667	Opng.	5,900	970		6,870	8,125
0200　　To 12' wide	"	.40	40	"	7,075	1,450		8,525	10,200
0400　　Over 12' wide, add per L.F. of excess				L.F.	800			800	880
1000　Swing doors, to 5' wide	2 Skwk	.80	20	Ea.	3,500	725		4,225	5,075
1860　Add for controls, wall pushbutton, 3 button		4	4		240	145		385	510
1870　　Control pull cord		4.30	3.721		195	135		330	445

08 71 Door Hardware

08 71 20 – Hardware

08 71 20.10 Bolts, Flush

		Crew	Daily Output	Labor-Hours	Unit	Material	2014 Bare Costs Labor	Equipment	Total	Total Incl O&P
0010	**BOLTS, FLUSH**									
0020	Standard, concealed	1 Carp	7	1.143	Ea.	23.50	41		64.50	94
0800	Automatic fire exit	"	5	1.600		260	57		317	380
1600	For electric release, add	1 Elec	3	2.667		127	114		241	325
3000	Barrel, brass, 2" long	1 Carp	40	.200		6.80	7.15		13.95	19.55
3020	4" long		40	.200		12.25	7.15		19.40	25.50
3060	6" long		40	.200		25	7.15		32.15	39.50

08 71 20.15 Hardware

		Crew	Daily Output	Labor-Hours	Unit	Material	2014 Bare Costs Labor	Equipment	Total	Total Incl O&P
0010	**HARDWARE**									
0020	Average percentage for hardware, total job cost									
0025	Minimum				Job					2%
0050	Maximum									5%
0500	Total hardware for building, average distribution					85%	15%			
1000	Door hardware, apartment, interior	1 Carp	4	2	Door	450	71.50		521.50	620
1300	Average, door hardware, motel/hotel interior, with access card		4	2		580	71.50		651.50	760
1500	Hospital bedroom, minimum		4	2		620	71.50		691.50	800
2000	Maximum		3	2.667		725	95.50		820.50	955
2100	Pocket door		6	1.333	Ea.	100	47.50		147.50	190
2250	School, single exterior, incl. lever, incl. panic device		3	2.667	Door	1,275	95.50		1,370.50	1,550
2500	Single interior, regular use, lever included		3	2.667		615	95.50		710.50	840
2550	Average, door hdwe., school, classroom, ANSI F84, lever handle		3	2.667		845	95.50		940.50	1,100
2600	Average, door hdwe., school, classroom, ANSI F88, incl. lever		3	2.667		905	95.50		1,000.50	1,150
2850	Stairway, single interior		3	2.667		540	95.50		635.50	755
3100	Double exterior, with panic device		2	4	Pr.	2,375	143		2,518	2,850
6020	Add for fire alarm door holder, electro-magnetic	1 Elec	4	2	Ea.	102	85.50		187.50	252

08 71 20.20 Door Protectors

		Crew	Daily Output	Labor-Hours	Unit	Material	2014 Bare Costs Labor	Equipment	Total	Total Incl O&P
0010	**DOOR PROTECTORS**									
0020	1-3/4" x 3/4" U channel	2 Carp	80	.200	L.F.	37	7.15		44.15	52.50
0021	1-3/4" x 1-1/4" U channel		80	.200	"	39	7.15		46.15	55
1000	Tear drop, spring-stl, 8" high x 19" long		15	1.067	Ea.	98	38		136	172
1010	8" high x 32" long		15	1.067		121	38		159	197
1100	Tear drop, stainless stl., 8" high x 19" long		15	1.067		255	38		293	345
1200	8" high x 32" long		15	1.067		315	38		353	415

08 71 20.30 Door Closers

		Crew	Daily Output	Labor-Hours	Unit	Material	2014 Bare Costs Labor	Equipment	Total	Total Incl O&P
0010	**DOOR CLOSERS** Adjustable backcheck, multiple mounting									
0015	and rack and pinion									
0020	Standard Regular Arm	1 Carp	6	1.333	Ea.	188	47.50		235.50	287
0040	Hold open arm		6	1.333		200	47.50		247.50	300
0100	Fusible link		6.50	1.231		162	44		206	252
0210	Light duty, regular arm		6	1.333		93.50	47.50		141	183
0220	Parallel arm		6	1.333		125	47.50		172.50	217
0230	Hold open arm		6	1.333		117	47.50		164.50	209
0240	Fusible link arm		6	1.333		148	47.50		195.50	243
0250	Medium duty, regular arm		6	1.333		117	47.50		164.50	209
0500	Surface mount regular arm		6.50	1.231		125	44		169	212
0550	Fusible link		6.50	1.231		131	44		175	218
1520	Overhead concealed, all sizes, regular arm		5.50	1.455		200	52		252	310
1525	Concealed arm		5	1.600		310	57		367	435
1530	Concealed in door, all sizes, regular arm		5.50	1.455		320	52		372	440
1535	Concealed arm		5	1.600		253	57		310	375
1560	Floor concealed, all sizes, single acting		2.20	3.636		500	130		630	770

08 71 Door Hardware

08 71 20 – Hardware

08 71 20.30 Door Closers

		Crew	Daily Output	Labor-Hours	Unit	Material	2014 Bare Costs Labor	Equipment	Total	Total Incl O&P
1565	Double acting	1 Carp	2.20	3.636	Ea.	410	130		540	670
1610	Hold open arm		6	1.333		420	47.50		467.50	540
1620	Double acting, standard arm		6	1.333		700	47.50		747.50	850
1630	Hold open arm		6	1.333		700	47.50		747.50	850
1640	Floor, center hung, single acting, bottom arm		6	1.333		410	47.50		457.50	530
1650	Double acting		6	1.333		465	47.50		512.50	590
1660	Offset hung, single acting, bottom arm		6	1.333		550	47.50		597.50	685
2000	Backcheck and adjustable power, hinge face mount									
5000	For cast aluminum cylinder, deduct				Ea.	35			35	38.50
5010	For delayed action add	1 Carp	6	1.333		34	47.50		81.50	118
5040	For delayed action, add					46			46	50.50
5080	For fusible link arm, add					35			35	38.50
5120	For shock absorbing arm, add					50			50	55
5160	For spring power adjustment, add					40			40	44
6000	Closer-holder, hinge face mount, all sizes, exposed arm	1 Carp	6.50	1.231		201	44		245	295
6500	Electro magnetic closer/holder									
6510	Single point, no detector	1 Carp	4	2	Ea.	470	71.50		541.50	635
6515	Including detector		4	2		665	71.50		736.50	855
6520	Multi-point, no detector		4	2		875	71.50		946.50	1,075
6524	Including detector		4	2		1,275	71.50		1,346.50	1,525
6550	Electric automatic operators									
6555	Operator	1 Carp	4	2	Ea.	1,975	71.50		2,046.50	2,300
6570	Wall plate actuator		4	2		217	71.50		288.50	360
7000	Electronic closer-holder, hinge facemount, concealed arm		5	1.600		420	57		477	555
7400	With built-in detector		5	1.600		605	57		662	760
8000	Surface mounted, stand. duty, parallel arm, primed, traditional		6	1.333		207	47.50		254.50	310
8030	Light duty		6	1.333		137	47.50		184.50	230
8042	Extra duty parallel arm		6	1.333		125	47.50		172.50	217
8044	Hold open arm		6	1.333		190	47.50		237.50	289
8046	Positive stop arm		6	1.333		212	47.50		259.50	315
8050	Heavy duty		6	1.333		234	47.50		281.50	335
8052	Heavy duty, regular arm		6	1.333		215	47.50		262.50	315
8054	Top jamb mount		6	1.333		215	47.50		262.50	315
8056	Extra duty parallel arm		6	1.333		215	47.50		262.50	315
8058	Hold open arm		6	1.333		261	47.50		308.50	365
8060	Positive stop arm		6	1.333		238	47.50		285.50	340
8062	Fusible link arm		6	1.333		257	47.50		304.50	365
8080	Universal heavy duty, regular arm		6	1.333		225	47.50		272.50	325
8084	Parallel arm		6	1.333		225	47.50		272.50	325
8088	Extra duty, parallel arm		6	1.333		257	47.50		304.50	365
8090	Hold open arm		6	1.333		265	47.50		312.50	370
8094	Positive stop arm		6	1.333		275	47.50		322.50	380
8100	Standard duty, parallel arm, modern		6	1.333		243	47.50		290.50	350
8150	Heavy duty		6	1.333		274	47.50		321.50	380

08 71 20.35 Panic Devices

		Crew	Daily Output	Labor-Hours	Unit	Material	2014 Bare Costs Labor	Equipment	Total	Total Incl O&P
0010	**PANIC DEVICES**									
0015	For rim locks, single door exit only	1 Carp	6	1.333	Ea.	460	47.50		507.50	585
0020	Outside key and pull		5	1.600		570	57		627	725
0200	Bar and vertical rod, exit only		5	1.600		865	57		922	1,050
0210	Outside key and pull		4	2		940	71.50		1,011.50	1,150
0400	Bar and concealed rod		4	2		745	71.50		816.50	940
0600	Touch bar, exit only		6	1.333		555	47.50		602.50	690

08 71 Door Hardware

08 71 20 - Hardware

08 71 20.35 Panic Devices

		Crew	Daily Output	Labor-Hours	Unit	Material	2014 Bare Costs Labor	Equipment	Total	Total Incl O&P
0610	Outside key and pull	1 Carp	5	1.600	Ea.	685	57		742	845
0700	Touch bar and vertical rod, exit only		5	1.600		845	57		902	1,025
0710	Outside key and pull		4	2		970	71.50		1,041.50	1,200
1000	Mortise, bar, exit only		4	2		690	71.50		761.50	880
1600	Touch bar, exit only		4	2		740	71.50		811.50	935
2000	Narrow stile, rim mounted, bar, exit only		6	1.333		615	47.50		662.50	755
2010	Outside key and pull		5	1.600		890	57		947	1,075
2200	Bar and vertical rod, exit only		5	1.600		920	57		977	1,100
2210	Outside key and pull		4	2		920	71.50		991.50	1,125
2400	Bar and concealed rod, exit only		3	2.667		1,025	95.50		1,120.50	1,300
3000	Mortise, bar, exit only		4	2		600	71.50		671.50	780
3600	Touch bar, exit only		4	2		790	71.50		861.50	990

08 71 20.40 Lockset

		Crew	Daily Output	Labor-Hours	Unit	Material	2014 Bare Costs Labor	Equipment	Total	Total Incl O&P
0010	**LOCKSET**, Standard duty									
0020	Non-keyed, passage, w/sect.trim	1 Carp	12	.667	Ea.	63.50	24		87.50	110
0100	Privacy		12	.667		75	24		99	123
0400	Keyed, single cylinder function		10	.800		108	28.50		136.50	166
0420	Hotel (see also Section 08 71 20.15)		8	1		205	36		241	286
0500	Lever handled, keyed, single cylinder function		10	.800		128	28.50		156.50	189
1000	Heavy duty with sectional trim, non-keyed, passages		12	.667		125	24		149	178
1100	Privacy		12	.667		155	24		179	211
1400	Keyed, single cylinder function		10	.800		185	28.50		213.50	252
1420	Hotel		8	1		450	36		486	555
1600	Communicating		10	.800		290	28.50		318.50	370
1690	For re-core cylinder, add					50			50	55
1700	Residential, interior door, minimum	1 Carp	16	.500		30	17.90		47.90	63
1720	Maximum		8	1		120	36		156	192
1800	Exterior, minimum		14	.571		50	20.50		70.50	89.50
1810	Average		8	1		72.50	36		108.50	140
1820	Maximum		8	1		220	36		256	300
3980	Keyless, pushbutton type									
4000	Residential/light commercial, deadbolt, standard	1 Carp	9	.889	Ea.	140	32		172	208
4010	Heavy duty		9	.889		230	32		262	305
4020	Industrial, heavy duty, with deadbolt		9	.889		355	32		387	445
4030	Key override		9	.889		390	32		422	485
4040	Lever activated handle		9	.889		415	32		447	510
4050	Key override		9	.889		430	32		462	525
4060	Double sided pushbutton type		8	1		755	36		791	890
4070	Key override		8	1		790	36		826	930

08 71 20.41 Dead Locks

		Crew	Daily Output	Labor-Hours	Unit	Material	2014 Bare Costs Labor	Equipment	Total	Total Incl O&P
0010	**DEAD LOCKS**									
0011	Mortise heavy duty outside key (security item)	1 Carp	9	.889	Ea.	200	32		232	274
0020	Double cylinder		9	.889		200	32		232	274
0100	Medium duty, outside key		10	.800		110	28.50		138.50	169
0110	Double cylinder		10	.800		120	28.50		148.50	180
1000	Tubular, standard duty, outside key		10	.800		45	28.50		73.50	97.50
1010	Double cylinder		10	.800		60	28.50		88.50	114
1200	Night latch, outside key		10	.800		45	28.50		73.50	97.50

08 71 20.42 Mortise Locksets

		Crew	Daily Output	Labor-Hours	Unit	Material	2014 Bare Costs Labor	Equipment	Total	Total Incl O&P
0010	**MORTISE LOCKSETS**, Comm., wrought knobs & full escutcheon trim									
0015	Assumes mortise is cut									
0020	Non-keyed, passage, minimum	1 Carp	9	.889	Ea.	149	32		181	218

08 71 20.42 Mortise Locksets

		Crew	Daily Output	Labor-Hours	Unit	Material	2014 Bare Costs Labor	Equipment	Total	Total Incl O&P
0030	Maximum	1 Carp	8	1	Ea.	405	36		441	505
0040	Privacy, minimum		9	.889		169	32		201	240
0050	Maximum		8	1		455	36		491	560
0100	Keyed, office/entrance/apartment, minimum		8	1		197	36		233	277
0110	Maximum		7	1.143		515	41		556	640
0120	Single cylinder, typical, minimum		8	1		189	36		225	268
0130	Maximum		7	1.143		495	41		536	615
0200	Hotel, minimum (see also Section 08 71 20.15)		7	1.143		189	41		230	277
0210	Maximum (see also Section 08 71 20.15)		6	1.333		505	47.50		552.50	640
0300	Communication, double cylinder, minimum		8	1		225	36		261	310
0310	Maximum		7	1.143		515	41		556	640
1000	Wrought knobs and sectional trim, non-keyed, passage, minimum		10	.800		130	28.50		158.50	191
1010	Maximum		9	.889		405	32		437	500
1040	Privacy, minimum		10	.800		145	28.50		173.50	208
1050	Maximum		9	.889		455	32		487	555
1100	Keyed, entrance, office/apartment, minimum		9	.889		220	32		252	296
1110	Maximum		8	1		515	36		551	630
1120	Single cylinder, typical, minimum		9	.889		225	32		257	300
1130	Maximum		8	1		495	36		531	605
2000	Cast knobs and full escutcheon trim									
2010	Non-keyed, passage, minimum	1 Carp	9	.889	Ea.	275	32		307	360
2020	Maximum		8	1		380	36		416	480
2040	Privacy, minimum		9	.889		320	32		352	405
2050	Maximum		8	1		440	36		476	545
2120	Keyed, single cylinder, typical, minimum		8	1		330	36		366	425
2130	Maximum		7	1.143		525	41		566	650
3000	Cast knob and sectional trim, non-keyed, passage, minimum		10	.800		210	28.50		238.50	279
3010	Maximum		10	.800		380	28.50		408.50	470
3040	Privacy, minimum		10	.800		225	28.50		253.50	296
3050	Maximum		10	.800		440	28.50		468.50	535
3100	Keyed, office/entrance/apartment, minimum		9	.889		255	32		287	335
3110	Maximum		9	.889		580	32		612	690
3120	Single cylinder, typical, minimum		9	.889		260	32		292	340
3130	Maximum		9	.889		525	32		557	635
3190	For re-core cylinder, add					50			50	55

08 71 20.45 Peepholes

		Crew	Daily Output	Labor-Hours	Unit	Material	2014 Bare Costs Labor	Equipment	Total	Total Incl O&P
0010	**PEEPHOLES**									
2010	Peephole	1 Carp	32	.250	Ea.	15.80	8.95		24.75	32.50
2020	Peephole, wide view	"	32	.250	"	16.50	8.95		25.45	33

08 71 20.50 Door Stops

		Crew	Daily Output	Labor-Hours	Unit	Material	2014 Bare Costs Labor	Equipment	Total	Total Incl O&P
0010	**DOOR STOPS**									
0020	Holder & bumper, floor or wall	1 Carp	32	.250	Ea.	34.50	8.95		43.45	52.50
1300	Wall bumper, 4" diameter, with rubber pad, aluminum		32	.250		11.70	8.95		20.65	28
1600	Door bumper, floor type, aluminum		32	.250		8.10	8.95		17.05	24
1620	Brass		32	.250		9.65	8.95		18.60	25.50
1630	Bronze		32	.250		18.20	8.95		27.15	35
1900	Plunger type, door mounted		32	.250		28	8.95		36.95	45.50
2500	Holder, floor type, aluminum		32	.250		33.50	8.95		42.45	52
2520	Wall type, aluminum		32	.250		35	8.95		43.95	53.50
2530	Overhead type, bronze		32	.250		101	8.95		109.95	126
2540	Plunger type, aluminum		32	.250		28	8.95		36.95	45.50
2560	Brass		32	.250		43	8.95		51.95	62

08 71 20.50 Door Stops

	Crew	Daily Output	Labor-Hours	Unit	Material	2014 Bare Costs Labor	Equipment	Total	Total Incl O&P
3000 Electro-magnetic, wall mounted, US3	1 Carp	3	2.667	Ea.	258	95.50		353.50	445
3020 Floor mounted, US3		3	2.667		315	95.50		410.50	510
4000 Doorstop, ceiling mounted		3	2.667		20	95.50		115.50	182
4030 Doorstop, header		3	2.667		45	95.50		140.50	210

08 71 20.55 Push-Pull Plates

	Crew	Daily Output	Labor-Hours	Unit	Material	2014 Bare Costs Labor	Equipment	Total	Total Incl O&P
0010 **PUSH-PULL PLATES**									
0090 Push plate, 0.050 thick, 3" x 12", aluminum	1 Carp	12	.667	Ea.	6.25	24		30.25	47
0100 4" x 16"		12	.667		11.10	24		35.10	52.50
0110 6" x 16"		12	.667		8.50	24		32.50	49.50
0120 8" x 16"		12	.667		9.90	24		33.90	51
0200 Push plate, 0.050 thick, 3" x 12", brass		12	.667		14	24		38	55.50
0210 4" x 16"		12	.667		17.50	24		41.50	59.50
0220 6" x 16"		12	.667		27	24		51	69.50
0230 8" x 16"		12	.667		35	24		59	78.50
0250 Push plate, 0.050 thick, 3" x 12", satin brass		12	.667		14.25	24		38.25	55.50
0260 4" x 16"		12	.667		17.70	24		41.70	59.50
0270 6" x 16"		12	.667		27	24		51	69.50
0280 8" x 16"		12	.667		35	24		59	78.50
0490 Push plate, 0.050 thick, 3" x 12", bronze		12	.667		17	24		41	58.50
0500 4" x 16"		12	.667		25	24		49	67.50
0510 6" x 16"		12	.667		32	24		56	75
0520 8" x 16"		12	.667		38.50	24		62.50	82.50
0740 Push plate, 0.050 thick, 3" x 12", stainless steel		12	.667		12	24		36	53
0760 6" x 16"		12	.667		18.65	24		42.65	60.50
0780 8" x 16"		12	.667		23.50	24		47.50	66
0790 Push plate, 0.050 thick, 3" x 12", satin stainless steel		12	.667		7	24		31	47.50
0820 6" x 16"		12	.667		11.70	24		35.70	53
0830 8" x 16"		12	.667		9	24		33	50
0980 Pull plate, 0.050 thick, 3" x 12", aluminum		12	.667		25.50	24		49.50	68
1050 Pull plate, 0.050 thick, 3" x 12", brass		12	.667		39.50	24		63.50	83.50
1080 Pull plate, 0.050 thick, 3" x 12", bronze		12	.667		50	24		74	95
1180 Pull plate, 0.050 thick, 3" x 12", stainless steel		12	.667		45.50	24		69.50	90
1250 Pull plate, 0.050 thick, 3" x 12", chrome		12	.667		44.50	24		68.50	89
1500 Pull handle and push bar, aluminum		11	.727		118	26		144	174
2000 Bronze		10	.800		159	28.50		187.50	223
3000 Push plate both sides, aluminum		14	.571		27	20.50		47.50	64
3500 Bronze		13	.615		61.50	22		83.50	105
4000 Door pull, designer style, cast aluminum, minimum		12	.667		88.50	24		112.50	138
5000 Maximum		8	1		370	36		406	465
6000 Cast bronze, minimum		12	.667		87	24		111	136
7000 Maximum		8	1		405	36		441	505
8000 Walnut, minimum		12	.667		70	24		94	117
9000 Maximum		8	1		380	36		416	480

08 71 20.60 Entrance Locks

	Crew	Daily Output	Labor-Hours	Unit	Material	2014 Bare Costs Labor	Equipment	Total	Total Incl O&P
0010 **ENTRANCE LOCKS**									
0015 Cylinder, grip handle deadlocking latch	1 Carp	9	.889	Ea.	175	32		207	247
0020 Deadbolt		8	1		175	36		211	253
0100 Push and pull plate, dead bolt		8	1		225	36		261	310
0900 For handicapped lever, add					150			150	165

08 71 Door Hardware

08 71 20 – Hardware

08 71 20.65 Thresholds

		Crew	Daily Output	Labor-Hours	Unit	Material	2014 Bare Costs Labor	2014 Bare Costs Equipment	Total	Total Incl O&P
0010	**THRESHOLDS**									
0011	Threshold 3' long saddles aluminum	1 Carp	48	.167	L.F.	8.15	5.95		14.10	19
0100	Aluminum, 8" wide, 1/2" thick		12	.667	Ea.	49	24		73	93.50
0500	Bronze		60	.133	L.F.	41.50	4.77		46.27	53.50
0600	Bronze, panic threshold, 5" wide, 1/2" thick		12	.667	Ea.	158	24		182	213
0700	Rubber, 1/2" thick, 5-1/2" wide		20	.400		40	14.30		54.30	68
0800	2-3/4" wide		20	.400		37.50	14.30		51.80	65.50
1950	ADA Compliant Thresholds									
2300	Threshold, aluminum 4" wide x 36" long	1 Carp	12	.667	Ea.	33	24		57	76.50
2310	4" wide x 48" long		12	.667		41	24		65	85
2320	4" wide x 72" long		12	.667		66	24		90	113
2360	6" wide x 36" long		12	.667		53	24		77	98.50
2370	6" wide x 48" long		12	.667		68	24		92	115
2380	6" wide x 72" long		12	.667		106	24		130	157
2500	Threshold, ramp, aluminum or rubber 24" x 24"		12	.667		190	24		214	249

08 71 20.70 Floor Checks

		Crew	Daily Output	Labor-Hours	Unit	Material	2014 Bare Costs Labor	2014 Bare Costs Equipment	Total	Total Incl O&P
0010	**FLOOR CHECKS**									
0020	For over 3' wide doors single acting	1 Carp	2.50	3.200	Ea.	745	114		859	1,000
0500	Double acting	"	2.50	3.200	"	860	114		974	1,125

08 71 20.75 Door Hardware Accessories

		Crew	Daily Output	Labor-Hours	Unit	Material	2014 Bare Costs Labor	2014 Bare Costs Equipment	Total	Total Incl O&P
0010	**DOOR HARDWARE ACCESSORIES**									
0050	Door closing coordinator, 36" (for paired openings up to 56")	1 Carp	8	1	Ea.	98	36		134	168
0060	48" (for paired openings up to 84")		8	1		105	36		141	176
0070	56" (for paired openings up to 96")		8	1		116	36		152	187

08 71 20.80 Hasps

		Crew	Daily Output	Labor-Hours	Unit	Material	2014 Bare Costs Labor	2014 Bare Costs Equipment	Total	Total Incl O&P
0010	**HASPS**, steel assembly									
0015	3"	1 Carp	26	.308	Ea.	4.90	11		15.90	24
0020	4-1/2"		13	.615		6.60	22		28.60	44.50
0040	6"		12.50	.640		8.70	23		31.70	48

08 71 20.90 Hinges

		Crew	Daily Output	Labor-Hours	Unit	Material	2014 Bare Costs Labor	2014 Bare Costs Equipment	Total	Total Incl O&P
0010	**HINGES** R087120-10									
0012	Full mortise, avg. freq., steel base, USP, 4-1/2" x 4-1/2"				Pr.	36			36	40
0100	5" x 5", USP					57.50			57.50	63
0200	6" x 6", USP					119			119	131
0400	Brass base, 4-1/2" x 4-1/2", US10					58.50			58.50	64.50
0500	5" x 5", US10					86			86	94.50
0600	6" x 6", US10					162			162	178
0800	Stainless steel base, 4-1/2" x 4-1/2", US32					74			74	81.50
0900	For non removable pin, add (security item)				Ea.	4.88			4.88	5.35
0910	For floating pin, driven tips, add					3.30			3.30	3.63
0930	For hospital type tip on pin, add					13.95			13.95	15.35
0940	For steeple type tip on pin, add					18.95			18.95	21
0950	Full mortise, high frequency, steel base, 3-1/2" x 3-1/2", US26D				Pr.	30			30	33
1000	4-1/2" x 4-1/2", USP					63			63	69
1100	5" x 5", USP					50			50	55
1200	6" x 6", USP					134			134	148
1400	Brass base, 3-1/2" x 3-1/2", US4					51			51	56
1430	4-1/2" x 4-1/2", US10					73.50			73.50	81
1500	5" x 5", US10					122			122	134
1600	6" x 6", US10					166			166	183
1800	Stainless steel base, 4-1/2" x 4-1/2", US32					103			103	114

08 71 20.90 Hinges

		Crew	Daily Output	Labor-Hours	Unit	Material	2014 Bare Costs Labor	2014 Bare Costs Equipment	Total	Total Incl O&P
1810	5" x 4-1/2", US32				Pr.	137			137	151
1930	For hospital type tip on pin, add				Ea.	13.15			13.15	14.45
1950	Full mortise, low frequency, steel base, 3-1/2" x 3-1/2", US26D				Pr.	23			23	25.50
2000	4-1/2" x 4-1/2", USP					22			22	24.50
2100	5" x 5", USP					47.50			47.50	52
2200	6" x 6", USP					89			89	98
2300	4-1/2" x 4-1/2", US3					17.70			17.70	19.45
2310	5" x 5", US3					42.50			42.50	46.50
2400	Brass bass, 4-1/2" x 4-1/2", US10					53			53	58.50
2500	5" x 5", US10					76.50			76.50	84
2800	Stainless steel base, 4-1/2" x 4-1/2", US32					74.50			74.50	82
8000	Install hinge	1 Carp	34	.235			8.40		8.40	14.15

08 71 20.91 Special Hinges

		Crew	Daily Output	Labor-Hours	Unit	Material	2014 Bare Costs Labor	2014 Bare Costs Equipment	Total	Total Incl O&P
0010	**SPECIAL HINGES**									
0015	Paumelle, high frequency									
0020	Steel base, 6" x 4-1/2", US10				Pr.	145			145	160
0100	Brass base, 5" x 4-1/2", US10				Ea.	248			248	273
0200	Paumelle, average frequency, steel base, 4-1/2" x 3-1/2", US10				Pr.	98.50			98.50	108
0400	Olive knuckle, low frequency, brass base, 6" x 4-1/2", US10				Ea.	142			142	156
1000	Electric hinge with concealed conductor, average frequency									
1010	Steel base, 4-1/2" x 4-1/2", US26D				Pr.	310			310	340
1100	Bronze base, 4-1/2" x 4-1/2", US26D				"	320			320	350
1200	Electric hinge with concealed conductor, high frequency									
1210	Steel base, 4-1/2" x 4-1/2", US26D				Pr.	262			262	288
1600	Double weight, 800 lb., steel base, removable pin, 5" x 6", USP					310			310	340
1700	Steel base-welded pin, 5" x 6", USP					166			166	183
1800	Triple weight, 2000 lb., steel base, welded pin, 5" x 6", USP					400			400	440
2000	Pivot reinf., high frequency, steel base, 7-3/4" door plate, USP					149			149	164
2200	Bronze base, 7-3/4" door plate, US10					232			232	255
3000	Swing clear, full mortise, full or half surface, high frequency,									
3010	Steel base, 5" high, USP				Pr.	143			143	157
3200	Swing clear, full mortise, average frequency									
3210	Steel base, 4-1/2" high, USP				Pr.	128			128	141
4000	Wide throw, average frequency, steel base, 4-1/2" x 6", USP					94.50			94.50	104
4200	High frequency, steel base, 4-1/2" x 6", USP					112			112	124
4600	Spring hinge, single acting, 6" flange, steel				Ea.	50			50	55
4700	Brass					94.50			94.50	104
4900	Double acting, 6" flange, steel					80			80	88
4950	Brass					133			133	146
8000	Continuous hinges									
8010	Steel, piano, 2" x 72"	1 Carp	20	.400	Ea.	22	14.30		36.30	48
8020	Brass, piano, 1-1/16" x 30"		30	.267		8	9.55		17.55	25
8030	Acrylic, piano, 1-3/4" x 12"		40	.200		15	7.15		22.15	28.50
8040	Aluminum, door, standard duty, 7'		3	2.667		135	95.50		230.50	310
8050	Heavy duty, 7'		3	2.667		142	95.50		237.50	315
8060	8'		3	2.667		160	95.50		255.50	335
8070	Steel, door, heavy duty, 7'		3	2.667		200	95.50		295.50	380
8080	8'		3	2.667		250	95.50		345.50	435
8090	Stainless steel, door, heavy duty, 7'		3	2.667		260	95.50		355.50	445
8100	8'		3	2.667		280	95.50		375.50	470
9000	Continuous hinge, steel, full mortise, heavy duty, 96 inch		2	4		460	143		603	745

08 71 Door Hardware

08 71 20 – Hardware

08 71 20.95 Kick Plates	Crew	Daily Output	Labor-Hours	Unit	Material	2014 Bare Costs Labor	2014 Bare Costs Equipment	Total	Total Incl O&P
0010 KICK PLATES									
0020 Stainless steel, .050, 16 ga., 8" x 28", US32	1 Carp	15	.533	Ea.	38	19.05		57.05	74
0030 8" x 30"		15	.533		41	19.05		60.05	77
0040 8" x 34"		15	.533		46	19.05		65.05	82.50
0050 10" x 28"		15	.533		76	19.05		95.05	116
0060 10" x 30"		15	.533		82	19.05		101.05	122
0070 10" x 34"		15	.533		92	19.05		111.05	133
0080 Mop/Kick, 4" x 28"		15	.533		34	19.05		53.05	69.50
0090 4" x 30"		15	.533		36	19.05		55.05	71.50
0100 4" x 34"		15	.533		41	19.05		60.05	77
0110 6" x 28"		15	.533		43	19.05		62.05	79.50
0120 6" x 30"		15	.533		47	19.05		66.05	83.50
0130 6" x 34"		15	.533		53	19.05		72.05	90.50
0500 Bronze, .050", 8" x 28"		15	.533		66.50	19.05		85.55	106
0510 8" x 30"		15	.533		65	19.05		84.05	104
0520 8" x 34"		15	.533		73	19.05		92.05	113
0530 10" x 28"		15	.533		75	19.05		94.05	115
0540 10" x 30"		15	.533		80	19.05		99.05	120
0550 10" x 34"		15	.533		91	19.05		110.05	132
0560 Mop/Kick, 4" x 28"		15	.533		33	19.05		52.05	68.50
0570 4" x 30"		15	.533		36	19.05		55.05	71.50
0580 4" x 34"		15	.533		37	19.05		56.05	72.50
0590 6" x 28"		15	.533		46	19.05		65.05	82.50
0600 6" x 30"		15	.533		52	19.05		71.05	89
0610 6" x 34"		15	.533		56	19.05		75.05	93.50
1000 Acrylic, .125", 8" x 26"		15	.533		28	19.05		47.05	63
1010 8" x 36"		15	.533		38	19.05		57.05	74
1020 8" x 42"		15	.533		45	19.05		64.05	81.50
1030 10" x 26"		15	.533		35	19.05		54.05	70.50
1040 10" x 36"		15	.533		48	19.05		67.05	85
1050 10" x 42"		15	.533		68.50	19.05		87.55	108
1060 Mop/Kick, 4" x 26"		15	.533		17	19.05		36.05	50.50
1070 4" x 36"		15	.533		24	19.05		43.05	58.50
1080 4" x 42"		15	.533		27	19.05		46.05	61.50
1090 6" x 26"		15	.533		23	19.05		42.05	57.50
1100 6" x 36"		15	.533		34	19.05		53.05	69.50
1110 6" x 42"		15	.533		39	19.05		58.05	75
1220 Brass, .050", 8" x 26"		15	.533		56	19.05		75.05	93.50
1230 8" x 36"		15	.533		75	19.05		94.05	115
1240 8" x 42"		15	.533		86	19.05		105.05	127
1250 10" x 26"		15	.533		71	19.05		90.05	110
1260 10" x 36"		15	.533		91	19.05		110.05	132
1270 10" x 42"		15	.533		105	19.05		124.05	148
1320 Mop/Kick, 4" x 26"		15	.533		28	19.05		47.05	63
1330 4" x 36"		15	.533		39	19.05		58.05	75
1340 4" x 42"		15	.533		44	19.05		63.05	80.50
1350 6" x 26"		15	.533		38	19.05		57.05	74
1360 6" x 36"		15	.533		48	19.05		67.05	85
1370 6" x 42"		15	.533		55	19.05		74.05	92.50
1800 Aluminum, .050", 8" x 26"		15	.533		29	19.05		48.05	64
1810 8" x 36"		15	.533		40	19.05		59.05	76
1820 8" x 42"		15	.533		47	19.05		66.05	83.50

08 71 Door Hardware

08 71 20 – Hardware

08 71 20.95 Kick Plates

		Crew	Daily Output	Labor-Hours	Unit	Material	2014 Bare Costs Labor	Equipment	Total	Total Incl O&P
1830	10" x 26"	1 Carp	15	.533	Ea.	36	19.05		55.05	71.50
1840	10" x 36"		15	.533		50	19.05		69.05	87
1850	10" x 42"		15	.533		59	19.05		78.05	97
1860	Mop/Kick, 4" x 26"		15	.533		15	19.05		34.05	48.50
1870	4" x 36"		15	.533		20	19.05		39.05	54
1880	4" x 42"		15	.533		24	19.05		43.05	58.50
1890	6" x 26"		15	.533		22	19.05		41.05	56
1900	6" x 36"		15	.533		30	19.05		49.05	65
1910	6" x 42"		15	.533		35	19.05		54.05	70.50

08 71 21 – Astragals

08 71 21.10 Exterior Mouldings, Astragals

		Crew	Daily Output	Labor-Hours	Unit	Material	2014 Bare Costs Labor	Equipment	Total	Total Incl O&P
0010	**EXTERIOR MOULDINGS, ASTRAGALS**									
0400	One piece, overlapping cadmium plated steel, flat, 3/16" x 2"	1 Carp	90	.089	L.F.	4	3.18		7.18	9.75
0600	Prime coated steel, flat, 1/8" x 3"		90	.089		5.75	3.18		8.93	11.70
0800	Stainless steel, flat, 3/32" x 1-5/8"		90	.089		16	3.18		19.18	23
1000	Aluminum, flat, 1/8" x 2"		90	.089		4.10	3.18		7.28	9.85
1200	Nail on, "T" extrusion		120	.067		1.90	2.38		4.28	6.10
1300	Vinyl bulb insert		105	.076		2.50	2.72		5.22	7.35
1600	Screw on, "T" extrusion		90	.089		3.20	3.18		6.38	8.85
1700	Vinyl insert		75	.107		4.50	3.81		8.31	11.35
2000	"L" extrusion, neoprene bulbs		75	.107		4.10	3.81		7.91	10.90
2100	Neoprene sponge insert		75	.107		6.90	3.81		10.71	14
2200	Magnetic		75	.107		10.60	3.81		14.41	18.05
2400	Spring hinged security seal, with cam		75	.107		6.80	3.81		10.61	13.90
2600	Spring loaded locking bolt, vinyl insert		45	.178		9.20	6.35		15.55	21
2800	Neoprene sponge strip, "Z" shaped, aluminum		60	.133		8.25	4.77		13.02	17.10
2900	Solid neoprene strip, nail on aluminum strip		90	.089		4.05	3.18		7.23	9.80
3000	One piece stile protection									
3020	Neoprene fabric loop, nail on aluminum strips	1 Carp	60	.133	L.F.	1.10	4.77		5.87	9.20
3110	Flush mounted aluminum extrusion, 1/2" x 1-1/4"		60	.133		6.90	4.77		11.67	15.60
3140	3/4" x 1-3/8"		60	.133		4.10	4.77		8.87	12.50
3160	1-1/8" x 1-3/4"		60	.133		4.70	4.77		9.47	13.15
3300	Mortise, 9/16" x 3/4"		60	.133		4.10	4.77		8.87	12.50
3320	13/16" x 1-3/8"		60	.133		4.30	4.77		9.07	12.75
3600	Spring bronze strip, nail on type		105	.076		1.85	2.72		4.57	6.60
3620	Screw on, with retainer		75	.107		2.70	3.81		6.51	9.35
3800	Flexible stainless steel housing, pile insert, 1/2" door		105	.076		7.25	2.72		9.97	12.60
3820	3/4" door		105	.076		8.10	2.72		10.82	13.50
4000	Extruded aluminum retainer, flush mount, pile insert		105	.076		2.25	2.72		4.97	7.05
4080	Mortise, felt insert		90	.089		4.55	3.18		7.73	10.35
4160	Mortise with spring, pile insert		90	.089		3.40	3.18		6.58	9.10
4400	Rigid vinyl retainer, mortise, pile insert		105	.076		2.70	2.72		5.42	7.55
4600	Wool pile filler strip, aluminum backing		105	.076		2.70	2.72		5.42	7.55
5000	Two piece overlapping astragal, extruded aluminum retainer									
5010	Pile insert	1 Carp	60	.133	L.F.	3.35	4.77		8.12	11.70
5020	Vinyl bulb insert		60	.133		1.85	4.77		6.62	10.05
5040	Vinyl flap insert		60	.133		3.65	4.77		8.42	12
5060	Solid neoprene flap insert		60	.133		6.55	4.77		11.32	15.20
5080	Hypalon rubber flap insert		60	.133		6.65	4.77		11.42	15.30
5090	Snap on cover, pile insert		60	.133		9.45	4.77		14.22	18.40
5400	Magnetic aluminum, surface mounted		60	.133		23	4.77		27.77	33
5500	Interlocking aluminum, 5/8" x 1" neoprene bulb insert		45	.178		5.70	6.35		12.05	16.95

08 71 Door Hardware

08 71 21 – Astragals

08 71 21.10 Exterior Mouldings, Astragals

08 71 21.10 Exterior Mouldings, Astragals	Crew	Daily Output	Labor-Hours	Unit	Material	2014 Bare Costs Labor	Equipment	Total	Total Incl O&P
5600	Adjustable aluminum, 9/16" x 21/32", pile insert	1 Carp	45	.178	L.F.	17.55	6.35		23.90	30
5790	For vinyl bulb, deduct					.75			.75	.83
5800	Magnetic, adjustable, 9/16" x 21/32"	1 Carp	45	.178	↓	23	6.35		29.35	35.50
6000	Two piece stile protection									
6010	Cloth backed rubber loop, 1" gap, nail on aluminum strips	1 Carp	45	.178	L.F.	4.35	6.35		10.70	15.50
6040	Screw on aluminum strips		45	.178		6.55	6.35		12.90	17.90
6100	1-1/2" gap, screw on aluminum extrusion		45	.178		5.85	6.35		12.20	17.15
6240	Vinyl fabric loop, slotted aluminum extrusion, 1" gap		45	.178		2.20	6.35		8.55	13.10
6300	1-1/4" gap	↓	45	.178	↓	6.20	6.35		12.55	17.50

08 71 25 – Weatherstripping

08 71 25.10 Mechanical Seals, Weatherstripping

08 71 25.10 Mechanical Seals, Weatherstripping	Crew	Daily Output	Labor-Hours	Unit	Material	2014 Bare Costs Labor	Equipment	Total	Total Incl O&P
0010	**MECHANICAL SEALS, WEATHERSTRIPPING**									
1000	Doors, wood frame, interlocking, for 3' x 7' door, zinc	1 Carp	3	2.667	Opng.	44	95.50		139.50	209
1100	Bronze		3	2.667		56	95.50		151.50	222
1300	6' x 7' opening, zinc		2	4		54	143		197	300
1400	Bronze	↓	2	4	↓	65	143		208	315
1700	Wood frame, spring type, bronze									
1800	3' x 7' door	1 Carp	7.60	1.053	Opng.	23	37.50		60.50	89
1900	6' x 7' door	"	7	1.143	"	29.50	41		70.50	101
2200	Metal frame, spring type, bronze									
2300	3' x 7' door	1 Carp	3	2.667	Opng.	46.50	95.50		142	211
2400	6' x 7' door	"	2.50	3.200	"	52	114		166	249
2500	For stainless steel, spring type, add					133%				
2700	Metal frame, extruded sections, 3' x 7' door, aluminum	1 Carp	3	2.667	Opng.	28	95.50		123.50	191
2800	Bronze		3	2.667		82	95.50		177.50	250
3100	6' x 7' door, aluminum		1.50	5.333		35	191		226	360
3200	Bronze	↓	1.50	5.333	↓	137	191		328	470
3500	Threshold weatherstripping									
3650	Door sweep, flush mounted, aluminum	1 Carp	25	.320	Ea.	19	11.45		30.45	40.50
3700	Vinyl		25	.320		18	11.45		29.45	39
5000	Garage door bottom weatherstrip, 12' aluminum, clear		14	.571		25	20.50		45.50	62
5010	Bronze		14	.571		90	20.50		110.50	134
5050	Bottom protection, Rubber		14	.571		37	20.50		57.50	75
5100	Threshold	↓	14	.571	↓	72	20.50		92.50	114

08 74 Access Control Hardware

08 74 13 – Card Key Access Control Hardware

08 74 13.50 Card Key Access

08 74 13.50 Card Key Access	Crew	Daily Output	Labor-Hours	Unit	Material	2014 Bare Costs Labor	Equipment	Total	Total Incl O&P
0010	**CARD KEY ACCESS**									
0020	Computerized system , processor, proximity reader and cards									
0030	Does not inculde door hardware, lockset or wiring									
0040	Card key system for 1 door				Ea.	1,175			1,175	1,300
0060	Card key system for 2 doors					2,125			2,125	2,350
0080	Card key system for 4 doors					2,650			2,650	2,900
0100	Processor for card key access system					850			850	935
0160	Magnetic lock for electric access, 600 Pound holding force					190			190	209
0170	Magnetic lock for electric access, 1200 Pound holding force					190			190	209
0200	Proximify card reader				↓	125			125	138

08 74 Access Control Hardware

08 74 19 – Biometric Identity Access Control Hardware

08 74 19.50 Biometric Identity Access		Crew	Daily Output	Labor-Hours	Unit	Material	2014 Bare Costs Labor	Equipment	Total	Total Incl O&P
0010	**BIOMETRIC IDENTITY ACCESS**									
0220	Hand geometry scanner, mem of 512 users, excl striker/power	1 Elec	3	2.667	Ea.	2,100	114		2,214	2,475
0230	Memory upgrade for, adds 9,700 user profiles		8	1		300	42.50		342.50	400
0240	Adds 32,500 user profiles		8	1		600	42.50		642.50	730
0250	Prison type, memory of 256 users, excl striker, power		3	2.667		2,600	114		2,714	3,025
0260	Memory upgrade for, adds 3,300 user profiles		8	1		250	42.50		292.50	345
0270	Adds 9,700 user profiles		8	1		460	42.50		502.50	575
0280	Adds 27,900 user profiles		8	1		610	42.50		652.50	740
0290	All weather, mem of 512 users, excl striker/power		3	2.667		3,900	114		4,014	4,475
0300	Facial & fingerprint scanner, combination unit, excl striker/power		3	2.667		4,300	114		4,414	4,900
0310	Access for, for initial setup, excl striker/power		3	2.667		1,100	114		1,214	1,375

08 75 Window Hardware

08 75 30 – Weatherstripping

08 75 30.10 Mechanical Weather Seals

08 75 30.10 Mechanical Weather Seals		Crew	Daily Output	Labor-Hours	Unit	Material	2014 Bare Costs Labor	Equipment	Total	Total Incl O&P
0010	**MECHANICAL WEATHER SEALS**, Window, double hung, 3' X 5'									
0020	Zinc	1 Carp	7.20	1.111	Opng.	20	39.50		59.50	89
0100	Bronze		7.20	1.111		39	39.50		78.50	110
0500	As above but heavy duty, zinc		4.60	1.739		20	62		82	127
0600	Bronze		4.60	1.739		70	62		132	182

08 79 Hardware Accessories

08 79 13 – Key Storage Equipment

08 79 13.10 Key Cabinets

08 79 13.10 Key Cabinets		Crew	Daily Output	Labor-Hours	Unit	Material	2014 Bare Costs Labor	Equipment	Total	Total Incl O&P
0010	**KEY CABINETS**									
0020	Wall mounted, 60 key capacity	1 Carp	20	.400	Ea.	113	14.30		127.30	149
0200	Drawer type, 600 key capacity	1 Clab	15	.533		800	15.05		815.05	905
0300	2,400 key capacity		20	.400		4,200	11.30		4,211.30	4,650
0400	Tray type, 20 key capacity		50	.160		62.50	4.51		67.01	76.50
0500	50 key capacity		40	.200		102	5.65		107.65	122

08 79 20 – Door Accessories

08 79 20.10 Door Hardware Accessories

08 79 20.10 Door Hardware Accessories		Crew	Daily Output	Labor-Hours	Unit	Material	2014 Bare Costs Labor	Equipment	Total	Total Incl O&P
0010	**DOOR HARDWARE ACCESSORIES**									
0140	Door bolt, surface, 4"	1 Carp	32	.250	Ea.	11.70	8.95		20.65	28
0160	Door latch	"	12	.667	"	8.55	24		32.55	49.50
0200	Sliding closet door									
0220	Track and hanger, single	1 Carp	10	.800	Ea.	56	28.50		84.50	110
0240	Double		8	1		80	36		116	148
0260	Door guide, single		48	.167		30	5.95		35.95	43
0280	Double		48	.167		40	5.95		45.95	54
0600	Deadbolt and lock cover plate, brass or stainless steel		30	.267		28	9.55		37.55	47
0620	Hole cover plate, brass or chrome		35	.229		8	8.15		16.15	22.50
2240	Mortise lockset, passage, lever handle		9	.889		170	32		202	241
4000	Security chain, standard		18	.444		10	15.90		25.90	37.50

08 81 Glass Glazing

08 81 10 – Float Glass

08 81 10.10 Various Types and Thickness of Float Glass

		Crew	Daily Output	Labor-Hours	Unit	Material	2014 Bare Costs Labor	Equipment	Total	Total Incl O&P
0010	**VARIOUS TYPES AND THICKNESS OF FLOAT GLASS** R088110-10									
0020	3/16" Plain	2 Glaz	130	.123	S.F.	4.93	4.28		9.21	12.50
0200	Tempered, clear		130	.123		6.85	4.28		11.13	14.65
0300	Tinted		130	.123		7.80	4.28		12.08	15.70
0600	1/4" thick, clear, plain		120	.133		5.75	4.64		10.39	14.05
0700	Tinted		120	.133		9.10	4.64		13.74	17.70
0800	Tempered, clear		120	.133		8.70	4.64		13.34	17.25
0900	Tinted		120	.133		10.70	4.64		15.34	19.50
1600	3/8" thick, clear, plain		75	.213		10.05	7.40		17.45	23.50
1700	Tinted		75	.213		15.70	7.40		23.10	29.50
1800	Tempered, clear		75	.213		16.40	7.40		23.80	30.50
1900	Tinted		75	.213		18.55	7.40		25.95	33
2200	1/2" thick, clear, plain		55	.291		17	10.10		27.10	35.50
2300	Tinted		55	.291		27.50	10.10		37.60	47
2400	Tempered, clear		55	.291		24.50	10.10		34.60	43.50
2500	Tinted		55	.291		25.50	10.10		35.60	45
2800	5/8" thick, clear, plain		45	.356		27.50	12.35		39.85	50.50
2900	Tempered, clear		45	.356		31.50	12.35		43.85	55
3200	3/4" thick, clear, plain		35	.457		35.50	15.90		51.40	65.50
3300	Tempered, clear		35	.457		41	15.90		56.90	72
3600	1" thick, clear, plain		30	.533		59	18.55		77.55	95.50
8900	For low emissivity coating for 3/16" & 1/4" only, add to above					18%				

08 81 13 – Decorative Glass Glazing

08 81 13.10 Beveled Glass

		Crew	Daily Output	Labor-Hours	Unit	Material	2014 Bare Costs Labor	Equipment	Total	Total Incl O&P
0010	**BEVELED GLASS**, with design patterns									
0020	Minimum	2 Glaz	150	.107	S.F.	60.50	3.71		64.21	72.50
0050	Average		125	.128		133	4.45		137.45	153
0100	Maximum		100	.160		233	5.55		238.55	266
0102	Maximum, per L.F. for 30" cabinet	1 Glaz	40	.200	L.F.	585	6.95		591.95	650

08 81 13.20 Faceted Glass

		Crew	Daily Output	Labor-Hours	Unit	Material	2014 Bare Costs Labor	Equipment	Total	Total Incl O&P
0010	**FACETED GLASS**, Color tinted 3/4" thick									
0020	Minimum	2 Glaz	95	.168	S.F.	48.50	5.85		54.35	63
0100	Maximum	"	75	.213	"	83	7.40		90.40	104

08 81 13.30 Sandblasted Glass

		Crew	Daily Output	Labor-Hours	Unit	Material	2014 Bare Costs Labor	Equipment	Total	Total Incl O&P
0010	**SANDBLASTED GLASS**, float glass									
0020	1/8" thick	2 Glaz	160	.100	S.F.	11	3.48		14.48	17.90
0100	3/16" thick		130	.123		12.15	4.28		16.43	20.50
0500	1/4" thick		120	.133		12.65	4.64		17.29	21.50
0600	3/8" thick		75	.213		13.60	7.40		21	27.50

08 81 13.40 Glass Column Covers

		Crew	Daily Output	Labor-Hours	Unit	Material	2014 Bare Costs Labor	Equipment	Total	Total Incl O&P
0010	**GLASS COLUMN COVERS**									
0020	Tempered glass column cover, 24" dia., up to 12' high	2 Glaz	30	.533	V.L.F.	82	18.55		100.55	121
0040	up to 20' high	"	24	.667	"	120	23		143	171

08 81 20 – Vision Panels

08 81 20.10 Full Vision

		Crew	Daily Output	Labor-Hours	Unit	Material	2014 Bare Costs Labor	Equipment	Total	Total Incl O&P
0010	**FULL VISION**, window system with 3/4" glass mullions									
0020	Up to 10' high	H-2	130	.185	S.F.	62.50	6		68.50	79
0100	10' to 20' high, minimum		110	.218		67	7.10		74.10	85.50
0150	Average		100	.240		72	7.80		79.80	92.50
0200	Maximum		80	.300		81	9.80		90.80	105

08 81 Glass Glazing

08 81 25 – Glazing Variables

08 81 25.10 Applications of Glazing		Crew	Daily Output	Labor-Hours	Unit	Material	2014 Bare Costs Labor	Equipment	Total	Total Incl O&P
0010	**APPLICATIONS OF GLAZING**	R088110-10								
0500	For high rise glazing, exterior, add per S.F. per story				S.F.					.41
0600	For glass replacement, add				"		100%			
0700	For gasket settings, add				L.F.	5.75			5.75	6.35
0900	For sloped glazing, add				S.F.		26%			
2000	Fabrication, polished edges, 1/4" thick				Inch	.55			.55	.61
2100	1/2" thick					1.30			1.30	1.43
2500	Mitered edges, 1/4" thick					1.30			1.30	1.43
2600	1/2" thick					2.15			2.15	2.37

08 81 30 – Insulating Glass

08 81 30.10 Reduce Heat Transfer Glass

			Crew	Daily Output	Labor-Hours	Unit	Material	Labor	Equipment	Total	Total Incl O&P
0010	**REDUCE HEAT TRANSFER GLASS**		R088110-10								
0015	2 lites 1/8" float, 1/2" thk under 15 S.F.										
0020	Clear	G	2 Glaz	95	.168	S.F.	9.95	5.85		15.80	20.50
0100	Tinted	G		95	.168		13.80	5.85		19.65	25
0200	2 lites 3/16" float, for 5/8" thk unit, 15 to 30 S.F., clear	G		90	.178		13.70	6.20		19.90	25.50
0300	Tinted	G		90	.178		13.75	6.20		19.95	25.50
0400	1" thk, dbl. glazed, 1/4" float, 30-70 S.F., clear	G		75	.213		16.60	7.40		24	30.50
0500	Tinted	G		75	.213		23.50	7.40		30.90	38.50
0600	1" thick double glazed, 1/4" float, 1/4" wire			75	.213		23	7.40		30.40	38
0700	1/4" float, 1/4" tempered			75	.213		30.50	7.40		37.90	46
0800	1/4" wire, 1/4" tempered			75	.213		29	7.40		36.40	44.50
0900	Both lites, 1/4" wire			75	.213		37	7.40		44.40	53.50
2000	Both lites, light & heat reflective	G		85	.188		31.50	6.55		38.05	45.50
2500	Heat reflective, film inside, 1" thick unit, clear	G		85	.188		27.50	6.55		34.05	41.50
2600	Tinted	G		85	.188		28.50	6.55		35.05	42.50
3000	Film on weatherside, clear, 1/2" thick unit	G		95	.168		19.60	5.85		25.45	31.50
3100	5/8" thick unit	G		90	.178		19.90	6.20		26.10	32.50
3200	1" thick unit	G		85	.188		27	6.55		33.55	41

08 81 35 – Translucent Glass

08 81 35.10 Obscure Glass

		Crew	Daily Output	Labor-Hours	Unit	Material	Labor	Equipment	Total	Total Incl O&P
0010	**OBSCURE GLASS**									
0020	1/8" thick, Minimum	2 Glaz	140	.114	S.F.	11.60	3.98		15.58	19.35
0100	Maximum		125	.128		13.70	4.45		18.15	22.50
0300	7/32" thick, minimum		120	.133		12.70	4.64		17.34	21.50
0400	Maximum		105	.152		15.95	5.30		21.25	26.50

08 81 35.20 Patterned Glass

		Crew	Daily Output	Labor-Hours	Unit	Material	Labor	Equipment	Total	Total Incl O&P
0010	**PATTERNED GLASS**, colored									
0020	1/8" thick, Minimum	2 Glaz	140	.114	S.F.	9.30	3.98		13.28	16.85
0100	Maximum		125	.128		15.80	4.45		20.25	25
0300	7/32" thick, minimum		120	.133		11.65	4.64		16.29	20.50
0400	Maximum		105	.152		16.95	5.30		22.25	27.50

08 81 45 – Sheet Glass

08 81 45.10 Window Glass, Sheet

		Crew	Daily Output	Labor-Hours	Unit	Material	Labor	Equipment	Total	Total Incl O&P
0010	**WINDOW GLASS, SHEET** gray									
0020	1/8" thick	2 Glaz	160	.100	S.F.	5.70	3.48		9.18	12.05
0200	1/4" thick	"	130	.123	"	7	4.28		11.28	14.80

08 81 Glass Glazing

08 81 50 – Spandrel Glass

08 81 50.10 Glass for Non Vision Areas

		Crew	Daily Output	Labor-Hours	Unit	Material	2014 Bare Costs Labor	Equipment	Total	Total Incl O&P
0010	**GLASS FOR NON VISION AREAS**, 1/4" thick standard colors									
0020	Up to 1000 S.F.	2 Glaz	110	.145	S.F.	16.50	5.05		21.55	26.50
0200	1,000 to 2,000 S.F.	"	120	.133	"	15.30	4.64		19.94	24.50
0300	For custom colors, add				Total	10%				
0500	For 3/8" thick, add				S.F.	11.90			11.90	13.10
1000	For double coated, 1/4" thick, add					4.25			4.25	4.68
1200	For insulation on panels, add					6.95			6.95	7.65
2000	Panels, insulated, with aluminum backed fiberglass, 1" thick	2 Glaz	120	.133		16.85	4.64		21.49	26.50
2100	2" thick	"	120	.133	▼	20	4.64		24.64	29.50

08 81 55 – Window Glass

08 81 55.10 Sheet Glass

		Crew	Daily Output	Labor-Hours	Unit	Material	2014 Bare Costs Labor	Equipment	Total	Total Incl O&P
0010	**SHEET GLASS** (window), clear float, stops, putty bed									
0015	1/8" thick, clear float	2 Glaz	480	.033	S.F.	3.60	1.16		4.76	5.90
0500	3/16" thick, clear		480	.033		5.80	1.16		6.96	8.35
0600	Tinted		480	.033		7.45	1.16		8.61	10.15
0700	Tempered	▼	480	.033	▼	9.20	1.16		10.36	12.05

08 81 65 – Wire Glass

08 81 65.10 Glass Reinforced With Wire

		Crew	Daily Output	Labor-Hours	Unit	Material	2014 Bare Costs Labor	Equipment	Total	Total Incl O&P
0010	**GLASS REINFORCED WITH WIRE**									
0012	1/4" thick rough obscure	2 Glaz	135	.119	S.F.	23.50	4.12		27.62	32.50
1000	Polished wire, 1/4" thick, diamond, clear		135	.119		27.50	4.12		31.62	37
1500	Pinstripe, obscure	▼	135	.119	▼	40.50	4.12		44.62	51.50

08 83 Mirrors

08 83 13 – Mirrored Glass Glazing

08 83 13.10 Mirrors

		Crew	Daily Output	Labor-Hours	Unit	Material	2014 Bare Costs Labor	Equipment	Total	Total Incl O&P
0010	**MIRRORS**, No frames, wall type, 1/4" plate glass, polished edge									
0100	Up to 5 S.F.	2 Glaz	125	.128	S.F.	9.50	4.45		13.95	17.85
0200	Over 5 S.F.		160	.100		9.25	3.48		12.73	16
0500	Door type, 1/4" plate glass, up to 12 S.F.		160	.100		8.55	3.48		12.03	15.20
1000	Float glass, up to 10 S.F., 1/8" thick		160	.100		5.65	3.48		9.13	12
1100	3/16" thick		150	.107		6.95	3.71		10.66	13.80
1500	12" x 12" wall tiles, square edge, clear		195	.082		2.22	2.86		5.08	7.20
1600	Veined		195	.082		5.80	2.86		8.66	11.15
2000	1/4" thick, stock sizes, one way transparent		125	.128		18.95	4.45		23.40	28.50
2010	Bathroom, unframed, laminated	▼	160	.100	▼	13.30	3.48		16.78	20.50

08 83 13.15 Reflective Glass

			Crew	Daily Output	Labor-Hours	Unit	Material	2014 Bare Costs Labor	Equipment	Total	Total Incl O&P
0010	**REFLECTIVE GLASS**										
0100	1/4" float with fused metallic oxide fixed	**G**	2 Glaz	115	.139	S.F.	16.95	4.84		21.79	26.50
0500	1/4" float glass with reflective applied coating	**G**	"	115	.139	"	13.70	4.84		18.54	23

08 84 Plastic Glazing

08 84 10 – Plexiglass Glazing

08 84 10.10 Plexiglass Acrylic		Crew	Daily Output	Labor-Hours	Unit	Material	2014 Bare Costs Labor	Equipment	Total	Total Incl O&P
0010	**PLEXIGLASS ACRYLIC**, clear, masked,									
0020	1/8" thick, cut sheets	2 Glaz	170	.094	S.F.	12	3.28		15.28	18.65
0200	Full sheets		195	.082		5	2.86		7.86	10.25
0500	1/4" thick, cut sheets		165	.097		14	3.37		17.37	21
0600	Full sheets		185	.086		9	3.01		12.01	14.90
0900	3/8" thick, cut sheets		155	.103		20	3.59		23.59	28
1000	Full sheets		180	.089		15	3.09		18.09	21.50
1300	1/2" thick, cut sheets		135	.119		28	4.12		32.12	38
1400	Full sheets		150	.107		20	3.71		23.71	28
1700	3/4" thick, cut sheets		115	.139		69	4.84		73.84	84
1800	Full sheets		130	.123		40	4.28		44.28	51
2100	1" thick, cut sheets		105	.152		77.50	5.30		82.80	94.50
2200	Full sheets		125	.128		48	4.45		52.45	60.50
3000	Colored, 1/8" thick, cut sheets		170	.094		18	3.28		21.28	25.50
3200	Full sheets		195	.082		11	2.86		13.86	16.85
3500	1/4" thick, cut sheets		165	.097		20	3.37		23.37	27.50
3600	Full sheets		185	.086		14	3.01		17.01	20.50
4000	Mirrors, untinted, cut sheets, 1/8" thick		185	.086		12	3.01		15.01	18.20
4200	1/4" thick		180	.089		16	3.09		19.09	23

08 84 20 – Polycarbonate

08 84 20.10 Thermoplastic

		Crew	Daily Output	Labor-Hours	Unit	Material	2014 Bare Costs Labor	Equipment	Total	Total Incl O&P
0010	**THERMOPLASTIC**, clear, masked, cut sheets									
0020	1/8" thick	2 Glaz	170	.094	S.F.	14	3.28		17.28	21
0500	3/16" thick		165	.097		16	3.37		19.37	23
1000	1/4" thick		155	.103		17	3.59		20.59	24.50
1500	3/8" thick		150	.107		26	3.71		29.71	34.50

08 87 Glazing Surface Films

08 87 13 – Solar Control Films

08 87 13.10 Solar Films On Glass

			Crew	Daily Output	Labor-Hours	Unit	Material	2014 Bare Costs Labor	Equipment	Total	Total Incl O&P
0010	**SOLAR FILMS ON GLASS** (glass not included)										
2000	Minimum	G	2 Glaz	180	.089	S.F.	6.80	3.09		9.89	12.65
2050	Maximum	G	"	225	.071	"	15.30	2.47		17.77	21

08 87 23 – Safety and Security Films

08 87 23.16 Security Films

			Crew	Daily Output	Labor-Hours	Unit	Material	2014 Bare Costs Labor	Equipment	Total	Total Incl O&P
0010	**SECURITY FILMS**, clear, 32000 psi tensile strength, adhered to glass	R088110-10									
0100	.002" thick, daylight installation		H-2	950	.025	S.F.	2.70	.82		3.52	4.34
0150	.004" thick, daylight installation			800	.030		3.35	.98		4.33	5.30
0200	.006" thick, daylight installation			700	.034		3.60	1.12		4.72	5.80
0210	Install for anchorage			600	.040		4	1.30		5.30	6.55
0400	.007" thick, daylight installation			600	.040		4.45	1.30		5.75	7.05
0410	Install for anchorage			500	.048		4.94	1.56		6.50	8.05
0500	.008" thick, daylight installation			500	.048		5	1.56		6.56	8.10
0510	Install for anchorage			500	.048		5.55	1.56		7.11	8.70
0600	.015" thick, daylight installation			400	.060		8.80	1.96		10.76	12.95
0610	Install for anchorage			400	.060		5.55	1.96		7.51	9.35
0900	Security film anchorage, mechanical attachment and cover plate		H-3	370	.043	L.F.	9.75	1.33		11.08	12.95
0950	Security film anchorage, wet glaze structural caulking		1 Glaz	225	.036	"	.92	1.24		2.16	3.07
1000	Adhered security film removal		1 Clab	275	.029	S.F.		.82		.82	1.38

08 88 Special Function Glazing

08 88 40 – Acoustical Glass Units

08 88 40.10 Sound Reduction Units	Crew	Daily Output	Labor-Hours	Unit	Material	2014 Bare Costs Labor	Equipment	Total	Total Incl O&P
0010 **SOUND REDUCTION UNITS**, 1 lite at 3/8", 1 lite at 3/16"									
0020 For 1" thick	2 Glaz	100	.160	S.F.	34	5.55		39.55	47
0100 For 4" thick	"	80	.200	"	58.50	6.95		65.45	75.50

08 88 56 – Ballistics-Resistant Glazing

08 88 56.10 Laminated Glass	Crew	Daily Output	Labor-Hours	Unit	Material	2014 Bare Costs Labor	Equipment	Total	Total Incl O&P
0010 **LAMINATED GLASS**									
0020 Clear float .03" vinyl 1/4"	2 Glaz	90	.178	S.F.	12.10	6.20		18.30	23.50
0100 3/8" thick		78	.205		22.50	7.15		29.65	36.50
0200 .06" vinyl, 1/2" thick		65	.246		25.50	8.55		34.05	42.50
1000 5/8" thick		90	.178		29.50	6.20		35.70	43
2000 Bullet-resisting, 1-3/16" thick, to 15 S.F.		16	1		93	35		128	160
2100 Over 15 S.F.		16	1		108	35		143	176
2500 2-1/4" thick, to 15 S.F.		12	1.333		149	46.50		195.50	241
2600 Over 15 S.F.		12	1.333		140	46.50		186.50	231
2700 Level 2 (.357 magnum), NIJ and UL		12	1.333		76	46.50		122.50	161
2750 Level 3A (.44 magnum) NIJ, UL 3		12	1.333		81	46.50		127.50	166
2800 Level 4 (AK-47) NIJ, UL 7 & 8		12	1.333		112	46.50		158.50	200
2850 Level 5 (M-16) UL		12	1.333		115	46.50		161.50	204
2900 Level 3 (7.62 Armor Piercing) NIJ, UL 4 & 5		12	1.333		136	46.50		182.50	227

08 91 Louvers

08 91 19 – Fixed Louvers

08 91 19.10 Aluminum Louvers	Crew	Daily Output	Labor-Hours	Unit	Material	2014 Bare Costs Labor	Equipment	Total	Total Incl O&P
0010 **ALUMINUM LOUVERS**									
0020 Aluminum with screen, residential, 8" x 8"	1 Carp	38	.211	Ea.	17.50	7.55		25.05	32
0100 12" x 12"		38	.211		15	7.55		22.55	29
0200 12" x 18"		35	.229		19	8.15		27.15	35
0250 14" x 24"		30	.267		26	9.55		35.55	44.50
0300 18" x 24"		27	.296		29	10.60		39.60	50
0500 24" x 30"		24	.333		62.50	11.90		74.40	89
0700 Triangle, adjustable, small		20	.400		47.50	14.30		61.80	76.50
0800 Large		15	.533		59	19.05		78.05	97
1200 Extruded aluminum, see Section 23 37 15.40									
2100 Midget, aluminum, 3/4" deep, 1" diameter	1 Carp	85	.094	Ea.	.78	3.36		4.14	6.50
2150 3" diameter		60	.133		2.28	4.77		7.05	10.50
2200 4" diameter		50	.160		3.64	5.70		9.34	13.60
2250 6" diameter		30	.267		4.10	9.55		13.65	20.50

08 91 26 – Door Louvers

08 91 26.10 Steel Louvers, 18 Gauge, Fixed Blade	Crew	Daily Output	Labor-Hours	Unit	Material	2014 Bare Costs Labor	Equipment	Total	Total Incl O&P
0010 **STEEL LOUVERS, 18 GAUGE, FIXED BLADE**									
0050 12" x 12", with enamel or powder coat	1 Carp	20	.400	Ea.	82	14.30		96.30	114
0055 18" x 12"		20	.400		94	14.30		108.30	127
0060 18" x 18"		20	.400		87.50	14.30		101.80	121
0065 24" x 12"		20	.400		113	14.30		127.30	148
0070 24" x 18"		20	.400		126	14.30		140.30	163
0075 24" x 24"		20	.400		150	14.30		164.30	189
0100 12" x 12", galvanized		20	.400		65	14.30		79.30	95.50
0105 18" x 12"		20	.400		76.50	14.30		90.80	108
0115 24" x 12"		20	.400		89.50	14.30		103.80	123
0125 24" x 24"		20	.400		127	14.30		141.30	163

08 95 Vents

08 95 13 – Soffit Vents

08 95 13.10 Wall Louvers

		Crew	Daily Output	Labor-Hours	Unit	Material	2014 Bare Costs Labor	Equipment	Total	Total Incl O&P
0010	**WALL LOUVERS**									
2330	Soffit vent, continuous, 3" wide, aluminum, mill finish	1 Carp	200	.040	L.F.	.62	1.43		2.05	3.09
2340	Baked enamel finish		200	.040	"	.68	1.43		2.11	3.16
2400	Under eaves vent, aluminum, mill finish, 16" x 4"		48	.167	Ea.	1.90	5.95		7.85	12.15
2500	16" x 8"		48	.167	"	2.18	5.95		8.13	12.45

08 95 16 – Wall Vents

08 95 16.10 Louvers

		Crew	Daily Output	Labor-Hours	Unit	Material	2014 Bare Costs Labor	Equipment	Total	Total Incl O&P
0010	**LOUVERS**									
0020	Redwood, 2'-0" diameter, full circle	1 Carp	16	.500	Ea.	190	17.90		207.90	239
0100	Half circle		16	.500		190	17.90		207.90	239
0200	Octagonal		16	.500		142	17.90		159.90	186
0300	Triangular, 5/12 pitch, 5'-0" at base		16	.500		200	17.90		217.90	250
7000	Vinyl gable vent, 8" x 8"		38	.211		14	7.55		21.55	28
7020	12" x 12"		38	.211		27	7.55		34.55	42
7080	12" x 18"		35	.229		35	8.15		43.15	52.50
7200	18" x 24"		30	.267		45	9.55		54.55	65.50

Estimating Tips

General

- Room Finish Schedule: A complete set of plans should contain a room finish schedule. If one is not available, it would be well worth the time and effort to obtain one.

09 20 00 Plaster and Gypsum Board

- Lath is estimated by the square yard plus a 5% allowance for waste. Furring, channels, and accessories are measured by the linear foot. An extra foot should be allowed for each accessory miter or stop.
- Plaster is also estimated by the square yard. Deductions for openings vary by preference, from zero deduction to 50% of all openings over 2 feet in width. The estimator should allow one extra square foot for each linear foot of horizontal interior or exterior angle located below the ceiling level. Also, double the areas of small radius work.
- Drywall accessories, studs, track, and acoustical caulking are all measured by the linear foot. Drywall taping is figured by the square foot. Gypsum wallboard is estimated by the square foot. No material deductions should be made for door or window openings under 32 S.F.

09 60 00 Flooring

- Tile and terrazzo areas are taken off on a square foot basis. Trim and base materials are measured by the linear foot. Accent tiles are listed per each. Two basic methods of installation are used. Mud set is approximately 30% more expensive than thin set. In terrazzo work, be sure to include the linear footage of embedded decorative strips, grounds, machine rubbing, and power cleanup.
- Wood flooring is available in strip, parquet, or block configuration. The latter two types are set in adhesives with quantities estimated by the square foot. The laying pattern will influence labor costs and material waste. In addition to the material and labor for laying wood floors, the estimator must make allowances for sanding and finishing these areas unless the flooring is prefinished.
- Sheet flooring is measured by the square yard. Roll widths vary, so consideration should be given to use the most economical width, as waste must be figured into the total quantity. Consider also the installation methods available, direct glue down or stretched.

09 70 00 Wall Finishes

- Wall coverings are estimated by the square foot. The area to be covered is measured, length by height of wall above baseboards, to calculate the square footage of each wall. This figure is divided by the number of square feet in the single roll which is being used. Deduct, in full, the areas of openings such as doors and windows. Where a pattern match is required allow 25%–30% waste.

09 80 00 Acoustic Treatment

- Acoustical systems fall into several categories. The takeoff of these materials should be by the square foot of area with a 5% allowance for waste. Do not forget about scaffolding, if applicable, when estimating these systems.

09 90 00 Painting and Coating

- A major portion of the work in painting involves surface preparation. Be sure to include cleaning, sanding, filling, and masking costs in the estimate.
- Protection of adjacent surfaces is not included in painting costs. When considering the method of paint application, an important factor is the amount of protection and masking required. These must be estimated separately and may be the determining factor in choosing the method of application.

Reference Numbers

Reference numbers are shown in shaded boxes at the beginning of some major classifications. These numbers refer to related items in the Reference Section. The reference information may be an estimating procedure, an alternate pricing method, or technical information.

Note: Not all subdivisions listed here necessarily appear in this publication.

09 01 Maintenance of Finishes

09 01 60 – Maintenance of Flooring

09 01 60.10 Carpet Maintenance

		Crew	Daily Output	Labor-Hours	Unit	Material	2014 Bare Costs Labor	2014 Bare Costs Equipment	Total	Total Incl O&P
0010	**CARPET MAINTENANCE**									
0020	Steam clean, per cleaning, minimum	1 Clab	3000	.003	S.F.	.05	.08		.13	.19
0500	Maximum	"	2000	.004	"	.07	.11		.18	.27

09 01 70 – Maintenance of Wall Finishes

09 01 70.10 Gypsum Wallboard Repairs

		Crew	Daily Output	Labor-Hours	Unit	Material	Labor	Equipment	Total	Total Incl O&P
0010	**GYPSUM WALLBOARD REPAIRS**									
0100	Fill and sand, pin/nail holes	1 Carp	960	.008	Ea.		.30		.30	.50
0110	Screw head pops		480	.017			.60		.60	1
0120	Dents, up to 2" square		48	.167		.01	5.95		5.96	10.05
0130	2" to 4" square		24	.333		.04	11.90		11.94	20
0140	Cut square, patch, sand and finish, holes, up to 2" square		12	.667		.04	24		24.04	40
0150	2" to 4" square		11	.727		.09	26		26.09	44
0160	4" to 8" square		10	.800		.24	28.50		28.74	48.50
0170	8" to 12" square		8	1		.47	36		36.47	60.50
0180	12" to 32" square		6	1.333		1.55	47.50		49.05	81.50
0210	16" by 48"		5	1.600		2.61	57		59.61	99
0220	32" by 48"		4	2		4.12	71.50		75.62	125
0230	48" square		3.50	2.286		5.80	81.50		87.30	143
0240	60" square		3.20	2.500		9.35	89.50		98.85	160
0500	Skim coat surface with joint compound		1600	.005	S.F.	.03	.18		.21	.34
0510	Prepare, retape and refinish joints		60	.133	L.F.	.67	4.77		5.44	8.75

09 05 Common Work Results for Finishes

09 05 05 – Selective Finishes Demolition

09 05 05.10 Selective Demolition, Ceilings

			Crew	Daily Output	Labor-Hours	Unit	Material	Labor	Equipment	Total	Total Incl O&P
0010	**SELECTIVE DEMOLITION, CEILINGS**	R024119-10									
0200	Ceiling, drywall, furred and nailed or screwed		2 Clab	800	.020	S.F.		.56		.56	.95
0220	On metal frame			760	.021			.59		.59	1
0240	On suspension system, including system			720	.022			.63		.63	1.05
1000	Plaster, lime and horse hair, on wood lath, incl. lath			700	.023			.64		.64	1.08
1020	On metal lath			570	.028			.79		.79	1.33
1100	Gypsum, on gypsum lath			720	.022			.63		.63	1.05
1120	On metal lath			500	.032			.90		.90	1.52
1200	Suspended ceiling, mineral fiber, 2' x 2' or 2' x 4'			1500	.011			.30		.30	.51
1250	On suspension system, incl. system			1200	.013			.38		.38	.63
1500	Tile, wood fiber, 12" x 12", glued			900	.018			.50		.50	.84
1540	Stapled			1500	.011			.30		.30	.51
1580	On suspension system, incl. system			760	.021			.59		.59	1
2000	Wood, tongue and groove, 1" x 4"			1000	.016			.45		.45	.76
2040	1" x 8"			1100	.015			.41		.41	.69
2400	Plywood or wood fiberboard, 4' x 8' sheets			1200	.013			.38		.38	.63

09 05 05.20 Selective Demolition, Flooring

			Crew	Daily Output	Labor-Hours	Unit	Material	Labor	Equipment	Total	Total Incl O&P
0010	**SELECTIVE DEMOLITION, FLOORING**	R024119-10									
0200	Brick with mortar		2 Clab	475	.034	S.F.		.95		.95	1.60
0400	Carpet, bonded, including surface scraping			2000	.008			.23		.23	.38
0440	Scrim applied			8000	.002			.06		.06	.09
0480	Tackless			9000	.002			.05		.05	.08
0550	Carpet tile, releasable adhesive			5000	.003			.09		.09	.15
0560	Permanent adhesive			1850	.009			.24		.24	.41
0601	Composition		1 Clab	200	.040			1.13		1.13	1.90

09 05 Common Work Results for Finishes

09 05 05 – Selective Finishes Demolition

09 05 05.20 Selective Demolition, Flooring

		Crew	Daily Output	Labor-Hours	Unit	Material	2014 Bare Costs Labor	Equipment	Total	Total Incl O&P
0800	Resilient, sheet goods	2 Clab	1400	.011	S.F.		.32		.32	.54
0820	For gym floors	"	900	.018	↓		.50		.50	.84
0850	Vinyl or rubber cove base	1 Clab	1000	.008	L.F.		.23		.23	.38
0860	Vinyl or rubber cove base, molded corner	"	1000	.008	Ea.		.23		.23	.38
0870	For glued and caulked installation, add to labor						50%			
0900	Vinyl composition tile, 12" x 12"	2 Clab	1000	.016	S.F.		.45		.45	.76
2000	Tile, ceramic, thin set		675	.024			.67		.67	1.12
2020	Mud set		625	.026			.72		.72	1.21
2200	Marble, slate, thin set		675	.024			.67		.67	1.12
2220	Mud set		625	.026			.72		.72	1.21
2600	Terrazzo, thin set		450	.036			1		1	1.69
2620	Mud set		425	.038			1.06		1.06	1.79
2640	Terrazzo, cast in place	↓	300	.053			1.50		1.50	2.53
3000	Wood, block, on end	1 Carp	400	.020			.72		.72	1.20
3200	Parquet		450	.018			.64		.64	1.07
3400	Strip flooring, interior, 2-1/4" x 25/32" thick		325	.025			.88		.88	1.48
3500	Exterior, porch flooring, 1" x 4"		220	.036			1.30		1.30	2.19
3800	Subfloor, tongue and groove, 1" x 6"		325	.025			.88		.88	1.48
3820	1" x 8"		430	.019			.67		.67	1.12
3840	1" x 10"		520	.015			.55		.55	.93
4000	Plywood, nailed		600	.013			.48		.48	.80
4100	Glued and nailed		400	.020			.72		.72	1.20
4200	Hardboard, 1/4" thick	↓	760	.011			.38		.38	.63
8000	Remove flooring, bead blast, minimum	A-1A	1000	.008			.29	.21	.50	.73
8100	Maximum		400	.020			.73	.54	1.27	1.82
8150	Mastic only	↓	1500	.005	↓		.19	.14	.33	.49

09 05 05.30 Selective Demolition, Walls and Partitions

		Crew	Daily Output	Labor-Hours	Unit	Material	2014 Bare Costs Labor	Equipment	Total	Total Incl O&P
0010	**SELECTIVE DEMOLITION, WALLS AND PARTITIONS** R024119-10									
0020	Walls, concrete, reinforced	B-39	120	.400	C.F.		11.40	1.95	13.35	21.50
0025	Plain	"	160	.300			8.55	1.46	10.01	16
0100	Brick, 4" to 12" thick	B-9	220	.182	↓		5.20	1.06	6.26	9.90
0200	Concrete block, 4" thick		1150	.035	S.F.		.99	.20	1.19	1.89
0280	8" thick		1050	.038			1.09	.22	1.31	2.07
0300	Exterior stucco 1" thick over mesh	↓	3200	.013			.36	.07	.43	.68
1000	Drywall, nailed or screwed	1 Clab	1000	.008			.23		.23	.38
1010	2 layers		400	.020			.56		.56	.95
1020	Glued and nailed		900	.009			.25		.25	.42
1500	Fiberboard, nailed		900	.009			.25		.25	.42
1520	Glued and nailed		800	.010			.28		.28	.47
1568	Plenum barrier, sheet lead		300	.027			.75		.75	1.27
2000	Movable walls, metal, 5' high		300	.027			.75		.75	1.27
2020	8' high	↓	400	.020			.56		.56	.95
2200	Metal or wood studs, finish 2 sides, fiberboard	B-1	520	.046			1.33		1.33	2.24
2250	Lath and plaster		260	.092			2.67		2.67	4.48
2300	Plasterboard (drywall)		520	.046			1.33		1.33	2.24
2350	Plywood	↓	450	.053			1.54		1.54	2.59
2800	Paneling, 4' x 8' sheets	1 Clab	475	.017			.47		.47	.80
3000	Plaster, lime and horsehair, on wood lath		400	.020			.56		.56	.95
3020	On metal lath		335	.024			.67		.67	1.13
3400	Gypsum or perlite, on gypsum lath		410	.020			.55		.55	.93
3420	On metal lath		300	.027	↓		.75		.75	1.27
3450	Plaster, interior gypsum, acoustic, or cement	↓	60	.133	S.Y.		3.76		3.76	6.35

09 05 Common Work Results for Finishes

09 05 05 – Selective Finishes Demolition

09 05 05.30 Selective Demolition, Walls and Partitions

09 05 05.30 Selective Demolition, Walls and Partitions	Crew	Daily Output	Labor-Hours	Unit	Material	2014 Bare Costs Labor	Equipment	Total	Total Incl O&P
3500	Stucco, on masonry	1 Clab	145	.055	S.Y.		1.56		1.56	2.62
3510	Commercial 3-coat		80	.100			2.82		2.82	4.75
3520	Interior stucco	↓	25	.320	↓		9		9	15.20
3600	Plywood, one side	B-1	1500	.016	S.F.		.46		.46	.78
3750	Terra cotta block and plaster, to 6" thick	"	175	.137			3.96		3.96	6.65
3760	Tile, ceramic, on walls, thin set	1 Clab	300	.027			.75		.75	1.27
3765	Mud set		250	.032	↓		.90		.90	1.52
3800	Toilet partitions, slate or marble		5	1.600	Ea.		45		45	76
3820	Metal or plastic	↓	8	1	"		28		28	47.50

09 21 Plaster and Gypsum Board Assemblies

09 21 13 – Plaster Assemblies

09 21 13.10 Plaster Partition Wall

		Crew	Daily Output	Labor-Hours	Unit	Material	2014 Bare Costs Labor	Equipment	Total	Total Incl O&P
0010	**PLASTER PARTITION WALL**									
0400	Stud walls, 3.4 lb. metal lath, 3 coat gypsum plaster, 2 sides									
0600	2" x 4" wood studs, 16" O.C.	J-2	315	.152	S.F.	3.32	4.77	.46	8.55	11.95
0700	2-1/2" metal studs, 25 ga., 12" O.C.		325	.148		3.08	4.62	.44	8.14	11.50
0800	3-5/8" metal studs, 25 ga., 16" O.C.	↓	320	.150	↓	3.10	4.69	.45	8.24	11.60
0900	Gypsum lath, 2 coat vermiculite plaster, 2 sides									
1000	2" x 4" wood studs, 16" O.C.	J-2	355	.135	S.F.	3.70	4.23	.40	8.33	11.45
1200	2-1/2" metal studs, 25 ga., 12" O.C.		365	.132		3.28	4.11	.39	7.78	10.80
1300	3-5/8" metal studs, 25 ga., 16" O.C.	↓	360	.133	↓	3.37	4.17	.40	7.94	11

09 21 16 – Gypsum Board Assemblies

09 21 16.23 Gypsum Board Shaft Wall Assemblies

		Crew	Daily Output	Labor-Hours	Unit	Material	2014 Bare Costs Labor	Equipment	Total	Total Incl O&P
0010	**GYPSUM BOARD SHAFT WALL ASSEMBLIES**									
0030	1" thick coreboard wall liner on shaft side									
0040	2-hour assembly with double layer									
0060	5/8" fire rated gypsum board on room side	2 Carp	220	.073	S.F.	2.02	2.60		4.62	6.60
0100	3-hour assembly with triple layer									
0300	5/8" fire rated gypsum board on room side	2 Carp	180	.089	S.F.	1.70	3.18		4.88	7.20
0400	4-hour assembly, 1" coreboard, 5/8" fire rated gypsum board									
0600	and 3/4" galv. metal furring channels, 24" O.C., with									
0700	Double layer 5/8" fire rated gypsum board on room side	2 Carp	110	.145	S.F.	1.59	5.20		6.79	10.50
0900	For taping & finishing, add per side	1 Carp	1050	.008	"	.05	.27		.32	.51
1000	For insulation, see Section 07 21									
5200	For work over 8' high, add	2 Carp	3060	.005	S.F.		.19		.19	.31
5300	For distribution cost over 3 stories high, add per story	"	6100	.003	"		.09		.09	.16

09 21 16.33 Partition Wall

		Crew	Daily Output	Labor-Hours	Unit	Material	2014 Bare Costs Labor	Equipment	Total	Total Incl O&P
0010	**PARTITION WALL** Stud wall, 8' to 12' high									
0050	1/2", interior, gypsum board, std, tape & finish 2 sides									
0500	Installed on and incl., 2" x 4" wood studs, 16" O.C.	2 Carp	310	.052	S.F.	1.12	1.85		2.97	4.33
1000	Metal studs, NLB, 25 ga., 16" O.C., 3-5/8" wide		350	.046		1.06	1.63		2.69	3.92
1200	6" wide		330	.048		1.20	1.73		2.93	4.24
1400	Water resistant, on 2" x 4" wood studs, 16" O.C.		310	.052		1.28	1.85		3.13	4.51
1600	Metal studs, NLB, 25 ga., 16" O.C., 3-5/8" wide		350	.046		1.22	1.63		2.85	4.10
1800	6" wide		330	.048		1.36	1.73		3.09	4.42
2000	Fire res., 2 layers, 1-1/2 hr., on 2" x 4" wood studs, 16" O.C.		210	.076		1.80	2.72		4.52	6.55
2200	Metal studs, NLB, 25 ga., 16" O.C., 3-5/8" wide		250	.064		1.74	2.29		4.03	5.75
2400	6" wide		230	.070		1.88	2.49		4.37	6.25
2600	Fire & water res., 2 layers, 1-1/2 hr., 2" x 4" studs, 16" O.C.		210	.076		1.80	2.72		4.52	6.55

09 21 Plaster and Gypsum Board Assemblies

09 21 16 – Gypsum Board Assemblies

09 21 16.33 Partition Wall

		Crew	Daily Output	Labor-Hours	Unit	Material	2014 Bare Costs Labor	Equipment	Total	Total Incl O&P
2800	Metal studs, NLB, 25 ga., 16" O.C., 3-5/8" wide	2 Carp	250	.064	S.F.	1.74	2.29		4.03	5.75
3000	6" wide	↓	230	.070	↓	1.88	2.49		4.37	6.25
3200	5/8", interior, gypsum board, standard, tape & finish 2 sides									
3400	Installed on and including 2" x 4" wood studs, 16" O.C.	2 Carp	300	.053	S.F.	1.16	1.91		3.07	4.49
3600	24" O.C.		330	.048		1.07	1.73		2.80	4.09
3800	Metal studs, NLB, 25 ga., 16" O.C., 3-5/8" wide		340	.047		1.10	1.68		2.78	4.04
4000	6" wide		320	.050		1.24	1.79		3.03	4.38
4200	24" O.C., 3-5/8" wide		360	.044		1.01	1.59		2.60	3.78
4400	6" wide		340	.047		1.11	1.68		2.79	4.05
4800	Water resistant, on 2" x 4" wood studs, 16" O.C.		300	.053		1.42	1.91		3.33	4.77
5000	24" O.C.		330	.048		1.33	1.73		3.06	4.38
5200	Metal studs, NLB, 25 ga. 16" O.C., 3-5/8" wide		340	.047		1.36	1.68		3.04	4.33
5400	6" wide		320	.050		1.50	1.79		3.29	4.66
5600	24" O.C., 3-5/8" wide		360	.044		1.27	1.59		2.86	4.06
5800	6" wide		340	.047		1.37	1.68		3.05	4.34
6000	Fire resistant, 2 layers, 2 hr., on 2" x 4" wood studs, 16" O.C.		205	.078		1.79	2.79		4.58	6.65
6200	24" O.C.		235	.068		1.79	2.43		4.22	6.05
6400	Metal studs, NLB, 25 ga., 16" O.C., 3-5/8" wide		245	.065		1.85	2.33		4.18	5.95
6600	6" wide		225	.071		1.96	2.54		4.50	6.45
6800	24" O.C., 3-5/8" wide		265	.060		1.73	2.16		3.89	5.55
7000	6" wide		245	.065		1.83	2.33		4.16	5.95
7200	Fire & water resistant, 2 layers, 2 hr., 2" x 4" studs, 16" O.C.		205	.078		1.88	2.79		4.67	6.75
7400	24" O.C.		235	.068		1.79	2.43		4.22	6.05
7600	Metal studs, NLB, 25 ga., 16" O.C., 3-5/8" wide		245	.065		1.82	2.33		4.15	5.95
7800	6" wide		225	.071		1.96	2.54		4.50	6.45
8000	24" O.C., 3-5/8" wide		265	.060		1.73	2.16		3.89	5.55
8200	6" wide	↓	245	.065	↓	1.83	2.33		4.16	5.95
8600	1/2" blueboard, mesh tape both sides									
8620	Installed on and including 2" x 4" wood studs, 16" O.C.	2 Carp	300	.053	S.F.	1.16	1.91		3.07	4.49
8640	Metal studs, NLB, 25 ga., 16" O.C., 3-5/8" wide		340	.047		1.10	1.68		2.78	4.04
8660	6" wide	↓	320	.050	↓	1.24	1.79		3.03	4.38
9000	Exterior, 1/2" gypsum sheathing, 1/2" gypsum finished, interior,									
9100	including foil faced insulation, metal studs, 20 ga.									
9200	16" O.C., 3-5/8" wide	2 Carp	290	.055	S.F.	1.70	1.97		3.67	5.20
9400	6" wide	↓	270	.059		1.95	2.12		4.07	5.70
9600	Partitions, for work over 8' high, add	↓	1530	.010	↓		.37		.37	.63

09 22 Supports for Plaster and Gypsum Board

09 22 03 – Fastening Methods for Finishes

09 22 03.20 Drilling Plaster/Drywall

		Crew	Daily Output	Labor-Hours	Unit	Material	2014 Bare Costs Labor	Equipment	Total	Total Incl O&P
0010	**DRILLING PLASTER/DRYWALL**									
1100	Drilling & layout for drywall/plaster walls, up to 1" deep, no anchor									
1200	Holes, 1/4" diameter	1 Carp	150	.053	Ea.	.01	1.91		1.92	3.22
1300	3/8" diameter		140	.057		.01	2.04		2.05	3.45
1400	1/2" diameter		130	.062		.01	2.20		2.21	3.71
1500	3/4" diameter		120	.067		.01	2.38		2.39	4.03
1600	1" diameter		110	.073		.02	2.60		2.62	4.39
1700	1-1/4" diameter		100	.080		.03	2.86		2.89	4.84
1800	1-1/2" diameter	↓	90	.089		.04	3.18		3.22	5.40
1900	For ceiling installations, add				↓		40%			

09 22 Supports for Plaster and Gypsum Board

09 22 13 – Metal Furring

09 22 13.13 Metal Channel Furring		Crew	Daily Output	Labor-Hours	Unit	Material	2014 Bare Costs Labor	Equipment	Total	Total Incl O&P
0010	**METAL CHANNEL FURRING**									
0030	Beams and columns, 7/8" channels, galvanized, 12" O.C.	1 Lath	155	.052	S.F.	.37	1.63		2	3.04
0050	16" O.C.		170	.047		.31	1.49		1.80	2.74
0070	24" O.C.		185	.043		.20	1.37		1.57	2.42
0100	Ceilings, on steel, 7/8" channels, galvanized, 12" O.C.		210	.038		.34	1.21		1.55	2.31
0300	16" O.C.		290	.028		.31	.87		1.18	1.75
0400	24" O.C.		420	.019		.20	.60		.80	1.19
0600	1-5/8" channels, galvanized, 12" O.C.		190	.042		.46	1.33		1.79	2.66
0700	16" O.C.		260	.031		.41	.97		1.38	2.03
0900	24" O.C.		390	.021		.28	.65		.93	1.35
0930	7/8" channels with sound isolation clips, 12" O.C.		120	.067		1.72	2.11		3.83	5.30
0940	16" O.C.		100	.080		1.29	2.53		3.82	5.50
0950	24" O.C.		165	.048		.86	1.53		2.39	3.41
0960	1-5/8" channels, galvanized, 12" O.C.		110	.073		1.83	2.30		4.13	5.75
0970	16" O.C.		100	.080		1.38	2.53		3.91	5.60
0980	24" O.C.		155	.052		.92	1.63		2.55	3.64
1000	Walls, 7/8" channels, galvanized, 12" O.C.		235	.034		.34	1.08		1.42	2.10
1200	16" O.C.		265	.030		.31	.96		1.27	1.88
1300	24" O.C.		350	.023		.20	.72		.92	1.38
1500	1-5/8" channels, galvanized, 12" O.C.		210	.038		.46	1.21		1.67	2.45
1600	16" O.C.		240	.033		.41	1.05		1.46	2.16
1800	24" O.C.		305	.026		.28	.83		1.11	1.64
1920	7/8" channels with sound isolation clips, 12" O.C.		125	.064		1.72	2.03		3.75	5.15
1940	16" O.C.		100	.080		1.29	2.53		3.82	5.50
1950	24" O.C.		150	.053		.86	1.69		2.55	3.66
1960	1-5/8" channels, galvanized, 12" O.C.		115	.070		1.83	2.20		4.03	5.55
1970	16" O.C.		95	.084		1.38	2.67		4.05	5.80
1980	24" O.C.		140	.057		.92	1.81		2.73	3.92

09 22 16 – Non-Structural Metal Framing

09 22 16.13 Non-Structural Metal Stud Framing		Crew	Daily Output	Labor-Hours	Unit	Material	2014 Bare Costs Labor	Equipment	Total	Total Incl O&P
0010	**NON-STRUCTURAL METAL STUD FRAMING**									
1600	Non-load bearing, galv., 8' high, 25 ga. 1-5/8" wide, 16" O.C.	1 Carp	619	.013	S.F.	.27	.46		.73	1.08
1610	24" O.C.		950	.008		.20	.30		.50	.74
1620	2-1/2" wide, 16" O.C.		613	.013		.32	.47		.79	1.14
1630	24" O.C.		938	.009		.24	.30		.54	.78
1640	3-5/8" wide, 16" O.C.		600	.013		.39	.48		.87	1.22
1650	24" O.C.		925	.009		.29	.31		.60	.84
1660	4" wide, 16" O.C.		594	.013		.42	.48		.90	1.28
1670	24" O.C.		925	.009		.32	.31		.63	.87
1680	6" wide, 16" O.C.		588	.014		.53	.49		1.02	1.40
1690	24" O.C.		906	.009		.40	.32		.72	.97
1700	20 ga. studs, 1-5/8" wide, 16" O.C.		494	.016		.38	.58		.96	1.38
1710	24" O.C.		763	.010		.28	.37		.65	.94
1720	2-1/2" wide, 16" O.C.		488	.016		.46	.59		1.05	1.49
1730	24" O.C.		750	.011		.35	.38		.73	1.02
1740	3-5/8" wide, 16" O.C.		481	.017		.50	.59		1.09	1.55
1750	24" O.C.		738	.011		.37	.39		.76	1.06
1760	4" wide, 16" O.C.		475	.017		.60	.60		1.20	1.67
1770	24" O.C.		738	.011		.45	.39		.84	1.15
1780	6" wide, 16" O.C.		469	.017		.76	.61		1.37	1.86
1790	24" O.C.		725	.011		.57	.39		.96	1.29
2000	Non-load bearing, galv., 10' high, 25 ga. 1-5/8" wide, 16" O.C.		495	.016		.26	.58		.84	1.25

09 22 Supports for Plaster and Gypsum Board

09 22 16 – Non-Structural Metal Framing

09 22 16.13 Non-Structural Metal Stud Framing	Crew	Daily Output	Labor-Hours	Unit	Material	2014 Bare Costs Labor	Equipment	Total	Total Incl O&P
2100	24" O.C.	1 Carp	760	.011	S.F.	.19	.38		.57	.84
2200	2-1/2" wide, 16" O.C.		490	.016		.30	.58		.88	1.31
2250	24" O.C.		750	.011		.22	.38		.60	.89
2300	3-5/8" wide, 16" O.C.		480	.017		.36	.60		.96	1.40
2350	24" O.C.		740	.011		.27	.39		.66	.95
2400	4" wide, 16" O.C.		475	.017		.40	.60		1	1.45
2450	24" O.C.		740	.011		.30	.39		.69	.97
2500	6" wide, 16" O.C.		470	.017		.50	.61		1.11	1.57
2550	24" O.C.		725	.011		.37	.39		.76	1.07
2600	20 ga. studs, 1-5/8" wide, 16" O.C.		395	.020		.36	.72		1.08	1.61
2650	24" O.C.		610	.013		.26	.47		.73	1.08
2700	2-1/2" wide, 16" O.C.		390	.021		.43	.73		1.16	1.71
2750	24" O.C.		600	.013		.32	.48		.80	1.15
2800	3-5/8" wide, 16" OC		385	.021		.47	.74		1.21	1.77
2850	24" O.C.		590	.014		.35	.48		.83	1.20
2900	4" wide, 16" O.C.		380	.021		.57	.75		1.32	1.90
2950	24" O.C.		590	.014		.42	.48		.90	1.28
3000	6" wide, 16" O.C.		375	.021		.72	.76		1.48	2.07
3050	24" O.C.		580	.014		.53	.49		1.02	1.41
3060	Non-load bearing, galv., 12' high, 25 ga. 1-5/8" wide, 16" O.C.		413	.019		.25	.69		.94	1.44
3070	24" O.C.		633	.013		.18	.45		.63	.96
3080	2-1/2" wide, 16" O.C.		408	.020		.29	.70		.99	1.50
3090	24" O.C.		625	.013		.21	.46		.67	1
3100	3-5/8" wide, 16" O.C.		400	.020		.35	.72		1.07	1.58
3110	24" O.C.		617	.013		.25	.46		.71	1.06
3120	4" wide, 16" O.C.		396	.020		.38	.72		1.10	1.64
3130	24" O.C.		617	.013		.28	.46		.74	1.09
3140	6" wide, 16" O.C.		392	.020		.48	.73		1.21	1.76
3150	24" O.C.		604	.013		.35	.47		.82	1.18
3160	20 ga. studs, 1-5/8" wide, 16" O.C.		329	.024		.34	.87		1.21	1.83
3170	24" O.C.		508	.016		.25	.56		.81	1.22
3180	2-1/2" wide, 16" O.C.		325	.025		.41	.88		1.29	1.93
3190	24" O.C.		500	.016		.30	.57		.87	1.29
3200	3-5/8" wide, 16" O.C.		321	.025		.45	.89		1.34	2
3210	24" O.C.		492	.016		.33	.58		.91	1.34
3220	4" wide, 16" O.C.		317	.025		.55	.90		1.45	2.12
3230	24" O.C.		492	.016		.40	.58		.98	1.42
3240	6" wide, 16" O.C.		313	.026		.69	.91		1.60	2.30
3250	24" O.C.		483	.017		.50	.59		1.09	1.55
5000	Load bearing studs, see Section 05 41 13.30									

09 22 26 – Suspension Systems

09 22 26.13 Ceiling Suspension Systems

		Crew	Daily Output	Labor-Hours	Unit	Material	2014 Bare Costs Labor	Equipment	Total	Total Incl O&P
0010	**CEILING SUSPENSION SYSTEMS** for gypsum board or plaster									
8000	Suspended ceilings, including carriers									
8200	1-1/2" carriers, 24" O.C. with:									
8300	7/8" channels, 16" O.C.	1 Lath	275	.029	S.F.	.51	.92		1.43	2.04
8320	24" O.C.		310	.026		.41	.82		1.23	1.77
8400	1-5/8" channels, 16" O.C.		205	.039		.62	1.24		1.86	2.67
8420	24" O.C.		250	.032		.48	1.01		1.49	2.16
8600	2" carriers, 24" O.C. with:									
8700	7/8" channels, 16" O.C.	1 Lath	250	.032	S.F.	.56	1.01		1.57	2.24
8720	24" O.C.		285	.028		.45	.89		1.34	1.93

09 22 Supports for Plaster and Gypsum Board

09 22 26 – Suspension Systems

09 22 26.13 Ceiling Suspension Systems	Crew	Daily Output	Labor-Hours	Unit	Material	2014 Bare Costs Labor	Equipment	Total	Total Incl O&P
8800	1-5/8" channels, 16" O.C.	1 Lath	190	.042	S.F.	.66	1.33		1.99	2.88
8820	24" O.C.		225	.036		.53	1.13		1.66	2.39

09 22 36 – Lath

09 22 36.13 Gypsum Lath

0010	**GYPSUM LATH** R092000-50									
0020	Plain or perforated, nailed, 3/8" thick	1 Lath	85	.094	S.Y.	2.70	2.98		5.68	7.75
0100	1/2" thick		80	.100		2.43	3.17		5.60	7.75
0300	Clipped to steel studs, 3/8" thick		75	.107		2.70	3.38		6.08	8.40
0400	1/2" thick		70	.114		2.43	3.62		6.05	8.45
1500	For ceiling installations, add		216	.037			1.17		1.17	1.89
1600	For columns and beams, add		170	.047			1.49		1.49	2.40

09 22 36.23 Metal Lath

0010	**METAL LATH** R092000-50									
0020	Diamond, expanded, 2.5 lb. per S.Y., painted				S.Y.	4.24			4.24	4.66
0100	Galvanized					3.05			3.05	3.36
0300	3.4 lb. per S.Y., painted					3.47			3.47	3.82
0400	Galvanized					3.80			3.80	4.18
0600	For 15# asphalt sheathing paper, add					.49			.49	.53
0900	Flat rib, 1/8" high, 2.75 lb., painted					3.26			3.26	3.59
1000	Foil backed					3.14			3.14	3.45
1200	3.4 lb. per S.Y., painted					4.28			4.28	4.71
1300	Galvanized					5.85			5.85	6.40
1500	For 15# asphalt sheathing paper, add					.49			.49	.53
1800	High rib, 3/8" high, 3.4 lb. per S.Y., painted					4.39			4.39	4.83
1900	Galvanized					3.71			3.71	4.08
2400	3/4" high, painted, .60 lb. per S.F.				S.F.	.62			.62	.68
2500	.75 lb. per S.F.				"	1.33			1.33	1.46
2800	Stucco mesh, painted, 3.6 lb.				S.Y.	4.03			4.03	4.43
3000	K-lath, perforated, absorbent paper, regular					4.42			4.42	4.86
3100	Heavy duty					5.20			5.20	5.75
3300	Waterproof, heavy duty, grade B backing					5.10			5.10	5.60
3400	Fire resistant backing					5.65			5.65	6.20
3600	2.5 lb. diamond painted, on wood framing, on walls	1 Lath	85	.094		4.24	2.98		7.22	9.45
3700	On ceilings		75	.107		4.24	3.38		7.62	10.10
3900	3.4 lb. diamond painted, on wood framing, on walls		80	.100		4.28	3.17		7.45	9.80
4000	On ceilings		70	.114		4.28	3.62		7.90	10.50
4200	3.4 lb. diamond painted, wired to steel framing		75	.107		4.28	3.38		7.66	10.15
4300	On ceilings		60	.133		4.28	4.22		8.50	11.50
4500	Columns and beams, wired to steel		40	.200		4.28	6.35		10.63	14.90
4600	Cornices, wired to steel		35	.229		4.28	7.25		11.53	16.35
4800	Screwed to steel studs, 2.5 lb.		80	.100		4.24	3.17		7.41	9.75
4900	3.4 lb.		75	.107		3.47	3.38		6.85	9.25
5100	Rib lath, painted, wired to steel, on walls, 2.5 lb.		75	.107		3.26	3.38		6.64	9.05
5200	3.4 lb.		70	.114		4.39	3.62		8.01	10.65
5400	4.0 lb.		65	.123		5.70	3.90		9.60	12.50
5500	For self-furring lath, add					.11			.11	.12
5700	Suspended ceiling system, incl. 3.4 lb. diamond lath, painted	1 Lath	15	.533		3.58	16.90		20.48	31
5800	Galvanized	"	15	.533		4.53	16.90		21.43	32
6000	Hollow metal stud partitions, 3.4 lb. painted lath both sides									
6010	Non-load bearing, 25 ga., w/rib lath 2-1/2" studs, 12" O.C.	1 Lath	20.30	.394	S.Y.	12.25	12.45		24.70	33.50
6300	16" O.C.		21.10	.379		11.50	12		23.50	32
6350	24" O.C.		22.70	.352		10.80	11.15		21.95	30

09 22 Supports for Plaster and Gypsum Board

09 22 36 – Lath

09 22 36.23 Metal Lath

		Crew	Daily Output	Labor-Hours	Unit	Material	2014 Bare Costs Labor	2014 Bare Costs Equipment	Total	Total Incl O&P
6400	3-5/8" studs, 16" O.C.	1 Lath	19.50	.410	S.Y.	12.05	13		25.05	34.50
6600	24" O.C.		20.40	.392		11.20	12.40		23.60	32.50
6700	4" studs, 16" O.C.		20.40	.392		12.40	12.40		24.80	33.50
6900	24" O.C.		21.60	.370		11.45	11.70		23.15	31.50
7000	6" studs, 16" O.C.		19.50	.410		13.30	13		26.30	35.50
7100	24" O.C.		21.10	.379		12.10	12		24.10	32.50
7200	L.B. partitions, 16 ga., w/rib lath, 2-1/2" studs, 16" O.C.		20	.400		12.45	12.65		25.10	34
7300	3-5/8" studs, 16 ga.		19.70	.406		14.15	12.85		27	36
7500	4" studs, 16 ga.		19.50	.410		14.70	13		27.70	37
7600	6" studs, 16 ga.		18.70	.428		17.35	13.55		30.90	41

09 22 36.43 Security Mesh

		Crew	Daily Output	Labor-Hours	Unit	Material	2014 Bare Costs Labor	2014 Bare Costs Equipment	Total	Total Incl O&P
0010	**SECURITY MESH**, expanded metal, flat, screwed to framing									
0100	On walls, 3/4", 1.76 lb./S.F.	2 Carp	1500	.011	S.F.	1.77	.38		2.15	2.59
0110	1-1/2", 1.14 lb./S.F.		1600	.010		1.52	.36		1.88	2.27
0200	On ceilings, 3/4", 1.76 lb./S.F.		1350	.012		1.77	.42		2.19	2.66
0210	1-1/2", 1.14 lb./S.F.		1450	.011		1.52	.39		1.91	2.33

09 22 36.83 Accessories, Plaster

		Crew	Daily Output	Labor-Hours	Unit	Material	2014 Bare Costs Labor	2014 Bare Costs Equipment	Total	Total Incl O&P
0010	**ACCESSORIES, PLASTER**									
0020	Casing bead, expanded flange, galvanized	1 Lath	2.70	2.963	C.L.F.	50.50	94		144.50	207
0200	Foundation weep screed, galvanized	"	2.70	2.963		52	94		146	208
0900	Channels, cold rolled, 16 ga., 3/4" deep, galvanized					34			34	37.50
1200	1-1/2" deep, 16 ga., galvanized					46			46	50.50
1620	Corner bead, expanded bullnose, 3/4" radius, #10, galvanized	1 Lath	2.60	3.077		25	97.50		122.50	185
1650	#1, galvanized		2.55	3.137		44	99.50		143.50	209
1670	Expanded wing, 2-3/4" wide, #1, galvanized		2.65	3.019		37	95.50		132.50	195
1700	Inside corner (corner rite), 3" x 3", painted		2.60	3.077		21	97.50		118.50	181
1750	Strip-ex, 4" wide, painted		2.55	3.137		37	99.50		136.50	201
1800	Expansion joint, 3/4" grounds, limited expansion, galv., 1 piece		2.70	2.963		81.50	94		175.50	241
2100	Extreme expansion, galvanized, 2 piece		2.60	3.077		149	97.50		246.50	320

09 23 Gypsum Plastering

09 23 13 – Acoustical Gypsum Plastering

09 23 13.10 Perlite or Vermiculite Plaster

		Crew	Daily Output	Labor-Hours	Unit	Material	2014 Bare Costs Labor	2014 Bare Costs Equipment	Total	Total Incl O&P
0010	**PERLITE OR VERMICULITE PLASTER** R092000-50									
0020	In 100 lb. bags, under 200 bags				Bag	16.65			16.65	18.30
0100	Over 200 bags				"	15.80			15.80	17.40
0300	2 coats, no lath included, on walls	J-1	92	.435	S.Y.	3.78	13.55	1.56	18.89	28.50
0400	On ceilings	"	79	.506		3.78	15.80	1.82	21.40	32
0600	On and incl. 3/8" gypsum lath, on metal studs	J-2	84	.571		7.50	17.90	1.71	27.11	39.50
0700	On ceilings	"	70	.686		7.50	21.50	2.05	31.05	45.50
0900	3 coats, no lath included, on walls	J-1	74	.541		6.30	16.90	1.94	25.14	37
1000	On ceilings	"	63	.635		6.30	19.80	2.28	28.38	42
1200	On and incl. painted metal lath, on metal studs	J-2	72	.667		10.70	21	1.99	33.69	48
1300	On ceilings		61	.787		10.70	24.50	2.35	37.55	55
1500	On and incl. suspended metal lath ceiling		37	1.297		9.90	40.50	3.88	54.28	81.50
1700	For irregular or curved surfaces, add to above						30%			
1800	For columns and beams, add to above						50%			
1900	For soffits, add to ceiling prices						40%			

09 23 Gypsum Plastering

09 23 20 – Gypsum Plaster

09 23 20.10 Gypsum Plaster On Walls and Ceilings

	09 23 20.10 Gypsum Plaster On Walls and Ceilings	Crew	Daily Output	Labor-Hours	Unit	Material	2014 Bare Costs Labor	2014 Bare Costs Equipment	Total	Total Incl O&P
0010	**GYPSUM PLASTER ON WALLS AND CEILINGS** R092000-50									
0020	80# bag, less than 1 ton				Bag	14.45			14.45	15.85
0100	Over 1 ton				"	12.70			12.70	13.95
0300	2 coats, no lath included, on walls	J-1	105	.381	S.Y.	3.37	11.90	1.37	16.64	25
0400	On ceilings	"	92	.435		3.37	13.55	1.56	18.48	28
0600	On and incl. 3/8" gypsum lath on steel, on walls	J-2	97	.495		6.05	15.50	1.48	23.03	34
0700	On ceilings	"	83	.578		6.05	18.10	1.73	25.88	38
0900	3 coats, no lath included, on walls	J-1	87	.460		4.82	14.35	1.65	20.82	30.50
1000	On ceilings	"	78	.513		4.82	16	1.84	22.66	34
1200	On and including painted metal lath, on wood studs	J-2	86	.558		9.55	17.45	1.67	28.67	41
1300	On ceilings	"	76.50	.627		9.55	19.65	1.88	31.08	44.50
1600	For irregular or curved surfaces, add						30%			
1800	For columns & beams, add						50%			

09 23 20.20 Gauging Plaster

		Crew	Daily Output	Labor-Hours	Unit	Material	Labor	Equipment	Total	Total Incl O&P
0010	**GAUGING PLASTER** R092000-50									
0020	100 lb. bags, less than 1 ton				Bag	19.60			19.60	21.50
0100	Over 1 ton				"	17.95			17.95	19.75

09 23 20.30 Keenes Cement

		Crew	Daily Output	Labor-Hours	Unit	Material	Labor	Equipment	Total	Total Incl O&P
0010	**KEENES CEMENT** R092000-50									
0020	In 100 lb. bags, less than 1 ton				Bag	20.50			20.50	22.50
0100	Over 1 ton				"	19.35			19.35	21.50
0300	Finish only, add to plaster prices, standard	J-1	215	.186	S.Y.	1.86	5.80	.67	8.33	12.35
0400	High quality	"	144	.278	"	1.88	8.65	1	11.53	17.40

09 24 Cement Plastering

09 24 23 – Cement Stucco

09 24 23.40 Stucco

		Crew	Daily Output	Labor-Hours	Unit	Material	Labor	Equipment	Total	Total Incl O&P
0010	**STUCCO** R092000-50									
0015	3 coats 1" thick, float finish, with mesh, on wood frame	J-2	63	.762	S.Y.	6.55	24	2.28	32.83	48.50
0100	On masonry construction, no mesh incl.	J-1	67	.597		2.50	18.65	2.14	23.29	35.50
0300	For trowel finish, add	1 Plas	170	.047			1.54		1.54	2.53
0400	For 3/4" thick, on masonry, deduct	J-1	880	.045		.62	1.42	.16	2.20	3.19
0600	For coloring and special finish, add, minimum		685	.058		.39	1.82	.21	2.42	3.66
0700	Maximum		200	.200		1.38	6.25	.72	8.35	12.55
0900	For soffits, add	J-2	155	.310		2.14	9.70	.93	12.77	19.25
1000	Exterior stucco, with bonding agent, 3 coats, on walls, no mesh incl.	J-1	200	.200		3.58	6.25	.72	10.55	15
1200	Ceilings		180	.222		3.58	6.95	.80	11.33	16.20
1300	Beams		80	.500		3.58	15.60	1.80	20.98	31.50
1500	Columns		100	.400		3.58	12.50	1.44	17.52	26
1600	Mesh, painted, nailed to wood, 1.8 lb.	1 Lath	60	.133		6.20	4.22		10.42	13.60
1800	3.6 lb.		55	.145		4.03	4.60		8.63	11.85
1900	Wired to steel, painted, 1.8 lb.		53	.151		6.20	4.78		10.98	14.50
2100	3.6 lb.		50	.160		4.03	5.05		9.08	12.60

09 25 Other Plastering

09 25 23 – Lime Based Plastering

09 25 23.10 Venetian Plaster		Crew	Daily Output	Labor-Hours	Unit	Material	2014 Bare Costs Labor	Equipment	Total	Total Incl O&P
0010	**VENETIAN PLASTER**									
0100	Walls, 1 coat primer, roller applied	1 Plas	950	.008	S.F.	.16	.28		.44	.63
0200	Plaster, 3 coats, incl. sanding	2 Plas	700	.023	"	.44	.75		1.19	1.72
0210	For pigment, light colors add per gal. plaster				Gal.	12			12	13.20
0220	For pigment, dark colors add				"	50			50	55
0300	For sealer/wax coat incl. burnishing, add	1 Plas	300	.027	S.F.	.41	.87		1.28	1.88

09 26 Veneer Plastering

09 26 13 – Gypsum Veneer Plastering

09 26 13.20 Blueboard

		Crew	Daily Output	Labor-Hours	Unit	Material	2014 Bare Costs Labor	Equipment	Total	Total Incl O&P
0010	**BLUEBOARD** For use with thin coat									
0100	plaster application see Section 09 26 13.80									
1000	3/8" thick, on walls or ceilings, standard, no finish included	2 Carp	1900	.008	S.F.	.31	.30		.61	.85
1100	With thin coat plaster finish		875	.018		.41	.65		1.06	1.55
1400	On beams, columns, or soffits, standard, no finish included		675	.024		.36	.85		1.21	1.82
1450	With thin coat plaster finish		475	.034		.46	1.20		1.66	2.53
3000	1/2" thick, on walls or ceilings, standard, no finish included		1900	.008		.31	.30		.61	.85
3100	With thin coat plaster finish		875	.018		.41	.65		1.06	1.55
3300	Fire resistant, no finish included		1900	.008		.31	.30		.61	.85
3400	With thin coat plaster finish		875	.018		.41	.65		1.06	1.55
3450	On beams, columns, or soffits, standard, no finish included		675	.024		.36	.85		1.21	1.82
3500	With thin coat plaster finish		475	.034		.46	1.20		1.66	2.53
3700	Fire resistant, no finish included		675	.024		.36	.85		1.21	1.82
3800	With thin coat plaster finish		475	.034		.46	1.20		1.66	2.53
5000	5/8" thick, on walls or ceilings, fire resistant, no finish included		1900	.008		.33	.30		.63	.87
5100	With thin coat plaster finish		875	.018		.43	.65		1.08	1.57
5500	On beams, columns, or soffits, no finish included		675	.024		.38	.85		1.23	1.85
5600	With thin coat plaster finish		475	.034		.48	1.20		1.68	2.56
6000	For high ceilings, over 8' high, add		3060	.005			.19		.19	.31
6500	For over 3 stories high, add per story		6100	.003			.09		.09	.16

09 26 13.80 Thin Coat Plaster

			Crew	Daily Output	Labor-Hours	Unit	Material	2014 Bare Costs Labor	Equipment	Total	Total Incl O&P
0010	**THIN COAT PLASTER**	R092000-50									
0012	1 coat veneer, not incl. lath		J-1	3600	.011	S.F.	.10	.35	.04	.49	.72
1000	In 50 lb. bags					Bag	13.70			13.70	15.10

09 28 Backing Boards and Underlayments

09 28 13 – Cementitious Backing Boards

09 28 13.10 Cementitious Backerboard

		Crew	Daily Output	Labor-Hours	Unit	Material	2014 Bare Costs Labor	Equipment	Total	Total Incl O&P
0010	**CEMENTITIOUS BACKERBOARD**									
0070	Cementitious backerboard, on floor, 3' x 4' x 1/2" sheets	2 Carp	525	.030	S.F.	.80	1.09		1.89	2.71
0080	3' x 5' x 1/2" sheets		525	.030		.74	1.09		1.83	2.65
0090	3' x 6' x 1/2" sheets		525	.030		.74	1.09		1.83	2.64
0100	3' x 4' x 5/8" sheets		525	.030		1.02	1.09		2.11	2.95
0110	3' x 5' x 5/8" sheets		525	.030		.99	1.09		2.08	2.91
0120	3' x 6' x 5/8" sheets		525	.030		.96	1.09		2.05	2.89
0150	On wall, 3' x 4' x 1/2" sheets		350	.046		.80	1.63		2.43	3.63
0160	3' x 5' x 1/2" sheets		350	.046		.74	1.63		2.37	3.57
0170	3' x 6' x 1/2" sheets		350	.046		.74	1.63		2.37	3.56
0180	3' x 4' x 5/8" sheets		350	.046		1.02	1.63		2.65	3.87

09 28 Backing Boards and Underlayments

09 28 13 – Cementitious Backing Boards

09 28 13.10 Cementitious Backerboard	Crew	Daily Output	Labor-Hours	Unit	Material	2014 Bare Costs Labor	Equipment	Total	Total Incl O&P
0190	3' x 5' x 5/8" sheets	2 Carp	350	.046	S.F.	.99	1.63		2.62	3.83
0200	3' x 6' x 5/8" sheets		350	.046		.96	1.63		2.59	3.81
0250	On counter, 3' x 4' x 1/2" sheets		180	.089		.80	3.18		3.98	6.25
0260	3' x 5' x 1/2" sheets		180	.089		.74	3.18		3.92	6.15
0270	3' x 6' x 1/2" sheets		180	.089		.74	3.18		3.92	6.15
0300	3' x 4' x 5/8" sheets		180	.089		1.02	3.18		4.20	6.45
0310	3' x 5' x 5/8" sheets		180	.089		.99	3.18		4.17	6.45
0320	3' x 6' x 5/8" sheets		180	.089		.96	3.18		4.14	6.40

09 29 Gypsum Board

09 29 10 – Gypsum Board Panels

09 29 10.30 Gypsum Board

		Crew	Daily Output	Labor-Hours	Unit	Material	2014 Bare Costs Labor	Equipment	Total	Total Incl O&P
0010	**GYPSUM BOARD** on walls & ceilings R092910-10									
0100	Nailed or screwed to studs unless otherwise noted									
0110	1/4" thick, on walls or ceilings, standard, no finish included	2 Carp	1330	.012	S.F.	.31	.43		.74	1.06
0115	1/4" thick, on walls or ceilings, flexible, no finish included		1050	.015		.47	.54		1.01	1.44
0117	1/4" thick, on columns or soffits, flexible, no finish included		1050	.015		.47	.54		1.01	1.44
0130	1/4" thick, standard, no finish included, less than 800 S.F.		510	.031		.31	1.12		1.43	2.23
0150	3/8" thick, on walls, standard, no finish included		2000	.008		.31	.29		.60	.82
0200	On ceilings, standard, no finish included		1800	.009		.31	.32		.63	.87
0250	On beams, columns, or soffits, no finish included		675	.024		.31	.85		1.16	1.77
0300	1/2" thick, on walls, standard, no finish included		2000	.008		.30	.29		.59	.81
0350	Taped and finished (level 4 finish)		965	.017		.35	.59		.94	1.38
0390	With compound skim coat (level 5 finish)		775	.021		.41	.74		1.15	1.69
0400	Fire resistant, no finish included		2000	.008		.32	.29		.61	.83
0450	Taped and finished (level 4 finish)		965	.017		.37	.59		.96	1.41
0490	With compound skim coat (level 5 finish)		775	.021		.43	.74		1.17	1.71
0500	Water resistant, no finish included		2000	.008		.38	.29		.67	.90
0550	Taped and finished (level 4 finish)		965	.017		.43	.59		1.02	1.47
0590	With compound skim coat (level 5 finish)		775	.021		.49	.74		1.23	1.77
0600	Prefinished, vinyl, clipped to studs		900	.018		.48	.64		1.12	1.60
0700	Mold resistant, no finish included		2000	.008		.40	.29		.69	.92
0710	Taped and finished (level 4 finish)		965	.017		.45	.59		1.04	1.49
0720	With compound skim coat (level 5 finish)		775	.021		.51	.74		1.25	1.80
1000	On ceilings, standard, no finish included		1800	.009		.30	.32		.62	.86
1050	Taped and finished (level 4 finish)		765	.021		.35	.75		1.10	1.64
1090	With compound skim coat (level 5 finish)		610	.026		.41	.94		1.35	2.03
1100	Fire resistant, no finish included		1800	.009		.32	.32		.64	.88
1150	Taped and finished (level 4 finish)		765	.021		.37	.75		1.12	1.67
1195	With compound skim coat (level 5 finish)		610	.026		.43	.94		1.37	2.05
1200	Water resistant, no finish included		1800	.009		.38	.32		.70	.95
1250	Taped and finished (level 4 finish)		765	.021		.43	.75		1.18	1.73
1290	With compound skim coat (level 5 finish)		610	.026		.49	.94		1.43	2.11
1310	Mold resistant, no finish included		1800	.009		.40	.32		.72	.97
1320	Taped and finished (level 4 finish)		765	.021		.45	.75		1.20	1.75
1330	With compound skim coat (level 5 finish)		610	.026		.51	.94		1.45	2.14
1350	Sag resistant, no finish included		1600	.010		.32	.36		.68	.95
1360	Taped and finished (level 4 finish)		765	.021		.37	.75		1.12	1.67
1370	With compound skim coat (level 5 finish)		610	.026		.43	.94		1.37	2.05
1500	On beams, columns, or soffits, standard, no finish included		675	.024		.35	.85		1.20	1.81
1550	Taped and finished (level 4 finish)		540	.030		.35	1.06		1.41	2.16

09 29 Gypsum Board

09 29 10 – Gypsum Board Panels

09 29 10.30 Gypsum Board	Crew	Daily Output	Labor-Hours	Unit	Material	2014 Bare Costs Labor	2014 Bare Costs Equipment	Total	Total Incl O&P
1590	With compound skim coat (level 5 finish)	2 Carp	475	.034	S.F.	.41	1.20		1.61	2.48
1600	Fire resistant, no finish included		675	.024		.32	.85		1.17	1.78
1650	Taped and finished (level 4 finish)		540	.030		.37	1.06		1.43	2.19
1690	With compound skim coat (level 5 finish)		475	.034		.43	1.20		1.63	2.50
1700	Water resistant, no finish included		675	.024		.44	.85		1.29	1.91
1750	Taped and finished (level 4 finish)		540	.030		.43	1.06		1.49	2.25
1790	With compound skim coat (level 5 finish)		475	.034		.49	1.20		1.69	2.56
1800	Mold resistant, no finish included		675	.024		.46	.85		1.31	1.94
1810	Taped and finished (level 4 finish)		540	.030		.45	1.06		1.51	2.27
1820	With compound skim coat (level 5 finish)		475	.034		.51	1.20		1.71	2.59
1850	Sag resistant, no finish included		675	.024		.37	.85		1.22	1.83
1860	Taped and finished (level 4 finish)		540	.030		.37	1.06		1.43	2.19
1870	With compound skim coat (level 5 finish)		475	.034		.43	1.20		1.63	2.50
2000	5/8" thick, on walls, standard, no finish included		2000	.008		.32	.29		.61	.83
2050	Taped and finished (level 4 finish)		965	.017		.37	.59		.96	1.41
2090	With compound skim coat (level 5 finish)		775	.021		.43	.74		1.17	1.71
2100	Fire resistant, no finish included		2000	.008		.34	.29		.63	.85
2150	Taped and finished (level 4 finish)		965	.017		.39	.59		.98	1.43
2195	With compound skim coat (level 5 finish)		775	.021		.45	.74		1.19	1.73
2200	Water resistant, no finish included		2000	.008		.45	.29		.74	.98
2250	Taped and finished (level 4 finish)		965	.017		.50	.59		1.09	1.55
2290	With compound skim coat (level 5 finish)		775	.021		.56	.74		1.30	1.85
2300	Prefinished, vinyl, clipped to studs		900	.018		.89	.64		1.53	2.05
2510	Mold resistant, no finish included		2000	.008		.45	.29		.74	.98
2520	Taped and finished (level 4 finish)		965	.017		.50	.59		1.09	1.55
2530	With compound skim coat (level 5 finish)		775	.021		.56	.74		1.30	1.85
3000	On ceilings, standard, no finish included		1800	.009		.32	.32		.64	.88
3050	Taped and finished (level 4 finish)		765	.021		.37	.75		1.12	1.67
3090	With compound skim coat (level 5 finish)		615	.026		.43	.93		1.36	2.04
3100	Fire resistant, no finish included		1800	.009		.34	.32		.66	.90
3150	Taped and finished (level 4 finish)		765	.021		.39	.75		1.14	1.69
3190	With compound skim coat (level 5 finish)		615	.026		.45	.93		1.38	2.06
3200	Water resistant, no finish included		1800	.009		.45	.32		.77	1.03
3250	Taped and finished (level 4 finish)		765	.021		.50	.75		1.25	1.81
3290	With compound skim coat (level 5 finish)		615	.026		.56	.93		1.49	2.18
3300	Mold resistant, no finish included		1800	.009		.45	.32		.77	1.03
3310	Taped and finished (level 4 finish)		765	.021		.50	.75		1.25	1.81
3320	With compound skim coat (level 5 finish)		615	.026		.56	.93		1.49	2.18
3500	On beams, columns, or soffits, no finish included		675	.024		.37	.85		1.22	1.83
3550	Taped and finished (level 4 finish)		475	.034		.43	1.20		1.63	2.50
3590	With compound skim coat (level 5 finish)		380	.042		.49	1.51		2	3.07
3600	Fire resistant, no finish included		675	.024		.39	.85		1.24	1.86
3650	Taped and finished (level 4 finish)		475	.034		.45	1.20		1.65	2.52
3690	With compound skim coat (level 5 finish)		380	.042		.45	1.51		1.96	3.02
3700	Water resistant, no finish included		675	.024		.52	.85		1.37	2
3750	Taped and finished (level 4 finish)		475	.034		.56	1.20		1.76	2.64
3790	With compound skim coat (level 5 finish)		380	.042		.57	1.51		2.08	3.16
3800	Mold resistant, no finish included		675	.024		.52	.85		1.37	2
3810	Taped and finished (level 4 finish)		475	.034		.56	1.20		1.76	2.64
3820	With compound skim coat (level 5 finish)		380	.042		.57	1.51		2.08	3.16
4000	Fireproofing, beams or columns, 2 layers, 1/2" thick, incl finish		330	.048		.74	1.73		2.47	3.73
4010	Mold resistant		330	.048		.90	1.73		2.63	3.91
4050	5/8" thick		300	.053		.78	1.91		2.69	4.07

09 29 10.30 Gypsum Board	Crew	Daily Output	Labor-Hours	Unit	Material	2014 Bare Costs Labor	Equipment	Total	Total Incl O&P
4060	Mold resistant	2 Carp	300	.053	S.F.	1	1.91		2.91	4.31
4100	3 layers, 1/2" thick		225	.071		1.11	2.54		3.65	5.50
4110	Mold resistant		225	.071		1.35	2.54		3.89	5.75
4150	5/8" thick		210	.076		1.17	2.72		3.89	5.85
4160	Mold resistant		210	.076		1.50	2.72		4.22	6.25
5050	For 1" thick coreboard on columns		480	.033		.74	1.19		1.93	2.81
5100	For foil-backed board, add					.15			.15	.17
5200	For work over 8' high, add	2 Carp	3060	.005			.19		.19	.31
5270	For textured spray, add	2 Lath	1600	.010		.04	.32		.36	.55
5300	For distribution cost over 3 stories high, add per story	2 Carp	6100	.003			.09		.09	.16
5350	For finishing inner corners, add		950	.017	L.F.	.11	.60		.71	1.13
5355	For finishing outer corners, add		1250	.013		.23	.46		.69	1.03
5500	For acoustical sealant, add per bead	1 Carp	500	.016		.04	.57		.61	1.01
5550	Sealant, 1 quart tube				Ea.	7.05			7.05	7.80
6000	Gypsum sound dampening panels									
6010	1/2" thick on walls, multi-layer, light weight, no finish included	2 Carp	1500	.011	S.F.	1.87	.38		2.25	2.70
6015	Taped and finished (level 4 finish)		725	.022		1.92	.79		2.71	3.44
6020	With compound skim coat (level 5 finish)		580	.028		1.98	.99		2.97	3.83
6025	5/8" thick on walls, for wood studs, no finish included		1500	.011		2.70	.38		3.08	3.61
6030	Taped and finished (level 4 finish)		725	.022		2.75	.79		3.54	4.35
6035	With compound skim coat (level 5 finish)		580	.028		2.81	.99		3.80	4.75
6040	For metal stud, no finish included		1500	.011		2.06	.38		2.44	2.91
6045	Taped and finished (level 4 finish)		725	.022		2.11	.79		2.90	3.65
6050	With compound skim coat (level 5 finish)		580	.028		2.17	.99		3.16	4.04
6055	Abuse resist, no finish included		1500	.011		3.75	.38		4.13	4.77
6060	Taped and finished (level 4 finish)		725	.022		3.80	.79		4.59	5.50
6065	With compound skim coat (level 5 finish)		580	.028		3.86	.99		4.85	5.90
6070	Shear rated, no finish included		1500	.011		4.30	.38		4.68	5.35
6075	Taped and finished (level 4 finish)		725	.022		4.35	.79		5.14	6.10
6080	With compound skim coat (level 5 finish)		580	.028		4.41	.99		5.40	6.50
6085	For SCIF applications, no finish included		1500	.011		4.72	.38		5.10	5.85
6090	Taped and finished (level 4 finish)		725	.022		4.77	.79		5.56	6.60
6095	With compound skim coat (level 5 finish)		580	.028		4.83	.99		5.82	6.95
6100	1-3/8" thick on walls, THX Certified, no finish included		1500	.011		8.40	.38		8.78	9.90
6105	Taped and finished (level 4 finish)		725	.022		8.45	.79		9.24	10.65
6110	With compound skim coat (level 5 finish)		580	.028		8.50	.99		9.49	11
6115	5/8" thick on walls, score & snap installation, no finish included		2000	.008		1.78	.29		2.07	2.44
6120	Taped and finished (level 4 finish)		965	.017		1.83	.59		2.42	3.01
6125	With compound skim coat (level 5 finish)		775	.021		1.89	.74		2.63	3.31
7020	5/8" thick on ceilings, for wood joists, no finish included		1200	.013		2.70	.48		3.18	3.77
7025	Taped and finished (level 4 finish)		510	.031		2.75	1.12		3.87	4.91
7030	With compound skim coat (level 5 finish)		410	.039		2.81	1.40		4.21	5.45
7035	For metal joists, no finish included		1200	.013		2.06	.48		2.54	3.07
7040	Taped and finished (level 4 finish)		510	.031		2.11	1.12		3.23	4.21
7045	With compound skim coat (level 5 finish)		410	.039		2.17	1.40		3.57	4.73
7050	Abuse resist, no finish included		1200	.013		3.75	.48		4.23	4.93
7055	Taped and finished (level 4 finish)		510	.031		3.80	1.12		4.92	6.05
7060	With compound skim coat (level 5 finish)		410	.039		3.86	1.40		5.26	6.60
7065	Shear rated, no finish included		1200	.013		4.30	.48		4.78	5.55
7070	Taped and finished (level 4 finish)		510	.031		4.35	1.12		5.47	6.65
7075	With compound skim coat (level 5 finish)		410	.039		4.41	1.40		5.81	7.20
7080	For SCIF applications, no finish included		1200	.013		4.72	.48		5.20	6
7085	Taped and finished (level 4 finish)		510	.031		4.77	1.12		5.89	7.15

09 29 Gypsum Board

09 29 10 – Gypsum Board Panels

09 29 10.30 Gypsum Board

		Crew	Daily Output	Labor-Hours	Unit	Material	2014 Bare Costs Labor	Equipment	Total	Total Incl O&P
7090	With compound skim coat (level 5 finish)	2 Carp	410	.039	S.F.	4.83	1.40		6.23	7.65
8010	5/8" thick on ceilings, score & snap installation, no finish included		1600	.010		1.78	.36		2.14	2.56
8015	Taped and finished (level 4 finish)		680	.024		1.83	.84		2.67	3.43
8020	With compound skim coat (level 5 finish)	↓	545	.029	↓	1.89	1.05		2.94	3.84

09 29 10.50 High Abuse Gypsum Board

		Crew	Daily Output	Labor-Hours	Unit	Material	2014 Bare Costs Labor	Equipment	Total	Total Incl O&P
0010	**HIGH ABUSE GYPSUM BOARD**, fiber reinforced, nailed or									
0100	screwed to studs unless otherwise noted									
0110	1/2" thick, on walls, no finish included	2 Carp	1800	.009	S.F.	.61	.32		.93	1.20
0120	Taped and finished (level 4 finish)		870	.018		.66	.66		1.32	1.84
0130	With compound skim coat (level 5 finish)		700	.023		.72	.82		1.54	2.17
0150	On ceilings, no finish included		1620	.010		.61	.35		.96	1.26
0160	Taped and finished (level 4 finish)		690	.023		.66	.83		1.49	2.12
0170	With compound skim coat (level 5 finish)		550	.029		.72	1.04		1.76	2.54
0210	5/8" thick, on walls, no finish included		1800	.009		.77	.32		1.09	1.38
0220	Taped and finished (level 4 finish)		870	.018		.82	.66		1.48	2.01
0230	With compound skim coat (level 5 finish)		700	.023		.88	.82		1.70	2.34
0250	On ceilings, no finish included		1620	.010		.77	.35		1.12	1.44
0260	Taped and finished (level 4 finish)		690	.023		.82	.83		1.65	2.29
0270	With compound skim coat (level 5 finish)		550	.029		.88	1.04		1.92	2.71
0310	5/8" thick, on walls, very high impact, no finish included		1800	.009		.99	.32		1.31	1.62
0320	Taped and finished (level 4 finish)		870	.018		1.04	.66		1.70	2.25
0330	With compound skim coat (level 5 finish)		700	.023		1.10	.82		1.92	2.58
0350	On ceilings, no finish included		1620	.010		.99	.35		1.34	1.68
0360	Taped and finished (level 4 finish)		690	.023		1.04	.83		1.87	2.53
0370	With compound skim coat (level 5 finish)	↓	550	.029	↓	1.10	1.04		2.14	2.95
0400	High abuse, gypsum core, paper face									
0410	1/2" thick, on walls, no finish included	2 Carp	1800	.009	S.F.	.57	.32		.89	1.16
0420	Taped and finished (level 4 finish)		870	.018		.62	.66		1.28	1.79
0430	With compound skim coat (level 5 finish)		700	.023		.68	.82		1.50	2.12
0450	On ceilings, no finish included		1620	.010		.57	.35		.92	1.22
0460	Taped and finished (level 4 finish)		690	.023		.62	.83		1.45	2.07
0470	With compound skim coat (level 5 finish)		550	.029		.68	1.04		1.72	2.49
0510	5/8" thick, on walls, no finish included		1800	.009		.77	.32		1.09	1.38
0520	Taped and finished (level 4 finish)		870	.018		.82	.66		1.48	2.01
0530	With compound skim coat (level 5 finish)		700	.023		.88	.82		1.70	2.34
0550	On ceilings, no finish included		1620	.010		.77	.35		1.12	1.44
0560	Taped and finished (level 4 finish)		690	.023		.82	.83		1.65	2.29
0570	With compound skim coat (level 5 finish)		550	.029		.88	1.04		1.92	2.71
1000	For high ceilings, over 8' high, add		2750	.006			.21		.21	.35
1010	For distribution cost over 3 stories high, add per story	↓	5500	.003	↓		.10		.10	.18

09 29 15 – Gypsum Board Accessories

09 29 15.10 Accessories, Gypsum Board

		Crew	Daily Output	Labor-Hours	Unit	Material	2014 Bare Costs Labor	Equipment	Total	Total Incl O&P
0010	**ACCESSORIES, GYPSUM BOARD**									
0020	Casing bead, galvanized steel	1 Carp	2.90	2.759	C.L.F.	24.50	98.50		123	193
0100	Vinyl		3	2.667		22	95.50		117.50	184
0300	Corner bead, galvanized steel, 1" x 1"		4	2		15.15	71.50		86.65	137
0400	1-1/4" x 1-1/4"		3.50	2.286		16	81.50		97.50	155
0600	Vinyl		4	2		16.25	71.50		87.75	138
0900	Furring channel, galv. steel, 7/8" deep, standard		2.60	3.077		32.50	110		142.50	221
1000	Resilient		2.55	3.137		29	112		141	221
1100	J trim, galvanized steel, 1/2" wide		3	2.667		21.50	95.50		117	184
1120	5/8" wide	↓	2.95	2.712	↓	27.50	97		124.50	193

09 29 Gypsum Board

09 29 15 – Gypsum Board Accessories

09 29 15.10 Accessories, Gypsum Board	Crew	Daily Output	Labor-Hours	Unit	Material	2014 Bare Costs Labor	Equipment	Total	Total Incl O&P
1140	L trim, galvanized	1 Carp	3	2.667	C.L.F.	21.50	95.50		117	184
1150	U trim, galvanized	↓	2.95	2.712	↓	29	97		126	195
1160	Screws #6 x 1" A				M	9.45			9.45	10.40
1170	#6 x 1-5/8" A				"	13.65			13.65	15
1200	For stud partitions, see Section 05 41 13.30 and 09 22 16.13									
1500	Z stud, galvanized steel, 1-1/2" wide	1 Carp	2.60	3.077	C.L.F.	36	110		146	225
1600	2" wide	"	2.55	3.137	"	60.50	112		172.50	256

09 30 Tiling

09 30 13 – Ceramic Tiling

09 30 13.10 Ceramic Tile

		Crew	Daily Output	Labor-Hours	Unit	Material	2014 Bare Costs Labor	Equipment	Total	Total Incl O&P
0010	**CERAMIC TILE**									
0020	Backsplash, thinset, average grade tiles	1 Tilf	50	.160	S.F.	2.45	5.25		7.70	11.15
0022	Custom grade tiles		50	.160		4.90	5.25		10.15	13.85
0024	Luxury grade tiles		50	.160		9.80	5.25		15.05	19.20
0026	Economy grade tiles	↓	50	.160	↓	2.24	5.25		7.49	10.90
0050	Base, using 1' x 4" high pc. with 1" x 1" tiles, mud set	D-7	82	.195	L.F.	5.15	5.75		10.90	14.90
0100	Thin set	"	128	.125		4.77	3.67		8.44	11.15
0300	For 6" high base, 1" x 1" tile face, add					.76			.76	.84
0400	For 2" x 2" tile face, add to above					.41			.41	.45
0600	Cove base, 4-1/4" x 4-1/4" high, mud set	D-7	91	.176		3.88	5.15		9.03	12.60
0700	Thin set		128	.125		3.95	3.67		7.62	10.25
0900	6" x 4-1/4" high, mud set		100	.160		4.05	4.70		8.75	12.05
1000	Thin set		137	.117		3.93	3.43		7.36	9.85
1200	Sanitary cove base, 6" x 4-1/4" high, mud set		93	.172		4.11	5.05		9.16	12.70
1300	Thin set		124	.129		3.99	3.79		7.78	10.50
1500	6" x 6" high, mud set		84	.190		5.10	5.60		10.70	14.60
1600	Thin set		117	.137	↓	4.96	4.01		8.97	11.95
1800	Bathroom accessories, average (soap dish, tooth brush holder)		82	.195	Ea.	12	5.75		17.75	22.50
1900	Bathtub, 5', rec. 4-1/4" x 4-1/4" tile wainscot, adhesive set 6' high		2.90	5.517		156	162		318	435
2100	7' high wainscot		2.50	6.400		179	188		367	500
2200	8' high wainscot		2.20	7.273	↓	190	213		403	555
2400	Bullnose trim, 4-1/4" x 4-1/4", mud set		82	.195	L.F.	3.81	5.75		9.56	13.45
2500	Thin set		128	.125		3.73	3.67		7.40	10
2700	2" x 6" bullnose trim, mud set		84	.190		4.27	5.60		9.87	13.70
2800	Thin set		124	.129	↓	4.21	3.79		8	10.75
3000	Floors, natural clay, random or uniform, thin set, color group 1		183	.087	S.F.	4.15	2.57		6.72	8.70
3100	Color group 2		183	.087		5.85	2.57		8.42	10.60
3255	Floors, glazed, thin Set, 6" x 6", color group 1		300	.053		4.45	1.57		6.02	7.40
3260	8" x 8" tile		300	.053		4.45	1.57		6.02	7.40
3270	12" x 12" tile		290	.055		5.85	1.62		7.47	9.05
3280	16" x 16" tile		280	.057		6.70	1.68		8.38	10.10
3281	18" x 18" tile		270	.059		8.15	1.74		9.89	11.80
3282	20" x 20" tile		260	.062		9.30	1.81		11.11	13.10
3283	24" x 24" tile		250	.064		10.60	1.88		12.48	14.70
3285	Border, 6" x 12" tile		200	.080		15.25	2.35		17.60	20.50
3290	3" x 12" tile		200	.080		38.50	2.35		40.85	46
3300	Porcelain type, 1 color, color group 2, 1" x 1"		183	.087		5.20	2.57		7.77	9.85
3310	2" x 2" or 2" x 1", thin set	↓	190	.084		5.95	2.47		8.42	10.55
3350	For random blend, 2 colors, add					1			1	1.10
3360	4 colors, add				↓	1.50			1.50	1.65

09 30 Tiling

09 30 13 – Ceramic Tiling

09 30 13.10 Ceramic Tile

		Crew	Daily Output	Labor-Hours	Unit	Material	2014 Bare Costs Labor	Equipment	Total	Total Incl O&P
3370	For color group 3, add				S.F.	.65			.65	.72
3380	For abrasive non-slip tile, add					.44			.44	.48
4300	Specialty tile, 4-1/4" x 4-1/4" x 1/2", decorator finish	D-7	183	.087		10.40	2.57		12.97	15.60
4500	Add for epoxy grout, 1/16" joint, 1" x 1" tile		800	.020		.66	.59		1.25	1.68
4600	2" x 2" tile	↓	820	.020	↓	.61	.57		1.18	1.59
4800	Pregrouted sheets, walls, 4-1/4" x 4-1/4", 6" x 4-1/4"									
4810	and 8-1/2" x 4-1/4", 4 S.F. sheets, silicone grout	D-7	240	.067	S.F.	5.05	1.96		7.01	8.70
5100	Floors, unglazed, 2 S.F. sheets,									
5110	Urethane adhesive	D-7	180	.089	S.F.	5.05	2.61		7.66	9.75
5400	Walls, interior, thin set, 4-1/4" x 4-1/4" tile		190	.084		2.26	2.47		4.73	6.45
5500	6" x 4-1/4" tile		190	.084		2.92	2.47		5.39	7.20
5700	8-1/2" x 4-1/4" tile		190	.084		4.86	2.47		7.33	9.35
5800	6" x 6" tile		175	.091		3.12	2.68		5.80	7.75
5810	8" x 8" tile		170	.094		4.27	2.76		7.03	9.15
5820	12" x 12" tile		160	.100		4.35	2.94		7.29	9.50
5830	16" x 16" tile		150	.107		4.77	3.13		7.90	10.30
6000	Decorated wall tile, 4-1/4" x 4-1/4", minimum		270	.059		3.18	1.74		4.92	6.30
6100	Maximum		180	.089		49.50	2.61		52.11	58.50
6300	Exterior walls, frostproof, mud set, 4-1/4" x 4-1/4"		102	.157		7.15	4.60		11.75	15.30
6400	1-3/8" x 1-3/8"		93	.172		5.20	5.05		10.25	13.85
6600	Crystalline glazed, 4-1/4" x 4-1/4", mud set, plain		100	.160		4.27	4.70		8.97	12.30
6700	4-1/4" x 4-1/4", scored tile		100	.160		5.80	4.70		10.50	14
6900	6" x 6" plain		93	.172		6.50	5.05		11.55	15.30
7000	For epoxy grout, 1/16" joints, 4-1/4" tile, add		800	.020		.41	.59		1	1.40
7200	For tile set in dry mortar, add		1735	.009			.27		.27	.44
7300	For tile set in Portland cement mortar, add		290	.055		.16	1.62		1.78	2.79
9300	Ceramic tiles, recycled glass, standard colors, 2" x 2" thru 6" x 6" G		190	.084		20	2.47		22.47	26
9310	6" x 6" G		175	.091		20	2.68		22.68	26.50
9320	8" x 8" G		170	.094		22	2.76		24.76	29
9330	12" x 12" G		160	.100		22	2.94		24.94	29
9340	Earthtones, 2" x 2" to 4" x 8" G		190	.084		25	2.47		27.47	31.50
9350	6" x 6" G		175	.091		25	2.68		27.68	32
9360	8" x 8" G		170	.094		26	2.76		28.76	33
9370	12" x 12" G		160	.100		26	2.94		28.94	33
9380	Deep colors, 2" x 2" to 4" x 8" G		190	.084		29.50	2.47		31.97	36.50
9390	6" x 6" G		175	.091		29.50	2.68		32.18	37
9400	8" x 8" G		170	.094		31	2.76		33.76	38.50
9410	12" x 12" G	↓	160	.100	↓	31	2.94		33.94	38.50

09 30 13.20 Ceramic Tile Repairs

		Crew	Daily Output	Labor-Hours	Unit	Material	2014 Bare Costs Labor	Equipment	Total	Total Incl O&P
0010	**CERAMIC TILE REPAIRS**									
1000	Grout removal, carbide tipped, rotary grinder	1 Clab	240	.033	L.F.		.94		.94	1.58
1100	Regrout tile 4-1/2 x 4-1/2, or larger, wall	1 Tilf	100	.080	S.F.	.14	2.62		2.76	4.38
1150	Floor		125	.064		.15	2.10		2.25	3.55
1200	Seal tile and grout	↓	360	.022	↓		.73		.73	1.18

09 30 13.45 Ceramic Tile Accessories

		Crew	Daily Output	Labor-Hours	Unit	Material	2014 Bare Costs Labor	Equipment	Total	Total Incl O&P
0010	**CERAMIC TILE ACCESSORIES**									
0100	Spacers, 1/8"				C	1.98			1.98	2.18
1310	Sealer for natural stone tile, installed	1 Tilf	650	.012	S.F.	.05	.40		.45	.71

09 30 Tiling

09 30 16 – Quarry Tiling

09 30 16.10 Quarry Tile

		Crew	Daily Output	Labor-Hours	Unit	Material	2014 Bare Costs Labor	2014 Bare Costs Equipment	Total	Total Incl O&P
0010	**QUARRY TILE**									
0100	Base, cove or sanitary, mud set, to 5" high, 1/2" thick	D-7	110	.145	L.F.	5.35	4.27		9.62	12.80
0300	Bullnose trim, red, mud set, 6" x 6" x 1/2" thick		120	.133		4.39	3.91		8.30	11.15
0400	4" x 4" x 1/2" thick		110	.145		4.50	4.27		8.77	11.85
0600	4" x 8" x 1/2" thick, using 8" as edge		130	.123		4.50	3.61		8.11	10.80
0700	Floors, mud set, 1,000 S.F. lots, red, 4" x 4" x 1/2" thick		120	.133	S.F.	7.05	3.91		10.96	14.05
0900	6" x 6" x 1/2" thick		140	.114		7.30	3.35		10.65	13.45
1000	4" x 8" x 1/2" thick		130	.123		6.05	3.61		9.66	12.50
1300	For waxed coating, add					.74			.74	.81
1500	For non-standard colors, add					.45			.45	.50
1600	For abrasive surface, add					.51			.51	.56
1800	Brown tile, imported, 6" x 6" x 3/4"	D-7	120	.133		7.85	3.91		11.76	14.90
1900	8" x 8" x 1"		110	.145		8.55	4.27		12.82	16.30
2100	For thin set mortar application, deduct		700	.023			.67		.67	1.08
2200	For epoxy grout & mortar, 6" x 6" x 1/2", add		350	.046		2.02	1.34		3.36	4.39
2700	Stair tread, 6" x 6" x 3/4", plain		50	.320		6.95	9.40		16.35	23
2800	Abrasive		47	.340		5.95	10		15.95	22.50
3000	Wainscot, 6" x 6" x 1/2", thin set, red		105	.152		4.63	4.47		9.10	12.30
3100	Non-standard colors		105	.152		5.15	4.47		9.62	12.85
3300	Window sill, 6" wide, 3/4" thick		90	.178	L.F.	6.20	5.20		11.40	15.20
3400	Corners		80	.200	Ea.	6.65	5.85		12.50	16.80

09 30 23 – Glass Mosaic Tiling

09 30 23.10 Glass Mosaics

		Crew	Daily Output	Labor-Hours	Unit	Material	2014 Bare Costs Labor	2014 Bare Costs Equipment	Total	Total Incl O&P
0010	**GLASS MOSAICS** 3/4" tile on 12" sheets, standard grout									
0300	Color group 1 & 2	D-7	73	.219	S.F.	16.45	6.45		22.90	28.50
0350	Color group 3		73	.219		20.50	6.45		26.95	33
0400	Color group 4		73	.219		26	6.45		32.45	39
0450	Color group 5		73	.219		27.50	6.45		33.95	40.50
0500	Color group 6		73	.219		35.50	6.45		41.95	49.50
0600	Color group 7		73	.219		43.50	6.45		49.95	58.50
0700	Color group 8, golds, silvers & specialties		64	.250		54	7.35		61.35	71.50
1020	1" tile on 12" sheets, opalescent finish		73	.219		17.55	6.45		24	29.50
1040	1" x 2" tile on 12" sheet, blend		73	.219		17.30	6.45		23.75	29.50
1060	2" tile on 12" sheet, blend		73	.219		17.10	6.45		23.55	29
1080	5/8" x random tile, linear, on 12" sheet, blend		73	.219		28	6.45		34.45	41.50
1600	Dots on 12" sheet		73	.219		28	6.45		34.45	41.50
1700	For glass mosaic tiles set in dry mortar, add		290	.055		.45	1.62		2.07	3.11
1720	For glass mosaic tile set in Portland cement mortar, add		290	.055		.01	1.62		1.63	2.62
1730	For polyblend sanded tile grout		96.15	.166	Lb.	2.19	4.88		7.07	10.30

09 30 29 – Metal Tiling

09 30 29.10 Metal Tile

		Crew	Daily Output	Labor-Hours	Unit	Material	2014 Bare Costs Labor	2014 Bare Costs Equipment	Total	Total Incl O&P
0010	**METAL TILE** 4' x 4' sheet, 24 ga., tile pattern, nailed									
0200	Stainless steel	2 Carp	512	.031	S.F.	27.50	1.12		28.62	32
0400	Aluminized steel	"	512	.031	"	14.80	1.12		15.92	18.15

09 34 Waterproofing-Membrane Tiling

09 34 13 – Waterproofing-Membrane Ceramic Tiling

09 34 13.10 Ceramic Tile Waterproofing Membrane	Crew	Daily Output	Labor-Hours	Unit	Material	2014 Bare Costs Labor	Equipment	Total	Total Incl O&P
0010	**CERAMIC TILE WATERPROOFING MEMBRANE**									
0020	On floors, including thinset									
0030	Fleece laminated polyethylene grid, 1/8" thick	D-7	250	.064	S.F.	2.23	1.88		4.11	5.50
0040	5/16" thick	"	250	.064	"	2.55	1.88		4.43	5.85
0050	On walls, including thinset									
0060	Fleece laminated polyethylene sheet, 8 mil thick	D-7	480	.033	S.F.	2.23	.98		3.21	4.03
0070	Accessories, including thinset									
0080	Joint and corner sheet, 4 mils thick, 5" wide	1 Tilf	240	.033	L.F.	1.32	1.09		2.41	3.21
0090	7-1/4" wide		180	.044		1.68	1.46		3.14	4.20
0100	10" wide		120	.067		2.05	2.18		4.23	5.75
0110	Pre-formed corners, inside		32	.250	Ea.	6.20	8.20		14.40	20
0120	Outside		32	.250		7.35	8.20		15.55	21.50
0130	2" flanged floor drain with 6" stainless steel grate		16	.500		380	16.40		396.40	440
0140	EPS, sloped shower floor		480	.017	S.F.	4.77	.55		5.32	6.15
0150	Curb		32	.250	L.F.	13.50	8.20		21.70	28

09 51 Acoustical Ceilings

09 51 23 – Acoustical Tile Ceilings

09 51 23.10 Suspended Acoustic Ceiling Tiles	Crew	Daily Output	Labor-Hours	Unit	Material	2014 Bare Costs Labor	Equipment	Total	Total Incl O&P
0010	**SUSPENDED ACOUSTIC CEILING TILES**, not including									
0100	suspension system									
0300	Fiberglass boards, film faced, 2' x 2' or 2' x 4', 5/8" thick	1 Carp	625	.013	S.F.	1.02	.46		1.48	1.89
0400	3/4" thick		600	.013		1.67	.48		2.15	2.64
0500	3" thick, thermal, R11		450	.018		1.90	.64		2.54	3.16
0600	Glass cloth faced fiberglass, 3/4" thick		500	.016		2.01	.57		2.58	3.17
0700	1" thick		485	.016		2.74	.59		3.33	4
0820	1-1/2" thick, nubby face		475	.017		2.50	.60		3.10	3.76
1110	Mineral fiber tile, lay-in, 2' x 2' or 2' x 4', 5/8" thick, fine texture		625	.013		1.25	.46		1.71	2.15
1115	Rough textured		625	.013		1.21	.46		1.67	2.10
1125	3/4" thick, fine textured		600	.013		1.66	.48		2.14	2.63
1130	Rough textured		600	.013		1.65	.48		2.13	2.62
1135	Fissured		600	.013		2.70	.48		3.18	3.77
1150	Tegular, 5/8" thick, fine textured		470	.017		1.64	.61		2.25	2.82
1155	Rough textured		470	.017		1.18	.61		1.79	2.32
1165	3/4" thick, fine textured		450	.018		2.70	.64		3.34	4.04
1170	Rough textured		450	.018		1.54	.64		2.18	2.76
1175	Fissured		450	.018		2.70	.64		3.34	4.04
1185	For plastic film face, add					.84			.84	.92
1190	For fire rating, add					.45			.45	.50
1300	Mirror tile, acrylic, 2' x 2'	1 Carp	500	.016		10.70	.57		11.27	12.70
1900	Eggcrate, acrylic, 1/2" x 1/2" x 1/2" cubes		500	.016		1.86	.57		2.43	3.01
2100	Polystyrene eggcrate, 3/8" x 3/8" x 1/2" cubes		510	.016		1.56	.56		2.12	2.66
2200	1/2" x 1/2" x 1/2" cubes		500	.016		1.74	.57		2.31	2.87
2400	Luminous panels, prismatic, acrylic		400	.020		2.26	.72		2.98	3.69
2500	Polystyrene		400	.020		1.16	.72		1.88	2.48
2700	Flat white acrylic		400	.020		3.94	.72		4.66	5.55
2800	Polystyrene		400	.020		2.70	.72		3.42	4.17
3000	Drop pan, white, acrylic		400	.020		5.75	.72		6.47	7.55
3100	Polystyrene		400	.020		4.82	.72		5.54	6.50
3600	Perforated aluminum sheets, .024" thick, corrugated, painted		490	.016		2.34	.58		2.92	3.55
3700	Plain		500	.016		3.92	.57		4.49	5.25

09 51 Acoustical Ceilings

09 51 23 – Acoustical Tile Ceilings

09 51 23.10 Suspended Acoustic Ceiling Tiles		Crew	Daily Output	Labor-Hours	Unit	Material	2014 Bare Costs Labor	Equipment	Total	Total Incl O&P
3720	Mineral fiber, 24" x 24" or 48", reveal edge, painted, 5/8" thick	1 Carp	600	.013	S.F.	1.18	.48		1.66	2.10
3740	3/4" thick		575	.014		1.54	.50		2.04	2.53
5020	66 – 78% recycled content, 3/4" thick	G	600	.013		1.87	.48		2.35	2.86
5040	Mylar, 42% recycled content, 3/4" thick	G	600	.013		4.41	.48		4.89	5.65

09 51 23.30 Suspended Ceilings, Complete		Crew	Daily Output	Labor-Hours	Unit	Material	2014 Bare Costs Labor	Equipment	Total	Total Incl O&P
0010	**SUSPENDED CEILINGS, COMPLETE**, including standard									
0100	suspension system but not incl. 1-1/2" carrier channels									
0600	Fiberglass ceiling board, 2' x 4' x 5/8", plain faced	1 Carp	500	.016	S.F.	1.72	.57		2.29	2.85
0700	Offices, 2' x 4' x 3/4"		380	.021		2.37	.75		3.12	3.88
0800	Mineral fiber, on 15/16" T bar susp. 2' x 2' x 3/4" lay-in board		345	.023		2.57	.83		3.40	4.21
0810	2' x 4' x 5/8" tile		380	.021		2.65	.75		3.40	4.18
0820	Tegular, 2' x 2' x 5/8" tile on 9/16" grid		250	.032		3.12	1.14		4.26	5.35
0830	2' x 4' x 3/4" tile		275	.029		3.02	1.04		4.06	5.05
0900	Luminous panels, prismatic, acrylic		255	.031		2.96	1.12		4.08	5.15
1200	Metal pan with acoustic pad, steel		75	.107		4.48	3.81		8.29	11.35
1300	Painted aluminum		75	.107		3.04	3.81		6.85	9.75
1500	Aluminum, degreased finish		75	.107		5.15	3.81		8.96	12.10
1600	Stainless steel		75	.107		9.70	3.81		13.51	17.05
1800	Tile, Z bar suspension, 5/8" mineral fiber tile		150	.053		2.32	1.91		4.23	5.75
1900	3/4" mineral fiber tile		150	.053		2.48	1.91		4.39	5.95
2400	For strip lighting, see Section 26 51 13.50									
2500	For rooms under 500 S.F., add				S.F.		25%			

09 51 53 – Direct-Applied Acoustical Ceilings

09 51 53.10 Ceiling Tile

09 51 53.10 Ceiling Tile		Crew	Daily Output	Labor-Hours	Unit	Material	2014 Bare Costs Labor	Equipment	Total	Total Incl O&P
0010	**CEILING TILE**, stapled or cemented									
0100	12" x 12" or 12" x 24", not including furring									
0600	Mineral fiber, vinyl coated, 5/8" thick	1 Carp	300	.027	S.F.	1.87	.95		2.82	3.66
0700	3/4" thick		300	.027		1.78	.95		2.73	3.56
0900	Fire rated, 3/4" thick, plain faced		300	.027		1.29	.95		2.24	3.02
1000	Plastic coated face		300	.027		1.29	.95		2.24	3.02
1200	Aluminum faced, 5/8" thick, plain		300	.027		1.61	.95		2.56	3.37
3700	Wall application of above, add		1000	.008			.29		.29	.48
3900	For ceiling primer, add					.13			.13	.14
4000	For ceiling cement, add					.38			.38	.42

09 53 Acoustical Ceiling Suspension Assemblies

09 53 23 – Metal Acoustical Ceiling Suspension Assemblies

09 53 23.30 Ceiling Suspension Systems

09 53 23.30 Ceiling Suspension Systems		Crew	Daily Output	Labor-Hours	Unit	Material	2014 Bare Costs Labor	Equipment	Total	Total Incl O&P
0010	**CEILING SUSPENSION SYSTEMS** for boards and tile									
0050	Class A suspension system, 15/16" T bar, 2' x 4' grid	1 Carp	800	.010	S.F.	.70	.36		1.06	1.37
0300	2' x 2' grid		650	.012		.91	.44		1.35	1.74
0310	25% recycled steel, 2' x 4' grid	G	800	.010		.76	.36		1.12	1.43
0320	2' x 2' grid	G	650	.012		.95	.44		1.39	1.78
0350	For 9/16" grid, add					.16			.16	.18
0360	For fire rated grid, add					.09			.09	.10
0370	For colored grid, add					.21			.21	.23
0400	Concealed Z bar suspension system, 12" module	1 Carp	520	.015		.78	.55		1.33	1.79
0600	1-1/2" carrier channels, 4' O.C., add	"	470	.017		.11	.61		.72	1.14
0700	Carrier channels for ceilings with									
0900	recessed lighting fixtures, add	1 Carp	460	.017	S.F.	.20	.62		.82	1.27

09 53 Acoustical Ceiling Suspension Assemblies

09 53 23 – Metal Acoustical Ceiling Suspension Assemblies

09 53 23.30 Ceiling Suspension Systems

		Crew	Daily Output	Labor-Hours	Unit	Material	2014 Bare Costs Labor	Equipment	Total	Total Incl O&P
1040	Hanging wire, 12 ga., 4' long	1 Carp	65	.123	C.S.F.	.31	4.40		4.71	7.75
1080	8' long	↓	65	.123	"	.62	4.40		5.02	8.10
3000	Seismic ceiling bracing, IBC Site Class D, Occupancy Category II									
3050	For ceilings less than 2500 S.F.									
3060	Seismic clips at attached walls	1 Carp	180	.044	Ea.	1	1.59		2.59	3.77
3100	For ceilings greater than 2500 S.F., add									
3120	Seismic clips, joints at cross tees	1 Carp	120	.067	Ea.	2.90	2.38		5.28	7.20
3140	At cross tees and mains, mains field cut	"	60	.133	"	2.90	4.77		7.67	11.20
3200	Compression posts, telescopic, attached to structure above									
3210	To 30" high	1 Carp	26	.308	Ea.	27	11		38	48.50
3220	30" to 48" high	↓	25.50	.314		43.50	11.20		54.70	67
3230	48" to 84" high		25	.320		52.50	11.45		63.95	77
3240	84" to 102" high		24.50	.327		60	11.65		71.65	85.50
3250	102" to 120" high		24	.333		85.50	11.90		97.40	115
3260	120" to 144" high	↓	24	.333	↓	95	11.90		106.90	125
3300	Stabilizer bars									
3310	12" long	1 Carp	240	.033	Ea.	.78	1.19		1.97	2.86
3320	24" long		235	.034		.77	1.22		1.99	2.90
3330	36" long		230	.035		.72	1.24		1.96	2.88
3340	48" long	↓	220	.036	↓	.73	1.30		2.03	2.99
3400	Wire support for light fixtures, per L.F. height to structure above									
3410	Less than 10 lb.	1 Carp	400	.020	L.F.	.28	.72		1	1.50
3420	10 lb. to 56 lb.	"	240	.033	"	.55	1.19		1.74	2.61

09 54 Specialty Ceilings

09 54 33 – Decorative Panel Ceilings

09 54 33.20 Metal Panel Ceilings

		Crew	Daily Output	Labor-Hours	Unit	Material	2014 Bare Costs Labor	Equipment	Total	Total Incl O&P
0010	**METAL PANEL CEILINGS**									
0020	Lay-in or screwed to furring, not including grid									
0100	Tin ceilings, 2' x 2' or 2' x 4', bare steel finish	2 Carp	300	.053	S.F.	2.46	1.91		4.37	5.90
0120	Painted white finish		300	.053	"	3.67	1.91		5.58	7.25
0140	Copper, chrome or brass finish		300	.053	L.F.	6.45	1.91		8.36	10.30
0200	Cornice molding, 2-1/2" to 3-1/2" wide, 4' long, bare steel finish		200	.080	S.F.	2.21	2.86		5.07	7.25
0220	Painted white finish		200	.080		2.92	2.86		5.78	8
0240	Copper, chrome or brass finish		200	.080		3.91	2.86		6.77	9.10
0320	5" to 6-1/2" wide, 4' long, bare steel finish		150	.107		3.19	3.81		7	9.90
0340	Painted white finish		150	.107		4.25	3.81		8.06	11.05
0360	Copper, chrome or brass finish		150	.107		6.50	3.81		10.31	13.55
0420	Flat molding, 3-1/2" to 5" wide, 4' long, bare steel finish		250	.064		3.29	2.29		5.58	7.45
0440	Painted white finish		250	.064		3.80	2.29		6.09	8.05
0460	Copper, chrome or brass finish	↓	250	.064	↓	7.35	2.29		9.64	11.95

09 62 Specialty Flooring

09 62 19 – Laminate Flooring

09 62 19.10 Floating Floor

		Crew	Daily Output	Labor-Hours	Unit	Material	2014 Bare Costs Labor	Equipment	Total	Total Incl O&P
0010	**FLOATING FLOOR**									
8300	Floating floor, laminate, wood pattern strip, complete	1 Clab	133	.060	S.F.	5.05	1.70		6.75	8.40
8310	Components, T & G wood composite strips					4.02			4.02	4.42
8320	Film					.14			.14	.15
8330	Foam					.25			.25	.28
8340	Adhesive					.65			.65	.72
8350	Installation kit					.17			.17	.19
8360	Trim, 2" wide x 3' long				L.F.	3.85			3.85	4.24
8370	Reducer moulding				"	5.20			5.20	5.70

09 62 23 – Bamboo Flooring

09 62 23.10 Flooring, Bamboo

			Crew	Daily Output	Labor-Hours	Unit	Material	Labor	Equipment	Total	Total Incl O&P
0010	**FLOORING, BAMBOO**										
8600	Flooring, wood, bamboo strips, unfinished, 5/8" x 4" x 3'	G	1 Carp	255	.031	S.F.	4.53	1.12		5.65	6.85
8610	5/8" x 4" x 4'	G		275	.029		4.70	1.04		5.74	6.90
8620	5/8" x 4" x 6'	G		295	.027		5.15	.97		6.12	7.35
8630	Finished, 5/8" x 4" x 3'	G		255	.031		4.99	1.12		6.11	7.40
8640	5/8" x 4" x 4'	G		275	.029		5.20	1.04		6.24	7.50
8650	5/8" x 4" x 6'	G		295	.027		4.54	.97		5.51	6.60
8660	Stair treads, unfinished, 1-1/16" x 11-1/2" x 4'	G		18	.444	Ea.	43.50	15.90		59.40	74.50
8670	Finished, 1-1/16" x 11-1/2" x 4'	G		18	.444		77	15.90		92.90	111
8680	Stair risers, unfinished, 5/8" x 7-1/2" x 4'	G		18	.444		16.05	15.90		31.95	44
8690	Finished, 5/8" x 7-1/2" x 4'	G		18	.444		30.50	15.90		46.40	60
8700	Stair nosing, unfinished, 6' long	G		16	.500		35.50	17.90		53.40	69
8710	Finished, 6' long	G		16	.500		42	17.90		59.90	76

09 63 Masonry Flooring

09 63 13 – Brick Flooring

09 63 13.10 Miscellaneous Brick Flooring

			Crew	Daily Output	Labor-Hours	Unit	Material	Labor	Equipment	Total	Total Incl O&P
0010	**MISCELLANEOUS BRICK FLOORING**										
0020	Acid-proof shales, red, 8" x 3-3/4" x 1-1/4" thick		D-7	.43	37.209	M	685	1,100		1,785	2,525
0050	2-1/4" thick		D-1	.40	40		950	1,300		2,250	3,200
0200	Acid-proof clay brick, 8" x 3-3/4" x 2-1/4" thick	G		.40	40		930	1,300		2,230	3,175
0250	9" x 4-1/2" x 3"	G		95	.168	S.F.	4.14	5.45		9.59	13.60
0260	Cast ceramic, pressed, 4" x 8" x 1/2", unglazed		D-7	100	.160		6.25	4.70		10.95	14.50
0270	Glazed			100	.160		8.35	4.70		13.05	16.75
0280	Hand molded flooring, 4" x 8" x 3/4", unglazed			95	.168		8.25	4.94		13.19	17.10
0290	Glazed			95	.168		10.35	4.94		15.29	19.40
0300	8" hexagonal, 3/4" thick, unglazed			85	.188		9.05	5.50		14.55	18.85
0310	Glazed			85	.188		16.35	5.50		21.85	27
0400	Heavy duty industrial, cement mortar bed, 2" thick, not incl. brick		D-1	80	.200		.83	6.45		7.28	11.65
0450	Acid-proof joints, 1/4" wide		"	65	.246		1.44	7.95		9.39	14.80
0500	Pavers, 8" x 4", 1" to 1-1/4" thick, red		D-7	95	.168		3.64	4.94		8.58	12
0510	Ironspot		"	95	.168		5.15	4.94		10.09	13.65
0540	1-3/8" to 1-3/4" thick, red		D-1	95	.168		3.51	5.45		8.96	12.90
0560	Ironspot			95	.168		5.10	5.45		10.55	14.65
0580	2-1/4" thick, red			90	.178		3.57	5.75		9.32	13.50
0590	Ironspot			90	.178		5.55	5.75		11.30	15.65
0700	Paver, adobe brick, 6" x 12", 1/2" joint	G		42	.381		1.38	12.30		13.68	22
0710	Mexican red, 12" x 12"	G	1 Tilf	48	.167		1.66	5.45		7.11	10.65
0720	Saltillo, 12" x 12"	G	"	48	.167		1.40	5.45		6.85	10.35

09 63 Masonry Flooring

09 63 13 – Brick Flooring

09 63 13.10 Miscellaneous Brick Flooring

		Crew	Daily Output	Labor-Hours	Unit	Material	2014 Bare Costs Labor	Equipment	Total	Total Incl O&P
0800	For sidewalks and patios with pavers, see Section 32 14 16.10									
0870	For epoxy joints, add	D-1	600	.027	S.F.	2.77	.86		3.63	4.48
0880	For Furan underlayment, add	"	600	.027		2.30	.86		3.16	3.96
0890	For waxed surface, steam cleaned, add	A-1H	1000	.008	↓	.20	.23	.08	.51	.68

09 63 40 – Stone Flooring

09 63 40.10 Marble

		Crew	Daily Output	Labor-Hours	Unit	Material	2014 Bare Costs Labor	Equipment	Total	Total Incl O&P
0010	**MARBLE**									
0020	Thin gauge tile, 12" x 6", 3/8", white Carara	D-7	60	.267	S.F.	14.90	7.85		22.75	29
0100	Travertine		60	.267		13.30	7.85		21.15	27.50
0200	12" x 12" x 3/8", thin set, floors		60	.267		9	7.85		16.85	22.50
0300	On walls		52	.308	↓	9.85	9.05		18.90	25.50
1000	Marble threshold, 4" wide x 36" long x 5/8" thick, white	↓	60	.267	Ea.	9	7.85		16.85	22.50

09 63 40.20 Slate Tile

		Crew	Daily Output	Labor-Hours	Unit	Material	2014 Bare Costs Labor	Equipment	Total	Total Incl O&P
0010	**SLATE TILE**									
0020	Vermont, 6" x 6" x 1/4" thick, thin set	D-7	180	.089	S.F.	7	2.61		9.61	11.90
0200	See also Section 32 14 40.10									

09 64 Wood Flooring

09 64 16 – Wood Block Flooring

09 64 16.10 End Grain Block Flooring

		Crew	Daily Output	Labor-Hours	Unit	Material	2014 Bare Costs Labor	Equipment	Total	Total Incl O&P
0010	**END GRAIN BLOCK FLOORING**									
0020	End grain flooring, coated, 2" thick	1 Carp	295	.027	S.F.	3.52	.97		4.49	5.50
0400	Natural finish, 1" thick, fir		125	.064		3.64	2.29		5.93	7.85
0600	1-1/2" thick, pine		125	.064		3.57	2.29		5.86	7.80
0700	2" thick, pine	↓	125	.064	↓	4.12	2.29		6.41	8.40

09 64 19 – Wood Composition Flooring

09 64 19.10 Wood Composition

		Crew	Daily Output	Labor-Hours	Unit	Material	2014 Bare Costs Labor	Equipment	Total	Total Incl O&P
0010	**WOOD COMPOSITION** Gym floors									
0100	2-1/4" x 6-7/8" x 3/8", on 2" grout setting bed	D-7	150	.107	S.F.	6.05	3.13		9.18	11.70
0200	Thin set, on concrete	"	250	.064		5.50	1.88		7.38	9.10
0300	Sanding and finishing, add	1 Carp	200	.040	↓	.83	1.43		2.26	3.32

09 64 23 – Wood Parquet Flooring

09 64 23.10 Wood Parquet

		Crew	Daily Output	Labor-Hours	Unit	Material	2014 Bare Costs Labor	Equipment	Total	Total Incl O&P
0010	**WOOD PARQUET** flooring									
5200	Parquetry, standard, 5/16" thick, not incl. finish, oak, minimum	1 Carp	160	.050	S.F.	4.14	1.79		5.93	7.55
5300	Maximum		100	.080		7	2.86		9.86	12.50
5500	Teak, minimum		160	.050		4.86	1.79		6.65	8.35
5600	Maximum		100	.080		8.50	2.86		11.36	14.15
5650	13/16" thick, select grade oak, minimum		160	.050		9.50	1.79		11.29	13.45
5700	Maximum		100	.080		14.40	2.86		17.26	20.50
5800	Custom parquetry, including finish, minimum		100	.080		15.65	2.86		18.51	22
5900	Maximum		50	.160		21	5.70		26.70	32.50
6700	Parquetry, prefinished white oak, 5/16" thick, minimum		160	.050		4.27	1.79		6.06	7.70
6800	Maximum		100	.080		4.69	2.86		7.55	9.95
7000	Walnut or teak, parquetry, minimum		160	.050		5.35	1.79		7.14	8.90
7100	Maximum	↓	100	.080	↓	9.35	2.86		12.21	15.10
7200	Acrylic wood parquet blocks, 12" x 12" x 5/16",									
7210	Irradiated, set in epoxy	1 Carp	160	.050	S.F.	7.80	1.79		9.59	11.55

09 64 Wood Flooring

09 64 29 – Wood Strip and Plank Flooring

09 64 29.10 Wood		Crew	Daily Output	Labor-Hours	Unit	Material	2014 Bare Costs Labor	2014 Bare Costs Equipment	Total	Total Incl O&P
0010	**WOOD**									
0020	Fir, vertical grain, 1" x 4", not incl. finish, grade B & better	1 Carp	255	.031	S.F.	2.74	1.12		3.86	4.90
0100	C grade & better		255	.031		2.58	1.12		3.70	4.73
4000	Maple, strip, 25/32" x 2-1/4", not incl. finish, select		170	.047		5.75	1.68		7.43	9.20
4100	#2 & better		170	.047		4.29	1.68		5.97	7.55
4300	33/32" x 3-1/4", not incl. finish, #1 grade		170	.047		4.49	1.68		6.17	7.75
4400	#2 & better		170	.047		4	1.68		5.68	7.25
4600	Oak, white or red, 25/32" x 2-1/4", not incl. finish									
4700	#1 common	1 Carp	170	.047	S.F.	2.98	1.68		4.66	6.10
4900	Select quartered, 2-1/4" wide		170	.047		4.24	1.68		5.92	7.50
5000	Clear		170	.047		4.12	1.68		5.80	7.35
6100	Prefinished, white oak, prime grade, 2-1/4" wide		170	.047		4.69	1.68		6.37	8
6200	3-1/4" wide		185	.043		5.10	1.55		6.65	8.20
6400	Ranch plank		145	.055		7.15	1.97		9.12	11.15
6500	Hardwood blocks, 9" x 9", 25/32" thick		160	.050		5.90	1.79		7.69	9.50
7400	Yellow pine, 3/4" x 3-1/8", T & G, C & better, not incl. finish		200	.040		1.49	1.43		2.92	4.05
7500	Refinish wood floor, sand, 2 coats poly, wax, soft wood, min.	1 Clab	400	.020		.88	.56		1.44	1.92
7600	Hard wood, max.		130	.062		1.31	1.74		3.05	4.36
7800	Sanding and finishing, 2 coats polyurethane		295	.027		.88	.76		1.64	2.26
7900	Subfloor and underlayment, see Section 06 16									
8015	Transition molding, 2 1/4" wide, 5' long	1 Carp	19.20	.417	Ea.	10.70	14.90		25.60	37

09 64 66 – Wood Athletic Flooring

09 64 66.10 Gymnasium Flooring		Crew	Daily Output	Labor-Hours	Unit	Material	2014 Bare Costs Labor	2014 Bare Costs Equipment	Total	Total Incl O&P
0010	**GYMNASIUM FLOORING**									
0600	Gym floor, in mastic, over 2 ply felt, #2 & better									
0700	25/32" thick maple	1 Carp	100	.080	S.F.	3.77	2.86		6.63	8.95
0900	33/32" thick maple		98	.082		4.76	2.92		7.68	10.15
1000	For 1/2" corkboard underlayment, add		750	.011		.97	.38		1.35	1.71
1300	For #1 grade maple, add					.50			.50	.55
1600	Maple flooring, over sleepers, #2 & better									
1700	25/32" thick	1 Carp	85	.094	S.F.	4.63	3.36		7.99	10.75
1900	33/32" thick	"	83	.096		5.40	3.45		8.85	11.75
2000	For #1 grade, add					.54			.54	.59
2200	For 3/4" subfloor, add	1 Carp	350	.023		1.20	.82		2.02	2.70
2300	With two 1/2" subfloors, 25/32" thick	"	69	.116		5.80	4.14		9.94	13.30
2500	Maple, incl. finish, #2 & btr., 25/32" thick, on rubber									
2600	Sleepers, with two 1/2" subfloors	1 Carp	76	.105	S.F.	6.20	3.76		9.96	13.20
2800	With steel spline, double connection to channels	"	73	.110		6.65	3.92		10.57	13.90
2900	For 33/32" maple, add					.71			.71	.78
3100	For #1 grade maple, add					.54			.54	.59
3500	For termite proofing all of the above, add					.29			.29	.32
3700	Portable hardwood, prefinished panels	1 Carp	83	.096		8.30	3.45		11.75	14.90
3720	Insulated with polystyrene, 1" thick, add		165	.048		.71	1.73		2.44	3.70
3750	Running tracks, Sitka spruce surface, 25/32" x 2-1/4"		62	.129		15.20	4.61		19.81	24.50
3770	3/4" plywood surface, finished		100	.080		3.60	2.86		6.46	8.75

09 65 Resilient Flooring

09 65 10 – Resilient Tile Underlayment

09 65 10.10 Latex Underlayment

		Crew	Daily Output	Labor-Hours	Unit	Material	2014 Bare Costs Labor	2014 Bare Costs Equipment	Total	Total Incl O&P
0010	**LATEX UNDERLAYMENT**									
3600	Latex underlayment, 1/8" thk., cementitious for resilient flooring	1 Tilf	160	.050	S.F.	1.16	1.64		2.80	3.92
4000	Liquid, fortified				Gal.	34			34	37.50

09 65 13 – Resilient Base and Accessories

09 65 13.13 Resilient Base

		Crew	Daily Output	Labor-Hours	Unit	Material	2014 Bare Costs Labor	2014 Bare Costs Equipment	Total	Total Incl O&P
0010	**RESILIENT BASE**									
0690	1/8" vinyl base, 2 1/2" H, straight or cove, standard colors	1 Tilf	315	.025	L.F.	1.34	.83		2.17	2.81
0700	4" high		315	.025		1.26	.83		2.09	2.73
0710	6" high		315	.025		1.52	.83		2.35	3.01
0720	Corners, 2 1/2" high		315	.025	Ea.	2.02	.83		2.85	3.56
0730	4" high		315	.025		2.56	.83		3.39	4.16
0740	6" high		315	.025		2.99	.83		3.82	4.63
0800	1/8" rubber base, 2 1/2" H, straight or cove, standard colors		315	.025	L.F.	1.13	.83		1.96	2.58
1100	4" high		315	.025		1.26	.83		2.09	2.73
1110	6" high		315	.025		1.65	.83		2.48	3.16
1150	Corners, 2 1/2" high		315	.025	Ea.	1.70	.83		2.53	3.21
1153	4" high		315	.025		2.51	.83		3.34	4.10
1155	6" high		315	.025		3.15	.83		3.98	4.81
1450	For premium color/finish add					50%				
1500	Millwork profile	1 Tilf	315	.025	L.F.	5.85	.83		6.68	7.80

09 65 13.23 Resilient Stair Treads and Risers

		Crew	Daily Output	Labor-Hours	Unit	Material	2014 Bare Costs Labor	2014 Bare Costs Equipment	Total	Total Incl O&P
0010	**RESILIENT STAIR TREADS AND RISERS**									
0300	Rubber, molded tread, 12" wide, 5/16" thick, black	1 Tilf	115	.070	L.F.	14.10	2.28		16.38	19.20
0400	Colors		115	.070		14.50	2.28		16.78	19.65
0600	1/4" thick, black		115	.070		13.60	2.28		15.88	18.65
0700	Colors		115	.070		14.10	2.28		16.38	19.20
0900	Grip strip safety tread, colors, 5/16" thick		115	.070		22	2.28		24.28	28
1000	3/16" thick		120	.067		16.10	2.18		18.28	21.50
1200	Landings, smooth sheet rubber, 1/8" thick		120	.067	S.F.	6.95	2.18		9.13	11.15
1300	3/16" thick		120	.067	"	8.75	2.18		10.93	13.15
1500	Nosings, 3" wide, 3/16" thick, black		140	.057	L.F.	3.94	1.87		5.81	7.35
1600	Colors		140	.057		4.29	1.87		6.16	7.75
1800	Risers, 7" high, 1/8" thick, flat		250	.032		6.65	1.05		7.70	9.05
1900	Coved		250	.032		8.25	1.05		9.30	10.80
2100	Vinyl, molded tread, 12" wide, colors, 1/8" thick		115	.070		6.95	2.28		9.23	11.35
2200	1/4" thick		115	.070		8.75	2.28		11.03	13.35
2300	Landing material, 1/8" thick		200	.040	S.F.	6.95	1.31		8.26	9.75
2400	Riser, 7" high, 1/8" thick, coved		175	.046	L.F.	3.95	1.50		5.45	6.75
2500	Tread and riser combined, 1/8" thick		80	.100	"	10.45	3.28		13.73	16.80

09 65 16 – Resilient Sheet Flooring

09 65 16.10 Rubber and Vinyl Sheet Flooring

			Crew	Daily Output	Labor-Hours	Unit	Material	2014 Bare Costs Labor	2014 Bare Costs Equipment	Total	Total Incl O&P
0010	**RUBBER AND VINYL SHEET FLOORING**										
5500	Linoleum, sheet goods	G	1 Tilf	360	.022	S.F.	3.59	.73		4.32	5.10
5900	Rubber, sheet goods, 36" wide, 1/8" thick			120	.067		7.65	2.18		9.83	11.90
5950	3/16" thick			100	.080		10.35	2.62		12.97	15.65
6000	1/4" thick			90	.089		12.25	2.91		15.16	18.20
8000	Vinyl sheet goods, backed, .065" thick, minimum			250	.032		4.10	1.05		5.15	6.20
8050	Maximum			200	.040		5	1.31		6.31	7.60
8100	.080" thick, minimum			230	.035		4.10	1.14		5.24	6.35
8150	Maximum			200	.040		5.90	1.31		7.21	8.60
8200	.125" thick, minimum			230	.035		4.25	1.14		5.39	6.50

09 65 Resilient Flooring

09 65 16 – Resilient Sheet Flooring

09 65 16.10 Rubber and Vinyl Sheet Flooring

		Crew	Daily Output	Labor-Hours	Unit	Material	2014 Bare Costs Labor	Equipment	Total	Total Incl O&P
8250	Maximum	1 Tilf	200	.040	S.F.	7.50	1.31		8.81	10.35
8400	For welding seams, add	↓	100	.080	L.F.	.20	2.62		2.82	4.45
8700	Adhesive cement, 1 gallon per 200 to 300 S.F.				Gal.	27			27	29.50
8800	Asphalt primer, 1 gallon per 300 S.F.					14			14	15.40
8900	Emulsion, 1 gallon per 140 S.F.				↓	18			18	19.80

09 65 19 – Resilient Tile Flooring

09 65 19.10 Miscellaneous Resilient Tile Flooring

			Crew	Daily Output	Labor-Hours	Unit	Material	2014 Bare Costs Labor	Equipment	Total	Total Incl O&P
0010	**MISCELLANEOUS RESILIENT TILE FLOORING**										
2200	Cork tile, standard finish, 1/8" thick	G	1 Tilf	315	.025	S.F.	7	.83		7.83	9.05
2250	3/16" thick	G		315	.025		7.75	.83		8.58	9.90
2300	5/16" thick	G		315	.025		8.45	.83		9.28	10.60
2350	1/2" thick	G		315	.025		10.70	.83		11.53	13.10
2500	Urethane finish, 1/8" thick	G		315	.025		9.50	.83		10.33	11.80
2550	3/16" thick	G		315	.025		10.30	.83		11.13	12.70
2600	5/16" thick	G		315	.025		11.70	.83		12.53	14.20
2650	1/2" thick	G		315	.025		15.75	.83		16.58	18.70
6050	Rubber tile, marbleized colors, 12" x 12", 1/8" thick			400	.020		7.25	.66		7.91	9
6100	3/16" thick			400	.020		9.25	.66		9.91	11.25
6300	Special tile, plain colors, 1/8" thick			400	.020		10	.66		10.66	12.05
6350	3/16" thick			400	.020		10.25	.66		10.91	12.35
6410	Raised, radial or square, minimum			400	.020		8	.66		8.66	9.85
6430	Maximum			400	.020		11	.66		11.66	13.15
6450	For golf course, skating rink, etc., 1/4" thick			275	.029		13.95	.95		14.90	16.90
6700	Synthetic turf, 3/8" thick		↓	90	.089	↓	6.95	2.91		9.86	12.35
6750	Interlocking 2' x 2' squares, 1/2" thick, not										
6810	cemented, for playgrounds, minimum		1 Tilf	210	.038	S.F.	6.25	1.25		7.50	8.90
6850	Maximum			190	.042		13.40	1.38		14.78	17
7000	Vinyl composition tile, 12" x 12", 1/16" thick			500	.016		.86	.52		1.38	1.80
7050	Embossed			500	.016		2.21	.52		2.73	3.28
7100	Marbleized			500	.016		2.21	.52		2.73	3.28
7150	Solid			500	.016		2.85	.52		3.37	3.99
7200	3/32" thick, embossed			500	.016		1.46	.52		1.98	2.46
7250	Marbleized			500	.016		2.54	.52		3.06	3.64
7300	Solid			500	.016		2.36	.52		2.88	3.45
7350	1/8" thick, marbleized			500	.016		2.22	.52		2.74	3.29
7400	Solid			500	.016		2.26	.52		2.78	3.34
7450	Conductive			500	.016		6.70	.52		7.22	8.20
7500	Vinyl tile, 12" x 12", .050" thick, minimum			500	.016		3.42	.52		3.94	4.61
7550	Maximum			500	.016		7	.52		7.52	8.55
7600	1/8" thick, minimum			500	.016		4.99	.52		5.51	6.35
7650	Solid colors			500	.016		3.65	.52		4.17	4.87
7700	Marbleized or Travertine pattern			500	.016		5.90	.52		6.42	7.35
7750	Florentine pattern			500	.016		6.30	.52		6.82	7.80
7800	Maximum		↓	500	.016	↓	13	.52		13.52	15.15

09 65 33 – Conductive Resilient Flooring

09 65 33.10 Conductive Rubber and Vinyl Flooring

		Crew	Daily Output	Labor-Hours	Unit	Material	2014 Bare Costs Labor	Equipment	Total	Total Incl O&P
0010	**CONDUCTIVE RUBBER AND VINYL FLOORING**									
1700	Conductive flooring, rubber tile, 1/8" thick	1 Tilf	315	.025	S.F.	6.60	.83		7.43	8.60
1800	Homogeneous vinyl tile, 1/8" thick	"	315	.025	"	8.75	.83		9.58	11

09 66 Terrazzo Flooring

09 66 13 – Portland Cement Terrazzo Flooring

09 66 13.10 Portland Cement Terrazzo

		Crew	Daily Output	Labor-Hours	Unit	Material	2014 Bare Costs Labor	Equipment	Total	Total Incl O&P
0010	**PORTLAND CEMENT TERRAZZO**, cast-in-place	R096613-10								
0101	Curb, 6" high and 6" wide	J-3	12	1.333	L.F.	6	40	24	70	97
0300	Divider strip for floors, 14 ga., 1-1/4" deep, zinc	1 Mstz	375	.021		1.46	.69		2.15	2.73
0400	Brass		375	.021		2.56	.69		3.25	3.94
0600	Heavy top strip 1/4" thick, 1-1/4" deep, zinc		300	.027		2.08	.87		2.95	3.69
0900	Galv. bottoms, brass		300	.027		3.32	.87		4.19	5.05
1200	For thin set floors, 16 ga., 1/2" x 1/2", zinc		350	.023		.98	.74		1.72	2.28
1300	Brass	↓	350	.023	↓	2.39	.74		3.13	3.83
1500	Floor, bonded to concrete, 1-3/4" thick, gray cement	J-3	75	.213	S.F.	3.28	6.35	3.87	13.50	18.10
1600	White cement, mud set		75	.213		3.65	6.35	3.87	13.87	18.55
1800	Not bonded, 3" total thickness, gray cement		70	.229		4.08	6.80	4.15	15.03	20
1900	White cement, mud set	↓	70	.229	↓	4.76	6.80	4.15	15.71	21
2100	For Venetian terrazzo, 1" topping, add					50%	50%			
2200	For heavy duty abrasive terrazzo, add					50%	50%			
2700	Monolithic terrazzo, 1/2" thick									
2710	10' panels	J-3	125	.128	S.F.	3.08	3.82	2.32	9.22	12.10
3000	Stairs, cast in place, pan filled treads		30	.533	L.F.	3.31	15.90	9.70	28.91	40
3100	Treads and risers	↓	14	1.143	"	5.85	34	21	60.85	84.50
3300	For stair landings, add to floor prices						50%			
3400	Stair stringers and fascia	J-3	30	.533	S.F.	5.50	15.90	9.70	31.10	42
3600	For abrasive metal nosings on stairs, add		150	.107	L.F.	9.05	3.18	1.94	14.17	17.25
3700	For abrasive surface finish, add		600	.027	S.F.	1.52	.80	.48	2.80	3.48
3900	For raised abrasive strips, add		150	.107	L.F.	1.32	3.18	1.94	6.44	8.75
4000	Wainscot, bonded, 1-1/2" thick		30	.533	S.F.	3.88	15.90	9.70	29.48	40.50
4200	1/4" thick	↓	40	.400	"	5.45	11.95	7.25	24.65	33
4300	Stone chips, onyx gemstone, per 50 lb. bag				Bag	16.50			16.50	18.15

09 66 16 – Terrazzo Floor Tile

09 66 16.10 Tile or Terrazzo Base

		Crew	Daily Output	Labor-Hours	Unit	Material	2014 Bare Costs Labor	Equipment	Total	Total Incl O&P
0010	**TILE OR TERRAZZO BASE**									
0020	Scratch coat only	1 Mstz	150	.053	S.F.	.43	1.73		2.16	3.27
0500	Scratch and brown coat only	"	75	.107	"	.82	3.47		4.29	6.50

09 66 16.13 Portland Cement Terrazzo Floor Tile

		Crew	Daily Output	Labor-Hours	Unit	Material	2014 Bare Costs Labor	Equipment	Total	Total Incl O&P
0010	**PORTLAND CEMENT TERRAZZO FLOOR TILE**									
1200	Floor tiles, non-slip, 1" thick, 12" x 12"	D-1	60	.267	S.F.	19.70	8.60		28.30	36
1300	1-1/4" thick, 12" x 12"		60	.267		20.50	8.60		29.10	37
1500	16" x 16"		50	.320		22	10.30		32.30	41.50
1600	1-1/2" thick, 16" x 16"	↓	45	.356		20.50	11.45		31.95	41.50
1800	For Venetian terrazzo, add					6.10			6.10	6.70
1900	For white cement, add	↓			↓	.57			.57	.63

09 66 16.16 Plastic Matrix Terrazzo Floor Tile

		Crew	Daily Output	Labor-Hours	Unit	Material	2014 Bare Costs Labor	Equipment	Total	Total Incl O&P
0010	**PLASTIC MATRIX TERRAZZO FLOOR TILE**									
0100	12" x 12", 3/16" thick, Floor tiles w/marble chips	1 Tilf	500	.016	S.F.	7.30	.52		7.82	8.90
0200	12" x 12", 3/16" thick, Floor tiles w/glass chips		500	.016		7.90	.52		8.42	9.50
0300	12" x 12", 3/16" thick, Floor tiles w/recycled content	↓	500	.016	↓	6.20	.52		6.72	7.70

09 66 16.30 Terrazzo, Precast

		Crew	Daily Output	Labor-Hours	Unit	Material	2014 Bare Costs Labor	Equipment	Total	Total Incl O&P
0010	**TERRAZZO, PRECAST**									
0020	Base, 6" high, straight	1 Mstz	70	.114	L.F.	11.85	3.71		15.56	19
0100	Cove		60	.133		12.80	4.33		17.13	21
0300	8" high, straight		60	.133		11.45	4.33		15.78	19.60
0400	Cove	↓	50	.160		16.85	5.20		22.05	27
0600	For white cement, add				↓	.45			.45	.50

09 66 Terrazzo Flooring

09 66 16 – Terrazzo Floor Tile

09 66 16.30 Terrazzo, Precast

		Crew	Daily Output	Labor-Hours	Unit	Material	2014 Bare Costs Labor	Equipment	Total	Total Incl O&P
0700	For 16 ga. zinc toe strip, add				L.F.	1.72			1.72	1.89
0900	Curbs, 4" x 4" high	1 Mstz	40	.200		32.50	6.50		39	46
1000	8" x 8" high	"	30	.267		37.50	8.65		46.15	55
2401	Stair treads, 1-1/2" thick, non-slip, three line pattern	2 Mstz	70	.229		41	7.45		48.45	57
2501	Nosing and two lines	J-3	70	.229		41	6.80	4.15	51.95	60.50
2701	2" thick treads, straight	2 Mstz	60	.267		47	8.65		55.65	66
2801	Curved		50	.320		65	10.40		75.40	88.50
3001	Stair risers, straight sections, 1" thick, to 6" high		60	.267		10.35	8.65		19	25.50
3101	Cove		50	.320		16.20	10.40		26.60	34.50
3301	Curved, 1" thick, to 6" high, vertical		48	.333		27	10.85		37.85	47
3402	Cove		38	.421		42	13.70		55.70	68
3601	Stair tread and riser, single piece, straight, minimum		60	.267		52	8.65		60.65	71.50
3701	Maximum	↓	40	.400		67.50	13		80.50	95
3901	Curved tread and riser, minimum	J-3	40	.400		73	11.95	7.25	92.20	107
4001	Maximum	"	32	.500		92	14.90	9.10	116	135
4201	Stair stringers, notched, 1" thick	2 Mstz	25	.640		31	21		52	67.50
4301	2" thick		22	.727	↓	36	23.50		59.50	77.50
4501	Stair landings, structural, non-slip, 1-1/2" thick		85	.188	S.F.	29	6.10		35.10	41.50
4601	3" thick	↓	14	1.143		35.50	37		72.50	99
4800	Wainscot, 12" x 12" x 1" tiles	1 Mstz	12	.667		6.85	21.50		28.35	42.50
4900	16" x 16" x 1-1/2" tiles	"	8	1	↓	14.25	32.50		46.75	68

09 66 23 – Resinous Matrix Terrazzo Flooring

09 66 23.13 Polyacrylate Modified Cementitious Terrazzo Flooring

		Crew	Daily Output	Labor-Hours	Unit	Material	Labor	Equipment	Total	Total Incl O&P
0010	**POLYACRYLATE MODIFIED CEMENTITIOUS TERRAZZO FLOORING**									
3150	Polyacrylate, 1/4" thick, minimum	C-6	735	.065	S.F.	3.53	1.93	.09	5.55	7.20
3170	Maximum		480	.100		4.48	2.96	.14	7.58	10
3200	3/8" thick, minimum		620	.077		4.55	2.29	.11	6.95	8.95
3220	Maximum	↓	480	.100	↓	6.35	2.96	.14	9.45	12.10

09 66 23.16 Epoxy-Resin Terrazzo Flooring

		Crew	Daily Output	Labor-Hours	Unit	Material	Labor	Equipment	Total	Total Incl O&P
0010	**EPOXY-RESIN TERRAZZO FLOORING**									
1800	Epoxy terrazzo, 1/4" thick, chemical resistant, minimum	J-3	200	.080	S.F.	5.95	2.39	1.45	9.79	11.95
1900	Maximum		150	.107		9	3.18	1.94	14.12	17.20
2500	Epoxy terrazzo, 1/4" thick, minimum		200	.080		5.05	2.39	1.45	8.89	11.05
2550	Average		175	.091		5.85	2.73	1.66	10.24	12.70
2600	Maximum	↓	150	.107	↓	6.25	3.18	1.94	11.37	14.15

09 66 33 – Conductive Terrazzo Flooring

09 66 33.10 Conductive Terrazzo

		Crew	Daily Output	Labor-Hours	Unit	Material	Labor	Equipment	Total	Total Incl O&P
0010	**CONDUCTIVE TERRAZZO**									
2400	Bonded conductive floor for hospitals	J-3	90	.178	S.F.	4.71	5.30	3.23	13.24	17.30

09 66 33.13 Conductive Epoxy-Resin Terrazzo

		Crew	Daily Output	Labor-Hours	Unit	Material	Labor	Equipment	Total	Total Incl O&P
0010	**CONDUCTIVE EPOXY-RESIN TERRAZZO**									
2100	Epoxy terrazzo, 1/4" thick, conductive, minimum	J-3	100	.160	S.F.	7.95	4.77	2.91	15.63	19.60
2200	Maximum	"	90	.178	"	10.35	5.30	3.23	18.88	23.50

09 66 33.19 Conductive Plastic-Matrix Terrazzo Flooring

		Crew	Daily Output	Labor-Hours	Unit	Material	Labor	Equipment	Total	Total Incl O&P
0010	**CONDUCTIVE PLASTIC-MATRIX TERRAZZO FLOORING**									
3300	Conductive, 1/4" thick, minimum	C-6	450	.107	S.F.	7.20	3.15	.15	10.50	13.35
3330	Maximum		305	.157		9.90	4.65	.22	14.77	18.90
3350	3/8" thick, minimum		365	.132		9.45	3.89	.18	13.52	17.10
3370	Maximum		255	.188		12.65	5.55	.26	18.46	23.50
3450	Granite, conductive, 1/4" thick, minimum		695	.069		9.15	2.04	.10	11.29	13.55
3470	Maximum	↓	420	.114	↓	11.80	3.38	.16	15.34	18.80

09 66 Terrazzo Flooring

09 66 33 – Conductive Terrazzo Flooring

09 66 33.19 Conductive Plastic-Matrix Terrazzo Flooring		Crew	Daily Output	Labor-Hours	Unit	Material	2014 Bare Costs Labor	Equipment	Total	Total Incl O&P
3500	3/8" thick, minimum	C-6	695	.069	S.F.	13.35	2.04	.10	15.49	18.20
3520	Maximum	↓	380	.126	↓	16.15	3.73	.17	20.05	24

09 67 Fluid-Applied Flooring

09 67 13 – Elastomeric Liquid Flooring

09 67 13.13 Elastomeric Liquid Flooring

		Crew	Daily Output	Labor-Hours	Unit	Material	2014 Bare Costs Labor	Equipment	Total	Total Incl O&P
0010	**ELASTOMERIC LIQUID FLOORING**									
0020	Cementitious acrylic, 1/4" thick	C-6	520	.092	S.F.	1.63	2.73	.13	4.49	6.50
0100	3/8" thick	"	450	.107		2.06	3.15	.15	5.36	7.70
0200	Methyl methachrylate, 1/4" thick	C-8A	3000	.016		5.80	.49		6.29	7.15
0210	1/8" thick	"	3000	.016		3.18	.49		3.67	4.31
0300	Cupric oxychloride, on bond coat, minimum	C-6	480	.100		3.51	2.96	.14	6.61	8.95
0400	Maximum		420	.114		5.85	3.38	.16	9.39	12.25
2400	Mastic, hot laid, 2 coat, 1-1/2" thick, standard, minimum		690	.070		4.07	2.06	.10	6.23	8.05
2500	Maximum		520	.092		5.25	2.73	.13	8.11	10.45
2700	Acid-proof, minimum		605	.079		5.25	2.35	.11	7.71	9.80
2800	Maximum		350	.137		7.25	4.05	.19	11.49	14.90
3000	Neoprene, troweled on, 1/4" thick, minimum		545	.088		4.01	2.60	.12	6.73	8.90
3100	Maximum		430	.112		5.50	3.30	.15	8.95	11.70
4300	Polyurethane, with suspended vinyl chips, minimum		1065	.045		7.50	1.33	.06	8.89	10.55
4500	Maximum	↓	860	.056	↓	10.80	1.65	.08	12.53	14.75

09 67 26 – Quartz Flooring

09 67 26.26 Quartz Flooring

		Crew	Daily Output	Labor-Hours	Unit	Material	2014 Bare Costs Labor	Equipment	Total	Total Incl O&P
0010	**QUARTZ FLOORING**									
0600	Epoxy, with colored quartz chips, broadcast, minimum	C-6	675	.071	S.F.	2.75	2.10	.10	4.95	6.65
0700	Maximum		490	.098		3.97	2.90	.14	7.01	9.35
0900	Troweled, minimum		560	.086		3.50	2.53	.12	6.15	8.20
1000	Maximum	↓	480	.100	↓	5.25	2.96	.14	8.35	10.90
1200	Heavy duty epoxy topping, 1/4" thick,									
1300	500 to 1,000 S.F.	C-6	420	.114	S.F.	5.55	3.38	.16	9.09	11.90
1500	1,000 to 2,000 S.F.		450	.107		5	3.15	.15	8.30	10.90
1600	Over 10,000 S.F.		480	.100		4.63	2.96	.14	7.73	10.20
3600	Polyester, with colored quartz chips, 1/16" thick, minimum		1065	.045		3.14	1.33	.06	4.53	5.75
3700	Maximum		560	.086		4.15	2.53	.12	6.80	8.95
3900	1/8" thick, minimum		810	.059		3.65	1.75	.08	5.48	7.05
4000	Maximum		675	.071		4.70	2.10	.10	6.90	8.75
4200	Polyester, heavy duty, compared to epoxy, add	↓	2590	.019		1.51	.55	.03	2.09	2.61

09 67 66 – Fluid-Applied Athletic Flooring

09 67 66.10 Polyurethane

		Crew	Daily Output	Labor-Hours	Unit	Material	2014 Bare Costs Labor	Equipment	Total	Total Incl O&P
0010	**POLYURETHANE**									
4400	Thermoset, prefabricated in place, indoor									
4500	3/8" thick for basketball, gyms, etc.	1 Tilf	100	.080	S.F.	5.40	2.62		8.02	10.20
4600	1/2" thick for professional sports		95	.084		7.25	2.76		10.01	12.40
5000	Poured in place, indoor, with finish, 1/4" thick		80	.100		3.99	3.28		7.27	9.70
5050	3/8" thick		65	.123		4.84	4.03		8.87	11.80
5100	1/2" thick	↓	50	.160	↓	6.75	5.25		12	15.90

09 68 Carpeting

09 68 05 – Carpet Accessories

09 68 05.11 Flooring Transition Strip

		Crew	Daily Output	Labor-Hours	Unit	Material	2014 Bare Costs Labor	2014 Bare Costs Equipment	Total	Total Incl O&P
0010	**FLOORING TRANSITION STRIP**									
0107	Clamp down brass divider, 12' strip, vinyl to carpet	1 Tilf	31.25	.256	Ea.	11.05	8.40		19.45	26
0117	Vinyl to hard surface	"	31.25	.256	"	11.05	8.40		19.45	26

09 68 10 – Carpet Pad

09 68 10.10 Commercial Grade Carpet Pad

		Crew	Daily Output	Labor-Hours	Unit	Material	Labor	Equipment	Total	Total Incl O&P
0010	**COMMERCIAL GRADE CARPET PAD**									
9000	Sponge rubber pad, minimum	1 Tilf	150	.053	S.Y.	4.30	1.75		6.05	7.55
9100	Maximum		150	.053		10.20	1.75		11.95	14
9200	Felt pad, minimum		150	.053		5.10	1.75		6.85	8.40
9300	Maximum		150	.053		7.60	1.75		9.35	11.15
9400	Bonded urethane pad, minimum		150	.053		5.05	1.75		6.80	8.35
9500	Maximum		150	.053		9.20	1.75		10.95	12.90
9600	Prime urethane pad, minimum		150	.053		3.21	1.75		4.96	6.35
9700	Maximum		150	.053		5.45	1.75		7.20	8.80

09 68 13 – Tile Carpeting

09 68 13.10 Carpet Tile

		Crew	Daily Output	Labor-Hours	Unit	Material	Labor	Equipment	Total	Total Incl O&P
0010	**CARPET TILE**									
0100	Tufted nylon, 18" x 18", hard back, 20 oz.	1 Tilf	80	.100	S.Y.	22.50	3.28		25.78	30.50
0110	26 oz.		80	.100		38.50	3.28		41.78	48
0200	Cushion back, 20 oz.		80	.100		28.50	3.28		31.78	36.50
0210	26 oz.		80	.100		44.50	3.28		47.78	54.50
1100	Tufted, 24" x 24", hard back, 24 oz. nylon		80	.100		29	3.28		32.28	37.50
1180	35 oz.		80	.100		35.50	3.28		38.78	45
5060	42 oz.		80	.100		46	3.28		49.28	56.50

09 68 16 – Sheet Carpeting

09 68 16.10 Sheet Carpet

		Crew	Daily Output	Labor-Hours	Unit	Material	Labor	Equipment	Total	Total Incl O&P
0010	**SHEET CARPET**									
0700	Nylon, level loop, 26 oz., light to medium traffic	1 Tilf	75	.107	S.Y.	30	3.49		33.49	38.50
0720	28 oz., light to medium traffic		75	.107		31.50	3.49		34.99	40
0900	32 oz., medium traffic		75	.107		38	3.49		41.49	47.50
1100	40 oz., medium to heavy traffic		75	.107		56	3.49		59.49	67
2920	Nylon plush, 30 oz., medium traffic		57	.140		29.50	4.60		34.10	40
3000	36 oz., medium traffic		75	.107		39.50	3.49		42.99	49
3100	42 oz., medium to heavy traffic		70	.114		44.50	3.74		48.24	54.50
3200	46 oz., medium to heavy traffic		70	.114		52	3.74		55.74	63
3300	54 oz., heavy traffic		70	.114		56.50	3.74		60.24	68
3340	60 oz., heavy traffic		70	.114		77.50	3.74		81.24	91
3665	Olefin, 24 oz., light to medium traffic		75	.107		17.75	3.49		21.24	25
3670	26 oz., medium traffic		75	.107		19.25	3.49		22.74	26.50
3680	28 oz., medium to heavy traffic		75	.107		21	3.49		24.49	28.50
3700	32 oz., medium to heavy traffic		75	.107		26	3.49		29.49	34
3730	42 oz., heavy traffic		70	.114		28	3.74		31.74	36.50
4110	Wool, level loop, 40 oz., medium traffic		75	.107		131	3.49		134.49	150
4500	50 oz., medium to heavy traffic		75	.107		132	3.49		135.49	151
4700	Patterned, 32 oz., medium to heavy traffic		70	.114		131	3.74		134.74	150
4900	48 oz., heavy traffic		70	.114		135	3.74		138.74	155
5000	For less than full roll (approx. 1500 S.F.), add					25%				
5100	For small rooms, less than 12' wide, add						25%			
5200	For large open areas (no cuts), deduct						25%			
5600	For bound carpet baseboard, add	1 Tilf	300	.027	L.F.	3	.87		3.87	4.71
5610	For stairs, not incl. price of carpet, add	"	30	.267	Riser		8.75		8.75	14.10

09 68 Carpeting

09 68 16 – Sheet Carpeting

09 68 16.10 Sheet Carpet	Crew	Daily Output	Labor-Hours	Unit	Material	2014 Bare Costs Labor	Equipment	Total	Total Incl O&P
5620	For borders and patterns, add to labor						18%			
8950	For tackless, stretched installation, add padding from 09 68 10.10 to above									
9850	For brand-named specific fiber, add				S.Y.	25%				

09 68 20 – Athletic Carpet

09 68 20.10 Indoor Athletic Carpet

	09 68 20.10 Indoor Athletic Carpet	Crew	Daily Output	Labor-Hours	Unit	Material	2014 Bare Costs Labor	Equipment	Total	Total Incl O&P
0010	**INDOOR ATHLETIC CARPET**									
3700	Polyethylene, in rolls, no base incl., landscape surfaces	1 Tilf	275	.029	S.F.	4.07	.95		5.02	6
3800	Nylon action surface, 1/8" thick		275	.029		3.76	.95		4.71	5.70
3900	1/4" thick		275	.029		5.45	.95		6.40	7.50
4000	3/8" thick		275	.029		6.80	.95		7.75	9.05
4100	Golf tee surface with foam back		235	.034		6.75	1.11		7.86	9.25
4200	Practice putting, knitted nylon surface		235	.034		5.70	1.11		6.81	8.10
5500	Polyvinyl chloride, sheet goods for gyms, 1/4" thick		80	.100		9.60	3.28		12.88	15.85
5600	3/8" thick		60	.133		11	4.37		15.37	19.15

09 69 Access Flooring

09 69 13 – Rigid-Grid Access Flooring

09 69 13.10 Access Floors

	09 69 13.10 Access Floors	Crew	Daily Output	Labor-Hours	Unit	Material	2014 Bare Costs Labor	Equipment	Total	Total Incl O&P
0010	**ACCESS FLOORS**									
0015	Access floor package including panel, pedestal, stringers & laminate cover									
0100	Computer room, greater than 6,000 S.F.	4 Carp	750	.043	S.F.	7.50	1.53		9.03	10.80
0110	Less than 6,000 S.F.	2 Carp	375	.043		8.15	1.53		9.68	11.55
0120	Office, greater than 6,000 S.F.	4 Carp	1050	.030		5.35	1.09		6.44	7.75
0250	Panels, particle board or steel, 1250# load, no covering, under 6,000 S.F.	2 Carp	600	.027		3.75	.95		4.70	5.75
0300	Over 6,000 S.F.		640	.025		3.21	.89		4.10	5.05
0400	Aluminum, 24" panels		500	.032		32.50	1.14		33.64	38
0600	For carpet covering, add					8.75			8.75	9.65
0700	For vinyl floor covering, add					9.05			9.05	9.95
0900	For high pressure laminate covering, add					7.50			7.50	8.25
0910	For snap on stringer system, add	2 Carp	1000	.016		1.56	.57		2.13	2.68
0950	Office applications, steel or concrete panels,									
0960	no covering, over 6,000 S.F.	2 Carp	960	.017	S.F.	10.55	.60		11.15	12.60
1000	Machine cutouts after initial installation	1 Carp	50	.160	Ea.	20	5.70		25.70	31.50
1050	Pedestals, 6" to 12"	2 Carp	85	.188		8.30	6.75		15.05	20.50
1100	Air conditioning grilles, 4" x 12"	1 Carp	17	.471		68	16.80		84.80	104
1150	4" x 18"	"	14	.571		93.50	20.50		114	138
1200	Approach ramps, minimum	2 Carp	60	.267	S.F.	24.50	9.55		34.05	43
1300	Maximum	"	40	.400	"	34	14.30		48.30	61.50
1500	Handrail, 2 rail, aluminum	1 Carp	15	.533	L.F.	100	19.05		119.05	142

09 72 Wall Coverings

09 72 19 – Textile Wall Covering

09 72 19.10 Textile Wall Covering

		Crew	Daily Output	Labor-Hours	Unit	Material	2014 Bare Costs Labor	2014 Bare Costs Equipment	Total	Total Incl O&P
0010	**TEXTILE WALL COVERING**, including sizing; add 10-30% waste @ takeoff									
0020	Silk	1 Pape	640	.013	S.F.	4.09	.39		4.48	5.15
0030	Cotton		640	.013		6.55	.39		6.94	7.85
0040	Linen		640	.013		1.82	.39		2.21	2.65
0050	Blend		640	.013		2.93	.39		3.32	3.87

09 72 20 – Natural Fiber Wall Covering

09 72 20.10 Natural Fiber Wall Covering

		Crew	Daily Output	Labor-Hours	Unit	Material	Labor	Equipment	Total	Total Incl O&P
0010	**NATURAL FIBER WALL COVERING**, including sizing; add 10-30% waste @ takeoff									
0015	Bamboo	1 Pape	640	.013	S.F.	2.23	.39		2.62	3.10
0030	Burlap		640	.013		2	.39		2.39	2.85
0045	Jute		640	.013		1.27	.39		1.66	2.05
0060	Sisal		640	.013		1.44	.39		1.83	2.23

09 72 23 – Wallpapering

09 72 23.10 Wallpaper

			Crew	Daily Output	Labor-Hours	Unit	Material	Labor	Equipment	Total	Total Incl O&P
0010	**WALLPAPER** including sizing; add 10-30 percent waste @ takeoff	R097223-10									
0050	Aluminum foil		1 Pape	275	.029	S.F.	1.04	.91		1.95	2.64
0100	Copper sheets, .025" thick, vinyl backing			240	.033		5.55	1.05		6.60	7.80
0300	Phenolic backing			240	.033		7.20	1.05		8.25	9.65
0600	Cork tiles, light or dark, 12" x 12" x 3/16"			240	.033		5.05	1.05		6.10	7.25
0700	5/16" thick			235	.034		2.95	1.07		4.02	5
0900	1/4" basketweave			240	.033		3.50	1.05		4.55	5.55
1000	1/2" natural, non-directional pattern			240	.033		7.60	1.05		8.65	10.10
1200	Granular surface, 12" x 36", 1/2" thick			385	.021		1.29	.65		1.94	2.49
1300	1" thick			370	.022		1.66	.68		2.34	2.95
1500	Polyurethane coated, 12" x 12" x 3/16" thick			240	.033		4.03	1.05		5.08	6.15
1600	5/16" thick			235	.034		6.30	1.07		7.37	8.65
1800	Cork wallpaper, paperbacked, natural			480	.017		2.04	.52		2.56	3.10
1900	Colors			480	.017		2.84	.52		3.36	3.98
2100	Flexible wood veneer, 1/32" thick, plain woods			100	.080		2.41	2.52		4.93	6.80
2200	Exotic woods			95	.084		3.65	2.65		6.30	8.35
2400	Gypsum-based, fabric-backed, fire resistant										
2501	resistant for masonry walls, minimum		1 Pord	800	.010	S.F.	.84	.31		1.15	1.43
2700	Maximum (small quantities)		1 Pape	640	.013		1.40	.39		1.79	2.19
2750	Acrylic, modified, semi-rigid PVC, .028" thick		2 Carp	330	.048		1.21	1.73		2.94	4.25
2800	.040" thick		"	320	.050		1.78	1.79		3.57	4.97
3001	Vinyl wall covering, fabric-backed, lightweight		1 Pord	640	.013		.93	.39		1.32	1.66
3301	Medium weight			480	.017		1.14	.52		1.66	2.11
3401	Heavy weight			435	.018		1.52	.57		2.09	2.62
3600	Adhesive, 5 gal. lots (18 S.Y./gal.)					Gal.	14.20			14.20	15.60
3700	Wallpaper, average workmanship, solid pattern, low cost paper		1 Pape	640	.013	S.F.	.43	.39		.82	1.12
3900	basic patterns (matching required), avg. cost paper			535	.015		.98	.47		1.45	1.85
4000	Paper at $85 per double roll, quality workmanship			435	.018		1.94	.58		2.52	3.08
4100	Linen wall covering, paper backed										
4150	Flame treatment, minimum					S.F.	1.01			1.01	1.11
4180	Maximum						1.65			1.65	1.82
4190	Grass cloth, natural fabric [G]		1 Pape	400	.020		1.87	.63		2.50	3.09
4200	Grass cloths with lining paper, minimum [G]			400	.020		.66	.63		1.29	1.76
4300	Maximum [G]			350	.023		2.66	.72		3.38	4.11

09 77 Special Wall Surfacing

09 77 33 – Fiberglass Reinforced Panels

09 77 33.10 Fiberglass Reinforced Plastic Panels	Crew	Daily Output	Labor-Hours	Unit	Material	2014 Bare Costs Labor	Equipment	Total	Total Incl O&P
0010 **FIBERGLASS REINFORCED PLASTIC PANELS**, .090" thick									
0020 On walls, adhesive mounted, embossed surface	2 Carp	640	.025	S.F.	1.11	.89		2	2.72
0030 Smooth surface		640	.025		1.37	.89		2.26	3.01
0040 Fire rated, embossed surface		640	.025		1.99	.89		2.88	3.69
0050 Nylon rivet mounted, on drywall, embossed surface		480	.033		1.11	1.19		2.30	3.22
0060 Smooth surface		480	.033		1.37	1.19		2.56	3.51
0070 Fire rated, embossed surface		480	.033		1.99	1.19		3.18	4.19
0080 On masonry, embossed surface		320	.050		1.11	1.79		2.90	4.23
0090 Smooth surface		320	.050		1.37	1.79		3.16	4.52
0100 Fire rated, embossed surface		320	.050		1.99	1.79		3.78	5.20
0110 Nylon rivet and adhesive mounted, on drywall, embossed surface		240	.067		1.26	2.38		3.64	5.40
0120 Smooth surface		240	.067		1.26	2.38		3.64	5.40
0130 Fire rated, embossed surface		240	.067		2.19	2.38		4.57	6.40
0140 On masonry, embossed surface		190	.084		1.26	3.01		4.27	6.45
0150 Smooth surface		190	.084		1.26	3.01		4.27	6.45
0160 Fire rated, embossed surface		190	.084		2.19	3.01		5.20	7.45
0170 For moldings add	1 Carp	250	.032	L.F.	.26	1.14		1.40	2.21
0180 On ceilings, for lay in grid system, embossed surface		400	.020	S.F.	1.11	.72		1.83	2.42
0190 Smooth surface		400	.020		1.37	.72		2.09	2.71
0200 Fire rated, embossed surface		400	.020		1.99	.72		2.71	3.39

09 81 Acoustic Insulation

09 81 16 – Acoustic Blanket Insulation

09 81 16.10 Sound Attenuation Blanket	Crew	Daily Output	Labor-Hours	Unit	Material	2014 Bare Costs Labor	Equipment	Total	Total Incl O&P
0010 **SOUND ATTENUATION BLANKET**									
0020 Blanket, 1" thick	1 Carp	925	.009	S.F.	.26	.31		.57	.81
0500 1-1/2" thick		920	.009		.27	.31		.58	.82
1000 2" thick		915	.009		.36	.31		.67	.93
1500 3" thick		910	.009		.52	.31		.83	1.10
3000 Thermal or acoustical batt above ceiling, 2" thick		900	.009		.50	.32		.82	1.08
3100 3" thick		900	.009		.75	.32		1.07	1.36
3200 4" thick		900	.009		.94	.32		1.26	1.56
3400 Urethane plastic foam, open cell, on wall, 2" thick	2 Carp	2050	.008		3.11	.28		3.39	3.89
3500 3" thick		1550	.010		4.13	.37		4.50	5.15
3600 4" thick		1050	.015		5.80	.54		6.34	7.25
3700 On ceiling, 2" thick		1700	.009		3.10	.34		3.44	3.98
3800 3" thick		1300	.012		4.13	.44		4.57	5.30
3900 4" thick		900	.018		5.80	.64		6.44	7.40
4000 Nylon matting 0.4" thick, with carbon black spinerette									
4010 plus polyester fabric, on floor	D-7	1600	.010	S.F.	1.36	.29		1.65	1.97
4200 Fiberglass reinf. backer board underlayment, 7/16" thick, on floor	"	1500	.011	"	1.66	.31		1.97	2.34

09 84 Acoustic Room Components

09 84 13 – Fixed Sound-Absorptive Panels

09 84 13.10 Fixed Panels	Crew	Daily Output	Labor-Hours	Unit	Material	2014 Bare Costs Labor	Equipment	Total	Total Incl O&P
0010 **FIXED PANELS** Perforated steel facing, painted with									
0100 Fiberglass or mineral filler, no backs, 2-1/4" thick, modular									
0200 space units, ceiling or wall hung, white or colored	1 Carp	100	.080	S.F.	8.70	2.86		11.56	14.40
0300 Fiberboard sound deadening panels, 1/2" thick	"	600	.013	"	.33	.48		.81	1.16
0500 Fiberglass panels, 4' x 8' x 1" thick, with									
0600 glass cloth face for walls, cemented	1 Carp	155	.052	S.F.	7.60	1.85		9.45	11.45
0700 1-1/2" thick, dacron covered, inner aluminum frame,									
0710 wall mounted	1 Carp	300	.027	S.F.	8.90	.95		9.85	11.40
0900 Mineral fiberboard panels, fabric covered, 30" x 108",									
1000 3/4" thick, concealed spline, wall mounted	1 Carp	150	.053	S.F.	6.40	1.91		8.31	10.25

09 84 36 – Sound-Absorbing Ceiling Units

09 84 36.10 Barriers	Crew	Daily Output	Labor-Hours	Unit	Material	2014 Bare Costs Labor	Equipment	Total	Total Incl O&P
0010 **BARRIERS** Plenum									
0600 Aluminum foil, fiberglass reinf., parallel with joists	1 Carp	275	.029	S.F.	1.05	1.04		2.09	2.91
0700 Perpendicular to joists		180	.044		1.05	1.59		2.64	3.83
0900 Aluminum mesh, kraft paperbacked		275	.029		.79	1.04		1.83	2.62
0970 Fiberglass batts, kraft faced, 3-1/2" thick		1400	.006		.37	.20		.57	.75
0980 6" thick		1300	.006		.66	.22		.88	1.10
1000 Sheet lead, 1 lb., 1/64" thick, perpendicular to joists		150	.053		5.50	1.91		7.41	9.25
1100 Vinyl foam reinforced, 1/8" thick, 1.0 lb. per S.F.		150	.053		4.49	1.91		6.40	8.15

09 91 Painting

09 91 03 – Paint Restoration

09 91 03.20 Sanding

	Crew	Daily Output	Labor-Hours	Unit	Material	2014 Bare Costs Labor	Equipment	Total	Total Incl O&P
0010 **SANDING** and puttying interior trim, compared to									
0100 Painting 1 coat, on quality work				L.F.	100%				
0300 Medium work					50%				
0400 Industrial grade					25%				
0500 Surface protection, placement and removal									
0510 Basic drop cloths	1 Pord	6400	.001	S.F.		.04		.04	.06
0520 Masking with paper		800	.010		.04	.31		.35	.55
0530 Volume cover up (using plastic sheathing, or building paper)		16000	.001			.02		.02	.03

09 91 03.30 Exterior Surface Preparation

	Crew	Daily Output	Labor-Hours	Unit	Material	2014 Bare Costs Labor	Equipment	Total	Total Incl O&P
0010 **EXTERIOR SURFACE PREPARATION**									
0015 Doors, per side, not incl. frames or trim									
0020 Scrape & sand									
0030 Wood, flush	1 Pord	616	.013	S.F.		.41		.41	.67
0040 Wood, detail		496	.016			.50		.50	.83
0050 Wood, louvered		280	.029			.89		.89	1.47
0060 Wood, overhead		616	.013			.41		.41	.67
0070 Wire brush									
0080 Metal, flush	1 Pord	640	.013	S.F.		.39		.39	.64
0090 Metal, detail		520	.015			.48		.48	.79
0100 Metal, louvered		360	.022			.69		.69	1.14
0110 Metal or fibr., overhead		640	.013			.39		.39	.64
0120 Metal, roll up		560	.014			.45		.45	.73
0130 Metal, bulkhead		640	.013			.39		.39	.64
0140 Power wash, based on 2500 lb. operating pressure									
0150 Metal, flush	A-1H	2240	.004	S.F.		.10	.03	.13	.21
0160 Metal, detail		2120	.004			.11	.04	.15	.22

09 91 03.30 Exterior Surface Preparation

		Crew	Daily Output	Labor-Hours	Unit	Material	2014 Bare Costs Labor	2014 Bare Costs Equipment	Total	Total Incl O&P
0170	Metal, louvered	A-1H	2000	.004	S.F.		.11	.04	.15	.23
0180	Metal or fibr., overhead		2400	.003			.09	.03	.12	.19
0190	Metal, roll up		2400	.003			.09	.03	.12	.19
0200	Metal, bulkhead	↓	2200	.004	↓		.10	.03	.13	.21
0400	Windows, per side, not incl. trim									
0410	Scrape & sand									
0420	Wood, 1-2 lite	1 Pord	320	.025	S.F.		.78		.78	1.29
0430	Wood, 3-6 lite		280	.029			.89		.89	1.47
0440	Wood, 7-10 lite		240	.033			1.04		1.04	1.71
0450	Wood, 12 lite		200	.040			1.25		1.25	2.06
0460	Wood, Bay/Bow	↓	320	.025	↓		.78		.78	1.29
0470	Wire brush									
0480	Metal, 1-2 lite	1 Pord	480	.017	S.F.		.52		.52	.86
0490	Metal, 3-6 lite		400	.020			.63		.63	1.03
0500	Metal, Bay/Bow	↓	480	.017	↓		.52		.52	.86
0510	Power wash, based on 2500 lb. operating pressure									
0520	1-2 lite	A-1H	4400	.002	S.F.		.05	.02	.07	.11
0530	3-6 lite		4320	.002			.05	.02	.07	.11
0540	7-10 lite		4240	.002			.05	.02	.07	.11
0550	12 lite		4160	.002			.05	.02	.07	.11
0560	Bay/Bow	↓	4400	.002	↓		.05	.02	.07	.11
0600	Siding, scrape and sand, light=10-30%, med.=30-70%									
0610	Heavy=70-100% of surface to sand									
0650	Texture 1-11, light	1 Pord	480	.017	S.F.		.52		.52	.86
0660	Med.		440	.018			.57		.57	.93
0670	Heavy		360	.022			.69		.69	1.14
0680	Wood shingles, shakes, light		440	.018			.57		.57	.93
0690	Med.		360	.022			.69		.69	1.14
0700	Heavy		280	.029			.89		.89	1.47
0710	Clapboard, light		520	.015			.48		.48	.79
0720	Med.		480	.017			.52		.52	.86
0730	Heavy	↓	400	.020	↓		.63		.63	1.03
0740	Wire brush									
0750	Aluminum, light	1 Pord	600	.013	S.F.		.42		.42	.69
0760	Med.		520	.015			.48		.48	.79
0770	Heavy	↓	440	.018	↓		.57		.57	.93
0780	Pressure wash, based on 2500 lb. operating pressure									
0790	Stucco	A-1H	3080	.003	S.F.		.07	.02	.09	.15
0800	Aluminum or vinyl		3200	.003			.07	.02	.09	.15
0810	Siding, masonry, brick & block	↓	2400	.003	↓		.09	.03	.12	.19
1300	Miscellaneous, wire brush									
1310	Metal, pedestrian gate	1 Pord	100	.080	S.F.		2.50		2.50	4.11
8020	For sand blasting, see Section 03 35 29.60 and 05 01 10.51									

09 91 03.40 Interior Surface Preparation

		Crew	Daily Output	Labor-Hours	Unit	Material	2014 Bare Costs Labor	2014 Bare Costs Equipment	Total	Total Incl O&P
0010	**INTERIOR SURFACE PREPARATION**									
0020	Doors, per side, not incl. frames or trim									
0030	Scrape & sand									
0040	Wood, flush	1 Pord	616	.013	S.F.		.41		.41	.67
0050	Wood, detail		496	.016			.50		.50	.83
0060	Wood, louvered	↓	280	.029	↓		.89		.89	1.47
0070	Wire brush									
0080	Metal, flush	1 Pord	640	.013	S.F.		.39		.39	.64

09 91 03 – Paint Restoration

09 91 03.40 Interior Surface Preparation		Crew	Daily Output	Labor-Hours	Unit	Material	2014 Bare Costs Labor	2014 Bare Costs Equipment	Total	Total Incl O&P
0090	Metal, detail	1 Pord	520	.015	S.F.		.48		.48	.79
0100	Metal, louvered	↓	360	.022	↓		.69		.69	1.14
0110	Hand wash									
0120	Wood, flush	1 Pord	2160	.004	S.F.		.12		.12	.19
0130	Wood, detailed		2000	.004			.13		.13	.21
0140	Wood, louvered		1360	.006			.18		.18	.30
0150	Metal, flush		2160	.004			.12		.12	.19
0160	Metal, detail		2000	.004			.13		.13	.21
0170	Metal, louvered	↓	1360	.006	↓		.18		.18	.30
0400	Windows, per side, not incl. trim									
0410	Scrape & sand									
0420	Wood, 1-2 lite	1 Pord	360	.022	S.F.		.69		.69	1.14
0430	Wood, 3-6 lite		320	.025			.78		.78	1.29
0440	Wood, 7-10 lite		280	.029			.89		.89	1.47
0450	Wood, 12 lite		240	.033			1.04		1.04	1.71
0460	Wood, Bay/Bow	↓	360	.022	↓		.69		.69	1.14
0470	Wire brush									
0480	Metal, 1-2 lite	1 Pord	520	.015	S.F.		.48		.48	.79
0490	Metal, 3-6 lite		440	.018			.57		.57	.93
0500	Metal, Bay/Bow	↓	520	.015	↓		.48		.48	.79
0600	Walls, sanding, light=10-30%, medium - 30-70%,									
0610	heavy=70-100% of surface to sand									
0650	Walls, sand									
0660	Gypsum board or plaster, light	1 Pord	3077	.003	S.F.		.08		.08	.13
0670	Gypsum board or plaster, medium		2160	.004			.12		.12	.19
0680	Gypsum board or plaster, heavy		923	.009			.27		.27	.45
0690	Wood, T&G, light		2400	.003			.10		.10	.17
0700	Wood, T&G, med.		1600	.005			.16		.16	.26
0710	Wood, T&G, heavy	↓	800	.010	↓		.31		.31	.51
0720	Walls, wash									
0730	Gypsum board or plaster	1 Pord	3200	.003	S.F.		.08		.08	.13
0740	Wood, T&G		3200	.003			.08		.08	.13
0750	Masonry, brick & block, smooth		2800	.003			.09		.09	.15
0760	Masonry, brick & block, coarse	↓	2000	.004	↓		.13		.13	.21
8020	For sand blasting, see Section 03 35 29.60 and 05 01 10.51									

09 91 13 – Exterior Painting

09 91 13.30 Fences

		Crew	Daily Output	Labor-Hours	Unit	Material	Labor	Equipment	Total	Total Incl O&P
0010	**FENCES** R099100-20									
0100	Chain link or wire metal, one side, water base									
0110	Roll & brush, first coat	1 Pord	960	.008	S.F.	.08	.26		.34	.51
0120	Second coat		1280	.006		.07	.20		.27	.40
0130	Spray, first coat		2275	.004		.08	.11		.19	.26
0140	Second coat	↓	2600	.003	↓	.08	.10		.18	.24
0150	Picket, water base									
0160	Roll & brush, first coat	1 Pord	865	.009	S.F.	.08	.29		.37	.57
0170	Second coat		1050	.008		.08	.24		.32	.48
0180	Spray, first coat		2275	.004		.08	.11		.19	.27
0190	Second coat	↓	2600	.003	↓	.08	.10		.18	.25
0200	Stockade, water base									
0210	Roll & brush, first coat	1 Pord	1040	.008	S.F.	.08	.24		.32	.49
0220	Second coat		1200	.007		.08	.21		.29	.43
0230	Spray, first coat	↓	2275	.004		.08	.11		.19	.27

09 91 13 – Exterior Painting

09 91 13.30 Fences

		Crew	Daily Output	Labor-Hours	Unit	Material	2014 Bare Costs Labor	2014 Bare Costs Equipment	Total	Total Incl O&P
0240	Second coat	1 Pord	2600	.003	S.F.	.08	.10		.18	.25

09 91 13.42 Miscellaneous, Exterior

		Crew	Daily Output	Labor-Hours	Unit	Material	2014 Bare Costs Labor	2014 Bare Costs Equipment	Total	Total Incl O&P
0010	**MISCELLANEOUS, EXTERIOR** R099100-20									
0015	For painting metals, see Section 09 97 13.23									
0100	Railing, ext., decorative wood, incl. cap & baluster									
0110	Newels & spindles @ 12" O.C.									
0120	Brushwork, stain, sand, seal & varnish									
0130	First coat	1 Pord	90	.089	L.F.	.75	2.78		3.53	5.40
0140	Second coat	"	120	.067	"	.75	2.08		2.83	4.25
0150	Rough sawn wood, 42" high, 2" x 2" verticals, 6" O.C.									
0160	Brushwork, stain, each coat	1 Pord	90	.089	L.F.	.24	2.78		3.02	4.84
0170	Wrought iron, 1" rail, 1/2" sq. verticals									
0180	Brushwork, zinc chromate, 60" high, bars 6" O.C.									
0190	Primer	1 Pord	130	.062	L.F.	.86	1.92		2.78	4.11
0200	Finish coat		130	.062		1.13	1.92		3.05	4.40
0210	Additional coat		190	.042		1.32	1.32		2.64	3.61
0220	Shutters or blinds, single panel, 2' x 4', paint all sides									
0230	Brushwork, primer	1 Pord	20	.400	Ea.	.69	12.50		13.19	21.50
0240	Finish coat, exterior latex		20	.400		.61	12.50		13.11	21
0250	Primer & 1 coat, exterior latex		13	.615		1.15	19.25		20.40	33
0260	Spray, primer		35	.229		1	7.15		8.15	12.85
0270	Finish coat, exterior latex		35	.229		1.30	7.15		8.45	13.20
0280	Primer & 1 coat, exterior latex		20	.400		1.08	12.50		13.58	21.50
0290	For louvered shutters, add				S.F.	10%				
0300	Stair stringers, exterior, metal									
0310	Roll & brush, zinc chromate, to 14", each coat	1 Pord	320	.025	L.F.	.38	.78		1.16	1.70
0320	Rough sawn wood, 4" x 12"									
0330	Roll & brush, exterior latex, each coat	1 Pord	215	.037	L.F.	.09	1.16		1.25	2.01
0340	Trellis/lattice, 2" x 2" @ 3" O.C. with 2" x 8" supports									
0350	Spray, latex, per side, each coat	1 Pord	475	.017	S.F.	.09	.53		.62	.97
0450	Decking, ext., sealer, alkyd, brushwork, sealer coat		1140	.007		.09	.22		.31	.46
0460	1st coat		1140	.007		.09	.22		.31	.46
0470	2nd coat		1300	.006		.07	.19		.26	.40
0500	Paint, alkyd, brushwork, primer coat		1140	.007		.10	.22		.32	.47
0510	1st coat		1140	.007		.16	.22		.38	.53
0520	2nd coat		1300	.006		.12	.19		.31	.45
0600	Sand paint, alkyd, brushwork, 1 coat		150	.053		.13	1.67		1.80	2.88

09 91 13.60 Siding Exterior

		Crew	Daily Output	Labor-Hours	Unit	Material	2014 Bare Costs Labor	2014 Bare Costs Equipment	Total	Total Incl O&P
0010	**SIDING EXTERIOR**, Alkyd (oil base)									
0450	Steel siding, oil base, paint 1 coat, brushwork	2 Pord	2015	.008	S.F.	.13	.25		.38	.55
0500	Spray		4550	.004		.19	.11		.30	.39
0800	Paint 2 coats, brushwork		1300	.012		.25	.38		.63	.91
1000	Spray		2750	.006		.17	.18		.35	.49
1200	Stucco, rough, oil base, paint 2 coats, brushwork		1300	.012		.25	.38		.63	.91
1400	Roller		1625	.010		.27	.31		.58	.80
1600	Spray		2925	.005		.28	.17		.45	.59
1800	Texture 1-11 or clapboard, oil base, primer coat, brushwork		1300	.012		.13	.38		.51	.78
2000	Spray		4550	.004		.13	.11		.24	.33
2400	Paint 2 coats, brushwork		810	.020		.37	.62		.99	1.42
2600	Spray		2600	.006		.41	.19		.60	.77
3400	Stain 2 coats, brushwork		950	.017		.16	.53		.69	1.05
4000	Spray		3050	.005		.18	.16		.34	.47

09 91 Painting

09 91 13 – Exterior Painting

09 91 13.60 Siding Exterior

		Crew	Daily Output	Labor-Hours	Unit	Material	2014 Bare Costs Labor	Equipment	Total	Total Incl O&P
4200	Wood shingles, oil base primer coat, brushwork	2 Pord	1300	.012	S.F.	.12	.38		.50	.77
4400	Spray		3900	.004		.12	.13		.25	.34
5000	Paint 2 coats, brushwork		810	.020		.31	.62		.93	1.36
5200	Spray		2275	.007		.29	.22		.51	.68
6500	Stain 2 coats, brushwork		950	.017		.16	.53		.69	1.05
7000	Spray		2660	.006		.22	.19		.41	.56
8000	For latex paint, deduct					10%				
8100	For work over 12' H, from pipe scaffolding, add						15%			
8200	For work over 12' H, from extension ladder, add						25%			
8300	For work over 12' H, from swing staging, add						35%			

09 91 13.62 Siding, Misc.

		Crew	Daily Output	Labor-Hours	Unit	Material	2014 Bare Costs Labor	Equipment	Total	Total Incl O&P
0010	**SIDING, MISC.,** latex paint R099100-10									
0100	Aluminum siding									
0110	Brushwork, primer	2 Pord	2275	.007	S.F.	.06	.22		.28	.43
0120	Finish coat, exterior latex		2275	.007		.05	.22		.27	.42
0130	Primer & 1 coat exterior latex		1300	.012		.13	.38		.51	.77
0140	Primer & 2 coats exterior latex		975	.016		.18	.51		.69	1.04
0150	Mineral fiber shingles									
0160	Brushwork, primer	2 Pord	1495	.011	S.F.	.13	.33		.46	.70
0170	Finish coat, industrial enamel		1495	.011		.18	.33		.51	.75
0180	Primer & 1 coat enamel		810	.020		.32	.62		.94	1.37
0190	Primer & 2 coats enamel		540	.030		.50	.93		1.43	2.07
0200	Roll, primer		1625	.010		.15	.31		.46	.67
0210	Finish coat, industrial enamel		1625	.010		.20	.31		.51	.73
0220	Primer & 1 coat enamel		975	.016		.35	.51		.86	1.22
0230	Primer & 2 coats enamel		650	.025		.54	.77		1.31	1.87
0240	Spray, primer		3900	.004		.12	.13		.25	.34
0250	Finish coat, industrial enamel		3900	.004		.16	.13		.29	.39
0260	Primer & 1 coat enamel		2275	.007		.28	.22		.50	.67
0270	Primer & 2 coats enamel		1625	.010		.44	.31		.75	1
0280	Waterproof sealer, first coat		4485	.004		.08	.11		.19	.26
0290	Second coat		5235	.003		.07	.10		.17	.24
0300	Rough wood incl. shingles, shakes or rough sawn siding									
0310	Brushwork, primer	2 Pord	1280	.013	S.F.	.14	.39		.53	.79
0320	Finish coat, exterior latex		1280	.013		.10	.39		.49	.75
0330	Primer & 1 coat exterior latex		960	.017		.23	.52		.75	1.12
0340	Primer & 2 coats exterior latex		700	.023		.33	.71		1.04	1.54
0350	Roll, primer		2925	.005		.18	.17		.35	.48
0360	Finish coat, exterior latex		2925	.005		.12	.17		.29	.41
0370	Primer & 1 coat exterior latex		1790	.009		.30	.28		.58	.79
0380	Primer & 2 coats exterior latex		1300	.012		.42	.38		.80	1.09
0390	Spray, primer		3900	.004		.16	.13		.29	.38
0400	Finish coat, exterior latex		3900	.004		.09	.13		.22	.31
0410	Primer & 1 coat exterior latex		2600	.006		.25	.19		.44	.59
0420	Primer & 2 coats exterior latex		2080	.008		.33	.24		.57	.77
0430	Waterproof sealer, first coat		4485	.004		.14	.11		.25	.33
0440	Second coat		4485	.004		.08	.11		.19	.26
0450	Smooth wood incl. butt, T&G, beveled, drop or B&B siding									
0460	Brushwork, primer	2 Pord	2325	.007	S.F.	.10	.22		.32	.46
0470	Finish coat, exterior latex		1280	.013		.10	.39		.49	.75
0480	Primer & 1 coat exterior latex		800	.020		.20	.63		.83	1.25
0490	Primer & 2 coats exterior latex		630	.025		.29	.79		1.08	1.63

09 91 Painting

09 91 13 – Exterior Painting

09 91 13.62 Siding, Misc.

		Crew	Daily Output	Labor-Hours	Unit	Material	2014 Bare Costs Labor	Equipment	Total	Total Incl O&P
0500	Roll, primer	2 Pord	2275	.007	S.F.	.11	.22		.33	.48
0510	Finish coat, exterior latex		2275	.007		.10	.22		.32	.47
0520	Primer & 1 coat exterior latex		1300	.012		.21	.38		.59	.87
0530	Primer & 2 coats exterior latex		975	.016		.32	.51		.83	1.19
0540	Spray, primer		4550	.004		.09	.11		.20	.27
0550	Finish coat, exterior latex		4550	.004		.09	.11		.20	.28
0560	Primer & 1 coat exterior latex		2600	.006		.18	.19		.37	.51
0570	Primer & 2 coats exterior latex		1950	.008		.26	.26		.52	.71
0580	Waterproof sealer, first coat		5230	.003		.08	.10		.18	.24
0590	Second coat	↓	5980	.003		.08	.08		.16	.22
0600	For oil base paint, add				↓	10%				

09 91 13.70 Doors and Windows, Exterior

		Crew	Daily Output	Labor-Hours	Unit	Material	2014 Bare Costs Labor	Equipment	Total	Total Incl O&P
0010	**DOORS AND WINDOWS, EXTERIOR**									
0100	Door frames & trim, only									
0110	Brushwork, primer	R099100-20 1 Pord	512	.016	L.F.	.06	.49		.55	.87
0120	Finish coat, exterior latex		512	.016		.08	.49		.57	.88
0130	Primer & 1 coat, exterior latex		300	.027		.14	.83		.97	1.52
0140	Primer & 2 coats, exterior latex	↓	265	.030	↓	.22	.94		1.16	1.79
0150	Doors, flush, both sides, incl. frame & trim									
0160	Roll & brush, primer	1 Pord	10	.800	Ea.	4.74	25		29.74	46
0170	Finish coat, exterior latex		10	.800		5.85	25		30.85	47.50
0180	Primer & 1 coat, exterior latex		7	1.143		10.55	35.50		46.05	70
0190	Primer & 2 coats, exterior latex		5	1.600		16.40	50		66.40	100
0200	Brushwork, stain, sealer & 2 coats polyurethane	↓	4	2	↓	26	62.50		88.50	132
0210	Doors, French, both sides, 10-15 lite, incl. frame & trim									
0220	Brushwork, primer	1 Pord	6	1.333	Ea.	2.37	41.50		43.87	71
0230	Finish coat, exterior latex		6	1.333		2.92	41.50		44.42	71.50
0240	Primer & 1 coat, exterior latex		3	2.667		5.30	83.50		88.80	143
0250	Primer & 2 coats, exterior latex		2	4		8.05	125		133.05	215
0260	Brushwork, stain, sealer & 2 coats polyurethane	↓	2.50	3.200	↓	9.45	100		109.45	174
0270	Doors, louvered, both sides, incl. frame & trim									
0280	Brushwork, primer	1 Pord	7	1.143	Ea.	4.74	35.50		40.24	63.50
0290	Finish coat, exterior latex		7	1.143		5.85	35.50		41.35	65
0300	Primer & 1 coat, exterior latex		4	2		10.55	62.50		73.05	115
0310	Primer & 2 coats, exterior latex		3	2.667		16.05	83.50		99.55	155
0320	Brushwork, stain, sealer & 2 coats polyurethane	↓	4.50	1.778	↓	26	55.50		81.50	120
0330	Doors, panel, both sides, incl. frame & trim									
0340	Roll & brush, primer	1 Pord	6	1.333	Ea.	4.74	41.50		46.24	73.50
0350	Finish coat, exterior latex		6	1.333		5.85	41.50		47.35	75
0360	Primer & 1 coat, exterior latex		3	2.667		10.55	83.50		94.05	149
0370	Primer & 2 coats, exterior latex		2.50	3.200		16.05	100		116.05	182
0380	Brushwork, stain, sealer & 2 coats polyurethane	↓	3	2.667		26	83.50		109.50	166
0400	Windows, per ext. side, based on 15 S.F.									
0410	1 to 6 lite									
0420	Brushwork, primer	1 Pord	13	.615	Ea.	.94	19.25		20.19	32.50
0430	Finish coat, exterior latex		13	.615		1.15	19.25		20.40	33
0440	Primer & 1 coat, exterior latex		8	1		2.09	31.50		33.59	54
0450	Primer & 2 coats, exterior latex		6	1.333		3.17	41.50		44.67	72
0460	Stain, sealer & 1 coat varnish	↓	7	1.143	↓	3.73	35.50		39.23	62.50
0470	7 to 10 lite									
0480	Brushwork, primer	1 Pord	11	.727	Ea.	.94	22.50		23.44	38.50
0490	Finish coat, exterior latex	↓	11	.727	↓	1.15	22.50		23.65	39

09 91 Painting

09 91 13 – Exterior Painting

09 91 13.70 Doors and Windows, Exterior

		Crew	Daily Output	Labor-Hours	Unit	Material	2014 Bare Costs Labor	Equipment	Total	Total Incl O&P
0500	Primer & 1 coat, exterior latex	1 Pord	7	1.143	Ea.	2.09	35.50		37.59	61
0510	Primer & 2 coats, exterior latex		5	1.600		3.17	50		53.17	85.50
0520	Stain, sealer & 1 coat varnish	↓	6	1.333	↓	3.73	41.50		45.23	72.50
0530	12 lite									
0540	Brushwork, primer	1 Pord	10	.800	Ea.	.94	25		25.94	42
0550	Finish coat, exterior latex		10	.800		1.15	25		26.15	42.50
0560	Primer & 1 coat, exterior latex		6	1.333		2.09	41.50		43.59	71
0570	Primer & 2 coats, exterior latex		5	1.600		3.17	50		53.17	85.50
0580	Stain, sealer & 1 coat varnish	↓	6	1.333	↓	3.87	41.50		45.37	73
0590	For oil base paint, add					10%				

09 91 13.80 Trim, Exterior

		Crew	Daily Output	Labor-Hours	Unit	Material	2014 Bare Costs Labor	Equipment	Total	Total Incl O&P
0010	**TRIM, EXTERIOR** R099100-10									
0100	Door frames & trim (see Doors, interior or exterior)									
0110	Fascia, latex paint, one coat coverage									
0120	1" x 4", brushwork	1 Pord	640	.013	L.F.	.02	.39		.41	.66
0130	Roll		1280	.006		.03	.20		.23	.35
0140	Spray		2080	.004		.02	.12		.14	.22
0150	1" x 6" to 1" x 10", brushwork		640	.013		.08	.39		.47	.73
0160	Roll		1230	.007		.09	.20		.29	.42
0170	Spray		2100	.004		.07	.12		.19	.27
0180	1" x 12", brushwork		640	.013		.08	.39		.47	.73
0190	Roll		1050	.008		.09	.24		.33	.48
0200	Spray		2200	.004	↓	.07	.11		.18	.26
0210	Gutters & downspouts, metal, zinc chromate paint									
0220	Brushwork, gutters, 5", first coat	1 Pord	640	.013	L.F.	.40	.39		.79	1.08
0230	Second coat		960	.008		.38	.26		.64	.84
0240	Third coat		1280	.006		.30	.20		.50	.66
0250	Downspouts, 4", first coat		640	.013		.40	.39		.79	1.08
0260	Second coat		960	.008		.38	.26		.64	.84
0270	Third coat		1280	.006	↓	.30	.20		.50	.66
0280	Gutters & downspouts, wood									
0290	Brushwork, gutters, 5", primer	1 Pord	640	.013	L.F.	.06	.39		.45	.71
0300	Finish coat, exterior latex		640	.013		.07	.39		.46	.72
0310	Primer & 1 coat exterior latex		400	.020		.14	.63		.77	1.18
0320	Primer & 2 coats exterior latex		325	.025		.22	.77		.99	1.51
0330	Downspouts, 4", primer		640	.013		.06	.39		.45	.71
0340	Finish coat, exterior latex		640	.013		.07	.39		.46	.72
0350	Primer & 1 coat exterior latex		400	.020		.14	.63		.77	1.18
0360	Primer & 2 coats exterior latex		325	.025	↓	.11	.77		.88	1.39
0370	Molding, exterior, up to 14" wide									
0380	Brushwork, primer	1 Pord	640	.013	L.F.	.07	.39		.46	.72
0390	Finish coat, exterior latex		640	.013		.08	.39		.47	.73
0400	Primer & 1 coat exterior latex		400	.020		.17	.63		.80	1.21
0410	Primer & 2 coats exterior latex		315	.025		.17	.79		.96	1.49
0420	Stain & fill		1050	.008		.10	.24		.34	.50
0430	Shellac		1850	.004		.13	.14		.27	.36
0440	Varnish		1275	.006	↓	.11	.20		.31	.44

09 91 13.90 Walls, Masonry (CMU), Exterior

		Crew	Daily Output	Labor-Hours	Unit	Material	2014 Bare Costs Labor	Equipment	Total	Total Incl O&P
0010	**WALLS, MASONRY (CMU), EXTERIOR**									
0360	Concrete masonry units (CMU), smooth surface									
0370	Brushwork, latex, first coat	1 Pord	640	.013	S.F.	.07	.39		.46	.72
0380	Second coat	↓	960	.008	↓	.06	.26		.32	.49

09 91 Painting

09 91 13 – Exterior Painting

09 91 13.90 Walls, Masonry (CMU), Exterior

		Crew	Daily Output	Labor-Hours	Unit	Material	2014 Bare Costs Labor	Equipment	Total	Total Incl O&P
0390	Waterproof sealer, first coat	1 Pord	736	.011	S.F.	.25	.34		.59	.83
0400	Second coat		1104	.007		.25	.23		.48	.64
0410	Roll, latex, paint, first coat		1465	.005		.09	.17		.26	.37
0420	Second coat		1790	.004		.07	.14		.21	.30
0430	Waterproof sealer, first coat		1680	.005		.25	.15		.40	.51
0440	Second coat		2060	.004		.25	.12		.37	.47
0450	Spray, latex, paint, first coat		1950	.004		.07	.13		.20	.28
0460	Second coat		2600	.003		.05	.10		.15	.22
0470	Waterproof sealer, first coat		2245	.004		.25	.11		.36	.45
0480	Second coat		2990	.003		.25	.08		.33	.41
0490	Concrete masonry unit (CMU), porous									
0500	Brushwork, latex, first coat	1 Pord	640	.013	S.F.	.14	.39		.53	.80
0510	Second coat		960	.008		.07	.26		.33	.51
0520	Waterproof sealer, first coat		736	.011		.25	.34		.59	.83
0530	Second coat		1104	.007		.25	.23		.48	.64
0540	Roll latex, first coat		1465	.005		.11	.17		.28	.40
0550	Second coat		1790	.004		.07	.14		.21	.31
0560	Waterproof sealer, first coat		1680	.005		.25	.15		.40	.51
0570	Second coat		2060	.004		.25	.12		.37	.47
0580	Spray latex, first coat		1950	.004		.08	.13		.21	.30
0590	Second coat		2600	.003		.05	.10		.15	.22
0600	Waterproof sealer, first coat		2245	.004		.25	.11		.36	.45
0610	Second coat		2990	.003		.25	.08		.33	.41

09 91 23 – Interior Painting

09 91 23.20 Cabinets and Casework

			Crew	Daily Output	Labor-Hours	Unit	Material	2014 Bare Costs Labor	Equipment	Total	Total Incl O&P
0010	**CABINETS AND CASEWORK**	R099100-10									
1000	Primer coat, oil base, brushwork		1 Pord	650	.012	S.F.	.06	.38		.44	.70
2000	Paint, oil base, brushwork, 1 coat			650	.012		.11	.38		.49	.75
3000	Stain, brushwork, wipe off			650	.012		.08	.38		.46	.72
4000	Shellac, 1 coat, brushwork			650	.012		.10	.38		.48	.75
4500	Varnish, 3 coats, brushwork, sand after 1st coat			325	.025		.28	.77		1.05	1.58
5000	For latex paint, deduct						10%				

09 91 23.33 Doors and Windows, Interior Alkyd (Oil Base)

		Crew	Daily Output	Labor-Hours	Unit	Material	2014 Bare Costs Labor	Equipment	Total	Total Incl O&P
0010	**DOORS AND WINDOWS, INTERIOR ALKYD (OIL BASE)**									
0500	Flush door & frame, 3' x 7', oil, primer, brushwork	1 Pord	10	.800	Ea.	3.32	25		28.32	44.50
1000	Paint, 1 coat		10	.800		4.11	25		29.11	45.50
1400	Stain, brushwork, wipe off		18	.444		1.71	13.90		15.61	25
1600	Shellac, 1 coat, brushwork		25	.320		2.20	10		12.20	18.85
1800	Varnish, 3 coats, brushwork, sand after 1st coat		9	.889		5.95	28		33.95	52
2000	Panel door & frame, 3' x 7', oil, primer, brushwork		6	1.333		2.44	41.50		43.94	71
2200	Paint, 1 coat		6	1.333		4.11	41.50		45.61	73
2600	Stain, brushwork, panel door, 3' x 7', not incl. frame		16	.500		1.71	15.65		17.36	27.50
2800	Shellac, 1 coat, brushwork		22	.364		2.20	11.35		13.55	21
3000	Varnish, 3 coats, brushwork, sand after 1st coat		7.50	1.067		5.95	33.50		39.45	61.50
4400	Windows, including frame and trim, per side									
4600	Colonial type, 6/6 lites, 2' x 3', oil, primer, brushwork	1 Pord	14	.571	Ea.	.38	17.85		18.23	30
5800	Paint, 1 coat		14	.571		.65	17.85		18.50	30
6200	3' x 5' opening, 6/6 lites, primer coat, brushwork		12	.667		.96	21		21.96	35.50
6400	Paint, 1 coat		12	.667		1.62	21		22.62	36.50
6800	4' x 8' opening, 6/6 lites, primer coat, brushwork		8	1		2.05	31.50		33.55	54
7000	Paint, 1 coat		8	1		3.46	31.50		34.96	55.50
8000	Single lite type, 2' x 3', oil base, primer coat, brushwork		33	.242		.38	7.60		7.98	12.85

09 91 23.33 Doors and Windows, Interior Alkyd (Oil Base)	Crew	Daily Output	Labor-Hours	Unit	Material	2014 Bare Costs Labor	Equipment	Total	Total Incl O&P
8200	Paint, 1 coat	1 Pord	33	.242	Ea.	.65	7.60		8.25	13.15
8600	3' x 5' opening, primer coat, brushwork		20	.400		.96	12.50		13.46	21.50
8800	Paint, 1 coat		20	.400		1.62	12.50		14.12	22.50
9200	4' x 8' opening, primer coat, brushwork		14	.571		2.05	17.85		19.90	32
9400	Paint, 1 coat		14	.571		3.46	17.85		21.31	33.50

09 91 23.35 Doors and Windows, Interior Latex	Crew	Daily Output	Labor-Hours	Unit	Material	2014 Bare Costs Labor	Equipment	Total	Total Incl O&P
0010	**DOORS & WINDOWS, INTERIOR LATEX** R099100-10									
0100	Doors, flush, both sides, incl. frame & trim									
0110	Roll & brush, primer	1 Pord	10	.800	Ea.	3.97	25		28.97	45.50
0120	Finish coat, latex		10	.800		5.35	25		30.35	47
0130	Primer & 1 coat latex		7	1.143		9.35	35.50		44.85	69
0140	Primer & 2 coats latex		5	1.600		14.40	50		64.40	98
0160	Spray, both sides, primer		20	.400		4.18	12.50		16.68	25
0170	Finish coat, latex		20	.400		5.65	12.50		18.15	26.50
0180	Primer & 1 coat latex		11	.727		9.90	22.50		32.40	48.50
0190	Primer & 2 coats latex		8	1		15.25	31.50		46.75	68.50
0200	Doors, French, both sides, 10-15 lite, incl. frame & trim									
0210	Roll & brush, primer	1 Pord	6	1.333	Ea.	1.99	41.50		43.49	70.50
0220	Finish coat, latex		6	1.333		2.68	41.50		44.18	71.50
0230	Primer & 1 coat latex		3	2.667		4.67	83.50		88.17	142
0240	Primer & 2 coats latex		2	4		7.20	125		132.20	214
0260	Doors, louvered, both sides, incl. frame & trim									
0270	Roll & brush, primer	1 Pord	7	1.143	Ea.	3.97	35.50		39.47	63
0280	Finish coat, latex		7	1.143		5.35	35.50		40.85	64.50
0290	Primer & 1 coat, latex		4	2		9.10	62.50		71.60	113
0300	Primer & 2 coats, latex		3	2.667		14.70	83.50		98.20	153
0320	Spray, both sides, primer		20	.400		4.18	12.50		16.68	25
0330	Finish coat, latex		20	.400		5.65	12.50		18.15	26.50
0340	Primer & 1 coat, latex		11	.727		9.90	22.50		32.40	48.50
0350	Primer & 2 coats, latex		8	1		15.55	31.50		47.05	68.50
0360	Doors, panel, both sides, incl. frame & trim									
0370	Roll & brush, primer	1 Pord	6	1.333	Ea.	4.18	41.50		45.68	73
0380	Finish coat, latex		6	1.333		5.35	41.50		46.85	74.50
0390	Primer & 1 coat, latex		3	2.667		9.35	83.50		92.85	147
0400	Primer & 2 coats, latex		2.50	3.200		14.70	100		114.70	180
0420	Spray, both sides, primer		10	.800		4.18	25		29.18	45.50
0430	Finish coat, latex		10	.800		5.65	25		30.65	47
0440	Primer & 1 coat, latex		5	1.600		9.90	50		59.90	93
0450	Primer & 2 coats, latex		4	2		15.55	62.50		78.05	120
0460	Windows, per interior side, based on 15 S.F.									
0470	1 to 6 lite									
0480	Brushwork, primer	1 Pord	13	.615	Ea.	.78	19.25		20.03	32.50
0490	Finish coat, enamel		13	.615		1.06	19.25		20.31	32.50
0500	Primer & 1 coat enamel		8	1		1.84	31.50		33.34	53.50
0510	Primer & 2 coats enamel		6	1.333		2.90	41.50		44.40	71.50
0530	7 to 10 lite									
0540	Brushwork, primer	1 Pord	11	.727	Ea.	.78	22.50		23.28	38.50
0550	Finish coat, enamel		11	.727		1.06	22.50		23.56	38.50
0560	Primer & 1 coat enamel		7	1.143		1.84	35.50		37.34	60.50
0570	Primer & 2 coats enamel		5	1.600		2.90	50		52.90	85
0590	12 lite									
0600	Brushwork, primer	1 Pord	10	.800	Ea.	.78	25		25.78	42

09 91 Painting

09 91 23 – Interior Painting

09 91 23.35 Doors and Windows, Interior Latex		Crew	Daily Output	Labor-Hours	Unit	Material	2014 Bare Costs Labor	Equipment	Total	Total Incl O&P
0610	Finish coat, enamel	1 Pord	10	.800	Ea.	1.06	25		26.06	42
0620	Primer & 1 coat enamel		6	1.333		1.84	41.50		43.34	70.50
0630	Primer & 2 coats enamel	↓	5	1.600		2.90	50		52.90	85
0650	For oil base paint, add				↓	10%				

09 91 23.39 Doors and Windows, Interior Latex, Zero Voc

			Crew	Daily Output	Labor-Hours	Unit	Material	2014 Bare Costs Labor	Equipment	Total	Total Incl O&P
0010	**DOORS & WINDOWS, INTERIOR LATEX, ZERO VOC**										
0100	Doors flush, both sides, incl. frame & trim										
0110	Roll & brush, primer	G	1 Pord	10	.800	Ea.	4.84	25		29.84	46.50
0120	Finish coat, latex	G		10	.800		5.65	25		30.65	47
0130	Primer & 1 coat latex	G		7	1.143		10.45	35.50		45.95	70
0140	Primer & 2 coats latex	G		5	1.600		15.80	50		65.80	99.50
0160	Spray, both sides, primer	G		20	.400		5.10	12.50		17.60	26
0170	Finish coat, latex	G		20	.400		5.90	12.50		18.40	27
0180	Primer & 1 coat latex	G		11	.727		11.10	22.50		33.60	49.50
0190	Primer & 2 coats latex	G	↓	8	1	↓	16.70	31.50		48.20	70
0200	Doors, French, both sides, 10-15 lite, incl. frame & trim										
0210	Roll & brush, primer	G	1 Pord	6	1.333	Ea.	2.42	41.50		43.92	71
0220	Finish coat, latex	G		6	1.333		2.81	41.50		44.31	71.50
0230	Primer & 1 coat latex	G		3	2.667		5.25	83.50		88.75	143
0240	Primer & 2 coats latex	G	↓	2	4	↓	7.90	125		132.90	215
0360	Doors, panel, both sides, incl. frame & trim										
0370	Roll & brush, primer	G	1 Pord	6	1.333	Ea.	5.10	41.50		46.60	74
0380	Finish coat, latex	G		6	1.333		5.65	41.50		47.15	74.50
0390	Primer & 1 coat, latex	G		3	2.667		10.45	83.50		93.95	149
0400	Primer & 2 coats, latex	G		2.50	3.200		16.10	100		116.10	182
0420	Spray, both sides, primer	G		10	.800		5.10	25		30.10	46.50
0430	Finish coat, latex	G		10	.800		5.90	25		30.90	47.50
0440	Primer & 1 coat, latex	G		5	1.600		11.10	50		61.10	94
0450	Primer & 2 coats, latex	G	↓	4	2	↓	17.05	62.50		79.55	122
0460	Windows, per interior side, based on 15 S.F.										
0470	1 to 6 lite										
0480	Brushwork, primer	G	1 Pord	13	.615	Ea.	.96	19.25		20.21	32.50
0490	Finish coat, enamel	G		13	.615		1.11	19.25		20.36	32.50
0500	Primer & 1 coat enamel	G		8	1		2.07	31.50		33.57	54
0510	Primer & 2 coats enamel	G	↓	6	1.333	↓	3.18	41.50		44.68	72

09 91 23.40 Floors, Interior

		Crew	Daily Output	Labor-Hours	Unit	Material	2014 Bare Costs Labor	Equipment	Total	Total Incl O&P
0010	**FLOORS, INTERIOR**									
0100	Concrete paint, latex									
0110	Brushwork									
0120	1st coat	1 Pord	975	.008	S.F.	.15	.26		.41	.59
0130	2nd coat		1150	.007		.10	.22		.32	.47
0140	3rd coat	↓	1300	.006	↓	.08	.19		.27	.41
0150	Roll									
0160	1st coat	1 Pord	2600	.003	S.F.	.20	.10		.30	.38
0170	2nd coat		3250	.002		.12	.08		.20	.26
0180	3rd coat	↓	3900	.002	↓	.09	.06		.15	.21
0190	Spray									
0200	1st coat	1 Pord	2600	.003	S.F.	.18	.10		.28	.35
0210	2nd coat		3250	.002		.10	.08		.18	.24
0220	3rd coat	↓	3900	.002	↓	.08	.06		.14	.19
0300	Acid stain and sealer									
0310	Stain, one coat	1 Pord	650	.012	S.F.	.11	.38		.49	.75

09 91 23.40 Floors, Interior	Crew	Daily Output	Labor-Hours	Unit	Material	2014 Bare Costs Labor	Equipment	Total	Total Incl O&P
0320	Two coats	1 Pord	570	.014	S.F.	.22	.44		.66	.96
0330	Acrylic sealer, one coat		2600	.003		.18	.10		.28	.36
0340	Two coats	↓	1400	.006	↓	.37	.18		.55	.70

09 91 23.52 Miscellaneous, Interior	Crew	Daily Output	Labor-Hours	Unit	Material	2014 Bare Costs Labor	Equipment	Total	Total Incl O&P
0010	**MISCELLANEOUS, INTERIOR**									
2400	Floors, conc./wood, oil base, primer/sealer coat, brushwork	2 Pord	1950	.008	S.F.	.08	.26		.34	.51
2450	Roller		5200	.003		.09	.10		.19	.26
2600	Spray		6000	.003		.09	.08		.17	.24
2650	Paint 1 coat, brushwork		1950	.008		.08	.26		.34	.51
2800	Roller		5200	.003		.08	.10		.18	.25
2850	Spray		6000	.003		.09	.08		.17	.24
3000	Stain, wood floor, brushwork, 1 coat		4550	.004		.08	.11		.19	.27
3200	Roller		5200	.003		.09	.10		.19	.25
3250	Spray		6000	.003		.09	.08		.17	.23
3400	Varnish, wood floor, brushwork		4550	.004		.09	.11		.20	.28
3450	Roller		5200	.003		.10	.10		.20	.27
3600	Spray	↓	6000	.003	↓	.11	.08		.19	.26
3650	For dust proofing or anti skid, see Section 03 35 29.30									
3800	Grilles, per side, oil base, primer coat, brushwork	1 Pord	520	.015	S.F.	.13	.48		.61	.93
3850	Spray		1140	.007		.13	.22		.35	.51
3920	Paint 2 coats, brushwork		325	.025		.42	.77		1.19	1.73
3940	Spray	↓	650	.012	↓	.48	.38		.86	1.16
5000	Pipe, 1" - 4" diameter, primer or sealer coat, oil base, brushwork	2 Pord	1250	.013	L.F.	.09	.40		.49	.76
5100	Spray		2165	.007		.08	.23		.31	.47
5350	Paint 2 coats, brushwork		775	.021		.19	.65		.84	1.27
5400	Spray		1240	.013		.22	.40		.62	.90
6300	13" - 16" diameter, primer or sealer coat, brushwork		310	.052		.35	1.61		1.96	3.04
6350	Spray		540	.030		.39	.93		1.32	1.95
6500	Paint 2 coats, brushwork		195	.082		.78	2.56		3.34	5.10
6550	Spray	↓	310	.052	↓	.86	1.61		2.47	3.60
7000	Trim, wood, incl. putting, under 6" wide									
7200	Primer coat, oil base, brushwork	1 Pord	650	.012	L.F.	.03	.38		.41	.67
7250	Paint, 1 coat, brushwork		650	.012		.05	.38		.43	.69
7450	3 coats		325	.025		.16	.77		.93	1.44
7500	Over 6" wide, primer coat, brushwork		650	.012		.06	.38		.44	.70
7550	Paint, 1 coat, brushwork		650	.012		.11	.38		.49	.75
7650	3 coats		325	.025	↓	.31	.77		1.08	1.61
8000	Cornice, simple design, primer coat, oil base, brushwork		650	.012	S.F.	.06	.38		.44	.70
8250	Paint, 1 coat		650	.012		.11	.38		.49	.75
8350	Ornate design, primer coat		350	.023		.06	.71		.77	1.25
8400	Paint, 1 coat		350	.023		.11	.71		.82	1.30
8600	Balustrades, primer coat, oil base, brushwork		520	.015		.06	.48		.54	.86
8650	Paint, 1 coat		520	.015		.11	.48		.59	.91
8900	Trusses and wood frames, primer coat, oil base, brushwork		800	.010		.06	.31		.37	.58
8950	Spray		1200	.007		.07	.21		.28	.41
9220	Paint 2 coats, brushwork		500	.016		.21	.50		.71	1.05
9240	Spray		600	.013		.23	.42		.65	.95
9260	Stain, brushwork, wipe off		600	.013		.08	.42		.50	.78
9280	Varnish, 3 coats, brushwork	↓	275	.029		.28	.91		1.19	1.81
9350	For latex paint, deduct				↓	10%				

09 91 Painting

09 91 23 – Interior Painting

09 91 23.62 Electrostatic Painting

	Crew	Daily Output	Labor-Hours	Unit	Material	2014 Bare Costs Labor	Equipment	Total	Total Incl O&P
0010 **ELECTROSTATIC PAINTING**									
0100 In shop									
0200 Flat surfaces (lockers, casework, elevator doors. etc.)									
0300 One coat	1 Pord	200	.040	S.F.	.53	1.25		1.78	2.64
0400 Two coats	"	120	.067	"	.77	2.08		2.85	4.27
0500 Irregular surfaces (furniture, door frames, etc.)									
0600 One coat	1 Pord	150	.053	S.F.	.53	1.67		2.20	3.32
0700 Two coats	"	100	.080	"	.77	2.50		3.27	4.95
0800 On site									
0900 Flat surfaces (lockers, casework, elevator doors, etc.)									
1000 One coat	1 Pord	150	.053	S.F.	.53	1.67		2.20	3.32
1100 Two coats	"	100	.080	"	.77	2.50		3.27	4.95
1200 Irregular surfaces (furniture, door frames, etc)									
1300 One coat	1 Pord	115	.070	S.F.	.53	2.17		2.70	4.16
1400 Two coats	"	70	.114	"	.77	3.57		4.34	6.70

09 91 23.72 Walls and Ceilings, Interior

	Crew	Daily Output	Labor-Hours	Unit	Material	2014 Bare Costs Labor	Equipment	Total	Total Incl O&P
0010 **WALLS AND CEILINGS, INTERIOR** R099100-10									
0100 Concrete, drywall or plaster, latex , primer or sealer coat R099100-20									
0200 Smooth finish, brushwork	1 Pord	1150	.007	S.F.	.06	.22		.28	.43
0240 Roller		1350	.006		.06	.19		.25	.37
0280 Spray		2750	.003		.05	.09		.14	.21
0300 Sand finish, brushwork		975	.008		.06	.26		.32	.49
0340 Roller		1150	.007		.06	.22		.28	.43
0380 Spray		2275	.004		.05	.11		.16	.24
0800 Paint 2 coats, smooth finish, brushwork		680	.012		.13	.37		.50	.74
0840 Roller		800	.010		.13	.31		.44	.65
0880 Spray		1625	.005		.12	.15		.27	.38
0900 Sand finish, brushwork		605	.013		.13	.41		.54	.82
0940 Roller		1020	.008		.13	.25		.38	.54
0980 Spray		1700	.005		.12	.15		.27	.37
1200 Paint 3 coats, smooth finish, brushwork		510	.016		.19	.49		.68	1.02
1240 Roller		650	.012		.19	.38		.57	.84
1280 Spray		1625	.005		.18	.15		.33	.45
1600 Glaze coating, 2 coats, spray, clear		1200	.007		.49	.21		.70	.88
1640 Multicolor		1200	.007		.98	.21		1.19	1.42
1660 Painting walls, complete, including surface prep, primer &									
1670 2 coats finish, on drywall or plaster, with roller	1 Pord	325	.025	S.F.	.20	.77		.97	1.48
1700 For oil base paint, add					10%				
1800 For ceiling installations, add						25%			
2000 Masonry or concrete block, primer/sealer, latex paint									
2100 Primer, smooth finish, brushwork	1 Pord	1000	.008	S.F.	.10	.25		.35	.52
2110 Roller		1150	.007		.10	.22		.32	.47
2180 Spray		2400	.003		.09	.10		.19	.27
2200 Sand finish, brushwork		850	.009		.10	.29		.39	.59
2210 Roller		975	.008		.10	.26		.36	.53
2280 Spray		2050	.004		.09	.12		.21	.30
2800 Primer plus one finish coat, smooth brush		525	.015		.29	.48		.77	1.10
2810 Roller		615	.013		.18	.41		.59	.87
2880 Spray		1200	.007		.16	.21		.37	.52
2900 Sand finish, brushwork		450	.018		.18	.56		.74	1.11
2910 Roller		515	.016		.18	.49		.67	1
2980 Spray		1025	.008		.16	.24		.40	.58

09 91 23.72 Walls and Ceilings, Interior

09 91 23.72 Walls and Ceilings, Interior		Crew	Daily Output	Labor-Hours	Unit	Material	2014 Bare Costs Labor	Equipment	Total	Total Incl O&P
3600	Glaze coating, 3 coats, spray, clear	1 Pord	900	.009	S.F.	.70	.28		.98	1.23
3620	Multicolor		900	.009		1.13	.28		1.41	1.71
4000	Block filler, 1 coat, brushwork		425	.019		.12	.59		.71	1.10
4100	Silicone, water repellent, 2 coats, spray		2000	.004		.29	.13		.42	.53
4120	For oil base paint, add					10%				
8200	For work 8' - 15' H, add						10%			
8300	For work over 15' H, add						20%			
8400	For light textured surfaces, add						10%			
8410	Heavy textured, add						25%			

09 91 23.74 Walls and Ceilings, Interior, Zero VOC Latex

09 91 23.74 Walls and Ceilings, Interior, Zero VOC Latex			Crew	Daily Output	Labor-Hours	Unit	Material	2014 Bare Costs Labor	Equipment	Total	Total Incl O&P
0010	**WALLS AND CEILINGS, INTERIOR, ZERO VOC LATEX**										
0100	Concrete, dry wall or plaster, latex, primer or sealer coat										
0200	Smooth finish, brushwork	G	1 Pord	1150	.007	S.F.	.06	.22		.28	.43
0240	Roller	G		1350	.006		.06	.19		.25	.37
0280	Spray	G		2750	.003		.05	.09		.14	.20
0300	Sand finish, brushwork	G		975	.008		.06	.26		.32	.49
0340	Roller	G		1150	.007		.07	.22		.29	.43
0380	Spray	G		2275	.004		.05	.11		.16	.24
0800	Paint 2 coats, smooth finish, brushwork	G		680	.012		.14	.37		.51	.76
0840	Roller	G		800	.010		.15	.31		.46	.67
0880	Spray	G		1625	.005		.13	.15		.28	.39
0900	Sand finish, brushwork	G		605	.013		.14	.41		.55	.83
0940	Roller	G		1020	.008		.15	.25		.40	.56
0980	Spray	G		1700	.005		.13	.15		.28	.38
1200	Paint 3 coats, smooth finish, brushwork	G		510	.016		.21	.49		.70	1.04
1240	Roller	G		650	.012		.22	.38		.60	.87
1280	Spray	G		1625	.005		.19	.15		.34	.46
1800	For ceiling installations, add	G						25%			
8200	For work 8' - 15' H, add							10%			
8300	For work over 15' H, add							20%			

09 91 23.75 Dry Fall Painting

09 91 23.75 Dry Fall Painting		Crew	Daily Output	Labor-Hours	Unit	Material	2014 Bare Costs Labor	Equipment	Total	Total Incl O&P
0010	**DRY FALL PAINTING**									
0100	Sprayed on walls, gypsum board or plaster									
0220	One coat	1 Pord	2600	.003	S.F.	.06	.10		.16	.22
0250	Two coats		1560	.005		.11	.16		.27	.38
0280	Concrete or textured plaster, one coat		1560	.005		.06	.16		.22	.32
0310	Two coats		1300	.006		.11	.19		.30	.44
0340	Concrete block, one coat		1560	.005		.06	.16		.22	.32
0370	Two coats		1300	.006		.11	.19		.30	.44
0400	Wood, one coat		877	.009		.06	.29		.35	.53
0430	Two coats		650	.012		.11	.38		.49	.75
0440	On ceilings, gypsum board or plaster									
0470	One coat	1 Pord	1560	.005	S.F.	.06	.16		.22	.32
0500	Two coats		1300	.006		.11	.19		.30	.44
0530	Concrete or textured plaster, one coat		1560	.005		.06	.16		.22	.32
0560	Two coats		1300	.006		.11	.19		.30	.44
0570	Structural steel, bar joists or metal deck, one coat		1560	.005		.06	.16		.22	.32
0580	Two coats		1040	.008		.11	.24		.35	.52

09 93 Staining and Transparent Finishing

09 93 23 – Interior Staining and Finishing

09 93 23.10 Varnish

		Crew	Daily Output	Labor-Hours	Unit	Material	2014 Bare Costs Labor	Equipment	Total	Total Incl O&P
0010	**VARNISH**									
0012	1 coat + sealer, on wood trim, brush, no sanding included	1 Pord	400	.020	S.F.	.07	.63		.70	1.11
0020	1 coat + sealer, on wood trim, brush, no sanding included, no VOC		400	.020		.18	.63		.81	1.23
0100	Hardwood floors, 2 coats, no sanding included, roller		1890	.004		.15	.13		.28	.39

09 96 High-Performance Coatings

09 96 23 – Graffiti-Resistant Coatings

09 96 23.10 Graffiti Resistant Treatments

		Crew	Daily Output	Labor-Hours	Unit	Material	2014 Bare Costs Labor	Equipment	Total	Total Incl O&P
0010	**GRAFFITI RESISTANT TREATMENTS**, sprayed on walls									
0100	Non-sacrificial, permanent non-stick coating, clear, on metals	1 Pord	2000	.004	S.F.	2.06	.13		2.19	2.48
0200	Concrete		2000	.004		2.35	.13		2.48	2.79
0300	Concrete block		2000	.004		3.03	.13		3.16	3.55
0400	Brick		2000	.004		3.44	.13		3.57	3.99
0500	Stone		2000	.004		3.44	.13		3.57	3.99
0600	Unpainted wood		2000	.004		3.97	.13		4.10	4.58
2000	Semi-permanent cross linking polymer primer, on metals		2000	.004		.67	.13		.80	.94
2100	Concrete		2000	.004		.80	.13		.93	1.09
2200	Concrete block		2000	.004		1	.13		1.13	1.31
2300	Brick		2000	.004		.80	.13		.93	1.09
2400	Stone		2000	.004		.80	.13		.93	1.09
2500	Unpainted wood		2000	.004		1.11	.13		1.24	1.43
3000	Top coat, on metals		2000	.004		.55	.13		.68	.81
3100	Concrete		2000	.004		.62	.13		.75	.90
3200	Concrete block		2000	.004		.87	.13		1	1.17
3300	Brick		2000	.004		.73	.13		.86	1.01
3400	Stone		2000	.004		.73	.13		.86	1.01
3500	Unpainted wood		2000	.004		.87	.13		1	1.17
5000	Sacrificial, water based, on metal		2000	.004		.32	.13		.45	.57
5100	Concrete		2000	.004		.32	.13		.45	.57
5200	Concrete block		2000	.004		.32	.13		.45	.57
5300	Brick		2000	.004		.32	.13		.45	.57
5400	Stone		2000	.004		.32	.13		.45	.57
5500	Unpainted wood		2000	.004		.32	.13		.45	.57
8000	Cleaner for use after treatment									
8100	Towels or wipes, per package of 30				Ea.	.63			.63	.70
8200	Aerosol spray, 24 oz. can				"	18			18	19.80

09 96 46 – Intumescent Coatings

09 96 46.10 Coatings, Intumescent

		Crew	Daily Output	Labor-Hours	Unit	Material	2014 Bare Costs Labor	Equipment	Total	Total Incl O&P
0010	**COATINGS, INTUMESCENT**, spray applied									
0100	On exterior structural steel, 0.25" d.f.t.	1 Pord	475	.017	S.F.	.41	.53		.94	1.32
0150	0.51" d.f.t.		350	.023		.41	.71		1.12	1.63
0200	0.98" d.f.t.		280	.029		.41	.89		1.30	1.92
0300	On interior structural steel, 0.108" d.f.t.		300	.027		.41	.83		1.24	1.82
0350	0.310" d.f.t.		150	.053		.41	1.67		2.08	3.19
0400	0.670" d.f.t.		100	.080		.41	2.50		2.91	4.56

09 96 53 – Elastomeric Coatings

09 96 53.10 Coatings, Elastomeric

		Crew	Daily Output	Labor-Hours	Unit	Material	2014 Bare Costs Labor	Equipment	Total	Total Incl O&P
0010	**COATINGS, ELASTOMERIC**									
0020	High build, water proof, one coat system									
0100	Concrete, brush	1 Pord	650	.012	S.F.	.31	.38		.69	.97

09 96 High-Performance Coatings

09 96 56 – Epoxy Coatings

09 96 56.20 Wall Coatings

		Crew	Daily Output	Labor-Hours	Unit	Material	2014 Bare Costs Labor	Equipment	Total	Total Incl O&P
0010	**WALL COATINGS**									
0100	Acrylic glazed coatings, minimum	1 Pord	525	.015	S.F.	.31	.48		.79	1.12
0200	Maximum		305	.026		.65	.82		1.47	2.07
0300	Epoxy coatings, minimum		525	.015		.40	.48		.88	1.22
0400	Maximum		170	.047		1.20	1.47		2.67	3.74
0600	Exposed aggregate, troweled on, 1/16" to 1/4", minimum		235	.034		.61	1.06		1.67	2.42
0700	Maximum (epoxy or polyacrylate)		130	.062		1.31	1.92		3.23	4.60
0900	1/2" to 5/8" aggregate, minimum		130	.062		1.19	1.92		3.11	4.47
1000	Maximum		80	.100		2.06	3.13		5.19	7.40
1500	Exposed aggregate, sprayed on, 1/8" aggregate, minimum		295	.027		.56	.85		1.41	2.01
1600	Maximum		145	.055		1.04	1.72		2.76	3.98
1800	High build epoxy, 50 mil, minimum		390	.021		.67	.64		1.31	1.79
1900	Maximum		95	.084		1.14	2.63		3.77	5.60
2100	Laminated epoxy with fiberglass, minimum		295	.027		.72	.85		1.57	2.18
2200	Maximum		145	.055		1.30	1.72		3.02	4.27
2400	Sprayed perlite or vermiculite, 1/16" thick, minimum		2935	.003		.27	.09		.36	.44
2500	Maximum		640	.013		.73	.39		1.12	1.44
2700	Vinyl plastic wall coating, minimum		735	.011		.33	.34		.67	.92
2800	Maximum		240	.033		.81	1.04		1.85	2.60
3000	Urethane on smooth surface, 2 coats, minimum		1135	.007		.27	.22		.49	.66
3100	Maximum		665	.012		.58	.38		.96	1.26
3600	Ceramic-like glazed coating, cementitious, minimum		440	.018		.47	.57		1.04	1.45
3700	Maximum		345	.023		.80	.72		1.52	2.07
3900	Resin base, minimum		640	.013		.33	.39		.72	1
4000	Maximum		330	.024		.53	.76		1.29	1.83

09 97 Special Coatings

09 97 13 – Steel Coatings

09 97 13.23 Exterior Steel Coatings

			Crew	Daily Output	Labor-Hours	Unit	Material	2014 Bare Costs Labor	Equipment	Total	Total Incl O&P
0010	**EXTERIOR STEEL COATINGS**	R050516-30									
6101	Cold galvanizing, brush in field		1 Pord	1100	.007	S.F.	.12	.23		.35	.51
6510	Paints & protective coatings, sprayed in field										
6520	Alkyds, primer		2 Psst	3600	.004	S.F.	.08	.14		.22	.37
6540	Gloss topcoats			3200	.005		.08	.16		.24	.40
6560	Silicone alkyd			3200	.005		.15	.16		.31	.47
6610	Epoxy, primer			3000	.005		.29	.17		.46	.65
6630	Intermediate or topcoat			2800	.006		.26	.18		.44	.65
6650	Enamel coat			2800	.006		.33	.18		.51	.72
6700	Epoxy ester, primer			2800	.006		.40	.18		.58	.80
6720	Topcoats			2800	.006		.22	.18		.40	.60
6810	Latex primer			3600	.004		.06	.14		.20	.35
6830	Topcoats			3200	.005		.06	.16		.22	.38
6910	Universal primers, one part, phenolic, modified alkyd			2000	.008		.40	.26		.66	.94
6940	Two part, epoxy spray			2000	.008		.30	.26		.56	.83
7000	Zinc rich primers, self cure, spray, inorganic			1800	.009		.86	.28		1.14	1.50
7010	Epoxy, spray, organic			1800	.009		.26	.28		.54	.84
7020	Above one story, spray painting simple structures, add							25%			
7030	Intricate structures, add							50%			

Estimating Tips

General

- The items in this division are usually priced per square foot or each.
- Many items in Division 10 require some type of support system or special anchors that are not usually furnished with the item. The required anchors must be added to the estimate in the appropriate division.
- Some items in Division 10, such as lockers, may require assembly before installation. Verify the amount of assembly required. Assembly can often exceed installation time.

10 20 00 Interior Specialties

- Support angles and blocking are not included in the installation of toilet compartments, shower/dressing compartments, or cubicles. Appropriate line items from Divisions 5 or 6 may need to be added to support the installations.
- Toilet partitions are priced by the stall. A stall consists of a side wall, pilaster, and door with hardware. Toilet tissue holders and grab bars are extra.
- The required acoustical rating of a folding partition can have a significant impact on costs. Verify the sound transmission coefficient rating of the panel priced to the specification requirements.

- Grab bar installation does not include supplemental blocking or backing to support the required load. When grab bars are installed at an existing facility, provisions must be made to attach the grab bars to solid structure.

Reference Numbers

Reference numbers are shown in shaded boxes at the beginning of some major classifications. These numbers refer to related items in the Reference Section. The reference information may be an estimating procedure, an alternate pricing method, or technical information.

Note: Not all subdivisions listed here necessarily appear in this publication.

Division 10 – Specialties

10 05 Common Work Results for Specialties

10 05 05 – Selective Specialties Demolition

10 05 05.10 Selective Demolition, Specialties

10 05 05.10 Selective Demolition, Specialties	Crew	Daily Output	Labor-Hours	Unit	Material	2014 Bare Costs Labor	Equipment	Total	Total Incl O&P
0010 **SELECTIVE DEMOLITION, SPECIALTIES**									
1100 Boards and panels, wall mounted	2 Clab	15	1.067	Ea.		30		30	50.50
1200 Cases, for directory and/or bulletin boards, including doors		24	.667			18.80		18.80	31.50
1850 Shower partitions, cabinet or stall, including base and door	↓	8	2			56.50		56.50	95
1855 Shower receptor, terrazzo or concrete	1 Clab	14	.571	↓		16.10		16.10	27
1900 Curtain track or rod, hospital type, ceiling mounted or suspended	"	220	.036	L.F.		1.03		1.03	1.73
1910 Toilet cubicles, remove	2 Clab	8	2	Ea.		56.50		56.50	95
1930 Urinal screen, remove	1 Clab	12	.667	"		18.80		18.80	31.50
2650 Wall guard, misc. wall or corner protection	"	320	.025	L.F.		.71		.71	1.19
2750 Access floor, metal panel system, including pedestals, covering	2 Clab	850	.019	S.F.		.53		.53	.89
3050 Fireplace, prefab, freestanding or wall hung, including hood and screen	1 Clab	2	4	Ea.		113		113	190
3054 Chimney top, simulated brick, 4' high	"	15	.533			15.05		15.05	25.50
3200 Stove, woodburning, cast iron	2 Clab	2	8			226		226	380
3440 Weathervane, residential	1 Clab	12	.667			18.80		18.80	31.50
3500 Flagpole, groundset, to 70' high, excluding base/foundation	K-1	1	16			515	335	850	1,225
3555 To 30' high	"	2.50	6.400			207	133	340	490
4300 Letter, signs or plaques, exterior on wall	1 Clab	20	.400			11.30		11.30	19
4310 Signs, street, reflective aluminum, including post and bracket		60	.133			3.76		3.76	6.35
4320 Door signs interior on door 6" x 6", selective demolition	↓	20	.400			11.30		11.30	19
4550 Turnstiles, manual or electric	2 Clab	2	8	↓		226		226	380
5050 Lockers	1 Clab	15	.533	Opng.		15.05		15.05	25.50
5250 Cabinets, recessed	Q-12	12	1.333	Ea.		49		49	81
5260 Mail boxes, Horiz., Key Lock, front loading, Remove	1 Carp	34	.235	"		8.40		8.40	14.15
5350 Awning, fabric, including frame	2 Clab	100	.160	S.F.		4.51		4.51	7.60
6050 Partition, woven wire		1400	.011			.32		.32	.54
6100 Folding gate, security, door or window		500	.032			.90		.90	1.52
6580 Acoustic air wall		650	.025	↓		.69		.69	1.17
7550 Telephone enclosure, exterior, post mounted		3	5.333	Ea.		150		150	253
8850 Scale, platform, excludes foundation or pit	↓	.25	64	"		1,800		1,800	3,025

10 11 Visual Display Units

10 11 13 – Chalkboards

10 11 13.13 Fixed Chalkboards

	Crew	Daily Output	Labor-Hours	Unit	Material	2014 Bare Costs Labor	Equipment	Total	Total Incl O&P
0010 **FIXED CHALKBOARDS** Porcelain enamel steel									
3900 Wall hung									
4000 Aluminum frame and chalktrough									
4200 3' x 4'	2 Carp	16	1	Ea.	240	36		276	325
4300 3' x 5'		15	1.067		310	38		348	405
4500 4' x 8'		14	1.143		425	41		466	535
4600 4' x 12'	↓	13	1.231	↓	585	44		629	720
4700 Wood frame and chalktrough									
4800 3' x 4'	2 Carp	16	1	Ea.	217	36		253	298
5000 3' x 5'		15	1.067		267	38		305	360
5100 4' x 5'		14	1.143		275	41		316	370
5300 4' x 8'	↓	13	1.231	↓	355	44		399	465
5400 Liquid chalk, white porcelain enamel, wall hung									
5420 Deluxe units, aluminum trim and chalktrough									
5450 4' x 4'	2 Carp	16	1	Ea.	252	36		288	335
5500 4' x 8'		14	1.143		380	41		421	490
5550 4' x 12'	↓	12	1.333	↓	535	47.50		582.50	670
5700 Wood trim and chalktrough									

10 11 Visual Display Units

10 11 13 – Chalkboards

10 11 13.13 Fixed Chalkboards

		Crew	Daily Output	Labor-Hours	Unit	Material	2014 Bare Costs Labor	Equipment	Total	Total Incl O&P
5900	4' x 4'	2 Carp	16	1	Ea.	715	36		751	845
6000	4' x 6'		15	1.067		810	38		848	955
6200	4' x 8'	↓	14	1.143		970	41		1,011	1,150
6300	Liquid chalk, felt tip markers					2.04			2.04	2.24
6500	Erasers					1.81			1.81	1.99
6600	Board cleaner, 8 oz. bottle				↓	6			6	6.60

10 11 13.23 Modular-Support-Mounted Chalkboards

		Crew	Daily Output	Labor-Hours	Unit	Material	2014 Bare Costs Labor	Equipment	Total	Total Incl O&P
0010	**MODULAR-SUPPORT-MOUNTED CHALKBOARDS**									
0400	Sliding chalkboards									
0450	Vertical, one sliding board with back panel, wall mounted									
0500	8' x 4'	2 Carp	8	2	Ea.	2,225	71.50		2,296.50	2,575
0520	8' x 8'		7.50	2.133		3,225	76.50		3,301.50	3,675
0540	8' x 12'	↓	7	2.286	↓	4,175	81.50		4,256.50	4,725
0600	Two sliding boards, with back panel									
0620	8' x 4'	2 Carp	8	2	Ea.	3,500	71.50		3,571.50	3,975
0640	8' x 8'		7.50	2.133		5,025	76.50		5,101.50	5,675
0660	8' x 12'	↓	7	2.286	↓	8,400	81.50		8,481.50	9,375
0700	Horizontal, two track									
0800	4' x 8', 2 sliding panels	2 Carp	8	2	Ea.	1,950	71.50		2,021.50	2,275
0820	4' x 12', 2 sliding panels		7.50	2.133		2,550	76.50		2,626.50	2,925
0840	4' x 16', 4 sliding panels	↓	7	2.286	↓	3,425	81.50		3,506.50	3,900
0900	Four track, four sliding panels									
0920	4' x 8'	2 Carp	8	2	Ea.	3,150	71.50		3,221.50	3,575
0940	4' x 12'		7.50	2.133		4,100	76.50		4,176.50	4,650
0960	4' x 16'	↓	7	2.286	↓	5,350	81.50		5,431.50	6,000
1200	Vertical, motor operated									
1400	One sliding panel with back panel									
1450	10' x 4'	2 Carp	4	4	Ea.	5,650	143		5,793	6,475
1500	10' x 10'		3.75	4.267		6,825	153		6,978	7,750
1550	10' x 16'	↓	3.50	4.571	↓	8,050	163		8,213	9,125
1700	Two sliding panels with back panel									
1750	10' x 4'	2 Carp	4	4	Ea.	10,000	143		10,143	11,200
1800	10' x 10'		3.75	4.267		11,700	153		11,853	13,100
1850	10' x 16'	↓	3.50	4.571	↓	13,300	163		13,463	15,000
2000	Three sliding panels with back panel									
2100	10' x 4'	2 Carp	4	4	Ea.	14,000	143		14,143	15,600
2150	10' x 10'		3.75	4.267		15,300	153		15,453	17,200
2200	10' x 16'	↓	3.50	4.571	↓	18,500	163		18,663	20,700
2400	For projection screen, glass beaded, add				S.F.	8.10			8.10	8.90
2500	For remote control, 1 panel control, add				Ea.	380			380	420
2600	2 panel control, add				"	655			655	725
2800	For units without back panels, deduct				S.F.	5.10			5.10	5.65
2850	For liquid chalk porcelain panels, add				"	5.50			5.50	6.05
3000	Swing leaf, any comb. of chalkboard & cork, aluminum frame									
3100	Floor style, 6 panels									
3150	30" x 40" panels				Ea.	1,575			1,575	1,750
3200	48" x 40" panels				"	2,650			2,650	2,925
3300	Wall mounted, 6 panels									
3400	30" x 40" panels	2 Carp	16	1	Ea.	1,500	36		1,536	1,700
3450	48" x 40" panels	"	16	1	"	1,850	36		1,886	2,075
3600	Extra panels for swing leaf units									
3700	30" x 40" panels				Ea.	299			299	330

10 11 Visual Display Units

10 11 13 – Chalkboards

10 11 13.23 Modular-Support-Mounted Chalkboards

		Crew	Daily Output	Labor-Hours	Unit	Material	2014 Bare Costs Labor	Equipment	Total	Total Incl O&P
3750	48" x 40" panels				Ea.	370			370	405

10 11 13.43 Portable Chalkboards

		Crew	Daily Output	Labor-Hours	Unit	Material	2014 Bare Costs Labor	Equipment	Total	Total Incl O&P
0010	**PORTABLE CHALKBOARDS**									
0100	Freestanding, reversible									
0120	Economy, wood frame, 4' x 6'									
0140	Chalkboard both sides				Ea.	615			615	680
0160	Chalkboard one side, cork other side				"	565			565	620
0200	Standard, lightweight satin finished aluminum, 4' x 6'									
0220	Chalkboard both sides				Ea.	675			675	745
0240	Chalkboard one side, cork other side				"	705			705	775
0300	Deluxe, heavy duty extruded aluminum, 4' x 6'									
0320	Chalkboard both sides				Ea.	1,050			1,050	1,150
0340	Chalkboard one side, cork other side				"	1,025			1,025	1,125

10 11 16 – Markerboards

10 11 16.53 Electronic Markerboards

		Crew	Daily Output	Labor-Hours	Unit	Material	2014 Bare Costs Labor	Equipment	Total	Total Incl O&P
0010	**ELECTRONIC MARKERBOARDS**									
0100	Wall hung or free standing, 3' x 4' to 4' x 6'	2 Carp	8	2	S.F.	84	71.50		155.50	212
0150	5' x 6' to 4' x 8'		8	2	"	63	71.50		134.50	189
0500	Interactive projection module for existing whiteboards		8	2	Ea.	1,300	71.50		1,371.50	1,550

10 11 23 – Tackboards

10 11 23.10 Fixed Tackboards

		Crew	Daily Output	Labor-Hours	Unit	Material	2014 Bare Costs Labor	Equipment	Total	Total Incl O&P
0010	**FIXED TACKBOARDS**									
0020	Cork sheets, unbacked, no frame, 1/4" thick	2 Carp	290	.055	S.F.	2.07	1.97		4.04	5.60
0100	1/2" thick		290	.055		4.14	1.97		6.11	7.85
0300	Fabric-face, no frame, on 7/32" cork underlay		290	.055		6.30	1.97		8.27	10.25
0400	On 1/4" cork on 1/4" hardboard		290	.055		8.30	1.97		10.27	12.45
0600	With edges wrapped		290	.055		10.60	1.97		12.57	15
0700	On 7/16" fire retardant core		290	.055		6.50	1.97		8.47	10.45
0900	With edges wrapped		290	.055		8.05	1.97		10.02	12.15
1000	Designer fabric only, cut to size					2.70			2.70	2.97
1200	1/4" vinyl cork, on 1/4" hardboard, no frame	2 Carp	290	.055		8.75	1.97		10.72	12.90
1300	On 1/4" coreboard		290	.055		5.30	1.97		7.27	9.15
2000	For map and display rail, economy, add		385	.042	L.F.	3.06	1.49		4.55	5.85
2100	Deluxe, add		350	.046	"	4.70	1.63		6.33	7.90
2120	Prefabricated, 1/4" cork, 3' x 5' with aluminum frame		16	1	Ea.	124	36		160	196
2140	Wood frame		16	1		156	36		192	231
2160	4' x 4' with aluminum frame		16	1		134	36		170	207
2180	Wood frame		16	1		180	36		216	258
2200	4' x 8' with aluminum frame		14	1.143		270	41		311	365
2210	With wood frame		14	1.143		235	41		276	330
2220	4' x 12' with aluminum frame		12	1.333		400	47.50		447.50	520
2230	Bulletin board case, single glass door, with lock									
2240	36" x 24", economy	2 Carp	12	1.333	Ea.	310	47.50		357.50	420
2250	Deluxe		12	1.333		405	47.50		452.50	525
2260	42" x 30", economy		12	1.333		365	47.50		412.50	480
2270	Deluxe		12	1.333		525	47.50		572.50	660
2300	Glass enclosed cabinets, alum., cork panel, hinged doors									
2400	3' x 3', 1 door	2 Carp	12	1.333	Ea.	605	47.50		652.50	745
2500	4' x 4', 2 door		11	1.455		1,000	52		1,052	1,200
2600	4' x 7', 3 door		10	1.600		1,775	57		1,832	2,050
2800	4' x 10', 4 door		8	2		2,350	71.50		2,421.50	2,725

10 11 Visual Display Units

10 11 23 – Tackboards

10 11 23.10 Fixed Tackboards

		Crew	Daily Output	Labor-Hours	Unit	Material	2014 Bare Costs Labor	Equipment	Total	Total Incl O&P
2900	For lights, add per door opening	1 Elec	13	.615	Ea.	161	26.50		187.50	221
3100	Horizontal sliding units, 4 doors, 4' x 8', 8' x 4'	2 Carp	9	1.778		1,950	63.50		2,013.50	2,250
3200	4' x 12'		7	2.286		2,550	81.50		2,631.50	2,925
3400	8 doors, 4' x 16'		5	3.200		3,450	114		3,564	3,975
3500	4' x 24'		4	4		4,650	143		4,793	5,350

10 11 23.20 Control Boards

		Crew	Daily Output	Labor-Hours	Unit	Material	2014 Bare Costs Labor	Equipment	Total	Total Incl O&P
0010	**CONTROL BOARDS**									
0020	Magnetic, porcelain finish, 18" x 24", framed	2 Carp	8	2	Ea.	199	71.50		270.50	340
0100	24" x 36"		7.50	2.133		295	76.50		371.50	455
0200	36" x 48"		7	2.286		390	81.50		471.50	565
0300	48" x 72"		6	2.667		860	95.50		955.50	1,100
0400	48" x 96"		5	3.200		1,075	114		1,189	1,375

10 13 Directories

10 13 10 – Building Directories

10 13 10.10 Directory Boards

		Crew	Daily Output	Labor-Hours	Unit	Material	2014 Bare Costs Labor	Equipment	Total	Total Incl O&P
0010	**DIRECTORY BOARDS**									
0050	Plastic, glass covered, 30" x 20"	2 Carp	3	5.333	Ea.	234	191		425	575
0100	36" x 48"		2	8		845	286		1,131	1,400
0300	Grooved cork, 30" x 20"		3	5.333		405	191		596	765
0400	36" x 48"		2	8		555	286		841	1,100
0600	Black felt, 30" x 20"		3	5.333		231	191		422	575
0700	36" x 48"		2	8		445	286		731	970
0900	Outdoor, weatherproof, black plastic, 36" x 24"		2	8		760	286		1,046	1,325
1000	36" x 36"		1.50	10.667		880	380		1,260	1,600
1800	Indoor, economy, open face, 18" x 24"		7	2.286		157	81.50		238.50	310
1900	24" x 36"		7	2.286		154	81.50		235.50	305
2000	36" x 24"		6	2.667		154	95.50		249.50	330
2100	36" x 48"		6	2.667		251	95.50		346.50	435
2400	Building directory, alum., black felt panels, 1 door, 24" x 18"		4	4		315	143		458	585
2500	36" x 24"		3.50	4.571		370	163		533	685
2600	48" x 32"		3	5.333		610	191		801	990
2700	2 door, 36" x 48"		2.50	6.400		655	229		884	1,100
2800	36" x 60"		2	8		860	286		1,146	1,425
2900	48" x 60"		1	16		970	570		1,540	2,025
3100	For bronze enamel finish, add					15%				
3200	For bronze anodized finish, add					25%				
3400	For illuminated directory, single door unit, add					135			135	148
3500	For 6" header panel, 6 letters per foot, add				L.F.	21.50			21.50	23.50
6050	Building directory, electronic display, alum. frame, wall mounted	2 Carp	32	.500	S.F.	2,275	17.90		2,292.90	2,525
6100	Free standing	"	60	.267	"	2,800	9.55		2,809.55	3,100

10 14 19 – Dimensional Letter Signage

10 14 19.10 Exterior Signs		Crew	Daily Output	Labor-Hours	Unit	Material	2014 Bare Costs Labor	Equipment	Total	Total Incl O&P
0010	**EXTERIOR SIGNS**									
0020	Letters, 2" high, 3/8" deep, cast bronze	1 Carp	24	.333	Ea.	25.50	11.90		37.40	48
0140	1/2" deep, cast aluminum		18	.444		25.50	15.90		41.40	54.50
0160	Cast bronze		32	.250		31	8.95		39.95	49.50
0300	6" high, 5/8" deep, cast aluminum		24	.333		29	11.90		40.90	52
0400	Cast bronze		24	.333		59	11.90		70.90	85
0600	8" high, 3/4" deep, cast aluminum		14	.571		37	20.50		57.50	75.50
0700	Cast bronze		20	.400		82.50	14.30		96.80	115
0900	10" high, 1" deep, cast aluminum		18	.444		48	15.90		63.90	79.50
1000	Bronze		18	.444		114	15.90		129.90	152
1200	12" high, 1-1/4" deep, cast aluminum		12	.667		55	24		79	100
1500	Cast bronze		18	.444		136	15.90		151.90	177
1600	14" high, 2-5/16" deep, cast aluminum		12	.667		82	24		106	130
1800	Fabricated stainless steel, 6" high, 2" deep		20	.400		41.50	14.30		55.80	69.50
1900	12" high, 3" deep		18	.444		67	15.90		82.90	101
2100	18" high, 3" deep		12	.667		109	24		133	159
2200	24" high, 4" deep		10	.800		212	28.50		240.50	281
2700	Acrylic, on high density foam, 12" high, 2" deep		20	.400		16.90	14.30		31.20	42.50
2800	18" high, 2" deep		18	.444		39	15.90		54.90	69.50
3900	Plaques, custom, 20" x 30", for up to 450 letters, cast aluminum	2 Carp	4	4		1,425	143		1,568	1,800
4000	Cast bronze		4	4		1,875	143		2,018	2,300
4200	30" x 36", up to 900 letters cast aluminum		3	5.333		2,350	191		2,541	2,900
4300	Cast bronze		3	5.333		4,225	191		4,416	4,975
4500	36" x 48", for up to 1300 letters, cast bronze		2	8		4,600	286		4,886	5,550
4800	Signs, reflective alum. directional signs, dbl. face, 2-way, w/bracket		30	.533		144	19.05		163.05	190
4900	4-way		30	.533		231	19.05		250.05	286
5100	Exit signs, 24 ga. alum., 14" x 12" surface mounted	1 Carp	30	.267		47.50	9.55		57.05	68.50
5200	10" x 7"		20	.400		25.50	14.30		39.80	52
5400	Bracket mounted, double face, 12" x 10"		30	.267		56	9.55		65.55	78
5500	Sticky back, stock decals, 14" x 10"	1 Clab	50	.160		27	4.51		31.51	37
6000	Interior elec., wall mount, fiberglass panels, 2 lamps, 6"	1 Elec	8	1		87	42.50		129.50	166
6100	8"	"	8	1		103	42.50		145.50	184
6400	Replacement sign faces, 6" or 8"	1 Clab	50	.160		62.50	4.51		67.01	76

10 14 23 – Panel Signage

10 14 23.13 Engraved Panel Signage

		Crew	Daily Output	Labor-Hours	Unit	Material	2014 Bare Costs Labor	Equipment	Total	Total Incl O&P
0010	**ENGRAVED PANEL SIGNAGE**, interior									
1010	Flexible door sign, adhesive back, w/Braille, 5/8" letters, 4" x 4"	1 Clab	32	.250	Ea.	30.50	7.05		37.55	45.50
1050	6" x 6"		32	.250		46.50	7.05		53.55	63
1100	8" x 2"		32	.250		30.50	7.05		37.55	45.50
1150	8" x 4"		32	.250		39.50	7.05		46.55	55.50
1200	8" x 8"		32	.250		52.50	7.05		59.55	70
1250	12" x 2"		32	.250		35	7.05		42.05	50.50
1300	12" x 6"		32	.250		50	7.05		57.05	67
1350	12" x 12"		32	.250		105	7.05		112.05	128
1500	Graphic symbols, 2" x 2"		32	.250		12	7.05		19.05	25
1550	6" x 6"		32	.250		31	7.05		38.05	46
1600	8" x 8"		32	.250		39	7.05		46.05	54.50
2010	Corridor, stock acrylic, 2-sided, with mounting bracket, 2" x 8"	1 Carp	24	.333		24.50	11.90		36.40	47
2020	2" x 10"		24	.333		33.50	11.90		45.40	57
2050	3" x 8"		24	.333		28.50	11.90		40.40	51.50
2060	3" x 10"		24	.333		42	11.90		53.90	66.50
2070	3" x 12"		24	.333		47	11.90		58.90	71.50

10 14 Signage

10 14 23 – Panel Signage

10 14 23.13 Engraved Panel Signage

		Crew	Daily Output	Labor-Hours	Unit	Material	2014 Bare Costs Labor	2014 Bare Costs Equipment	Total	Total Incl O&P
2100	4" x 8"	1 Carp	24	.333	Ea.	21	11.90		32.90	43
2110	4" x 10"		24	.333		37	11.90		48.90	60.50
2120	4" x 12"		24	.333		50.50	11.90		62.40	75.50

10 14 53 – Traffic Signage

10 14 53.20 Traffic Signs

		Crew	Daily Output	Labor-Hours	Unit	Material	2014 Bare Costs Labor	2014 Bare Costs Equipment	Total	Total Incl O&P
0010	**TRAFFIC SIGNS**									
0012	Stock, 24" x 24", no posts, .080" alum. reflectorized	B-80	70	.343	Ea.	83	9.90	10.85	103.75	120
0100	High intensity		70	.343		95.50	9.90	10.85	116.25	134
0300	30" x 30", reflectorized		70	.343		121	9.90	10.85	141.75	162
0400	High intensity		70	.343		133	9.90	10.85	153.75	175
0600	Guide and directional signs, 12" x 18", reflectorized		70	.343		34.50	9.90	10.85	55.25	66.50
0700	High intensity		70	.343		51	9.90	10.85	71.75	85
0900	18" x 24", stock signs, reflectorized		70	.343		46	9.90	10.85	66.75	79.50
1000	High intensity		70	.343		51	9.90	10.85	71.75	85
1200	24" x 24", stock signs, reflectorized		70	.343		56	9.90	10.85	76.75	90
1300	High intensity		70	.343		61	9.90	10.85	81.75	95.50
1500	Add to above for steel posts, galvanized, 10'-0" upright, bolted		200	.120		32.50	3.46	3.79	39.75	46
1600	12'-0" upright, bolted		140	.171		39	4.95	5.40	49.35	57.50
1800	Highway road signs, aluminum, over 20 S.F., reflectorized		350	.069	S.F.	33.50	1.98	2.17	37.65	42.50
2000	High intensity		350	.069		33.50	1.98	2.17	37.65	42.50
2200	Highway, suspended over road, 80 S.F. min., reflectorized		165	.145		31	4.20	4.59	39.79	46
2300	High intensity		165	.145		29.50	4.20	4.59	38.29	44.50

10 17 Telephone Specialties

10 17 16 – Telephone Enclosures

10 17 16.10 Commercial Telephone Enclosures

		Crew	Daily Output	Labor-Hours	Unit	Material	2014 Bare Costs Labor	2014 Bare Costs Equipment	Total	Total Incl O&P
0010	**COMMERCIAL TELEPHONE ENCLOSURES**									
0300	Shelf type, wall hung, minimum	2 Carp	5	3.200	Ea.	1,025	114		1,139	1,325
0400	Maximum	"	5	3.200	"	2,850	114		2,964	3,325

10 21 Compartments and Cubicles

10 21 13 – Toilet Compartments

10 21 13.13 Metal Toilet Compartments

		Crew	Daily Output	Labor-Hours	Unit	Material	2014 Bare Costs Labor	2014 Bare Costs Equipment	Total	Total Incl O&P
0010	**METAL TOILET COMPARTMENTS**									
0110	Cubicles, ceiling hung									
0200	Powder coated steel	2 Carp	4	4	Ea.	515	143		658	805
0500	Stainless steel	"	4	4		1,075	143		1,218	1,425
0600	For handicap units, incl. 52" grab bars, add ♿					430			430	475
0900	Floor and ceiling anchored									
1000	Powder coated steel	2 Carp	5	3.200	Ea.	590	114		704	835
1300	Stainless steel	"	5	3.200		1,150	114		1,264	1,475
1400	For handicap units, incl. 52" grab bars, add ♿					296			296	325
1610	Floor anchored									
1700	Powder coated steel	2 Carp	7	2.286	Ea.	585	81.50		666.50	775
2000	Stainless steel	"	7	2.286		1,400	81.50		1,481.50	1,675
2100	For handicap units, incl. 52" grab bars, add ♿					310			310	345
2200	For juvenile units, deduct					41.50			41.50	45.50
2450	Floor anchored, headrail braced									
2500	Powder coated steel	2 Carp	6	2.667	Ea.	380	95.50		475.50	575

10 21 13 – Toilet Compartments

10 21 13.13 Metal Toilet Compartments

		Crew	Daily Output	Labor-Hours	Unit	Material	2014 Bare Costs Labor	Equipment	Total	Total Incl O&P
2804	Stainless steel	2 Carp	4.60	3.478	Ea.	1,050	124		1,174	1,350
2900	For handicap units, incl. 52" grab bars, add					370			370	410
3000	Wall hung partitions, powder coated steel	2 Carp	7	2.286		635	81.50		716.50	835
3300	Stainless steel	"	7	2.286		1,650	81.50		1,731.50	1,950
3400	For handicap units, incl. 52" grab bars, add					370			370	410
4000	Screens, entrance, floor mounted, 58" high, 48" wide									
4200	Powder coated steel	2 Carp	15	1.067	Ea.	242	38		280	330
4500	Stainless steel	"	15	1.067	"	910	38		948	1,075
4650	Urinal screen, 18" wide									
4704	Powder coated steel	2 Carp	6.15	2.602	Ea.	206	93		299	385
5004	Stainless steel	"	6.15	2.602	"	580	93		673	795
5100	Floor mounted, head rail braced									
5300	Powder coated steel	2 Carp	8	2	Ea.	230	71.50		301.50	375
5600	Stainless steel	"	8	2	"	595	71.50		666.50	775
5750	Pilaster, flush									
5800	Powder coated steel	2 Carp	10	1.600	Ea.	278	57		335	400
6100	Stainless steel		10	1.600		615	57		672	770
6300	Post braced, powder coated steel		10	1.600		153	57		210	264
6600	Stainless steel		10	1.600		450	57		507	590
6700	Wall hung, bracket supported									
6800	Powder coated steel	2 Carp	10	1.600	Ea.	153	57		210	264
7100	Stainless steel		10	1.600		227	57		284	345
7400	Flange supported, powder coated steel		10	1.600		106	57		163	212
7700	Stainless steel		10	1.600		310	57		367	435
7800	Wedge type, powder coated steel		10	1.600		134	57		191	244
8100	Stainless steel		10	1.600		575	57		632	730

10 21 13.14 Metal Toilet Compartment Components

		Crew	Daily Output	Labor-Hours	Unit	Material	2014 Bare Costs Labor	Equipment	Total	Total Incl O&P
0010	**METAL TOILET COMPARTMENT COMPONENTS**									
0100	Pilasters									
0110	Overhead braced, powder coated steel, 7" wide x 82" high	2 Carp	22.20	.721	Ea.	69.50	26		95.50	120
0120	Stainless steel		22.20	.721		124	26		150	181
0130	Floor braced, powder coated steel, 7" wide x 70" high		23.30	.687		123	24.50		147.50	178
0140	Stainless steel		23.30	.687		242	24.50		266.50	310
0150	Ceiling hung, powder coated steel, 7" wide x 83" high		13.30	1.203		131	43		174	217
0160	Stainless steel		13.30	1.203		271	43		314	370
0170	Wall hung, powder coated steel, 3" wide x 58" high		18.90	.847		129	30.50		159.50	193
0180	Stainless steel		18.90	.847		191	30.50		221.50	261
0200	Panels									
0210	Powder coated steel, 31" wide x 58" high	2 Carp	18.90	.847	Ea.	132	30.50		162.50	196
0220	Stainless steel		18.90	.847		360	30.50		390.50	450
0230	Powder coated steel, 53" wide x 58" high		18.90	.847		164	30.50		194.50	231
0240	Stainless steel		18.90	.847		470	30.50		500.50	565
0250	Powder coated steel, 63" wide x 58" high		18.90	.847		200	30.50		230.50	271
0260	Stainless steel		18.90	.847		515	30.50		545.50	615
0300	Doors									
0310	Powder coated steel, 24" wide x 58" high	2 Carp	14.10	1.135	Ea.	138	40.50		178.50	220
0320	Stainless steel		14.10	1.135		287	40.50		327.50	385
0330	Powder coated steel, 26" wide x 58" high		14.10	1.135		140	40.50		180.50	223
0340	Stainless steel		14.10	1.135		296	40.50		336.50	395
0350	Powder coated steel, 28" wide x 58" high		14.10	1.135		160	40.50		200.50	245
0360	Stainless steel		14.10	1.135		330	40.50		370.50	435
0370	Powder coated steel, 36" wide x 58" high		14.10	1.135		172	40.50		212.50	259

10 21 Compartments and Cubicles

10 21 13 – Toilet Compartments

10 21 13.14 Metal Toilet Compartment Components

	Crew	Daily Output	Labor-Hours	Unit	Material	2014 Bare Costs Labor	2014 Bare Costs Equipment	Total	Total Incl O&P
0380	Stainless steel	2 Carp	14.10	1.135	Ea.	370	40.50		410.50	480
0400	Headrails									
0410	For powder coated steel, 62" long	2 Carp	65	.246	Ea.	21.50	8.80		30.30	38.50
0420	Stainless steel		65	.246		22.50	8.80		31.30	40
0430	For powder coated steel, 84" long		50	.320		32	11.45		43.45	55
0440	Stainless steel		50	.320		34.50	11.45		45.95	57.50
0450	For powder coated steel, 120" long		30	.533		42.50	19.05		61.55	79
0460	Stainless steel	↓	30	.533	↓	46.50	19.05		65.55	83

10 21 13.16 Plastic-Laminate-Clad Toilet Compartments

	Crew	Daily Output	Labor-Hours	Unit	Material	2014 Bare Costs Labor	2014 Bare Costs Equipment	Total	Total Incl O&P
0010	**PLASTIC-LAMINATE-CLAD TOILET COMPARTMENTS**									
0110	Cubicles, ceiling hung									
0300	Plastic laminate on particle board	2 Carp	4	4	Ea.	520	143		663	810
0600	For handicap units, incl. 52" grab bars, add				"	430			430	475
0900	Floor and ceiling anchored									
1100	Plastic laminate on particle board	2 Carp	5	3.200	Ea.	785	114		899	1,050
1400	For handicap units, incl. 52" grab bars, add				"	296			296	325
1610	Floor mounted									
1800	Plastic laminate on particle board	2 Carp	7	2.286	Ea.	490	81.50		571.50	675
2450	Floor mounted, headrail braced									
2600	Plastic laminate on particle board	2 Carp	6	2.667	Ea.	750	95.50		845.50	985
3400	For handicap units, incl. 52" grab bars, add					370			370	410
4300	Entrance screen, floor mtd., plas. lam., 58" high, 48" wide	2 Carp	15	1.067		610	38		648	735
4800	Urinal screen, 18" wide, ceiling braced, plastic laminate		8	2		184	71.50		255.50	320
5400	Floor mounted, headrail braced		8	2		190	71.50		261.50	330
5900	Pilaster, flush, plastic laminate		10	1.600		505	57		562	655
6400	Post braced, plastic laminate	↓	10	1.600	↓	300	57		357	425
6700	Wall hung, bracket supported									
6900	Plastic laminate on particle board	2 Carp	10	1.600	Ea.	92.50	57		149.50	198
7450	Flange supported									
7500	Plastic laminate on particle board	2 Carp	10	1.600	Ea.	230	57		287	350

10 21 13.17 Plastic-Laminate Clad Toilet Compartment Components

	Crew	Daily Output	Labor-Hours	Unit	Material	2014 Bare Costs Labor	2014 Bare Costs Equipment	Total	Total Incl O&P
0010	**PLASTIC-LAMINATE CLAD TOILET COMPARTMENT COMPONENTS**									
0100	Pilasters									
0110	Overhead braced, 7" wide x 82" high	2 Carp	22.20	.721	Ea.	95	26		121	149
0130	Floor anchored, 7" wide x 70" high		23.30	.687		95	24.50		119.50	146
0150	Ceiling hung, 7" wide x 83" high		13.30	1.203		99.50	43		142.50	182
0180	Wall hung, 3" wide x 58" high	↓	18.90	.847	↓	93	30.50		123.50	153
0200	Panels									
0210	31" wide x 58" high	2 Carp	18.90	.847	Ea.	143	30.50		173.50	208
0230	51" wide x 58" high		18.90	.847		196	30.50		226.50	267
0250	63" wide x 58" high	↓	18.90	.847	↓	229	30.50		259.50	305
0300	Doors									
0310	24" wide x 58" high	2 Carp	14.10	1.135	Ea.	141	40.50		181.50	224
0330	26" wide x 58" high		14.10	1.135		146	40.50		186.50	229
0350	28" wide x 58" high		14.10	1.135		150	40.50		190.50	234
0370	36" wide x 58" high	↓	14.10	1.135	↓	180	40.50		220.50	267
0400	Headrails									
0410	62" long	2 Carp	65	.246	Ea.	22.50	8.80		31.30	40
0430	84" long		60	.267	↓	31.50	9.55		41.05	50.50
0450	120" long	↓	30	.533	↓	42	19.05		61.05	78

10 21 13 – Toilet Compartments

10 21 13.19 Plastic Toilet Compartments

		Crew	Daily Output	Labor-Hours	Unit	Material	2014 Bare Costs Labor	2014 Bare Costs Equipment	Total	Total Incl O&P
0010	**PLASTIC TOILET COMPARTMENTS**									
0110	Cubicles, ceiling hung									
0250	Phenolic	2 Carp	4	4	Ea.	865	143		1,008	1,200
0600	For handicap units, incl. 52" grab bars, add				"	430			430	475
0900	Floor and ceiling anchored									
1050	Phenolic	2 Carp	5	3.200	Ea.	825	114		939	1,100
1400	For handicap units, incl. 52" grab bars, add				"	296			296	325
1610	Floor mounted									
1750	Phenolic	2 Carp	7	2.286	Ea.	795	81.50		876.50	1,000
2100	For handicap units, incl. 52" grab bars, add					310			310	345
2200	For juvenile units, deduct					41.50			41.50	45.50
2450	Floor mounted, headrail braced									
2550	Phenolic	2 Carp	6	2.667	Ea.	795	95.50		890.50	1,025

10 21 13.20 Plastic Toilet Compartment Components

		Crew	Daily Output	Labor-Hours	Unit	Material	2014 Bare Costs Labor	2014 Bare Costs Equipment	Total	Total Incl O&P
0010	**PLASTIC TOILET COMPARTMENT COMPONENTS**									
0100	Pilasters									
0110	Overhead braced, polymer plastic, 7" wide x 82" high	2 Carp	22.20	.721	Ea.	121	26		147	177
0120	Phenolic		22.20	.721		148	26		174	207
0130	Floor braced, polymer plastic, 7" wide x 70" high		23.30	.687		169	24.50		193.50	228
0140	Phenolic		23.30	.687		140	24.50		164.50	196
0150	Ceiling hung, polymer plastic, 7" wide x 83" high		13.30	1.203		166	43		209	256
0160	Phenolic		13.30	1.203		158	43		201	247
0180	Wall hung, phenolic, 3" wide x 58" high		18.90	.847		96	30.50		126.50	156
0200	Panels									
0203	Polymer plastic, 18" high x 55" high	2 Carp	18.90	.847	Ea.	200	30.50		230.50	271
0206	Phenolic, 18" wide x 58" high		18.90	.847		193	30.50		223.50	263
0210	Polymer plastic, 31" high x 55" high		18.90	.847		305	30.50		335.50	385
0220	Phenolic, 31" wide x 58" high		18.90	.847		260	30.50		290.50	335
0223	Polymer plastic, 48" high x 55" high		18.90	.847		470	30.50		500.50	565
0226	Phenolic, 48" wide x 58" high		18.90	.847		550	30.50		580.50	655
0230	Polymer plastic, 51" wide x 55" high		18.90	.847		405	30.50		435.50	495
0240	Phenolic, 51" wide x 58" high		18.90	.847		395	30.50		425.50	485
0250	Polymer plastic, 63" wide x 55" high		18.90	.847		555	30.50		585.50	660
0260	Phenolic, 63" wide x 58" high		18.90	.847		415	30.50		445.50	510
0300	Doors									
0310	Polymer plastic, 24" wide x 55" high	2 Carp	14.10	1.135	Ea.	208	40.50		248.50	298
0320	Phenolic, 24" wide x 58" high		14.10	1.135		292	40.50		332.50	390
0330	Polymer plastic, 26" high x 55" high		14.10	1.135		222	40.50		262.50	315
0340	Phenolic, 26" wide x 58" high		14.10	1.135		310	40.50		350.50	410
0350	Polymer plastic, 28" wide x 55" high		14.10	1.135		247	40.50		287.50	340
0360	Phenolic, 28" wide x 58" high		14.10	1.135		330	40.50		370.50	430
0370	Polymer plastic, 36" wide x 55" high		14.10	1.135		288	40.50		328.50	385
0380	Phenolic, 36" wide x 58" high		14.10	1.135		410	40.50		450.50	520
0400	Headrails									
0410	For polymer plastic, 62" long	2 Carp	65	.246	Ea.	22.50	8.80		31.30	40
0420	Phenolic		65	.246		22.50	8.80		31.30	40
0430	For polymer plastic, 84" long		50	.320		33	11.45		44.45	55.50
0440	Phenolic		50	.320		33	11.45		44.45	55.50
0450	For polymer plastic, 120" long		30	.533		43	19.05		62.05	79.50
0460	Phenolic		30	.533		43	19.05		62.05	79.50

10 21 Compartments and Cubicles

10 21 13 – Toilet Compartments

10 21 13.40 Stone Toilet Compartments

		Crew	Daily Output	Labor-Hours	Unit	Material	2014 Bare Costs Labor	Equipment	Total	Total Incl O&P
0010	**STONE TOILET COMPARTMENTS**									
0100	Cubicles, ceiling hung, marble	2 Marb	2	8	Ea.	1,625	264		1,889	2,225
0600	For handicap units, incl. 52" grab bars, add					430			430	475
0800	Floor & ceiling anchored, marble	2 Marb	2.50	6.400		2,025	211		2,236	2,600
1400	For handicap units, incl. 52" grab bars, add					296			296	325
1600	Floor mounted, marble	2 Marb	3	5.333		1,200	176		1,376	1,625
2401	Floor mounted, headrail braced, marble	2 Ston	3	5.333		1,150	186		1,336	1,575
2900	For handicap units, incl. 52" grab bars, add					370			370	410
4100	Entrance screen, floor mounted marble, 58" high, 48" wide	2 Marb	9	1.778		755	58.50		813.50	930
4600	Urinal screen, 18" wide, ceiling braced, marble	D-1	6	2.667		755	86		841	975
5100	Floor mounted, head rail braced									
5200	Marble	D-1	6	2.667	Ea.	645	86		731	855
5700	Pilaster, flush, marble		9	1.778		840	57.50		897.50	1,025
6200	Post braced, marble		9	1.778		825	57.50		882.50	1,000

10 21 16 – Shower and Dressing Compartments

10 21 16.10 Partitions, Shower

		Crew	Daily Output	Labor-Hours	Unit	Material	2014 Bare Costs Labor	Equipment	Total	Total Incl O&P
0010	**PARTITIONS, SHOWER** floor mounted, no plumbing									
0400	Cabinet, one piece, fiberglass, 32" x 32"	2 Carp	5	3.200	Ea.	510	114		624	750
0420	36" x 36"		5	3.200		610	114		724	860
0440	36" x 48"		5	3.200		1,300	114		1,414	1,625
0460	Acrylic, 32" x 32"		5	3.200		299	114		413	520
0480	36" x 36"		5	3.200		1,000	114		1,114	1,300
0500	36" x 48"		5	3.200		1,500	114		1,614	1,850
0520	Shower door for above, clear plastic, 24" wide	1 Carp	8	1		177	36		213	255
0540	28" wide		8	1		201	36		237	282
0560	Tempered glass, 24" wide		8	1		191	36		227	270
0580	28" wide		8	1		216	36		252	297
2400	Glass stalls, with doors, no receptors, chrome on brass	2 Shee	3	5.333		1,650	216		1,866	2,175
2700	Anodized aluminum	"	4	4		1,150	162		1,312	1,550
2901	Marble shower stall, stock design, with shower door	2 Ston	1.20	13.333		2,475	465		2,940	3,500
3001	With curtain	"	1.30	12.308		2,200	430		2,630	3,125
3200	Receptors, precast terrazzo, 32" x 32"	2 Marb	14	1.143		330	37.50		367.50	430
3300	48" x 34"	"	9.50	1.684		440	55.50		495.50	580
3501	Plastic, simulated terrazzo receptor, 32" x 32"	2 Ston	14	1.143		148	40		188	230
3600	32" x 48"	2 Marb	12	1.333		215	44		259	310
3801	Precast concrete, colors, 32" x 32"	2 Ston	14	1.143		186	40		226	272
3900	48" x 48"	2 Marb	8	2		251	66		317	385
4100	Shower doors, economy plastic, 24" wide	1 Shee	9	.889		144	36		180	218
4200	Tempered glass door, economy		8	1		260	40.50		300.50	355
4400	Folding, tempered glass, aluminum frame		6	1.333		390	54		444	520
4500	Sliding, tempered glass, 48" opening		6	1.333		540	54		594	680
4700	Deluxe, tempered glass, chrome on brass frame, minimum		8	1		385	40.50		425.50	490
4800	Maximum		1	8		625	325		950	1,225
4850	On anodized aluminum frame, minimum		2	4		540	162		702	860
4900	Maximum		1	8		625	325		950	1,225
5100	Shower enclosure, tempered glass, anodized alum. frame									
5120	2 panel & door, corner unit, 32" x 32"	1 Shee	2	4	Ea.	1,025	162		1,187	1,425
5140	Neo-angle corner unit, 16" x 24" x 16"	"	2	4		1,075	162		1,237	1,475
5200	Shower surround, 3 wall, polypropylene, 32" x 32"	1 Carp	4	2		455	71.50		526.50	620
5220	PVC, 32" x 32"		4	2		380	71.50		451.50	540
5240	Fiberglass		4	2		420	71.50		491.50	580
5250	2 wall, polypropylene, 32" x 32"		4	2		315	71.50		386.50	470

10 21 Compartments and Cubicles

10 21 16 – Shower and Dressing Compartments

10 21 16.10 Partitions, Shower

10 21 16.10 Partitions, Shower		Crew	Daily Output	Labor-Hours	Unit	Material	2014 Bare Costs Labor	Equipment	Total	Total Incl O&P
5270	PVC	1 Carp	4	2	Ea.	395	71.50		466.50	555
5290	Fiberglass		4	2		400	71.50		471.50	560
5300	Tub doors, tempered glass & frame, minimum	1 Shee	8	1		229	40.50		269.50	320
5400	Maximum		6	1.333		535	54		589	680
5600	Chrome plated, brass frame, minimum		8	1		305	40.50		345.50	405
5700	Maximum		6	1.333		745	54		799	905
5900	Tub/shower enclosure, temp. glass, alum. frame, minimum		2	4		410	162		572	720
6200	Maximum		1.50	5.333		855	216		1,071	1,300
6500	On chrome-plated brass frame, minimum		2	4		565	162		727	895
6600	Maximum		1.50	5.333		1,200	216		1,416	1,675
6800	Tub surround, 3 wall, polypropylene	1 Carp	4	2		256	71.50		327.50	400
6900	PVC		4	2		390	71.50		461.50	550
7000	Fiberglass, minimum		4	2		400	71.50		471.50	560
7100	Maximum		3	2.667		680	95.50		775.50	910

10 21 23 – Cubicle Curtains and Track

10 21 23.16 Cubicle Track and Hardware

10 21 23.16 Cubicle Track and Hardware		Crew	Daily Output	Labor-Hours	Unit	Material	2014 Bare Costs Labor	Equipment	Total	Total Incl O&P
0010	**CUBICLE TRACK AND HARDWARE**									
0020	Curtain track, box channel, ceiling mounted	1 Carp	135	.059	L.F.	6.20	2.12		8.32	10.35
0100	Suspended	"	100	.080	"	8.20	2.86		11.06	13.80
0300	Curtains, nylon mesh tops, fire resistant, 11 oz. per lineal yard									
0310	Polyester oxford cloth, 9' ceiling height	1 Carp	425	.019	L.F.	15.10	.67		15.77	17.75
0500	8' ceiling height		425	.019		9.45	.67		10.12	11.55
0700	Designer oxford cloth		425	.019		9.85	.67		10.52	11.95
0800	I.V. track systems									
0820	I.V. track, oval	1 Carp	135	.059	L.F.	5.35	2.12		7.47	9.45
0830	I.V. trolley		32	.250	Ea.	41	8.95		49.95	60
0840	I.V. pendent, (tree, 5 hook)		32	.250	"	167	8.95		175.95	198

10 22 Partitions

10 22 13 – Wire Mesh Partitions

10 22 13.10 Partitions, Woven Wire

10 22 13.10 Partitions, Woven Wire		Crew	Daily Output	Labor-Hours	Unit	Material	2014 Bare Costs Labor	Equipment	Total	Total Incl O&P
0010	**PARTITIONS, WOVEN WIRE** for tool or stockroom enclosures									
0100	Channel frame, 1-1/2" diamond mesh, 10 ga. wire, painted									
0300	Wall panels, 4'-0" wide, 7' high	2 Carp	25	.640	Ea.	142	23		165	195
0400	8' high		23	.696		162	25		187	220
0600	10' high		18	.889		191	32		223	264
0700	For 5' wide panels, add					5%				
0900	Ceiling panels, 10' long, 2' wide	2 Carp	25	.640		148	23		171	202
1000	4' wide		15	1.067		171	38		209	252
1200	Panel with service window & shelf, 5' wide, 7' high		20	.800		355	28.50		383.50	440
1300	8' high		15	1.067		445	38		483	555
1500	Sliding doors, full height, 3' wide, 7' high		6	2.667		460	95.50		555.50	670
1600	10' high		5	3.200		525	114		639	770
1800	6' wide sliding door, 7' full height		5	3.200		635	114		749	890
1900	10' high		4	4		820	143		963	1,150
2100	Swinging doors, 3' wide, 7' high, no transom		6	2.667		292	95.50		387.50	480
2200	7' high, 3' transom		5	3.200		370	114		484	595

10 22 Partitions

10 22 16 – Folding Gates

10 22 16.10 Security Gates

	Crew	Daily Output	Labor-Hours	Unit	Material	2014 Bare Costs Labor	Equipment	Total	Total Incl O&P
0010 **SECURITY GATES** for roll up type, see Section 08 33 13.10									
0300 Scissors type folding gate, ptd. steel, single, 6-1/2' high, 5-1/2' wide	2 Sswk	4	4	Opng.	223	153		376	535
0350 6-1/2' wide		4	4		243	153		396	560
0400 7-1/2' wide		4	4		253	153		406	570
0600 Double gate, 8' high, 8' wide		2.50	6.400		380	245		625	885
0650 10' wide		2.50	6.400		415	245		660	925
0700 12' wide		2	8		610	305		915	1,250
0750 14' wide		2	8		700	305		1,005	1,350
0900 Door gate, folding steel, 4' wide, 61" high		4	4		138	153		291	445
1000 71" high		4	4		169	153		322	475
1200 81" high		4	4		182	153		335	490
1300 Window gates, 2' to 4' wide, 31" high		4	4		78	153		231	380
1500 55" high		3.75	4.267		122	164		286	445
1600 79" high		3.50	4.571		144	175		319	495

10 22 19 – Demountable Partitions

10 22 19.43 Demountable Composite Partitions

	Crew	Daily Output	Labor-Hours	Unit	Material	2014 Bare Costs Labor	Equipment	Total	Total Incl O&P
0010 **DEMOUNTABLE COMPOSITE PARTITIONS**, add for doors									
0100 Do not deduct door openings from total L.F.									
0900 Demountable gypsum system on 2" to 2-1/2"									
1000 steel studs, 9' high, 3" to 3-3/4" thick									
1200 Vinyl clad gypsum	2 Carp	48	.333	L.F.	59	11.90		70.90	85
1300 Fabric clad gypsum		44	.364		147	13		160	184
1500 Steel clad gypsum		40	.400		164	14.30		178.30	204
1600 1.75 system, aluminum framing, vinyl clad hardboard,									
1800 paper honeycomb core panel, 1-3/4" to 2-1/2" thick									
1900 9' high	2 Carp	48	.333	L.F.	99	11.90		110.90	129
2100 7' high		60	.267		89	9.55		98.55	114
2200 5' high		80	.200		75	7.15		82.15	94.50
2250 Unitized gypsum system									
2300 Unitized panel, 9' high, 2" to 2-1/2" thick									
2350 Vinyl clad gypsum	2 Carp	48	.333	L.F.	127	11.90		138.90	160
2400 Fabric clad gypsum	"	44	.364	"	210	13		223	253
2500 Unitized mineral fiber system									
2510 Unitized panel, 9' high, 2-1/4" thick, aluminum frame									
2550 Vinyl clad mineral fiber	2 Carp	48	.333	L.F.	127	11.90		138.90	159
2600 Fabric clad mineral fiber	"	44	.364	"	189	13		202	230
2800 Movable steel walls, modular system									
2900 Unitized panels, 9' high, 48" wide									
3100 Baked enamel, pre-finished	2 Carp	60	.267	L.F.	144	9.55		153.55	174
3200 Fabric clad steel		56	.286	"	207	10.20		217.20	245
5310 Trackless wall, cork finish, semi-acoustic, 1-5/8" thick, minimum		325	.049	S.F.	37.50	1.76		39.26	44.50
5320 Maximum		190	.084		42	3.01		45.01	51
5330 Acoustic, 2" thick, minimum		305	.052		35.50	1.88		37.38	42.50
5340 Maximum		225	.071		54.50	2.54		57.04	64.50
5500 For acoustical partitions, add, minimum					2.31			2.31	2.54
5550 Maximum					10.80			10.80	11.85
5700 For doors, see Sections 08 11 & 08 16									
5800 For door hardware, see Section 08 71									
6100 In-plant modular office system, w/prehung hollow core door									
6200 3" thick polystyrene core panels									
6250 12' x 12', 2 wall	2 Clab	3.80	4.211	Ea.	4,125	119		4,244	4,725
6300 4 wall		1.90	8.421		7,300	237		7,537	8,425

10 22 Partitions

10 22 19 - Demountable Partitions

10 22 19.43 Demountable Composite Partitions	Crew	Daily Output	Labor-Hours	Unit	Material	2014 Bare Costs Labor	Equipment	Total	Total Incl O&P
6350	16' x 16', 2 wall	2 Clab	3.60	4.444	Ea.	6,175	125		6,300	7,000
6400	4 wall	↓	1.80	8.889	↓	8,650	251		8,901	9,950

10 22 23 - Portable Partitions, Screens, and Panels

10 22 23.13 Wall Screens

		Crew	Daily Output	Labor-Hours	Unit	Material	2014 Bare Costs Labor	Equipment	Total	Total Incl O&P
0010	**WALL SCREENS**, divider panels, free standing, fiber core									
0020	Fabric face straight									
0100	3'-0" long, 4'-0" high	2 Carp	100	.160	L.F.	149	5.70		154.70	174
0200	5'-0" high		90	.178		105	6.35		111.35	127
0500	6'-0" high		75	.213		122	7.65		129.65	148
0900	5'-0" long, 4'-0" high		175	.091		92	3.27		95.27	107
1000	5'-0" high		150	.107		100	3.81		103.81	116
1500	6"-0" high		125	.128		117	4.58		121.58	136
1600	6'-0" long, 5'-0" high		162	.099		97	3.53		100.53	113
3200	Economical panels, fabric face, 4'-0" long, 5'-0" high		132	.121		49	4.33		53.33	61.50
3250	6'-0" high		112	.143		53	5.10		58.10	66.50
3300	5'-0" long, 5'-0" high		150	.107		51.50	3.81		55.31	63
3350	6'-0" high		125	.128		43	4.58		47.58	55
3450	Acoustical panels, 60 to 90 NRC, 3'-0" long, 5'-0" high		90	.178		88.50	6.35		94.85	108
3550	6'-0" high		75	.213		98	7.65		105.65	121
3600	5'-0" long, 5'-0" high		150	.107		65	3.81		68.81	78
3650	6'-0" high		125	.128		68	4.58		72.58	82.50
3700	6'-0" long, 5'-0" high		162	.099		56	3.53		59.53	67.50
3750	6'-0" high		138	.116		55	4.14		59.14	67.50
3800	Economy acoustical panels, 40 N.R.C., 4'-0" long, 5'-0" high		132	.121		49	4.33		53.33	61.50
3850	6'-0" high		112	.143		53	5.10		58.10	66.50
3900	5'-0" long, 6'-0" high		125	.128		43	4.58		47.58	55
3950	6'-0" long, 5'-0" high		162	.099		43	3.53		46.53	53.50
4000	Metal chalkboard, 6'-6" high, chalkboard, 1 side		125	.128		119	4.58		123.58	139
4100	Metal chalkboard, 2 sides		120	.133		136	4.77		140.77	157
4300	Tackboard, both sides	↓	123	.130	↓	107	4.65		111.65	126

10 22 33 - Accordion Folding Partitions

10 22 33.10 Partitions, Accordion Folding

		Crew	Daily Output	Labor-Hours	Unit	Material	2014 Bare Costs Labor	Equipment	Total	Total Incl O&P
0010	**PARTITIONS, ACCORDION FOLDING**									
0100	Vinyl covered, over 150 S.F., frame not included									
0300	Residential, 1.25 lb. per S.F., 8' maximum height	2 Carp	300	.053	S.F.	23	1.91		24.91	28
0400	Commercial, 1.75 lb. per S.F., 8' maximum height		225	.071		26	2.54		28.54	33
0600	2 lb. per S.F., 17' maximum height		150	.107		27	3.81		30.81	36
0700	Industrial, 4 lb. per S.F., 20' maximum height		75	.213		40.50	7.65		48.15	57.50
0900	Acoustical, 3 lb. per S.F., 17' maximum height		100	.160		29	5.70		34.70	41
1200	5 lb. per S.F., 20' maximum height		95	.168		40	6		46	54
1300	5.5 lb. per S.F., 17' maximum height		90	.178		47	6.35		53.35	62
1400	Fire rated, 4.5 psf, 20' maximum height		160	.100		47	3.58		50.58	57.50
1500	Vinyl clad wood or steel, electric operation, 5.0 psf		160	.100		57	3.58		60.58	69
1900	Wood, non-acoustic, birch or mahogany, to 10' high	↓	300	.053	↓	30.50	1.91		32.41	37

10 22 39 - Folding Panel Partitions

10 22 39.10 Partitions, Folding Panel

		Crew	Daily Output	Labor-Hours	Unit	Material	2014 Bare Costs Labor	Equipment	Total	Total Incl O&P
0010	**PARTITIONS, FOLDING PANEL**, acoustic, wood									
0100	Vinyl faced, to 18' high, 6 psf, minimum	2 Carp	60	.267	S.F.	57	9.55		66.55	78.50
0150	Average		45	.356		68	12.70		80.70	96
0200	Maximum		30	.533		87.50	19.05		106.55	129
0400	Plastic laminate or hardwood finish, minimum	↓	60	.267	↓	58.50	9.55		68.05	80.50

10 22 Partitions

10 22 39 - Folding Panel Partitions

10 22 39.10 Partitions, Folding Panel		Crew	Daily Output	Labor-Hours	Unit	Material	2014 Bare Costs Labor	2014 Bare Costs Equipment	Total	Total Incl O&P
0500	Maximum	2 Carp	30	.533	S.F.	62.50	19.05		81.55	101
0600	Wood, low acoustical type, 4.5 psf, to 14' high		50	.320		42.50	11.45		53.95	66.50
1100	Steel, acoustical, 9 to 12 lb. per S.F., vinyl faced, minimum		60	.267		60.50	9.55		70.05	82.50
1200	Maximum		30	.533		74	19.05		93.05	114
1700	Aluminum framed, acoustical, to 12' high, 5.5 psf, minimum		60	.267		41	9.55		50.55	61
1800	Maximum		30	.533		49.50	19.05		68.55	86
2000	6.5 lb. per S.F., minimum		60	.267		43	9.55		52.55	63
2100	Maximum		30	.533		53	19.05		72.05	90.50

10 22 43 - Sliding Partitions

10 22 43.10 Partitions, Sliding		Crew	Daily Output	Labor-Hours	Unit	Material	2014 Bare Costs Labor	2014 Bare Costs Equipment	Total	Total Incl O&P
0010	**PARTITIONS, SLIDING**									
0020	Acoustic air wall, 1-5/8" thick, minimum	2 Carp	375	.043	S.F.	33	1.53		34.53	39
0100	Maximum		365	.044		56.50	1.57		58.07	64.50
0300	2-1/4" thick, minimum		360	.044		37	1.59		38.59	43.50
0400	Maximum		330	.048		65	1.73		66.73	74.50
0600	For track type, add to above				L.F.	121			121	133
0700	Overhead track type, acoustical, 3" thick, 11 psf, minimum	2 Carp	350	.046	S.F.	83.50	1.63		85.13	94.50
0800	Maximum	"	300	.053	"	100	1.91		101.91	113

10 26 Wall and Door Protection

10 26 13 - Corner Guards

10 26 13.10 Metal Corner Guards		Crew	Daily Output	Labor-Hours	Unit	Material	2014 Bare Costs Labor	2014 Bare Costs Equipment	Total	Total Incl O&P
0010	**METAL CORNER GUARDS**									
0020	Steel angle w/anchors, 1" x 1" x 1/4", 1.5#/L.F.	2 Carp	160	.100	L.F.	6.25	3.58		9.83	12.90
0101	2" x 2" x 1/4" angles, 3.2#/L.F.		150	.107		10.20	3.81		14.01	17.60
0201	3" x 3" x 5/16" angles, 6.1#/L.F.		140	.114		16.45	4.09		20.54	25
0301	4" x 4" x 5/16" angles, 8.2#/L.F.		120	.133		17.40	4.77		22.17	27
0350	For angles drilled and anchored to masonry, add					15%	120%			
0370	Drilled and anchored to concrete, add					20%	170%			
0400	For galvanized angles, add					35%				
0450	For stainless steel angles, add					100%				
0501	Steel door track/wheel guard, 4' - 0" high	2 Carp	12	1.333	Ea.	109	47.50		156.50	200
0801	Pipe bumper for truck doors, conc. filled, 8' long, 6" diam.		10	1.600		685	57		742	845
0901	8" diameter		10	1.600		930	57		987	1,125
1000	Wall protection, stainless steel, 16 ga, 48" x 36" tall, screwed to studs	2 Skwk	500	.032	S.F.	8.45	1.16		9.61	11.25
1050	Wall end guard, stainless steel, 16 ga, 36" tall, screwed to studs	1 Skwk	30	.267	Ea.	19	9.70		28.70	37.50

10 26 13.20 Corner Protection		Crew	Daily Output	Labor-Hours	Unit	Material	2014 Bare Costs Labor	2014 Bare Costs Equipment	Total	Total Incl O&P
0010	**CORNER PROTECTION**									
0100	Stainless steel, 16 ga., adhesive mount, 3-1/2" leg	1 Carp	80	.100	L.F.	23	3.58		26.58	31
0200	12 ga. stainless, adhesive mount	"	80	.100		26.50	3.58		30.08	35
0300	For screw mount, add					10%				
0500	Vinyl acrylic, adhesive mount, 3" leg	1 Carp	128	.063		8.60	2.23		10.83	13.25
0550	1-1/2" leg		160	.050		4.83	1.79		6.62	8.30
0600	Screw mounted, 3" leg		80	.100		9.55	3.58		13.13	16.50
0650	1-1/2" leg		100	.080		4.83	2.86		7.69	10.10
0700	Clear plastic, screw mounted, 2-1/2"		60	.133		4.37	4.77		9.14	12.80
1000	Vinyl cover, alum. retainer, surface mount, 3" x 3"		48	.167		10.45	5.95		16.40	21.50
1050	2" x 2"		48	.167		9.45	5.95		15.40	20.50
1100	Flush mounted, 3" x 3"		32	.250		20.50	8.95		29.45	37.50
1150	2" x 2"		32	.250		16.70	8.95		25.65	33.50

10 26 Wall and Door Protection

10 26 16 – Bumper Guards

10 26 16.10 Wallguard

10 26 16.10 Wallguard		Crew	Daily Output	Labor-Hours	Unit	Material	2014 Bare Costs Labor	Equipment	Total	Total Incl O&P
0010	**WALLGUARD**									
0400	Rub rail, vinyl, adhesive mounted	1 Carp	185	.043	L.F.	8.70	1.55		10.25	12.15
0500	Neoprene, aluminum backing, 1-1/2" x 2"		110	.073		8.80	2.60		11.40	14.05
1000	Trolley rail, PVC, clipped to wall, 5" high		185	.043		8.80	1.55		10.35	12.30
1050	8" high		180	.044		14.70	1.59		16.29	18.80
1200	Bed bumper, vinyl acrylic, alum. retainer, 21" long		10	.800	Ea.	40.50	28.50		69	92.50
1300	53" long with aligner		9	.889	"	102	32		134	167
1400	Bumper, vinyl cover, alum. retain., cush. mnt., 1-1/2" x 2-3/4"		80	.100	L.F.	14.20	3.58		17.78	21.50
1500	2" x 4-1/4"		80	.100		20.50	3.58		24.08	29
1600	Surface mounted, 1-3/4" x 3-5/8"		80	.100		11.95	3.58		15.53	19.15
1700	Bumper rail, stainless steel, flat bar on brackets, 4" x 1/4"	2 Skwk	120	.133		44	4.84		48.84	56.50
1750	Wallguard stainless steel baseboard, 12" tall, adhesive applied	"	260	.062		32	2.23		34.23	39.50
2000	Crash rail, vinyl cover, alum. retainer, 1" x 4"	1 Carp	110	.073		11.05	2.60		13.65	16.50
2100	1" x 8"		90	.089		18.15	3.18		21.33	25.50
2150	Vinyl inserts, aluminum plate, 1" x 2-1/2"		110	.073		14.90	2.60		17.50	21
2200	1" x 5"		90	.089		23	3.18		26.18	31
3000	Handrail/bumper, vinyl cover, alum. retainer									
3010	Bracket mounted, flat rail, 5-1/2"	1 Carp	80	.100	L.F.	18.30	3.58		21.88	26
3100	6-1/2"		80	.100		23	3.58		26.58	31
3200	Bronze bracket, 1-3/4" diam. rail		80	.100		16.50	3.58		20.08	24

10 28 Toilet, Bath, and Laundry Accessories

10 28 13 – Toilet Accessories

10 28 13.13 Commercial Toilet Accessories

10 28 13.13 Commercial Toilet Accessories		Crew	Daily Output	Labor-Hours	Unit	Material	2014 Bare Costs Labor	Equipment	Total	Total Incl O&P
0010	**COMMERCIAL TOILET ACCESSORIES**									
0200	Curtain rod, stainless steel, 5' long, 1" diameter	1 Carp	13	.615	Ea.	26.50	22		48.50	66
0300	1-1/4" diameter		13	.615		30.50	22		52.50	70.50
0350	Chrome, 1" diameter		13	.615		32.50	22		54.50	72.50
0360	For vinyl curtain, add		1950	.004	S.F.	.84	.15		.99	1.17
0400	Diaper changing station, horizontal, wall mounted, plastic		10	.800	Ea.	223	28.50		251.50	293
0500	Dispenser units, combined soap & towel dispensers,									
0510	mirror and shelf, flush mounted	1 Carp	10	.800	Ea.	310	28.50		338.50	390
0600	Towel dispenser and waste receptacle,									
0610	18 gallon capacity	1 Carp	10	.800	Ea.	286	28.50		314.50	365
0800	Grab bar, straight, 1-1/4" diameter, stainless steel, 18" long		24	.333		29	11.90		40.90	52
0900	24" long		23	.348		29.50	12.45		41.95	53.50
1000	30" long		22	.364		31.50	13		44.50	56.50
1100	36" long		20	.400		38.50	14.30		52.80	66.50
1105	42" long		20	.400		46	14.30		60.30	74.50
1120	Corner, 36" long		20	.400		85.50	14.30		99.80	118
1200	1-1/2" diameter, 24" long		23	.348		31	12.45		43.45	55
1300	36" long		20	.400		33.50	14.30		47.80	61
1310	42" long		18	.444		43	15.90		58.90	74
1500	Tub bar, 1-1/4" diameter, 24" x 36"		14	.571		92.50	20.50		113	137
1600	Plus vertical arm		12	.667		97.50	24		121.50	147
1900	End tub bar, 1" diameter, 90° angle, 16" x 32"		12	.667		109	24		133	160
2010	Tub/shower/toilet, 2-wall, 36" x 24"		12	.667		83	24		107	132
2300	Hand dryer, surface mounted, electric, 115 volt, 20 amp		4	2		430	71.50		501.50	595
2400	230 volt, 10 amp		4	2		745	71.50		816.50	940
2450	Hand dryer, touch free, 1400 watt, 81,000 rpm		4	2		1,025	71.50		1,096.50	1,250

10 28 Toilet, Bath, and Laundry Accessories

10 28 13 – Toilet Accessories

10 28 13.13 Commercial Toilet Accessories

		Crew	Daily Output	Labor-Hours	Unit	Material	2014 Bare Costs Labor	Equipment	Total	Total Incl O&P
2600	Hat and coat strip, stainless steel, 4 hook, 36" long	1 Carp	24	.333	Ea.	75	11.90		86.90	103
2700	6 hook, 60" long		20	.400		131	14.30		145.30	168
3000	Mirror, with stainless steel 3/4" square frame, 18" x 24"		20	.400		47	14.30		61.30	75.50
3100	36" x 24"		15	.533		103	19.05		122.05	145
3200	48" x 24"		10	.800		139	28.50		167.50	201
3300	72" x 24"		6	1.333		256	47.50		303.50	360
3500	With 5" stainless steel shelf, 18" x 24"		20	.400		186	14.30		200.30	229
3600	36" x 24"		15	.533		217	19.05		236.05	271
3700	48" x 24"		10	.800		245	28.50		273.50	315
3800	72" x 24"		6	1.333		300	47.50		347.50	410
4100	Mop holder strip, stainless steel, 5 holders, 48" long		20	.400		89	14.30		103.30	122
4200	Napkin/tampon dispenser, recessed		15	.533		525	19.05		544.05	605
4220	Semi-recessed		6.50	1.231		310	44		354	415
4250	Napkin receptacle, recessed		6.50	1.231		165	44		209	256
4300	Robe hook, single, regular		36	.222		18.10	7.95		26.05	33.50
4400	Heavy duty, concealed mounting		36	.222		21	7.95		28.95	36.50
4600	Soap dispenser, chrome, surface mounted, liquid		20	.400		46.50	14.30		60.80	75
4700	Powder		20	.400		55	14.30		69.30	84.50
5000	Recessed stainless steel, liquid		10	.800		137	28.50		165.50	199
5600	Shelf, stainless steel, 5" wide, 18 ga., 24" long		24	.333		68.50	11.90		80.40	95.50
5700	48" long		16	.500		135	17.90		152.90	179
5800	8" wide shelf, 18 ga., 24" long		22	.364		69	13		82	98
5900	48" long		14	.571		121	20.50		141.50	168
6000	Toilet seat cover dispenser, stainless steel, recessed		20	.400		167	14.30		181.30	207
6050	Surface mounted		15	.533		34.50	19.05		53.55	69.50
6100	Toilet tissue dispenser, surface mounted, SS, single roll		30	.267		17.80	9.55		27.35	35.50
6200	Double roll		24	.333		23.50	11.90		35.40	46
6240	Plastic, twin/jumbo dbl. roll		24	.333		26	11.90		37.90	48.50
6400	Towel bar, stainless steel, 18" long		23	.348		41.50	12.45		53.95	67
6500	30" long		21	.381		111	13.60		124.60	146
6700	Towel dispenser, stainless steel, surface mounted		16	.500		44.50	17.90		62.40	79
6800	Flush mounted, recessed		10	.800		257	28.50		285.50	330
6900	Plastic, touchless, battery operated		16	.500		80.50	17.90		98.40	119
7000	Towel holder, hotel type, 2 guest size		20	.400		51.50	14.30		65.80	80.50
7200	Towel shelf, stainless steel, 24" long, 8" wide		20	.400		59.50	14.30		73.80	89.50
7400	Tumbler holder, tumbler only		30	.267		15.90	9.55		25.45	33.50
7410	Tumbler holder		20	.400		9.10	14.30		23.40	34
7500	Soap, tumbler & toothbrush		30	.267		19.60	9.55		29.15	37.50
7510	Tumbler & toothbrush holder		20	.400		12.60	14.30		26.90	38
7700	Wall urn ash receiver, surface mount, 11" long		12	.667		95	24		119	144
7800	7-1/2", long		18	.444		128	15.90		143.90	167
8000	Waste receptacles, stainless steel, with top, 13 gallon		10	.800		295	28.50		323.50	375
8100	36 gallon		8	1		395	36		431	495

10 28 16 – Bath Accessories

10 28 16.20 Medicine Cabinets

		Crew	Daily Output	Labor-Hours	Unit	Material	2014 Bare Costs Labor	Equipment	Total	Total Incl O&P
0010	**MEDICINE CABINETS**									
0020	With mirror, sst frame, 16" x 22", unlighted	1 Carp	14	.571	Ea.	95	20.50		115.50	140
0100	Wood frame		14	.571		136	20.50		156.50	185
0300	Sliding mirror doors, 20" x 16" x 4-3/4", unlighted		7	1.143		125	41		166	206
0400	24" x 19" x 8-1/2", lighted		5	1.600		179	57		236	293
0600	Triple door, 30" x 32", unlighted, plywood body		7	1.143		320	41		361	420
0700	Steel body		7	1.143		350	41		391	455

10 28 Toilet, Bath, and Laundry Accessories

10 28 16 – Bath Accessories

10 28 16.20 Medicine Cabinets		Crew	Daily Output	Labor-Hours	Unit	Material	2014 Bare Costs Labor	Equipment	Total	Total Incl O&P
0900	Oak door, wood body, beveled mirror, single door	1 Carp	7	1.143	Ea.	195	41		236	283
1000	Double door		6	1.333		390	47.50		437.50	510
1200	Hotel cabinets, stainless, with lower shelf, unlighted		10	.800		200	28.50		228.50	267
1300	Lighted		5	1.600		305	57		362	430

10 28 23 – Laundry Accessories

10 28 23.13 Built-In Ironing Boards

		Crew	Daily Output	Labor-Hours	Unit	Material	Labor	Equipment	Total	Total Incl O&P
0010	**BUILT-IN IRONING BOARDS**									
0020	Including cabinet, board & light, minimum	1 Carp	2	4	Ea.	365	143		508	640
0100	Maximum, see also Section 11 23 23.13	"	1.50	5.333	"	595	191		786	975

10 31 Manufactured Fireplaces

10 31 13 – Manufactured Fireplace Chimneys

10 31 13.10 Fireplace Chimneys

		Crew	Daily Output	Labor-Hours	Unit	Material	Labor	Equipment	Total	Total Incl O&P
0010	**FIREPLACE CHIMNEYS**									
0500	Chimney dbl. wall, all stainless, over 8'-6", 7" diam., add to fireplace	1 Carp	33	.242	V.L.F.	83.50	8.65		92.15	106
0600	10" diameter, add to fireplace		32	.250		112	8.95		120.95	139
0700	12" diameter, add to fireplace		31	.258		159	9.25		168.25	191
0800	14" diameter, add to fireplace		30	.267		243	9.55		252.55	283
1000	Simulated brick chimney top, 4' high, 16" x 16"		10	.800	Ea.	425	28.50		453.50	520
1100	24" x 24"		7	1.143	"	540	41		581	665

10 31 13.20 Chimney Accessories

		Crew	Daily Output	Labor-Hours	Unit	Material	Labor	Equipment	Total	Total Incl O&P
0010	**CHIMNEY ACCESSORIES**									
0020	Chimney screens, galv., 13" x 13" flue	1 Bric	8	1	Ea.	58.50	35.50		94	124
0050	24" x 24" flue		5	1.600		124	57		181	232
0200	Stainless steel, 13" x 13" flue		8	1		97.50	35.50		133	167
0250	20" x 20" flue		5	1.600		152	57		209	262
2400	Squirrel and bird screens, galvanized, 8" x 8" flue		16	.500		53	17.80		70.80	88
2450	13" x 13" flue		12	.667		55	23.50		78.50	100

10 31 16 – Manufactured Fireplace Forms

10 31 16.10 Fireplace Forms

		Crew	Daily Output	Labor-Hours	Unit	Material	Labor	Equipment	Total	Total Incl O&P
0010	**FIREPLACE FORMS**									
1800	Fireplace forms, no accessories, 32" opening	1 Bric	3	2.667	Ea.	670	95		765	900
1900	36" opening		2.50	3.200		855	114		969	1,125
2000	40" opening		2	4		1,125	142		1,267	1,475
2100	78" opening		1.50	5.333		1,650	190		1,840	2,150

10 31 23 – Prefabricated Fireplaces

10 31 23.10 Fireplace, Prefabricated

		Crew	Daily Output	Labor-Hours	Unit	Material	Labor	Equipment	Total	Total Incl O&P
0010	**FIREPLACE, PREFABRICATED**, free standing or wall hung									
0100	With hood & screen, minimum	1 Carp	1.30	6.154	Ea.	1,200	220		1,420	1,700
0150	Average		1	8		1,450	286		1,736	2,075
0200	Maximum		.90	8.889		2,725	320		3,045	3,525
1500	Simulated logs, gas fired, 40,000 BTU, 2' long, minimum		7	1.143	Set	485	41		526	605
1600	Maximum		6	1.333		1,125	47.50		1,172.50	1,325
1700	Electric, 1,500 BTU, 1'-6" long, minimum		7	1.143		200	41		241	289
1800	11,500 BTU, maximum		6	1.333		300	47.50		347.50	415
2000	Fireplace, built-in, 36" hearth, radiant		1.30	6.154	Ea.	660	220		880	1,100
2100	Recirculating, small fan		1	8		945	286		1,231	1,525
2150	Large fan		.90	8.889		1,900	320		2,220	2,625
2200	42" hearth, radiant		1.20	6.667		890	238		1,128	1,375

10 31 Manufactured Fireplaces

10 31 23 – Prefabricated Fireplaces

10 31 23.10 Fireplace, Prefabricated	Crew	Daily Output	Labor-Hours	Unit	Material	2014 Bare Costs Labor	Equipment	Total	Total Incl O&P
2300	Recirculating, small fan	1 Carp	.90	8.889	Ea.	1,175	320		1,495	1,825
2350	Large fan		.80	10		1,300	360		1,660	2,025
2400	48" hearth, radiant		1.10	7.273		2,075	260		2,335	2,700
2500	Recirculating, small fan		.80	10		2,350	360		2,710	3,200
2550	Large fan		.70	11.429		2,375	410		2,785	3,275
3000	See through, including doors		.80	10		2,525	360		2,885	3,400
3200	Corner (2 wall)		1	8		3,250	286		3,536	4,050

10 32 Fireplace Specialties

10 32 13 – Fireplace Dampers

10 32 13.10 Dampers

10 32 13.10 Dampers	Crew	Daily Output	Labor-Hours	Unit	Material	2014 Bare Costs Labor	Equipment	Total	Total Incl O&P
0010	**DAMPERS**									
0800	Damper, rotary control, steel, 30" opening	1 Bric	6	1.333	Ea.	119	47.50		166.50	210
0850	Cast iron, 30" opening		6	1.333		125	47.50		172.50	216
0880	36" opening		6	1.333		127	47.50		174.50	219
0900	48" opening		6	1.333		167	47.50		214.50	263
0920	60" opening		6	1.333		355	47.50		402.50	470
0950	72" opening		5	1.600		425	57		482	560
1000	84" opening, special order		5	1.600		910	57		967	1,100
1050	96" opening, special order		4	2		925	71		996	1,150
1200	Steel plate, poker control, 60" opening		8	1		320	35.50		355.50	415
1250	84" opening, special order		5	1.600		585	57		642	740
1400	"Universal" type, chain operated, 32" x 20" opening		8	1		250	35.50		285.50	335
1450	48" x 24" opening		5	1.600		375	57		432	505

10 32 23 – Fireplace Doors

10 32 23.10 Doors

10 32 23.10 Doors	Crew	Daily Output	Labor-Hours	Unit	Material	2014 Bare Costs Labor	Equipment	Total	Total Incl O&P
0010	**DOORS**									
0400	Cleanout doors and frames, cast iron, 8" x 8"	1 Bric	12	.667	Ea.	41	23.50		64.50	84.50
0450	12" x 12"		10	.800		108	28.50		136.50	167
0500	18" x 24"		8	1		150	35.50		185.50	225
0550	Cast iron frame, steel door, 24" x 30"		5	1.600		315	57		372	440
1600	Dutch Oven door and frame, cast iron, 12" x 15" opening		13	.615		131	22		153	182
1650	Copper plated, 12" x 15" opening		13	.615		257	22		279	320

10 35 Stoves

10 35 13 – Heating Stoves

10 35 13.10 Woodburning Stoves

10 35 13.10 Woodburning Stoves	Crew	Daily Output	Labor-Hours	Unit	Material	2014 Bare Costs Labor	Equipment	Total	Total Incl O&P
0010	**WOODBURNING STOVES**									
0015	Cast iron, minimum	2 Carp	1.30	12.308	Ea.	980	440		1,420	1,825
0020	Average		1	16		1,825	570		2,395	2,975
0030	Maximum		.80	20		2,525	715		3,240	3,975
0050	For gas log lighter, add					45			45	49.50

10 43 Emergency Aid Specialties

10 43 13 – Defibrillator Cabinets

10 43 13.05 Defibrillator Cabinets	Crew	Daily Output	Labor-Hours	Unit	Material	2014 Bare Costs Labor	Equipment	Total	Total Incl O&P
0010 **DEFIBRILLATOR CABINETS**, not equipped, stainless steel									
0050 Defibrillator cabinet, stainless steel with strobe & alarm 12" x 27"	1 Carp	10	.800	Ea.	430	28.50		458.50	520
0100 Automatic External Defibrillator	"	30	.267	"	1,350	9.55		1,359.55	1,500

10 44 Fire Protection Specialties

10 44 13 – Fire Protection Cabinets

10 44 13.53 Fire Equipment Cabinets

	Crew	Daily Output	Labor-Hours	Unit	Material	Labor	Equipment	Total	Total Incl O&P
0010 **FIRE EQUIPMENT CABINETS**, not equipped, 20 ga. steel box									
0040 recessed, D.S. glass in door, box size given									
1000 Portable extinguisher, single, 8" x 12" x 27", alum. door & frame	Q-12	8	2	Ea.	151	74		225	289
1100 Steel door and frame		8	2		105	74		179	237
2700 Fire blanket & extinguisher cab, inc blanket, rec stl., 14" x 40" x 8"		7	2.286		179	84.50		263.50	335
2800 Fire blanket cab, inc blanket, surf mtd, stl, 15"x10"x5", w/pwdr coat fin		8	2		90	74		164	221
3000 Hose rack assy., 1-1/2" valve & 100' hose, 24" x 40" x 5-1/2"									
3100 Aluminum door and frame	Q-12	6	2.667	Ea.	350	98.50		448.50	545
3200 Steel door and frame		6	2.667		234	98.50		332.50	420
3300 Stainless steel door and frame		6	2.667		475	98.50		573.50	680
4000 Hose rack assy., 2-1/2" x 1-1/2" valve, 100' hose, 24" x 40" x 8"									
4100 Aluminum door and frame	Q-12	6	2.667	Ea.	355	98.50		453.50	550
4200 Steel door and frame		6	2.667		241	98.50		339.50	425
4300 Stainless steel door and frame		6	2.667		475	98.50		573.50	680
5000 Hose rack assy., 2-1/2" x 1-1/2" valve, 100' hose									
5010 and extinguisher, 30" x 40" x 8"									
5100 Aluminum door and frame	Q-12	5	3.200	Ea.	455	118		573	695
5200 Steel door and frame		5	3.200		300	118		418	525
5300 Stainless steel door and frame		5	3.200		550	118		668	800
8000 Valve cabinet for 2-1/2" FD angle valve, 18" x 18" x 8"									
8100 Aluminum door and frame	Q-12	12	1.333	Ea.	156	49		205	253
8200 Steel door and frame		12	1.333		129	49		178	223
8300 Stainless steel door and frame		12	1.333		210	49		259	310

10 44 16 – Fire Extinguishers

10 44 16.13 Portable Fire Extinguishers

	Crew	Daily Output	Labor-Hours	Unit	Material	Labor	Equipment	Total	Total Incl O&P
0010 **PORTABLE FIRE EXTINGUISHERS**									
0140 CO_2, with hose and "H" horn, 10 lb.				Ea.	268			268	295
0160 15 lb.					345			345	380
0180 20 lb.					380			380	420
1000 Dry chemical, pressurized									
1040 Standard type, portable, painted, 2-1/2 lb.				Ea.	36.50			36.50	40
1060 5 lb.					50			50	55
1080 10 lb.					79.50			79.50	87.50
1100 20 lb.					134			134	148
1120 30 lb.					395			395	435
1300 Standard type, wheeled, 150 lb.					2,350			2,350	2,600
2000 ABC all purpose type, portable, 2-1/2 lb.					21			21	23.50
2060 5 lb.					26.50			26.50	29
2080 9-1/2 lb.					44			44	48
2100 20 lb.					79.50			79.50	87.50
3500 Halotron 1, 2-1/2 lb.					126			126	139
3600 5 lb.					198			198	218
3700 11 lb.					390			390	430

10 44 Fire Protection Specialties

10 44 16 – Fire Extinguishers

10 44 16.13 Portable Fire Extinguishers

		Crew	Daily Output	Labor-Hours	Unit	Material	2014 Bare Costs Labor	Equipment	Total	Total Incl O&P
5000	Pressurized water, 2-1/2 gallon, stainless steel				Ea.	102			102	112
5060	With anti-freeze					106			106	116
9400	Installation of extinguishers, 12 or more, on nailable surface	1 Carp	30	.267			9.55		9.55	16.05
9420	On masonry or concrete	"	15	.533	↓		19.05		19.05	32

10 44 16.16 Wheeled Fire Extinguisher Units

		Crew	Daily Output	Labor-Hours	Unit	Material	2014 Bare Costs Labor	Equipment	Total	Total Incl O&P
0010	**WHEELED FIRE EXTINGUISHER UNITS**									
0350	CO$_2$, portable, with swivel horn									
0360	Wheeled type, cart mounted, 50 lb.				Ea.	1,100			1,100	1,200
0400	100 lb.				"	4,125			4,125	4,550
2200	ABC all purpose type									
2300	Wheeled, 45 lb.				Ea.	735			735	810
2360	150 lb.				"	1,850			1,850	2,025

10 51 Lockers

10 51 13 – Metal Lockers

10 51 13.10 Lockers

		Crew	Daily Output	Labor-Hours	Unit	Material	2014 Bare Costs Labor	Equipment	Total	Total Incl O&P
0011	**LOCKERS** steel, baked enamel, pre-assembled									
0110	Single tier box locker, 12" x 15" x 72"	1 Shee	20	.400	Ea.	239	16.20		255.20	290
0120	18" x 15" x 72"		20	.400		263	16.20		279.20	315
0130	12" x 18" x 72"		20	.400		267	16.20		283.20	320
0140	18" x 18" x 72"		20	.400		278	16.20		294.20	330
0410	Double tier, 12" x 15" x 36"		30	.267		236	10.80		246.80	278
0420	18" x 15" x 36"		30	.267		235	10.80		245.80	277
0430	12" x 18" x 36"		30	.267		266	10.80		276.80	310
0440	18" x 18" x 36"		30	.267		257	10.80		267.80	300
0500	Two person, 18" x 15" x 72"		20	.400		285	16.20		301.20	340
0510	18" x 18" x 72"		20	.400		293	16.20		309.20	350
0520	Duplex, 15" x 15" x 72"		20	.400		287	16.20		303.20	340
0530	15" x 21" x 72"		20	.400	↓	335	16.20		351.20	390
0600	5 tier box lockers, minimum		30	.267	Opng.	45	10.80		55.80	67
0700	Maximum		24	.333		52	13.50		65.50	79.50
0900	6 tier box lockers, minimum		36	.222		39.50	9		48.50	58.50
1000	Maximum		30	.267	↓	47	10.80		57.80	69.50
1100	Wire meshed wardrobe, floor. mtd., open front varsity type	↓	7.50	1.067	Ea.	261	43		304	360
2400	16-person locker unit with clothing rack									
2500	72 wide x 15" deep x 72" high	1 Shee	15	.533	Ea.	455	21.50		476.50	535
2550	18" deep	"	15	.533	"	625	21.50		646.50	725
3000	Wall mounted lockers, 4 person, with coat bar									
3100	48" wide x 18" deep x 12" high	1 Shee	20	.400	Ea.	315	16.20		331.20	370
3250	Rack w/24 wire mesh baskets		1.50	5.333	Set	365	216		581	760
3260	30 baskets		1.25	6.400		360	259		619	825
3270	36 baskets		.95	8.421		475	340		815	1,100
3280	42 baskets	↓	.80	10	↓	540	405		945	1,275
3300	For built-in lock with 2 keys, add				Ea.	13.30			13.30	14.60
3600	For hanger rods, add					1.86			1.86	2.05
3650	For number plate kit, 100 plates #1 - #100, add	1 Shee	4	2		70	81		151	212
3700	For locker base, closed front panel		90	.089		7.15	3.60		10.75	13.85
3710	End panel, bolted		36	.222		8.90	9		17.90	25
3800	For sloping top, 12" wide		24	.333		30.50	13.50		44	56.50
3810	15" wide		24	.333		33.50	13.50		47	59.50
3820	18" wide	↓	24	.333	↓	35.50	13.50		49	61.50

10 51 Lockers

10 51 13 – Metal Lockers

10 51 13.10 Lockers		Crew	Daily Output	Labor-Hours	Unit	Material	2014 Bare Costs Labor	Equipment	Total	Total Incl O&P
3850	Sloping top end panel, 12" deep	1 Shee	72	.111	Ea.	11.10	4.49		15.59	19.70
3860	15" deep		72	.111		12.90	4.49		17.39	21.50
3870	18" deep		72	.111		13.65	4.49		18.14	22.50
3900	For finish end panels, steel, 60" high, 15" deep		12	.667		50	27		77	100
3910	72" high, 12" deep		12	.667		50	27		77	100
3920	18" deep		12	.667		56	27		83	107
5000	For 'ready to assemble' lockers,									
5010	Add to labor						75%			
5020	Deduct from material					20%				

10 51 26 – Plastic Lockers

10 51 26.13 Recycled Plastic Lockers

0011	**RECYCLED PLASTIC LOCKERS**, 30% recycled									
0110	Single tier box locker, 12" x 12" x 72"	G 1 Shee	8	1	Ea.	435	40.50		475.50	·550
0120	12" x 15" x 72"	G	8	1		435	40.50		475.50	550
0130	12" x 18" x 72"	G	8	1		450	40.50		490.50	565
0410	Double tier, 12" x 12" x 72"	G	21	.381		455	15.40		470.40	525
0420	12" x 15" x 72"	G	21	.381		465	15.40		480.40	535
0430	12" x 18" x 72"	G	21	.381		475	15.40		490.40	545

10 51 53 – Locker Room Benches

10 51 53.10 Benches

0010	**BENCHES**									
2100	Locker bench, laminated maple, top only	1 Shee	100	.080	L.F.	18	3.24		21.24	25
2200	Pedestals, steel pipe		25	.320	Ea.	43.50	12.95		56.45	69
2250	Plastic, 9.5" top with PVC pedestals		80	.100	L.F.	58	4.05		62.05	71

10 55 Postal Specialties

10 55 23 – Mail Boxes

10 55 23.10 Commercial Mail Boxes

0010	**COMMERCIAL MAIL BOXES**									
0020	Horiz., key lock, 5"H x 6"W x 15"D, alum., rear load	1 Carp	34	.235	Ea.	35	8.40		43.40	52.50
0100	Front loading		34	.235		35	8.40		43.40	52.50
0200	Double, 5"H x 12"W x 15"D, rear loading		26	.308		66.50	11		77.50	92
0300	Front loading		26	.308		70	11		81	95.50
0500	Quadruple, 10"H x 12"W x 15"D, rear loading		20	.400		98.50	14.30		112.80	132
0600	Front loading		20	.400		96.50	14.30		110.80	130
0800	Vertical, front load, 15"H x 5"W x 6"D, alum., per compartment		34	.235		30	8.40		38.40	47
0900	Bronze, duranodic finish		34	.235		40	8.40		48.40	58
1000	Steel, enameled		34	.235		30	8.40		38.40	47
1700	Alphabetical directories, 120 names		10	.800		132	28.50		160.50	194
1800	Letter collection box		6	1.333		650	47.50		697.50	795
1830	Lobby collection boxes, aluminum	2 Shee	5	3.200		1,700	129		1,829	2,100
1840	Bronze or stainless	"	4.50	3.556		1,700	144		1,844	2,125
1900	Letter slot, residential	1 Carp	20	.400		80	14.30		94.30	112
2000	Post office type		8	1		105	36		141	176
2250	Key keeper, single key, aluminum		26	.308		37.50	11		48.50	59.50
2300	Steel, enameled		26	.308		116	11		127	147

10 56 Storage Assemblies

10 56 13 – Metal Storage Shelving

10 56 13.10 Shelving

		Crew	Daily Output	Labor-Hours	Unit	Material	2014 Bare Costs Labor	2014 Bare Costs Equipment	Total	Total Incl O&P
0010	**SHELVING**									
0020	Metal, industrial, cross-braced, 3' wide, 12" deep	1 Sswk	175	.046	SF Shlf	7.45	1.75		9.20	11.55
0100	24" deep		330	.024		4.95	.93		5.88	7.20
0300	4' wide, 12" deep		185	.043		6.35	1.66		8.01	10.15
0400	24" deep		380	.021		4.55	.81		5.36	6.55
1200	Enclosed sides, cross-braced back, 3' wide, 12" deep		175	.046		11.70	1.75		13.45	16.20
1300	24" deep		290	.028		8.10	1.06		9.16	10.90
1500	Fully enclosed, sides and back, 3' wide, 12" deep		150	.053		13.90	2.05		15.95	19.20
1600	24" deep		255	.031		9.35	1.20		10.55	12.55
1800	4' wide, 12" deep		150	.053		9.50	2.05		11.55	14.35
1900	24" deep		290	.028		7.45	1.06		8.51	10.20
2200	Wide span, 1600 lb. capacity per shelf, 6' wide, 24" deep		380	.021		6.30	.81		7.11	8.50
2400	36" deep		440	.018		6.75	.70		7.45	8.80
2600	8' wide, 24" deep		440	.018		6.35	.70		7.05	8.35
2800	36" deep		520	.015		6.10	.59		6.69	7.80
4000	Pallet racks, steel frame 5,000 lb. capacity, 8' long, 36" deep	2 Sswk	450	.036		9.10	1.36		10.46	12.60
4200	42" deep		500	.032		8.25	1.23		9.48	11.45
4400	48" deep		520	.031		7.40	1.18		8.58	10.35

10 56 13.20 Parts Bins

		Crew	Daily Output	Labor-Hours	Unit	Material	2014 Bare Costs Labor	2014 Bare Costs Equipment	Total	Total Incl O&P
0010	**PARTS BINS** metal, gray baked enamel finish									
0100	6'-3" high, 3' wide									
0300	12 bins, 18" wide x 12" high, 12" deep	2 Clab	10	1.600	Ea.	315	45		360	420
0400	24" deep		10	1.600		395	45		440	505
0600	72 bins, 6" wide x 6" high, 12" deep		8	2		525	56.50		581.50	670
0700	18" deep		8	2		825	56.50		881.50	1,000
1000	7'-3" high, 3' wide									
1200	14 bins, 18" wide x 12" high, 12" deep	2 Clab	10	1.600	Ea.	345	45		390	455
1300	24" deep		10	1.600		435	45		480	550
1500	84 bins, 6" wide x 6" high, 12" deep		8	2		890	56.50		946.50	1,075
1600	24" deep		8	2		1,075	56.50		1,131.50	1,300

10 57 Wardrobe and Closet Specialties

10 57 13 – Hat and Coat Racks

10 57 13.10 Coat Racks and Wardrobes

		Crew	Daily Output	Labor-Hours	Unit	Material	2014 Bare Costs Labor	2014 Bare Costs Equipment	Total	Total Incl O&P
0010	**COAT RACKS AND WARDROBES**									
0020	Hat & coat rack, floor model, 6 hangers									
0050	Standing, beech wood, 21" x 21" x 72", chrome				Ea.	237			237	260
0100	18 ga. tubular steel, 21" x 21" x 69", wood walnut				"	299			299	330
0500	16 ga. steel frame, 22 ga. steel shelves									
0650	Single pedestal, 30" x 18" x 63"				Ea.	262			262	289
0800	Single face rack, 29" x 18-1/2" x 62"					291			291	320
0900	51" x 18-1/2" x 70"					410			410	450
0910	Double face rack, 39" x 26" x 70"					370			370	405
0920	63" x 26" x 70"					465			465	515
0940	For 2" ball casters, add				Set	88			88	97
1400	Utility hook strips, 3/8" x 2-1/2" x 18", 6 hooks	1 Carp	48	.167	Ea.	61	5.95		66.95	77
1500	34" long, 12 hooks	"	48	.167	"	62	5.95		67.95	78
1650	Wall mounted racks, 16 ga. steel frame, 22 ga. steel shelves									
1850	12" x 15" x 26", 6 hangers	1 Carp	32	.250	Ea.	155	8.95		163.95	185
2000	12" x 15" x 50", 12 hangers	"	32	.250	"	181	8.95		189.95	214
2150	Wardrobe cabinet, steel, baked enamel finish									

10 57 Wardrobe and Closet Specialties

10 57 13 – Hat and Coat Racks

10 57 13.10 Coat Racks and Wardrobes

		Crew	Daily Output	Labor-Hours	Unit	Material	2014 Bare Costs Labor	Equipment	Total	Total Incl O&P
2300	36" x 21" x 78", incl. top shelf & hanger rod				Ea.	315			315	350
2400	Wardrobe, 24" x 24" x 76", KD, w/door, hospital, baked enamel steel	1 Carp	2	4		570	143		713	865
2500	Hardwood	"	2	4	↓	1,275	143		1,418	1,650

10 57 23 – Closet and Utility Shelving

10 57 23.19 Wood Closet and Utility Shelving

		Crew	Daily Output	Labor-Hours	Unit	Material	2014 Bare Costs Labor	Equipment	Total	Total Incl O&P
0010	**WOOD CLOSET AND UTILITY SHELVING**									
0020	Pine, clear grade, no edge band, 1" x 8"	1 Carp	115	.070	L.F.	3.04	2.49		5.53	7.50
0100	1" x 10"		110	.073		3.78	2.60		6.38	8.55
0200	1" x 12"		105	.076		4.56	2.72		7.28	9.60
0600	Plywood, 3/4" thick with lumber edge, 12" wide		75	.107		1.78	3.81		5.59	8.35
0700	24" wide		70	.114	↓	3.18	4.09		7.27	10.35
0900	Bookcase, clear grade pine, shelves 12" O.C., 8" deep, per S.F. shelf		70	.114	S.F.	9.90	4.09		13.99	17.70
1000	12" deep shelves		65	.123	"	14.80	4.40		19.20	23.50
1200	Adjustable closet rod and shelf, 12" wide, 3' long		20	.400	Ea.	10.95	14.30		25.25	36
1300	8' long		15	.533	"	20	19.05		39.05	54
1500	Prefinished shelves with supports, stock, 8" wide		75	.107	L.F.	3.38	3.81		7.19	10.10
1600	10" wide	↓	70	.114	"	4.75	4.09		8.84	12.10

10 73 Protective Covers

10 73 13 – Awnings

10 73 13.10 Awnings, Fabric

		Crew	Daily Output	Labor-Hours	Unit	Material	2014 Bare Costs Labor	Equipment	Total	Total Incl O&P
0010	**AWNINGS, FABRIC**									
0020	Including acrylic canvas and frame, standard design									
0100	Door and window, slope, 3' high, 4' wide	1 Carp	4.50	1.778	Ea.	720	63.50		783.50	895
0110	6' wide		3.50	2.286		925	81.50		1,006.50	1,150
0120	8' wide		3	2.667		1,125	95.50		1,220.50	1,400
0200	Quarter round convex, 4' wide		3	2.667		1,125	95.50		1,220.50	1,375
0210	6' wide		2.25	3.556		1,450	127		1,577	1,825
0220	8' wide		1.80	4.444		1,775	159		1,934	2,225
0300	Dome, 4' wide		7.50	1.067		430	38		468	540
0310	6' wide		3.50	2.286		970	81.50		1,051.50	1,200
0320	8' wide		2	4		1,725	143		1,868	2,150
0350	Elongated dome, 4' wide		1.33	6.015		1,625	215		1,840	2,125
0360	6' wide		1.11	7.207		1,925	258		2,183	2,550
0370	8' wide	↓	1	8		2,275	286		2,561	2,975
1000	Entry or walkway, peak, 12' long, 4' wide	2 Carp	.90	17.778		5,125	635		5,760	6,700
1010	6' wide		.60	26.667		7,875	955		8,830	10,300
1020	8' wide		.40	40		10,900	1,425		12,325	14,400
1100	Radius with dome end, 4' wide		1.10	14.545		3,875	520		4,395	5,150
1110	6' wide		.70	22.857		6,225	815		7,040	8,225
1120	8' wide	↓	.50	32	↓	8,875	1,150		10,025	11,700
2000	Retractable lateral arm awning, manual									
2010	To 12' wide, 8'-6" projection	2 Carp	1.70	9.412	Ea.	1,150	335		1,485	1,850
2020	To 14' wide, 8'-6" projection		1.10	14.545		1,350	520		1,870	2,350
2030	To 19' wide, 8'-6" projection		.85	18.824		1,825	675		2,500	3,150
2040	To 24' wide, 8'-6" projection	↓	.67	23.881		2,300	855		3,155	3,975
2050	Motor for above, add	1 Carp	2.67	3	↓	990	107		1,097	1,275
3000	Patio/deck canopy with frame									
3010	12' wide, 12' projection	2 Carp	2	8	Ea.	1,625	286		1,911	2,275
3020	16' wide, 14' projection	"	1.20	13.333	↓	2,550	475		3,025	3,600

10 73 Protective Covers

10 73 13 – Awnings

10 73 13.10 Awnings, Fabric

		Crew	Daily Output	Labor-Hours	Unit	Material	2014 Bare Costs Labor	Equipment	Total	Total Incl O&P
9000	For fire retardant canvas, add				Ea.	7%				
9010	For lettering or graphics, add					35%				
9020	For painted or coated acrylic canvas, deduct					8%				
9030	For translucent or opaque vinyl canvas, add					10%				
9040	For 6 or more units, deduct					20%	15%			

10 73 16 – Canopies

10 73 16.20 Metal Canopies

		Crew	Daily Output	Labor-Hours	Unit	Material	Labor	Equipment	Total	Total Incl O&P
0010	**METAL CANOPIES**									
0020	Wall hung, .032", aluminum, prefinished, 8' x 10'	K-2	1.30	18.462	Ea.	1,950	660	256	2,866	3,650
0300	8' x 20'		1.10	21.818		3,425	780	305	4,510	5,550
0500	10' x 10'		1.30	18.462		2,575	660	256	3,491	4,325
0700	10' x 20'		1.10	21.818		4,300	780	305	5,385	6,500
1000	12' x 20'		1	24		5,150	860	335	6,345	7,625
1360	12' x 30'		.80	30		7,725	1,075	415	9,215	10,900
1700	12' x 40'		.60	40		10,300	1,425	555	12,280	14,600
1900	For free standing units, add					20%	10%			
2300	Aluminum entrance canopies, flat soffit, .032"									
2500	3'-6" x 4'-0", clear anodized	2 Carp	4	4	Ea.	915	143		1,058	1,250
2700	Bronze anodized		4	4		1,625	143		1,768	2,025
3000	Polyurethane painted		4	4		1,300	143		1,443	1,700
3300	4'-6" x 10'-0", clear anodized		2	8		2,525	286		2,811	3,250
3500	Bronze anodized		2	8		3,225	286		3,511	4,025
3700	Polyurethane painted		2	8		2,700	286		2,986	3,450
4000	Wall downspout, 10 L.F., clear anodized	1 Carp	7	1.143		157	41		198	242
4300	Bronze anodized		7	1.143		274	41		315	370
4500	Polyurethane painted		7	1.143		236	41		277	330
7000	Carport, baked vinyl finish, .032", 20' x 10', no foundations, min.	K-2	4	6	Car	4,000	215	83.50	4,298.50	4,875
7250	Maximum		2	12	"	7,150	430	167	7,747	8,825
7500	Walkway cover, to 12' wide, stl., vinyl finish, .032",no fndtns., min.		250	.096	S.F.	26.50	3.44	1.33	31.27	37
7750	Maximum		200	.120	"	60	4.30	1.67	65.97	75.50

10 74 Manufactured Exterior Specialties

10 74 23 – Cupolas

10 74 23.10 Wood Cupolas

		Crew	Daily Output	Labor-Hours	Unit	Material	Labor	Equipment	Total	Total Incl O&P
0010	**WOOD CUPOLAS**									
0020	Stock units, pine, painted, 18" sq., 28" high, alum. roof	1 Carp	4.10	1.951	Ea.	184	70		254	320
0100	Copper roof		3.80	2.105		255	75.50		330.50	410
0300	23" square, 33" high, aluminum roof		3.70	2.162		360	77.50		437.50	525
0400	Copper roof		3.30	2.424		470	86.50		556.50	660
0600	30" square, 37" high, aluminum roof		3.70	2.162		560	77.50		637.50	745
0700	Copper roof		3.30	2.424		670	86.50		756.50	880
0900	Hexagonal, 31" wide, 46" high, copper roof		4	2		860	71.50		931.50	1,075
1000	36" wide, 50" high, copper roof		3.50	2.286		1,400	81.50		1,481.50	1,675
1200	For deluxe stock units, add to above					25%				
1400	For custom built units, add to above					50%	50%			

10 74 29 – Steeples

10 74 29.10 Prefabricated Steeples

		Crew	Daily Output	Labor-Hours	Unit	Material	Labor	Equipment	Total	Total Incl O&P
0010	**PREFABRICATED STEEPLES**									
4000	Steeples, translucent fiberglass, 30" square, 15' high	F-3	2	20	Ea.	8,275	655	330	9,260	10,600
4150	25' high		1.80	22.222		9,650	730	370	10,750	12,200

10 74 Manufactured Exterior Specialties

10 74 29 – Steeples

10 74 29.10 Prefabricated Steeples		Crew	Daily Output	Labor-Hours	Unit	Material	2014 Bare Costs Labor	Equipment	Total	Total Incl O&P
4350	Opaque fiberglass, 24" square, 14' high	F-3	2	20	Ea.	6,875	655	330	7,860	9,050
4500	28' high	↓	1.80	22.222		6,300	730	370	7,400	8,550
4600	Aluminum, baked finish, 16" square, 14' high					5,625			5,625	6,200
4620	20' high, 3'-6" base					9,425			9,425	10,400
4640	35' high, 8' base					36,300			36,300	39,900
4660	60' high, 14' base					76,500			76,500	84,000
4680	152' high, custom					624,500			624,500	687,000
4700	Porcelain enamel steeples, custom, 40' high	F-3	.50	80		14,100	2,625	1,325	18,050	21,500
4800	60' high	"	.30	133	↓	24,500	4,375	2,200	31,075	36,800

10 74 33 – Weathervanes

10 74 33.10 Residential Weathervanes		Crew	Daily Output	Labor-Hours	Unit	Material	2014 Bare Costs Labor	Equipment	Total	Total Incl O&P
0010	**RESIDENTIAL WEATHERVANES**									
0020	Residential types, minimum	1 Carp	8	1	Ea.	151	36		187	226
0100	Maximum	"	2	4	"	1,700	143		1,843	2,125

10 74 46 – Window Wells

10 74 46.10 Area Window Wells		Crew	Daily Output	Labor-Hours	Unit	Material	2014 Bare Costs Labor	Equipment	Total	Total Incl O&P
0010	**AREA WINDOW WELLS**, Galvanized steel									
0020	20 ga., 3'-2" wide, 1' deep	1 Sswk	29	.276	Ea.	16.95	10.60		27.55	38.50
0100	2' deep		23	.348		27.50	13.35		40.85	55.50
0300	16 ga., 3'-2" wide, 1' deep		29	.276		23	10.60		33.60	45.50
0400	3' deep		23	.348		47	13.35		60.35	77
0600	Welded grating for above, 15 lb., painted		45	.178		87.50	6.80		94.30	109
0700	Galvanized		45	.178		118	6.80		124.80	143
0900	Translucent plastic cap for above	↓	60	.133	↓	17.65	5.10		22.75	29

10 75 Flagpoles

10 75 16 – Ground-Set Flagpoles

10 75 16.10 Flagpoles		Crew	Daily Output	Labor-Hours	Unit	Material	2014 Bare Costs Labor	Equipment	Total	Total Incl O&P
0010	**FLAGPOLES**, ground set									
0050	Not including base or foundation									
0100	Aluminum, tapered, ground set 20' high	K-1	2	8	Ea.	980	258	166	1,404	1,700
0200	25' high		1.70	9.412		1,150	305	196	1,651	1,975
0300	30' high		1.50	10.667		1,275	345	222	1,842	2,225
0400	35' high		1.40	11.429		1,800	370	238	2,408	2,850
0500	40' high		1.20	13.333		2,525	430	277	3,232	3,800
0600	50' high		1	16		3,100	515	335	3,950	4,625
0700	60' high		.90	17.778		5,075	575	370	6,020	6,975
0800	70' high		.80	20		8,250	645	415	9,310	10,600
1100	Counterbalanced, internal halyard, 20' high		1.80	8.889		2,600	287	185	3,072	3,550
1200	30' high		1.50	10.667		2,900	345	222	3,467	4,025
1300	40' high		1.30	12.308		6,400	400	256	7,056	8,000
1400	50' high		1	16		8,900	515	335	9,750	11,000
2820	Aluminum, electronically operated, 30' high		1.40	11.429		4,375	370	238	4,983	5,700
2840	35' high		1.30	12.308		4,725	400	256	5,381	6,150
2860	39' high		1.10	14.545		5,150	470	305	5,925	6,800
2880	45' high		1	16		6,575	515	335	7,425	8,475
2900	50' high		.90	17.778		7,000	575	370	7,945	9,075
3000	Fiberglass, tapered, ground set, 23' high		2	8		580	258	166	1,004	1,250
3100	29'-7" high		1.50	10.667		1,525	345	222	2,092	2,500
3200	36'-1" high	↓	1.40	11.429	↓	1,975	370	238	2,583	3,050

10 75 Flagpoles

10 75 16 – Ground-Set Flagpoles

10 75 16.10 Flagpoles		Crew	Daily Output	Labor-Hours	Unit	Material	2014 Bare Costs Labor	Equipment	Total	Total Incl O&P
3300	39'-5" high	K-1	1.20	13.333	Ea.	2,200	430	277	2,907	3,450
3400	49'-2" high		1	16		4,100	515	335	4,950	5,750
3500	59' high		.90	17.778		5,225	575	370	6,170	7,125
4300	Steel, direct imbedded installation									
4400	Internal halyard, 20' high	K-1	2.50	6.400	Ea.	1,300	207	133	1,640	1,925
4500	25' high		2.50	6.400		1,950	207	133	2,290	2,650
4600	30' high		2.30	6.957		2,325	225	145	2,695	3,100
4700	40' high		2.10	7.619		3,125	246	159	3,530	4,000
4800	50' high		1.90	8.421		4,125	272	175	4,572	5,175
5000	60' high		1.80	8.889		6,875	287	185	7,347	8,225
5100	70' high		1.60	10		7,475	325	208	8,008	9,000
5200	80' high		1.40	11.429		9,625	370	238	10,233	11,500
5300	90' high		1.20	13.333		15,000	430	277	15,707	17,500
5500	100' high		1	16		15,500	515	335	16,350	18,300
6400	Wood poles, tapered, clear vertical grain fir with tilting									
6410	base, not incl. foundation, 4" butt, 25' high	K-1	1.90	8.421	Ea.	1,400	272	175	1,847	2,175
6800	6" butt, 30' high	"	1.30	12.308	"	2,575	400	256	3,231	3,775
7300	Foundations for flagpoles, including									
7400	excavation and concrete, to 35' high poles	C-1	10	3.200	Ea.	675	101		776	915
7600	40' to 50' high		3.50	9.143		1,250	289		1,539	1,850
7700	Over 60' high		2	16		1,550	505		2,055	2,575

10 75 23 – Wall-Mounted Flagpoles

10 75 23.10 Flagpoles		Crew	Daily Output	Labor-Hours	Unit	Material	2014 Bare Costs Labor	Equipment	Total	Total Incl O&P
0010	**FLAGPOLES**, structure mounted									
0100	Fiberglass, vertical wall set, 19'-8" long	K-1	1.50	10.667	Ea.	1,350	345	222	1,917	2,325
0200	23' long		1.40	11.429		1,450	370	238	2,058	2,450
0300	26'-3" long		1.30	12.308		1,850	400	256	2,506	2,975
0800	19'-8" long outrigger		1.30	12.308		1,225	400	256	1,881	2,300
1300	Aluminum, vertical wall set, tapered, with base, 20' high		1.20	13.333		965	430	277	1,672	2,100
1400	29'-6" high		1	16		2,650	515	335	3,500	4,150
2400	Outrigger poles with base, 12' long		1.30	12.308		1,100	400	256	1,756	2,150
2500	14' long		1	16		1,425	515	335	2,275	2,800

10 81 Pest Control Devices

10 81 13 – Bird Control Devices

10 81 13.10 Bird Control Netting		Crew	Daily Output	Labor-Hours	Unit	Material	2014 Bare Costs Labor	Equipment	Total	Total Incl O&P
0010	**BIRD CONTROL NETTING**									
0020	1/8" square mesh	4 Clab	4000	.008	S.F.	.67	.23		.90	1.12
0100	1/4" square mesh		4000	.008		.78	.23		1.01	1.24
0120	1/2" square mesh		4000	.008		.12	.23		.35	.51
0140	5/8" x 3/4" mesh		4000	.008		.07	.23		.30	.46
0160	1-1/4" x 1-1/2" mesh		4000	.008		.13	.23		.36	.52
0200	4" square mesh		4000	.008		.10	.23		.33	.49
1000	Poly clips				Ea.	.05			.05	.06

10 88 Scales

10 88 05 – Commercial Scales

10 88 05.10 Scales		Crew	Daily Output	Labor-Hours	Unit	Material	2014 Bare Costs			Total	Total Incl O&P
							Labor	Equipment			
0010	**SCALES**										
0700	Truck scales, incl. steel weigh bridge,										
0800	not including foundation, pits										
1550	Digital, electronic, 100 ton capacity, steel deck 12' x 10' platform	3 Carp	.20	120	Ea.	13,500	4,300			17,800	22,100
1600	40' x 10' platform		.14	171		27,000	6,125			33,125	40,000
1640	60' x 10' platform		.13	184		35,700	6,600			42,300	50,500
1680	70' x 10' platform		.12	200		37,900	7,150			45,050	53,500
2000	For standard automatic printing device, add					1,400				1,400	1,525
2100	For remote reading electronic system, add					2,625				2,625	2,900
2300	Concrete foundation pits for above, 8' x 6', 5 C.Y. required	C-1	.50	64		1,025	2,025			3,050	4,525
2400	14' x 6' platform, 10 C.Y. required		.35	91.429		1,500	2,900			4,400	6,525
2600	50' x 10' platform, 30 C.Y. required		.25	128		2,025	4,050			6,075	9,050
2700	70' x 10' platform, 40 C.Y. required		.15	213		4,450	6,750			11,200	16,300
2750	Crane scales, dial, 1 ton capacity					1,125				1,125	1,225
2780	5 ton capacity					1,500				1,500	1,650
2800	Digital, 1 ton capacity					1,900				1,900	2,075
2850	10 ton capacity					5,050				5,050	5,550
2900	Low profile electronic warehouse scale,										
3000	not incl. printer, 4' x 4' platform, 10,000 lb. capacity	2 Carp	.30	53.333	Ea.	1,425	1,900			3,325	4,750
3300	5' x 7' platform, 10,000 lb. capacity		.25	64		4,625	2,300			6,925	8,950
3400	20,000 lb. capacity		.20	80		5,700	2,850			8,550	11,100
3500	For printers, incl. time, date & numbering, add					1,000				1,000	1,100
3800	Portable, beam type, capacity 1000#, platform 18" x 24"					770				770	845
3900	Dial type, capacity 2000#, platform 24" x 24"					1,375				1,375	1,500
4000	Digital type, capacity 1000#, platform 24" x 30"					2,175				2,175	2,400
4100	Portable contractor truck scales, 50 ton cap., 40' x 10' platform					33,000				33,000	36,300
4200	60' x 10' platform					30,400				30,400	33,400

Estimating Tips

General

- The items in this division are usually priced per square foot or each. Many of these items are purchased by the owner for installation by the contractor. Check the specifications for responsibilities and include time for receiving, storage, installation, and mechanical and electrical hookups in the appropriate divisions.

- Many items in Division 11 require some type of support system that is not usually furnished with the item. Examples of these systems include blocking for the attachment of casework and support angles for ceiling-hung projection screens. The required blocking or supports must be added to the estimate in the appropriate division.

- Some items in Division 11 may require assembly or electrical hookups. Verify the amount of assembly required or the need for a hard electrical connection and add the appropriate costs.

Reference Numbers

Reference numbers are shown in shaded boxes at the beginning of some major classifications. These numbers refer to related items in the Reference Section. The reference information may be an estimating procedure, an alternate pricing method, or technical information.

Note: Not all subdivisions listed here necessarily appear in this publication.

Division 11 - Equipment

11 05 05.10 Selective Demolition	Crew	Daily Output	Labor-Hours	Unit	Material	2014 Bare Costs Labor	2014 Bare Costs Equipment	Total	Total Incl O&P
0010 **SELECTIVE DEMOLITION**									
0130 Central vacuum, motor unit, residential or commercial	1 Clab	2	4	Ea.		113		113	190
0210 Vault door and frame	2 Skwk	2	8			290		290	490
0215 Day gate, for vault	"	3	5.333			194		194	325
0380 Bank equipment, teller window, bullet resistant	1 Clab	1.20	6.667	↓		188		188	315
0381 Counter	2 Clab	1.50	10.667	Station		300		300	505
0382 Drive-up window, including drawer and glass		1.50	10.667	"		300		300	505
0383 Thru-wall boxes and chests, selective demolition		2.50	6.400	Ea.		180		180	305
0384 Bullet resistant partitions	↓	20	.800	L.F.		22.50		22.50	38
0385 Pneumatic tube system, 2 lane drive-up	L-3	.45	22.222	Ea.		825		825	1,375
0386 Safety deposit box	1 Clab	50	.160	Opng.		4.51		4.51	7.60
0387 Surveillance system, video, complete	2 Elec	2	8	Ea.		340		340	560
0410 Church equipment, misc moveable fixtures	2 Clab	1	16			450		450	760
0412 Steeple, to 28' high	F-3	3	13.333			435	221	656	980
0414 40' to 60' high	"	.80	50	↓		1,650	830	2,480	3,650
0510 Library equipment, bookshelves, wood, to 90" high	1 Clab	20	.400	L.F.		11.30		11.30	19
0515 Carrels, hardwood, 36" x 24"	"	9	.889	Ea.		25		25	42
0630 Stage equipment, light control panel	1 Elec	1	8	"		340		340	560
0632 Border lights		40	.200	L.F.		8.55		8.55	14
0634 Spotlights	↓	8	1	Ea.		42.50		42.50	70
0636 Telescoping platforms and risers	2 Clab	175	.091	SF Stg.		2.58		2.58	4.34
1020 Barber equipment, hydraulic chair	1 Clab	40	.200	Ea.		5.65		5.65	9.50
1030 Checkout counter, supermarket or warehouse conveyor	2 Clab	18	.889			25		25	42
1040 Food cases, refrigerated or frozen	Q-5	6	2.667			104		104	171
1190 Laundry equipment, commercial	L-6	3	4			171		171	281
1360 Movie equipment, lamphouse, to 4000 watt, incl rectifier	1 Elec	4	2			85.50		85.50	140
1365 Sound system, incl amplifier	"	1.25	6.400			273		273	445
1410 Air compressor, to 5 H.P.	2 Clab	2.50	6.400	↓		180		180	305
1412 Lubrication equipment, automotive, 3 reel type, incl pump, excl piping	L-4	1	16	Set		505		505	855
1414 Booth, spray paint, complete, to 26' long	"	.80	20	"		630		630	1,075
1560 Parking equipment, cashier booth	B-22	2	15	Ea.		460	105	565	890
1600 Loading dock equipment, dock bumpers, rubber	1 Clab	50	.160	"		4.51		4.51	7.60
1610 Door seal for door perimeter	"	50	.160	L.F.		4.51		4.51	7.60
1620 Platform lifter, fixed, 6' x 8', 5000 lb. capacity	E-16	1.50	10.667	Ea.		420	94.50	514.50	905
1630 Dock leveller	"	2	8			315	71	386	680
1640 Lights, single or double arm	1 Elec	8	1			42.50		42.50	70
1650 Shelter, fabric, truck or train	1 Clab	1.50	5.333			150		150	253
1790 Waste handling equipment, commercial compactor	L-4	2	8			253		253	425
1792 Commercial or municipal incinerator, gas	"	2	8			253		253	425
1795 Crematory, excluding building	Q-3	.25	128			4,900		4,900	8,100
1910 Detection equipment, cell bar front	E-4	4	8			310	35.50	345.50	630
1912 Cell door and frame		8	4			155	17.75	172.75	315
1914 Prefab cell, 4' to 5' wide, 7' to 8' high, 7' deep		8	4			155	17.75	172.75	315
1916 Cot, bolted, single		40	.800			31	3.55	34.55	63
1918 Visitor cubicle	↓	4	8			310	35.50	345.50	630
2850 Hydraulic gates, canal, flap, knife, slide or sluice, to 18" diameter	L-5A	8	4			156	76	232	370
2852 19" to 36" diameter		6	5.333			208	101	309	495
2854 37" to 48" diameter		2	16			625	305	930	1,475
2856 49" to 60" diameter		1	32			1,250	605	1,855	2,975
2858 Over 60" diameter	↓	.30	106			4,150	2,025	6,175	9,875
3100 Sewage pumping system, prefabricated, to 1000 GPM	C-17D	.20	420			15,500	4,125	19,625	30,700
3110 Sewage treatment, holding tank for recirc chemical water closet	1 Plum	8	1			42.50		42.50	70.50
3900 Wastewater treatment system, to 1500 gallons	B-21	2	14	↓		425	70	495	785

11 05 Common Work Results for Equipment

11 05 05 – Selective Equipment Demolition

11 05 05.10 Selective Demolition

		Crew	Daily Output	Labor-Hours	Unit	Material	2014 Bare Costs Labor	2014 Bare Costs Equipment	Total	Total Incl O&P
4050	Food storage equipment, walk-in refrigerator/freezer	2 Clab	64	.250	S.F.		7.05		7.05	11.85
4052	Shelving, stainless steel, 4 tier or dunnage rack	1 Clab	12	.667	Ea.		18.80		18.80	31.50
4100	Food preparation equipment, small countertop		18	.444			12.55		12.55	21
4150	Food delivery carts, heated cabinets		18	.444			12.55		12.55	21
4200	Cooking equipment, commercial range	Q-1	12	1.333			51		51	84.50
4250	Hood and ventilation equipment, kitchen exhaust hood, excl fire prot	1 Clab	3	2.667			75		75	127
4255	Fire protection system	Q-1	3	5.333			205		205	335
4300	Food dispensing equipment, countertop items	1 Clab	15	.533			15.05		15.05	25.50
4310	Serving counter	"	65	.123	L.F.		3.47		3.47	5.85
4350	Ice machine, ice cube maker, flakers and storage bins, to 2000 lb./day	Q-1	1.60	10	Ea.		385		385	635
4400	Cleaning and disposal, commercial dishwasher, to 50 racks per hour	L-6	1	12			510		510	840
4405	To 275 racks per hour	L-4	1	16			505		505	855
4410	Dishwasher hood	2 Clab	5	3.200			90		90	152
4420	Garbage disposal, commercial, to 5 H.P.	L-1	8	1.250			53.50		53.50	88
4540	Water heater, residential, to 80 gal/day	"	5	2			85		85	140
4542	Water softener, automatic	2 Plum	10	1.600			68		68	112
4544	Disappearing stairway, to 15' floor height	2 Clab	6	2.667			75		75	127
4710	Darkroom equipment, light	L-7	10	2.600			80		80	135
4712	Heavy	"	1.50	17.333			535		535	900
4720	Doors	2 Clab	3.50	4.571	Opng.		129		129	217
4830	Bowling alley, complete, incl pinsetter, scorer, counters, misc supplies	4 Clab	.40	80	Lane		2,250		2,250	3,800
4840	Health club equipment, circuit training apparatus	2 Clab	2	8	Set		226		226	380
4842	Squat racks	"	10	1.600	Ea.		45		45	76
4860	School equipment, basketball backstop	L-2	2	8			251		251	420
4862	Table and benches, folding, in wall, 14' long	L-4	4	4			126		126	214
4864	Bleachers, telescoping, to 30 tier	F-5	120	.267	Seat		8.35		8.35	14.10
4866	Boxing ring, elevated	L-4	.20	80	Ea.		2,525		2,525	4,275
4867	Boxing ring, floor level	"	2	8			253		253	425
4868	Exercise equipment	1 Clab	6	1.333			37.50		37.50	63.50
4870	Gym divider	L-4	1000	.016	S.F.		.51		.51	.85
4875	Scoreboard	R-3	2	10	Ea.		420	70	490	765
4880	Shooting range, incl bullet traps, targets, excl structure	L-9	1	36	Point		1,200		1,200	2,025
5200	Vocational shop equipment	2 Clab	8	2	Ea.		56.50		56.50	95
6200	Fume hood, incl countertop, excl HVAC	"	6	2.667	L.F.		75		75	127
7100	Medical sterilizing, distiller, water, steam heated, 50 gal. capacity	1 Plum	2.80	2.857	Ea.		122		122	201
7200	Medical equipment, surgery table, minor	1 Clab	1	8			226		226	380
7210	Surgical lights, doctors office, single or double arm	2 Elec	3	5.333			228		228	375
7300	Physical therapy, table	2 Clab	4	4			113		113	190
7310	Whirlpool bath, fixed, incl mixing valves	1 Plum	4	2			85		85	141
7400	Dental equipment, chair, electric or hydraulic	1 Clab	.75	10.667			300		300	505
7410	Central suction system	1 Plum	2	4			170		170	281
7420	Drill console with accessories	1 Clab	3.20	2.500			70.50		70.50	119
7430	X-ray unit	"	4	2			56.50		56.50	95
7440	X-ray developer	1 Plum	10	.800			34		34	56

11 05 10 – Equipment Installation

11 05 10.10 Industrial Equipment Installation

		Crew	Daily Output	Labor-Hours	Unit	Material	2014 Bare Costs Labor	2014 Bare Costs Equipment	Total	Total Incl O&P
0010	**INDUSTRIAL EQUIPMENT INSTALLATION**									
0020	Industrial equipment, minimum	E-2	12	4	Ton		155	127	282	430
0200	Maximum	"	2	24	"		930	765	1,695	2,575

11 11 Vehicle Service Equipment

11 11 13 – Compressed-Air Vehicle Service Equipment

11 11 13.10 Compressed Air Equipment

11 11 13.10 Compressed Air Equipment		Crew	Daily Output	Labor-Hours	Unit	Material	2014 Bare Costs Labor	2014 Bare Costs Equipment	Total	Total Incl O&P
0010	COMPRESSED AIR EQUIPMENT									
0030	Compressors, electric, 1-1/2 H.P., standard controls	L-4	1.50	10.667	Ea.	450	335		785	1,050
0550	Dual controls		1.50	10.667		800	335		1,135	1,450
0600	5 H.P., 115/230 volt, standard controls		1	16		2,550	505		3,055	3,650
0650	Dual controls	↓	1	16	↓	3,100	505		3,605	4,250

11 11 19 – Vehicle Lubrication Equipment

11 11 19.10 Lubrication Equipment

11 11 19.10 Lubrication Equipment		Crew	Daily Output	Labor-Hours	Unit	Material	Labor	Equipment	Total	Total Incl O&P
0010	LUBRICATION EQUIPMENT									
3000	Lube equipment, 3 reel type, with pumps, not including piping	L-4	.50	32	Set	8,700	1,000		9,700	11,300
3100	Hose reel, including hose, oil/lube, 1000 PSI	2 Sswk	2	8	Ea.	730	305		1,035	1,400
3200	Grease, 5000 PSI		2	8		790	305		1,095	1,450
3300	Air, 50 feet, 160 PSI		2	8		865	305		1,170	1,525
3350	25 feet, 160 PSI	↓	2	8	↓	520	305		825	1,150

11 11 33 – Vehicle Spray Painting Equipment

11 11 33.10 Spray Painting Equipment

11 11 33.10 Spray Painting Equipment		Crew	Daily Output	Labor-Hours	Unit	Material	Labor	Equipment	Total	Total Incl O&P
0010	SPRAY PAINTING EQUIPMENT									
4000	Spray painting booth, 26' long, complete	L-4	.40	40	Ea.	16,200	1,275		17,475	19,900

11 12 Parking Control Equipment

11 12 13 – Parking Key and Card Control Units

11 12 13.10 Parking Control Units

11 12 13.10 Parking Control Units		Crew	Daily Output	Labor-Hours	Unit	Material	Labor	Equipment	Total	Total Incl O&P
0010	PARKING CONTROL UNITS									
5100	Card reader	1 Elec	2	4	Ea.	1,925	171		2,096	2,400
5120	Proximity with customer display	2 Elec	1	16		5,500	685		6,185	7,175
6000	Parking control software, minimum	1 Elec	.50	16		23,600	685		24,285	27,000
6020	Maximum	"	.20	40	↓	103,000	1,700		104,700	116,500

11 12 16 – Parking Ticket Dispensers

11 12 16.10 Ticket Dispensers

11 12 16.10 Ticket Dispensers		Crew	Daily Output	Labor-Hours	Unit	Material	Labor	Equipment	Total	Total Incl O&P
0010	TICKET DISPENSERS									
5900	Ticket spitter with time/date stamp, standard	2 Elec	2	8	Ea.	6,400	340		6,740	7,575
5920	Mag stripe encoding	"	2	8	"	18,600	340		18,940	21,000

11 12 26 – Parking Fee Collection Equipment

11 12 26.13 Parking Fee Coin Collection Equipment

11 12 26.13 Parking Fee Coin Collection Equipment		Crew	Daily Output	Labor-Hours	Unit	Material	Labor	Equipment	Total	Total Incl O&P
0010	PARKING FEE COIN COLLECTION EQUIPMENT									
5200	Cashier booth, average	B-22	1	30	Ea.	10,300	925	210	11,435	13,100
5300	Collector station, pay on foot	2 Elec	.20	80		109,500	3,425		112,925	126,000
5320	Credit card only	"	.50	32	↓	20,200	1,375		21,575	24,500

11 12 26.23 Fee Equipment

11 12 26.23 Fee Equipment		Crew	Daily Output	Labor-Hours	Unit	Material	Labor	Equipment	Total	Total Incl O&P
0010	FEE EQUIPMENT									
5600	Fee computer	1 Elec	1.50	5.333	Ea.	14,000	228		14,228	15,800

11 12 33 – Parking Gates

11 12 33.13 Lift Arm Parking Gates

11 12 33.13 Lift Arm Parking Gates		Crew	Daily Output	Labor-Hours	Unit	Material	Labor	Equipment	Total	Total Incl O&P
0010	LIFT ARM PARKING GATES									
5000	Barrier gate with programmable controller	2 Elec	3	5.333	Ea.	3,350	228		3,578	4,050
5020	Industrial		3	5.333		5,000	228		5,228	5,875
5500	Exit verifier	↓	1	16		17,400	685		18,085	20,300
5700	Full sign, 4" letters	1 Elec	2	4		1,225	171		1,396	1,600
5800	Inductive loop	2 Elec	4	4	↓	169	171		340	465

11 12 Parking Control Equipment

11 12 33 – Parking Gates

11 12 33.13 Lift Arm Parking Gates	Crew	Daily Output	Labor-Hours	Unit	Material	2014 Bare Costs Labor	Equipment	Total	Total Incl O&P
5950	Vehicle detector, microprocessor based	1 Elec	3	2.667	Ea.	420	114		534	650

11 13 Loading Dock Equipment

11 13 13 – Loading Dock Bumpers

11 13 13.10 Dock Bumpers

		Crew	Daily Output	Labor-Hours	Unit	Material	2014 Bare Costs Labor	Equipment	Total	Total Incl O&P
0010	**DOCK BUMPERS** Bolts not included									
0020	2" x 6" to 4" x 8", average	1 Carp	.30	26.667	M.B.F.	1,325	955		2,280	3,075
0050	Bumpers, rubber blocks 4-1/2" thick, 10" high, 14" long		26	.308	Ea.	63	11		74	88
0200	24" long		22	.364		95	13		108	126
0300	36" long		17	.471		72.50	16.80		89.30	108
0500	12" high, 14" long		25	.320		100	11.45		111.45	129
0550	24" long		20	.400		111	14.30		125.30	146
0600	36" long		15	.533		123	19.05		142.05	168
0800	Rubber blocks 6" thick, 10" high, 14" long		22	.364		103	13		116	135
0850	24" long		18	.444		121	15.90		136.90	160
0900	36" long		13	.615		186	22		208	241
0910	20" high, 11" long		13	.615		147	22		169	198
0920	Extruded rubber bumpers, T section, 22" x 22" x 3" thick		41	.195		64.50	7		71.50	83
0940	Molded rubber bumpers, 24" x 12" x 3" thick		20	.400		57	14.30		71.30	86.50
1000	Welded installation of above bumpers	E-14	8	1		3.74	38.50	17.75	59.99	96.50
1100	For drilled anchors, add per anchor	1 Carp	36	.222		6.70	7.95		14.65	20.50
1300	Steel bumpers, see Section 10 26 13.10									

11 13 16 – Loading Dock Seals and Shelters

11 13 16.10 Dock Seals and Shelters

		Crew	Daily Output	Labor-Hours	Unit	Material	2014 Bare Costs Labor	Equipment	Total	Total Incl O&P
0010	**DOCK SEALS AND SHELTERS**									
3600	Door seal for door perimeter, 12" x 12", vinyl covered	1 Carp	26	.308	L.F.	32	11		43	53.50
3900	Folding gates, see Section 10 22 16.10									
6200	Shelters, fabric, for truck or train, scissor arms, minimum	1 Carp	1	8	Ea.	1,750	286		2,036	2,400
6300	Maximum	"	.50	16	"	2,400	570		2,970	3,600

11 13 19 – Stationary Loading Dock Equipment

11 13 19.10 Dock Equipment

		Crew	Daily Output	Labor-Hours	Unit	Material	2014 Bare Costs Labor	Equipment	Total	Total Incl O&P
0010	**DOCK EQUIPMENT**									
2200	Dock boards, heavy duty, 60" x 60", aluminum, 5,000 lb. capacity				Ea.	1,450			1,450	1,600
2700	9,000 lb. capacity					1,600			1,600	1,750
3200	15,000 lb. capacity					1,725			1,725	1,900
4200	Platform lifter, 6' x 6', portable, 3,000 lb. capacity					9,150			9,150	10,100
4250	4,000 lb. capacity					11,300			11,300	12,400
4400	Fixed, 6' x 8', 5,000 lb. capacity	E-16	.70	22.857		9,850	900	203	10,953	12,700
4500	Levelers, hinged for trucks, 10 ton capacity, 6' x 8'		1.08	14.815		4,975	585	132	5,692	6,725
4650	7' x 8'		1.08	14.815		5,925	585	132	6,642	7,750
4670	Air bag power operated, 10 ton cap., 6' x 8'		1.08	14.815		5,775	585	132	6,492	7,600
4680	7' x 8'		1.08	14.815		5,800	585	132	6,517	7,625
4700	Hydraulic, 10 ton capacity, 6' x 8'		1.08	14.815		8,650	585	132	9,367	10,800
4800	7' x 8'		1.08	14.815		9,325	585	132	10,042	11,400
5800	Loading dock safety restraints, manual style		1.08	14.815		3,175	585	132	3,892	4,725
5900	Automatic style		1.08	14.815		5,325	585	132	6,042	7,100

11 13 Loading Dock Equipment

11 13 26 – Loading Dock Lights

11 13 26.10 Dock Lights	Crew	Daily Output	Labor-Hours	Unit	Material	2014 Bare Costs Labor	Equipment	Total	Total Incl O&P
0010 **DOCK LIGHTS**									
5000 Lights for loading docks, single arm, 24" long	1 Elec	3.80	2.105	Ea.	136	90		226	297
5700 Double arm, 60" long	"	3.80	2.105	"	209	90		299	375

11 14 Pedestrian Control Equipment

11 14 13 – Pedestrian Gates

11 14 13.13 Portable Posts and Railings

	Crew	Daily Output	Labor-Hours	Unit	Material	Labor	Equipment	Total	Total Incl O&P
0010 **PORTABLE POSTS AND RAILINGS**									
0020 Portable for pedestrian traffic control, standard, minimum				Ea.	132			132	146
0100 Maximum					184			184	202
0300 Deluxe posts, minimum					208			208	229
0400 Maximum					420			420	460
0600 Ropes for above posts, plastic covered, 1-1/2" diameter				L.F.	17.05			17.05	18.75
0700 Chain core				"	11.50			11.50	12.65
1500 Portable security or safety barrier, black with 7' yellow strap				Ea.	210			210	231
1510 12' yellow strap					235			235	258
1550 Sign holder, standard design					75			75	82.50

11 14 13.19 Turnstiles

	Crew	Daily Output	Labor-Hours	Unit	Material	Labor	Equipment	Total	Total Incl O&P
0010 **TURNSTILES**									
0020 One way, 4 arm, 46" diameter, economy, manual	2 Carp	5	3.200	Ea.	1,675	114		1,789	2,050
0100 Electric		1.20	13.333		2,025	475		2,500	3,050
0300 High security, galv., 5'-5" diameter, 7' high, manual		1	16		5,800	570		6,370	7,350
0350 Electric		.60	26.667		8,125	955		9,080	10,500
0420 Three arm, 24" opening, light duty, manual		2	8		3,375	286		3,661	4,200
0450 Heavy duty		1.50	10.667		4,950	380		5,330	6,075
0460 Manual, with registering & controls, light duty		2	8		3,725	286		4,011	4,575
0470 Heavy duty		1.50	10.667		4,050	380		4,430	5,100
0480 Electric, heavy duty		1.10	14.545		4,725	520		5,245	6,075
0500 For coin or token operating, add					700			700	770
1200 One way gate with horizontal bars, 5'-5" diameter									
1300 7' high, recreation or transit type	2 Carp	.80	20	Ea.	5,300	715		6,015	7,025
1500 For electronic counter, add				"	208			208	229

11 16 Vault Equipment

11 16 16 – Safes

11 16 16.10 Commercial Safes

	Crew	Daily Output	Labor-Hours	Unit	Material	Labor	Equipment	Total	Total Incl O&P
0010 **COMMERCIAL SAFES**									
0200 Office, 1 hr. rating, 30" x 18" x 18"				Ea.	2,275			2,275	2,500
0250 40" x 18" x 18"					4,850			4,850	5,325
0300 60" x 36" x 18", double door					7,350			7,350	8,075
0600 Data, 1 hr. rating, 27" x 19" x 16"					4,550			4,550	5,000
0700 63" x 34" x 16"					14,400			14,400	15,900
0750 Diskette, 1 hr., 14" x 12" x 11", inside					4,025			4,025	4,425
0800 Money, "B" label, 9" x 14" x 14"					540			540	595
0900 Tool resistive, 24" x 24" x 20"					4,125			4,125	4,525
1050 Tool and torch resistive, 24" x 24" x 20"					7,850			7,850	8,625
1150 Jewelers, 23" x 20" x 18"					8,725			8,725	9,600
1200 63" x 25" x 18"					14,300			14,300	15,700

11 16 Vault Equipment

11 16 16 – Safes

11 16 16.10 Commercial Safes	Crew	Daily Output	Labor-Hours	Unit	Material	2014 Bare Costs Labor	2014 Bare Costs Equipment	Total	Total Incl O&P
1300	For handling into building, add, minimum	A-2	8.50	2.824	Ea.		80	32	112	170
1400	Maximum	"	.78	30.769	↓		875	345	1,220	1,850

11 17 Teller and Service Equipment

11 17 13 – Teller Equipment Systems

11 17 13.10 Bank Equipment

	11 17 13.10 Bank Equipment	Crew	Daily Output	Labor-Hours	Unit	Material	2014 Bare Costs Labor	2014 Bare Costs Equipment	Total	Total Incl O&P
0010	**BANK EQUIPMENT**									
0020	Alarm system, police	2 Elec	1.60	10	Ea.	4,900	425		5,325	6,100
0100	With vault alarm	"	.40	40		19,500	1,700		21,200	24,200
0400	Bullet resistant teller window, 44" x 60"	1 Glaz	.60	13.333		3,800	465		4,265	4,975
0500	48" x 60"	"	.60	13.333	↓	5,525	465		5,990	6,850
3000	Counters for banks, frontal only	2 Carp	1	16	Station	1,825	570		2,395	2,975
3100	Complete with steel undercounter	"	.50	32	"	3,575	1,150		4,725	5,850
4600	Door and frame, bullet-resistant, with vision panel, minimum	2 Sswk	1.10	14.545	Ea.	5,500	560		6,060	7,125
4700	Maximum		1.10	14.545		7,475	560		8,035	9,275
4800	Drive-up window, drawer & mike, not incl. glass, minimum		1	16		6,825	615		7,440	8,675
4900	Maximum		.50	32		9,100	1,225		10,325	12,400
5000	Night depository, with chest, minimum		1	16		7,450	615		8,065	9,375
5100	Maximum		.50	32		10,600	1,225		11,825	14,100
5200	Package receiver, painted		3.20	5		1,375	192		1,567	1,875
5300	Stainless steel		3.20	5	↓	2,325	192		2,517	2,925
5400	Partitions, bullet-resistant, 1-3/16" glass, 8' high	2 Carp	10	1.600	L.F.	198	57		255	315
5450	Acrylic	"	10	1.600	"	375	57		432	510
5500	Pneumatic tube systems, 2 lane drive-up, complete	L-3	.25	40	Total	25,800	1,475		27,275	30,900
5550	With T.V. viewer	"	.20	50	"	50,000	1,850		51,850	58,000
5570	Safety deposit boxes, minimum	1 Sswk	44	.182	Opng.	57.50	6.95		64.45	76.50
5580	Maximum, 10" x 15" opening		19	.421		122	16.15		138.15	165
5590	Teller locker, average	↓	15	.533	↓	1,575	20.50		1,595.50	1,775
5600	Pass thru, bullet-res. window, painted steel, 24" x 36"	2 Sswk	1.60	10	Ea.	2,625	385		3,010	3,625
5700	48" x 48"		1.20	13.333		2,675	510		3,185	3,900
5800	72" x 40"	↓	.80	20	↓	4,200	765		4,965	6,075
5900	For stainless steel frames, add					20%				
6100	Surveillance system, video camera, complete	2 Elec	1	16	Ea.	9,500	685		10,185	11,500
6110	For each additional camera, add				"	990			990	1,100
6120	CCTV system, see Section 27 41 33.10									
6200	Twenty-four hour teller, single unit,									
6300	automated deposit, cash and memo	L-3	.25	40	Ea.	44,300	1,475		45,775	51,000
7000	Vault front, see Section 08 34 59.10									

11 19 Detention Equipment

11 19 30 – Detention Cell Equipment

11 19 30.10 Cell Equipment

	11 19 30.10 Cell Equipment	Crew	Daily Output	Labor-Hours	Unit	Material	2014 Bare Costs Labor	2014 Bare Costs Equipment	Total	Total Incl O&P
0010	**CELL EQUIPMENT**									
3000	Toilet apparatus including wash basin, average	L-8	1.50	13.333	Ea.	3,350	450		3,800	4,450

11 21 Mercantile and Service Equipment

11 21 13 – Cash Registers and Checking Equipment

11 21 13.10 Checkout Counter	Crew	Daily Output	Labor-Hours	Unit	Material	2014 Bare Costs Labor	Equipment	Total	Total Incl O&P
0010 **CHECKOUT COUNTER**									
0020 Supermarket conveyor, single belt	2 Clab	10	1.600	Ea.	3,125	45		3,170	3,525
0100 Double belt, power take-away		9	1.778		4,525	50		4,575	5,050
0400 Double belt, power take-away, incl. side scanning		7	2.286		5,300	64.50		5,364.50	5,925
0800 Warehouse or bulk type		6	2.667		6,275	75		6,350	7,025
1000 Scanning system, 2 lanes, w/registers, scan gun & memory				System	16,400			16,400	18,100
1100 10 lanes, single processor, full scan, with scales				"	156,000			156,000	171,500
2000 Register, restaurant, minimum				Ea.	730			730	805
2100 Maximum					3,075			3,075	3,400
2150 Store, minimum					730			730	805
2200 Maximum					3,075			3,075	3,400

11 21 53 – Barber and Beauty Shop Equipment

11 21 53.10 Barber Equipment

	Crew	Daily Output	Labor-Hours	Unit	Material	Labor	Equipment	Total	Total Incl O&P
0010 **BARBER EQUIPMENT**									
0020 Chair, hydraulic, movable, minimum	1 Carp	24	.333	Ea.	555	11.90		566.90	630
0050 Maximum	"	16	.500		3,425	17.90		3,442.90	3,800
0200 Wall hung styling station with mirrors, minimum	L-2	8	2		455	62.50		517.50	605
0300 Maximum	"	4	4		2,300	125		2,425	2,725
0500 Sink, hair washing basin, rough plumbing not incl.	1 Plum	8	1		490	42.50		532.50	610
1000 Sterilizer, liquid solution for tools					159			159	175
1100 Total equipment, rule of thumb, per chair, minimum	L-8	1	20		1,900	670		2,570	3,225
1150 Maximum	"	1	20		5,100	670		5,770	6,725

11 23 Commercial Laundry and Dry Cleaning Equipment

11 23 13 – Dry Cleaning Equipment

11 23 13.13 Dry Cleaners

	Crew	Daily Output	Labor-Hours	Unit	Material	Labor	Equipment	Total	Total Incl O&P
0010 **DRY CLEANERS** Not incl. rough-in									
2000 Dry cleaners, electric, 20 lb. capacity	L-1	.20	50	Ea.	33,300	2,125		35,425	40,100
2050 25 lb. capacity		.17	58.824		48,000	2,500		50,500	57,000
2100 30 lb. capacity		.15	66.667		50,500	2,850		53,350	60,000
2150 60 lb. capacity		.09	111		78,000	4,725		82,725	94,000

11 23 16 – Drying and Conditioning Equipment

11 23 16.13 Dryers

	Crew	Daily Output	Labor-Hours	Unit	Material	Labor	Equipment	Total	Total Incl O&P
0010 **DRYERS**, Not including rough-in									
1500 Industrial, 30 lb. capacity	1 Plum	2	4	Ea.	3,125	170		3,295	3,725
1600 50 lb. capacity	"	1.70	4.706		3,350	200		3,550	4,025
4700 Lint collector, ductwork not included, 8,000 to 10,000 CFM	Q-10	.30	80		9,100	3,025		12,125	15,000

11 23 19 – Finishing Equipment

11 23 19.13 Folders and Spreaders

	Crew	Daily Output	Labor-Hours	Unit	Material	Labor	Equipment	Total	Total Incl O&P
0010 **FOLDERS AND SPREADERS**									
3500 Folders, blankets & sheets, minimum	1 Elec	.17	47.059	Ea.	32,700	2,000		34,700	39,300
3700 King size with automatic stacker		.10	80		59,000	3,425		62,425	70,500
3800 For conveyor delivery, add		.45	17.778		14,300	760		15,060	17,100

11 23 23 – Commercial Ironing Equipment

11 23 23.13 Irons and Pressers

	Crew	Daily Output	Labor-Hours	Unit	Material	Labor	Equipment	Total	Total Incl O&P
0010 **IRONS AND PRESSERS**									
4500 Ironers, institutional, 110", single roll	1 Elec	.20	40	Ea.	31,700	1,700		33,400	37,700

11 23 Commercial Laundry and Dry Cleaning Equipment

11 23 26 – Commercial Washers and Extractors

11 23 26.13 Washers and Extractors

		Crew	Daily Output	Labor-Hours	Unit	Material	2014 Bare Costs Labor	2014 Bare Costs Equipment	Total	Total Incl O&P
0010	**WASHERS AND EXTRACTORS**, not including rough-in									
6000	Combination washer/extractor, 20 lb. capacity	L-6	1.50	8	Ea.	5,875	340		6,215	7,000
6100	30 lb. capacity		.80	15		9,150	640		9,790	11,200
6200	50 lb. capacity		.68	17.647		10,700	750		11,450	13,100
6300	75 lb. capacity		.30	40		20,200	1,700		21,900	25,000
6350	125 lb. capacity		.16	75		27,300	3,200		30,500	35,400

11 23 33 – Coin-Operated Laundry Equipment

11 23 33.13 Coin Operated Washers and Dryers

		Crew	Daily Output	Labor-Hours	Unit	Material	2014 Bare Costs Labor	2014 Bare Costs Equipment	Total	Total Incl O&P
0010	**COIN OPERATED WASHERS AND DRYERS**									
0990	Dryer, gas fired									
1000	Commercial, 30 lb. capacity, coin operated, single	1 Plum	3	2.667	Ea.	3,250	114		3,364	3,750
1100	Double stacked	"	2	4	"	7,200	170		7,370	8,200
5290	Clothes washer									
5300	Commercial, coin operated, average	1 Plum	3	2.667	Ea.	1,250	114		1,364	1,550

11 24 Maintenance Equipment

11 24 19 – Vacuum Cleaning Systems

11 24 19.10 Vacuum Cleaning

		Crew	Daily Output	Labor-Hours	Unit	Material	2014 Bare Costs Labor	2014 Bare Costs Equipment	Total	Total Incl O&P
0010	**VACUUM CLEANING**									
0020	Central, 3 inlet, residential	1 Skwk	.90	8.889	Total	1,050	325		1,375	1,725
0200	Commercial		.70	11.429		1,225	415		1,640	2,025
0400	5 inlet system, residential		.50	16		1,475	580		2,055	2,600
0600	7 inlet system, commercial		.40	20		1,675	725		2,400	3,075
0800	9 inlet system, residential		.30	26.667		3,700	970		4,670	5,700
4010	Rule of thumb: First 1200 S.F., installed								1,425	1,575
4020	For each additional S.F., add				S.F.					.26

11 26 Unit Kitchens

11 26 13 – Metal Unit Kitchens

11 26 13.10 Commercial Unit Kitchens

		Crew	Daily Output	Labor-Hours	Unit	Material	2014 Bare Costs Labor	2014 Bare Costs Equipment	Total	Total Incl O&P
0010	**COMMERCIAL UNIT KITCHENS**									
1500	Combination range, refrigerator and sink, 30" wide, minimum	L-1	2	5	Ea.	1,100	213		1,313	1,550
1550	Maximum		1	10		1,450	425		1,875	2,300
1570	60" wide, average		1.40	7.143		1,525	305		1,830	2,175
1590	72" wide, average		1.20	8.333		1,600	355		1,955	2,325
1600	Office model, 48" wide		2	5		2,000	213		2,213	2,550
1620	Refrigerator and sink only		2.40	4.167		2,500	178		2,678	3,050
1640	Combination range, refrigerator, sink, microwave									
1660	Oven and ice maker	L-1	.80	12.500	Ea.	4,500	535		5,035	5,825

11 27 13 – Darkroom Processing Equipment

11 27 13.10 Darkroom Equipment	Crew	Daily Output	Labor-Hours	Unit	Material	2014 Bare Costs Labor	Equipment	Total	Total Incl O&P
0010 **DARKROOM EQUIPMENT**									
0020 Developing sink, 5" deep, 24" x 48"	Q-1	2	8	Ea.	4,100	305		4,405	5,025
0050 48" x 52"		1.70	9.412		4,375	360		4,735	5,425
0200 10" deep, 24" x 48"		1.70	9.412		1,525	360		1,885	2,275
0250 24" x 108"		1.50	10.667		3,625	410		4,035	4,650
0500 Dryers, dehumidified filtered air, 36" x 25" x 68" high	L-7	6	4.333		4,250	134		4,384	4,900
0550 48" x 25" x 68" high		5	5.200		10,000	160		10,160	11,300
2000 Processors, automatic, color print, minimum		4	6.500		15,700	200		15,900	17,600
2050 Maximum		.60	43.333		24,700	1,325		26,025	29,500
2300 Black and white print, minimum		2	13		11,900	400		12,300	13,800
2350 Maximum		.80	32.500		61,500	1,000		62,500	69,000
2600 Manual processor, 16" x 20" maximum print size		2	13		9,450	400		9,850	11,100
2650 20" x 24" maximum print size		1	26		8,975	800		9,775	11,200
3000 Viewing lights, 20" x 24"		6	4.333		285	134		419	540
3100 20" x 24" with color correction		6	4.333		340	134		474	600
3500 Washers, round, minimum sheet 11" x 14"	Q-1	2	8		3,225	305		3,530	4,050
3550 Maximum sheet 20" x 24"		1	16		3,575	615		4,190	4,925
3800 Square, minimum sheet 20" x 24"		1	16		3,125	615		3,740	4,425
3900 Maximum sheet 50" x 56"		.80	20		4,850	765		5,615	6,600
4500 Combination tank sink, tray sink, washers, with									
4510 Dry side tables, average	Q-1	.45	35.556	Ea.	10,600	1,375		11,975	14,000

11 31 Residential Appliances

11 31 13 – Residential Kitchen Appliances

11 31 13.13 Cooking Equipment

	Crew	Daily Output	Labor-Hours	Unit	Material	Labor	Equipment	Total	Total Incl O&P
0010 **COOKING EQUIPMENT**									
0020 Cooking range, 30" free standing, 1 oven, minimum	2 Clab	10	1.600	Ea.	435	45		480	555
0050 Maximum		4	4		2,000	113		2,113	2,400
0150 2 oven, minimum		10	1.600		1,200	45		1,245	1,400
0200 Maximum		10	1.600		2,525	45		2,570	2,850
0350 Built-in, 30" wide, 1 oven, minimum	1 Elec	6	1.333		675	57		732	835
0400 Maximum	2 Carp	2	8		1,350	286		1,636	1,950
0500 2 oven, conventional, minimum		4	4		1,300	143		1,443	1,675
0550 1 conventional, 1 microwave, maximum		2	8		1,775	286		2,061	2,425
0700 Free-standing, 1 oven, 21" wide range, minimum	2 Clab	10	1.600		450	45		495	570
0750 21" wide, maximum	"	4	4		445	113		558	680
0900 Countertop cooktops, 4 burner, standard, minimum	1 Elec	6	1.333		293	57		350	415
0950 Maximum		3	2.667		1,300	114		1,414	1,600
1050 As above, but with grill and griddle attachment, minimum		6	1.333		1,225	57		1,282	1,450
1100 Maximum		3	2.667		3,650	114		3,764	4,200
1200 Induction cooktop, 30" wide		3	2.667		1,175	114		1,289	1,475
1250 Microwave oven, minimum		4	2		119	85.50		204.50	271
1300 Maximum		2	4		460	171		631	785

11 31 13.23 Refrigeration Equipment

	Crew	Daily Output	Labor-Hours	Unit	Material	Labor	Equipment	Total	Total Incl O&P
0010 **REFRIGERATION EQUIPMENT**									
2000 Deep freeze, 15 to 23 C.F., minimum	2 Clab	10	1.600	Ea.	605	45		650	740
2050 Maximum		5	3.200		810	90		900	1,050
2200 30 C.F., minimum		8	2		695	56.50		751.50	860
2250 Maximum		3	5.333		900	150		1,050	1,250
5200 Icemaker, automatic, 20 lb. per day	1 Plum	7	1.143		885	48.50		933.50	1,050
5350 51 lb. per day	"	2	4		1,575	170		1,745	2,000

11 31 Residential Appliances

11 31 13 – Residential Kitchen Appliances

11 31 13.23 Refrigeration Equipment

		Crew	Daily Output	Labor-Hours	Unit	Material	2014 Bare Costs Labor	Equipment	Total	Total Incl O&P
5500	Refrigerator, no frost, 10 C.F. to 12 C.F., minimum	2 Clab	10	1.600	Ea.	420	45		465	535
5600	Maximum		6	2.667		445	75		520	610
5750	14 C.F. to 16 C.F., minimum		9	1.778		500	50		550	635
5800	Maximum		5	3.200		615	90		705	825
5950	18 C.F. to 20 C.F., minimum		8	2		620	56.50		676.50	780
6000	Maximum		4	4		1,400	113		1,513	1,750
6150	21 C.F. to 29 C.F., minimum		7	2.286		955	64.50		1,019.50	1,150
6200	Maximum		3	5.333		3,325	150		3,475	3,925
6790	Energy-star qualified, 18 C.F., minimum	G	2 Carp	4	4	505	143		648	795
6795	Maximum	G		2	8	1,150	286		1,436	1,750
6797	21.7 C.F., minimum	G		4	4	1,025	143		1,168	1,375
6799	Maximum	G		4	4	2,075	143		2,218	2,550

11 31 13.33 Kitchen Cleaning Equipment

		Crew	Daily Output	Labor-Hours	Unit	Material	Labor	Equipment	Total	Total Incl O&P
0010	**KITCHEN CLEANING EQUIPMENT**									
2750	Dishwasher, built-in, 2 cycles, minimum	L-1	4	2.500	Ea.	235	107		342	435
2800	Maximum		2	5		430	213		643	820
2950	4 or more cycles, minimum		4	2.500		370	107		477	585
2960	Average		4	2.500		495	107		602	720
3000	Maximum		2	5		1,075	213		1,288	1,550
3100	Energy-star qualified, minimum	G	4	2.500		365	107		472	575
3110	Maximum	G	2	5		1,500	213		1,713	2,000

11 31 13.43 Waste Disposal Equipment

		Crew	Daily Output	Labor-Hours	Unit	Material	Labor	Equipment	Total	Total Incl O&P
0010	**WASTE DISPOSAL EQUIPMENT**									
1750	Compactor, residential size, 4 to 1 compaction, minimum	1 Carp	5	1.600	Ea.	640	57		697	800
1800	Maximum	"	3	2.667		1,000	95.50		1,095.50	1,250
3300	Garbage disposal, sink type, minimum	L-1	10	1		86.50	42.50		129	165
3350	Maximum	"	10	1		217	42.50		259.50	310

11 31 13.53 Kitchen Ventilation Equipment

		Crew	Daily Output	Labor-Hours	Unit	Material	Labor	Equipment	Total	Total Incl O&P
0010	**KITCHEN VENTILATION EQUIPMENT**									
4150	Hood for range, 2 speed, vented, 30" wide, minimum	L-3	5	2	Ea.	69.50	74.50		144	201
4200	Maximum		3	3.333		770	124		894	1,050
4300	42" wide, minimum		5	2		166	74.50		240.50	305
4330	Custom		5	2		1,650	74.50		1,724.50	1,925
4350	Maximum		3	3.333		2,000	124		2,124	2,400
4500	For ventless hood, 2 speed, add					18.45			18.45	20.50
4650	For vented 1 speed, deduct from maximum					49.50			49.50	54.50

11 31 23 – Residential Laundry Appliances

11 31 23.13 Washers

		Crew	Daily Output	Labor-Hours	Unit	Material	Labor	Equipment	Total	Total Incl O&P
0010	**WASHERS**									
5000	Residential, 4 cycle, average	1 Plum	3	2.667	Ea.	865	114		979	1,150
6650	Washing machine, automatic, minimum		3	2.667		480	114		594	710
6700	Maximum		1	8		1,500	340		1,840	2,200
6750	Energy star qualified, front loading, minimum	G	3	2.667		645	114		759	895
6760	Maximum	G	1	8		1,575	340		1,915	2,275
6764	Top loading, minimum	G	3	2.667		445	114		559	675
6766	Maximum	G	3	2.667		1,225	114		1,339	1,525

11 31 23.23 Dryers

		Crew	Daily Output	Labor-Hours	Unit	Material	Labor	Equipment	Total	Total Incl O&P
0010	**DRYERS**									
0500	Gas fired residential, 16 lb. capacity, average	1 Plum	3	2.667	Ea.	665	114		779	920
6770	Electric, front loading, energy-star qualified, minimum	G	L-2	3	5.333	380	167		547	700
6780	Maximum	G	"	2	8	1,900	251		2,151	2,500

11 31 Residential Appliances

11 31 23 – Residential Laundry Appliances

11 31 23.23 Dryers		Crew	Daily Output	Labor-Hours	Unit	Material	2014 Bare Costs Labor	Equipment	Total	Total Incl O&P
7450	Vent kits for dryers	1 Carp	10	.800	Ea.	38.50	28.50		67	90

11 31 33 – Miscellaneous Residential Appliances

11 31 33.13 Sump Pumps

		Crew	Daily Output	Labor-Hours	Unit	Material	Labor	Equipment	Total	Total Incl O&P
0010	**SUMP PUMPS**									
6400	Cellar drainer, pedestal, 1/3 H.P., molded PVC base	1 Plum	3	2.667	Ea.	135	114		249	335
6450	Solid brass	"	2	4	"	289	170		459	600
6460	Sump pump, see also Section 22 14 29.16									

11 31 33.23 Water Heaters

		Crew	Daily Output	Labor-Hours	Unit	Material	Labor	Equipment	Total	Total Incl O&P
0010	**WATER HEATERS**									
6900	Electric, glass lined, 30 gallon, minimum	L-1	5	2	Ea.	430	85		515	610
6950	Maximum		3	3.333		595	142		737	890
7100	80 gallon, minimum		2	5		1,225	213		1,438	1,700
7150	Maximum		1	10		1,700	425		2,125	2,550
7180	Gas, glass lined, 30 gallon, minimum	2 Plum	5	3.200		805	136		941	1,100
7220	Maximum		3	5.333		1,125	227		1,352	1,600
7260	50 gallon, minimum		2.50	6.400		845	273		1,118	1,375
7300	Maximum		1.50	10.667		1,175	455		1,630	2,025
7310	Water heater, see also Section 22 33 30.13									

11 31 33.43 Air Quality

		Crew	Daily Output	Labor-Hours	Unit	Material	Labor	Equipment	Total	Total Incl O&P
0010	**AIR QUALITY**									
2450	Dehumidifier, portable, automatic, 15 pint	1 Elec	4	2	Ea.	150	85.50		235.50	305
2550	40 pint					207			207	228
3550	Heater, electric, built-in, 1250 watt, ceiling type, minimum	1 Elec	4	2		106	85.50		191.50	256
3600	Maximum		3	2.667		172	114		286	375
3700	Wall type, minimum		4	2		170	85.50		255.50	325
3750	Maximum		3	2.667		183	114		297	385
3900	1500 watt wall type, with blower		4	2		170	85.50		255.50	325
3950	3000 watt		3	2.667		350	114		464	570
4850	Humidifier, portable, 8 gallons per day					131			131	144
5000	15 gallons per day					208			208	229

11 33 Retractable Stairs

11 33 10 – Disappearing Stairs

11 33 10.10 Disappearing Stairway

		Crew	Daily Output	Labor-Hours	Unit	Material	Labor	Equipment	Total	Total Incl O&P
0010	**DISAPPEARING STAIRWAY** No trim included									
0100	Custom grade, pine, 8'-6" ceiling, minimum	1 Carp	4	2	Ea.	175	71.50		246.50	315
0150	Average		3.50	2.286		250	81.50		331.50	410
0200	Maximum		3	2.667		320	95.50		415.50	515
0500	Heavy duty, pivoted, from 7'-7" to 12'-10" floor to floor		3	2.667		735	95.50		830.50	965
0600	16'-0" ceiling		2	4		1,500	143		1,643	1,900
0800	Economy folding, pine, 8'-6" ceiling		4	2		174	71.50		245.50	310
0900	9'-6" ceiling		4	2		194	71.50		265.50	335
1100	Automatic electric, aluminum, floor to floor height, 8' to 9'	2 Carp	1	16		8,425	570		8,995	10,200
1400	11' to 12'		.90	17.778		8,975	635		9,610	10,900
1700	14' to 15'		.70	22.857		9,675	815		10,490	12,000

11 41 Foodservice Storage Equipment

11 41 13 – Refrigerated Food Storage Cases

11 41 13.10 Refrigerated Food Cases	Crew	Daily Output	Labor-Hours	Unit	Material	2014 Bare Costs Labor	Equipment	Total	Total Incl O&P
0010 **REFRIGERATED FOOD CASES**									
0030 Dairy, multi-deck, 12' long	Q-5	3	5.333	Ea.	11,200	208		11,408	12,600
0100 For rear sliding doors, add					1,800			1,800	1,975
0200 Delicatessen case, service deli, 12' long, single deck	Q-5	3.90	4.103		7,650	160		7,810	8,700
0300 Multi-deck, 18 S.F. shelf display		3	5.333		7,075	208		7,283	8,125
0400 Freezer, self-contained, chest-type, 30 C.F.		3.90	4.103		8,425	160		8,585	9,550
0500 Glass door, upright, 78 C.F.		3.30	4.848		10,100	189		10,289	11,400
0600 Frozen food, chest type, 12' long		3.30	4.848		8,125	189		8,314	9,225
0700 Glass door, reach-in, 5 door		3	5.333		13,900	208		14,108	15,600
0800 Island case, 12' long, single deck		3.30	4.848		7,200	189		7,389	8,225
0900 Multi-deck		3	5.333		8,400	208		8,608	9,600
1000 Meat case, 12' long, single deck		3.30	4.848		7,200	189		7,389	8,225
1050 Multi-deck		3.10	5.161		10,300	201		10,501	11,600
1100 Produce, 12' long, single deck		3.30	4.848		6,775	189		6,964	7,750
1200 Multi-deck		3.10	5.161		8,625	201		8,826	9,800

11 41 13.20 Refrigerated Food Storage Equipment

	Crew	Daily Output	Labor-Hours	Unit	Material	2014 Bare Costs Labor	Equipment	Total	Total Incl O&P
0010 **REFRIGERATED FOOD STORAGE EQUIPMENT**									
2350 Cooler, reach-in, beverage, 6' long	Q-1	6	2.667	Ea.	3,550	102		3,652	4,075
4300 Freezers, reach-in, 44 C.F.		4	4		4,350	153		4,503	5,050
4500 68 C.F.		3	5.333		4,775	205		4,980	5,575
4600 Freezer, pre-fab, 8' x 8' w/refrigeration	2 Carp	.45	35.556		10,900	1,275		12,175	14,200
4620 8' x 12'		.35	45.714		11,000	1,625		12,625	14,900
4640 8' x 16'		.25	64		14,900	2,300		17,200	20,300
4660 8' x 20'		.17	94.118		19,200	3,375		22,575	26,800
4680 Reach-in, 1 compartment	Q-1	4	4		2,475	153		2,628	2,975
4685 Energy star rated G	R-18	7.80	3.333		2,550	110		2,660	2,975
4700 2 compartment	Q-1	3	5.333		4,050	205		4,255	4,800
4705 Energy star rated G	R-18	6.20	4.194		3,075	138		3,213	3,600
4710 3 compartment	Q-1	3	5.333		5,225	205		5,430	6,075
4715 Energy star rated G	R-18	5.60	4.643		3,850	153		4,003	4,475
8320 Refrigerator, reach-in, 1 compartment		7.80	3.333		2,400	110		2,510	2,800
8325 Energy star rated G		7.80	3.333		2,550	110		2,660	2,975
8330 2 compartment		6.20	4.194		3,750	138		3,888	4,350
8335 Energy star rated G		6.20	4.194		3,075	138		3,213	3,600
8340 3 compartment		5.60	4.643		4,700	153		4,853	5,425
8345 Energy star rated G		5.60	4.643		3,850	153		4,003	4,475
8350 Pre-fab, with refrigeration, 8' x 8'	2 Carp	.45	35.556		6,975	1,275		8,250	9,825
8360 8' x 12'		.35	45.714		7,900	1,625		9,525	11,500
8370 8' x 16'		.25	64		12,200	2,300		14,500	17,300
8380 8' x 20'		.17	94.118		15,500	3,375		18,875	22,700
8390 Pass-thru/roll-in, 1 compartment	R-18	7.80	3.333		4,450	110		4,560	5,075
8400 2 compartment		6.24	4.167		6,250	138		6,388	7,100
8410 3 compartment		5.60	4.643		8,525	153		8,678	9,625
8420 Walk-in, alum, door & floor only, no refrig, 6' x 6' x 7'-6"	2 Carp	1.40	11.429		8,675	410		9,085	10,200
8430 10' x 6' x 7'-6"		.55	29.091		12,500	1,050		13,550	15,600
8440 12' x 14' x 7'-6"		.25	64		17,300	2,300		19,600	22,900
8450 12' x 20' x 7'-6"		.17	94.118		19,100	3,375		22,475	26,700
8460 Refrigerated cabinets, mobile					3,875			3,875	4,275
8470 Refrigerator/freezer, reach-in, 1 compartment	R-18	5.60	4.643		5,725	153		5,878	6,550
8480 2 compartment	"	4.80	5.417		7,475	179		7,654	8,525

11 41 Foodservice Storage Equipment

11 41 13 – Refrigerated Food Storage Cases

11 41 13.30 Wine Cellar	Crew	Daily Output	Labor-Hours	Unit	Material	2014 Bare Costs Labor	Equipment	Total	Total Incl O&P
0010 **WINE CELLAR**, refrigerated, Redwood interior, carpeted, walk-in type									
0020 6'-8" high, including racks									
0200 80" W x 48" D for 900 bottles	2 Carp	1.50	10.667	Ea.	4,250	380		4,630	5,325
0250 80" W x 72" D for 1300 bottles		1.33	12.030		5,175	430		5,605	6,425
0300 80" W x 94" D for 1900 bottles		1.17	13.675		6,275	490		6,765	7,725
0400 80" W x 124" D for 2500 bottles		1	16		7,375	570		7,945	9,050
0600 Portable cabinets, red oak, reach-in temp.& humidity controlled									
0650 26-5/8"W x 26-1/2"D x 68"H for 235 bottles				Ea.	3,525			3,525	3,875
0660 32"W x 21-1/2"D x 73-1/2"H for 144 bottles					2,875			2,875	3,150
0670 32"W x 29-1/2"D x 73-1/2"H for 288 bottles					3,825			3,825	4,225
0680 39-1/2"W x 29-1/2"D x 86-1/2"H for 440 bottles					4,050			4,050	4,450
0690 52-1/2"W x 29-1/2"D x 73-1/2"H for 468 bottles					4,325			4,325	4,775
0700 52-1/2"W x 29-1/2"D x 86-1/2"H for 572 bottles					4,425			4,425	4,875
0730 Portable, red oak, can be built-in with glass door									
0750 23-7/8"W x 24"D x 34-1/2"H for 50 bottles				Ea.	930			930	1,025

11 41 33 – Foodservice Shelving

11 41 33.20 Metal Food Storage Shelving

	Crew	Daily Output	Labor-Hours	Unit	Material	2014 Bare Costs Labor	Equipment	Total	Total Incl O&P
0010 **METAL FOOD STORAGE SHELVING**									
8600 Stainless steel shelving, louvered 4-tier, 20" x 3'	1 Clab	6	1.333	Ea.	1,400	37.50		1,437.50	1,600
8605 20" x 4'		6	1.333		1,525	37.50		1,562.50	1,750
8610 20" x 6'		6	1.333		2,175	37.50		2,212.50	2,475
8615 24" x 3'		6	1.333		1,950	37.50		1,987.50	2,225
8620 24" x 4'		6	1.333		2,325	37.50		2,362.50	2,650
8625 24" x 6'		6	1.333		3,250	37.50		3,287.50	3,625
8630 Flat 4-tier, 20" x 3'		6	1.333		1,150	37.50		1,187.50	1,325
8635 20" x 4'		6	1.333		1,400	37.50		1,437.50	1,600
8640 20" x 5'		6	1.333		1,600	37.50		1,637.50	1,850
8645 24" x 3'		6	1.333		1,250	37.50		1,287.50	1,450
8650 24" x 4'		6	1.333		2,200	37.50		2,237.50	2,475
8655 24" x 6'		6	1.333		2,650	37.50		2,687.50	2,975
8700 Galvanized shelving, louvered 4-tier, 20" x 3'		6	1.333		750	37.50		787.50	890
8705 20" x 4'		6	1.333		850	37.50		887.50	1,000
8710 20" x 6'		6	1.333		995	37.50		1,032.50	1,175
8715 24" x 3'		6	1.333		700	37.50		737.50	835
8720 24" x 4'		6	1.333		985	37.50		1,022.50	1,150
8725 24" x 6'		6	1.333		1,300	37.50		1,337.50	1,525
8730 Flat 4-tier, 20" x 3'		6	1.333		695	37.50		732.50	830
8735 20" x 4'		6	1.333		685	37.50		722.50	820
8740 20" x 6'		6	1.333		895	37.50		932.50	1,050
8745 24" x 3'		6	1.333		660	37.50		697.50	795
8750 24" x 4'		6	1.333		745	37.50		782.50	885
8755 24" x 6'		6	1.333		940	37.50		977.50	1,100
8760 Stainless steel dunnage rack, 24" x 3'		8	1		325	28		353	410
8765 24" x 4'		8	1		420	28		448	510
8770 Galvanized dunnage rack, 24" x 3'		8	1		166	28		194	231
8775 24" x 4'		8	1		187	28		215	254

11 42 Food Preparation Equipment

11 42 10 – Commercial Food Preparation Equipment

11 42 10.10 Choppers, Mixers and Misc. Equipment

		Daily Output	Labor-Hours	Unit	Material	2014 Bare Costs Labor	2014 Bare Costs Equipment	Total	Total Incl O&P
0010	**CHOPPERS, MIXERS AND MISC. EQUIPMENT**	Crew							
1700	Choppers, 5 pounds	R-18	7	3.714	Ea.	2,125	123		2,248	2,550
1720	16 pounds		5	5.200		2,175	172		2,347	2,675
1740	35 to 40 pounds		4	6.500		3,500	215		3,715	4,200
1840	Coffee brewer, 5 burners	1 Plum	3	2.667		1,300	114		1,414	1,625
1850	Coffee urn, twin 6 gallon urns		2	4		2,375	170		2,545	2,900
1860	Single, 3 gallon		3	2.667		1,800	114		1,914	2,150
3000	Fast food equipment, total package, minimum	6 Skwk	.08	600		201,000	21,800		222,800	258,500
3100	Maximum	"	.07	685		274,000	24,900		298,900	343,500
3800	Food mixers, bench type, 20 quarts	L-7	7	3.714		2,925	115		3,040	3,425
3850	40 quarts		5.40	4.815		6,650	148		6,798	7,575
3900	60 quarts		5	5.200		11,200	160		11,360	12,600
4040	80 quarts		3.90	6.667		12,500	206		12,706	14,100
4100	Floor type, 20 quarts		15	1.733		3,200	53.50		3,253.50	3,600
4120	60 quarts		14	1.857		9,825	57.50		9,882.50	10,900
4140	80 quarts		12	2.167		15,200	67		15,267	16,900
4160	140 quarts		8.60	3.023		25,300	93		25,393	28,000
6700	Peelers, small	R-18	8	3.250		1,875	107		1,982	2,225
6720	Large	"	6	4.333		4,775	143		4,918	5,500
6800	Pulper/extractor, close coupled, 5 HP	1 Plum	1.90	4.211		3,475	179		3,654	4,125
8580	Slicer with table	R-18	9	2.889		4,625	95.50		4,720.50	5,225

11 43 Food Delivery Carts and Conveyors

11 43 13 – Food Delivery Carts

11 43 13.10 Mobile Carts, Racks and Trays

		Daily Output	Labor-Hours	Unit	Material	2014 Bare Costs Labor	2014 Bare Costs Equipment	Total	Total Incl O&P
0010	**MOBILE CARTS, RACKS AND TRAYS**	Crew							
1650	Cabinet, heated, 1 compartment, reach-in	R-18	5.60	4.643	Ea.	3,250	153		3,403	3,825
1655	Pass-thru roll-in		5.60	4.643		3,775	153		3,928	4,400
1660	2 compartment, reach-in		4.80	5.417		8,925	179		9,104	10,100
1670	Mobile					3,500			3,500	3,825
6850	Mobile rack w/pan slide					1,375			1,375	1,500
9180	Tray and silver dispenser, mobile	1 Clab	16	.500		905	14.10		919.10	1,025

11 44 Food Cooking Equipment

11 44 13 – Commercial Ranges

11 44 13.10 Cooking Equipment

		Daily Output	Labor-Hours	Unit	Material	2014 Bare Costs Labor	2014 Bare Costs Equipment	Total	Total Incl O&P
0010	**COOKING EQUIPMENT**	Crew							
0020	Bake oven, gas, one section	Q-1	8	2	Ea.	5,550	76.50		5,626.50	6,225
0300	Two sections		7	2.286		8,975	87.50		9,062.50	10,000
0600	Three sections		6	2.667		12,400	102		12,502	13,800
0900	Electric convection, single deck	L-7	4	6.500		6,150	200		6,350	7,075
1300	Broiler, without oven, standard	Q-1	8	2		3,500	76.50		3,576.50	3,975
1550	Infrared	L-7	4	6.500		7,325	200		7,525	8,400
4750	Fryer, with twin baskets, modular model	Q-1	7	2.286		1,250	87.50		1,337.50	1,525
5000	Floor model, on 6" legs	"	5	3.200		2,400	123		2,523	2,850
5100	Extra single basket, large					98.50			98.50	108
5170	Energy star rated, 50 lb. capacity G	R-18	4	6.500		4,575	215		4,790	5,400
5175	85 lb. capacity G	"	4	6.500		8,425	215		8,640	9,625
5300	Griddle, SS, 24" plate, w/4" legs, elec, 208 V, 3 phase, 3' long	Q-1	7	2.286		1,375	87.50		1,462.50	1,675

11 44 13 – Commercial Ranges

11 44 13.10 Cooking Equipment	Crew	Daily Output	Labor-Hours	Unit	Material	2014 Bare Costs Labor	Equipment	Total	Total Incl O&P
5550	4' long	Q-1	6	2.667	Ea.	2,225	102		2,327	2,625
6200	Iced tea brewer	1 Plum	3.44	2.326		745	99		844	980
6350	Kettle, w/steam jacket, tilting, w/positive lock, SS, 20 gallons	L-7	7	3.714		8,125	115		8,240	9,150
6600	60 gallons	"	6	4.333		10,800	134		10,934	12,100
6900	Range, restaurant type, 6 burners and 1 standard oven, 36" wide	Q-1	7	2.286		2,575	87.50		2,662.50	2,975
6950	Convection		7	2.286		4,400	87.50		4,487.50	5,000
7150	2 standard ovens, 24" griddle, 60" wide		6	2.667		4,500	102		4,602	5,150
7200	1 standard, 1 convection oven		6	2.667		9,350	102		9,452	10,500
7450	Heavy duty, single 34" standard oven, open top		5	3.200		4,750	123		4,873	5,425
7500	Convection oven		5	3.200		5,375	123		5,498	6,125
7700	Griddle top		6	2.667		2,825	102		2,927	3,275
7750	Convection oven	▼	6	2.667		7,700	102		7,802	8,625
8850	Steamer, electric 27 KW	L-7	7	3.714		10,600	115		10,715	11,900
9100	Electric, 10 KW or gas 100,000 BTU	"	5	5.200		6,250	160		6,410	7,150
9150	Toaster, conveyor type, 16-22 slices per minute					1,075			1,075	1,175
9160	Pop-up, 2 slot				▼	610			610	670
9200	For deluxe models of above equipment, add					75%				
9400	Rule of thumb: Equipment cost based									
9410	on kitchen work area									
9420	Office buildings, minimum	L-7	77	.338	S.F.	89.50	10.40		99.90	116
9450	Maximum		58	.448		151	13.85		164.85	189
9550	Public eating facilities, minimum		77	.338		117	10.40		127.40	147
9600	Maximum		46	.565		191	17.45		208.45	240
9750	Hospitals, minimum		58	.448		121	13.85		134.85	156
9800	Maximum	▼	39	.667	▼	222	20.50		242.50	279

11 46 Food Dispensing Equipment

11 46 16 – Service Line Equipment

11 46 16.10 Commercial Food Dispensing Equipment

		Crew	Daily Output	Labor-Hours	Unit	Material	Labor	Equipment	Total	Total Incl O&P
0010	**COMMERCIAL FOOD DISPENSING EQUIPMENT**									
1050	Butter pat dispenser	1 Clab	13	.615	Ea.	995	17.35		1,012.35	1,125
1100	Bread dispenser, counter top		13	.615		880	17.35		897.35	995
1900	Cup and glass dispenser, drop in		4	2		1,075	56.50		1,131.50	1,275
1920	Disposable cup, drop in		16	.500		490	14.10		504.10	565
2650	Dish dispenser, drop in, 12"		11	.727		2,225	20.50		2,245.50	2,475
2660	Mobile	▼	10	.800		2,600	22.50		2,622.50	2,900
3300	Food warmer, counter, 1.2 KW					660			660	725
3550	1.6 KW					2,100			2,100	2,325
3600	Well, hot food, built-in, rectangular, 12" x 20"	R-30	10	2.600		805	88		893	1,025
3610	Circular, 7 qt.		10	2.600		415	88		503	600
3620	Refrigerated, 2 compartments		10	2.600		3,025	88		3,113	3,475
3630	3 compartments		9	2.889		3,650	98		3,748	4,200
3640	4 compartments		8	3.250		4,300	110		4,410	4,900
4720	Frost cold plate	▼	9	2.889		18,200	98		18,298	20,200
5700	Hot chocolate dispenser	1 Plum	4	2		1,150	85		1,235	1,425
5750	Ice dispenser 567 pound	Q-1	6	2.667		5,150	102		5,252	5,850
6250	Jet spray dispenser	R-18	4.50	5.778		3,125	191		3,316	3,775
6300	Juice dispenser, concentrate	"	4.50	5.778		1,875	191		2,066	2,375
6690	Milk dispenser, bulk, 2 flavor	R-30	8	3.250		1,825	110		1,935	2,200
6695	3 flavor	"	8	3.250	▼	2,450	110		2,560	2,875
8800	Serving counter, straight	1 Carp	40	.200	L.F.	915	7.15		922.15	1,000

11 46 Food Dispensing Equipment

11 46 16 – Service Line Equipment

11 46 16.10 Commercial Food Dispensing Equipment		Crew	Daily Output	Labor-Hours	Unit	Material	2014 Bare Costs Labor	Equipment	Total	Total Incl O&P
8820	Curved section	1 Carp	30	.267	L.F.	1,125	9.55		1,134.55	1,250
8825	Solid surface, see Section 12 36 61.16									
8860	Sneeze guard with lights, 60" L	1 Clab	16	.500	Ea.	390	14.10		404.10	455
9100	Soft serve ice cream machine, medium	R-18	11	2.364		11,900	78		11,978	13,200
9110	Large	"	9	2.889		21,500	95.50		21,595.50	23,900

11 47 Ice Machines

11 47 10 – Commercial Ice Machines

11 47 10.10 Commercial Ice Equipment

		Crew	Daily Output	Labor-Hours	Unit	Material	2014 Bare Costs Labor	Equipment	Total	Total Incl O&P
0010	**COMMERCIAL ICE EQUIPMENT**									
5800	Ice cube maker, 50 pounds per day	Q-1	6	2.667	Ea.	1,600	102		1,702	1,925
5900	250 pounds per day		1.20	13.333		2,650	510		3,160	3,775
6050	500 pounds per day		4	4		2,750	153		2,903	3,275
6060	With bin		1.20	13.333		3,350	510		3,860	4,550
6090	1000 pounds per day, with bin		1	16		4,875	615		5,490	6,375
6100	Ice flakers, 300 pounds per day		1.60	10		2,750	385		3,135	3,650
6120	600 pounds per day		.95	16.842		3,900	645		4,545	5,350
6130	1000 pounds per day		.75	21.333		4,700	820		5,520	6,525
6140	2000 pounds per day		.65	24.615		21,300	945		22,245	25,000
6160	Ice storage bin, 500 pound capacity	Q-5	1	16		1,025	625		1,650	2,150
6180	1000 pound	"	.56	28.571		2,500	1,125		3,625	4,575

11 48 Cleaning and Disposal Equipment

11 48 13 – Commercial Dishwashers

11 48 13.10 Dishwashers

			Crew	Daily Output	Labor-Hours	Unit	Material	2014 Bare Costs Labor	Equipment	Total	Total Incl O&P
0010	**DISHWASHERS**										
2700	Dishwasher, commercial, rack type										
2720	10 to 12 racks per hour		Q-1	3.20	5	Ea.	3,475	192		3,667	4,150
2730	Energy star rated, 35 to 40 racks/hour	G		1.30	12.308		4,650	470		5,120	5,875
2740	50 to 60 racks/hour	G		1.30	12.308		10,100	470		10,570	11,900
2800	Automatic, 190 to 230 racks per hour		L-6	.35	34.286		13,800	1,450		15,250	17,500
2820	235 to 275 racks per hour			.25	48		31,100	2,050		33,150	37,600
2840	8,750 to 12,500 dishes per hour			.10	120		54,500	5,125		59,625	68,500
2950	Dishwasher hood, canopy type		L-3A	10	1.200	L.F.	855	46.50		901.50	1,025
2960	Pant leg type		"	2.50	4.800	Ea.	8,600	186		8,786	9,775
5200	Garbage disposal 1.5 HP, 100 GPH		L-1	4.80	2.083		2,150	89		2,239	2,525
5210	3 HP, 120 GPH			4.60	2.174		2,600	92.50		2,692.50	3,000
5220	5 HP, 250 GPH			4.50	2.222		3,575	94.50		3,669.50	4,075
6750	Pot sink, 3 compartment		1 Plum	7.25	1.103	L.F.	970	47		1,017	1,150
6760	Pot washer, low temp wash/rinse			1.60	5	Ea.	4,000	213		4,213	4,750
6770	High pressure wash, high temperature rinse			1.20	6.667		36,500	284		36,784	40,600
9170	Trash compactor, small, up to 125 lb. compacted weight		L-4	4	4		23,900	126		24,026	26,500
9175	Large, up to 175 lb. compacted weight		"	3	5.333		29,200	169		29,369	32,400

11 52 Audio-Visual Equipment

11 52 13 – Projection Screens

11 52 13.10 Projection Screens, Wall or Ceiling Hung	Crew	Daily Output	Labor-Hours	Unit	Material	2014 Bare Costs Labor	Equipment	Total	Total Incl O&P
0010 **PROJECTION SCREENS, WALL OR CEILING HUNG**, matte white									
0100 Manually operated, economy	2 Carp	500	.032	S.F.	5.85	1.14		6.99	8.35
0300 Intermediate		450	.036		6.80	1.27		8.07	9.65
0400 Deluxe		400	.040		9.45	1.43		10.88	12.75
0600 Electric operated, matte white, 25 S.F., economy		5	3.200	Ea.	855	114		969	1,125
0700 Deluxe		4	4		1,775	143		1,918	2,200
0900 50 S.F., economy		3	5.333		695	191		886	1,075
1000 Deluxe		2	8		1,975	286		2,261	2,650
1200 Heavy duty, electric operated, 200 S.F.		1.50	10.667		3,900	380		4,280	4,950
1300 400 S.F.		1	16		4,800	570		5,370	6,250
1500 Rigid acrylic in wall, for rear projection, 1/4" thick	2 Glaz	30	.533	S.F.	47	18.55		65.55	83
1600 1/2" thick (maximum size 10' x 20')	"	25	.640	"	83.50	22.50		106	129

11 52 16 – Projectors

11 52 16.10 Movie Equipment	Crew	Daily Output	Labor-Hours	Unit	Material	2014 Bare Costs Labor	Equipment	Total	Total Incl O&P
0010 **MOVIE EQUIPMENT**									
0020 Changeover, minimum				Ea.	465			465	510
0100 Maximum					905			905	995
0400 Film transport, incl. platters and autowind, minimum					5,025			5,025	5,525
0500 Maximum					14,300			14,300	15,700
0800 Lamphouses, incl. rectifiers, xenon, 1,000 watt	1 Elec	2	4		6,650	171		6,821	7,575
0900 1,600 watt		2	4		7,100	171		7,271	8,075
1000 2,000 watt		1.50	5.333		7,625	228		7,853	8,750
1100 4,000 watt		1.50	5.333		9,425	228		9,653	10,800
1400 Lenses, anamorphic, minimum					1,275			1,275	1,400
1500 Maximum					2,875			2,875	3,150
1800 Flat 35 mm, minimum					1,100			1,100	1,225
1900 Maximum					1,725			1,725	1,900
2200 Pedestals, for projectors					1,475			1,475	1,625
2300 Console type					10,700			10,700	11,800
2600 Projector mechanisms, incl. soundhead, 35 mm, minimum					11,100			11,100	12,200
2700 Maximum					15,200			15,200	16,700
3000 Projection screens, rigid, in wall, acrylic, 1/4" thick	2 Glaz	195	.082	S.F.	42	2.86		44.86	50.50
3100 1/2" thick	"	130	.123	"	48.50	4.28		52.78	60.50
3300 Electric operated, heavy duty, 400 S.F.	2 Carp	1	16	Ea.	2,950	570		3,520	4,200
3320 Theater projection screens, matte white, including frames	"	200	.080	S.F.	6.65	2.86		9.51	12.10
3400 Also see Section 11 52 13.10									
3700 Sound systems, incl. amplifier, mono, minimum	1 Elec	.90	8.889	Ea.	3,300	380		3,680	4,250
3800 Dolby/Super Sound, maximum		.40	20		18,100	855		18,955	21,300
4100 Dual system, 2 channel, front surround, minimum		.70	11.429		4,625	490		5,115	5,900
4200 Dolby/Super Sound, 4 channel, maximum		.40	20		16,500	855		17,355	19,600
4500 Sound heads, 35 mm					5,300			5,300	5,825
4900 Splicer, tape system, minimum					740			740	815
5000 Tape type, maximum					1,325			1,325	1,450
5300 Speakers, recessed behind screen, minimum	1 Elec	2	4		1,050	171		1,221	1,450
5400 Maximum	"	1	8		3,100	340		3,440	3,950
5700 Seating, painted steel, upholstered, minimum	2 Carp	35	.457		132	16.35		148.35	173
5800 Maximum	"	28	.571		420	20.50		440.50	500
6100 Rewind tables, minimum					2,650			2,650	2,900
6200 Maximum					4,725			4,725	5,175
7000 For automation, varying sophistication, minimum	1 Elec	1	8	System	2,375	340		2,715	3,175
7100 Maximum	2 Elec	.30	53.333	"	5,575	2,275		7,850	9,850

11 52 Audio-Visual Equipment

11 52 16 – Projectors

11 52 16.20 Movie Equipment- Digital	Crew	Daily Output	Labor-Hours	Unit	Material	2014 Bare Costs Labor	Equipment	Total	Total Incl O&P
0010 **MOVIE EQUIPMENT- DIGITAL**									
1000 Digital 2K projection system, 98" DMD	1 Elec	2	4	Ea.	44,000	171		44,171	48,700
1100 OEM lens		2	4		5,375	171		5,546	6,175
2000 Pedestal with power distribution		2	4		2,050	171		2,221	2,525
3000 Software		2	4		1,725	171		1,896	2,175

11 53 Laboratory Equipment

11 53 03 – Laboratory Test Equipment

11 53 03.13 Test Equipment

	Crew	Daily Output	Labor-Hours	Unit	Material	Labor	Equipment	Total	Total Incl O&P
0010 **TEST EQUIPMENT**									
1700 Thermometer, electric, portable				Ea.	490			490	540
1800 Titration unit, four 2000 ml reservoirs				"	5,500			5,500	6,050

11 53 13 – Laboratory Fume Hoods

11 53 13.13 Recirculating Laboratory Fume Hoods

	Crew	Daily Output	Labor-Hours	Unit	Material	Labor	Equipment	Total	Total Incl O&P
0010 **RECIRCULATING LABORATORY FUME HOODS**									
0600 Fume hood, with countertop & base, not including HVAC									
0610 Simple, minimum	2 Carp	5.40	2.963	L.F.	495	106		601	720
0620 Complex, including fixtures		2.40	6.667		795	238		1,033	1,275
0630 Special, maximum		1.70	9.412		830	335		1,165	1,475
0670 Service fixtures, average				Ea.	237			237	261
0680 For sink assembly with hot and cold water, add	1 Plum	1.40	5.714		725	243		968	1,200
0750 Glove box, fiberglass, bacteriological					16,900			16,900	18,600
0760 Controlled atmosphere					19,400			19,400	21,300
0770 Radioisotope					16,900			16,900	18,600
0780 Carcinogenic					16,900			16,900	18,600

11 53 13.23 Exhaust Hoods

	Crew	Daily Output	Labor-Hours	Unit	Material	Labor	Equipment	Total	Total Incl O&P
0010 **EXHAUST HOODS**									
0650 Ductwork, minimum	2 Shee	1	16	Hood	4,025	645		4,670	5,500
0660 Maximum	"	.50	32	"	6,200	1,300		7,500	8,975

11 53 16 – Laboratory Incubators

11 53 16.13 Incubators

	Crew	Daily Output	Labor-Hours	Unit	Material	Labor	Equipment	Total	Total Incl O&P
0010 **INCUBATORS**									
1000 Incubators, minimum				Ea.	3,000			3,000	3,300
1010 Maximum				"	11,700			11,700	12,800

11 53 19 – Laboratory Sterilizers

11 53 19.13 Sterilizers

	Crew	Daily Output	Labor-Hours	Unit	Material	Labor	Equipment	Total	Total Incl O&P
0010 **STERILIZERS**									
0700 Glassware washer, undercounter, minimum	L-1	1.80	5.556	Ea.	6,250	237		6,487	7,275
0710 Maximum	"	1	10		13,100	425		13,525	15,100
1850 Utensil washer-sanitizer	1 Plum	2	4		11,100	170		11,270	12,500

11 53 23 – Laboratory Refrigerators

11 53 23.13 Refrigerators

	Crew	Daily Output	Labor-Hours	Unit	Material	Labor	Equipment	Total	Total Incl O&P
0010 **REFRIGERATORS**									
1200 Blood bank, 28.6 C.F. emergency signal				Ea.	9,550			9,550	10,500
1210 Reach-in, 16.9 C.F.				"	8,425			8,425	9,275

11 53 Laboratory Equipment

11 53 33 – Emergency Safety Appliances

11 53 33.13 Emergency Equipment

	11 53 33.13 Emergency Equipment	Crew	Daily Output	Labor-Hours	Unit	Material	2014 Bare Costs Labor	Equipment	Total	Total Incl O&P
0010	**EMERGENCY EQUIPMENT**									
1400	Safety equipment, eye wash, hand held				Ea.	405			405	445
1450	Deluge shower				"	760			760	840

11 53 43 – Service Fittings and Accessories

11 53 43.13 Fittings

	11 53 43.13 Fittings	Crew	Daily Output	Labor-Hours	Unit	Material	2014 Bare Costs Labor	Equipment	Total	Total Incl O&P
0010	**FITTINGS**									
1600	Sink, one piece plastic, flask wash, hose, free standing	1 Plum	1.60	5	Ea.	1,925	213		2,138	2,475
1610	Epoxy resin sink, 25" x 16" x 10"	"	2	4	"	218	170		388	520
1950	Utility table, acid resistant top with drawers	2 Carp	30	.533	L.F.	162	19.05		181.05	210
8000	Alternate pricing method: as percent of lab furniture									
8050	Installation, not incl. plumbing & duct work				% Furn.				22%	22%
8100	Plumbing, final connections, simple system								10%	10%
8110	Moderately complex system								15%	15%
8120	Complex system								20%	20%
8150	Electrical, simple system								10%	10%
8160	Moderately complex system								20%	20%
8170	Complex system								35%	35%

11 57 Vocational Shop Equipment

11 57 10 – Shop Equipment

11 57 10.10 Vocational School Shop Equipment

	11 57 10.10 Vocational School Shop Equipment	Crew	Daily Output	Labor-Hours	Unit	Material	2014 Bare Costs Labor	Equipment	Total	Total Incl O&P
0010	**VOCATIONAL SCHOOL SHOP EQUIPMENT**									
0020	Benches, work, wood, average	2 Carp	5	3.200	Ea.	630	114		744	880
0100	Metal, average		5	3.200		545	114		659	785
0400	Combination belt & disc sander, 6"		4	4		1,650	143		1,793	2,050
0700	Drill press, floor mounted, 12", 1/2 H.P.		4	4		410	143		553	690
0800	Dust collector, not incl. ductwork, 6" diameter	1 Shee	1.10	7.273		4,600	294		4,894	5,575
0810	Dust collector bag, 20" diameter	"	5	1.600		435	64.50		499.50	590
1000	Grinders, double wheel, 1/2 H.P.	2 Carp	5	3.200		215	114		329	430
1300	Jointer, 4", 3/4 H.P.		4	4		1,350	143		1,493	1,750
1600	Kilns, 16 C.F., to 2000°		4	4		1,450	143		1,593	1,850
1900	Lathe, woodworking, 10", 1/2 H.P.		4	4		540	143		683	835
2200	Planer, 13" x 6"		4	4		1,075	143		1,218	1,450
2500	Potter's wheel, motorized		4	4		1,125	143		1,268	1,475
2800	Saws, band, 14", 3/4 H.P.		4	4		920	143		1,063	1,275
3100	Metal cutting band saw, 14"		4	4		2,500	143		2,643	3,000
3400	Radial arm saw, 10", 2 H.P.		4	4		1,350	143		1,493	1,750
3700	Scroll saw, 24"		4	4		580	143		723	880
4000	Table saw, 10", 3 H.P.		4	4		2,675	143		2,818	3,200
4300	Welder AC arc, 30 amp capacity.		4	4		3,150	143		3,293	3,700

11 61 Broadcast, Theater, and Stage Equipment

11 61 23 – Folding and Portable Stages

11 61 23.10 Portable Stages

11 61 23.10 Portable Stages	Crew	Daily Output	Labor-Hours	Unit	Material	2014 Bare Costs Labor	Equipment	Total	Total Incl O&P
0010 **PORTABLE STAGES**									
1500 Flooring, portable oak parquet, 3' x 3' sections				S.F.	13.40			13.40	14.70
1600 Cart to carry 225 S.F. of flooring				Ea.	400			400	440
5000 Stages, portable with steps, folding legs, stock, 8" high				SF Stg.	32			32	35.50
5100 16" high					49			49	54
5200 32" high					53			53	58
5300 40" high					59.50			59.50	65
6000 Telescoping platforms, extruded alum., straight, minimum	4 Carp	157	.204		34	7.30		41.30	49.50
6100 Maximum		77	.416		47	14.85		61.85	77
6500 Pie-shaped, minimum		150	.213		73.50	7.65		81.15	93.50
6600 Maximum	↓	70	.457		82	16.35		98.35	118
6800 For 3/4" plywood covered deck, deduct					4.16			4.16	4.58
7000 Band risers, steel frame, plywood deck, minimum	4 Carp	275	.116		30.50	4.16		34.66	40.50
7100 Maximum	"	138	.232	↓	69	8.30		77.30	90
7500 Chairs for above, self-storing, minimum	2 Carp	43	.372	Ea.	109	13.30		122.30	143
7600 Maximum	"	40	.400	"	192	14.30		206.30	235

11 61 33 – Rigging Systems and Controls

11 61 33.10 Controls

	Crew	Daily Output	Labor-Hours	Unit	Material	2014 Bare Costs Labor	Equipment	Total	Total Incl O&P
0010 **CONTROLS**									
0050 Control boards with dimmers and breakers, minimum	1 Elec	1	8	Ea.	12,500	340		12,840	14,300
0100 Average		.50	16		39,200	685		39,885	44,200
0150 Maximum	↓	.20	40	↓	127,500	1,700		129,200	143,500
8000 Rule of thumb: total stage equipment, minimum	4 Carp	100	.320	SF Stg.	97	11.45		108.45	126
8100 Maximum	"	25	1.280	"	545	46		591	675

11 61 43 – Stage Curtains

11 61 43.10 Curtains

	Crew	Daily Output	Labor-Hours	Unit	Material	2014 Bare Costs Labor	Equipment	Total	Total Incl O&P
0010 **CURTAINS**									
0500 Curtain track, straight, light duty	2 Carp	20	.800	L.F.	27.50	28.50		56	78
0600 Heavy duty		18	.889		61.50	32		93.50	121
0700 Curved sections		12	1.333	↓	175	47.50		222.50	273
1000 Curtains, velour, medium weight		600	.027	S.F.	7.90	.95		8.85	10.30
1150 Silica based yarn, inherently fire retardant	↓	50	.320	"	15.20	11.45		26.65	36

11 62 Musical Equipment

11 62 16 – Carillons

11 62 16.10 Bell Tower Equipment

	Crew	Daily Output	Labor-Hours	Unit	Material	2014 Bare Costs Labor	Equipment	Total	Total Incl O&P
0010 **BELL TOWER EQUIPMENT**									
0300 Carillon, 4 octave (48 bells), with keyboard				System	984,000			984,000	1,082,500
0320 2 octave (24 bells)					463,000			463,000	509,500
0340 3 to 4 bell peal, minimum					116,000			116,000	127,500
0360 Maximum				↓	694,500			694,500	764,000
0380 Cast bronze bell, average				Ea.	104,000			104,000	114,500
0400 Electronic, digital, minimum					17,400			17,400	19,100
0410 With keyboard, maximum				↓	87,000			87,000	95,500

11 66 13 – Exercise Equipment

11 66 13.10 Physical Training Equipment	Crew	Daily Output	Labor-Hours	Unit	Material	2014 Bare Costs Labor	Equipment	Total	Total Incl O&P
0010 **PHYSICAL TRAINING EQUIPMENT**									
0020 Abdominal rack, 2 board capacity				Ea.	480			480	530
0050 Abdominal board, upholstered					655			655	720
0200 Bicycle trainer, minimum					480			480	525
0300 Deluxe, electric					4,300			4,300	4,725
0400 Barbell set, chrome plated steel, 25 lb.					249			249	274
0420 100 lb.					460			460	505
0450 200 lb.					700			700	770
0500 Weight plates, cast iron, per lb.				Lb.	5.20			5.20	5.70
0520 Storage rack, 10 station				Ea.	900			900	990
0600 Circuit training apparatus, 12 machines minimum	2 Clab	1.25	12.800	Set	28,700	360		29,060	32,100
0700 Average		1	16		35,200	450		35,650	39,500
0800 Maximum	↓	.75	21.333		41,700	600		42,300	46,900
0820 Dumbbell set, cast iron, with rack and 5 pair			↓		620			620	680
0900 Squat racks	2 Clab	5	3.200	Ea.	890	90		980	1,125
1200 Multi-station gym machine, 5 station					5,000			5,000	5,500
1250 9 station					11,600			11,600	12,800
1280 Rowing machine, hydraulic					1,750			1,750	1,925
1300 Treadmill, manual					1,100			1,100	1,200
1320 Motorized					3,500			3,500	3,850
1340 Electronic					3,700			3,700	4,075
1360 Cardio-testing					4,525			4,525	5,000
1400 Treatment/massage tables, minimum					590			590	645
1420 Deluxe, with accessories					720			720	790
4150 Exercise equipment, bicycle trainer					750			750	825
4180 Chinning bar, adjustable, wall mounted	1 Carp	5	1.600		210	57		267	325
4200 Exercise ladder, 16' x 1'-7", suspended	L-2	3	5.333		1,350	167		1,517	1,750
4210 High bar, floor plate attached	1 Carp	4	2		2,225	71.50		2,296.50	2,550
4240 Parallel bars, adjustable		4	2		1,750	71.50		1,821.50	2,050
4270 Uneven parallel bars, adjustable	↓	4	2	↓	3,200	71.50		3,271.50	3,625
4280 Wall mounted, adjustable	L-2	1.50	10.667	Set	855	335		1,190	1,500
4300 Rope, ceiling mounted, 18' long	1 Carp	3.66	2.186	Ea.	188	78		266	340
4330 Side horse, vaulting		5	1.600		1,350	57		1,407	1,575
4360 Treadmill, motorized, deluxe, training type		5	1.600		3,800	57		3,857	4,275
4390 Weight lifting multi-station, minimum	2 Clab	1	16		330	450		780	1,125
4450 Maximum	"	.50	32	↓	14,700	900		15,600	17,700

11 66 23 – Gymnasium Equipment

11 66 23.13 Basketball Equipment

	Crew	Daily Output	Labor-Hours	Unit	Material	Labor	Equipment	Total	Total Incl O&P
0010 **BASKETBALL EQUIPMENT**									
1000 Backstops, wall mtd., 6' extended, fixed, minimum	L-2	1	16	Ea.	1,375	500		1,875	2,350
1100 Maximum		1	16		1,875	500		2,375	2,925
1200 Swing up, minimum		1	16		1,425	500		1,925	2,425
1250 Maximum		1	16		2,800	500		3,300	3,950
1300 Portable, manual, heavy duty, spring operated		1.90	8.421		12,600	264		12,864	14,200
1400 Ceiling suspended, stationary, minimum		.78	20.513		4,000	645		4,645	5,475
1450 Fold up, with accessories, maximum	↓	.40	40		6,000	1,250		7,250	8,700
1600 For electrically operated, add	1 Elec	1	8	↓	2,300	340		2,640	3,100
5800 Wall pads, 1-1/2" thick, standard (not fire rated)	2 Carp	640	.025	S.F.	6.20	.89		7.09	8.30

11 66 23.19 Boxing Ring

	Crew	Daily Output	Labor-Hours	Unit	Material	Labor	Equipment	Total	Total Incl O&P
0010 **BOXING RING**									
4100 Elevated, 22' x 22'	L-4	.10	160	Ea.	7,000	5,050		12,050	16,300
4110 For cellular plastic foam padding, add	↓	.10	160	↓	1,025	5,050		6,075	9,675

11 66 Athletic Equipment

11 66 23 – Gymnasium Equipment

11 66 23.19 Boxing Ring

		Crew	Daily Output	Labor-Hours	Unit	Material	2014 Bare Costs Labor	Equipment	Total	Total Incl O&P
4120	Floor level, including posts and ropes only, 20' x 20'	L-4	.80	20	Ea.	4,500	630		5,130	6,025
4130	Canvas, 30' x 30'	↓	5	3.200	↓	1,250	101		1,351	1,550

11 66 23.47 Gym Mats

0010	**GYM MATS**									
5500	2" thick, naugahyde covered				S.F.	3.67			3.67	4.04
5600	Vinyl/nylon covered					7.95			7.95	8.70
6000	Wrestling mats, 1" thick, heavy duty				↓	5.55			5.55	6.10

11 66 43 – Interior Scoreboards

11 66 43.10 Scoreboards

		Crew	Daily Output	Labor-Hours	Unit	Material	Labor	Equipment	Total	Total Incl O&P
0010	**SCOREBOARDS**									
7000	Baseball, minimum	R-3	1.30	15.385	Ea.	4,075	650	108	4,833	5,650
7200	Maximum		.05	400		17,900	16,800	2,800	37,500	50,500
7300	Football, minimum		.86	23.256		5,275	980	163	6,418	7,575
7400	Maximum		.20	100		15,700	4,200	700	20,600	25,000
7500	Basketball (one side), minimum		2.07	9.662		2,375	405	67.50	2,847.50	3,375
7600	Maximum		.30	66.667		3,475	2,800	465	6,740	8,950
7700	Hockey-basketball (four sides), minimum		.25	80		5,600	3,375	560	9,535	12,300
7800	Maximum	↓	.15	133	↓	5,675	5,625	935	12,235	16,500

11 66 53 – Gymnasium Dividers

11 66 53.10 Divider Curtains

		Crew	Daily Output	Labor-Hours	Unit	Material	Labor	Equipment	Total	Total Incl O&P
0010	**DIVIDER CURTAINS**									
4500	Gym divider curtain, mesh top, vinyl bottom, manual	L-4	500	.032	S.F.	8.90	1.01		9.91	11.50
4700	Electric roll up	L-7	400	.065	"	11.90	2		13.90	16.45

11 67 Recreational Equipment

11 67 13 – Bowling Alley Equipment

11 67 13.10 Bowling Alleys

		Crew	Daily Output	Labor-Hours	Unit	Material	Labor	Equipment	Total	Total Incl O&P
0010	**BOWLING ALLEYS** Including alley, pinsetter, scorer,									
0020	Counters and misc. supplies, minimum	4 Carp	.20	160	Lane	41,700	5,725		47,425	55,500
0150	Average		.19	168		45,900	6,025		51,925	60,500
0300	Maximum	↓	.18	177		53,000	6,350		59,350	68,500
0400	Combo table ball rack, add					1,150			1,150	1,250
0600	For automatic scorer, add, minimum					8,225			8,225	9,050
0700	Maximum				↓	9,875			9,875	10,900

11 67 23 – Shooting Range Equipment

11 67 23.10 Shooting Range

		Crew	Daily Output	Labor-Hours	Unit	Material	Labor	Equipment	Total	Total Incl O&P
0010	**SHOOTING RANGE** Incl. bullet traps, target provisions, controls,									
0100	Separators, ceiling system, etc. Not incl. structural shell									
0200	Commercial	L-9	.64	56.250	Point	28,000	1,875		29,875	34,000
0300	Law enforcement		.28	128		38,000	4,275		42,275	49,000
0400	National Guard armories		.71	50.704		20,500	1,675		22,175	25,500
0500	Reserve training centers		.71	50.704		15,800	1,675		17,475	20,200
0600	Schools and colleges		.32	112		35,000	3,750		38,750	44,800
0700	Major academies	↓	.19	189		52,000	6,300		58,300	67,500
0800	For acoustical treatment, add					10%	10%			
0900	For lighting, add					28%	25%			
1000	For plumbing, add					5%	5%			
1100	For ventilating system, add, minimum					40%	40%			
1200	Add, average				↓	25%	25%			

11 67 23 – Shooting Range Equipment

11 67 23.10 Shooting Range	Crew	Daily Output	Labor-Hours	Unit	Material	2014 Bare Costs Labor	Equipment	Total	Total Incl O&P
1300	Add, maximum				Point	35%	35%			

11 68 Play Field Equipment and Structures

11 68 13 – Playground Equipment

11 68 13.10 Free-Standing Playground Equipment

			Crew	Daily Output	Labor-Hours	Unit	Material	Labor	Equipment	Total	Total Incl O&P
0010	**FREE-STANDING PLAYGROUND EQUIPMENT** See also individual items										
0200	Bike rack, 10' long, permanent	G	B-1	12	2	Ea.	420	57.50		477.50	560
0400	Horizontal monkey ladder, 14' long, 6' high			4	6		895	173		1,068	1,275
0590	Parallel bars, 10' long			4	6		315	173		488	640
0600	Posts, tether ball set, 2-3/8" O.D.			12	2		450	57.50		507.50	590
0800	Poles, multiple purpose, 10'-6" long			12	2	Pr.	176	57.50		233.50	291
1000	Ground socket for movable posts, 2-3/8" post			10	2.400		101	69.50		170.50	228
1100	3-1/2" post			10	2.400		165	69.50		234.50	298
1300	See-saw, spring, steel, 2 units			6	4	Ea.	735	115		850	1,000
1400	4 units			4	6		1,275	173		1,448	1,700
1500	6 units			3	8		1,650	231		1,881	2,225
1700	Shelter, fiberglass golf tee, 3 person			4.60	5.217		4,300	151		4,451	5,000
1900	Slides, stainless steel bed, 12' long, 6' high			3	8		3,275	231		3,506	4,025
2000	20' long, 10' high			2	12		3,650	345		3,995	4,575
2200	Swings, plain seats, 8' high, 4 seats			2	12		1,150	345		1,495	1,825
2300	8 seats			1.30	18.462		2,150	535		2,685	3,250
2500	12' high, 4 seats			2	12		2,125	345		2,470	2,900
2600	8 seats			1.30	18.462		3,475	535		4,010	4,725
2800	Whirlers, 8' diameter			3	8		2,725	231		2,956	3,400
2900	10' diameter			3	8		6,200	231		6,431	7,225

11 68 13.20 Modular Playground

			Crew	Daily Output	Labor-Hours	Unit	Material	Labor	Equipment	Total	Total Incl O&P
0010	**MODULAR PLAYGROUND** Basic components										
0100	Deck, square, steel, 48" x 48"		B-1	1	24	Ea.	515	695		1,210	1,750
0110	Recycled polyurethane			1	24		510	695		1,205	1,725
0120	Triangular, steel, 48" side			1	24		670	695		1,365	1,925
0130	Post, steel, 5" square			18	1.333	L.F.	40	38.50		78.50	109
0140	Aluminum, 2-3/8" square			20	1.200	"	39	34.50		73.50	102
0160	Roof, square poly, 54" side			18	1.333	Ea.	1,400	38.50		1,438.50	1,600
0170	Wheelchair transfer module, for 3' high deck			3	8	"	2,925	231		3,156	3,600
0180	Guardrail, pipe, 36" high			60	.400	L.F.	196	11.55		207.55	235
0190	Steps, deck-to-deck, 3 – 8" steps			8	3	Ea.	1,100	86.50		1,186.50	1,375
0200	Activity panel, crawl through panel			2	12		495	345		840	1,125
0210	Alphabet/spelling panel			2	12		550	345		895	1,200
0360	With guardrails			3	8		1,825	231		2,056	2,400
0370	Crawl tunnel, straight, 56" long			4	6		1,200	173		1,373	1,625
0380	90°, 4' long			4	6		1,375	173		1,548	1,825
1200	Slide, tunnel, for 56" high deck			8	3		1,725	86.50		1,811.50	2,050
1210	Straight, poly			8	3		385	86.50		471.50	570
1220	Stainless steel, 54" high deck			6	4		680	115		795	945
1230	Curved, poly, 40" high deck			6	4		855	115		970	1,125
1240	Spiral slide, 56" - 72" high			5	4.800		4,425	139		4,564	5,075
1300	Ladder, vertical, for 24" - 72" high deck			5	4.800		550	139		689	840
1310	Horizontal, 8' long			5	4.800		690	139		829	990
1320	Corkscrew climber, 6' high			3	8		1,125	231		1,356	1,625
1330	Fire pole for 72" high deck			6	4		650	115		765	910
1340	Bridge, ring climber, 8' long			4	6		1,875	173		2,048	2,350

11 68 Play Field Equipment and Structures

11 68 13 – Playground Equipment

11 68 13.20 Modular Playground	Crew	Daily Output	Labor-Hours	Unit	Material	2014 Bare Costs Labor	2014 Bare Costs Equipment	Total	Total Incl O&P
1350	Suspension	B-1	4	6	L.F.	355	173		528	685

11 68 16 – Play Structures

11 68 16.10 Handball/Squash Court

		Crew	Daily Output	Labor-Hours	Unit	Material	Labor	Equipment	Total	Total Incl O&P
0010	**HANDBALL/SQUASH COURT**, outdoor									
0900	Handball or squash court, outdoor, wood	2 Carp	.50	32	Ea.	4,975	1,150		6,125	7,400
1000	Masonry handball/squash court	D-1	.30	53.333	"	23,900	1,725		25,625	29,200

11 68 16.30 Platform/Paddle Tennis Court

		Crew	Daily Output	Labor-Hours	Unit	Material	Labor	Equipment	Total	Total Incl O&P
0010	**PLATFORM/PADDLE TENNIS COURT** Complete with lighting, etc.									
0100	Aluminum slat deck with aluminum frame	B-1	.08	300	Court	60,000	8,650		68,650	80,500
0500	Aluminum slat deck with wood frame	C-1	.12	266		62,500	8,450		70,950	83,000
0800	Aluminum deck heater, add	B-1	1.18	20.339		2,550	585		3,135	3,800
0900	Douglas fir planking with wood frame 2" x 6" x 30'	C-1	.12	266		59,000	8,450		67,450	78,500
1000	Plywood deck with steel frame		.12	266		59,000	8,450		67,450	78,500
1100	Steel slat deck with wood frame		.12	266		38,900	8,450		47,350	57,000

11 68 33 – Athletic Field Equipment

11 68 33.13 Football Field Equipment

		Crew	Daily Output	Labor-Hours	Unit	Material	Labor	Equipment	Total	Total Incl O&P
0010	**FOOTBALL FIELD EQUIPMENT**									
0020	Goal posts, steel, football, double post	B-1	1.50	16	Pr.	3,750	460		4,210	4,900
0100	Deluxe, single post		1.50	16		2,600	460		3,060	3,625
0300	Football, convertible to soccer		1.50	16		2,800	460		3,260	3,850
0500	Soccer, regulation		2	12		1,400	345		1,745	2,125

11 71 Medical Sterilizing Equipment

11 71 10 – Medical Sterilizers & Distillers

11 71 10.10 Sterilizers and Distillers

		Crew	Daily Output	Labor-Hours	Unit	Material	Labor	Equipment	Total	Total Incl O&P
0010	**STERILIZERS AND DISTILLERS**									
0700	Distiller, water, steam heated, 50 gal. capacity	1 Plum	1.40	5.714	Ea.	19,000	243		19,243	21,300
5600	Sterilizers, floor loading, 26" x 62" x 42", single door, steam					121,000			121,000	133,000
5650	Double door, steam					204,000			204,000	224,000
5800	General purpose, 20" x 20" x 38", single door					12,900			12,900	14,200
6000	Portable, counter top, steam, minimum					3,500			3,500	3,850
6020	Maximum					4,275			4,275	4,700
6050	Portable, counter top, gas, 17" x 15" x 32-1/2"					39,300			39,300	43,200
6150	Manual washer/sterilizer, 16" x 16" x 26"	1 Plum	2	4		54,000	170		54,170	59,500
6200	Steam generators, electric 10 kW to 180 kW, freestanding									
6250	Minimum	1 Elec	3	2.667	Ea.	8,675	114		8,789	9,725
6300	Maximum	"	.70	11.429		28,800	490		29,290	32,500
8200	Bed pan washer-sanitizer	1 Plum	2	4		7,425	170		7,595	8,425

413

11 72 Examination and Treatment Equipment

11 72 13 – Examination Equipment

11 72 13.13 Examination Equipment

11 72 13.13 Examination Equipment	Crew	Daily Output	Labor-Hours	Unit	Material	2014 Bare Costs Labor	Equipment	Total	Total Incl O&P
0010 **EXAMINATION EQUIPMENT**									
0300 Blood pressure unit, mercurial, wall				Ea.	150			150	165
0400 Diagnostic set, wall					770			770	845
4400 Scale, physician's, with height rod				↓	315			315	350

11 72 53 – Treatment Equipment

11 72 53.13 Medical Treatment Equipment

	Crew	Daily Output	Labor-Hours	Unit	Material	2014 Bare Costs Labor	Equipment	Total	Total Incl O&P
0010 **MEDICAL TREATMENT EQUIPMENT**									
6500 Surgery table, minor minimum	1 Sswk	.70	11.429	Ea.	12,000	440		12,440	14,000
6520 Maximum	"	.50	16		20,000	615		20,615	23,200
6700 Surgical lights, doctor's office, single arm	2 Elec	2	8		2,325	340		2,665	3,100
6750 Dual arm	"	1	16	↓	4,525	685		5,210	6,100

11 73 Patient Care Equipment

11 73 10 – Patient Treatment Equipment

11 73 10.10 Treatment Equipment

	Crew	Daily Output	Labor-Hours	Unit	Material	2014 Bare Costs Labor	Equipment	Total	Total Incl O&P
0010 **TREATMENT EQUIPMENT**									
0750 Exam room furnishings, average per room				Ea.	6,975			6,975	7,675
1800 Heat therapy unit, humidified, 26" x 78" x 28"				"	3,550			3,550	3,925
2100 Hubbard tank with accessories, stainless steel,									
2110 125 GPM at 45 psi water pressure				Ea.	26,800			26,800	29,500
2150 For electric overhead hoist, add					2,925			2,925	3,225
2900 K-Module for heat therapy, 20 oz. capacity, 75°F to 110°F					420			420	460
3600 Paraffin bath, 126°F, auto controlled					1,100			1,100	1,200
3900 Parallel bars for walking training, 12'-0"					1,425			1,425	1,575
4600 Station, dietary, medium, with ice					16,500			16,500	18,200
4700 Medicine					7,450			7,450	8,200
7000 Tables, physical therapy, walk off, electric	2 Carp	3	5.333		3,325	191		3,516	4,000
7150 Standard, vinyl top with base cabinets, minimum		3	5.333		1,000	191		1,191	1,425
7200 Maximum		2	8		5,550	286		5,836	6,575
8400 Whirlpool bath, mobile, sst, 18" x 24" x 60"					4,850			4,850	5,325
8450 Fixed, incl. mixing valves	1 Plum	2	4	↓	9,575	170		9,745	10,800

11 73 10.20 Bariatric Equipment

	Crew	Daily Output	Labor-Hours	Unit	Material	2014 Bare Costs Labor	Equipment	Total	Total Incl O&P
0010 **BARIATRIC EQUIPMENT**									
5000 Patient lift, electric operated, arm style									
5110 400 lb. capacity				Ea.	1,975			1,975	2,175
5120 450 lb. capacity					3,000			3,000	3,300
5130 600 lb. capacity					3,150			3,150	3,475
5140 700 lb. capacity					5,000			5,000	5,500
5150 1,000 lb. capacity					10,700			10,700	11,800
5200 Overhead, 4-post, 1,000 lb. capacity					10,300			10,300	11,300
5300 Overhead, track type, 450 lb. capacity, not including track					2,950			2,950	3,250
5500 For fabric sling, add					310			310	340
5550 For digital scale, add				↓	770			770	845

11 74 Dental Equipment

11 74 10 – Dental Office Equipment

11 74 10.10 Diagnostic and Treatment Equipment

		Crew	Daily Output	Labor-Hours	Unit	Material	2014 Bare Costs Labor	2014 Bare Costs Equipment	Total	Total Incl O&P
0010	**DIAGNOSTIC AND TREATMENT EQUIPMENT**									
0020	Central suction system, minimum	1 Plum	1.20	6.667	Ea.	1,550	284		1,834	2,175
0100	Maximum	"	.90	8.889		4,400	380		4,780	5,475
0300	Air compressor, minimum	1 Skwk	.80	10		3,000	365		3,365	3,925
0400	Maximum		.50	16		8,850	580		9,430	10,700
0600	Chair, electric or hydraulic, minimum		.50	16		2,225	580		2,805	3,425
0700	Maximum		.25	32		7,725	1,150		8,875	10,500
0800	Doctor's/assistant's stool, minimum					251			251	276
0850	Maximum					705			705	775
1000	Drill console with accessories, minimum	1 Skwk	1.60	5		2,075	182		2,257	2,575
1100	Maximum		1.60	5		4,850	182		5,032	5,625
2000	Light, ceiling mounted, minimum		8	1		1,150	36.50		1,186.50	1,325
2100	Maximum		8	1		2,000	36.50		2,036.50	2,250
2200	Unit light, minimum	2 Skwk	5.33	3.002		730	109		839	985
2210	Maximum		5.33	3.002		1,550	109		1,659	1,900
2220	Track light, minimum		3.20	5		1,550	182		1,732	2,025
2230	Maximum		3.20	5		2,625	182		2,807	3,200
2300	Sterilizers, steam portable, minimum					1,300			1,300	1,425
2350	Maximum					10,400			10,400	11,400
2600	Steam, institutional					3,250			3,250	3,550
2650	Dry heat, electric, portable, 3 trays					1,225			1,225	1,325
2700	Ultra-sonic cleaner, portable, minimum					440			440	485
2750	Maximum (institutional)					1,325			1,325	1,450
3000	X-ray unit, wall, minimum	1 Skwk	4	2		2,325	72.50		2,397.50	2,675
3010	Maximum		4	2		4,000	72.50		4,072.50	4,525
3100	Panoramic unit		.60	13.333		15,500	485		15,985	17,900
3105	Deluxe, minimum	2 Skwk	1.60	10		16,500	365		16,865	18,700
3110	Maximum	"	1.60	10		40,500	365		40,865	45,100
3500	Developers, X-ray, average	1 Plum	5.33	1.501		4,950	64		5,014	5,550
3600	Maximum	"	5.33	1.501		8,100	64		8,164	9,000

11 76 Operating Room Equipment

11 76 10 – Operating Room Equipment

11 76 10.10 Surgical Equipment

		Crew	Daily Output	Labor-Hours	Unit	Material	2014 Bare Costs Labor	2014 Bare Costs Equipment	Total	Total Incl O&P
0010	**SURGICAL EQUIPMENT**									
5000	Scrub, surgical, stainless steel, single station, minimum	1 Plum	3	2.667	Ea.	4,250	114		4,364	4,850
5100	Maximum					6,900			6,900	7,600
6550	Major surgery table, minimum	1 Sswk	.50	16		26,000	615		26,615	29,800
6570	Maximum	"	.50	16		28,000	615		28,615	32,000
6800	Surgical lights, major operating room, dual head, minimum	2 Elec	1	16		4,450	685		5,135	6,000
6850	Maximum	"	1	16		29,700	685		30,385	33,800

11 77 Radiology Equipment

11 77 10 – Radiology Equipment

11 77 10.10 X-Ray Equipment	Crew	Daily Output	Labor-Hours	Unit	Material	2014 Bare Costs Labor	Equipment	Total	Total Incl O&P
0010 **X-RAY EQUIPMENT**									
8700 X-ray, mobile, minimum				Ea.	16,600			16,600	18,300
8750 Maximum					77,000			77,000	84,500
8900 Stationary, minimum					42,700			42,700	47,000
8950 Maximum					222,000			222,000	244,000
9150 Developing processors, minimum					4,700			4,700	5,175
9200 Maximum					12,700			12,700	14,000

11 78 Mortuary Equipment

11 78 13 – Mortuary Refrigerators

11 78 13.10 Mortuary and Autopsy Equipment

	Crew	Daily Output	Labor-Hours	Unit	Material	Labor	Equipment	Total	Total Incl O&P
0010 **MORTUARY AND AUTOPSY EQUIPMENT**									
0015 Autopsy table, standard	1 Plum	1	8	Ea.	9,625	340		9,965	11,200
0020 Deluxe	"	.60	13.333		14,900	570		15,470	17,300
3200 Mortuary refrigerator, end operated, 2 capacity					12,200			12,200	13,400
3300 6 capacity					21,900			21,900	24,100

11 78 16 – Crematorium Equipment

11 78 16.10 Crematory

	Crew	Daily Output	Labor-Hours	Unit	Material	Labor	Equipment	Total	Total Incl O&P
0010 **CREMATORY**									
1500 Crematory, not including building, 1 place	Q-3	.20	160	Ea.	71,500	6,125		77,625	89,000
1750 2 place	"	.10	320	"	102,500	12,300		114,800	132,500

11 82 Solid Waste Handling Equipment

11 82 19 – Packaged Incinerators

11 82 19.10 Packaged Gas Fired Incinerators

	Crew	Daily Output	Labor-Hours	Unit	Material	Labor	Equipment	Total	Total Incl O&P
0010 **PACKAGED GAS FIRED INCINERATORS**									
4400 Incinerator, gas, not incl. chimney, elec. or pipe, 50#/hr., minimum	Q-3	.80	40	Ea.	38,000	1,525		39,525	44,300
4420 Maximum		.70	45.714		40,000	1,750		41,750	46,900
4440 200 lb. per hr., minimum (batch type)		.60	53.333		67,000	2,050		69,050	77,000
4460 Maximum (with feeder)		.50	64		75,000	2,450		77,450	86,500
4480 400 lb. per hr., minimum (batch type)		.30	106		78,000	4,100		82,100	93,000
4500 Maximum (with feeder)		.25	128		100,000	4,900		104,900	118,000
4520 800 lb. per hr., with feeder, minimum		.20	160		120,000	6,125		126,125	142,000
4540 Maximum		.17	188		180,000	7,225		187,225	210,000
4560 1,200 lb. per hr., with feeder, minimum		.15	213		152,000	8,175		160,175	180,500
4580 Maximum		.11	290		197,500	11,200		208,700	236,000
4600 2,000 lb. per hr., with feeder, minimum		.10	320		400,000	12,300		412,300	460,000
4620 Maximum		.05	640		600,000	24,500		624,500	700,500
4700 For heat recovery system, add, minimum		.25	128		80,000	4,900		84,900	96,000
4710 Add, maximum		.11	290		250,000	11,200		261,200	293,500
4720 For automatic ash conveyer, add		.50	64		33,300	2,450		35,750	40,700
4750 Large municipal incinerators, incl. stack, minimum		.25	128	Ton/day	20,200	4,900		25,100	30,300
4850 Maximum		.10	320	"	54,000	12,300		66,300	79,000

11 82 26 – Facility Waste Compactors

11 82 26.10 Compactors

	Crew	Daily Output	Labor-Hours	Unit	Material	Labor	Equipment	Total	Total Incl O&P
0010 **COMPACTORS**									
0020 Compactors, 115 volt, 250#/hr., chute fed	L-4	1	16	Ea.	11,900	505		12,405	14,000
0100 Hand fed		2.40	6.667		14,900	211		15,111	16,800

11 82 Solid Waste Handling Equipment

11 82 26 – Facility Waste Compactors

11 82 26.10 Compactors	Crew	Daily Output	Labor-Hours	Unit	Material	2014 Bare Costs Labor	Equipment	Total	Total Incl O&P
0300	Multi-bag, 230 volt, 600#/hr., chute fed	L-4	1	16	Ea.	14,900	505		15,405	17,300
0400	Hand fed		1	16		15,100	505		15,605	17,500
0500	Containerized, hand fed, 2 to 6 C.Y. containers, 250#/hr.		1	16		14,900	505		15,405	17,300
0550	For chute fed, add per floor		1	16		1,375	505		1,880	2,375
1000	Heavy duty industrial compactor, 0.5 C.Y. capacity		1	16		10,000	505		10,505	11,900
1050	1.0 C.Y. capacity		1	16		15,000	505		15,505	17,400
1100	3.0 C.Y. capacity		.50	32		25,600	1,000		26,600	29,900
1150	5.0 C.Y. capacity		.50	32		32,200	1,000		33,200	37,100
1200	Combination shredder/compactor (5,000 lb./hr.)	↓	.50	32		62,500	1,000		63,500	70,500
1400	For handling hazardous waste materials, 55 gallon drum packer, std.					19,500			19,500	21,500
1410	55 gallon drum packer w/HEPA filter					24,300			24,300	26,700
1420	55 gallon drum packer w/charcoal & HEPA filter					32,400			32,400	35,600
1430	All of the above made explosion proof, add					1,425			1,425	1,575
5500	Shredder, municipal use, 35 ton per hour					301,000			301,000	331,000
5600	60 ton per hour					641,000			641,000	705,000
5750	Shredder & baler, 50 ton per day					601,000			601,000	661,000
5800	Shredder, industrial, minimum					23,700			23,700	26,100
5850	Maximum					127,000			127,000	139,500
5900	Baler, industrial, minimum					9,500			9,500	10,500
5950	Maximum				↓	554,000			554,000	609,500
6000	Transfer station compactor, with power unit									
6050	and pedestal, not including pit, 50 ton per hour				Ea.	190,000			190,000	209,000

11 91 Religious Equipment

11 91 13 – Baptisteries

11 91 13.10 Baptistry

		Crew	Daily Output	Labor-Hours	Unit	Material	Labor	Equipment	Total	Total Incl O&P
0010	**BAPTISTRY**									
0150	Fiberglass, 3'-6" deep, x 13'-7" long,									
0160	steps at both ends, incl. plumbing, minimum	L-8	1	20	Ea.	5,650	670		6,320	7,350
0200	Maximum	"	.70	28.571		9,225	960		10,185	11,700
0250	Add for filter, heater and lights			↓		1,825			1,825	2,025

11 91 23 – Sanctuary Equipment

11 91 23.10 Sanctuary Furnishings

		Crew	Daily Output	Labor-Hours	Unit	Material	Labor	Equipment	Total	Total Incl O&P
0010	**SANCTUARY FURNISHINGS**									
0020	Altar, wood, custom design, plain	1 Carp	1.40	5.714	Ea.	2,525	204		2,729	3,125
0050	Deluxe	"	.20	40		12,200	1,425		13,625	15,800
0071	Granite or marble, average	2 Ston	.50	32		13,200	1,125		14,325	16,400
0091	Deluxe	"	.20	80		37,500	2,800		40,300	46,000
0100	Arks, prefabricated, plain	2 Carp	.80	20		9,650	715		10,365	11,800
0130	Deluxe, maximum	"	.20	80		137,000	2,850		139,850	155,500
0500	Reconciliation room, wood, prefabricated, single, plain	1 Carp	.60	13.333		3,150	475		3,625	4,250
0550	Deluxe		.40	20		8,650	715		9,365	10,700
0650	Double, plain		.40	20		6,275	715		6,990	8,125
0700	Deluxe		.20	40		18,800	1,425		20,225	23,000
1000	Lecterns, wood, plain		5	1.600		835	57		892	1,000
1100	Deluxe		2	4		6,050	143		6,193	6,900
2000	Pulpits, hardwood, prefabricated, plain		2	4		1,475	143		1,618	1,875
2100	Deluxe		1.60	5	↓	10,000	179		10,179	11,300
2500	Railing, hardwood, average		25	.320	L.F.	206	11.45		217.45	245
3000	Seating, individual, oak, contour, laminated	↓	21	.381	Person	176	13.60		189.60	217

11 91 23.10 Sanctuary Furnishings		Crew	Daily Output	Labor-Hours	Unit	Material	2014 Bare Costs Labor	Equipment	Total	Total Incl O&P
3100	Cushion seat	1 Carp	21	.381	Person	160	13.60		173.60	199
3200	Fully upholstered		21	.381		156	13.60		169.60	195
3300	Combination, self-rising	↓	21	.381		300	13.60		313.60	355
3500	For cherry, add				↓	30%				
5000	Wall cross, aluminum, extruded, 2" x 2" section	1 Carp	34	.235	L.F.	215	8.40		223.40	251
5150	4" x 4" section		29	.276		310	9.85		319.85	355
5300	Bronze, extruded, 1" x 2" section		31	.258		425	9.25		434.25	480
5350	2-1/2" x 2-1/2" section		34	.235		640	8.40		648.40	720
5450	Solid bar stock, 1/2" x 3" section		29	.276		845	9.85		854.85	945
5600	Fiberglass, stock		34	.235		145	8.40		153.40	174
5700	Stainless steel, 4" deep, channel section		29	.276		680	9.85		689.85	765
5800	4" deep box section	↓	29	.276	↓	925	9.85		934.85	1,050

Estimating Tips

General

• The items in this division are usually priced per square foot or each. Most of these items are purchased by the owner and installed by the contractor. Do not assume the items in Division 12 will be purchased and installed by the contractor. Check the specifications for responsibilities and include receiving, storage, installation, and mechanical and electrical hookups in the appropriate divisions.

• Some items in this division require some type of support system that is not usually furnished with the item. Examples of these systems include blocking for the attachment of casework and heavy drapery rods. The required blocking must be added to the estimate in the appropriate division.

Reference Numbers

Reference numbers are shown in shaded boxes at the beginning of some major classifications. These numbers refer to related items in the Reference Section. The reference information may be an estimating procedure, an alternate pricing method, or technical information.

Note: Not all subdivisions listed here necessarily appear in this publication.

Division 12 - Furnishings

12 21 Window Blinds

12 21 13 – Horizontal Louver Blinds

12 21 13.13 Metal Horizontal Louver Blinds	Crew	Daily Output	Labor-Hours	Unit	Material	2014 Bare Costs Labor	Equipment	Total	Total Incl O&P
0010	**METAL HORIZONTAL LOUVER BLINDS**									
0020	Horizontal, 1" aluminum slats, solid color, stock	1 Carp	590	.014	S.F.	4.80	.48		5.28	6.10
0070	Horizontal, 1" aluminum slats, custom color		590	.014		5.30	.48		5.78	6.60
0250	2" aluminum slats, solid color, stock		590	.014		7.65	.48		8.13	9.20
0275	2" aluminum slats, custom color		590	.014		5.60	.48		6.08	6.95

12 21 13.33 Vinyl Horizontal Louver Blinds

		Crew	Daily Output	Labor-Hours	Unit	Material	2014 Bare Costs Labor	Equipment	Total	Total Incl O&P
0010	**VINYL HORIZONTAL LOUVER BLINDS**									
0100	2" composite, 48" wide, 48" high	1 Carp	30	.267	Ea.	90	9.55		99.55	115
0120	72" high		29	.276		129	9.85		138.85	158
0140	96" high		28	.286		177	10.20		187.20	211
0200	60" wide, 60" high		27	.296		97.50	10.60		108.10	125
0220	72" high		25	.320		112	11.45		123.45	142
0240	96" high		24	.333		178	11.90		189.90	216
0300	72" wide, 72" high		25	.320		190	11.45		201.45	229
0320	96" high		23	.348		266	12.45		278.45	315
0400	96" wide, 96" high		20	.400		310	14.30		324.30	365
1000	2" faux wood, 48" wide, 48" high		30	.267		58	9.55		67.55	80
1020	72" high		29	.276		79	9.85		88.85	104
1040	96" high		28	.286		98	10.20		108.20	125
1300	72" wide, 72" high		25	.320		122	11.45		133.45	154
1320	96" high		23	.348		192	12.45		204.45	232
1400	96" wide, 96" high		20	.400		212	14.30		226.30	258

12 21 16 – Vertical Louver Blinds

12 21 16.13 Metal Vertical Louver Blinds

		Crew	Daily Output	Labor-Hours	Unit	Material	2014 Bare Costs Labor	Equipment	Total	Total Incl O&P
0010	**METAL VERTICAL LOUVER BLINDS**									
1500	Vertical, 3" PVC strips, minimum	1 Carp	460	.017	S.F.	7.80	.62		8.42	9.60
1600	Maximum		400	.020		23	.72		23.72	26.50
1800	4" aluminum slats, minimum		460	.017		7.95	.62		8.57	9.80
1900	Maximum		400	.020		14.65	.72		15.37	17.35

12 22 Curtains and Drapes

12 22 16 – Drapery Track and Accessories

12 22 16.10 Drapery Hardware

		Crew	Daily Output	Labor-Hours	Unit	Material	2014 Bare Costs Labor	Equipment	Total	Total Incl O&P
0010	**DRAPERY HARDWARE**									
0030	Standard traverse, per foot, minimum	1 Carp	59	.136	L.F.	6.85	4.85		11.70	15.65
0100	Maximum		51	.157	"	10	5.60		15.60	20.50
4000	Traverse rods, adjustable, 28" to 48"		22	.364	Ea.	22.50	13		35.50	46.50
4020	48" to 84"		20	.400		28.50	14.30		42.80	55
4040	66" to 120"		18	.444		34.50	15.90		50.40	64
4060	84" to 156"		16	.500		39	17.90		56.90	73
4080	100" to 180"		14	.571		45.50	20.50		66	84.50
4100	228" to 312"		13	.615		63	22		85	107
4600	Valance, pinch pleated fabric, 12" deep, up to 54" long, minimum					38.50			38.50	42.50
4610	Maximum					96			96	106
4620	Up to 77" long, minimum					59			59	65
4630	Maximum					155			155	171
5000	Stationary rods, first 2'					8.10			8.10	8.90
5020	Each additional foot, add				L.F.	3.82			3.82	4.20

12 22 Curtains and Drapes

12 22 16 – Drapery Track and Accessories

12 22 16.20 Blast Curtains	Crew	Daily Output	Labor-Hours	Unit	Material	2014 Bare Costs Labor	Equipment	Total	Total Incl O&P
0010 **BLAST CURTAINS** per L.F. horizontal opening width, off-white or gray fabric									
0100 Blast curtains, drapery system, complete, including hardware, minimum	1 Carp	10.25	.780	L.F.	185	28		213	251
0120 Average		10.25	.780		200	28		228	267
0140 Maximum		10.25	.780		230	28		258	300

12 23 Interior Shutters

12 23 10 – Wood Interior Shutters

12 23 10.10 Wood Interior Shutters

	Crew	Daily Output	Labor-Hours	Unit	Material	Labor	Equipment	Total	Total Incl O&P
0010 **WOOD INTERIOR SHUTTERS**, louvered									
0200 Two panel, 27" wide, 36" high	1 Carp	5	1.600	Set	147	57		204	258
0300 33" wide, 36" high		5	1.600		190	57		247	305
0500 47" wide, 36" high		5	1.600		255	57		312	375
1000 Four panel, 27" wide, 36" high		5	1.600		216	57		273	335
1100 33" wide, 36" high		5	1.600		276	57		333	400
1300 47" wide, 36" high		5	1.600		370	57		427	500

12 23 10.13 Wood Panels

	Crew	Daily Output	Labor-Hours	Unit	Material	Labor	Equipment	Total	Total Incl O&P
0010 **WOOD PANELS**									
3000 Wood folding panels with movable louvers, 7" x 20" each	1 Carp	17	.471	Pr.	78	16.80		94.80	115
3300 8" x 28" each		17	.471		78	16.80		94.80	115
3450 9" x 36" each		17	.471		90	16.80		106.80	128
3600 10" x 40" each		17	.471		98	16.80		114.80	137
4000 Fixed louver type, stock units, 8" x 20" each		17	.471		92	16.80		108.80	130
4150 10" x 28" each		17	.471		78	16.80		94.80	114
4300 12" x 36" each		17	.471		92	16.80		108.80	130
4450 18" x 40" each		17	.471		132	16.80		148.80	174
5000 Insert panel type, stock, 7" x 20" each		17	.471		20.50	16.80		37.30	51
5150 8" x 28" each		17	.471		37.50	16.80		54.30	69.50
5300 9" x 36" each		17	.471		47.50	16.80		64.30	80.50
5450 10" x 40" each		17	.471		51	16.80		67.80	84.50
5600 Raised panel type, stock, 10" x 24" each		17	.471		243	16.80		259.80	296
5650 12" x 26" each		17	.471		243	16.80		259.80	296
5700 14" x 30" each		17	.471		268	16.80		284.80	325
5750 16" x 36" each		17	.471		296	16.80		312.80	355
6000 For custom built pine, add					22%				
6500 For custom built hardwood blinds, add					42%				

12 24 Window Shades

12 24 13 – Roller Window Shades

12 24 13.10 Shades

	Crew	Daily Output	Labor-Hours	Unit	Material	Labor	Equipment	Total	Total Incl O&P
0010 **SHADES**									
0020 Basswood, roll-up, stain finish, 3/8" slats	1 Carp	300	.027	S.F.	14.65	.95		15.60	17.70
0200 7/8" slats		300	.027		13.85	.95		14.80	16.80
0300 Vertical side slide, stain finish, 3/8" slats		300	.027		18.95	.95		19.90	22.50
0400 7/8" slats		300	.027		18.95	.95		19.90	22.50
0500 For fire retardant finishes, add					16%				
0600 For "B" rated finishes, add					20%				
0900 Mylar, single layer, non-heat reflective	1 Carp	685	.012		4.96	.42		5.38	6.15
0910 Mylar, single layer, heat reflective		685	.012		5.35	.42		5.77	6.60

12 24 Window Shades

12 24 13 – Roller Window Shades

12 24 13.10 Shades		Crew	Daily Output	Labor-Hours	Unit	Material	2014 Bare Costs Labor	2014 Bare Costs Equipment	Total	Total Incl O&P
1000	Double layered, heat reflective	1 Carp	685	.012	S.F.	5.75	.42		6.17	7
1100	Triple layered, heat reflective	↓	685	.012	↓	6.25	.42		6.67	7.60
1200	For metal roller instead of wood, add per				Shade	4.42			4.42	4.86
1300	Vinyl coated cotton, standard	1 Carp	685	.012	S.F.	2.84	.42		3.26	3.82
1400	Lightproof decorator shades		685	.012		2.94	.42		3.36	3.93
1500	Vinyl, lightweight, 4 ga.		685	.012		.60	.42		1.02	1.36
1600	Heavyweight, 6 ga.		685	.012		1.83	.42		2.25	2.71
1700	Vinyl laminated fiberglass, 6 ga., translucent		685	.012		2.55	.42		2.97	3.51
1800	Lightproof	↓	685	.012	↓	4.19	.42		4.61	5.30

12 32 Manufactured Wood Casework

12 32 16 – Manufactured Plastic-Laminate-Clad Casework

12 32 16.20 Plastic Laminate Casework Doors

		Crew	Daily Output	Labor-Hours	Unit	Material	2014 Bare Costs Labor	2014 Bare Costs Equipment	Total	Total Incl O&P
0010	**PLASTIC LAMINATE CASEWORK DOORS**									
1000	For casework frames, see Section 12 32 23.15									
1100	For casework hardware, see Section 12 32 23.35									
6000	Plastic laminate on particle board									
6100	12" wide, 18" high	1 Carp	25	.320	Ea.	24	11.45		35.45	46
6140	30" high		23	.348		40	12.45		52.45	65
6500	18" wide, 18" high		24	.333		36	11.90		47.90	59.50
6600	30" high	↓	22	.364	↓	60	13		73	88

12 32 16.25 Plastic Laminate Drawer Fronts

		Crew	Daily Output	Labor-Hours	Unit	Material	2014 Bare Costs Labor	2014 Bare Costs Equipment	Total	Total Incl O&P
0010	**PLASTIC LAMINATE DRAWER FRONTS**									
2800	Plastic laminate on particle board front									
3000	4" high, 12" wide	1 Carp	17	.471	Ea.	3.93	16.80		20.73	33
3200	18" wide	"	16	.500	"	5.90	17.90		23.80	36.50

12 32 23 – Hardwood Casework

12 32 23.10 Manufactured Wood Casework, Stock Units

		Crew	Daily Output	Labor-Hours	Unit	Material	2014 Bare Costs Labor	2014 Bare Costs Equipment	Total	Total Incl O&P
0010	**MANUFACTURED WOOD CASEWORK, STOCK UNITS**									
0300	Built-in drawer units, pine, 18" deep, 32" high, unfinished									
0400	Minimum	2 Carp	53	.302	L.F.	114	10.80		124.80	143
0500	Maximum	"	40	.400	"	134	14.30		148.30	172
0700	Kitchen base cabinets, hardwood, not incl. counter tops,									
0710	24" deep, 35" high, prefinished									
0800	One top drawer, one door below, 12" wide	2 Carp	24.80	.645	Ea.	254	23		277	320
0840	18" wide		23.30	.687		287	24.50		311.50	355
0880	24" wide		22.30	.717		350	25.50		375.50	430
1000	Four drawers, 12" wide		24.80	.645		267	23		290	330
1040	18" wide		23.30	.687		298	24.50		322.50	370
1060	24" wide		22.30	.717		330	25.50		355.50	405
1200	Two top drawers, two doors below, 27" wide		22	.727		375	26		401	460
1260	36" wide		20.30	.788		435	28		463	530
1300	48" wide		18.90	.847		495	30.50		525.50	595
1500	Range or sink base, two doors below, 30" wide		21.40	.748		335	26.50		361.50	415
1540	36" wide		20.30	.788		380	28		408	465
1580	48" wide	↓	18.90	.847		415	30.50		445.50	510
1800	For sink front units, deduct					154			154	169
2000	Corner base cabinets, 36" wide, standard	2 Carp	18	.889		600	32		632	715
2100	Lazy Susan with revolving door	"	16.50	.970	↓	805	34.50		839.50	945
4000	Kitchen wall cabinets, hardwood, 12" deep with two doors									

12 32 Manufactured Wood Casework

12 32 23 – Hardwood Casework

12 32 23.10 Manufactured Wood Casework, Stock Units

		Crew	Daily Output	Labor-Hours	Unit	Material	2014 Bare Costs Labor	Equipment	Total	Total Incl O&P
4050	12" high, 30" wide	2 Carp	24.80	.645	Ea.	227	23		250	289
4100	36" wide		24	.667		270	24		294	335
4400	15" high, 30" wide		24	.667		231	24		255	294
4440	36" wide		22.70	.705		277	25		302	350
4700	24" high, 30" wide		23.30	.687		310	24.50		334.50	380
4720	36" wide		22.70	.705		340	25		365	420
5000	30" high, one door, 12" wide		22	.727		207	26		233	271
5040	18" wide		20.90	.766		254	27.50		281.50	325
5060	24" wide		20.30	.788		296	28		324	375
5300	Two doors, 27" wide		19.80	.808		325	29		354	405
5340	36" wide		18.80	.851		395	30.50		425.50	480
5380	48" wide		18.40	.870		480	31		511	585
6000	Corner wall, 30" high, 24" wide		18	.889		340	32		372	430
6050	30" wide		17.20	.930		360	33.50		393.50	455
6100	36" wide		16.50	.970		410	34.50		444.50	510
6500	Revolving Lazy Susan		15.20	1.053		460	37.50		497.50	570
7000	Broom cabinet, 84" high, 24" deep, 18" wide		10	1.600		625	57		682	780
7500	Oven cabinets, 84" high, 24" deep, 27" wide		8	2		960	71.50		1,031.50	1,175
7750	Valance board trim		396	.040	L.F.	13	1.44		14.44	16.75
7780	Toe kick trim	1 Carp	256	.031	"	2.79	1.12		3.91	4.95
7790	Base cabinet corner filler		16	.500	Ea.	41.50	17.90		59.40	75.50
7800	Cabinet filler, 3" x 24"		20	.400		18.05	14.30		32.35	44
7810	3" x 30"		20	.400		22.50	14.30		36.80	49
7820	3" x 42"		18	.444		31.50	15.90		47.40	61
7830	3" x 80"		16	.500		60	17.90		77.90	96
7850	Cabinet panel		50	.160	S.F.	8.35	5.70		14.05	18.75
9000	For deluxe models of all cabinets, add					40%				
9500	For custom built in place, add					25%	10%			
9558	Rule of thumb, kitchen cabinets not including									
9560	appliances & counter top, minimum	2 Carp	30	.533	L.F.	168	19.05		187.05	217
9600	Maximum	"	25	.640	"	380	23		403	455
9610	For metal cabinets, see Section 12 35 70.13									

12 32 23.15 Manufactured Wood Casework Frames

		Crew	Daily Output	Labor-Hours	Unit	Material	2014 Bare Costs Labor	Equipment	Total	Total Incl O&P
0010	**MANUFACTURED WOOD CASEWORK FRAMES**									
0050	Base cabinets, counter storage, 36" high									
0100	One bay, 18" wide	1 Carp	2.70	2.963	Ea.	164	106		270	360
0400	Two bay, 36" wide		2.20	3.636		250	130		380	495
1100	Three bay, 54" wide		1.50	5.333		298	191		489	645
2800	Bookcases, one bay, 7' high, 18" wide		2.40	3.333		193	119		312	415
3500	Two bay, 36" wide		1.60	5		280	179		459	610
4100	Three bay, 54" wide		1.20	6.667		465	238		703	910
5100	Coat racks, one bay, 7' high, 24" wide		4.50	1.778		192	63.50		255.50	320
5300	Two bay, 48" wide		2.75	2.909		268	104		372	470
5800	Three bay, 72" wide		2.10	3.810		395	136		531	665
6100	Wall mounted cabinet, one bay, 24" high, 18" wide		3.60	2.222		106	79.50		185.50	250
6800	Two bay, 36" wide		2.20	3.636		154	130		284	390
7400	Three bay, 54" wide		1.70	4.706		192	168		360	495
8400	30" high, one bay, 18" wide		3.60	2.222		115	79.50		194.50	260
9000	Two bay, 36" wide		2.15	3.721		153	133		286	390
9400	Three bay, 54" wide		1.60	5		191	179		370	510
9800	Wardrobe, 7' high, single, 24" wide		2.70	2.963		212	106		318	410
9880	Partition & adjustable shelves, 48" wide		1.70	4.706		270	168		438	580

12 32 Manufactured Wood Casework

12 32 23 – Hardwood Casework

12 32 23.15 Manufactured Wood Casework Frames	Crew	Daily Output	Labor-Hours	Unit	Material	2014 Bare Costs Labor	Equipment	Total	Total Incl O&P
9950 Partition, adjustable shelves & drawers, 48" wide	1 Carp	1.40	5.714	Ea.	405	204		609	790

12 32 23.20 Manufactured Hardwood Casework Doors

	Crew	Daily Output	Labor-Hours	Unit	Material	2014 Bare Costs Labor	Equipment	Total	Total Incl O&P
0010 **MANUFACTURED HARDWOOD CASEWORK DOORS**									
2000 Glass panel, hardwood frame									
2200 12" wide, 18" high	1 Carp	34	.235	Ea.	25.50	8.40		33.90	42
2600 30" high		32	.250		42.50	8.95		51.45	62
4450 18" wide, 18" high		32	.250		38.50	8.95		47.45	57
4550 30" high	↓	29	.276	↓	64	9.85		73.85	86.50
5000 Hardwood, raised panel									
5100 12" wide, 18" high	1 Carp	16	.500	Ea.	28.50	17.90		46.40	61.50
5200 30" high		15	.533		47.50	19.05		66.55	84.50
5500 18" wide, 18" high		15	.533		43	19.05		62.05	79
5600 30" high	↓	14	.571	↓	71.50	20.50		92	113

12 32 23.25 Manufactured Wood Casework Drawer Fronts

	Crew	Daily Output	Labor-Hours	Unit	Material	2014 Bare Costs Labor	Equipment	Total	Total Incl O&P
0010 **MANUFACTURED WOOD CASEWORK DRAWER FRONTS**									
0100 Solid hardwood front									
1000 4" high, 12" wide	1 Carp	17	.471	Ea.	4.33	16.80		21.13	33.50
1200 18" wide	"	16	.500	"	6.50	17.90		24.40	37

12 32 23.30 Manufactured Wood Casework Vanities

	Crew	Daily Output	Labor-Hours	Unit	Material	2014 Bare Costs Labor	Equipment	Total	Total Incl O&P
0010 **MANUFACTURED WOOD CASEWORK VANITIES**									
8000 Vanity bases, 2 doors, 30" high, 21" deep, 24" wide	2 Carp	20	.800	Ea.	297	28.50		325.50	375
8050 30" wide		16	1		355	36		391	450
8100 36" wide		13.33	1.200		345	43		388	450
8150 48" wide	↓	11.43	1.400		450	50		500	580
9000 For deluxe models of all vanities, add to above					40%				
9500 For custom built in place, add to above				↓	25%	10%			

12 32 23.35 Manufactured Wood Casework Hardware

	Crew	Daily Output	Labor-Hours	Unit	Material	2014 Bare Costs Labor	Equipment	Total	Total Incl O&P
0010 **MANUFACTURED WOOD CASEWORK HARDWARE**									
1000 Catches, minimum	1 Carp	235	.034	Ea.	1.17	1.22		2.39	3.34
1040 Maximum	"	80	.100	"	7.20	3.58		10.78	13.95
2000 Door/drawer pulls, handles									
2200 Handles and pulls, projecting, metal, minimum	1 Carp	48	.167	Ea.	4.80	5.95		10.75	15.35
2240 Maximum		36	.222		10.15	7.95		18.10	24.50
2300 Wood, minimum		48	.167		5.05	5.95		11	15.60
2340 Maximum		36	.222		9.25	7.95		17.20	23.50
2600 Flush, metal, minimum		48	.167		5.05	5.95		11	15.60
2640 Maximum		36	.222	↓	9.25	7.95		17.20	23.50
3000 Drawer tracks/glides, minimum		48	.167	Pr.	8.55	5.95		14.50	19.45
3040 Maximum		24	.333		25	11.90		36.90	47.50
4000 Cabinet hinges, minimum		160	.050		2.90	1.79		4.69	6.20
4040 Maximum	↓	68	.118	↓	11	4.21		15.21	19.20

12 35 Specialty Casework

12 35 50 – Educational/Library Casework

12 35 50.13 Educational Casework

		Crew	Daily Output	Labor-Hours	Unit	Material	2014 Bare Costs Labor	Equipment	Total	Total Incl O&P
0010	**EDUCATIONAL CASEWORK**									
5000	School, 24" deep, metal, 84" high units	2 Carp	15	1.067	L.F.	420	38		458	525
5150	Counter height units		20	.800		282	28.50		310.50	360
5450	Wood, custom fabricated, 32" high counter		20	.800		235	28.50		263.50	305
5600	Add for counter top		56	.286		25	10.20		35.20	44.50
5800	84" high wall units		15	1.067		455	38		493	565
6000	Laminated plastic finish is same price as wood									

12 35 53 – Laboratory Casework

12 35 53.13 Metal Laboratory Casework

		Crew	Daily Output	Labor-Hours	Unit	Material	2014 Bare Costs Labor	Equipment	Total	Total Incl O&P
0010	**METAL LABORATORY CASEWORK**									
0020	Cabinets, base, door units, metal	2 Carp	18	.889	L.F.	228	32		260	305
0300	Drawer units		18	.889		505	32		537	615
0700	Tall storage cabinets, open, 7' high		20	.800		485	28.50		513.50	585
0900	With glazed doors		20	.800		735	28.50		763.50	855
1300	Wall cabinets, metal, 12-1/2" deep, open		20	.800		164	28.50		192.50	229
1500	With doors		20	.800		340	28.50		368.50	425
6300	Rule of thumb: lab furniture including installation & connection									
6320	High school				S.F.				35	39
6340	College								52	57
6360	Clinical, health care								45	49.50
6380	Industrial								72.50	79.50

12 35 59 – Display Casework

12 35 59.10 Display Cases

		Crew	Daily Output	Labor-Hours	Unit	Material	2014 Bare Costs Labor	Equipment	Total	Total Incl O&P
0010	**DISPLAY CASES** Free standing, all glass									
0020	Aluminum frame, 42" high x 36" x 12" deep	2 Carp	8	2	Ea.	1,225	71.50		1,296.50	1,450
0100	70" high x 48" x 18" deep	"	6	2.667		3,725	95.50		3,820.50	4,250
0500	For wood bases, add					9%				
0600	For hardwood frames, deduct					8%				
0700	For bronze, baked enamel finish, add					10%				
2000	Wall mounted, glass front, aluminum frame									
2010	Non-illuminated, one section 3' x 4' x 1'-4"	2 Carp	5	3.200	Ea.	2,150	114		2,264	2,550
2100	5' x 4' x 1'-4"		5	3.200		2,475	114		2,589	2,925
2200	6' x 4' x 1'-4"		4	4		2,975	143		3,118	3,525
2500	Two sections, 8' x 4' x 1'-4"		2	8		2,175	286		2,461	2,875
2600	10' x 4' x 1'-4"		2	8		2,675	286		2,961	3,400
3000	Three sections, 16' x 4' x 1'-4"		1.50	10.667		4,050	380		4,430	5,100
3500	For fluorescent lights, add				Section	330			330	365
4000	Table exhibit cases, 2' wide, 3' high, 4' long, flat top	2 Carp	5	3.200	Ea.	1,375	114		1,489	1,700
4100	3' wide, 3' high, 4' long, sloping top	"	3	5.333	"	810	191		1,001	1,200

12 35 70 – Healthcare Casework

12 35 70.13 Hospital Casework

		Crew	Daily Output	Labor-Hours	Unit	Material	2014 Bare Costs Labor	Equipment	Total	Total Incl O&P
0010	**HOSPITAL CASEWORK**									
0500	Base cabinets, laminated plastic	2 Carp	10	1.600	L.F.	269	57		326	390
1000	Stainless steel	"	10	1.600		495	57		552	640
1200	For all drawers, add					28			28	31
1300	Cabinet base trim, 4" high, enameled steel	2 Carp	200	.080		45	2.86		47.86	54.50
1400	Stainless steel		200	.080		90.50	2.86		93.36	104
1450	Countertop, laminated plastic, no backsplash		40	.400		46.50	14.30		60.80	75
1650	With backsplash		40	.400		58	14.30		72.30	87.50
1800	For sink cutout, add		12.20	1.311	Ea.		47		47	79
1900	Stainless steel counter top		40	.400	L.F.	150	14.30		164.30	189

425

12 35 Specialty Casework

12 35 70 – Healthcare Casework

12 35 70.13 Hospital Casework

		Crew	Daily Output	Labor-Hours	Unit	Material	2014 Bare Costs Labor	Equipment	Total	Total Incl O&P
2000	For drop-in stainless 43" x 21" sink, add				Ea.	990			990	1,100
2500	Wall cabinets, laminated plastic	2 Carp	15	1.067	L.F.	202	38		240	286
2600	Enameled steel		15	1.067		248	38		286	335
2700	Stainless steel		15	1.067		495	38		533	605

12 35 70.16 Nurse Station Casework

		Crew	Daily Output	Labor-Hours	Unit	Material	2014 Bare Costs Labor	Equipment	Total	Total Incl O&P
0010	**NURSE STATION CASEWORK**									
2100	Door type, laminated plastic	2 Carp	10	1.600	L.F.	310	57		367	440
2200	Enameled steel		10	1.600		298	57		355	425
2300	Stainless steel		10	1.600		595	57		652	750
2400	For drawer type, add					253			253	279

12 35 80 – Commercial Kitchen Casework

12 35 80.13 Metal Kitchen Casework

		Crew	Daily Output	Labor-Hours	Unit	Material	2014 Bare Costs Labor	Equipment	Total	Total Incl O&P
0010	**METAL KITCHEN CASEWORK**									
3500	Base cabinets, metal, minimum	2 Carp	30	.533	L.F.	72.50	19.05		91.55	112
3600	Maximum		25	.640		184	23		207	242
3700	Wall cabinets, metal, minimum		30	.533		72.50	19.05		91.55	112
3800	Maximum		25	.640		167	23		190	222

12 36 Countertops

12 36 16 – Metal Countertops

12 36 16.10 Stainless Steel Countertops

		Crew	Daily Output	Labor-Hours	Unit	Material	2014 Bare Costs Labor	Equipment	Total	Total Incl O&P
0010	**STAINLESS STEEL COUNTERTOPS**									
3200	Stainless steel, custom	1 Carp	24	.333	S.F.	150	11.90		161.90	185

12 36 19 – Wood Countertops

12 36 19.10 Maple Countertops

		Crew	Daily Output	Labor-Hours	Unit	Material	2014 Bare Costs Labor	Equipment	Total	Total Incl O&P
0010	**MAPLE COUNTERTOPS**									
2900	Solid, laminated, 1-1/2" thick, no splash	1 Carp	28	.286	L.F.	74	10.20		84.20	98.50
3000	With square splash		28	.286	"	88	10.20		98.20	114
3400	Recessed cutting block with trim, 16" x 20" x 1"		8	1	Ea.	90	36		126	159

12 36 23 – Plastic Countertops

12 36 23.13 Plastic-Laminate-Clad Countertops

		Crew	Daily Output	Labor-Hours	Unit	Material	2014 Bare Costs Labor	Equipment	Total	Total Incl O&P
0010	**PLASTIC-LAMINATE-CLAD COUNTERTOPS**									
0020	Stock, 24" wide w/backsplash, minimum	1 Carp	30	.267	L.F.	16.65	9.55		26.20	34.50
0100	Maximum		25	.320		34	11.45		45.45	56.50
0300	Custom plastic, 7/8" thick, aluminum molding, no splash		30	.267		29.50	9.55		39.05	48.50
0400	Cove splash		30	.267		28.50	9.55		38.05	47.50
0600	1-1/4" thick, no splash		28	.286		34.50	10.20		44.70	55
0700	Square splash		28	.286		41.50	10.20		51.70	62.50
0900	Square edge, plastic face, 7/8" thick, no splash		30	.267		32.50	9.55		42.05	52
1000	With splash		30	.267		38.50	9.55		48.05	58.50
1200	For stainless channel edge, 7/8" thick, add					3.06			3.06	3.37
1300	1-1/4" thick, add					3.65			3.65	4.02
1500	For solid color suede finish, add					4			4	4.40
1700	For end splash, add				Ea.	18			18	19.80
1900	For cut outs, standard, add, minimum	1 Carp	32	.250		12	8.95		20.95	28.50
2000	Maximum		8	1		6	36		42	66.50
2100	Postformed, including backsplash and front edge		30	.267	L.F.	10	9.55		19.55	27
2110	Mitred, add		12	.667	Ea.		24		24	40
2200	Built-in place, 25" wide, plastic laminate		25	.320	L.F.	40.50	11.45		51.95	64

12 36 Countertops

12 36 33 – Tile Countertops

12 36 33.10 Ceramic Tile Countertops	Crew	Daily Output	Labor-Hours	Unit	Material	2014 Bare Costs Labor	Equipment	Total	Total Incl O&P
0010 **CERAMIC TILE COUNTERTOPS**									
2300 Ceramic tile mosaic	1 Carp	25	.320	L.F.	33	11.45		44.45	56

12 36 40 – Stone Countertops

12 36 40.10 Natural Stone Countertops

	Crew	Daily Output	Labor-Hours	Unit	Material	Labor	Equipment	Total	Total Incl O&P
0010 **NATURAL STONE COUNTERTOPS**									
2500 Marble, stock, with splash, 1/2" thick, minimum	1 Bric	17	.471	L.F.	41	16.75		57.75	73
2700 3/4" thick, maximum		13	.615		103	22		125	150
2800 Granite, average, 1-1/4" thick, 24" wide, no splash		13.01	.615		135	22		157	186

12 36 53 – Laboratory Countertops

12 36 53.10 Laboratory Countertops and Sinks

	Crew	Daily Output	Labor-Hours	Unit	Material	Labor	Equipment	Total	Total Incl O&P
0010 **LABORATORY COUNTERTOPS AND SINKS**									
0020 Countertops, not incl. base cabinets, acid-proof, minimum	2 Carp	82	.195	S.F.	40	7		47	56
0030 Maximum		70	.229		49.50	8.15		57.65	68.50
0040 Stainless steel		82	.195		129	7		136	154

12 36 61 – Simulated Stone Countertops

12 36 61.16 Solid Surface Countertops

	Crew	Daily Output	Labor-Hours	Unit	Material	Labor	Equipment	Total	Total Incl O&P
0010 **SOLID SURFACE COUNTERTOPS**, Acrylic polymer									
0020 Pricing for orders of 100 L.F. or greater									
0100 25" wide, solid colors	2 Carp	28	.571	L.F.	53.50	20.50		74	93.50
0200 Patterned colors		28	.571		68	20.50		88.50	109
0300 Premium patterned colors		28	.571		85	20.50		105.50	128
0400 With silicone attached 4" backsplash, solid colors		27	.593		58.50	21		79.50	100
0500 Patterned colors		27	.593		74.50	21		95.50	118
0600 Premium patterned colors		27	.593		92.50	21		113.50	138
0700 With hard seam attached 4" backsplash, solid colors		23	.696		58.50	25		83.50	107
0800 Patterned colors		23	.696		74.50	25		99.50	124
0900 Premium patterned colors		23	.696		92.50	25		117.50	144
1000 Pricing for order of 51 – 99 L.F.									
1100 25" wide, solid colors	2 Carp	24	.667	L.F.	61.50	24		85.50	108
1200 Patterned colors		24	.667		78	24		102	126
1300 Premium patterned colors		24	.667		97.50	24		121.50	147
1400 With silicone attached 4" backsplash, solid colors		23	.696		67.50	25		92.50	117
1500 Patterned colors		23	.696		85.50	25		110.50	136
1600 Premium patterned colors		23	.696		107	25		132	159
1700 With hard seam attached 4" backsplash, solid colors		20	.800		67.50	28.50		96	123
1800 Patterned colors		20	.800		85.50	28.50		114	142
1900 Premium patterned colors		20	.800		107	28.50		135.50	165
2000 Pricing for order of 1 – 50 L.F.									
2100 25" wide, solid colors	2 Carp	20	.800	L.F.	72.50	28.50		101	128
2200 Patterned colors		20	.800		91.50	28.50		120	149
2300 Premium patterned colors		20	.800		115	28.50		143.50	174
2400 With silicone attached 4" backsplash, solid colors		19	.842		79.50	30		109.50	138
2500 Patterned colors		19	.842		100	30		130	161
2600 Premium patterned colors		19	.842		125	30		155	189
2700 With hard seam attached 4" backsplash, solid colors		15	1.067		79.50	38		117.50	151
2800 Patterned colors		15	1.067		100	38		138	174
2900 Premium patterned colors		15	1.067		125	38		163	202
3000 Sinks, pricing for order of 100 or greater units									
3100 Single bowl, hard seamed, solid colors, 13" x 17"	1 Carp	3	2.667	Ea.	360	95.50		455.50	560
3200 10" x 15"		7	1.143		167	41		208	253

12 36 Countertops

12 36 61 – Simulated Stone Countertops

12 36 61.16 Solid Surface Countertops		Crew	Daily Output	Labor-Hours	Unit	Material	2014 Bare Costs Labor	Equipment	Total	Total Incl O&P
3300	Cutouts for sinks	1 Carp	8	1	Ea.		36		36	60
3400	Sinks, pricing for order of 51 – 99 units									
3500	Single bowl, hard seamed, solid colors, 13" x 17"	1 Carp	2.55	3.137	Ea.	415	112		527	645
3600	10" x 15"		6	1.333		192	47.50		239.50	291
3700	Cutouts for sinks		7	1.143			41		41	68.50
3800	Sinks, pricing for order of 1 – 50 units									
3900	Single bowl, hard seamed, solid colors, 13" x 17"	1 Carp	2	4	Ea.	490	143		633	775
4000	10" x 15"		4.55	1.758		226	63		289	355
4100	Cutouts for sinks		5.25	1.524			54.50		54.50	91.50
4200	Cooktop cutouts, pricing for 100 or greater units		4	2		26.50	71.50		98	150
4300	51 – 99 units		3.40	2.353		30.50	84		114.50	176
4400	1 – 50 units		3	2.667		36	95.50		131.50	200

12 36 61.17 Solid Surface Vanity Tops		Crew	Daily Output	Labor-Hours	Unit	Material	2014 Bare Costs Labor	Equipment	Total	Total Incl O&P
0010	**SOLID SURFACE VANITY TOPS**									
0015	Solid surface, center bowl, 17" x 19"	1 Carp	12	.667	Ea.	186	24		210	245
0020	19" x 25"		12	.667		190	24		214	249
0030	19" x 31"		12	.667		223	24		247	285
0040	19" x 37"		12	.667		259	24		283	325
0050	22" x 25"		10	.800		340	28.50		368.50	425
0060	22" x 31"		10	.800		395	28.50		423.50	485
0070	22" x 37"		10	.800		460	28.50		488.50	560
0080	22" x 43"		10	.800		525	28.50		553.50	630
0090	22" x 49"		10	.800		585	28.50		613.50	690
0110	22" x 55"		8	1		660	36		696	790
0120	22" x 61"		8	1		755	36		791	890
0220	Double bowl, 22" x 61"		8	1		855	36		891	1,000
0230	Double bowl, 22" x 73"		8	1		930	36		966	1,075
0240	For aggregate colors, add					35%				
0250	For faucets and fittings, see Section 22 41 39.10									

12 36 61.19 Quartz Agglomerate Countertops		Crew	Daily Output	Labor-Hours	Unit	Material	2014 Bare Costs Labor	Equipment	Total	Total Incl O&P
0010	**QUARTZ AGGLOMERATE COUNTERTOPS**									
0100	25" wide, 4" backsplash, color group A, minimum	2 Carp	15	1.067	L.F.	63	38		101	134
0110	Maximum		15	1.067		88.50	38		126.50	161
0120	Color group B, minimum		15	1.067		65.50	38		103.50	136
0130	Maximum		15	1.067		92.50	38		130.50	166
0140	Color group C, minimum		15	1.067		76.50	38		114.50	148
0150	Maximum		15	1.067		105	38		143	179
0160	Color group D, minimum		15	1.067		83	38		121	155
0170	Maximum		15	1.067		112	38		150	188

12 46 Furnishing Accessories

12 46 13 – Ash Receptacles

12 46 13.10 Ash/Trash Receivers		Crew	Daily Output	Labor-Hours	Unit	Material	2014 Bare Costs Labor	Equipment	Total	Total Incl O&P
0010	**ASH/TRASH RECEIVERS**									
1000	Ash urn, cylindrical metal									
1020	8" diameter, 20" high	1 Clab	60	.133	Ea.	155	3.76		158.76	176
1060	10" diameter, 26" high	"	60	.133	"	124	3.76		127.76	142
2000	Combination ash/trash urn, metal									
2020	8" diameter, 20" high	1 Clab	60	.133	Ea.	155	3.76		158.76	176
2050	10" diameter, 26" high	"	60	.133	"	124	3.76		127.76	142

12 46 Furnishing Accessories

12 46 19 – Clocks

12 46 19.50 Wall Clocks		Crew	Daily Output	Labor-Hours	Unit	Material	2014 Bare Costs Labor	2014 Bare Costs Equipment	Total	Total Incl O&P
0010	**WALL CLOCKS**									
0080	12" diameter, single face	1 Elec	8	1	Ea.	128	42.50		170.50	210
0100	Double face	"	6.20	1.290	"	294	55		349	415

12 46 33 – Waste Receptacles

12 46 33.13 Trash Receptacles

12 46 33.13 Trash Receptacles		Crew	Daily Output	Labor-Hours	Unit	Material	Labor	Equipment	Total	Total Incl O&P
0010	**TRASH RECEPTACLES**									
4000	Trash receptacle, metal									
4020	8" diameter, 15" high	1 Clab	60	.133	Ea.	72	3.76		75.76	85.50
4040	10" diameter, 18" high		60	.133		135	3.76		138.76	154
5040	16" x 8" x 14" high	↓	60	.133	↓	25.50	3.76		29.26	34.50
5500	Plastic, with lid									
5520	35 gallon	1 Clab	60	.133	Ea.	135	3.76		138.76	154
5540	45 gallon		60	.133		217	3.76		220.76	245
5550	Plastic recycling barrel, w/lid & wheels, 32 gal.	G	60	.133		83	3.76		86.76	98
5560	65 gal.	G	60	.133		535	3.76		538.76	590
5570	95 gal.	G	60	.133	↓	995	3.76		998.76	1,100

12 48 Rugs and Mats

12 48 13 – Entrance Floor Mats and Frames

12 48 13.13 Entrance Floor Mats

12 48 13.13 Entrance Floor Mats		Crew	Daily Output	Labor-Hours	Unit	Material	Labor	Equipment	Total	Total Incl O&P
0010	**ENTRANCE FLOOR MATS**									
0020	Recessed, in-laid black rubber, 3/8" thick, solid	1 Clab	155	.052	S.F.	25.50	1.46		26.96	30.50
0050	Perforated		155	.052		15.80	1.46		17.26	19.85
0100	1/2" thick, solid		155	.052		19	1.46		20.46	23.50
0150	Perforated		155	.052		23	1.46		24.46	27.50
0200	In colors, 3/8" thick, solid		155	.052		20.50	1.46		21.96	25
0250	Perforated		155	.052		21	1.46		22.46	26
0300	1/2" thick, solid		155	.052		26.50	1.46		27.96	31.50
0350	Perforated		155	.052		27	1.46		28.46	32.50
2000	Recycled rubber tire tile, 12" x 12" x 3/8" thick	G	125	.064		9.90	1.80		11.70	13.95
2510	Natural cocoa fiber, 1/2" thick	G	125	.064		8.20	1.80		10	12.05
2520	3/4" thick	G	125	.064		6.80	1.80		8.60	10.50
2530	1" thick	G	125	.064	↓	9.40	1.80		11.20	13.40

12 51 Office Furniture

12 51 16 – Case Goods

12 51 16.13 Metal Case Goods

12 51 16.13 Metal Case Goods		Crew	Daily Output	Labor-Hours	Unit	Material	Labor	Equipment	Total	Total Incl O&P
0010	**METAL CASE GOODS**									
0020	Desks, 29" high, double pedestal, 30" x 60", metal, minimum				Ea.	580			580	635
0030	Maximum					1,475			1,475	1,625
0600	Desks, single pedestal, 30" x 60", metal, minimum					540			540	595
0620	Maximum					1,200			1,200	1,325
0720	Desks, secretarial, 30" x 60", metal, minimum					470			470	520
0730	Maximum					830			830	910
0740	Return, 20" x 42", minimum					350			350	385
0750	Maximum					540			540	595
0940	59" x 12" x 23" high, steel, minimum					300			300	330
0960	Maximum				↓	380			380	420

12 51 Office Furniture

12 51 16 – Case Goods

12 51 16.16 Wood Case Goods

12 51 16.16 Wood Case Goods	Crew	Daily Output	Labor-Hours	Unit	Material	2014 Bare Costs Labor	Equipment	Total	Total Incl O&P
0010 **WOOD CASE GOODS**									
0150 Desk, 29" high, double pedestal, 30" x 60"									
0160 Wood, minimum				Ea.	840			840	925
0180 Maximum				"	2,875			2,875	3,175
0630 Single pedestal, 30" x 60"									
0640 Wood, minimum				Ea.	595			595	655
0650 Maximum					900			900	990
0670 Executive return, 24" x 42", with box, file, wood, minimum					380			380	420
0680 Maximum					900			900	990
0790 Desk, 29" high, secretarial, 30" x 60"									
0800 Wood, minimum				Ea.	485			485	535
0810 Maximum					2,925			2,925	3,200
0820 Return, 20" x 42", minimum					305			305	335
0830 Maximum					1,100			1,100	1,225
0900 Desktop organizer, 72" x 14" x 36" high, wood, minimum					172			172	189
0920 Maximum					455			455	500
1110 Furniture, credenza, 29" high, 18" to 22" x 60" to 72"									

12 51 23 – Office Tables

12 51 23.33 Conference Tables

12 51 23.33 Conference Tables	Crew	Daily Output	Labor-Hours	Unit	Material	2014 Bare Costs Labor	Equipment	Total	Total Incl O&P
0010 **CONFERENCE TABLES**									
6050 Boat, 96" x 42", minimum				Ea.	780			780	855
6150 Maximum					3,575			3,575	3,925
6720 Rectangle, 96" x 42", minimum					1,275			1,275	1,400
6740 Maximum					3,575			3,575	3,925

12 52 Seating

12 52 23 – Office Seating

12 52 23.13 Office Chairs

12 52 23.13 Office Chairs	Crew	Daily Output	Labor-Hours	Unit	Material	2014 Bare Costs Labor	Equipment	Total	Total Incl O&P
0010 **OFFICE CHAIRS**									
2000 Standard office chair, executive, minimum				Ea.	320			320	355
2150 Maximum					2,050			2,050	2,275
2200 Management, minimum					223			223	245
2250 Maximum					2,175			2,175	2,400
2280 Task, minimum					162			162	178
2290 Maximum					550			550	605
2300 Arm kit, minimum					68			68	75
2320 Maximum					123			123	135

12 54 Hospitality Furniture

12 54 13 – Hotel and Motel Furniture

12 54 13.10 Hotel Furniture	Crew	Daily Output	Labor-Hours	Unit	Material	2014 Bare Costs Labor	Equipment	Total	Total Incl O&P
0010 **HOTEL FURNITURE**									
0020 Standard quality set, minimum				Room	2,375			2,375	2,600
0200 Maximum				"	8,425			8,425	9,275

12 54 16 – Restaurant Furniture

12 54 16.10 Tables, Folding

12 54 16.10 Tables, Folding	Crew	Daily Output	Labor-Hours	Unit	Material	Labor	Equipment	Total	Total Incl O&P
0010 **TABLES, FOLDING** Laminated plastic tops									
1000 Tubular steel legs with glides									
1020 18" x 60", minimum				Ea.	256			256	282
1040 Maximum					1,500			1,500	1,650
1840 36" x 96", minimum					310			310	340
1860 Maximum					3,025			3,025	3,325
2000 Round, wood stained, plywood top, 60" diameter, minimum					238			238	262
2020 Maximum					320			320	350

12 54 16.20 Furniture, Restaurant

12 54 16.20 Furniture, Restaurant	Crew	Daily Output	Labor-Hours	Unit	Material	Labor	Equipment	Total	Total Incl O&P
0010 **FURNITURE, RESTAURANT**									
0020 Bars, built-in, front bar	1 Carp	5	1.600	L.F.	274	57		331	395
0200 Back bar	"	5	1.600	"	199	57		256	315
0300 Booth seating, see Section 12 54 16.70									
2000 Chair, bentwood side chair, metal, minimum				Ea.	97			97	107
2020 Maximum					114			114	125
2600 Upholstered seat & back, arms, minimum					158			158	174
2620 Maximum					450			450	495

12 54 16.70 Booths

12 54 16.70 Booths	Crew	Daily Output	Labor-Hours	Unit	Material	Labor	Equipment	Total	Total Incl O&P
0010 **BOOTHS**									
1000 Banquet, upholstered seat and back, custom									
1500 Straight, minimum	2 Carp	40	.400	L.F.	193	14.30		207.30	236
1520 Maximum		36	.444		375	15.90		390.90	435
1600 "L" or "U" shape, minimum		35	.457		196	16.35		212.35	244
1620 Maximum		30	.533		350	19.05		369.05	415
1800 Upholstered outside finished backs for									
1810 single booths and custom banquets									
1820 Minimum	2 Carp	44	.364	L.F.	22	13		35	46.50
1840 Maximum	"	40	.400	"	66.50	14.30		80.80	97
3000 Fixed seating, one piece plastic chair and									
3010 plastic laminate table top									
3100 Two seat, 24" x 24" table, minimum	F-7	30	1.067	Ea.	775	34		809	915
3120 Maximum		26	1.231		1,100	39.50		1,139.50	1,300
3200 Four seat, 24" x 48" table, minimum		28	1.143		770	36.50		806.50	905
3220 Maximum		24	1.333		1,300	42.50		1,342.50	1,525
5000 Mount in floor, wood fiber core with									
5010 plastic laminate face, single booth									
5050 24" wide	F-7	30	1.067	Ea.	298	34		332	385
5100 48" wide	"	28	1.143	"	380	36.50		416.50	475

12 55 Detention Furniture

12 55 13 – Detention Bunks

12 55 13.13 Cots		Crew	Daily Output	Labor-Hours	Unit	Material	2014 Bare Costs Labor	Equipment	Total	Total Incl O&P
0010	**COTS**									
2500	Bolted, single, painted steel	E-4	20	1.600	Ea.	330	62	7.10	399.10	490
2700	Stainless steel	"	20	1.600	"	960	62	7.10	1,029.10	1,175

12 56 Institutional Furniture

12 56 33 – Classroom Furniture

12 56 33.10 Furniture, School

		Crew	Daily Output	Labor-Hours	Unit	Material	Labor	Equipment	Total	Total Incl O&P
0010	**FURNITURE, SCHOOL**									
0500	Classroom, movable chair & desk type, minimum				Set				73.50	81
0600	Maximum				"				155	171
1000	Chair, molded plastic									
1100	Integral tablet arm, minimum				Ea.	100			100	110
1150	Maximum					182			182	200
2000	Desk, single pedestal, top book compartment, minimum					142			142	156
2020	Maximum					167			167	184
2200	Flip top, minimum					228			228	250
2220	Maximum					276			276	305

12 56 43 – Dormitory Furniture

12 56 43.10 Dormitory Furnishings

		Crew	Daily Output	Labor-Hours	Unit	Material	Labor	Equipment	Total	Total Incl O&P
0010	**DORMITORY FURNISHINGS**									
0300	Bunkable bed, twin, minimum				Ea.	370			370	405
0320	Maximum					540			540	595
1000	Chest, four drawer, minimum					355			355	390
1020	Maximum					675			675	745
1050	Built-in, minimum	2 Carp	13	1.231	L.F.	114	44		158	199
1150	Maximum		10	1.600		211	57		268	330
1200	Desk top, built-in, laminated plastic, 24" deep, minimum		50	.320		43.50	11.45		54.95	67
1300	Maximum		40	.400		130	14.30		144.30	167
1450	30" deep, minimum		50	.320		55.50	11.45		66.95	80.50
1550	Maximum		40	.400		242	14.30		256.30	291
1750	Dressing unit, built-in, minimum		12	1.333		171	47.50		218.50	268
1850	Maximum		8	2		515	71.50		586.50	685
8000	Rule of thumb: total cost for furniture, minimum				Student				2,525	2,800
8050	Maximum				"				4,850	5,350

12 56 51 – Library Furniture

12 56 51.10 Library Furnishings

		Crew	Daily Output	Labor-Hours	Unit	Material	Labor	Equipment	Total	Total Incl O&P
0010	**LIBRARY FURNISHINGS**									
0100	Attendant desk, 36" x 62" x 29" high	1 Carp	16	.500	Ea.	1,825	17.90		1,842.90	2,050
0200	Book display, "A" frame display, both sides, 42" x 42" x 60" high		16	.500		1,125	17.90		1,142.90	1,275
0220	Table with bulletin board, 42" x 24" x 49" high		16	.500		735	17.90		752.90	835
0800	Card catalogue, 30 tray unit		16	.500		2,950	17.90		2,967.90	3,250
0840	60 tray unit		16	.500		5,625	17.90		5,642.90	6,225
0880	72 tray unit	2 Carp	16	1		8,000	36		8,036	8,850
1000	Carrels, single face, initial unit	1 Carp	16	.500		800	17.90		817.90	910
1500	Double face, initial unit	2 Carp	16	1		1,125	36		1,161	1,275
1710	Carrels, hardwood, 36" x 24", minimum	1 Carp	5	1.600		765	57		822	940
1720	Maximum	"	4	2		1,950	71.50		2,021.50	2,275
2700	Card catalog file, 60 trays, complete					7,775			7,775	8,550
2720	Alternate method: each tray					129			129	142
3800	Charging desk, built-in, with counter, plastic laminated top	1 Carp	7	1.143	L.F.	298	41		339	400

12 56 Institutional Furniture

12 56 51 – Library Furniture

12 56 51.10 Library Furnishings

		Crew	Daily Output	Labor-Hours	Unit	Material	2014 Bare Costs Labor	Equipment	Total	Total Incl O&P
4000	Dictionary stand, stationary	1 Carp	16	.500	Ea.	750	17.90		767.90	855
4020	Revolving		16	.500		211	17.90		228.90	262
4200	Exhibit case, table style, 60" x 28" x 36"		11	.727		2,775	26		2,801	3,100
6010	Bookshelf, metal, 90" high, 10" shelf, double face		11.50	.696	L.F.	150	25		175	207
6020	Single face		12	.667	"	121	24		145	173
6050	For 8" shelving, subtract from above					10%				
6060	For 12" shelving, add to above					10%				
6070	For 42" high with countertop, subtract from above					20%				
6100	Mobile compacted shelving, hand crank, 9'-0" high									
6110	Double face, including track, 3' section				Ea.	1,150			1,150	1,250
6150	For electrical operation, add					25%				
6200	Magazine shelving, 82" high, 12" deep, single face	1 Carp	11.50	.696	L.F.	148	25		173	205
6210	Double face	"	11.50	.696	"	243	25		268	310
7200	Reading table, laminated top, 60" x 36"				Ea.	690			690	760

12 56 70 – Healthcare Furniture

12 56 70.10 Furniture, Hospital

		Crew	Daily Output	Labor-Hours	Unit	Material	2014 Bare Costs Labor	Equipment	Total	Total Incl O&P
0010	**FURNITURE, HOSPITAL**									
0020	Beds, manual, minimum				Ea.	785			785	865
0100	Maximum					2,500			2,500	2,750
0600	All electric hospital beds, minimum					1,600			1,600	1,775
0700	Maximum					4,400			4,400	4,850
0900	Manual, nursing home beds, minimum					755			755	830
1000	Maximum					2,150			2,150	2,375
1020	Overbed table, laminated top, minimum					450			450	495
1040	Maximum					870			870	955
1100	Patient wall systems, not incl. plumbing, minimum				Room	1,400			1,400	1,550
1200	Maximum				"	1,900			1,900	2,100
2000	Geriatric chairs, minimum				Ea.	430			430	470
2020	Maximum				"	750			750	825

12 61 Fixed Audience Seating

12 61 13 – Upholstered Audience Seating

12 61 13.13 Auditorium Chairs

		Crew	Daily Output	Labor-Hours	Unit	Material	2014 Bare Costs Labor	Equipment	Total	Total Incl O&P
0010	**AUDITORIUM CHAIRS**									
2000	All veneer construction	2 Carp	22	.727	Ea.	227	26		253	294
2200	Veneer back, padded seat		22	.727		237	26		263	305
2350	Fully upholstered, spring seat		22	.727		237	26		263	305
2450	For tablet arms, add					66.50			66.50	73
2500	For fire retardancy, CATB-133, add					29.50			29.50	32.50

12 61 13.23 Lecture Hall Seating

		Crew	Daily Output	Labor-Hours	Unit	Material	2014 Bare Costs Labor	Equipment	Total	Total Incl O&P
0010	**LECTURE HALL SEATING**									
1000	Pedestal type, minimum	2 Carp	22	.727	Ea.	187	26		213	250
1200	Maximum	"	14.50	1.103	"	480	39.50		519.50	595

12 63 Stadium and Arena Seating

12 63 13 – Stadium and Arena Bench Seating

12 63 13.13 Bleachers		Crew	Daily Output	Labor-Hours	Unit	Material	2014 Bare Costs Labor	Equipment	Total	Total Incl O&P
0010	**BLEACHERS**									
3000	Telescoping, manual to 15 tier, minimum	F-5	65	.492	Seat	90.50	15.40		105.90	126
3100	Maximum		60	.533		136	16.70		152.70	177
3300	16 to 20 tier, minimum		60	.533		217	16.70		233.70	267
3400	Maximum		55	.582		271	18.25		289.25	330
3600	21 to 30 tier, minimum		50	.640		226	20		246	283
3700	Maximum		40	.800		299	25		324	370
3900	For integral power operation, add, minimum	2 Elec	300	.053		45	2.28		47.28	53.50
4000	Maximum	"	250	.064		72.50	2.73		75.23	84
5000	Benches, folding, in wall, 14' table, 2 benches	L-4	2	8	Set	765	253		1,018	1,275

12 67 Pews and Benches

12 67 13 – Pews

12 67 13.13 Sanctuary Pews		Crew	Daily Output	Labor-Hours	Unit	Material	2014 Bare Costs Labor	Equipment	Total	Total Incl O&P
0010	**SANCTUARY PEWS**									
1500	Bench type, hardwood, minimum	1 Carp	20	.400	L.F.	93.50	14.30		107.80	127
1550	Maximum	"	15	.533		185	19.05		204.05	236
1570	For kneeler, add					22			22	24.50

12 92 Interior Planters and Artificial Plants

12 92 33 – Interior Planters

12 92 33.10 Planters		Crew	Daily Output	Labor-Hours	Unit	Material	2014 Bare Costs Labor	Equipment	Total	Total Incl O&P
0010	**PLANTERS**									
1000	Fiberglass, hanging, 12" diameter, 7" high				Ea.	115			115	127
1500	Rectangular, 48" long, 16" high x 15" wide					655			655	720
1650	60" long, 30" high, 28" wide					995			995	1,100
2000	Round, 12" diameter, 13" high					152			152	168
2050	25" high					199			199	219
5000	Square, 10" side, 20" high					189			189	208
5100	14" side, 15" high					229			229	252
6000	Metal bowl, 32" diameter, 8" high, minimum					545			545	600
6050	Maximum					740			740	810
8750	Wood, fiberglass liner, square									
8780	14" square, 15" high, minimum				Ea.	445			445	490
8800	Maximum					550			550	605
9400	Plastic cylinder, molded, 10" diameter, 10" high					18.05			18.05	19.90
9500	11" diameter, 11" high					34.50			34.50	38

434

12 93 Site Furnishings

12 93 23 – Trash and Litter Receptacles

12 93 23.10 Trash Receptacles

		Crew	Daily Output	Labor-Hours	Unit	Material	2014 Bare Costs Labor	Equipment	Total	Total Incl O&P
0010	**TRASH RECEPTACLES**									
0020	Fiberglass, 2' square, 18" high	2 Clab	30	.533	Ea.	550	15.05		565.05	630
0100	2' square, 2'-6" high		30	.533		780	15.05		795.05	880
0300	Circular , 2' diameter, 18" high		30	.533		465	15.05		480.05	535
0400	2' diameter, 2'-6" high		30	.533		520	15.05		535.05	595
0500	Recycled plastic, var colors, round, 32 gal., 28" x 38" H [G]		5	3.200		500	90		590	700
0510	32 gal., 31" x 32" H [G]		5	3.200		575	90		665	780

12 93 23.20 Trash Closure

		Crew	Daily Output	Labor-Hours	Unit	Material	2014 Bare Costs Labor	Equipment	Total	Total Incl O&P
0010	**TRASH CLOSURE**									
0020	Steel with pullover cover, 2'-3" wide, 4'-7" high, 6'-2" long	2 Clab	5	3.200	Ea.	1,925	90		2,015	2,250
0100	10'-1" long		4	4		2,375	113		2,488	2,825
0300	Wood, 10' wide, 6' high, 10' long		1.20	13.333		1,725	375		2,100	2,500

12 93 33 – Manufactured Planters

12 93 33.10 Planters

		Crew	Daily Output	Labor-Hours	Unit	Material	2014 Bare Costs Labor	Equipment	Total	Total Incl O&P
0010	**PLANTERS**									
0012	Concrete, sandblasted, precast, 48" diameter, 24" high	2 Clab	15	1.067	Ea.	620	30		650	730
0100	Fluted, precast, 7' diameter, 36" high		10	1.600		1,550	45		1,595	1,775
0300	Fiberglass, circular, 36" diameter, 24" high		15	1.067		710	30		740	830
0320	36" diameter, 27" high		12	1.333		710	37.50		747.50	845
0330	33" high		15	1.067		755	30		785	880
0335	24" diameter, 36" high		15	1.067		415	30		445	510
0340	60" diameter, 39" high		8	2		1,250	56.50		1,306.50	1,475
0400	60" diameter, 24" high		10	1.600		1,100	45		1,145	1,275
0600	Square, 24" side, 36" high		15	1.067		605	30		635	720
0610	24" side, 27" high		12	1.333		660	37.50		697.50	795
0620	24" side, 16" high		20	.800		315	22.50		337.50	385
0700	48" side, 36" high		15	1.067		995	30		1,025	1,150
0900	Planter/bench, 72" square, 36" high		5	3.200		1,750	90		1,840	2,075
1000	96" square, 27" high		5	3.200		2,175	90		2,265	2,550
1200	Wood, square, 48" side, 24" high		15	1.067		1,375	30		1,405	1,575
1300	Circular, 48" diameter, 30" high		10	1.600		965	45		1,010	1,125
1500	72" diameter, 30" high		10	1.600		1,700	45		1,745	1,950
1600	Planter/bench, 72"		5	3.200		3,225	90		3,315	3,675

12 93 43 – Site Seating and Tables

12 93 43.13 Site Seating

		Crew	Daily Output	Labor-Hours	Unit	Material	2014 Bare Costs Labor	Equipment	Total	Total Incl O&P
0010	**SITE SEATING**									
0012	Seating, benches, park, precast conc., w/backs, wood rails, 4' long	2 Clab	5	3.200	Ea.	580	90		670	785
0100	8' long		4	4		935	113		1,048	1,225
0300	Fiberglass, without back, one piece, 4' long		10	1.600		605	45		650	745
0400	8' long		7	2.286		780	64.50		844.50	970
0500	Steel barstock pedestals w/backs, 2" x 3" wood rails, 4' long		10	1.600		1,100	45		1,145	1,275
0510	8' long		7	2.286		1,400	64.50		1,464.50	1,650
0520	3" x 8" wood plank, 4' long		10	1.600		1,175	45		1,220	1,375
0530	8' long		7	2.286		1,450	64.50		1,514.50	1,700
0540	Backless, 4" x 4" wood plank, 4' square		10	1.600		920	45		965	1,100
0550	8' long		7	2.286		990	64.50		1,054.50	1,200
0600	Aluminum pedestals, with backs, aluminum slats, 8' long		8	2		470	56.50		526.50	610
0610	15' long		5	3.200		955	90		1,045	1,200
0620	Portable, aluminum slats, 8' long		8	2		455	56.50		511.50	595
0630	15' long		5	3.200		550	90		640	755
0800	Cast iron pedestals, back & arms, wood slats, 4' long		8	2		415	56.50		471.50	555

12 93 43.13 Site Seating		Crew	Daily Output	Labor-Hours	Unit	Material	2014 Bare Costs Labor	Equipment	Total	Total Incl O&P
0820	8' long	2 Clab	5	3.200	Ea.	920	90		1,010	1,175
0840	Backless, wood slats, 4' long		8	2		580	56.50		636.50	735
0860	8' long		5	3.200		1,150	90		1,240	1,400
1700	Steel frame, fir seat, 10' long		10	1.600		345	45		390	450

Estimating Tips

General

- The items and systems in this division are usually estimated, purchased, supplied, and installed as a unit by one or more subcontractors. The estimator must ensure that all parties are operating from the same set of specifications and assumptions, and that all necessary items are estimated and will be provided. Many times the complex items and systems are covered, but the more common ones, such as excavation or a crane, are overlooked for the very reason that everyone assumes nobody could miss them. The estimator should be the central focus and be able to ensure that all systems are complete.

- Another area where problems can develop in this division is at the interface between systems. The estimator must ensure, for instance, that anchor bolts, nuts, and washers are estimated and included for the air-supported structures and pre-engineered buildings to be bolted to their foundations. Utility supply is a common area where essential items or pieces of equipment can be missed or overlooked due to the fact that each subcontractor may feel it is another's responsibility. The estimator should also be aware of certain items which may be supplied as part of a package but installed by others, and ensure that the installing contractor's estimate includes the cost of installation. Conversely, the estimator must also ensure that items are not costed by two different subcontractors, resulting in an inflated overall estimate.

13 30 00 Special Structures

- The foundations and floor slab, as well as rough mechanical and electrical, should be estimated, as this work is required for the assembly and erection of the structure.

Generally, as noted in the book, the pre-engineered building comes as a shell. Pricing is based on the size and structural design parameters stated in the reference section. Additional features, such as windows and doors with their related structural framing, must also be included by the estimator. Here again, the estimator must have a clear understanding of the scope of each portion of the work and all the necessary interfaces.

Reference Numbers

Reference numbers are shown in shaded boxes at the beginning of some major classifications. These numbers refer to related items in the Reference Section. The reference information may be an estimating procedure, an alternate pricing method, or technical information.

Note: Not all subdivisions listed here necessarily appear in this publication.

13 05 05.10 Selective Demolition, Air Supported Structures	Crew	Daily Output	Labor-Hours	Unit	Material	2014 Bare Costs Labor	Equipment	Total	Total Incl O&P
0010 **SELECTIVE DEMOLITION, AIR SUPPORTED STRUCTURES**									
0020 Tank covers, scrim, dbl. layer, vinyl poly w/hdwe., blower & controls									
0050 Round and rectangular R024119-10	B-2	9000	.004	S.F.		.13		.13	.21
0100 Warehouse structures									
0120 Poly/vinyl fabric, 28 oz., incl. tension cables & inflation system	4 Clab	9000	.004	SF Flr.		.10		.10	.17
0150 Reinforced vinyl, 12 oz., 3000 S.F.	"	5000	.006			.18		.18	.30
0200 12,000 to 24,000 S.F.	8 Clab	20000	.003			.09		.09	.15
0250 Tedlar vinyl fabric, 28 oz. w/liner, to 3000 S.F.	4 Clab	5000	.006			.18		.18	.30
0300 12,000 to 24,000 S.F.	8 Clab	20000	.003	↓		.09		.09	.15
0350 Greenhouse/shelter, woven polyethylene with liner									
0400 3000 S.F.	4 Clab	5000	.006	SF Flr.		.18		.18	.30
0450 12,000 to 24,000 S.F.	8 Clab	20000	.003			.09		.09	.15
0500 Tennis/gymnasium, poly/vinyl fabric, 28 oz., incl. thermal liner	4 Clab	9000	.004			.10		.10	.17
0600 Stadium/convention center, teflon coated fiberglass, incl. thermal liner	9 Clab	40000	.002	↓		.05		.05	.09
0700 Doors, air lock, 15' long, 10' x 10'	2 Carp	1.50	10.667	Ea.		380		380	640
0720 15' x 15'		.80	20			715		715	1,200
0750 Revolving personnel door, 6' diam. x 6'-6" high	↓	1.50	10.667	↓		380		380	640

13 05 05.20 Selective Demolition, Garden Houses

	Crew	Daily Output	Labor-Hours	Unit	Material	Labor	Equipment	Total	Total Incl O&P
0010 **SELECTIVE DEMOLITION, GARDEN HOUSES** R024119-10									
0020 Prefab, wood, excl foundation, average	2 Clab	400	.040	SF Flr.		1.13		1.13	1.90

13 05 05.25 Selective Demolition, Geodesic Domes

	Crew	Daily Output	Labor-Hours	Unit	Material	Labor	Equipment	Total	Total Incl O&P
0010 **SELECTIVE DEMOLITION, GEODESIC DOMES**									
0050 Shell only, interlocking plywood panels, 30' diameter	F-5	3.20	10	Ea.		315		315	530
0060 34' diameter		2.30	13.913			435		435	735
0070 39' diameter	↓	2	16			500		500	845
0080 45' diameter	F-3	2.20	18.182			595	300	895	1,325
0090 55' diameter		2	20			655	330	985	1,475
0100 60' diameter		2	20			655	330	985	1,475
0110 65' diameter	↓	1.60	25	↓		820	415	1,235	1,825

13 05 05.30 Selective Demolition, Greenhouses

	Crew	Daily Output	Labor-Hours	Unit	Material	Labor	Equipment	Total	Total Incl O&P
0010 **SELECTIVE DEMOLITION, GREENHOUSES** R024119-10									
0020 Resi-type, free standing, excl. foundations, 9' long x 8' wide	2 Clab	160	.100	SF Flr.		2.82		2.82	4.75
0030 9' long x 11' wide		170	.094			2.65		2.65	4.47
0040 9' long x 14' wide		220	.073			2.05		2.05	3.45
0050 9' long x 17' wide		320	.050			1.41		1.41	2.37
0060 Lean-to type, 4' wide		64	.250			7.05		7.05	11.85
0070 7' wide		120	.133	↓		3.76		3.76	6.35
0080 Geodesic hemisphere, 1/8" plexiglass glazing, 8' diam.		4	4	Ea.		113		113	190
0090 24' diam.		.80	20			565		565	950
0100 48' diam.	↓	.40	40	↓		1,125		1,125	1,900

13 05 05.35 Selective Demolition, Hangars

	Crew	Daily Output	Labor-Hours	Unit	Material	Labor	Equipment	Total	Total Incl O&P
0010 **SELECTIVE DEMOLITION, HANGARS**									
0020 T type hangars, prefab, steel, galv roof & walls, incl doors, excl fndtn	E-2	2550	.019	SF Flr.		.73	.60	1.33	2.02
0030 Circular type, prefab, steel frame, plastic skin, incl foundation, 80' diam	"	.50	96	Total		3,725	3,050	6,775	10,300

13 05 05.45 Selective Demolition, Lightning Protection

	Crew	Daily Output	Labor-Hours	Unit	Material	Labor	Equipment	Total	Total Incl O&P
0010 **SELECTIVE DEMOLITION, LIGHTNING PROTECTION**									
0020 Air terminal & base, copper, 3/8" diam. x 10", to 75' h	1 Clab	16	.500	Ea.		14.10		14.10	23.50
0030 1/2" diam. x 12", over 75' h		16	.500			14.10		14.10	23.50
0050 Aluminum, 1/2" diam. x 12", to 75' h		16	.500			14.10		14.10	23.50
0060 5/8" diam. x 12", over 75' h		16	.500	↓		14.10		14.10	23.50
0070 Cable, copper, 220 lb. per thousand feet, to 75' high	↓	640	.013	L.F.		.35		.35	.59

13 05 Common Work Results for Special Construction

13 05 05 – Selective Special Construction Demolition

13 05 05.45 Selective Demolition, Lightning Protection

		Crew	Daily Output	Labor-Hours	Unit	Material	2014 Bare Costs Labor	Equipment	Total	Total Incl O&P
0080	375 lb. per thousand feet, over 75' high	1 Clab	460	.017	L.F.		.49		.49	.83
0090	Aluminum, 101 lb. per thousand feet, to 75' high		560	.014			.40		.40	.68
0100	199 lb. per thousand feet, over 75' high		480	.017	▼		.47		.47	.79
0110	Arrester, 175 V AC, to ground		16	.500	Ea.		14.10		14.10	23.50
0120	650 V AC, to ground	▼	13	.615	"		17.35		17.35	29

13 05 05.50 Selective Demolition, Pre-Engineered Steel Buildings

		Crew	Daily Output	Labor-Hours	Unit	Material	2014 Bare Costs Labor	Equipment	Total	Total Incl O&P
0010	**SELECTIVE DEMOLITION, PRE-ENGINEERED STEEL BUILDINGS**									
0500	Pre-engd. steel bldgs., rigid frame, clear span & multi post, excl. salvage									
0550	3,500 to 7,500 S.F.	L-10	1000	.024	SF Flr.		.94	.66	1.60	2.44
0600	7,501 to 12,500 S.F.		1500	.016			.63	.44	1.07	1.63
0650	12,500 S.F. or greater	▼	1650	.015	▼		.57	.40	.97	1.48
0700	Pre-engd. steel building components									
0710	Entrance canopy, including frame 4' x 4'	E-24	8	4	Ea.		153	93	246	385
0720	4' x 8'	"	7	4.571			175	107	282	435
0730	HM doors, self framing, single leaf	2 Skwk	8	2			72.50		72.50	123
0740	Double leaf		5	3.200	▼		116		116	196
0760	Gutter, eave type		600	.027	L.F.		.97		.97	1.63
0770	Sash, single slide, double slide or fixed		24	.667	Ea.		24		24	41
0780	Skylight, fiberglass, to 30 S.F.		16	1			36.50		36.50	61.50
0785	Roof vents, circular, 12" to 24" diameter		12	1.333			48.50		48.50	81.50
0790	Continuous, 10' long	▼	8	2	▼		72.50		72.50	123
0900	Shelters, aluminum frame									
0910	Acrylic glazing, 3' x 9' x 8' high	2 Skwk	2	8	Ea.		290		290	490
0920	9' x 12' x 8' high	"	1.50	10.667	"		385		385	655

13 05 05.60 Selective Demolition, Silos

		Crew	Daily Output	Labor-Hours	Unit	Material	2014 Bare Costs Labor	Equipment	Total	Total Incl O&P
0010	**SELECTIVE DEMOLITION, SILOS**									
0020	Conc stave, indstrl, conical/sloping bott, excl fndtn, 12' diam., 35' h	E-24	.18	177	Ea.		6,800	4,150	10,950	17,100
0030	16' diam., 45' h		.12	266			10,200	6,225	16,425	25,600
0040	25' diam., 75' h	▼	.08	400			15,300	9,325	24,625	38,500
0050	Steel, factory fabricated, 30,000 gal. cap, painted or epoxy lined	L-5	2	28	▼		1,075	375	1,450	2,425

13 05 05.65 Selective Demolition, Sound Control

		Crew	Daily Output	Labor-Hours	Unit	Material	2014 Bare Costs Labor	Equipment	Total	Total Incl O&P
0010	**SELECTIVE DEMOLITION, SOUND CONTROL** R024119-10									
0120	Acoustical enclosure, 4" thick walls & ceiling panels, 8 lb./S.F.	3 Carp	144	.167	SF Surf		5.95		5.95	10.05
0130	10.5 lb./S.F.		128	.188			6.70		6.70	11.30
0140	Reverb chamber, parallel walls, 4" thick		120	.200			7.15		7.15	12.05
0150	Skewed walls, parallel roof, 4" thick		110	.218			7.80		7.80	13.10
0160	Skewed walls/roof, 4" layer/air space		96	.250			8.95		8.95	15.05
0170	Sound-absorbing panels, painted metal, 2'-6" x 8', under 1,000 S.F.		430	.056			2		2	3.36
0180	Over 1,000 S.F.	▼	480	.050			1.79		1.79	3.01
0190	Flexible transparent curtain, clear	3 Shee	430	.056			2.26		2.26	3.76
0192	50% clear, 50% foam		430	.056			2.26		2.26	3.76
0194	25% clear, 75% foam		430	.056			2.26		2.26	3.76
0196	100% foam	▼	430	.056	▼		2.26		2.26	3.76
0200	Audio-masking sys., incl. speakers, amplfr., signal gnrtr.									
0205	Ceiling mounted, 5,000 S.F.	2 Elec	4800	.003	S.F.		.14		.14	.23
0210	10,000 S.F.		5600	.003			.12		.12	.20
0220	Plenum mounted, 5,000 S.F.		7600	.002			.09		.09	.15
0230	10,000 S.F.	▼	8800	.002	▼		.08		.08	.13

13 05 05.70 Selective Demolition, Special Purpose Rooms

		Crew	Daily Output	Labor-Hours	Unit	Material	2014 Bare Costs Labor	Equipment	Total	Total Incl O&P
0010	**SELECTIVE DEMOLITION, SPECIAL PURPOSE ROOMS** R024119-10									
0100	Audiometric rooms, under 500 S.F. surface	4 Carp	200	.160	SF Surf		5.70		5.70	9.60
0110	Over 500 S.F. surface	"	240	.133	"		4.77		4.77	8

13 05 05 – Selective Special Construction Demolition

13 05 05.70 Selective Demolition, Special Purpose Rooms	Crew	Daily Output	Labor-Hours	Unit	Material	2014 Bare Costs Labor	2014 Bare Costs Equipment	Total	Total Incl O&P
0200	Clean rooms, 12' x 12' soft wall, class 100	1 Carp	.30	26.667	Ea.		955		955	1,600
0210	Class 1000		.30	26.667			955		955	1,600
0220	Class 10,000		.35	22.857			815		815	1,375
0230	Class 100,000		.35	22.857			815		815	1,375
0300	Darkrooms, shell complete, 8' high	2 Carp	220	.073	SF Flr.		2.60		2.60	4.37
0310	12' high		110	.145	"		5.20		5.20	8.75
0350	Darkrooms doors, mini-cylindrical, revolving		4	4	Ea.		143		143	241
0400	Music room, practice modular		140	.114	SF Surf		4.09		4.09	6.85
0500	Refrigeration structures and finishes									
0510	Wall finish, 2 coat portland cement plaster, 1/2" thick	1 Clab	200	.040	S.F.		1.13		1.13	1.90
0520	Fiberglass panels, 1/8" thick		400	.020			.56		.56	.95
0530	Ceiling finish, polystyrene plastic, 1" to 2" thick		500	.016			.45		.45	.76
0540	4" thick		450	.018			.50		.50	.84
0550	Refrigerator, prefab aluminum walk-in, 7'-6" high, 6' x 6' OD	2 Carp	100	.160	SF Flr.		5.70		5.70	9.60
0560	10' x 10' OD		160	.100			3.58		3.58	6
0570	Over 150 S.F.		200	.080			2.86		2.86	4.81
0600	Sauna, prefabricated, including heater & controls, 7' high, to 30 S.F.		120	.133			4.77		4.77	8
0610	To 40 S.F.		140	.114			4.09		4.09	6.85
0620	To 60 S.F.		175	.091			3.27		3.27	5.50
0630	To 100 S.F.		220	.073			2.60		2.60	4.37
0640	To 130 S.F.		250	.064			2.29		2.29	3.85
0650	Steam bath, heater, timer, head, single, to 140 C.F.	1 Plum	2.20	3.636	Ea.		155		155	256
0660	To 300 C.F.		2.20	3.636			155		155	256
0670	Steam bath, comm. size, w/blow-down assembly, to 800 C.F.		1.80	4.444			189		189	310
0680	To 2500 C.F.		1.60	5			213		213	350
0690	Steam bath, comm. size, multiple, for motels, apts, 500 C.F., 2 baths		2	4			170		170	281
0700	1,000 C.F., 4 baths		1.40	5.714			243		243	400

13 05 05.75 Selective Demolition, Storage Tanks		Crew	Daily Output	Labor-Hours	Unit	Material	Labor	Equipment	Total	Total Incl O&P
0010	**SELECTIVE DEMOLITION, STORAGE TANKS**									
0500	Steel tank, single wall, above ground, not incl. fdn., pumps or piping									
0510	Single wall, 275 gallon	R024119-10	Q-1	3	5.333	Ea.		205		205	335
0520	550 thru 2,000 gallon		B-34P	2	12			440	350	790	1,100
0530	5,000 thru 10,000 gallon		B-34Q	2	12			445	640	1,085	1,425
0540	15,000 thru 30,000 gallon		B-34S	2	16			620	1,800	2,420	3,000
0600	Steel tank, double wall, above ground not incl. fdn., pumps & piping									
0620	500 thru 2,000 gallon		B-34P	2	12	Ea.		440	350	790	1,100

13 05 05.85 Selective Demolition, Swimming Pool Equip	Crew	Daily Output	Labor-Hours	Unit	Material	Labor	Equipment	Total	Total Incl O&P
0010	**SELECTIVE DEMOLITION, SWIMMING POOL EQUIP**									
0020	Diving stand, stainless steel, 3 meter	2 Clab	3	5.333	Ea.		150		150	253
0030	1 meter		5	3.200			90		90	152
0040	Diving board, 16' long, aluminum		5.40	2.963			83.50		83.50	141
0050	Fiberglass		5.40	2.963			83.50		83.50	141
0070	Ladders, heavy duty, stainless steel, 2 tread		14	1.143			32		32	54
0080	4 tread		12	1.333			37.50		37.50	63.50
0090	Lifeguard chair, stainless steel, fixed		5	3.200			90		90	152
0100	Slide, tubular, fiberglass, aluminum handrails & ladder, 5', straight		4	4			113		113	190
0110	8', curved		6	2.667			75		75	127
0120	10', curved		3	5.333			150		150	253
0130	12' straight, with platform		2.50	6.400			180		180	305
0140	Removable access ramp, stainless steel		4	4			113		113	190
0150	Removable stairs, stainless steel, collapsible		4	4			113		113	190

13 05 Common Work Results for Special Construction

13 05 05 – Selective Special Construction Demolition

13 05 05.90 Selective Demolition, Tension Structures

		Crew	Daily Output	Labor-Hours	Unit	Material	2014 Bare Costs Labor	Equipment	Total	Total Incl O&P
0010	**SELECTIVE DEMOLITION, TENSION STRUCTURES**									
0020	Steel/alum. frame, fabric shell, 60' clear span, 6,000 S.F.	B-41	2000	.022	SF Flr.		.64	.15	.79	1.24
0030	12,000 S.F.		2200	.020			.59	.13	.72	1.13
0040	80' clear span, 20,800 S.F.		2440	.018			.53	.12	.65	1.02
0050	100' clear span, 10,000 S.F.	L-5	4350	.013			.50	.17	.67	1.12
0060	26,000 S.F.		4600	.012			.47	.16	.63	1.06
0070	36,000 S.F.		5000	.011			.43	.15	.58	.97

13 05 05.95 Selective Demo, X-Ray/Radio Freq Protection

		Crew	Daily Output	Labor-Hours	Unit	Material	2014 Bare Costs Labor	Equipment	Total	Total Incl O&P
0010	**SELECTIVE DEMO, X-RAY/RADIO FREQ PROTECTION**									
0020	Shielding lead, lined door frame, excl. hdwe., 1/16" thick	1 Clab	4.80	1.667	Ea.		47		47	79
0030	Lead sheets, 1/16" thick	2 Clab	270	.059	S.F.		1.67		1.67	2.81
0040	1/8" thick		240	.067			1.88		1.88	3.16
0050	Lead shielding, 1/4" thick		270	.059			1.67		1.67	2.81
0060	1/2" thick		240	.067			1.88		1.88	3.16
0070	Lead glass, 1/4" thick, 2.0 mm LE, 12" x 16"	2 Glaz	16	1	Ea.		35		35	58
0080	24" x 36"		8	2			69.50		69.50	116
0090	36" x 60"		4	4			139		139	231
0100	Lead glass window frame, with 1/16" lead & voice passage, 36" x 60"		4	4			139		139	231
0110	Lead glass window frame, 24" x 36"		8	2			69.50		69.50	116
0120	Lead gypsum board, 5/8" thick with 1/16" lead	2 Clab	320	.050	S.F.		1.41		1.41	2.37
0130	1/8" lead		280	.057			1.61		1.61	2.71
0140	1/32" lead		400	.040			1.13		1.13	1.90
0150	Butt joints, 1/8" lead or thicker, 2" x 7' long batten strip		480	.033	Ea.		.94		.94	1.58
0160	X-ray protection, average radiography room, up to 300 S.F., 1/16" lead, min		.50	32	Total		900		900	1,525
0170	Maximum		.30	53.333			1,500		1,500	2,525
0180	Deep therapy X-ray room, 250 kV cap, up to 300 S.F., 1/4" lead, min		.20	80			2,250		2,250	3,800
0190	Maximum		.12	133			3,750		3,750	6,325
0880	Radio frequency shielding, prefab or screen-type copper or steel, minimum		360	.044	SF Surf		1.25		1.25	2.11
0890	Average		310	.052			1.46		1.46	2.45
0895	Maximum		290	.055			1.56		1.56	2.62

13 11 Swimming Pools

13 11 13 – Below-Grade Swimming Pools

13 11 13.50 Swimming Pools

		Crew	Daily Output	Labor-Hours	Unit	Material	2014 Bare Costs Labor	Equipment	Total	Total Incl O&P
0010	**SWIMMING POOLS** Residential in-ground, vinyl lined, concrete									
0020	Sides including equipment, sand bottom	B-52	300	.187	SF Surf	21.50	5.80	1.98	29.28	35.50
0100	Metal or polystyrene sides R131113-20	B-14	410	.117		17.75	3.50	.89	22.14	26.50
0200	Add for vermiculite bottom					1.35			1.35	1.49
0500	Gunite bottom and sides, white plaster finish									
0600	12' x 30' pool	B-52	145	.386	SF Surf	39.50	11.95	4.11	55.56	68
0720	16' x 32' pool		155	.361		35.50	11.20	3.84	50.54	62
0750	20' x 40' pool		250	.224		32	6.95	2.38	41.33	49.50
0810	Concrete bottom and sides, tile finish									
0820	12' x 30' pool	B-52	80	.700	SF Surf	40	21.50	7.45	68.95	88.50
0830	16' x 32' pool		95	.589		33	18.25	6.25	57.50	74
0840	20' x 40' pool		130	.431		26.50	13.35	4.58	44.43	56.50
1100	Motel, gunite with plaster finish, incl. medium									
1150	capacity filtration & chlorination	B-52	115	.487	SF Surf	48.50	15.05	5.20	68.75	84.50
1200	Municipal, gunite with plaster finish, incl. high									
1250	capacity filtration & chlorination	B-52	100	.560	SF Surf	63	17.35	5.95	86.30	105

13 11 13 – Below-Grade Swimming Pools

13 11 13.50 Swimming Pools

		Crew	Daily Output	Labor-Hours	Unit	Material	2014 Bare Costs Labor	Equipment	Total	Total Incl O&P
1350	Add for formed gutters				L.F.	92.50			92.50	102
1360	Add for stainless steel gutters				"	274			274	300
1600	For water heating system, see Section 23 52 28.10									
1700	Filtration and deck equipment only, as % of total				Total				20%	20%
1800	Deck equipment, rule of thumb, 20' x 40' pool				SF Pool				1.18	1.30
1900	5000 S.F. pool				"				1.73	1.90
3000	Painting pools, preparation + 3 coats, 20' x 40' pool, epoxy	2 Pord	.33	48.485	Total	1,775	1,525		3,300	4,450
3100	Rubber base paint, 18 gallons	"	.33	48.485		1,325	1,525		2,850	3,950
3500	42' x 82' pool, 75 gallons, epoxy paint	3 Pord	.14	171		7,500	5,350		12,850	17,100
3600	Rubber base paint	"	.14	171		5,450	5,350		10,800	14,800

13 11 46 – Swimming Pool Accessories

13 11 46.50 Swimming Pool Equipment

		Crew	Daily Output	Labor-Hours	Unit	Material	2014 Bare Costs Labor	Equipment	Total	Total Incl O&P
0010	**SWIMMING POOL EQUIPMENT**									
0020	Diving stand, stainless steel, 3 meter	2 Carp	.40	40	Ea.	14,500	1,425		15,925	18,300
0300	1 meter		2.70	5.926		8,825	212		9,037	10,100
0600	Diving boards, 16' long, aluminum		2.70	5.926		3,975	212		4,187	4,700
0700	Fiberglass		2.70	5.926		3,200	212		3,412	3,875
0800	14' long, aluminum		2.70	5.926		3,900	212		4,112	4,650
0850	Fiberglass		2.70	5.926		3,100	212		3,312	3,750
1200	Ladders, heavy duty, stainless steel, 2 tread		7	2.286		775	81.50		856.50	990
1500	4 tread		6	2.667		1,050	95.50		1,145.50	1,300
1800	Lifeguard chair, stainless steel, fixed		2.70	5.926		3,150	212		3,362	3,800
1900	Portable					2,725			2,725	3,000
2100	Lights, underwater, 12 volt, with transformer, 300 watt	1 Elec	1	8		335	340		675	930
2200	110 volt, 500 watt, standard		1	8		293	340		633	880
2400	Low water cutoff type		1	8		300	340		640	890
2800	Heaters, see Section 23 52 28.10									
3000	Pool covers, reinforced vinyl	3 Clab	1800	.013	S.F.	.35	.38		.73	1.02
3050	Automatic, electric								8.75	9.65
3100	Vinyl water tube	3 Clab	3200	.008		.21	.21		.42	.59
3200	Maximum	"	3000	.008		.41	.23		.64	.83
3250	Sealed air bubble polyethylene solar blanket, 16 mils					.24			.24	.26
3300	Slides, tubular, fiberglass, aluminum handrails & ladder, 5'-0", straight	2 Carp	1.60	10	Ea.	3,400	360		3,760	4,350
3320	8'-0", curved		3	5.333		6,750	191		6,941	7,750
3400	10'-0", curved		1	16		21,800	570		22,370	25,000
3420	12'-0", straight with platform		1.20	13.333		13,400	475		13,875	15,500
4500	Hydraulic lift, movable pool bottom, single ram									
4520	Under 1,000 S.F. area	L-9	72	.500	S.F.	130	16.65		146.65	171
4600	Four ram lift, over 1,000 S.F.	"	109	.330	"	105	11		116	135
5000	Removable access ramp, stainless steel	2 Clab	2	8	Ea.	5,800	226		6,026	6,750

13 17 Tubs and Pools

13 17 13 – Hot Tubs

13 17 13.10 Redwood Hot Tub System	Crew	Daily Output	Labor-Hours	Unit	Material	2014 Bare Costs Labor	Equipment	Total	Total Incl O&P
0010 **REDWOOD HOT TUB SYSTEM**									
7050 4' diameter x 4' deep	Q-1	1	16	Ea.	3,225	615		3,840	4,550
7100 5' diameter x 4' deep		1	16		4,100	615		4,715	5,500
7150 6' diameter x 4' deep		.80	20		4,950	765		5,715	6,700
7200 8' diameter x 4' deep	↓	.80	20	↓	7,250	765		8,015	9,250

13 17 33 – Whirlpool Tubs

13 17 33.10 Whirlpool Bath	Crew	Daily Output	Labor-Hours	Unit	Material	2014 Bare Costs Labor	Equipment	Total	Total Incl O&P
0010 **WHIRLPOOL BATH**									
6000 Whirlpool, bath with vented overflow, molded fiberglass									
6100 66" x 36" x 24"	Q-1	1	16	Ea.	3,325	615		3,940	4,650

13 18 Ice Rinks

13 18 13 – Ice Rink Floor Systems

13 18 13.50 Ice Skating	Crew	Daily Output	Labor-Hours	Unit	Material	2014 Bare Costs Labor	Equipment	Total	Total Incl O&P
0010 **ICE SKATING** Equipment incl. refrigeration, plumbing & cooling									
0020 coils & concrete slab, 85' x 200' rink									
0300 55° system, 5 mos., 100 ton				Total	575,000			575,000	632,500
0700 90° system, 12 mos., 135 ton				"	650,000			650,000	715,000
1200 Subsoil heating system (recycled from compressor), 85' x 200'	Q-7	.27	118	Ea.	40,000	4,625		44,625	51,500
1300 Subsoil insulation, 2 lb. polystyrene with vapor barrier, 85' x 200'	2 Carp	.14	114	"	30,000	4,075		34,075	39,900

13 18 16 – Ice Rink Dasher Boards

13 18 16.50 Ice Rink Dasher Boards	Crew	Daily Output	Labor-Hours	Unit	Material	2014 Bare Costs Labor	Equipment	Total	Total Incl O&P
0010 **ICE RINK DASHER BOARDS**									
1000 Dasher boards, 1/2" H.D. polyethylene faced steel frame, 3' acrylic									
1020 screen at sides, 5' acrylic ends, 85' x 200'	F-5	.06	533	Ea.	135,000	16,700		151,700	176,500
1100 Fiberglass & aluminum construction, same sides and ends	"	.06	533	"	155,000	16,700		171,700	198,500

13 21 Controlled Environment Rooms

13 21 13 – Clean Rooms

13 21 13.50 Clean Room Components	Crew	Daily Output	Labor-Hours	Unit	Material	2014 Bare Costs Labor	Equipment	Total	Total Incl O&P
0010 **CLEAN ROOM COMPONENTS**									
1100 Clean room, soft wall, 12' x 12', Class 100	1 Carp	.18	44.444	Ea.	17,200	1,600		18,800	21,700
1110 Class 1,000		.18	44.444		14,000	1,600		15,600	18,100
1120 Class 10,000		.21	38.095		12,400	1,350		13,750	15,900
1130 Class 100,000	↓	.21	38.095	↓	11,600	1,350		12,950	15,100
2800 Ceiling grid support, slotted channel struts 4'-0" O.C., ea. way				S.F.				5.90	6.50
3000 Ceiling panel, vinyl coated foil on mineral substrate									
3020 Sealed, non-perforated				S.F.				1.27	1.40
4000 Ceiling panel seal, silicone sealant, 150 L.F./gal.	1 Carp	150	.053	L.F.	.34	1.91		2.25	3.58
4100 Two sided adhesive tape	"	240	.033	"	.12	1.19		1.31	2.13
4200 Clips, one per panel				Ea.	.99			.99	1.09
6000 HEPA filter, 2' x 4', 99.97% eff., 3" dp beveled frame (silicone seal)					480			480	530
6040 6" deep skirted frame (channel seal)					420			420	460
6100 99.99% efficient, 3" deep beveled frame (silicone seal)					555			555	610
6140 6" deep skirted frame (channel seal)					435			435	475
6200 99.999% efficient, 3" deep beveled frame (silicone seal)					625			625	690
6240 6" deep skirted frame (channel seal)				↓	450			450	495
7000 Wall panel systems, including channel strut framing									

13 21 Controlled Environment Rooms

13 21 13 – Clean Rooms

13 21 13.50 Clean Room Components	Crew	Daily Output	Labor-Hours	Unit	Material	2014 Bare Costs Labor	Equipment	Total	Total Incl O&P
7020	Polyester coated aluminum, particle board				S.F.				18.20	20
7100	Porcelain coated aluminum, particle board								32	35
7400	Wall panel support, slotted channel struts, to 12' high				↓				16.35	18

13 21 26 – Cold Storage Rooms

13 21 26.50 Refrigeration

		Crew	Daily Output	Labor-Hours	Unit	Material	2014 Bare Costs Labor	Equipment	Total	Total Incl O&P
0010	**REFRIGERATION**									
0020	Curbs, 12" high, 4" thick, concrete	2 Carp	58	.276	L.F.	4.94	9.85		14.79	22
1000	Doors, see Section 08 34 13.10									
2400	Finishes, 2 coat portland cement plaster, 1/2" thick	1 Plas	48	.167	S.F.	1.36	5.45		6.81	10.45
2500	For galvanized reinforcing mesh, add	1 Lath	335	.024		.90	.76		1.66	2.21
2700	3/16" thick latex cement	1 Plas	88	.091		2.31	2.97		5.28	7.45
2900	For glass cloth reinforced ceilings, add	"	450	.018		.55	.58		1.13	1.57
3100	Fiberglass panels, 1/8" thick	1 Carp	149.45	.054		3.06	1.91		4.97	6.60
3200	Polystyrene, plastic finish ceiling, 1" thick		274	.029		2.83	1.04		3.87	4.87
3400	2" thick		274	.029		3.23	1.04		4.27	5.30
3500	4" thick	↓	219	.037		3.57	1.31		4.88	6.15
3800	Floors, concrete, 4" thick	1 Cefi	93	.086		1.29	2.95		4.24	6.20
3900	6" thick	"	85	.094	↓	2.01	3.23		5.24	7.45
4000	Insulation, 1" to 6" thick, cork				B.F.	1.30			1.30	1.43
4100	Urethane					.51			.51	.56
4300	Polystyrene, regular					.52			.52	.57
4400	Bead board					.24			.24	.26
4600	Installation of above, add per layer	2 Carp	657.60	.024	S.F.	.43	.87		1.30	1.93
4700	Wall and ceiling juncture		298.90	.054	L.F.	2.11	1.91		4.02	5.55
4900	Partitions, galvanized sandwich panels, 4" thick, stock		219.20	.073	S.F.	8.85	2.61		11.46	14.15
5000	Aluminum or fiberglass	↓	219.20	.073	"	9.70	2.61		12.31	15.05
5200	Prefab walk-in, 7'-6" high, aluminum, incl. refrigeration, door & floor									
5210	not incl. partitions, 6' x 6'	2 Carp	54.80	.292	SF Flr.	158	10.45		168.45	192
5500	10' x 10'		82.20	.195		127	6.95		133.95	152
5700	12' x 14'		109.60	.146		114	5.20		119.20	135
5800	12' x 20'	↓	109.60	.146		99.50	5.20		104.70	118
6100	For 8'-6" high, add					5%				
6300	Rule of thumb for complete units, w/o doors & refrigeration, cooler	2 Carp	146	.110		143	3.92		146.92	165
6400	Freezer		109.60	.146	↓	170	5.20		175.20	195
6600	Shelving, plated or galvanized, steel wire type		360	.044	SF Hor.	12.55	1.59		14.14	16.45
6700	Slat shelf type	↓	375	.043		15.50	1.53		17.03	19.60
6900	For stainless steel shelving, add				↓	300%				
7000	Vapor barrier, on wood walls	2 Carp	1644	.010	S.F.	.19	.35		.54	.80
7200	On masonry walls	"	1315	.012	"	.47	.44		.91	1.25
7500	For air curtain doors, see Section 23 34 33.10									

13 21 48 – Sound-Conditioned Rooms

13 21 48.10 Anechoic Chambers

		Crew	Daily Output	Labor-Hours	Unit	Material	2014 Bare Costs Labor	Equipment	Total	Total Incl O&P
0010	**ANECHOIC CHAMBERS** Standard units, 7' ceiling heights									
0100	Area for pricing is net inside dimensions									
0300	200 cycles per second cutoff, 25 S.F. floor area				SF Flr.	1,625			1,625	1,800
0400	50 S.F.								1,050	1,150
0600	75 S.F.								1,000	1,100
0700	100 S.F.					1,225			1,225	1,350
0900	For 150 cycles per second cutoff, add to 100 S.F. room								30%	30%
1000	For 100 cycles per second cutoff, add to 100 S.F. room				↓				45%	45%

13 21 Controlled Environment Rooms

13 21 48 – Sound-Conditioned Rooms

13 21 48.15 Audiometric Rooms	Crew	Daily Output	Labor-Hours	Unit	Material	2014 Bare Costs Labor	Equipment	Total	Total Incl O&P
0010 **AUDIOMETRIC ROOMS**									
0020 Under 500 S.F. surface	4 Carp	98	.327	SF Surf	52.50	11.65		64.15	77
0100 Over 500 S.F. surface	"	120	.267	"	50	9.55		59.55	71

13 21 53 – Darkrooms

13 21 53.50 Darkrooms

13 21 53.50 Darkrooms	Crew	Daily Output	Labor-Hours	Unit	Material	2014 Bare Costs Labor	Equipment	Total	Total Incl O&P
0010 **DARKROOMS**									
0020 Shell, complete except for door, 64 S.F., 8' high	2 Carp	128	.125	SF Flr.	38.50	4.47		42.97	49.50
0100 12' high		64	.250		49	8.95		57.95	69
0500 120 S.F. floor, 8' high		120	.133		28	4.77		32.77	38.50
0600 12' high		60	.267		37.50	9.55		47.05	57.50
0800 240 S.F. floor, 8' high		120	.133		20.50	4.77		25.27	30.50
0900 12' high		60	.267		27.50	9.55		37.05	46
1200 Mini-cylindrical, revolving, unlined, 4' diameter		3.50	4.571	Ea.	2,875	163		3,038	3,450
1400 5'-6" diameter		2.50	6.400		5,175	229		5,404	6,075
1600 Add for lead lining, inner cylinder, 1/32" thick					1,650			1,650	1,825
1700 1/16" thick					4,450			4,450	4,875
1800 Add for lead lining, inner and outer cylinder, 1/32" thick					3,050			3,050	3,375
1900 1/16" thick					6,825			6,825	7,500
2000 For darkroom door, see Section 08 34 36.10									

13 21 56 – Music Rooms

13 21 56.50 Music Rooms

13 21 56.50 Music Rooms	Crew	Daily Output	Labor-Hours	Unit	Material	2014 Bare Costs Labor	Equipment	Total	Total Incl O&P
0010 **MUSIC ROOMS**									
0020 Practice room, modular, perforated steel, under 500 S.F.	2 Carp	70	.229	SF Surf	32	8.15		40.15	49.50
0100 Over 500 S.F.	"	80	.200	"	27	7.15		34.15	42

13 24 Special Activity Rooms

13 24 16 – Saunas

13 24 16.50 Saunas and Heaters

13 24 16.50 Saunas and Heaters	Crew	Daily Output	Labor-Hours	Unit	Material	2014 Bare Costs Labor	Equipment	Total	Total Incl O&P
0010 **SAUNAS AND HEATERS**									
0020 Prefabricated, incl. heater & controls, 7' high, 6' x 4', C/C	L-7	2.20	11.818	Ea.	5,375	365		5,740	6,550
0050 6' x 4', C/P		2	13		4,875	400		5,275	6,050
0400 6' x 5', C/C		2	13		5,675	400		6,075	6,925
0450 6' x 5', C/P		2	13		5,150	400		5,550	6,325
0600 6' x 6', C/C		1.80	14.444		6,275	445		6,720	7,650
0650 6' x 6', C/P		1.80	14.444		5,725	445		6,170	7,050
0800 6' x 9', C/C		1.60	16.250		7,750	500		8,250	9,375
0850 6' x 9', C/P		1.60	16.250		7,000	500		7,500	8,550
1000 8' x 12', C/C		1.10	23.636		11,600	730		12,330	14,000
1050 8' x 12', C/P		1.10	23.636		10,500	730		11,230	12,700
1200 8' x 8', C/C		1.40	18.571		9,150	575		9,725	11,100
1250 8' x 8', C/P		1.40	18.571		8,450	575		9,025	10,200
1400 8' x 10', C/C		1.20	21.667		10,100	670		10,770	12,300
1450 8' x 10', C/P		1.20	21.667		9,225	670		9,895	11,300
1600 10' x 12', C/C		1	26		12,300	800		13,100	14,900
1650 10' x 12', C/P		1	26		10,900	800		11,700	13,400
1700 Door only, cedar, 2'x6', with 1'x4' tempered insulated glass window	2 Carp	3.40	4.706		735	168		903	1,100
1800 Prehung, incl. jambs, pulls & hardware	"	12	1.333		730	47.50		777.50	880
2500 Heaters only (incl. above), wall mounted, to 200 C.F.					675			675	745
2750 To 300 C.F.					910			910	1,000

13 24 Special Activity Rooms

13 24 16 – Saunas

13 24 16.50 Saunas and Heaters	Crew	Daily Output	Labor-Hours	Unit	Material	2014 Bare Costs Labor	Equipment	Total	Total Incl O&P
3000	Floor standing, to 720 C.F., 10,000 watts, w/controls	1 Elec	3	2.667	Ea.	2,900	114		3,014	3,375
3250	To 1,000 C.F., 16,000 watts	"	3	2.667	↓	3,700	114		3,814	4,250

13 24 26 – Steam Baths

13 24 26.50 Steam Baths and Components	Crew	Daily Output	Labor-Hours	Unit	Material	Labor	Equipment	Total	Total Incl O&P
0010	**STEAM BATHS AND COMPONENTS**									
0020	Heater, timer & head, single, to 140 C.F.	1 Plum	1.20	6.667	Ea.	1,450	284		1,734	2,075
0500	To 300 C.F.		1.10	7.273		1,550	310		1,860	2,200
1000	Commercial size, with blow-down assembly, to 800 C.F.		.90	8.889		7,350	380		7,730	8,700
1500	To 2500 C.F.	↓	.80	10		9,125	425		9,550	10,700
2000	Multiple, motels, apts., 2 baths, w/blow-down assm., 500 C.F.	Q-1	1.30	12.308		7,950	470		8,420	9,525
2500	4 baths	"	.70	22.857		10,700	875		11,575	13,300
2700	Conversion unit for residential tub, including door				↓	3,600			3,600	3,950

13 28 Athletic and Recreational Special Construction

13 28 33 – Athletic and Recreational Court Walls

13 28 33.50 Sport Court	Crew	Daily Output	Labor-Hours	Unit	Material	Labor	Equipment	Total	Total Incl O&P
0010	**SPORT COURT**									
0020	Floors, No. 2 & better maple, 25/32" thick				SF Flr.				6.05	6.65
0100	Walls, laminated plastic bonded to galv. steel studs				SF Wall				7.70	8.45
0150	Laminated fiberglass surfacing, minimum								1.91	2.10
0180	Maximum				↓				2.15	2.37
0300	Squash, regulation court in existing building, minimum				Court	36,800			36,800	40,400
0400	Maximum				"	41,000			41,000	45,000
0450	Rule of thumb for components:									
0470	Walls	3 Carp	.15	160	Court	11,000	5,725		16,725	21,700
0500	Floor	"	.25	96		8,725	3,425		12,150	15,400
0550	Lighting	2 Elec	.60	26.667		2,100	1,150		3,250	4,175
0600	Handball, racquetball court in existing building, minimum	C-1	.20	160		39,800	5,075		44,875	52,500
0800	Maximum	"	.10	320		43,100	10,100		53,200	64,500
0900	Rule of thumb for components: walls	3 Carp	.12	200		12,600	7,150		19,750	25,900
1000	Floor		.25	96		8,725	3,425		12,150	15,400
1100	Ceiling	↓	.33	72.727		4,200	2,600		6,800	9,000
1200	Lighting	2 Elec	.60	26.667	↓	2,200	1,150		3,350	4,300

13 31 Fabric Structures

13 31 13 – Air-Supported Fabric Structures

13 31 13.09 Air Supported Tank Covers	Crew	Daily Output	Labor-Hours	Unit	Material	Labor	Equipment	Total	Total Incl O&P
0010	**AIR SUPPORTED TANK COVERS**, vinyl polyester									
0100	Scrim, double layer, with hardware, blower, standby & controls									
0200	Round, 75' diameter	B-2	4500	.009	S.F.	10.20	.25		10.45	11.70
0300	100' diameter		5000	.008		9.30	.23		9.53	10.60
0400	150' diameter		5000	.008		7.35	.23		7.58	8.50
0500	Rectangular, 20' x 20'		4500	.009		23	.25		23.25	26
0600	30' x 40'		4500	.009		23	.25		23.25	26
0700	50' x 60'	↓	4500	.009		23	.25		23.25	26
0800	For single wall construction, deduct, minimum					.79			.79	.87
0900	Maximum					2.33			2.33	2.56
1000	For maximum resistance to atmosphere or cold, add				↓	1.14			1.14	1.25
1100	For average shipping charges, add				Total	1,975			1,975	2,175

13 31 Fabric Structures

13 31 13 – Air-Supported Fabric Structures

13 31 13.13 Single-Walled Air-Supported Structures	Crew	Daily Output	Labor-Hours	Unit	Material	2014 Bare Costs Labor	Equipment	Total	Total Incl O&P
0010 **SINGLE-WALLED AIR-SUPPORTED STRUCTURES** R133113-10									
0020 Site preparation, incl. anchor placement and utilities	B-11B	1000	.016	SF Flr.	1.16	.52	.30	1.98	2.47
0030 For concrete, see Section 03 30 53.40									
0050 Warehouse, polyester/vinyl fabric, 28 oz., over 10 yr. life, welded									
0060 Seams, tension cables, primary & auxiliary inflation system,									
0070 airlock, personnel doors and liner									
0100 5,000 S.F.	4 Clab	5000	.006	SF Flr.	25	.18		25.18	28
0250 12,000 S.F.	"	6000	.005		18	.15		18.15	20
0400 24,000 S.F.	8 Clab	12000	.005		12.65	.15		12.80	14.20
0500 50,000 S.F.	"	12500	.005		11.75	.14		11.89	13.15
0700 12 oz. reinforced vinyl fabric, 5 yr. life, sewn seams,									
0710 accordion door, including liner									
0750 3000 S.F.	4 Clab	3000	.011	SF Flr.	12	.30		12.30	13.70
0800 12,000 S.F.	"	6000	.005		10.20	.15		10.35	11.50
0850 24,000 S.F.	8 Clab	12000	.005		8.65	.15		8.80	9.75
0950 Deduct for single layer					1.03			1.03	1.13
1000 Add for welded seams					1.01			1.01	1.11
1050 Add for double layer, welded seams included					2.08			2.08	2.29
1250 Tedlar/vinyl fabric, 28 oz., with liner, over 10 yr. life,									
1260 incl. overhead and personnel doors									
1300 3000 S.F.	4 Clab	3000	.011	SF Flr.	24.50	.30		24.80	27.50
1450 12,000 S.F.	"	6000	.005		17.20	.15		17.35	19.20
1550 24,000 S.F.	8 Clab	12000	.005		13.30	.15		13.45	14.90
1700 Deduct for single layer					1.44			1.44	1.58
2250 Greenhouse/shelter, woven polyethylene with liner, 2 yr. life,									
2260 sewn seams, including doors									
2300 3000 S.F.	4 Clab	3000	.011	SF Flr.	6.60	.30		6.90	7.75
2350 12,000 S.F.	"	6000	.005		6.70	.15		6.85	7.65
2450 24,000 S.F.	8 Clab	12000	.005		5.60	.15		5.75	6.40
2550 Deduct for single layer					.63			.63	.69
2600 Tennis/gymnasium, polyester/vinyl fabric, 28 oz., over 10 yr. life,									
2610 including thermal liner, heat and lights									
2650 7,200 S.F.	4 Clab	6000	.005	SF Flr.	23.50	.15		23.65	26.50
2750 13,000 S.F.	"	6500	.005		18	.14		18.14	20
2850 Over 24,000 S.F.	8 Clab	12000	.005		16.45	.15		16.60	18.30
2860 For low temperature conditions, add					1.14			1.14	1.25
2870 For average shipping charges, add				Total	5,600			5,600	6,150
2900 Thermal liner, translucent reinforced vinyl				SF Flr.	1.14			1.14	1.25
2950 Metalized mylar fabric and mesh, double liner				"	2.33			2.33	2.56
3050 Stadium/convention center, teflon coated fiberglass, heavy weight,									
3060 over 20 yr. life, incl. thermal liner and heating system									
3100 Minimum	9 Clab	26000	.003	SF Flr.	57.50	.08		57.58	63
3110 Maximum	"	19000	.004	"	68	.11		68.11	75
3400 Doors, air lock, 15' long, 10' x 10'	2 Carp	.80	20	Ea.	20,400	715		21,115	23,700
3600 15' x 15'	"	.50	32		30,300	1,150		31,450	35,300
3700 For each added 5' length, add					5,425			5,425	5,950
3900 Revolving personnel door, 6' diameter, 6'-6" high	2 Carp	.80	20		15,200	715		15,915	17,900
4200 Double wall, self supporting, shell only, minimum				SF Flr.				19.10	21
4300 Maximum				"				35.50	39

13 31 Fabric Structures

13 31 23 – Tensioned Fabric Structures

13 31 23.50 Tension Structures	Crew	Daily Output	Labor-Hours	Unit	Material	2014 Bare Costs Labor	Equipment	Total	Total Incl O&P
0010 **TENSION STRUCTURES** Rigid steel/alum. frame, vinyl coated poly									
0100 Fabric shell, 60' clear span, not incl. foundations or floors									
0200 6,000 S.F.	B-41	1000	.044	SF Flr.	13.80	1.29	.29	15.38	17.70
0300 12,000 S.F.		1100	.040		13.20	1.17	.27	14.64	16.80
0400 80' to 99' clear span, 20,800 S.F.	↓	1220	.036		13	1.06	.24	14.30	16.35
0410 100' to 119' clear span, 10,000 S.F.	L-5	2175	.026		13.70	1	.34	15.04	17.30
0430 26,000 S.F.		2300	.024		12.75	.94	.32	14.01	16.15
0450 36,000 S.F.		2500	.022		12.60	.87	.30	13.77	15.80
0460 120' to 149' clear span, 24,000 S.F.		3000	.019		13.90	.72	.25	14.87	16.85
0470 150' to 199' clear span, 30,000 S.F.	↓	6000	.009		14.45	.36	.12	14.93	16.65
0480 200' clear span, 40,000 S.F.	E-6	8000	.015	↓	17.75	.58	.23	18.56	21
0500 For roll-up door, 12' x 14', add	L-2	1	16	Ea.	5,500	500		6,000	6,900
0600 For personnel doors, add, minimum				SF Flr.	5%				
0700 Add, maximum					15%				
0800 For site work, simple foundation, etc., add, minimum								1.25	1.95
0900 Add, maximum				↓				2.75	3.05

13 34 Fabricated Engineered Structures

13 34 13 – Glazed Structures

13 34 13.13 Greenhouses

	Crew	Daily Output	Labor-Hours	Unit	Material	2014 Bare Costs Labor	Equipment	Total	Total Incl O&P
0010 **GREENHOUSES**, Shell only, stock units, not incl. 2' stub walls,									
0020 foundation, floors, heat or compartments									
0300 Residential type, free standing, 8'-6" long x 7'-6" wide	2 Carp	59	.271	SF Flr.	31.50	9.70		41.20	51.50
0400 10'-6" wide		85	.188		24	6.75		30.75	38
0600 13'-6" wide		108	.148		23.50	5.30		28.80	35
0700 17'-0" wide		160	.100		19.20	3.58		22.78	27
0900 Lean-to type, 3'-10" wide		34	.471		36.50	16.80		53.30	69
1000 6'-10" wide	↓	58	.276	↓	44.50	9.85		54.35	65.50
1500 Commercial, custom, truss frame, incl. equip., plumbing, elec.,									
1510 benches and controls, under 2,000 S.F., minimum				SF Flr.				27.50	30
1550 Maximum					17.40			17.40	19.10
1700 Over 5,000 S.F., minimum					15.70			15.70	17.25
1750 Maximum				↓				27.50	30
2000 Institutional, custom, rigid frame, including compartments and									
2010 multi-controls, under 500 S.F., minimum				SF Flr.	45			45	49.50
2050 Maximum					35.50			35.50	39
2150 Over 2,000 S.F., minimum					11.70			11.70	12.90
2200 Maximum					59			59	65
2400 Concealed rigid frame, under 500 S.F., minimum								82	90
2450 Maximum								100	110
2550 Over 2,000 S.F., minimum								62	68
2600 Maximum								72	79
2800 Lean-to type, under 500 S.F., minimum								72.50	80
2850 Maximum								109	120
3000 Over 2,000 S.F., minimum								40	44
3050 Maximum				↓				66.50	73
3700 For 1/4" tempered glass, add				SF Surf	1.34			1.34	1.47
3900 Cooling, 1200 CFM exhaust fan, add				Ea.	289			289	320
4000 7850 CFM					995			995	1,100
4200 For heaters, 10 MBH, add				↓	209			209	230

13 34 Fabricated Engineered Structures

13 34 13 – Glazed Structures

13 34 13.13 Greenhouses

		Crew	Daily Output	Labor-Hours	Unit	Material	2014 Bare Costs Labor	Equipment	Total	Total Incl O&P
4300	60 MBH, add				Ea.	760			760	835
4500	For benches, 2' x 8', add					157			157	173
4600	4' x 10', add					190			190	209
4800	For controls, add, minimum				Total	240			240	264
4900	Maximum				"	750			750	825
5100	For humidification equipment, add				Ea.	400			400	440
5200	For vinyl shading, add				S.F.	.24			.24	.26
6000	Geodesic hemisphere, 1/8" plexiglass glazing									
6050	8' diameter	2 Carp	2	8	Ea.	6,250	286		6,536	7,350
6150	24' diameter		.35	45.714		14,000	1,625		15,625	18,100
6250	48' diameter		.20	80		33,000	2,850		35,850	41,000

13 34 13.19 Swimming Pool Enclosures

		Crew	Daily Output	Labor-Hours	Unit	Material	2014 Bare Costs Labor	Equipment	Total	Total Incl O&P
0010	**SWIMMING POOL ENCLOSURES** Translucent, free standing									
0020	not including foundations, heat or light									
0200	Economy, minimum	2 Carp	200	.080	SF Hor.	60	2.86		62.86	71
0300	Maximum		100	.160		65	5.70		70.70	81
0400	Deluxe, minimum		100	.160		72	5.70		77.70	88.50
0600	Maximum		70	.229		93	8.15		101.15	116
0700	For motorized roof, 40% opening, solid roof, add					21			21	23
0800	Skylight type roof, add					13.50			13.50	14.85
0900	Air-inflated, including blowers and heaters, minimum								3.18	3.50
1000	Maximum								6.10	6.70

13 34 16 – Grandstands and Bleachers

13 34 16.13 Grandstands

		Crew	Daily Output	Labor-Hours	Unit	Material	2014 Bare Costs Labor	Equipment	Total	Total Incl O&P
0010	**GRANDSTANDS** Permanent, municipal, including foundation									
0050	Steel understructure w/aluminum closed deck, minimum				Seat				118	130
0100	Maximum								205	225
0300	Steel, minimum					18.10			18.10	19.90
0400	Maximum					20.50			20.50	22.50
0600	Aluminum, extruded, stock design, minimum								63.50	70
0700	Maximum								105	115
0900	Composite, steel, wood and plastic, stock design, minimum					35			35	38.50
1000	Maximum					62			62	68.50

13 34 16.53 Bleachers

		Crew	Daily Output	Labor-Hours	Unit	Material	2014 Bare Costs Labor	Equipment	Total	Total Incl O&P
0010	**BLEACHERS**									
0020	Bleachers, outdoor, portable, 5 tiers, 42 seats	2 Sswk	120	.133	Seat	90	5.10		95.10	109
0100	5 tiers, 54 seats		80	.200		80.50	7.65		88.15	103
0200	10 tiers, 104 seats		120	.133		91	5.10		96.10	110
0300	10 tiers, 144 seats		80	.200		82	7.65		89.65	105
0500	Permanent bleachers, aluminum seat, steel frame, 24" row									
0600	8 tiers, 80 seats	2 Sswk	60	.267	Seat	66	10.25		76.25	92
0700	8 tiers, 160 seats		48	.333		57	12.80		69.80	87.50
0925	15 tiers, 154 to 165 seats		60	.267		99	10.25		109.25	129
0975	15 tiers, 214 to 225 seats		60	.267		90	10.25		100.25	119
1050	15 tiers, 274 to 285 seats		60	.267		81	10.25		91.25	109
1200	Seat backs only, 30" row, fiberglass		160	.100		40	3.84		43.84	51.50
1300	Steel and wood		160	.100		18.15	3.84		21.99	27.50
1400	NOTE: average seating is 1.5' in width									

13 34 19.50 Pre-Engineered Steel Buildings	Crew	Daily Output	Labor-Hours	Unit	Material	2014 Bare Costs Labor	Equipment	Total	Total Incl O&P
0010 **PRE-ENGINEERED STEEL BUILDINGS** R133419-10									
0100 Clear span rigid frame, 26 ga. colored roofing and siding									
0150 20' to 29' wide, 10' eave height	E-2	425	.113	SF Flr.	8.50	4.38	3.60	16.48	21.50
0160 14' eave height		350	.137		9.20	5.30	4.37	18.87	25
0170 16' eave height		320	.150		9.85	5.80	4.78	20.43	27
0180 20' eave height		275	.175		10.75	6.75	5.55	23.05	30.50
0190 24' eave height		240	.200		11.85	7.75	6.35	25.95	34.50
0200 30' to 49' wide, 10' eave height		535	.090		6.45	3.48	2.86	12.79	16.75
0300 14' eave height		450	.107		7	4.13	3.40	14.53	19.15
0400 16' eave height		415	.116		7.45	4.48	3.68	15.61	20.50
0500 20' eave height		360	.133		8.10	5.15	4.25	17.50	23
0600 24' eave height		320	.150		8.90	5.80	4.78	19.48	26
0700 50' to 100' wide, 10' eave height		770	.062		5.50	2.42	1.99	9.91	12.75
0900 16' eave height		600	.080		6.30	3.10	2.55	11.95	15.55
1000 20' eave height		490	.098		6.85	3.80	3.12	13.77	18.05
1100 24' eave height	▼	435	.110	▼	7.55	4.27	3.51	15.33	20
1200 Clear span tapered beam frame, 26 ga. colored roofing/siding									
1300 30' to 39' wide, 10' eave height	E-2	535	.090	SF Flr.	7.35	3.48	2.86	13.69	17.70
1400 14' eave height		450	.107		8.10	4.13	3.40	15.63	20.50
1500 16' eave height		415	.116		8.50	4.48	3.68	16.66	22
1600 20' eave height		360	.133		9.35	5.15	4.25	18.75	24.50
1700 40' wide, 10' eave height		600	.080		6.50	3.10	2.55	12.15	15.75
1800 14' eave height		510	.094		7.20	3.65	3	13.85	18
1900 16' eave height		475	.101		7.55	3.91	3.22	14.68	19.15
2000 20' eave height		415	.116		8.30	4.48	3.68	16.46	21.50
2100 50' to 79' wide, 10' eave height		770	.062		6.05	2.42	1.99	10.46	13.35
2200 14' eave height		675	.071		6.60	2.75	2.26	11.61	14.90
2300 16' eave height		635	.076		6.85	2.93	2.41	12.19	15.65
2400 20' eave height		490	.098		7.45	3.80	3.12	14.37	18.70
2410 80' to 100' wide, 10' eave height		935	.051		5.40	1.99	1.64	9.03	11.40
2420 14' eave height		750	.064		5.90	2.48	2.04	10.42	13.35
2430 16' eave height		685	.070		6.20	2.71	2.23	11.14	14.30
2440 20' eave height		560	.086		6.60	3.32	2.73	12.65	16.50
2460 101' to 120' wide, 10' eave height		950	.051		4.94	1.96	1.61	8.51	10.85
2470 14' eave height		770	.062		5.50	2.42	1.99	9.91	12.75
2480 16' eave height		675	.071		5.85	2.75	2.26	10.86	14.05
2490 20' eave height	▼	560	.086	▼	6.25	3.32	2.73	12.30	16.05
2500 Single post 2-span frame, 26 ga. colored roofing and siding									
2600 80' wide, 14' eave height	E-2	740	.065	SF Flr.	5.50	2.51	2.07	10.08	13
2700 16' eave height		695	.069		5.85	2.68	2.20	10.73	13.80
2800 20' eave height		625	.077		6.30	2.98	2.45	11.73	15.20
2900 24' eave height		570	.084		6.90	3.26	2.68	12.84	16.65
3000 100' wide, 14' eave height		835	.057		5.35	2.23	1.83	9.41	12
3100 16' eave height		795	.060		4.95	2.34	1.92	9.21	11.95
3200 20' eave height		730	.066		6	2.55	2.09	10.64	13.65
3300 24' eave height		670	.072		6.65	2.78	2.28	11.71	15
3400 120' wide, 14' eave height		870	.055		6.25	2.14	1.76	10.15	12.75
3500 16' eave height		830	.058		5.55	2.24	1.84	9.63	12.30
3600 20' eave height		765	.063		6	2.43	2	10.43	13.35
3700 24' eave height	▼	705	.068	▼	6.60	2.64	2.17	11.41	14.55
3800 Double post 3-span frame, 26 ga. colored roofing and siding									
3900 150' wide, 14' eave height	E-2	925	.052	SF Flr.	4.35	2.01	1.65	8.01	10.35

13 34 19.50 Pre-Engineered Steel Buildings	Crew	Daily Output	Labor-Hours	Unit	Material	2014 Bare Costs Labor	Equipment	Total	Total Incl O&P
4000	16' eave height	E-2	890	.054	SF Flr.	4.53	2.09	1.72	8.34	10.75
4100	20' eave height		820	.059		4.93	2.27	1.86	9.06	11.70
4200	24' eave height	↓	765	.063	↓	5.45	2.43	2	9.88	12.75
4300	Triple post 4-span frame, 26 ga. colored roofing and siding									
4400	160' wide, 14' eave height	E-2	970	.049	SF Flr.	4.28	1.92	1.58	7.78	10
4500	16' eave height		930	.052		4.46	2	1.64	8.10	10.45
4600	20' eave height		870	.055		4.37	2.14	1.76	8.27	10.70
4700	24' eave height		815	.059		4.97	2.28	1.88	9.13	11.75
4800	200' wide, 14' eave height		1030	.047		3.90	1.81	1.48	7.19	9.30
4900	16' eave height		995	.048		4.05	1.87	1.54	7.46	9.65
5000	20' eave height		935	.051		4.47	1.99	1.64	8.10	10.45
5100	24' eave height	↓	885	.054	↓	5	2.10	1.73	8.83	11.30
5200	Accessory items: add to the basic building cost above									
5250	Eave overhang, 2' wide, 26 ga., with soffit	E-2	360	.133	L.F.	29.50	5.15	4.25	38.90	47
5300	4' wide, without soffit		300	.160		26	6.20	5.10	37.30	45.50
5350	With soffit		250	.192		38	7.45	6.10	51.55	62
5400	6' wide, without soffit		250	.192		34	7.45	6.10	47.55	58
5450	With soffit		200	.240	↓	45.50	9.30	7.65	62.45	76
5500	Entrance canopy, incl. frame, 4' x 4'		25	1.920	Ea.	475	74.50	61	610.50	725
5550	4' x 8'		19	2.526	"	550	98	80.50	728.50	875
5600	End wall roof overhang, 4' wide, without soffit		850	.056	L.F.	16.55	2.19	1.80	20.54	24.50
5650	With soffit	↓	500	.096	"	27	3.72	3.06	33.78	40
5700	Doors, HM self-framing, incl. butts, lockset and trim									
5750	Single leaf, 3070 (3' x 7'), economy	2 Sswk	5	3.200	Opng.	585	123		708	880
5800	Deluxe		4	4		640	153		793	995
5825	Glazed		4	4		745	153		898	1,100
5850	3670 (3'-6" x 7')		4	4		815	153		968	1,200
5900	4070 (4' x 7')		3	5.333		885	205		1,090	1,350
5950	Double leaf, 6070 (6' x 7')		2	8		1,100	305		1,405	1,775
6000	Glazed		2	8		1,400	305		1,705	2,125
6050	Framing only, for openings, 3' x 7'		4	4		185	153		338	495
6100	10' x 10'		3	5.333		610	205		815	1,050
6150	For windows below, 2020 (2' x 2')		6	2.667		196	102		298	410
6200	4030 (4' x 3')		5	3.200	↓	239	123		362	495
6250	Flashings, 26 ga., corner or eave, painted		240	.067	L.F.	4.30	2.56		6.86	9.60
6300	Galvanized		240	.067		4.10	2.56		6.66	9.40
6350	Rake flashing, painted		240	.067		4.64	2.56		7.20	9.95
6400	Galvanized		240	.067		4.40	2.56		6.96	9.70
6450	Ridge flashing, 18" wide, painted		240	.067		6.20	2.56		8.76	11.65
6500	Galvanized		240	.067		7.10	2.56		9.66	12.65
6550	Gutter, eave type, 26 ga., painted		320	.050		6.70	1.92		8.62	11.05
6650	Valley type, between buildings, painted	↓	120	.133	↓	12.85	5.10		17.95	24
6710	Insulation, rated .6 lb. density, unfaced 4" thick, R13	2 Carp	2300	.007	S.F.	.39	.25		.64	.85
6720	6" thick, R19		2300	.007		.52	.25		.77	.99
6730	10" thick, R30	↓	2300	.007	↓	1	.25		1.25	1.52
6750	Insulation, rated .6 lb. density, poly/scrim/foil (PSF) faced									
6801	1-1/2" thick, R5	2 Clab	2300	.007	S.F.	.28	.20		.48	.64
6851	3" thick, R10		2300	.007		.30	.20		.50	.66
6901	4" thick, R13		2300	.007		.40	.20		.60	.77
6930	10" thick, R30	2 Carp	2300	.007		1.32	.25		1.57	1.87
6951	Foil faced, 1-1/2" thick, R5	2 Clab	2300	.007		.30	.20		.50	.66
7001	2" thick, R6		2300	.007		.39	.20		.59	.76
7051	3" thick, R10	↓	2300	.007	↓	.41	.20		.61	.78

13 34 19 – Metal Building Systems

13 34 19.50 Pre-Engineered Steel Buildings	Crew	Daily Output	Labor-Hours	Unit	Material	2014 Bare Costs Labor	Equipment	Total	Total Incl O&P
7101	4" thick, R13	2 Clab	2300	.007	S.F.	.43	.20		.63	.80
7110	6" thick, R19	2 Carp	2300	.007		.60	.25		.85	1.08
7120	10" thick, R30	"	2300	.007		.84	.25		1.09	1.34
7151	Metalized polyester facing, 1-1/2" thick, R5	2 Clab	2300	.007		.49	.20		.69	.87
7201	2" thick, R6		2300	.007		.58	.20		.78	.97
7251	3" thick, R11		2300	.007		.66	.20		.86	1.06
7301	4" thick, R13		2300	.007		.75	.20		.95	1.16
7310	6" thick, R19	2 Carp	2300	.007		.97	.25		1.22	1.49
7351	Vinyl, scrim foil (SD), 1-1/2" thick, R5	2 Clab	2300	.007		.43	.20		.63	.80
7401	2" thick, R6		2300	.007		.55	.20		.75	.94
7451	3" thick, R10		2300	.007		.59	.20		.79	.98
7501	4" thick, R13		2300	.007		.73	.20		.93	1.13
7510	Vinyl/scrim/vinyl (VSV) 4" thick, R13	2 Carp	2300	.007		.48	.25		.73	.95
7520	6" thick, R19		2300	.007		.62	.25		.87	1.10
7530	9 1/2" thick, R30		2300	.007		.84	.25		1.09	1.34
7540	Polyprop/scrim/polyester (PSP), 4", R13		2300	.007		.53	.25		.78	1
7550	6" thick, R19		2300	.007		.66	.25		.91	1.15
7555	10" thick, R30		2300	.007		1.17	.25		1.42	1.71
7560	Polyprop/scrim/kraft/polyester (PSKP), 4" thick, R13		2300	.007		.49	.25		.74	.96
7570	6" thick, R19		2300	.007		.68	.25		.93	1.17
7580	10" thick, R19		2300	.007		1.29	.25		1.54	1.84
7585	Vinyl/scrim/polyester (VSP), 4" thick, R13		2300	.007		.52	.25		.77	.99
7590	6" thick, R19		2300	.007		.64	.25		.89	1.12
7600	10" thick, R30		2300	.007		1	.25		1.25	1.52
7635	Insulation installation, over the purlin, second layer, up to 4" thick, add						90%			
7640	Insulation installation, between the purlins, up to 4" thick, add						100%			
7650	Sash, single slide, glazed, with screens, 2020 (2' x 2')	E-1	22	.727	Opng.	125	28	6.45	159.45	198
7700	3030 (3' x 3')		14	1.143		282	44	10.15	336.15	405
7750	4030 (4' x 3')		13	1.231		375	47	10.95	432.95	515
7800	6040 (6' x 4')		12	1.333		750	51	11.85	812.85	935
7850	Double slide sash, 3030 (3' x 3')		14	1.143		220	44	10.15	274.15	335
7900	6040 (6' x 4')		12	1.333		585	51	11.85	647.85	755
7950	Fixed glass, no screens, 3030 (3' x 3')		14	1.143		215	44	10.15	269.15	330
8000	6040 (6' x 4')		12	1.333		575	51	11.85	637.85	740
8050	Prefinished storm sash, 3030 (3' x 3')		70	.229		75	8.75	2.03	85.78	101
8100	Siding and roofing, see Sections 07 41 13.00 & 07 42 13.00									
8200	Skylight, fiberglass panels, to 30 S.F.	E-1	10	1.600	Ea.	107	61.50	14.20	182.70	250
8250	Larger sizes, add for excess over 30 S.F.	"	300	.053	S.F.	3.55	2.05	.47	6.07	8.35
8300	Roof vents, turbine ventilator, wind driven									
8350	No damper, includes base, galvanized									
8400	12" diameter	Q-9	10	1.600	Ea.	91	58		149	197
8450	20" diameter		8	2		257	73		330	405
8500	24" diameter		8	2		405	73		478	565
8600	Continuous, 26 ga., 10' long, 9" wide	2 Sswk	4	4		36	153		189	330
8650	12" wide	"	4	4		36	153		189	330

13 34 23 – Fabricated Structures

13 34 23.10 Comfort Stations

		Crew	Daily Output	Labor-Hours	Unit	Material	Labor	Equipment	Total	Total Incl O&P
0010	**COMFORT STATIONS** Prefab., stock, w/doors, windows & fixt.									
0100	Not incl. interior finish or electrical									
0300	Mobile, on steel frame, 2 unit				S.F.	196			196	215
0350	7 unit					249			249	274
0400	Permanent, including concrete slab, 2 unit	B-12J	50	.320		249	10.70	17.65	277.35	310

13 34 Fabricated Engineered Structures

13 34 23 – Fabricated Structures

13 34 23.10 Comfort Stations

		Crew	Daily Output	Labor-Hours	Unit	Material	2014 Bare Costs Labor	Equipment	Total	Total Incl O&P
0500	6 unit	B-12J	43	.372	S.F.	191	12.45	20.50	223.95	255
0600	Alternate pricing method, mobile, 2 fixture				Fixture	5,575			5,575	6,150
0650	7 fixture					8,975			8,975	9,875
0700	Permanent, 2 unit	B-12J	.70	22.857		20,500	765	1,250	22,515	25,300
0750	6 unit	"	.50	32	↓	17,400	1,075	1,775	20,250	22,900

13 34 23.15 Domes

		Crew	Daily Output	Labor-Hours	Unit	Material	2014 Bare Costs Labor	Equipment	Total	Total Incl O&P
0010	**DOMES**									
0020	Domes, rev. alum., elec. drive, for astronomy obsv. shell only, stock units									
0600	10'-6" diameter	2 Carp	.25	64	Ea.	30,000	2,300		32,300	36,900
0900	18'-6" diameter		.17	94.118		70,000	3,375		73,375	82,500
1200	24'-6" diameter	↓	.08	200	↓	95,500	7,150		102,650	117,000
1500	Domes, bulk storage, shell only, dual radius hemisphere, arch, steel									
1600	framing, corrugated steel covering, 150' diameter	E-2	550	.087	SF Flr.	28	3.38	2.78	34.16	40
1700	400' diameter	"	720	.067		22.50	2.58	2.12	27.20	32
1800	Wood framing, wood decking, to 400' diameter	F-4	400	.100	↓	37.50	3.28	2.84	43.62	50
1900	Radial framed wood (2" x 6"), 1/2" thick									
2000	plywood, asphalt shingles, 50' diameter	F-3	2000	.020	SF Flr.	72.50	.66	.33	73.49	81
2100	60' diameter		1900	.021		62	.69	.35	63.04	69.50
2200	72' diameter		1800	.022		51.50	.73	.37	52.60	58
2300	116' diameter		1730	.023		35	.76	.38	36.14	40
2400	150' diameter	↓	1500	.027	↓	37.50	.87	.44	38.81	43.50

13 34 23.16 Fabricated Control Booths

		Crew	Daily Output	Labor-Hours	Unit	Material	2014 Bare Costs Labor	Equipment	Total	Total Incl O&P
0010	**FABRICATED CONTROL BOOTHS**									
0100	Guard House, prefab conc. w/bullet resistant doors & windows, roof & wiring									
0110	8' x 8', Level III	L-10	1	24	Ea.	38,400	940	665	40,005	44,700
0120	8' x 8', Level IV	"	1	24	"	43,800	940	665	45,405	50,500

13 34 23.25 Garage Costs

		Crew	Daily Output	Labor-Hours	Unit	Material	2014 Bare Costs Labor	Equipment	Total	Total Incl O&P
0010	**GARAGE COSTS**									
0020	Public parking, average				Car				18,100	19,900
0100	See also Square Foot Costs in Reference Section									
0300	Residential, wood, 12' x 20', one car prefab shell, stock, economy	2 Carp	1	16	Total	5,225	570		5,795	6,700
0350	Custom		.67	23.881		6,250	855		7,105	8,275
0400	Two car, 24' x 20', economy		.67	23.881		9,875	855		10,730	12,300
0450	Custom	↓	.50	32	↓	11,700	1,150		12,850	14,700

13 34 23.30 Garden House

		Crew	Daily Output	Labor-Hours	Unit	Material	2014 Bare Costs Labor	Equipment	Total	Total Incl O&P
0010	**GARDEN HOUSE** Prefab wood, no floors or foundations									
0100	6' x 6'	2 Carp	200	.080	SF Flr.	47	2.86		49.86	57
0300	8' x 12'	"	48	.333	"	28	11.90		39.90	51

13 34 23.35 Geodesic Domes

		Crew	Daily Output	Labor-Hours	Unit	Material	2014 Bare Costs Labor	Equipment	Total	Total Incl O&P
0010	**GEODESIC DOMES** Shell only, interlocking plywood panels R133423-30									
0400	30' diameter	F-5	1.60	20	Ea.	23,000	625		23,625	26,400
0500	33' diameter		1.14	28.070		24,300	880		25,180	28,200
0600	40' diameter	↓	1	32		28,200	1,000		29,200	32,700
0700	45' diameter	F-3	1.13	35.556		29,500	1,175	590	31,265	35,100
0750	56' diameter		1	40		53,000	1,300	665	54,965	61,500
0800	60' diameter		1	40		60,000	1,300	665	61,965	69,000
0850	67' diameter	↓	.80	50	↓	84,500	1,650	830	86,980	96,500
1100	Aluminum panel, with 6" insulation									
1200	100' diameter				SF Flr.	30.50			30.50	33.50
1300	500' diameter				"	29.50			29.50	32.50
1600	Aluminum framed, plexiglass closure panels									

13 34 Fabricated Engineered Structures

13 34 23 – Fabricated Structures

13 34 23.35 Geodesic Domes

		Crew	Daily Output	Labor-Hours	Unit	Material	Labor	Equipment	Total	Total Incl O&P
1700	40' diameter				SF Flr.	75.50			75.50	83
1800	200' diameter				"	69.50			69.50	76.50
2100	Aluminum framed, aluminum closure panels									
2200	40' diameter				SF Flr.	24.50			24.50	27
2300	100' diameter					23.50			23.50	26
2400	200' diameter					23.50			23.50	26
2500	For VRP faced bonded fiberglass insulation, add									10
2700	Aluminum framed, fiberglass sandwich panel closure									
2800	6' diameter	2 Carp	150	.107	SF Flr.	33	3.81		36.81	43
2900	28' diameter	"	350	.046	"	30	1.63		31.63	36

13 34 23.45 Kiosks

		Crew	Daily Output	Labor-Hours	Unit	Material	Labor	Equipment	Total	Total Incl O&P
0010	**KIOSKS**									
0020	Round, advertising type, 5' diameter, 7' high, aluminum wall, illuminated				Ea.	23,500			23,500	25,800
0100	Aluminum wall, non-illuminated					22,500			22,500	24,700
0500	Rectangular, 5' x 9', 7'-6" high, aluminum wall, illuminated					25,500			25,500	28,000
0600	Aluminum wall, non-illuminated					24,000			24,000	26,400

13 34 23.60 Portable Booths

		Crew	Daily Output	Labor-Hours	Unit	Material	Labor	Equipment	Total	Total Incl O&P
0010	**PORTABLE BOOTHS** Prefab. aluminum with doors, windows, ext. roof									
0100	lights wiring & insulation, 15 S.F. building, O.D., painted, minimum				S.F.	258			258	284
0300	30 S.F. building					208			208	229
0400	50 S.F. building					164			164	180
0600	80 S.F. building					142			142	156
0700	100 S.F. building					123			123	135
0900	Acoustical booth, 27 Db @ 1,000 Hz, 15 S.F. floor				Ea.	3,550			3,550	3,925
1000	7' x 7'-6", including light & ventilation					7,325			7,325	8,050
1200	Ticket booth, galv. steel, not incl. foundations., 4' x 4'					4,375			4,375	4,800
1300	4' x 6'					6,625			6,625	7,300

13 34 23.70 Shelters

		Crew	Daily Output	Labor-Hours	Unit	Material	Labor	Equipment	Total	Total Incl O&P
0010	**SHELTERS**									
0020	Aluminum frame, acrylic glazing, 3' x 9' x 8' high	2 Sswk	1.14	14.035	Ea.	2,400	540		2,940	3,650
0100	9' x 12' x 8' high	"	.73	21.918	"	5,700	840		6,540	7,850

13 34 43 – Aircraft Hangars

13 34 43.50 Hangars

		Crew	Daily Output	Labor-Hours	Unit	Material	Labor	Equipment	Total	Total Incl O&P
0010	**HANGARS** Prefabricated steel T hangars, Galv. steel roof &									
0100	walls, incl. electric bi-folding doors									
0110	not including floors or foundations, 4 unit	E-2	1275	.038	SF Flr.	12.45	1.46	1.20	15.11	17.75
0130	8 unit		1063	.045		11.35	1.75	1.44	14.54	17.30
0900	With bottom rolling doors, 4 unit		1386	.035		11.50	1.34	1.10	13.94	16.35
1000	8 unit		966	.050		10.30	1.93	1.58	13.81	16.70
1200	Alternate pricing method:									
1300	Galv. roof and walls, electric bi-folding doors, 4 plane	E-2	1.06	45.283	Plane	16,500	1,750	1,450	19,700	23,100
1500	8 plane		.91	52.747		13,500	2,050	1,675	17,225	20,600
1600	With bottom rolling doors, 4 plane		1.25	38.400		15,300	1,500	1,225	18,025	20,900
1800	8 plane		.97	49.485		12,300	1,925	1,575	15,800	18,900
2000	Circular type, prefab., steel frame, plastic skin, electric									
2010	door, including foundations, 80' diameter,									

13 34 53 – Agricultural Structures

13 34 53.50 Silos

		Crew	Daily Output	Labor-Hours	Unit	Material	Labor	Equipment	Total	Total Incl O&P
0010	**SILOS**									
0500	Steel, factory fab., 30,000 gallon cap., painted, minimum	L-5	1	56	Ea.	22,100	2,175	745	25,020	29,200
0700	Maximum		.50	112		35,100	4,325	1,500	40,925	48,400

13 34 Fabricated Engineered Structures

13 34 53 – Agricultural Structures

13 34 53.50 Silos		Crew	Daily Output	Labor-Hours	Unit	Material	2014 Bare Costs Labor	Equipment	Total	Total Incl O&P
0800	Epoxy lined, minimum	L-5	1	56	Ea.	36,100	2,175	745	39,020	44,600
1000	Maximum	↓	.50	112	↓	45,700	4,325	1,500	51,525	60,500

13 34 63 – Natural Fiber Construction

13 34 63.50 Straw Bale Construction

13 34 63.50 Straw Bale Construction			Crew	Daily Output	Labor-Hours	Unit	Material	Labor	Equipment	Total	Total Incl O&P
0010	**STRAW BALE CONSTRUCTION**										
2000	Straw bales wall, incl. labor & material complete, minimum	G				SF Flr.					130
2010	Maximum	G				"					160
2020	Straw bales in walls w/modified post and beam frame	G	2 Carp	320	.050	S.F.	6.05	1.79		7.84	9.65

13 36 Towers

13 36 13 – Metal Towers

13 36 13.50 Control Towers

13 36 13.50 Control Towers		Crew	Daily Output	Labor-Hours	Unit	Material	Labor	Equipment	Total	Total Incl O&P
0010	**CONTROL TOWERS**									
0020	Modular 12' x 10', incl. instruments				Ea.	810,000			810,000	891,000
0100	Maximum								970,000	1,067,000
0500	With standard 40' tower				↓	1,400,000			1,400,000	1,540,000
1000	Temporary portable control towers, 8' x 12',									
1010	complete with one position communications, minimum				Ea.				266,000	293,000
2000	For fixed facilities, depending on height, minimum								57,000	63,000
2010	Maximum				↓				115,000	127,000

13 42 Building Modules

13 42 63 – Detention Cell Modules

13 42 63.16 Steel Detention Cell Modules

13 42 63.16 Steel Detention Cell Modules		Crew	Daily Output	Labor-Hours	Unit	Material	Labor	Equipment	Total	Total Incl O&P
0010	**STEEL DETENTION CELL MODULES**									
2000	Cells, prefab., 5' to 6' wide, 7' to 8' high, 7' to 8' deep,									
2010	bar front, cot, not incl. plumbing	E-4	1.50	21.333	Ea.	9,650	830	94.50	10,574.50	12,300

13 48 Sound, Vibration, and Seismic Control

13 48 13 – Manufactured Sound and Vibration Control Components

13 48 13.50 Audio Masking

13 48 13.50 Audio Masking		Crew	Daily Output	Labor-Hours	Unit	Material	Labor	Equipment	Total	Total Incl O&P
0010	**AUDIO MASKING**, acoustical enclosure, 4" thick wall and ceiling									
0020	8# per S.F., up to 12' span	3 Carp	72	.333	SF Surf	33	11.90		44.90	56
0300	Better quality panels, 10.5# per S.F.		64	.375		37	13.40		50.40	63.50
0400	Reverb-chamber, 4" thick, parallel walls		60	.400		46.50	14.30		60.80	75
0600	Skewed wall, parallel roof, 4" thick panels		55	.436		53	15.60		68.60	85
0700	Skewed walls, skewed roof, 4" layers, 4" air space		48	.500		59.50	17.90		77.40	95.50
0900	Sound-absorbing panels, pntd. mtl., 2'-6" x 8', under 1,000 S.F.		215	.112		12.30	3.99		16.29	20.50
1100	Over 1000 S.F.		240	.100		11.85	3.58		15.43	19.05
1200	Fabric faced	↓	240	.100		9.60	3.58		13.18	16.60
1500	Flexible transparent curtain, clear	3 Shee	215	.112		7.45	4.52		11.97	15.75
1600	50% foam		215	.112		10.40	4.52		14.92	18.95
1700	75% foam		215	.112		10.40	4.52		14.92	18.95
1800	100% foam	↓	215	.112	↓	10.40	4.52		14.92	18.95
3100	Audio masking system, including speakers, amplification									
3110	and signal generator									
3200	Ceiling mounted, 5,000 S.F.	2 Elec	2400	.007	S.F.	1.26	.28		1.54	1.86

13 48 Sound, Vibration, and Seismic Control

13 48 13 – Manufactured Sound and Vibration Control Components

13 48 13.50 Audio Masking	Crew	Daily Output	Labor-Hours	Unit	Material	2014 Bare Costs Labor	Equipment	Total	Total Incl O&P
3300	10,000 S.F.	2 Elec	2800	.006	S.F.	1.02	.24		1.26	1.52
3400	Plenum mounted, 5,000 S.F.		3800	.004		1.08	.18		1.26	1.48
3500	10,000 S.F.	↓	4400	.004	↓	.73	.16		.89	1.05

13 49 Radiation Protection

13 49 13 – Integrated X-Ray Shielding Assemblies

13 49 13.50 Lead Sheets

		Crew	Daily Output	Labor-Hours	Unit	Material	2014 Bare Costs Labor	Equipment	Total	Total Incl O&P
0010	**LEAD SHEETS**									
0300	Lead sheets, 1/16" thick	2 Lath	135	.119	S.F.	10.05	3.75		13.80	17.10
0400	1/8" thick		120	.133		20	4.22		24.22	29
0500	Lead shielding, 1/4" thick		135	.119		49	3.75		52.75	60
0550	1/2" thick	↓	120	.133	↓	83.50	4.22		87.72	98.50
0950	Lead headed nails (average 1 lb. per sheet)				Lb.	8.05			8.05	8.85
1000	Butt joints in 1/8" lead or thicker, 2" batten strip x 7' long	2 Lath	240	.067	Ea.	28	2.11		30.11	34.50
1200	X-ray protection, average radiography or fluoroscopy									
1210	room, up to 300 S.F. floor, 1/16" lead, minimum	2 Lath	.25	64	Total	10,100	2,025		12,125	14,400
1500	Maximum, 7'-0" walls	"	.15	106	"	12,200	3,375		15,575	18,800
1600	Deep therapy X-ray room, 250 kV capacity,									
1800	up to 300 S.F. floor, 1/4" lead, minimum	2 Lath	.08	200	Total	28,300	6,325		34,625	41,300
1900	Maximum, 7'-0" walls	"	.06	266	"	34,900	8,450		43,350	52,000

13 49 19 – Lead-Lined Materials

13 49 19.50 Shielding Lead

		Crew	Daily Output	Labor-Hours	Unit	Material	2014 Bare Costs Labor	Equipment	Total	Total Incl O&P
0010	**SHIELDING LEAD**									
0100	Laminated lead in wood doors, 1/16" thick, no hardware				S.F.	45			45	49.50
0200	Lead lined door frame, not incl. hardware,									
0210	1/16" thick lead, butt prepared for hardware	1 Lath	2.40	3.333	Ea.	770	106		876	1,025
0850	Window frame with 1/16" lead and voice passage, 36" x 60"	2 Glaz	2	8		5,550	278		5,828	6,550
0870	24" x 36" frame		4	4	↓	2,700	139		2,839	3,200
0900	Lead gypsum board, 5/8" thick with 1/16" lead		160	.100	S.F.	10.15	3.48		13.63	16.95
0910	1/8" lead		140	.114		22	3.98		25.98	30.50
0930	1/32" lead	2 Lath	200	.080		7.60	2.53		10.13	12.45

13 49 21 – Lead Glazing

13 49 21.50 Lead Glazing

		Crew	Daily Output	Labor-Hours	Unit	Material	2014 Bare Costs Labor	Equipment	Total	Total Incl O&P
0010	**LEAD GLAZING**									
0600	Lead glass, 1/4" thick, 2.0 mm LE, 12" x 16"	2 Glaz	13	1.231	Ea.	360	43		403	470
0700	24" x 36"		8	2		1,275	69.50		1,344.50	1,525
0800	36" x 60"	↓	2	8		3,500	278		3,778	4,300
2000	X-ray viewing panels, clear lead plastic									
2010	7 mm thick, 0.3 mm LE, 2.3 lb./S.F.	H-3	139	.115	S.F.	234	3.55		237.55	263
2020	12 mm thick, 0.5 mm LE, 3.9 lb./S.F.		82	.195		345	6		351	390
2030	18 mm thick, 0.8 mm LE, 5.9 lb./S.F.		54	.296		395	9.15		404.15	450
2040	22 mm thick, 1.0 mm LE, 7.2 lb./S.F.		44	.364		515	11.20		526.20	585
2050	35 mm thick, 1.5 mm LE, 11.5 lb./S.F.		28	.571		790	17.65		807.65	900
2060	46 mm thick, 2.0 mm LE, 15.0 lb./S.F.	↓	21	.762	↓	1,025	23.50		1,048.50	1,175
2090	For panels 12 S.F. to 48 S.F., add crating charge				Ea.					50

13 49 23 – Integrated RFI/EMI Shielding Assemblies

13 49 23.50 Modular Shielding Partitions	Crew	Daily Output	Labor-Hours	Unit	Material	2014 Bare Costs Labor	2014 Bare Costs Equipment	Total	Total Incl O&P
0010 **MODULAR SHIELDING PARTITIONS**									
4000 X-ray barriers, modular, panels mounted within framework for									
4002 attaching to floor, wall or ceiling, upper portion is clear lead									
4005 plastic window panels 48"H, lower portion is opaque leaded									
4008 steel panels 36"H, structural supports not incl.									
4010 1-section barrier, 36"W x 84"H overall									
4020 0.5 mm LE panels	H-3	6.40	2.500	Ea.	5,725	77		5,802	6,425
4030 0.8 mm LE panels		6.40	2.500		6,350	77		6,427	7,100
4040 1.0 mm LE panels		5.33	3.002		7,775	92.50		7,867.50	8,700
4050 1.5 mm LE panels		5.33	3.002		11,100	92.50		11,192.50	12,400
4060 2-section barrier, 72"W x 84"H overall									
4070 0.5 mm LE panels	H-3	4	4	Ea.	11,400	123		11,523	12,800
4080 0.8 mm LE panels		4	4		12,700	123		12,823	14,100
4090 1.0 mm LE panels		3.56	4.494		15,600	139		15,739	17,300
5000 1.5 mm LE panels		3.20	5		22,200	154		22,354	24,700
5010 3-section barrier, 108"W x 84"H overall									
5020 0.5 mm LE panels	H-3	3.20	5	Ea.	17,200	154		17,354	19,200
5030 0.8 mm LE panels		3.20	5		19,000	154		19,154	21,200
5040 1.0 mm LE panels		2.67	5.993		23,300	185		23,485	26,000
5050 1.5 mm LE panels		2.46	6.504		33,200	201		33,401	36,800
7000 X-ray barriers, mobile, mounted within framework w/casters on									
7005 bottom, clear lead plastic window panels on upper portion,									
7010 opaque on lower, 30"W x 75"H overall, incl. framework									
7020 24"H upper w/0.5 mm LE, 48"H lower w/0.8 mm LE	1 Carp	16	.500	Ea.	3,700	17.90		3,717.90	4,075
7030 48"W x 75"H overall, incl. framework									
7040 36"H upper w/0.5 mm LE, 36"H lower w/0.8 mm LE	1 Carp	16	.500	Ea.	6,000	17.90		6,017.90	6,625
7050 36"H upper w/1.0 mm LE, 36"H lower w/1.5 mm LE	"	16	.500	"	7,100	17.90		7,117.90	7,825
7060 72"W x 75"H overall, incl. framework									
7070 36"H upper w/0.5 mm LE, 36"H lower w/0.8 mm LE	1 Carp	16	.500	Ea.	7,100	17.90		7,117.90	7,825
7080 36"H upper w/1.0 mm LE, 36"H lower w/1.5 mm LE	"	16	.500	"	8,900	17.90		8,917.90	9,800

13 49 33 – Radio Frequency Shielding

13 49 33.50 Shielding, Radio Frequency	Crew	Daily Output	Labor-Hours	Unit	Material	2014 Bare Costs Labor	2014 Bare Costs Equipment	Total	Total Incl O&P
0010 **SHIELDING, RADIO FREQUENCY**									
0020 Prefabricated, galvanized steel	2 Carp	375	.043	SF Surf	4.46	1.53		5.99	7.50
0040 5 oz., copper floor panel		480	.033		3.68	1.19		4.87	6.05
0050 5 oz., copper wall/ceiling panel		155	.103		3.68	3.69		7.37	10.25
0100 12 oz., copper floor panel		470	.034		7.85	1.22		9.07	10.70
0110 12 oz., copper wall/ceiling panel		140	.114		7.85	4.09		11.94	15.50
0150 Door, copper/wood laminate, 4' x 7'		1.50	10.667	Ea.	7,400	380		7,780	8,775

13 53 Meteorological Instrumentation

13 53 09 – Weather Instrumentation

13 53 09.50 Weather Station	Crew	Daily Output	Labor-Hours	Unit	Material	2014 Bare Costs Labor	2014 Bare Costs Equipment	Total	Total Incl O&P
0010 **WEATHER STATION**									
0020 Remote recording, solar powered, with rain gauge & display, 400 ft range				Ea.	1,625			1,625	1,775
0100 1 mile range				"	1,825			1,825	2,025

Division Notes

	CREW	DAILY OUTPUT	LABOR-HOURS	UNIT	BARE COSTS				TOTAL INCL O&P
					MAT.	LABOR	EQUIP.	TOTAL	

Estimating Tips

General

- Many products in Division 14 will require some type of support or blocking for installation not included with the item itself. Examples are supports for conveyors or tube systems, attachment points for lifts, and footings for hoists or cranes. Add these supports in the appropriate division.

14 10 00 Dumbwaiters
14 20 00 Elevators

- Dumbwaiters and elevators are estimated and purchased in a method similar to buying a car. The manufacturer has a base unit with standard features. Added to this base unit price will be whatever options the owner or specifications require. Increased load capacity, additional vertical travel, additional stops, higher speed, and cab finish options are items to be considered. When developing an estimate for dumbwaiters and elevators, remember that some items needed by the installers may have to be included as part of the general contract.

Examples are:
- — shaftway
- — rail support brackets
- — machine room
- — electrical supply
- — sill angles
- — electrical connections
- — pits
- — roof penthouses
- — pit ladders

Check the job specifications and drawings before pricing.

- Installation of elevators and handicapped lifts in historic structures can require significant additional costs. The associated structural requirements may involve cutting into and repairing finishes, mouldings, flooring, etc. The estimator must account for these special conditions.

14 30 00 Escalators and Moving Walks

- Escalators and moving walks are specialty items installed by specialty contractors. There are numerous options associated with these items. For specific options, contact a manufacturer or contractor. In a method similar to estimating dumbwaiters and elevators, you should verify the extent of general contract work and add items as necessary.

14 40 00 Lifts
14 90 00 Other Conveying Equipment

- Products such as correspondence lifts, chutes, and pneumatic tube systems, as well as other items specified in this subdivision, may require trained installers. The general contractor might not have any choice as to who will perform the installation or when it will be performed. Long lead times are often required for these products, making early decisions in scheduling necessary.

Reference Numbers

Reference numbers are shown in shaded boxes at the beginning of some major classifications. These numbers refer to related items in the Reference Section. The reference information may be an estimating procedure, an alternate pricing method, or technical information.

Note: Not all subdivisions listed here necessarily appear in this publication.

14 11 Manual Dumbwaiters

14 11 10 – Hand Operated Dumbwaiters

14 11 10.20 Manual Dumbwaiters	Crew	Daily Output	Labor-Hours	Unit	Material	2014 Bare Costs Labor	Equipment	Total	Total Incl O&P
0010 **MANUAL DUMBWAITERS**									
0020 2 stop, minimum	2 Elev	.75	21.333	Ea.	2,925	1,175		4,100	5,175
0100 Maximum		.50	32	"	6,650	1,775		8,425	10,300
0300 For each additional stop, add	↓	.75	21.333	Stop	1,050	1,175		2,225	3,125

14 12 Electric Dumbwaiters

14 12 10 – Dumbwaiters

14 12 10.10 Electric Dumbwaiters

	Crew	Daily Output	Labor-Hours	Unit	Material	2014 Bare Costs Labor	Equipment	Total	Total Incl O&P
0010 **ELECTRIC DUMBWAITERS**									
0020 2 stop, minimum	2 Elev	.13	123	Ea.	7,375	6,850		14,225	19,300
0100 Maximum		.11	145	"	22,200	8,100		30,300	37,600
0600 For each additional stop, add	↓	.54	29.630	Stop	3,250	1,650		4,900	6,275
0750 Correspondence lift, 1 floor, 2 stop, 45 lb. capacity	2 Elec	.20	80	Ea.	8,350	3,425		11,775	14,800

14 21 Electric Traction Elevators

14 21 13 – Electric Traction Freight Elevators

14 21 13.10 Electric Traction Freight Elevators and Options

	Crew	Daily Output	Labor-Hours	Unit	Material	2014 Bare Costs Labor	Equipment	Total	Total Incl O&P
0010 **ELECTRIC TRACTION FREIGHT ELEVATORS AND OPTIONS** R142000-10									
0425 Electric freight, base unit, 4000 lb., 200 fpm, 4 stop, std. fin.	2 Elev	.05	320	Ea.	106,500	17,800		124,300	146,500
0450 For 5000 lb. capacity, add					5,750			5,750	6,325
0500 For 6000 lb. capacity, add					14,400			14,400	15,800
0525 For 7000 lb. capacity, add					17,900			17,900	19,700
0550 For 8000 lb. capacity, add					35,800			35,800	39,300
0575 For 10000 lb. capacity, add					30,000			30,000	33,000
0600 For 12000 lb. capacity, add					36,400			36,400	40,100
0625 For 16000 lb. capacity, add					44,100			44,100	48,500
0650 For 20000 lb. capacity, add					49,100			49,100	54,000
0675 For increased speed, 250 fpm, add					17,000			17,000	18,700
0700 300 fpm, geared electric, add					21,400			21,400	23,600
0725 350 fpm, geared electric, add					26,100			26,100	28,700
0750 400 fpm, geared electric, add					30,500			30,500	33,600
0775 500 fpm, gearless electric, add					37,600			37,600	41,300
0800 600 fpm, gearless electric, add					45,000			45,000	49,500
0825 700 fpm, gearless electric, add					53,500			53,500	59,000
0850 800 fpm, gearless electric, add					61,500			61,500	68,000
0875 For class "B" loading, add					4,975			4,975	5,475
0900 For class "C-1" loading, add					7,100			7,100	7,825
0925 For class "C-2" loading, add					8,150			8,150	8,975
0950 For class "C-3" loading, add					10,800			10,800	11,900
0975 For travel over 40 V.L.F., add	2 Elev	7.25	2.207	V.L.F.	660	123		783	925
1000 For number of stops over 4, add	"	.27	59.259	Stop	4,075	3,300		7,375	9,900

14 21 23 – Electric Traction Passenger Elevators

14 21 23.10 Electric Traction Passenger Elevators and Options

	Crew	Daily Output	Labor-Hours	Unit	Material	2014 Bare Costs Labor	Equipment	Total	Total Incl O&P
0010 **ELECTRIC TRACTION PASSENGER ELEVATORS AND OPTIONS**									
1625 Electric pass., base unit, 2000 lb., 200 fpm, 4 stop, std. fin.	2 Elev	.05	320	Ea.	90,000	17,800		107,800	128,000
1650 For 2500 lb. capacity, add					3,675			3,675	4,050
1675 For 3000 lb. capacity, add					4,325			4,325	4,750
1700 For 3500 lb. capacity, add					5,500			5,500	6,050
1725 For 4000 lb. capacity, add	↓				6,700			6,700	7,350

14 21 Electric Traction Elevators

14 21 23 – Electric Traction Passenger Elevators

14 21 23.10 Electric Traction Passenger Elevators and Options	Crew	Daily Output	Labor-Hours	Unit	Material	2014 Bare Costs Labor	Equipment	Total	Total Incl O&P
1750	For 4500 lb. capacity, add				Ea.	8,800			8,800	9,675
1775	For 5000 lb. capacity, add					11,200			11,200	12,300
1800	For increased speed, 250 fpm, geared electric, add					4,975			4,975	5,475
1825	300 fpm, geared electric, add					7,825			7,825	8,600
1850	350 fpm, geared electric, add					9,000			9,000	9,900
1875	400 fpm, geared electric, add					11,800			11,800	12,900
1900	500 fpm, gearless electric, add					27,000			27,000	29,700
1925	600 fpm, gearless electric, add					42,800			42,800	47,100
1950	700 fpm, gearless electric, add					48,300			48,300	53,000
1975	800 fpm, gearless electric, add					53,000			53,000	58,500
2000	For travel over 40 V.L.F., add	2 Elev	7.25	2.207	V.L.F.	805	123		928	1,075
2025	For number of stops over 4, add		.27	59.259	Stop	5,550	3,300		8,850	11,500
2400	Electric hospital, base unit, 4000 lb., 200 fpm, 4 stop, std fin.		.05	320	Ea.	76,000	17,800		93,800	112,500
2425	For 4500 lb. capacity, add					5,225			5,225	5,750
2450	For 5000 lb. capacity, add					6,850			6,850	7,525
2475	For increased speed, 250 fpm, geared electric, add					5,075			5,075	5,575
2500	300 fpm, geared electric, add					7,750			7,750	8,525
2525	350 fpm, geared electric, add					8,950			8,950	9,825
2550	400 fpm, geared electric, add					11,700			11,700	12,800
2575	500 fpm, gearless electric, add					31,100			31,100	34,200
2600	600 fpm, gearless electric, add					45,300			45,300	49,800
2625	700 fpm, gearless electric, add					50,000			50,000	55,000
2650	800 fpm, gearless electric, add					56,000			56,000	61,500
2675	For travel over 40 V.L.F., add	2 Elev	7.25	2.207	V.L.F.	455	123		578	700
2700	For number of stops over 4, add	"	.27	59.259	Stop	4,150	3,300		7,450	9,950

14 21 33 – Electric Traction Residential Elevators

14 21 33.20 Residential Elevators

		Crew	Daily Output	Labor-Hours	Unit	Material	Labor	Equipment	Total	Total Incl O&P
0010	**RESIDENTIAL ELEVATORS**									
7000	Residential, cab type, 1 floor, 2 stop, minimum	2 Elev	.20	80	Ea.	11,200	4,450		15,650	19,700
7100	Maximum		.10	160		19,000	8,900		27,900	35,500
7200	2 floor, 3 stop, minimum		.12	133		16,700	7,425		24,125	30,500
7300	Maximum		.06	266		27,200	14,800		42,000	54,000

14 24 Hydraulic Elevators

14 24 13 – Hydraulic Freight Elevators

14 24 13.10 Hydraulic Freight Elevators and Options

		Crew	Daily Output	Labor-Hours	Unit	Material	Labor	Equipment	Total	Total Incl O&P
0010	**HYDRAULIC FREIGHT ELEVATORS AND OPTIONS**									
1025	Hydraulic freight, base unit, 2000 lb., 50 fpm, 2 stop, std. fin.	2 Elev	.10	160	Ea.	78,500	8,900		87,400	101,000
1050	For 2500 lb. capacity, add					3,775			3,775	4,175
1075	For 3000 lb. capacity, add					6,575			6,575	7,225
1100	For 3500 lb. capacity, add					11,700			11,700	12,800
1125	For 4000 lb. capacity, add					12,600			12,600	13,900
1150	For 4500 lb. capacity, add					14,800			14,800	16,300
1175	For 5000 lb. capacity, add					18,800			18,800	20,700
1200	For 6000 lb. capacity, add					23,000			23,000	25,300
1225	For 7000 lb. capacity, add					28,100			28,100	31,000
1250	For 8000 lb. capacity, add					31,700			31,700	34,900
1275	For 10000 lb. capacity, add					39,100			39,100	43,000
1300	For 12000 lb. capacity, add					50,500			50,500	56,000
1325	For 16000 lb. capacity, add					69,000			69,000	76,000

14 24 Hydraulic Elevators

14 24 13 – Hydraulic Freight Elevators

14 24 13.10 Hydraulic Freight Elevators and Options		Crew	Daily Output	Labor-Hours	Unit	Material	2014 Bare Costs Labor	Equipment	Total	Total Incl O&P
1350	For 20000 lb. capacity, add				Ea.	83,500			83,500	92,000
1375	For increased speed, 100 fpm, add					1,600			1,600	1,775
1400	125 fpm, add					3,525			3,525	3,875
1425	150 fpm, add					4,575			4,575	5,050
1450	175 fpm, add					7,350			7,350	8,075
1475	For class "B" loading, add					4,725			4,725	5,200
1500	For class "C-1" loading, add					7,075			7,075	7,775
1525	For class "C-2" loading, add					8,125			8,125	8,925
1550	For class "C-3" loading, add					10,400			10,400	11,500
1575	For travel over 20 V.L.F., add	2 Elev	7.25	2.207	V.L.F.	1,250	123		1,373	1,575
1600	For number of stops over 2, add	"	.27	59.259	Stop	3,375	3,300		6,675	9,125

14 24 23 – Hydraulic Passenger Elevators

14 24 23.10 Hydraulic Passenger Elevators and Options		Crew	Daily Output	Labor-Hours	Unit	Material	2014 Bare Costs Labor	Equipment	Total	Total Incl O&P
0010	**HYDRAULIC PASSENGER ELEVATORS AND OPTIONS**									
2050	Hyd. pass., base unit, 1500 lb., 100 fpm, 2 stop, std. fin.	2 Elev	.10	160	Ea.	38,600	8,900		47,500	57,000
2075	For 2000 lb. capacity, add					1,425			1,425	1,575
2100	For 2500 lb. capacity, add					2,750			2,750	3,025
2125	For 3000 lb. capacity, add					3,900			3,900	4,300
2150	For 3500 lb. capacity, add					6,575			6,575	7,250
2175	For 4000 lb. capacity, add					7,875			7,875	8,650
2200	For 4500 lb. capacity, add					10,300			10,300	11,300
2225	For 5000 lb. capacity, add					14,500			14,500	16,000
2250	For increased speed, 125 fpm, add					2,075			2,075	2,275
2275	150 fpm, add					2,800			2,800	3,075
2300	175 fpm, add					4,625			4,625	5,100
2325	200 fpm, add					8,850			8,850	9,725
2350	For travel over 12 V.L.F., add	2 Elev	7.25	2.207	V.L.F.	740	123		863	1,000
2375	For number of stops over 2, add		.27	59.259	Stop	1,800	3,300		5,100	7,400
2725	Hydraulic hospital, base unit, 4000 lb., 100 fpm, 2 stop, std. fin.		.10	160	Ea.	57,000	8,900		65,900	77,500
2775	For 4500 lb. capacity, add					6,400			6,400	7,050
2800	For 5000 lb. capacity, add					9,375			9,375	10,300
2825	For increased speed, 125 fpm, add					2,525			2,525	2,775
2850	150 fpm, add					3,300			3,300	3,625
2875	175 fpm, add					5,500			5,500	6,050
2900	200 fpm, add					8,050			8,050	8,850
2925	For travel over 12 V.L.F., add	2 Elev	7.25	2.207	V.L.F.	545	123		668	800
2950	For number of stops over 2, add	"	.27	59.259	Stop	4,000	3,300		7,300	9,800

14 27 Custom Elevator Cabs and Doors

14 27 13 – Custom Elevator Cab Finishes

14 27 13.10 Cab Finishes		Crew	Daily Output	Labor-Hours	Unit	Material	2014 Bare Costs Labor	Equipment	Total	Total Incl O&P
0010	**CAB FINISHES**									
3325	Passenger elevator cab finishes (based on 3500 lb. cab size)									
3350	Acrylic panel ceiling				Ea.	730			730	800
3375	Aluminum eggcrate ceiling					890			890	980
3400	Stainless steel doors					3,775			3,775	4,150
3425	Carpet flooring					595			595	655
3450	Epoxy flooring					450			450	495
3475	Quarry tile flooring					850			850	935
3500	Slate flooring					1,525			1,525	1,675

14 27 Custom Elevator Cabs and Doors

14 27 13 – Custom Elevator Cab Finishes

14 27 13.10 Cab Finishes

		Crew	Daily Output	Labor-Hours	Unit	Material	2014 Bare Costs Labor	Equipment	Total	Total Incl O&P
3525	Textured rubber flooring				Ea.	635			635	700
3550	Stainless steel walls					4,275			4,275	4,700
3575	Stainless steel returns at door					1,125			1,125	1,225
4450	Hospital elevator cab finishes (based on 3500 lb. cab size)									
4475	Aluminum eggcrate ceiling				Ea.	890			890	980
4500	Stainless steel doors					3,775			3,775	4,150
4525	Epoxy flooring					450			450	495
4550	Quarry tile flooring					850			850	935
4575	Textured rubber flooring					635			635	700
4600	Stainless steel walls					4,375			4,375	4,800
4625	Stainless steel returns at door					940			940	1,025

14 28 Elevator Equipment and Controls

14 28 10 – Elevator Equipment and Control Options

14 28 10.10 Elevator Controls and Doors

		Crew	Daily Output	Labor-Hours	Unit	Material	2014 Bare Costs Labor	Equipment	Total	Total Incl O&P
0010	**ELEVATOR CONTROLS AND DOORS**									
2975	Passenger elevator options									
3000	2 car group automatic controls	2 Elev	.66	24.242	Ea.	4,800	1,350		6,150	7,475
3025	3 car group automatic controls		.44	36.364		9,200	2,025		11,225	13,400
3050	4 car group automatic controls		.33	48.485		18,400	2,700		21,100	24,700
3075	5 car group automatic controls		.26	61.538		33,300	3,425		36,725	42,300
3100	6 car group automatic controls		.22	72.727		67,500	4,050		71,550	80,500
3125	Intercom service		3	5.333		995	297		1,292	1,575
3150	Duplex car selective collective		.66	24.242		8,500	1,350		9,850	11,600
3175	Center opening 1 speed doors		2	8		1,900	445		2,345	2,825
3200	Center opening 2 speed doors		2	8		2,650	445		3,095	3,625
3225	Rear opening doors (opposite front)		2	8		4,050	445		4,495	5,200
3250	Side opening 2 speed doors		2	8		4,300	445		4,745	5,450
3275	Automatic emergency power switching		.66	24.242		1,150	1,350		2,500	3,450
3300	Manual emergency power switching		8	2		495	111		606	725
3625	Hall finishes, stainless steel doors					1,625			1,625	1,800
3650	Stainless steel frames					1,400			1,400	1,525
3675	12 month maintenance contract								3,600	3,950
3700	Signal devices, hall lanterns	2 Elev	8	2		505	111		616	735
3725	Position indicators, up to 3		9.40	1.702		470	94.50		564.50	670
3750	Position indicators, per each over 3		32	.500		420	28		448	505
3775	High speed heavy duty door opener					3,200			3,200	3,525
3800	Variable voltage, O.H. gearless machine, min.	2 Elev	.16	100		51,500	5,575		57,075	65,500
3815	Maximum		.07	228		80,000	12,700		92,700	109,000
3825	Basement installed geared machine		.33	48.485		49,100	2,700		51,800	58,500
3850	Freight elevator options									
3875	Doors, bi-parting	2 Elev	.66	24.242	Ea.	7,475	1,350		8,825	10,400
3900	Power operated door and gate	"	.66	24.242		23,700	1,350		25,050	28,200
3925	Finishes, steel plate floor					1,800			1,800	1,975
3950	14 ga. 1/4" x 4' steel plate walls					1,950			1,950	2,150
3975	12 month maintenance contract								3,600	3,950
4000	Signal devices, hall lanterns	2 Elev	8	2		495	111		606	725
4025	Position indicators, up to 3		9.40	1.702		485	94.50		579.50	685
4050	Position indicators, per each over 3		32	.500		425	28		453	510
4075	Variable voltage basement installed geared machine		.66	24.242		19,500	1,350		20,850	23,600
4100	Hospital elevator options									

14 28 10 – Elevator Equipment and Control Options

14 28 10.10 Elevator Controls and Doors

		Crew	Daily Output	Labor-Hours	Unit	Material	2014 Bare Costs Labor	Equipment	Total	Total Incl O&P
4125	2 car group automatic controls	2 Elev	.66	24.242	Ea.	4,800	1,350		6,150	7,500
4150	3 car group automatic controls		.44	36.364		9,200	2,025		11,225	13,400
4175	4 car group automatic controls		.33	48.485		18,400	2,700		21,100	24,600
4200	5 car group automatic controls		.26	61.538		33,300	3,425		36,725	42,300
4225	6 car group automatic controls		.22	72.727		67,500	4,050		71,550	80,500
4250	Intercom service		3	5.333		990	297		1,287	1,575
4275	Duplex car selective collective		.66	24.242		8,500	1,350		9,850	11,500
4300	Center opening 1 speed doors		2	8		1,900	445		2,345	2,800
4325	Center opening 2 speed doors		2	8		2,475	445		2,920	3,450
4350	Rear opening doors (opposite front)		2	8		4,075	445		4,520	5,200
4375	Side opening 2 speed doors		2	8		6,150	445		6,595	7,500
4400	Automatic emergency power switching		.66	24.242		1,125	1,350		2,475	3,425
4425	Manual emergency power switching		8	2		485	111		596	715
4675	Hall finishes, stainless steel doors					1,575			1,575	1,725
4700	Stainless steel frames					1,400			1,400	1,550
4725	12 month maintenance contract								3,600	3,950
4750	Signal devices, hall lanterns	2 Elev	8	2		475	111		586	705
4775	Position indicators, up to 3		9.40	1.702		470	94.50		564.50	670
4800	Position indicators, per each over 3		32	.500		415	28		443	505
4825	High speed heavy duty door opener					3,200			3,200	3,525
4850	Variable voltage, O.H. gearless machine, min.	2 Elev	.16	100		51,000	5,575		56,575	65,000
4865	Maximum		.07	228		78,500	12,700		91,200	107,500
4875	Basement installed geared machine		.33	48.485		20,100	2,700		22,800	26,500
5000	Drilling for piston, casing included, 18" diameter	B-48	80	.600	V.L.F.	53.50	18.15	36.50	108.15	130

14 31 10 – Glass and Steel Escalators

14 31 10.10 Escalators

			Crew	Daily Output	Labor-Hours	Unit	Material	2014 Bare Costs Labor	Equipment	Total	Total Incl O&P
0010	**ESCALATORS**	R143110-10									
1000	Glass, 32" wide x 10' floor to floor height		M-1	.07	457	Ea.	83,500	24,200	685	108,385	132,000
1010	48" wide x 10' floor to floor height			.07	457		89,500	24,200	685	114,385	139,000
1020	32" wide x 15' floor to floor height			.06	533		87,500	28,200	800	116,500	143,500
1030	48" wide x 15' floor to floor height			.06	533		92,500	28,200	800	121,500	148,500
1040	32" wide x 20' floor to floor height			.05	653		92,500	34,500	980	127,980	159,500
1050	48" wide x 20' floor to floor height			.05	653		100,500	34,500	980	135,980	168,000
1060	32" wide x 25' floor to floor height			.04	800		101,000	42,300	1,200	144,500	181,500
1070	48" wide x 25' floor to floor height			.04	800		116,500	42,300	1,200	160,000	198,500
1080	Enameled steel, 32" wide x 10' floor to floor height			.07	457		89,500	24,200	685	114,385	139,000
1090	48" wide x 10' floor to floor height			.07	457		97,000	24,200	685	121,885	147,000
1110	32" wide x 15' floor to floor height			.06	533		94,500	28,200	800	123,500	151,000
1120	48" wide x 15' floor to floor height			.06	533		100,000	28,200	800	129,000	157,000
1130	32" wide x 20' floor to floor height			.05	653		100,000	34,500	980	135,480	168,000
1140	48" wide x 20' floor to floor height			.05	653		108,500	34,500	980	143,980	177,000
1150	32" wide x 25' floor to floor height			.04	800		108,500	42,300	1,200	152,000	190,000
1160	48" wide x 25' floor to floor height			.04	800		125,000	42,300	1,200	168,500	208,000
1170	Stainless steel, 32" wide x 10' floor to floor height			.07	457		94,500	24,200	685	119,385	144,500
1180	48" wide x 10' floor to floor height			.07	457		101,500	24,200	685	126,385	152,000
1500	32" wide x 15' floor to floor height			.06	533		100,000	28,200	800	129,000	157,000
1700	48" wide x 15' floor to floor height			.06	533		105,000	28,200	800	134,000	162,500
1750	32" wide x 18' floor to floor height			.05	615		102,500	32,500	925	135,925	166,500
1775	48" wide x 18' floor to floor height			.05	615		111,500	32,500	925	144,925	176,500

14 31 Escalators

14 31 10 – Glass and Steel Escalators

14 31 10.10 Escalators		Crew	Daily Output	Labor-Hours	Unit	Material	2014 Bare Costs Labor	Equipment	Total	Total Incl O&P
2300	32" wide x 25' floor to floor height	M-1	.04	800	Ea.	114,000	42,300	1,200	157,500	196,000
2500	48" wide x 25' floor to floor height	↓	.04	800	↓	131,500	42,300	1,200	175,000	215,000

14 32 Moving Walks

14 32 10 – Moving Walkways

14 32 10.10 Moving Walks			Crew	Daily Output	Labor-Hours	Unit	Material	2014 Bare Costs Labor	Equipment	Total	Total Incl O&P
0010	**MOVING WALKS**	R143210-20									
0020	Walk, 27" tread width, minimum		M-1	6.50	4.923	L.F.	850	260	7.40	1,117.40	1,375
0100	300' to 500', maximum			4.43	7.223		1,175	380	10.85	1,565.85	1,925
0300	48" tread width walk, minimum			4.43	7.223		1,925	380	10.85	2,315.85	2,750
0400	100' to 350', maximum			3.82	8.377		2,250	445	12.55	2,707.55	3,225
0600	Ramp, 12° incline, 36" tread width, minimum			5.27	6.072		1,575	320	9.10	1,904.10	2,250
0700	70' to 90' maximum			3.82	8.377		2,250	445	12.55	2,707.55	3,225
0900	48" tread width, minimum			3.57	8.964		2,300	475	13.45	2,788.45	3,325
1000	40' to 70', maximum		↓	2.91	10.997	↓	2,900	580	16.50	3,496.50	4,175

14 42 Wheelchair Lifts

14 42 13 – Inclined Wheelchair Lifts

14 42 13.10 Inclined Wheelchair Lifts and Stairclimbers		Crew	Daily Output	Labor-Hours	Unit	Material	2014 Bare Costs Labor	Equipment	Total	Total Incl O&P
0010	**INCLINED WHEELCHAIR LIFTS AND STAIRCLIMBERS**									
7700	Stair climber (chair lift), single seat, minimum	2 Elev	1	16	Ea.	5,325	890		6,215	7,325
7800	Maximum		.20	80		7,350	4,450		11,800	15,400
8700	Stair lift, minimum		1	16		14,500	890		15,390	17,400
8900	Maximum	↓	.20	80	↓	22,900	4,450		27,350	32,500

14 42 16 – Vertical Wheelchair Lifts

14 42 16.10 Wheelchair Lifts		Crew	Daily Output	Labor-Hours	Unit	Material	2014 Bare Costs Labor	Equipment	Total	Total Incl O&P
0010	**WHEELCHAIR LIFTS**									
8000	Wheelchair lift, minimum	2 Elev	1	16	Ea.	7,325	890		8,215	9,500
8500	Maximum	"	.50	32	"	17,300	1,775		19,075	21,900

14 45 Vehicle Lifts

14 45 10 – Hydraulic Vehicle Lifts

14 45 10.10 Hydraulic Lifts		Crew	Daily Output	Labor-Hours	Unit	Material	2014 Bare Costs Labor	Equipment	Total	Total Incl O&P
0010	**HYDRAULIC LIFTS**									
2200	Single post, 8000 lb. capacity	L-4	.40	40	Ea.	5,500	1,275		6,775	8,175
2810	Double post, 6000 lb. capacity		2.67	5.993		7,750	189		7,939	8,850
2815	9000 lb. capacity		2.29	6.987		18,400	221		18,621	20,600
2820	15,000 lb. capacity		2	8		20,800	253		21,053	23,200
2822	26,000 lb. capacity		1.80	8.889		13,700	281		13,981	15,600
2825	30,000 lb. capacity		1.60	10		45,900	315		46,215	51,000
2830	Ramp style, 4 post, 25,000 lb. capacity		2	8		18,000	253		18,253	20,200
2835	35,000 lb. capacity		1	16		83,500	505		84,005	93,000
2840	50,000 lb. capacity		1	16		93,500	505		94,005	104,000
2845	75,000 lb. capacity	↓	1	16		108,500	505		109,005	120,500
2850	For drive thru tracks, add, minimum					1,150			1,150	1,275
2855	Maximum					1,975			1,975	2,175
2860	Ramp extensions, 3' (set of 2)				↓	945			945	1,050

465

14 45 Vehicle Lifts

14 45 10 – Hydraulic Vehicle Lifts

14 45 10.10 Hydraulic Lifts

	14 45 10.10 Hydraulic Lifts	Crew	Daily Output	Labor-Hours	Unit	Material	2014 Bare Costs Labor	Equipment	Total	Total Incl O&P
2865	Rolling jack platform				Ea.	3,300			3,300	3,625
2870	Electric/hydraulic jacking beam					8,825			8,825	9,700
2880	Scissor lift, portable, 6000 lb. capacity				↓	8,650			8,650	9,525

14 51 Correspondence and Parcel Lifts

14 51 10 – Electric Correspondence and Parcel Lifts

14 51 10.10 Correspondence Lifts

	14 51 10.10 Correspondence Lifts	Crew	Daily Output	Labor-Hours	Unit	Material	2014 Bare Costs Labor	Equipment	Total	Total Incl O&P
0010	**CORRESPONDENCE LIFTS**									
0020	1 floor, 2 stop, 25 lb. capacity, electric	2 Elev	.20	80	Ea.	6,500	4,450		10,950	14,400
0100	Hand, 5 lb. capacity	"	.20	80	"	2,500	4,450		6,950	10,000

14 51 10.20 Parcel Lifts

	14 51 10.20 Parcel Lifts	Crew	Daily Output	Labor-Hours	Unit	Material	2014 Bare Costs Labor	Equipment	Total	Total Incl O&P
0010	**PARCEL LIFTS**									
0020	20" x 20", 100 lb. capacity, electric, per floor	2 Mill	.25	64	Ea.	10,000	2,400		12,400	14,900

14 91 Facility Chutes

14 91 33 – Laundry and Linen Chutes

14 91 33.10 Chutes

	14 91 33.10 Chutes	Crew	Daily Output	Labor-Hours	Unit	Material	2014 Bare Costs Labor	Equipment	Total	Total Incl O&P
0011	**CHUTES**, linen, trash or refuse									
0050	Aluminized steel, 16 ga., 18" diameter	2 Shee	3.50	4.571	Floor	1,700	185		1,885	2,175
0100	24" diameter		3.20	5		1,775	202		1,977	2,275
0200	30" diameter		3	5.333		2,125	216		2,341	2,675
0300	36" diameter		2.80	5.714		2,625	231		2,856	3,275
0400	Galvanized steel, 16 ga., 18" diameter		3.50	4.571		1,000	185		1,185	1,400
0500	24" diameter		3.20	5		1,125	202		1,327	1,575
0600	30" diameter		3	5.333		1,275	216		1,491	1,750
0700	36" diameter		2.80	5.714		1,500	231		1,731	2,025
0800	Stainless steel, 18" diameter		3.50	4.571		3,000	185		3,185	3,600
0900	24" diameter		3.20	5		3,150	202		3,352	3,775
1000	30" diameter		3	5.333		3,750	216		3,966	4,475
1005	36" diameter		2.80	5.714	↓	3,950	231		4,181	4,700
1200	Linen chute bottom collector, aluminized steel		4	4	Ea.	1,400	162		1,562	1,825
1300	Stainless steel		4	4		1,800	162		1,962	2,250
1500	Refuse, bottom hopper, aluminized steel, 18" diameter		3	5.333		1,025	216		1,241	1,475
1600	24" diameter		3	5.333		1,250	216		1,466	1,725
1800	36" diameter		3	5.333	↓	2,500	216		2,716	3,100

14 91 82 – Trash Chutes

14 91 82.10 Trash Chutes and Accessories

	14 91 82.10 Trash Chutes and Accessories	Crew	Daily Output	Labor-Hours	Unit	Material	2014 Bare Costs Labor	Equipment	Total	Total Incl O&P
0010	**TRASH CHUTES AND ACCESSORIES**									
2900	Package chutes, spiral type, minimum	2 Shee	4.50	3.556	Floor	2,425	144		2,569	2,925
3000	Maximum	"	1.50	10.667	"	6,325	430		6,755	7,700

14 92 Pneumatic Tube Systems

14 92 10 – Conventional, Automatic and Computer Controlled Pneumatic Tube Systems

14 92 10.10 Pneumatic Tube Systems	Crew	Daily Output	Labor-Hours	Unit	Material	2014 Bare Costs Labor	2014 Bare Costs Equipment	Total	Total Incl O&P
0010 **PNEUMATIC TUBE SYSTEMS**									
0020 100' long, single tube, 2 stations, stock									
0100 3" diameter	2 Stpi	.12	133	Total	6,600	5,775		12,375	16,800
0300 4" diameter	"	.09	177	"	7,450	7,700		15,150	20,900
0400 Twin tube, two stations or more, conventional system									
0600 2-1/2" round	2 Stpi	62.50	.256	L.F.	36	11.10		47.10	58
0700 3" round		46	.348		36	15.05		51.05	64.50
0900 4" round		49.60	.323		44	13.95		57.95	71.50
1000 4" x 7" oval		37.60	.426		76	18.45		94.45	114
1050 Add for blower		2	8	System	5,200	345		5,545	6,300
1110 Plus for each round station, add		7.50	2.133	Ea.	1,275	92.50		1,367.50	1,550
1150 Plus for each oval station, add		7.50	2.133	"	1,275	92.50		1,367.50	1,550
1200 Alternate pricing method: base cost, minimum		.75	21.333	Total	6,375	925		7,300	8,550
1300 Maximum		.25	64	"	12,700	2,775		15,475	18,500
1500 Plus total system length, add, minimum		93.40	.171	L.F.	8.20	7.40		15.60	21.50
1600 Maximum		37.60	.426	"	24.50	18.45		42.95	57
1800 Completely automatic system, 4" round, 15 to 50 stations		.29	55.172	Station	20,100	2,400		22,500	26,100
2200 51 to 144 stations		.32	50		15,600	2,175		17,775	20,800
2400 6" round or 4" x 7" oval, 15 to 50 stations		.24	66.667		25,200	2,875		28,075	32,500
2800 51 to 144 stations		.23	69.565		21,100	3,000		24,100	28,200

Division Notes

	CREW	DAILY OUTPUT	LABOR-HOURS	UNIT	BARE COSTS				TOTAL INCL O&P
					MAT.	LABOR	EQUIP.	TOTAL	

Estimating Tips

Pipe for fire protection and all uses is located in Subdivisions 21 11 13 and 22 11 13.

The labor adjustment factors listed in Subdivision 22 01 02.20 also apply to Division 21.

Many, but not all, areas in the U.S. require backflow protection in the fire system. It is advisable to check local building codes for specific requirements.

For your reference, the following is a list of the most applicable Fire Codes and Standards which may be purchased from the NFPA, 1 Batterymarch Park, Quincy, MA 02169-7471.

NFPA 1: Uniform Fire Code

NFPA 10: Portable Fire Extinguishers

NFPA 11: Low-, Medium-, and High-Expansion Foam

NFPA 12: Carbon Dioxide Extinguishing Systems (Also companion 12A)

NFPA 13: Installation of Sprinkler Systems (Also companion 13D, 13E, and 13R)

NFPA 14: Installation of Standpipe and Hose Systems

NFPA 15: Water Spray Fixed Systems for Fire Protection

NFPA 16: Installation of Foam-Water Sprinkler and Foam-Water Spray Systems

NFPA 17: Dry Chemical Extinguishing Systems (Also companion 17A)

NFPA 18: Wetting Agents

NFPA 20: Installation of Stationary Pumps for Fire Protection

NFPA 22: Water Tanks for Private Fire Protection

NFPA 24: Installation of Private Fire Service Mains and their Appurtenances

NFPA 25: Inspection, Testing and Maintenance of Water-Based Fire Protection

Reference Numbers

Reference numbers are shown in shaded boxes at the beginning of some major classifications. These numbers refer to related items in the Reference Section. The reference information may be an estimating procedure, an alternate pricing method, or technical information.

Note: Not all subdivisions listed here necessarily appear in this publication.

Note: **Trade Service,** *in part, has been used as a reference source for some of the material prices used in Division 21.*

21 05 Common Work Results for Fire Suppression

21 05 23 – General-Duty Valves for Water-Based Fire-Suppression Piping

21 05 23.50 General-Duty Valves	Crew	Daily Output	Labor-Hours	Unit	Material	2014 Bare Costs Labor	Equipment	Total	Total Incl O&P
0010 **GENERAL-DUTY VALVES**, for water-based fire suppression									
6200 Valves and components									
6500 Check, swing, C.I. body, brass fittings, auto. ball drip									
6520 4" size	Q-12	3	5.333	Ea.	335	197		532	690
6800 Check, wafer, butterfly type, C.I. body, bronze fittings									
6820 4" size	Q-12	4	4	Ea.	460	148		608	750

21 11 Facility Fire-Suppression Water-Service Piping

21 11 16 – Facility Fire Hydrants

21 11 16.50 Fire Hydrants for Buildings

	Crew	Daily Output	Labor-Hours	Unit	Material	2014 Bare Costs Labor	Equipment	Total	Total Incl O&P
0010 **FIRE HYDRANTS FOR BUILDINGS**									
3750 Hydrants, wall, w/caps, single, flush, polished brass									
3800 2-1/2" x 2-1/2"	Q-12	5	3.200	Ea.	193	118		311	405
3840 2-1/2" x 3"	"	5	3.200		410	118		528	645
3900 For polished chrome, add					20%				
3950 Double, flush, polished brass									
4000 2-1/2" x 2-1/2" x 4"	Q-12	5	3.200	Ea.	545	118		663	795
4040 2-1/2" x 2-1/2" x 6"	"	4.60	3.478		785	128		913	1,075
4200 For polished chrome, add					10%				
4350 Double, projecting, polished brass									
4400 2-1/2" x 2-1/2" x 4"	Q-12	5	3.200	Ea.	242	118		360	460
4450 2-1/2" x 2-1/2" x 6"	"	4.60	3.478	"	495	128		623	755
4460 Valve control, dbl. flush/projecting hydrant, cap &									
4470 chain, extension rod & cplg., escutcheon, polished brass	Q-12	8	2	Ea.	288	74		362	435

21 11 19 – Fire-Department Connections

21 11 19.50 Connections for the Fire-Department

	Crew	Daily Output	Labor-Hours	Unit	Material	2014 Bare Costs Labor	Equipment	Total	Total Incl O&P
0010 **CONNECTIONS FOR THE FIRE-DEPARTMENT**									
7140 Standpipe connections, wall, w/plugs & chains									
7160 Single, flush, brass, 2-1/2" x 2-1/2"	Q-12	5	3.200	Ea.	151	118		269	360
7180 2-1/2" x 3"	"	5	3.200	"	156	118		274	365
7240 For polished chrome, add					15%				
7280 Double, flush, polished brass									
7300 2-1/2" x 2-1/2" x 4"	Q-12	5	3.200	Ea.	495	118		613	740
7330 2-1/2" x 2-1/2" x 6"	"	4.60	3.478	"	690	128		818	965
7400 For polished chrome, add					15%				
7440 For sill cock combination, add				Ea.	86			86	94.50
7900 Three way, flush, polished brass									
7920 2-1/2" (3) x 4"	Q-12	4.80	3.333	Ea.	1,575	123		1,698	1,950
7930 2-1/2" (3) x 6"	"	4.80	3.333		1,575	123		1,698	1,950
8000 For polished chrome, add					9%				
8020 Three way, projecting, polished brass									
8040 2-1/2" (3) x 4"	Q-12	4.80	3.333	Ea.	1,400	123		1,523	1,750

470

21 12 Fire-Suppression Standpipes

21 12 13 – Fire-Suppression Hoses and Nozzles

21 12 13.50 Fire Hoses and Nozzles	Crew	Daily Output	Labor-Hours	Unit	Material	2014 Bare Costs Labor	Equipment	Total	Total Incl O&P
0010 **FIRE HOSES AND NOZZLES**									
0200 Adapters, rough brass, straight hose threads									
0220 One piece, female to male, rocker lugs									
0240 1" x 1"				Ea.	46			46	50.50
0320 2" x 2"					42			42	46
0380 2-1/2" x 2-1/2"					19			19	21
2200 Hose, less couplings									
2260 Synthetic jacket, lined, 300 lb. test, 1-1/2" diameter	Q-12	2600	.006	L.F.	3.09	.23		3.32	3.77
2280 2-1/2" diameter		2200	.007		5.30	.27		5.57	6.30
2360 High strength, 500 lb. test, 1-1/2" diameter		2600	.006		3.18	.23		3.41	3.87
2380 2-1/2" diameter		2200	.007		5.65	.27		5.92	6.65
5600 Nozzles, brass									
5620 Adjustable fog, 3/4" booster line				Ea.	106			106	116
5630 1" booster line					125			125	137
5640 1-1/2" leader line					75.50			75.50	83
5660 2-1/2" direct connection					143			143	158
5780 For chrome plated, add					8%				
5850 Electrical fire, adjustable fog, no shock									
5900 1-1/2"				Ea.	390			390	430
5920 2-1/2"					525			525	575
5980 For polished chrome, add					6%				
6200 Heavy duty, comb. adj. fog and str. stream, with handle									
6210 1" booster line				Ea.	375			375	410

21 12 19 – Fire-Suppression Hose Racks

21 12 19.50 Fire Hose Racks

	Crew	Daily Output	Labor-Hours	Unit	Material	Labor	Equipment	Total	Total Incl O&P
0010 **FIRE HOSE RACKS**									
2600 Hose rack, swinging, for 1-1/2" diameter hose,									
2620 Enameled steel, 50' & 75' lengths of hose	Q-12	20	.800	Ea.	58	29.50		87.50	113
2640 100' and 125' lengths of hose	"	20	.800	"	58	29.50		87.50	113

21 12 23 – Fire-Suppression Hose Valves

21 12 23.70 Fire Hose Valves

	Crew	Daily Output	Labor-Hours	Unit	Material	Labor	Equipment	Total	Total Incl O&P
0010 **FIRE HOSE VALVES**									
0080 Wheel handle, 300 lb., 1-1/2"	1 Spri	12	.667	Ea.	86	27.50		113.50	140
0090 2-1/2"	"	7	1.143	"	167	47		214	261
0100 For polished brass, add					35%				
0110 For polished chrome, add					50%				

21 13 Fire-Suppression Sprinkler Systems

21 13 13 – Wet-Pipe Sprinkler Systems

21 13 13.50 Wet-Pipe Sprinkler System Components

	Crew	Daily Output	Labor-Hours	Unit	Material	Labor	Equipment	Total	Total Incl O&P
0010 **WET-PIPE SPRINKLER SYSTEM COMPONENTS**									
2600 Sprinkler heads, not including supply piping									
3700 Standard spray, pendent or upright, brass, 135°F to 286°F									
3730 1/2" NPT, 7/16" orifice	1 Spri	16	.500	Ea.	14.35	20.50		34.85	50
3740 1/2" NPT, 1/2" orifice	"	16	.500		9.35	20.50		29.85	44.50
3860 For wax and lead coating, add					33			33	36
3880 For wax coating, add					19.75			19.75	21.50
3900 For lead coating, add					21.50			21.50	23.50
3920 For 360°F, same cost									
3930 For 400°F				Ea.	87.50			87.50	96.50

21 13 Fire-Suppression Sprinkler Systems

21 13 13 – Wet-Pipe Sprinkler Systems

21 13 13.50 Wet-Pipe Sprinkler System Components

	Crew	Daily Output	Labor-Hours	Unit	Material	2014 Bare Costs Labor	Equipment	Total	Total Incl O&P
3940 For 500°F				Ea.	87.50			87.50	96.50
4500 Sidewall, horizontal, brass, 135°F to 286°F									
4520 1/2" NPT, 1/2" orifice	1 Spri	16	.500	Ea.	23.50	20.50		44	60
4540 For 360°F, same cost									
4800 Recessed pendent, brass, 135°F to 286°F									
4820 1/2" NPT, 3/8" orifice	1 Spri	10	.800	Ea.	45	33		78	104
4830 1/2" NPT, 7/16" orifice		10	.800		22	33		55	78
4840 1/2" NPT, 1/2" orifice	↓	10	.800	↓	18.15	33		51.15	74

21 13 16 – Dry-Pipe Sprinkler Systems

21 13 16.50 Dry-Pipe Sprinkler System Components

	Crew	Daily Output	Labor-Hours	Unit	Material	2014 Bare Costs Labor	Equipment	Total	Total Incl O&P
0010 **DRY-PIPE SPRINKLER SYSTEM COMPONENTS**									
0600 Accelerator	1 Spri	8	1	Ea.	715	41		756	855
2600 Sprinkler heads, not including supply piping									
2640 Dry, pendent, 1/2" orifice, 3/4" or 1" NPT									
2700 15-1/4" to 18" length	1 Spri	14	.571	Ea.	137	23.50		160.50	190
2710 18-1/4" to 21" length		13	.615		142	25		167	198
2720 21-1/4" to 24" length		13	.615		147	25		172	204
2730 24-1/4" to 27" length	↓	13	.615	↓	153	25		178	210
6330 Valves and components									

21 13 26 – Deluge Fire-Suppression Sprinkler Systems

21 13 26.50 Deluge Fire-Suppression Sprinkler Sys. Comp.

	Crew	Daily Output	Labor-Hours	Unit	Material	2014 Bare Costs Labor	Equipment	Total	Total Incl O&P
0010 **DELUGE FIRE-SUPPRESSION SPRINKLER SYSTEM COMPONENTS**									
1400 Deluge system, monitoring panel w/deluge valve & trim	1 Spri	18	.444	Ea.	10,300	18.20		10,318.20	11,300
6200 Valves and components									
7000 Deluge, assembly, incl. trim, pressure									
7020 operated relief, emergency release, gauges									
7040 2" size	Q-12	2	8	Ea.	3,500	295		3,795	4,325
7060 3" size	"	1.50	10.667	"	3,925	395		4,320	4,950

21 13 39 – Foam-Water Systems

21 13 39.50 Foam-Water System Components

	Crew	Daily Output	Labor-Hours	Unit	Material	2014 Bare Costs Labor	Equipment	Total	Total Incl O&P
0010 **FOAM-WATER SYSTEM COMPONENTS**									
2600 Sprinkler heads, not including supply piping									
3600 Foam-water, pendent or upright, 1/2" NPT	1 Spri	12	.667	Ea.	198	27.50		225.50	262

21 21 Carbon-Dioxide Fire-Extinguishing Systems

21 21 16 – Carbon-Dioxide Fire-Extinguishing Equipment

21 21 16.50 CO2 Fire Extinguishing System

	Crew	Daily Output	Labor-Hours	Unit	Material	2014 Bare Costs Labor	Equipment	Total	Total Incl O&P
0010 **CO₂ FIRE EXTINGUISHING SYSTEM**									
0042 For detectors and control stations, see Section 28 31 23.50									
0100 Control panel, single zone with batteries (2 zones det., 1 suppr.)	1 Elec	1	8	Ea.	1,675	340		2,015	2,400
0150 Multizone (4) with batteries (8 zones det., 4 suppr.)	"	.50	16		3,200	685		3,885	4,625
1000 Dispersion nozzle, CO₂, 3" x 5"	1 Plum	18	.444		65	18.95		83.95	103
2000 Extinguisher, CO₂ system, high pressure, 75 lb. cylinder	Q-1	6	2.667		1,250	102		1,352	1,525
2100 100 lb. cylinder	"	5	3.200		1,275	123		1,398	1,600
3000 Electro/mechanical release	L-1	4	2.500		163	107		270	355
3400 Manual pull station	1 Plum	6	1.333		58.50	57		115.50	158
4000 Pneumatic damper release	"	8	1	↓	217	42.50		259.50	310

21 22 Clean-Agent Fire-Extinguishing Systems

21 22 16 – Clean-Agent Fire-Extinguishing Equipment

21 22 16.50 FM200 Fire Extinguishing System	Crew	Daily Output	Labor-Hours	Unit	Material	2014 Bare Costs Labor	Equipment	Total	Total Incl O&P
0010 **FM200 FIRE EXTINGUISHING SYSTEM**									
1100 Dispersion nozzle FM200, 1-1/2"	1 Plum	14	.571	Ea.	65	24.50		89.50	112
2400 Extinguisher, FM200 system, filled, with mounting bracket									
2520 101 lb. container	Q-1	5	3.200	Ea.	4,650	123		4,773	5,300
2540 196 lb. container	"	4	4	"	7,550	153		7,703	8,550
6000 Average FM200 system, minimum				C.F.	1.71			1.71	1.88
6020 Maximum				"	3.40			3.40	3.74

21 31 Centrifugal Fire Pumps

21 31 13 – Electric-Drive, Centrifugal Fire Pumps

21 31 13.50 Electric-Drive Fire Pumps

	Crew	Daily Output	Labor-Hours	Unit	Material	2014 Bare Costs Labor	Equipment	Total	Total Incl O&P
0010 **ELECTRIC-DRIVE FIRE PUMPS** Including controller, fittings and relief valve									
3100 250 GPM, 55 psi, 15 HP, 3550 RPM, 2" pump	Q-13	.70	45.714	Ea.	15,200	1,675		16,875	19,600
3200 500 GPM, 50 psi, 27 HP, 1770 RPM, 4" pump		.68	47.059		15,500	1,725		17,225	20,000
3350 750 GPM, 50 psi, 44 HP, 1770 RPM, 5" pump		.64	50		16,200	1,850		18,050	20,900
3400 750 GPM, 100 psi, 66 HP, 3550 RPM, 4" pump		.58	55.172		18,700	2,025		20,725	23,900
5000 For jockey pump 1", 3 HP, with control, add	Q-12	2	8		2,525	295		2,820	3,250

21 31 16 – Diesel-Drive, Centrifugal Fire Pumps

21 31 16.50 Diesel-Drive Fire Pumps

	Crew	Daily Output	Labor-Hours	Unit	Material	2014 Bare Costs Labor	Equipment	Total	Total Incl O&P
0010 **DIESEL-DRIVE FIRE PUMPS** Including controller, fittings and relief valve									
0050 500 GPM, 50 psi, 27 HP, 4" pump	Q-13	.64	50	Ea.	35,300	1,850		37,150	41,900
0200 750 GPM, 50 psi, 44 HP, 5" pump		.60	53.333		36,300	1,975		38,275	43,200
0400 1000 GPM, 100 psi, 89 HP, 4" pump		.56	57.143		39,800	2,100		41,900	47,200
0700 2000 GPM, 100 psi, 167 HP, 6" pump		.34	94.118		50,500	3,475		53,975	61,000
0950 3500 GPM, 100 psi, 300 HP, 10" pump		.24	133		70,500	4,925		75,425	85,500

Division Notes

	CREW	DAILY OUTPUT	LABOR-HOURS	UNIT	BARE COSTS				TOTAL INCL O&P
					MAT.	LABOR	EQUIP.	TOTAL	

Estimating Tips

22 10 00 Plumbing Piping and Pumps

This subdivision is primarily basic pipe and related materials. The pipe may be used by any of the mechanical disciplines, i.e., plumbing, fire protection, heating, and air conditioning.

Note: CPVC plastic piping approved for fire protection is located in 21 11 13.

- The labor adjustment factors listed in Subdivision 22 01 02.20 apply throughout Divisions 21, 22, and 23. CAUTION: the correct percentage may vary for the same items. For example, the percentage add for the basic pipe installation should be based on the maximum height that the craftsman must install for that particular section. If the pipe is to be located 14' above the floor but it is suspended on threaded rod from beams, the bottom flange of which is 18' high (4' rods), then the height is actually 18' and the add is 20%. The pipe coverer, however, does not have to go above the 14', and so his or her add should be 10%.

- Most pipe is priced first as straight pipe with a joint (coupling, weld, etc.) every 10' and a hanger usually every 10'.

There are exceptions with hanger spacing such as for cast iron pipe (5') and plastic pipe (3 per 10'). Following each type of pipe there are several lines listing sizes and the amount to be subtracted to delete couplings and hangers. This is for pipe that is to be buried or supported together on trapeze hangers. The reason that the couplings are deleted is that these runs are usually long, and frequently longer lengths of pipe are used. By deleting the couplings, the estimator is expected to look up and add back the correct reduced number of couplings.

- When preparing an estimate, it may be necessary to approximate the fittings. Fittings usually run between 25% and 50% of the cost of the pipe. The lower percentage is for simpler runs, and the higher number is for complex areas, such as mechanical rooms.

- For historic restoration projects, the systems must be as invisible as possible, and pathways must be sought for pipes, conduit, and ductwork. While installations in accessible spaces (such as basements and attics) are relatively straightforward to estimate, labor costs may be more difficult to determine when delivery systems must be concealed.

22 40 00 Plumbing Fixtures

- Plumbing fixture costs usually require two lines: the fixture itself and its "rough-in, supply, and waste."

- In the Assemblies Section (Plumbing D2010) for the desired fixture, the System Components Group at the center of the page shows the fixture on the first line. The rest of the list (fittings, pipe, tubing, etc.) will total up to what we refer to in the Unit Price section as "Rough-in, supply, waste, and vent." Note that for most fixtures we allow a nominal 5' of tubing to reach from the fixture to a main or riser.

- Remember that gas- and oil-fired units need venting.

Reference Numbers

Reference numbers are shown in shaded boxes at the beginning of some major classifications. These numbers refer to related items in the Reference Section. The reference information may be an estimating procedure, an alternate pricing method, or technical information.

Note: Not all subdivisions listed here necessarily appear in this publication.

Note: **Trade Service,** *in part, has been used as a reference source for some of the material prices used in Division 22.*

22 01 Operation and Maintenance of Plumbing

22 01 02 – Labor Adjustments

22 01 02.10 Boilers, General		Crew	Daily Output	Labor-Hours	Unit	Material	2014 Bare Costs Labor	2014 Bare Costs Equipment	Total	Total Incl O&P
0010	**BOILERS, GENERAL**, Prices do not include flue piping, elec. wiring,									
0020	gas or oil piping, boiler base, pad, or tankless unless noted									
0100	Boiler H.P.: 10 KW = 34 lb./steam/hr. = 33,475 BTU/hr.									
0150	To convert SFR to BTU rating: Hot water, 150 x SFR; R235000-50									
0160	Forced hot water, 180 x SFR; steam, 240 x SFR									

22 01 02.20 Labor Adjustment Factors		Crew	Daily Output	Labor-Hours	Unit	Material	2014 Bare Costs Labor	2014 Bare Costs Equipment	Total	Total Incl O&P
0010	**LABOR ADJUSTMENT FACTORS**, (For Div. 21, 22 and 23) R220102-20									
0100	Labor factors, The below are reasonable suggestions, however									
0110	each project must be evaluated for its own peculiarities, and									
0120	the adjustments be increased or decreased depending on the									
0130	severity of the special conditions.									
1000	Add to labor for elevated installation (Above floor level)									
1080	10' to 14.5' high						10%			
1100	15' to 19.5' high						20%			
1120	20' to 24.5' high						25%			
1140	25' to 29.5' high						35%			
1160	30' to 34.5' high						40%			
1180	35' to 39.5' high						50%			
1200	40' and higher						55%			
2000	Add to labor for crawl space									
2100	3' high						40%			
2140	4' high						30%			
3000	Add to labor for multi-story building									
3100	Add per floor for floors 3 thru 19						2%			
3140	Add per floor for floors 20 and up						4%			
4000	Add to labor for working in existing occupied buildings									
4100	Hospital						35%			
4140	Office building						25%			
4180	School						20%			
4220	Factory or warehouse						15%			
4260	Multi dwelling						15%			
5000	Add to labor, miscellaneous									
5100	Cramped shaft						35%			
5140	Congested area						15%			
5180	Excessive heat or cold						30%			
9000	Labor factors, The above are reasonable suggestions, however									
9010	each project should be evaluated for its own peculiarities.									
9100	Other factors to be considered are:									
9140	Movement of material and equipment through finished areas									
9180	Equipment room									
9220	Attic space									
9260	No service road									
9300	Poor unloading/storage area									
9340	Congested site area/heavy traffic									

22 05 Common Work Results for Plumbing

22 05 05 – Selective Plumbing Demolition

22 05 05.10 Plumbing Demolition

		Daily Output	Labor-Hours	Unit	Material	2014 Bare Costs Labor	Equipment	Total	Total Incl O&P
		Crew							
0010	**PLUMBING DEMOLITION**								
1020	Fixtures, including 10' piping								
1101	Bathtubs, cast iron	1 Clab	4	2	Ea.		56.50		56.50	95
1121	Fiberglass		6	1.333			37.50		37.50	63.50
1141	Steel		5	1.600			45		45	76
1201	Lavatory, wall hung		10	.800			22.50		22.50	38
1221	Counter top		16	.500			14.10		14.10	23.50
1301	Sink, single compartment		16	.500			14.10		14.10	23.50
1321	Double		10	.800			22.50		22.50	38
1401	Water closet, floor mounted		16	.500			14.10		14.10	23.50
1421	Wall mounted		7	1.143			32		32	54
1501	Urinal, floor mounted		4	2			56.50		56.50	95
1521	Wall mounted		7	1.143			32		32	54
1601	Water fountains, free standing		8	1			28		28	47.50
1621	Wall or deck mounted		6	1.333			37.50		37.50	63.50
2001	Piping, metal, to 1-1/2" diameter		200	.040	L.F.		1.13		1.13	1.90
2051	2" thru 3-1/2" diameter		150	.053			1.50		1.50	2.53
2101	4" thru 6" diameter		100	.080			2.26		2.26	3.80
2151	16" thru 20" diameter		50	.160			4.51		4.51	7.60
2160	Plastic pipe with fittings, up thru 1-1/2" diameter	1 Plum	250	.032			1.36		1.36	2.25
2162	2" thru 3" diameter	"	200	.040			1.70		1.70	2.81
2164	4" thru 6" diameter	Q-1	200	.080			3.07		3.07	5.05
2166	8" thru 14" diameter		150	.107			4.09		4.09	6.75
2168	16" diameter		100	.160			6.15		6.15	10.10
2212	Deduct for salvage, aluminum scrap				Ton				700	770
2214	Brass scrap								2,450	2,675
2216	Copper scrap								3,200	3,525
2218	Lead scrap								520	570
2220	Steel scrap								180	200

22 05 23 – General-Duty Valves for Plumbing Piping

22 05 23.10 Valves, Brass

		Crew	Daily Output	Labor-Hours	Unit	Material	2014 Bare Costs Labor	Equipment	Total	Total Incl O&P
0010	**VALVES, BRASS**									
0500	Gas cocks, threaded									
0530	1/2"	1 Plum	24	.333	Ea.	13.15	14.20		27.35	38
0540	3/4"		22	.364		15.50	15.50		31	42.50
0550	1"		19	.421		31	17.95		48.95	63.50
0560	1-1/4"		15	.533		44.50	22.50		67	86.50

22 05 23.20 Valves, Bronze

		Crew	Daily Output	Labor-Hours	Unit	Material	2014 Bare Costs Labor	Equipment	Total	Total Incl O&P
0010	**VALVES, BRONZE**									
1020	Angle, 150 lb., rising stem, threaded									
1030	1/8"	1 Plum	24	.333	Ea.	135	14.20		149.20	172
1040	1/4"		24	.333		135	14.20		149.20	172
1050	3/8"		24	.333		135	14.20		149.20	172
1060	1/2"		22	.364		135	15.50		150.50	174
1070	3/4"		20	.400		184	17.05		201.05	230
1080	1"		19	.421		265	17.95		282.95	320
1100	1-1/2"		13	.615		445	26		471	535
1110	2"		11	.727		715	31		746	835
1300	Ball									
1398	Threaded, 150 psi									
1400	1/4"	1 Plum	24	.333	Ea.	13.55	14.20		27.75	38.50
1430	3/8"		24	.333		13.55	14.20		27.75	38.50

22 05 23.20 Valves, Bronze		Crew	Daily Output	Labor-Hours	Unit	Material	2014 Bare Costs Labor	Equipment	Total	Total Incl O&P
1450	1/2"	1 Plum	22	.364	Ea.	13.55	15.50		29.05	40.50
1460	3/4"		20	.400		22.50	17.05		39.55	52.50
1470	1"		19	.421		32	17.95		49.95	64.50
1480	1-1/4"		15	.533		56	22.50		78.50	99
1490	1-1/2"		13	.615		69.50	26		95.50	120
1500	2"		11	.727		88	31		119	148
1750	Check, swing, class 150, regrinding disc, threaded									
1800	1/8"	1 Plum	24	.333	Ea.	63	14.20		77.20	93
1830	1/4"		24	.333		63	14.20		77.20	93
1840	3/8"		24	.333		67	14.20		81.20	97
1850	1/2"		24	.333		72	14.20		86.20	103
1860	3/4"		20	.400		95	17.05		112.05	132
1870	1"		19	.421		137	17.95		154.95	180
1880	1-1/4"		15	.533		198	22.50		220.50	256
1890	1-1/2"		13	.615		230	26		256	297
1900	2"		11	.727		340	31		371	420
1910	2-1/2"	Q-1	15	1.067		760	41		801	905
2000	For 200 lb., add					5%	10%			
2040	For 300 lb., add					15%	15%			
2850	Gate, N.R.S., soldered, 125 psi									
2900	3/8"	1 Plum	24	.333	Ea.	54.50	14.20		68.70	83.50
2920	1/2"		24	.333		46.50	14.20		60.70	75
2940	3/4"		20	.400		53	17.05		70.05	86
2950	1"		19	.421		75	17.95		92.95	112
2960	1-1/4"		15	.533		115	22.50		137.50	164
2970	1-1/2"		13	.615		129	26		155	186
2980	2"		11	.727		182	31		213	252
2990	2-1/2"	Q-1	15	1.067		455	41		496	575
3000	3"	"	13	1.231		595	47		642	735
3850	Rising stem, soldered, 300 psi									
3950	1"	1 Plum	19	.421	Ea.	189	17.95		206.95	238
3980	2"	"	11	.727		505	31		536	610
4000	3"	Q-1	13	1.231		1,675	47		1,722	1,925
4250	Threaded, class 150									
4310	1/4"	1 Plum	24	.333	Ea.	71	14.20		85.20	102
4320	3/8"		24	.333		71	14.20		85.20	102
4330	1/2"		24	.333		65	14.20		79.20	95
4340	3/4"		20	.400		76	17.05		93.05	112
4350	1"		19	.421		102	17.95		119.95	142
4360	1-1/4"		15	.533		139	22.50		161.50	191
4370	1-1/2"		13	.615		175	26		201	236
4380	2"		11	.727		235	31		266	310
4390	2-1/2"	Q-1	15	1.067		550	41		591	675
4400	3"	"	13	1.231		765	47		812	920
4500	For 300 psi, threaded, add					100%	15%			
4540	For chain operated type, add					15%				
4850	Globe, class 150, rising stem, threaded									
4920	1/4"	1 Plum	24	.333	Ea.	102	14.20		116.20	136
4940	3/8" size		24	.333		101	14.20		115.20	135
4950	1/2"		24	.333		101	14.20		115.20	135
4960	3/4"		20	.400		135	17.05		152.05	176
4970	1"		19	.421		212	17.95		229.95	263
4980	1-1/4"		15	.533		335	22.50		357.50	410

22 05 23 – General-Duty Valves for Plumbing Piping

22 05 23.20 Valves, Bronze		Crew	Daily Output	Labor-Hours	Unit	Material	2014 Bare Costs Labor	Equipment	Total	Total Incl O&P
4990	1-1/2"	1 Plum	13	.615	Ea.	410	26		436	495
5000	2"	↓	11	.727		615	31		646	725
5010	2-1/2"	Q-1	15	1.067		1,225	41		1,266	1,425
5020	3"	"	13	1.231	↓	1,750	47		1,797	2,000
5120	For 300 lb. threaded, add					50%	15%			
5600	Relief, pressure & temperature, self-closing, ASME, threaded									
5640	3/4"	1 Plum	28	.286	Ea.	253	12.15		265.15	298
5650	1"		24	.333		405	14.20		419.20	470
5660	1-1/4"		20	.400		895	17.05		912.05	1,025
5670	1-1/2"		18	.444		1,250	18.95		1,268.95	1,400
5680	2"	↓	16	.500	↓	1,350	21.50		1,371.50	1,525
5950	Pressure, poppet type, threaded									
6000	1/2"	1 Plum	30	.267	Ea.	68.50	11.35		79.85	94.50
6040	3/4"	"	28	.286	"	73.50	12.15		85.65	101
6400	Pressure, water, ASME, threaded									
6440	3/4"	1 Plum	28	.286	Ea.	116	12.15		128.15	147
6450	1"		24	.333		260	14.20		274.20	310
6460	1-1/4"		20	.400		390	17.05		407.05	460
6470	1-1/2"		18	.444		570	18.95		588.95	655
6480	2"		16	.500		820	21.50		841.50	940
6490	2-1/2"	↓	15	.533	↓	3,150	22.50		3,172.50	3,525
6900	Reducing, water pressure									
6920	300 psi to 25-75 psi, threaded or sweat									
6940	1/2"	1 Plum	24	.333	Ea.	395	14.20		409.20	460
6950	3/4"		20	.400		395	17.05		412.05	465
6960	1"		19	.421		615	17.95		632.95	705
6970	1-1/4"		15	.533		1,100	22.50		1,122.50	1,250
6980	1-1/2"	↓	13	.615	↓	1,650	26		1,676	1,875
8350	Tempering, water, sweat connections									
8400	1/2"	1 Plum	24	.333	Ea.	109	14.20		123.20	144
8440	3/4"	"	20	.400	"	126	17.05		143.05	167
8650	Threaded connections									
8700	1/2"	1 Plum	24	.333	Ea.	126	14.20		140.20	163
8740	3/4"		20	.400		770	17.05		787.05	875
8750	1"		19	.421		865	17.95		882.95	985
8760	1-1/4"		15	.533		1,350	22.50		1,372.50	1,525
8770	1-1/2"		13	.615		1,475	26		1,501	1,650
8780	2"	↓	11	.727	↓	2,200	31		2,231	2,475

22 05 23.60 Valves, Plastic										
0010	**VALVES, PLASTIC**									
1100	Angle, PVC, threaded									
1110	1/4"	1 Plum	26	.308	Ea.	74	13.10		87.10	103
1120	1/2"		26	.308		74	13.10		87.10	103
1130	3/4"		25	.320		87.50	13.65		101.15	119
1140	1"	↓	23	.348	↓	106	14.80		120.80	142
1150	Ball, PVC, socket or threaded, single union									
1230	1/2"	1 Plum	26	.308	Ea.	28	13.10		41.10	52.50
1240	3/4"		25	.320		32	13.65		45.65	58
1250	1"		23	.348		40	14.80		54.80	69
1260	1-1/4"		21	.381		54	16.25		70.25	86.50
1270	1-1/2"		20	.400		64.50	17.05		81.55	99
1280	2"	↓	17	.471	↓	93.50	20		113.50	136

22 05 23 – General-Duty Valves for Plumbing Piping

22 05 23.60 Valves, Plastic		Crew	Daily Output	Labor-Hours	Unit	Material	2014 Bare Costs Labor	Equipment	Total	Total Incl O&P
1360	For PVC, flanged, add				Ea.	100%	15%			
1650	CPVC, socket or threaded, single union									
1700	1/2"	1 Plum	26	.308	Ea.	56	13.10		69.10	83
1720	3/4"		25	.320		70	13.65		83.65	99.50
1730	1"		23	.348		84	14.80		98.80	117
1750	1-1/4"		21	.381		134	16.25		150.25	175
1760	1-1/2"		20	.400		134	17.05		151.05	176
1840	For CPVC, flanged, add					65%	15%			
1880	For true union, socket or threaded, add					50%	5%			
2050	Polypropylene, threaded									
2100	1/4"	1 Plum	26	.308	Ea.	45	13.10		58.10	71
2120	3/8"		26	.308		45	13.10		58.10	71
2130	1/2"		26	.308		45	13.10		58.10	71
2140	3/4"		25	.320		54.50	13.65		68.15	82.50
2150	1"		23	.348		62.50	14.80		77.30	93
2160	1-1/4"		21	.381		84	16.25		100.25	120
2170	1-1/2"		20	.400		103	17.05		120.05	142
2180	2"		17	.471		138	20		158	185
4850	Foot valve, PVC, socket or threaded									
4900	1/2"	1 Plum	34	.235	Ea.	73	10		83	96.50
4930	3/4"		32	.250		83	10.65		93.65	109
4940	1"		28	.286		107	12.15		119.15	138
4950	1-1/4"		27	.296		206	12.60		218.60	248
4960	1-1/2"		26	.308		206	13.10		219.10	249
6350	Y sediment strainer, PVC, socket or threaded									
6400	1/2"	1 Plum	26	.308	Ea.	55	13.10		68.10	82
6440	3/4"		24	.333		58.50	14.20		72.70	87.50
6450	1"		23	.348		69.50	14.80		84.30	101
6460	1-1/4"		21	.381		117	16.25		133.25	155
6470	1-1/2"		20	.400		117	17.05		134.05	156

22 05 48 – Vibration and Seismic Controls for Plumbing Piping and Equipment

22 05 48.10 Seismic Bracing Supports		Crew	Daily Output	Labor-Hours	Unit	Material	2014 Bare Costs Labor	Equipment	Total	Total Incl O&P
0010	**SEISMIC BRACING SUPPORTS**									
0020	Clamps									
0030	C-clamp, for mounting on steel beam									
0040	3/8" threaded rod	1 Skwk	160	.050	Ea.	1.95	1.82		3.77	5.20
0050	1/2" threaded rod		160	.050		2.09	1.82		3.91	5.35
0060	5/8" threaded rod		160	.050		3.52	1.82		5.34	6.95
0070	3/4" threaded rod		160	.050		4.34	1.82		6.16	7.85
0100	Brackets									
0110	Beam side or wall mallable iron									
0120	3/8" threaded rod	1 Skwk	48	.167	Ea.	2.96	6.05		9.01	13.45
0130	1/2" threaded rod		48	.167		4.18	6.05		10.23	14.80
0140	5/8" threaded rod		48	.167		7.85	6.05		13.90	18.80
0150	3/4" threaded rod		48	.167		10.75	6.05		16.80	22
0160	7/8" threaded rod		48	.167		11.10	6.05		17.15	22.50
0170	For concrete installation, add						30%			
0180	Wall, welded steel									
0190	0 size 12" wide 18" deep	1 Skwk	34	.235	Ea.	164	8.55		172.55	194
0200	1 size 18" wide 24" deep		34	.235		201	8.55		209.55	235
0210	2 size 24" wide 30" deep		34	.235		276	8.55		284.55	320
0300	Rod, carbon steel									

22 05 48 – Vibration and Seismic Controls for Plumbing Piping and Equipment

22 05 48.10 Seismic Bracing Supports

		Crew	Daily Output	Labor-Hours	Unit	Material	2014 Bare Costs Labor	2014 Bare Costs Equipment	Total	Total Incl O&P
0310	Continuous thread									
0320	1/4" thread	1 Skwk	144	.056	L.F.	1.62	2.02		3.64	5.20
0330	3/8" thread		144	.056		1.72	2.02		3.74	5.30
0340	1/2" thread		144	.056		2.72	2.02		4.74	6.40
0350	5/8" thread		144	.056		3.86	2.02		5.88	7.65
0360	3/4" thread		144	.056		6.80	2.02		8.82	10.90
0370	7/8" thread		144	.056		8.55	2.02		10.57	12.80
0380	For galvanized, add					30%				
0400	Channel, steel									
0410	3/4" x 1-1/2"	1 Skwk	80	.100	L.F.	4.83	3.63		8.46	11.45
0420	1-1/2" x 1-1/2"		70	.114		6.35	4.15		10.50	14
0430	1-7/8" x 1-1/2"		60	.133		22.50	4.84		27.34	32.50
0440	3" x 1-1/2"		50	.160		38	5.80		43.80	51.50
0450	Spring nuts									
0460	3/8"	1 Skwk	100	.080	Ea.	1.40	2.90		4.30	6.45
0470	1/2"	"	80	.100	"	1.67	3.63		5.30	8
0500	Welding, field									
0510	Cleaning and welding plates, bars, or rods									
0520	To existing beams, columns, or trusses									
0530	1" weld	1 Skwk	144	.056	Ea.	.22	2.02		2.24	3.65
0540	2" weld		72	.111		.38	4.03		4.41	7.20
0550	3" weld		54	.148		.59	5.40		5.99	9.75
0560	4" weld		36	.222		.81	8.05		8.86	14.50
0570	5" weld		30	.267		1.02	9.70		10.72	17.45
0580	6" weld		24	.333		1.15	12.10		13.25	22
0600	Vibration absorbers									
0610	Hangers, neoprene flex									
0620	10-120 lb. capacity	1 Skwk	8	1	Ea.	25.50	36.50		62	90
0630	75-550 lb. capacity		8	1		36	36.50		72.50	101
0640	250-1100 lb. capacity		6	1.333		66.50	48.50		115	155
0650	1000-4000 lb. capacity		6	1.333		124	48.50		172.50	219

22 05 76 – Facility Drainage Piping Cleanouts

22 05 76.10 Cleanouts

		Crew	Daily Output	Labor-Hours	Unit	Material	2014 Bare Costs Labor	2014 Bare Costs Equipment	Total	Total Incl O&P
0010	**CLEANOUTS**									
0060	Floor type									
0080	Round or square, scoriated nickel bronze top									
0100	2" pipe size	1 Plum	10	.800	Ea.	183	34		217	257
0120	3" pipe size		8	1		274	42.50		316.50	370
0140	4" pipe size		6	1.333		274	57		331	395
0980	Round top, recessed for terrazzo									
1000	2" pipe size	1 Plum	9	.889	Ea.	183	38		221	264
1080	3" pipe size		6	1.333		274	57		331	395
1100	4" pipe size		4	2		274	85		359	440
1120	5" pipe size	Q-1	6	2.667		345	102		447	550

22 05 76.20 Cleanout Tees

		Crew	Daily Output	Labor-Hours	Unit	Material	2014 Bare Costs Labor	2014 Bare Costs Equipment	Total	Total Incl O&P
0010	**CLEANOUT TEES**									
0100	Cast iron, B&S, with countersunk plug									
0200	2" pipe size	1 Plum	4	2	Ea.	248	85		333	415
0220	3" pipe size		3.60	2.222		270	94.50		364.50	455
0240	4" pipe size		3.30	2.424		335	103		438	540
0280	6" pipe size	Q-1	5	3.200		910	123		1,033	1,200
0500	For round smooth access cover, same price									

22 05 76 – Facility Drainage Piping Cleanouts

22 05 76.20 Cleanout Tees		Crew	Daily Output	Labor-Hours	Unit	Material	2014 Bare Costs Labor	2014 Bare Costs Equipment	Total	Total Incl O&P
4000	Plastic, tees and adapters. Add plugs									
4010	ABS, DWV									
4020	Cleanout tee, 1-1/2" pipe size	1 Plum	15	.533	Ea.	20	22.50		42.50	59.50
4030	2" pipe size	Q-1	27	.593		22.50	22.50		45	62.50
4040	3" pipe size		21	.762		43.50	29		72.50	96
4050	4" pipe size		16	1		87	38.50		125.50	160
4100	Cleanout plug, 1-1/2" pipe size	1 Plum	32	.250		2.97	10.65		13.62	21
4110	2" pipe size	Q-1	56	.286		3.90	10.95		14.85	22.50
4120	3" pipe size		36	.444		6.30	17.05		23.35	35
4130	4" pipe size		30	.533		11	20.50		31.50	46
4180	Cleanout adapter fitting, 1-1/2" pipe size	1 Plum	32	.250		4.70	10.65		15.35	23
4190	2" pipe size	Q-1	56	.286		7.20	10.95		18.15	26
4200	3" pipe size		36	.444		18.45	17.05		35.50	48.50
4210	4" pipe size		30	.533		34	20.50		54.50	71.50
5000	PVC, DWV									
5010	Cleanout tee, 1-1/2" pipe size	1 Plum	15	.533	Ea.	12.75	22.50		35.25	51.50
5020	2" pipe size	Q-1	27	.593		14.85	22.50		37.35	54
5030	3" pipe size		21	.762		29	29		58	79.50
5040	4" pipe size		16	1		51.50	38.50		90	121
5090	Cleanout plug, 1-1/2" pipe size	1 Plum	32	.250		3.04	10.65		13.69	21
5100	2" pipe size	Q-1	56	.286		3.30	10.95		14.25	21.50
5110	3" pipe size		36	.444		6.05	17.05		23.10	34.50
5120	4" pipe size		30	.533		8.90	20.50		29.40	44
5130	6" pipe size		24	.667		29.50	25.50		55	74.50
5170	Cleanout adapter fitting, 1-1/2" pipe size	1 Plum	32	.250		4.06	10.65		14.71	22
5180	2" pipe size	Q-1	56	.286		5.20	10.95		16.15	24
5190	3" pipe size		36	.444		14.70	17.05		31.75	44
5200	4" pipe size		30	.533		23.50	20.50		44	60
5210	6" pipe size		24	.667		70.50	25.50		96	120

22 07 19 – Plumbing Piping Insulation

22 07 19.10 Piping Insulation

			Crew	Daily Output	Labor-Hours	Unit	Material	2014 Bare Costs Labor	2014 Bare Costs Equipment	Total	Total Incl O&P
0010	**PIPING INSULATION**										
0100	Rule of thumb, as a percentage of total mechanical costs					Job				10%	10%
0110	Insulation req'd. is based on the surface size/area to be covered										
0600	Pipe covering (price copper tube one size less than IPS)										
6600	Fiberglass, with all service jacket										
6840	1" wall, 1/2" iron pipe size	G	Q-14	240	.067	L.F.	.89	2.27		3.16	4.83
6870	1" iron pipe size	G		220	.073		1.04	2.48		3.52	5.35
6900	2" iron pipe size	G		200	.080		1.32	2.73		4.05	6.05
6920	3" iron pipe size	G		180	.089		1.60	3.03		4.63	6.90
6940	4" iron pipe size	G		150	.107		2.12	3.64		5.76	8.50
7320	2" wall, 1/2" iron pipe size	G		220	.073		2.62	2.48		5.10	7.10
7440	6" iron pipe size	G		100	.160		5.25	5.45		10.70	15.05
7460	8" iron pipe size	G		80	.200		6.40	6.80		13.20	18.55
7480	10" iron pipe size	G		70	.229		7.65	7.80		15.45	21.50
7490	12" iron pipe size	G		65	.246		8.55	8.40		16.95	23.50
7800	For fiberglass with standard canvas jacket, deduct						5%				
7802	For fittings, add 3 L.F. for each fitting										
7804	plus 4 L.F. for each flange of the fitting										

22 07 Plumbing Insulation

22 07 19 – Plumbing Piping Insulation

22 07 19.10 Piping Insulation		Crew	Daily Output	Labor-Hours	Unit	Material	2014 Bare Costs Labor	Equipment	Total	Total Incl O&P
7810	Finishes									
7812	For .016" aluminum jacket, add	G	Q-14	200	.080	S.F.	.92	2.73		3.65	5.65
7813	For .010" stainless steel, add	G	"	160	.100	"	2.88	3.41		6.29	8.95
7814	For single layer of felt, add						10%	10%			
7816	For roofing paper, 45 lb. to 55 lb., add						25%	10%			
7879	Rubber tubing, flexible closed cell foam										
7880	3/8" wall, 1/4" iron pipe size	G	1 Asbe	120	.067	L.F.	.33	2.52		2.85	4.64
7910	1/2" iron pipe size	G		115	.070		.41	2.63		3.04	4.92
7920	3/4" iron pipe size	G		115	.070		.46	2.63		3.09	4.98
7930	1" iron pipe size	G		110	.073		.52	2.75		3.27	5.25
7950	1-1/2" iron pipe size	G		110	.073		.73	2.75		3.48	5.45
8100	1/2" wall, 1/4" iron pipe size	G		90	.089		.54	3.36		3.90	6.30
8130	1/2" iron pipe size	G		89	.090		.67	3.40		4.07	6.50
8140	3/4" iron pipe size	G		89	.090		.75	3.40		4.15	6.60
8150	1" iron pipe size	G		88	.091		.82	3.44		4.26	6.75
8170	1-1/2" iron pipe size	G		87	.092		1.15	3.48		4.63	7.15
8180	2" iron pipe size	G		86	.093		1.47	3.52		4.99	7.55
8200	3" iron pipe size	G		85	.094		2.06	3.56		5.62	8.30
8300	3/4" wall, 1/4" iron pipe size	G		90	.089		.85	3.36		4.21	6.65
8330	1/2" iron pipe size	G		89	.090		1.10	3.40		4.50	6.95
8340	3/4" iron pipe size	G		89	.090		1.35	3.40		4.75	7.25
8350	1" iron pipe size	G		88	.091		1.54	3.44		4.98	7.55
8370	1-1/2" iron pipe size	G		87	.092		2.32	3.48		5.80	8.45
8380	2" iron pipe size	G		86	.093		2.68	3.52		6.20	8.90
8400	3" iron pipe size	G		85	.094		4.08	3.56		7.64	10.55
8444	1" wall, 1/2" iron pipe size	G		86	.093		2.05	3.52		5.57	8.20
8445	3/4" iron pipe size	G		84	.095		2.48	3.60		6.08	8.85
8446	1" iron pipe size	G		84	.095		2.89	3.60		6.49	9.30
8447	1-1/4" iron pipe size	G		82	.098		3.23	3.69		6.92	9.80
8448	1-1/2" iron pipe size	G		82	.098		3.76	3.69		7.45	10.40
8449	2" iron pipe size	G		80	.100		4.95	3.79		8.74	11.85
8450	2-1/2" iron pipe size	G		80	.100		6.45	3.79		10.24	13.50
8456	Rubber insulation tape, 1/8" x 2" x 30'	G				Ea.	12.05			12.05	13.25

22 11 Facility Water Distribution

22 11 13 – Facility Water Distribution Piping

22 11 13.14 Pipe, Brass

		Crew	Daily Output	Labor-Hours	Unit	Material	2014 Bare Costs Labor	Equipment	Total	Total Incl O&P
0010	**PIPE, BRASS**, Plain end										
0900	Field threaded, coupling & clevis hanger assembly 10' O.C.										
0920	Regular weight										
1120	1/2" diameter		1 Plum	48	.167	L.F.	6.40	7.10		13.50	18.75
1140	3/4" diameter			46	.174		8.60	7.40		16	21.50
1160	1" diameter			43	.186		12.50	7.95		20.45	27
1180	1-1/4" diameter		Q-1	72	.222		19.10	8.50		27.60	35
1200	1-1/2" diameter			65	.246		23	9.45		32.45	40.50
1220	2" diameter			53	.302		32	11.60		43.60	54.50

22 11 13.23 Pipe/Tube, Copper

		Crew	Daily Output	Labor-Hours	Unit	Material	2014 Bare Costs Labor	Equipment	Total	Total Incl O&P
0010	**PIPE/TUBE, COPPER**, Solder joints										
1000	Type K tubing, couplings & clevis hanger assemblies 10' O.C.										
1100	1/4" diameter		1 Plum	84	.095	L.F.	4.62	4.06		8.68	11.80
1200	1" diameter			66	.121		10.60	5.15		15.75	20

22 11 13.23 Pipe/Tube, Copper

		Crew	Daily Output	Labor-Hours	Unit	Material	Labor	Equipment	Total	Total Incl O&P
1260	2" diameter	1 Plum	40	.200	L.F.	26.50	8.50		35	43
2000	Type L tubing, couplings & clevis hanger assemblies 10' O.C.									
2100	1/4" diameter	1 Plum	88	.091	L.F.	2.30	3.87		6.17	8.95
2120	3/8" diameter		84	.095		3.13	4.06		7.19	10.15
2140	1/2" diameter		81	.099		3.37	4.21		7.58	10.65
2160	5/8" diameter		79	.101		5.35	4.31		9.66	12.95
2180	3/4" diameter		76	.105		5.15	4.48		9.63	13.05
2200	1" diameter		68	.118		7.85	5		12.85	16.90
2220	1-1/4" diameter		58	.138		11.25	5.90		17.15	22
2240	1-1/2" diameter		52	.154		14.35	6.55		20.90	26.50
2260	2" diameter		42	.190		22	8.10		30.10	37.50
2280	2-1/2" diameter	Q-1	62	.258		35.50	9.90		45.40	55.50
2300	3" diameter		56	.286		48.50	10.95		59.45	71.50
2320	3-1/2" diameter		43	.372		70.50	14.25		84.75	101
2340	4" diameter		39	.410		85.50	15.75		101.25	120
2360	5" diameter		34	.471		168	18.05		186.05	215
2380	6" diameter	Q-2	40	.600		244	22		266	305
2400	8" diameter	"	36	.667		370	24.50		394.50	450
2410	For other than full hard temper, add					21%				
2590	For silver solder, add						15%			
4000	Type DWV tubing, couplings & clevis hanger assemblies 10' O.C.									
4100	1-1/4" diameter	1 Plum	60	.133	L.F.	9.95	5.70		15.65	20.50
4120	1-1/2" diameter		54	.148		12.45	6.30		18.75	24
4140	2" diameter		44	.182		17.05	7.75		24.80	31.50
4160	3" diameter	Q-1	58	.276		35	10.60		45.60	56
4180	4" diameter		40	.400		62	15.35		77.35	93.50
4200	5" diameter		36	.444		154	17.05		171.05	198
4220	6" diameter	Q-2	42	.571		230	21		251	288

22 11 13.44 Pipe, Steel

		Crew	Daily Output	Labor-Hours	Unit	Material	Labor	Equipment	Total	Total Incl O&P
0010	**PIPE, STEEL** R221113-50									
0020	All pipe sizes are to Spec. A-53 unless noted otherwise									
0050	Schedule 40, threaded, with couplings, and clevis hanger									
0060	assemblies sized for covering, 10' O.C.									
0540	Black, 1/4" diameter	1 Plum	66	.121	L.F.	4.51	5.15		9.66	13.45
0550	3/8" diameter		65	.123		5.10	5.25		10.35	14.25
0560	1/2" diameter		63	.127		2.73	5.40		8.13	11.95
0570	3/4" diameter		61	.131		3.17	5.60		8.77	12.70
0580	1" diameter		53	.151		4.64	6.45		11.09	15.70
0590	1-1/4" diameter	Q-1	89	.180		5.75	6.90		12.65	17.70
0600	1-1/2" diameter		80	.200		6.70	7.65		14.35	20
0610	2" diameter		64	.250		8.95	9.60		18.55	25.50
0620	2-1/2" diameter		50	.320		14.05	12.25		26.30	36
0630	3" diameter		43	.372		18	14.25		32.25	43.50
0640	3-1/2" diameter		40	.400		24.50	15.35		39.85	52.50
0650	4" diameter		36	.444		27	17.05		44.05	58
1280	All pipe sizes are to Spec. A-53 unless noted otherwise									
1281	Schedule 40, threaded, with couplings and clevis hanger									
1282	assemblies sized for covering, 10' O. C.									
1290	Galvanized, 1/4" diameter	1 Plum	66	.121	L.F.	6.40	5.15		11.55	15.55
1300	3/8" diameter		65	.123		7.05	5.25		12.30	16.40
1310	1/2" diameter		63	.127		3.76	5.40		9.16	13.10
1320	3/4" diameter		61	.131		4.45	5.60		10.05	14.10

22 11 Facility Water Distribution

22 11 13 – Facility Water Distribution Piping

22 11 13.44 Pipe, Steel

		Crew	Daily Output	Labor-Hours	Unit	Material	2014 Bare Costs Labor	Equipment	Total	Total Incl O&P
1330	1" diameter	1 Plum	53	.151	L.F.	6.10	6.45		12.55	17.30
1340	1-1/4" diameter	Q-1	89	.180		7.70	6.90		14.60	19.90
1350	1-1/2" diameter		80	.200		9.05	7.65		16.70	22.50
1360	2" diameter		64	.250		12.15	9.60		21.75	29
1370	2-1/2" diameter		50	.320		20	12.25		32.25	42.50
1380	3" diameter		43	.372		25.50	14.25		39.75	52
1390	3-1/2" diameter		40	.400		33	15.35		48.35	62
1400	4" diameter		36	.444		38	17.05		55.05	69.50
2000	Welded, sch. 40, on yoke & roll hanger assy's, sized for covering, 10' O.C.									
2040	Black, 1" diameter	Q-15	93	.172	L.F.	3.91	6.60	.60	11.11	15.85
2070	2" diameter		61	.262		7.05	10.05	.91	18.01	25.50
2090	3" diameter		43	.372		15.40	14.25	1.29	30.94	42
2110	4" diameter		37	.432		21.50	16.60	1.50	39.60	52.50
2120	5" diameter		32	.500		34	19.20	1.73	54.93	71
2130	6" diameter	Q-16	36	.667		42.50	26.50	1.53	70.53	92
2140	8" diameter		29	.828		68	33	1.90	102.90	131
2150	10" diameter		24	1		88.50	40	2.30	130.80	165
2160	12" diameter		19	1.263		104	50	2.91	156.91	200

22 11 13.48 Pipe, Fittings and Valves, Steel, Grooved-Joint

		Crew	Daily Output	Labor-Hours	Unit	Material	2014 Bare Costs Labor	Equipment	Total	Total Incl O&P
0010	**PIPE, FITTINGS AND VALVES, STEEL, GROOVED-JOINT**									
0012	Fittings are ductile iron. Steel fittings noted.									
0020	Pipe includes coupling & clevis type hanger assemblies, 10' O.C.									
1000	Schedule 40, black									
1040	3/4" diameter	1 Plum	71	.113	L.F.	4.62	4.80		9.42	13
1050	1" diameter		63	.127		4.41	5.40		9.81	13.80
1060	1-1/4" diameter		58	.138		5.70	5.90		11.60	15.95
1070	1-1/2" diameter		51	.157		6.50	6.70		13.20	18.20
1080	2" diameter		40	.200		7.85	8.50		16.35	22.50
1090	2-1/2" diameter	Q-1	57	.281		13.45	10.75		24.20	32.50
1100	3" diameter		50	.320		16.55	12.25		28.80	38.50
1110	4" diameter		45	.356		22.50	13.65		36.15	47.50
1120	5" diameter		37	.432		36.50	16.60		53.10	68
1130	6" diameter	Q-2	42	.571		47	21		68	87
1800	Galvanized									
1840	3/4" diameter	1 Plum	71	.113	L.F.	5.85	4.80		10.65	14.35
1850	1" diameter		63	.127		5.55	5.40		10.95	15.05
1860	1-1/4" diameter		58	.138		7.20	5.90		13.10	17.65
1870	1-1/2" diameter		51	.157		8.40	6.70		15.10	20.50
1880	2" diameter		40	.200		12	8.50		20.50	27.50
1890	2-1/2" diameter	Q-1	57	.281		18.20	10.75		28.95	38
1900	3" diameter		50	.320		23	12.25		35.25	46
1910	4" diameter		45	.356		32	13.65		45.65	58
1920	5" diameter		37	.432		58.50	16.60		75.10	92
1930	6" diameter	Q-2	42	.571		63.50	21		84.50	105
3990	Fittings: coupling material required at joints not incl. in fitting price.									
3994	Add 1 selected coupling, material only, per joint for installed price.									
4000	Elbow, 90° or 45°, painted									
4030	3/4" diameter	1 Plum	50	.160	Ea.	56	6.80		62.80	73.50
4040	1" diameter		50	.160		30	6.80		36.80	44.50
4050	1-1/4" diameter		40	.200		30	8.50		38.50	47
4060	1-1/2" diameter		33	.242		30	10.35		40.35	50
4070	2" diameter		25	.320		30	13.65		43.65	55.50

22 11 Facility Water Distribution

22 11 13 – Facility Water Distribution Piping

22 11 13.48 Pipe, Fittings and Valves, Steel, Grooved-Joint	Crew	Daily Output	Labor-Hours	Unit	Material	2014 Bare Costs Labor	Equipment	Total	Total Incl O&P
4080	2-1/2" diameter	Q-1	40	.400	Ea.	30	15.35		45.35	58.50
4090	3" diameter		33	.485		53	18.60		71.60	89
4100	4" diameter		25	.640		57.50	24.50		82	104
4110	5" diameter		20	.800		137	30.50		167.50	202
4120	6" diameter	Q-2	25	.960		161	35.50		196.50	237
4250	For galvanized elbows, add					26%				
4690	Tee, painted									
4700	3/4" diameter	1 Plum	38	.211	Ea.	60.50	8.95		69.45	81.50
4740	1" diameter		33	.242		46.50	10.35		56.85	68.50
4750	1-1/4" diameter		27	.296		46.50	12.60		59.10	72.50
4760	1-1/2" diameter		22	.364		46.50	15.50		62	77
4770	2" diameter		17	.471		46.50	20		66.50	84.50
4780	2-1/2" diameter	Q-1	27	.593		46.50	22.50		69	89
4790	3" diameter		22	.727		64	28		92	116
4800	4" diameter		17	.941		97	36		133	167
4810	5" diameter		13	1.231		226	47		273	325
4820	6" diameter	Q-2	17	1.412		261	52		313	375
4900	For galvanized tees, add					24%				
4906	Couplings, rigid style, painted									
4908	1" diameter	1 Plum	100	.080	Ea.	23	3.41		26.41	31
4909	1-1/4" diameter		100	.080		23	3.41		26.41	31
4910	1-1/2" diameter		67	.119		23	5.10		28.10	34
4912	2" diameter		50	.160		29.50	6.80		36.30	44
4914	2-1/2" diameter	Q-1	80	.200		33.50	7.65		41.15	49.50
4916	3" diameter		67	.239		39	9.15		48.15	58
4918	4" diameter		50	.320		54.50	12.25		66.75	80.50
4920	5" diameter		40	.400		70	15.35		85.35	103
4922	6" diameter	Q-2	50	.480		93	17.75		110.75	132
4924	8" diameter		42	.571		146	21		167	196
4926	10" diameter		35	.686		211	25.50		236.50	275
4928	12" diameter		32	.750		236	27.50		263.50	305
4930	14" diameter		24	1		257	37		294	345
4931	16" diameter		20	1.200		335	44.50		379.50	445
4932	18" diameter		18	1.333		385	49		434	505
4933	20" diameter		16	1.500		530	55.50		585.50	670
4934	24" diameter		13	1.846		675	68		743	855
4940	Flexible, standard, painted									
4950	3/4" diameter	1 Plum	100	.080	Ea.	16.60	3.41		20.01	24
4960	1" diameter		100	.080		16.60	3.41		20.01	24
4970	1-1/4" diameter		80	.100		22	4.26		26.26	31
4980	1-1/2" diameter		67	.119		24	5.10		29.10	34.50
4990	2" diameter		50	.160		25.50	6.80		32.30	39.50
5000	2-1/2" diameter	Q-1	80	.200		29.50	7.65		37.15	45
5010	3" diameter		67	.239		33	9.15		42.15	51.50
5020	3-1/2" diameter		57	.281		47	10.75		57.75	69.50
5030	4" diameter		50	.320		47.50	12.25		59.75	72.50
5040	5" diameter		40	.400		72	15.35		87.35	105
5050	6" diameter	Q-2	50	.480		85	17.75		102.75	123
5200	For galvanized couplings, add					33%				

22 11 13 – Facility Water Distribution Piping

22 11 13.64 Pipe, Stainless Steel

		Crew	Daily Output	Labor-Hours	Unit	Material	2014 Bare Costs Labor	Equipment	Total	Total Incl O&P
0010	**PIPE, STAINLESS STEEL**									
3500	Threaded, couplings and clevis hanger assemblies, 10' O.C.									
3520	Schedule 40, type 304									
3540	1/4" diameter	1 Plum	54	.148	L.F.	10.10	6.30		16.40	21.50
3550	3/8" diameter		53	.151		10.35	6.45		16.80	22
3560	1/2" diameter		52	.154		12.05	6.55		18.60	24
3580	1" diameter	↓	45	.178		18.50	7.55		26.05	33
3610	2" diameter	Q-1	57	.281		44	10.75		54.75	66.50
3640	4" diameter	Q-2	51	.471		137	17.40		154.40	179
3740	For small quantities, add				↓	10%				
4250	Schedule 40, type 316									
4290	1/4" diameter	1 Plum	54	.148	L.F.	10.90	6.30		17.20	22.50
4300	3/8" diameter		53	.151		12	6.45		18.45	24
4310	1/2" diameter		52	.154		14.70	6.55		21.25	27
4320	3/4" diameter		51	.157		17.15	6.70		23.85	30
4330	1" diameter	↓	45	.178		24.50	7.55		32.05	39.50
4360	2" diameter	Q-1	57	.281		52.50	10.75		63.25	75.50
4390	4" diameter	Q-2	51	.471		152	17.40		169.40	196
4490	For small quantities, add				↓	10%				

22 11 13.74 Pipe, Plastic

		Crew	Daily Output	Labor-Hours	Unit	Material	2014 Bare Costs Labor	Equipment	Total	Total Incl O&P
0010	**PIPE, PLASTIC**									
1800	PVC, couplings 10' O.C., clevis hanger assemblies, 3 per 10'									
1820	Schedule 40									
1860	1/2" diameter	1 Plum	54	.148	L.F.	3.02	6.30		9.32	13.75
1870	3/4" diameter		51	.157		3.33	6.70		10.03	14.70
1880	1" diameter		46	.174		3.96	7.40		11.36	16.60
1890	1-1/4" diameter		42	.190		4.94	8.10		13.04	18.85
1900	1-1/2" diameter		36	.222		4.76	9.45		14.21	21
1910	2" diameter	Q-1	59	.271		5.95	10.40		16.35	23.50
1920	2-1/2" diameter		56	.286		9.15	10.95		20.10	28
1930	3" diameter		53	.302		11.05	11.60		22.65	31.50
1940	4" diameter		48	.333		14.20	12.80		27	36.50
1950	5" diameter		43	.372		28	14.25		42.25	54.50
1960	6" diameter	↓	39	.410	↓	29.50	15.75		45.25	58.50
4100	DWV type, schedule 40, couplings 10' O.C., clevis hanger assy's, 3 per 10'									
4210	ABS, schedule 40, foam core type									
4212	Plain end black									
4214	1-1/2" diameter	1 Plum	39	.205	L.F.	2.96	8.75		11.71	17.65
4216	2" diameter	Q-1	62	.258		3.40	9.90		13.30	20
4218	3" diameter		56	.286		6.10	10.95		17.05	25
4220	4" diameter		51	.314		8.70	12.05		20.75	29.50
4222	6" diameter	↓	42	.381	↓	20.50	14.60		35.10	46.50
4240	To delete coupling & hangers, subtract									
4244	1-1/2" diam. to 6" diam.					43%	48%			
4400	PVC									
4410	1-1/4" diameter	1 Plum	42	.190	L.F.	3.41	8.10		11.51	17.15
4420	1-1/2" diameter	"	36	.222		2.98	9.45		12.43	18.90
4460	2" diameter	Q-1	59	.271		3.39	10.40		13.79	21
4470	3" diameter		53	.302		6.05	11.60		17.65	26
4480	4" diameter		48	.333		8.35	12.80		21.15	30
4490	6" diameter	↓	39	.410		17.25	15.75		33	45
5300	CPVC, socket joint, couplings 10' O.C., clevis hanger assemblies, 3 per 10'									

22 11 Facility Water Distribution

22 11 13 – Facility Water Distribution Piping

22 11 13.74 Pipe, Plastic

		Crew	Daily Output	Labor-Hours	Unit	Material	2014 Bare Costs Labor	Equipment	Total	Total Incl O&P
5302	Schedule 40									
5304	1/2" diameter	1 Plum	54	.148	L.F.	3.65	6.30		9.95	14.40
5305	3/4" diameter		51	.157		4.30	6.70		11	15.80
5306	1" diameter		46	.174		5.50	7.40		12.90	18.30
5307	1-1/4" diameter		42	.190		6.90	8.10		15	21
5308	1-1/2" diameter		36	.222		8.05	9.45		17.50	24.50
5309	2" diameter	Q-1	59	.271		9.90	10.40		20.30	28
5310	2-1/2" diameter		56	.286		16.60	10.95		27.55	36.50
5311	3" diameter		53	.302		20	11.60		31.60	41
5360	CPVC, threaded, couplings 10' O.C., clevis hanger assemblies, 3 per 10'									
5380	Schedule 40									
5460	1/2" diameter	1 Plum	54	.148	L.F.	4.45	6.30		10.75	15.30
5470	3/4" diameter		51	.157		5.70	6.70		12.40	17.30
5480	1" diameter		46	.174		6.95	7.40		14.35	19.85
5490	1-1/4" diameter		42	.190		8	8.10		16.10	22
5500	1-1/2" diameter		36	.222		9	9.45		18.45	25.50
5510	2" diameter	Q-1	59	.271		11.10	10.40		21.50	29.50
5520	2-1/2" diameter		56	.286		17.85	10.95		28.80	38
5530	3" diameter		53	.302		22	11.60		33.60	43

22 11 19 – Domestic Water Piping Specialties

22 11 19.10 Flexible Connectors

		Crew	Daily Output	Labor-Hours	Unit	Material	2014 Bare Costs Labor	Equipment	Total	Total Incl O&P
0010	**FLEXIBLE CONNECTORS**, Corrugated, 7/8" O.D., 1/2" I.D.									
0050	Gas, seamless brass, steel fittings									
0200	12" long	1 Plum	36	.222	Ea.	17.40	9.45		26.85	35
0220	18" long		36	.222		21.50	9.45		30.95	39.50
0240	24" long		34	.235		25.50	10		35.50	44.50
0280	36" long		32	.250		30.50	10.65		41.15	51
0340	60" long		30	.267		46	11.35		57.35	69.50
2000	Water, copper tubing, dielectric separators									
2100	12" long	1 Plum	36	.222	Ea.	17.35	9.45		26.80	34.50
2260	24" long	"	34	.235	"	26	10		36	45

22 11 19.14 Flexible Metal Hose

		Crew	Daily Output	Labor-Hours	Unit	Material	2014 Bare Costs Labor	Equipment	Total	Total Incl O&P
0010	**FLEXIBLE METAL HOSE**, Connectors, standard lengths									
0100	Bronze braided, bronze ends									
0120	3/8" diameter x 12"	1 Stpi	26	.308	Ea.	19.60	13.30		32.90	43.50
0160	3/4" diameter x 12"		20	.400		29.50	17.30		46.80	61
0180	1" diameter x 18"		19	.421		35.50	18.25		53.75	69
0200	1-1/2" diameter x 18"		13	.615		48	26.50		74.50	96.50
0220	2" diameter x 18"		11	.727		63	31.50		94.50	122

22 11 19.26 Pressure Regulators

		Crew	Daily Output	Labor-Hours	Unit	Material	2014 Bare Costs Labor	Equipment	Total	Total Incl O&P
0010	**PRESSURE REGULATORS**									
3000	Steam, high capacity, bronze body, stainless steel trim									
3020	Threaded, 1/2" diameter	1 Stpi	24	.333	Ea.	1,975	14.45		1,989.45	2,200
3030	3/4" diameter		24	.333		2,150	14.45		2,164.45	2,375
3040	1" diameter		19	.421		2,400	18.25		2,418.25	2,675
3060	1-1/4" diameter		15	.533		2,500	23		2,523	2,800
3080	1-1/2" diameter		13	.615		3,025	26.50		3,051.50	3,375
3100	2" diameter		11	.727		3,725	31.50		3,756.50	4,125
3120	2-1/2" diameter	Q-5	12	1.333		4,650	52		4,702	5,200
3140	3" diameter	"	11	1.455		5,075	56.50		5,131.50	5,675
3500	Flanged connection, iron body, 125 lb. W.S.P.									
3520	3" diameter	Q-5	11	1.455	Ea.	5,800	56.50		5,856.50	6,500

22 11 Facility Water Distribution

22 11 19 – Domestic Water Piping Specialties

22 11 19.26 Pressure Regulators	Crew	Daily Output	Labor-Hours	Unit	Material	2014 Bare Costs Labor	Equipment	Total	Total Incl O&P
3540 4" diameter	Q-5	5	3.200	Ea.	7,325	125		7,450	8,250

22 11 19.38 Water Supply Meters

	Crew	Daily Output	Labor-Hours	Unit	Material	Labor	Equipment	Total	Total Incl O&P
0010 **WATER SUPPLY METERS**									
2000 Domestic/commercial, bronze									
2020 Threaded									
2060 5/8" diameter, to 20 GPM	1 Plum	16	.500	Ea.	48.50	21.50		70	88.50
2080 3/4" diameter, to 30 GPM		14	.571		88.50	24.50		113	138
2100 1" diameter, to 50 GPM		12	.667		134	28.50		162.50	195
2300 Threaded/flanged									
2340 1-1/2" diameter, to 100 GPM	1 Plum	8	1	Ea.	330	42.50		372.50	430
2360 2" diameter, to 160 GPM	"	6	1.333	"	445	57		502	585
2600 Flanged, compound									
2640 3" diameter, 320 GPM	Q-1	3	5.333	Ea.	3,025	205		3,230	3,650
2660 4" diameter, to 500 GPM		1.50	10.667		4,850	410		5,260	6,000
2680 6" diameter, to 1,000 GPM		1	16		7,725	615		8,340	9,500
2700 8" diameter, to 1,800 GPM		.80	20		12,100	765		12,865	14,600

22 11 19.42 Backflow Preventers

	Crew	Daily Output	Labor-Hours	Unit	Material	Labor	Equipment	Total	Total Incl O&P
0010 **BACKFLOW PREVENTERS**, Includes valves									
0020 and four test cocks, corrosion resistant, automatic operation									
4000 Reduced pressure principle									
4100 Threaded, bronze, valves are ball									
4120 3/4" pipe size	1 Plum	16	.500	Ea.	445	21.50		466.50	525
4140 1" pipe size		14	.571		480	24.50		504.50	565
4150 1-1/4" pipe size		12	.667		845	28.50		873.50	975
4160 1-1/2" pipe size		10	.800		960	34	–	994	1,100
4180 2" pipe size		7	1.143		1,075	48.50		1,123.50	1,275
5000 Flanged, bronze, valves are OS&Y									
5060 2-1/2" pipe size	Q-1	5	3.200	Ea.	4,025	123		4,148	4,625
5080 3" pipe size		4.50	3.556		4,650	136		4,786	5,325
5100 4" pipe size		3	5.333		5,500	205		5,705	6,375
5120 6" pipe size	Q-2	3	8		8,750	295		9,045	10,100
5600 Flanged, iron, valves are OS&Y									
5660 2-1/2" pipe size	Q-1	5	3.200	Ea.	3,025	123		3,148	3,525
5680 3" pipe size		4.50	3.556		3,175	136		3,311	3,725
5700 4" pipe size		3	5.333		3,975	205		4,180	4,700
5720 6" pipe size	Q-2	3	8		5,775	295		6,070	6,825
5740 8" pipe size		2	12		10,100	445		10,545	11,800
5760 10" pipe size		1	24		13,600	885		14,485	16,400

22 11 19.50 Vacuum Breakers

	Crew	Daily Output	Labor-Hours	Unit	Material	Labor	Equipment	Total	Total Incl O&P
0010 **VACUUM BREAKERS**									
0013 See also backflow preventers Section 22 11 19.42									
1000 Anti-siphon continuous pressure type									
1010 Max. 150 PSI - 210°F									
1020 Bronze body									
1030 1/2" size	1 Stpi	24	.333	Ea.	187	14.45		201.45	230
1040 3/4" size		20	.400		187	17.30		204.30	235
1050 1" size		19	.421		194	18.25		212.25	243
1060 1-1/4" size		15	.533		380	23		403	460
1070 1-1/2" size		13	.615		470	26.50		496.50	560
1080 2" size		11	.727		485	31.50		516.50	580
1200 Max. 125 PSI with atmospheric vent									
1210 Brass, in-line construction									

22 11 19.50 Vacuum Breakers		Crew	Daily Output	Labor-Hours	Unit	Material	2014 Bare Costs Labor	Equipment	Total	Total Incl O&P
1220	1/4" size	1 Stpi	24	.333	Ea.	117	14.45		131.45	153
1230	3/8" size	"	24	.333		117	14.45		131.45	153
1260	For polished chrome finish, add					13%				
2000	Anti-siphon, non-continuous pressure type									
2010	Hot or cold water 125 PSI - 210°F									
2020	Bronze body									
2030	1/4" size	1 Stpi	24	.333	Ea.	64	14.45		78.45	94.50
2040	3/8" size		24	.333		64	14.45		78.45	94.50
2050	1/2" size		24	.333		72.50	14.45		86.95	104
2060	3/4" size		20	.400		86.50	17.30		103.80	124
2070	1" size		19	.421		134	18.25		152.25	177
2080	1-1/4" size		15	.533		235	23		258	296
2090	1-1/2" size		13	.615		276	26.50		302.50	350
2100	2" size		11	.727		430	31.50		461.50	520
2110	2-1/2" size		8	1		1,225	43.50		1,268.50	1,425
2120	3" size		6	1.333		1,625	57.50		1,682.50	1,900
2150	For polished chrome finish, add					50%				

22 11 19.54 Water Hammer Arresters/Shock Absorbers										
0010	**WATER HAMMER ARRESTERS/SHOCK ABSORBERS**									
0490	Copper									
0500	3/4" male I.P.S. For 1 to 11 fixtures	1 Plum	12	.667	Ea.	28	28.50		56.50	78
0600	1" male I.P.S. For 12 to 32 fixtures		8	1		45.50	42.50		88	121
0700	1-1/4" male I.P.S. For 33 to 60 fixtures		8	1		47	42.50		89.50	122
0800	1-1/2" male I.P.S. For 61 to 113 fixtures		8	1		67.50	42.50		110	145
0900	2" male I.P.S. For 114 to 154 fixtures		8	1		98.50	42.50		141	179
1000	2-1/2" male I.P.S. For 155 to 330 fixtures		4	2		305	85		390	475

22 11 19.64 Hydrants										
0010	**HYDRANTS**									
0050	Wall type, moderate climate, bronze, encased									
0200	3/4" IPS connection	1 Plum	16	.500	Ea.	705	21.50		726.50	815
0300	1" IPS connection		14	.571		810	24.50		834.50	930
0500	Anti-siphon type, 3/4" connection		16	.500		610	21.50		631.50	705
1000	Non-freeze, bronze, exposed									
1100	3/4" IPS connection, 4" to 9" thick wall	1 Plum	14	.571	Ea.	480	24.50		504.50	565
1120	10" to 14" thick wall		12	.667		515	28.50		543.50	615
1140	15" to 19" thick wall		12	.667		580	28.50		608.50	680
1160	20" to 24" thick wall		10	.800		625	34		659	745
1200	For 1" IPS connection, add					15%	10%			
1240	For 3/4" adapter type vacuum breaker, add				Ea.	60			60	66
1280	For anti-siphon type, add				"	126			126	139
2000	Non-freeze bronze, encased, anti-siphon type									
2100	3/4" IPS connection, 5" to 9" thick wall	1 Plum	14	.571	Ea.	1,225	24.50		1,249.50	1,375
2120	10" to 14" thick wall		12	.667		1,250	28.50		1,278.50	1,425
2140	15" to 19" thick wall		12	.667		1,300	28.50		1,328.50	1,500
3000	Ground box type, bronze frame, 3/4" IPS connection									
3080	Non-freeze, all bronze, polished face, set flush									
3100	2 feet depth of bury	1 Plum	8	1	Ea.	905	42.50		947.50	1,075
3140	4 feet depth of bury		8	1		1,050	42.50		1,092.50	1,225
3180	6 feet depth of bury		7	1.143		1,175	48.50		1,223.50	1,375
3220	8 feet depth of bury		5	1.600		1,325	68		1,393	1,550
3400	For 1" IPS connection, add					15%	10%			
3550	For 2" connection, add					445%	24%			

22 11 Facility Water Distribution

22 11 19 – Domestic Water Piping Specialties

22 11 19.64 Hydrants

		Crew	Daily Output	Labor-Hours	Unit	Material	2014 Bare Costs Labor	Equipment	Total	Total Incl O&P
3600	For tapped drain port in box, add				Ea.	82			82	90
5000	Moderate climate, all bronze, polished face									
5020	and scoriated cover, set flush									
5100	3/4" IPS connection	1 Plum	16	.500	Ea.	625	21.50		646.50	725
5120	1" IPS connection	"	14	.571		770	24.50		794.50	885
5200	For tapped drain port in box, add					82			82	90

22 11 23 – Domestic Water Pumps

22 11 23.10 General Utility Pumps

		Crew	Daily Output	Labor-Hours	Unit	Material	2014 Bare Costs Labor	Equipment	Total	Total Incl O&P
0010	**GENERAL UTILITY PUMPS**									
2000	Single stage									
3000	Double suction,									
3190	75 HP, to 2500 GPM	Q-3	.28	114	Ea.	20,100	4,375		24,475	29,300
3220	100 HP, to 3000 GPM		.26	123		25,500	4,725		30,225	35,900
3240	150 HP, to 4000 GPM		.24	133		36,000	5,125		41,125	48,000

22 13 Facility Sanitary Sewerage

22 13 16 – Sanitary Waste and Vent Piping

22 13 16.20 Pipe, Cast Iron

		Crew	Daily Output	Labor-Hours	Unit	Material	2014 Bare Costs Labor	Equipment	Total	Total Incl O&P
0010	**PIPE, CAST IRON,** Soil, on clevis hanger assemblies, 5' O.C.									
0020	Single hub, service wt., lead & oakum joints 10' O.C.									
2120	2" diameter	Q-1	63	.254	L.F.	9.30	9.75		19.05	26.50
2140	3" diameter		60	.267		12.95	10.25		23.20	31
2160	4" diameter		55	.291		16.85	11.15		28	37
2180	5" diameter	Q-2	76	.316		23	11.65		34.65	45
2200	6" diameter	"	73	.329		29	12.15		41.15	52
2220	8" diameter	Q-3	59	.542		44	21		65	83
2240	10" diameter		54	.593		71	22.50		93.50	116
2260	12" diameter		48	.667		101	25.50		126.50	153
2320	For service weight, double hub, add					10%				
2340	For extra heavy, single hub, add					48%	4%			
2360	For extra heavy, double hub, add					71%	4%			
2400	Lead for caulking, (1#/diam. in.)	Q-1	160	.100	Lb.	1.04	3.84		4.88	7.50
2420	Oakum for caulking, (1/8#/diam. in.)	"	40	.400	"	4.80	15.35		20.15	31
4000	No hub, couplings 10' O.C.									
4100	1-1/2" diameter	Q-1	71	.225	L.F.	9.15	8.65		17.80	24.50
4120	2" diameter		67	.239		9.40	9.15		18.55	25.50
4140	3" diameter		64	.250		13.35	9.60		22.95	30.50
4160	4" diameter		58	.276		16.95	10.60		27.55	36

22 13 16.50 Shower Drains

		Crew	Daily Output	Labor-Hours	Unit	Material	2014 Bare Costs Labor	Equipment	Total	Total Incl O&P
0010	**SHOWER DRAINS**									
2780	Shower, with strainer, uniform diam. trap, bronze top									
2800	2" and 3" pipe size	Q-1	8	2	Ea.	395	76.50		471.50	560
2820	4" pipe size	"	7	2.286		435	87.50		522.50	620
2840	For galvanized body, add					175			175	193

22 13 16.60 Traps

		Crew	Daily Output	Labor-Hours	Unit	Material	2014 Bare Costs Labor	Equipment	Total	Total Incl O&P
0010	**TRAPS**									
0030	Cast iron, service weight									
0050	Running P trap, without vent									
1100	2"	Q-1	16	1	Ea.	164	38.50		202.50	244
1140	3"		14	1.143		164	44		208	253

22 13 16 – Sanitary Waste and Vent Piping

22 13 16.60 Traps

		Crew	Daily Output	Labor-Hours	Unit	Material	2014 Bare Costs Labor	Equipment	Total	Total Incl O&P
1150	4"	Q-1	13	1.231	Ea.	164	47		211	258
1160	6"	Q-2	17	1.412	↓	605	52		657	750
1180	Running trap, single hub, with vent									
2080	3" pipe size, 3" vent	Q-1	14	1.143	Ea.	109	44		153	193
2120	4" pipe size, 4" vent	"	13	1.231	↓	149	47		196	242
2300	For double hub, vent, add					10%	20%			
3000	P trap, B&S, 2" pipe size	Q-1	16	1		32.50	38.50		71	99.50
3040	3" pipe size	"	14	1.143	↓	49	44		93	126
3350	Deep seal trap, B&S									
3400	1-1/4" pipe size	Q-1	14	1.143	Ea.	51	44		95	129
3410	1-1/2" pipe size		14	1.143		51	44		95	129
3420	2" pipe size		14	1.143		46	44		90	123
3440	3" pipe size	↓	12	1.333	↓	60	51		111	151
4700	Copper, drainage, drum trap									
4800	3" x 5" solid, 1-1/2 pipe size	1 Plum	16	.500	Ea.	286	21.50		307.50	350
4840	3" x 6" swivel, 1-1/2 pipe size	"	16	.500	"	455	21.50		476.50	535
5100	P trap, standard pattern									
5200	1-1/4" pipe size	1 Plum	18	.444	Ea.	211	18.95		229.95	263
5240	1-1/2" pipe size		17	.471		204	20		224	258
5260	2" pipe size		15	.533		315	22.50		337.50	385
5280	3" pipe size	↓	11	.727	↓	760	31		791	885
5340	With cleanout, swivel joint and slip joint									
5360	1-1/4" pipe size	1 Plum	18	.444	Ea.	148	18.95		166.95	194
5400	1-1/2" pipe size	"	17	.471	"	310	20		330	375

22 13 16.80 Vent Flashing and Caps

		Crew	Daily Output	Labor-Hours	Unit	Material	2014 Bare Costs Labor	Equipment	Total	Total Incl O&P
0010	**VENT FLASHING AND CAPS**									
0120	Vent caps									
0140	Cast iron									
0180	2-1/2" - 3-5/8" pipe	1 Plum	21	.381	Ea.	45	16.25		61.25	76.50
0190	4" - 4-1/8" pipe	"	19	.421	"	55	17.95		72.95	90
0900	Vent flashing									
1000	Aluminum with lead ring									
1020	1-1/4" pipe	1 Plum	20	.400	Ea.	11.80	17.05		28.85	41
1030	1-1/2" pipe		20	.400		14.15	17.05		31.20	43.50
1040	2" pipe		18	.444		12.70	18.95		31.65	45
1050	3" pipe		17	.471		14.05	20		34.05	48.50
1060	4" pipe	↓	16	.500	↓	16.95	21.50		38.45	53.50
1350	Copper with neoprene ring									
1400	1-1/4" pipe	1 Plum	20	.400	Ea.	20.50	17.05		37.55	50.50
1430	1-1/2" pipe		20	.400		20.50	17.05		37.55	50.50
1440	2" pipe		18	.444		21.50	18.95		40.45	54.50
1450	3" pipe		17	.471		25.50	20		45.50	61
1460	4" pipe	↓	16	.500		28	21.50		49.50	65.50

22 13 19 – Sanitary Waste Piping Specialties

22 13 19.13 Sanitary Drains

		Crew	Daily Output	Labor-Hours	Unit	Material	2014 Bare Costs Labor	Equipment	Total	Total Incl O&P
0010	**SANITARY DRAINS**									
0400	Deck, auto park, C.I., 13" top									
0440	3", 4", 5", and 6" pipe size	Q-1	8	2	Ea.	1,325	76.50		1,401.50	1,600
0480	For galvanized body, add				"	720			720	790
2000	Floor, medium duty, C.I., deep flange, 7" diam. top									
2040	2" and 3" pipe size	Q-1	12	1.333	Ea.	186	51		237	290
2080	For galvanized body, add				↓	89.50			89.50	98.50

22 13 Facility Sanitary Sewerage

22 13 19 – Sanitary Waste Piping Specialties

22 13 19.13 Sanitary Drains

		Crew	Daily Output	Labor-Hours	Unit	Material	2014 Bare Costs Labor	Equipment	Total	Total Incl O&P
2120	With polished bronze top				Ea.	291			291	320
2400	Heavy duty, with sediment bucket, C.I., 12" diam. loose grate									
2420	2", 3", 4", 5", and 6" pipe size	Q-1	9	1.778	Ea.	640	68		708	820
2460	With polished bronze top				"	905			905	995
2500	Heavy duty, cleanout & trap w/bucket, C.I., 15" top									
2540	2", 3", and 4" pipe size	Q-1	6	2.667	Ea.	6,075	102		6,177	6,875
2560	For galvanized body, add					1,550			1,550	1,725
2580	With polished bronze top					6,575			6,575	7,250

22 13 23 – Sanitary Waste Interceptors

22 13 23.10 Interceptors

		Crew	Daily Output	Labor-Hours	Unit	Material	2014 Bare Costs Labor	Equipment	Total	Total Incl O&P
0010	**INTERCEPTORS**									
0150	Grease, fabricated steel, 4 GPM, 8 lb. fat capacity	1 Plum	4	2	Ea.	1,100	85		1,185	1,350
0200	7 GPM, 14 lb. fat capacity		4	2		1,525	85		1,610	1,825
1000	10 GPM, 20 lb. fat capacity		4	2		1,800	85		1,885	2,125
1040	15 GPM, 30 lb. fat capacity		4	2		2,650	85		2,735	3,075
1060	20 GPM, 40 lb. fat capacity		3	2.667		3,250	114		3,364	3,750
1160	100 GPM, 200 lb. fat capacity	Q-1	2	8		13,600	305		13,905	15,400
1580	For seepage pan, add					7%				
3000	Hair, cast iron, 1-1/4" and 1-1/2" pipe connection	1 Plum	8	1	Ea.	415	42.50		457.50	525
3100	For chrome-plated cast iron, add					253			253	279
4000	Oil, fabricated steel, 10 GPM, 2" pipe size	1 Plum	4	2		2,450	85		2,535	2,850
4100	15 GPM, 2" or 3" pipe size		4	2		3,375	85		3,460	3,850
4120	20 GPM, 2" or 3" pipe size		3	2.667		4,075	114		4,189	4,650
4220	100 GPM, 3" pipe size	Q-1	2	8		13,600	305		13,905	15,400
6000	Solids, precious metals recovery, C.I., 1-1/4" to 2" pipe	1 Plum	4	2		620	85		705	825
6100	Dental Lab., large, C.I., 1-1/2" to 2" pipe	"	3	2.667		2,175	114		2,289	2,575

22 13 29 – Sanitary Sewerage Pumps

22 13 29.13 Wet-Pit-Mounted, Vertical Sewerage Pumps

		Crew	Daily Output	Labor-Hours	Unit	Material	2014 Bare Costs Labor	Equipment	Total	Total Incl O&P
0010	**WET-PIT-MOUNTED, VERTICAL SEWERAGE PUMPS**									
0020	Controls incl. alarm/disconnect panel w/wire. Excavation not included									
0260	Simplex, 9 GPM at 60 PSIG, 91 gal. tank				Ea.	3,325			3,325	3,650
0300	Unit with manway, 26" I.D., 18" high					3,700			3,700	4,050
0340	26" I.D., 36" high					3,750			3,750	4,125
0380	43" I.D., 4' high					3,975			3,975	4,375
3000	Indoor residential type installation									
3020	Simplex, 9 GPM at 60 PSIG, 91 gal. HDPE tank				Ea.	3,350			3,350	3,675

22 13 29.14 Sewage Ejector Pumps

		Crew	Daily Output	Labor-Hours	Unit	Material	2014 Bare Costs Labor	Equipment	Total	Total Incl O&P
0010	**SEWAGE EJECTOR PUMPS**, With operating and level controls									
0100	Simplex system incl. tank, cover, pump 15' head									
0500	37 gal. PE tank, 12 GPM, 1/2 HP, 2" discharge	Q-1	3.20	5	Ea.	480	192		672	840
0510	3" discharge		3.10	5.161		520	198		718	895
0530	87 GPM, .7 HP, 2" discharge		3.20	5		735	192		927	1,125
0540	3" discharge		3.10	5.161		795	198		993	1,200
0600	45 gal. coated stl. tank, 12 GPM, 1/2 HP, 2" discharge		3	5.333		855	205		1,060	1,275
0610	3" discharge		2.90	5.517		890	212		1,102	1,325
0630	87 GPM, .7 HP, 2" discharge		3	5.333		1,100	205		1,305	1,525
0640	3" discharge		2.90	5.517		1,150	212		1,362	1,625
0660	134 GPM, 1 HP, 2" discharge		2.80	5.714		1,175	219		1,394	1,650
0680	3" discharge		2.70	5.926		1,250	227		1,477	1,750
0700	70 gal. PE tank, 12 GPM, 1/2 HP, 2" discharge		2.60	6.154		920	236		1,156	1,425
0710	3" discharge		2.40	6.667		980	256		1,236	1,500

22 13 Facility Sanitary Sewerage

22 13 29 – Sanitary Sewerage Pumps

22 13 29.14 Sewage Ejector Pumps

		Crew	Daily Output	Labor-Hours	Unit	Material	2014 Bare Costs Labor	Equipment	Total	Total Incl O&P
0730	87 GPM, 0.7 HP, 2" discharge	Q-1	2.50	6.400	Ea.	1,200	245		1,445	1,700
0740	3" discharge		2.30	6.957		1,275	267		1,542	1,850
0760	134 GPM, 1 HP, 2" discharge		2.20	7.273		1,300	279		1,579	1,875
0770	3" discharge		2	8		1,375	305		1,680	2,025

22 14 Facility Storm Drainage

22 14 23 – Storm Drainage Piping Specialties

22 14 23.33 Backwater Valves

		Crew	Daily Output	Labor-Hours	Unit	Material	2014 Bare Costs Labor	Equipment	Total	Total Incl O&P
0010	**BACKWATER VALVES**, C.I. Body									
6980	Bronze gate and automatic flapper valves									
7000	3" and 4" pipe size	Q-1	13	1.231	Ea.	1,900	47		1,947	2,150
7100	5" and 6" pipe size	"	13	1.231	"	2,900	47		2,947	3,275
7240	Bronze flapper valve, bolted cover									
7260	2" pipe size	Q-1	16	1	Ea.	555	38.50		593.50	675
7300	4" pipe size	"	13	1.231		1,075	47		1,122	1,250
7340	6" pipe size	Q-2	17	1.412		1,525	52		1,577	1,750

22 14 26 – Facility Storm Drains

22 14 26.13 Roof Drains

		Crew	Daily Output	Labor-Hours	Unit	Material	2014 Bare Costs Labor	Equipment	Total	Total Incl O&P
0010	**ROOF DRAINS**									
0140	Cornice, C.I., 45° or 90° outlet									
0200	3" and 4" pipe size	Q-1	12	1.333	Ea.	360	51		411	480
0260	For galvanized body, add					70			70	77
0280	For polished bronze dome, add					87.50			87.50	96.50
3860	Roof, flat metal deck, C.I. body, 12" C.I. dome									
3890	3" pipe size	Q-1	14	1.143	Ea.	365	44		409	475
3920	6" pipe size	"	10	1.600	"	635	61.50		696.50	800
4620	Main, all aluminum, 12" low profile dome									
4640	2", 3" and 4" pipe size	Q-1	14	1.143	Ea.	405	44		449	520

22 14 26.16 Facility Area Drains

		Crew	Daily Output	Labor-Hours	Unit	Material	2014 Bare Costs Labor	Equipment	Total	Total Incl O&P
0010	**FACILITY AREA DRAINS**									
4980	Scupper floor, oblique strainer, C.I.									
5000	6" x 7" top, 2", 3" and 4" pipe size	Q-1	16	1	Ea.	262	38.50		300.50	350
5100	8" x 12" top, 5" and 6" pipe size	"	14	1.143		510	44		554	635
5160	For galvanized body, add					40%				
5200	For polished bronze strainer, add					85%				

22 14 26.19 Facility Trench Drains

		Crew	Daily Output	Labor-Hours	Unit	Material	2014 Bare Costs Labor	Equipment	Total	Total Incl O&P
0010	**FACILITY TRENCH DRAINS**									
5980	Trench, floor, heavy duty, modular, C.I., 12" x 12" top									
6000	2", 3", 4", 5", & 6" pipe size	Q-1	8	2	Ea.	830	76.50		906.50	1,050
6100	For unit with polished bronze top	"	8	2	"	1,250	76.50		1,326.50	1,475
6600	Trench, floor, for cement concrete encasement									
6610	Not including trenching or concrete									
6640	Polyester polymer concrete									
6650	4" internal width, with grate									
6660	Light duty steel grate	Q-1	120	.133	L.F.	34	5.10		39.10	46
6670	Medium duty steel grate		115	.139		39	5.35		44.35	52
6680	Heavy duty iron grate		110	.145		60	5.60		65.60	75
6700	12" internal width, with grate									
6770	Heavy duty galvanized grate	Q-1	80	.200	L.F.	164	7.65		171.65	193
6800	Fiberglass									

22 14 Facility Storm Drainage

22 14 26 – Facility Storm Drains

22 14 26.19 Facility Trench Drains	Crew	Daily Output	Labor-Hours	Unit	Material	2014 Bare Costs Labor	Equipment	Total	Total Incl O&P
6810	8" internal width, with grate									
6820	Medium duty galvanized grate	Q-1	115	.139	L.F.	96.50	5.35		101.85	115
6830	Heavy duty iron grate	"	110	.145	"	102	5.60		107.60	122

22 14 29 – Sump Pumps

22 14 29.13 Wet-Pit-Mounted, Vertical Sump Pumps

		Crew	Daily Output	Labor-Hours	Unit	Material	Labor	Equipment	Total	Total Incl O&P
0010	**WET-PIT-MOUNTED, VERTICAL SUMP PUMPS**									
0400	Molded PVC base, 21 GPM at 15' head, 1/3 HP	1 Plum	5	1.600	Ea.	135	68		203	261
0800	Iron base, 21 GPM at 15' head, 1/3 HP		5	1.600		164	68		232	292
1200	Solid brass, 21 GPM at 15' head, 1/3 HP		5	1.600		289	68		357	430
2000	Sump pump, single stage									
2010	25 GPM, 1 HP, 1-1/2" discharge	Q-1	1.80	8.889	Ea.	3,625	340		3,965	4,525
2020	75 GPM, 1-1/2 HP, 2" discharge		1.50	10.667		3,825	410		4,235	4,875
2030	100 GPM, 2 HP, 2-1/2" discharge		1.30	12.308		3,900	470		4,370	5,050
2040	150 GPM, 3 HP, 3" discharge		1.10	14.545		3,900	560		4,460	5,200
2050	200 GPM, 3 HP, 3" discharge		1	16		4,125	615		4,740	5,550
2060	300 GPM, 10 HP, 4" discharge	Q-2	1.20	20		4,450	740		5,190	6,125
2070	500 GPM, 15 HP, 5" discharge		1.10	21.818		5,075	805		5,880	6,900
2080	800 GPM, 20 HP, 6" discharge		1	24		6,000	885		6,885	8,050
2090	1000 GPM, 30 HP, 6" discharge		.85	28.235		6,575	1,050		7,625	8,975
2100	1600 GPM, 50 HP, 8" discharge		.72	33.333		10,300	1,225		11,525	13,300
2110	2000 GPM, 60 HP, 8" discharge	Q-3	.85	37.647		10,500	1,450		11,950	14,000
2202	For general purpose float switch, copper coated float, add	Q-1	5	3.200		108	123		231	320

22 14 29.16 Submersible Sump Pumps

		Crew	Daily Output	Labor-Hours	Unit	Material	Labor	Equipment	Total	Total Incl O&P
0010	**SUBMERSIBLE SUMP PUMPS**									
7000	Sump pump, automatic									
7100	Plastic, 1-1/4" discharge, 1/4 HP	1 Plum	6	1.333	Ea.	134	57		191	241
7140	1/3 HP		5	1.600		194	68		262	325
7160	1/2 HP		5	1.600		238	68		306	375
7180	1-1/2" discharge, 1/2 HP		4	2		272	85		357	440
7500	Cast iron, 1-1/4" discharge, 1/4 HP		6	1.333		189	57		246	300
7540	1/3 HP		6	1.333		222	57		279	340
7560	1/2 HP		5	1.600		269	68		337	405

22 31 Domestic Water Softeners

22 31 13 – Residential Domestic Water Softeners

22 31 13.10 Residential Water Softeners

		Crew	Daily Output	Labor-Hours	Unit	Material	Labor	Equipment	Total	Total Incl O&P
0010	**RESIDENTIAL WATER SOFTENERS**									
7350	Water softener, automatic, to 30 grains per gallon	2 Plum	5	3.200	Ea.	400	136		536	665
7400	To 100 grains per gallon	"	4	4	"	650	170		820	995

22 31 16 – Commercial Domestic Water Softeners

22 31 16.10 Water Softeners

		Crew	Daily Output	Labor-Hours	Unit	Material	Labor	Equipment	Total	Total Incl O&P
0010	**WATER SOFTENERS**									
5800	Softener systems, automatic, intermediate sizes									
5820	available, may be used in multiples.									
6000	Hardness capacity between regenerations and flow									
6100	150,000 grains, 37 GPM cont., 51 GPM peak	Q-1	1.20	13.333	Ea.	5,300	510		5,810	6,700
6200	300,000 grains, 81 GPM cont., 113 GPM peak		1	16		9,375	615		9,990	11,300
6300	750,000 grains, 160 GPM cont., 230 GPM peak		.80	20		12,200	765		12,965	14,700
6400	900,000 grains, 185 GPM cont., 270 GPM peak		.70	22.857		19,700	875		20,575	23,100

22 33 Electric Domestic Water Heaters

22 33 13 – Instantaneous Electric Domestic Water Heaters

22 33 13.10 Hot Water Dispensers

		Crew	Daily Output	Labor-Hours	Unit	Material	2014 Bare Costs Labor	Equipment	Total	Total Incl O&P
0010	**HOT WATER DISPENSERS**									
0160	Commercial, 100 cup, 11.3 amp	1 Plum	14	.571	Ea.	510	24.50		534.50	605
3180	Household, 60 cup	"	14	.571	"	269	24.50		293.50	335

22 33 30 – Residential, Electric Domestic Water Heaters

22 33 30.13 Residential, Small-Capacity Elec. Water Heaters

		Crew	Daily Output	Labor-Hours	Unit	Material	Labor	Equipment	Total	Total Incl O&P
0010	**RESIDENTIAL, SMALL-CAPACITY ELECTRIC DOMESTIC WATER HEATERS**									
1000	Residential, electric, glass lined tank, 5 yr., 10 gal., single element	1 Plum	2.30	3.478	Ea.	330	148		478	605
1040	20 gallon, single element		2.20	3.636		410	155		565	705
1060	30 gallon, double element		2.20	3.636		475	155		630	780
1080	40 gallon, double element		2	4		800	170		970	1,150
1100	52 gallon, double element		2	4		895	170		1,065	1,275
1180	120 gallon, double element		1.40	5.714		1,900	243		2,143	2,475

22 33 33 – Light-Commercial Electric Domestic Water Heaters

22 33 33.10 Commercial Electric Water Heaters

		Crew	Daily Output	Labor-Hours	Unit	Material	Labor	Equipment	Total	Total Incl O&P
0010	**COMMERCIAL ELECTRIC WATER HEATERS**									
4000	Commercial, 100° rise. NOTE: for each size tank, a range of									
4010	heaters between the ones shown are available									
4020	Electric									
4100	5 gal., 3 kW, 12 GPH, 208 volt	1 Plum	2	4	Ea.	2,750	170		2,920	3,300
4120	10 gal., 6 kW, 25 GPH, 208 volt		2	4		3,050	170		3,220	3,625
4130	30 gal., 24 kW, 98 GPH, 208 volt		1.92	4.167		4,725	178		4,903	5,500
4136	40 gal., 36 kW, 148 GPH, 208 volt		1.88	4.255		5,650	181		5,831	6,525
4140	50 gal., 9 kW, 37 GPH, 208 volt		1.80	4.444		4,175	189		4,364	4,900
4160	50 gal., 36 kW, 148 GPH, 208 volt		1.80	4.444		6,400	189		6,589	7,325
4300	200 gal., 15 kW, 61 GPH, 480 volt	Q-1	1.70	9.412		19,700	360		20,060	22,300
4320	200 gal., 120 kW , 490 GPH, 480 volt		1.70	9.412		26,900	360		27,260	30,200
4460	400 gal., 30 kW, 123 GPH, 480 volt		1	16		26,800	615		27,415	30,500
5400	Modulating step control for under 90 kW, 2-5 steps	1 Elec	5.30	1.509		810	64.50		874.50	995
5440	1 through 5 steps beyond standard		3.20	2.500		221	107		328	420
5460	6 through 10 steps beyond standard		2.70	2.963		455	127		582	705
5480	11 through 18 steps beyond standard		1.60	5		680	214		894	1,100

22 34 Fuel-Fired Domestic Water Heaters

22 34 13 – Instantaneous, Tankless, Gas Domestic Water Heaters

22 34 13.10 Instantaneous, Tankless, Gas Water Heaters

			Crew	Daily Output	Labor-Hours	Unit	Material	Labor	Equipment	Total	Total Incl O&P
0010	**INSTANTANEOUS, TANKLESS, GAS WATER HEATERS**										
9410	Natural gas/propane, 3.2 GPM	G	1 Plum	2	4	Ea.	365	170		535	680
9420	6.4 GPM	G		1.90	4.211		745	179		924	1,125
9430	8.4 GPM	G		1.80	4.444		890	189		1,079	1,300
9440	9.5 GPM	G		1.60	5		1,150	213		1,363	1,600

22 34 30 – Residential Gas Domestic Water Heaters

22 34 30.13 Residential, Atmos, Gas Domestic Wtr Heaters

		Crew	Daily Output	Labor-Hours	Unit	Material	Labor	Equipment	Total	Total Incl O&P
0010	**RESIDENTIAL, ATMOSPHERIC, GAS DOMESTIC WATER HEATERS**									
2000	Gas fired, foam lined tank, 10 yr., vent not incl.									
2040	30 gallon	1 Plum	2	4	Ea.	895	170		1,065	1,275
2100	75 gallon		1.50	5.333		1,350	227		1,577	1,875
2120	100 gallon		1.30	6.154		1,525	262		1,787	2,100

22 34 Fuel-Fired Domestic Water Heaters

22 34 36 – Commercial Gas Domestic Water Heaters

22 34 36.13 Commercial, Atmos., Gas Domestic Water Htrs.

		Crew	Daily Output	Labor-Hours	Unit	Material	2014 Bare Costs Labor	Equipment	Total	Total Incl O&P
0010	**COMMERCIAL, ATMOSPHERIC, GAS DOMESTIC WATER HEATERS**									
6000	Gas fired, flush jacket, std. controls, vent not incl.									
6040	75 MBH input, 73 GPH	1 Plum	1.40	5.714	Ea.	3,500	243		3,743	4,250
6060	98 MBH input, 95 GPH		1.40	5.714		5,300	243		5,543	6,225
6080	120 MBH input, 110 GPH		1.20	6.667		5,500	284		5,784	6,500
6180	200 MBH input, 192 GPH		.60	13.333		8,925	570		9,495	10,800
6200	250 MBH input, 245 GPH		.50	16		9,325	680		10,005	11,400
6900	For low water cutoff, add		8	1		340	42.50		382.50	440
6960	For bronze body hot water circulator, add	↓	4	2	↓	1,925	85		2,010	2,275

22 34 46 – Oil-Fired Domestic Water Heaters

22 34 46.10 Residential Oil-Fired Water Heaters

		Crew	Daily Output	Labor-Hours	Unit	Material	Labor	Equipment	Total	Total Incl O&P
0010	**RESIDENTIAL OIL-FIRED WATER HEATERS**									
3000	Oil fired, glass lined tank, 5 yr., vent not included, 30 gallon	1 Plum	2	4	Ea.	1,175	170		1,345	1,550
3040	50 gallon		1.80	4.444		1,375	189		1,564	1,825
3060	70 gallon	↓	1.50	5.333	↓	1,975	227		2,202	2,550

22 34 46.20 Commercial Oil-Fired Water Heaters

		Crew	Daily Output	Labor-Hours	Unit	Material	Labor	Equipment	Total	Total Incl O&P
0010	**COMMERCIAL OIL-FIRED WATER HEATERS**									
8000	Oil fired, glass lined, UL listed, std. controls, vent not incl.									
8060	140 gal., 140 MBH input, 134 GPH	Q-1	2.13	7.512	Ea.	19,900	288		20,188	22,400
8080	140 gal., 199 MBH input, 191 GPH		2	8		20,600	305		20,905	23,200
8100	140 gal., 255 MBH input, 247 GPH		1.60	10		21,200	385		21,585	23,900
8160	140 gal., 540 MBH input, 519 GPH		.96	16.667		28,100	640		28,740	32,000
8180	140 gal., 720 MBH input, 691 GPH	↓	.92	17.391		28,600	665		29,265	32,600
8280	201 gal., 1250 MBH input, 1200 GPH	Q-2	1.22	19.672		43,900	725		44,625	49,500
8300	201 gal., 1500 MBH input, 1441 GPH	"	1.16	20.690		47,800	765		48,565	54,000
8900	For low water cutoff, add	1 Plum	8	1		325	42.50		367.50	430
8960	For bronze body hot water circulator, add	"	4	2	↓	710	85		795	920

22 35 Domestic Water Heat Exchangers

22 35 30 – Water Heating by Steam

22 35 30.10 Water Heating Transfer Package

		Crew	Daily Output	Labor-Hours	Unit	Material	Labor	Equipment	Total	Total Incl O&P
0010	**WATER HEATING TRANSFER PACKAGE**, Complete controls,									
0020	expansion tank, converter, air separator									
1000	Hot water, 180°F enter, 200°F leaving, 15# steam									
1010	One pump system, 28 GPM	Q-6	.75	32	Ea.	19,500	1,200		20,700	23,500
1020	35 GPM		.70	34.286		21,200	1,275		22,475	25,400
1040	55 GPM		.65	36.923		25,100	1,375		26,475	29,900
1060	130 GPM		.55	43.636		31,700	1,650		33,350	37,500
1080	255 GPM		.40	60		41,800	2,250		44,050	49,600
1100	550 GPM	↓	.30	80	↓	53,000	3,000		56,000	63,000

22 41 06 – Plumbing Fixtures General

22 41 06.10 Plumbing Fixture Notes	Crew	Daily Output	Labor-Hours	Unit	Material	2014 Bare Costs Labor	Equipment	Total	Total Incl O&P
0010 **PLUMBING FIXTURE NOTES**, Incl. trim fittings unless otherwise noted R224000-40									
0080 For rough-in, supply, waste, and vent, see add for each type									
0122 For electric water coolers, see Section 22 47 16.10									
0160 For color, unless otherwise noted, add				Ea.	20%				

22 41 13 – Residential Water Closets, Urinals, and Bidets

22 41 13.40 Water Closets

	Crew	Daily Output	Labor-Hours	Unit	Material	Labor	Equipment	Total	Total Incl O&P
0010 **WATER CLOSETS** R224000-40									
0032 For automatic flush, see Line 22 42 39.10 0972									
0150 Tank type, vitreous china, incl. seat, supply pipe w/stop, 1.6 gpf or noted									
0200 Wall hung									
0400 Two piece, close coupled	Q-1	5.30	3.019	Ea.	630	116		746	880
0960 For rough-in, supply, waste, vent and carrier	"	2.73	5.861	"	810	225		1,035	1,250
0999 Floor mounted									
1100 Two piece, close coupled	Q-1	5.30	3.019	Ea.	233	116		349	445
1102 Economy		5.30	3.019		130	116		246	335
1110 Two piece, close coupled, dual flush		5.30	3.019		299	116		415	520
1140 Two piece, close coupled, 1.28 gpf, ADA [G]		5.30	3.019		305	116		421	525
1960 For color, add					30%				
1980 For rough-in, supply, waste and vent	Q-1	3.05	5.246	Ea.	330	201		531	695

22 41 16 – Residential Lavatories and Sinks

22 41 16.10 Lavatories

	Crew	Daily Output	Labor-Hours	Unit	Material	Labor	Equipment	Total	Total Incl O&P
0010 **LAVATORIES**, With trim, white unless noted otherwise R224000-40									
0500 Vanity top, porcelain enamel on cast iron									
0600 20" x 18"	Q-1	6.40	2.500	Ea.	330	96		426	520
0640 33" x 19" oval		6.40	2.500		690	96		786	920
0720 19" round		6.40	2.500		425	96		521	630
0860 For color, add					25%				
1000 Cultured marble, 19" x 17", single bowl	Q-1	6.40	2.500	Ea.	175	96		271	350
1040 25" x 19", single bowl	"	6.40	2.500	"	206	96		302	385
1580 For color, same price									
1900 Stainless steel, self-rimming, 25" x 22", single bowl, ledge	Q-1	6.40	2.500	Ea.	365	96		461	565
1960 17" x 22", single bowl		6.40	2.500		355	96		451	550
2600 Steel, enameled, 20" x 17", single bowl		5.80	2.759		197	106		303	390
2660 19" round		5.80	2.759		171	106		277	365
2900 Vitreous china, 20" x 16", single bowl		5.40	2.963		260	114		374	475
2960 20" x 17", single bowl		5.40	2.963		176	114		290	380
3020 19" round, single bowl		5.40	2.963		174	114		288	380
3200 22" x 13", single bowl		5.40	2.963		267	114		381	480
3560 For color, add					50%				
3580 Rough-in, supply, waste and vent for all above lavatories	Q-1	2.30	6.957	Ea.	415	267		682	895
4000 Wall hung									
4040 Porcelain enamel on cast iron, 16" x 14", single bowl	Q-1	8	2	Ea.	510	76.50		586.50	685
4180 20" x 18", single bowl		8	2		277	76.50		353.50	430
4240 22" x 19", single bowl		8	2		685	76.50		761.50	880
4580 For color, add					30%				
6000 Vitreous china, 18" x 15", single bowl with backsplash	Q-1	7	2.286	Ea.	231	87.50		318.50	400
6500 For color, add					30%				
6960 Rough-in, supply, waste and vent for above lavatories	Q-1	1.66	9.639	Ea.	470	370		840	1,125
7000 Pedestal type									
7600 Vitreous china, 27" x 21", white	Q-1	6.60	2.424	Ea.	690	93		783	915
7610 27" x 21", colored		6.60	2.424		865	93		958	1,100
7620 27" x 21", premium color		6.60	2.424		970	93		1,063	1,225

22 41 16 – Residential Lavatories and Sinks

22 41 16.10 Lavatories

		Crew	Daily Output	Labor-Hours	Unit	Material	2014 Bare Costs Labor	Equipment	Total	Total Incl O&P
7660	26" x 20", white	Q-1	6.60	2.424	Ea.	770	93		863	1,000
7670	26" x 20", colored		6.60	2.424		770	93		863	1,000
7680	26" x 20", premium color		6.60	2.424		970	93		1,063	1,225
7700	24" x 20", white		6.60	2.424		395	93		488	590
7710	24" x 20", colored		6.60	2.424		480	93		573	680
7720	24" x 20", premium color		6.60	2.424		535	93		628	745
7760	21" x 18", white		6.60	2.424		284	93		377	470
7770	21" x 18", colored		6.60	2.424		300	93		393	485
7990	Rough-in, supply, waste and vent for pedestal lavatories		1.66	9.639		470	370		840	1,125

22 41 16.30 Sinks

		Crew	Daily Output	Labor-Hours	Unit	Material	2014 Bare Costs Labor	Equipment	Total	Total Incl O&P
0010	**SINKS**, With faucets and drain R224000-40									
2000	Kitchen, counter top style, P.E. on C.I., 24" x 21" single bowl	Q-1	5.60	2.857	Ea.	275	110		385	480
2100	31" x 22" single bowl		5.60	2.857		575	110		685	810
2200	32" x 21" double bowl		4.80	3.333		340	128		468	585
3000	Stainless steel, self rimming, 19" x 18" single bowl		5.60	2.857		590	110		700	830
3100	25" x 22" single bowl		5.60	2.857		660	110		770	905
4000	Steel, enameled, with ledge, 24" x 21" single bowl		5.60	2.857		505	110		615	735
4100	32" x 21" double bowl		4.80	3.333		495	128		623	755
4960	For color sinks except stainless steel, add					10%				
4980	For rough-in, supply, waste and vent, counter top sinks	Q-1	2.14	7.477		460	287		747	980
5000	Kitchen, raised deck, P.E. on C.I.									
5100	32" x 21", dual level, double bowl	Q-1	2.60	6.154	Ea.	410	236		646	840
5700	For color, add					20%				
5790	For rough-in, supply, waste & vent, sinks	Q-1	1.85	8.649		460	330		790	1,050

22 41 19 – Residential Bathtubs

22 41 19.10 Baths

		Crew	Daily Output	Labor-Hours	Unit	Material	2014 Bare Costs Labor	Equipment	Total	Total Incl O&P
0010	**BATHS**									
0100	Tubs, recessed porcelain enamel on cast iron, with trim									
0180	48" x 42"	Q-1	4	4	Ea.	2,625	153		2,778	3,150
0220	72" x 36"		3	5.333		2,725	205		2,930	3,325
2000	Enameled formed steel, 4'-6" long		5.80	2.759		495	106		601	720
4000	Soaking, acrylic, w/pop-up drain 66" x 36" x 20" deep		5.50	2.909		1,825	112		1,937	2,175
4100	60" x 42" x 20" deep		5	3.200		1,150	123		1,273	1,475
9600	Rough-in, supply, waste and vent, for all above tubs, add		2.07	7.729		485	296		781	1,025

22 41 23 – Residential Showers

22 41 23.20 Showers

		Crew	Daily Output	Labor-Hours	Unit	Material	2014 Bare Costs Labor	Equipment	Total	Total Incl O&P
0010	**SHOWERS**									
1500	Stall, with drain only. Add for valve and door/curtain									
3000	Fiberglass, one piece, with 3 walls, 32" x 32" square	Q-1	5.50	2.909	Ea.	490	112		602	725
3100	36" x 36" square		5.50	2.909		505	112		617	740
3250	64" x 65-3/4" x 81-1/2" fold. seat, whlchr.		3.80	4.211		2,200	161		2,361	2,700
4000	Polypropylene, stall only, w/molded-stone floor, 30" x 30"		2	8		635	305		940	1,200
4200	Rough-in, supply, waste and vent for above showers		2.05	7.805		540	299		839	1,075

22 41 23.40 Shower System Components

		Crew	Daily Output	Labor-Hours	Unit	Material	2014 Bare Costs Labor	Equipment	Total	Total Incl O&P
0010	**SHOWER SYSTEM COMPONENTS**									
4500	Receptor only									
4510	For tile, 36" x 36"	1 Plum	4	2	Ea.	365	85		450	545
4520	Fiberglass receptor only, 32" x 32"		8	1		107	42.50		149.50	189
4530	34" x 34"		7.80	1.026		126	43.50		169.50	211
4540	36" x 36"		7.60	1.053		132	45		177	219
4600	Rectangular									

22 41 Residential Plumbing Fixtures

22 41 23 – Residential Showers

22 41 23.40 Shower System Components	Crew	Daily Output	Labor-Hours	Unit	Material	2014 Bare Costs Labor	Equipment	Total	Total Incl O&P
4620	32" x 48"	1 Plum	7.40	1.081	Ea.	149	46		195	239
4630	32" x 54"		7.20	1.111		196	47.50		243.50	293
4640	32" x 60"		7	1.143		208	48.50		256.50	310
5000	Built-in, head, arm, 2.5 GPM valve		4	2		80	85		165	229
5200	Head, arm, by-pass, integral stops, handles		3.60	2.222		255	94.50		349.50	435

22 41 36 – Residential Laundry Trays

22 41 36.10 Laundry Sinks

22 41 36.10 Laundry Sinks	Crew	Daily Output	Labor-Hours	Unit	Material	Labor	Equipment	Total	Total Incl O&P
0010	**LAUNDRY SINKS**, With trim									
0020	Porcelain enamel on cast iron, black iron frame									
0050	24" x 21", single compartment	Q-1	6	2.667	Ea.	580	102		682	805
0100	26" x 21", single compartment	"	6	2.667	"	610	102		712	840
2000	Molded stone, on wall hanger or legs									
2020	22" x 23", single compartment	Q-1	6	2.667	Ea.	134	102		236	315
2100	45" x 21", double compartment	"	5	3.200	"	330	123		453	570
3000	Plastic, on wall hanger or legs									
3020	18" x 23", single compartment	Q-1	6.50	2.462	Ea.	135	94.50		229.50	305
3300	40" x 24", double compartment		5.50	2.909		278	112		390	490
5000	Stainless steel, counter top, 22" x 17" single compartment		6	2.667		64	102		166	240
5200	33" x 22", double compartment		5	3.200		79	123		202	290
9600	Rough-in, supply, waste and vent, for all laundry sinks		2.14	7.477		460	287		747	980

22 41 39 – Residential Faucets, Supplies and Trim

22 41 39.10 Faucets and Fittings

22 41 39.10 Faucets and Fittings	Crew	Daily Output	Labor-Hours	Unit	Material	Labor	Equipment	Total	Total Incl O&P
0010	**FAUCETS AND FITTINGS**									
0150	Bath, faucets, diverter spout combination, sweat	1 Plum	8	1	Ea.	86.50	42.50		129	166
0200	For integral stops, IPS unions, add					109			109	120
0420	Bath, press-bal mix valve w/diverter, spout, shower head, arm/flange	1 Plum	8	1		168	42.50		210.50	256
0810	Bidet									
0812	Fitting, over the rim, swivel spray/pop-up drain	1 Plum	8	1	Ea.	206	42.50		248.50	298
1000	Kitchen sink faucets, top mount, cast spout		10	.800		61.50	34		95.50	124
1100	For spray, add		24	.333		16.15	14.20		30.35	41.50
1300	Single control lever handle									
1310	With pull out spray									
1320	Polished chrome	1 Plum	10	.800	Ea.	196	34		230	271
2000	Laundry faucets, shelf type, IPS or copper unions		12	.667		49.50	28.50		78	102
2100	Lavatory faucet, centerset, without drain		10	.800		44.50	34		78.50	105
2210	Porcelain cross handles and pop-up drain									
2220	Polished chrome	1 Plum	6.66	1.201	Ea.	189	51		240	293
2230	Polished brass	"	6.66	1.201	"	284	51		335	395
2260	Single lever handle and pop-up drain									
2280	Satin nickel	1 Plum	6.66	1.201	Ea.	277	51		328	390
2290	Polished chrome		6.66	1.201		198	51		249	305
2810	Automatic sensor and operator, with faucet head G		6.15	1.301		450	55.50		505.50	585
4000	Shower by-pass valve with union		18	.444		68.50	18.95		87.45	106
4200	Shower thermostatic mixing valve, concealed, with shower head trim kit		8	1		330	42.50		372.50	430
4220	Shower pressure balancing mixing valve,									
4230	With shower head, arm, flange and diverter tub spout									
4240	Chrome	1 Plum	6.14	1.303	Ea.	350	55.50		405.50	475
4250	Satin nickel		6.14	1.303		475	55.50		530.50	610
4260	Polished graphite		6.14	1.303		475	55.50		530.50	610
5000	Sillcock, compact, brass, IPS or copper to hose		24	.333		9.70	14.20		23.90	34

22 42 Commercial Plumbing Fixtures

22 42 13 – Commercial Water Closets, Urinals, and Bidets

22 42 13.30 Urinals

		Crew	Daily Output	Labor-Hours	Unit	Material	2014 Bare Costs Labor	Equipment	Total	Total Incl O&P
0010	**URINALS**									
3000	Wall hung, vitreous china, with hanger & self-closing valve									
3100	Siphon jet type	Q-1	3	5.333	Ea.	315	205		520	685
3120	Blowout type		3	5.333		450	205		655	830
3140	Water saving .5 gpf [G]		3	5.333		585	205		790	980
3300	Rough-in, supply, waste & vent		2.83	5.654		570	217		787	990
5000	Stall type, vitreous china, includes valve		2.50	6.400		715	245		960	1,200
6980	Rough-in, supply, waste and vent		1.99	8.040		585	310		895	1,150

22 42 13.40 Water Closets

		Crew	Daily Output	Labor-Hours	Unit	Material	2014 Bare Costs Labor	Equipment	Total	Total Incl O&P
0010	**WATER CLOSETS**									
3000	Bowl only, with flush valve, seat, 1.6 gpf unless noted									
3100	Wall hung	Q-1	5.80	2.759	Ea.	755	106		861	1,000
3200	For rough-in, supply, waste and vent, single WC		2.56	6.250		890	240		1,130	1,375
3300	Floor mounted		5.80	2.759		355	106		461	565
3350	With wall outlet		5.80	2.759		530	106		636	755
3360	With floor outlet, 1.28 gpf [G]		5.80	2.759		585	106		691	820
3362	With floor outlet, 1.28 gpf, ADA [G]		5.80	2.759		620	106		726	860
3370	For rough-in, supply, waste and vent, single WC		2.84	5.634		410	216		626	810
3390	Floor mounted children's size, 10-3/4" high									
3392	With automatic flush sensor, 1.6 gpf	Q-1	6.20	2.581	Ea.	610	99		709	835
3396	With automatic flush sensor, 1.28 gpf		6.20	2.581		610	99		709	835
3400	For rough-in, supply, waste and vent, single WC		2.84	5.634		410	216		626	810

22 42 16 – Commercial Lavatories and Sinks

22 42 16.14 Lavatories

		Crew	Daily Output	Labor-Hours	Unit	Material	2014 Bare Costs Labor	Equipment	Total	Total Incl O&P
0010	**LAVATORIES**, With trim, white unless noted otherwise									
0020	Commercial lavatories same as residential. See Section 22 41 16.10									

22 42 16.40 Service Sinks

		Crew	Daily Output	Labor-Hours	Unit	Material	2014 Bare Costs Labor	Equipment	Total	Total Incl O&P
0010	**SERVICE SINKS**									
6650	Service, floor, corner, P.E. on C.I., 28" x 28"	Q-1	4.40	3.636	Ea.	990	139		1,129	1,325
6790	For rough-in, supply, waste & vent, floor service sinks		1.64	9.756		1,475	375		1,850	2,250
7000	Service, wall, P.E. on C.I., roll rim, 22" x 18"		4	4		750	153		903	1,075
7100	24" x 20"		4	4		835	153		988	1,175
8600	Vitreous china, 22" x 20"		4	4		595	153		748	910
8960	For stainless steel rim guard, front or one side, add					56			56	62
8980	For rough-in, supply, waste & vent, wall service sinks	Q-1	1.30	12.308		1,800	470		2,270	2,775

22 42 23 – Commercial Showers

22 42 23.30 Group Showers

		Crew	Daily Output	Labor-Hours	Unit	Material	2014 Bare Costs Labor	Equipment	Total	Total Incl O&P
0010	**GROUP SHOWERS**									
6000	Group, w/pressure balancing valve, rough-in and rigging not included									
6800	Column, 6 heads, no receptors, less partitions	Q-1	3	5.333	Ea.	3,000	205		3,205	3,625
6900	With stainless steel partitions		1	16		9,250	615		9,865	11,200
7600	5 heads, no receptors, less partitions		3	5.333		2,475	205		2,680	3,050
7620	4 heads (1 handicap) no receptors, less partitions		3	5.333		3,975	205		4,180	4,700
7700	With stainless steel partitions		1	16		7,600	615		8,215	9,350
8000	Wall, 2 heads, no receptors, less partitions		4	4		1,375	153		1,528	1,775
8100	With stainless steel partitions		2	8		3,225	305		3,530	4,050

22 42 Commercial Plumbing Fixtures

22 42 33 – Wash Fountains

22 42 33.20 Commercial Wash Fountains		Crew	Daily Output	Labor-Hours	Unit	Material	2014 Bare Costs Labor	Equipment	Total	Total Incl O&P
0010	**COMMERCIAL WASH FOUNTAINS**									
1900	Group, foot control									
2000	Precast terrazzo, circular, 36" diam., 5 or 6 persons	Q-2	3	8	Ea.	5,800	295		6,095	6,850
2100	54" diameter for 8 or 10 persons		2.50	9.600		9,025	355		9,380	10,500
2400	Semi-circular, 36" diam. for 3 persons		3	8		4,775	295		5,070	5,725
2500	54" diam. for 4 or 5 persons		2.50	9.600		6,775	355		7,130	8,025
2700	Quarter circle (corner), 54" for 3 persons		3.50	6.857		6,000	253		6,253	7,025
3000	Stainless steel, circular, 36" diameter		3.50	6.857		4,850	253		5,103	5,750
3100	54" diameter		2.80	8.571		7,050	315		7,365	8,275
3400	Semi-circular, 36" diameter		3.50	6.857		4,800	253		5,053	5,700
3500	54" diameter		2.80	8.571		5,425	315		5,740	6,475
5610	Group, infrared control, barrier free									
5614	Precast terrazzo									
5620	Semi-circular 36" diam. for 3 persons	Q-2	3	8	Ea.	7,150	295		7,445	8,350
5630	46" diam. for 4 persons		2.80	8.571		7,725	315		8,040	9,025
5640	Circular, 54" diam. for 8 persons, button control		2.50	9.600		9,125	355		9,480	10,600
5700	Rough-in, supply, waste and vent for above wash fountains	Q-1	1.82	8.791		660	335		995	1,275
6200	Duo for small washrooms, stainless steel		2	8		2,725	305		3,030	3,475
6500	Rough-in, supply, waste & vent for duo fountains		2.02	7.921		405	305		710	945

22 42 39 – Commercial Faucets, Supplies, and Trim

22 42 39.10 Faucets and Fittings

		Crew	Daily Output	Labor-Hours	Unit	Material	Labor	Equipment	Total	Total Incl O&P
0010	**FAUCETS AND FITTINGS**									
0840	Flush valves, with vacuum breaker									
0850	Water closet									
0860	Exposed, rear spud	1 Plum	8	1	Ea.	148	42.50		190.50	234
0870	Top spud		8	1		149	42.50		191.50	234
0880	Concealed, rear spud		8	1		197	42.50		239.50	287
0890	Top spud		8	1		159	42.50		201.50	246
0900	Wall hung		8	1		177	42.50		219.50	266
0920	Urinal									
0930	Exposed, stall	1 Plum	8	1	Ea.	149	42.50		191.50	235
0940	Wall, (washout)		8	1		149	42.50		191.50	234
0950	Pedestal, top spud		8	1		143	42.50		185.50	228
0960	Concealed, stall		8	1		156	42.50		198.50	243
0970	Wall (washout)		8	1		168	42.50		210.50	256
0971	Automatic flush sensor and operator for									
0972	urinals or water closets, standard	G	1 Plum	8	1	Ea.	450	42.50		492.50	565
0980	High efficiency water saving									
0984	Water closets, 1.28 gpf	G	1 Plum	8	1	Ea.	415	42.50		457.50	530
0988	Urinals, .5 gpf	G	"	8	1	"	415	42.50		457.50	530
2790	Faucets for lavatories									
2800	Self-closing, center set	1 Plum	10	.800	Ea.	131	34		165	200
2810	Automatic sensor and operator, with faucet head		6.15	1.301		450	55.50		505.50	585
3000	Service sink faucet, cast spout, pail hook, hose end		14	.571		80	24.50		104.50	128

22 42 39.30 Carriers and Supports

		Crew	Daily Output	Labor-Hours	Unit	Material	Labor	Equipment	Total	Total Incl O&P
0010	**CARRIERS AND SUPPORTS**, For plumbing fixtures									
0500	Drinking fountain, wall mounted									
0600	Plate type with studs, top back plate	1 Plum	7	1.143	Ea.	83.50	48.50		132	172
0700	Top front and back plate		7	1.143		102	48.50		150.50	193
0800	Top & bottom, front & back plates, w/bearing jacks		7	1.143		148	48.50		196.50	243
3000	Lavatory, concealed arm									

22 42 39.30 Carriers and Supports		Crew	Daily Output	Labor-Hours	Unit	Material	2014 Bare Costs Labor	Equipment	Total	Total Incl O&P
3050	Floor mounted, single									
3100	High back fixture	1 Plum	6	1.333	Ea.	465	57		522	605
3200	Flat slab fixture		6	1.333		400	57		457	535
3220	Paraplegic		6	1.333		515	57		572	665
3250	Floor mounted, back to back									
3300	High back fixtures	1 Plum	5	1.600	Ea.	660	68		728	835
3400	Flat slab fixtures		5	1.600		810	68		878	1,000
3430	Paraplegic		5	1.600		755	68		823	940
3500	Wall mounted, in stud or masonry									
3600	High back fixture	1 Plum	6	1.333	Ea.	274	57		331	395
3700	Flat slab fixture	"	6	1.333	"	237	57		294	355
4600	Sink, floor mounted									
4650	Exposed arm system									
4700	Single heavy fixture	1 Plum	5	1.600	Ea.	770	68		838	960
4750	Single heavy sink with slab		5	1.600		990	68		1,058	1,200
4800	Back to back, standard fixtures		5	1.600		570	68		638	735
4850	Back to back, heavy fixtures		5	1.600		875	68		943	1,075
4900	Back to back, heavy sink with slab		5	1.600		875	68		943	1,075
4950	Exposed offset arm system									
5000	Single heavy deep fixture	1 Plum	5	1.600	Ea.	735	68		803	920
5100	Plate type system									
5200	With bearing jacks, single fixture	1 Plum	5	1.600	Ea.	845	68		913	1,050
5300	With exposed arms, single heavy fixture		5	1.600		1,075	68		1,143	1,300
5400	Wall mounted, exposed arms, single heavy fixture		5	1.600		395	68		463	545
6000	Urinal, floor mounted, 2" or 3" coupling, blowout type		6	1.333		490	57		547	635
6100	With fixture or hanger bolts, blowout or washout		6	1.333		350	57		407	480
6200	With bearing plate		6	1.333		390	57		447	525
6300	Wall mounted, plate type system		6	1.333		300	57		357	430
6980	Water closet, siphon jet									
7000	Horizontal, adjustable, caulk									
7040	Single, 4" pipe size	1 Plum	5.33	1.501	Ea.	655	64		719	825
7050	4" pipe size, paraplegic		5.33	1.501		655	64		719	825
7060	5" pipe size		5.33	1.501		845	64		909	1,025
7100	Double, 4" pipe size		5	1.600		1,225	68		1,293	1,450
7110	4" pipe size, paraplegic		5	1.600		1,225	68		1,293	1,450
7120	5" pipe size		5	1.600		1,475	68		1,543	1,725
7160	Horizontal, adjustable, extended, caulk									
7180	Single, 4" pipe size	1 Plum	5.33	1.501	Ea.	885	64		949	1,075
7200	5" pipe size		5.33	1.501		1,125	64		1,189	1,325
7240	Double, 4" pipe size		5	1.600		1,550	68		1,618	1,800
7260	5" pipe size		5	1.600		1,875	68		1,943	2,150
7400	Vertical, adjustable, caulk or thread									
7440	Single, 4" pipe size	1 Plum	5.33	1.501	Ea.	905	64		969	1,100
7460	5" pipe size		5.33	1.501		1,125	64		1,189	1,325
7480	6" pipe size		5	1.600		1,275	68		1,343	1,500
7520	Double, 4" pipe size		5	1.600		1,350	68		1,418	1,575
7540	5" pipe size		5	1.600		1,550	68		1,618	1,800
7560	6" pipe size		4	2		1,725	85		1,810	2,050
7600	Vertical, adjustable, extended, caulk									
7620	Single, 4" pipe size	1 Plum	5.33	1.501	Ea.	905	64		969	1,100
7640	5" pipe size		5.33	1.501		1,125	64		1,189	1,325
7680	6" pipe size		5	1.600		1,275	68		1,343	1,500
7720	Double, 4" pipe size		5	1.600		1,350	68		1,418	1,575

22 42 Commercial Plumbing Fixtures

22 42 39 – Commercial Faucets, Supplies, and Trim

22 42 39.30 Carriers and Supports		Crew	Daily Output	Labor-Hours	Unit	Material	2014 Bare Costs Labor	Equipment	Total	Total Incl O&P
7740	5" pipe size	1 Plum	5	1.600	Ea.	1,550	68		1,618	1,800
7760	6" pipe size	↓	4	2	↓	1,725	85		1,810	2,050
7780	Water closet, blow out									
7800	Vertical offset, caulk or thread									
7820	Single, 4" pipe size	1 Plum	5.33	1.501	Ea.	665	64		729	840
7840	Double, 4" pipe size	"	5	1.600	"	1,150	68		1,218	1,350
7880	Vertical offset, extended, caulk									
7900	Single, 4" pipe size	1 Plum	5.33	1.501	Ea.	835	64		899	1,025
7920	Double, 4" pipe size	"	5	1.600	"	1,300	68		1,368	1,550
7960	Vertical, for floor mounted back-outlet									
7980	Single, 4" thread, 2" vent	1 Plum	5.33	1.501	Ea.	585	64		649	750
8000	Double, 4" thread, 2" vent	"	6	1.333	"	1,725	57		1,782	2,000
8040	Vertical, for floor mounted back-outlet, extended									
8060	Single, 4" caulk, 2" vent	1 Plum	6	1.333	Ea.	585	57		642	740
8080	Double, 4" caulk, 2" vent	"	6	1.333	"	1,725	57		1,782	2,000
8200	Water closet, residential									
8220	Vertical centerline, floor mount									
8240	Single, 3" caulk, 2" or 3" vent	1 Plum	6	1.333	Ea.	535	57		592	680
8260	4" caulk, 2" or 4" vent		6	1.333		690	57		747	850
8280	3" copper sweat, 3" vent		6	1.333		480	57		537	620
8300	4" copper sweat, 4" vent	↓	6	1.333	↓	580	57		637	735
8400	Vertical offset, floor mount									
8420	Single, 3" or 4" caulk, vent	1 Plum	4	2	Ea.	665	85		750	875
8440	3" or 4" copper sweat, vent		5	1.600		665	68		733	845
8460	Double, 3" or 4" caulk, vent		4	2		1,150	85		1,235	1,400
8480	3" or 4" copper sweat, vent	↓	5	1.600	↓	1,150	68		1,218	1,350
9000	Water cooler (electric), floor mounted									
9100	Plate type with bearing plate, single	1 Plum	6	1.333	Ea.	335	57		392	465

22 45 Emergency Plumbing Fixtures

22 45 13 – Emergency Showers

22 45 13.10 Emergency Showers

		Crew	Daily Output	Labor-Hours	Unit	Material	Labor	Equipment	Total	Total Incl O&P
0010	**EMERGENCY SHOWERS**, Rough-in not included									
5000	Shower, single head, drench, ball valve, pull, freestanding	Q-1	4	4	Ea.	380	153		533	675
5200	Horizontal or vertical supply		4	4		540	153		693	850
6000	Multi-nozzle, eye/face wash combination		4	4		640	153		793	960
6400	Multi-nozzle, 12 spray, shower only		4	4		1,950	153		2,103	2,400
6600	For freeze-proof, add	↓	6	2.667	↓	455	102		557	670

22 45 16 – Eyewash Equipment

22 45 16.10 Eyewash Safety Equipment

		Crew	Daily Output	Labor-Hours	Unit	Material	Labor	Equipment	Total	Total Incl O&P
0010	**EYEWASH SAFETY EQUIPMENT**, Rough-in not included									
1000	Eye wash fountain									
1400	Plastic bowl, pedestal mounted	Q-1	4	4	Ea.	269	153		422	550
1600	Unmounted		4	4		240	153		393	515
1800	Wall mounted		4	4		435	153		588	735
2000	Stainless steel, pedestal mounted		4	4		340	153		493	630
2200	Unmounted		4	4		266	153		419	545
2400	Wall mounted	↓	4	4	↓	282	153		435	565

22 45 Emergency Plumbing Fixtures

22 45 19 – Self-Contained Eyewash Equipment

22 45 19.10 Self-Contained Eyewash Safety Equipment	Crew	Daily Output	Labor-Hours	Unit	Material	2014 Bare Costs Labor	Equipment	Total	Total Incl O&P
0010 **SELF-CONTAINED EYEWASH SAFETY EQUIPMENT**									
3000 Eye wash, portable, self-contained				Ea.	990			990	1,100

22 45 26 – Eye/Face Wash Equipment

22 45 26.10 Eye/Face Wash Safety Equipment

	Crew	Daily Output	Labor-Hours	Unit	Material	Labor	Equipment	Total	Total Incl O&P
0010 **EYE/FACE WASH SAFETY EQUIPMENT**, Rough-in not included									
4000 Eye and face wash, combination fountain									
4200 Stainless steel, pedestal mounted	Q-1	4	4	Ea.	1,050	153		1,203	1,400
4400 Unmounted		4	4		266	153		419	545
4600 Wall mounted		4	4		282	153		435	565

22 47 Drinking Fountains and Water Coolers

22 47 13 – Drinking Fountains

22 47 13.10 Drinking Water Fountains

	Crew	Daily Output	Labor-Hours	Unit	Material	Labor	Equipment	Total	Total Incl O&P
0010 **DRINKING WATER FOUNTAINS**, For connection to cold water supply									
1000 Wall mounted, non-recessed									
1400 Bronze, with no back	1 Plum	4	2	Ea.	990	85		1,075	1,250
1800 Cast aluminum, enameled, for correctional institutions		4	2		1,625	85		1,710	1,950
2000 Fiberglass, 12" back, single bubbler unit		4	2		1,875	85		1,960	2,200
2040 Dual bubbler		3.20	2.500		2,100	107		2,207	2,500
2400 Precast stone, no back		4	2		950	85		1,035	1,200
2700 Stainless steel, single bubbler, no back		4	2		1,025	85		1,110	1,300
2740 With back		4	2		540	85		625	730
2780 Dual handle & wheelchair projection type		4	2		730	85		815	945
2820 Dual level for handicapped type		3.20	2.500		1,500	107		1,607	1,825
3300 Vitreous china									
3340 7" back	1 Plum	4	2	Ea.	610	85		695	810
3940 For vandal-resistant bottom plate, add					73.50			73.50	81
3960 For freeze-proof valve system, add	1 Plum	2	4		700	170		870	1,050
3980 For rough-in, supply and waste, add	"	2.21	3.620		365	154		519	655
4000 Wall mounted, semi-recessed									
4200 Poly-marble, single bubbler	1 Plum	4	2	Ea.	955	85		1,040	1,200
4600 Stainless steel, satin finish, single bubbler		4	2		1,125	85		1,210	1,400
4900 Vitreous china, single bubbler		4	2		880	85		965	1,100
5980 For rough-in, supply and waste, add		1.83	4.372		365	186		551	705
6000 Wall mounted, fully recessed									
6400 Poly-marble, single bubbler	1 Plum	4	2	Ea.	1,600	85		1,685	1,900
6800 Stainless steel, single bubbler		4	2		1,525	85		1,610	1,825
7560 For freeze-proof valve system, add		2	4		795	170		965	1,150
7580 For rough-in, supply and waste, add		1.83	4.372		365	186		551	705
7600 Floor mounted, pedestal type									
7700 Aluminum, architectural style, C.I. base	1 Plum	2	4	Ea.	2,250	170		2,420	2,750
7780 Wheelchair handicap unit		2	4		1,625	170		1,795	2,050
8400 Stainless steel, architectural style		2	4		1,750	170		1,920	2,200
8600 Enameled iron, heavy duty service, 2 bubblers		2	4		2,575	170		2,745	3,125
8660 4 bubblers		2	4		3,950	170		4,120	4,600
8880 For freeze-proof valve system, add		2	4		665	170		835	1,000
8900 For rough-in, supply and waste, add		1.83	4.372		365	186		551	705
9100 Deck mounted									
9500 Stainless steel, circular receptor	1 Plum	4	2	Ea.	415	85		500	595
9760 White enameled steel, 14" x 9" receptor		4	2		360	85		445	535

505

22 47 Drinking Fountains and Water Coolers

22 47 13 – Drinking Fountains

22 47 13.10 Drinking Water Fountains	Crew	Daily Output	Labor-Hours	Unit	Material	2014 Bare Costs Labor	Equipment	Total	Total Incl O&P
9860	White enameled cast iron, 24" x 16" receptor	1 Plum	3	2.667	Ea.	445	114		559	675
9980	For rough-in, supply and waste, add	↓	1.83	4.372	↓	365	186		551	705

22 47 16 – Pressure Water Coolers

22 47 16.10 Electric Water Coolers

		Crew	Daily Output	Labor-Hours	Unit	Material	2014 Bare Costs Labor	Equipment	Total	Total Incl O&P
0010	**ELECTRIC WATER COOLERS** R224000-50									
0100	Wall mounted, non-recessed									
0140	4 GPH	Q-1	4	4	Ea.	680	153		833	1,000
0160	8 GPH, barrier free, sensor operated		4	4		1,025	153		1,178	1,400
0180	8.2 GPH		4	4		725	153		878	1,050
0600	8 GPH hot and cold water	↓	4	4		1,050	153		1,203	1,425
0640	For stainless steel cabinet, add					84			84	92
1000	Dual height, 8.2 GPH	Q-1	3.80	4.211		2,025	161		2,186	2,500
1040	14.3 GPH	"	3.80	4.211		975	161		1,136	1,350
1240	For stainless steel cabinet, add					171			171	188
2600	Wheelchair type, 8 GPH	Q-1	4	4		915	153		1,068	1,250
3300	Semi-recessed, 8.1 GPH		4	4		715	153		868	1,050
3320	12 GPH	↓	4	4	↓	820	153		973	1,150
4600	Floor mounted, flush-to-wall									
4640	4 GPH	1 Plum	3	2.667	Ea.	705	114		819	960
4680	8.2 GPH		3	2.667		740	114		854	1,000
4720	14.3 GPH		3	2.667		850	114		964	1,125
4960	14 GPH hot and cold water	↓	3	2.667		1,100	114		1,214	1,400
4980	For stainless steel cabinet, add					128			128	141
5000	Dual height, 8.2 GPH	1 Plum	2	4		1,100	170		1,270	1,500
5040	14.3 GPH	"	2	4		1,150	170		1,320	1,550
5120	For stainless steel cabinet, add					186			186	205
9800	For supply, waste & vent, all coolers	1 Plum	2.21	3.620	↓	365	154		519	655

22 51 Swimming Pool Plumbing Systems

22 51 19 – Swimming Pool Water Treatment Equipment

22 51 19.50 Swimming Pool Filtration Equipment

		Crew	Daily Output	Labor-Hours	Unit	Material	2014 Bare Costs Labor	Equipment	Total	Total Incl O&P
0010	**SWIMMING POOL FILTRATION EQUIPMENT**									
0900	Filter system, sand or diatomite type, incl. pump, 6,000 gal./hr.	2 Plum	1.80	8.889	Total	1,925	380		2,305	2,750
1020	Add for chlorination system, 800 S.F. pool		3	5.333	Ea.	177	227		404	570
1040	5,000 S.F. pool	↓	3	5.333	"	1,875	227		2,102	2,450

22 52 Fountain Plumbing Systems

22 52 16 – Fountain Pumps

22 52 16.10 Fountain Water Pumps

		Crew	Daily Output	Labor-Hours	Unit	Material	2014 Bare Costs Labor	Equipment	Total	Total Incl O&P
0010	**FOUNTAIN WATER PUMPS**									
0100	Pump w/controls									
0200	Single phase, 100' cord, 1/2 H.P. pump	2 Skwk	4.40	3.636	Ea.	1,275	132		1,407	1,625
0300	3/4 H.P. pump		4.30	3.721		2,175	135		2,310	2,625
0400	1 H.P. pump		4.20	3.810		2,350	138		2,488	2,825
0500	1-1/2 H.P. pump		4.10	3.902		2,800	142		2,942	3,325
0600	2 H.P. pump		4	4		3,775	145		3,920	4,425
0700	Three phase, 200' cord, 5 H.P. pump		3.90	4.103		5,175	149		5,324	5,950
0800	7-1/2 H.P. pump		3.80	4.211		9,000	153		9,153	10,200
0900	10 H.P. pump	↓	3.70	4.324		13,300	157		13,457	15,000

22 52 Fountain Plumbing Systems

22 52 16 – Fountain Pumps

	22 52 16.10 Fountain Water Pumps	Crew	Daily Output	Labor-Hours	Unit	Material	2014 Bare Costs Labor	Equipment	Total	Total Incl O&P
1000	15 H.P. pump	2 Skwk	3.60	4.444	Ea.	16,800	161		16,961	18,800
2000	DESIGN NOTE: Use two horsepower per surface acre.									

22 52 33 – Fountain Ancillary

22 52 33.10 Fountain Miscellaneous

		Crew	Daily Output	Labor-Hours	Unit	Material	2014 Bare Costs Labor	Equipment	Total	Total Incl O&P
0010	**FOUNTAIN MISCELLANEOUS**									
1100	Nozzles, minimum	2 Skwk	8	2	Ea.	149	72.50		221.50	287
1200	Maximum		8	2		320	72.50		392.50	475
1300	Lights w/mounting kits, 200 watt		18	.889		1,050	32.50		1,082.50	1,200
1400	300 watt		18	.889		1,275	32.50		1,307.50	1,450
1500	500 watt		18	.889		1,425	32.50		1,457.50	1,625
1600	Color blender	↓	12	1.333	↓	555	48.50		603.50	690

22 66 Chemical-Waste Systems for Lab. and Healthcare Facilities

22 66 53 – Laboratory Chemical-Waste and Vent Piping

22 66 53.30 Glass Pipe

		Crew	Daily Output	Labor-Hours	Unit	Material	2014 Bare Costs Labor	Equipment	Total	Total Incl O&P
0010	**GLASS PIPE**, Borosilicate, couplings & clevis hanger assemblies, 10' O.C.									
0020	Drainage									
1100	1-1/2" diameter	Q-1	52	.308	L.F.	10.60	11.80		22.40	31
1120	2" diameter		44	.364		13.85	13.95		27.80	38.50
1140	3" diameter		39	.410		18.70	15.75		34.45	46.50
1160	4" diameter		30	.533		33.50	20.50		54	70.50
1180	6" diameter	↓	26	.615	↓	58	23.50		81.50	103

22 66 53.60 Corrosion Resistant Pipe

		Crew	Daily Output	Labor-Hours	Unit	Material	2014 Bare Costs Labor	Equipment	Total	Total Incl O&P
0010	**CORROSION RESISTANT PIPE**, No couplings or hangers									
0020	Iron alloy, drain, mechanical joint									
1000	1-1/2" diameter	Q-1	70	.229	L.F.	46	8.75		54.75	65
1100	2" diameter		66	.242		47	9.30		56.30	67
1120	3" diameter		60	.267		60.50	10.25		70.75	83.50
1140	4" diameter	↓	52	.308	↓	77.50	11.80		89.30	105
2980	Plastic, epoxy, fiberglass filament wound, B&S joint									
3000	2" diameter	Q-1	62	.258	L.F.	12	9.90		21.90	29.50
3100	3" diameter		51	.314		14	12.05		26.05	35.50
3120	4" diameter		45	.356		20	13.65		33.65	44.50
3140	6" diameter	↓	32	.500	↓	28	19.20		47.20	62.50
3980	Polyester, fiberglass filament wound, B&S joint									
4000	2" diameter	Q-1	62	.258	L.F.	13.05	9.90		22.95	30.50
4100	3" diameter		51	.314		17	12.05		29.05	38.50
4120	4" diameter		45	.356		25	13.65		38.65	50
4140	6" diameter	↓	32	.500	↓	36	19.20		55.20	71
4980	Polypropylene, acid resistant, fire retardant, schedule 40									
5000	1-1/2" diameter	Q-1	68	.235	L.F.	7.90	9		16.90	23.50
5100	2" diameter		62	.258		12.45	9.90		22.35	30
5120	3" diameter		51	.314		22	12.05		34.05	44.50
5140	4" diameter	↓	45	.356	↓	28	13.65		41.65	53.50
5980	Proxylene, fire retardant, Schedule 40									
6000	1-1/2" diameter	Q-1	68	.235	L.F.	12.40	9		21.40	28.50
6100	2" diameter		62	.258		17	9.90		26.90	35
6120	3" diameter		51	.314		30.50	12.05		42.55	54
6140	4" diameter	↓	45	.356	↓	43.50	13.65		57.15	70

Division Notes

	CREW	DAILY OUTPUT	LABOR-HOURS	UNIT	BARE COSTS				TOTAL INCL O&P
					MAT.	LABOR	EQUIP.	TOTAL	

Estimating Tips

The labor adjustment factors listed in Subdivision 22 01 02.20 also apply to Division 23.

23 10 00 Facility Fuel Systems

- The prices in this subdivision for above- and below-ground storage tanks do not include foundations or hold-down slabs, unless noted. The estimator should refer to Divisions 3 and 31 for foundation system pricing. In addition to the foundations, required tank accessories, such as tank gauges, leak detection devices, and additional manholes and piping, must be added to the tank prices.

23 50 00 Central Heating Equipment

- When estimating the cost of an HVAC system, check to see who is responsible for providing and installing the temperature control system. It is possible to overlook controls, assuming that they would be included in the electrical estimate.

- When looking up a boiler, be careful on specified capacity. Some manufacturers rate their products on output while others use input.

- Include HVAC insulation for pipe, boiler, and duct (wrap and liner).

- Be careful when looking up mechanical items to get the correct pressure rating and connection type (thread, weld, flange).

23 70 00 Central HVAC Equipment

- Combination heating and cooling units are sized by the air conditioning requirements. (See Reference No. R236000-20 for preliminary sizing guide.)

- A ton of air conditioning is nominally 400 CFM.

- Rectangular duct is taken off by the linear foot for each size, but its cost is usually estimated by the pound. Remember that SMACNA standards now base duct on internal pressure.

- Prefabricated duct is estimated and purchased like pipe: straight sections and fittings.

- Note that cranes or other lifting equipment are not included on any lines in Division 23. For example, if a crane is required to lift a heavy piece of pipe into place high above a gym floor, or to put a rooftop unit on the roof of a four-story building, etc., it must be added. Due to the potential for extreme variation—from nothing additional required to a major crane or helicopter—we feel that including a nominal amount for "lifting contingency" would be useless and detract from the accuracy of the estimate. When using equipment rental cost data from RSMeans, do not forget to include the cost of the operator(s).

Reference Numbers

Reference numbers are shown in shaded boxes at the beginning of some major classifications. These numbers refer to related items in the Reference Section. The reference information may be an estimating procedure, an alternate pricing method, or technical information.

Note: Not all subdivisions listed here necessarily appear in this publication.

Note: **Trade Service,** *in part, has been used as a reference source for some of the material prices used in Division 23.*

23 05 Common Work Results for HVAC

23 05 02 – HVAC General

23 05 02.10 Air Conditioning, General	Crew	Daily Output	Labor-Hours	Unit	Material	2014 Bare Costs Labor	Equipment	Total	Total Incl O&P
0010 **AIR CONDITIONING, GENERAL** Prices are for standard efficiencies (SEER 13)									
0020 for upgrade to SEER 14 add					10%				

23 05 05 – Selective HVAC Demolition

23 05 05.10 HVAC Demolition

	Crew	Daily Output	Labor-Hours	Unit	Material	2014 Bare Costs Labor	Equipment	Total	Total Incl O&P
0010 **HVAC DEMOLITION**									
0100 Air conditioner, split unit, 3 ton	Q-5	2	8	Ea.		310		310	515
0150 Package unit, 3 ton	Q-6	3	8	"		300		300	495
0298 Boilers									
0300 Electric, up thru 148 kW	Q-19	2	12	Ea.		485		485	795
0310 150 thru 518 kW	"	1	24			965		965	1,600
0320 550 thru 2000 kW	Q-21	.40	80			3,275		3,275	5,400
0330 2070 kW and up	"	.30	106			4,375		4,375	7,200
0340 Gas and/or oil, up thru 150 MBH	Q-7	2.20	14.545			565		565	935
0350 160 thru 2000 MBH		.80	40			1,550		1,550	2,575
0360 2100 thru 4500 MBH		.50	64			2,500		2,500	4,125
0370 4600 thru 7000 MBH		.30	106			4,150		4,150	6,850
0380 7100 thru 12,000 MBH		.16	200			7,800		7,800	12,900
0390 12,200 thru 25,000 MBH		.12	266			10,400		10,400	17,100
1000 Ductwork, 4" high, 8" wide	1 Clab	200	.040	L.F.		1.13		1.13	1.90
1100 6" high, 8" wide		165	.048			1.37		1.37	2.30
1200 10" high, 12" wide		125	.064			1.80		1.80	3.04
1300 12"-14" high, 16"-18" wide		85	.094			2.65		2.65	4.47
1400 18" high, 24" wide		67	.119			3.37		3.37	5.65
1500 30" high, 36" wide		56	.143			4.03		4.03	6.80
1540 72" wide		50	.160			4.51		4.51	7.60
3000 Mechanical equipment, light items. Unit is weight, not cooling.	Q-5	.90	17.778	Ton		695		695	1,150
3600 Heavy items	"	1.10	14.545	"		565		565	935
3700 Deduct for salvage (when applicable), minimum				Job				73	80
3710 Maximum				"				455	500
5090 Remove refrigerant from system	1 Stpi	40	.200	Lb.		8.65		8.65	14.30

23 05 23 – General-Duty Valves for HVAC Piping

23 05 23.30 Valves, Iron Body

	Crew	Daily Output	Labor-Hours	Unit	Material	2014 Bare Costs Labor	Equipment	Total	Total Incl O&P
0010 **VALVES, IRON BODY**									
1020 Butterfly, wafer type, gear actuator, 200 lb.									
1030 2"	1 Plum	14	.571	Ea.	96	24.50		120.50	145
1040 2-1/2"	Q-1	9	1.778		97.50	68		165.50	220
1050 3"		8	2		101	76.50		177.50	238
1060 4"		5	3.200		113	123		236	325
1070 5"	Q-2	5	4.800		126	177		303	430
1080 6"	"	5	4.800		143	177		320	450
1650 Gate, 125 lb., N.R.S.									
2150 Flanged									
2200 2"	1 Plum	5	1.600	Ea.	680	68		748	860
2240 2-1/2"	Q-1	5	3.200		700	123		823	975
2260 3"		4.50	3.556		780	136		916	1,075
2280 4"		3	5.333		1,125	205		1,330	1,550
2300 6"	Q-2	3	8		1,900	295		2,195	2,575
3550 OS&Y, 125 lb., flanged									
3600 2"	1 Plum	5	1.600	Ea.	455	68		523	610
3660 3"	Q-1	4.50	3.556		495	136		631	770
3680 4"	"	3	5.333		730	205		935	1,150
3700 6"	Q-2	3	8		1,175	295		1,470	1,775

23 05 Common Work Results for HVAC

23 05 23 – General-Duty Valves for HVAC Piping

23 05 23.30 Valves, Iron Body

		Crew	Daily Output	Labor-Hours	Unit	Material	2014 Bare Costs Labor	2014 Bare Costs Equipment	Total	Total Incl O&P
3900	For 175 lb., flanged, add					200%	10%			
5450	Swing check, 125 lb., threaded									
5470	1"	1 Plum	13	.615	Ea.	635	26		661	745
5500	2"	"	11	.727		410	31		441	500
5540	2-1/2"	Q-1	15	1.067		525	41		566	650
5550	3"		13	1.231		570	47		617	705
5560	4"		10	1.600		905	61.50		966.50	1,100
5950	Flanged									
6000	2"	1 Plum	5	1.600	Ea.	395	68		463	545
6040	2-1/2"	Q-1	5	3.200		365	123		488	605
6050	3"		4.50	3.556		390	136		526	650
6060	4"		3	5.333		610	205		815	1,000
6070	6"	Q-2	3	8		1,050	295		1,345	1,625

23 05 23.80 Valves, Steel

		Crew	Daily Output	Labor-Hours	Unit	Material	2014 Bare Costs Labor	2014 Bare Costs Equipment	Total	Total Incl O&P
0010	**VALVES, STEEL**									
0800	Cast									
1350	Check valve, swing type, 150 lb., flanged									
1370	1"	1 Plum	10	.800	Ea.	390	34		424	485
1400	2"	"	8	1		705	42.50		747.50	845
1440	2-1/2"	Q-1	5	3.200		820	123		943	1,100
1450	3"		4.50	3.556		835	136		971	1,150
1460	4"		3	5.333		1,200	205		1,405	1,650
1540	For 300 lb., flanged, add					50%	15%			
1548	For 600 lb., flanged, add					110%	20%			
1950	Gate valve, 150 lb., flanged									
2000	2"	1 Plum	8	1	Ea.	760	42.50		802.50	905
2040	2-1/2"	Q-1	5	3.200		1,075	123		1,198	1,375
2050	3"		4.50	3.556		1,075	136		1,211	1,400
2060	4"		3	5.333		1,325	205		1,530	1,800
2070	6"	Q-2	3	8		2,075	295		2,370	2,750
3650	Globe valve, 150 lb., flanged									
3700	2"	1 Plum	8	1	Ea.	955	42.50		997.50	1,125
3740	2-1/2"	Q-1	5	3.200		1,200	123		1,323	1,525
3750	3"		4.50	3.556		1,200	136		1,336	1,550
3760	4"		3	5.333		1,775	205		1,980	2,275
3770	6"	Q-2	3	8		2,775	295		3,070	3,525
5150	Forged									
5650	Check valve, class 800, horizontal, socket									
5698	Threaded									
5700	1/4"	1 Plum	24	.333	Ea.	94.50	14.20		108.70	128
5720	3/8"		24	.333		94.50	14.20		108.70	128
5730	1/2"		24	.333		94.50	14.20		108.70	128
5740	3/4"		20	.400		101	17.05		118.05	139
5750	1"		19	.421		119	17.95		136.95	161
5760	1-1/4"		15	.533		233	22.50		255.50	294

23 05 93 – Testing, Adjusting, and Balancing for HVAC

23 05 93.10 Balancing, Air

		Crew	Daily Output	Labor-Hours	Unit	Material	2014 Bare Costs Labor	2014 Bare Costs Equipment	Total	Total Incl O&P
0010	**BALANCING, AIR** (Subcontractor's quote incl. material and labor)									
0900	Heating and ventilating equipment									
1000	Centrifugal fans, utility sets				Ea.				365	400
1100	Heating and ventilating unit								545	600
1200	In-line fan								530	585

23 05 Common Work Results for HVAC

23 05 93 – Testing, Adjusting, and Balancing for HVAC

23 05 93.10 Balancing, Air

	23 05 93.10 Balancing, Air	Crew	Daily Output	Labor-Hours	Unit	Material	2014 Bare Costs Labor	Equipment	Total	Total Incl O&P
1300	Propeller and wall fan				Ea.				103	114
1400	Roof exhaust fan								243	267
2000	Air conditioning equipment, central station								790	870
2100	Built-up low pressure unit								730	800
2200	Built-up high pressure unit								850	935
2500	Multi-zone A.C. and heating unit								545	600
2600	For each zone over one, add								122	134
2700	Package A.C. unit								305	335
2800	Rooftop heating and cooling unit								425	470
3000	Supply, return, exhaust, registers & diffusers, avg. height ceiling								73	80
3100	High ceiling								109	120
3200	Floor height								61	67

23 05 93.20 Balancing, Water

	23 05 93.20 Balancing, Water	Crew	Daily Output	Labor-Hours	Unit	Material	2014 Bare Costs Labor	Equipment	Total	Total Incl O&P
0010	**BALANCING, WATER** (Subcontractor's quote incl. material and labor)									
0050	Air cooled condenser				Ea.				225	247
0080	Boiler								455	500
0100	Cabinet unit heater								77	85
0200	Chiller								545	600
0300	Convector								64.50	70.50
0500	Cooling tower								420	460
0600	Fan coil unit, unit ventilator								116	127
0700	Fin tube and radiant panels								129	141
0800	Main and duct re-heat coils								119	131
0810	Heat exchanger								119	131
1000	Pumps								283	310
1100	Unit heater								90	99

23 07 HVAC Insulation

23 07 13 – Duct Insulation

23 07 13.10 Duct Thermal Insulation

	23 07 13.10 Duct Thermal Insulation	Crew	Daily Output	Labor-Hours	Unit	Material	2014 Bare Costs Labor	Equipment	Total	Total Incl O&P
0010	**DUCT THERMAL INSULATION**									
0100	Rule of thumb, as a percentage of total mechanical costs				Job				10%	10%
0110	Insulation req'd. is based on the surface size/area to be covered									
3000	Ductwork									
3020	Blanket type, fiberglass, flexible									
3140	FSK vapor barrier wrap, .75 lb. density									
3160	1" thick	[G] Q-14	350	.046	S.F.	.19	1.56		1.75	2.85
3170	1-1/2" thick	[G]	320	.050		.23	1.70		1.93	3.14
3180	2" thick	[G]	300	.053		.27	1.82		2.09	3.38
3190	3" thick	[G]	260	.062		.38	2.10		2.48	3.98
3200	4" thick	[G]	242	.066		.64	2.25		2.89	4.52
3210	Vinyl jacket, same as FSK									
3280	Unfaced, 1 lb. density									
3310	1" thick	[G] Q-14	360	.044	S.F.	.20	1.51		1.71	2.79
3320	1-1/2" thick	[G]	330	.048		.25	1.65		1.90	3.08
3330	2" thick	[G]	310	.052		.33	1.76		2.09	3.34
3400	FSK facing, 1 lb. density									
3420	1-1/2" thick	[G] Q-14	310	.052	S.F.	.31	1.76		2.07	3.32
3430	2" thick	[G] "	300	.053	"	.37	1.82		2.19	3.49
3450	FSK facing, 1.5 lb. density									
3470	1-1/2" thick	[G] Q-14	300	.053	S.F.	.38	1.82		2.20	3.50

23 07 HVAC Insulation

23 07 13 – Duct Insulation

23 07 13.10 Duct Thermal Insulation

23 07 13.10 Duct Thermal Insulation		Crew	Daily Output	Labor-Hours	Unit	Material	2014 Bare Costs Labor	Equipment	Total	Total Incl O&P
3480	2" thick	G	Q-14	290	.055	S.F.	.46	1.88		2.34	3.70
3795	Finishes										
3800	Stainless steel woven mesh		Q-14	100	.160	S.F.	.74	5.45		6.19	10.05
3810	For .010" stainless steel, add			160	.100		2.88	3.41		6.29	8.95
3820	18 oz. fiberglass cloth, pasted on			170	.094		.67	3.21		3.88	6.20
3900	8 oz. canvas, pasted on			180	.089		.21	3.03		3.24	5.40
3940	For .016" aluminum jacket, add			200	.080		.92	2.73		3.65	5.65
7878	Contact cement, quart can					Ea.	10.50			10.50	11.55

23 07 16 – HVAC Equipment Insulation

23 07 16.10 HVAC Equipment Thermal Insulation

0010	**HVAC EQUIPMENT THERMAL INSULATION**										
0100	Rule of thumb, as a percentage of total mechanical costs					Job				10%	10%
0110	Insulation req'd. is based on the surface size/area to be covered										
1000	Boiler, 1-1/2" calcium silicate only	G	Q-14	110	.145	S.F.	3.77	4.96		8.73	12.55
1020	Plus 2" fiberglass	G	"	80	.200	"	4.74	6.80		11.54	16.75
2000	Breeching, 2" calcium silicate										
2020	Rectangular	G	Q-14	42	.381	S.F.	7.40	13		20.40	30
2040	Round	G	"	38.70	.413	"	7.70	14.10		21.80	32.50

23 09 Instrumentation and Control for HVAC

23 09 33 – Electric and Electronic Control System for HVAC

23 09 33.10 Electronic Control Systems

0010	**ELECTRONIC CONTROL SYSTEMS**										
0020	For electronic costs, add to Section 23 09 43.10					Ea.				15%	15%

23 09 43 – Pneumatic Control System for HVAC

23 09 43.10 Pneumatic Control Systems

0010	**PNEUMATIC CONTROL SYSTEMS**										
0011	Including a nominal 50 ft. of tubing. Add control panelboard if req'd.										
0100	Heating and ventilating, split system										
0200	Mixed air control, economizer cycle, panel readout, tubing										
0220	Up to 10 tons	G	Q-19	.68	35.294	Ea.	4,075	1,425		5,500	6,800
0240	For 10 to 20 tons	G		.63	37.915		4,350	1,525		5,875	7,300
0260	For over 20 tons	G		.58	41.096		4,725	1,650		6,375	7,925
0300	Heating coil, hot water, 3 way valve,										
0320	Freezestat, limit control on discharge, readout		Q-5	.69	23.088	Ea.	3,025	900		3,925	4,800
0500	Cooling coil, chilled water, room										
0520	Thermostat, 3 way valve		Q-5	2	8	Ea.	1,350	310		1,660	2,000
0600	Cooling tower, fan cycle, damper control,										
0620	Control system including water readout in/out at panel		Q-19	.67	35.821	Ea.	5,350	1,450		6,800	8,275
1000	Unit ventilator, day/night operation,										
1100	freezestat, ASHRAE, cycle 2		Q-19	.91	26.374	Ea.	2,975	1,050		4,025	5,000
2000	Compensated hot water from boiler, valve control,										
2100	readout and reset at panel, up to 60 GPM		Q-19	.55	43.956	Ea.	5,550	1,775		7,325	9,000
2120	For 120 GPM			.51	47.059		5,925	1,900		7,825	9,650
2140	For 240 GPM			.49	49.180		6,200	1,975		8,175	10,100
3000	Boiler room combustion air, damper to 5 S.F., controls			1.37	17.582		2,675	705		3,380	4,125
3500	Fan coil, heating and cooling valves, 4 pipe control system			3	8		1,200	320		1,520	1,850
3600	Heat exchanger system controls			.86	27.907		2,600	1,125		3,725	4,700
4000	Pneumatic thermostat, including controlling room radiator valve		Q-5	2.43	6.593		805	257		1,062	1,300
4060	Pump control system		Q-19	3	8		1,225	320		1,545	1,875

23 09 Instrumentation and Control for HVAC

23 09 43 – Pneumatic Control System for HVAC

23 09 43.10 Pneumatic Control Systems	Crew	Daily Output	Labor-Hours	Unit	Material	2014 Bare Costs Labor	Equipment	Total	Total Incl O&P
4500	Air supply for pneumatic control system									
4600	Tank mounted duplex compressor, starter, alternator,									
4620	piping, dryer, PRV station and filter									
4630	1/2 HP	Q-19	.68	35.139	Ea.	9,950	1,425		11,375	13,200
4660	1-1/2 HP		.58	41.739		12,100	1,675		13,775	16,200
4690	5 HP		.42	57.143		28,900	2,300		31,200	35,600

23 13 Facility Fuel-Storage Tanks

23 13 13 – Facility Underground Fuel-Oil, Storage Tanks

23 13 13.09 Single-Wall Steel Fuel-Oil Tanks

		Crew	Daily Output	Labor-Hours	Unit	Material	Labor	Equipment	Total	Total Incl O&P
0010	**SINGLE-WALL STEEL FUEL-OIL TANKS**									
5000	Tanks, steel ugnd., sti-p3, not incl. hold-down bars									
5500	Excavation, pad, pumps and piping not included									
5510	Single wall, 500 gallon capacity, 7 ga. shell	Q-5	2.70	5.926	Ea.	2,050	231		2,281	2,625
5520	1,000 gallon capacity, 7 ga. shell	"	2.50	6.400		3,825	249		4,074	4,600
5530	2,000 gallon capacity, 1/4" thick shell	Q-7	4.60	6.957		6,200	271		6,471	7,275
5535	2,500 gallon capacity, 7 ga. shell	Q-5	3	5.333		6,850	208		7,058	7,875
5540	5,000 gallon capacity, 1/4" thick shell	Q-7	3.20	10		11,500	390		11,890	13,300
5580	15,000 gallon capacity, 5/16" thick shell		1.70	18.824		19,000	735		19,735	22,100
5600	20,000 gallon capacity, 5/16" thick shell		1.50	21.333		36,300	830		37,130	41,400
5610	25,000 gallon capacity, 3/8" thick shell		1.30	24.615		37,900	960		38,860	43,300
5620	30,000 gallon capacity, 3/8" thick shell		1.10	29.091		38,400	1,125		39,525	44,100
5630	40,000 gallon capacity, 3/8" thick shell		.90	35.556		42,000	1,375		43,375	48,500
5640	50,000 gallon capacity, 3/8" thick shell		.80	40		46,600	1,550		48,150	54,000

23 13 13.23 Glass-Fiber-Reinfcd-Plastic, Fuel-Oil, Storage

		Crew	Daily Output	Labor-Hours	Unit	Material	Labor	Equipment	Total	Total Incl O&P
0010	**GLASS-FIBER-REINFCD-PLASTIC, UNDERGRND. FUEL-OIL, STORAGE**									
0210	Fiberglass, underground, single wall, U.L. listed, not including									
0220	manway or hold-down strap									
0240	2,000 gallon capacity	Q-7	4.57	7.002	Ea.	5,675	273		5,948	6,675
0245	3,000 gallon capacity		3.90	8.205		6,800	320		7,120	8,000
0250	4,000 gallon capacity		3.55	9.014		7,875	350		8,225	9,250
0255	5,000 gallon capacity		3.20	10		8,750	390		9,140	10,300
0260	6,000 gallon capacity		2.67	11.985		8,950	465		9,415	10,600
0280	10,000 gallon capacity		2	16		12,200	625		12,825	14,400
0284	15,000 gallon capacity		1.68	19.048		19,500	740		20,240	22,600
0290	20,000 gallon capacity		1.45	22.069		25,100	860		25,960	29,000
0500	For manway, fittings and hold-downs, add					20%	15%			
1020	Fiberglass, underground, double wall, U.L. listed									
1030	includes manways, not incl. hold-down straps									
1040	600 gallon capacity	Q-5	2.42	6.612	Ea.	6,850	258		7,108	7,950
1050	1,000 gallon capacity	"	2.25	7.111		9,350	277		9,627	10,800
1060	2,500 gallon capacity	Q-7	4.16	7.692		14,100	300		14,400	16,000
1070	3,000 gallon capacity		3.90	8.205		15,300	320		15,620	17,300
1080	4,000 gallon capacity		3.64	8.791		15,500	345		15,845	17,600
1090	6,000 gallon capacity		2.42	13.223		20,100	515		20,615	23,100
1100	8,000 gallon capacity		2.08	15.385		22,400	600		23,000	25,700
1110	10,000 gallon capacity		1.82	17.582		26,000	685		26,685	29,700
1120	12,000 gallon capacity		1.70	18.824		32,400	735		33,135	36,900
2210	Fiberglass, underground, single wall, U.L. listed, including									
2220	hold-down straps, no manways									
2240	2,000 gallon capacity	Q-7	3.55	9.014	Ea.	6,100	350		6,450	7,275

23 13 Facility Fuel-Storage Tanks

23 13 13 – Facility Underground Fuel-Oil, Storage Tanks

23 13 13.23 Glass-Fiber-Reinfcd-Plastic, Fuel-Oil, Storage

		Crew	Daily Output	Labor-Hours	Unit	Material	2014 Bare Costs Labor	Equipment	Total	Total Incl O&P
2250	4,000 gallon capacity	Q-7	2.90	11.034	Ea.	8,300	430		8,730	9,825
2260	6,000 gallon capacity		2	16		9,800	625		10,425	11,800
2280	10,000 gallon capacity		1.60	20		13,100	780		13,880	15,700
2284	15,000 gallon capacity		1.39	23.022		20,300	895		21,195	23,900
2290	20,000 gallon capacity		1.14	28.070		26,400	1,100		27,500	30,800
3020	Fiberglass, underground, double wall, U.L. listed									
3030	includes manways and hold-down straps									
3040	600 gallon capacity	Q-5	1.86	8.602	Ea.	7,275	335		7,610	8,550
3050	1,000 gallon capacity	"	1.70	9.412		9,775	365		10,140	11,400
3060	2,500 gallon capacity	Q-7	3.29	9.726		14,500	380		14,880	16,500
3070	3,000 gallon capacity		3.13	10.224		15,700	400		16,100	17,900
3080	4,000 gallon capacity		2.93	10.922		15,900	425		16,325	18,200
3090	6,000 gallon capacity		1.86	17.204		21,000	670		21,670	24,200
3100	8,000 gallon capacity		1.65	19.394		23,300	755		24,055	26,900
3110	10,000 gallon capacity		1.48	21.622		26,800	845		27,645	30,900
3120	12,000 gallon capacity		1.40	22.857		33,300	890		34,190	38,100

23 13 23 – Facility Aboveground Fuel-Oil, Storage Tanks

23 13 23.13 Vertical, Steel, Abvground Fuel-Oil, Stor. Tanks

		Crew	Daily Output	Labor-Hours	Unit	Material	2014 Bare Costs Labor	Equipment	Total	Total Incl O&P
0010	**VERTICAL, STEEL, ABOVEGROUND FUEL-OIL, STORAGE TANKS**									
4000	Fixed roof oil storage tanks, steel, (1 BBL=42 gal. w/foundation 3'D x 1'W)									
4200	5,000 barrels				Ea.				194,000	213,500
4300	24,000 barrels								333,500	367,000
4500	56,000 barrels								729,000	802,000
4600	110,000 barrels								1,060,000	1,166,000
4800	143,000 barrels								1,250,000	1,375,000
4900	225,000 barrels								1,360,000	1,496,000
5100	Floating roof gasoline tanks, steel, 5,000 barrels (w/foundation 3'D x 1'W)								204,000	225,000
5200	25,000 barrels								381,000	419,000
5400	55,000 barrels								839,000	923,000
5500	100,000 barrels								1,253,000	1,379,000
5700	150,000 barrels								1,532,000	1,685,000
5800	225,000 barrels								2,300,000	2,783,000

23 13 23.16 Horizontal, Stl, Abvgrd Fuel-Oil, Storage Tanks

		Crew	Daily Output	Labor-Hours	Unit	Material	2014 Bare Costs Labor	Equipment	Total	Total Incl O&P
0010	**HORIZONTAL, STEEL, ABOVEGROUND FUEL-OIL, STORAGE TANKS**									
3000	Steel, storage, above ground, including cradles, coating,									
3020	fittings, not including foundation, pumps or piping									
3040	Single wall, 275 gallon	Q-5	5	3.200	Ea.	490	125		615	745
3060	550 gallon	"	2.70	5.926		3,400	231		3,631	4,125
3080	1,000 gallon	Q-7	5	6.400		5,600	249		5,849	6,550
3100	1,500 gallon		4.75	6.737		7,975	263		8,238	9,200
3120	2,000 gallon		4.60	6.957		9,675	271		9,946	11,000
3140	5,000 gallon		3.20	10		19,100	390		19,490	21,600
3150	10,000 gallon		2	16		31,900	625		32,525	36,100
3160	15,000 gallon		1.70	18.824		41,000	735		41,735	46,300
3170	20,000 gallon		1.45	22.069		53,000	860		53,860	60,000
3180	25,000 gallon		1.30	24.615		62,000	960		62,960	69,500
3190	30,000 gallon		1.10	29.091		74,000	1,125		75,125	83,500
3320	Double wall, 500 gallon capacity	Q-5	2.40	6.667		2,625	260		2,885	3,300
3330	2000 gallon capacity	Q-7	4.15	7.711		9,975	300		10,275	11,500
3340	4000 gallon capacity		3.60	8.889		17,800	345		18,145	20,200
3350	6000 gallon capacity		2.40	13.333		21,000	520		21,520	24,000
3360	8000 gallon capacity		2	16		27,000	625		27,625	30,700

23 13 Facility Fuel-Storage Tanks

23 13 23 – Facility Aboveground Fuel-Oil, Storage Tanks

23 13 23.16 Horizontal, Stl, Abvgrd Fuel-Oil, Storage Tanks

		Crew	Daily Output	Labor-Hours	Unit	Material	2014 Bare Costs Labor	Equipment	Total	Total Incl O&P
3370	10000 gallon capacity	Q-7	1.80	17.778	Ea.	30,200	695		30,895	34,400
3380	15000 gallon capacity		1.50	21.333		45,900	830		46,730	52,000
3390	20000 gallon capacity		1.30	24.615		52,500	960		53,460	59,000
3400	25000 gallon capacity		1.15	27.826		63,500	1,075		64,575	72,000
3410	30000 gallon capacity		1	32		69,500	1,250		70,750	78,500

23 13 23.26 Horizontal, Conc., Abvgrd Fuel-Oil, Stor. Tanks

		Crew	Daily Output	Labor-Hours	Unit	Material	2014 Bare Costs Labor	Equipment	Total	Total Incl O&P
0010	**HORIZONTAL, CONCRETE, ABOVEGROUND FUEL-OIL, STORAGE TANKS**									
0050	Concrete, storage, above ground, including pad & pump									
0100	500 gallon	F-3	2	20	Ea.	10,000	655	330	10,985	12,500
0200	1,000 gallon	"	2	20		14,000	655	330	14,985	16,900
0300	2,000 gallon	F-4	2	20		18,000	655	570	19,225	21,500
0400	4,000 gallon		2	20		23,000	655	570	24,225	27,000
0500	8,000 gallon		2	20		36,000	655	570	37,225	41,300
0600	12,000 gallon		2	20		48,000	655	570	49,225	54,500

23 21 Hydronic Piping and Pumps

23 21 20 – Hydronic HVAC Piping Specialties

23 21 20.10 Air Control

		Crew	Daily Output	Labor-Hours	Unit	Material	2014 Bare Costs Labor	Equipment	Total	Total Incl O&P
0010	**AIR CONTROL**									
0030	Air separator, with strainer									
0040	2" diameter	Q-5	6	2.667	Ea.	1,175	104		1,279	1,475
0080	2-1/2" diameter		5	3.200		1,325	125		1,450	1,650
0100	3" diameter		4	4		2,050	156		2,206	2,500
0120	4" diameter		3	5.333		2,950	208		3,158	3,575
0130	5" diameter	Q-6	3.60	6.667		3,750	250		4,000	4,550
0140	6" diameter	"	3.40	7.059		4,500	265		4,765	5,375

23 21 20.18 Automatic Air Vent

		Crew	Daily Output	Labor-Hours	Unit	Material	2014 Bare Costs Labor	Equipment	Total	Total Incl O&P
0010	**AUTOMATIC AIR VENT**									
0020	Cast iron body, stainless steel internals, float type									
0060	1/2" NPT inlet, 300 psi	1 Stpi	12	.667	Ea.	107	29		136	166
0220	3/4" NPT inlet, 250 psi	"	10	.800		335	34.50		369.50	425
0340	1-1/2" NPT inlet, 250 psi	Q-5	12	1.333		1,050	52		1,102	1,225

23 21 20.42 Expansion Joints

		Crew	Daily Output	Labor-Hours	Unit	Material	2014 Bare Costs Labor	Equipment	Total	Total Incl O&P
0010	**EXPANSION JOINTS**									
0100	Bellows type, neoprene cover, flanged spool									
0140	6" face to face, 1-1/4" diameter	1 Stpi	11	.727	Ea.	255	31.50		286.50	335
0160	1-1/2" diameter	"	10.60	.755		255	32.50		287.50	335
0180	2" diameter	Q-5	13.30	1.203		258	47		305	360
0190	2-1/2" diameter		12.40	1.290		267	50.50		317.50	375
0200	3" diameter		11.40	1.404		299	54.50		353.50	420
0480	10" face to face, 2" diameter		13	1.231		370	48		418	490
0500	2-1/2" diameter		12	1.333		390	52		442	515
0520	3" diameter		11	1.455		400	56.50		456.50	535
0540	4" diameter		8	2		455	78		533	630
0560	5" diameter		7	2.286		540	89		629	740
0580	6" diameter		6	2.667		560	104		664	785

23 21 20.46 Expansion Tanks

		Crew	Daily Output	Labor-Hours	Unit	Material	2014 Bare Costs Labor	Equipment	Total	Total Incl O&P
0010	**EXPANSION TANKS**									
1507	Underground fuel-oil storage tanks, see Section 23 13 13									
1512	Tank leak detection systems, see Section 28 33 33.50									

23 21 20 – Hydronic HVAC Piping Specialties

23 21 20.46 Expansion Tanks

		Crew	Daily Output	Labor-Hours	Unit	Material	2014 Bare Costs Labor	Equipment	Total	Total Incl O&P
2000	Steel, liquid expansion, ASME, painted, 15 gallon capacity	Q-5	17	.941	Ea.	640	36.50		676.50	760
2020	24 gallon capacity		14	1.143		715	44.50		759.50	860
2040	30 gallon capacity		12	1.333		715	52		767	870
2060	40 gallon capacity		10	1.600		835	62.50		897.50	1,025
2080	60 gallon capacity		8	2		1,000	78		1,078	1,225
2100	80 gallon capacity		7	2.286		1,075	89		1,164	1,325
2120	100 gallon capacity		6	2.667		1,450	104		1,554	1,775
3000	Steel ASME expansion, rubber diaphragm, 19 gal. cap. accept.		12	1.333		2,425	52		2,477	2,750
3020	31 gallon capacity		8	2		2,700	78		2,778	3,100
3040	61 gallon capacity		6	2.667		3,800	104		3,904	4,350
3080	119 gallon capacity		4	4		4,100	156		4,256	4,750
3100	158 gallon capacity		3.80	4.211		5,675	164		5,839	6,525
3140	317 gallon capacity		2.80	5.714		8,575	223		8,798	9,800
3180	528 gallon capacity	▼	2.40	6.667	▼	13,900	260		14,160	15,700

23 21 20.58 Hydronic Heating Control Valves

		Crew	Daily Output	Labor-Hours	Unit	Material	2014 Bare Costs Labor	Equipment	Total	Total Incl O&P
0010	**HYDRONIC HEATING CONTROL VALVES**									
0050	Hot water, nonelectric, thermostatic									
0100	Radiator supply, 1/2" diameter	1 Stpi	24	.333	Ea.	68.50	14.45		82.95	99
0120	3/4" diameter		20	.400		68.50	17.30		85.80	104
0140	1" diameter		19	.421		88	18.25		106.25	127
0160	1-1/4" diameter	▼	15	.533	▼	212	23		235	271
0500	For low pressure steam, add					25%				

23 21 20.70 Steam Traps

		Crew	Daily Output	Labor-Hours	Unit	Material	2014 Bare Costs Labor	Equipment	Total	Total Incl O&P
0010	**STEAM TRAPS**									
0030	Cast iron body, threaded									
0040	Inverted bucket									
0050	1/2" pipe size	1 Stpi	12	.667	Ea.	152	29		181	215
0070	3/4" pipe size		10	.800		266	34.50		300.50	350
0100	1" pipe size		9	.889		410	38.50		448.50	515
0120	1-1/4" pipe size	▼	8	1	▼	615	43.50		658.50	750
1000	Float & thermostatic, 15 psi									
1010	3/4" pipe size	1 Stpi	16	.500	Ea.	124	21.50		145.50	173
1020	1" pipe size		15	.533		150	23		173	202
1040	1-1/2" pipe size		9	.889		263	38.50		301.50	355
1060	2" pipe size	▼	6	1.333		485	57.50		542.50	625

23 21 20.76 Strainers, Y Type, Bronze Body

		Crew	Daily Output	Labor-Hours	Unit	Material	2014 Bare Costs Labor	Equipment	Total	Total Incl O&P
0010	**STRAINERS, Y TYPE, BRONZE BODY**									
0050	Screwed, 125 lb., 1/4" pipe size	1 Stpi	24	.333	Ea.	23	14.45		37.45	49.50
0070	3/8" pipe size		24	.333		27.50	14.45		41.95	54.50
0100	1/2" pipe size		20	.400		27.50	17.30		44.80	59
0140	1" pipe size		17	.471		40.50	20.50		61	78
0160	1-1/2" pipe size		14	.571		87.50	24.50		112	137
0180	2" pipe size		13	.615		116	26.50		142.50	172
0182	3" pipe size	▼	12	.667		845	29		874	980
0200	300 lb., 2-1/2" pipe size	Q-5	17	.941		510	36.50		546.50	620
0220	3" pipe size		16	1		1,000	39		1,039	1,175
0240	4" pipe size	▼	15	1.067	▼	2,300	41.50		2,341.50	2,600
0500	For 300 lb. rating 1/4" thru 2", add					15%				
1000	Flanged, 150 lb., 1-1/2" pipe size	1 Stpi	11	.727	Ea.	475	31.50		506.50	570
1020	2" pipe size	"	8	1		640	43.50		683.50	775
1030	2-1/2" pipe size	Q-5	5	3.200		950	125		1,075	1,250
1040	3" pipe size	▼	4.50	3.556	▼	1,175	139		1,314	1,500

23 21 20 – Hydronic HVAC Piping Specialties

23 21 20.76 Strainers, Y Type, Bronze Body		Crew	Daily Output	Labor-Hours	Unit	Material	2014 Bare Costs Labor	Equipment	Total	Total Incl O&P
1060	4" pipe size	Q-5	3	5.333	Ea.	1,775	208		1,983	2,300
1100	6" pipe size	Q-6	3	8		3,400	300		3,700	4,225
1106	8" pipe size	"	2.60	9.231		3,725	345		4,070	4,675
1500	For 300 lb. rating, add					40%				

23 21 20.78 Strainers, Y Type, Iron Body

		Crew	Daily Output	Labor-Hours	Unit	Material	Labor	Equipment	Total	Total Incl O&P
0010	**STRAINERS, Y TYPE, IRON BODY**									
0050	Screwed, 250 lb., 1/4" pipe size	1 Stpi	20	.400	Ea.	11.05	17.30		28.35	40.50
0070	3/8" pipe size		20	.400		11.05	17.30		28.35	40.50
0100	1/2" pipe size		20	.400		11.05	17.30		28.35	40.50
0140	1" pipe size		16	.500		18.25	21.50		39.75	55.50
0160	1-1/2" pipe size		12	.667		30	29		59	80
0180	2" pipe size		8	1		44.50	43.50		88	121
0220	3" pipe size	Q-5	11	1.455		289	56.50		345.50	415
0240	4" pipe size	"	5	3.200		490	125		615	745
0500	For galvanized body, add					50%				
1000	Flanged, 125 lb., 1-1/2" pipe size	1 Stpi	11	.727	Ea.	155	31.50		186.50	222
1020	2" pipe size	"	8	1		113	43.50		156.50	196
1040	3" pipe size	Q-5	4.50	3.556		150	139		289	395
1060	4" pipe size	"	3	5.333		247	208		455	615
1080	5" pipe size	Q-6	3.40	7.059		385	265		650	860
1100	6" pipe size	"	3	8		495	300		795	1,050
1500	For 250 lb. rating, add					20%				
2000	For galvanized body, add					50%				
2500	For steel body, add					40%				

23 21 20.88 Venturi Flow

		Crew	Daily Output	Labor-Hours	Unit	Material	Labor	Equipment	Total	Total Incl O&P
0010	**VENTURI FLOW**, Measuring device									
0050	1/2" diameter	1 Stpi	24	.333	Ea.	281	14.45		295.45	335
0120	1" diameter		19	.421		276	18.25		294.25	335
0140	1-1/4" diameter		15	.533		340	23		363	415
0160	1-1/2" diameter		13	.615		355	26.50		381.50	435
0180	2" diameter		11	.727		365	31.50		396.50	455
0220	3" diameter	Q-5	14	1.143		515	44.50		559.50	645
0240	4" diameter	"	11	1.455		775	56.50		831.50	945
0280	6" diameter	Q-6	3.50	6.857		1,125	257		1,382	1,675
0500	For meter, add					2,125			2,125	2,350

23 21 23 – Hydronic Pumps

23 21 23.13 In-Line Centrifugal Hydronic Pumps

		Crew	Daily Output	Labor-Hours	Unit	Material	Labor	Equipment	Total	Total Incl O&P
0010	**IN-LINE CENTRIFUGAL HYDRONIC PUMPS**									
0600	Bronze, sweat connections, 1/40 HP, in line									
0640	3/4" size	Q-1	16	1	Ea.	212	38.50		250.50	297
1000	Flange connection, 3/4" to 1-1/2" size									
1040	1/12 HP	Q-1	6	2.667	Ea.	545	102		647	770
1060	1/8 HP		6	2.667		940	102		1,042	1,200
1100	1/3 HP		6	2.667		1,050	102		1,152	1,325
1140	2" size, 1/6 HP		5	3.200		1,350	123		1,473	1,675
1180	2-1/2" size, 1/4 HP		5	3.200		1,775	123		1,898	2,150
2000	Cast iron, flange connection									
2040	3/4" to 1-1/2" size, in line, 1/12 HP	Q-1	6	2.667	Ea.	355	102		457	560
2101	Pumps, circulating, 3/4" to 1-1/2" size, 1/3 HP		6	2.667		765	102		867	1,025
2140	2" size, 1/6 HP		5	3.200		720	123		843	1,000
2180	2-1/2" size, 1/4 HP		5	3.200		960	123		1,083	1,250
2220	3" size, 1/4 HP		4	4		975	153		1,128	1,325

23 21 Hydronic Piping and Pumps

23 21 23 – Hydronic Pumps

23 21 23.13 In-Line Centrifugal Hydronic Pumps	Crew	Daily Output	Labor-Hours	Unit	Material	2014 Bare Costs Labor	Equipment	Total	Total Incl O&P
2600	For nonferrous impeller, add					3%			

23 21 29 – Automatic Condensate Pump Units

23 21 29.10 Condensate Removal Pump System

		Crew	Daily Output	Labor-Hours	Unit	Material	Labor	Equipment	Total	Total Incl O&P
0010	**CONDENSATE REMOVAL PUMP SYSTEM**									
0020	Pump with 1 gal. ABS tank									
0100	115 V									
0120	1/50 HP, 200 GPH [G]	1 Stpi	12	.667	Ea.	191	29		220	258
0140	1/18 HP, 270 GPH [G]		10	.800		204	34.50		238.50	281
0160	1/5 HP, 450 GPH [G]		8	1		455	43.50		498.50	570
0200	230 V									
0240	1/18 HP, 270 GPH [G]	1 Stpi	10	.800	Ea.	211	34.50		245.50	289
0260	1/5 HP, 450 GPH [G]	"	8	1	"	505	43.50		548.50	625

23 22 Steam and Condensate Piping and Pumps

23 22 13 – Steam and Condensate Heating Piping

23 22 13.23 Aboveground Steam and Condensate Piping

		Crew	Daily Output	Labor-Hours	Unit	Material	Labor	Equipment	Total	Total Incl O&P
0010	**ABOVEGROUND STEAM AND CONDENSATE HEATING PIPING**									
0020	Condensate meter									
0100	500 lb. per hour	1 Stpi	14	.571	Ea.	3,275	24.50		3,299.50	3,650
0140	1500 lb. per hour	"	7	1.143	"	3,575	49.50		3,624.50	4,000

23 22 23 – Steam Condensate Pumps

23 22 23.10 Condensate Return System

		Crew	Daily Output	Labor-Hours	Unit	Material	Labor	Equipment	Total	Total Incl O&P
0010	**CONDENSATE RETURN SYSTEM**									
2000	Simplex									
2010	With pump, motor, CI receiver, float switch									
2020	3/4 HP, 15 GPM	Q-1	1.80	8.889	Ea.	6,100	340		6,440	7,275
2100	Duplex									
2110	With 2 pumps and motors, CI receiver, float switch, alternator									
2120	3/4 HP, 15 GPM, 15 gal. CI rcvr.	Q-1	1.40	11.429	Ea.	6,675	440		7,115	8,050
2130	1 HP, 25 GPM		1.20	13.333		8,000	510		8,510	9,650
2140	1-1/2 HP, 45 GPM		1	16		9,300	615		9,915	11,200
2150	1-1/2 HP, 60 GPM		1	16		10,400	615		11,015	12,500

23 31 HVAC Ducts and Casings

23 31 13 – Metal Ducts

23 31 13.13 Rectangular Metal Ducts

			Crew	Daily Output	Labor-Hours	Unit	Material	Labor	Equipment	Total	Total Incl O&P
0010	**RECTANGULAR METAL DUCTS**	R233100-20									
0020	Fabricated rectangular, includes fittings, joints, supports,										
0021	allowance for flexible connections and field sketches.										
0030	Does not include "as-built dwgs." or insulation.										
0031	NOTE: Fabrication and installation are combined										
0040	as LABOR cost. Approx. 25% fittings assumed.										
0042	Fabrication/Inst. is to commercial quality standards										
0043	(SMACNA or equiv.) for structure, sealing, leak testing, etc.										
0100	Aluminum, alloy 3003-H14, under 100 lb.		Q-10	75	.320	Lb.	3.66	12.10		15.76	24
0110	100 to 500 lb.			80	.300		2.38	11.35		13.73	21.50
0120	500 to 1,000 lb.			95	.253		2.25	9.55		11.80	18.40
0140	1,000 to 2,000 lb.			120	.200		2.16	7.55		9.71	15

23 31 HVAC Ducts and Casings

23 31 13 – Metal Ducts

23 31 13.13 Rectangular Metal Ducts

		Crew	Daily Output	Labor-Hours	Unit	Material	2014 Bare Costs Labor	2014 Bare Costs Equipment	Total	Total Incl O&P
0150	2,000 to 5,000 lb.	Q-10	130	.185	Lb.	2.16	6.95		9.11	14
0160	Over 5,000 lb.		145	.166		2.16	6.25		8.41	12.80
0500	Galvanized steel, under 200 lb.		235	.102		.66	3.86		4.52	7.20
0520	200 to 500 lb.		245	.098		.62	3.70		4.32	6.85
0540	500 to 1,000 lb.		255	.094		.61	3.55		4.16	6.55
0560	1,000 to 2,000 lb.		265	.091		.60	3.42		4.02	6.35
0580	Over 5,000 lb.		285	.084		.60	3.18		3.78	5.95
1000	Stainless steel, type 304, under 100 lb.		165	.145		6.35	5.50		11.85	16.10
1020	100 to 500 lb.		175	.137		4.05	5.20		9.25	13.10
1030	500 to 1,000 lb.		190	.126		2.95	4.77		7.72	11.20
1040	1,000 to 2,000 lb.		200	.120		2.89	4.53		7.42	10.75
1050	2,000 to 5,000 lb.		225	.107		2.39	4.03		6.42	9.35
1060	Over 5,000 lb.		235	.102		2.35	3.86		6.21	9.05
1100	For medium pressure ductwork, add						15%			
1200	For high pressure ductwork, add						40%			
1210	For welded ductwork, add						85%			
1220	For 30% fittings, add						11%			
1224	For 40% fittings, add						34%			
1228	For 50% fittings, add						56%			
1232	For 60% fittings, add						79%			
1236	For 70% fittings, add						101%			
1240	For 80% fittings, add						124%			
1244	For 90% fittings, add						147%			
1248	For 100% fittings, add						169%			
1252	Note: Fittings add includes time for detailing and installation.									

23 31 13.19 Metal Duct Fittings

		Crew	Daily Output	Labor-Hours	Unit	Material	2014 Bare Costs Labor	2014 Bare Costs Equipment	Total	Total Incl O&P
0010	**METAL DUCT FITTINGS**									
2000	Fabrics for flexible connections, with metal edge	1 Shee	100	.080	L.F.	3.44	3.24		6.68	9.20
2100	Without metal edge	"	160	.050	"	2.46	2.02		4.48	6.10

23 31 16 – Nonmetal Ducts

23 31 16.13 Fibrous-Glass Ducts

		Crew	Daily Output	Labor-Hours	Unit	Material	2014 Bare Costs Labor	2014 Bare Costs Equipment	Total	Total Incl O&P
0010	**FIBROUS-GLASS DUCTS**	R233100-20								
3490	Rigid fiberglass duct board, foil reinf. kraft facing									
3500	Rectangular, 1" thick, alum. faced, (FRK), std. weight	Q-10	350	.069	SF Surf	.77	2.59		3.36	5.15

23 33 Air Duct Accessories

23 33 13 – Dampers

23 33 13.13 Volume-Control Dampers

		Crew	Daily Output	Labor-Hours	Unit	Material	2014 Bare Costs Labor	2014 Bare Costs Equipment	Total	Total Incl O&P
0010	**VOLUME-CONTROL DAMPERS**									
5990	Multi-blade dampers, opposed blade, 8" x 6"	1 Shee	24	.333	Ea.	21.50	13.50		35	46.50
5994	8" x 8"		22	.364		22.50	14.70		37.20	49
5996	10" x 10"		21	.381		26.50	15.40		41.90	55
6000	12" x 12"		21	.381		29.50	15.40		44.90	58
6020	12" x 18"		18	.444		39.50	18		57.50	73.50
6030	14" x 10"		20	.400		29	16.20		45.20	58.50
6031	14" x 14"		17	.471		35.50	19.05		54.55	70.50
6033	16" x 12"		17	.471		35.50	19.05		54.55	70.50
6035	16" x 16"		16	.500		44	20		64	82
6037	18" x 16"		15	.533		48	21.50		69.50	89
6038	18" x 18"		15	.533		52	21.50		73.50	93

23 33 AirDuct Accessories

23 33 13 – Dampers

23 33 13.13 Volume-Control Dampers

		Crew	Daily Output	Labor-Hours	Unit	Material	2014 Bare Costs Labor	2014 Bare Costs Equipment	Total	Total Incl O&P
6070	20" x 16"	1 Shee	14	.571	Ea.	52	23		75	95.50
6072	20" x 20"		13	.615		62.50	25		87.50	111
6074	22" x 18"		14	.571		62.50	23		85.50	108
6076	24" x 16"		11	.727		61	29.50		90.50	117
6078	24" x 20"		8	1		72.50	40.50		113	148
6080	24" x 24"		8	1		85	40.50		125.50	161
6110	26" x 26"		6	1.333		95	54		149	195
6133	30" x 30"	Q-9	6.60	2.424		137	88		225	297
6135	32" x 32"		6.40	2.500		154	91		245	320
6180	48" x 36"		5.60	2.857		253	104		357	450
8000	Multi-blade dampers, parallel blade									
8100	8" x 8"	1 Shee	24	.333	Ea.	82	13.50		95.50	113
8140	16" x 10"		20	.400		103	16.20		119.20	141
8200	24" x 16"		11	.727		134	29.50		163.50	197
8260	30" x 18"		7	1.143		186	46		232	281

23 33 13.16 Fire Dampers

		Crew	Daily Output	Labor-Hours	Unit	Material	2014 Bare Costs Labor	2014 Bare Costs Equipment	Total	Total Incl O&P
0010	**FIRE DAMPERS**									
3000	Fire damper, curtain type, 1-1/2 hr. rated, vertical, 6" x 6"	1 Shee	24	.333	Ea.	24	13.50		37.50	49
3020	8" x 6"		22	.364		24	14.70		38.70	51
3240	16" x 14"		18	.444		44	18		62	78.50
3400	24" x 20"		8	1		54	40.50		94.50	127

23 33 13.28 Splitter Damper Assembly

		Crew	Daily Output	Labor-Hours	Unit	Material	2014 Bare Costs Labor	2014 Bare Costs Equipment	Total	Total Incl O&P
0010	**SPLITTER DAMPER ASSEMBLY**									
7000	Self locking, 1' rod	1 Shee	24	.333	Ea.	23.50	13.50		37	48
7020	3' rod		22	.364		30	14.70		44.70	57.50
7040	4' rod		20	.400		33.50	16.20		49.70	64
7060	6' rod		18	.444		41	18		59	75

23 33 19 – Duct Silencers

23 33 19.10 Duct Silencers

		Crew	Daily Output	Labor-Hours	Unit	Material	2014 Bare Costs Labor	2014 Bare Costs Equipment	Total	Total Incl O&P
0010	**DUCT SILENCERS**									
9000	Silencers, noise control for air flow, duct				MCFM	57			57	63

23 33 33 – Duct-Mounting Access Doors

23 33 33.13 Duct Access Doors

		Crew	Daily Output	Labor-Hours	Unit	Material	2014 Bare Costs Labor	2014 Bare Costs Equipment	Total	Total Incl O&P
0010	**DUCT ACCESS DOORS**									
1000	Duct access door, insulated, 6" x 6"	1 Shee	14	.571	Ea.	16.05	23		39.05	56
1020	10" x 10"		11	.727		18.45	29.50		47.95	69.50
1040	12" x 12"		10	.800		20	32.50		52.50	76
1050	12" x 18"		9	.889		37	36		73	101
1070	18" x 18"		8	1		32.50	40.50		73	103
1074	24" x 18"		8	1		44	40.50		84.50	116

23 33 46 – Flexible Ducts

23 33 46.10 Flexible Air Ducts

		Crew	Daily Output	Labor-Hours	Unit	Material	2014 Bare Costs Labor	2014 Bare Costs Equipment	Total	Total Incl O&P
0010	**FLEXIBLE AIR DUCTS** R233100-20									
1300	Flexible, coated fiberglass fabric on corr. resist. metal helix									
1400	pressure to 12" (WG) UL-181									
1500	Noninsulated, 3" diameter	Q-9	400	.040	L.F.	1.12	1.46		2.58	3.66
1540	5" diameter		320	.050		1.30	1.82		3.12	4.47
1561	Ductwork, flexible, non-insulated, 6" diameter		280	.057		1.50	2.08		3.58	5.10
1580	7" diameter		240	.067		1.53	2.43		3.96	5.75
1600	8" diameter		200	.080		1.91	2.91		4.82	6.95

23 33 Air Duct Accessories

23 33 46 – Flexible Ducts

23 33 46.10 Flexible Air Ducts

23 33 46.10 Flexible Air Ducts		Crew	Daily Output	Labor-Hours	Unit	Material	2014 Bare Costs Labor	Equipment	Total	Total Incl O&P
1640	10" diameter	Q-9	160	.100	L.F.	2.46	3.64		6.10	8.75
1660	12" diameter		120	.133		2.94	4.85		7.79	11.35
1900	Insulated, 1" thick, PE jacket, 3" diameter [G]		380	.042		2.60	1.53		4.13	5.40
1910	4" diameter [G]		340	.047		2.60	1.71		4.31	5.70
1920	5" diameter [G]		300	.053		2.60	1.94		4.54	6.10
1940	6" diameter [G]		260	.062		2.94	2.24		5.18	6.95
1960	7" diameter [G]		220	.073		3.20	2.65		5.85	7.95
1980	8" diameter [G]		180	.089		3.49	3.24		6.73	9.25
2020	10" diameter [G]		140	.114		4.25	4.16		8.41	11.65
2040	12" diameter [G]	↓	100	.160	↓	4.90	5.80		10.70	15.10

23 33 53 – Duct Liners

23 33 53.10 Duct Liner Board

23 33 53.10 Duct Liner Board		Crew	Daily Output	Labor-Hours	Unit	Material	2014 Bare Costs Labor	Equipment	Total	Total Incl O&P
0010	**DUCT LINER BOARD**									
3340	Board type fiberglass liner, FSK, 1-1/2 lb. density									
3344	1" thick [G]	Q-14	150	.107	S.F.	.60	3.64		4.24	6.80
3345	1-1/2" thick [G]		130	.123		.66	4.19		4.85	7.85
3346	2" thick [G]		120	.133		.77	4.54		5.31	8.55
3348	3" thick [G]		110	.145		.99	4.96		5.95	9.50
3350	4" thick [G]		100	.160		1.22	5.45		6.67	10.60
3356	3 lb. density, 1" thick [G]		150	.107		.77	3.64		4.41	7
3358	1-1/2" thick [G]		130	.123		.97	4.19		5.16	8.15
3360	2" thick [G]		120	.133		1.18	4.54		5.72	9
3362	2-1/2" thick [G]		110	.145		1.38	4.96		6.34	9.90
3364	3" thick [G]		100	.160		1.59	5.45		7.04	11
3366	4" thick [G]		90	.178		2	6.05		8.05	12.50
3370	6 lb. density, 1" thick [G]		140	.114		1.09	3.90		4.99	7.80
3374	1-1/2" thick [G]		120	.133		1.46	4.54		6	9.30
3378	2" thick [G]	↓	100	.160	↓	1.82	5.45		7.27	11.25
3490	Board type, fiberglass liner, 3 lb. density									
3680	No finish									
3700	1" thick [G]	Q-14	170	.094	S.F.	.43	3.21		3.64	5.90
3710	1-1/2" thick [G]		140	.114		.64	3.90		4.54	7.30
3720	2" thick [G]	↓	130	.123	↓	.86	4.19		5.05	8.05
3940	Board type, non-fibrous foam									
3950	Temperature, bacteria and fungi resistant									
3960	1" thick [G]	Q-14	150	.107	S.F.	2.38	3.64		6.02	8.75
3970	1-1/2" thick [G]		130	.123		3.28	4.19		7.47	10.70
3980	2" thick [G]	↓	120	.133	↓	3.98	4.54		8.52	12.10

23 34 HVAC Fans

23 34 13 – Axial HVAC Fans

23 34 13.10 Axial Flow HVAC Fans

23 34 13.10 Axial Flow HVAC Fans		Crew	Daily Output	Labor-Hours	Unit	Material	2014 Bare Costs Labor	Equipment	Total	Total Incl O&P
0010	**AXIAL FLOW HVAC FANS** R233400-10									
0020	Air conditioning and process air handling									
0030	Axial flow, compact, low sound, 2.5" S.P.									
0050	3,800 CFM, 5 HP	Q-20	3.40	5.882	Ea.	5,025	222		5,247	5,925
0080	6,400 CFM, 5 HP		2.80	7.143		5,625	269		5,894	6,650
0100	10,500 CFM, 7-1/2 HP		2.40	8.333		7,000	315		7,315	8,225
0120	15,600 CFM, 10 HP		1.60	12.500		8,825	470		9,295	10,500
1500	Vaneaxial, low pressure, 2000 CFM, 1/2 HP	↓	3.60	5.556	↓	2,150	209		2,359	2,725

23 34 HVAC Fans

23 34 13 – Axial HVAC Fans

23 34 13.10 Axial Flow HVAC Fans

	Crew	Daily Output	Labor-Hours	Unit	Material	2014 Bare Costs Labor	Equipment	Total	Total Incl O&P
1520	4,000 CFM, 1 HP	Q-20	3.20	6.250	Ea.	2,525	235		2,760	3,175
1540	8,000 CFM, 2 HP	↓	2.80	7.143	↓	3,200	269		3,469	3,950

23 34 14 – Blower HVAC Fans

23 34 14.10 Blower Type HVAC Fans

		Crew	Daily Output	Labor-Hours	Unit	Material	Labor	Equipment	Total	Total Incl O&P
0010	BLOWER TYPE HVAC FANS									
2500	Ceiling fan, right angle, extra quiet, 0.10" S.P.									
2520	95 CFM	Q-20	20	1	Ea.	287	37.50		324.50	380
2540	210 CFM		19	1.053		340	39.50		379.50	440
2560	385 CFM		18	1.111		430	42		472	545
2580	885 CFM		16	1.250		850	47		897	1,025
2600	1,650 CFM		13	1.538		1,175	58		1,233	1,400
2620	2,960 CFM	↓	11	1.818		1,575	68.50		1,643.50	1,850
2640	For wall or roof cap, add	1 Shee	16	.500		287	20		307	350
2660	For straight thru fan, add					10%				
2680	For speed control switch, add	1 Elec	16	.500	↓	157	21.50		178.50	207
7500	Utility set, steel construction, pedestal, 1/4" S.P.									
7520	Direct drive, 150 CFM, 1/8 HP	Q-20	6.40	3.125	Ea.	845	118		963	1,125
7540	485 CFM, 1/6 HP		5.80	3.448		1,075	130		1,205	1,400
7560	1950 CFM, 1/2 HP		4.80	4.167		1,250	157		1,407	1,625
7580	2410 CFM, 3/4 HP		4.40	4.545		2,300	171		2,471	2,800
7600	3328 CFM, 1-1/2 HP	↓	3	6.667	↓	2,575	251		2,826	3,250
7680	V-belt drive, drive cover, 3 phase									
7700	800 CFM, 1/4 HP	Q-20	6	3.333	Ea.	955	126		1,081	1,250
7720	1,300 CFM, 1/3 HP		5	4		1,000	151		1,151	1,350
7740	2,000 CFM, 1 HP		4.60	4.348		1,175	164		1,339	1,575
7760	2,900 CFM, 3/4 HP	↓	4.20	4.762	↓	1,600	179		1,779	2,050

23 34 16 – Centrifugal HVAC Fans

23 34 16.10 Centrifugal Type HVAC Fans

		Crew	Daily Output	Labor-Hours	Unit	Material	Labor	Equipment	Total	Total Incl O&P
0010	CENTRIFUGAL TYPE HVAC FANS									
0200	In-line centrifugal, supply/exhaust booster									
0220	aluminum wheel/hub, disconnect switch, 1/4" S.P.									
0240	500 CFM, 10" diameter connection	Q-20	3	6.667	Ea.	1,250	251		1,501	1,800
0260	1,380 CFM, 12" diameter connection		2	10		1,325	375		1,700	2,075
0280	1,520 CFM, 16" diameter connection		2	10		1,450	375		1,825	2,225
0300	2,560 CFM, 18" diameter connection		1	20		1,575	755		2,330	2,975
0320	3,480 CFM, 20" diameter connection		.80	25		1,875	940		2,815	3,625
0326	5,080 CFM, 20" diameter connection	↓	.75	26.667	↓	2,025	1,000		3,025	3,900
3500	Centrifugal, airfoil, motor and drive, complete									
3520	1000 CFM, 1/2 HP	Q-20	2.50	8	Ea.	1,850	300		2,150	2,525
3540	2,000 CFM, 1 HP		2	10		2,075	375		2,450	2,925
3560	4,000 CFM, 3 HP		1.80	11.111		2,650	420		3,070	3,600
3580	8,000 CFM, 7-1/2 HP		1.40	14.286		3,975	540		4,515	5,275
3600	12,000 CFM, 10 HP	↓	1	20	↓	5,300	755		6,055	7,075
5000	Utility set, centrifugal, V belt drive, motor									
5020	1/4" S.P., 1200 CFM, 1/4 HP	Q-20	6	3.333	Ea.	1,650	126		1,776	2,025
5040	1520 CFM, 1/3 HP		5	4		2,125	151		2,276	2,600
5060	1850 CFM, 1/2 HP		4	5		2,125	188		2,313	2,650
5080	2180 CFM, 3/4 HP		3	6.667		2,525	251		2,776	3,200
5100	1/2" S.P., 3600 CFM, 1 HP		2	10		2,975	375		3,350	3,900
5120	4250 CFM, 1-1/2 HP		1.60	12.500		3,150	470		3,620	4,250
5140	4800 CFM, 2 HP	↓	1.40	14.286	↓	3,825	540		4,365	5,100
7000	Roof exhauster, centrifugal, aluminum housing, 12" galvanized									

23 34 HVAC Fans

23 34 16 – Centrifugal HVAC Fans

23 34 16.10 Centrifugal Type HVAC Fans

		Crew	Daily Output	Labor-Hours	Unit	Material	2014 Bare Costs Labor	Equipment	Total	Total Incl O&P
7020	curb, bird screen, back draft damper, 1/4" S.P.									
7100	Direct drive, 320 CFM, 11" sq. damper	Q-20	7	2.857	Ea.	665	108		773	915
7120	600 CFM, 11" sq. damper		6	3.333		865	126		991	1,150
7140	815 CFM, 13" sq. damper		5	4		865	151		1,016	1,200
7160	1450 CFM, 13" sq. damper		4.20	4.762		1,400	179		1,579	1,850
7180	2050 CFM, 16" sq. damper		4	5		1,675	188		1,863	2,175
7200	V-belt drive, 1650 CFM, 12" sq. damper		6	3.333		1,250	126		1,376	1,600
7220	2750 CFM, 21" sq. damper		5	4		1,500	151		1,651	1,900
7230	3500 CFM, 21" sq. damper		4.50	4.444		1,675	167		1,842	2,125
7240	4910 CFM, 23" sq. damper		4	5		2,050	188		2,238	2,600
7260	8525 CFM, 28" sq. damper		3	6.667		2,725	251		2,976	3,425
7280	13,760 CFM, 35" sq. damper		2	10		3,800	375		4,175	4,825
7300	20,558 CFM, 43" sq. damper	▼	1	20		7,625	755		8,380	9,625
7320	For 2 speed winding, add					15%				
7340	For explosionproof motor, add					580			580	635
7360	For belt driven, top discharge, add				▼	15%				
8500	Wall exhausters, centrifugal, auto damper, 1/8" S.P.									
8520	Direct drive, 610 CFM, 1/20 HP	Q-20	14	1.429	Ea.	405	54		459	535
8540	796 CFM, 1/12 HP		13	1.538		845	58		903	1,025
8560	822 CFM, 1/6 HP		12	1.667		1,025	63		1,088	1,225
8580	1,320 CFM, 1/4 HP	▼	12	1.667	▼	2,125	63		2,188	2,425
9500	V-belt drive, 3 phase									
9520	2,800 CFM, 1/4 HP	Q-20	9	2.222	Ea.	1,825	83.50		1,908.50	2,150
9540	3,740 CFM, 1/2 HP	"	8	2.500	"	1,900	94		1,994	2,250

23 34 23 – HVAC Power Ventilators

23 34 23.10 HVAC Power Circulators and Ventilators

			Crew	Daily Output	Labor-Hours	Unit	Material	Labor	Equipment	Total	Total Incl O&P
0010	**HVAC POWER CIRCULATORS AND VENTILATORS**										
3000	Paddle blade air circulator, 3 speed switch										
3020	42", 5,000 CFM high, 3000 CFM low	G	1 Elec	2.40	3.333	Ea.	163	142		305	410
3040	52", 6,500 CFM high, 4000 CFM low	G	"	2.20	3.636	"	170	155		325	440
3100	For antique white motor, same cost										
3200	For brass plated motor, same cost										
3300	For light adaptor kit, add	G				Ea.	41			41	45
6000	Propeller exhaust, wall shutter										
6020	Direct drive, one speed, .075" S.P.										
6100	653 CFM, 1/30 HP		Q-20	10	2	Ea.	183	75.50		258.50	325
6120	1033 CFM, 1/20 HP			9	2.222		273	83.50		356.50	440
6140	1323 CFM, 1/15 HP		▼	8	2.500	▼	305	94		399	490
6300	V-belt drive, 3 phase										
6320	6175 CFM, 3/4 HP		Q-20	5	4	Ea.	2,850	151		3,001	3,375
6340	7500 CFM, 3/4 HP			5	4		2,925	151		3,076	3,450
6360	10,100 CFM, 1 HP			4.50	4.444		3,075	167		3,242	3,650
6380	14,300 CFM, 1-1/2 HP		▼	4	5	▼	3,325	188		3,513	3,975
6650	Residential, bath exhaust, grille, back draft damper										
6660	50 CFM		Q-20	24	.833	Ea.	61	31.50		92.50	120
6670	110 CFM			22	.909		94.50	34		128.50	161
6680	Light combination, squirrel cage, 100 watt, 70 CFM		▼	24	.833	▼	108	31.50		139.50	170
6700	Light/heater combination, ceiling mounted										
6710	70 CFM, 1450 watt		Q-20	24	.833	Ea.	155	31.50		186.50	223
6800	Heater combination, recessed, 70 CFM			24	.833		64.50	31.50		96	123
6820	With 2 infrared bulbs			23	.870		101	33		134	166
6900	Kitchen exhaust, grille, complete, 160 CFM			22	.909		104	34		138	171

23 34 HVAC Fans

23 34 23 – HVAC Power Ventilators

23 34 23.10 HVAC Power Circulators and Ventilators

		Crew	Daily Output	Labor-Hours	Unit	Material	2014 Bare Costs Labor	2014 Bare Costs Equipment	Total	Total Incl O&P
6910	180 CFM	Q-20	20	1	Ea.	87	37.50		124.50	158
6920	270 CFM		18	1.111		164	42		206	251
6930	350 CFM	↓	16	1.250	↓	124	47		171	214
6940	Residential roof jacks and wall caps									
6944	Wall cap with back draft damper									
6946	3" & 4" diam. round duct	1 Shee	11	.727	Ea.	24.50	29.50		54	76
6948	6" diam. round duct	"	11	.727	"	61.50	29.50		91	117
6958	Roof jack with bird screen and back draft damper									
6960	3" & 4" diam. round duct	1 Shee	11	.727	Ea.	25	29.50		54.50	76.50
6962	3-1/4" x 10" rectangular duct	"	10	.800	"	46.50	32.50		79	105
6980	Transition									
6982	3-1/4" x 10" to 6" diam. round	1 Shee	20	.400	Ea.	31	16.20		47.20	61

23 34 33 – Air Curtains

23 34 33.10 Air Barrier Curtains

		Crew	Daily Output	Labor-Hours	Unit	Material	2014 Bare Costs Labor	2014 Bare Costs Equipment	Total	Total Incl O&P
0010	**AIR BARRIER CURTAINS**, Incl. motor starters, transformers,									
0050	and door switches									
2450	Conveyor openings or service windows									
3000	Service window, 5' high x 25" wide	2 Shee	5	3.200	Ea.	305	129		434	550
3100	Environmental separation									
3110	Door heights up to 8', low profile, super quiet									
3120	Unheated, variable speed									
3130	36" wide	2 Shee	4	4	Ea.	610	162		772	940
3134	42" wide		3.80	4.211		635	170		805	985
3138	48" wide		3.60	4.444		655	180		835	1,025
3142	60" wide	↓	3.40	4.706		685	190		875	1,075
3146	72" wide	Q-3	4.60	6.957		850	267		1,117	1,375
3150	96" wide		4.40	7.273		1,300	279		1,579	1,875
3154	120" wide		4.20	7.619		1,400	292		1,692	2,000
3158	144" wide	↓	4	8	↓	1,700	305		2,005	2,375
3200	Door heights up to 10'									
3210	Unheated									
3230	36" wide	2 Shee	3.80	4.211	Ea.	645	170		815	995
3234	42" wide		3.60	4.444		665	180		845	1,025
3238	48" wide		3.40	4.706		685	190		875	1,075
3242	60" wide	↓	3.20	5		1,025	202		1,227	1,450
3246	72" wide	Q-3	4.40	7.273		1,075	279		1,354	1,650
3250	96" wide		4.20	7.619		1,275	292		1,567	1,875
3254	120" wide		4	8		1,775	305		2,080	2,450
3258	144" wide	↓	3.80	8.421	↓	1,925	325		2,250	2,625
3300	Door heights up to 12'									
3310	Unheated									
3334	42" wide	2 Shee	3.40	4.706	Ea.	920	190		1,110	1,325
3338	48" wide		3.20	5		925	202		1,127	1,350
3342	60" wide	↓	3	5.333		945	216		1,161	1,400
3346	72" wide	Q-3	4.20	7.619		1,675	292		1,967	2,300
3350	96" wide		4	8		1,825	305		2,130	2,500
3354	120" wide		3.80	8.421		2,225	325		2,550	2,975
3358	144" wide	↓	3.60	8.889	↓	2,375	340		2,715	3,175
3400	Door heights up to 16'									
3410	Unheated									
3438	48" wide	2 Shee	3	5.333	Ea.	1,100	216		1,316	1,575
3442	60" wide	"	2.80	5.714	↓	1,175	231		1,406	1,650

23 34 HVAC Fans

23 34 33 – Air Curtains

23 34 33.10 Air Barrier Curtains		Crew	Daily Output	Labor-Hours	Unit	Material	2014 Bare Costs Labor	Equipment	Total	Total Incl O&P
3446	72" wide	Q-3	3.80	8.421	Ea.	2,000	325		2,325	2,725
3450	96" wide		3.60	8.889		2,075	340		2,415	2,850
3454	120" wide		3.40	9.412		2,825	360		3,185	3,700
3458	144" wide	↓	3.20	10	↓	2,925	385		3,310	3,825
3470	Heated, electric									
3474	48" wide	2 Shee	2.90	5.517	Ea.	1,850	223		2,073	2,400
3478	60" wide	"	2.70	5.926		1,875	240		2,115	2,475
3482	72" wide	Q-3	3.70	8.649		3,175	330		3,505	4,050
3486	96" wide		3.50	9.143		3,275	350		3,625	4,175
3490	120" wide		3.30	9.697		3,325	370		3,695	4,300
3494	144" wide	↓	3.10	10.323	↓	4,475	395		4,870	5,575

23 37 Air Outlets and Inlets

23 37 13 – Diffusers, Registers, and Grilles

23 37 13.10 Diffusers

		Crew	Daily Output	Labor-Hours	Unit	Material	2014 Bare Costs Labor	Equipment	Total	Total Incl O&P
0010	**DIFFUSERS**, Aluminum, opposed blade damper unless noted									
0100	Ceiling, linear, also for sidewall									
0500	Perforated, 24" x 24" lay-in panel size, 6" x 6"	1 Shee	16	.500	Ea.	151	20		171	200
0520	8" x 8"		15	.533		159	21.50		180.50	211
0530	9" x 9"		14	.571		161	23		184	216
0540	10" x 10"		14	.571		162	23		185	217
0560	12" x 12"		12	.667		168	27		195	230
0590	16" x 16"		11	.727		189	29.50		218.50	256
0600	18" x 18"		10	.800		202	32.50		234.50	276
0610	20" x 20"		10	.800		218	32.50		250.50	294
0620	24" x 24"		9	.889		239	36		275	325
1000	Rectangular, 1 to 4 way blow, 6" x 6"		16	.500		50	20		70	88.50
1010	8" x 8"		15	.533		58	21.50		79.50	99.50
1014	9" x 9"		15	.533		66	21.50		87.50	109
1016	10" x 10"		15	.533		80	21.50		101.50	124
1020	12" x 6"		15	.533		71.50	21.50		93	115
1040	12" x 9"		14	.571		75.50	23		98.50	122
1060	12" x 12"		12	.667		84.50	27		111.50	138
1070	14" x 6"		13	.615		77.50	25		102.50	127
1074	14" x 14"		12	.667		128	27		155	185
1150	18" x 18"		9	.889		138	36		174	211
1160	21" x 21"		8	1		215	40.50		255.50	305
1170	24" x 12"		10	.800		163	32.50		195.50	234
1500	Round, butterfly damper, steel, diffuser size, 6" diameter		18	.444		9	18		27	40
1520	8" diameter		16	.500		9.55	20		29.55	44
1540	10" diameter		14	.571		11.85	23		34.85	51.50
1560	12" diameter		12	.667		15.65	27		42.65	62
1580	14" diameter		10	.800		19.55	32.50		52.05	75.50
2000	T bar mounting, 24" x 24" lay-in frame, 6" x 6"		16	.500		49	20		69	87.50
2020	8" x 8"		14	.571		51	23		74	95
2040	12" x 12"		12	.667		60.50	27		87.50	112
2060	16" x 16"		11	.727		81	29.50		110.50	138
2080	18" x 18"	↓	10	.800		90	32.50		122.50	153
6000	For steel diffusers instead of aluminum, deduct				↓	10%				

23 37 Air Outlets and Inlets

23 37 13 – Diffusers, Registers, and Grilles

23 37 13.30 Grilles

		Crew	Daily Output	Labor-Hours	Unit	Material	2014 Bare Costs Labor	2014 Bare Costs Equipment	Total	Total Incl O&P
0010	**GRILLES**									
0020	Aluminum, unless noted otherwise									
1000	Air return, steel, 6" x 6"	1 Shee	26	.308	Ea.	18.70	12.45		31.15	41.50
1020	10" x 6"		24	.333		18.70	13.50		32.20	43
1080	16" x 8"		22	.364		26.50	14.70		41.20	53.50
1100	12" x 12"		22	.364		26.50	14.70		41.20	53.50
1120	24" x 12"		18	.444		36	18		54	69.50
1220	24" x 18"		16	.500		43.50	20		63.50	81.50
1280	36" x 24"		14	.571		75	23		98	121
3000	Filter grille with filter, 12" x 12"		24	.333		53	13.50		66.50	80.50
3020	18" x 12"		20	.400		71	16.20		87.20	105
3040	24" x 18"		18	.444		83.50	18		101.50	122
3060	24" x 24"	↓	16	.500	↓	98	20		118	142
6000	For steel grilles instead of aluminum in above, deduct					10%				

23 37 13.60 Registers

		Crew	Daily Output	Labor-Hours	Unit	Material	2014 Bare Costs Labor	2014 Bare Costs Equipment	Total	Total Incl O&P
0010	**REGISTERS**									
0980	Air supply									
1000	Ceiling/wall, O.B. damper, anodized aluminum									
1010	One or two way deflection, adj. curved face bars									
1020	8" x 4"	1 Shee	26	.308	Ea.	11.55	12.45		24	34
1120	12" x 12"		18	.444		21	18		39	53.50
1240	20" x 6"		18	.444		18.90	18		36.90	51
1340	24" x 8"		13	.615		25.50	25		50.50	69.50
1350	24" x 18"	↓	12	.667	↓	47.50	27		74.50	97
2700	Above registers in steel instead of aluminum, deduct					10%				
4000	Floor, toe operated damper, enameled steel									
4020	4" x 8"	1 Shee	32	.250	Ea.	9	10.10		19.10	27
4100	8" x 10"		22	.364		11	14.70		25.70	36.50
4140	10" x 10"		20	.400		13.15	16.20		29.35	41.50
4220	14" x 14"		16	.500		42	20		62	80
4240	14" x 20"	↓	15	.533	↓	49.50	21.50		71	90
4980	Air return									
5000	Ceiling or wall, fixed 45° face blades									
5010	Adjustable O.B. damper, anodized aluminum									
5020	4" x 8"	1 Shee	26	.308	Ea.	11.85	12.45		24.30	34
5060	6" x 10"		19	.421		14.20	17.05		31.25	44
5280	24" x 24"		11	.727		65	29.50		94.50	121
5300	24" x 36"	↓	8	1	↓	110	40.50		150.50	189
6000	For steel construction instead of aluminum, deduct					10%				

23 37 15 – Louvers

23 37 15.40 HVAC Louvers

		Crew	Daily Output	Labor-Hours	Unit	Material	2014 Bare Costs Labor	2014 Bare Costs Equipment	Total	Total Incl O&P
0010	**HVAC LOUVERS**									
0100	Aluminum, extruded, with screen, mill finish									
1002	Brick vent, see also Section 04 05 23.19									
1100	Standard, 4" deep, 8" wide, 5" high	1 Shee	24	.333	Ea.	34.50	13.50		48	60
1200	Modular, 4" deep, 7-3/4" wide, 5" high		24	.333		36	13.50		49.50	62
1300	Speed brick, 4" deep, 11-5/8" wide, 3-7/8" high		24	.333		36	13.50		49.50	62
1400	Fuel oil brick, 4" deep, 8" wide, 5" high		24	.333	↓	61.50	13.50		75	90.50
2000	Cooling tower and mechanical equip., screens, light weight		40	.200	S.F.	15.40	8.10		23.50	30.50
2020	Standard weight		35	.229		41	9.25		50.25	60.50
2500	Dual combination, automatic, intake or exhaust	↓	20	.400	↓	56	16.20		72.20	88.50

23 37 15 – Louvers

23 37 15.40 HVAC Louvers	Crew	Daily Output	Labor-Hours	Unit	Material	2014 Bare Costs Labor	Equipment	Total	Total Incl O&P
2520	Manual operation	1 Shee	20	.400	S.F.	41.50	16.20		57.70	73
2540	Electric or pneumatic operation		20	.400	↓	41.50	16.20		57.70	73
2560	Motor, for electric or pneumatic	↓	14	.571	Ea.	480	23		503	570
3000	Fixed blade, continuous line									
3100	Mullion type, stormproof	1 Shee	28	.286	S.F.	41.50	11.55		53.05	65.50
3200	Stormproof		28	.286		41.50	11.55		53.05	65.50
3300	Vertical line	↓	28	.286	↓	49.50	11.55		61.05	73.50
3500	For damper to use with above, add					50%	30%			
3520	Motor, for damper, electric or pneumatic	1 Shee	14	.571	Ea.	480	23		503	570
4000	Operating, 45°, manual, electric or pneumatic		24	.333	S.F.	50	13.50		63.50	77.50
4100	Motor, for electric or pneumatic		14	.571	Ea.	480	23		503	570
4200	Penthouse, roof		56	.143	S.F.	24.50	5.80		30.30	36.50
4300	Walls		40	.200		58	8.10		66.10	77.50
5000	Thinline, under 4" thick, fixed blade	↓	40	.200	↓	24	8.10		32.10	40
5010	Finishes, applied by mfr. at additional cost, available in colors									
5020	Prime coat only, add				S.F.	3.30			3.30	3.63
5040	Baked enamel finish coating, add					6.10			6.10	6.70
5060	Anodized finish, add					6.60			6.60	7.25
5080	Duranodic finish, add					12			12	13.20
5100	Fluoropolymer finish coating, add					18.90			18.90	21
9980	For small orders (under 10 pieces), add				↓	25%				

23 37 23 – HVAC Gravity Ventilators

23 37 23.10 HVAC Gravity Air Ventilators

		Crew	Daily Output	Labor-Hours	Unit	Material	2014 Bare Costs Labor	Equipment	Total	Total Incl O&P
0010	**HVAC GRAVITY AIR VENTILATORS,** Includes base R233400-10									
1280	Rotary ventilators, wind driven, galvanized									
1300	4" neck diameter	Q-9	20	.800	Ea.	64.50	29		93.50	120
1340	6" neck diameter		16	1		64.50	36.50		101	132
1400	12" neck diameter		10	1.600		91	58		149	197
1500	24" neck diameter		8	2		405	73		478	565
1540	36" neck diameter	↓	6	2.667	↓	655	97		752	880
2000	Stationary, gravity, syphon, galvanized									
2160	6" neck diameter, 66 CFM	Q-9	16	1	Ea.	45	36.50		81.50	110
2240	12" neck diameter, 160 CFM		10	1.600		106	58		164	214
2340	24" neck diameter, 900 CFM		8	2		360	73		433	515
2380	36" neck diameter, 2,000 CFM		6	2.667		440	97		537	645
4200	Stationary mushroom, aluminum, 16" orifice diameter		10	1.600		590	58		648	745
4220	26" orifice diameter		6.15	2.602		870	94.50		964.50	1,125
4230	30" orifice diameter		5.71	2.802		1,275	102		1,377	1,575
4240	38" orifice diameter		5	3.200		1,825	116		1,941	2,200
4250	42" orifice diameter		4.70	3.404		2,425	124		2,549	2,875
4260	50" orifice diameter	↓	4.44	3.604	↓	2,875	131		3,006	3,400
5000	Relief vent									
5500	Rectangular, aluminum, galvanized curb									
5510	intake/exhaust, 0.033" SP									
5580	500 CFM, 12" x 12"	Q-9	8.60	1.860	Ea.	685	67.50		752.50	865
5600	600 CFM, 12" x 16"		8	2		765	73		838	965
5640	1000 CFM, 12" x 24"		6.60	2.424		860	88		948	1,100
5680	3000 CFM, 20" x 42"	↓	4	4	↓	1,500	146		1,646	1,900
5880	Size is throat area, volume is at 500 fpm									
7000	Note: sizes based on exhaust. Intake, with 0.125" SP									
7100	loss, approximately twice listed capacity.									

23 38 Ventilation Hoods

23 38 13 - Commercial-Kitchen Hoods

23 38 13.10 Hood and Ventilation Equipment	Crew	Daily Output	Labor-Hours	Unit	Material	2014 Bare Costs Labor	Equipment	Total	Total Incl O&P
0010 **HOOD AND VENTILATION EQUIPMENT**									
2970 Exhaust hood, sst, gutter on all sides, 4' x 4' x 2'	1 Carp	1.80	4.444	Ea.	4,675	159		4,834	5,400
2980 4' x 4' x 7'	"	1.60	5	"	7,425	179		7,604	8,475

23 41 Particulate Air Filtration

23 41 13 - Panel Air Filters

23 41 13.10 Panel Type Air Filters

		Crew	Daily Output	Labor-Hours	Unit	Material	Labor	Equipment	Total	Total Incl O&P
0010	**PANEL TYPE AIR FILTERS**									
2950	Mechanical media filtration units									
3000	High efficiency type, with frame, non-supported [G]				MCFM	65			65	71.50
3100	Supported type [G]				"	60			60	66
5500	Throwaway glass or paper media type				Ea.	3.35			3.35	3.69

23 41 16 - Renewable-Media Air Filters

23 41 16.10 Disposable Media Air Filters

		Crew	Daily Output	Labor-Hours	Unit	Material	Labor	Equipment	Total	Total Incl O&P
0010	**DISPOSABLE MEDIA AIR FILTERS**									
5000	Renewable disposable roll				MCFM	19.35			19.35	21.50

23 41 19 - Washable Air Filters

23 41 19.10 Permanent Air Filters

		Crew	Daily Output	Labor-Hours	Unit	Material	Labor	Equipment	Total	Total Incl O&P
0010	**PERMANENT AIR FILTERS**									
4500	Permanent washable [G]				MCFM	20			20	22

23 41 23 - Extended Surface Filters

23 41 23.10 Expanded Surface Filters

		Crew	Daily Output	Labor-Hours	Unit	Material	Labor	Equipment	Total	Total Incl O&P
0010	**EXPANDED SURFACE FILTERS**									
4000	Medium efficiency, extended surface [G]				MCFM	5.50			5.50	6.05

23 42 Gas-Phase Air Filtration

23 42 13 - Activated-Carbon Air Filtration

23 42 13.10 Charcoal Type Air Filtration

		Crew	Daily Output	Labor-Hours	Unit	Material	Labor	Equipment	Total	Total Incl O&P
0010	**CHARCOAL TYPE AIR FILTRATION**									
0050	Activated charcoal type, full flow				MCFM	600			600	660
0060	Full flow, impregnated media 12" deep					225			225	248
0070	HEPA filter & frame for field erection					350			350	385
0080	HEPA filter-diffuser, ceiling install.				↓	300			300	330

23 43 Electronic Air Cleaners

23 43 13 - Washable Electronic Air Cleaners

23 43 13.10 Electronic Air Cleaners

		Crew	Daily Output	Labor-Hours	Unit	Material	Labor	Equipment	Total	Total Incl O&P
0010	**ELECTRONIC AIR CLEANERS**									
2000	Electronic air cleaner, duct mounted									
2150	1000 CFM	1 Shee	4	2	Ea.	420	81		501	600
2200	1200 CFM	↓	3.80	2.105	↓	505	85		590	695
2250	1400 CFM	↓	3.60	2.222	↓	520	90		610	725

23 51 Breechings, Chimneys, and Stacks

23 51 13 – Draft Control Devices

23 51 13.13 Draft-Induction Fans	Crew	Daily Output	Labor-Hours	Unit	Material	2014 Bare Costs Labor	Equipment	Total	Total Incl O&P
0010 **DRAFT-INDUCTION FANS**									
1000 Breeching installation									
1800 Hot gas, 600°F, variable pitch pulley and motor									
1860 8" diam. inlet, 1/4 H.P., 1phase, 1120 CFM	Q-9	4	4	Ea.	2,150	146		2,296	2,600
1900 12" diam. inlet, 3/4 H.P., 3 phase, 2960 CFM		3	5.333		2,925	194		3,119	3,525
1980 24" diam. inlet, 7-1/2 H.P., 3 phase, 17,760 CFM	↓	.80	20	↓	8,375	730		9,105	10,500
2300 For multi-blade damper at fan inlet, add					20%				

23 51 23 – Gas Vents

23 51 23.10 Gas Chimney Vents

	Crew	Daily Output	Labor-Hours	Unit	Material	2014 Bare Costs Labor	Equipment	Total	Total Incl O&P
0010 **GAS CHIMNEY VENTS**, Prefab metal, U.L. listed									
0020 Gas, double wall, galvanized steel									
0080 3" diameter	Q-9	72	.222	V.L.F.	5.55	8.10		13.65	19.60
0100 4" diameter		68	.235		7.20	8.55		15.75	22.50
0120 5" diameter		64	.250		7.80	9.10		16.90	24
0140 6" diameter		60	.267		9.45	9.70		19.15	26.50
0160 7" diameter		56	.286		15.10	10.40		25.50	34
0180 8" diameter		52	.308		17.40	11.20		28.60	38
0200 10" diameter		48	.333		36	12.15		48.15	60
0220 12" diameter		44	.364		43	13.25		56.25	69.50
0260 16" diameter	↓	40	.400		103	14.55		117.55	139
0300 20" diameter	Q-10	36	.667	↓	150	25		175	207

23 51 26 – All-Fuel Vent Chimneys

23 51 26.30 All-Fuel Vent Chimneys, Double Wall, St. Stl.

	Crew	Daily Output	Labor-Hours	Unit	Material	2014 Bare Costs Labor	Equipment	Total	Total Incl O&P
0010 **ALL-FUEL VENT CHIMNEYS, DOUBLE WALL, STAINLESS STEEL**									
7780 All fuel, pressure tight, double wall, 4" insulation, U.L. listed, 1400°F.									
7790 304 stainless steel liner, aluminized steel outer jacket									
7800 6" diameter	Q-9	60	.267	V.L.F.	62	9.70		71.70	84
7804 8" diameter		52	.308		71	11.20		82.20	96.50
7806 10" diameter		48	.333		79	12.15		91.15	107
7808 12" diameter		44	.364		90.50	13.25		103.75	122
7810 14" diameter	↓	42	.381	↓	102	13.85		115.85	135
7880 For 316 stainless steel liner add				L.F.	30%				

23 52 Heating Boilers

23 52 13 – Electric Boilers

23 52 13.10 Electric Boilers, ASME

	Crew	Daily Output	Labor-Hours	Unit	Material	2014 Bare Costs Labor	Equipment	Total	Total Incl O&P
0010 **ELECTRIC BOILERS, ASME**, Standard controls and trim									
1000 Steam, 6 KW, 20.5 MBH	Q-19	1.20	20	Ea.	3,950	805		4,755	5,675
1160 60 KW, 205 MBH		1	24		6,650	965		7,615	8,925
1220 112 KW, 382 MBH		.75	32		9,375	1,275		10,650	12,400
1280 222 KW, 758 MBH	↓	.55	43.636		23,800	1,750		25,550	29,100
1380 518 KW, 1768 MBH	Q-21	.36	88.889		32,600	3,650		36,250	41,900
1480 814 KW, 2778 MBH	↓	.25	128		40,600	5,250		45,850	53,500
1600 2,340 KW, 7984 MBH	↓	.16	200		86,500	8,200		94,700	108,500
2000 Hot water, 7.5 KW, 25.6 MBH	Q-19	1.30	18.462		4,975	745		5,720	6,700
2100 90 KW, 307 MBH		1.10	21.818		6,000	880		6,880	8,050
2220 296 KW, 1010 MBH	↓	.55	43.636		16,100	1,750		17,850	20,600
2500 1036 KW, 3536 MBH	Q-21	.34	94.118		35,500	3,850		39,350	45,500
2680 2400 KW, 8191 MBH	↓	.25	128		68,000	5,250		73,250	83,000
2820 3600 KW, 12,283 MBH	↓	.16	200	↓	94,000	8,200		102,200	117,000

23 52 Heating Boilers

23 52 23 – Cast-Iron Boilers

23 52 23.20 Gas-Fired Boilers

		Crew	Daily Output	Labor-Hours	Unit	Material	2014 Bare Costs Labor	Equipment	Total	Total Incl O&P
0010	**GAS-FIRED BOILERS**, Natural or propane, standard controls, packaged									
1000	Cast iron, with insulated jacket									
2000	Steam, gross output, 81 MBH	Q-7	1.40	22.857	Ea.	2,350	890		3,240	4,050
2080	203 MBH		.90	35.556		3,650	1,375		5,025	6,275
2180	400 MBH		.56	56.838		5,575	2,225		7,800	9,775
2240	765 MBH		.43	74.419		11,200	2,900		14,100	17,100
2320	1,875 MBH		.30	106		22,900	4,150		27,050	32,100
2440	4,720 MBH		.15	207		91,500	8,100		99,600	114,000
2480	6,100 MBH		.13	246		101,500	9,600		111,100	127,500
2540	6,970 MBH		.10	320		110,500	12,500		123,000	142,000
3000	Hot water, gross output, 80 MBH		1.46	21.918		2,150	855		3,005	3,775
3140	320 MBH		.80	40		4,500	1,550		6,050	7,525
3260	1,088 MBH		.40	80		13,500	3,125		16,625	20,100
3360	2,856 MBH		.20	160		28,300	6,225		34,525	41,400
3380	3,264 MBH		.18	179		30,000	7,000		37,000	44,600
3480	6,100 MBH		.13	250		101,500	9,750		111,250	127,500
3540	6,970 MBH		.09	359		110,500	14,000		124,500	144,500
7000	For tankless water heater, add					10%				

23 52 23.30 Gas/Oil Fired Boilers

		Crew	Daily Output	Labor-Hours	Unit	Material	2014 Bare Costs Labor	Equipment	Total	Total Incl O&P
0010	**GAS/OIL FIRED BOILERS**, Combination with burners and controls, packaged									
1000	Cast iron with insulated jacket									
2000	Steam, gross output, 720 MBH	Q-7	.43	74.074	Ea.	14,400	2,875		17,275	20,600
2080	1,600 MBH		.30	107		20,400	4,175		24,575	29,400
2140	2,700 MBH		.19	165		27,500	6,475		33,975	40,900
2280	5,520 MBH		.14	235		88,500	9,175		97,675	112,000
2340	6,390 MBH		.11	296		94,500	11,500		106,000	123,000
2380	6,970 MBH		.09	372		100,500	14,500		115,000	134,500
2900	Hot water, gross output									
2910	200 MBH	Q-6	.62	39.024	Ea.	10,400	1,475		11,875	13,800
2920	300 MBH		.49	49.080		10,400	1,850		12,250	14,500
2930	400 MBH		.41	57.971		12,200	2,175		14,375	17,000
2940	500 MBH		.36	67.039		13,100	2,525		15,625	18,600
3000	584 MBH	Q-7	.44	72.072		14,500	2,800		17,300	20,600
3060	1,460 MBH		.28	113		28,400	4,400		32,800	38,600
3160	4,088 MBH		.16	195		61,000	7,600		68,600	79,500
3300	13,500 MBH, 403.3 BHP		.04	727		188,500	28,300		216,800	254,000

23 52 23.40 Oil-Fired Boilers

		Crew	Daily Output	Labor-Hours	Unit	Material	2014 Bare Costs Labor	Equipment	Total	Total Incl O&P
0010	**OIL-FIRED BOILERS**, Standard controls, flame retention burner, packaged									
1000	Cast iron, with insulated flush jacket									
2000	Steam, gross output, 109 MBH	Q-7	1.20	26.667	Ea.	2,175	1,050		3,225	4,125
2060	207 MBH		.90	35.556		3,000	1,375		4,375	5,575
2180	1,084 MBH		.38	85.106		10,500	3,325		13,825	17,100
2280	3,000 MBH		.19	170		22,800	6,625		29,425	36,000
2380	5,520 MBH		.14	235		76,000	9,175		85,175	98,500
2460	6,970 MBH		.09	363		97,500	14,200		111,700	130,500
3000	Hot water, same price as steam									
4000	For tankless coil in smaller sizes, add				Ea.	15%				

23 52 Heating Boilers

23 52 26 – Steel Boilers

23 52 26.40 Oil-Fired Boilers	Crew	Daily Output	Labor-Hours	Unit	Material	2014 Bare Costs Labor	Equipment	Total	Total Incl O&P
0010 **OIL-FIRED BOILERS**, Standard controls, flame retention burner									
5000 Steel, with insulated flush jacket									
7000 Hot water, gross output, 103 MBH	Q-6	1.60	15	Ea.	1,775	565		2,340	2,875
7120 420 MBH		.70	34.483		6,700	1,300		8,000	9,500
7320 3,150 MBH		.13	184		41,200	6,925		48,125	56,500
7340 For tankless coil in steam or hot water, add					7%				

23 52 28 – Swimming Pool Boilers

23 52 28.10 Swimming Pool Heaters

	Crew	Daily Output	Labor-Hours	Unit	Material	Labor	Equipment	Total	Total Incl O&P
0010 **SWIMMING POOL HEATERS**, Not including wiring, external									
0020 piping, base or pad,									
0160 Gas fired, input, 155 MBH	Q-6	1.50	16	Ea.	1,900	600		2,500	3,100
0200 199 MBH		1	24		2,025	900		2,925	3,700
0280 500 MBH		.40	60		8,475	2,250		10,725	13,000
0400 1,800 MBH		.14	171		18,400	6,425		24,825	30,800
2000 Electric, 12 KW, 4,800 gallon pool	Q-19	3	8		2,075	320		2,395	2,800
2020 15 KW, 7,200 gallon pool		2.80	8.571		2,100	345		2,445	2,900
2040 24 KW, 9,600 gallon pool		2.40	10		2,425	400		2,825	3,325
2100 57 KW, 24,000 gallon pool		1.20	20		3,575	805		4,380	5,250

23 54 Furnaces

23 54 13 – Electric-Resistance Furnaces

23 54 13.10 Electric Furnaces

	Crew	Daily Output	Labor-Hours	Unit	Material	Labor	Equipment	Total	Total Incl O&P
0010 **ELECTRIC FURNACES**, Hot air, blowers, std. controls									
0011 not including gas, oil or flue piping									
1000 Electric, UL listed									
1100 34.1 MBH	Q-20	4.40	4.545	Ea.	560	171		731	900

23 54 16 – Fuel-Fired Furnaces

23 54 16.13 Gas-Fired Furnaces

	Crew	Daily Output	Labor-Hours	Unit	Material	Labor	Equipment	Total	Total Incl O&P
0010 **GAS-FIRED FURNACES**									
3000 Gas, AGA certified, upflow, direct drive models									
3020 45 MBH input	Q-9	4	4	Ea.	535	146		681	835
3040 60 MBH input		3.80	4.211		535	153		688	845
3060 75 MBH input		3.60	4.444		575	162		737	905
3100 100 MBH input		3.20	5		625	182		807	995

23 54 16.16 Oil-Fired Furnaces

	Crew	Daily Output	Labor-Hours	Unit	Material	Labor	Equipment	Total	Total Incl O&P
0010 **OIL-FIRED FURNACES**									
6000 Oil, UL listed, atomizing gun type burner									
6020 56 MBH output	Q-9	3.60	4.444	Ea.	1,550	162		1,712	1,975
6030 84 MBH output		3.50	4.571		1,850	166		2,016	2,325
6040 95 MBH output		3.40	4.706		1,875	171		2,046	2,350
6060 134 MBH output		3.20	5		2,175	182		2,357	2,700
6080 151 MBH output		3	5.333		2,250	194		2,444	2,800

23 55 Fuel-Fired Heaters

23 55 13 – Fuel-Fired Duct Heaters

23 55 13.16 Gas-Fired Duct Heaters

	Crew	Daily Output	Labor-Hours	Unit	Material	2014 Bare Costs Labor	Equipment	Total	Total Incl O&P
0010 **GAS-FIRED DUCT HEATERS**, Includes burner, controls, stainless steel									
0020 heat exchanger. Gas fired, electric ignition									
0030 Indoor installation									
0100 120 MBH output	Q-5	4	4	Ea.	2,575	156		2,731	3,100
0130 200 MBH output		2.70	5.926		3,175	231		3,406	3,850
0140 240 MBH output		2.30	6.957		3,600	271		3,871	4,400
0180 320 MBH output	↓	1.60	10		4,175	390		4,565	5,250
0300 For powered venter and adapter, add				↓	510			510	560
0502 For required flue pipe, see Section 23 51 23.10									
1000 Outdoor installation, with power venter									
1020 75 MBH output	Q-5	4	4	Ea.	2,950	156		3,106	3,500
1060 120 MBH output		4	4		3,275	156		3,431	3,850
1100 187 MBH output		3	5.333		4,150	208		4,358	4,925
1140 300 MBH output		1.80	8.889		7,325	345		7,670	8,625
1180 450 MBH output	↓	1.40	11.429		9,075	445		9,520	10,700

23 55 33 – Fuel-Fired Unit Heaters

23 55 33.13 Oil-Fired Unit Heaters

	Crew	Daily Output	Labor-Hours	Unit	Material	2014 Bare Costs Labor	Equipment	Total	Total Incl O&P
0010 **OIL-FIRED UNIT HEATERS**, Cabinet, grilles, fan, ctrl., burner, no piping									
6000 Oil fired, suspension mounted, 94 MBH output	Q-5	4	4	Ea.	4,475	156		4,631	5,150
6040 140 MBH output		3	5.333		4,850	208		5,058	5,675
6060 184 MBH output	↓	3	5.333	↓	5,150	208		5,358	6,025

23 55 33.16 Gas-Fired Unit Heaters

	Crew	Daily Output	Labor-Hours	Unit	Material	2014 Bare Costs Labor	Equipment	Total	Total Incl O&P
0010 **GAS-FIRED UNIT HEATERS**, Cabinet, grilles, fan, ctrls., burner, no piping									
0022 thermostat, no piping. For flue see Section 23 51 23.10									
1000 Gas fired, floor mounted									
1100 60 MBH output	Q-5	10	1.600	Ea.	870	62.50		932.50	1,050
1140 100 MBH output		8	2		960	78		1,038	1,175
1180 180 MBH output		6	2.667		1,375	104		1,479	1,675
2000 Suspension mounted, propeller fan, 20 MBH output		8.50	1.882		1,025	73.50		1,098.50	1,250
2040 60 MBH output		7	2.286		1,225	89		1,314	1,475
2060 80 MBH output		6	2.667		1,375	104		1,479	1,700
2100 130 MBH output		5	3.200		1,725	125		1,850	2,100
2240 320 MBH output	↓	2	8		3,525	310		3,835	4,400
2500 For powered venter and adapter, add					420			420	460
5000 Wall furnace, 17.5 MBH output	Q-5	6	2.667		760	104		864	1,000
5020 24 MBH output		5	3.200		770	125		895	1,050
5040 35 MBH output	↓	4	4	↓	770	156		926	1,100

23 56 Solar Energy Heating Equipment

23 56 16 – Packaged Solar Heating Equipment

23 56 16.40 Solar Heating Systems

		Crew	Daily Output	Labor-Hours	Unit	Material	2014 Bare Costs Labor	Equipment	Total	Total Incl O&P
0010 **SOLAR HEATING SYSTEMS**	R235616-60									
0020 System/Package prices, not including connecting										
0030 pipe, insulation, or special heating/plumbing fixtures										
0500 Hot water, standard package, low temperature										
0540 1 collector, circulator, fittings, 65 gal. tank	G	Q-1	.50	32	Ea.	3,575	1,225		4,800	5,950
0580 2 collectors, circulator, fittings, 120 gal. tank	G		.40	40		4,700	1,525		6,225	7,675
0620 3 collectors, circulator, fittings, 120 gal. tank	G	↓	.34	47.059	↓	6,325	1,800		8,125	9,950
0700 Medium temperature package										
0720 1 collector, circulator, fittings, 80 gal. tank	G	Q-1	.50	32	Ea.	4,950	1,225		6,175	7,475

23 56 Solar Energy Heating Equipment

23 56 16 – Packaged Solar Heating Equipment

23 56 16.40 Solar Heating Systems

		Crew	Daily Output	Labor-Hours	Unit	Material	2014 Bare Costs Labor	2014 Bare Costs Equipment	Total	Total Incl O&P
0740	2 collectors, circulator, fittings, 120 gal. tank	G	Q-1	.40	40	Ea.	6,400	1,525		7,925	9,550
0780	3 collectors, circulator, fittings, 120 gal. tank	G	↓	.30	53.333		7,225	2,050		9,275	11,300
0980	For each additional 120 gal. tank, add	G				↓	1,675			1,675	1,850

23 56 19 – Solar Heating Components

23 56 19.50 Solar Heating Ancillary

		Crew	Daily Output	Labor-Hours	Unit	Material	2014 Bare Costs Labor	2014 Bare Costs Equipment	Total	Total Incl O&P
0010	**SOLAR HEATING ANCILLARY**										
2300	Circulators, air										
2310	Blowers										
2400	Reversible fan, 20" diameter, 2 speed	G	Q-9	18	.889	Ea.	113	32.50		145.50	178
2800	Circulators, liquid, 1/25 HP, 5.3 GPM	G	Q-1	14	1.143		274	44		318	375
2870	1/12 HP, 30 GPM	G	"	10	1.600	↓	345	61.50		406.50	480
3000	Collector panels, air with aluminum absorber plate										
3010	Wall or roof mount										
3040	Flat black, plastic glazing										
3080	4' x 8'	G	Q-9	6	2.667	Ea.	660	97		757	890
3200	Flush roof mount, 10' to 16' x 22" wide	G	"	96	.167	L.F.	132	6.05		138.05	155
3300	Collector panels, liquid with copper absorber plate										
3330	Alum. frame, 4' x 8', 5/32" single glazing	G	Q-1	9.50	1.684	Ea.	995	64.50		1,059.50	1,200
3390	Alum. frame, 4' x 10', 5/32" single glazing	G		6	2.667		1,150	102		1,252	1,425
3450	Flat black, alum. frame, 3.5' x 7.5'	G		9	1.778		730	68		798	915
3500	4' x 8'	G		5.50	2.909		915	112		1,027	1,175
3520	4' x 10'	G		10	1.600		1,025	61.50		1,086.50	1,225
3540	4' x 12.5'	G		5	3.200		1,225	123		1,348	1,550
3600	Liquid, full wetted, plastic, alum. frame, 4' x 10'	G		5	3.200		247	123		370	475
3650	Collector panel mounting, flat roof or ground rack	G		7	2.286	↓	244	87.50		331.50	415
3670	Roof clamps	G	↓	70	.229	Set	2.80	8.75		11.55	17.55
3700	Roof strap, teflon	G	1 Plum	205	.039	L.F.	23.50	1.66		25.16	28.50
3900	Differential controller with two sensors										
3930	Thermostat, hard wired	G	1 Plum	8	1	Ea.	101	42.50		143.50	182
4100	Five station with digital read-out	G	"	3	2.667	"	236	114		350	445
4300	Heat exchanger										
4315	includes coil, blower, circulator										
4316	and controller for DHW and space hot air										
4580	Fluid to fluid package includes two circulating pumps										
4590	expansion tank, check valve, relief valve										
4600	controller, high temperature cutoff and sensors	G	Q-1	2.50	6.400	Ea.	770	245		1,015	1,250
4650	Heat transfer fluid										
4700	Propylene glycol, inhibited anti-freeze	G	1 Plum	28	.286	Gal.	15.45	12.15		27.60	37
8250	Water storage tank with heat exchanger and electric element										
8300	80 gal. with 2" x 2 lb. density insulation	G	1 Plum	1.60	5	Ea.	1,600	213		1,813	2,125
8380	120 gal. with 2" x 2 lb. density insulation	G		1.40	5.714		1,825	243		2,068	2,425
8400	120 gal. with 2" x 2 lb. density insul., 40 S.F. heat coil	G	↓	1.40	5.714	↓	2,325	243		2,568	2,950

23 57 Heat Exchangers for HVAC

23 57 16 – Steam-to-Water Heat Exchangers

23 57 16.10 Shell/Tube Type Steam-to-Water Heat Exch.	Crew	Daily Output	Labor- Hours	Unit	Material	2014 Bare Costs Labor	Equipment	Total	Total Incl O&P
0010 **SHELL AND TUBE TYPE STEAM-TO-WATER HEAT EXCHANGERS**									
0016 Shell & tube type, 2 or 4 pass, 3/4" O.D. copper tubes,									
0020 C.I. heads, C.I. tube sheet, steel shell									
0100 Hot water 40°F to 180°F, by steam at 10 PSI									
0120 8 GPM	Q-5	6	2.667	Ea.	2,150	104		2,254	2,550
0140 10 GPM		5	3.200		3,250	125		3,375	3,775
0160 40 GPM		4	4		5,025	156		5,181	5,775
0180 64 GPM		2	8		7,700	310		8,010	8,975
0200 96 GPM	↓	1	16		10,300	625		10,925	12,300
0220 120 GPM	Q-6	1.50	16	↓	13,500	600		14,100	15,900

23 57 19 – Liquid-to-Liquid Heat Exchangers

23 57 19.13 Plate-Type, Liquid-to-Liquid Heat Exchangers

	Crew	Daily Output	Labor- Hours	Unit	Material	Labor	Equipment	Total	Total Incl O&P
0010 **PLATE-TYPE, LIQUID-TO-LIQUID HEAT EXCHANGERS**									
3000 Plate type,									
3100 400 GPM	Q-6	.80	30	Ea.	35,600	1,125		36,725	41,100
3120 800 GPM	"	.50	48		61,500	1,800		63,300	70,500
3140 1200 GPM	Q-7	.34	94.118		91,500	3,675		95,175	106,500
3160 1800 GPM	"	.24	133	↓	121,000	5,200		126,200	141,500

23 57 19.16 Shell-Type, Liquid-to-Liquid Heat Exchangers

	Crew	Daily Output	Labor- Hours	Unit	Material	Labor	Equipment	Total	Total Incl O&P
0010 **SHELL-TYPE, LIQUID-TO-LIQUID HEAT EXCHANGERS**									
1000 Hot water 40°F to 140°F, by water at 200°F									
1020 7 GPM	Q-5	6	2.667	Ea.	2,650	104		2,754	3,075
1040 16 GPM		5	3.200		3,750	125		3,875	4,325
1060 34 GPM		4	4		5,675	156		5,831	6,475
1100 74 GPM	↓	1.50	10.667	↓	10,300	415		10,715	12,000

23 63 Refrigerant Condensers

23 63 13 – Air-Cooled Refrigerant Condensers

23 63 13.10 Air-Cooled Refrig. Condensers

	Crew	Daily Output	Labor- Hours	Unit	Material	Labor	Equipment	Total	Total Incl O&P
0010 **AIR-COOLED REFRIG. CONDENSERS**, Ratings for 30°F TD, R-22.									
0080 Air cooled, belt drive, propeller fan									
0240 50 ton	Q-6	.69	34.985	Ea.	10,600	1,325		11,925	13,800
0280 59 ton		.58	41.308		12,700	1,550		14,250	16,600
0320 73 ton		.47	51.173		16,600	1,925		18,525	21,500
0360 86 ton		.40	60.302		19,200	2,275		21,475	24,800
0380 88 ton	↓	.39	61.697	↓	20,600	2,325		22,925	26,500
1550 Air cooled, direct drive, propeller fan									
1590 1 ton	Q-5	3.80	4.211	Ea.	725	164		889	1,075
1600 1-1/2 ton		3.60	4.444		890	173		1,063	1,250
1620 2 ton		3.20	5		955	195		1,150	1,375
1640 5 ton		2	8		1,950	310		2,260	2,650
1660 10 ton		1.40	11.429		3,000	445		3,445	4,025
1690 16 ton		1.10	14.545		4,225	565		4,790	5,575
1720 26 ton	↓	.84	19.002		5,450	740		6,190	7,225
1760 41 ton	Q-6	.77	31.008		10,300	1,175		11,475	13,200
1800 63 ton	"	.55	44.037	↓	16,100	1,650		17,750	20,500

23 64 Packaged Water Chillers

23 64 13 – Absorption Water Chillers

23 64 13.16 Indirect-Fired Absorption Water Chillers	Crew	Daily Output	Labor-Hours	Unit	Material	2014 Bare Costs Labor	Equipment	Total	Total Incl O&P
0010 **INDIRECT-FIRED ABSORPTION WATER CHILLERS**									
0020 Steam or hot water, water cooled									
0400 420 ton	Q-7	.10	323	Ea.	366,500	12,600		379,100	424,000

23 64 16 – Centrifugal Water Chillers

23 64 16.10 Centrifugal Type Water Chillers

	Crew	Daily Output	Labor-Hours	Unit	Material	Labor	Equipment	Total	Total Incl O&P
0010 **CENTRIFUGAL TYPE WATER CHILLERS**, With standard controls									
0020 Centrifugal liquid chiller, water cooled									
0030 not including water tower									
0100 2000 ton (twin 1000 ton units)	Q-7	.07	477	Ea.	895,000	18,600		913,600	1,015,500

23 64 19 – Reciprocating Water Chillers

23 64 19.10 Reciprocating Type Water Chillers

	Crew	Daily Output	Labor-Hours	Unit	Material	Labor	Equipment	Total	Total Incl O&P
0010 **RECIPROCATING TYPE WATER CHILLERS**, With standard controls									
0494 Water chillers, integral air cooled condenser									
0600 100 ton cooling	Q-7	.25	129	Ea.	75,000	5,025		80,025	91,000
0980 Water cooled, multiple compressor, semi-hermetic, tower not incl.									
1000 15 ton cooling	Q-6	.36	65.934	Ea.	19,400	2,475		21,875	25,400
1020 25 ton cooling	Q-7	.41	78.049		19,900	3,050		22,950	26,900
1060 35 ton cooling		.31	101		24,800	3,975		28,775	33,900
1090 45 ton cooling		.29	111		35,100	4,325		39,425	45,800
1100 50 ton cooling		.28	113		36,500	4,450		40,950	47,500
1160 100 ton cooling		.18	179		62,000	7,000		69,000	80,000
1180 125 ton cooling		.16	196		71,000	7,650		78,650	90,500
1200 145 ton cooling		.16	202		82,000	7,900		89,900	103,500
1451 Water cooled, dual compressors, semi-hermetic, tower not incl.									
1500 80 ton cooling	Q-7	.14	222	Ea.	29,600	8,650		38,250	46,900
1520 100 ton cooling		.14	228		40,000	8,900		48,900	58,500
1540 120 ton cooling		.14	231		48,500	9,050		57,550	68,500

23 64 23 – Scroll Water Chillers

23 64 23.10 Scroll Water Chillers

	Crew	Daily Output	Labor-Hours	Unit	Material	Labor	Equipment	Total	Total Incl O&P
0010 **SCROLL WATER CHILLERS**, With standard controls									
0480 Packaged w/integral air cooled condenser									
0482 10 ton cooling	Q-7	.34	94.118	Ea.	20,500	3,675		24,175	28,600
0490 15 ton cooling		.37	86.486		22,200	3,375		25,575	30,000
0500 20 ton cooling		.34	94.118		28,200	3,675		31,875	37,100
0520 40 ton cooling		.30	108		36,700	4,225		40,925	47,400
0680 Scroll water cooled, single compressor, hermetic, tower not incl.									
0700 2 ton cooling	Q-5	.57	28.070	Ea.	3,500	1,100		4,600	5,650
0710 5 ton cooling		.57	28.070		4,175	1,100		5,275	6,400
0740 8 ton cooling		.31	52.117		5,750	2,025		7,775	9,675
0760 10 ton cooling	Q-6	.36	67.039		6,625	2,525		9,150	11,400
0800 20 ton cooling	Q-7	.38	83.990		11,800	3,275		15,075	18,400
0820 30 ton cooling	"	.33	96.096		13,200	3,750		16,950	20,800

23 64 26 – Rotary-Screw Water Chillers

23 64 26.10 Rotary-Screw Type Water Chillers

	Crew	Daily Output	Labor-Hours	Unit	Material	Labor	Equipment	Total	Total Incl O&P
0010 **ROTARY-SCREW TYPE WATER CHILLERS**, With standard controls									
0110 Screw, liquid chiller, air cooled, insulated evaporator									
0120 130 ton	Q-7	.14	228	Ea.	91,500	8,900		100,400	115,000
0124 160 ton		.13	246		112,500	9,600		122,100	139,500
0128 180 ton		.13	250		126,500	9,750		136,250	155,000
0132 210 ton		.12	258		139,000	10,100		149,100	169,500

23 64 Packaged Water Chillers

23 64 26 – Rotary-Screw Water Chillers

23 64 26.10 Rotary-Screw Type Water Chillers	Crew	Daily Output	Labor-Hours	Unit	Material	2014 Bare Costs Labor	Equipment	Total	Total Incl O&P
0136	270 ton	Q-7	.12	266	Ea.	159,000	10,400		169,400	192,000
0140	320 ton	↓	.12	275	↓	199,500	10,800		210,300	237,000
1450	Water cooled, tower not included									
1580	150 ton cooling, screw compressors	Q-7	.13	240	Ea.	69,000	9,375		78,375	91,000
1620	200 ton cooling, screw compressors	↓	.13	250		95,000	9,750		104,750	120,500
1660	291 ton cooling, screw compressors	↓	.12	260	↓	99,000	10,100		109,100	125,500

23 65 Cooling Towers

23 65 13 – Forced-Draft Cooling Towers

23 65 13.10 Forced-Draft Type Cooling Towers

		Crew	Daily Output	Labor-Hours	Unit	Material	2014 Bare Costs Labor	Equipment	Total	Total Incl O&P
0010	**FORCED-DRAFT TYPE COOLING TOWERS**, Packaged units									
0070	Galvanized steel									
0080	Induced draft, crossflow									
0100	Vertical, belt drive, 61 tons	Q-6	90	.267	TonAC	211	10		221	249
0150	100 ton		100	.240		203	9		212	239
0200	115 ton		109	.220		177	8.25		185.25	209
0250	131 ton		120	.200		213	7.50		220.50	246
0260	162 ton	↓	132	.182	↓	172	6.80		178.80	200
1000	For higher capacities, use multiples									
1500	Induced air, double flow									
1900	Vertical, gear drive, 167 ton	Q-6	126	.190	TonAC	167	7.15		174.15	195
2000	297 ton		129	.186		103	7		110	125
2100	582 ton		132	.182		57	6.80		63.80	74.50
2150	849 ton		142	.169		77	6.35		83.35	95
2200	1016 ton	↓	150	.160	↓	77.50	6		83.50	95.50
3000	For higher capacities, use multiples									
3500	For pumps and piping, add	Q-6	38	.632	TonAC	105	23.50		128.50	155
4000	For absorption systems, add				"	75%	75%			
4100	Cooling water chemical feeder	Q-5	3	5.333	Ea.	365	208		573	745
5000	Fiberglass tower on galvanized steel support structure									
5010	Draw thru									
5100	100 ton	Q-6	1.40	17.143	Ea.	13,100	645		13,745	15,500
5120	120 ton		1.20	20		15,200	750		15,950	18,100
5140	140 ton		1	24		16,500	900		17,400	19,600
5160	160 ton		.80	30		18,300	1,125		19,425	22,000
5180	180 ton		.65	36.923		20,800	1,375		22,175	25,200
5200	200 ton	↓	.48	50	↓	23,500	1,875		25,375	29,000
5300	For stainless steel support structure, add					30%				
5360	For higher capacities, use multiples of each size									
6000	Stainless steel									
6010	Induced draft, crossflow, horizontal, belt drive									
6100	57 ton	Q-6	1.50	16	Ea.	26,500	600		27,100	30,200
6120	91 ton		.99	24.242		32,100	910		33,010	36,800
6140	111 ton		.43	55.814		40,800	2,100		42,900	48,400
6160	126 ton	↓	.22	109	↓	40,800	4,100		44,900	51,500
6170	Induced draft, crossflow, vertical, gear drive									
6172	167 ton	Q-6	.75	32	Ea.	52,000	1,200		53,200	59,500
6174	297 ton		.43	55.814		58,000	2,100		60,100	67,000
6176	582 ton		.23	104		92,000	3,925		95,925	107,500
6178	849 ton		.17	141		129,500	5,300		134,800	151,500
6180	1016 ton	↓	.15	160		155,500	6,000		161,500	181,500

23 73 Indoor Central-Station Air-Handling Units

23 73 39 – Indoor, Direct Gas-Fired Heating and Ventilating Units

23 73 39.10 Make-Up Air Unit	Crew	Daily Output	Labor-Hours	Unit	Material	2014 Bare Costs Labor	Equipment	Total	Total Incl O&P
0010 **MAKE-UP AIR UNIT**									
0020 Indoor suspension, natural/LP gas, direct fired,									
0032 standard control. For flue see Section 23 51 23.10									
0040 70°F temperature rise, MBH is input									
0100 75 MBH input	Q-6	3.60	6.667	Ea.	4,900	250		5,150	5,825
0160 150 MBH input		3	8		5,975	300		6,275	7,075
0220 225 MBH input		2.40	10		6,675	375		7,050	7,975
0300 400 MBH input		1.60	15		16,600	565		17,165	19,100
0600 For discharge louver assembly, add					5%				
0700 For filters, add					10%				
0800 For air shut-off damper section, add					30%				

23 74 Packaged Outdoor HVAC Equipment

23 74 33 – Dedicated Outdoor-Air Units

23 74 33.10 Rooftop Air Conditioners

23 74 33.10 Rooftop Air Conditioners		Crew	Daily Output	Labor-Hours	Unit	Material	2014 Bare Costs Labor	Equipment	Total	Total Incl O&P
0010 **ROOFTOP AIR CONDITIONERS**, Standard controls, curb, economizer										
1000 Single zone, electric cool, gas heat										
1100 3 ton cooling, 60 MBH heating	R236000-20	Q-5	.70	22.857	Ea.	3,850	890		4,740	5,700
1120 4 ton cooling, 95 MBH heating			.61	26.403		4,525	1,025		5,550	6,675
1140 5 ton cooling, 112 MBH heating			.56	28.521		5,275	1,100		6,375	7,625
1145 6 ton cooling, 140 MBH heating			.52	30.769		6,200	1,200		7,400	8,800
1150 7.5 ton cooling, 170 MBH heating			.50	32.258		8,125	1,250		9,375	11,000
1156 8.5 ton cooling, 170 MBH heating			.46	34.783		8,800	1,350		10,150	11,900
1160 10 ton cooling, 200 MBH heating		Q-6	.67	35.982		11,600	1,350		12,950	15,000
1170 12.5 ton cooling, 230 MBH heating			.63	37.975		14,900	1,425		16,325	18,800
1190 17.5 ton cooling, 330 MBH heating			.52	45.889		17,800	1,725		19,525	22,500
1200 20 ton cooling, 360 MBH heating		Q-7	.67	47.976		23,800	1,875		25,675	29,200
1210 25 ton cooling, 450 MBH heating			.56	57.554		27,700	2,250		29,950	34,200
1220 30 ton cooling, 540 MBH heating			.47	68.376		28,600	2,675		31,275	35,900
1240 40 ton cooling, 675 MBH heating			.35	91.168		36,900	3,550		40,450	46,500
2000 Multizone, electric cool, gas heat, economizer										
2100 15 ton cooling, 360 MBH heating		Q-7	.61	52.545	Ea.	65,000	2,050		67,050	75,000
2120 20 ton cooling, 360 MBH heating			.53	60.038		70,000	2,350		72,350	81,000
2200 40 ton cooling, 540 MBH heating			.28	113		122,500	4,450		126,950	142,000
2210 50 ton cooling, 540 MBH heating			.23	142		152,000	5,550		157,550	176,500
2220 70 ton cooling, 1500 MBH heating			.16	198		164,500	7,750		172,250	194,000
2240 80 ton cooling, 1500 MBH heating			.14	228		188,000	8,900		196,900	221,500
2260 90 ton cooling, 1500 MBH heating			.13	256		197,500	9,975		207,475	233,500
2280 105 ton cooling, 1500 MBH heating			.11	290		217,500	11,300		228,800	257,500
2400 For hot water heat coil, deduct						5%				
2500 For steam heat coil, deduct						2%				
2600 For electric heat, deduct						3%	5%			

23 81 Decentralized Unitary HVAC Equipment

23 81 13 – Packaged Terminal Air-Conditioners

23 81 13.10 Packaged Cabinet Type Air-Conditioners	Crew	Daily Output	Labor-Hours	Unit	Material	2014 Bare Costs Labor	2014 Bare Costs Equipment	Total	Total Incl O&P
0010 **PACKAGED CABINET TYPE AIR-CONDITIONERS**, Cabinet, wall sleeve,									
0100 louver, electric heat, thermostat, manual changeover, 208 V									
0200 6,000 BTUH cooling, 8800 BTU heat	Q-5	6	2.667	Ea.	775	104		879	1,025
0220 9,000 BTUH cooling, 13,900 BTU heat		5	3.200		850	125		975	1,150
0240 12,000 BTUH cooling, 13,900 BTU heat		4	4		920	156		1,076	1,250
0260 15,000 BTUH cooling, 13,900 BTU heat		3	5.333		1,150	208		1,358	1,625
0500 For hot water coil, increase heat by 10%, add					5%	10%			
1000 For steam, increase heat output by 30%, add					8%	10%			

23 81 19 – Self-Contained Air-Conditioners

23 81 19.20 Self-Contained Single Package

	Crew	Daily Output	Labor-Hours	Unit	Material	Labor	Equipment	Total	Total Incl O&P
0010 **SELF-CONTAINED SINGLE PACKAGE**									
0100 Air cooled, for free blow or duct, not incl. remote condenser									
0110 Constant volume									
0200 3 ton cooling	Q-5	1	16	Ea.	3,750	625		4,375	5,125
0220 5 ton cooling	Q-6	1.20	20		4,450	750		5,200	6,150
0240 10 ton cooling	Q-7	1	32		7,375	1,250		8,625	10,200
0260 20 ton cooling		.90	35.556		17,200	1,375		18,575	21,200
0280 30 ton cooling		.80	40		25,300	1,550		26,850	30,400
0340 60 ton cooling	Q-8	.40	80		56,000	3,300	138	59,438	67,000
0490 For duct mounting no price change									
0500 For steam heating coils, add				Ea.	10%	10%			
1000 Water cooled for free blow or duct, not including tower									
1010 Constant volume									
1100 3 ton cooling	Q-6	1	24	Ea.	3,725	900		4,625	5,550
1120 5 ton cooling	"	1	24		4,850	900		5,750	6,825
1140 10 ton cooling	Q-7	.90	35.556		9,075	1,375		10,450	12,300
1160 20 ton cooling		.80	40		28,600	1,550		30,150	34,000
1180 30 ton cooling		.70	45.714		37,900	1,775		39,675	44,700
1300 For hot water or steam heat coils, add					12%	10%			

23 81 23 – Computer-Room Air-Conditioners

23 81 23.10 Computer Room Units

	Crew	Daily Output	Labor-Hours	Unit	Material	Labor	Equipment	Total	Total Incl O&P
0010 **COMPUTER ROOM UNITS**									
1000 Air cooled, includes remote condenser but not									
1020 interconnecting tubing or refrigerant									
1080 3 ton	Q-5	.50	32	Ea.	18,200	1,250		19,450	22,200
1120 5 ton		.45	35.556		19,500	1,375		20,875	23,700
1160 6 ton		.30	53.333		35,900	2,075		37,975	42,900
1200 8 ton		.27	59.259		36,400	2,300		38,700	43,800
1240 10 ton		.25	64		38,000	2,500		40,500	45,900
1260 12 ton		.24	66.667		39,300	2,600		41,900	47,600
1280 15 ton		.22	72.727		41,800	2,825		44,625	50,500
1290 18 ton		.20	80		47,900	3,125		51,025	57,500
1300 20 ton	Q-6	.26	92.308		50,000	3,475		53,475	60,500
1320 22 ton		.24	100		50,500	3,750		54,250	61,500
1360 30 ton		.21	114		62,500	4,300		66,800	75,500
2200 Chilled water, for connection to									
2220 existing chiller system of adequate capacity									
2260 5 ton	Q-5	.74	21.622	Ea.	13,900	845		14,745	16,700

23 81 Decentralized Unitary HVAC Equipment

23 81 43 – Air-Source Unitary Heat Pumps

23 81 43.10 Air-Source Heat Pumps

23 81 43.10 Air-Source Heat Pumps	Crew	Daily Output	Labor-Hours	Unit	Material	2014 Bare Costs Labor	Equipment	Total	Total Incl O&P
0010 **AIR-SOURCE HEAT PUMPS**, Not including interconnecting tubing									
1000 Air to air, split system, not including curbs, pads, fan coil and ductwork									
1012 Outside condensing unit only, for fan coil see Section 23 82 19.10									
1020 2 ton cooling, 8.5 MBH heat @ 0°F	Q-5	2	8	Ea.	2,300	310		2,610	3,075
1060 5 ton cooling, 27 MBH heat @ 0°F		.50	32		3,625	1,250		4,875	6,025
1080 7.5 ton cooling, 33 MBH heat @ 0°F	↓	.45	35.556		6,325	1,375		7,700	9,250
1100 10 ton cooling, 50 MBH heat @ 0°F	Q-6	.64	37.500		8,675	1,400		10,075	11,900
1120 15 ton cooling, 64 MBH heat @ 0°F		.50	48		13,400	1,800		15,200	17,800
1130 20 ton cooling, 85 MBH heat @ 0°F		.35	68.571		17,000	2,575		19,575	23,000
1140 25 ton cooling, 119 MBH heat @ 0°F	↓	.25	96	↓	20,400	3,600		24,000	28,500
1500 Single package, not including curbs, pads, or plenums									
1520 2 ton cooling, 6.5 MBH heat @ 0°F	Q-5	1.50	10.667	Ea.	2,950	415		3,365	3,925
1580 4 ton cooling, 13 MBH heat @ 0°F		.96	16.667		4,125	650		4,775	5,625
1640 7.5 ton cooling, 35 MBH heat @ 0°F	↓	.40	40		7,250	1,550		8,800	10,600

23 81 46 – Water-Source Unitary Heat Pumps

23 81 46.10 Water Source Heat Pumps

23 81 46.10 Water Source Heat Pumps	Crew	Daily Output	Labor-Hours	Unit	Material	Labor	Equipment	Total	Total Incl O&P
0010 **WATER SOURCE HEAT PUMPS**, Not incl. connecting tubing or water source									
2000 Water source to air, single package									
2100 1 ton cooling, 13 MBH heat @ 75°F	Q-5	2	8	Ea.	1,825	310		2,135	2,525
2140 2 ton cooling, 19 MBH heat @ 75°F		1.70	9.412		2,050	365		2,415	2,850
2220 5 ton cooling, 29 MBH heat @ 75°F	↓	.90	17.778		3,025	695		3,720	4,475
3960 For supplementary heat coil, add				↓	10%				
4000 For increase in capacity thru use									
4020 of solar collector, size boiler at 60%									

23 82 Convection Heating and Cooling Units

23 82 16 – Air Coils

23 82 16.10 Flanged Coils

	Crew	Daily Output	Labor-Hours	Unit	Material	Labor	Equipment	Total	Total Incl O&P
0010 **FLANGED COILS**									
0500 Chilled water cooling, 6 rows, 24" x 48"	Q-5	3.20	5	Ea.	4,025	195		4,220	4,750
1000 Direct expansion cooling, 6 rows, 24" x 48"		2.80	5.714		4,350	223		4,573	5,175
1500 Hot water heating, 1 row, 24" x 48"		4	4		1,600	156		1,756	2,025
2000 Steam heating, 1 row, 24" x 48"	↓	3.06	5.229	↓	2,275	204		2,479	2,825

23 82 16.20 Duct Heaters

	Crew	Daily Output	Labor-Hours	Unit	Material	Labor	Equipment	Total	Total Incl O&P
0010 **DUCT HEATERS**, Electric, 480 V, 3 Ph.									
0020 Finned tubular insert, 500°F									
0100 8" wide x 6" high, 4.0 kW	Q-20	16	1.250	Ea.	795	47		842	955
0120 12" high, 8.0 kW		15	1.333		1,325	50		1,375	1,525
0140 18" high, 12.0 kW		14	1.429		1,850	54		1,904	2,125
0160 24" high, 16.0 kW		13	1.538		2,375	58		2,433	2,700
0180 30" high, 20.0 kW		12	1.667		2,900	63		2,963	3,300
0300 12" wide x 6" high, 6.7 kW		15	1.333		845	50		895	1,000
0320 12" high, 13.3 kW		14	1.429		1,350	54		1,404	1,600
0340 18" high, 20.0 kW		13	1.538		1,900	58		1,958	2,200
0360 24" high, 26.7 kW		12	1.667		2,450	63		2,513	2,800
0700 24" wide x 6" high, 17.8 kW		13	1.538		1,000	58		1,058	1,200
0760 24" high, 71.1 kW	↓	10	2	↓	3,075	75.50		3,150.50	3,500
8000 To obtain BTU multiply kW by 3413									

23 82 Convection Heating and Cooling Units

23 82 19 – Fan Coil Units

23 82 19.10 Fan Coil Air Conditioning	Crew	Daily Output	Labor-Hours	Unit	Material	2014 Bare Costs Labor	Equipment	Total	Total Incl O&P
0010 **FAN COIL AIR CONDITIONING**									
0030 Fan coil AC, cabinet mounted, filters and controls									
0100 Chilled water, 1/2 ton cooling	Q-5	8	2	Ea.	810	78		888	1,025
0120 1 ton cooling		6	2.667		935	104		1,039	1,200
0180 3 ton cooling	↓	4	4	↓	1,875	156		2,031	2,325
0262 For hot water coil, add					40%	10%			
0940 Direct expansion, for use w/air cooled condensing unit, 1.5 ton cooling	Q-5	5	3.200	Ea.	755	125		880	1,025
1000 5 ton cooling	"	3	5.333		1,450	208		1,658	1,950
1040 10 ton cooling	Q-6	2.60	9.231		3,175	345		3,520	4,075
1060 20 ton cooling	"	.70	34.286		6,250	1,275		7,525	9,000
1500 For hot water coil, add				↓	40%	10%			

23 82 19.20 Heating and Ventilating Units

	Crew	Daily Output	Labor-Hours	Unit	Material	2014 Bare Costs Labor	Equipment	Total	Total Incl O&P
0010 **HEATING AND VENTILATING UNITS**, Classroom units									
0020 Includes filter, heating/cooling coils, standard controls									
0080 750 CFM, 2 tons cooling	Q-6	2	12	Ea.	4,050	450		4,500	5,225
0120 1250 CFM, 3 tons cooling		1.40	17.143		4,950	645		5,595	6,500
0140 1500 CFM, 4 tons cooling	↓	.80	30		5,300	1,125		6,425	7,675
0500 For electric heat, add					35%				
1000 For no cooling, deduct				↓	25%	10%			

23 82 27 – Infrared Units

23 82 27.10 Infrared Type Heating Units

	Crew	Daily Output	Labor-Hours	Unit	Material	2014 Bare Costs Labor	Equipment	Total	Total Incl O&P
0010 **INFRARED TYPE HEATING UNITS**									
0020 Gas fired, unvented, electric ignition, 100% shutoff.									
0030 Piping and wiring not included									
0060 Input, 15 MBH	Q-5	7	2.286	Ea.	555	89		644	755
0120 45 MBH		5	3.200		1,150	125		1,275	1,475
0160 60 MBH		4	4		1,200	156		1,356	1,575
0240 120 MBH	↓	2	8	↓	1,500	310		1,810	2,175
1000 Gas fired, vented, electric ignition, tubular									
1020 Piping and wiring not included, 20' to 80' lengths									
1030 Single stage, input, 60 MBH	Q-6	4.50	5.333	Ea.	1,400	200		1,600	1,875
1040 80 MBH		3.90	6.154		1,400	231		1,631	1,925
1050 100 MBH		3.40	7.059		1,400	265		1,665	1,975
1060 125 MBH		2.90	8.276		1,625	310		1,935	2,275
1070 150 MBH		2.70	8.889		1,625	335		1,960	2,325
1080 170 MBH		2.50	9.600		1,625	360		1,985	2,375
1090 200 MBH	↓	2.20	10.909	↓	1,825	410		2,235	2,675
1100 Note: Final pricing may vary due to									
1110 tube length and configuration package selected									
1130 Two stage, input, 60 MBH high, 45 MBH low	Q-6	4.50	5.333	Ea.	1,525	200		1,725	2,000
1140 80 MBH high, 60 MBH low		3.90	6.154		1,525	231		1,756	2,050
1150 100 MBH high, 65 MBH low		3.40	7.059		1,525	265		1,790	2,100
1160 125 MBH high, 95 MBH low		2.90	8.276		1,725	310		2,035	2,400
1170 150 MBH high, 100 MBH low		2.70	8.889		1,725	335		2,060	2,450
1180 170 MBH high, 125 MBH low		2.50	9.600		1,925	360		2,285	2,725
1190 200 MBH high, 150 MBH low	↓	2.20	10.909	↓	1,925	410		2,335	2,800
1220 Note: Final pricing may vary due to									
1230 tube length and configuration package selected									

23 82 Convection Heating and Cooling Units

23 82 29 – Radiators

23 82 29.10 Hydronic Heating	Crew	Daily Output	Labor-Hours	Unit	Material	2014 Bare Costs Labor	2014 Bare Costs Equipment	Total	Total Incl O&P
0010 **HYDRONIC HEATING**, Terminal units, not incl. main supply pipe									
1000 Radiation									
1100 Panel, baseboard, C.I., including supports, no covers	Q-5	46	.348	L.F.	36.50	13.55		50.05	62.50
3000 Radiators, cast iron									
3100 Free standing or wall hung, 6 tube, 25" high	Q-5	96	.167	Section	44	6.50		50.50	59
3200 4 tube, 19" high	"	96	.167	"	30.50	6.50		37	44
3250 Adj. brackets, 2 per wall radiator up to 30 sections	1 Stpi	32	.250	Ea.	34	10.85		44.85	55.50
9500 To convert SFR to BTU rating: Hot water, 150 x SFR									
9510 Forced hot water, 180 x SFR; steam, 240 x SFR									

23 82 33 – Convectors

23 82 33.10 Convector Units

	Crew	Daily Output	Labor-Hours	Unit	Material	2014 Bare Costs Labor	2014 Bare Costs Equipment	Total	Total Incl O&P
0010 **CONVECTOR UNITS**, Terminal units, not incl. main supply pipe									
2204 Convector, multifin, 2 pipe w/cabinet									
2210 17" H x 24" L	Q-5	10	1.600	Ea.	99	62.50		161.50	212
2214 17" H x 36" L		8.60	1.860		148	72.50		220.50	283
2218 17" H x 48" L		7.40	2.162		198	84.50		282.50	355
2222 21" H x 24" L		9	1.778		99	69.50		168.50	223
2226 21" H x 36" L		8.20	1.951		148	76		224	288
2228 21" H x 48" L		6.80	2.353		198	91.50		289.50	370
2240 For knob operated damper, add					140%				
2241 For metal trim strips, add	Q-5	64	.250	Ea.	19.25	9.75		29	37
2243 For snap-on inlet grille, add					10%	10%			
2245 For hinged access door, add	Q-5	64	.250	Ea.	35.50	9.75		45.25	55
2246 For air chamber, auto-venting, add	"	58	.276	"	6.85	10.75		17.60	25.50

23 82 36 – Finned-Tube Radiation Heaters

23 82 36.10 Finned Tube Radiation

	Crew	Daily Output	Labor-Hours	Unit	Material	2014 Bare Costs Labor	2014 Bare Costs Equipment	Total	Total Incl O&P
0010 **FINNED TUBE RADIATION**, Terminal units, not incl. main supply pipe									
1150 Fin tube, wall hung, 14" slope top cover, with damper									
1200 1-1/4" copper tube, 4-1/4" alum. fin	Q-5	38	.421	L.F.	42	16.40		58.40	73
1250 1-1/4" steel tube, 4-1/4" steel fin	"	36	.444	"	39.50	17.30		56.80	71.50
1500 Note: fin tube may also require corners, caps, etc.									

23 82 39 – Unit Heaters

23 82 39.16 Propeller Unit Heaters

	Crew	Daily Output	Labor-Hours	Unit	Material	2014 Bare Costs Labor	2014 Bare Costs Equipment	Total	Total Incl O&P
0010 **PROPELLER UNIT HEATERS**									
3950 Unit heaters, propeller, 115 V 2 psi steam, 60°F entering air									
4000 Horizontal, 12 MBH	Q-5	12	1.333	Ea.	360	52		412	480
4060 43.9 MBH		8	2		545	78		623	730
4140 96.8 MBH		6	2.667		795	104		899	1,050
4180 157.6 MBH		4	4		1,050	156		1,206	1,425
4240 286.9 MBH		2	8		1,650	310		1,960	2,350
4260 364 MBH		1.80	8.889		2,075	345		2,420	2,850
4270 404 MBH		1.60	10		2,150	390		2,540	3,025
4300 Vertical diffuser same price									
4310 Vertical flow, 40 MBH	Q-5	11	1.455	Ea.	540	56.50		596.50	690
4314 58.5 MBH		8	2		560	78		638	745
4326 131.0 MBH		4	4		845	156		1,001	1,175
4346 297.0 MBH		1.80	8.889		1,600	345		1,945	2,350
4354 420 MBH, (460 V)	Q-6	1.80	13.333		2,150	500		2,650	3,200
4358 500 MBH, (460 V)		1.71	14.035		2,875	525		3,400	4,025
4362 570 MBH, (460 V)		1.40	17.143		3,925	645		4,570	5,375

23 82 Convection Heating and Cooling Units

23 82 39 – Unit Heaters

23 82 39.16 Propeller Unit Heaters		Crew	Daily Output	Labor-Hours	Unit	Material	2014 Bare Costs Labor	Equipment	Total	Total Incl O&P
4366	620 MBH, (460 V)	Q-6	1.30	18.462	Ea.	3,925	695		4,620	5,475
4370	960 MBH, (460 V)	↓	1.10	21.818	↓	7,450	820		8,270	9,550

23 83 Radiant Heating Units

23 83 33 – Electric Radiant Heaters

23 83 33.10 Electric Heating

		Crew	Daily Output	Labor-Hours	Unit	Material	Labor	Equipment	Total	Total Incl O&P
0010	**ELECTRIC HEATING**, not incl. conduit or feed wiring									
1100	Rule of thumb: Baseboard units, including control	1 Elec	4.40	1.818	kW	101	77.50		178.50	238
1300	Baseboard heaters, 2' long, 350 watt		8	1	Ea.	30	42.50		72.50	103
1400	3' long, 750 watt		8	1		34.50	42.50		77	108
1600	4' long, 1000 watt		6.70	1.194		41	51		92	129
1800	5' long, 935 watt		5.70	1.404		51	60		111	154
2000	6' long, 1500 watt		5	1.600		56	68.50		124.50	174
2400	8' long, 2000 watt	↓	4	2	↓	69.50	85.50		155	216
2950	Wall heaters with fan, 120 to 277 volt									
3160	Recessed, residential, 750 watt	1 Elec	6	1.333	Ea.	134	57		191	240
3170	1000 watt		6	1.333		134	57		191	240
3180	1250 watt		5	1.600		134	68.50		202.50	259
3190	1500 watt		4	2		134	85.50		219.50	287
3600	Thermostats, integral		16	.500		30	21.50		51.50	68
3800	Line voltage, 1 pole	↓	8	1	↓	20.50	42.50		63	92.50

23 84 Humidity Control Equipment

23 84 13 – Humidifiers

23 84 13.10 Humidifier Units

		Crew	Daily Output	Labor-Hours	Unit	Material	Labor	Equipment	Total	Total Incl O&P
0010	**HUMIDIFIER UNITS**									
0520	Steam, room or duct, filter, regulators, auto. controls, 220 V									
0540	11 lb. per hour	Q-5	6	2.667	Ea.	2,625	104		2,729	3,050
0560	22 lb. per hour		5	3.200		2,900	125		3,025	3,375
0580	33 lb. per hour		4	4		2,975	156		3,131	3,525
0600	50 lb. per hour		4	4		3,425	156		3,581	4,025
0620	100 lb. per hour	↓	3	5.333	↓	4,350	208		4,558	5,150

Division Notes

	CREW	DAILY OUTPUT	LABOR-HOURS	UNIT	BARE COSTS				TOTAL INCL O&P
					MAT.	LABOR	EQUIP.	TOTAL	

Estimating Tips

26 05 00 Common Work Results for Electrical

- Conduit should be taken off in three main categories—power distribution, branch power, and branch lighting—so the estimator can concentrate on systems and components, therefore making it easier to ensure all items have been accounted for.
- For cost modifications for elevated conduit installation, add the percentages to labor according to the height of installation, and only to the quantities exceeding the different height levels, not to the total conduit quantities.
- Remember that aluminum wiring of equal ampacity is larger in diameter than copper and may require larger conduit.
- If more than three wires at a time are being pulled, deduct percentages from the labor hours of that grouping of wires.
- When taking off grounding systems, identify separately the type and size of wire, and list each unique type of ground connection.

- The estimator should take the weights of materials into consideration when completing a takeoff. Topics to consider include: How will the materials be supported? What methods of support are available? How high will the support structure have to reach? Will the final support structure be able to withstand the total burden? Is the support material included or separate from the fixture, equipment, and material specified?
- Do not overlook the costs for equipment used in the installation. If scaffolding or highlifts are available in the field, contractors may use them in lieu of the proposed ladders and rolling staging.

26 20 00 Low-Voltage Electrical Transmission

- Supports and concrete pads may be shown on drawings for the larger equipment, or the support system may be only a piece of plywood for the back of a panelboard. In either case, it must be included in the costs.

26 40 00 Electrical and Cathodic Protection

- When taking off cathodic protections systems, identify the type and size of cable, and list each unique type of anode connection.

26 50 00 Lighting

- Fixtures should be taken off room by room, using the fixture schedule, specifications, and the ceiling plan. For large concentrations of lighting fixtures in the same area, deduct the percentages from labor hours.

Reference Numbers

Reference numbers are shown in shaded boxes at the beginning of some major classifications. These numbers refer to related items in the Reference Section. The reference information may be an estimating procedure, an alternate pricing method, or technical information.

Note: Not all subdivisions listed here necessarily appear in this publication.

Note: **Trade Service,** *in part, has been used as a reference source for some of the material prices used in Division 26.*

26 05 05.10 Electrical Demolition	Crew	Daily Output	Labor-Hours	Unit	Material	2014 Bare Costs Labor	2014 Bare Costs Equipment	Total	Total Incl O&P
0010	**ELECTRICAL DEMOLITION**									
0020	Conduit to 15' high, including fittings & hangers									
0100	Rigid galvanized steel, 1/2" to 1" diameter	1 Elec	242	.033	L.F.		1.41		1.41	2.31
0120	1-1/4" to 2"	"	200	.040			1.71		1.71	2.80
0140	2-1/2" to 3-1/2"	2 Elec	302	.053			2.26		2.26	3.70
0160	4" to 6"	"	160	.100			4.27		4.27	7
0200	Electric metallic tubing (EMT), 1/2" to 1"	1 Elec	394	.020			.87		.87	1.42
0220	1-1/4" to 1-1/2"		326	.025			1.05		1.05	1.72
0240	2" to 3"	↓	236	.034			1.45		1.45	2.37
0260	3-1/2" to 4"	2 Elec	310	.052	↓		2.20		2.20	3.61
0270	Armored cable, (BX) avg. 50' runs									
0280	#14, 2 wire	1 Elec	690	.012	L.F.		.49		.49	.81
0290	#14, 3 wire		571	.014			.60		.60	.98
0300	#12, 2 wire		605	.013			.56		.56	.92
0310	#12, 3 wire		514	.016			.66		.66	1.09
0320	#10, 2 wire		514	.016			.66		.66	1.09
0330	#10, 3 wire		425	.019			.80		.80	1.32
0340	#8, 3 wire	↓	342	.023	↓		1		1	1.64
0350	Non metallic sheathed cable (Romex)									
0360	#14, 2 wire	1 Elec	720	.011	L.F.		.47		.47	.78
0370	#14, 3 wire		657	.012			.52		.52	.85
0380	#12, 2 wire		629	.013			.54		.54	.89
0390	#10, 3 wire	↓	450	.018	↓		.76		.76	1.24
0400	Wiremold raceway, including fittings & hangers									
0420	No. 3000	1 Elec	250	.032	L.F.		1.37		1.37	2.24
0440	No. 4000		217	.037			1.57		1.57	2.58
0460	No. 6000		166	.048			2.06		2.06	3.37
0462	Plugmold with receptacle		114	.070	↓		3		3	4.91
0465	Telephone/power pole		12	.667	Ea.		28.50		28.50	46.50
0470	Non-metallic, straight section	↓	480	.017	L.F.		.71		.71	1.17
0500	Channels, steel, including fittings & hangers									
0520	3/4" x 1-1/2"	1 Elec	308	.026	L.F.		1.11		1.11	1.82
0540	1-1/2" x 1-1/2"		269	.030			1.27		1.27	2.08
0560	1-1/2" x 1-7/8"	↓	229	.035	↓		1.49		1.49	2.44
0600	Copper bus duct, indoor, 3 phase									
0610	Including hangers & supports									
0620	225 amp	2 Elec	135	.119	L.F.		5.05		5.05	8.30
0640	400 amp		106	.151			6.45		6.45	10.55
0660	600 amp		86	.186			7.95		7.95	13
0680	1000 amp		60	.267			11.40		11.40	18.65
0700	1600 amp		40	.400			17.10		17.10	28
0720	3000 amp	↓	10	1.600	↓		68.50		68.50	112
1300	Transformer, dry type, 1 phase, incl. removal of									
1320	supports, wire & conduit terminations									
1340	1 kVA	1 Elec	7.70	1.039	Ea.		44.50		44.50	72.50
1420	75 kVA	2 Elec	2.50	6.400	"		273		273	445
1440	3 phase to 600V, primary									
1460	3 kVA	1 Elec	3.85	2.078	Ea.		88.50		88.50	145
1520	75 kVA	2 Elec	2.70	5.926			253		253	415
1550	300 kVA	R-3	1.80	11.111			470	78	548	850
1570	750 kVA	"	1.10	18.182	↓		765	127	892	1,400
1800	Wire, THW-THWN-THHN, removed from									
1810	in place conduit, to 15' high									

26 05 Common Work Results for Electrical

26 05 05 – Selective Electrical Demolition

26 05 05.10 Electrical Demolition

		Crew	Daily Output	Labor-Hours	Unit	Material	2014 Bare Costs Labor	Equipment	Total	Total Incl O&P
1830	#14	1 Elec	65	.123	C.L.F.		5.25		5.25	8.60
1840	#12		55	.145			6.20		6.20	10.15
1850	#10		45.50	.176			7.50		7.50	12.30
1860	#8		40.40	.198			8.45		8.45	13.85
1870	#6		32.60	.245			10.50		10.50	17.15
1880	#4	2 Elec	53	.302			12.90		12.90	21
1890	#3		50	.320			13.65		13.65	22.50
1900	#2		44.60	.359			15.30		15.30	25
1910	1/0		33.20	.482			20.50		20.50	33.50
1920	2/0		29.20	.548			23.50		23.50	38.50
1930	3/0		25	.640			27.50		27.50	44.50
1940	4/0		22	.727			31		31	51
1950	250 kcmil		20	.800			34		34	56
1960	300 kcmil		19	.842			36		36	59
1970	350 kcmil		18	.889			38		38	62
1980	400 kcmil		17	.941			40		40	66
1990	500 kcmil		16.20	.988			42		42	69
2000	Interior fluorescent fixtures, incl. supports									
2010	& whips, to 15' high									
2100	Recessed drop-in 2' x 2', 2 lamp	2 Elec	35	.457	Ea.		19.50		19.50	32
2120	2' x 4', 2 lamp		33	.485			20.50		20.50	34
2140	2' x 4', 4 lamp		30	.533			23		23	37.50
2160	4' x 4', 4 lamp		20	.800			34		34	56
2180	Surface mount, acrylic lens & hinged frame									
2200	1' x 4', 2 lamp	2 Elec	44	.364	Ea.		15.55		15.55	25.50
2220	2' x 2', 2 lamp		44	.364			15.55		15.55	25.50
2260	2' x 4', 4 lamp		33	.485			20.50		20.50	34
2280	4' x 4', 4 lamp		23	.696			29.50		29.50	48.50
2300	Strip fixtures, surface mount									
2320	4' long, 1 lamp	2 Elec	53	.302	Ea.		12.90		12.90	21
2340	4' long, 2 lamp		50	.320			13.65		13.65	22.50
2360	8' long, 1 lamp		42	.381			16.25		16.25	26.50
2380	8' long, 2 lamp		40	.400			17.10		17.10	28
2400	Pendant mount, industrial, incl. removal									
2410	of chain or rod hangers, to 15' high									
2420	4' long, 2 lamp	2 Elec	35	.457	Ea.		19.50		19.50	32
2440	8' long, 2 lamp	"	27	.593	"		25.50		25.50	41.50

26 05 13 – Medium-Voltage Cables

26 05 13.16 Medium-Voltage, Single Cable

		Crew	Daily Output	Labor-Hours	Unit	Material	2014 Bare Costs Labor	Equipment	Total	Total Incl O&P
0010	**MEDIUM-VOLTAGE, SINGLE CABLE** Splicing & terminations not included									
0040	Copper, XLP shielding, 5 kV, #6	2 Elec	4.40	3.636	C.L.F.	158	155		313	430
0050	#4		4.40	3.636		205	155		360	480
0100	#2		4	4		242	171		413	545
0200	#1		4	4		278	171		449	585
0400	1/0		3.80	4.211		305	180		485	630
0600	2/0		3.60	4.444		385	190		575	735
0800	4/0		3.20	5		500	214		714	900
1000	250 kcmil	3 Elec	4.50	5.333		620	228		848	1,050
1200	350 kcmil		3.90	6.154		800	263		1,063	1,300
1400	500 kcmil		3.60	6.667		975	285		1,260	1,550
1600	15 kV, ungrounded neutral, #1	2 Elec	4	4		340	171		511	650
1800	1/0		3.80	4.211		405	180		585	740

26 05 Common Work Results for Electrical

26 05 13 – Medium-Voltage Cables

26 05 13.16 Medium-Voltage, Single Cable	Crew	Daily Output	Labor-Hours	Unit	Material	2014 Bare Costs Labor	Equipment	Total	Total Incl O&P
2000	2/0	2 Elec	3.60	4.444	C.L.F.	460	190		650	815
2200	4/0	↓	3.20	5		610	214		824	1,025
2400	250 kcmil	3 Elec	4.50	5.333		675	228		903	1,125
2600	350 kcmil		3.90	6.154		855	263		1,118	1,375
2800	500 kcmil	↓	3.60	6.667	↓	1,050	285		1,335	1,625

26 05 19 – Low-Voltage Electrical Power Conductors and Cables

26 05 19.20 Armored Cable

		Crew	Daily Output	Labor-Hours	Unit	Material	2014 Bare Costs Labor	Equipment	Total	Total Incl O&P
0010	**ARMORED CABLE**									
0050	600 volt, copper (BX), #14, 2 conductor, solid	1 Elec	2.40	3.333	C.L.F.	54	142		196	293
0100	3 conductor, solid		2.20	3.636		83.50	155		238.50	345
0150	#12, 2 conductor, solid		2.30	3.478		54.50	149		203.50	305
0200	3 conductor, solid		2	4		88.50	171		259.50	380
0250	#10, 2 conductor, solid		2	4		100	171		271	390
0300	3 conductor, solid		1.60	5		139	214		353	505
0340	#8, 2 conductor, stranded		1.50	5.333		262	228		490	665
0350	3 conductor, stranded		1.30	6.154		262	263		525	720
0400	3 conductor with PVC jacket, in cable tray, #6	↓	3.10	2.581		455	110		565	680
0450	#4	2 Elec	5.40	2.963		565	127		692	825
0500	#2		4.60	3.478		710	149		859	1,025
0550	#1		4	4		940	171		1,111	1,300
0600	1/0		3.60	4.444		1,025	190		1,215	1,425
0650	2/0		3.40	4.706		1,250	201		1,451	1,700
0700	3/0		3.20	5		1,575	214		1,789	2,075
0750	4/0	↓	3	5.333		1,825	228		2,053	2,400
0800	250 kcmil	3 Elec	3.60	6.667		2,100	285		2,385	2,775
0850	350 kcmil		3.30	7.273		2,825	310		3,135	3,600
0900	500 kcmil	↓	3	8	↓	3,800	340		4,140	4,725
1050	5 kV, copper, 3 conductor with PVC jacket,									
1060	non-shielded, in cable tray, #4	2 Elec	380	.042	L.F.	7.35	1.80		9.15	11
1100	#2		360	.044		9.55	1.90		11.45	13.60
1200	#1		300	.053		12.15	2.28		14.43	17.10
1400	1/0		290	.055		14	2.36		16.36	19.25
1600	2/0		260	.062		16.20	2.63		18.83	22
2000	4/0		240	.067		21.50	2.85		24.35	28.50
2100	250 kcmil	3 Elec	330	.073		29.50	3.11		32.61	37.50
2150	350 kcmil		315	.076		36.50	3.25		39.75	45.50
2200	500 kcmil		270	.089	↓	51	3.80		54.80	62
2400	15 kV, copper, 3 conductor with PVC jacket galv., steel armored									
2500	grounded neutral, in cable tray, #2	2 Elec	300	.053	L.F.	15.40	2.28		17.68	20.50
2600	#1		280	.057		16.40	2.44		18.84	22
2800	1/0		260	.062		18.75	2.63		21.38	25
2900	2/0		220	.073		25	3.11		28.11	32.50
3000	4/0	↓	190	.084		28.50	3.60		32.10	37
3100	250 kcmil	3 Elec	270	.089		31.50	3.80		35.30	40.50
3150	350 kcmil		240	.100		37	4.27		41.27	48
3200	500 kcmil	↓	210	.114	↓	50	4.88		54.88	63
3400	15 kV, copper, 3 conductor with PVC jacket,									
3450	ungrounded neutral, in cable tray, #2	2 Elec	260	.062	L.F.	16.60	2.63		19.23	22.50
3500	#1		230	.070		18.40	2.97		21.37	25.50
3600	1/0		200	.080		21	3.42		24.42	28.50
3700	2/0		190	.084		26	3.60		29.60	34.50
3800	4/0	↓	160	.100	↓	31	4.27		35.27	41.50

26 05 19 – Low-Voltage Electrical Power Conductors and Cables

26 05 19.20 Armored Cable		Crew	Daily Output	Labor-Hours	Unit	Material	2014 Bare Costs Labor	Equipment	Total	Total Incl O&P
4000	250 kcmil	3 Elec	210	.114	L.F.	36.50	4.88		41.38	48
4050	350 kcmil		195	.123		48	5.25		53.25	61
4100	500 kcmil		180	.133		58.50	5.70		64.20	73.50
9010	600 volt, copper (MC) steel clad, #14, 2 wire	1 Elec	2.40	3.333	C.L.F.	55	142		197	294
9020	3 wire		2.20	3.636		85	155		240	350
9030	4 wire		2	4		118	171		289	410
9040	#12, 2 wire		2.30	3.478		55.50	149		204.50	305
9050	3 wire		2	4		94	171		265	385
9070	#10, 2 wire		2	4		116	171		287	410
9080	3 wire		1.60	5		162	214		376	530
9100	#8, 2 wire, stranded		1.80	4.444		223	190		413	555
9110	3 wire, stranded		1.30	6.154		315	263		578	775
9200	600 volt, copper (MC) aluminum clad, #14, 2 wire		2.65	3.019		53.50	129		182.50	270
9210	3 wire		2.45	3.265		83.50	139		222.50	320
9220	4 wire		2.20	3.636		117	155		272	380
9230	#12, 2 wire		2.55	3.137		55.50	134		189.50	280
9240	3 wire		2.20	3.636		92.50	155		247.50	355
9250	4 wire		2	4		125	171		296	420
9260	#10, 2 wire		2.20	3.636		115	155		270	380
9270	3 wire		1.80	4.444		161	190		351	485
9280	4 wire		1.55	5.161		253	220		473	640

26 05 19.35 Cable Terminations

		Crew	Daily Output	Labor-Hours	Unit	Material	2014 Bare Costs Labor	Equipment	Total	Total Incl O&P
0010	**CABLE TERMINATIONS**									
0015	Wire connectors, screw type, #22 to #14	1 Elec	260	.031	Ea.	.06	1.31		1.37	2.22
0020	#18 to #12		240	.033		.08	1.42		1.50	2.42
0025	#18 to #10		240	.033		.14	1.42		1.56	2.48
0030	Screw-on connectors, insulated, #18 to #12		240	.033		.22	1.42		1.64	2.57
0035	#16 to #10		230	.035		.25	1.49		1.74	2.71
0040	#14 to #8		210	.038		.30	1.63		1.93	2.99
0045	#12 to #6		180	.044		.62	1.90		2.52	3.79
0050	Terminal lugs, solderless, #16 to #10		50	.160		.37	6.85		7.22	11.60
0100	#8 to #4		30	.267		.73	11.40		12.13	19.45
0150	#2 to #1		22	.364		1.03	15.55		16.58	26.50
0200	1/0 to 2/0		16	.500		1.64	21.50		23.14	37
0250	3/0		12	.667		2.87	28.50		31.37	49.50
0300	4/0		11	.727		3.51	31		34.51	55
0350	250 kcmil		9	.889		3.41	38		41.41	66
0400	350 kcmil		7	1.143		4.44	49		53.44	85
0450	500 kcmil		6	1.333		8.20	57		65.20	102
1600	Crimp 1 hole lugs, copper or aluminum, 600 volt									
1620	#14	1 Elec	60	.133	Ea.	.60	5.70		6.30	9.95
1630	#12		50	.160		.92	6.85		7.77	12.20
1640	#10		45	.178		.92	7.60		8.52	13.45
1780	#8		36	.222		1.91	9.50		11.41	17.65
1800	#6		30	.267		2.48	11.40		13.88	21.50
2000	#4		27	.296		3.38	12.65		16.03	24
2200	#2		24	.333		5.30	14.25		19.55	29.50
2400	#1		20	.400		5.50	17.10		22.60	34
2500	1/0		17.50	.457		5.85	19.50		25.35	38.50
2600	2/0		15	.533		6.80	23		29.80	45
2800	3/0		12	.667		8	28.50		36.50	55.50
3000	4/0		11	.727		8.90	31		39.90	61

26 05 Common Work Results for Electrical

26 05 19 – Low-Voltage Electrical Power Conductors and Cables

		Crew	Daily Output	Labor-Hours	Unit	Material	2014 Bare Costs Labor	2014 Bare Costs Equipment	Total	Total Incl O&P
26 05 19.35 Cable Terminations										
3200	250 kcmil	1 Elec	9	.889	Ea.	10.50	38		48.50	73.50
3400	300 kcmil		8	1		12	42.50		54.50	83
3500	350 kcmil		7	1.143		13.60	49		62.60	95
3600	400 kcmil		6.50	1.231		15.10	52.50		67.60	103
3800	500 kcmil		6	1.333		17.70	57		74.70	112
26 05 19.50 Mineral Insulated Cable										
0010	**MINERAL INSULATED CABLE** 600 volt									
0100	1 conductor, #12	1 Elec	1.60	5	C.L.F.	360	214		574	745
0200	#10		1.60	5		465	214		679	860
0400	#8		1.50	5.333		515	228		743	945
0500	#6		1.40	5.714		615	244		859	1,075
0600	#4	2 Elec	2.40	6.667		825	285		1,110	1,375
0800	#2		2.20	7.273		1,175	310		1,485	1,775
0900	#1		2.10	7.619		1,350	325		1,675	2,000
1000	1/0		2	8		1,575	340		1,915	2,275
1100	2/0		1.90	8.421		1,875	360		2,235	2,675
1200	3/0		1.80	8.889		2,250	380		2,630	3,100
1400	4/0		1.60	10		2,600	425		3,025	3,575
1410	250 kcmil	3 Elec	2.40	10		2,950	425		3,375	3,925
1420	350 kcmil		1.95	12.308		3,350	525		3,875	4,550
1430	500 kcmil		1.95	12.308		4,325	525		4,850	5,600
26 05 19.55 Non-Metallic Sheathed Cable										
0010	**NON-METALLIC SHEATHED CABLE** 600 volt									
0100	Copper with ground wire, (Romex)									
0150	#14, 2 conductor	1 Elec	2.70	2.963	C.L.F.	25.50	127		152.50	235
0200	3 conductor		2.40	3.333		35.50	142		177.50	272
0250	#12, 2 conductor		2.50	3.200		38.50	137		175.50	267
0300	3 conductor		2.20	3.636		54	155		209	315
0350	#10, 2 conductor		2.20	3.636		60	155		215	320
0400	3 conductor		1.80	4.444		85.50	190		275.50	405
0430	#8, 2 conductor		1.60	5		94.50	214		308.50	455
0450	3 conductor		1.50	5.333		138	228		366	525
0500	#6, 3 conductor		1.40	5.714		224	244		468	645
0550	SE type SER aluminum cable, 3 RHW and									
0600	1 bare neutral, 3 #8 & 1 #8	1 Elec	1.60	5	C.L.F.	137	214		351	500
0650	3 #6 & 1 #6	"	1.40	5.714		156	244		400	570
0700	3 #4 & 1 #6	2 Elec	2.40	6.667		144	285		429	625
0750	3 #2 & 1 #4		2.20	7.273		257	310		567	790
0800	3 #1/0 & 1 #2		2	8		390	340		730	990
0850	3 #2/0 & 1 #1		1.80	8.889		460	380		840	1,125
0900	3 #4/0 & 1 #2/0		1.60	10		655	425		1,080	1,425
26 05 19.90 Wire										
0010	**WIRE**	R260519-92								
0020	600 volt, copper type THW, solid, #14	1 Elec	13	.615	C.L.F.	8.30	26.50		34.80	52
0030	#12	R260533-22	11	.727		12.50	31		43.50	65
0040	#10		10	.800		19.80	34		53.80	78
0050	Stranded, #14		13	.615		9.40	26.50		35.90	53.50
0100	#12		11	.727		14.45	31		45.45	67
0120	#10		10	.800		23	34		57	81
0140	#8		8	1		37.50	42.50		80	112
0160	#6		6.50	1.231		64	52.50		116.50	157
0180	#4	2 Elec	10.60	1.509		101	64.50		165.50	217

26 05 Common Work Results for Electrical

26 05 19 – Low-Voltage Electrical Power Conductors and Cables

26 05 19.90 Wire		Crew	Daily Output	Labor-Hours	Unit	Material	2014 Bare Costs Labor	Equipment	Total	Total Incl O&P
0200	#3	2 Elec	10	1.600	C.L.F.	126	68.50		194.50	251
0220	#2		9	1.778		160	76		236	300
0240	#1		8	2		202	85.50		287.50	360
0260	1/0		6.60	2.424		251	104		355	445
0280	2/0		5.80	2.759		315	118		433	540
0300	3/0		5	3.200		395	137		532	660
0350	4/0		4.40	3.636		505	155		660	810
0400	250 kcmil	3 Elec	6	4		590	171		761	930
0420	300 kcmil		5.70	4.211		705	180		885	1,075
0450	350 kcmil		5.40	4.444		860	190		1,050	1,250
0480	400 kcmil		5.10	4.706		990	201		1,191	1,425
0490	500 kcmil		4.80	5		1,175	214		1,389	1,625
0540	600 volt, aluminum type THHN, stranded, #6	1 Elec	8	1		37.50	42.50		80	111
0560	#4	2 Elec	13	1.231		46.50	52.50		99	137
0580	#2		10.60	1.509		63	64.50		127.50	175
0600	#1		9	1.778		92	76		168	225
0620	1/0		8	2		110	85.50		195.50	261
0640	2/0		7.20	2.222		130	95		225	298
0680	3/0		6.60	2.424		162	104		266	345
0700	4/0		6.20	2.581		180	110		290	380
0720	250 kcmil	3 Elec	8.70	2.759		219	118		337	435
0740	300 kcmil		8.10	2.963		305	127		432	540
0760	350 kcmil		7.50	3.200		310	137		447	565
0780	400 kcmil		6.90	3.478		360	149		509	640
0800	500 kcmil		6	4		395	171		566	715
0850	600 kcmil		5.70	4.211		505	180		685	850
0880	700 kcmil		5.10	4.706		580	201		781	970
0900	750 kcmil		4.80	5		600	214		814	1,000
0910	1000 kcmil		3.78	6.349		890	271		1,161	1,425
0920	600 volt, copper type THWN-THHN, solid, #14	1 Elec	13	.615		8.95	26.50		35.45	53
0940	#12		11	.727		13.55	31		44.55	66
0960	#10		10	.800		21.50	34		55.50	79.50
1000	Stranded, #14		13	.615		10.25	26.50		36.75	54.50
1200	#12		11	.727		15.70	31		46.70	68.50
1250	#10		10	.800		24.50	34		58.50	82.50
1300	#8		8	1		38	42.50		80.50	112
1350	#6		6.50	1.231		65	52.50		117.50	158
1400	#4	2 Elec	10.60	1.509		103	64.50		167.50	219

26 05 23 – Control-Voltage Electrical Power Cables

26 05 23.10 Control Cable

		Crew	Daily Output	Labor-Hours	Unit	Material	2014 Bare Costs Labor	Equipment	Total	Total Incl O&P
0010	**CONTROL CABLE**									
0020	600 volt, copper, #14 THWN wire with PVC jacket, 2 wires	1 Elec	9	.889	C.L.F.	26.50	38		64.50	91
0030	3 wires		8	1		37	42.50		79.50	111
0100	4 wires		7	1.143		45.50	49		94.50	130
0150	5 wires		6.50	1.231		56	52.50		108.50	148
0200	6 wires		6	1.333		85.50	57		142.50	187
0300	8 wires		5.30	1.509		98	64.50		162.50	214
0400	10 wires		4.80	1.667		123	71		194	253
0500	12 wires		4.30	1.860		144	79.50		223.50	288
0600	14 wires		3.80	2.105		172	90		262	335
0700	16 wires		3.50	2.286		177	97.50		274.50	355
0800	18 wires		3.30	2.424		193	104		297	380

26 05 23 – Control-Voltage Electrical Power Cables

26 05 23.10 Control Cable	Crew	Daily Output	Labor-Hours	Unit	Material	2014 Bare Costs Labor	Equipment	Total	Total Incl O&P
0810	19 wires	1 Elec	3.10	2.581	C.L.F.	218	110		328	420
0900	20 wires		3	2.667		236	114		350	445
1000	22 wires	↓	2.80	2.857	↓	243	122		365	465

26 05 26 – Grounding and Bonding for Electrical Systems

26 05 26.80 Grounding

		Crew	Daily Output	Labor-Hours	Unit	Material	Labor	Equipment	Total	Total Incl O&P
0010	**GROUNDING**									
0030	Rod, copper clad, 8' long, 1/2" diameter	1 Elec	5.50	1.455	Ea.	20.50	62		82.50	125
0050	3/4" diameter		5.30	1.509		34	64.50		98.50	144
0080	10' long, 1/2" diameter		4.80	1.667		22.50	71		93.50	142
0100	3/4" diameter		4.40	1.818		39	77.50		116.50	170
0130	15' long, 3/4" diameter		4	2	↓	63.50	85.50		149	210
0390	Bare copper wire, stranded, #8		11	.727	C.L.F.	35	31		66	89.50
0400	#6	↓	10	.800		61	34		95	123
0600	#2	2 Elec	10	1.600		162	68.50		230.50	291
0800	3/0		6.60	2.424		365	104		469	575
1000	4/0	↓	5.70	2.807		460	120		580	700
1200	250 kcmil	3 Elec	7.20	3.333	↓	545	142		687	835
1800	Water pipe ground clamps, heavy duty									
2000	Bronze, 1/2" to 1" diameter	1 Elec	8	1	Ea.	23.50	42.50		66	95.50
2100	1-1/4" to 2" diameter		8	1		32.50	42.50		75	106
2200	2-1/2" to 3" diameter		6	1.333		49	57		106	147
2800	Brazed connections, #6 wire		12	.667		16	28.50		44.50	64
3000	#2 wire		10	.800		21.50	34		55.50	79.50
3100	3/0 wire		8	1		32	42.50		74.50	106
3200	4/0 wire		7	1.143		37	49		86	121
3400	250 kcmil wire		5	1.600		43	68.50		111.50	159
3600	500 kcmil wire	↓	4	2	↓	53	85.50		138.50	198

26 05 33 – Raceway and Boxes for Electrical Systems

26 05 33.13 Conduit

		Crew	Daily Output	Labor-Hours	Unit	Material	Labor	Equipment	Total	Total Incl O&P
0010	**CONDUIT** To 15' high, includes 2 terminations, 2 elbows,	R260533-22								
0020	11 beam clamps, and 11 couplings per 100 L.F.									
0300	Aluminum, 1/2" diameter	1 Elec	100	.080	L.F.	1.83	3.42		5.25	7.60
0500	3/4" diameter		90	.089		2.46	3.80		6.26	8.90
0700	1" diameter		80	.100		3.53	4.27		7.80	10.90
1000	1-1/4" diameter		70	.114		4.35	4.88		9.23	12.80
1030	1-1/2" diameter		65	.123		5.50	5.25		10.75	14.65
1050	2" diameter		60	.133		7.80	5.70		13.50	17.85
1070	2-1/2" diameter		50	.160		11.40	6.85		18.25	24
1100	3" diameter	2 Elec	90	.178		15.95	7.60		23.55	30
1130	3-1/2" diameter		80	.200		20.50	8.55		29.05	36.50
1140	4" diameter	↓	70	.229		25	9.75		34.75	43.50
1750	Rigid galvanized steel, 1/2" diameter	1 Elec	90	.089		2.40	3.80		6.20	8.85
1770	3/4" diameter		80	.100		2.56	4.27		6.83	9.80
1800	1" diameter		65	.123		3.69	5.25		8.94	12.65
1830	1-1/4" diameter		60	.133		4.84	5.70		10.54	14.65
1850	1-1/2" diameter		55	.145		5.75	6.20		11.95	16.45
1870	2" diameter		45	.178		7.45	7.60		15.05	20.50
1900	2-1/2" diameter		35	.229		13.30	9.75		23.05	30.50
1930	3" diameter	2 Elec	50	.320		15.50	13.65		29.15	39.50
1950	3-1/2" diameter		44	.364		19.45	15.55		35	47
1970	4" diameter	↓	40	.400		23	17.10		40.10	53
2500	Steel, intermediate conduit (IMC), 1/2" diameter	1 Elec	100	.080	↓	1.72	3.42		5.14	7.50

26 05 33 – Raceway and Boxes for Electrical Systems

26 05 33.13 Conduit

		Crew	Daily Output	Labor-Hours	Unit	Material	2014 Bare Costs Labor	Equipment	Total	Total Incl O&P
2530	3/4" diameter	1 Elec	90	.089	L.F.	2.06	3.80		5.86	8.45
2550	1" diameter		70	.114		3.04	4.88		7.92	11.35
2570	1-1/4" diameter		65	.123		3.73	5.25		8.98	12.70
2600	1-1/2" diameter		60	.133		4.92	5.70		10.62	14.70
2630	2" diameter		50	.160		5.95	6.85		12.80	17.70
2650	2-1/2" diameter		40	.200		10.60	8.55		19.15	25.50
2670	3" diameter	2 Elec	60	.267		14.50	11.40		25.90	34.50
2700	3-1/2" diameter		54	.296		19.15	12.65		31.80	41.50
2730	4" diameter		50	.320		21	13.65		34.65	45.50
5000	Electric metallic tubing (EMT), 1/2" diameter	1 Elec	170	.047		.56	2.01		2.57	3.91
5020	3/4" diameter		130	.062		.86	2.63		3.49	5.25
5040	1" diameter		115	.070		1.48	2.97		4.45	6.50
5060	1-1/4" diameter		100	.080		2.45	3.42		5.87	8.30
5080	1-1/2" diameter		90	.089		3.16	3.80		6.96	9.70
5100	2" diameter		80	.100		4.02	4.27		8.29	11.40
5120	2-1/2" diameter		60	.133		9.55	5.70		15.25	19.80
5140	3" diameter	2 Elec	100	.160		11.05	6.85		17.90	23.50
5160	3-1/2" diameter		90	.178		14	7.60		21.60	28
5180	4" diameter		80	.200		15.35	8.55		23.90	31
9900	Add to labor for higher elevated installation									
9910	15' to 20' high, add						10%			
9920	20' to 25' high, add						20%			
9930	25' to 30' high, add						25%			
9940	30' to 35' high, add						30%			
9950	35' to 40' high, add						35%			
9960	Over 40' high, add						40%			
9980	Allowance for conduit fittings 5% min.-20% max.									

26 05 33.16 Outlet Boxes

		Crew	Daily Output	Labor-Hours	Unit	Material	2014 Bare Costs Labor	Equipment	Total	Total Incl O&P
0010	**OUTLET BOXES**									
0020	Pressed steel, octagon, 4"	1 Elec	20	.400	Ea.	3.07	17.10		20.17	31.50
0060	Covers, blank		64	.125		1.29	5.35		6.64	10.15
0100	Extension rings		40	.200		5.10	8.55		13.65	19.60
0150	Square, 4"		20	.400		2.10	17.10		19.20	30.50
0200	Extension rings		40	.200		5.15	8.55		13.70	19.65
0250	Covers, blank		64	.125		1.39	5.35		6.74	10.30
0300	Plaster rings		64	.125		2.83	5.35		8.18	11.85
0650	Switchbox		27	.296		4.91	12.65		17.56	26
1100	Concrete, floor, 1 gang		5.30	1.509		89	64.50		153.50	204
2000	Poke-thru fitting, fire rated, for 3-3/4" floor		6.80	1.176		129	50		179	223
2040	For 7" floor		6.80	1.176		143	50		193	239
2100	Pedestal, 15 amp, duplex receptacle & blank plate		5.25	1.524		136	65		201	257
2120	Duplex receptacle and telephone plate		5.25	1.524		136	65		201	257
2140	Pedestal, 20 amp, duplex recept. & phone plate		5	1.600		137	68.50		205.50	263
2200	Abandonment plate		32	.250		38	10.70		48.70	59.50

26 05 33.18 Pull Boxes

		Crew	Daily Output	Labor-Hours	Unit	Material	2014 Bare Costs Labor	Equipment	Total	Total Incl O&P
0010	**PULL BOXES**									
0100	Sheet metal, pull box, NEMA 1, type SC, 6" W x 6" H x 4" D	1 Elec	8	1	Ea.	10.75	42.50		53.25	82
0200	8" W x 8" H x 4" D		8	1		15.30	42.50		57.80	87
0300	10" W x 12" H x 6" D		5.30	1.509		29	64.50		93.50	138
0400	16" W x 20" H x 8" D		4	2		86	85.50		171.50	235
0500	20" W x 24" H x 8" D		3.20	2.500		97.50	107		204.50	282
0600	24" W x 36" H x 8" D		2.70	2.963		140	127		267	360

26 05 33.18 Pull Boxes		Crew	Daily Output	Labor-Hours	Unit	Material	2014 Bare Costs Labor	Equipment	Total	Total Incl O&P
0650	Pull box, hinged , NEMA 1, 6" W x 6" H x 4" D	1 Elec	8	1	Ea.	10.90	42.50		53.40	82
0800	12" W x 16" H x 6" D		4.70	1.702		43	72.50		115.50	167
1000	20" W x 20" H x 6" D		3.60	2.222		74.50	95		169.50	237
1200	20" W x 20" H x 8" D		3.20	2.500		148	107		255	340
1400	24" W x 36" H x 8" D		2.70	2.963		228	127		355	460
1600	24" W x 42" H x 8" D	▼	2	4	▼	345	171		516	660
2100	Pull box, NEMA 3R, type SC, raintight & weatherproof									
2150	6" L x 6" W x 6" D	1 Elec	10	.800	Ea.	18.85	34		52.85	76.50
2200	8" L x 6" W x 6" D		8	1		28	42.50		70.50	101
2250	10" L x 6" W x 6" D		7	1.143		37	49		86	121
2300	12" L x 12" W x 6" D		5	1.600		44	68.50		112.50	161
2350	16" L x 16" W x 6" D		4.50	1.778		115	76		191	250
2400	20" L x 20" W x 6" D		4	2		142	85.50		227.50	296
2450	24" L x 18" W x 8" D		3	2.667		125	114		239	325
2500	24" L x 24" W x 10" D		2.50	3.200		161	137		298	400
2550	30" L x 24" W x 12" D		2	4		380	171		551	695
2600	36" L x 36" W x 12" D	▼	1.50	5.333	▼	430	228		658	845
2800	Cast iron, pull boxes for surface mounting									
3000	NEMA 4, watertight & dust tight									
3050	6" L x 6" W x 6" D	1 Elec	4	2	Ea.	248	85.50		333.50	410
3100	8" L x 6" W x 6" D		3.20	2.500		345	107		452	555
3150	10" L x 6" W x 6" D		2.50	3.200		385	137		522	650
3200	12" L x 12" W x 6" D		2.30	3.478		705	149		854	1,025
3250	16" L x 16" W x 6" D		1.30	6.154		1,125	263		1,388	1,675
3300	20" L x 20" W x 6" D		.80	10		2,100	425		2,525	3,025
3350	24" L x 18" W x 8" D		.70	11.429		2,600	490		3,090	3,675
3400	24" L x 24" W x 10" D		.50	16		4,925	685		5,610	6,550
3450	30" L x 24" W x 12" D		.40	20		9,025	855		9,880	11,300
3500	36" L x 36" W x 12" D	▼	.20	40	▼	7,025	1,700		8,725	10,500
4000	NEMA 7, explosionproof									
4050	6" L x 6" W x 6" D	1 Elec	2	4	Ea.	685	171		856	1,025
4100	8" L x 6" W x 6" D		1.80	4.444		920	190		1,110	1,300
4150	10" L x 6" W x 6" D		1.60	5		1,275	214		1,489	1,750
4200	12" L x 12" W x 6" D		1	8		2,150	340		2,490	2,900
4250	16" L x 14" W x 6" D		.60	13.333		3,025	570		3,595	4,250
4300	18" L x 18" W x 8" D		.50	16		5,575	685		6,260	7,275
4350	24" L x 18" W x 8" D		.40	20		7,100	855		7,955	9,200
4400	24" L x 24" W x 10" D		.30	26.667		9,675	1,150		10,825	12,500
4450	30" L x 24" W x 12" D	▼	.20	40	▼	14,100	1,700		15,800	18,300
6000	J.I.C. wiring boxes, NEMA 12, dust tight & drip tight									
6050	6" L x 8" W x 4" D	1 Elec	10	.800	Ea.	51.50	34		85.50	113
6100	8" L x 10" W x 4" D		8	1		64	42.50		106.50	141
6150	12" L x 14" W x 6" D		5.30	1.509		109	64.50		173.50	225
6200	14" L x 16" W x 6" D		4.70	1.702		127	72.50		199.50	259
6250	16" L x 20" W x 6" D		4.40	1.818		224	77.50		301.50	375
6300	24" L x 30" W x 6" D		3.20	2.500		330	107		437	535
6350	24" L x 30" W x 8" D		2.90	2.759		355	118		473	585
6400	24" L x 36" W x 8" D		2.70	2.963		390	127		517	635
6450	24" L x 42" W x 8" D		2.30	3.478		425	149		574	715
6500	24" L x 48" W x 8" D	▼	2	4	▼	465	171		636	790

26 05 Common Work Results for Electrical

26 05 33 – Raceway and Boxes for Electrical Systems

26 05 33.23 Wireway

		Crew	Daily Output	Labor-Hours	Unit	Material	2014 Bare Costs Labor	Equipment	Total	Total Incl O&P
0010	**WIREWAY** to 15' high									
0100	NEMA 1, Screw cover w/fittings and supports, 2-1/2" x 2-1/2"	1 Elec	45	.178	L.F.	10.35	7.60		17.95	24
0200	4" x 4"	"	40	.200		11.50	8.55		20.05	26.50
0400	6" x 6"	2 Elec	60	.267		19.50	11.40		30.90	40
0600	8" x 8"	"	40	.400		28	17.10		45.10	59
4475	NEMA 3R, Screw cover w/fittings and supports, 4" x 4"	1 Elec	36	.222		19.45	9.50		28.95	37
4480	6" x 6"	2 Elec	55	.291		26	12.40		38.40	49
4485	8" x 8"		36	.444		40	19		59	75
4490	12" x 12"		18	.889		64	38		102	133
9980	Allow. for wireway ftngs., 5% min.-20% max.									

26 05 33.35 Flexible Metallic Conduit

		Crew	Daily Output	Labor-Hours	Unit	Material	2014 Bare Costs Labor	Equipment	Total	Total Incl O&P
0010	**FLEXIBLE METALLIC CONDUIT**									
0050	Steel, 3/8" diameter	1 Elec	200	.040	L.F.	.51	1.71		2.22	3.36
0100	1/2" diameter		200	.040		.57	1.71		2.28	3.43
0200	3/4" diameter		160	.050		.78	2.14		2.92	4.36
0250	1" diameter		100	.080		1.42	3.42		4.84	7.15
0300	1-1/4" diameter		70	.114		1.84	4.88		6.72	10
0350	1-1/2" diameter		50	.160		3	6.85		9.85	14.50
0370	2" diameter		40	.200		3.66	8.55		12.21	18.05
0420	Connectors, plain, 3/8" diameter		100	.080	Ea.	2.31	3.42		5.73	8.15
0430	1/2" diameter		80	.100		2.67	4.27		6.94	9.95
0440	3/4" diameter		70	.114		3.06	4.88		7.94	11.35
0450	1" diameter		50	.160		6.50	6.85		13.35	18.35
0452	1-1/4" diameter		45	.178		8	7.60		15.60	21.50
0454	1-1/2" diameter		40	.200		11.75	8.55		20.30	27
0456	2" diameter		28	.286		17.60	12.20		29.80	39.50
0490	Insulated, 1" diameter		40	.200		7.10	8.55		15.65	22
0500	1-1/4" diameter		40	.200		13.10	8.55		21.65	28.50
0550	1-1/2" diameter		32	.250		19.70	10.70		30.40	39
0600	2" diameter		23	.348		32.50	14.85		47.35	60.50

26 05 36 – Cable Trays for Electrical Systems

26 05 36.10 Cable Tray Ladder Type

		Crew	Daily Output	Labor-Hours	Unit	Material	2014 Bare Costs Labor	Equipment	Total	Total Incl O&P
0010	**CABLE TRAY LADDER TYPE** w/ftngs. & supports, 4" dp., to 15' elev.									
0160	Galvanized steel tray									
0170	4" rung spacing, 6" wide	2 Elec	98	.163	L.F.	17.95	6.95		24.90	31
0200	12" wide		86	.186		21.50	7.95		29.45	36.50
0400	18" wide		82	.195		25	8.35		33.35	41
0600	24" wide		78	.205		29	8.75		37.75	46.50
3200	Aluminum tray, 4" deep, 6" rung spacing, 6" wide		134	.119		17.80	5.10		22.90	28
3220	12" wide		124	.129		19.95	5.50		25.45	31
3230	18" wide		114	.140		22	6		28	34.50
3240	24" wide		106	.151		26	6.45		32.45	39
9980	Allow. for tray ftngs., 5% min.-20% max.									

26 05 39 – Underfloor Raceways for Electrical Systems

26 05 39.30 Conduit In Concrete Slab

		Crew	Daily Output	Labor-Hours	Unit	Material	2014 Bare Costs Labor	Equipment	Total	Total Incl O&P
0010	**CONDUIT IN CONCRETE SLAB** Including terminations,									
0020	fittings and supports									
3230	PVC, schedule 40, 1/2" diameter	1 Elec	270	.030	L.F.	.64	1.27		1.91	2.77
3250	3/4" diameter		230	.035		.75	1.49		2.24	3.25
3270	1" diameter		200	.040		.94	1.71		2.65	3.84
3300	1-1/4" diameter		170	.047		1.36	2.01		3.37	4.78

26 05 Common Work Results for Electrical

26 05 39 – Underfloor Raceways for Electrical Systems

26 05 39.30 Conduit In Concrete Slab

		Crew	Daily Output	Labor-Hours	Unit	Material	2014 Bare Costs Labor	Equipment	Total	Total Incl O&P
3330	1-1/2" diameter	1 Elec	140	.057	L.F.	1.63	2.44		4.07	5.80
3350	2" diameter		120	.067		2.07	2.85		4.92	6.95
4350	Rigid galvanized steel, 1/2" diameter		200	.040		2.31	1.71		4.02	5.35
4400	3/4" diameter		170	.047		2.44	2.01		4.45	6
4450	1" diameter		130	.062		3.36	2.63		5.99	8
4500	1-1/4" diameter		110	.073		4.59	3.11		7.70	10.15
4600	1-1/2" diameter		100	.080		5.15	3.42		8.57	11.25
4800	2" diameter		90	.089		6.40	3.80		10.20	13.25

26 05 39.40 Conduit In Trench

		Crew	Daily Output	Labor-Hours	Unit	Material	2014 Bare Costs Labor	Equipment	Total	Total Incl O&P
0010	**CONDUIT IN TRENCH** Includes terminations and fittings									
0020	Does not include excavation or backfill, see Section 31 23 16.00									
0200	Rigid galvanized steel, 2" diameter	1 Elec	150	.053	L.F.	6	2.28		8.28	10.35
0400	2-1/2" diameter	"	100	.080		11.75	3.42		15.17	18.55
0600	3" diameter	2 Elec	160	.100		13.90	4.27		18.17	22.50
0800	3-1/2" diameter		140	.114		18.35	4.88		23.23	28
1000	4" diameter		100	.160		20.50	6.85		27.35	33.50
1200	5" diameter		80	.200		42.50	8.55		51.05	61
1400	6" diameter		60	.267		62.50	11.40		73.90	87.50

26 05 43 – Underground Ducts and Raceways for Electrical Systems

26 05 43.10 Trench Duct

		Crew	Daily Output	Labor-Hours	Unit	Material	2014 Bare Costs Labor	Equipment	Total	Total Incl O&P
0010	**TRENCH DUCT** Steel with cover									
0020	Standard adjustable, depths to 4"									
0100	Straight, single compartment, 9" wide	2 Elec	40	.400	L.F.	116	17.10		133.10	156
0200	12" wide		32	.500		133	21.50		154.50	181
0400	18" wide		26	.615		163	26.50		189.50	222
0600	24" wide		22	.727		195	31		226	265
0800	30" wide		20	.800		226	34		260	305
1000	36" wide		16	1		259	42.50		301.50	355
1200	Horizontal elbow, 9" wide		5.40	2.963	Ea.	380	127		507	625
1400	12" wide		4.60	3.478		440	149		589	730
1600	18" wide		4	4		565	171		736	900
1800	24" wide		3.20	5		795	214		1,009	1,225
2000	30" wide		2.60	6.154		1,050	263		1,313	1,600
2200	36" wide		2.40	6.667		1,400	285		1,685	2,000
2400	Vertical elbow, 9" wide		5.40	2.963		134	127		261	355
2600	12" wide		4.60	3.478		145	149		294	400
2800	18" wide		4	4		166	171		337	465
3000	24" wide		3.20	5		207	214		421	575
3200	30" wide		2.60	6.154		228	263		491	680
3400	36" wide		2.40	6.667		251	285		536	740
3600	Cross, 9" wide		4	4		625	171		796	970
3800	12" wide		3.20	5		665	214		879	1,075
4000	18" wide		2.60	6.154		795	263		1,058	1,300
4200	24" wide		2.20	7.273		1,000	310		1,310	1,600
4400	30" wide		2	8		1,300	340		1,640	2,000
4600	36" wide		1.80	8.889		1,625	380		2,005	2,425
4800	End closure, 9" wide		14.40	1.111		39	47.50		86.50	121
5000	12" wide		12	1.333		45	57		102	143
5200	18" wide		10	1.600		68.50	68.50		137	188
5400	24" wide		8	2		90.50	85.50		176	240
5600	30" wide		6.60	2.424		113	104		217	294
5800	36" wide		5.80	2.759		135	118		253	340

26 05 43 – Underground Ducts and Raceways for Electrical Systems

26 05 43.10 Trench Duct

		Crew	Daily Output	Labor-Hours	Unit	Material	2014 Bare Costs Labor	Equipment	Total	Total Incl O&P
6000	Tees, 9" wide	2 Elec	4	4	Ea.	380	171		551	700
6200	12" wide		3.60	4.444		440	190		630	795
6400	18" wide		3.20	5		565	214		779	970
6600	24" wide		3	5.333		815	228		1,043	1,275
6800	30" wide		2.60	6.154		1,050	263		1,313	1,600
7000	36" wide		2	8		1,400	340		1,740	2,075
7200	Riser, and cabinet connector, 9" wide		5.40	2.963		166	127		293	390
7400	12" wide		4.60	3.478		194	149		343	455
7600	18" wide		4	4		238	171		409	540
7800	24" wide		3.20	5		289	214		503	665
8000	30" wide		2.60	6.154		330	263		593	795
8200	36" wide		2	8		385	340		725	985
8400	Insert assembly, cell to conduit adapter, 1-1/4"	1 Elec	16	.500		66	21.50		87.50	108

26 05 43.20 Underfloor Duct

		Crew	Daily Output	Labor-Hours	Unit	Material	2014 Bare Costs Labor	Equipment	Total	Total Incl O&P
0010	**UNDERFLOOR DUCT**									
0100	Duct, 1-3/8" x 3-1/8" blank, standard	2 Elec	160	.100	L.F.	14.10	4.27		18.37	22.50
0200	1-3/8" x 7-1/4" blank, super duct		120	.133		28	5.70		33.70	40.50
0400	7/8" or 1-3/8" insert type, 24" O.C., 1-3/8" x 3-1/8", std.		140	.114		18.85	4.88		23.73	29
0600	1-3/8" x 7-1/4", super duct		100	.160		33	6.85		39.85	47.50
0800	Junction box, single duct, 1 level, 3-1/8"	1 Elec	4	2	Ea.	425	85.50		510.50	605
1000	Junction box, single duct, 1 level, 7-1/4"		2.70	2.963		495	127		622	745
1200	1 level, 2 duct, 3-1/8"		3.20	2.500		565	107		672	795
1400	Junction box, 1 level, 2 duct, 7-1/4"		2.30	3.478		1,450	149		1,599	1,850
1580	Junction box, 1 level, one 3-1/8" + one 7-1/4" x same		2.30	3.478		960	149		1,109	1,300
1600	Triple duct, 3-1/8"		2.30	3.478		960	149		1,109	1,300
1800	Insert to conduit adapter, 3/4" & 1"		32	.250		34.50	10.70		45.20	55.50
2000	Support, single cell		27	.296		52	12.65		64.65	78
2200	Super duct		16	.500		52	21.50		73.50	92.50
2400	Double cell		16	.500		52	21.50		73.50	92.50
2600	Triple cell		11	.727		52	31		83	109
2800	Vertical elbow, standard duct		10	.800		93.50	34		127.50	159
3000	Super duct		8	1		93.50	42.50		136	173
3200	Cabinet connector, standard duct		32	.250		70.50	10.70		81.20	95
3400	Super duct		27	.296		70.50	12.65		83.15	98
3600	Conduit adapter, 1" to 1-1/4"		32	.250		70.50	10.70		81.20	95
3800	2" to 1-1/4"		27	.296		84.50	12.65		97.15	114
4000	Outlet, low tension (tele, computer, etc.)		8	1		98.50	42.50		141	178
4200	High tension, receptacle (120 volt)		8	1		98.50	42.50		141	178

26 05 80 – Wiring Connections

26 05 80.10 Motor Connections

		Crew	Daily Output	Labor-Hours	Unit	Material	2014 Bare Costs Labor	Equipment	Total	Total Incl O&P
0010	**MOTOR CONNECTIONS**									
0020	Flexible conduit and fittings, 115 volt, 1 phase, up to 1 HP motor	1 Elec	8	1	Ea.	7.25	42.50		49.75	78
0200	25 HP motor		2.70	2.963		33.50	127		160.50	244
0400	50 HP motor		2.20	3.636		67	155		222	330
0600	100 HP motor		1.50	5.333		158	228		386	550

26 05 90 – Residential Applications

26 05 90.10 Residential Wiring

0010	**RESIDENTIAL WIRING**									
0020	20' avg. runs and #14/2 wiring incl. unless otherwise noted									
1000	Service & panel, includes 24' SE-AL cable, service eye, meter,									
1010	Socket, panel board, main bkr., ground rod, 15 or 20 amp									

26 05 90.10 Residential Wiring	Crew	Daily Output	Labor-Hours	Unit	Material	Labor	Equipment	Total	Total Incl O&P
1020	1-pole circuit breakers, and misc. hardware									
1100	100 amp, with 10 branch breakers	1 Elec	1.19	6.723	Ea.	540	287		827	1,075
1110	With PVC conduit and wire		.92	8.696		595	370		965	1,275
1120	With RGS conduit and wire		.73	10.959		740	470		1,210	1,575
1150	150 amp, with 14 branch breakers		1.03	7.767		840	330		1,170	1,475
1170	With PVC conduit and wire		.82	9.756		955	415		1,370	1,725
1180	With RGS conduit and wire		.67	11.940		1,225	510		1,735	2,175
1200	200 amp, with 18 branch breakers	2 Elec	1.80	8.889		1,125	380		1,505	1,850
1220	With PVC conduit and wire		1.46	10.959		1,225	470		1,695	2,125
1230	With RGS conduit and wire		1.24	12.903		1,600	550		2,150	2,650
1800	Lightning surge suppressor	1 Elec	32	.250		50.50	10.70		61.20	73.50
2000	Switch devices									
2100	Single pole, 15 amp, Ivory, with a 1-gang box, cover plate,									
2110	Type NM (Romex) cable	1 Elec	17.10	.468	Ea.	12.30	20		32.30	46
2120	Type MC (BX) cable		14.30	.559		23.50	24		47.50	65
2130	EMT & wire		5.71	1.401		29.50	60		89.50	131
2150	3-way, #14/3, type NM cable		14.55	.550		15.60	23.50		39.10	55.50
2170	Type MC cable		12.31	.650		31	28		59	79.50
2180	EMT & wire		5	1.600		32.50	68.50		101	148
2200	4-way, #14/3, type NM cable		14.55	.550		22.50	23.50		46	63
2220	Type MC cable		12.31	.650		37.50	28		65.50	87
2230	EMT & wire		5	1.600		39.50	68.50		108	156
2250	S.P., 20 amp, #12/2, type NM cable		13.33	.600		21	25.50		46.50	65.50
2270	Type MC cable		11.43	.700		30	30		60	82
2280	EMT & wire		4.85	1.649		40	70.50		110.50	159
2290	S.P. rotary dimmer, 600W, no wiring		17	.471		27	20		47	62.50
2300	S.P. rotary dimmer, 600W, type NM cable		14.55	.550		32	23.50		55.50	73.50
2320	Type MC cable		12.31	.650		43.50	28		71.50	93
2330	EMT & wire		5	1.600		51	68.50		119.50	168
2350	3-way rotary dimmer, type NM cable		13.33	.600		31.50	25.50		57	76.50
2370	Type MC cable		11.43	.700		42.50	30		72.50	96
2380	EMT & wire		4.85	1.649		50	70.50		120.50	170
2400	Interval timer wall switch, 20 amp, 1-30 min., #12/2									
2410	Type NM cable	1 Elec	14.55	.550	Ea.	54	23.50		77.50	98
2420	Type MC cable		12.31	.650		59	28		87	111
2430	EMT & wire		5	1.600		73	68.50		141.50	193
2500	Decorator style									
2510	S.P., 15 amp, type NM cable	1 Elec	17.10	.468	Ea.	16.15	20		36.15	50.50
2520	Type MC cable		14.30	.559		27.50	24		51.50	69
2530	EMT & wire		5.71	1.401		33.50	60		93.50	135
2550	3-way, #14/3, type NM cable		14.55	.550		19.40	23.50		42.90	60
2570	Type MC cable		12.31	.650		34.50	28		62.50	83.50
2580	EMT & wire		5	1.600		36.50	68.50		105	152
2600	4-way, #14/3, type NM cable		14.55	.550		26.50	23.50		50	67.50
2620	Type MC cable		12.31	.650		41.50	28		69.50	91
2630	EMT & wire		5	1.600		43	68.50		111.50	160
2650	S.P., 20 amp, #12/2, type NM cable		13.33	.600		25	25.50		50.50	69.50
2670	Type MC cable		11.43	.700		34	30		64	86
2680	EMT & wire		4.85	1.649		44	70.50		114.50	163
2700	S.P., slide dimmer, type NM cable		17.10	.468		32	20		52	68
2720	Type MC cable		14.30	.559		43.50	24		67.50	87
2730	EMT & wire		5.71	1.401		51	60		111	154
2750	S.P., touch dimmer, type NM cable		17.10	.468		29.50	20		49.50	64.50

26 05 90.10 Residential Wiring	Crew	Daily Output	Labor-Hours	Unit	Material	2014 Bare Costs Labor	Equipment	Total	Total Incl O&P
2770	Type MC cable	1 Elec	14.30	.559	Ea.	40.50	24		64.50	83.50
2780	EMT & wire		5.71	1.401		48	60		108	151
2800	3-way touch dimmer, type NM cable		13.33	.600		51.50	25.50		77	98.50
2820	Type MC cable		11.43	.700		63	30		93	118
2830	EMT & wire		4.85	1.649		70.50	70.50		141	193
3000	Combination devices									
3100	S.P. switch/15 amp recpt., Ivory, 1-gang box, plate									
3110	Type NM cable	1 Elec	11.43	.700	Ea.	24	30		54	75.50
3120	Type MC cable		10	.800		35.50	34		69.50	95
3130	EMT & wire		4.40	1.818		43	77.50		120.50	174
3150	S.P. switch/pilot light, type NM cable		11.43	.700		24	30		54	75.50
3170	Type MC cable		10	.800		35.50	34		69.50	95
3180	EMT & wire		4.43	1.806		43	77		120	174
3190	2-S.P. switches, 2-#14/2, no wiring		14	.571		6.95	24.50		31.45	47.50
3200	2-S.P. switches, 2-#14/2, type NM cables		10	.800		27.50	34		61.50	86.50
3220	Type MC cable		8.89	.900		44.50	38.50		83	112
3230	EMT & wire		4.10	1.951		46.50	83.50		130	187
3250	3-way switch/15 amp recpt., #14/3, type NM cable		10	.800		31.50	34		65.50	90.50
3270	Type MC cable		8.89	.900		46.50	38.50		85	114
3280	EMT & wire		4.10	1.951		48	83.50		131.50	189
3300	2-3 way switches, 2-#14/3, type NM cables		8.89	.900		41	38.50		79.50	108
3320	Type MC cable		8	1		66	42.50		108.50	143
3330	EMT & wire		4	2		56	85.50		141.50	202
3350	S.P. switch/20 amp recpt., #12/2, type NM cable		10	.800		32	34		66	91.50
3370	Type MC cable		8.89	.900		37	38.50		75.50	104
3380	EMT & wire		4.10	1.951		51	83.50		134.50	192
3400	Decorator style									
3410	S.P. switch/15 amp recpt., type NM cable	1 Elec	11.43	.700	Ea.	28	30		58	79.50
3420	Type MC cable		10	.800		39	34		73	99
3430	EMT & wire		4.40	1.818		46.50	77.50		124	179
3450	S.P. switch/pilot light, type NM cable		11.43	.700		28	30		58	80
3470	Type MC cable		10	.800		39.50	34		73.50	99.50
3480	EMT & wire		4.40	1.818		47	77.50		124.50	179
3500	2-S.P. switches, 2-#14/2, type NM cables		10	.800		31.50	34		65.50	90.50
3520	Type MC cable		8.89	.900		48.50	38.50		87	116
3530	EMT & wire		4.10	1.951		50	83.50		133.50	191
3550	3-way/15 amp recpt., #14/3, type NM cable		10	.800		35	34		69	94.50
3570	Type MC cable		8.89	.900		50.50	38.50		89	119
3580	EMT & wire		4.10	1.951		52	83.50		135.50	193
3650	2-3 way switches, 2-#14/3, type NM cables		8.89	.900		45	38.50		83.50	113
3670	Type MC cable		8	1		69.50	42.50		112	147
3680	EMT & wire		4	2		59.50	85.50		145	206
3700	S.P. switch/20 amp recpt., #12/2, type NM cable		10	.800		36	34		70	95.50
3720	Type MC cable		8.89	.900		41	38.50		79.50	108
3730	EMT & wire		4.10	1.951		55	83.50		138.50	196
4000	Receptacle devices									
4010	Duplex outlet, 15 amp recpt., Ivory, 1-gang box, plate									
4015	Type NM cable	1 Elec	14.55	.550	Ea.	11	23.50		34.50	50.50
4020	Type MC cable		12.31	.650		22.50	28		50.50	70
4030	EMT & wire		5.33	1.501		28	64		92	136
4050	With #12/2, type NM cable		12.31	.650		13.65	28		41.65	60.50
4070	Type MC cable		10.67	.750		22.50	32		54.50	77
4080	EMT & wire		4.71	1.699		32.50	72.50		105	155

26 05 90.10 Residential Wiring	Crew	Daily Output	Labor-Hours	Unit	Material	2014 Bare Costs Labor	2014 Bare Costs Equipment	Total	Total Incl O&P
4100	20 amp recpt., #12/2, type NM cable	1 Elec	12.31	.650	Ea.	21	28		49	68.50
4120	Type MC cable		10.67	.750		29.50	32		61.50	85
4130	EMT & wire		4.71	1.699		39.50	72.50		112	163
4140	For GFI see Section 26 05 90.10 line 4300 below									
4150	Decorator style, 15 amp recpt., type NM cable	1 Elec	14.55	.550	Ea.	14.80	23.50		38.30	55
4170	Type MC cable		12.31	.650		26	28		54	74
4180	EMT & wire		5.33	1.501		32	64		96	140
4200	With #12/2, type NM cable		12.31	.650		17.45	28		45.45	64.50
4220	Type MC cable		10.67	.750		26	32		58	81.50
4230	EMT & wire		4.71	1.699		36	72.50		108.50	159
4250	20 amp recpt. #12/2, type NM cable		12.31	.650		24.50	28		52.50	72.50
4270	Type MC cable		10.67	.750		33.50	32		65.50	89
4280	EMT & wire		4.71	1.699		43.50	72.50		116	167
4300	GFI, 15 amp recpt., type NM cable		12.31	.650		47.50	28		75.50	97.50
4320	Type MC cable		10.67	.750		58.50	32		90.50	117
4330	EMT & wire		4.71	1.699		64.50	72.50		137	190
4350	GFI with #12/2, type NM cable		10.67	.750		50	32		82	108
4370	Type MC cable		9.20	.870		58.50	37		95.50	126
4380	EMT & wire		4.21	1.900		68.50	81		149.50	209
4400	20 amp recpt., #12/2 type NM cable		10.67	.750		52	32		84	110
4420	Type MC cable		9.20	.870		61	37		98	128
4430	EMT & wire		4.21	1.900		71	81		152	211
4500	Weather-proof cover for above receptacles, add		32	.250		4.08	10.70		14.78	22
4550	Air conditioner outlet, 20 amp-240 volt recpt.									
4560	30' of #12/2, 2 pole circuit breaker									
4570	Type NM cable	1 Elec	10	.800	Ea.	63	34		97	125
4580	Type MC cable		9	.889		73	38		111	143
4590	EMT & wire		4	2		81.50	85.50		167	230
4600	Decorator style, type NM cable		10	.800		67.50	34		101.50	131
4620	Type MC cable		9	.889		78	38		116	148
4630	EMT & wire		4	2		86.50	85.50		172	235
4650	Dryer outlet, 30 amp-240 volt recpt., 20' of #10/3									
4660	2 pole circuit breaker									
4670	Type NM cable	1 Elec	6.41	1.248	Ea.	64	53.50		117.50	158
4680	Type MC cable		5.71	1.401		69	60		129	174
4690	EMT & wire		3.48	2.299		75.50	98		173.50	244
4700	Range outlet, 50 amp-240 volt recpt., 30' of #8/3									
4710	Type NM cable	1 Elec	4.21	1.900	Ea.	92	81		173	234
4720	Type MC cable		4	2		136	85.50		221.50	290
4730	EMT & wire		2.96	2.703		106	115		221	305
4750	Central vacuum outlet, Type NM cable		6.40	1.250		60	53.50		113.50	154
4770	Type MC cable		5.71	1.401		75.50	60		135.50	181
4780	EMT & wire		3.48	2.299		81.50	98		179.50	251
4800	30 amp-110 volt locking recpt., #10/2 circ. bkr.									
4810	Type NM cable	1 Elec	6.20	1.290	Ea.	69	55		124	166
4820	Type MC cable		5.40	1.481		86.50	63.50		150	199
4830	EMT & wire		3.20	2.500		92	107		199	276
4900	Low voltage outlets									
4910	Telephone recpt., 20' of 4/C phone wire	1 Elec	26	.308	Ea.	10.95	13.15		24.10	33.50
4920	TV recpt., 20' of RG59U coax wire, F type connector	"	16	.500	"	19.20	21.50		40.70	56
4950	Door bell chime, transformer, 2 buttons, 60' of bellwire									
4970	Economy model	1 Elec	11.50	.696	Ea.	58	29.50		87.50	113
4980	Custom model		11.50	.696		123	29.50		152.50	184

26 05 90.10 Residential Wiring		Crew	Daily Output	Labor-Hours	Unit	Material	2014 Bare Costs Labor	Equipment	Total	Total Incl O&P
4990	Luxury model, 3 buttons	1 Elec	9.50	.842	Ea.	305	36		341	395
6000	Lighting outlets									
6050	Wire only (for fixture), type NM cable	1 Elec	32	.250	Ea.	7.20	10.70		17.90	25.50
6070	Type MC cable		24	.333		13.85	14.25		28.10	38.50
6080	EMT & wire		10	.800		18.65	34		52.65	76.50
6100	Box (4"), and wire (for fixture), type NM cable		25	.320		16.10	13.65		29.75	40.50
6120	Type MC cable		20	.400		23	17.10		40.10	53
6130	EMT & wire		11	.727		27.50	31		58.50	81.50
6200	Fixtures (use with lines 6050 or 6100 above)									
6210	Canopy style, economy grade	1 Elec	40	.200	Ea.	37.50	8.55		46.05	55
6220	Custom grade		40	.200		57.50	8.55		66.05	77
6250	Dining room chandelier, economy grade		19	.421		93.50	18		111.50	133
6260	Custom grade		19	.421		274	18		292	330
6270	Luxury grade		15	.533		620	23		643	720
6310	Kitchen fixture (fluorescent), economy grade		30	.267		69.50	11.40		80.90	95
6320	Custom grade		25	.320		190	13.65		203.65	232
6350	Outdoor, wall mounted, economy grade		30	.267		35.50	11.40		46.90	57.50
6360	Custom grade		30	.267		121	11.40		132.40	153
6370	Luxury grade		25	.320		274	13.65		287.65	325
6410	Outdoor PAR floodlights, 1 lamp, 150 watt		20	.400		38	17.10		55.10	70
6420	2 lamp, 150 watt each		20	.400		63	17.10		80.10	97
6425	Motion sensing, 2 lamp, 150 watt each		20	.400		76	17.10		93.10	112
6430	For infrared security sensor, add		32	.250		127	10.70		137.70	158
6450	Outdoor, quartz-halogen, 300 watt flood		20	.400		46	17.10		63.10	78.50
6600	Recessed downlight, round, pre-wired, 50 or 75 watt trim		30	.267		47	11.40		58.40	70
6610	With shower light trim		30	.267		58	11.40		69.40	82.50
6620	With wall washer trim		28	.286		70	12.20		82.20	97
6630	With eye-ball trim		28	.286		70	12.20		82.20	97
6640	For direct contact with insulation, add					2.49			2.49	2.74
6700	Porcelain lamp holder	1 Elec	40	.200		3.50	8.55		12.05	17.85
6710	With pull switch		40	.200		5.70	8.55		14.25	20.50
6750	Fluorescent strip, 1-20 watt tube, wrap around diffuser, 24"		24	.333		58.50	14.25		72.75	88
6760	1-34 watt tube, 48"		24	.333		75.50	14.25		89.75	107
6770	2-34 watt tubes, 48"		20	.400		89.50	17.10		106.60	127
6780	With residential ballast		20	.400		100	17.10		117.10	138
6800	Bathroom heat lamp, 1-250 watt		28	.286		51.50	12.20		63.70	76.50
6810	2-250 watt lamps		28	.286		82	12.20		94.20	110
6820	For timer switch, see Section 26 05 90.10 line 2400									
6900	Outdoor post lamp, incl. post, fixture, 35' of #14/2									
6910	Type NMC cable	1 Elec	3.50	2.286	Ea.	226	97.50		323.50	410
6920	Photo-eye, add		27	.296		38	12.65		50.65	62.50
6950	Clock dial time switch, 24 hr., w/enclosure, type NM cable		11.43	.700		70.50	30		100.50	127
6970	Type MC cable		11	.727		82	31		113	141
6980	EMT & wire		4.85	1.649		88	70.50		158.50	212
7000	Alarm systems									
7050	Smoke detectors, box, #14/3, type NM cable	1 Elec	14.55	.550	Ea.	35	23.50		58.50	77.50
7070	Type MC cable		12.31	.650		46.50	28		74.50	96.50
7080	EMT & wire		5	1.600		48.50	68.50		117	165
7090	For relay output to security system, add					14.10			14.10	15.55
8000	Residential equipment									
8050	Disposal hook-up, incl. switch, outlet box, 3' of flex									
8060	20 amp-1 pole circ. bkr., and 25' of #12/2									
8070	Type NM cable	1 Elec	10	.800	Ea.	32.50	34		66.50	92

26 05 90.10 Residential Wiring	Crew	Daily Output	Labor-Hours	Unit	Material	2014 Bare Costs Labor	Equipment	Total	Total Incl O&P
8080	Type MC cable	1 Elec	8	1	Ea.	42	42.50		84.50	117
8090	EMT & wire	↓	5	1.600	↓	53.50	68.50		122	171
8100	Trash compactor or dishwasher hook-up, incl. outlet box,									
8110	3' of flex, 15 amp-1 pole circ. bkr., and 25' of #14/2									
8120	Type NM cable	1 Elec	10	.800	Ea.	24	34		58	82.50
8130	Type MC cable		8	1		37	42.50		79.50	111
8140	EMT & wire	↓	5	1.600	↓	45	68.50		113.50	162
8150	Hot water sink dispensor hook-up, use line 8100									
8200	Vent/exhaust fan hook-up, type NM cable	1 Elec	32	.250	Ea.	7.20	10.70		17.90	25.50
8220	Type MC cable		24	.333		13.85	14.25		28.10	38.50
8230	EMT & wire	↓	10	.800	↓	18.65	34		52.65	76.50
8250	Bathroom vent fan, 50 CFM (use with above hook-up)									
8260	Economy model	1 Elec	15	.533	Ea.	27	23		50	67.50
8270	Low noise model		15	.533		37	23		60	78
8280	Custom model	↓	12	.667	↓	127	28.50		155.50	187
8300	Bathroom or kitchen vent fan, 110 CFM									
8310	Economy model	1 Elec	15	.533	Ea.	75.50	23		98.50	121
8320	Low noise model	"	15	.533	"	93.50	23		116.50	141
8350	Paddle fan, variable speed (w/o lights)									
8360	Economy model (AC motor)	1 Elec	10	.800	Ea.	125	34		159	193
8362	With light kit		10	.800		166	34		200	238
8370	Custom model (AC motor)		10	.800		197	34		231	273
8372	With light kit		10	.800		238	34		272	320
8380	Luxury model (DC motor)		8	1		390	42.50		432.50	500
8382	With light kit		8	1		430	42.50		472.50	545
8390	Remote speed switch for above, add	↓	12	.667	↓	32.50	28.50		61	82
8500	Whole house exhaust fan, ceiling mount, 36", variable speed									
8510	Remote switch, incl. shutters, 20 amp-1 pole circ. bkr.									
8520	30' of #12/2, type NM cable	1 Elec	4	2	Ea.	1,250	85.50		1,335.50	1,525
8530	Type MC cable		3.50	2.286		1,275	97.50		1,372.50	1,550
8540	EMT & wire	↓	3	2.667	↓	1,275	114		1,389	1,575
8600	Whirlpool tub hook-up, incl. timer switch, outlet box									
8610	3' of flex, 20 amp-1 pole GFI circ. bkr.									
8620	30' of #12/2, type NM cable	1 Elec	5	1.600	Ea.	127	68.50		195.50	251
8630	Type MC cable		4.20	1.905		131	81.50		212.50	278
8640	EMT & wire	↓	3.40	2.353	↓	141	100		241	320
8650	Hot water heater hook-up, incl. 1-2 pole circ. bkr., box;									
8660	3' of flex, 20' of #10/2, type NM cable	1 Elec	5	1.600	Ea.	34	68.50		102.50	149
8670	Type MC cable		4.20	1.905		47.50	81.50		129	185
8680	EMT & wire	↓	3.40	2.353	↓	48.50	100		148.50	217
9000	Heating/air conditioning									
9050	Furnace/boiler hook-up, incl. firestat, local on-off switch									
9060	Emergency switch, and 40' of type NM cable	1 Elec	4	2	Ea.	52.50	85.50		138	198
9070	Type MC cable		3.50	2.286		69.50	97.50		167	237
9080	EMT & wire	↓	1.50	5.333	↓	81	228		309	465
9100	Air conditioner hook-up, incl. local 60 amp disc. switch									
9110	3' sealtite, 40 amp, 2 pole circuit breaker									
9130	40' of #8/2, type NM cable	1 Elec	3.50	2.286	Ea.	182	97.50		279.50	360
9140	Type MC cable		3	2.667		249	114		363	460
9150	EMT & wire	↓	1.30	6.154	↓	218	263		481	670
9200	Heat pump hook-up, 1-40 & 1-100 amp 2 pole circ. bkr.									
9210	Local disconnect switch, 3' sealtite									
9220	40' of #8/2 & 30' of #3/2									

26 25 Enclosed Bus Assemblies

26 25 13 – Bus Duct/Busway and Fittings

26 25 13.40 Copper Bus Duct	Crew	Daily Output	Labor-Hours	Unit	Material	2014 Bare Costs Labor	Equipment	Total	Total Incl O&P
5800	400 amp	2 Elec	4.60	3.478	Ea.	1,375	149		1,524	1,775
5900	600 amp		4	4		1,375	171		1,546	1,800
6000	800 amp		3.20	5		1,675	214		1,889	2,175
6100	1000 amp		3	5.333		1,925	228		2,153	2,500
6200	1350 amp		2.60	6.154		2,375	263		2,638	3,025
6300	1600 amp		2.40	6.667		2,675	285		2,960	3,425
6400	2000 amp		2	8		3,250	340		3,590	4,100
6490	Tee fittings, 225 amp		2.40	6.667		1,875	285		2,160	2,550
6500	400 amp		2	8		1,875	340		2,215	2,625
6600	600 amp		1.80	8.889		1,875	380		2,255	2,700
6700	800 amp		1.60	10		2,175	425		2,600	3,075
6800	1350 amp		1.20	13.333		2,950	570		3,520	4,175
7000	1600 amp		1	16		3,375	685		4,060	4,825
7100	2000 amp		.80	20		4,000	855		4,855	5,800
7200	Plug-in fusible switches w/3 fuses, 600 volt, 3 pole, 30 amp	1 Elec	4	2		840	85.50		925.50	1,075
7300	60 amp		3.60	2.222		945	95		1,040	1,200
7400	100 amp		2.70	2.963		1,450	127		1,577	1,775
7500	200 amp	2 Elec	3.20	5		2,575	214		2,789	3,175
7600	400 amp		1.40	11.429		7,550	490		8,040	9,100
7700	600 amp		.90	17.778		8,550	760		9,310	10,700
7800	800 amp		.66	24.242		12,000	1,025		13,025	14,900
7900	1200 amp		.50	32		22,500	1,375		23,875	27,000
8000	Plug-in circuit breakers, molded case, 15 to 50 amp	1 Elec	4.40	1.818		795	77.50		872.50	1,000
8100	70 to 100 amp	"	3.10	2.581		885	110		995	1,150
8200	150 to 225 amp	2 Elec	3.40	4.706		2,400	201		2,601	2,975
8300	250 to 400 amp		1.40	11.429		4,200	490		4,690	5,425
8400	500 to 600 amp		1	16		5,675	685		6,360	7,375
8500	700 to 800 amp		.64	25		7,000	1,075		8,075	9,450
8600	900 to 1000 amp		.56	28.571		10,000	1,225		11,225	13,000
8700	1200 amp		.44	36.364		12,000	1,550		13,550	15,900

26 27 Low-Voltage Distribution Equipment

26 27 16 – Electrical Cabinets and Enclosures

26 27 16.10 Cabinets

		Crew	Daily Output	Labor-Hours	Unit	Material	2014 Bare Costs Labor	Equipment	Total	Total Incl O&P
0010	**CABINETS**									
7000	Cabinets, current transformer									
7050	Single door, 24" H x 24" W x 10" D	1 Elec	1.60	5	Ea.	178	214		392	545
7100	30" H x 24" W x 10" D		1.30	6.154		166	263		429	615
7150	36" H x 24" W x 10" D		1.10	7.273		186	310		496	715
7200	30" H x 30" W x 10" D		1	8		194	340		534	775
7250	36" H x 30" W x 10" D		.90	8.889		227	380		607	870
7300	36" H x 36" W x 10" D		.80	10		235	425		660	960
7500	Double door, 48" H x 36" W x 10" D		.60	13.333		555	570		1,125	1,550
7550	24" H x 24" W x 12" D		1	8		165	340		505	740

26 27 23 – Indoor Service Poles

26 27 23.40 Surface Raceway

		Crew	Daily Output	Labor-Hours	Unit	Material	2014 Bare Costs Labor	Equipment	Total	Total Incl O&P
0010	**SURFACE RACEWAY**									
0090	Metal, straight section									
0100	No. 500	1 Elec	100	.080	L.F.	1.04	3.42		4.46	6.75
0110	No. 700		100	.080		1.17	3.42		4.59	6.90

26 27 Low-Voltage Distribution Equipment

26 27 23 – Indoor Service Poles

26 27 23.40 Surface Raceway

		Crew	Daily Output	Labor-Hours	Unit	Material	2014 Bare Costs Labor	Equipment	Total	Total Incl O&P
0400	No. 1500, small pancake	1 Elec	90	.089	L.F.	2.15	3.80		5.95	8.55
0600	No. 2000, base & cover, blank		90	.089		2.19	3.80		5.99	8.60
0800	No. 3000, base & cover, blank		75	.107		4.40	4.55		8.95	12.30
1000	No. 4000, base & cover, blank		65	.123		7.30	5.25		12.55	16.65
1200	No. 6000, base & cover, blank		50	.160		11.40	6.85		18.25	23.50
2400	Fittings, elbows, No. 500		40	.200	Ea.	1.90	8.55		10.45	16.10
2800	Elbow cover, No. 2000		40	.200		3.57	8.55		12.12	17.95
2880	Tee, No. 500		42	.190		3.66	8.15		11.81	17.35
2900	No. 2000		27	.296		11.85	12.65		24.50	33.50
3000	Switch box, No. 500		16	.500		11	21.50		32.50	47
3400	Telephone outlet, No. 1500		16	.500		14.10	21.50		35.60	50.50
3600	Junction box, No. 1500		16	.500		9.65	21.50		31.15	45.50
3800	Plugmold wired sections, No. 2000									
4000	1 circuit, 6 outlets, 3 ft. long	1 Elec	8	1	Ea.	36	42.50		78.50	110
4100	2 circuits, 8 outlets, 6 ft. long	"	5.30	1.509	"	53	64.50		117.50	165

26 27 26 – Wiring Devices

26 27 26.10 Low Voltage Switching

		Crew	Daily Output	Labor-Hours	Unit	Material	2014 Bare Costs Labor	Equipment	Total	Total Incl O&P
0010	**LOW VOLTAGE SWITCHING**									
3600	Relays, 120 V or 277 V standard	1 Elec	12	.667	Ea.	41	28.50		69.50	92
3800	Flush switch, standard		40	.200		11.40	8.55		19.95	26.50
4000	Interchangeable		40	.200		14.90	8.55		23.45	30.50
4100	Surface switch, standard		40	.200		8.05	8.55		16.60	23
4200	Transformer 115 V to 25 V		12	.667		129	28.50		157.50	189
4400	Master control, 12 circuit, manual		4	2		125	85.50		210.50	277
4500	25 circuit, motorized		4	2		139	85.50		224.50	292
4600	Rectifier, silicon		12	.667		45	28.50		73.50	96
4800	Switchplates, 1 gang, 1, 2 or 3 switch, plastic		80	.100		4.95	4.27		9.22	12.45
5000	Stainless steel		80	.100		11.25	4.27		15.52	19.40
5400	2 gang, 3 switch, stainless steel		53	.151		22.50	6.45		28.95	35.50
5500	4 switch, plastic		53	.151		10.25	6.45		16.70	22
5800	3 gang, 9 switch, stainless steel		32	.250		64	10.70		74.70	88

26 27 26.20 Wiring Devices Elements

		Crew	Daily Output	Labor-Hours	Unit	Material	2014 Bare Costs Labor	Equipment	Total	Total Incl O&P
0010	**WIRING DEVICES ELEMENTS**									
0200	Toggle switch, quiet type, single pole, 15 amp	1 Elec	40	.200	Ea.	5.70	8.55		14.25	20.50
0600	3 way, 15 amp		23	.348		5.95	14.85		20.80	31
0900	4 way, 15 amp		15	.533		10.75	23		33.75	49.50
1650	Dimmer switch, 120 volt, incandescent, 600 watt, 1 pole [G]		16	.500		18.40	21.50		39.90	55
2460	Receptacle, duplex, 120 volt, grounded, 15 amp		40	.200		1.22	8.55		9.77	15.35
2470	20 amp		27	.296		8.35	12.65		21	29.50
2490	Dryer, 30 amp		15	.533		5.20	23		28.20	43
2500	Range, 50 amp		11	.727		11.85	31		42.85	64
2600	Wall plates, stainless steel, 1 gang		80	.100		2.53	4.27		6.80	9.80
2800	2 gang		53	.151		4.29	6.45		10.74	15.25
3200	Lampholder, keyless		26	.308		11	13.15		24.15	33.50
3400	Pullchain with receptacle		22	.364		20.50	15.55		36.05	48

26 27 73 – Door Chimes

26 27 73.10 Doorbell System

		Crew	Daily Output	Labor-Hours	Unit	Material	2014 Bare Costs Labor	Equipment	Total	Total Incl O&P
0010	**DOORBELL SYSTEM**, incl. transformer, button & signal									
0100	6" bell	1 Elec	4	2	Ea.	113	85.50		198.50	264
0200	Buzzer	"	4	2	"	104	85.50		189.50	254

27 51 Distributed Audio-Video Communications Systems

27 51 19 – Sound Masking Systems

27 51 19.10 Sound System	Crew	Daily Output	Labor-Hours	Unit	Material	2014 Bare Costs Labor	Equipment	Total	Total Incl O&P
1800	Cabinets	1 Elec	1	8	Ea.	840	340		1,180	1,475
2000	Intercom, 30 station capacity, master station	2 Elec	2	8		2,300	340		2,640	3,075
2200	Remote station	1 Elec	8	1		162	42.50		204.50	248
2400	Intercom outlets		8	1		95	42.50		137.50	174
2600	Handset		4	2		315	85.50		400.50	485
2800	Emergency call system, 12 zones, annunciator		1.30	6.154		945	263		1,208	1,475
3000	Bell		5.30	1.509		98	64.50		162.50	214
3200	Light or relay		8	1		49	42.50		91.50	124
3400	Transformer		4	2		215	85.50		300.50	375
3600	House telephone, talking station		1.60	5		460	214		674	860
3800	Press to talk, release to listen		5.30	1.509		108	64.50		172.50	224
4000	System-on button					64.50			64.50	71
4200	Door release	1 Elec	4	2		115	85.50		200.50	267
4400	Combination speaker and microphone		8	1		196	42.50		238.50	286
4600	Termination box		3.20	2.500		61.50	107		168.50	243
4800	Amplifier or power supply		5.30	1.509		710	64.50		774.50	885
5000	Vestibule door unit		16	.500	Name	130	21.50		151.50	178
5200	Strip cabinet		27	.296	Ea.	246	12.65		258.65	292
5400	Directory		16	.500	"	116	21.50		137.50	162

27 52 Healthcare Communications and Monitoring Systems

27 52 23 – Nurse Call/Code Blue Systems

27 52 23.10 Nurse Call Systems	Crew	Daily Output	Labor-Hours	Unit	Material	2014 Bare Costs Labor	Equipment	Total	Total Incl O&P
0010	**NURSE CALL SYSTEMS**									
0100	Single bedside call station	1 Elec	8	1	Ea.	228	42.50		270.50	320
0200	Ceiling speaker station		8	1		66.50	42.50		109	144
0400	Emergency call station		8	1		71.50	42.50		114	149
0600	Pillow speaker		8	1		176	42.50		218.50	263
0800	Double bedside call station		4	2		141	85.50		226.50	295
1000	Duty station		4	2		146	85.50		231.50	300
1200	Standard call button		8	1		86	42.50		128.50	165
1400	Lights, corridor, dome or zone indicator		8	1		48.50	42.50		91	124
1600	Master control station for 20 stations	2 Elec	.65	24.615	Total	3,950	1,050		5,000	6,050

27 53 Distributed Systems

27 53 13 – Clock Systems

27 53 13.50 Clock Equipments	Crew	Daily Output	Labor-Hours	Unit	Material	2014 Bare Costs Labor	Equipment	Total	Total Incl O&P
0010	**CLOCK EQUIPMENTS**, not including wires & conduits									
0100	Time system components, master controller	1 Elec	.33	24.242	Ea.	1,850	1,025		2,875	3,725
0200	Program bell		8	1		86	42.50		128.50	165
0400	Combination clock & speaker		3.20	2.500		212	107		319	410
0600	Frequency generator		2	4		2,375	171		2,546	2,900
0800	Job time automatic stamp recorder		4	2		535	85.50		620.50	730
1600	Master time clock system, clocks & bells, 20 room	4 Elec	.20	160		6,100	6,825		12,925	17,900
1800	50 room	"	.08	400		12,500	17,100		29,600	41,800
1900	Time clock	1 Elec	3.20	2.500		440	107		547	660
2000	100 cards in & out, 1 color					9.05			9.05	10
2200	2 colors					9.05			9.05	10
2800	Metal rack for 25 cards	1 Elec	7	1.143		43.50	49		92.50	128

Division Notes

	CREW	DAILY OUTPUT	LABOR-HOURS	UNIT	BARE COSTS				TOTAL INCL O&P
					MAT.	LABOR	EQUIP.	TOTAL	

Estimating Tips

- When estimating material costs for electronic safety and security systems, it is always prudent to obtain manufacturers' quotations for equipment prices and special installation requirements that affect the total cost.

- Fire alarm systems consist of control panels, annunciator panels, battery with rack, charger, and fire alarm actuating and indicating devices. Some fire alarm systems include speakers, telephone lines, door closer controls, and other components. Be careful not to overlook the costs related to installation for these items.

Also be aware of costs for integrated automation instrumentation and terminal devices, control equipment, control wiring, and programming.

- Security equipment includes items such as CCTV, access control, and other detection and identification systems to perform alert and alarm functions. Be sure to consider the costs related to installation for this security equipment, such as for integrated automation instrumentation and terminal devices, control equipment, control wiring, and programming.

Reference Numbers

Reference numbers are shown in shaded boxes at the beginning of some major classifications. These numbers refer to related items in the Reference Section. The reference information may be an estimating procedure, an alternate pricing method, or technical information.

Note: Not all subdivisions listed here necessarily appear in this publication.

Division 28 - Electronic Safety and Security

28 13 Access Control

28 13 53 – Security Access Detection

28 13 53.13 Security Access Metal Detectors	Crew	Daily Output	Labor-Hours	Unit	Material	2014 Bare Costs Labor	Equipment	Total	Total Incl O&P
0010 **SECURITY ACCESS METAL DETECTORS**									
0240 Metal detector, hand-held, wand type, unit only				Ea.	89			89	98
0250 Metal detector, walk through portal type, single zone	1 Elec	2	4		3,675	171		3,846	4,300
0260 Multi-zone	"	2	4		4,650	171		4,821	5,400

28 13 53.16 Security Access X-Ray Equipment

	Crew	Daily Output	Labor-Hours	Unit	Material	Labor	Equipment	Total	Total Incl O&P
0010 **SECURITY ACCESS X-RAY EQUIPMENT**									
0290 X-ray machine, desk top, for mail/small packages/letters	1 Elec	4	2	Ea.	3,400	85.50		3,485.50	3,875
0300 Conveyor type, incl monitor, minimum		2	4		15,800	171		15,971	17,700
0310 Maximum		2	4		28,300	171		28,471	31,400
0320 X-ray machine, large unit, for airports, incl monitor, min.	2 Elec	1	16		39,600	685		40,285	44,700
0330 Maximum	"	.50	32		68,000	1,375		69,375	76,500

28 13 53.23 Security Access Explosive Detection Equipment

	Crew	Daily Output	Labor-Hours	Unit	Material	Labor	Equipment	Total	Total Incl O&P
0010 **SECURITY ACCESS EXPLOSIVE DETECTION EQUIPMENT**									
0270 Explosives detector, walk through portal type	1 Elec	2	4	Ea.	43,700	171		43,871	48,400
0280 Hand-held, battery operated				"				25,500	28,100

28 16 Intrusion Detection

28 16 16 – Intrusion Detection Systems Infrastructure

28 16 16.50 Intrusion Detection

	Crew	Daily Output	Labor-Hours	Unit	Material	Labor	Equipment	Total	Total Incl O&P
0010 **INTRUSION DETECTION**, not including wires & conduits									
0100 Burglar alarm, battery operated, mechanical trigger	1 Elec	4	2	Ea.	275	85.50		360.50	440
0200 Electrical trigger		4	2		330	85.50		415.50	500
0400 For outside key control, add		8	1		83	42.50		125.50	162
0600 For remote signaling circuitry, add		8	1		124	42.50		166.50	206
0800 Card reader, flush type, standard		2.70	2.963		920	127		1,047	1,225
1000 Multi-code		2.70	2.963		1,175	127		1,302	1,500
1200 Door switches, hinge switch		5.30	1.509		58	64.50		122.50	170
1400 Magnetic switch		5.30	1.509		68.50	64.50		133	182
1600 Exit control locks, horn alarm		4	2		274	85.50		359.50	440
1800 Flashing light alarm		4	2		300	85.50		385.50	470
2000 Indicating panels, 1 channel		2.70	2.963		365	127		492	605
2200 10 channel	2 Elec	3.20	5		1,250	214		1,464	1,725
2400 20 channel		2	8		2,425	340		2,765	3,225
2600 40 channel		1.14	14.035		4,425	600		5,025	5,825
2800 Ultrasonic motion detector, 12 volt	1 Elec	2.30	3.478		227	149		376	495
3000 Infrared photoelectric detector	"	4	2		188	85.50		273.50	345

28 23 Video Surveillance

28 23 13 – Video Surveillance Control and Management Systems

28 23 13.10 Closed Circuit Television System

	Crew	Daily Output	Labor-Hours	Unit	Material	Labor	Equipment	Total	Total Incl O&P
0010 **CLOSED CIRCUIT TELEVISION SYSTEM**									
2000 Surveillance, one station (camera & monitor)	2 Elec	2.60	6.154	Total	1,350	263		1,613	1,900
2200 For additional camera stations, add	1 Elec	2.70	2.963	Ea.	750	127		877	1,025
2400 Industrial quality, one station (camera & monitor)	2 Elec	2.60	6.154	Total	2,775	263		3,038	3,475
2600 For additional camera stations, add	1 Elec	2.70	2.963	Ea.	1,700	127		1,827	2,075
2610 For low light, add		2.70	2.963		1,375	127		1,502	1,700
2620 For very low light, add		2.70	2.963		10,100	127		10,227	11,300
2800 For weatherproof camera station, add		1.30	6.154		1,050	263		1,313	1,575
3000 For pan and tilt, add		1.30	6.154		2,700	263		2,963	3,400

28 23 Video Surveillance

28 23 13 – Video Surveillance Control and Management Systems

28 23 13.10 Closed Circuit Television System

		Crew	Daily Output	Labor-Hours	Unit	Material	2014 Bare Costs Labor	Equipment	Total	Total Incl O&P
3200	For zoom lens - remote control, add, minimum	1 Elec	2	4	Ea.	2,500	171		2,671	3,025
3400	Maximum		2	4		9,125	171		9,296	10,300
3410	For automatic iris for low light, add	↓	2	4	↓	2,175	171		2,346	2,675
3600	Educational T.V. studio, basic 3 camera system, black & white,									
3800	electrical & electronic equip. only, minimum	4 Elec	.80	40	Total	13,000	1,700		14,700	17,100
4000	Maximum (full console)		.28	114		55,000	4,875		59,875	68,500
4100	As above, but color system, minimum		.28	114		73,000	4,875		77,875	88,500
4120	Maximum	↓	.12	266	↓	317,500	11,400		328,900	368,000
4200	For film chain, black & white, add	1 Elec	1	8	Ea.	14,800	340		15,140	16,900
4250	Color, add		.25	32		18,000	1,375		19,375	22,000
4400	For video recorders, add, minimum	↓	1	8		3,125	340		3,465	3,975
4600	Maximum	4 Elec	.40	80	↓	25,900	3,425		29,325	34,100

28 23 23 – Video Surveillance Systems Infrastructure

28 23 23.50 Video Surveillance Equipments

		Crew	Daily Output	Labor-Hours	Unit	Material	2014 Bare Costs Labor	Equipment	Total	Total Incl O&P
0010	**VIDEO SURVEILLANCE EQUIPMENTS**									
0200	Video cameras, wireless, hidden in exit signs, clocks, etc., incl. receiver	1 Elec	3	2.667	Ea.	107	114		221	305
0210	Accessories for video recorder, single camera		3	2.667		181	114		295	385
0220	For multiple cameras		3	2.667		1,750	114		1,864	2,100
0230	Video cameras, wireless, for under vehicle searching, complete	↓	2	4	↓	10,100	171		10,271	11,400

28 31 Fire Detection and Alarm

28 31 23 – Fire Detection and Alarm Annunciation Panels and Fire Stations

28 31 23.50 Alarm Panels and Devices

		Crew	Daily Output	Labor-Hours	Unit	Material	2014 Bare Costs Labor	Equipment	Total	Total Incl O&P
0010	**ALARM PANELS AND DEVICES**, not including wires & conduits									
3594	Fire, alarm control panel									
3600	4 zone	2 Elec	2	8	Ea.	395	340		735	995
3800	8 zone		1	16		775	685		1,460	1,975
4000	12 zone	↓	.67	23.988		2,375	1,025		3,400	4,275
4020	Alarm device	1 Elec	8	1		235	42.50		277.50	330
4050	Actuating device		8	1		335	42.50		377.50	435
4200	Battery and rack		4	2		410	85.50		495.50	590
4400	Automatic charger		8	1		580	42.50		622.50	705
4600	Signal bell		8	1		78	42.50		120.50	156
4800	Trouble buzzer or manual station		8	1		82.50	42.50		125	161
5600	Strobe and horn		5.30	1.509		151	64.50		215.50	272
5800	Fire alarm horn		6.70	1.194		60.50	51		111.50	150
6000	Door holder, electro-magnetic		4	2		102	85.50		187.50	252
6200	Combination holder and closer		3.20	2.500		122	107		229	310
6600	Drill switch		8	1		365	42.50		407.50	475
6800	Master box		2.70	2.963		6,350	127		6,477	7,175
7000	Break glass station		8	1		55	42.50		97.50	131
7800	Remote annunciator, 8 zone lamp	↓	1.80	4.444		207	190		397	535
8000	12 zone lamp	2 Elec	2.60	6.154		330	263		593	795
8200	16 zone lamp	"	2.20	7.273	↓	415	310		725	965

28 31 Fire Detection and Alarm

28 31 43 – Fire Detection Sensors

28 31 43.50 Fire and Heat Detectors	Crew	Daily Output	Labor-Hours	Unit	Material	2014 Bare Costs Labor	Equipment	Total	Total Incl O&P
0010 **FIRE & HEAT DETECTORS**									
5000 Detector, rate of rise	1 Elec	8	1	Ea.	50.50	42.50		93	126

28 31 46 – Smoke Detection Sensors

28 31 46.50 Smoke Detectors

	Crew	Daily Output	Labor-Hours	Unit	Material	Labor	Equipment	Total	Total Incl O&P
0010 **SMOKE DETECTORS**									
5200 Smoke detector, ceiling type	1 Elec	6.20	1.290	Ea.	109	55		164	210
5400 Duct type	"	3.20	2.500	"	325	107		432	530

28 33 Gas Detection and Alarm

28 33 33 – Gas Detection Sensors

28 33 33.50 Tank Leak Detection Systems

	Crew	Daily Output	Labor-Hours	Unit	Material	Labor	Equipment	Total	Total Incl O&P
0010 **TANK LEAK DETECTION SYSTEMS** Liquid and vapor									
0100 For hydrocarbons and hazardous liquids/vapors									
0120 Controller, data acquisition, incl. printer, modem, RS232 port									
0140 24 channel, for use with all probes				Ea.	4,125			4,125	4,525
0160 9 channel, for external monitoring				"	905			905	1,000
0170 Integrated control panel with monitoring system and printer									
0180 1 to 2 tanks, double wall	2 Elec	4	4	Ea.	2,075	171		2,246	2,550
0181 1 to 8 tanks, single wall		4	4		2,075	171		2,246	2,550
0190 2 to 8 tanks, double wall	↓	2.50	6.400	↓	5,800	273		6,073	6,850
0200 Probes									
0210 Well monitoring									
0220 Liquid phase detection				Ea.	470			470	520
0230 Hydrocarbon vapor, fixed position					475			475	525
0240 Hydrocarbon vapor, float mounted					475			475	525
0250 Both liquid and vapor hydrocarbon				↓	475			475	525
0300 Secondary containment, liquid phase									
0310 Pipe trench/manway sump				Ea.	815			815	895
0320 Double wall pipe and manual sump					815			815	895
0330 Double wall fiberglass annular space					320			320	350
0340 Double wall steel tank annular space				↓	335			335	365
0500 Accessories									
0510 Modem, non-dedicated phone line				Ea.	300			300	330
0600 Monitoring, internal									
0610 Automatic tank gauge, incl. overfill				Ea.	1,150			1,150	1,250
0620 Product line				"	1,150			1,150	1,250
0700 Monitoring, special									
0710 Cathodic protection				Ea.	715			715	790
0720 Annular space chemical monitor				"	975			975	1,075

28 39 10 – Notification Systems

28 39 10.10 Mass Notification System	Crew	Daily Output	Labor-Hours	Unit	Material	2014 Bare Costs Labor	Equipment	Total	Total Incl O&P
0010 **MASS NOTIFICATION SYSTEM**									
0100 Wireless command center, 10,000 devices	2 Elec	1.33	12.030	Ea.	3,575	515		4,090	4,775
0200 Option, email notification					1,750			1,750	1,925
0210 Remote device supervision & monitor					2,425			2,425	2,650
0300 Antenna VHF or UHF, for medium range	1 Elec	4	2		128	85.50		213.50	281
0310 For high-power transmitter		2	4		665	171		836	1,000
0400 Transmitter, 25 watt		4	2		2,000	85.50		2,085.50	2,350
0410 40 watt		2.66	3.008		2,675	128		2,803	3,150
0420 100 watt		1.33	6.015		6,700	257		6,957	7,800
0500 Wireless receiver/control module for speaker		8	1		262	42.50		304.50	360
0600 Desktop paging controller, stand alone		4	2		365	85.50		450.50	545

Division Notes

	CREW	DAILY OUTPUT	LABOR-HOURS	UNIT	BARE COSTS				TOTAL INCL O&P
					MAT.	LABOR	EQUIP.	TOTAL	

Estimating Tips

31 05 00 Common Work Results for Earthwork

- Estimating the actual cost of performing earthwork requires careful consideration of the variables involved. This includes items such as type of soil, whether water will be encountered, dewatering, whether banks need bracing, disposal of excavated earth, and length of haul to fill or spoil sites, etc. If the project has large quantities of cut or fill, consider raising or lowering the site to reduce costs, while paying close attention to the effect on site drainage and utilities.

- If the project has large quantities of fill, creating a borrow pit on the site can significantly lower the costs.

- It is very important to consider what time of year the project is scheduled for completion. Bad weather can create large cost overruns from dewatering, site repair, and lost productivity from cold weather.

Reference Numbers

Reference numbers are shown in shaded boxes at the beginning of some major classifications. These numbers refer to related items in the Reference Section. The reference information may be an estimating procedure, an alternate pricing method, or technical information.

Note: Not all subdivisions listed here necessarily appear in this publication.

Division 31 – Earthwork

31 05 Common Work Results for Earthwork

31 05 13 – Soils for Earthwork

31 05 13.10 Borrow

		Crew	Daily Output	Labor-Hours	Unit	Material	2014 Bare Costs Labor	Equipment	Total	Total Incl O&P
0010	**BORROW** R312316-40									
0020	Spread, 200 H.P. dozer, no compaction, 2 mi. RT haul									
0200	Common borrow	B-15	600	.047	C.Y.	12.35	1.48	4.52	18.35	21
0700	Screened loam		600	.047		28	1.48	4.52	34	38
0800	Topsoil, weed free	↓	600	.047		24.50	1.48	4.52	30.50	34.50
0900	For 5 mile haul, add	B-34B	200	.040	↓		1.19	3.46	4.65	5.80

31 05 16 – Aggregates for Earthwork

31 05 16.10 Borrow

		Crew	Daily Output	Labor-Hours	Unit	Material	2014 Bare Costs Labor	Equipment	Total	Total Incl O&P
0010	**BORROW** R312316-40									
0020	Spread, with 200 H.P. dozer, no compaction, 2 mi. RT haul									
0100	Bank run gravel	B-15	600	.047	L.C.Y.	22	1.48	4.52	28	31.50
0300	Crushed stone (1.40 tons per CY) , 1-1/2"		600	.047		28.50	1.48	4.52	34.50	38.50
0320	3/4"		600	.047		28.50	1.48	4.52	34.50	38.50
0340	1/2"		600	.047		27	1.48	4.52	33	37
0360	3/8"		600	.047		25.50	1.48	4.52	31.50	36
0400	Sand, washed, concrete		600	.047		42	1.48	4.52	48	53.50
0500	Dead or bank sand		600	.047		17.55	1.48	4.52	23.55	26.50
0600	Select structural fill	↓	600	.047		21	1.48	4.52	27	30.50
0900	For 5 mile haul, add	B-34B	200	.040	↓		1.19	3.46	4.65	5.80

31 05 23 – Cement and Concrete for Earthwork

31 05 23.30 Plant Mixed Bituminous Concrete

		Crew	Daily Output	Labor-Hours	Unit	Material	2014 Bare Costs Labor	Equipment	Total	Total Incl O&P
0010	**PLANT MIXED BITUMINOUS CONCRETE**									
0020	Asphaltic concrete plant mix (145 lb. per C.F.)				Ton	68			68	75
0040	Asphaltic concrete less than 300 tons add trucking costs									
0050	See Section 31 23 23.20 for hauling costs									
0200	All weather patching mix, hot				Ton	68			68	75
0250	Cold patch					78			78	86
0300	Berm mix				↓	68			68	75

31 06 Schedules for Earthwork

31 06 60 – Schedules for Special Foundations and Load Bearing Elements

31 06 60.14 Piling Special Costs

		Crew	Daily Output	Labor-Hours	Unit	Material	2014 Bare Costs Labor	Equipment	Total	Total Incl O&P
0010	**PILING SPECIAL COSTS**									
0011	Piling special costs, pile caps, see Section 03 30 53.40									
0500	Cutoffs, concrete piles, plain	1 Pile	5.50	1.455	Ea.		50.50		50.50	87
0600	With steel thin shell, add		38	.211			7.30		7.30	12.55
0700	Steel pile or "H" piles		19	.421			14.55		14.55	25
0800	Wood piles	↓	38	.211	↓		7.30		7.30	12.55
0900	Pre-augering up to 30' deep, average soil, 24" diameter	B-43	180	.222	L.F.		6.35	14.15	20.50	26.50
0920	36" diameter		115	.348			9.95	22	31.95	41.50
0960	48" diameter		70	.571			16.35	36.50	52.85	67.50
0980	60" diameter	↓	50	.800	↓		23	51	74	94.50
1000	Testing, any type piles, test load is twice the design load									
1050	50 ton design load, 100 ton test				Ea.				14,000	15,500
1100	100 ton design load, 200 ton test								20,000	22,000
1150	150 ton design load, 300 ton test								26,000	28,500
1200	200 ton design load, 400 ton test								28,000	31,000
1250	400 ton design load, 800 ton test				↓				32,000	35,000
1500	Wet conditions, soft damp ground									
1600	Requiring mats for crane, add								40%	40%

31 06 Schedules for Earthwork

31 06 60 – Schedules for Special Foundations and Load Bearing Elements

31 06 60.14 Piling Special Costs	Crew	Daily Output	Labor-Hours	Unit	Material	2014 Bare Costs Labor	Equipment	Total	Total Incl O&P
1700 Barge mounted driving rig, add								30%	30%

31 06 60.15 Mobilization

		Crew	Daily Output	Labor-Hours	Unit	Material	Labor	Equipment	Total	Total Incl O&P
0010	**MOBILIZATION**									
0020	Set up & remove, air compressor, 600 CFM	A-5	3.30	5.455	Ea.		154	20.50	174.50	282
0100	1200 CFM	"	2.20	8.182			231	30.50	261.50	425
0200	Crane, with pile leads and pile hammer, 75 ton	B-19	.60	93.333			3,225	3,075	6,300	8,900
0300	150 ton	"	.36	155			5,375	5,125	10,500	14,800
0500	Drill rig, for caissons, to 36", minimum	B-43	2	20			570	1,275	1,845	2,375
0520	Maximum		.50	80			2,300	5,100	7,400	9,450
0600	Up to 84"		1	40			1,150	2,550	3,700	4,725
0800	Auxiliary boiler, for steam small	A-5	1.66	10.843			305	40.50	345.50	560
0900	Large	"	.83	21.687			615	81.50	696.50	1,125
1100	Rule of thumb: complete pile driving set up, small	B-19	.45	124			4,300	4,100	8,400	11,900
1200	Large	"	.27	207			7,175	6,825	14,000	19,800
1500	Mobilization, barge, by tug boat	B-83	25	.640	Mile		21	35.50	56.50	74

31 11 Clearing and Grubbing

31 11 10 – Clearing and Grubbing Land

31 11 10.10 Clear and Grub Site

		Crew	Daily Output	Labor-Hours	Unit	Material	Labor	Equipment	Total	Total Incl O&P
0010	**CLEAR AND GRUB SITE**									
0020	Cut & chip light trees to 6" diam.	B-7	1	48	Acre		1,450	1,675	3,125	4,275
0150	Grub stumps and remove	B-30	2	12			390	1,200	1,590	1,975
0200	Cut & chip medium, trees to 12" diam.	B-7	.70	68.571			2,075	2,400	4,475	6,100
0250	Grub stumps and remove	B-30	1	24			775	2,425	3,200	3,950
0300	Cut & chip heavy, trees to 24" diam.	B-7	.30	160			4,825	5,600	10,425	14,200
0350	Grub stumps and remove	B-30	.50	48			1,550	4,825	6,375	7,900
0400	If burning is allowed, deduct cut & chip								40%	40%
3000	Chipping stumps, to 18" deep, 12" diam.	B-86	20	.400	Ea.		15.05	8.10	23.15	34
3040	18" diameter		16	.500			18.85	10.15	29	42
3080	24" diameter		14	.571			21.50	11.60	33.10	48.50
3100	30" diameter		12	.667			25	13.50	38.50	56.50
3120	36" diameter		10	.800			30	16.20	46.20	68
3160	48" diameter		8	1			37.50	20.50	58	85
5000	Tree thinning, feller buncher, conifer									
5080	Up to 8" diameter	B-93	240	.033	Ea.		1.25	3.04	4.29	5.40
5120	12" diameter		160	.050			1.88	4.56	6.44	8.10
5240	Hardwood, up to 4" diameter		240	.033			1.25	3.04	4.29	5.40
5280	8" diameter		180	.044			1.67	4.05	5.72	7.20
5320	12" diameter		120	.067			2.51	6.10	8.61	10.85
7000	Tree removal, congested area, aerial lift truck									
7040	8" diameter	B-85	7	5.714	Ea.		174	149	323	455
7080	12" diameter		6	6.667			203	174	377	530
7120	18" diameter		5	8			243	209	452	635
7160	24" diameter		4	10			305	262	567	800
7240	36" diameter		3	13.333			405	350	755	1,075
7280	48" diameter		2	20			610	525	1,135	1,600

31 13 Selective Tree and Shrub Removal and Trimming

31 13 13 – Selective Tree and Shrub Removal

31 13 13.10 Selective Clearing	Crew	Daily Output	Labor-Hours	Unit	Material	2014 Bare Costs Labor	2014 Bare Costs Equipment	Total	Total Incl O&P
0010 **SELECTIVE CLEARING**									
0020 Clearing brush with brush saw	A-1C	.25	32	Acre		900	125	1,025	1,650
0100 By hand	1 Clab	.12	66.667			1,875		1,875	3,175
0300 With dozer, ball and chain, light clearing	B-11A	2	8			263	660	923	1,175
0400 Medium clearing		1.50	10.667			350	885	1,235	1,550
0500 With dozer and brush rake, light		10	1.600			52.50	133	185.50	234
0550 Medium brush to 4" diameter		8	2			66	166	232	292
0600 Heavy brush to 4" diameter		6.40	2.500			82.50	207	289.50	365
1000 Brush mowing, tractor w/rotary mower, no removal									
1020 Light density	B-84	2	4	Acre		151	182	333	450
1040 Medium density		1.50	5.333			201	243	444	600
1080 Heavy density		1	8			300	365	665	900

31 13 13.20 Selective Tree Removal

31 13 13.20 Selective Tree Removal	Crew	Daily Output	Labor-Hours	Unit	Material	2014 Bare Costs Labor	2014 Bare Costs Equipment	Total	Total Incl O&P
0010 **SELECTIVE TREE REMOVAL**									
0011 With tractor, large tract, firm									
0020 level terrain, no boulders, less than 12" diam. trees									
0300 300 HP dozer, up to 400 trees/acre, 0 to 25% hardwoods	B-10M	.75	10.667	Acre		400	2,425	2,825	3,350
0340 25% to 50% hardwoods		.60	13.333			500	3,025	3,525	4,150
0370 75% to 100% hardwoods		.45	17.778			670	4,050	4,720	5,550
0400 500 trees/acre, 0% to 25% hardwoods		.60	13.333			500	3,025	3,525	4,150
0440 25% to 50% hardwoods		.48	16.667			630	3,775	4,405	5,225
0470 75% to 100% hardwoods		.36	22.222			835	5,050	5,885	6,925
0500 More than 600 trees/acre, 0 to 25% hardwoods		.52	15.385			580	3,500	4,080	4,800
0540 25% to 50% hardwoods		.42	19.048			715	4,325	5,040	5,950
0570 75% to 100% hardwoods		.31	25.806			970	5,850	6,820	8,050
0900 Large tract clearing per tree									
1500 300 HP dozer, to 12" diameter, softwood	B-10M	320	.025	Ea.		.94	5.70	6.64	7.80
1550 Hardwood		100	.080			3.01	18.15	21.16	25
1600 12" to 24" diameter, softwood		200	.040			1.51	9.10	10.61	12.50
1650 Hardwood		80	.100			3.77	22.50	26.27	31.50
1700 24" to 36" diameter, softwood		100	.080			3.01	18.15	21.16	25
1750 Hardwood		50	.160			6	36.50	42.50	50
1800 36" to 48" diameter, softwood		70	.114			4.30	26	30.30	35.50
1850 Hardwood		35	.229			8.60	52	60.60	71.50
2000 Stump removal on site by hydraulic backhoe, 1-1/2 C.Y.									
2040 4" to 6" diameter	B-17	60	.533	Ea.		16.30	13.05	29.35	42
2050 8" to 12" diameter	B-30	33	.727			23.50	73	96.50	120
2100 14" to 24" diameter		25	.960			31	96.50	127.50	158
2150 26" to 36" diameter		16	1.500			48.50	151	199.50	247
3000 Remove selective trees, on site using chain saws and chipper,									
3050 not incl. stumps, up to 6" diameter	B-7	18	2.667	Ea.		80.50	93	173.50	238
3100 8" to 12" diameter		12	4			120	140	260	355
3150 14" to 24" diameter		10	4.800			145	168	313	425
3200 26" to 36" diameter		8	6			181	210	391	535
3300 Machine load, 2 mile haul to dump, 12" diam. tree	A-3B	8	2			67.50	152	219.50	279

31 14 Earth Stripping and Stockpiling

31 14 13 - Soil Stripping and Stockpiling

31 14 13.23 Topsoil Stripping and Stockpiling

		Crew	Daily Output	Labor-Hours	Unit	Material	2014 Bare Costs Labor	Equipment	Total	Total Incl O&P
0010	**TOPSOIL STRIPPING AND STOCKPILING**									
0020	200 H.P. dozer, ideal conditions	B-10B	2300	.003	C.Y.		.13	.58	.71	.85
0100	Adverse conditions	"	1150	.007			.26	1.15	1.41	1.70
0200	300 H.P. dozer, ideal conditions	B-10M	3000	.003			.10	.61	.71	.84
0300	Adverse conditions	"	1650	.005			.18	1.10	1.28	1.51
0400	400 H.P. dozer, ideal conditions	B-10X	3900	.002			.08	.62	.70	.81
0500	Adverse conditions	"	2000	.004			.15	1.20	1.35	1.58
0600	Clay, dry and soft, 200 H.P. dozer, ideal conditions	B-10B	1600	.005			.19	.83	1.02	1.22
0700	Adverse conditions	"	800	.010			.38	1.66	2.04	2.44
1000	Medium hard, 300 H.P. dozer, ideal conditions	B-10M	2000	.004			.15	.91	1.06	1.25
1100	Adverse conditions	"	1100	.007			.27	1.65	1.92	2.27
1200	Very hard, 400 H.P. dozer, ideal conditions	B-10X	2600	.003			.12	.93	1.05	1.21
1300	Adverse conditions	"	1340	.006	▼		.22	1.80	2.02	2.35
1400	Loam or topsoil, remove and stockpile on site									
1420	6" deep, 200' haul	B-10B	865	.009	C.Y.		.35	1.53	1.88	2.27
1430	300' haul		520	.015			.58	2.55	3.13	3.76
1440	500' haul		225	.036	▼		1.34	5.90	7.24	8.70
1450	Alternate method: 6" deep, 200' haul		5090	.002	S.Y.		.06	.26	.32	.39
1460	500' haul	▼	1325	.006	"		.23	1	1.23	1.48
1500	Loam or topsoil, remove/stockpile on site									
1510	By hand, 6" deep, 50' haul, less than 100 S.Y.	B-1	100	.240	S.Y.		6.95		6.95	11.65
1520	By skid steer, 6" deep, 100' haul, 101-500 S.Y.	B-62	500	.048			1.48	.35	1.83	2.86
1530	100' haul, 501-900 S.Y.	"	900	.027			.82	.19	1.01	1.59
1540	200' haul, 901-1100 S.Y.	B-63	1000	.040			1.13	.17	1.30	2.09
1550	By dozer, 200' haul, 1101-4000 S.Y.	B-10B	4000	.002	▼		.08	.33	.41	.48

31 22 Grading

31 22 13 - Rough Grading

31 22 13.20 Rough Grading Sites

		Crew	Daily Output	Labor-Hours	Unit	Material	2014 Bare Costs Labor	Equipment	Total	Total Incl O&P
0010	**ROUGH GRADING SITES**									
0100	Rough grade sites 400 S.F. or less	B-1	2	12	Ea.		345		345	585
0120	410-1000 S.F.	"	1	24			695		695	1,175
0130	1100-3000 S.F.	B-62	1.50	16			495	116	611	955
0140	3100-5000 S.F.	"	1	24			740	174	914	1,450
0150	5100-8000 S.F.	B-63	1	40			1,125	174	1,299	2,100
0160	8100-10000 S.F.	"	.75	53.333			1,500	233	1,733	2,775
0170	8100-10000 S.F.	B-10L	1	8			300	480	780	1,025
0200	Rough grade open sites 10000-20000 S.F.	B-11L	1.80	8.889			293	395	688	920
0210	20100-25000 S.F.		1.40	11.429			375	505	880	1,175
0220	25100-30000 S.F.		1.20	13.333			440	590	1,030	1,375
0230	30100-35000 S.F.		1	16			525	705	1,230	1,650
0240	35100-40000 S.F.		.90	17.778			585	785	1,370	1,850
0250	40100-45000 S.F.		.80	20			660	885	1,545	2,075
0260	45100-50000 S.F.		.72	22.222			730	980	1,710	2,300
0270	50100-75000 S.F.		.50	32			1,050	1,425	2,475	3,300
0280	75100-100000 S.F.	▼	.36	44.444	▼		1,475	1,975	3,450	4,600

31 22 Grading

31 22 16 – Fine Grading

31 22 16.10 Finish Grading	Crew	Daily Output	Labor-Hours	Unit	Material	2014 Bare Costs Labor	2014 Bare Costs Equipment	Total	Total Incl O&P
0010 **FINISH GRADING**									
0012 Finish grading area to be paved with grader, small area	B-11L	400	.040	S.Y.		1.32	1.77	3.09	4.14
0100 Large area	↓	2000	.008			.26	.35	.61	.83
1100 Fine grade for slab on grade, machine	↓	1040	.015			.51	.68	1.19	1.59
1150 Hand grading	B-18	700	.034	↓		.99	.07	1.06	1.74
3500 Finish grading lagoon bottoms	B-11L	4	4	M.S.F.		132	177	309	415

31 23 Excavation and Fill

31 23 16 – Excavation

31 23 16.13 Excavating, Trench

31 23 16.13 Excavating, Trench	Crew	Daily Output	Labor-Hours	Unit	Material	2014 Bare Costs Labor	2014 Bare Costs Equipment	Total	Total Incl O&P
0010 **EXCAVATING, TRENCH**									
0011 Or continuous footing									
0020 Common earth with no sheeting or dewatering included									
0050 1' to 4' deep, 3/8 C.Y. excavator	B-11C	150	.107	B.C.Y.		3.51	2.44	5.95	8.55
0060 1/2 C.Y. excavator	B-11M	200	.080			2.63	1.99	4.62	6.60
0090 4' to 6' deep, 1/2 C.Y. excavator	"	200	.080			2.63	1.99	4.62	6.60
0101 5/8 C.Y. hydraulic excavator	B-12Q	250	.064			2.14	2.38	4.52	6.20
0300 1/2 C.Y. excavator, truck mounted	B-12J	200	.080			2.68	4.41	7.09	9.30
0500 6' to 10' deep, 3/4 C.Y. excavator	B-12F	225	.071			2.38	2.94	5.32	7.20
0510 1 C.Y. excavator	B-12A	400	.040			1.34	2.04	3.38	4.47
0600 1 C.Y. excavator, truck mounted	B-12K	400	.040			1.34	2.51	3.85	4.99
0610 1-1/2 C.Y. excavator	B-12B	600	.027			.89	1.72	2.61	3.38
0900 10' to 14' deep, 3/4 C.Y. excavator	B-12F	200	.080			2.68	3.31	5.99	8.10
0910 1 C.Y. excavator	B-12A	360	.044			1.49	2.26	3.75	4.97
1000 1-1/2 C.Y. excavator	B-12B	540	.030			.99	1.91	2.90	3.75
1300 14' to 20' deep, 1 C.Y. excavator	B-12A	320	.050			1.67	2.55	4.22	5.60
1310 1-1/2 C.Y. excavator	B-12B	480	.033			1.11	2.15	3.26	4.22
1320 2-1/2 C.Y. excavator	B-12S	765	.021			.70	2.14	2.84	3.52
1340 20' to 24' deep, 1 C.Y. excavator	B-12A	288	.056			1.86	2.83	4.69	6.20
1342 1-1/2 C.Y. excavator	B-12B	432	.037			1.24	2.39	3.63	4.70
1344 2-1/2 C.Y. excavator	B-12S	685	.023			.78	2.39	3.17	3.93
1352 4' to 6' deep, 1/2 C.Y. excavator w/trench box	B-13H	188	.085			2.85	5.15	8	10.40
1362 6' to 10' deep, 3/4 C.Y. excavator w/trench box	B-13G	212	.075			2.52	3.52	6.04	8.10
1370 1 C.Y. excavator	B-13D	376	.043			1.42	2.39	3.81	5
1371 1-1/2 C.Y. excavator	B-13E	564	.028			.95	1.98	2.93	3.75
1374 10' to 14' deep, 3/4 C.Y. excavator w/trench box	B-13G	188	.085			2.85	3.97	6.82	9.10
1375 1 C.Y. excavator	B-13D	338	.047			1.58	2.66	4.24	5.55
1376 1-1/2 C.Y. excavator	B-13E	508	.032			1.05	2.20	3.25	4.17
1381 14' to 20' deep, 1 C.Y. excavator w/trench box	B-13D	301	.053			1.78	2.99	4.77	6.25
1382 1-1/2 C.Y. excavator	B-13E	451	.035			1.19	2.47	3.66	4.70
1383 2-1/2 C.Y. excavator	B-13J	720	.022			.74	2.39	3.13	3.87
1386 20' to 24' deep, 1 C.Y. excavator w/trench box	B-13D	271	.059			1.97	3.32	5.29	6.95
1387 1-1/2 C.Y. excavator	B-13E	406	.039			1.32	2.75	4.07	5.20
1388 2-1/2 C.Y. excavator	B-13J	645	.025			.83	2.67	3.50	4.32
1400 By hand with pick and shovel 2' to 6' deep, light soil	1 Clab	8	1			28		28	47.50
1500 Heavy soil	"	4	2	↓		56.50		56.50	95
1700 For tamping backfilled trenches, air tamp, add	A-1G	100	.080	E.C.Y.		2.26	.56	2.82	4.42
1900 Vibrating plate, add	B-18	180	.133	"		3.85	.26	4.11	6.80
2100 Trim sides and bottom for concrete pours, common earth	↓	1500	.016	S.F.		.46	.03	.49	.81
2300 Hardpan	↓	600	.040	"		1.15	.08	1.23	2.02

31 23 16 – Excavation

31 23 16.13 Excavating, Trench	Crew	Daily Output	Labor-Hours	Unit	Material	2014 Bare Costs Labor	Equipment	Total	Total Incl O&P
2400	Pier and spread footing excavation, add to above				B.C.Y.			30%	30%
3000	Backfill trench, F.E. loader, wheel mtd., 1 C.Y. bucket								
3020	Minimal haul	B-10R	400	.020	L.C.Y.		.75	.74	1.49	2.06
3040	100' haul	"	200	.040			1.51	1.48	2.99	4.11
3080	2-1/4 C.Y. bucket, minimum haul	B-10T	600	.013			.50	.87	1.37	1.79
3090	100' haul	"	300	.027			1	1.74	2.74	3.58
5020	Loam & Sandy clay with no sheeting or dewatering included									
5050	1' to 4' deep, 3/8 C.Y. tractor loader/backhoe	B-11C	162	.099	B.C.Y.		3.25	2.25	5.50	7.90
5060	1/2 C.Y. excavator	B-11M	216	.074			2.44	1.84	4.28	6.10
5080	4' to 6' deep, 1/2 C.Y. excavator	"	216	.074			2.44	1.84	4.28	6.10
5130	1/2 C.Y. excavator, truck mounted	B-12J	216	.074			2.48	4.08	6.56	8.60
5140	6' to 10' deep, 3/4 C.Y. excavator	B-12F	243	.066			2.20	2.72	4.92	6.65
5150	1 C.Y. excavator	B-12A	432	.037			1.24	1.89	3.13	4.15
5160	1 C.Y. excavator, truck mounted	B-12K	432	.037			1.24	2.33	3.57	4.63
5170	1-1/2 C.Y. excavator	B-12B	648	.025			.83	1.59	2.42	3.13
5190	10' to 14' deep, 3/4 C.Y. excavator	B-12F	216	.074			2.48	3.07	5.55	7.50
5200	1 C.Y. excavator	B-12A	389	.041			1.38	2.09	3.47	4.59
5210	1-1/2 C.Y. excavator	B-12B	583	.027			.92	1.77	2.69	3.47
5250	14' to 20' deep, 1 C.Y. excavator	B-12A	346	.046			1.55	2.36	3.91	5.15
5260	1-1/2 C.Y. excavator	B-12B	518	.031			1.03	1.99	3.02	3.91
5270	2-1/2 C.Y. excavator	B-12S	826	.019			.65	1.98	2.63	3.26
5300	20' to 24' deep, 1 C.Y. excavator	B-12A	311	.051			1.72	2.62	4.34	5.75
5310	1-1/2 C.Y. excavator	B-12B	467	.034			1.15	2.21	3.36	4.34
5320	2-1/2 C.Y. excavator	B-12S	740	.022			.72	2.21	2.93	3.64
5352	4' to 6' deep, 1/2 C.Y. excavator w/trench box	B-13H	205	.078			2.61	4.71	7.32	9.55
5362	6' to 10' deep, 3/4 C.Y. excavator w/trench box	B-13G	231	.069			2.32	3.23	5.55	7.40
5364	1 C.Y. excavator	B-13D	410	.039			1.31	2.19	3.50	4.59
5366	1-1/2 C.Y. excavator	B-13E	616	.026			.87	1.81	2.68	3.44
5370	10' to 14' deep, 3/4 C.Y. excavator w/trench box	B-13G	205	.078			2.61	3.64	6.25	8.35
5372	1 C.Y. excavator	B-13D	370	.043			1.45	2.43	3.88	5.10
5374	1-1/2 C.Y. excavator	B-13E	554	.029			.97	2.01	2.98	3.82
5382	14' to 20' deep, 1 C.Y. excavator w/trench box	B-13D	329	.049			1.63	2.73	4.36	5.70
5384	1-1/2 C.Y. excavator	B-13E	492	.033			1.09	2.27	3.36	4.30
5386	2-1/2 C.Y. excavator	B-13J	780	.021			.69	2.21	2.90	3.57
5392	20' to 24' deep, 1 C.Y. excavator w/trench box	B-13D	295	.054			1.81	3.05	4.86	6.40
5394	1-1/2 C.Y. excavator	B-13E	444	.036			1.21	2.51	3.72	4.77
5396	2-1/2 C.Y. excavator	B-13J	695	.023			.77	2.48	3.25	4
6020	Sand & gravel with no sheeting or dewatering included									
6050	1' to 4' deep, 3/8 C.Y. excavator	B-11C	165	.097	B.C.Y.		3.19	2.21	5.40	7.75
6060	1/2 C.Y. excavator	B-11M	220	.073			2.40	1.81	4.21	6
6080	4' to 6' deep, 1/2 C.Y. excavator	"	220	.073			2.40	1.81	4.21	6
6130	1/2 C.Y. excavator, truck mounted	B-12J	220	.073			2.43	4.01	6.44	8.45
6140	6' to 10' deep, 3/4 C.Y. excavator	B-12F	248	.065			2.16	2.67	4.83	6.55
6150	1 C.Y. excavator	B-12A	440	.036			1.22	1.85	3.07	4.07
6160	1 C.Y. excavator, truck mounted	B-12K	440	.036			1.22	2.28	3.50	4.54
6170	1-1/2 C.Y. excavator	B-12B	660	.024			.81	1.56	2.37	3.07
6190	10' to 14' deep, 3/4 C.Y. excavator	B-12F	220	.073			2.43	3.01	5.44	7.35
6200	1 C.Y. excavator	B-12A	396	.040			1.35	2.06	3.41	4.51
6210	1-1/2 C.Y. excavator	B-12B	594	.027			.90	1.74	2.64	3.41
6250	14' to 20' deep, 1 C.Y. excavator	B-12A	352	.045			1.52	2.31	3.83	5.10
6260	1-1/2 C.Y. excavator	B-12B	528	.030			1.01	1.95	2.96	3.84
6270	2-1/2 C.Y. excavator	B-12S	840	.019			.64	1.95	2.59	3.20
6300	20' to 24' deep, 1 C.Y. excavator	B-12A	317	.050			1.69	2.57	4.26	5.65

31 23 16.13 Excavating, Trench

		Crew	Daily Output	Labor-Hours	Unit	Material	2014 Bare Costs Labor	Equipment	Total	Total Incl O&P
6310	1-1/2 C.Y. excavator	B-12B	475	.034	B.C.Y.		1.13	2.17	3.30	4.27
6320	2-1/2 C.Y. excavator	B-12S	755	.021			.71	2.17	2.88	3.56
6352	4' to 6' deep, 1/2 C.Y. excavator w/trench box	B-13H	209	.077			2.56	4.62	7.18	9.35
6362	6' to 10' deep, 3/4 C.Y. excavator w/trench box	B-13G	236	.068			2.27	3.16	5.43	7.25
6364	1 C.Y. excavator	B-13D	418	.038			1.28	2.15	3.43	4.51
6366	1-1/2 C.Y. excavator	B-13E	627	.026			.85	1.78	2.63	3.38
6370	10' to 14' deep, 3/4 C.Y. excavator w/trench box	B-13G	209	.077			2.56	3.57	6.13	8.20
6372	1 C.Y. excavator	B-13D	376	.043			1.42	2.39	3.81	5
6374	1-1/2 C.Y. excavator	B-13E	564	.028			.95	1.98	2.93	3.75
6382	14' to 20' deep, 1 C.Y. excavator w/trench box	B-13D	334	.048			1.60	2.69	4.29	5.65
6384	1-1/2 C.Y. excavator	B-13E	502	.032			1.07	2.22	3.29	4.22
6386	2-1/2 C.Y. excavator	B-13J	790	.020			.68	2.18	2.86	3.53
6392	20' to 24' deep, 1 C.Y. excavator w/trench box	B-13D	301	.053			1.78	2.99	4.77	6.25
6394	1-1/2 C.Y. excavator	B-13E	452	.035			1.18	2.47	3.65	4.68
6396	2-1/2 C.Y. excavator	B-13J	710	.023	▼		.75	2.42	3.17	3.93
7020	Dense hard clay with no sheeting or dewatering included									
7050	1' to 4' deep, 3/8 C.Y. excavator	B-11C	132	.121	B.C.Y.		3.99	2.77	6.76	9.70
7060	1/2 C.Y. excavator	B-11M	176	.091			2.99	2.26	5.25	7.50
7080	4' to 6' deep, 1/2 C.Y. excavator	"	176	.091			2.99	2.26	5.25	7.50
7130	1/2 C.Y. excavator, truck mounted	B-12J	176	.091			3.04	5	8.04	10.55
7140	6' to 10' deep, 3/4 C.Y. excavator	B-12F	198	.081			2.70	3.34	6.04	8.20
7150	1 C.Y. excavator	B-12A	352	.045			1.52	2.31	3.83	5.10
7160	1 C.Y. excavator, truck mounted	B-12K	352	.045			1.52	2.85	4.37	5.70
7170	1-1/2 C.Y. excavator	B-12B	528	.030			1.01	1.95	2.96	3.84
7190	10' to 14' deep, 3/4 C.Y. excavator	B-12F	176	.091			3.04	3.76	6.80	9.20
7200	1 C.Y. excavator	B-12A	317	.050			1.69	2.57	4.26	5.65
7210	1-1/2 C.Y. excavator	B-12B	475	.034			1.13	2.17	3.30	4.27
7250	14' to 20' deep, 1 C.Y. excavator	B-12A	282	.057			1.90	2.89	4.79	6.35
7260	1-1/2 C.Y. excavator	B-12B	422	.038			1.27	2.44	3.71	4.80
7270	2-1/2 C.Y. excavator	B-12S	675	.024			.79	2.42	3.21	3.99
7300	20' to 24' deep, 1 C.Y. excavator	B-12A	254	.063			2.11	3.21	5.32	7.05
7310	1-1/2 C.Y. excavator	B-12B	380	.042			1.41	2.71	4.12	5.35
7320	2-1/2 C.Y. excavator	B-12S	605	.026	▼		.88	2.71	3.59	4.46

31 23 16.14 Excavating, Utility Trench

		Crew	Daily Output	Labor-Hours	Unit	Material	2014 Bare Costs Labor	Equipment	Total	Total Incl O&P
0010	**EXCAVATING, UTILITY TRENCH**									
0011	Common earth									
0050	Trenching with chain trencher, 12 H.P., operator walking									
0100	4" wide trench, 12" deep	B-53	800	.010	L.F.		.28	.09	.37	.57
0150	18" deep		750	.011			.30	.10	.40	.61
0200	24" deep		700	.011			.32	.10	.42	.65
0300	6" wide trench, 12" deep		650	.012			.35	.11	.46	.70
0350	18" deep		600	.013			.38	.12	.50	.76
0400	24" deep		550	.015			.41	.13	.54	.83
0450	36" deep		450	.018			.50	.16	.66	1.01
0600	8" wide trench, 12" deep		475	.017			.47	.15	.62	.96
0650	18" deep		400	.020			.56	.18	.74	1.15
0700	24" deep		350	.023			.64	.20	.84	1.30
0750	36" deep	▼	300	.027	▼		.75	.24	.99	1.53
1000	Backfill by hand including compaction, add									
1050	4" wide trench, 12" deep	A-1G	800	.010	L.F.		.28	.07	.35	.55
1100	18" deep		530	.015			.43	.11	.54	.84
1150	24" deep	▼	400	.020	▼		.56	.14	.70	1.10

31 23 Excavation and Fill

31 23 16 – Excavation

31 23 16.14 Excavating, Utility Trench

		Crew	Daily Output	Labor-Hours	Unit	Material	2014 Bare Costs Labor	Equipment	Total	Total Incl O&P
1300	6" wide trench, 12" deep	A-1G	540	.015	L.F.		.42	.10	.52	.81
1350	18" deep		405	.020			.56	.14	.70	1.09
1400	24" deep		270	.030			.84	.21	1.05	1.64
1450	36" deep		180	.044			1.25	.31	1.56	2.45
1600	8" wide trench, 12" deep		400	.020			.56	.14	.70	1.10
1650	18" deep		265	.030			.85	.21	1.06	1.66
1700	24" deep		200	.040			1.13	.28	1.41	2.21
1750	36" deep		135	.059			1.67	.41	2.08	3.27
2000	Chain trencher, 40 H.P. operator riding									
2050	6" wide trench and backfill, 12" deep	B-54	1200	.007	L.F.		.24	.28	.52	.71
2100	18" deep		1000	.008			.29	.34	.63	.85
2150	24" deep		975	.008			.30	.35	.65	.87
2200	36" deep		900	.009			.32	.38	.70	.94
2250	48" deep		750	.011			.39	.45	.84	1.14
2300	60" deep		650	.012			.45	.52	.97	1.31
2400	8" wide trench and backfill, 12" deep		1000	.008			.29	.34	.63	.85
2450	18" deep		950	.008			.31	.36	.67	.90
2500	24" deep		900	.009			.32	.38	.70	.94
2550	36" deep		800	.010			.36	.42	.78	1.07
2600	48" deep		650	.012			.45	.52	.97	1.31
2700	12" wide trench and backfill, 12" deep		975	.008			.30	.35	.65	.87
2750	18" deep		860	.009			.34	.39	.73	.99
2800	24" deep		800	.010			.36	.42	.78	1.07
2850	36" deep		725	.011			.40	.47	.87	1.17
3000	16" wide trench and backfill, 12" deep		835	.010			.35	.41	.76	1.03
3050	18" deep		750	.011			.39	.45	.84	1.14
3100	24" deep		700	.011			.41	.49	.90	1.22
3200	Compaction with vibratory plate, add								35%	35%
5100	Hand excavate and trim for pipe bells after trench excavation									
5200	8" pipe	1 Clab	155	.052	L.F.		1.46		1.46	2.45
5300	18" pipe	"	130	.062	"		1.74		1.74	2.92

31 23 16.16 Structural Excavation for Minor Structures

		Crew	Daily Output	Labor-Hours	Unit	Material	2014 Bare Costs Labor	Equipment	Total	Total Incl O&P
0010	**STRUCTURAL EXCAVATION FOR MINOR STRUCTURES** R312316-40									
0015	Hand, pits to 6' deep, sandy soil	1 Clab	8	1	B.C.Y.		28		28	47.50
0100	Heavy soil or clay		4	2			56.50		56.50	95
0300	Pits 6' to 12' deep, sandy soil		5	1.600			45		45	76
0500	Heavy soil or clay		3	2.667			75		75	127
0700	Pits 12' to 18' deep, sandy soil		4	2			56.50		56.50	95
0900	Heavy soil or clay		2	4			113		113	190
1100	Hand loading trucks from stock pile, sandy soil		12	.667			18.80		18.80	31.50
1300	Heavy soil or clay		8	1			28		28	47.50
1500	For wet or muck hand excavation, add to above								50%	50%
6000	Machine excavation, for spread and mat footings, elevator pits,									
6001	and small building foundations									
6030	Common earth, hydraulic backhoe, 1/2 C.Y. bucket	B-12E	55	.291	B.C.Y.		9.75	8.15	17.90	25
6035	3/4 C.Y. bucket	B-12F	90	.178			5.95	7.35	13.30	18
6040	1 C.Y. bucket	B-12A	108	.148			4.96	7.55	12.51	16.55
6050	1-1/2 C.Y. bucket	B-12B	144	.111			3.72	7.15	10.87	14.10
6060	2 C.Y. bucket	B-12C	200	.080			2.68	5.90	8.58	10.90
6070	Sand and gravel, 3/4 C.Y. bucket	B-12F	100	.160			5.35	6.60	11.95	16.20
6080	1 C.Y. bucket	B-12A	120	.133			4.46	6.80	11.26	14.90
6090	1-1/2 C.Y. bucket	B-12B	160	.100			3.35	6.45	9.80	12.70

31 23 16 – Excavation

31 23 16.16 Structural Excavation for Minor Structures	Crew	Daily Output	Labor-Hours	Unit	Material	2014 Bare Costs Labor	Equipment	Total	Total Incl O&P
6100	2 C.Y. bucket	B-12C	220	.073	B.C.Y.		2.43	5.35	7.78	9.95
6110	Clay, till, or blasted rock, 3/4 C.Y. bucket	B-12F	80	.200			6.70	8.30	15	20.50
6120	1 C.Y. bucket	B-12A	95	.168			5.65	8.60	14.25	18.85
6130	1-1/2 C.Y. bucket	B-12B	130	.123			4.12	7.95	12.07	15.55
6140	2 C.Y. bucket	B-12C	175	.091			3.06	6.70	9.76	12.50
6230	Sandy clay & loam, hydraulic backhoe, 1/2 C.Y. bucket	B-12E	60	.267			8.90	7.45	16.35	23
6235	3/4 C.Y. bucket	B-12F	98	.163			5.45	6.75	12.20	16.55
6240	1 C.Y. bucket	B-12A	116	.138			4.61	7	11.61	15.45
6250	1-1/2 C.Y. bucket	B-12B	156	.103			3.43	6.60	10.03	12.95
9010	For mobilization or demobilization, see Section 01 54 36.50									
9020	For dewatering, see Section 31 23 19.20									
9022	For larger structures, see Bulk Excavation, Section 31 23 16.42									
9024	For loading onto trucks, add								15%	15%
9026	For hauling, see Section 31 23 23.20									
9030	For sheeting or soldier bms/lagging, see Section 31 52 16.10									
9040	For trench excavation of strip ftgs, see Section 31 23 16.13									

31 23 16.26 Rock Removal

		Crew	Daily Output	Labor-Hours	Unit	Material	Labor	Equipment	Total	Total Incl O&P
0010	**ROCK REMOVAL** R312316-40									
0015	Drilling only rock, 2" hole for rock bolts	B-47	316	.051	L.F.		1.48	5.15	6.63	8.15
0800	2-1/2" hole for pre-splitting		600	.027			.78	2.70	3.48	4.28
4600	Quarry operations, 2-1/2" to 3-1/2" diameter		715	.022			.65	2.27	2.92	3.60

31 23 16.30 Drilling and Blasting Rock

		Crew	Daily Output	Labor-Hours	Unit	Material	Labor	Equipment	Total	Total Incl O&P
0010	**DRILLING AND BLASTING ROCK**									
0020	Rock, open face, under 1500 C.Y.	B-47	225	.071	B.C.Y.	3.15	2.08	7.20	12.43	14.90
0100	Over 1500 C.Y.		300	.053		3.15	1.56	5.40	10.11	12.05
0200	Areas where blasting mats are required, under 1500 C.Y.		175	.091		3.15	2.67	9.25	15.07	18.15
0250	Over 1500 C.Y.		250	.064		3.15	1.87	6.50	11.52	13.75
0300	Bulk drilling and blasting, can vary greatly, average								9.65	12.20
0500	Pits, average								25.50	31.50
1300	Deep hole method, up to 1500 C.Y.	B-47	50	.320		3.15	9.35	32.50	45	54.50
1400	Over 1500 C.Y.		66	.242		3.15	7.10	24.50	34.75	42.50
1900	Restricted areas, up to 1500 C.Y.		13	1.231		3.15	36	125	164.15	201
2000	Over 1500 C.Y.		20	.800		3.15	23.50	81	107.65	132
2200	Trenches, up to 1500 C.Y.		22	.727		9.15	21	74	104.15	127
2300	Over 1500 C.Y.		26	.615		9.15	17.95	62.50	89.60	109
2500	Pier holes, up to 1500 C.Y.		22	.727		3.15	21	74	98.15	120
2600	Over 1500 C.Y.		31	.516		3.15	15.05	52.50	70.70	86.50
2800	Boulders under 1/2 C.Y., loaded on truck, no hauling	B-100	80	.100			3.77	12	15.77	19.45
2900	Boulders, drilled, blasted	B-47	100	.160		3.15	4.67	16.20	24.02	29
3100	Jackhammer operators with foreman compressor, air tools	B-9	1	40	Day		1,150	234	1,384	2,175
3300	Track drill, compressor, operator and foreman	B-47	1	16	"		465	1,625	2,090	2,550
3500	Blasting caps				Ea.	6.25			6.25	6.85
3700	Explosives					.46			.46	.51
3900	Blasting mats, rent, for first day					144			144	158
4000	Per added day					48			48	53
4200	Preblast survey for 6 room house, individual lot, minimum	A-6	2.40	6.667			237	29.50	266.50	430
4300	Maximum	"	1.35	11.852			420	53	473	765
4500	City block within zone of influence, minimum	A-8	25200	.001	S.F.		.05		.05	.08
4600	Maximum	"	15100	.002	"		.08		.08	.14

31 23 Excavation and Fill

31 23 16 – Excavation

31 23 16.42 Excavating, Bulk Bank Measure

		Crew	Daily Output	Labor-Hours	Unit	Material	2014 Bare Costs Labor	2014 Bare Costs Equipment	Total	Total Incl O&P
0010	**EXCAVATING, BULK BANK MEASURE** R312316-40									
0011	Common earth piled									
0020	For loading onto trucks, add								15%	15%
0050	For mobilization and demobilization, see Section 01 54 36.50 R312316-45									
0100	For hauling, see Section 31 23 23.20									
0200	Excavator, hydraulic, crawler mtd., 1 C.Y. cap. = 100 C.Y./hr.	B-12A	800	.020	B.C.Y.		.67	1.02	1.69	2.24
0250	1-1/2 C.Y. cap. = 125 C.Y./hr.	B-12B	1000	.016			.54	1.03	1.57	2.02
0260	2 C.Y. cap. = 165 C.Y./hr.	B-12C	1320	.012			.41	.89	1.30	1.66
0300	3 C.Y. cap. = 260 C.Y./hr.	B-12D	2080	.008			.26	1.17	1.43	1.72
0305	3-1/2 C.Y. cap. = 300 C.Y./hr.	"	2400	.007			.22	1.02	1.24	1.49
0310	Wheel mounted, 1/2 C.Y. cap. = 40 C.Y./hr.	B-12E	320	.050			1.67	1.40	3.07	4.33
0360	3/4 C.Y. cap. = 60 C.Y./hr.	B-12F	480	.033			1.11	1.38	2.49	3.38
0500	Clamshell, 1/2 C.Y. cap. = 20 C.Y./hr.	B-12G	160	.100			3.35	4.51	7.86	10.55
0550	1 C.Y. cap. = 35 C.Y./hr.	B-12H	280	.057			1.91	4.36	6.27	8
0950	Dragline, 1/2 C.Y. cap. = 30 C.Y./hr.	B-12I	240	.067			2.23	3.75	5.98	7.85
1000	3/4 C.Y. cap. = 35 C.Y./hr.	"	280	.057			1.91	3.22	5.13	6.75
1050	1-1/2 C.Y. cap. = 65 C.Y./hr.	B-12P	520	.031			1.03	2.33	3.36	4.29
1200	Front end loader, track mtd., 1-1/2 C.Y. cap. = 70 C.Y./hr.	B-10N	560	.014			.54	.93	1.47	1.92
1250	2-1/2 C.Y. cap. = 95 C.Y./hr.	B-10O	760	.011			.40	1.26	1.66	2.05
1300	3 C.Y. cap. = 130 C.Y./hr.	B-10P	1040	.008			.29	1.14	1.43	1.74
1350	5 C.Y. cap. = 160 C.Y./hr.	B-10Q	1280	.006			.24	1.20	1.44	1.71
1500	Wheel mounted, 3/4 C.Y. cap. = 45 C.Y./hr.	B-10R	360	.022			.84	.82	1.66	2.29
1550	1-1/2 C.Y. cap. = 80 C.Y./hr.	B-10S	640	.013			.47	.58	1.05	1.42
1600	2-1/4 C.Y. cap. = 100 C.Y./hr.	B-10T	800	.010			.38	.65	1.03	1.34
1650	5 C.Y. cap. = 185 C.Y./hr.	B-10U	1480	.005			.20	.71	.91	1.12
1800	Hydraulic excavator, truck mtd. 1/2 C.Y. = 30 C.Y./hr.	B-12J	240	.067			2.23	3.67	5.90	7.75
1850	48 inch bucket, 1 C.Y. = 45 C.Y./hr.	B-12K	360	.044			1.49	2.79	4.28	5.55
3700	Shovel, 1/2 C.Y. capacity = 55 C.Y./hr.	B-12L	440	.036			1.22	1.69	2.91	3.89
3750	3/4 C.Y. capacity = 85 C.Y./hr.	B-12M	680	.024			.79	1.39	2.18	2.84
3800	1 C.Y. capacity = 120 C.Y./hr.	B-12N	960	.017			.56	1.30	1.86	2.36
3850	1-1/2 C.Y. capacity = 160 C.Y./hr.	B-12O	1280	.013			.42	.98	1.40	1.78
3900	3 C.Y. cap. = 250 C.Y./hr.	B-12T	2000	.008			.27	.80	1.07	1.33
4000	For soft soil or sand, deduct								15%	15%
4100	For heavy soil or stiff clay, add								60%	60%
4200	For wet excavation with clamshell or dragline, add								100%	100%
4250	All other equipment, add								50%	50%
4400	Clamshell in sheeting or cofferdam, minimum	B-12H	160	.100			3.35	7.65	11	14
4450	Maximum	"	60	.267			8.90	20.50	29.40	37.50
5000	Excavating, bulk bank measure, sandy clay & loam piled									
5020	For loading onto trucks, add								15%	15%
5100	Excavator, hydraulic, crawler mtd., 1 C.Y. cap. = 120 C.Y./hr.	B-12A	960	.017	B.C.Y.		.56	.85	1.41	1.86
5150	1-1/2 C.Y. cap. = 150 C.Y./hr.	B-12B	1200	.013			.45	.86	1.31	1.68
5300	2 C.Y. cap. = 195 C.Y./hr.	B-12C	1560	.010			.34	.75	1.09	1.40
5400	3 C.Y. cap. = 300 C.Y./hr.	B-12D	2400	.007			.22	1.02	1.24	1.49
5500	3.5 C.Y. cap. = 350 C.Y./hr.	"	2800	.006			.19	.87	1.06	1.28
5610	Wheel mounted, 1/2 C.Y. cap. = 44 C.Y./hr.	B-12E	352	.045			1.52	1.27	2.79	3.94
5660	3/4 C.Y. cap. = 66 C.Y./hr.	B-12F	528	.030			1.01	1.25	2.26	3.07
8000	For hauling excavated material, see Section 31 23 23.20									

31 23 16 – Excavation

31 23 16.46 Excavating, Bulk, Dozer	Crew	Daily Output	Labor-Hours	Unit	Material	2014 Bare Costs Labor	2014 Bare Costs Equipment	Total	Total Incl O&P
0010 **EXCAVATING, BULK, DOZER**									
0011 Open site									
2000 80 H.P., 50' haul, sand & gravel	B-10L	460	.017	B.C.Y.		.65	1.05	1.70	2.23
2010 Sandy clay & loam		440	.018			.68	1.09	1.77	2.33
2020 Common earth		400	.020			.75	1.20	1.95	2.57
2040 Clay		250	.032			1.20	1.92	3.12	4.12
2200 150' haul, sand & gravel		230	.035			1.31	2.09	3.40	4.47
2210 Sandy clay & loam		220	.036			1.37	2.19	3.56	4.67
2220 Common earth		200	.040			1.51	2.41	3.92	5.15
2240 Clay		125	.064			2.41	3.85	6.26	8.20
2400 300' haul, sand & gravel		120	.067			2.51	4.01	6.52	8.55
2440 Clay		65	.123			4.63	7.40	12.03	15.80
3000 105 H.P., 50' haul, sand & gravel	B-10W	700	.011			.43	.85	1.28	1.64
3010 Sandy clay & loam		680	.012			.44	.87	1.31	1.69
3020 Common earth		610	.013			.49	.97	1.46	1.89
3040 Clay		385	.021			.78	1.54	2.32	2.99
3200 150' haul, sand & gravel		310	.026			.97	1.91	2.88	3.71
3210 Sandy clay & loam		300	.027			1	1.97	2.97	3.83
3220 Common earth		270	.030			1.12	2.19	3.31	4.26
3240 Clay		170	.047			1.77	3.48	5.25	6.75
3300 300' haul, sand & gravel		140	.057			2.15	4.23	6.38	8.20
3310 Sandy clay & loam		135	.059			2.23	4.38	6.61	8.50
3320 Common earth		120	.067			2.51	4.93	7.44	9.55
3340 Clay		100	.080			3.01	5.90	8.91	11.50
4000 200 H.P., 50' haul, sand & gravel	B-10B	1400	.006			.22	.95	1.17	1.40
4010 Sandy clay & loam		1360	.006			.22	.97	1.19	1.44
4020 Common earth		1230	.007			.24	1.08	1.32	1.59
4040 Clay		770	.010			.39	1.72	2.11	2.54
4200 150' haul, sand & gravel		595	.013			.51	2.23	2.74	3.29
4210 Sandy clay & loam		580	.014			.52	2.28	2.80	3.37
4220 Common earth		516	.016			.58	2.57	3.15	3.79
4240 Clay		325	.025			.93	4.08	5.01	6.05
4400 300' haul, sand & gravel		310	.026			.97	4.27	5.24	6.30
4410 Sandy clay & loam		300	.027			1	4.42	5.42	6.50
4420 Common earth		270	.030			1.12	4.91	6.03	7.25
4440 Clay		170	.047			1.77	7.80	9.57	11.50
5000 300 H.P., 50' haul, sand & gravel	B-10M	1900	.004			.16	.96	1.12	1.31
5010 Sandy clay & loam		1850	.004			.16	.98	1.14	1.35
5020 Common earth		1650	.005			.18	1.10	1.28	1.51
5040 Clay		1025	.008			.29	1.77	2.06	2.44
5200 150' haul, sand & gravel		920	.009			.33	1.98	2.31	2.71
5210 Sandy clay & loam		895	.009			.34	2.03	2.37	2.79
5220 Common earth		800	.010			.38	2.27	2.65	3.12
5240 Clay		500	.016			.60	3.63	4.23	5
5400 300' haul, sand & gravel		470	.017			.64	3.87	4.51	5.30
5410 Sandy clay & loam		455	.018			.66	3.99	4.65	5.50
5420 Common earth		410	.020			.73	4.43	5.16	6.10
5440 Clay		250	.032			1.20	7.25	8.45	10
5500 460 H.P., 50' haul, sand & gravel	B-10X	1930	.004			.16	1.25	1.41	1.63
5506 Sandy clay & loam		1880	.004			.16	1.28	1.44	1.68
5510 Common earth		1680	.005			.18	1.43	1.61	1.88
5520 Clay		1050	.008			.29	2.29	2.58	3

31 23 16 – Excavation

31 23 16.46 Excavating, Bulk, Dozer

		Crew	Daily Output	Labor-Hours	Unit	Material	2014 Bare Costs Labor	2014 Bare Costs Equipment	Total	Total Incl O&P
5530	150' haul, sand & gravel	B-10X	1290	.006	B.C.Y.		.23	1.87	2.10	2.44
5535	Sandy clay & loam		1250	.006			.24	1.93	2.17	2.52
5540	Common earth		1120	.007			.27	2.15	2.42	2.82
5550	Clay		700	.011			.43	3.44	3.87	4.50
5560	300' haul, sand & gravel		660	.012			.46	3.65	4.11	4.77
5565	Sandy clay & loam		640	.013			.47	3.76	4.23	4.92
5570	Common earth		575	.014			.52	4.19	4.71	5.50
5580	Clay		350	.023			.86	6.90	7.76	9
6000	700 H.P., 50' haul, sand & gravel	B-10V	3500	.002			.09	1.28	1.37	1.55
6006	Sandy clay & loam		3400	.002			.09	1.32	1.41	1.60
6010	Common earth		3035	.003			.10	1.48	1.58	1.79
6020	Clay		1925	.004			.16	2.33	2.49	2.83
6030	150' haul, sand & gravel		2025	.004			.15	2.21	2.36	2.69
6035	Sandy clay & loam		1960	.004			.15	2.29	2.44	2.77
6040	Common earth		1750	.005			.17	2.56	2.73	3.10
6050	Clay		1100	.007			.27	4.08	4.35	4.93
6060	300' haul, sand & gravel		1030	.008			.29	4.36	4.65	5.25
6065	Sandy clay & loam		1005	.008			.30	4.46	4.76	5.40
6070	Common earth		900	.009			.33	4.98	5.31	6.05
6080	Clay		550	.015			.55	8.15	8.70	9.85

31 23 16.50 Excavation, Bulk, Scrapers

			Crew	Daily Output	Labor-Hours	Unit	Material	2014 Bare Costs Labor	2014 Bare Costs Equipment	Total	Total Incl O&P
0010	**EXCAVATION, BULK, SCRAPERS**	R312316-40									
0100	Elev. scraper 11 C.Y., sand & gravel 1500' haul, 1/4 dozer		B-33F	690	.014	B.C.Y.		.55	2.37	2.92	3.50
0150	3000' haul			610	.016			.62	2.68	3.30	3.97
0200	5000' haul			505	.020			.75	3.24	3.99	4.79
0300	Common earth, 1500' haul			600	.017			.63	2.72	3.35	4.04
0350	3000' haul			530	.019			.71	3.08	3.79	4.57
0400	5000' haul			440	.023			.86	3.71	4.57	5.50
0410	Sandy clay & loam, 1500' haul			648	.015			.58	2.52	3.10	3.73
0420	3000' haul			572	.017			.66	2.86	3.52	4.23
0430	5000' haul			475	.021			.79	3.44	4.23	5.10
0500	Clay, 1500' haul			375	.027			1	4.36	5.36	6.45
0550	3000' haul			330	.030			1.14	4.95	6.09	7.35
0600	5000' haul			275	.036			1.37	5.95	7.32	8.80
1000	Self propelled scraper, 14 C.Y. 1/4 push dozer, sand										
1050	Sand and gravel, 1500' haul		B-33D	920	.011	B.C.Y.		.41	2.48	2.89	3.41
1100	3000' haul			805	.012			.47	2.84	3.31	3.89
1200	5000' haul			645	.016			.58	3.54	4.12	4.86
1300	Common earth, 1500' haul			800	.013			.47	2.85	3.32	3.92
1350	3000' haul			700	.014			.54	3.26	3.80	4.48
1400	5000' haul			560	.018			.67	4.08	4.75	5.60
1420	Sandy clay & loam, 1500' haul			864	.012			.44	2.64	3.08	3.63
1430	3000' haul			786	.013			.48	2.90	3.38	3.98
1440	5000' haul			605	.017			.62	3.77	4.39	5.20
1500	Clay, 1500' haul			500	.020			.75	4.57	5.32	6.25
1550	3000' haul			440	.023			.86	5.20	6.06	7.10
1600	5000' haul			350	.029			1.08	6.50	7.58	9
2000	21 C.Y., 1/4 push dozer, sand & gravel, 1500' haul		B-33E	1180	.008			.32	2.59	2.91	3.37
2100	3000' haul			910	.011			.41	3.36	3.77	4.38
2200	5000' haul			750	.013			.50	4.07	4.57	5.30
2300	Common earth, 1500' haul			1030	.010			.37	2.96	3.33	3.87
2350	3000' haul			790	.013			.48	3.87	4.35	5.05

31 23 Excavation and Fill

31 23 16 – Excavation

31 23 16.50 Excavation, Bulk, Scrapers

		Crew	Daily Output	Labor-Hours	Unit	Material	2014 Bare Costs Labor	2014 Bare Costs Equipment	Total	Total Incl O&P
2400	5000' haul	B-33E	650	.015	B.C.Y.		.58	4.70	5.28	6.10
2420	Sandy clay & loam, 1500' haul		1112	.009			.34	2.74	3.08	3.58
2430	3000' haul		854	.012			.44	3.58	4.02	4.66
2440	5000' haul		702	.014			.54	4.35	4.89	5.70
2500	Clay, 1500' haul		645	.016			.58	4.73	5.31	6.15
2550	3000' haul		495	.020			.76	6.15	6.91	8.05
2600	5000' haul		405	.025			.93	7.55	8.48	9.85
2700	Towed, 10 C.Y., 1/4 push dozer, sand & gravel, 1500' haul	B-33B	560	.018			.67	4.31	4.98	5.85
2720	3000' haul		450	.022			.84	5.35	6.19	7.30
2730	5000' haul		365	.027			1.03	6.60	7.63	8.95
2750	Common earth, 1500' haul		420	.024			.90	5.75	6.65	7.80
2770	3000' haul		400	.025			.94	6.05	6.99	8.20
2780	5000' haul		310	.032			1.21	7.80	9.01	10.55
2785	Sandy clay & Loam, 1500' haul		454	.022			.83	5.30	6.13	7.20
2790	3000' haul		432	.023			.87	5.60	6.47	7.60
2795	5000' haul		340	.029			1.11	7.10	8.21	9.65
2800	Clay, 1500' haul		315	.032			1.20	7.65	8.85	10.45
2820	3000' haul		300	.033			1.25	8.05	9.30	10.95
2840	5000' haul		225	.044			1.67	10.70	12.37	14.55
2900	15 C.Y., 1/4 push dozer, sand & gravel, 1500' haul	B-33C	800	.013			.47	3.04	3.51	4.12
2920	3000' haul		640	.016			.59	3.80	4.39	5.15
2940	5000' haul		520	.019			.72	4.67	5.39	6.35
2960	Common earth, 1500' haul		600	.017			.63	4.05	4.68	5.50
2980	3000' haul		560	.018			.67	4.34	5.01	5.90
3000	5000' haul		440	.023			.86	5.50	6.36	7.50
3005	Sandy clay & Loam, 1500' haul		648	.015			.58	3.75	4.33	5.10
3010	3000' haul		605	.017			.62	4.02	4.64	5.45
3015	5000' haul		475	.021			.79	5.10	5.89	6.95
3020	Clay, 1500' haul		450	.022			.84	5.40	6.24	7.35
3040	3000' haul		420	.024			.90	5.80	6.70	7.85
3060	5000' haul		320	.031			1.18	7.60	8.78	10.30

31 23 19 – Dewatering

31 23 19.20 Dewatering Systems

		Crew	Daily Output	Labor-Hours	Unit	Material	2014 Bare Costs Labor	2014 Bare Costs Equipment	Total	Total Incl O&P
0010	**DEWATERING SYSTEMS**									
0020	Excavate drainage trench, 2' wide, 2' deep	B-11C	90	.178	C.Y.		5.85	4.06	9.91	14.20
0100	2' wide, 3' deep, with backhoe loader	"	135	.119			3.90	2.71	6.61	9.50
0200	Excavate sump pits by hand, light soil	1 Clab	7.10	1.127			32		32	53.50
0300	Heavy soil	"	3.50	2.286			64.50		64.50	108
0500	Pumping 8 hr., attended 2 hrs. per day, including 20 L.F.									
0550	of suction hose & 100 L.F. discharge hose									
0601	2" diaphragm pump used for 8 hours	B-94A	4	2	Day		56.50	18.95	75.45	116
0652	4" diaphragm pump used for 8 hours	B-94B	4	2			56.50	31	87.50	129
0801	8 hrs. attended, 2" diaphragm pump	B-94A	1	8			226	76	302	465
0901	3" centrifugal pump	B-10J	1	8			300	84.50	384.50	595
1001	4" diaphragm pump	B-10I	1	8			300	124	424	635
1101	6" centrifugal pump	B-10K	1	8			300	365	665	900
1300	CMP, incl. excavation 3' deep, 12" diameter	B-6	115	.209	L.F.	8.35	6.45	3.18	17.98	23.50
1400	18" diameter		100	.240	"	12.55	7.40	3.65	23.60	30
1600	Sump hole construction, incl. excavation and gravel, pit		1250	.019	C.F.	1.12	.59	.29	2	2.54
1700	With 12" gravel collar, 12" pipe, corrugated, 16 ga.		70	.343	L.F.	21.50	10.60	5.20	37.30	47.50
1800	15" pipe, corrugated, 16 ga.		55	.436		28	13.45	6.65	48.10	60.50
1900	18" pipe, corrugated, 16 ga.		50	.480		32.50	14.80	7.30	54.60	69

31 23 19 – Dewatering

31 23 19.20 Dewatering Systems	Crew	Daily Output	Labor-Hours	Unit	Material	2014 Bare Costs Labor	Equipment	Total	Total Incl O&P
2000	24" pipe, corrugated, 14 ga.	B-6	40	.600	L.F.	39	18.55	9.15	66.70	84
2200	Wood lining, up to 4' x 4', add	↓	300	.080	SFCA	16.25	2.47	1.22	19.94	23.50
9950	See Section 31 23 19.40 for wellpoints									
9960	See Section 31 23 19.30 for deep well systems									

31 23 19.30 Wells

		Crew	Daily Output	Labor-Hours	Unit	Material	Labor	Equipment	Total	Total Incl O&P
0010	**WELLS**									
0011	For dewatering 10' to 20' deep, 2' diameter									
0020	with steel casing, minimum	B-6	165	.145	V.L.F.	38	4.49	2.21	44.70	51.50
0050	Average		98	.245		43	7.55	3.73	54.28	64.50
0100	Maximum	↓	49	.490	↓	48.50	15.15	7.45	71.10	87
0300	For dewatering pumps see 01 54 33 in Reference Section									
0500	For domestic water wells, see Section 33 21 13.10									

31 23 19.40 Wellpoints

		Crew	Daily Output	Labor-Hours	Unit	Material	Labor	Equipment	Total	Total Incl O&P
0010	**WELLPOINTS** R312319-90									
0011	For equipment rental, see 01 54 33 in Reference Section									
0100	Installation and removal of single stage system									
0110	Labor only, .75 labor-hours per L.F.	1 Clab	10.70	.748	LF Hdr		21		21	35.50
0200	2.0 labor-hours per L.F.	"	4	2	"		56.50		56.50	95
0400	Pump operation, 4 @ 6 hr. shifts									
0411	Per 24 hour day	4 Clab	1.27	25.197	Day		710		710	1,200
0501	Per 168 hour week, 160 hr. straight, 8 hr. double time		.18	177	Week		5,025		5,025	8,425
0551	Per 4.3 week month	↓	.04	800	Month		22,600		22,600	38,000
0600	Complete installation, operation, equipment rental, fuel &									
0610	removal of system with 2" wellpoints 5' O.C.									
0700	100' long header, 6" diameter, first month	4 Eqlt	3.23	9.907	LF Hdr	159	360		519	770
0800	Thereafter, per month		4.13	7.748		127	281		408	605
1000	200' long header, 8" diameter, first month		6	5.333		144	193		337	480
1100	Thereafter, per month		8.39	3.814		71.50	138		209.50	310
1300	500' long header, 8" diameter, first month		10.63	3.010		55.50	109		164.50	242
1400	Thereafter, per month		20.91	1.530		40	55.50		95.50	136
1600	1,000' long header, 10" diameter, first month		11.62	2.754		47.50	100		147.50	218
1700	Thereafter, per month	↓	41.81	.765	↓	24	27.50		51.50	72
1900	Note: above figures include pumping 168 hrs. per week									
1910	and include the pump operator and one stand-by pump.									

31 23 23 – Fill

31 23 23.13 Backfill

		Crew	Daily Output	Labor-Hours	Unit	Material	Labor	Equipment	Total	Total Incl O&P
0010	**BACKFILL** R312323-30									
0015	By hand, no compaction, light soil	1 Clab	14	.571	L.C.Y.		16.10		16.10	27
0100	Heavy soil	↓	11	.727	"		20.50		20.50	34.50
0300	Compaction in 6" layers, hand tamp, add to above	↓	20.60	.388	E.C.Y.		10.95		10.95	18.45
0400	Roller compaction operator walking, add	B-10A	100	.080			3.01	1.83	4.84	7
0500	Air tamp, add	B-9D	190	.211			6	1.40	7.40	11.70
0600	Vibrating plate, add	A-1D	60	.133			3.76	.60	4.36	7
0800	Compaction in 12" layers, hand tamp, add to above	1 Clab	34	.235			6.65		6.65	11.15
0900	Roller compaction operator walking, add	B-10A	150	.053			2.01	1.22	3.23	4.67
1000	Air tamp, add	B-9	285	.140			4.01	.82	4.83	7.65
1100	Vibrating plate, add	A-1E	90	.089	↓		2.51	.51	3.02	4.78
1300	Dozer backfilling, bulk, up to 300' haul, no compaction	B-10B	1200	.007	L.C.Y.		.25	1.10	1.35	1.64
1400	Air tamped, add	B-11B	80	.200	E.C.Y.		6.45	3.78	10.23	14.90
1600	Compacting backfill, 6" to 12" lifts, vibrating roller	B-10C	800	.010			.38	2.17	2.55	3.01
1700	Sheepsfoot roller	B-10D	750	.011	↓		.40	2.36	2.76	3.27
1900	Dozer backfilling, trench, up to 300' haul, no compaction	B-10B	900	.009	L.C.Y.		.33	1.47	1.80	2.17

31 23 Excavation and Fill

31 23 23 – Fill

31 23 23.13 Backfill

		Crew	Daily Output	Labor-Hours	Unit	Material	2014 Bare Costs Labor	2014 Bare Costs Equipment	Total	Total Incl O&P
2000	Air tamped, add	B-11B	80	.200	E.C.Y.		6.45	3.78	10.23	14.90
2200	Compacting backfill, 6" to 12" lifts, vibrating roller	B-10C	700	.011			.43	2.48	2.91	3.44
2300	Sheepsfoot roller	B-10D	650	.012	↓		.46	2.72	3.18	3.76

31 23 23.16 Fill By Borrow and Utility Bedding

		Crew	Daily Output	Labor-Hours	Unit	Material	Labor	Equipment	Total	Total Incl O&P
0010	**FILL BY BORROW AND UTILITY BEDDING**									
0015	Fill by borrow, load, 1 mile haul, spread with dozer									
0020	for embankments	B-15	1200	.023	L.C.Y.	12.35	.74	2.26	15.35	17.25
0035	Select fill for shoulders & embankments	"	1200	.023	"	21	.74	2.26	24	26.50
0040	Fill, for hauling over 1 mile, add to above per C.Y., see Section 31 23 23.20				Mile				1.41	1.73
0049	Utility bedding, for pipe & conduit, not incl. compaction									
0050	Crushed or screened bank run gravel	B-6	150	.160	L.C.Y.	25	4.94	2.44	32.38	38.50
0100	Crushed stone 3/4" to 1/2"		150	.160		28.50	4.94	2.44	35.88	42
0200	Sand, dead or bank	↓	150	.160	↓	17.55	4.94	2.44	24.93	30
0500	Compacting bedding in trench	A-1D	90	.089	E.C.Y.		2.51	.40	2.91	4.66
0600	If material source exceeds 2 miles, add for extra mileage.									
0610	See Section 31 23 23.20 for hauling mileage add.									

31 23 23.17 General Fill

		Crew	Daily Output	Labor-Hours	Unit	Material	Labor	Equipment	Total	Total Incl O&P
0010	**GENERAL FILL**									
0011	Spread dumped material, no compaction									
0020	By dozer, no compaction	B-10B	1000	.008	L.C.Y.		.30	1.33	1.63	1.96
0100	By hand	1 Clab	12	.667	"		18.80		18.80	31.50
0500	Gravel fill, compacted, under floor slabs, 4" deep	B-37	10000	.005	S.F.	.42	.14	.02	.58	.72
0600	6" deep		8600	.006		.63	.17	.02	.82	1
0700	9" deep		7200	.007		1.05	.20	.02	1.27	1.51
0800	12" deep		6000	.008	↓	1.48	.24	.03	1.75	2.05
1000	Alternate pricing method, 4" deep		120	.400	E.C.Y.	31.50	11.95	1.32	44.77	56.50
1100	6" deep		160	.300		31.50	8.95	.99	41.44	51
1200	9" deep		200	.240		31.50	7.15	.79	39.44	48
1300	12" deep		220	.218	↓	31.50	6.50	.72	38.72	46.50
1500	For fill under exterior paving, see Section 32 11 23.23									

31 23 23.20 Hauling

		Crew	Daily Output	Labor-Hours	Unit	Material	Labor	Equipment	Total	Total Incl O&P
0010	**HAULING**									
0011	Excavated or borrow, loose cubic yards									
0012	no loading equipment, including hauling, waiting, loading/dumping									
0013	time per cycle (wait, load, travel, unload or dump & return)									
0014	8 C.Y. truck, 15 MPH ave, cycle 0.5 miles, 10 min. wait/Ld./Uld.	B-34A	320	.025	L.C.Y.		.74	1.30	2.04	2.67
0016	cycle 1 mile		272	.029			.87	1.53	2.40	3.14
0018	cycle 2 miles		208	.038			1.14	2.01	3.15	4.11
0020	cycle 4 miles		144	.056			1.65	2.90	4.55	5.95
0022	cycle 6 miles		112	.071			2.12	3.73	5.85	7.65
0024	cycle 8 miles		88	.091			2.70	4.74	7.44	9.70
0026	20 MPH ave, cycle 0.5 mile		336	.024			.71	1.24	1.95	2.55
0028	cycle 1 mile		296	.027			.80	1.41	2.21	2.89
0030	cycle 2 miles		240	.033			.99	1.74	2.73	3.56
0032	cycle 4 miles		176	.045			1.35	2.37	3.72	4.86
0034	cycle 6 miles		136	.059			1.74	3.07	4.81	6.30
0036	cycle 8 miles		112	.071			2.12	3.73	5.85	7.65
0044	25 MPH ave, cycle 4 miles		192	.042			1.24	2.17	3.41	4.45
0046	cycle 6 miles		160	.050			1.48	2.61	4.09	5.35
0048	cycle 8 miles		128	.063			1.85	3.26	5.11	6.70
0050	30 MPH ave, cycle 4 miles		216	.037			1.10	1.93	3.03	3.96
0052	cycle 6 miles	↓	176	.045	↓		1.35	2.37	3.72	4.86

31 23 23 – Fill

31 23 23.20 Hauling	Crew	Daily Output	Labor-Hours	Unit	Material	2014 Bare Costs Labor	2014 Bare Costs Equipment	Total	Total Incl O&P
0054	cycle 8 miles	B-34A	144	.056	L.C.Y.		1.65	2.90	4.55	5.95
0114	15 MPH ave, cycle 0.5 mile, 15 min. wait/Ld./Uld.		224	.036			1.06	1.86	2.92	3.81
0116	cycle 1 mile		200	.040			1.19	2.09	3.28	4.27
0118	cycle 2 miles		168	.048			1.41	2.48	3.89	5.10
0120	cycle 4 miles		120	.067			1.98	3.48	5.46	7.10
0122	cycle 6 miles		96	.083			2.47	4.35	6.82	8.90
0124	cycle 8 miles		80	.100			2.97	5.20	8.17	10.70
0126	20 MPH ave, cycle 0.5 mile		232	.034			1.02	1.80	2.82	3.68
0128	cycle 1 mile		208	.038			1.14	2.01	3.15	4.11
0130	cycle 2 miles		184	.043			1.29	2.27	3.56	4.64
0132	cycle 4 miles		144	.056			1.65	2.90	4.55	5.95
0134	cycle 6 miles		112	.071			2.12	3.73	5.85	7.65
0136	cycle 8 miles		96	.083			2.47	4.35	6.82	8.90
0144	25 MPH ave, cycle 4 miles		152	.053			1.56	2.74	4.30	5.60
0146	cycle 6 miles		128	.063			1.85	3.26	5.11	6.70
0148	cycle 8 miles		112	.071			2.12	3.73	5.85	7.65
0150	30 MPH ave, cycle 4 miles		168	.048			1.41	2.48	3.89	5.10
0152	cycle 6 miles		144	.056			1.65	2.90	4.55	5.95
0154	cycle 8 miles		120	.067			1.98	3.48	5.46	7.10
0214	15 MPH ave, cycle 0.5 mile, 20 min wait/Ld./Uld.		176	.045			1.35	2.37	3.72	4.86
0216	cycle 1 mile		160	.050			1.48	2.61	4.09	5.35
0218	cycle 2 miles		136	.059			1.74	3.07	4.81	6.30
0220	cycle 4 miles		104	.077			2.28	4.01	6.29	8.20
0222	cycle 6 miles		88	.091			2.70	4.74	7.44	9.70
0224	cycle 8 miles		72	.111			3.29	5.80	9.09	11.85
0226	20 MPH ave, cycle 0.5 mile		176	.045			1.35	2.37	3.72	4.86
0228	cycle 1 mile		168	.048			1.41	2.48	3.89	5.10
0230	cycle 2 miles		144	.056			1.65	2.90	4.55	5.95
0232	cycle 4 miles		120	.067			1.98	3.48	5.46	7.10
0234	cycle 6 miles		96	.083			2.47	4.35	6.82	8.90
0236	cycle 8 miles		88	.091			2.70	4.74	7.44	9.70
0244	25 MPH ave, cycle 4 miles		128	.063			1.85	3.26	5.11	6.70
0246	cycle 6 miles		112	.071			2.12	3.73	5.85	7.65
0248	cycle 8 miles		96	.083			2.47	4.35	6.82	8.90
0250	30 MPH ave, cycle 4 miles		136	.059			1.74	3.07	4.81	6.30
0252	cycle 6 miles		120	.067			1.98	3.48	5.46	7.10
0254	cycle 8 miles		104	.077			2.28	4.01	6.29	8.20
0314	15 MPH ave, cycle 0.5 mile, 25 min wait/Ld./Uld.		144	.056			1.65	2.90	4.55	5.95
0316	cycle 1 mile		128	.063			1.85	3.26	5.11	6.70
0318	cycle 2 miles		112	.071			2.12	3.73	5.85	7.65
0320	cycle 4 miles		96	.083			2.47	4.35	6.82	8.90
0322	cycle 6 miles		80	.100			2.97	5.20	8.17	10.70
0324	cycle 8 miles		64	.125			3.71	6.50	10.21	13.35
0326	20 MPH ave, cycle 0.5 mile		144	.056			1.65	2.90	4.55	5.95
0328	cycle 1 mile		136	.059			1.74	3.07	4.81	6.30
0330	cycle 2 miles		120	.067			1.98	3.48	5.46	7.10
0332	cycle 4 miles		104	.077			2.28	4.01	6.29	8.20
0334	cycle 6 miles		88	.091			2.70	4.74	7.44	9.70
0336	cycle 8 miles		80	.100			2.97	5.20	8.17	10.70
0344	25 MPH ave, cycle 4 miles		112	.071			2.12	3.73	5.85	7.65
0346	cycle 6 miles		96	.083			2.47	4.35	6.82	8.90
0348	cycle 8 miles		88	.091			2.70	4.74	7.44	9.70
0350	30 MPH ave, cycle 4 miles		112	.071			2.12	3.73	5.85	7.65

31 23 23 – Fill

31 23 23.20 Hauling		Crew	Daily Output	Labor-Hours	Unit	Material	2014 Bare Costs Labor	2014 Bare Costs Equipment	Total	Total Incl O&P
0352	cycle 6 miles	B-34A	104	.077	L.C.Y.		2.28	4.01	6.29	8.20
0354	cycle 8 miles		96	.083			2.47	4.35	6.82	8.90
0414	15 MPH ave, cycle 0.5 mile, 30 min wait/Ld./Uld.		120	.067			1.98	3.48	5.46	7.10
0416	cycle 1 mile		112	.071			2.12	3.73	5.85	7.65
0418	cycle 2 miles		96	.083			2.47	4.35	6.82	8.90
0420	cycle 4 miles		80	.100			2.97	5.20	8.17	10.70
0422	cycle 6 miles		72	.111			3.29	5.80	9.09	11.85
0424	cycle 8 miles		64	.125			3.71	6.50	10.21	13.35
0426	20 MPH ave, cycle 0.5 mile		120	.067			1.98	3.48	5.46	7.10
0428	cycle 1 mile		112	.071			2.12	3.73	5.85	7.65
0430	cycle 2 miles		104	.077			2.28	4.01	6.29	8.20
0432	cycle 4 miles		88	.091			2.70	4.74	7.44	9.70
0434	cycle 6 miles		80	.100			2.97	5.20	8.17	10.70
0436	cycle 8 miles		72	.111			3.29	5.80	9.09	11.85
0444	25 MPH ave, cycle 4 miles		96	.083			2.47	4.35	6.82	8.90
0446	cycle 6 miles		88	.091			2.70	4.74	7.44	9.70
0448	cycle 8 miles		80	.100			2.97	5.20	8.17	10.70
0450	30 MPH ave, cycle 4 miles		96	.083			2.47	4.35	6.82	8.90
0452	cycle 6 miles		88	.091			2.70	4.74	7.44	9.70
0454	cycle 8 miles		80	.100			2.97	5.20	8.17	10.70
0514	15 MPH ave, cycle 0.5 mile, 35 min wait/Ld./Uld.		104	.077			2.28	4.01	6.29	8.20
0516	cycle 1 mile		96	.083			2.47	4.35	6.82	8.90
0518	cycle 2 miles		88	.091			2.70	4.74	7.44	9.70
0520	cycle 4 miles		72	.111			3.29	5.80	9.09	11.85
0522	cycle 6 miles		64	.125			3.71	6.50	10.21	13.35
0524	cycle 8 miles		56	.143			4.24	7.45	11.69	15.25
0526	20 MPH ave, cycle 0.5 mile		104	.077			2.28	4.01	6.29	8.20
0528	cycle 1 mile		96	.083			2.47	4.35	6.82	8.90
0530	cycle 2 miles		96	.083			2.47	4.35	6.82	8.90
0532	cycle 4 miles		80	.100			2.97	5.20	8.17	10.70
0534	cycle 6 miles		72	.111			3.29	5.80	9.09	11.85
0536	cycle 8 miles		64	.125			3.71	6.50	10.21	13.35
0544	25 MPH ave, cycle 4 miles		88	.091			2.70	4.74	7.44	9.70
0546	cycle 6 miles		80	.100			2.97	5.20	8.17	10.70
0548	cycle 8 miles		72	.111			3.29	5.80	9.09	11.85
0550	30 MPH ave, cycle 4 miles		88	.091			2.70	4.74	7.44	9.70
0552	cycle 6 miles		80	.100			2.97	5.20	8.17	10.70
0554	cycle 8 miles		72	.111			3.29	5.80	9.09	11.85
1014	12 C.Y. truck, cycle 0.5 mile, 15 MPH ave, 15 min. wait/Ld./Uld.	B-34B	336	.024			.71	2.06	2.77	3.45
1016	cycle 1 mile		300	.027			.79	2.31	3.10	3.86
1018	cycle 2 miles		252	.032			.94	2.75	3.69	4.59
1020	cycle 4 miles		180	.044			1.32	3.85	5.17	6.45
1022	cycle 6 miles		144	.056			1.65	4.81	6.46	8.05
1024	cycle 8 miles		120	.067			1.98	5.75	7.73	9.65
1025	cycle 10 miles		96	.083			2.47	7.20	9.67	12.05
1026	20 MPH ave, cycle 0.5 mile		348	.023			.68	1.99	2.67	3.33
1028	cycle 1 mile		312	.026			.76	2.22	2.98	3.71
1030	cycle 2 miles		276	.029			.86	2.51	3.37	4.19
1032	cycle 4 miles		216	.037			1.10	3.21	4.31	5.35
1034	cycle 6 miles		168	.048			1.41	4.12	5.53	6.90
1036	cycle 8 miles		144	.056			1.65	4.81	6.46	8.05
1038	cycle 10 miles		120	.067			1.98	5.75	7.73	9.65
1040	25 MPH ave, cycle 4 miles		228	.035			1.04	3.04	4.08	5.05

31 23 23 – Fill

31 23 23.20 Hauling	Crew	Daily Output	Labor-Hours	Unit	Material	2014 Bare Costs		Total	Total Incl O&P
						Labor	Equipment		
1042	cycle 6 miles	B-34B	192	.042	L.C.Y.		1.24	3.61	4.85	6.05
1044	cycle 8 miles		168	.048			1.41	4.12	5.53	6.90
1046	cycle 10 miles		144	.056			1.65	4.81	6.46	8.05
1050	30 MPH ave, cycle 4 miles		252	.032			.94	2.75	3.69	4.59
1052	cycle 6 miles		216	.037			1.10	3.21	4.31	5.35
1054	cycle 8 miles		180	.044			1.32	3.85	5.17	6.45
1056	cycle 10 miles		156	.051			1.52	4.44	5.96	7.40
1060	35 MPH ave, cycle 4 miles		264	.030			.90	2.62	3.52	4.38
1062	cycle 6 miles		228	.035			1.04	3.04	4.08	5.05
1064	cycle 8 miles		204	.039			1.16	3.39	4.55	5.65
1066	cycle 10 miles		180	.044			1.32	3.85	5.17	6.45
1068	cycle 20 miles		120	.067			1.98	5.75	7.73	9.65
1069	cycle 30 miles		84	.095			2.82	8.25	11.07	13.75
1070	cycle 40 miles		72	.111			3.29	9.60	12.89	16.10
1072	40 MPH ave, cycle 6 miles		240	.033			.99	2.88	3.87	4.82
1074	cycle 8 miles		216	.037			1.10	3.21	4.31	5.35
1076	cycle 10 miles		192	.042			1.24	3.61	4.85	6.05
1078	cycle 20 miles		120	.067			1.98	5.75	7.73	9.65
1080	cycle 30 miles		96	.083			2.47	7.20	9.67	12.05
1082	cycle 40 miles		72	.111			3.29	9.60	12.89	16.10
1084	cycle 50 miles		60	.133			3.95	11.55	15.50	19.30
1094	45 MPH ave, cycle 8 miles		216	.037			1.10	3.21	4.31	5.35
1096	cycle 10 miles		204	.039			1.16	3.39	4.55	5.65
1098	cycle 20 miles		132	.061			1.80	5.25	7.05	8.75
1100	cycle 30 miles		108	.074			2.20	6.40	8.60	10.70
1102	cycle 40 miles		84	.095			2.82	8.25	11.07	13.75
1104	cycle 50 miles		72	.111			3.29	9.60	12.89	16.10
1106	50 MPH ave, cycle 10 miles		216	.037			1.10	3.21	4.31	5.35
1108	cycle 20 miles		144	.056			1.65	4.81	6.46	8.05
1110	cycle 30 miles		108	.074			2.20	6.40	8.60	10.70
1112	cycle 40 miles		84	.095			2.82	8.25	11.07	13.75
1114	cycle 50 miles		72	.111			3.29	9.60	12.89	16.10
1214	15 MPH ave, cycle 0.5 mile, 20 min. wait/Ld./Uld.		264	.030			.90	2.62	3.52	4.38
1216	cycle 1 mile		240	.033			.99	2.88	3.87	4.82
1218	cycle 2 miles		204	.039			1.16	3.39	4.55	5.65
1220	cycle 4 miles		156	.051			1.52	4.44	5.96	7.40
1222	cycle 6 miles		132	.061			1.80	5.25	7.05	8.75
1224	cycle 8 miles		108	.074			2.20	6.40	8.60	10.70
1225	cycle 10 miles		96	.083			2.47	7.20	9.67	12.05
1226	20 MPH ave, cycle 0.5 mile		264	.030			.90	2.62	3.52	4.38
1228	cycle 1 mile		252	.032			.94	2.75	3.69	4.59
1230	cycle 2 miles		216	.037			1.10	3.21	4.31	5.35
1232	cycle 4 miles		180	.044			1.32	3.85	5.17	6.45
1234	cycle 6 miles		144	.056			1.65	4.81	6.46	8.05
1236	cycle 8 miles		132	.061			1.80	5.25	7.05	8.75
1238	cycle 10 miles		108	.074			2.20	6.40	8.60	10.70
1240	25 MPH ave, cycle 4 miles		192	.042			1.24	3.61	4.85	6.05
1242	cycle 6 miles		168	.048			1.41	4.12	5.53	6.90
1244	cycle 8 miles		144	.056			1.65	4.81	6.46	8.05
1246	cycle 10 miles		132	.061			1.80	5.25	7.05	8.75
1250	30 MPH ave, cycle 4 miles		204	.039			1.16	3.39	4.55	5.65
1252	cycle 6 miles		180	.044			1.32	3.85	5.17	6.45
1254	cycle 8 miles		156	.051			1.52	4.44	5.96	7.40

31 23 23.20 Hauling		Crew	Daily Output	Labor-Hours	Unit	Material	2014 Bare Costs			Total Incl O&P
							Labor	Equipment	Total	
1256	cycle 10 miles	B-34B	144	.056	L.C.Y.		1.65	4.81	6.46	8.05
1260	35 MPH ave, cycle 4 miles		216	.037			1.10	3.21	4.31	5.35
1262	cycle 6 miles		192	.042			1.24	3.61	4.85	6.05
1264	cycle 8 miles		168	.048			1.41	4.12	5.53	6.90
1266	cycle 10 miles		156	.051			1.52	4.44	5.96	7.40
1268	cycle 20 miles		108	.074			2.20	6.40	8.60	10.70
1269	cycle 30 miles		72	.111			3.29	9.60	12.89	16.10
1270	cycle 40 miles		60	.133			3.95	11.55	15.50	19.30
1272	40 MPH ave, cycle 6 miles		192	.042			1.24	3.61	4.85	6.05
1274	cycle 8 miles		180	.044			1.32	3.85	5.17	6.45
1276	cycle 10 miles		156	.051			1.52	4.44	5.96	7.40
1278	cycle 20 miles		108	.074			2.20	6.40	8.60	10.70
1280	cycle 30 miles		84	.095			2.82	8.25	11.07	13.75
1282	cycle 40 miles		72	.111			3.29	9.60	12.89	16.10
1284	cycle 50 miles		60	.133			3.95	11.55	15.50	19.30
1294	45 MPH ave, cycle 8 miles		180	.044			1.32	3.85	5.17	6.45
1296	cycle 10 miles		168	.048			1.41	4.12	5.53	6.90
1298	cycle 20 miles		120	.067			1.98	5.75	7.73	9.65
1300	cycle 30 miles		96	.083			2.47	7.20	9.67	12.05
1302	cycle 40 miles		72	.111			3.29	9.60	12.89	16.10
1304	cycle 50 miles		60	.133			3.95	11.55	15.50	19.30
1306	50 MPH ave, cycle 10 miles		180	.044			1.32	3.85	5.17	6.45
1308	cycle 20 miles		132	.061			1.80	5.25	7.05	8.75
1310	cycle 30 miles		96	.083			2.47	7.20	9.67	12.05
1312	cycle 40 miles		84	.095			2.82	8.25	11.07	13.75
1314	cycle 50 miles		72	.111			3.29	9.60	12.89	16.10
1414	15 MPH ave, cycle 0.5 mile, 25 min. wait/Ld./Uld.		204	.039			1.16	3.39	4.55	5.65
1416	cycle 1 mile		192	.042			1.24	3.61	4.85	6.05
1418	cycle 2 miles		168	.048			1.41	4.12	5.53	6.90
1420	cycle 4 miles		132	.061			1.80	5.25	7.05	8.75
1422	cycle 6 miles		120	.067			1.98	5.75	7.73	9.65
1424	cycle 8 miles		96	.083			2.47	7.20	9.67	12.05
1425	cycle 10 miles		84	.095			2.82	8.25	11.07	13.75
1426	20 MPH ave, cycle 0.5 mile		216	.037			1.10	3.21	4.31	5.35
1428	cycle 1 mile		204	.039			1.16	3.39	4.55	5.65
1430	cycle 2 miles		180	.044			1.32	3.85	5.17	6.45
1432	cycle 4 miles		156	.051			1.52	4.44	5.96	7.40
1434	cycle 6 miles		132	.061			1.80	5.25	7.05	8.75
1436	cycle 8 miles		120	.067			1.98	5.75	7.73	9.65
1438	cycle 10 miles		96	.083			2.47	7.20	9.67	12.05
1440	25 MPH ave, cycle 4 miles		168	.048			1.41	4.12	5.53	6.90
1442	cycle 6 miles		144	.056			1.65	4.81	6.46	8.05
1444	cycle 8 miles		132	.061			1.80	5.25	7.05	8.75
1446	cycle 10 miles		108	.074			2.20	6.40	8.60	10.70
1450	30 MPH ave, cycle 4 miles		168	.048			1.41	4.12	5.53	6.90
1452	cycle 6 miles		156	.051			1.52	4.44	5.96	7.40
1454	cycle 8 miles		132	.061			1.80	5.25	7.05	8.75
1456	cycle 10 miles		120	.067			1.98	5.75	7.73	9.65
1460	35 MPH ave, cycle 4 miles		180	.044			1.32	3.85	5.17	6.45
1462	cycle 6 miles		156	.051			1.52	4.44	5.96	7.40
1464	cycle 8 miles		144	.056			1.65	4.81	6.46	8.05
1466	cycle 10 miles		132	.061			1.80	5.25	7.05	8.75
1468	cycle 20 miles		96	.083			2.47	7.20	9.67	12.05

31 23 23.20 **Hauling**	Crew	Daily Output	Labor-Hours	Unit	Material	2014 Bare Costs Labor	Equipment	Total	Total Incl O&P
9080	cycle 20 miles	B-34I	180	.044	L.C.Y.		1.32	4.82	6.14	7.50
9082	cycle 30 miles		144	.056			1.65	6.05	7.70	9.40
9084	cycle 40 miles		108	.074			2.20	8.05	10.25	12.50
9086	cycle 50 miles		90	.089			2.64	9.65	12.29	15
9094	45 MPH ave, cycle 8 miles		324	.025			.73	2.68	3.41	4.17
9096	cycle 10 miles		306	.026			.78	2.83	3.61	4.41
9098	cycle 20 miles		198	.040			1.20	4.38	5.58	6.80
9100	cycle 30 miles		144	.056			1.65	6.05	7.70	9.40
9102	cycle 40 miles		126	.063			1.88	6.90	8.78	10.70
9104	cycle 50 miles		108	.074			2.20	8.05	10.25	12.50
9106	50 MPH ave, cycle 10 miles		324	.025			.73	2.68	3.41	4.17
9108	cycle 20 miles		216	.037			1.10	4.02	5.12	6.25
9110	cycle 30 miles		162	.049			1.46	5.35	6.81	8.35
9112	cycle 40 miles		126	.063			1.88	6.90	8.78	10.70
9114	cycle 50 miles		108	.074			2.20	8.05	10.25	12.50
9214	20 min. wait/Ld./Uld.,15 MPH, cycle 0.5 mi.		396	.020			.60	2.19	2.79	3.41
9216	cycle 1 mile		360	.022			.66	2.41	3.07	3.75
9218	cycle 2 miles		306	.026			.78	2.83	3.61	4.41
9220	cycle 4 miles		234	.034			1.01	3.71	4.72	5.75
9222	cycle 6 miles		198	.040			1.20	4.38	5.58	6.80
9224	cycle 8 miles		162	.049			1.46	5.35	6.81	8.35
9225	cycle 10 miles		144	.056			1.65	6.05	7.70	9.40
9226	20 MPH ave, cycle 0.5 mile		396	.020			.60	2.19	2.79	3.41
9228	cycle 1 mile		378	.021			.63	2.29	2.92	3.57
9230	cycle 2 miles		324	.025			.73	2.68	3.41	4.17
9232	cycle 4 miles		270	.030			.88	3.21	4.09	4.99
9234	cycle 6 miles		216	.037			1.10	4.02	5.12	6.25
9236	cycle 8 miles		198	.040			1.20	4.38	5.58	6.80
9238	cycle 10 miles		162	.049			1.46	5.35	6.81	8.35
9240	25 MPH ave, cycle 4 miles		288	.028			.82	3.01	3.83	4.68
9242	cycle 6 miles		252	.032			.94	3.44	4.38	5.35
9244	cycle 8 miles		216	.037			1.10	4.02	5.12	6.25
9246	cycle 10 miles		198	.040			1.20	4.38	5.58	6.80
9250	30 MPH ave, cycle 4 miles		306	.026			.78	2.83	3.61	4.41
9252	cycle 6 miles		270	.030			.88	3.21	4.09	4.99
9254	cycle 8 miles		234	.034			1.01	3.71	4.72	5.75
9256	cycle 10 miles		216	.037			1.10	4.02	5.12	6.25
9260	35 MPH ave, cycle 4 miles		324	.025			.73	2.68	3.41	4.17
9262	cycle 6 miles		288	.028			.82	3.01	3.83	4.68
9264	cycle 8 miles		252	.032			.94	3.44	4.38	5.35
9266	cycle 10 miles		234	.034			1.01	3.71	4.72	5.75
9268	cycle 20 miles		162	.049			1.46	5.35	6.81	8.35
9270	cycle 30 miles		108	.074			2.20	8.05	10.25	12.50
9272	cycle 40 miles		90	.089			2.64	9.65	12.29	15
9274	40 MPH ave, cycle 6 miles		288	.028			.82	3.01	3.83	4.68
9276	cycle 8 miles		270	.030			.88	3.21	4.09	4.99
9278	cycle 10 miles		234	.034			1.01	3.71	4.72	5.75
9280	cycle 20 miles		162	.049			1.46	5.35	6.81	8.35
9282	cycle 30 miles		126	.063			1.88	6.90	8.78	10.70
9284	cycle 40 miles		108	.074			2.20	8.05	10.25	12.50
9286	cycle 50 miles		90	.089			2.64	9.65	12.29	15
9294	45 MPH ave, cycle 8 miles		270	.030			.88	3.21	4.09	4.99
9296	cycle 10 miles		252	.032			.94	3.44	4.38	5.35

31 23 23.20 Hauling	Crew	Daily Output	Labor-Hours	Unit	Material	2014 Bare Costs Labor	2014 Bare Costs Equipment	Total	Total Incl O&P
9298	cycle 20 miles	B-34I	180	.044	L.C.Y.		1.32	4.82	6.14	7.50
9300	cycle 30 miles		144	.056			1.65	6.05	7.70	9.40
9302	cycle 40 miles		108	.074			2.20	8.05	10.25	12.50
9304	cycle 50 miles		90	.089			2.64	9.65	12.29	15
9306	50 MPH ave, cycle 10 miles		270	.030			.88	3.21	4.09	4.99
9308	cycle 20 miles		198	.040			1.20	4.38	5.58	6.80
9310	cycle 30 miles		144	.056			1.65	6.05	7.70	9.40
9312	cycle 40 miles		126	.063			1.88	6.90	8.78	10.70
9314	cycle 50 miles		108	.074			2.20	8.05	10.25	12.50
9414	25 min. wait/Ld./Uld.,15 MPH, cycle 0.5 mi.		306	.026			.78	2.83	3.61	4.41
9416	cycle 1 mile		288	.028			.82	3.01	3.83	4.68
9418	cycle 2 miles		252	.032			.94	3.44	4.38	5.35
9420	cycle 4 miles		198	.040			1.20	4.38	5.58	6.80
9422	cycle 6 miles		180	.044			1.32	4.82	6.14	7.50
9424	cycle 8 miles		144	.056			1.65	6.05	7.70	9.40
9425	cycle 10 miles		126	.063			1.88	6.90	8.78	10.70
9426	20 MPH ave, cycle 0.5 mile		324	.025			.73	2.68	3.41	4.17
9428	cycle 1 mile		306	.026			.78	2.83	3.61	4.41
9430	cycle 2 miles		270	.030			.88	3.21	4.09	4.99
9432	cycle 4 miles		234	.034			1.01	3.71	4.72	5.75
9434	cycle 6 miles		198	.040			1.20	4.38	5.58	6.80
9436	cycle 8 miles		180	.044			1.32	4.82	6.14	7.50
9438	cycle 10 miles		144	.056			1.65	6.05	7.70	9.40
9440	25 MPH ave, cycle 4 miles		252	.032			.94	3.44	4.38	5.35
9442	cycle 6 miles		216	.037			1.10	4.02	5.12	6.25
9444	cycle 8 miles		198	.040			1.20	4.38	5.58	6.80
9446	cycle 10 miles		180	.044			1.32	4.82	6.14	7.50
9450	30 MPH ave, cycle 4 miles		252	.032			.94	3.44	4.38	5.35
9452	cycle 6 miles		234	.034			1.01	3.71	4.72	5.75
9454	cycle 8 miles		198	.040			1.20	4.38	5.58	6.80
9456	cycle 10 miles		180	.044			1.32	4.82	6.14	7.50
9460	35 MPH ave, cycle 4 miles		270	.030			.88	3.21	4.09	4.99
9462	cycle 6 miles		234	.034			1.01	3.71	4.72	5.75
9464	cycle 8 miles		216	.037			1.10	4.02	5.12	6.25
9466	cycle 10 miles		198	.040			1.20	4.38	5.58	6.80
9468	cycle 20 miles		144	.056			1.65	6.05	7.70	9.40
9470	cycle 30 miles		108	.074			2.20	8.05	10.25	12.50
9472	cycle 40 miles		90	.089			2.64	9.65	12.29	15
9474	40 MPH ave, cycle 6 miles		252	.032			.94	3.44	4.38	5.35
9476	cycle 8 miles		234	.034			1.01	3.71	4.72	5.75
9478	cycle 10 miles		216	.037			1.10	4.02	5.12	6.25
9480	cycle 20 miles		144	.056			1.65	6.05	7.70	9.40
9482	cycle 30 miles		126	.063			1.88	6.90	8.78	10.70
9484	cycle 40 miles		90	.089			2.64	9.65	12.29	15
9486	cycle 50 miles		90	.089			2.64	9.65	12.29	15
9494	45 MPH ave, cycle 8 miles		234	.034			1.01	3.71	4.72	5.75
9496	cycle 10 miles		216	.037			1.10	4.02	5.12	6.25
9498	cycle 20 miles		162	.049			1.46	5.35	6.81	8.35
9500	cycle 30 miles		126	.063			1.88	6.90	8.78	10.70
9502	cycle 40 miles		108	.074			2.20	8.05	10.25	12.50
9504	cycle 50 miles		90	.089			2.64	9.65	12.29	15
9506	50 MPH ave, cycle 10 miles		234	.034			1.01	3.71	4.72	5.75
9508	cycle 20 miles		180	.044			1.32	4.82	6.14	7.50

31 23 23 – Fill

31 23 23.20 Hauling		Crew	Daily Output	Labor-Hours	Unit	Material	2014 Bare Costs Labor	Equipment	Total	Total Incl O&P
9510	cycle 30 miles	B-34I	144	.056	L.C.Y.		1.65	6.05	7.70	9.40
9512	cycle 40 miles		108	.074			2.20	8.05	10.25	12.50
9514	cycle 50 miles		90	.089			2.64	9.65	12.29	15
9614	30 min. wait/Ld./Uld.,15 MPH, cycle 0.5 mi.		270	.030			.88	3.21	4.09	4.99
9616	cycle 1 mile		252	.032			.94	3.44	4.38	5.35
9618	cycle 2 miles		216	.037			1.10	4.02	5.12	6.25
9620	cycle 4 miles		180	.044			1.32	4.82	6.14	7.50
9622	cycle 6 miles		162	.049			1.46	5.35	6.81	8.35
9624	cycle 8 miles		126	.063			1.88	6.90	8.78	10.70
9625	cycle 10 miles		126	.063			1.88	6.90	8.78	10.70
9626	20 MPH ave, cycle 0.5 mile		270	.030			.88	3.21	4.09	4.99
9628	cycle 1 mile		252	.032			.94	3.44	4.38	5.35
9630	cycle 2 miles		234	.034			1.01	3.71	4.72	5.75
9632	cycle 4 miles		198	.040			1.20	4.38	5.58	6.80
9634	cycle 6 miles		180	.044			1.32	4.82	6.14	7.50
9636	cycle 8 miles		162	.049			1.46	5.35	6.81	8.35
9638	cycle 10 miles		144	.056			1.65	6.05	7.70	9.40
9640	25 MPH ave, cycle 4 miles		216	.037			1.10	4.02	5.12	6.25
9642	cycle 6 miles		198	.040			1.20	4.38	5.58	6.80
9644	cycle 8 miles		180	.044			1.32	4.82	6.14	7.50
9646	cycle 10 miles		162	.049			1.46	5.35	6.81	8.35
9650	30 MPH ave, cycle 4 miles		216	.037			1.10	4.02	5.12	6.25
9652	cycle 6 miles		198	.040			1.20	4.38	5.58	6.80
9654	cycle 8 miles		180	.044			1.32	4.82	6.14	7.50
9656	cycle 10 miles		162	.049			1.46	5.35	6.81	8.35
9660	35 MPH ave, cycle 4 miles		234	.034			1.01	3.71	4.72	5.75
9662	cycle 6 miles		216	.037			1.10	4.02	5.12	6.25
9664	cycle 8 miles		198	.040			1.20	4.38	5.58	6.80
9666	cycle 10 miles		180	.044			1.32	4.82	6.14	7.50
9668	cycle 20 miles		126	.063			1.88	6.90	8.78	10.70
9670	cycle 30 miles		108	.074			2.20	8.05	10.25	12.50
9672	cycle 40 miles		90	.089			2.64	9.65	12.29	15
9674	40 MPH ave, cycle 6 miles		216	.037			1.10	4.02	5.12	6.25
9676	cycle 8 miles		198	.040			1.20	4.38	5.58	6.80
9678	cycle 10 miles		180	.044			1.32	4.82	6.14	7.50
9680	cycle 20 miles		144	.056			1.65	6.05	7.70	9.40
9682	cycle 30 miles		108	.074			2.20	8.05	10.25	12.50
9684	cycle 40 miles		90	.089			2.64	9.65	12.29	15
9686	cycle 50 miles		72	.111			3.29	12.05	15.34	18.75
9694	45 MPH ave, cycle 8 miles		216	.037			1.10	4.02	5.12	6.25
9696	cycle 10 miles		198	.040			1.20	4.38	5.58	6.80
9698	cycle 20 miles		144	.056			1.65	6.05	7.70	9.40
9700	cycle 30 miles		126	.063			1.88	6.90	8.78	10.70
9702	cycle 40 miles		108	.074			2.20	8.05	10.25	12.50
9704	cycle 50 miles		90	.089			2.64	9.65	12.29	15
9706	50 MPH ave, cycle 10 miles		198	.040			1.20	4.38	5.58	6.80
9708	cycle 20 miles		162	.049			1.46	5.35	6.81	8.35
9710	cycle 30 miles		126	.063			1.88	6.90	8.78	10.70
9712	cycle 40 miles		108	.074			2.20	8.05	10.25	12.50
9714	cycle 50 miles		90	.089			2.64	9.65	12.29	15

31 23 Excavation and Fill

31 23 23 – Fill

31 23 23.24 Compaction, Structural		Crew	Daily Output	Labor-Hours	Unit	Material	2014 Bare Costs Labor	Equipment	Total	Total Incl O&P
0010	**COMPACTION, STRUCTURAL**	R312323-30								
0020	Steel wheel tandem roller, 5 tons	B-10E	8	1	Hr.		37.50	19.90	57.40	84.50
0100	10 tons	B-10F	8	1	"		37.50	30.50	68	96
0300	Sheepsfoot or wobbly wheel roller, 8" lifts, common fill	B-10G	1300	.006	E.C.Y.		.23	.94	1.17	1.41
0400	Select fill	"	1500	.005			.20	.81	1.01	1.22
0600	Vibratory plate, 8" lifts, common fill	A-1D	200	.040			1.13	.18	1.31	2.10
0700	Select fill	"	216	.037	↓		1.04	.17	1.21	1.94

31 25 Erosion and Sedimentation Controls

31 25 14 – Stabilization Measures for Erosion and Sedimentation Control

31 25 14.16 Rolled Erosion Control Mats and Blankets

			Crew	Daily Output	Labor-Hours	Unit	Material	Labor	Equipment	Total	Total Incl O&P
0010	**ROLLED EROSION CONTROL MATS AND BLANKETS**										
0020	Jute mesh, 100 S.Y. per roll, 4' wide, stapled	G	B-80A	2400	.010	S.Y.	1.11	.28	.14	1.53	1.84
0100	Plastic netting, stapled, 2" x 1" mesh, 20 mil	G	B-1	2500	.010		.23	.28		.51	.72
0200	Polypropylene mesh, stapled, 6.5 oz./S.Y.	G		2500	.010		2.33	.28		2.61	3.03
0300	Tobacco netting, or jute mesh #2, stapled	G	↓	2500	.010	↓	.18	.28		.46	.67
1000	Silt fence, polypropylene, 3' high, ideal conditions	G	2 Clab	1600	.010	L.F.	.24	.28		.52	.73
1100	Adverse conditions	G	"	950	.017	"	.24	.47		.71	1.06
1200	Place and remove hay bales	G	A-2	3	8	Ton	241	227	90	558	745
1250	Hay bales, staked	G	"	2500	.010	L.F.	9.65	.27	.11	10.03	11.20

31 31 Soil Treatment

31 31 16 – Termite Control

31 31 16.13 Chemical Termite Control

		Crew	Daily Output	Labor-Hours	Unit	Material	Labor	Equipment	Total	Total Incl O&P
0010	**CHEMICAL TERMITE CONTROL**									
0020	Slab and walls, residential	1 Skwk	1200	.007	SF Flr.	.37	.24		.61	.82
0100	Commercial, minimum		2496	.003		.32	.12		.44	.55
0200	Maximum		1645	.005	↓	.48	.18		.66	.83
0400	Insecticides for termite control, minimum		14.20	.563	Gal.	63	20.50		83.50	104
0500	Maximum	↓	11	.727	"	108	26.50		134.50	164

31 32 Soil Stabilization

31 32 13 – Soil Mixing Stabilization

31 32 13.30 Calcium Chloride

		Crew	Daily Output	Labor-Hours	Unit	Material	Labor	Equipment	Total	Total Incl O&P
0010	**CALCIUM CHLORIDE**									
0020	Calcium chloride delivered, 100 lb. bags, truckload lots				Ton	385			385	425
0030	Solution, 4 lb. flake per gallon, tank truck delivery				Gal.	1.44			1.44	1.58

31 33 Rock Stabilization

31 33 13 – Rock Bolting and Grouting

31 33 13.10 Rock Bolting

		Crew	Daily Output	Labor-Hours	Unit	Material	2014 Bare Costs Labor	Equipment	Total	Total Incl O&P
0010	**ROCK BOLTING**									
2020	Hollow core, prestressable, anchor, 1" diameter, 5' long	2 Skwk	32	.500	Ea.	104	18.15		122.15	145
2025	10' long		24	.667		208	24		232	269
2060	2" diameter, 5' long		32	.500		395	18.15		413.15	465
2065	10' long		24	.667		775	24		799	895
2100	Super high-tensile, 3/4" diameter, 5' long		32	.500		23.50	18.15		41.65	56.50
2105	10' long		24	.667		47	24		71	93
2160	2" diameter, 5' long		32	.500		210	18.15		228.15	262
2165	10' long		24	.667		420	24		444	500
4400	Drill hole for rock bolt, 1-3/4" diam., 5' long (for 3/4" bolt)	B-56	17	.941			26.50	94.50	121	149
4405	10' long		9	1.778			50	179	229	281
4420	2" diameter, 5' long (for 1" bolt)		13	1.231			34.50	124	158.50	195
4425	10' long		7	2.286			64.50	230	294.50	360
4460	3-1/2" diameter, 5' long (for 2" bolt)		10	1.600			45	161	206	253
4465	10' long		5	3.200			90	320	410	505

31 36 Gabions

31 36 13 – Gabion Boxes

31 36 13.10 Gabion Box Systems

		Crew	Daily Output	Labor-Hours	Unit	Material	2014 Bare Costs Labor	Equipment	Total	Total Incl O&P
0010	**GABION BOX SYSTEMS**									
0400	Gabions, galvanized steel mesh mats or boxes, stone filled, 6" deep	B-13	200	.240	S.Y.	26.50	7.25	3.73	37.48	45.50
0500	9" deep		163	.294		38.50	8.90	4.58	51.98	62
0600	12" deep		153	.314		52	9.50	4.88	66.38	78.50
0700	18" deep		102	.471		73	14.25	7.30	94.55	113
0800	36" deep		60	.800		97.50	24	12.45	133.95	161

31 37 Riprap

31 37 13 – Machined Riprap

31 37 13.10 Riprap and Rock Lining

		Crew	Daily Output	Labor-Hours	Unit	Material	2014 Bare Costs Labor	Equipment	Total	Total Incl O&P
0010	**RIPRAP AND ROCK LINING**									
0011	Random, broken stone									
0100	Machine placed for slope protection	B-12G	62	.258	L.C.Y.	29.50	8.65	11.65	49.80	59.50
0110	3/8 to 1/4 C.Y. pieces, grouted	B-13	80	.600	S.Y.	56	18.15	9.30	83.45	102
0200	18" minimum thickness, not grouted	"	53	.906	"	18.45	27.50	14.05	60	82
0300	Dumped, 50 lb. average	B-11A	800	.020	Ton	25	.66	1.66	27.32	30.50
0350	100 lb. average		700	.023		25	.75	1.89	27.64	31
0370	300 lb. average		600	.027		25	.88	2.21	28.09	31.50

31 41 Shoring

31 41 13 – Timber Shoring

31 41 13.10 Building Shoring		Crew	Daily Output	Labor-Hours	Unit	Material	2014 Bare Costs Labor	Equipment	Total	Total Incl O&P
0010	**BUILDING SHORING**									
0020	Shoring, existing building, with timber, no salvage allowance	B-51	2.20	21.818	M.B.F.	760	625	123	1,508	2,025
1000	On cribbing with 35 ton screw jacks, per box and jack	"	3.60	13.333	Jack	71	380	75	526	800

31 41 16 – Sheet Piling

31 41 16.10 Sheet Piling Systems			Crew	Daily Output	Labor-Hours	Unit	Material	2014 Bare Costs Labor	Equipment	Total	Total Incl O&P
0010	**SHEET PILING SYSTEMS**										
0020	Sheet piling steel, not incl. wales, 22 psf, 15' excav., left in place		B-40	10.81	5.180	Ton	1,450	179	355	1,984	2,300
0100	Drive, extract & salvage	R314116-40		6	9.333		505	325	635	1,465	1,800
0300	20' deep excavation, 27 psf, left in place			12.95	4.324		1,450	149	295	1,894	2,175
0400	Drive, extract & salvage	R314116-45		6.55	8.550		505	295	585	1,385	1,700
0600	25' deep excavation, 38 psf, left in place			19	2.947		1,450	102	201	1,753	2,000
0700	Drive, extract & salvage			10.50	5.333		505	184	365	1,054	1,275
0900	40' deep excavation, 38 psf, left in place			21.20	2.642		1,450	91.50	180	1,721.50	1,950
1000	Drive, extract & salvage			12.25	4.571		505	158	310	973	1,175
1200	15' deep excavation, 22 psf, left in place			983	.057	S.F.	16.95	1.97	3.89	22.81	26.50
1300	Drive, extract & salvage			545	.103		5.65	3.55	7	16.20	19.95
1500	20' deep excavation, 27 psf, left in place			960	.058		21.50	2.02	3.98	27.50	31.50
1600	Drive, extract & salvage			485	.115		7.35	3.99	7.85	19.19	23.50
1800	25' deep excavation, 38 psf, left in place			1000	.056		31.50	1.94	3.82	37.26	42
1900	Drive, extract & salvage			553	.101		10.05	3.50	6.90	20.45	24.50
2100	Rent steel sheet piling and wales, first month					Ton	305			305	335
2200	Per added month						30.50			30.50	33.50
2300	Rental piling left in place, add to rental						1,150			1,150	1,275
2500	Wales, connections & struts, 2/3 salvage						475			475	525
2700	High strength piling, 50,000 psi, add						63			63	69.50
2800	55,000 psi, add						81			81	89
3000	Tie rod, not upset, 1-1/2" to 4" diameter with turnbuckle						2,100			2,100	2,300
3100	No turnbuckle						1,625			1,625	1,800
3300	Upset, 1-3/4" to 4" diameter with turnbuckle						2,375			2,375	2,600
3400	No turnbuckle						2,050			2,050	2,250
3600	Lightweight, 18" to 28" wide, 7 ga., 9.22 psf, and										
3610	9 ga., 8.6 psf, minimum					Lb.	.79			.79	.87
3700	Average						.90			.90	.99
3750	Maximum						1.05			1.05	1.16
3900	Wood, solid sheeting, incl. wales, braces and spacers,										
3910	drive, extract & salvage, 8' deep excavation		B-31	330	.121	S.F.	1.76	3.47	.66	5.89	8.50
4000	10' deep, 50 S.F./hr. in & 150 S.F./hr. out			300	.133		1.81	3.81	.73	6.35	9.20
4100	12' deep, 45 S.F./hr. in & 135 S.F./hr. out			270	.148		1.87	4.24	.81	6.92	10.10
4200	14' deep, 42 S.F./hr. in & 126 S.F./hr. out			250	.160		1.92	4.58	.88	7.38	10.80
4300	16' deep, 40 S.F./hr. in & 120 S.F./hr. out			240	.167		1.98	4.77	.91	7.66	11.20
4400	18' deep, 38 S.F./hr. in & 114 S.F./hr. out			230	.174		2.05	4.97	.95	7.97	11.65
4500	20' deep, 35 S.F./hr. in & 105 S.F./hr. out			210	.190		2.12	5.45	1.04	8.61	12.65
4520	Left in place, 8' deep, 55 S.F./hr.			440	.091		3.18	2.60	.50	6.28	8.40
4540	10' deep, 50 S.F./hr.			400	.100		3.34	2.86	.55	6.75	9.10
4560	12' deep, 45 S.F./hr.			360	.111		3.53	3.18	.61	7.32	9.90
4565	14' deep, 42 S.F./hr.			335	.119		3.74	3.41	.65	7.80	10.60
4570	16' deep, 40 S.F./hr.			320	.125		3.97	3.58	.69	8.24	11.10
4580	18' deep, 38 S.F./hr.			305	.131		4.23	3.75	.72	8.70	11.75
4590	20' deep, 35 S.F./hr.			280	.143		4.54	4.09	.78	9.41	12.75
4700	Alternate pricing, left in place, 8' deep			1.76	22.727	M.B.F.	715	650	125	1,490	2,025
4800	Drive, extract and salvage, 8' deep			1.32	30.303	"	635	865	166	1,666	2,325
5000	For treated lumber add cost of treatment to lumber										

31 43 Concrete Raising

31 43 13 – Pressure Grouting

31 43 13.13 Concrete Pressure Grouting	Crew	Daily Output	Labor-Hours	Unit	Material	2014 Bare Costs Labor	Equipment	Total	Total Incl O&P
0010 **CONCRETE PRESSURE GROUTING**									
0020 Grouting, pressure, cement & sand, 1:1 mix, minimum	B-61	124	.323	Bag	13.95	9.25	2.81	26.01	34
0100 Maximum		51	.784	"	13.95	22.50	6.85	43.30	61
0200 Cement and sand, 1:1 mix, minimum		250	.160	C.F.	28	4.58	1.40	33.98	39.50
0300 Maximum		100	.400		42	11.45	3.49	56.94	69
0400 Epoxy cement grout, minimum		137	.292		720	8.35	2.55	730.90	810
0500 Maximum		57	.702		720	20	6.10	746.10	835
0700 Alternate pricing method: (Add for materials)									
0710 5 person crew and equipment	B-61	1	40	Day		1,150	350	1,500	2,300

31 45 Vibroflotation and Densification

31 45 13 – Vibroflotation

31 45 13.10 Vibroflotation Densification

	Crew	Daily Output	Labor-Hours	Unit	Material	2014 Bare Costs Labor	Equipment	Total	Total Incl O&P
0010 **VIBROFLOTATION DENSIFICATION** R314513-90									
0900 Vibroflotation compacted sand cylinder, minimum	B-60	750	.064	V.L.F.		2.02	2.94	4.96	6.65
0950 Maximum		325	.148			4.67	6.80	11.47	15.25
1100 Vibro replacement compacted stone cylinder, minimum		500	.096			3.04	4.41	7.45	9.95
1150 Maximum		250	.192			6.05	8.85	14.90	19.85
1300 Mobilization and demobilization, minimum		.47	102	Total		3,225	4,700	7,925	10,600
1400 Maximum		.14	342	"		10,800	15,800	26,600	35,400

31 46 Needle Beams

31 46 13 – Cantilever Needle Beams

31 46 13.10 Needle Beams

	Crew	Daily Output	Labor-Hours	Unit	Material	2014 Bare Costs Labor	Equipment	Total	Total Incl O&P
0010 **NEEDLE BEAMS**									
0011 Incl. wood shoring 10' x 10' opening									
0400 Block, concrete, 8" thick	B-9	7.10	5.634	Ea.	50	161	33	244	360
0420 12" thick		6.70	5.970		58	171	35	264	390
0800 Brick, 4" thick with 8" backup block		5.70	7.018		58	201	41	300	450
1000 Brick, solid, 8" thick		6.20	6.452		50	185	37.50	272.50	405
1040 12" thick		4.90	8.163		58	233	47.50	338.50	510
1080 16" thick		4.50	8.889		74	254	52	380	570
2000 Add for additional floors of shoring	B-1	6	4		50	115		165	249

31 48 Underpinning

31 48 13 – Underpinning Piers

31 48 13.10 Underpinning Foundations

	Crew	Daily Output	Labor-Hours	Unit	Material	2014 Bare Costs Labor	Equipment	Total	Total Incl O&P
0010 **UNDERPINNING FOUNDATIONS**									
0011 Including excavation,									
0020 forming, reinforcing, concrete and equipment									
0100 5' to 16' below grade, 100 to 500 C.Y.	B-52	2.30	24.348	C.Y.	274	755	259	1,288	1,850
0200 Over 500 C.Y.		2.50	22.400		247	695	238	1,180	1,700
0400 16' to 25' below grade, 100 to 500 C.Y.		2	28		300	865	298	1,463	2,100
0500 Over 500 C.Y.		2.10	26.667		285	825	283	1,393	2,025
0700 26' to 40' below grade, 100 to 500 C.Y.		1.60	35		330	1,075	370	1,775	2,600
0800 Over 500 C.Y.		1.80	31.111		300	965	330	1,595	2,325
0900 For under 50 C.Y., add					10%	40%			

31 48 Underpinning

31 48 13 - Underpinning Piers

31 48 13.10 Underpinning Foundations	Crew	Daily Output	Labor-Hours	Unit	Material	2014 Bare Costs Labor	2014 Bare Costs Equipment	Total	Total Incl O&P
1000 For 50 C.Y. to 100 C.Y., add				C.Y.	5%	20%			

31 52 Cofferdams

31 52 16 - Timber Cofferdams

31 52 16.10 Cofferdams

		Crew	Daily Output	Labor-Hours	Unit	Material	2014 Bare Costs Labor	2014 Bare Costs Equipment	Total	Total Incl O&P
0010	**COFFERDAMS**									
0011	Incl. mobilization and temporary sheeting									
0080	Soldier beams & lagging H piles with 3" wood sheeting									
0090	horizontal between piles, including removal of wales & braces									
0100	No hydrostatic head, 15' deep, 1 line of braces, minimum	B-50	545	.191	S.F.	7.60	6.20	4.53	18.33	24
0200	Maximum		495	.210		8.45	6.85	4.99	20.29	26.50
0400	15' to 22' deep with 2 lines of braces, 10" H, minimum		360	.289		8.95	9.40	6.85	25.20	33.50
0500	Maximum		330	.315		10.15	10.30	7.50	27.95	37
0700	23' to 35' deep with 3 lines of braces, 12" H, minimum		325	.320		11.70	10.45	7.60	29.75	39
0800	Maximum		295	.353		12.70	11.50	8.35	32.55	43
1000	36' to 45' deep with 4 lines of braces, 14" H, minimum		290	.359		13.15	11.70	8.50	33.35	44
1100	Maximum		265	.392		13.85	12.80	9.30	35.95	47.50
1300	No hydrostatic head, left in place, 15' dp., 1 line of braces, min.		635	.164		10.15	5.35	3.89	19.39	24.50
1400	Maximum		575	.181		10.90	5.90	4.29	21.09	26.50
1600	15' to 22' deep with 2 lines of braces, minimum		455	.229		15.25	7.45	5.45	28.15	35.50
1700	Maximum		415	.251		16.95	8.15	5.95	31.05	39
1900	23' to 35' deep with 3 lines of braces, minimum		420	.248		18.15	8.05	5.90	32.10	40
2000	Maximum		380	.274		20	8.90	6.50	35.40	44.50
2200	36' to 45' deep with 4 lines of braces, minimum		385	.270		22	8.80	6.40	37.20	46
2300	Maximum		350	.297		25.50	9.70	7.05	42.25	52.50
2350	Lagging only, 3" thick wood between piles 8' O.C., minimum	B-46	400	.120		1.69	3.81	.11	5.61	8.50
2370	Maximum		250	.192		2.54	6.10	.18	8.82	13.40
2400	Open sheeting no bracing, for trenches to 10' deep, min.		1736	.028		.76	.88	.03	1.67	2.37
2450	Maximum		1510	.032		.85	1.01	.03	1.89	2.68
2500	Tie-back method, add to open sheeting, add, minimum								20%	20%
2550	Maximum								60%	60%
2700	Tie-backs only, based on tie-backs total length, minimum	B-46	86.80	.553	L.F.	14.50	17.55	.52	32.57	46.50
2750	Maximum		38.50	1.247	"	25.50	39.50	1.17	66.17	97
3500	Tie-backs only, typical average, 25' long		2	24	Ea.	640	760	22.50	1,422.50	2,025
3600	35' long		1.58	30.380	"	850	965	28.50	1,843.50	2,625

31 56 Slurry Walls

31 56 23 - Lean Concrete Slurry Walls

31 56 23.20 Slurry Trench

		Crew	Daily Output	Labor-Hours	Unit	Material	2014 Bare Costs Labor	2014 Bare Costs Equipment	Total	Total Incl O&P
0010	**SLURRY TRENCH**									
0011	Excavated slurry trench in wet soils									
0020	backfilled with 3000 PSI concrete, no reinforcing steel									
0050	Minimum	C-7	333	.216	C.F.	7.35	6.65	3.68	17.68	23
0100	Maximum		200	.360	"	12.30	11.05	6.15	29.50	38.50
0200	Alternate pricing method, minimum		150	.480	S.F.	14.65	14.75	8.15	37.55	49.50
0300	Maximum		120	.600		22	18.45	10.20	50.65	66.50
0500	Reinforced slurry trench, minimum	B-48	177	.271		11	8.20	16.45	35.65	44
0600	Maximum	"	69	.696		36.50	21	42	99.50	123
0800	Haul for disposal, 2 mile haul, excavated material, add	B-34B	99	.081	C.Y.		2.40	7	9.40	11.70

31 56 Slurry Walls

31 56 23 – Lean Concrete Slurry Walls

31 56 23.20 Slurry Trench	Crew	Daily Output	Labor-Hours	Unit	Material	2014 Bare Costs Labor	Equipment	Total	Total Incl O&P
0900	Haul bentonite castings for disposal, add	B-34B	40	.200	C.Y.		5.95	17.30	23.25	29

31 62 Driven Piles

31 62 13 – Concrete Piles

31 62 13.23 Prestressed Concrete Piles

		Crew	Daily Output	Labor-Hours	Unit	Material	2014 Bare Costs Labor	Equipment	Total	Total Incl O&P
0010	**PRESTRESSED CONCRETE PILES**, 200 piles									
0020	Unless specified otherwise, not incl. pile caps or mobilization									
2200	Precast, prestressed, 50' long, 12" diam., 2-3/8" wall	B-19	720	.078	V.L.F.	23.50	2.69	2.56	28.75	33.50
2300	14" diameter, 2-1/2" wall		680	.082		31.50	2.85	2.71	37.06	42.50
2500	16" diameter, 3" wall		640	.088		44.50	3.02	2.88	50.40	57.50
2600	18" diameter, 3" wall	B-19A	600	.093		56	3.23	3.76	62.99	71.50
2800	20" diameter, 3-1/2" wall		560	.100		67	3.46	4.03	74.49	84.50
2900	24" diameter, 3-1/2" wall		520	.108		75.50	3.72	4.34	83.56	94.50
3100	Precast, prestressed, 40' long, 10" thick, square	B-19	700	.080		18.05	2.76	2.63	23.44	27.50
3200	12" thick, square		680	.082		21.50	2.85	2.71	27.06	32
3400	14" thick, square		600	.093		25	3.23	3.07	31.30	36.50
3500	Octagonal		640	.088		34.50	3.02	2.88	40.40	46
3700	16" thick, square		560	.100		40.50	3.46	3.29	47.25	54
3800	Octagonal		600	.093		41	3.23	3.07	47.30	54.50
4000	18" thick, square	B-19A	520	.108		47	3.72	4.34	55.06	62.50
4100	Octagonal	B-19	560	.100		48.50	3.46	3.29	55.25	63
4300	20" thick, square	B-19A	480	.117		59.50	4.03	4.71	68.24	77.50
4400	Octagonal	B-19	520	.108		54	3.72	3.54	61.26	69
4600	24" thick, square	B-19A	440	.127		77	4.40	5.15	86.55	97.50
4700	Octagonal	B-19	480	.117		77.50	4.03	3.83	85.36	96.50
4730	Precast, prestressed, 60' long, 10" thick, square		700	.080		18.95	2.76	2.63	24.34	28.50
4740	12" thick, square (60' long)		680	.082		22.50	2.85	2.71	28.06	33
4750	Mobilization for 10,000 L.F. pile job, add		3300	.017			.59	.56	1.15	1.61
4800	25,000 L.F. pile job, add		8500	.007			.23	.22	.45	.63

31 62 16 – Steel Piles

31 62 16.13 Steel Piles

		Crew	Daily Output	Labor-Hours	Unit	Material	2014 Bare Costs Labor	Equipment	Total	Total Incl O&P
0010	**STEEL PILES**									
0100	Step tapered, round, concrete filled									
0110	8" tip, 60 ton capacity, 30' depth	B-19	760	.074	V.L.F.	11.35	2.55	2.42	16.32	19.50
0120	60' depth		740	.076		12.85	2.62	2.49	17.96	21.50
0130	80' depth		700	.080		13.30	2.76	2.63	18.69	22
0150	10" tip, 90 ton capacity, 30' depth		700	.080		13.65	2.76	2.63	19.04	22.50
0160	60' depth		690	.081		14.05	2.80	2.67	19.52	23
0170	80' depth		670	.084		15.15	2.89	2.75	20.79	24.50
0190	12" tip, 120 ton capacity, 30' depth		660	.085		18.10	2.93	2.79	23.82	28
0200	60' depth, 12" diameter		630	.089		17.45	3.07	2.92	23.44	27.50
0210	80' depth		590	.095		16.95	3.28	3.12	23.35	27.50
0250	"H" Sections, 50' long, HP8 x 36		640	.088		16.15	3.02	2.88	22.05	26
0400	HP10 X 42		610	.092		18.75	3.17	3.02	24.94	29
0500	HP10 X 57		610	.092		26	3.17	3.02	32.19	37
0700	HP12 X 53		590	.095		24	3.28	3.12	30.40	35.50
0800	HP12 X 74	B-19A	590	.095		33	3.28	3.83	40.11	46.50
1000	HP14 X 73		540	.104		32.50	3.58	4.18	40.26	47
1100	HP14 X 89		540	.104		39.50	3.58	4.18	47.26	54.50
1300	HP14 X 102		510	.110		45	3.79	4.43	53.22	61

31 62 Driven Piles

31 62 16 – Steel Piles

31 62 16.13 Steel Piles

		Crew	Daily Output	Labor-Hours	Unit	Material	2014 Bare Costs Labor	Equipment	Total	Total Incl O&P
1400	HP14 X 117	B-19A	510	.110	V.L.F.	51.50	3.79	4.43	59.72	68.50
1601	Splice on standard points, not in leads, 8" or 10"	1 Pile	5	1.600	Ea.	118	55.50		173.50	226
1701	12" or 14"		4	2		175	69		244	310
1901	Heavy duty points, not in leads, 10" wide		4	2		185	69		254	320
2101	14" wide		3.50	2.286		236	79		315	395

31 62 19 – Timber Piles

31 62 19.10 Wood Piles

		Crew	Daily Output	Labor-Hours	Unit	Material	2014 Bare Costs Labor	Equipment	Total	Total Incl O&P
0010	**WOOD PILES**									
0011	Friction or end bearing, not including									
0050	mobilization or demobilization									
0100	Untreated piles, up to 30' long, 12" butts, 8" points	B-19	625	.090	V.L.F.	17.40	3.10	2.95	23.45	27.50
0200	30' to 39' long, 12" butts, 8" points		700	.080		17.40	2.76	2.63	22.79	27
0300	40' to 49' long, 12" butts, 7" points		720	.078		17.40	2.69	2.56	22.65	26.50
0400	50' to 59' long, 13" butts, 7" points		800	.070		17.40	2.42	2.30	22.12	26
0500	60' to 69' long, 13" butts, 7" points		840	.067		19.60	2.30	2.19	24.09	28
0600	70' to 80' long, 13" butts, 6" points		840	.067		22	2.30	2.19	26.49	30.50
0800	Treated piles, 12 lb. per C.F.,									
0810	friction or end bearing, ASTM class B									
1000	Up to 30' long, 12" butts, 8" points	B-19	625	.090	V.L.F.	16.70	3.10	2.95	22.75	27
1100	30' to 39' long, 12" butts, 8" points		700	.080		18.20	2.76	2.63	23.59	27.50
1200	40' to 49' long, 12" butts, 7" points		720	.078		20.50	2.69	2.56	25.75	30
1300	50' to 59' long, 13" butts, 7" points		800	.070		21.50	2.42	2.30	26.22	30
1400	60' to 69' long, 13" butts, 6" points	B-19A	840	.067		26.50	2.30	2.69	31.49	36.50
1500	70' to 80' long, 13" butts, 6" points	"	840	.067		28	2.30	2.69	32.99	38
1600	Treated piles, C.C.A., 2.5# per C.F.									
1610	8" butts, 10' long	B-19	400	.140	V.L.F.	17.90	4.84	4.60	27.34	33
1620	11' to 16' long		500	.112		17.90	3.87	3.68	25.45	30.50
1630	17' to 20' long		575	.097		17.90	3.37	3.20	24.47	29
1640	10" butts, 10' to 16' long		500	.112		17.90	3.87	3.68	25.45	30.50
1650	17' to 20' long		575	.097		17.90	3.37	3.20	24.47	29
1660	21' to 40' long		700	.080		17.90	2.76	2.63	23.29	27.50
1670	12" butts, 10' to 20' long		575	.097		17.90	3.37	3.20	24.47	29
1680	21' to 35' long		650	.086		17.90	2.98	2.83	23.71	28
1690	36' to 40' long		700	.080		17.90	2.76	2.63	23.29	27.50
1695	14" butts, to 40' long		700	.080		17.90	2.76	2.63	23.29	27.50
1700	Boot for pile tip, minimum	1 Pile	27	.296	Ea.	23	10.25		33.25	43
1800	Maximum		21	.381		69	13.20		82.20	98.50
2000	Point for pile tip, minimum		20	.400		23	13.85		36.85	49.50
2100	Maximum		15	.533		83	18.45		101.45	123
2300	Splice for piles over 50' long, minimum	B-46	35	1.371		56.50	43.50	1.29	101.29	138
2400	Maximum		20	2.400		68	76	2.26	146.26	207
2600	Concrete encasement with wire mesh and tube		331	.145	V.L.F.	10.50	4.60	.14	15.24	19.55
2700	Mobilization for 10,000 L.F. pile job, add	B-19	3300	.017			.59	.56	1.15	1.61
2800	25,000 L.F. pile job, add	"	8500	.007			.23	.22	.45	.63

31 62 23 – Composite Piles

31 62 23.13 Concrete-Filled Steel Piles

		Crew	Daily Output	Labor-Hours	Unit	Material	2014 Bare Costs Labor	Equipment	Total	Total Incl O&P
0010	**CONCRETE-FILLED STEEL PILES** no mobilization or demobilization									
2600	Pipe piles, 50' lg. 8" diam., 29 lb. per L.F., no concrete	B-19	500	.112	V.L.F.	20.50	3.87	3.68	28.05	33.50
2700	Concrete filled		460	.122		21.50	4.21	4	29.71	35.50
2900	10" diameter, 34 lb. per L.F., no concrete		500	.112		27	3.87	3.68	34.55	40
3000	Concrete filled		450	.124		28.50	4.30	4.09	36.89	43.50
3200	12" diameter, 44 lb. per L.F., no concrete		475	.118		33.50	4.07	3.88	41.45	47.50

31 62 Driven Piles

31 62 23 – Composite Piles

31 62 23.13 Concrete-Filled Steel Piles	Crew	Daily Output	Labor-Hours	Unit	Material	2014 Bare Costs Labor	Equipment	Total	Total Incl O&P
3300	Concrete filled	B-19	415	.135	V.L.F.	36.50	4.66	4.44	45.60	53.50
3500	14" diameter, 46 lb. per L.F., no concrete		430	.130		35.50	4.50	4.28	44.28	51.50
3600	Concrete filled		355	.158		40.50	5.45	5.20	51.15	59.50
3800	16" diameter, 52 lb. per L.F., no concrete		385	.145		39.50	5.05	4.78	49.33	57.50
3900	Concrete filled		335	.167		44.50	5.80	5.50	55.80	65
4100	18" diameter, 59 lb. per L.F., no concrete		355	.158		50.50	5.45	5.20	61.15	70.50
4200	Concrete filled	↓	310	.181	↓	56.50	6.25	5.95	68.70	79
4400	Splices for pipe piles, not in leads, 8" diameter	1 Sswl	4.67	1.713	Ea.	90.50	65.50		156	225
4500	14" diameter		3.79	2.111		118	81		199	284
4600	16" diameter		3.03	2.640		146	101		247	355
4800	Points, standard, 8" diameter		4.61	1.735		150	66.50		216.50	292
4900	14" diameter		4.05	1.975		209	76		285	375
5000	16" diameter		3.37	2.374		254	91		345	455
5200	Points, heavy duty, 10" diameter		2.89	2.768		297	106		403	525
5300	14" or 16" diameter		2.02	3.960	↓	475	152		627	810
5500	For reinforcing steel, add		1150	.007	Lb.	.90	.27		1.17	1.50
5700	For thick wall sections, add	↓			"	.94			.94	1.03

31 63 Bored Piles

31 63 26 – Drilled Caissons

31 63 26.13 Fixed End Caisson Piles

		Crew	Daily Output	Labor-Hours	Unit	Material	2014 Bare Costs Labor	Equipment	Total	Total Incl O&P
0010	**FIXED END CAISSON PILES**									
0015	Including excavation, concrete, 50 lb. reinforcing									
0020	per C.Y., not incl. mobilization, boulder removal, disposal									
0100	Open style, machine drilled, to 50' deep, in stable ground, no	R316326-60								
0110	casings or ground water, 18" diam., 0.065 C.Y./L.F.	B-43	200	.200	V.L.F.	8.05	5.70	12.75	26.50	32.50
0200	24" diameter, 0.116 C.Y./L.F.		190	.211		14.40	6	13.45	33.85	40.50
0300	30" diameter, 0.182 C.Y./L.F.		150	.267		22.50	7.65	17	47.15	56.50
0400	36" diameter, 0.262 C.Y./L.F.		125	.320		32.50	9.15	20.50	62.15	73.50
0500	48" diameter, 0.465 C.Y./L.F.		100	.400		57.50	11.45	25.50	94.45	111
0600	60" diameter, 0.727 C.Y./L.F.		90	.444		90	12.70	28.50	131.20	152
0700	72" diameter, 1.05 C.Y./L.F.		80	.500		130	14.30	32	176.30	202
0800	84" diameter, 1.43 C.Y./L.F.	↓	75	.533	↓	177	15.25	34	226.25	258
1000	For bell excavation and concrete, add									
1020	4' bell diameter, 24" shaft, 0.444 C.Y.	B-43	20	2	Ea.	44	57	128	229	285
1040	6' bell diameter, 30" shaft, 1.57 C.Y.		5.70	7.018		155	201	450	806	1,000
1060	8' bell diameter, 36" shaft, 3.72 C.Y.		2.40	16.667		370	475	1,075	1,920	2,375
1080	9' bell diameter, 48" shaft, 4.48 C.Y.		2	20		445	570	1,275	2,290	2,850
1100	10' bell diameter, 60" shaft, 5.24 C.Y.		1.70	23.529		520	675	1,500	2,695	3,350
1120	12' bell diameter, 72" shaft, 8.74 C.Y.		1	40		865	1,150	2,550	4,565	5,675
1140	14' bell diameter, 84" shaft, 13.6 C.Y.	↓	.70	57.143	↓	1,350	1,625	3,650	6,625	8,225
1200	Open style, machine drilled, to 50' deep, in wet ground, pulled									
1300	casing and pumping, 18" diameter, 0.065 C.Y./L.F.	B-48	160	.300	V.L.F.	8.05	9.10	18.20	35.35	44
1400	24" diameter, 0.116 C.Y./L.F.		125	.384		14.40	11.65	23.50	49.55	61
1500	30" diameter, 0.182 C.Y./L.F.		85	.565		22.50	17.10	34	73.60	91
1600	36" diameter, 0.262 C.Y./L.F.	↓	60	.800		32.50	24	48.50	105	130
1700	48" diameter, 0.465 C.Y./L.F.	B-49	55	1.309		57.50	40.50	66.50	164.50	205
1800	60" diameter, 0.727 C.Y./L.F.		35	2.057		90	64	104	258	320
1900	72" diameter, 1.05 C.Y./L.F.		30	2.400		130	74.50	122	326.50	405
2000	84" diameter, 1.43 C.Y./L.F.	↓	25	2.880	↓	177	89.50	146	412.50	505
2100	For bell excavation and concrete, add									

31 63 Bored Piles

31 63 26 – Drilled Caissons

31 63 26.13 Fixed End Caisson Piles

		Crew	Daily Output	Labor-Hours	Unit	Material	2014 Bare Costs Labor	Equipment	Total	Total Incl O&P
2120	4' bell diameter, 24" shaft, 0.444 C.Y.	B-48	19.80	2.424	Ea.	44	73.50	147	264.50	335
2140	6' bell diameter, 30" shaft, 1.57 C.Y.		5.70	8.421		155	255	510	920	1,150
2160	8' bell diameter, 36" shaft, 3.72 C.Y.		2.40	20		370	605	1,200	2,175	2,750
2180	9' bell diameter, 48" shaft, 4.48 C.Y.	B-49	3.30	21.818		445	675	1,100	2,220	2,875
2200	10' bell diameter, 60" shaft, 5.24 C.Y.		2.80	25.714		520	795	1,300	2,615	3,350
2220	12' bell diameter, 72" shaft, 8.74 C.Y.		1.60	45		865	1,400	2,275	4,540	5,825
2240	14' bell diameter, 84" shaft, 13.6 C.Y.		1	72		1,350	2,225	3,650	7,225	9,275
2300	Open style, machine drilled, to 50' deep, in soft rocks and									
2400	medium hard shales, 18" diameter, 0.065 C.Y./L.F.	B-49	50	1.440	V.L.F.	8.05	44.50	73	125.55	165
2500	24" diameter, 0.116 C.Y./L.F.		30	2.400		14.40	74.50	122	210.90	276
2600	30" diameter, 0.182 C.Y./L.F.		20	3.600		22.50	112	183	317.50	415
2700	36" diameter, 0.262 C.Y./L.F.		15	4.800		32.50	149	244	425.50	555
2800	48" diameter, 0.465 C.Y./L.F.		10	7.200		57.50	223	365	645.50	840
2900	60" diameter, 0.727 C.Y./L.F.		7	10.286		90	320	520	930	1,225
3000	72" diameter, 1.05 C.Y./L.F.		6	12		130	370	610	1,110	1,450
3100	84" diameter, 1.43 C.Y./L.F.		5	14.400		177	445	730	1,352	1,750
3200	For bell excavation and concrete, add									
3220	4' bell diameter, 24" shaft, 0.444 C.Y.	B-49	10.90	6.606	Ea.	44	205	335	584	765
3240	6' bell diameter, 30" shaft, 1.57 C.Y.		3.10	23.226		155	720	1,175	2,050	2,700
3260	8' bell diameter, 36" shaft, 3.72 C.Y.		1.30	55.385		370	1,725	2,800	4,895	6,400
3280	9' bell diameter, 48" shaft, 4.48 C.Y.		1.10	65.455		445	2,025	3,325	5,795	7,575
3300	10' bell diameter, 60" shaft, 5.24 C.Y.		.90	80		520	2,475	4,050	7,045	9,250
3320	12' bell diameter, 72" shaft, 8.74 C.Y.		.60	120		865	3,725	6,100	10,690	14,000
3340	14' bell diameter, 84" shaft, 13.6 C.Y.		.40	180		1,350	5,575	9,150	16,075	21,000
3600	For rock excavation, sockets, add, minimum		120	.600	C.F.		18.60	30.50	49.10	65
3650	Average		95	.758			23.50	38.50	62	82
3700	Maximum		48	1.500			46.50	76	122.50	163
3900	For 50' to 100' deep, add				V.L.F.				7%	7%
4000	For 100' to 150' deep, add								25%	25%
4100	For 150' to 200' deep, add								30%	30%
4200	For casings left in place, add				Lb.	1.13			1.13	1.24
4300	For other than 50 lb. reinf. per C.Y., add or deduct				"	1.10			1.10	1.21
4400	For steel "I" beam cores, add	B-49	8.30	8.675	Ton	2,125	269	440	2,834	3,275
4500	Load and haul excess excavation, 2 miles	B-34B	178	.045	L.C.Y.		1.33	3.89	5.22	6.50
4600	For mobilization, 50 mile radius, rig to 36"	B-43	2	20	Ea.		570	1,275	1,845	2,375
4650	Rig to 84"	B-48	1.75	27.429			830	1,650	2,480	3,225
4700	For low headroom, add								50%	50%
5000	Bottom inspection	1 Skwk	1.20	6.667			242		242	410

31 63 26.16 Concrete Caissons for Marine Construction

		Crew	Daily Output	Labor-Hours	Unit	Material	2014 Bare Costs Labor	Equipment	Total	Total Incl O&P
0010	**CONCRETE CAISSONS FOR MARINE CONSTRUCTION**									
0100	Caissons, incl. mobilization and demobilization, up to 50 miles									
0200	Uncased shafts, 30 to 80 tons cap., 17" diam., 10' depth	B-44	88	.727	V.L.F.	19.80	24.50	21	65.30	87
0300	25' depth		165	.388		14.15	13.10	11.15	38.40	50.50
0400	80-150 ton capacity, 22" diameter, 10' depth		80	.800		25	27	23	75	98.50
0500	20' depth		130	.492		19.80	16.60	14.15	50.55	66
0700	Cased shafts, 10 to 30 ton capacity, 10-5/8" diam., 20' depth		175	.366		14.15	12.35	10.50	37	48
0800	30' depth		240	.267		13.20	9	7.65	29.85	38.50
0850	30 to 60 ton capacity, 12" diameter, 20' depth		160	.400		19.80	13.50	11.50	44.80	57.50
0900	40' depth		230	.278		15.25	9.40	8	32.65	41.50
1000	80 to 100 ton capacity, 16" diameter, 20' depth		160	.400		28.50	13.50	11.50	53.50	66.50
1100	40' depth		230	.278		26.50	9.40	8	43.90	54
1200	110 to 140 ton capacity, 17-5/8" diameter, 20' depth		160	.400		30.50	13.50	11.50	55.50	69

31 63 Bored Piles

31 63 26 – Drilled Caissons

31 63 26.16 Concrete Caissons for Marine Construction

		Crew	Daily Output	Labor-Hours	Unit	Material	2014 Bare Costs Labor	Equipment	Total	Total Incl O&P
1300	40' depth	B-44	230	.278	V.L.F.	28.50	9.40	8	45.90	56
1400	140 to 175 ton capacity, 19" diameter, 20' depth		130	.492		33	16.60	14.15	63.75	80.50
1500	40' depth	↓	210	.305	↓	30.50	10.30	8.75	49.55	60.50
1700	Over 30' long, L.F. cost tends to be lower									
1900	Maximum depth is about 90'									

31 63 29 – Drilled Concrete Piers and Shafts

31 63 29.13 Uncased Drilled Concrete Piers

		Crew	Daily Output	Labor-Hours	Unit	Material	2014 Bare Costs Labor	Equipment	Total	Total Incl O&P
0010	**UNCASED DRILLED CONCRETE PIERS**									
0020	Unless specified otherwise, not incl. pile caps or mobilization									
0050	Cast in place augered piles, no casing or reinforcing									
0060	8" diameter	B-43	540	.074	V.L.F.	4.04	2.12	4.72	10.88	13.20
0065	10" diameter		480	.083		6.40	2.38	5.30	14.08	16.90
0070	12" diameter		420	.095		9.05	2.72	6.05	17.82	21
0075	14" diameter		360	.111		12.20	3.18	7.10	22.48	26.50
0080	16" diameter		300	.133		16.45	3.81	8.50	28.76	34
0085	18" diameter	↓	240	.167	↓	20.50	4.77	10.65	35.92	42
0100	Cast in place, thin wall shell pile, straight sided,									
0110	not incl. reinforcing, 8" diam., 16 ga., 5.8 lb./L.F.	B-19	700	.080	V.L.F.	9.10	2.76	2.63	14.49	17.65
0200	10" diameter, 16 ga. corrugated, 7.3 lb./L.F.		650	.086		11.95	2.98	2.83	17.76	21.50
0300	12" diameter, 16 ga. corrugated, 8.7 lb./L.F.		600	.093		15.50	3.23	3.07	21.80	26
0400	14" diameter, 16 ga. corrugated, 10.0 lb./L.F.		550	.102		18.25	3.52	3.35	25.12	29.50
0500	16" diameter, 16 ga. corrugated, 11.6 lb./L.F.	↓	500	.112	↓	22.50	3.87	3.68	30.05	35
0800	Cast in place friction pile, 50' long, fluted,									
0810	tapered steel, 4000 psi concrete, no reinforcing									
0900	12" diameter, 7 ga.	B-19	600	.093	V.L.F.	29.50	3.23	3.07	35.80	41.50
1000	14" diameter, 7 ga.		560	.100		32	3.46	3.29	38.75	44.50
1100	16" diameter, 7 ga.		520	.108		37.50	3.72	3.54	44.76	51.50
1200	18" diameter, 7 ga.	↓	480	.117	↓	44	4.03	3.83	51.86	59.50
1300	End bearing, fluted, constant diameter,									
1320	4000 psi concrete, no reinforcing									
1340	12" diameter, 7 ga.	B-19	600	.093	V.L.F.	30.50	3.23	3.07	36.80	42.50
1360	14" diameter, 7 ga.		560	.100		38.50	3.46	3.29	45.25	51.50
1380	16" diameter, 7 ga.		520	.108		44.50	3.72	3.54	51.76	59
1400	18" diameter, 7 ga.	↓	480	.117	↓	49	4.03	3.83	56.86	65

31 63 29.20 Cast In Place Piles, Adds

		Crew	Daily Output	Labor-Hours	Unit	Material	2014 Bare Costs Labor	Equipment	Total	Total Incl O&P
0010	**CAST IN PLACE PILES, ADDS**									
1500	For reinforcing steel, add				Lb.	1			1	1.10
1700	For ball or pedestal end, add	B-19	11	5.091	C.Y.	148	176	167	491	645
1900	For lengths above 60', concrete, add	"	11	5.091	"	154	176	167	497	655
2000	For steel thin shell, pipe only				Lb.	1.25			1.25	1.38

Division Notes

	CREW	DAILY OUTPUT	LABOR-HOURS	UNIT	BARE COSTS				TOTAL INCL O&P
					MAT.	LABOR	EQUIP.	TOTAL	

Estimating Tips

32 01 00 Operations and Maintenance of Exterior Improvements

- Recycling of asphalt pavement is becoming very popular and is an alternative to removal and replacement. It can be a good value engineering proposal if removed pavement can be recycled, either at the project site or at another site that is reasonably close to the project site. Sections on repair of flexible and rigid pavement are included.

32 10 00 Bases, Ballasts, and Paving

- When estimating paving, keep in mind the project schedule. Also note that prices for asphalt and concrete are generally higher in the cold seasons. Lines for pavement markings, including tactile warning systems and fence lines, are included.

32 90 00 Planting

- The timing of planting and guarantee specifications often dictate the costs for establishing tree and shrub growth and a stand of grass or ground cover. Establish the work performance schedule to coincide with the local planting season. Maintenance and growth guarantees can add from 20%–100% to the total landscaping cost and can be contractually cumbersome. The cost to replace trees and shrubs can be as high as 5% of the total cost, depending on the planting zone, soil conditions, and time of year.

Reference Numbers

Reference numbers are shown in shaded boxes at the beginning of some major classifications. These numbers refer to related items in the Reference Section. The reference information may be an estimating procedure, an alternate pricing method, or technical information.

Note: Not all subdivisions listed here necessarily appear in this publication.

Division 32 - Exterior Improvements

32 01 Operation and Maintenance of Exterior Improvements

32 01 13 – Flexible Paving Surface Treatment

32 01 13.61 Slurry Seal (Latex Modified)

		Crew	Daily Output	Labor-Hours	Unit	Material	2014 Bare Costs Labor	Equipment	Total	Total Incl O&P
0010	**SLURRY SEAL (LATEX MODIFIED)**									
3780	Rubberized asphalt (latex) seal	B-45	5000	.003	S.Y.	2.78	.09	.06	2.93	3.29

32 01 13.64 Sand Seal

		Crew	Daily Output	Labor-Hours	Unit	Material	Labor	Equipment	Total	Total Incl O&P
0010	**SAND SEAL**									
2080	Sand sealing, sharp sand, asphalt emulsion, small area	B-91	10000	.006	S.Y.	1.47	.21	.24	1.92	2.24
2120	Roadway or large area	"	18000	.004	"	1.26	.12	.13	1.51	1.73

32 01 13.66 Fog Seal

		Crew	Daily Output	Labor-Hours	Unit	Material	Labor	Equipment	Total	Total Incl O&P
0010	**FOG SEAL**									
0012	Sealcoating, 2 coat coal tar pitch emulsion over 10,000 S.Y.	B-45	5000	.003	S.Y.	1.29	.09	.06	1.44	1.65
0030	1000 to 10,000 S.Y.	"	3000	.005		1.29	.15	.10	1.54	1.79
0100	Under 1000 S.Y.	B-1	1050	.023		1.29	.66		1.95	2.53
0300	Petroleum resistant, over 10,000 S.Y.	B-45	5000	.003		1.29	.09	.06	1.44	1.65
0320	1000 to 10,000 S.Y.	"	3000	.005		1.29	.15	.10	1.54	1.79
0400	Under 1000 S.Y.	B-1	1050	.023		1.29	.66		1.95	2.53
0600	Non-skid pavement renewal, over 10,000 S.Y.	B-45	5000	.003		1.36	.09	.06	1.51	1.73
0620	1000 to 10,000 S.Y.	"	3000	.005		1.36	.15	.10	1.61	1.87
0700	Under 1000 S.Y.	B-1	1050	.023		1.36	.66		2.02	2.61
0800	Prepare and clean surface for above	A-2	8545	.003	↓		.08	.03	.11	.16
1000	Hand seal asphalt curbing	B-1	4420	.005	L.F.	.61	.16		.77	.93
1900	Asphalt surface treatment, single course, small area									
1901	0.30 gal/S.Y. asphalt material, 20#/S.Y. aggregate	B-91	5000	.013	S.Y.	1.29	.43	.47	2.19	2.65
1910	Roadway or large area		10000	.006		1.19	.21	.24	1.64	1.93
1950	Asphalt surface treatment, dbl. course for small area		3000	.021		2.91	.71	.78	4.40	5.25
1960	Roadway or large area		6000	.011		2.62	.36	.39	3.37	3.90
1980	Asphalt surface treatment, single course, for shoulders	↓	7500	.009	↓	1.45	.28	.31	2.04	2.42

32 06 Schedules for Exterior Improvements

32 06 10 – Schedules for Bases, Ballasts, and Paving

32 06 10.10 Sidewalks, Driveways and Patios

		Crew	Daily Output	Labor-Hours	Unit	Material	Labor	Equipment	Total	Total Incl O&P
0010	**SIDEWALKS, DRIVEWAYS AND PATIOS** No base									
0020	Asphaltic concrete, 2" thick	B-37	720	.067	S.Y.	7.20	1.99	.22	9.41	11.50
0100	2-1/2" thick	"	660	.073	"	9.15	2.17	.24	11.56	13.95
0300	Concrete, 3000 psi, CIP, 6 x 6 - W1.4 x W1.4 mesh,									
0311	broomed finish, no base, 4" thick	3 Clab	600	.040	S.F.	1.65	1.13		2.78	3.72
0351	5" thick		545	.044		2.20	1.24		3.44	4.51
0401	6" thick	↓	510	.047		2.57	1.33		3.90	5.05
0450	For bank run gravel base, 4" thick, add	B-18	2500	.010		.51	.28	.02	.81	1.05
0520	8" thick, add	"	1600	.015		1.03	.43	.03	1.49	1.89
0550	Exposed aggregate finish, add to above, minimum	B-24	1875	.013		.10	.42		.52	.81
0600	Maximum	"	455	.053		.34	1.73		2.07	3.24
1000	Crushed stone, 1" thick, white marble	2 Clab	1700	.009		.40	.27		.67	.89
1050	Bluestone	"	1700	.009		.22	.27		.49	.69
1700	Redwood, prefabricated, 4' x 4' sections	2 Carp	316	.051		4.77	1.81		6.58	8.30
1750	Redwood planks, 1" thick, on sleepers	"	240	.067	↓	4.77	2.38		7.15	9.25
2250	Stone dust, 4" thick	B-62	900	.027	S.Y.	3.89	.82	.19	4.90	5.85

32 06 10.20 Steps

		Crew	Daily Output	Labor-Hours	Unit	Material	Labor	Equipment	Total	Total Incl O&P
0010	**STEPS**									
0011	Incl. excav., borrow & concrete base as required									
0100	Brick steps	B-24	35	.686	LF Riser	15	22.50		37.50	54
0300	Bluestone treads, 12" x 2" or 12" x 1-1/2"	"	30	.800	"	33	26		59	79.50

32 06 Schedules for Exterior Improvements

32 06 10 – Schedules for Bases, Ballasts, and Paving

32 06 10.20 Steps	Crew	Daily Output	Labor-Hours	Unit	Material	2014 Bare Costs Labor	2014 Bare Costs Equipment	Total	Total Incl O&P
0500 Concrete, cast in place, see Section 03 30 53.40									
0600 Precast concrete, see Section 03 41 23.50									

32 11 Base Courses

32 11 23 – Aggregate Base Courses

32 11 23.23 Base Course Drainage Layers

		Crew	Daily Output	Labor-Hours	Unit	Material	Labor	Equipment	Total	Total Incl O&P
0010	**BASE COURSE DRAINAGE LAYERS**									
0011	For roadways and large areas									
0050	Crushed 3/4" stone base, compacted, 3" deep	B-36C	5200	.008	S.Y.	2.76	.27	.79	3.82	4.34
0100	6" deep		5000	.008		5.50	.28	.82	6.60	7.40
0200	9" deep		4600	.009		8.30	.30	.89	9.49	10.60
0300	12" deep		4200	.010		11.05	.33	.98	12.36	13.75
0301	Crushed 1-1/2" stone base, compacted to 4" deep	B-36B	6000	.011		3.80	.36	.79	4.95	5.65
0302	6" deep		5400	.012		5.70	.40	.88	6.98	7.85
0303	8" deep		4500	.014		7.60	.47	1.05	9.12	10.30
0304	12" deep		3800	.017		11.40	.56	1.24	13.20	14.85
0350	Bank run gravel, spread and compacted									
0370	6" deep	B-32	6000	.005	S.Y.	4.26	.19	.38	4.83	5.40
0390	9" deep		4900	.007		6.40	.23	.46	7.09	7.95
0400	12" deep		4200	.008		8.55	.27	.54	9.36	10.45
6000	Stabilization fabric, polypropylene, 6 oz./S.Y.	B-6	10000	.002		1.27	.07	.04	1.38	1.56
6900	For small and irregular areas, add						50%	50%		
7000	Prepare and roll sub-base, small areas to 2500 S.Y.	B-32A	1500	.016	S.Y.		.55	.93	1.48	1.95
8000	Large areas over 2500 S.Y.	"	3500	.007			.24	.40	.64	.83
8050	For roadways	B-32	4000	.008			.28	.57	.85	1.10

32 11 26 – Asphaltic Base Courses

32 11 26.19 Bituminous-Stabilized Base Courses

		Crew	Daily Output	Labor-Hours	Unit	Material	Labor	Equipment	Total	Total Incl O&P
0010	**BITUMINOUS-STABILIZED BASE COURSES**									
0020	And large paved areas									
0700	Liquid application to gravel base, asphalt emulsion	B-45	6000	.003	Gal.	4.25	.08	.05	4.38	4.87
0800	Prime and seal, cut back asphalt		6000	.003	"	5	.08	.05	5.13	5.70
1000	Macadam penetration crushed stone, 2 gal. per S.Y., 4" thick		6000	.003	S.Y.	8.50	.08	.05	8.63	9.55
1100	6" thick, 3 gal. per S.Y.		4000	.004		12.75	.12	.08	12.95	14.30
1200	8" thick, 4 gal. per S.Y.		3000	.005		17	.15	.10	17.25	19.05
8900	For small and irregular areas, add						50%	50%		

32 12 Flexible Paving

32 12 16 – Asphalt Paving

32 12 16.13 Plant-Mix Asphalt Paving

		Crew	Daily Output	Labor-Hours	Unit	Material	Labor	Equipment	Total	Total Incl O&P
0010	**PLANT-MIX ASPHALT PAVING**									
0020	And large paved areas with no hauling included									
0025	See Section 31 23 23.20 for hauling costs									
0080	Binder course, 1-1/2" thick	B-25	7725	.011	S.Y.	5.55	.35	.36	6.26	7.10
0120	2" thick		6345	.014		7.40	.43	.44	8.27	9.35
0130	2-1/2" thick		5620	.016		9.25	.48	.49	10.22	11.50
0160	3" thick		4905	.018		11.10	.56	.56	12.22	13.75
0170	3-1/2" thick		4520	.019		12.95	.60	.61	14.16	15.95
0200	4" thick		4140	.021		14.80	.66	.67	16.13	18.10
0300	Wearing course, 1" thick	B-25B	10575	.009		3.67	.29	.28	4.24	4.83

32 12 Flexible Paving

32 12 16 – Asphalt Paving

32 12 16.13 Plant-Mix Asphalt Paving

		Crew	Daily Output	Labor-Hours	Unit	Material	Labor	Equipment	Total	Total Incl O&P
							2014 Bare Costs			
0340	1-1/2" thick	B-25B	7725	.012	S.Y.	6.15	.39	.39	6.93	7.90
0380	2" thick		6345	.015		8.30	.48	.47	9.25	10.40
0420	2-1/2" thick		5480	.018		10.20	.55	.55	11.30	12.75
0460	3" thick		4900	.020		12.20	.62	.61	13.43	15.10
0470	3-1/2" thick		4520	.021		14.30	.67	.66	15.63	17.55
0480	4" thick		4140	.023		16.35	.73	.73	17.81	19.95
0500	Open graded friction course	B-25C	5000	.010		2.04	.30	.48	2.82	3.29
0800	Alternate method of figuring paving costs									
0810	Binder course, 1-1/2" thick	B-25	630	.140	Ton	68	4.32	4.38	76.70	87
0811	2" thick		690	.128		68	3.95	4	75.95	86
0812	3" thick		800	.110		68	3.41	3.45	74.86	84.50
0813	4" thick		900	.098		68	3.03	3.07	74.10	83.50
0850	Wearing course, 1" thick	B-25B	575	.167		68	5.25	5.20	78.45	89.50
0851	1-1/2" thick		630	.152		68	4.80	4.76	77.56	88.50
0852	2" thick		690	.139		68	4.39	4.35	76.74	87
0853	2-1/2" thick		765	.125		68	3.96	3.92	75.88	86
0854	3" thick		800	.120		68	3.78	3.75	75.53	85.50
1000	Pavement replacement over trench, 2" thick	B-37	90	.533	S.Y.	7.65	15.95	1.77	25.37	37
1050	4" thick		70	.686		15.10	20.50	2.27	37.87	53.50
1080	6" thick		55	.873		24	26	2.89	52.89	73

32 12 16.14 Asphaltic Concrete Paving

		Crew	Daily Output	Labor-Hours	Unit	Material	Labor	Equipment	Total	Total Incl O&P
							2014 Bare Costs			
0011	**ASPHALTIC CONCRETE PAVING**, parking lots & driveways									
0015	No asphalt hauling included									
0018	Use 6.05 C.Y. per inch per M.S.F. for hauling									
0020	6" stone base, 2" binder course, 1" topping	B-25C	9000	.005	S.F.	1.74	.17	.27	2.18	2.49
0025	2" binder course, 2" topping		9000	.005		2.16	.17	.27	2.60	2.94
0030	3" binder course, 2" topping		9000	.005		2.57	.17	.27	3.01	3.40
0035	4" binder course, 2" topping		9000	.005		2.98	.17	.27	3.42	3.85
0040	1.5" binder course, 1" topping		9000	.005		1.54	.17	.27	1.98	2.26
0042	3" binder course, 1" topping		9000	.005		2.16	.17	.27	2.60	2.94
0045	3" binder course, 3" topping		9000	.005		2.98	.17	.27	3.42	3.85
0050	4" binder course, 3" topping		9000	.005		3.39	.17	.27	3.83	4.30
0055	4" binder course, 4" topping		9000	.005		3.80	.17	.27	4.24	4.75
0300	Binder course, 1-1/2" thick		35000	.001		.62	.04	.07	.73	.83
0400	2" thick		25000	.002		.80	.06	.10	.96	1.09
0500	3" thick		15000	.003		1.24	.10	.16	1.50	1.71
0600	4" thick		10800	.004		1.62	.14	.22	1.98	2.27
0800	Sand finish course, 3/4" thick		41000	.001		.32	.04	.06	.42	.47
0900	1" thick		34000	.001		.39	.04	.07	.50	.58
1000	Fill pot holes, hot mix, 2" thick	B-16	4200	.008		.84	.22	.16	1.22	1.47
1100	4" thick		3500	.009		1.23	.27	.20	1.70	2.02
1120	6" thick		3100	.010		1.65	.30	.22	2.17	2.57
1140	Cold patch, 2" thick	B-51	3000	.016		.98	.46	.09	1.53	1.94
1160	4" thick		2700	.018		1.86	.51	.10	2.47	3.01
1180	6" thick		1900	.025		2.89	.72	.14	3.75	4.56

32 13 Rigid Paving

32 13 13 – Concrete Paving

32 13 13.23 Concrete Paving Surface Treatment	Crew	Daily Output	Labor-Hours	Unit	Material	2014 Bare Costs Labor	Equipment	Total	Total Incl O&P
0010 **CONCRETE PAVING SURFACE TREATMENT**									
0015 Including joints, finishing and curing									
0020 Fixed form, 12' pass, unreinforced, 6" thick	B-26	3000	.029	S.Y.	21	.93	1.12	23.05	26.50
0100 8" thick		2750	.032		29	1.01	1.22	31.23	35
0110 8" thick, small area		1375	.064		29	2.02	2.45	33.47	38
0200 9" thick		2500	.035		33	1.11	1.35	35.46	40
0300 10" thick		2100	.042		36	1.32	1.60	38.92	44
0310 10" thick, small area		1050	.084		36	2.64	3.20	41.84	48
0400 12" thick		1800	.049		41.50	1.54	1.87	44.91	50
0410 Conc. pavement, w/jt.,fnsh.&curing,fix form,24' pass,unreinforced,6"T		6000	.015		20	.46	.56	21.02	23.50
0430 8" thick		5500	.016		27.50	.50	.61	28.61	31.50
0440 9" thick		5000	.018		31.50	.56	.67	32.73	36
0450 10" thick		4200	.021		34.50	.66	.80	35.96	40
0460 12" thick		3600	.024		40	.77	.93	41.70	46.50
0470 15" thick		3000	.029		52	.93	1.12	54.05	60.50
0500 Fixed form 12' pass 15" thick		1500	.059		52.50	1.85	2.24	56.59	63.50
0510 For small irregular areas, add				%	10%	100%	100%		
0520 Welded wire fabric, sheets for rigid paving 2.33 lb./S.Y.	2 Rodm	389	.041	S.Y.	1.31	1.56		2.87	4.11
0530 Reinforcing steel for rigid paving 12 lb./S.Y.		666	.024		6.30	.91		7.21	8.50
0540 Reinforcing steel for rigid paving 18 lb./S.Y.		444	.036		9.45	1.37		10.82	12.75
0620 Slip form, 12' pass, unreinforced, 6" thick	B-26A	5600	.016		20.50	.50	.63	21.63	24
0624 8" thick		5300	.017		28	.52	.67	29.19	32
0626 9" thick		4820	.018		32	.58	.73	33.31	37
0628 10" thick		4050	.022		35	.69	.87	36.56	40.50
0630 12" thick		3470	.025		40.50	.80	1.02	42.32	47
0632 15" thick		2890	.030		51	.96	1.22	53.18	59
0640 Slip form, 24' pass, unreinforced, 6" thick		11200	.008		20	.25	.32	20.57	23
0644 8" thick		10600	.008		27	.26	.33	27.59	30.50
0646 9" thick		9640	.009		31	.29	.37	31.66	35
0648 10" thick		8100	.011		34	.34	.44	34.78	38.50
0650 12" thick		6940	.013		39.50	.40	.51	40.41	44.50
0652 15" thick		5780	.015		49.50	.48	.61	50.59	56
0700 Finishing, broom finish small areas	2 Cefi	120	.133			4.58		4.58	7.40
1000 Curing, with sprayed membrane by hand	2 Clab	1500	.011		.99	.30		1.29	1.60
1650 For integral coloring, see Section 03 05 13.20									

32 14 Unit Paving

32 14 13 – Precast Concrete Unit Paving

32 14 13.13 Interlocking Precast Concrete Unit Paving

	Crew	Daily Output	Labor-Hours	Unit	Material	Labor	Equipment	Total	Total Incl O&P
0010 **INTERLOCKING PRECAST CONCRETE UNIT PAVING**									
0020 "V" blocks for retaining soil	D-1	205	.078	S.F.	10	2.52		12.52	15.20

32 14 13.16 Precast Concrete Unit Paving Slabs

	Crew	Daily Output	Labor-Hours	Unit	Material	Labor	Equipment	Total	Total Incl O&P
0010 **PRECAST CONCRETE UNIT PAVING SLABS**									
0750 Exposed local aggregate, natural	2 Bric	250	.064	S.F.	7.60	2.28		9.88	12.15
0800 Colors		250	.064		7.60	2.28		9.88	12.15
0850 Exposed granite or limestone aggregate		250	.064		7.35	2.28		9.63	11.90
0900 Exposed white tumblestone aggregate		250	.064		6.55	2.28		8.83	11.05

32 14 Unit Paving

32 14 13 – Precast Concrete Unit Paving

32 14 13.18 Precast Concrete Plantable Pavers	Crew	Daily Output	Labor-Hours	Unit	Material	2014 Bare Costs Labor	Equipment	Total	Total Incl O&P
0010 **PRECAST CONCRETE PLANTABLE PAVERS** (50% grass)									
0300 3/4" crushed stone base for plantable pavers, 6 inch depth	B-62	1000	.024	S.Y.	5.50	.74	.17	6.41	7.50
0400 8 inch depth		900	.027		7.40	.82	.19	8.41	9.75
0500 10 inch depth		800	.030		9.20	.93	.22	10.35	11.90
0600 12 inch depth		700	.034		11.05	1.06	.25	12.36	14.20
0700 Hydro seeding plantable pavers	B-81A	20	.800	M.S.F.	19.35	23	23.50	65.85	85
0800 Apply fertilizer and seed to plantable pavers	1 Clab	8	1	"	51.50	28		79.50	104

32 14 16 – Brick Unit Paving

32 14 16.10 Brick Paving

	Crew	Daily Output	Labor-Hours	Unit	Material	2014 Bare Costs Labor	Equipment	Total	Total Incl O&P
0010 **BRICK PAVING**									
0012 4" x 8" x 1-1/2", without joints (4.5 brick/S.F.)	D-1	110	.145	S.F.	2.21	4.69		6.90	10.25
0100 Grouted, 3/8" joint (3.9 brick/S.F.)		90	.178		2.15	5.75		7.90	11.90
0200 4" x 8" x 2-1/4", without joints (4.5 bricks/S.F.)		110	.145		2.48	4.69		7.17	10.55
0300 Grouted, 3/8" joint (3.9 brick/S.F.)		90	.178		2.15	5.75		7.90	11.90
0500 Bedding, asphalt, 3/4" thick	B-25	5130	.017		.68	.53	.54	1.75	2.23
0540 Course washed sand bed, 1" thick	B-18	5000	.005		.29	.14	.01	.44	.56
0580 Mortar, 1" thick	D-1	300	.053		.63	1.72		2.35	3.56
0620 2" thick		200	.080		1.27	2.58		3.85	5.70
1500 Brick on 1" thick sand bed laid flat, 4.5 per S.F.		100	.160		3.12	5.15		8.27	12.05
2000 Brick pavers, laid on edge, 7.2 per S.F.		70	.229		3.83	7.35		11.18	16.45
2500 For 4" thick concrete bed and joints, add		595	.027		1.15	.87		2.02	2.70
2800 For steam cleaning, add	A-1H	950	.008		.09	.24	.08	.41	.59

32 14 23 – Asphalt Unit Paving

32 14 23.10 Asphalt Blocks

	Crew	Daily Output	Labor-Hours	Unit	Material	2014 Bare Costs Labor	Equipment	Total	Total Incl O&P
0010 **ASPHALT BLOCKS**									
0020 Rectangular, 6" x 12" x 1-1/4", w/bed & neopr. adhesive	D-1	135	.119	S.F.	9.20	3.82		13.02	16.45
0100 3" thick		130	.123		12.90	3.97		16.87	21
0300 Hexagonal tile, 8" wide, 1-1/4" thick		135	.119		9.20	3.82		13.02	16.45
0400 2" thick		130	.123		12.90	3.97		16.87	21
0500 Square, 8" x 8", 1-1/4" thick		135	.119		9.20	3.82		13.02	16.45
0600 2" thick		130	.123		12.90	3.97		16.87	21
0900 For exposed aggregate (ground finish) add					.61			.61	.67
0910 For colors, add					.46			.46	.51

32 14 40 – Stone Paving

32 14 40.10 Stone Pavers

	Crew	Daily Output	Labor-Hours	Unit	Material	2014 Bare Costs Labor	Equipment	Total	Total Incl O&P
0010 **STONE PAVERS**									
1100 Flagging, bluestone, irregular, 1" thick,	D-1	81	.198	S.F.	6.35	6.35		12.70	17.60
1150 Snapped random rectangular, 1" thick		92	.174		9.60	5.60		15.20	19.95
1200 1-1/2" thick		85	.188		11.55	6.05		17.60	23
1250 2" thick		83	.193		13.45	6.20		19.65	25
1300 Slate, natural cleft, irregular, 3/4" thick		92	.174		9.15	5.60		14.75	19.40
1350 Random rectangular, gauged, 1/2" thick		105	.152		19.80	4.91		24.71	30
1400 Random rectangular, butt joint, gauged, 1/4" thick		150	.107		21.50	3.44		24.94	29
1500 For interior setting, add								25%	25%
1550 Granite blocks, 3-1/2" x 3-1/2" x 3-1/2"	D-1	92	.174	S.F.	11.60	5.60		17.20	22
1600 4" to 12" long, 3" to 5" wide, 3" to 5" thick		98	.163		9.70	5.25		14.95	19.40
1650 6" to 15" long, 3" to 6" wide, 3" to 5" thick		105	.152		5.15	4.91		10.06	13.85

32 16 13 – Curbs and Gutters

32 16 13.13 Cast-in-Place Concrete Curbs and Gutters	Crew	Daily Output	Labor-Hours	Unit	Material	2014 Bare Costs Labor	Equipment	Total	Total Incl O&P
0010 **CAST-IN-PLACE CONCRETE CURBS AND GUTTERS**									
0290 Forms only, no concrete									
0300 Concrete, wood forms, 6" x 18", straight	C-2	500	.096	L.F.	2.95	3.06		6.01	8.40
0400 6" x 18", radius	"	200	.240	"	3.06	7.65		10.71	16.25
0402 Forms and concrete complete									
0404 Concrete, wood forms, 6" x 18", straight & concrete	C-2A	500	.096	L.F.	5.70	3.32		9.02	11.85
0406 6" x 18", radius	"	200	.240		5.85	8.30		14.15	20.50
0415 Machine formed, 6" x 18", straight	B-69A	2000	.024		3.54	.75	.45	4.74	5.60
0416 6" x 18", radius	"	900	.053		3.57	1.66	1	6.23	7.80
0421 Curb and gutter, straight									
0422 with 6" high curb and 6" thick gutter, wood forms									
0430 24" wide, .055 C.Y. per L.F.	C-2A	375	.128	L.F.	15.20	4.43		19.63	24
0435 30" wide, .066 C.Y. per L.F.		340	.141		16.70	4.88		21.58	26.50
0440 Steel forms, 24" wide, straight		700	.069		6.80	2.37		9.17	11.40
0441 Radius		500	.096		6.60	3.32		9.92	12.85
0442 30" wide, straight		700	.069		7.95	2.37		10.32	12.65
0443 Radius		500	.096		7.50	3.32		10.82	13.80
0445 Machine formed, 24" wide, straight	B-69A	2000	.024		5.55	.75	.45	6.75	7.85
0446 Radius		900	.053		5.55	1.66	1	8.21	9.95
0447 30" wide, straight		2000	.024		6.45	.75	.45	7.65	8.85
0448 Radius		900	.053		6.45	1.66	1	9.11	10.95

32 16 13.23 Precast Concrete Curbs and Gutters

	Crew	Daily Output	Labor-Hours	Unit	Material	Labor	Equipment	Total	Total Incl O&P
0010 **PRECAST CONCRETE CURBS AND GUTTERS**									
0550 Precast, 6" x 18", straight	B-29	700	.069	L.F.	9.90	2.08	1.26	13.24	15.75
0600 6" x 18", radius	"	325	.148	"	10.40	4.47	2.71	17.58	22

32 16 13.33 Asphalt Curbs

	Crew	Daily Output	Labor-Hours	Unit	Material	Labor	Equipment	Total	Total Incl O&P
0010 **ASPHALT CURBS**									
0012 Curbs, asphaltic, machine formed, 8" wide, 6" high, 40 L.F./ton	B-27	1000	.032	L.F.	1.74	.92	.29	2.95	3.79
0100 8" wide, 8" high, 30 L.F. per ton		900	.036		2.33	1.02	.33	3.68	4.64
0150 Asphaltic berm, 12" W, 3"-6" H, 35 L.F./ton, before pavement		700	.046		.04	1.31	.42	1.77	2.71
0200 12" W, 1-1/2" to 4" H, 60 L.F. per ton, laid with pavement	B-2	1050	.038		.02	1.09		1.11	1.86

32 16 13.43 Stone Curbs

	Crew	Daily Output	Labor-Hours	Unit	Material	Labor	Equipment	Total	Total Incl O&P
0010 **STONE CURBS**									
1000 Granite, split face, straight, 5" x 16"	D-13	275	.175	L.F.	12.30	5.95	1.75	20	25.50
1100 6" x 18"	"	250	.192		16.15	6.55	1.93	24.63	31
1300 Radius curbing, 6" x 18", over 10' radius	B-29	260	.185		19.80	5.60	3.39	28.79	35
1400 Corners, 2' radius	"	80	.600	Ea.	66.50	18.15	11	95.65	116
1600 Edging, 4-1/2" x 12", straight	d-13	300	.160	L.F.	6.15	5.45	1.60	13.20	17.60
1800 Curb inlets, (guttermouth) straight	B-29	41	1.171	Ea.	148	35.50	21.50	205	245
2000 Indian granite (belgian block)									
2100 Jumbo, 10-1/2" x 7-1/2" x 4", grey	D-1	150	.107	L.F.	6.05	3.44		9.49	12.35
2150 Pink		150	.107		8.20	3.44		11.64	14.70
2200 Regular, 9" x 4-1/2" x 4-1/2", grey		160	.100		4.53	3.22		7.75	10.35
2250 Pink		160	.100		5.80	3.22		9.02	11.70
2300 Cubes, 4" x 4" x 4", grey		175	.091		3.30	2.95		6.25	8.55
2350 Pink		175	.091		3.58	2.95		6.53	8.85
2400 6" x 6" x 6", pink		155	.103		11.85	3.33		15.18	18.55
2500 Alternate pricing method for indian granite									
2550 Jumbo, 10-1/2" x 7-1/2" x 4" (30 lb.), grey				Ton	345			345	380
2600 Pink					475			475	525
2650 Regular, 9" x 4-1/2" x 4-1/2" (20 lb.), grey					320			320	350
2700 Pink					405			405	445

32 16 Curbs, Gutters, Sidewalks, and Driveways

32 16 13 – Curbs and Gutters

32 16 13.43 Stone Curbs	Crew	Daily Output	Labor-Hours	Unit	Material	2014 Bare Costs Labor	Equipment	Total	Total Incl O&P
2750	Cubes, 4" x 4" x 4" (5 lb.), grey				Ton	400			400	440
2800	Pink					460			460	505
2850	6" x 6" x 6" (25 lb.), pink					460			460	505
2900	For pallets, add					22			22	24

32 17 Paving Specialties

32 17 13 – Parking Bumpers

32 17 13.13 Metal Parking Bumpers

		Crew	Daily Output	Labor-Hours	Unit	Material	2014 Bare Costs Labor	Equipment	Total	Total Incl O&P
0010	**METAL PARKING BUMPERS**									
0015	Bumper rails for garages, 12 Ga. rail, 6" wide, with steel									
0020	posts 12'-6" O.C., minimum	E-4	190	.168	L.F.	17.30	6.55	.75	24.60	32.50
0030	Average		165	.194		21.50	7.55	.86	29.91	39.50
0100	Maximum		140	.229		26	8.90	1.01	35.91	46.50
0300	12" channel rail, minimum		160	.200		21.50	7.75	.89	30.14	40
0400	Maximum		120	.267		32.50	10.35	1.18	44.03	56.50
1300	Pipe bollards, conc. filled/paint, 8' L x 4' D hole, 6" diam.	B-6	20	1.200	Ea.	660	37	18.25	715.25	805
1400	8" diam.		15	1.600		890	49.50	24.50	964	1,100
1500	12" diam.		12	2		1,125	62	30.50	1,217.50	1,350
2030	Folding with individual padlocks	B-2	50	.800		600	23		623	700
8000	Parking lot control, see Section 11 12 13.10									
8900	Security bollards, SS, lighted, hyd., incl. controls, group of 3	L-7	.06	472	Ea.	48,400	14,600		63,000	77,500
8910	Group of 5	"	.04	634	"	65,000	19,600		84,600	104,500

32 17 13.16 Plastic Parking Bumpers

		Crew	Daily Output	Labor-Hours	Unit	Material	2014 Bare Costs Labor	Equipment	Total	Total Incl O&P
0010	**PLASTIC PARKING BUMPERS**									
1200	Thermoplastic, 6" x 10" x 6'-0"	B-2	120	.333	Ea.	52	9.55		61.55	73

32 17 13.19 Precast Concrete Parking Bumpers

		Crew	Daily Output	Labor-Hours	Unit	Material	2014 Bare Costs Labor	Equipment	Total	Total Incl O&P
0010	**PRECAST CONCRETE PARKING BUMPERS**									
1000	Wheel stops, precast concrete incl. dowels, 6" x 10" x 6'-0"	B-2	120	.333	Ea.	39.50	9.55		49.05	59
1100	8" x 13" x 6'-0"	"	120	.333	"	45.50	9.55		55.05	66

32 17 13.26 Wood Parking Bumpers

		Crew	Daily Output	Labor-Hours	Unit	Material	2014 Bare Costs Labor	Equipment	Total	Total Incl O&P
0010	**WOOD PARKING BUMPERS**									
0020	Parking barriers, timber w/saddles, treated type									
0100	4" x 4" for cars	B-2	520	.077	L.F.	2.79	2.20		4.99	6.75
0200	6" x 6" for trucks		520	.077	"	5.80	2.20		8	10.05
0600	Flexible fixed stanchion, 2' high, 3" diameter		100	.400	Ea.	40	11.45		51.45	63.50

32 17 23 – Pavement Markings

32 17 23.13 Painted Pavement Markings

		Crew	Daily Output	Labor-Hours	Unit	Material	2014 Bare Costs Labor	Equipment	Total	Total Incl O&P
0010	**PAINTED PAVEMENT MARKINGS**									
0020	Acrylic waterborne, white or yellow, 4" wide, less than 3000 L.F.	B-78	20000	.002	L.F.	.15	.06	.03	.24	.30
0200	6" wide, less than 3000 L.F.		11000	.004		.23	.10	.06	.39	.49
0500	8" wide, less than 3000 L.F.		10000	.004		.30	.11	.06	.47	.59
0600	12" wide, less than 3000 L.F.		4000	.010		.45	.29	.16	.90	1.16
0620	Arrows or gore lines		2300	.017	S.F.	.21	.50	.28	.99	1.38
0640	Temporary paint, white or yellow, less than 3000 L.F.		15000	.003	L.F.	.07	.08	.04	.19	.26
0660	Removal	1 Clab	300	.027			.75		.75	1.27
0680	Temporary tape	2 Clab	1500	.011		.47	.30		.77	1.03
0710	Thermoplastic, white or yellow, 4" wide, less than 6000 L.F.	B-79	15000	.003		.30	.08	.10	.48	.58
0730	6" wide, less than 6000 L.F.		14000	.003		.45	.08	.11	.64	.76
0740	8" wide, less than 6000 L.F.		12000	.003		.60	.10	.13	.83	.96
0750	12" wide, less than 6000 L.F.		6000	.007		.89	.19	.26	1.34	1.58

32 17 Paving Specialties

32 17 23 – Pavement Markings

32 17 23.13 Painted Pavement Markings

		Crew	Daily Output	Labor-Hours	Unit	Material	2014 Bare Costs Labor	Equipment	Total	Total Incl O&P
0760	Arrows	B-79	660	.061	S.F.	.60	1.74	2.38	4.72	6.20
0770	Gore lines		2500	.016		.60	.46	.63	1.69	2.12
0780	Letters	↓	660	.061	↓	.60	1.74	2.38	4.72	6.20
1000	Airport painted markings									
1050	Traffic safety flashing truck for airport painting	A-2B	1	8	Day		231	270	501	680
1100	Painting, white or yellow, taxiway markings	B-78	4000	.010	S.F.	.26	.29	.16	.71	.95
1110	with 12 lb. beads per 100 S.F.		4000	.010		.53	.29	.16	.98	1.24
1200	Runway markings		3500	.011		.26	.33	.18	.77	1.04
1210	with 12 lb. beads per 100 S.F.		3500	.011		.53	.33	.18	1.04	1.33
1300	Pavement location or direction signs		2500	.016		.26	.46	.26	.98	1.34
1310	with 12 lb. beads per 100 S.F.	↓	2500	.016	↓	.53	.46	.26	1.25	1.63
1350	Mobilization airport pavement painting		4	10	Ea.		286	161	447	655
1400	Paint markings or pavement signs removal daytime	B-78B	400	.045	S.F.		1.31	.98	2.29	3.28
1500	Removal nighttime		335	.054	"		1.56	1.17	2.73	3.91
1600	Mobilization pavement paint removal	↓	4	4.500	Ea.		131	98	229	330

32 17 23.14 Pavement Parking Markings

		Crew	Daily Output	Labor-Hours	Unit	Material	2014 Bare Costs Labor	Equipment	Total	Total Incl O&P
0010	**PAVEMENT PARKING MARKINGS**									
0790	Layout of pavement marking	A-2	25000	.001	L.F.		.03	.01	.04	.06
0800	Lines on pvmt., parking stall, paint, white, 4" wide	B-78B	400	.045	Stall	4.62	1.31	.98	6.91	8.40
0825	Parking stall, small quantities	2 Pord	80	.200		9.25	6.25		15.50	20.50
0830	Lines on pvmt., parking stall, thermoplastic, white, 4" wide	B-79	300	.133	↓	13	3.83	5.25	22.08	26.50
1000	Street letters and numbers	B-78B	1600	.011	S.F.	.70	.33	.24	1.27	1.59

32 18 Athletic and Recreational Surfacing

32 18 13 – Synthetic Grass Surfacing

32 18 13.10 Artificial Grass Surfacing

		Crew	Daily Output	Labor-Hours	Unit	Material	2014 Bare Costs Labor	Equipment	Total	Total Incl O&P
0010	**ARTIFICIAL GRASS SURFACING**									
0015	Not including asphalt base or drainage,									
0020	but including cushion pad, over 50,000 S.F.									
0200	1/2" pile and 5/16" cushion pad, standard	C-17	3200	.025	S.F.	10.20	.92		11.12	12.75
0300	Deluxe		2560	.031		15.10	1.15		16.25	18.55
0500	1/2" pile and 5/8" cushion pad, standard		2844	.028		14.70	1.03		15.73	17.95
0600	Deluxe	↓	2327	.034	↓	16.20	1.26		17.46	20
0800	For asphaltic concrete base, 2-1/2" thick,									
0900	with 6" crushed stone sub-base, add	B-25	12000	.007	S.F.	1.56	.23	.23	2.02	2.35

32 18 16 – Synthetic Resilient Surfacing

32 18 16.13 Playground Protective Surfacing

		Crew	Daily Output	Labor-Hours	Unit	Material	2014 Bare Costs Labor	Equipment	Total	Total Incl O&P
0010	**PLAYGROUND PROTECTIVE SURFACING**									
0100	Resilient rubber surface, poured in place, 4" thick, black	2 Skwk	300	.053	S.F.	11.15	1.94		13.09	15.50
0150	2" thick topping, colors	"	2800	.006		6.05	.21		6.26	7
0200	Wood chip mulch, 6" deep	1 Clab	300	.027	↓	.72	.75		1.47	2.06

32 18 23 – Athletic Surfacing

32 18 23.33 Running Track Surfacing

		Crew	Daily Output	Labor-Hours	Unit	Material	2014 Bare Costs Labor	Equipment	Total	Total Incl O&P
0010	**RUNNING TRACK SURFACING**									
0020	Running track, asphalt, incl base, 3" thick	B-37	300	.160	S.Y.	24	4.78	.53	29.31	34.50
0102	Surface, latex rubber system, 1/2" thick, black	B-20	115	.209		39	6.05		45.05	53
0152	Colors		115	.209		48	6.05		54.05	63
0302	Urethane rubber system, 1/2" thick, black		110	.218		29	6.30		35.30	42
0402	Color coating	↓	110	.218	↓	35.50	6.30		41.80	49.50

32 18 Athletic and Recreational Surfacing

32 18 23 – Athletic Surfacing

32 18 23.53 Tennis Court Surfacing	Crew	Daily Output	Labor-Hours	Unit	Material	2014 Bare Costs Labor	Equipment	Total	Total Incl O&P
0010 **TENNIS COURT SURFACING**									
0020 Tennis court, asphalt, incl. base, 2-1/2" thick, one court	B-37	450	.107	S.Y.	37.50	3.19	.35	41.04	46.50
0200 Two courts		675	.071		15.25	2.12	.24	17.61	20.50
0300 Clay courts		360	.133		42	3.98	.44	46.42	53.50
0400 Pulverized natural greenstone with 4" base, fast dry		250	.192		39.50	5.75	.64	45.89	54
0800 Rubber-acrylic base resilient pavement		600	.080		55.50	2.39	.26	58.15	66
1000 Colored sealer, acrylic emulsion, 3 coats	2 Clab	800	.020		6	.56		6.56	7.55
1100 3 coat, 2 colors	"	900	.018		8.45	.50		8.95	10.15
1200 For preparing old courts, add	1 Clab	825	.010			.27		.27	.46
1400 Posts for nets, 3-1/2" diameter with eye bolts	B-1	3.40	7.059	Pr.	300	204		504	675
1500 With pulley & reel		3.40	7.059	"	800	204		1,004	1,225
1700 Net, 42' long, nylon thread with binder		50	.480	Ea.	249	13.85		262.85	298
1800 All metal		6.50	3.692	"	495	107		602	725
2001 Paint markings on asphalt, 2 coat	1 Clab	2.50	3.200	Court	151	90		241	320
2200 Complete court with fence, etc., asphaltic conc., minimum	B-37	.20	240		28,400	7,175	795	36,370	44,100
2300 Maximum		.16	300		58,500	8,975	995	68,470	80,000
2800 Clay courts, minimum		.20	240		30,000	7,175	795	37,970	45,900
2900 Maximum		.16	300		55,000	8,975	995	64,970	76,500

32 31 Fences and Gates

32 31 13 – Chain Link Fences and Gates

32 31 13.20 Fence, Chain Link Industrial	Crew	Daily Output	Labor-Hours	Unit	Material	2014 Bare Costs Labor	Equipment	Total	Total Incl O&P
0010 **FENCE, CHAIN LINK INDUSTRIAL**									
0011 Schedule 40, including concrete									
0020 3 strands barb wire, 2" post @ 10' O.C., set in concrete, 6' H									
0200 9 ga. wire, galv. steel, in concrete	B-80C	240	.100	L.F.	19.10	2.84	1.16	23.10	27
0248 Fence, add for vinyl coated fabric				S.F.	.68			.68	.75
0300 Aluminized steel	B-80C	240	.100	L.F.	19.70	2.84	1.16	23.70	27.50
0500 6 ga. wire, galv. steel		240	.100		20.50	2.84	1.16	24.50	29
0600 Aluminized steel		240	.100		29.50	2.84	1.16	33.50	38.50
0800 6 ga. wire, 6' high but omit barbed wire, galv. steel		250	.096		19.40	2.73	1.11	23.24	27.50
0900 Aluminized steel, in concrete		250	.096		23.50	2.73	1.11	27.34	32
0920 8' H, 6 ga. wire, 2-1/2" line post, galv. steel, in concrete		180	.133		31	3.79	1.55	36.34	42
0940 Aluminized steel, in concrete		180	.133		37.50	3.79	1.55	42.84	49.50
1100 Add for corner posts, 3" diam., galv. steel, in concrete		40	.600	Ea.	91.50	17.05	6.95	115.50	136
1200 Aluminized steel, in concrete		40	.600		91.50	17.05	6.95	115.50	136
1300 Add for braces, galv. steel		80	.300		38.50	8.55	3.48	50.53	60.50
1350 Aluminized steel		80	.300		50	8.55	3.48	62.03	73
1400 Gate for 6' high fence, 1-5/8" frame, 3' wide, galv. steel		10	2.400		191	68	28	287	355
1500 Aluminized steel, in concrete		10	2.400		191	68	28	287	355
2000 5'-0" high fence, 9 ga., no barbed wire, 2" line post, in concrete									
2010 10' O.C., 1-5/8" top rail, in concrete									
2100 Galvanized steel, in concrete	B-80C	300	.080	L.F.	18.10	2.27	.93	21.30	24.50
2200 Aluminized steel, in concrete		300	.080	"	18.75	2.27	.93	21.95	25.50
2400 Gate, 4' wide, 5' high, 2" frame, galv. steel, in concrete		10	2.400	Ea.	176	68	28	272	340
2500 Aluminized steel, in concrete		10	2.400	"	192	68	28	288	355
3100 Overhead slide gate, chain link, 6' high, to 18' wide, in concrete		38	.632	L.F.	92.50	17.95	7.30	117.75	140
3110 Cantilever type, in concrete	B-80	48	.500		118	14.45	15.80	148.25	172
3120 8' high, in concrete		24	1		157	29	31.50	217.50	255
3130 10' high, in concrete		18	1.333		198	38.50	42	278.50	330

32 31 Fences and Gates

32 31 13 – Chain Link Fences and Gates

32 31 13.20 Fence, Chain Link Industrial

		Crew	Daily Output	Labor-Hours	Unit	Material	2014 Bare Costs Labor	2014 Bare Costs Equipment	Total	Total Incl O&P
5000	Double swing gates, incl. posts & hardware, in concrete									
5010	5' high, 12' opening, in concrete	B-80C	3.40	7.059	Opng.	365	201	82	648	825
5020	20' opening, in concrete		2.80	8.571		485	244	99.50	828.50	1,050
5060	6' high, 12' opening, in concrete		3.20	7.500		435	213	87	735	925
5070	20' opening, in concrete		2.60	9.231		605	262	107	974	1,225
5080	8' high, 12' opening, in concrete	B-80	2.13	11.252		435	325	355	1,115	1,400
5090	20' opening, in concrete		1.45	16.552		655	480	525	1,660	2,100
5100	10' high, 12' opening, in concrete		1.31	18.321		770	530	580	1,880	2,375
5110	20' opening, in concrete		1.03	23.301		835	675	735	2,245	2,850
5120	12' high, 12' opening, in concrete		1.05	22.857		1,250	660	720	2,630	3,275
5130	20' opening, in concrete		.85	28.235		1,325	815	890	3,030	3,800
5190	For aluminized steel add					20%				
7075	Fence, for small jobs 100 L.F. or less fence w/or wo gate, add				S.F.	20%				

32 31 13.25 Fence, Chain Link Residential

		Crew	Daily Output	Labor-Hours	Unit	Material	2014 Bare Costs Labor	2014 Bare Costs Equipment	Total	Total Incl O&P
0010	**FENCE, CHAIN LINK RESIDENTIAL**									
0011	Schedule 20, 11 ga. wire, 1-5/8" post									
0020	10' O.C., 1-3/8" top rail, 2" corner post, galv. stl. 3' high	B-80C	500	.048	L.F.	2	1.36	.56	3.92	5.10
0050	4' high		400	.060		7.05	1.71	.70	9.46	11.40
0100	6' high		200	.120		9.70	3.41	1.39	14.50	17.90
0150	Add for gate 3' wide, 1-3/8" frame, 3' high		12	2	Ea.	81	57	23	161	210
0170	4' high		10	2.400		87	68	28	183	240
0190	6' high		10	2.400		110	68	28	206	266
0200	Add for gate 4' wide, 1-3/8" frame, 3' high		9	2.667		88	76	31	195	258
0220	4' high		9	2.667		96	76	31	203	267
0240	6' high		8	3		120	85.50	35	240.50	315
0350	Aluminized steel, 11 ga. wire, 3' high		500	.048	L.F.	8.05	1.36	.56	9.97	11.75
0380	4' high		400	.060		9	1.71	.70	11.41	13.55
0400	6' high		200	.120		10.75	3.41	1.39	15.55	19.10
0450	Add for gate 3' wide, 1-3/8" frame, 3' high		12	2	Ea.	89	57	23	169	219
0470	4' high		10	2.400		97.50	68	28	193.50	252
0490	6' high		10	2.400		122	68	28	218	279
0500	Add for gate 4' wide, 1-3/8" frame, 3' high		10	2.400		98.50	68	28	194.50	253
0520	4' high		9	2.667		118	76	31	225	291
0540	6' high		8	3		131	85.50	35	251.50	325
0620	Vinyl covered, 9 ga. wire, 3' high		500	.048	L.F.	7.15	1.36	.56	9.07	10.75
0640	4' high		400	.060		8.15	1.71	.70	10.56	12.60
0660	6' high		200	.120		10.05	3.41	1.39	14.85	18.30
0720	Add for gate 3' wide, 1-3/8" frame, 3' high		12	2	Ea.	89	57	23	169	219
0740	4' high		10	2.400		96	68	28	192	251
0760	6' high		10	2.400		120	68	28	216	277
0780	Add for gate 4' wide, 1-3/8" frame, 3' high		10	2.400		96.50	68	28	192.50	251
0800	4' high		9	2.667		101	76	31	208	272
0820	6' high		8	3		128	85.50	35	248.50	320
7076	Fence, for small jobs 100 L.F. fence or less w/or wo gate, add				S.F.	20%				

32 31 13.26 Tennis Court Fences and Gates

		Crew	Daily Output	Labor-Hours	Unit	Material	2014 Bare Costs Labor	2014 Bare Costs Equipment	Total	Total Incl O&P
0010	**TENNIS COURT FENCES AND GATES**									
0860	Tennis courts, 11 ga. wire, 2-1/2" post set									
0870	in concrete, 10' O.C., 1-5/8" top rail									
0900	10' high	B-80	190	.126	L.F.	21.50	3.65	3.99	29.14	34
0920	12' high		170	.141	"	22.50	4.08	4.46	31.04	37
1000	Add for gate 4' wide, 1-5/8" frame 7' high		10	2.400	Ea.	228	69.50	76	373.50	450
1040	Aluminized steel, 11 ga. wire 10' high		190	.126	L.F.	19.35	3.65	3.99	26.99	32

32 31 13 – Chain Link Fences and Gates

32 31 13.26 Tennis Court Fences and Gates

	32 31 13.26 Tennis Court Fences and Gates	Crew	Daily Output	Labor-Hours	Unit	Material	2014 Bare Costs Labor	Equipment	Total	Total Incl O&P
1100	12' high	B-80	170	.141	L.F.	21.50	4.08	4.46	30.04	35.50
1140	Add for gate 4' wide, 1-5/8" frame, 7' high		10	2.400	Ea.	258	69.50	76	403.50	485
1250	Vinyl covered, 9 ga. wire, 10' high		190	.126	L.F.	19.80	3.65	3.99	27.44	32.50
1300	12' high		170	.141	"	23	4.08	4.46	31.54	37.50
1310	Fence, CL, tennis court, transom gate, single, galv., 4' x 7'	B-80A	8.72	2.752	Ea.	295	77.50	38	410.50	500
1400	Add for gate 4' wide, 1-5/8" frame, 7' high	B-80	10	2.400	"	310	69.50	76	455.50	540

32 31 13.33 Chain Link Backstops

	32 31 13.33 Chain Link Backstops	Crew	Daily Output	Labor-Hours	Unit	Material	2014 Bare Costs Labor	Equipment	Total	Total Incl O&P
0010	**CHAIN LINK BACKSTOPS**									
0015	Backstops, baseball, prefabricated, 30' wide, 12' high & 1 overhang	B-1	1	24	Ea.	2,550	695		3,245	3,975
0100	40' wide, 12' high & 2 overhangs	"	.75	32		6,825	925		7,750	9,050
0300	Basketball, steel, single goal	B-13	3.04	15.789		1,425	480	245	2,150	2,650
0400	Double goal	"	1.92	25		1,950	755	390	3,095	3,850
0600	Tennis, wire mesh with pair of ends	B-1	2.48	9.677	Set	2,675	279		2,954	3,400
0700	Enclosed court	"	1.30	18.462	Ea.	9,225	535		9,760	11,000

32 31 19 – Decorative Metal Fences and Gates

32 31 19.10 Decorative Fence

	32 31 19.10 Decorative Fence	Crew	Daily Output	Labor-Hours	Unit	Material	2014 Bare Costs Labor	Equipment	Total	Total Incl O&P
0010	**DECORATIVE FENCE**									
5300	Tubular picket, steel, 6' sections, 1-9/16" posts, 4' high	B-80C	300	.080	L.F.	30.50	2.27	.93	33.70	38.50
5400	2" posts, 5' high		240	.100		34.50	2.84	1.16	38.50	44
5600	2" posts, 6' high		200	.120		41	3.41	1.39	45.80	52.50
5700	Staggered picket 1-9/16" posts, 4' high		300	.080		30.50	2.27	.93	33.70	38.50
5800	2" posts, 5' high		240	.100		34.50	2.84	1.16	38.50	44
5900	2" posts, 6' high		200	.120		41	3.41	1.39	45.80	52.50
6200	Gates, 4' high, 3' wide	B-1	10	2.400	Ea.	274	69.50		343.50	415
6300	5' high, 3' wide		10	2.400		340	69.50		409.50	490
6400	6' high, 3' wide		10	2.400		390	69.50		459.50	545
6500	4' wide		10	2.400		415	69.50		484.50	570

32 31 26 – Wire Fences and Gates

32 31 26.10 Fences, Misc. Metal

	32 31 26.10 Fences, Misc. Metal	Crew	Daily Output	Labor-Hours	Unit	Material	2014 Bare Costs Labor	Equipment	Total	Total Incl O&P
0010	**FENCES, MISC. METAL**									
0012	Chicken wire, posts @ 4', 1" mesh, 4' high	B-80C	410	.059	L.F.	3.61	1.66	.68	5.95	7.50
0100	2" mesh, 6' high		350	.069		3.80	1.95	.79	6.54	8.30
0200	Galv. steel, 12 ga., 2" x 4" mesh, posts 5' O.C., 3' high		300	.080		2.75	2.27	.93	5.95	7.85
0300	5' high		300	.080		3.35	2.27	.93	6.55	8.50
0400	14 ga., 1" x 2" mesh, 3' high		300	.080		3.40	2.27	.93	6.60	8.55
0500	5' high		300	.080		4.55	2.27	.93	7.75	9.85
1000	Kennel fencing, 1-1/2" mesh, 6' long, 3'-6" wide, 6'-2" high	2 Clab	4	4	Ea.	500	113		613	740
1050	12' long		4	4		715	113		828	975
1200	Top covers, 1-1/2" mesh, 6' long		15	1.067		135	30		165	200
1250	12' long		12	1.333		190	37.50		227.50	273
1300	For kennel doors, see Section 08 31 13.40									
4500	Security fence, prison grade, set in concrete, 12' high	B-80	25	.960	L.F.	61	27.50	30.50	119	147
4600	16' high	"	20	1.200	"	79	34.50	38	151.50	187

32 31 26.20 Wire Fencing, General

	32 31 26.20 Wire Fencing, General	Crew	Daily Output	Labor-Hours	Unit	Material	2014 Bare Costs Labor	Equipment	Total	Total Incl O&P
0010	**WIRE FENCING, GENERAL**									
0015	Barbed wire, galvanized, domestic steel, hi-tensile 15-1/2 ga.				M.L.F.	91			91	100
0020	Standard, 12-3/4 ga.					103			103	113
0210	Barbless wire, 2-strand galvanized, 12-1/2 ga.					103			103	113
0500	Helical razor ribbon, stainless steel, 18" dia x 18" spacing				C.L.F.	168			168	185
0600	Hardware cloth galv., 1/4" mesh, 23 ga., 2' wide				C.S.F.	65			65	71.50
0700	3' wide					48			48	53

32 31 Fences and Gates

32 31 26 – Wire Fences and Gates

32 31 26.20 Wire Fencing, General

		Crew	Daily Output	Labor-Hours	Unit	Material	2014 Bare Costs Labor	Equipment	Total	Total Incl O&P
0900	1/2" mesh, 19 ga., 2' wide				C.S.F.	37.50			37.50	41
1000	4' wide					23.50			23.50	26
1200	Chain link fabric, steel, 2" mesh, 6 ga., galvanized					247			247	271
1300	9 ga., galvanized					86.50			86.50	95.50
1350	Vinyl coated					88.50			88.50	97
1360	Aluminized					80			80	88
1400	2-1/4" mesh, 11.5 ga., galvanized					54			54	59.50
1600	1-3/4" mesh (tennis courts), 11.5 ga. (core), vinyl coated					54			54	59.50
1700	9 ga., galvanized					84			84	92.50
2100	Welded wire fabric, galvanized, 1" x 2", 14 ga.					60			60	66
2200	2" x 4", 12-1/2 ga.					60			60	66

32 31 29 – Wood Fences and Gates

32 31 29.20 Fence, Wood Rail

		Crew	Daily Output	Labor-Hours	Unit	Material	2014 Bare Costs Labor	Equipment	Total	Total Incl O&P
0010	**FENCE, WOOD RAIL**									
0012	Picket, No. 2 cedar, Gothic, 2 rail, 3' high	B-1	160	.150	L.F.	7.55	4.33		11.88	15.60
0050	Gate, 3'-6" wide	B-80C	9	2.667	Ea.	76.50	76	31	183.50	245
0400	3 rail, 4' high		150	.160	L.F.	8.45	4.55	1.85	14.85	18.95
0500	Gate, 3'-6" wide		9	2.667	Ea.	94.50	76	31	201.50	265
0600	Open rail, rustic, No. 1 cedar, 2 rail, 3' high		160	.150	L.F.	5.85	4.26	1.74	11.85	15.50
0650	Gate, 3' wide		9	2.667	Ea.	80	76	31	187	249
0700	3 rail, 4' high		150	.160	L.F.	7	4.55	1.85	13.40	17.35
0900	Gate, 3' wide		9	2.667	Ea.	100	76	31	207	271
1200	Stockade, No. 2 cedar, treated wood rails, 6' high		160	.150	L.F.	8.80	4.26	1.74	14.80	18.75
1250	Gate, 3' wide		9	2.667	Ea.	95	76	31	202	266
1300	No. 1 cedar, 3-1/4" cedar rails, 6' high		160	.150	L.F.	19.85	4.26	1.74	25.85	31
1500	Gate, 3' wide		9	2.667	Ea.	215	76	31	322	400
1520	Open rail, split, No. 1 cedar, 2 rail, 3' high		160	.150	L.F.	5.90	4.26	1.74	11.90	15.55
1540	3 rail, 4'-0" high		150	.160		7.75	4.55	1.85	14.15	18.20
3300	Board, shadow box, 1" x 6", treated pine, 6' high		160	.150		12.40	4.26	1.74	18.40	22.50
3400	No. 1 cedar, 6' high		150	.160		24.50	4.55	1.85	30.90	36.50
3900	Basket weave, No. 1 cedar, 6' high		160	.150		33.50	4.26	1.74	39.50	46
3950	Gate, 3'-6" wide	B-1	8	3	Ea.	220	86.50		306.50	390
4000	Treated pine, 6' high		150	.160	L.F.	15.80	4.62		20.42	25
4200	Gate, 3'-6" wide		9	2.667	Ea.	160	77		237	305
5000	Fence rail, redwood, 2" x 4", merch. grade 8'		2400	.010	L.F.	2.39	.29		2.68	3.12
5050	Select grade, 8'		2400	.010	"	5.25	.29		5.54	6.30
6000	Fence post, select redwood, earthpacked & treated, 4" x 4" x 6'		96	.250	Ea.	13.50	7.20		20.70	27
6010	4" x 4" x 8'		96	.250		18.50	7.20		25.70	32.50
6020	Set in concrete, 4" x 4" x 6'		50	.480		21	13.85		34.85	46.50
6030	4" x 4" x 8'		50	.480		22	13.85		35.85	47.50
6040	Wood post, 4' high, set in concrete, incl. concrete		50	.480		13.50	13.85		27.35	38.50
6050	Earth packed		96	.250		16.50	7.20		23.70	30.50
6060	6' high, set in concrete, incl. concrete		50	.480		17	13.85		30.85	42
6070	Earth packed		96	.250		12.90	7.20		20.10	26.50

32 32 Retaining Walls

32 32 13 – Cast-in-Place Concrete Retaining Walls

32 32 13.10 Retaining Walls, Cast Concrete		Crew	Daily Output	Labor-Hours	Unit	Material	2014 Bare Costs Labor	Equipment	Total	Total Incl O&P
0010	**RETAINING WALLS, CAST CONCRETE**									
1800	Concrete gravity wall with vertical face including excavation & backfill									
1850	No reinforcing									
1900	6' high, level embankment	C-17C	36	2.306	L.F.	71.50	85	17.20	173.70	241
2000	33° slope embankment		32	2.594		84	95.50	19.35	198.85	275
2200	8' high, no surcharge		27	3.074		90	113	23	226	315
2300	33° slope embankment		24	3.458		109	127	26	262	365
2500	10' high, level embankment		19	4.368		129	161	32.50	322.50	450
2600	33° slope embankment	↓	18	4.611	↓	178	170	34.50	382.50	520
2800	Reinforced concrete cantilever, incl. excavation, backfill & reinf.									
2900	6' high, 33° slope embankment	C-17C	35	2.371	L.F.	66	87	17.70	170.70	239
3000	8' high, 33° slope embankment		29	2.862		76	105	21.50	202.50	286
3100	10' high, 33° slope embankment		20	4.150		99	153	31	283	400
3200	20' high, 500 lb. per L.F. surcharge	↓	7.50	11.067	↓	297	405	82.50	784.50	1,100
3500	Concrete cribbing, incl. excavation and backfill									
3700	12' high, open face	B-13	210	.229	S.F.	33	6.90	3.55	43.45	52
3900	Closed face	"	210	.229	"	31	6.90	3.55	41.45	49.50
4100	Concrete filled slurry trench, see Section 31 56 23.20									

32 32 23 – Segmental Retaining Walls

32 32 23.13 Segmental Conc. Unit Masonry Retaining Walls

		Crew	Daily Output	Labor-Hours	Unit	Material	2014 Bare Costs Labor	Equipment	Total	Total Incl O&P
0010	**SEGMENTAL CONC. UNIT MASONRY RETAINING WALLS**									
7100	Segmental Retaining Wall system, incl. pins, and void fill									
7120	base not included									
7140	Large unit, 8" high x 18" wide x 20" deep, 3 plane split	B-62	300	.080	S.F.	13.60	2.47	.58	16.65	19.70
7150	Straight split		300	.080		13.50	2.47	.58	16.55	19.60
7160	Medium, lt. wt., 8" high x 18" wide x 12" deep, 3 plane split		400	.060		10.45	1.85	.44	12.74	15.10
7170	Straight split		400	.060		9.85	1.85	.44	12.14	14.45
7180	Small unit, 4" x 18" x 10" deep, 3 plane split		400	.060		13.35	1.85	.44	15.64	18.25
7190	Straight split		400	.060		13	1.85	.44	15.29	17.90
7200	Cap unit, 3 plane split		300	.080		13.60	2.47	.58	16.65	19.70
7210	Cap unit, straight split		300	.080		13.60	2.47	.58	16.65	19.70
7250	Geo-grid soil reinforcement 4' x 50'	2 Clab	22500	.001		.70	.02		.72	.80
7255	Geo-grid soil reinforcement 6' x 150'	"	22500	.001	↓	.56	.02		.58	.65
8000	For higher walls, add components as necessary									

32 32 26 – Metal Crib Retaining Walls

32 32 26.10 Metal Bin Retaining Walls

		Crew	Daily Output	Labor-Hours	Unit	Material	2014 Bare Costs Labor	Equipment	Total	Total Incl O&P
0010	**METAL BIN RETAINING WALLS**									
0011	Aluminized steel bin, excavation									
0020	and backfill not included, 10' wide									
0100	4' high, 5.5' deep	B-13	650	.074	S.F.	27.50	2.24	1.15	30.89	35
0200	8' high, 5.5' deep		615	.078		31.50	2.36	1.21	35.07	40
0300	10' high, 7.7' deep		580	.083		34.50	2.51	1.29	38.30	43.50
0400	12' high, 7.7' deep		530	.091		37.50	2.74	1.41	41.65	47
0500	16' high, 7.7' deep		515	.093		39.50	2.82	1.45	43.77	50
0600	16' high, 9.9' deep		500	.096		42.50	2.91	1.49	46.90	53.50
0700	20' high, 9.9' deep		470	.102		48	3.09	1.59	52.68	60
0800	20' high, 12.1' deep		460	.104		43.50	3.16	1.62	48.28	54.50
0900	24' high, 12.1' deep		455	.105		46	3.19	1.64	50.83	58
1000	24' high, 14.3' deep		450	.107		54	3.23	1.66	58.89	66
1100	28' high, 14.3' deep	↓	440	.109	↓	56	3.30	1.70	61	69
1300	For plain galvanized bin type walls, deduct					10%				

32 32 Retaining Walls

32 32 29 – Timber Retaining Walls

32 32 29.10 Landscape Timber Retaining Walls	Crew	Daily Output	Labor-Hours	Unit	Material	2014 Bare Costs Labor	Equipment	Total	Total Incl O&P
0010	**LANDSCAPE TIMBER RETAINING WALLS**								
0100	Treated timbers, 6" x 6"	1 Clab	265	.030	L.F.	2	.85		2.85	3.63
0110	6" x 8"	"	200	.040	"	2.62	1.13		3.75	4.78
0120	Drilling holes in timbers for fastening, 1/2"	1 Carp	450	.018	Inch		.64		.64	1.07
0130	5/8"	"	450	.018	"		.64		.64	1.07
0140	Reinforcing rods for fastening, 1/2"	1 Clab	312	.026	L.F.	.37	.72		1.09	1.62
0150	5/8"	"	312	.026	"	.57	.72		1.29	1.85
0160	Reinforcing fabric	2 Clab	2500	.006	S.Y.	1.88	.18		2.06	2.37
0170	Gravel backfill		28	.571	C.Y.	19.90	16.10		36	49
0180	Perforated pipe, 4" diameter with silt sock		1200	.013	L.F.	1.29	.38		1.67	2.05
0190	Galvanized 60d common nails	1 Clab	625	.013	Ea.	.16	.36		.52	.79
0200	20d common nails	"	3800	.002	"	.04	.06		.10	.14

32 32 36 – Gabion Retaining Walls

32 32 36.10 Stone Gabion Retaining Walls

		Crew	Daily Output	Labor-Hours	Unit	Material	Labor	Equipment	Total	Total Incl O&P
0010	**STONE GABION RETAINING WALLS**									
4300	Stone filled gabions, not incl. excavation,									
4310	Stone, delivered, 3' wide									
4350	Galvanized, 6' high, 33° slope embankment	B-13	49	.980	L.F.	42	29.50	15.20	86.70	113
4500	Highway surcharge		27	1.778		84	54	27.50	165.50	214
4600	9' high, up to 33° slope embankment		24	2		94.50	60.50	31	186	240
4700	Highway surcharge		16	3		147	91	46.50	284.50	365
4900	12' high, up to 33° slope embankment		14	3.429		147	104	53.50	304.50	395
5000	Highway surcharge		11	4.364		210	132	68	410	530
5950	For PVC coating, add					12%				

32 32 60 – Stone Retaining Walls

32 32 60.10 Retaining Walls, Stone

		Crew	Daily Output	Labor-Hours	Unit	Material	Labor	Equipment	Total	Total Incl O&P
0010	**RETAINING WALLS, STONE**									
0015	Including excavation, concrete footing and									
0020	stone 3' below grade. Price is exposed face area.									
0200	Decorative random stone, to 6' high, 1'-6" thick, dry set	D-1	35	.457	S.F.	30.50	14.75		45.25	58
0300	Mortar set		40	.400		33.50	12.90		46.40	58.50
0500	Cut stone, to 6' high, 1'-6" thick, dry set		35	.457		31.50	14.75		46.25	59.50
0600	Mortar set		40	.400		32.50	12.90		45.40	57.50
0800	Random stone, 6' to 10' high, 2" thick, dry set		45	.356		41	11.45		52.45	64
0900	Mortar set		50	.320		42	10.30		52.30	63
1100	Cut stone, 6' to 10' high, 2" thick, dry set		45	.356		40	11.45		51.45	63
1200	Mortar set		50	.320		42	10.30		52.30	63

32 34 Fabricated Bridges

32 34 20 – Fabricated Pedestrian Bridges

32 34 20.10 Bridges, Pedestrian

		Crew	Daily Output	Labor-Hours	Unit	Material	Labor	Equipment	Total	Total Incl O&P
0010	**BRIDGES, PEDESTRIAN**									
0011	Spans over streams, roadways, etc.									
0020	including erection, not including foundations									
0050	Precast concrete, complete in place, 8' wide, 60' span	E-2	215	.223	S.F.	114	8.65	7.10	129.75	149
0100	100' span		185	.259		125	10.05	8.25	143.30	165
0150	120' span		160	.300		136	11.60	9.55	157.15	181
0200	150' span		145	.331		141	12.80	10.55	164.35	191
0300	Steel, trussed or arch spans, compl. in place, 8' wide, 40' span		320	.150		115	5.80	4.78	125.58	143

32 34 Fabricated Bridges

32 34 20 – Fabricated Pedestrian Bridges

32 34 20.10 Bridges, Pedestrian		Crew	Daily Output	Labor-Hours	Unit	Material	2014 Bare Costs Labor	Equipment	Total	Total Incl O&P
0400	50' span	E-2	395	.122	S.F.	103	4.71	3.87	111.58	126
0500	60' span		465	.103		103	4	3.29	110.29	124
0600	80' span		570	.084		123	3.26	2.68	128.94	144
0700	100' span		465	.103		173	4	3.29	180.29	201
0800	120' span		365	.132		218	5.10	4.19	227.29	254
0900	150' span		310	.155		232	6	4.93	242.93	272
1000	160' span		255	.188		232	7.30	6	245.30	275
1100	10' wide, 80' span		640	.075		123	2.91	2.39	128.30	143
1200	120' span		415	.116		159	4.48	3.68	167.16	187
1300	150' span		445	.108		178	4.18	3.44	185.62	208
1400	200' span	↓	205	.234		190	9.05	7.45	206.50	234
1600	Wood, laminated type, complete in place, 80' span	C-12	203	.236		85	8.35	3.27	96.62	111
1700	130' span	"	153	.314	↓	88.50	11.10	4.33	103.93	121

32 35 Screening Devices

32 35 16 – Sound Barriers

32 35 16.10 Traffic Barriers, Highway Sound Barriers

		Crew	Daily Output	Labor-Hours	Unit	Material	2014 Bare Costs Labor	Equipment	Total	Total Incl O&P
0010	**TRAFFIC BARRIERS, HIGHWAY SOUND BARRIERS**									
0020	Highway sound barriers, not including footing									
0100	Precast concrete, concrete columns @ 30' OC, 8" T, 8' H	C-12	400	.120	L.F.	130	4.24	1.66	135.90	152
0110	12' H		265	.181		195	6.40	2.50	203.90	229
0120	16' H		200	.240		260	8.50	3.31	271.81	305
0130	20' H	↓	160	.300		325	10.60	4.14	339.74	380
0400	Lt. Wt. composite panel, cementitious face, St. posts @ 12' OC, 8' H	B-80B	190	.168		154	5.10	1.31	160.41	179
0410	12' H		125	.256		231	7.75	1.99	240.74	269
0420	16' H		95	.337		310	10.20	2.61	322.81	360
0430	20' H	↓	75	.427	↓	385	12.90	3.31	401.21	450

32 84 Planting Irrigation

32 84 23 – Underground Sprinklers

32 84 23.10 Sprinkler Irrigation System

		Crew	Daily Output	Labor-Hours	Unit	Material	2014 Bare Costs Labor	Equipment	Total	Total Incl O&P
0010	**SPRINKLER IRRIGATION SYSTEM**									
0011	For lawns									
0100	Golf course with fully automatic system	C-17	.05	1600	9 holes	100,000	58,500		158,500	209,000
0200	24' diam. head at 15' O.C. incl. piping, auto oper., minimum	B-20	70	.343	Head	23.50	9.90		33.40	42
0300	Maximum		40	.600		56	17.30		73.30	90.50
0500	60' diam. head at 40' O.C. incl. piping, auto oper., minimum		28	.857		70.50	25		95.50	119
0600	Maximum		23	1.043	↓	190	30		220	260
0800	Residential system, custom, 1" supply		2000	.012	S.F.	.26	.35		.61	.87
0900	1-1/2" supply	↓	1800	.013	"	.49	.38		.87	1.19
1020	Pop up spray head w/risers, hi-pop, full circle pattern, 4"	2 Skwk	76	.211	Ea.	4.48	7.65		12.13	17.85
1030	1/2 circle pattern, 4"		76	.211		4.48	7.65		12.13	17.85
1040	6", full circle pattern		76	.211		9.85	7.65		17.50	24
1050	1/2 circle pattern, 6"		76	.211		8.50	7.65		16.15	22.50
1060	12", full circle pattern		76	.211		11.60	7.65		19.25	25.50
1070	1/2 circle pattern, 12"		76	.211		11.50	7.65		19.15	25.50
1080	Pop up bubbler head w/risers, hi-pop bubbler head, 4"		76	.211		4.35	7.65		12	17.70
1090	6"		76	.211		9.10	7.65		16.75	23
1100	12"	↓	76	.211		10.90	7.65		18.55	25

32 84 23.10 Sprinkler Irrigation System		Crew	Daily Output	Labor-Hours	Unit	Material	2014 Bare Costs Labor	Equipment	Total	Total Incl O&P
1110	Impact full/part circle sprinklers, 28'-54' 25-60 PSI	2 Skwk	37	.432	Ea.	19.60	15.70		35.30	48
1120	Spaced 37'-49' @ 25-50 PSI		37	.432		27.50	15.70		43.20	57
1130	Spaced 43'-61' @ 30-60 PSI		37	.432		77	15.70		92.70	111
1140	Spaced 54'-78' @ 40-80 PSI		37	.432		133	15.70		148.70	173
1145	Impact rotor pop-up full/part commercial circle sprinklers									
1150	Spaced 42'-65' 35-80 PSI	2 Skwk	25	.640	Ea.	17	23		40	57.50
1160	Spaced 48'-76' 45-85 PSI	"	25	.640	"	18.70	23		41.70	59.50
1165	Impact rotor pop-up part. circle comm., 53'-75', 55-100 PSI, w/accessories									
1170	Plastic case, metal cover	2 Skwk	25	.640	Ea.	82	23		105	129
1180	Rubber cover		25	.640		63	23		86	109
1190	Iron case, metal cover		22	.727		135	26.50		161.50	194
1200	Rubber cover		22	.727		143	26.50		169.50	202
1250	Plastic case, 2 nozzle, metal cover		25	.640		128	23		151	179
1260	Rubber cover		25	.640		131	23		154	183
1270	Iron case, 2 nozzle, metal cover		22	.727		185	26.50		211.50	249
1280	Rubber cover		22	.727		185	26.50		211.50	249
1282	Impact rotor pop-up full circle commercial, 39'-99', 30-100 PSI									
1284	Plastic case, metal cover	2 Skwk	25	.640	Ea.	138	23		161	191
1286	Rubber cover		25	.640		158	23		181	212
1288	Iron case, metal cover		22	.727		203	26.50		229.50	268
1290	Rubber cover		22	.727		210	26.50		236.50	276
1292	Plastic case, 2 nozzle, metal cover		22	.727		150	26.50		176.50	210
1294	Rubber cover		22	.727		150	26.50		176.50	210
1296	Iron case, 2 nozzle, metal cover		20	.800		198	29		227	266
1298	Rubber cover		20	.800		205	29		234	275
1305	Electric remote control valve, plastic, 3/4"		18	.889		17.30	32.50		49.80	73.50
1310	1"		18	.889		33	32.50		65.50	91
1320	1-1/2"		18	.889		60.50	32.50		93	121
1330	2"		18	.889		86	32.50		118.50	149
1335	Quick coupling valves, brass, locking cover									
1340	Inlet coupling valve, 3/4"	2 Skwk	18.75	.853	Ea.	22	31		53	76.50
1350	1"		18.75	.853		30.50	31		61.50	86.50
1360	Controller valve boxes, 6" round boxes		18.75	.853		7	31		38	60
1370	10" round boxes		14.25	1.123		11.30	41		52.30	81.50
1380	12" square box		9.75	1.641		15.90	59.50		75.40	118
1388	Electromech. control, 14 day 3-60 min., auto start to 23/day									
1390	4 station	2 Skwk	1.04	15.385	Ea.	185	560		745	1,150
1400	7 station		.64	25		201	910		1,111	1,750
1410	12 station		.40	40		220	1,450		1,670	2,700
1420	Dual programs, 18 station		.24	66.667		610	2,425		3,035	4,750
1430	23 station		.16	100		690	3,625		4,315	6,875
1435	Backflow preventer, bronze, 0-175 PSI, w/valves, test cocks									
1440	3/4"	2 Skwk	2	8	Ea.	103	290		393	605
1450	1"		2	8		118	290		408	620
1460	1-1/2"		2	8		280	290		570	800
1470	2"		2	8		345	290		635	870
1475	Pressure vacuum breaker, brass, 15-150 PSI									
1480	3/4"	2 Skwk	2	8	Ea.	60.50	290		350.50	555
1490	1"		2	8		65.50	290		355.50	560
1500	1-1/2"		2	8		270	290		560	785
1510	2"		2	8		325	290		615	850

32 91 13 – Soil Preparation

32 91 13.16 Mulching

		Crew	Daily Output	Labor-Hours	Unit	Material	2014 Bare Costs Labor	2014 Bare Costs Equipment	Total	Total Incl O&P
0010	**MULCHING**									
0100	Aged barks, 3" deep, hand spread	1 Clab	100	.080	S.Y.	3.38	2.26		5.64	7.50
0150	Skid steer loader	B-63	13.50	2.963	M.S.F.	375	83.50	12.90	471.40	570
0200	Hay, 1" deep, hand spread	1 Clab	475	.017	S.Y.	.48	.47		.95	1.33
0250	Power mulcher, small	B-64	180	.089	M.S.F.	53.50	2.54	2.39	58.43	65.50
0350	Large	B-65	530	.030	"	53.50	.86	1.12	55.48	61
0400	Humus peat, 1" deep, hand spread	1 Clab	700	.011	S.Y.	2.56	.32		2.88	3.36
0450	Push spreader	"	2500	.003	"	2.56	.09		2.65	2.97
0550	Tractor spreader	B-66	700	.011	M.S.F.	284	.41	.37	284.78	315
0600	Oat straw, 1" deep, hand spread	1 Clab	475	.017	S.Y.	.55	.47		1.02	1.41
0650	Power mulcher, small	B-64	180	.089	M.S.F.	61	2.54	2.39	65.93	74
0700	Large	B-65	530	.030	"	61	.86	1.12	62.98	69.50
0750	Add for asphaltic emulsion	B-45	1770	.009	Gal.	5.75	.26	.17	6.18	7
0800	Peat moss, 1" deep, hand spread	1 Clab	900	.009	S.Y.	2.63	.25		2.88	3.31
0850	Push spreader	"	2500	.003	"	2.63	.09		2.72	3.04
0950	Tractor spreader	B-66	700	.011	M.S.F.	292	.41	.37	292.78	320
1000	Polyethylene film, 6 mil	2 Clab	2000	.008	S.Y.	.44	.23		.67	.86
1100	Redwood nuggets, 3" deep, hand spread	1 Clab	150	.053	"	2.77	1.50		4.27	5.60
1150	Skid steer loader	B-63	13.50	2.963	M.S.F.	310	83.50	12.90	406.40	495
1200	Stone mulch, hand spread, ceramic chips, economy	1 Clab	125	.064	S.Y.	6.85	1.80		8.65	10.60
1250	Deluxe	"	95	.084	"	10.50	2.37		12.87	15.55
1300	Granite chips	B-1	10	2.400	C.Y.	69.50	69.50		139	194
1400	Marble chips		10	2.400		152	69.50		221.50	284
1600	Pea gravel		28	.857		75.50	25		100.50	125
1700	Quartz		10	2.400		188	69.50		257.50	325
1800	Tar paper, 15 lb. felt	1 Clab	800	.010	S.Y.	.49	.28		.77	1
1900	Wood chips, 2" deep, hand spread	"	220	.036	"	1.45	1.03		2.48	3.33
1950	Skid steer loader	B-63	20.30	1.970	M.S.F.	161	55.50	8.60	225.10	280

32 91 13.26 Planting Beds

		Crew	Daily Output	Labor-Hours	Unit	Material	2014 Bare Costs Labor	2014 Bare Costs Equipment	Total	Total Incl O&P
0010	**PLANTING BEDS**									
0100	Backfill planting pit, by hand, on site topsoil	2 Clab	18	.889	C.Y.		25		25	42
0200	Prepared planting mix, by hand	"	24	.667			18.80		18.80	31.50
0300	Skid steer loader, on site topsoil	B-62	340	.071			2.18	.51	2.69	4.21
0400	Prepared planting mix	"	410	.059			1.81	.43	2.24	3.49
1000	Excavate planting pit, by hand, sandy soil	2 Clab	16	1			28		28	47.50
1100	Heavy soil or clay	"	8	2			56.50		56.50	95
1200	1/2 C.Y. backhoe, sandy soil	B-11C	150	.107			3.51	2.44	5.95	8.55
1300	Heavy soil or clay	"	115	.139			4.58	3.18	7.76	11.15
2000	Mix planting soil, incl. loam, manure, peat, by hand	2 Clab	60	.267		43	7.50		50.50	60
2100	Skid steer loader	B-62	150	.160		43	4.94	1.16	49.10	57
3000	Pile sod, skid steer loader	"	2800	.009	S.Y.		.26	.06	.32	.51
3100	By hand	2 Clab	400	.040			1.13		1.13	1.90
4000	Remove sod, F.E. loader	B-10S	2000	.004			.15	.19	.34	.46
4100	Sod cutter	B-12K	3200	.005			.17	.31	.48	.63
4200	By hand	2 Clab	240	.067			1.88		1.88	3.16

32 91 19 – Landscape Grading

32 91 19.13 Topsoil Placement and Grading

		Crew	Daily Output	Labor-Hours	Unit	Material	2014 Bare Costs Labor	2014 Bare Costs Equipment	Total	Total Incl O&P
0010	**TOPSOIL PLACEMENT AND GRADING**									
0400	Spread from pile to rough finish grade, F.E. loader, 1.5 C.Y.	B-10S	200	.040	C.Y.		1.51	1.87	3.38	4.54
0500	Up to 200' radius, by hand	1 Clab	14	.571			16.10		16.10	27
0600	Top dress by hand, 1 C.Y. for 600 S.F.	"	11.50	.696		28	19.60		47.60	63.50
0700	Furnish and place, truck dumped, screened, 4" deep	B-10S	1300	.006	S.Y.	3.49	.23	.29	4.01	4.54

32 91 Planting Preparation

32 91 19 – Landscape Grading

32 91 19.13 Topsoil Placement and Grading	Crew	Daily Output	Labor-Hours	Unit	Material	2014 Bare Costs Labor	Equipment	Total	Total Incl O&P
0800	6" deep	B-10S	820	.010	S.Y.	4.46	.37	.46	5.29	6

32 92 Turf and Grasses

32 92 19 – Seeding

32 92 19.13 Mechanical Seeding

		Crew	Daily Output	Labor-Hours	Unit	Material	Labor	Equipment	Total	Total Incl O&P
0010	**MECHANICAL SEEDING**									
0020	Mechanical seeding, 215 lb./acre	B-66	1.50	5.333	Acre	650	193	173	1,016	1,225
0100	44 lb./M.S.Y.	"	2500	.003	S.Y.	.18	.12	.10	.40	.50
0101	$2.00/lb., 44 lb./M.S.Y.	1 Clab	13950	.001	S.F.	.02	.02		.04	.05
0300	Fine grading and seeding incl. lime, fertilizer & seed,									
0310	with equipment	B-14	1000	.048	S.Y.	.44	1.43	.37	2.24	3.29
0400	Fertilizer hand push spreader, 35 lb. per M.S.F.	1 Clab	200	.040	M.S.F.	14.95	1.13		16.08	18.30
0600	Limestone hand push spreader, 50 lb. per M.S.F.		180	.044		5.70	1.25		6.95	8.35
0800	Grass seed hand push spreader, 4.5 lb. per M.S.F.	↓	180	.044	↓	20	1.25		21.25	24
1000	Hydro or air seeding for large areas, incl. seed and fertilizer	B-81	8900	.002	S.Y.	.43	.05	.08	.56	.65
1100	With wood fiber mulch added	"	8900	.002	"	1.76	.05	.08	1.89	2.12
1300	Seed only, over 100 lb., field seed, minimum				Lb.	.75			.75	.83
1400	Maximum					4.30			4.30	4.73
1500	Lawn seed, minimum					1.25			1.25	1.38
1600	Maximum				↓	2.45			2.45	2.70
1800	Aerial operations, seeding only, field seed	B-58	50	.480	Acre	244	14.80	62	320.80	360
1900	Lawn seed		50	.480		405	14.80	62	481.80	540
2100	Seed and liquid fertilizer, field seed		50	.480		735	14.80	62	811.80	900
2200	Lawn seed	↓	50	.480	↓	895	14.80	62	971.80	1,075

32 92 23 – Sodding

32 92 23.10 Sodding Systems

		Crew	Daily Output	Labor-Hours	Unit	Material	Labor	Equipment	Total	Total Incl O&P
0010	**SODDING SYSTEMS**									
0020	Sodding, 1" deep, bluegrass sod, on level ground, over 8 M.S.F.	B-63	22	1.818	M.S.F.	250	51.50	7.95	309.45	370
0200	4 M.S.F.		17	2.353		265	66.50	10.25	341.75	415
0300	1000 S.F.		13.50	2.963		290	83.50	12.90	386.40	475
0500	Sloped ground, over 8 M.S.F.		6	6.667		250	188	29	467	620
0600	4 M.S.F.		5	8		265	226	35	526	710
0700	1000 S.F.		4	10		290	282	43.50	615.50	845
1000	Bent grass sod, on level ground, over 6 M.S.F.		20	2		253	56.50	8.70	318.20	385
1100	3 M.S.F.		18	2.222		265	62.50	9.70	337.20	410
1200	Sodding 1000 S.F. or less		14	2.857		293	80.50	12.45	385.95	475
1500	Sloped ground, over 6 M.S.F.		15	2.667		253	75	11.65	339.65	420
1600	3 M.S.F.		13.50	2.963		265	83.50	12.90	361.40	445
1700	1000 S.F.	↓	12	3.333	↓	293	94	14.55	401.55	500

32 93 Plants

32 93 10 – General Planting Costs

32 93 10.12 Travel		Crew	Daily Output	Labor-Hours	Unit	Material	2014 Bare Costs Labor	2014 Bare Costs Equipment	Total	Total Incl O&P
0010	**TRAVEL** add to all nursery items									
0015	10 to 20 miles one way, add				All				5%	5%
0100	30 to 50 miles one way, add				"				10%	10%

32 93 13 – Ground Covers

32 93 13.10 Ground Cover Plants

		Crew	Daily Output	Labor-Hours	Unit	Material	Labor	Equipment	Total	Total Incl O&P
0010	**GROUND COVER PLANTS**									
0012	Plants, pachysandra, in prepared beds	B-1	15	1.600	C	79.50	46		125.50	165
0200	Vinca minor, 1 yr., bare root, in prepared beds		12	2	"	64.50	57.50		122	168
0600	Stone chips, in 50 lb. bags, Georgia marble		520	.046	Bag	4.13	1.33		5.46	6.80
0700	Onyx gemstone		260	.092		16.50	2.67		19.17	22.50
0800	Quartz		260	.092		6.15	2.67		8.82	11.25
0900	Pea gravel, truckload lots		28	.857	Ton	24	25		49	67.50

32 93 33 – Shrubs

32 93 33.10 Shrubs and Trees

		Crew	Daily Output	Labor-Hours	Unit	Material	Labor	Equipment	Total	Total Incl O&P
0010	**SHRUBS AND TREES**									
0011	Evergreen, in prepared beds, B & B									
0100	Arborvitae pyramidal, 4'-5'	B-17	30	1.067	Ea.	110	32.50	26	168.50	204
0150	Globe, 12"-15"	B-1	96	.250		21.50	7.20		28.70	35.50
0300	Cedar, blue, 8'-10'	B-17	18	1.778		230	54.50	43.50	328	390
0500	Hemlock, Canadian, 2-1/2'-3'	B-1	36	.667		30.50	19.25		49.75	66
0550	Holly, Savannah, 8' - 10' H		9.68	2.479		258	71.50		329.50	405
0600	Juniper, andorra, 18"-24"		80	.300		36	8.65		44.65	54
0620	Wiltoni, 15"-18"		80	.300		28.50	8.65		37.15	46
0640	Skyrocket, 4-1/2'-5'	B-17	55	.582		117	17.80	14.25	149.05	174
0660	Blue pfitzer, 2'-2-1/2'	B-1	44	.545		42.50	15.75		58.25	73
0680	Ketleerie, 2-1/2'-3'		50	.480		51	13.85		64.85	79.50
0700	Pine, black, 2-1/2'-3'		50	.480		59.50	13.85		73.35	89
0720	Mugo, 18"-24"		60	.400		59	11.55		70.55	84.50
0740	White, 4'-5'	B-17	75	.427		51	13.05	10.45	74.50	89.50
0800	Spruce, blue, 18"-24"	B-1	60	.400		66.50	11.55		78.05	92.50
0840	Norway, 4'-5'	B-17	75	.427		82	13.05	10.45	105.50	124
0900	Yew, denisforma, 12"-15"	B-1	60	.400		36	11.55		47.55	59
1000	Capitata, 18"-24"		30	.800		32.50	23		55.50	75
1100	Hicksi, 2'-2-1/2'		30	.800		86.50	23		109.50	134

32 93 33.20 Shrubs

		Crew	Daily Output	Labor-Hours	Unit	Material	Labor	Equipment	Total	Total Incl O&P
0010	**SHRUBS**									
0011	Broadleaf Evergreen, planted in prepared beds									
0100	Andromeda, 15"-18", container	B-1	96	.250	Ea.	33	7.20		40.20	48.50
0200	Azalea, 15" - 18", container		96	.250		28.50	7.20		35.70	43.50
0300	Barberry, 9"-12", container		130	.185		17.55	5.35		22.90	28.50
0400	Boxwood, 15"-18", B&B		96	.250		42	7.20		49.20	58
0500	Euonymus, emerald gaiety, 12" to 15", container		115	.209		23	6.05		29.05	35.50
0600	Holly, 15"-18", B & B		96	.250		35.50	7.20		42.70	51.50
0900	Mount laurel, 18" - 24", B & B		80	.300		70	8.65		78.65	91.50
1000	Paxistema, 9 – 12" high		130	.185		22	5.35		27.35	33
1100	Rhododendron, 18"-24", container		48	.500		38	14.45		52.45	66.50
1200	Rosemary, 1 gal. container		600	.040		18	1.15		19.15	21.50
2000	Deciduous, planted in prepared beds, amelanchier, 2'-3', B & B		57	.421		120	12.15		132.15	153
2100	Azalea, 15"-18", B & B		96	.250		28.50	7.20		35.70	43.50
2300	Bayberry, 2'-3', B & B		57	.421		24	12.15		36.15	46.50
2600	Cotoneaster, 15"-18", B & B		80	.300		27	8.65		35.65	44

32 93 Plants

32 93 33 – Shrubs

	32 93 33.20 Shrubs	Crew	Daily Output	Labor-Hours	Unit	Material	2014 Bare Costs Labor	2014 Bare Costs Equipment	Total	Total Incl O&P
2800	Dogwood, 3'-4', B & B	B-17	40	.800	Ea.	31.50	24.50	19.55	75.55	97
2900	Euonymus, alatus compacta, 15" to 18", container	B-1	80	.300		25.50	8.65		34.15	42.50
3200	Forsythia, 2'-3', container	"	60	.400		18.70	11.55		30.25	40
3300	Hibiscus, 3'-4', B & B	B-17	75	.427		48	13.05	10.45	71.50	86
3400	Honeysuckle, 3'-4', B & B	B-1	60	.400		26	11.55		37.55	48
3500	Hydrangea, 2'-3', B & B	"	57	.421		29.50	12.15		41.65	53
3600	Lilac, 3'-4', B & B	B-17	40	.800		27.50	24.50	19.55	71.55	92.50
3900	Privet, bare root, 18"-24"	B-1	80	.300		14.25	8.65		22.90	30.50
4100	Quince, 2'-3', B & B	"	57	.421		28	12.15		40.15	51
4200	Russian olive, 3'-4', B & B	B-17	75	.427		26.50	13.05	10.45	50	62.50
4400	Spirea, 3'-4', B & B	B-1	70	.343		20	9.90		29.90	38.50
4500	Viburnum, 3'-4', B & B	B-17	40	.800		24	24.50	19.55	68.05	89

32 93 43 – Trees

32 93 43.20 Trees

	32 93 43.20 Trees		Crew	Daily Output	Labor-Hours	Unit	Material	Labor	Equipment	Total	Total Incl O&P
0010	**TREES**										
0011	Deciduous, in prep. beds, balled & burlapped (B&B)										
0100	Ash, 2" caliper	G	B-17	8	4	Ea.	185	122	98	405	515
0200	Beech, 5'-6'	G		50	.640		185	19.55	15.65	220.20	254
0300	Birch, 6'-8', 3 stems	G		20	1.600		170	49	39	258	310
0500	Crabapple, 6'-8'	G		20	1.600		140	49	39	228	279
0600	Dogwood, 4'-5'	G		40	.800		130	24.50	19.55	174.05	206
0700	Eastern redbud 4'-5'	G		40	.800		148	24.50	19.55	192.05	225
0800	Elm, 8'-10'	G		20	1.600		260	49	39	348	410
0900	Ginkgo, 6'-7'	G		24	1.333		150	41	32.50	223.50	269
1000	Hawthorn, 8'-10', 1" caliper	G		20	1.600		163	49	39	251	305
1100	Honeylocust, 10'-12', 1-1/2" caliper	G		10	3.200		205	98	78	381	475
1300	Larch, 8'	G		32	1		125	30.50	24.50	180	216
1400	Linden, 8'-10', 1" caliper	G		20	1.600		143	49	39	231	282
1500	Magnolia, 4'-5'	G		20	1.600		100	49	39	188	235
1600	Maple, red, 8'-10', 1-1/2" caliper	G		10	3.200		200	98	78	376	470
1700	Mountain ash, 8'-10', 1" caliper	G		16	2		175	61	49	285	350
1800	Oak, 2-1/2"-3" caliper	G		6	5.333		320	163	130	613	765
2100	Planetree, 9'-11', 1-1/4" caliper	G		10	3.200		240	98	78	416	515
2200	Plum, 6'-8', 1" caliper	G		20	1.600		80	49	39	168	213
2300	Poplar, 9'-11', 1-1/4" caliper	G		10	3.200		145	98	78	321	410
2500	Sumac, 2'-3'	G		75	.427		45	13.05	10.45	68.50	83
2700	Tulip, 5'-6'	G		40	.800		48	24.50	19.55	92.05	116
2800	Willow, 6'-8', 1" caliper	G		20	1.600		95	49	39	183	230

32 94 Planting Accessories

32 94 50 – Tree Guying

32 94 50.10 Tree Guying Systems

	32 94 50.10 Tree Guying Systems	Crew	Daily Output	Labor-Hours	Unit	Material	Labor	Equipment	Total	Total Incl O&P
0010	**TREE GUYING SYSTEMS**									
0015	Tree guying Including stakes, guy wire and wrap									
0100	Less than 3" caliper, 2 stakes	2 Clab	35	.457	Ea.	14.20	12.90		27.10	37
0200	3" to 4" caliper, 3 stakes	"	21	.762	"	19.20	21.50		40.70	57
1000	Including arrowhead anchor, cable, turnbuckles and wrap									
1100	Less than 3" caliper, 3" anchors	2 Clab	20	.800	Ea.	44.50	22.50		67	87
1200	3" to 6" caliper, 4" anchors		15	1.067		38	30		68	92.50
1300	6" caliper, 6" anchors		12	1.333		44.50	37.50		82	113

32 94 Planting Accessories

32 94 50 – Tree Guying

32 94 50.10 Tree Guying Systems	Crew	Daily Output	Labor-Hours	Unit	Material	2014 Bare Costs Labor	Equipment	Total	Total Incl O&P
1400	8" caliper, 8" anchors	2 Clab	9	1.778	Ea.	128	50		178	226

32 96 Transplanting

32 96 23 – Plant and Bulb Transplanting

32 96 23.23 Planting

		Crew	Daily Output	Labor-Hours	Unit	Material	Labor	Equipment	Total	Total Incl O&P
0010	**PLANTING**									
0011	Moving shrubs on site, 12" ball	3 Clab	28	.857	Ea.		24		24	40.50
0100	24" ball	B-62	22	1.091	"		33.50	7.90	41.40	65

32 96 23.43 Moving Trees

		Crew	Daily Output	Labor-Hours	Unit	Material	Labor	Equipment	Total	Total Incl O&P
0010	**MOVING TREES**, On site									
0300	Moving trees on site, 36" ball	B-6	3.75	6.400	Ea.		198	97.50	295.50	435
0400	60" ball	"	1	24	"		740	365	1,105	1,650

Estimating Tips

33 10 00 Water Utilities
33 30 00 Sanitary Sewerage Utilities
33 40 00 Storm Drainage Utilities

- Never assume that the water, sewer, and drainage lines will go in at the early stages of the project. Consider the site access needs before dividing the site in half with open trenches, loose pipe, and machinery obstructions. Always inspect the site to establish that the site drawings are complete. Check off all existing utilities on your drawings as you locate them. Be especially careful with underground utilities because appurtenances are sometimes buried during regrading or repaving operations. If you find any discrepancies, mark up the site plan for further research. Differing site conditions can be very costly if discovered later in the project.

- See also Section 33 01 00 for restoration of pipe where removal/replacement may be undesirable. Use of new types of piping materials can reduce the overall project cost. Owners/design engineers should consider the installing contractor as a valuable source of current information on utility products and local conditions that could lead to significant cost savings.

Reference Numbers

Reference numbers are shown in shaded boxes at the beginning of some major classifications. These numbers refer to related items in the Reference Section. The reference information may be an estimating procedure, an alternate pricing method, or technical information.

Note: Not all subdivisions listed here necessarily appear in this publication.

Note: **Trade Service,** *in part, has been used as a reference source for some of the material prices used in Division 33.*

33 01 Operation and Maintenance of Utilities

33 01 10 – Operation and Maintenance of Water Utilities

33 01 10.10 Corrosion Resistance

33 01 10.10 Corrosion Resistance	Crew	Daily Output	Labor-Hours	Unit	Material	2014 Bare Costs Labor	Equipment	Total	Total Incl O&P
0010 **CORROSION RESISTANCE**									
0012 Wrap & coat, add to pipe, 4" diameter				L.F.	2.53			2.53	2.78
0040 6" diameter					3.81			3.81	4.19
0060 8" diameter					4.53			4.53	4.98
0100 12" diameter					7.45			7.45	8.20
0200 24" diameter					14.40			14.40	15.85
0500 Coating, bituminous, per diameter inch, 1 coat, add					.64			.64	.70
0540 3 coat					1.93			1.93	2.12
0560 Coal tar epoxy, per diameter inch, 1 coat, add					.23			.23	.25
0600 3 coat					.69			.69	.76

33 01 30 – Operation and Maintenance of Sewer Utilities

33 01 30.72 Relining Sewers

33 01 30.72 Relining Sewers	Crew	Daily Output	Labor-Hours	Unit	Material	2014 Bare Costs Labor	Equipment	Total	Total Incl O&P
0010 **RELINING SEWERS**									
0011 With cement incl. bypass & cleaning									
0020 Less than 10,000 L.F., urban, 6" to 10"	C-17E	130	.615	L.F.	9.55	22.50	.73	32.78	49.50
0050 10" to 12"		125	.640		11.75	23.50	.76	36.01	53
0070 12" to 16"		115	.696		12.05	25.50	.82	38.37	57
0100 16" to 20"		95	.842		14.15	31	.99	46.14	68.50
0200 24" to 36"		90	.889		15.25	32.50	1.05	48.80	73
0300 48" to 72"		80	1		24.50	36.50	1.18	62.18	90

33 05 Common Work Results for Utilities

33 05 16 – Utility Structures

33 05 16.13 Precast Concrete Utility Boxes

33 05 16.13 Precast Concrete Utility Boxes	Crew	Daily Output	Labor-Hours	Unit	Material	2014 Bare Costs Labor	Equipment	Total	Total Incl O&P
0010 **PRECAST CONCRETE UTILITY BOXES**, 6" thick									
0050 5' x 10' x 6' high, I.D.	B-13	2	24	Ea.	3,675	725	375	4,775	5,650
0100 6' x 10' x 6' high, I.D.		2	24		3,800	725	375	4,900	5,825
0150 5' x 12' x 6' high, I.D.		2	24		4,025	725	375	5,125	6,050
0200 6' x 12' x 6' high, I.D.		1.80	26.667		4,525	805	415	5,745	6,775
0250 6' x 13' x 6' high, I.D.		1.50	32		5,925	970	495	7,390	8,700
0300 8' x 14' x 7' high, I.D.		1	48		6,400	1,450	745	8,595	10,300
0350 Hand hole, precast concrete, 1-1/2" thick									
0400 1'-0" x 2'-0" x 1'-9", I.D., light duty	B-1	4	6	Ea.	410	173		583	740
0450 4'-6" x 3'-2" x 2'-0", O.D., heavy duty	B-6	3	8	"	1,475	247	122	1,844	2,150

33 05 23 – Trenchless Utility Installation

33 05 23.19 Microtunneling

33 05 23.19 Microtunneling	Crew	Daily Output	Labor-Hours	Unit	Material	2014 Bare Costs Labor	Equipment	Total	Total Incl O&P
0010 **MICROTUNNELING**									
0011 Not including excavation, backfill, shoring,									
0020 or dewatering, average 50'/day, slurry method									
0100 24" to 48" outside diameter, minimum				L.F.				875	965
0110 Adverse conditions, add				%				50%	50%
1000 Rent microtunneling machine, average monthly lease				Month				97,500	107,000
1010 Operating technician				Day				630	705
1100 Mobilization and demobilization, minimum				Job				41,200	45,900
1110 Maximum				"				445,500	490,500

33 05 23.20 Horizontal Boring

33 05 23.20 Horizontal Boring	Crew	Daily Output	Labor-Hours	Unit	Material	2014 Bare Costs Labor	Equipment	Total	Total Incl O&P
0010 **HORIZONTAL BORING**									
0011 Casing only, 100' minimum,									
0020 not incl. jacking pits or dewatering									
0100 Roadwork, 1/2" thick wall, 24" diameter casing	B-42	20	2.800	L.F.	121	89.50	68.50	279	360

33 05 Common Work Results for Utilities

33 05 23 – Trenchless Utility Installation

33 05 23.20 Horizontal Boring

		Crew	Daily Output	Labor-Hours	Unit	Material	2014 Bare Costs Labor	Equipment	Total	Total Incl O&P
0200	36" diameter	B-42	16	3.500	L.F.	223	112	85.50	420.50	525
0300	48" diameter		15	3.733		310	120	91	521	640
0500	Railroad work, 24" diameter		15	3.733		121	120	91	332	435
0600	36" diameter		14	4		223	128	97.50	448.50	565
0700	48" diameter		12	4.667		310	150	114	574	715
0900	For ledge, add								20%	20%

33 05 26 – Utility Identification

33 05 26.10 Utility Accessories

		Crew	Daily Output	Labor-Hours	Unit	Material	2014 Bare Costs Labor	Equipment	Total	Total Incl O&P
0010	**UTILITY ACCESSORIES**									
0400	Underground tape, detectable, reinforced, alum. foil core, 2"	1 Clab	150	.053	C.L.F.	5.65	1.50		7.15	8.80
0500	6"	"	140	.057	"	27.50	1.61		29.11	33

33 11 Water Utility Distribution Piping

33 11 13 – Public Water Utility Distribution Piping

33 11 13.15 Water Supply, Ductile Iron Pipe

		Crew	Daily Output	Labor-Hours	Unit	Material	2014 Bare Costs Labor	Equipment	Total	Total Incl O&P
0010	**WATER SUPPLY, DUCTILE IRON PIPE** R331113-80									
0020	Not including excavation or backfill									
2000	Pipe, class 50 water piping, 18' lengths									
2020	Mechanical joint, 4" diameter	B-21A	200	.200	L.F.	15.60	6.95	2.41	24.96	31.50
2040	6" diameter		160	.250		17.75	8.70	3.01	29.46	37.50
2060	8" diameter		133.33	.300		24.50	10.45	3.61	38.56	48.50
2080	10" diameter		114.29	.350		35	12.15	4.21	51.36	63
2100	12" diameter		105.26	.380		42.50	13.20	4.57	60.27	74
2120	14" diameter		100	.400		60	13.90	4.81	78.71	94.50
2140	16" diameter		72.73	.550		63.50	19.10	6.60	89.20	109
2160	18" diameter		68.97	.580		74.50	20	7	101.50	123
2170	20" diameter		57.14	.700		85.50	24.50	8.40	118.40	144
2180	24" diameter		47.06	.850		108	29.50	10.25	147.75	179
3000	Tyton, push-on joint, 4" diameter		400	.100		17	3.48	1.20	21.68	26
3020	6" diameter		333.33	.120		17.85	4.17	1.44	23.46	28
3040	8" diameter		200	.200		23.50	6.95	2.41	32.86	39.50
3060	10" diameter		181.82	.220		35	7.65	2.65	45.30	54
3080	12" diameter		160	.250		37	8.70	3.01	48.71	59
3100	14" diameter		133.33	.300		41	10.45	3.61	55.06	66.50
3120	16" diameter		114.29	.350		49.50	12.15	4.21	65.86	79
3140	18" diameter		100	.400		55	13.90	4.81	73.71	89
3160	20" diameter		88.89	.450		57	15.65	5.40	78.05	95
3180	24" diameter		76.92	.520		64	18.10	6.25	88.35	107
8000	Fittings, mechanical joint									
8006	90° bend, 4" diameter	B-20A	16	2	Ea.	273	67.50		340.50	410
8020	6" diameter		12.80	2.500		405	84.50		489.50	585
8040	8" diameter		10.67	2.999		725	101		826	970
8060	10" diameter	B-21A	11.43	3.500		980	122	42	1,144	1,325
8080	12" diameter		10.53	3.799		1,375	132	45.50	1,552.50	1,775
8100	14" diameter		10	4		1,850	139	48	2,037	2,300
8120	16" diameter		7.27	5.502		2,400	191	66	2,657	3,025
8140	18" diameter		6.90	5.797		3,225	202	69.50	3,496.50	3,950
8160	20" diameter		5.71	7.005		4,050	244	84.50	4,378.50	4,950
8180	24" diameter		4.70	8.511		6,275	296	102	6,673	7,500
8200	Wye or tee, 4" diameter	B-20A	10.67	2.999		440	101		541	655

33 11 13 – Public Water Utility Distribution Piping

33 11 13.15 Water Supply, Ductile Iron Pipe		Crew	Daily Output	Labor-Hours	Unit	Material	2014 Bare Costs Labor	Equipment	Total	Total Incl O&P
8220	6" diameter	B-20A	8.53	3.751	Ea.	670	127		797	945
8240	8" diameter	↓	7.11	4.501		1,075	152		1,227	1,425
8260	10" diameter	B-21A	7.62	5.249		1,550	182	63	1,795	2,075
8280	12" diameter		7.02	5.698		2,025	198	68.50	2,291.50	2,625
8300	14" diameter		6.67	5.997		3,250	208	72	3,530	4,000
8320	16" diameter		4.85	8.247		3,600	287	99	3,986	4,550
8340	18" diameter		4.60	8.696		4,875	300	105	5,280	6,000
8360	20" diameter		3.81	10.499		6,825	365	126	7,316	8,275
8380	24" diameter	↓	3.14	12.739		11,600	445	153	12,198	13,600
8450	Decreaser, 6" x 4" diameter	B-20A	14.22	2.250		360	76		436	520
8460	8" x 6" diameter	"	11.64	2.749		525	93		618	735
8470	10" x 6" diameter	B-21A	13.33	3.001		645	104	36	785	925
8480	12" x 6" diameter		12.70	3.150		795	109	38	942	1,100
8490	16" x 6" diameter		10	4		1,425	139	48	1,612	1,850
8500	20" x 6" diameter	↓	8.42	4.751	↓	3,125	165	57	3,347	3,800
8550	Piping, butterfly valves, cast iron									
8560	4" diameter	B-20	6	4	Ea.	715	115		830	985
8570	6" diameter	"	5	4.800		850	139		989	1,175
8580	8" diameter	B-21	4	7		1,025	212	35	1,272	1,525
8590	10" diameter		3.50	8		1,500	242	40	1,782	2,100
8600	12" diameter		3	9.333		1,550	283	46.50	1,879.50	2,250
8610	14" diameter		2	14		3,700	425	70	4,195	4,850
8620	16" diameter	↓	2	14	↓	3,225	425	70	3,720	4,325

33 11 13.25 Water Supply, Polyvinyl Chloride Pipe

		Crew	Daily Output	Labor-Hours	Unit	Material	2014 Bare Costs Labor	Equipment	Total	Total Incl O&P
0010	**WATER SUPPLY, POLYVINYL CHLORIDE PIPE**									
0020	Not including excavation or backfill, unless specified									
2100	PVC pipe, Class 150, 1-1/2" diameter	Q-1A	750	.013	L.F.	.43	.57		1	1.42
2120	2" diameter		686	.015		.67	.63		1.30	1.77
2140	2-1/2" diameter	↓	500	.020		1.28	.86		2.14	2.83
2160	3" diameter	B-20	430	.056	↓	1.38	1.61		2.99	4.23
3010	AWWA C905, PR 100, DR 25									
3030	14" diameter	B-20A	213	.150	L.F.	13.65	5.05		18.70	23.50
3040	16" diameter		200	.160		19.20	5.40		24.60	30
3050	18" diameter		160	.200		24	6.75		30.75	38
3060	20" diameter		133	.241		30	8.15		38.15	46.50
3070	24" diameter		107	.299		43	10.10		53.10	64
3080	30" diameter		80	.400		81	13.50		94.50	112
3090	36" diameter		80	.400		126	13.50		139.50	161
3100	42" diameter		60	.533		168	18		186	215
3200	48" diameter		60	.533		220	18		238	272
4520	Pressure pipe Class 150, SDR 18, AWWA C900, 4" diameter		380	.084		2.61	2.84		5.45	7.60
4530	6" diameter		316	.101		5.25	3.42		8.67	11.50
4540	8" diameter		264	.121		8.90	4.09		12.99	16.55
4550	10" diameter		220	.145		15.45	4.91		20.36	25
4560	12" diameter	↓	186	.172	↓	20.50	5.80		26.30	32
8000	Fittings with rubber gasket									
8003	Class 150, DR 18									
8006	90° Bend , 4" diameter	B-20	100	.240	Ea.	42.50	6.95		49.45	58
8020	6" diameter		90	.267		74.50	7.70		82.20	95
8040	8" diameter		80	.300		144	8.65		152.65	174
8060	10" diameter		50	.480		330	13.85		343.85	385
8080	12" diameter	↓	30	.800	↓	425	23		448	505

33 11 Water Utility Distribution Piping

33 11 13 – Public Water Utility Distribution Piping

33 11 13.25 Water Supply, Polyvinyl Chloride Pipe

		Crew	Daily Output	Labor-Hours	Unit	Material	2014 Bare Costs Labor	Equipment	Total	Total Incl O&P
8100	Tee, 4" diameter	B-20	90	.267	Ea.	58	7.70		65.70	76.50
8120	6" diameter		80	.300		144	8.65		152.65	173
8140	8" diameter		70	.343		184	9.90		193.90	219
8160	10" diameter		40	.600		590	17.30		607.30	680
8180	12" diameter		20	1.200		765	34.50		799.50	900
8200	45° Bend, 4" diameter		100	.240		42	6.95		48.95	57.50
8220	6" diameter		90	.267		73	7.70		80.70	93
8240	8" diameter		50	.480		144	13.85		157.85	183
8260	10" diameter		50	.480		330	13.85		343.85	385
8280	12" diameter		30	.800		425	23		448	505
8300	Reducing tee 6" x 4"		100	.240		126	6.95		132.95	150
8320	8" x 6"		90	.267		224	7.70		231.70	259
8330	10" x 6"		90	.267		380	7.70		387.70	430
8340	10" x 8"		90	.267		395	7.70		402.70	445
8350	12" x 6"		90	.267		450	7.70		457.70	505
8360	12" x 8"		90	.267		470	7.70		477.70	530
8400	Tapped service tee (threaded type) 6" x 6" x 3/4"		100	.240		95	6.95		101.95	117
8430	6" x 6" x 1"		90	.267		95	7.70		102.70	118
8440	6" x 6" x 1-1/2"		90	.267		95	7.70		102.70	118
8450	6" x 6" x 2"		90	.267		95	7.70		102.70	118
8460	8" x 8" x 3/4"		90	.267		140	7.70		147.70	167
8470	8" x 8" x 1"		90	.267		140	7.70		147.70	167
8480	8" x 8" x 1-1/2"		90	.267		140	7.70		147.70	167
8490	8" x 8" x 2"		90	.267		140	7.70		147.70	167
8500	Repair coupling 4"		100	.240		22.50	6.95		29.45	36.50
8520	6" diameter		90	.267		34.50	7.70		42.20	51
8540	8" diameter		50	.480		83	13.85		96.85	115
8560	10" diameter		50	.480		208	13.85		221.85	253
8580	12" diameter		50	.480		233	13.85		246.85	281
8600	Plug end 4"		100	.240		22.50	6.95		29.45	36.50
8620	6" diameter		90	.267		40.50	7.70		48.20	57.50
8640	8" diameter		50	.480		69	13.85		82.85	99.50
8660	10" diameter		50	.480		96.50	13.85		110.35	130
8680	12" diameter		50	.480		119	13.85		132.85	155

33 12 Water Utility Distribution Equipment

33 12 19 – Water Utility Distribution Fire Hydrants

33 12 19.10 Fire Hydrants

		Crew	Daily Output	Labor-Hours	Unit	Material	2014 Bare Costs Labor	Equipment	Total	Total Incl O&P
0010	**FIRE HYDRANTS**									
0020	Mechanical joints unless otherwise noted									
1000	Fire hydrants, two way; excavation and backfill not incl.									
1100	4-1/2" valve size, depth 2'-0"	B-21	10	2.800	Ea.	1,650	85	14	1,749	1,975
1120	2'-6"		10	2.800		1,750	85	14	1,849	2,075
1140	3'-0"		10	2.800		1,875	85	14	1,974	2,200
1300	7'-0"		6	4.667		2,150	141	23.50	2,314.50	2,650
2400	Lower barrel extensions with stems, 1'-0"	B-20	14	1.714		355	49.50		404.50	475
2480	3'-0"	"	12	2		770	57.50		827.50	940

33 16 Water Utility Storage Tanks

33 16 13 – Aboveground Water Utility Storage Tanks

33 16 13.13 Steel Water Storage Tanks

	33 16 13.13 Steel Water Storage Tanks	Crew	Daily Output	Labor-Hours	Unit	Material	2014 Bare Costs Labor	Equipment	Total	Total Incl O&P
0010	**STEEL WATER STORAGE TANKS**									
0910	Steel, ground level, ht./diam. less than 1, not incl. fdn., 100,000 gallons				Ea.				202,000	244,500
1000	250,000 gallons								295,500	324,000
1200	500,000 gallons								417,000	458,500
1250	750,000 gallons								538,000	591,500
1300	1,000,000 gallons								558,000	725,500
1500	2,000,000 gallons								1,043,000	1,148,000
1600	4,000,000 gallons								2,121,000	2,333,000
1800	6,000,000 gallons								3,095,000	3,405,000
1850	8,000,000 gallons								4,068,000	4,475,000
1910	10,000,000 gallons				▼				5,050,000	5,554,500
2100	Steel standpipes, ht./diam. more than 1, 100' to overflow, no fdn.									
2200	500,000 gallons				Ea.				546,500	600,500
2400	750,000 gallons								722,500	794,500
2500	1,000,000 gallons								1,060,500	1,167,000
2700	1,500,000 gallons								1,749,000	1,923,000
2800	2,000,000 gallons				▼				2,327,000	2,559,000

33 16 13.16 Prestressed Conc. Water Storage Tanks

	33 16 13.16 Prestressed Conc. Water Storage Tanks	Crew	Daily Output	Labor-Hours	Unit	Material	Labor	Equipment	Total	Total Incl O&P
0010	**PRESTRESSED CONC. WATER STORAGE TANKS**									
0020	Not including fdn., pipe or pumps, 250,000 gallons				Ea.				299,000	329,500
0100	500,000 gallons								487,000	536,000
0300	1,000,000 gallons								707,000	807,500
0400	2,000,000 gallons								1,072,000	1,179,000
0600	4,000,000 gallons								1,706,000	1,877,000
0700	6,000,000 gallons								2,266,000	2,493,000
0750	8,000,000 gallons								2,924,000	3,216,000
0800	10,000,000 gallons				▼				3,533,000	3,886,000

33 16 13.23 Plastic-Coated Fabric Pillow Water Tanks

	33 16 13.23 Plastic-Coated Fabric Pillow Water Tanks	Crew	Daily Output	Labor-Hours	Unit	Material	Labor	Equipment	Total	Total Incl O&P
0010	**PLASTIC-COATED FABRIC PILLOW WATER TANKS**									
7000	Water tanks, vinyl coated fabric pillow tanks, freestanding, 5,000 gallons	4 Clab	4	8	Ea.	3,600	226		3,826	4,325
7100	Supporting embankment not included, 25,000 gallons	6 Clab	2	24		13,000	675		13,675	15,400
7200	50,000 gallons	8 Clab	1.50	42.667		18,100	1,200		19,300	21,900
7300	100,000 gallons	9 Clab	.90	80		41,500	2,250		43,750	49,500
7400	150,000 gallons		.50	144		59,500	4,050		63,550	72,500
7500	200,000 gallons		.40	180		73,500	5,075		78,575	89,500
7600	250,000 gallons	▼	.30	240	▼	103,500	6,775		110,275	125,500

33 16 19 – Elevated Water Utility Storage Tanks

33 16 19.50 Elevated Water Storage Tanks

	33 16 19.50 Elevated Water Storage Tanks	Crew	Daily Output	Labor-Hours	Unit	Material	Labor	Equipment	Total	Total Incl O&P
0010	**ELEVATED WATER STORAGE TANKS**									
0011	Not incl. pipe, pumps or foundation									
3000	Elevated water tanks, 100' to bottom capacity line, incl. painting									
3010	50,000 gallons				Ea.				185,000	204,000
3300	100,000 gallons								280,000	307,500
3400	250,000 gallons								751,500	826,500
3600	500,000 gallons								1,336,000	1,470,000
3700	750,000 gallons								1,622,000	1,783,500
3900	1,000,000 gallons				▼				2,322,000	2,556,000

33 21 Water Supply Wells

33 21 13 – Public Water Supply Wells

33 21 13.10 Wells and Accessories

33 21 13.10 Wells and Accessories	Crew	Daily Output	Labor-Hours	Unit	Material	2014 Bare Costs Labor	Equipment	Total	Total Incl O&P
0010 **WELLS & ACCESSORIES**									
0011 Domestic									
0100 Drilled, 4" to 6" diameter	B-23	120	.333	L.F.		9.55	24	33.55	42.50
0200 8" diameter	"	95.20	.420	"		12	30.50	42.50	53.50
0400 Gravel pack well, 40' deep, incl. gravel & casing, complete									
0500 24" diameter casing x 18" diameter screen	B-23	.13	307	Total	38,800	8,800	22,200	69,800	82,000
0600 36" diameter casing x 18" diameter screen		.12	333	"	40,000	9,525	24,000	73,525	86,500
0800 Observation wells, 1-1/4" riser pipe	↓	163	.245	V.L.F.	20.50	7	17.70	45.20	54
0900 For flush Buffalo roadway box, add	1 Skwk	16.60	.482	Ea.	51.50	17.50		69	86
1200 Test well, 2-1/2" diameter, up to 50' deep (15 to 50 GPM)	B-23	1.51	26.490	"	810	760	1,900	3,470	4,275
1300 Over 50' deep, add	"	121.80	.328	L.F.	21.50	9.40	23.50	54.40	65.50
1500 Pumps, installed in wells to 100' deep, 4" submersible									
1510 1/2 H.P.	Q-1	3.22	4.969	Ea.	450	191		641	810
1520 3/4 H.P.		2.66	6.015		590	231		821	1,025
1600 1 H.P.	↓	2.29	6.987		680	268		948	1,175
1700 1-1/2 H.P.	Q-22	1.60	10		735	385	415	1,535	1,900
1800 2 H.P.		1.33	12.030		890	460	500	1,850	2,300
1900 3 H.P.		1.14	14.035		1,375	540	580	2,495	3,025
2000 5 H.P.		1.14	14.035		2,300	540	580	3,420	4,050
2050 Remove and install motor only, 4 H.P.		1.14	14.035		1,100	540	580	2,220	2,725
3000 Pump, 6" submersible, 25' to 150' deep, 25 H.P., 249 to 297 GPM		.89	17.978		7,175	690	745	8,610	9,850
3100 25' to 500' deep, 30 H.P., 100 to 300 GPM	↓	.73	21.918	↓	8,600	840	910	10,350	11,800
9950 See Section 31 23 19.40 for wellpoints									
9960 See Section 31 23 19.30 for drainage wells									

33 21 13.20 Water Supply Wells, Pumps

33 21 13.20 Water Supply Wells, Pumps	Crew	Daily Output	Labor-Hours	Unit	Material	2014 Bare Costs Labor	Equipment	Total	Total Incl O&P
0010 **WATER SUPPLY WELLS, PUMPS**									
0011 With pressure control									
1000 Deep well, jet, 42 gal. galvanized tank									
1040 3/4 HP	1 Plum	.80	10	Ea.	1,100	425		1,525	1,925
3000 Shallow well, jet, 30 gal. galvanized tank									
3040 1/2 HP	1 Plum	2	4	Ea.	895	170		1,065	1,275

33 31 Sanitary Utility Sewerage Piping

33 31 13 – Public Sanitary Utility Sewerage Piping

33 31 13.15 Sewage Collection, Concrete Pipe

33 31 13.15 Sewage Collection, Concrete Pipe	Crew	Daily Output	Labor-Hours	Unit	Material	2014 Bare Costs Labor	Equipment	Total	Total Incl O&P
0010 **SEWAGE COLLECTION, CONCRETE PIPE**									
0020 See Section 33 41 13.60 for sewage/drainage collection, concrete pipe									

33 31 13.25 Sewage Collection, Polyvinyl Chloride Pipe

33 31 13.25 Sewage Collection, Polyvinyl Chloride Pipe	Crew	Daily Output	Labor-Hours	Unit	Material	2014 Bare Costs Labor	Equipment	Total	Total Incl O&P
0010 **SEWAGE COLLECTION, POLYVINYL CHLORIDE PIPE**									
0020 Not including excavation or backfill									
2000 20' lengths, SDR 35, B&S, 4" diameter	B-20	375	.064	L.F.	1.46	1.85		3.31	4.72
2040 6" diameter		350	.069		3.29	1.98		5.27	6.95
2080 13' lengths , SDR 35, B&S, 8" diameter	↓	335	.072		6.95	2.07		9.02	11.10
2120 10" diameter	B-21	330	.085		11.40	2.57	.42	14.39	17.35
2160 12" diameter		320	.088		12.75	2.65	.44	15.84	19
2200 15" diameter		240	.117		13	3.53	.58	17.11	21
4000 Piping, DWV PVC, no exc./bkfill., 10' L, Sch 40, 4" diameter	B-20	375	.064		4.64	1.85		6.49	8.20
4010 6" diameter		350	.069		10.20	1.98		12.18	14.55
4020 8" diameter	↓	335	.072	↓	19.70	2.07		21.77	25

33 36 Utility Septic Tanks

33 36 13 – Utility Septic Tank and Effluent Wet Wells

33 36 13.13 Concrete Utility Septic Tank

		Crew	Daily Output	Labor-Hours	Unit	Material	2014 Bare Costs Labor	2014 Bare Costs Equipment	Total	Total Incl O&P
0010	**CONCRETE UTILITY SEPTIC TANK**									
0011	Not including excavation or piping									
0015	Septic tanks, precast, 1,000 gallon	B-21	8	3.500	Ea.	1,075	106	17.50	1,198.50	1,400
0060	1,500 gallon		7	4		1,500	121	20	1,641	1,875
0100	2,000 gallon	↓	5	5.600		1,975	170	28	2,173	2,475
0200	5,000 gallon	B-13	3.50	13.714		9,475	415	213	10,103	11,300
0300	15,000 gallon, 4 piece	B-13B	1.70	32.941		21,700	1,025	670	23,395	26,300
0400	25,000 gallon, 4 piece		1.10	50.909		42,200	1,575	1,025	44,800	50,000
0500	40,000 gallon, 4 piece	↓	.80	70		54,000	2,150	1,425	57,575	64,500
0520	50,000 gallon, 5 piece	B-13C	.60	93.333		62,000	2,875	2,850	67,725	76,500
0640	75,000 gallon, cast in place	C-14C	.25	448		75,500	15,200	130	90,830	108,500
0660	100,000 gallon	"	.15	746		93,500	25,400	217	119,117	146,000
1150	Leaching field chambers, 13' x 3'-7" x 1'-4", standard	B-13	16	3		480	91	46.50	617.50	730
1200	Heavy duty, 8' x 4' x 1'-6"		14	3.429		284	104	53.50	441.50	545
1300	13' x 3'-9" x 1'-6"		12	4		1,125	121	62	1,308	1,525
1350	20' x 4' x 1'-6"	↓	5	9.600		1,175	291	149	1,615	1,925
1400	Leaching pit, precast concrete, 3' diameter, 3' deep	B-21	8	3.500		710	106	17.50	833.50	975
1500	6' diameter, 3' section		4.70	5.957		885	180	30	1,095	1,325
2000	Velocity reducing pit, precast conc., 6' diameter, 3' deep	↓	4.70	5.957	↓	1,600	180	30	1,810	2,100

33 36 13.19 Polyethylene Utility Septic Tank

		Crew	Daily Output	Labor-Hours	Unit	Material	2014 Bare Costs Labor	2014 Bare Costs Equipment	Total	Total Incl O&P
0010	**POLYETHYLENE UTILITY SEPTIC TANK**									
0015	High density polyethylene, 1,000 gallon	B-21	8	3.500	Ea.	1,300	106	17.50	1,423.50	1,625
0020	1,250 gallon		8	3.500		1,400	106	17.50	1,523.50	1,750
0025	1,500 gallon	↓	7	4	↓	1,650	121	20	1,791	2,050

33 36 19 – Utility Septic Tank Effluent Filter

33 36 19.13 Utility Septic Tank Effluent Tube Filter

		Crew	Daily Output	Labor-Hours	Unit	Material	2014 Bare Costs Labor	2014 Bare Costs Equipment	Total	Total Incl O&P
0010	**UTILITY SEPTIC TANK EFFLUENT TUBE FILTER**									
3000	Effluent filter, 4" diameter	1 Skwk	8	1	Ea.	55.50	36.50		92	123
3020	6" diameter	"	7	1.143	"	230	41.50		271.50	325

33 36 33 – Utility Septic Tank Drainage Field

33 36 33.13 Utility Septic Tank Tile Drainage Field

		Crew	Daily Output	Labor-Hours	Unit	Material	2014 Bare Costs Labor	2014 Bare Costs Equipment	Total	Total Incl O&P
0010	**UTILITY SEPTIC TANK TILE DRAINAGE FIELD**									
0015	Distribution box, concrete, 5 outlets	2 Clab	20	.800	Ea.	78.50	22.50		101	124
0020	7 outlets		16	1		78.50	28		106.50	134
0025	9 outlets		8	2		475	56.50		531.50	620
0115	Distribution boxes, HDPE, 5 outlets		20	.800		64.50	22.50		87	109
0120	8 outlets	↓	10	1.600		68.50	45		113.50	152
0240	Distribution boxes, Outlet Flow Leveler	1 Clab	50	.160	↓	2.22	4.51		6.73	10.05

33 36 50 – Drainage Field Systems

33 36 50.10 Drainage Field Excavation and Fill

		Crew	Daily Output	Labor-Hours	Unit	Material	2014 Bare Costs Labor	2014 Bare Costs Equipment	Total	Total Incl O&P
0010	**DRAINAGE FIELD EXCAVATION AND FILL**									
2200	Septic tank & drainage field excavation with 3/4 c.y backhoe	B-12F	145	.110	C.Y.		3.69	4.57	8.26	11.15
2400	4' trench for disposal field, 3/4 C.Y. backhoe	"	335	.048	L.F.		1.60	1.98	3.58	4.83
2600	Gravel fill, run of bank	B-6	150	.160	C.Y.	19.90	4.94	2.44	27.28	33
2800	Crushed stone, 3/4"	"	150	.160	"	34.50	4.94	2.44	41.88	48.50

33 41 13.40 Piping, Storm Drainage, Corrugated Metal

		Crew	Daily Output	Labor-Hours	Unit	Material	2014 Bare Costs Labor	2014 Bare Costs Equipment	Total	Total Incl O&P
0010	**PIPING, STORM DRAINAGE, CORRUGATED METAL**									
0020	Not including excavation or backfill									
2000	Corrugated metal pipe, galvanized									
2020	Bituminous coated with paved invert, 20' lengths									
2040	8" diameter, 16 ga.	B-14	330	.145	L.F.	8.70	4.35	1.11	14.16	18.05
2060	10" diameter, 16 ga.		260	.185		9.05	5.50	1.41	15.96	21
2080	12" diameter, 16 ga.		210	.229		11.10	6.85	1.74	19.69	25.50
2100	15" diameter, 16 ga.		200	.240		15.25	7.15	1.83	24.23	31
2120	18" diameter, 16 ga.		190	.253		16.75	7.55	1.92	26.22	33
2140	24" diameter, 14 ga.		160	.300		21.50	8.95	2.28	32.73	41
2160	30" diameter, 14 ga.	B-13	120	.400		28	12.10	6.20	46.30	58
2180	36" diameter, 12 ga.		120	.400		35.50	12.10	6.20	53.80	66.50
2200	48" diameter, 12 ga.		100	.480		53	14.55	7.45	75	90.50
2220	60" diameter, 10 ga.	B-13B	75	.747		80	23	15.15	118.15	143
2240	72" diameter, 8 ga.	"	45	1.244		95.50	38.50	25.50	159.50	197
2500	Galvanized, uncoated, 20' lengths									
2520	8" diameter, 16 ga.	B-14	355	.135	L.F.	7.85	4.04	1.03	12.92	16.60
2540	10" diameter, 16 ga.		280	.171		9	5.10	1.30	15.40	19.95
2560	12" diameter, 16 ga.		220	.218		10	6.50	1.66	18.16	24
2580	15" diameter, 16 ga.		220	.218		12.50	6.50	1.66	20.66	26.50
2600	18" diameter, 16 ga.		205	.234		15.10	7	1.78	23.88	30.50
2620	24" diameter, 14 ga.		175	.274		19	8.20	2.09	29.29	37
2640	30" diameter, 14 ga.	B-13	130	.369		25	11.20	5.75	41.95	52.50
2660	36" diameter, 12 ga.		130	.369		32	11.20	5.75	48.95	60
2680	48" diameter, 12 ga.		110	.436		47.50	13.20	6.80	67.50	82
2690	60" diameter, 10 ga.	B-13B	78	.718		72	22	14.55	108.55	132
2780	End sections, 8" diameter	B-14	35	1.371	Ea.	73	41	10.45	124.45	160
2785	10" diameter		35	1.371		77	41	10.45	128.45	165
2790	12" diameter		35	1.371		114	41	10.45	165.45	205
2800	18" diameter		30	1.600		115	48	12.20	175.20	220
2810	24" diameter	B-13	25	1.920		215	58	30	303	370
2820	30" diameter		25	1.920		330	58	30	418	490
2825	36" diameter		20	2.400		480	72.50	37.50	590	695
2830	48" diameter		10	4.800		950	145	74.50	1,169.50	1,375
2835	60" diameter	B-13B	5	11.200		1,650	345	227	2,222	2,625
2840	72" diameter	"	4	14		1,975	430	284	2,689	3,175

33 41 13.60 Sewage/Drainage Collection, Concrete Pipe

		Crew	Daily Output	Labor-Hours	Unit	Material	2014 Bare Costs Labor	2014 Bare Costs Equipment	Total	Total Incl O&P
0010	**SEWAGE/DRAINAGE COLLECTION, CONCRETE PIPE**									
0020	Not including excavation or backfill									
1000	Non-reinforced pipe, extra strength, B&S or T&G joints									
1010	6" diameter	B-14	265.04	.181	L.F.	5.60	5.40	1.38	12.38	16.75
1020	8" diameter		224	.214		6.15	6.40	1.63	14.18	19.35
1030	10" diameter		216	.222		6.85	6.65	1.69	15.19	20.50
1040	12" diameter		200	.240		8.15	7.15	1.83	17.13	23
1050	15" diameter		180	.267		11.25	7.95	2.03	21.23	28
1060	18" diameter		144	.333		13.20	9.95	2.54	25.69	34
1070	21" diameter		112	.429		16.30	12.80	3.26	32.36	43
1080	24" diameter		100	.480		22	14.35	3.65	40	52
2000	Reinforced culvert, class 3, no gaskets									
2010	12" diameter	B-14	150	.320	L.F.	10	9.55	2.44	21.99	29.50
2020	15" diameter		150	.320		13	9.55	2.44	24.99	33
2030	18" diameter		132	.364		16.75	10.85	2.77	30.37	39.50

33 41 Storm Utility Drainage Piping

33 41 13 - Public Storm Utility Drainage Piping

33 41 13.60 Sewage/Drainage Collection, Concrete Pipe

	33 41 13.60 Sewage/Drainage Collection, Concrete Pipe	Crew	Daily Output	Labor-Hours	Unit	Material	2014 Bare Costs Labor	Equipment	Total	Total Incl O&P
2035	21" diameter	B-14	120	.400	L.F.	21	11.95	3.04	35.99	46.50
2040	24" diameter	↓	100	.480		25	14.35	3.65	43	55.50
2045	27" diameter	B-13	92	.522		36	15.80	8.10	59.90	75
2050	30" diameter		88	.545		40.50	16.50	8.50	65.50	81.50
2060	36" diameter	↓	72	.667		55	20	10.35	85.35	106
2070	42" diameter	B-13B	72	.778		74	24	15.80	113.80	139
2080	48" diameter		64	.875		88	27	17.75	132.75	161
2090	60" diameter		48	1.167		135	36	23.50	194.50	235
2100	72" diameter		40	1.400		205	43	28.50	276.50	330
2120	84" diameter		32	1.750		250	54	35.50	339.50	405
2140	96" diameter	↓	24	2.333		300	72	47.50	419.50	500
2200	With gaskets, class 3, 12" diameter	B-21	168	.167		11	5.05	.83	16.88	21.50
2220	15" diameter		160	.175		14.30	5.30	.88	20.48	25.50
2230	18" diameter		152	.184		18.45	5.60	.92	24.97	31
2240	24" diameter	↓	136	.206		31.50	6.25	1.03	38.78	46
2260	30" diameter	B-13	88	.545		48	16.50	8.50	73	90
2270	36" diameter	"	72	.667		64.50	20	10.35	94.85	116
2290	48" diameter	B-13B	64	.875		100	27	17.75	144.75	175
2310	72" diameter	"	40	1.400		224	43	28.50	295.50	350
2330	Flared ends, 12" diameter	B-21	31	.903	Ea.	225	27.50	4.52	257.02	299
2340	15" diameter		25	1.120		266	34	5.60	305.60	355
2400	18" diameter		20	1.400		305	42.50	7	354.50	415
2420	24" diameter	↓	14	2		370	60.50	10	440.50	520
2440	36" diameter	B-13	10	4.800	↓	790	145	74.50	1,009.50	1,200
3080	Radius pipe, add to pipe prices, 12" to 60" diameter				L.F.	50%				
3090	Over 60" diameter, add				"	20%				
3500	Reinforced elliptical, 8' lengths, C507 class 3									
3520	14" x 23" inside, round equivalent 18" diameter	B-21	82	.341	L.F.	40.50	10.35	1.71	52.56	63.50
3530	24" x 38" inside, round equivalent 30" diameter	B-13	58	.828		61.50	25	12.85	99.35	124
3540	29" x 45" inside, round equivalent 36" diameter		52	.923		78	28	14.35	120.35	148
3550	38" x 60" inside, round equivalent 48" diameter		38	1.263		133	38.50	19.65	191.15	232
3560	48" x 76" inside, round equivalent 60" diameter		26	1.846		185	56	28.50	269.50	330
3570	58" x 91" inside, round equivalent 72" diameter	↓	22	2.182	↓	270	66	34	370	445
3780	Concrete slotted pipe, class 4 mortar joint									
3800	12" diameter	B-21	168	.167	L.F.	27	5.05	.83	32.88	39
3840	18" diameter	"	152	.184	"	31.50	5.60	.92	38.02	45
3900	Concrete slotted pipe, Class 4 O-ring joint									
3940	12" diameter	B-21	168	.167	L.F.	27	5.05	.83	32.88	39
3960	18" diameter	"	152	.184	"	31.50	5.60	.92	38.02	45

33 42 Culverts

33 42 16 - Concrete Culverts

33 42 16.15 Oval Arch Culverts

		Crew	Daily Output	Labor-Hours	Unit	Material	2014 Bare Costs Labor	Equipment	Total	Total Incl O&P
0010	**OVAL ARCH CULVERTS**									
3000	Corrugated galvanized or aluminum, coated & paved									
3020	17" x 13", 16 ga., 15" equivalent	B-14	200	.240	L.F.	13.25	7.15	1.83	22.23	28.50
3040	21" x 15", 16 ga., 18" equivalent		150	.320		16.05	9.55	2.44	28.04	36.50
3060	28" x 20", 14 ga., 24" equivalent		125	.384		24	11.45	2.92	38.37	48.50
3080	35" x 24", 14 ga., 30" equivalent	↓	100	.480		29.50	14.35	3.65	47.50	60.50
3100	42" x 29", 12 ga., 36" equivalent	B-13	100	.480		35.50	14.55	7.45	57.50	71.50
3120	49" x 33", 12 ga., 42" equivalent	↓	90	.533	↓	41	16.15	8.30	65.45	81.50

33 42 Culverts

33 42 16 – Concrete Culverts

33 42 16.15 Oval Arch Culverts

		Crew	Daily Output	Labor-Hours	Unit	Material	2014 Bare Costs Labor	Equipment	Total	Total Incl O&P
3140	57" x 38", 12 ga., 48" equivalent	B-13	75	.640	L.F.	57	19.40	9.95	86.35	106
3160	Steel, plain oval arch culverts, plain									
3180	17" x 13", 16 ga., 15" equivalent	B-14	225	.213	L.F.	11.95	6.35	1.62	19.92	25.50
3200	21" x 15", 16 ga., 18" equivalent		175	.274		14.45	8.20	2.09	24.74	32
3220	28" x 20", 14 ga., 24" equivalent	↓	150	.320		21.50	9.55	2.44	33.49	42
3240	35" x 24", 14 ga., 30" equivalent	B-13	108	.444		26.50	13.45	6.90	46.85	59
3260	42" x 29", 12 ga., 36" equivalent		108	.444		32	13.45	6.90	52.35	65.50
3280	49" x 33", 12 ga., 42" equivalent		92	.522		37	15.80	8.10	60.90	76.50
3300	57" x 38", 12 ga., 48" equivalent		75	.640	↓	51.50	19.40	9.95	80.85	100
3320	End sections, 17" x 13"		22	2.182	Ea.	144	66	34	244	310
3340	42" x 29"	↓	17	2.824	"	395	85.50	44	524.50	625
3360	Multi-plate arch, steel	B-20	1690	.014	Lb.	1.30	.41		1.71	2.12

33 44 Storm Utility Water Drains

33 44 13 – Utility Area Drains

33 44 13.13 Catchbasins

		Crew	Daily Output	Labor-Hours	Unit	Material	2014 Bare Costs Labor	Equipment	Total	Total Incl O&P
0010	**CATCHBASINS**									
0011	Not including footing & excavation									
1600	Frames & grates, C.I., 24" square, 500 lb.	B-6	7.80	3.077	Ea.	340	95	47	482	585
1700	26" D shape, 600 lb.		7	3.429		505	106	52	663	790
1800	Light traffic, 18" diameter, 100 lb.		10	2.400		122	74	36.50	232.50	298
1900	24" diameter, 300 lb.		8.70	2.759		196	85	42	323	405
2000	36" diameter, 900 lb.		5.80	4.138		570	128	63	761	910
2100	Heavy traffic, 24" diameter, 400 lb.		7.80	3.077		244	95	47	386	480
2200	36" diameter, 1150 lb.		3	8		795	247	122	1,164	1,425
2300	Mass. State standard, 26" diameter, 475 lb.		7	3.429		265	106	52	423	525
2400	30" diameter, 620 lb.		7	3.429		345	106	52	503	615
2500	Watertight, 24" diameter, 350 lb.		7.80	3.077		320	95	47	462	560
2600	26" diameter, 500 lb.		7	3.429		425	106	52	583	700
2700	32" diameter, 575 lb.	↓	6	4	↓	850	124	61	1,035	1,200
2800	3 piece cover & frame, 10" deep,									
2900	1200 lb., for heavy equipment	B-6	3	8	Ea.	1,050	247	122	1,419	1,700
3000	Raised for paving 1-1/4" to 2" high									
3100	4 piece expansion ring									
3200	20" to 26" diameter	1 Clab	3	2.667	Ea.	157	75		232	299
3300	30" to 36" diameter	"	3	2.667	"	216	75		291	365
3320	Frames and covers, existing, raised for paving, 2", including									
3340	row of brick, concrete collar, up to 12" wide frame	B-6	18	1.333	Ea.	44.50	41	20.50	106	141
3360	20" to 26" wide frame		11	2.182		66.50	67.50	33	167	223
3380	30" to 36" wide frame	↓	9	2.667		82.50	82.50	40.50	205.50	274
3400	Inverts, single channel brick	D-1	3	5.333		96	172		268	390
3500	Concrete		5	3.200		103	103		206	286
3600	Triple channel, brick		2	8		147	258		405	590
3700	Concrete	↓	3	5.333	↓	139	172		311	440

33 46 Subdrainage

33 46 16 – Subdrainage Piping

33 46 16.25 Piping, Subdrainage, Corrugated Metal

		Crew	Daily Output	Labor-Hours	Unit	Material	2014 Bare Costs Labor	Equipment	Total	Total Incl O&P
0010	**PIPING, SUBDRAINAGE, CORRUGATED METAL**									
0021	Not including excavation and backfill									
2010	Aluminum, perforated									
2020	6" diameter, 18 ga.	B-20	380	.063	L.F.	6.55	1.82		8.37	10.25
2200	8" diameter, 16 ga.	"	370	.065		8.60	1.87		10.47	12.60
2220	10" diameter, 16 ga.	B-21	360	.078		10.75	2.35	.39	13.49	16.20
2240	12" diameter, 16 ga.		285	.098		12	2.97	.49	15.46	18.75
2260	18" diameter, 16 ga.		205	.137		18	4.13	.68	22.81	27.50
3000	Uncoated galvanized, perforated									
3020	6" diameter, 18 ga.	B-20	380	.063	L.F.	6.05	1.82		7.87	9.70
3200	8" diameter, 16 ga.	"	370	.065		8.35	1.87		10.22	12.30
3220	10" diameter, 16 ga.	B-21	360	.078		8.85	2.35	.39	11.59	14.10
3240	12" diameter, 16 ga.		285	.098		9.85	2.97	.49	13.31	16.35
3260	18" diameter, 16 ga.		205	.137		15.05	4.13	.68	19.86	24.50
4000	Steel, perforated, asphalt coated									
4020	6" diameter 18 ga.	B-20	380	.063	L.F.	6.55	1.82		8.37	10.25
4030	8" diameter 18 ga.	"	370	.065		8.60	1.87		10.47	12.60
4040	10" diameter 16 ga.	B-21	360	.078		10.10	2.35	.39	12.84	15.50
4050	12" diameter 16 ga.		285	.098		11.10	2.97	.49	14.56	17.75
4060	18" diameter 16 ga.		205	.137		17.15	4.13	.68	21.96	26.50

33 46 16.40 Piping, Subdrainage, Polyvinyl Chloride

0010	**PIPING, SUBDRAINAGE, POLYVINYL CHLORIDE**									
0020	Perforated, price as solid pipe, Section 33 31 13.25									

33 49 Storm Drainage Structures

33 49 13 – Storm Drainage Manholes, Frames, and Covers

33 49 13.10 Storm Drainage Manholes, Frames and Covers

		Crew	Daily Output	Labor-Hours	Unit	Material	2014 Bare Costs Labor	Equipment	Total	Total Incl O&P
0010	**STORM DRAINAGE MANHOLES, FRAMES & COVERS**									
0020	Excludes footing, excavation, backfill (See line items for frame & cover)									
0050	Brick, 4' inside diameter, 4' deep	D-1	1	16	Ea.	510	515		1,025	1,425
0100	6' deep		.70	22.857		725	735		1,460	2,025
0150	8' deep		.50	32		935	1,025		1,960	2,750
0200	For depths over 8', add		4	4	V.L.F.	83.50	129		212.50	305
0400	Concrete blocks (radial), 4' I.D., 4' deep		1.50	10.667	Ea.	370	345		715	975
0500	6' deep		1	16		495	515		1,010	1,400
0600	8' deep		.70	22.857		620	735		1,355	1,900
0700	For depths over 8', add		5.50	2.909	V.L.F.	65	94		159	228
0800	Concrete, cast in place, 4' x 4', 8" thick, 4' deep	C-14H	2	24	Ea.	505	840	16.55	1,361.55	1,975
0900	6' deep		1.50	32		725	1,125	22	1,872	2,700
1000	8' deep		1	48		1,050	1,675	33	2,758	4,000
1100	For depths over 8', add		8	6	V.L.F.	118	210	4.14	332.14	485
1110	Precast, 4' I.D., 4' deep	B-22	4.10	7.317	Ea.	775	226	51	1,052	1,275
1120	6' deep		3	10		970	310	70	1,350	1,675
1130	8' deep		2	15		1,100	460	105	1,665	2,125
1140	For depths over 8', add		16	1.875	V.L.F.	125	58	13.15	196.15	249
1150	5' I.D., 4' deep	B-6	3	8	Ea.	1,625	247	122	1,994	2,325
1160	6' deep		2	12		1,675	370	183	2,228	2,650
1170	8' deep		1.50	16		2,350	495	244	3,089	3,700
1180	For depths over 8', add		12	2	V.L.F.	277	62	30.50	369.50	440
1190	6' I.D., 4' deep		2	12	Ea.	2,125	370	183	2,678	3,150
1200	6' deep		1.50	16		2,550	495	244	3,289	3,900

33 49 Storm Drainage Structures

33 49 13 – Storm Drainage Manholes, Frames, and Covers

33 49 13.10 Storm Drainage Manholes, Frames and Covers

		Crew	Daily Output	Labor-Hours	Unit	Material	2014 Bare Costs Labor	2014 Bare Costs Equipment	Total	Total Incl O&P
1210	8' deep	B-6	1	24	Ea.	3,150	740	365	4,255	5,100
1220	For depths over 8', add	↓	8	3	V.L.F.	375	92.50	45.50	513	615
1250	Slab tops, precast, 8" thick									
1300	4' diameter manhole	B-6	8	3	Ea.	245	92.50	45.50	383	475
1400	5' diameter manhole		7.50	3.200	↓	405	99	48.50	552.50	665
1500	6' diameter manhole	↓	7	3.429		625	106	52	783	920
3800	Steps, heavyweight cast iron, 7" x 9"	1 Bric	40	.200		19.05	7.10		26.15	33
3900	8" x 9"		40	.200		23	7.10		30.10	37
3928	12" x 10-1/2"		40	.200		26.50	7.10		33.60	41.50
4000	Standard sizes, galvanized steel		40	.200		21.50	7.10		28.60	35.50
4100	Aluminum		40	.200		24	7.10		31.10	38
4150	Polyethylene	↓	40	.200	↓	24.50	7.10		31.60	39

33 51 Natural-Gas Distribution

33 51 13 – Natural-Gas Piping

33 51 13.10 Piping, Gas Service and Distribution, P.E.

		Crew	Daily Output	Labor-Hours	Unit	Material	2014 Bare Costs Labor	2014 Bare Costs Equipment	Total	Total Incl O&P
0010	**PIPING, GAS SERVICE AND DISTRIBUTION, POLYETHYLENE**									
0020	Not including excavation or backfill									
1000	60 psi coils, compression coupling @ 100', 1/2" diameter, SDR 11	B-20A	608	.053	L.F.	.61	1.78		2.39	3.63
1010	1" diameter, SDR 11		544	.059		1.41	1.99		3.40	4.86
1040	1-1/4" diameter, SDR 11		544	.059		1.76	1.99		3.75	5.25
1100	2" diameter, SDR 11		488	.066		2.85	2.22		5.07	6.85
1160	3" diameter, SDR 11	↓	408	.078		5.60	2.65		8.25	10.55
1500	60 PSI 40' joints with coupling, 3" diameter, SDR 11	B-21A	408	.098		5.55	3.41	1.18	10.14	13.05
1540	4" diameter, SDR 11		352	.114		12.15	3.95	1.37	17.47	21.50
1600	6" diameter, SDR 11		328	.122		33.50	4.24	1.47	39.21	45.50
1640	8" diameter, SDR 11	↓	272	.147	↓	51.50	5.10	1.77	58.37	67

33 52 Liquid Fuel Distribution

33 52 16 – Gasoline Distribution

33 52 16.13 Gasoline Piping

		Crew	Daily Output	Labor-Hours	Unit	Material	2014 Bare Costs Labor	2014 Bare Costs Equipment	Total	Total Incl O&P
0010	**GASOLINE PIPING**									
0020	Primary containment pipe, fiberglass-reinforced									
0030	Plastic pipe 15' & 30' lengths									
0040	2" diameter	Q-6	425	.056	L.F.	5.95	2.12		8.07	10.05
0050	3" diameter		400	.060		10.40	2.25		12.65	15.10
0060	4" diameter	↓	375	.064	↓	13.70	2.40		16.10	19
0100	Fittings									
0110	Elbows, 90° & 45°, bell-ends, 2"	Q-6	24	1	Ea.	43.50	37.50		81	110
0120	3" diameter		22	1.091		55	41		96	128
0130	4" diameter		20	1.200		70	45		115	152
0200	Tees, bell ends, 2"		21	1.143		60.50	43		103.50	138
0210	3" diameter		18	1.333		64	50		114	153
0220	4" diameter		15	1.600		84	60		144	192
0230	Flanges bell ends, 2"		24	1		33.50	37.50		71	99
0240	3" diameter		22	1.091		39	41		80	111
0250	4" diameter		20	1.200		45	45		90	124
0260	Sleeve couplings, 2"		21	1.143		12.40	43		55.40	84.50
0270	3" diameter	↓	18	1.333		17.80	50		67.80	102

33 52 Liquid Fuel Distribution

33 52 16 – Gasoline Distribution

33 52 16.13 Gasoline Piping		Crew	Daily Output	Labor-Hours	Unit	Material	2014 Bare Costs Labor	Equipment	Total	Total Incl O&P
0280	4" diameter	Q-6	15	1.600	Ea.	23	60		83	125
0290	Threaded adapters 2"		21	1.143		18	43		61	91
0300	3" diameter		18	1.333		34	50		84	120
0310	4" diameter		15	1.600		38	60		98	141
0320	Reducers, 2"		27	.889		27.50	33.50		61	85
0330	3" diameter		22	1.091		27.50	41		68.50	97.50
0340	4" diameter		20	1.200		37	45		82	115
1010	Gas station product line for secondary containment (double wall)									
1100	Fiberglass reinforced plastic pipe 25' lengths									
1120	Pipe, plain end, 3" diameter	Q-6	375	.064	L.F.	26.50	2.40		28.90	33.50
1130	4" diameter		350	.069		32	2.57		34.57	40
1140	5" diameter		325	.074		35.50	2.77		38.27	43.50
1150	6" diameter		300	.080		39	3		42	48
1200	Fittings									
1230	Elbows, 90° & 45°, 3" diameter	Q-6	18	1.333	Ea.	136	50		186	233
1240	4" diameter		16	1.500		167	56.50		223.50	277
1250	5" diameter		14	1.714		184	64.50		248.50	310
1260	6" diameter		12	2		204	75		279	350
1270	Tees, 3" diameter		15	1.600		166	60		226	281
1280	4" diameter		12	2		202	75		277	345
1290	5" diameter		9	2.667		315	100		415	515
1300	6" diameter		6	4		375	150		525	665
1310	Couplings, 3" diameter		18	1.333		55	50		105	143
1320	4" diameter		16	1.500		119	56.50		175.50	224
1330	5" diameter		14	1.714		214	64.50		278.50	340
1340	6" diameter		12	2		315	75		390	475
1350	Cross-over nipples, 3" diameter		18	1.333		10.60	50		60.60	94
1360	4" diameter		16	1.500		12.75	56.50		69.25	107
1370	5" diameter		14	1.714		15.90	64.50		80.40	124
1380	6" diameter		12	2		19.10	75		94.10	145
1400	Telescoping, reducers, concentric 4" x 3"		18	1.333		47.50	50		97.50	135
1410	5" x 4"		17	1.412		95.50	53		148.50	193
1420	6" x 5"		16	1.500		234	56.50		290.50	350

33 71 Electrical Utility Transmission and Distribution

33 71 16 – Electrical Utility Poles

33 71 16.33 Wood Electrical Utility Poles

		Crew	Daily Output	Labor-Hours	Unit	Material	2014 Bare Costs Labor	Equipment	Total	Total Incl O&P
0010	**WOOD ELECTRICAL UTILITY POLES**									
0011	Excludes excavation, backfill and cast-in-place concrete									
6200	Electric & tel sitework, 20' high, treated wd., see Section 26 56 13.10	R-3	3.10	6.452	Ea.	223	272	45	540	740
6400	25' high		2.90	6.897		263	290	48.50	601.50	820
6600	30' high		2.60	7.692		430	325	54	809	1,075
6800	35' high		2.40	8.333		495	350	58.50	903.50	1,175
7000	40' high		2.30	8.696		710	365	61	1,136	1,450
7200	45' high		1.70	11.765		865	495	82.50	1,442.50	1,850
7400	Cross arms with hardware & insulators									
7600	4' long	1 Elec	2.50	3.200	Ea.	148	137		285	385
7800	5' long		2.40	3.333		170	142		312	420
8000	6' long		2.20	3.636		165	155		320	435

33 71 Electrical Utility Transmission and Distribution

33 71 19 – Electrical Underground Ducts and Manholes

33 71 19.17 Electric and Telephone Underground

33 71 19.17 Electric and Telephone Underground	Crew	Daily Output	Labor-Hours	Unit	Material	2014 Bare Costs Labor	2014 Bare Costs Equipment	Total	Total Incl O&P
0010 **ELECTRIC AND TELEPHONE UNDERGROUND**									
0011 Not including excavation									
0200 backfill and cast in place concrete									
0400 Hand holes, precast concrete, with concrete cover									
0600 2' x 2' x 3' deep	R-3	2.40	8.333	Ea.	415	350	58.50	823.50	1,100
0800 3' x 3' x 3' deep		1.90	10.526		535	445	73.50	1,053.50	1,400
1000 4' x 4' x 4' deep		1.40	14.286		1,200	600	100	1,900	2,400
1200 Manholes, precast with iron racks & pulling irons, C.I. frame									
1400 and cover, 4' x 6' x 7' deep	B-13	2	24	Ea.	5,925	725	375	7,025	8,150
1600 6' x 8' x 7' deep		1.90	25.263		6,650	765	395	7,810	9,025
1800 6' x 10' x 7' deep		1.80	26.667		7,450	805	415	8,670	10,000
4200 Underground duct, banks ready for concrete fill, min. of 7.5"									
4400 between conduits, center to center									
4580 PVC, type EB, 1 @ 2" diameter	2 Elec	480	.033	L.F.	.72	1.42		2.14	3.13
4600 2 @ 2" diameter		240	.067		1.45	2.85		4.30	6.25
4800 4 @ 2" diameter		120	.133		2.90	5.70		8.60	12.50
5000 2 @ 3" diameter		200	.080		1.98	3.42		5.40	7.75
5200 4 @ 3" diameter		100	.160		3.95	6.85		10.80	15.55
5400 2 @ 4" diameter		160	.100		3.03	4.27		7.30	10.35
5600 4 @ 4" diameter		80	.200		6.05	8.55		14.60	20.50
5800 6 @ 4" diameter		54	.296		9.10	12.65		21.75	30.50
6200 Rigid galvanized steel, 2 @ 2" diameter		180	.089		12.10	3.80		15.90	19.50
6400 4 @ 2" diameter		90	.178		24	7.60		31.60	39
6800 2 @ 3" diameter		100	.160		27.50	6.85		34.35	41
7000 4 @ 3" diameter		50	.320		55	13.65		68.65	83
7200 2 @ 4" diameter		70	.229		40	9.75		49.75	60
7400 4 @ 4" diameter		34	.471		80	20		100	121
7600 6 @ 4" diameter		22	.727		120	31		151	183

33 81 Communications Structures

33 81 13 – Communications Transmission Towers

33 81 13.10 Radio Towers

33 81 13.10 Radio Towers	Crew	Daily Output	Labor-Hours	Unit	Material	2014 Bare Costs Labor	2014 Bare Costs Equipment	Total	Total Incl O&P
0010 **RADIO TOWERS**									
0020 Guyed, 50' H, 40 lb. sect., 70 MPH basic wind spd.	2 Sswk	1	16	Ea.	2,750	615		3,365	4,200
0100 Wind load 90 MPH basic wind speed	"	1	16		3,700	615		4,315	5,250
0300 190' high, 40 lb. section, wind load 70 MPH basic wind speed	K-2	.33	72.727		9,550	2,600	1,000	13,150	16,400
0400 200' high, 70 lb. section, wind load 90 MPH basic wind speed		.33	72.727		15,900	2,600	1,000	19,500	23,400
0600 300' high, 70 lb. section, wind load 70 MPH basic wind speed		.20	120		25,500	4,300	1,675	31,475	37,800
0700 270' high, 90 lb. section, wind load 90 MPH basic wind speed		.20	120		27,600	4,300	1,675	33,575	40,100
0800 400' high, 100 lb. section, wind load 70 MPH basic wind speed		.14	171		38,100	6,150	2,375	46,625	56,000
0900 Self-supporting, 60' high, wind load 70 MPH basic wind speed		.80	30		4,500	1,075	415	5,990	7,375
0910 60' high, wind load 90 MPH basic wind speed		.45	53.333		5,275	1,900	740	7,915	10,100
1000 120' high, wind load 70 MPH basic wind speed		.40	60		10,000	2,150	835	12,985	15,900
1200 190' high, wind load 90 MPH basic wind speed		.20	120		28,300	4,300	1,675	34,275	40,900
2000 For states west of Rocky Mountains, add for shipping					10%				

Division Notes

		CREW	DAILY OUTPUT	LABOR-HOURS	UNIT	BARE COSTS				TOTAL INCL O&P
						MAT.	LABOR	EQUIP.	TOTAL	

Estimating Tips

34 11 00 Rail Tracks

This subdivision includes items that may involve either repair of existing, or construction of new, railroad tracks. Additional preparation work, such as the roadbed earthwork, would be found in Division 31. Additional new construction siding and turnouts are found in Subdivision 34 72. Maintenance of railroads is found under 34 01 23 Operation and Maintenance of Railways.

34 40 00 Traffic Signals

This subdivision includes traffic signal systems. Other traffic control devices such as traffic signs are found in Subdivision 10 14 53 Traffic Signage.

34 70 00 Vehicle Barriers

This subdivision includes security vehicle barriers, guide and guard rails, crash barriers, and delineators. The actual maintenance and construction of concrete and asphalt pavement is found in Division 32.

Reference Numbers

Reference numbers are shown in shaded boxes at the beginning of some major classifications. These numbers refer to related items in the Reference Section. The reference information may be an estimating procedure, an alternate pricing method, or technical information.

Note: Not all subdivisions listed here necessarily appear in this publication.

Division 34 - Transportation

34 01 Operation and Maintenance of Transportation

34 01 23 – Operation and Maintenance of Railways

34 01 23.51 Maintenance of Railroads	Crew	Daily Output	Labor-Hours	Unit	Material	2014 Bare Costs Labor	Equipment	Total	Total Incl O&P
0010 **MAINTENANCE OF RAILROADS**									
0400 Resurface and realign existing track	B-14	200	.240	L.F.		7.15	1.83	8.98	14.05
0600 For crushed stone ballast, add	"	500	.096	"	11.40	2.87	.73	15	18.15

34 11 Rail Tracks

34 11 13 – Track Rails

34 11 13.23 Heavy Rail Track

34 11 13.23 Heavy Rail Track	Crew	Daily Output	Labor-Hours	Unit	Material	2014 Bare Costs Labor	Equipment	Total	Total Incl O&P
0010 **HEAVY RAIL TRACK** R347216-10									
1000 Rail, 100 lb. prime grade				L.F.	35			35	38
1500 Relay rail				"	17.40			17.40	19.10

34 11 33 – Track Cross Ties

34 11 33.13 Concrete Track Cross Ties

34 11 33.13 Concrete Track Cross Ties	Crew	Daily Output	Labor-Hours	Unit	Material	2014 Bare Costs Labor	Equipment	Total	Total Incl O&P
0010 **CONCRETE TRACK CROSS TIES**									
1400 Ties, concrete, 8'-6" long, 30" O.C.	B-14	80	.600	Ea.	172	17.95	4.57	194.52	224

34 11 33.16 Timber Track Cross Ties

34 11 33.16 Timber Track Cross Ties	Crew	Daily Output	Labor-Hours	Unit	Material	2014 Bare Costs Labor	Equipment	Total	Total Incl O&P
0010 **TIMBER TRACK CROSS TIES**									
1600 Wood, pressure treated, 6" x 8" x 8'-6", C.L. lots	B-14	90	.533	Ea.	51.50	15.95	4.06	71.51	88
1700 L.C.L. lots		90	.533		54	15.95	4.06	74.01	90.50
1900 Heavy duty, 7" x 9" x 8'-6", C.L. lots		70	.686		57	20.50	5.20	82.70	103
2000 L.C.L. lots		70	.686		57	20.50	5.20	82.70	103

34 11 33.17 Timber Switch Ties

34 11 33.17 Timber Switch Ties	Crew	Daily Output	Labor-Hours	Unit	Material	2014 Bare Costs Labor	Equipment	Total	Total Incl O&P
0010 **TIMBER SWITCH TIES**									
1200 Switch timber, for a #8 switch, pressure treated	B-14	3.70	12.973	M.B.F.	3,100	390	98.50	3,588.50	4,150
1300 Complete set of timbers, 3.7 MBF for #8 switch	"	1	48	Total	11,900	1,425	365	13,690	15,900

34 11 93 – Track Appurtenances and Accessories

34 11 93.50 Track Accessories

34 11 93.50 Track Accessories	Crew	Daily Output	Labor-Hours	Unit	Material	2014 Bare Costs Labor	Equipment	Total	Total Incl O&P
0010 **TRACK ACCESSORIES**									
0020 Car bumpers, test	B-14	2	24	Ea.	3,875	715	183	4,773	5,675
0100 Heavy duty R347216-20		2	24		7,350	715	183	8,248	9,475
0200 Derails hand throw (sliding)		10	4.800		1,225	143	36.50	1,404.50	1,625
0300 Hand throw with standard timbers, open stand & target		8	6		1,325	179	45.50	1,549.50	1,800
2400 Wheel stops, fixed		18	2.667	Pr.	955	79.50	20.50	1,055	1,200
2450 Hinged		14	3.429	"	1,300	102	26	1,428	1,625

34 11 93.60 Track Material

34 11 93.60 Track Material	Crew	Daily Output	Labor-Hours	Unit	Material	2014 Bare Costs Labor	Equipment	Total	Total Incl O&P
0010 **TRACK MATERIAL**									
0020 Track bolts				Ea.	3.98			3.98	4.38
0100 Joint bars				Pr.	92.50			92.50	101
0200 Spikes				Ea.	1.31			1.31	1.44
0300 Tie plates				"	15.45			15.45	16.95

34 41 Roadway Signaling and Control Equipment

34 41 13 – Traffic Signals

34 41 13.10 Traffic Signals Systems

		Crew	Daily Output	Labor-Hours	Unit	Material	2014 Bare Costs Labor	Equipment	Total	Total Incl O&P
0010	**TRAFFIC SIGNALS SYSTEMS**									
0020	Mid block pedestrian crosswalk with pushbutton and mast arms	R-11	.30	186	Total	68,000	7,500	2,950	78,450	90,500
0600	Traffic signals, school flashing system, solar powered, remote controlled	"	1	56	Signal	12,000	2,250	890	15,140	17,900
1000	Intersection traffic signals, LED, mast, programmable, no lane control									
1010	Includes all labor, material and equip. for complete installation	R-11	1	56	Signal	158,000	2,250	890	161,140	178,500
1100	Intersection traffic signals, LED, mast, programmable, R/L lane control									
1110	Includes all labor, material and equip. for complete installation	R-11	1	56	Signal	216,000	2,250	890	219,140	242,000
1200	Add protective/permissive left turns to existing traffic light									
1210	Includes all labor, material and equip. for complete installation	R-11	1	56	Signal	66,000	2,250	890	69,140	77,000
1300	Replace existing light heads with LED heads wire hung									
1310	Includes all labor, material and equip. for complete installation	R-11	1	56	Signal	41,000	2,250	890	44,140	49,800
1400	Replace existing light heads with LED heads mast arm hung									
1410	Includes all labor, material and equip. for complete installation	R-11	1	56	Signal	77,000	2,250	890	80,140	89,000

34 71 Roadway Construction

34 71 13 – Vehicle Barriers

34 71 13.26 Vehicle Guide Rails

		Crew	Daily Output	Labor-Hours	Unit	Material	2014 Bare Costs Labor	Equipment	Total	Total Incl O&P
0010	**VEHICLE GUIDE RAILS**									
0012	Corrugated stl., galv. stl. posts, 6'-3" O.C.	B-80	850	.028	L.F.	21.50	.82	.89	23.21	26.50
0200	End sections, galvanized, flared		50	.480	Ea.	94	13.85	15.15	123	144
0300	Wrap around end		50	.480	"	137	13.85	15.15	166	191
0400	Timber guide rail, 4" x 8" with 6" x 8" wood posts, treated		960	.025	L.F.	11.80	.72	.79	13.31	15.10
0600	Cable guide rail, 3 at 3/4" cables, steel posts, single face		900	.027		10.60	.77	.84	12.21	13.90
0700	Wood posts		950	.025		12.70	.73	.80	14.23	16.05
0900	Guide rail, steel box beam, 6" x 6"		120	.200		33	5.75	6.30	45.05	53
1100	Median barrier, steel box beam, 6" x 8"		215	.112		44	3.22	3.53	50.75	58
1400	Resilient guide fence and light shield, 6' high	B-2	130	.308		37.50	8.80		46.30	56
1500	Concrete posts, individual, 6'-5", triangular	B-80	110	.218	Ea.	71	6.30	6.90	84.20	96.50
1550	Square	"	110	.218	"	76.50	6.30	6.90	89.70	103
2000	Median, precast concrete, 3'-6" high, 2' wide, single face	B-29	380	.126	L.F.	53	3.83	2.32	59.15	67.50
2200	Double face	"	340	.141	"	61	4.27	2.59	67.86	77
2400	Speed bumps, thermoplastic, 10-1/2" x 2-1/4" x 48" long	B-2	120	.333	Ea.	135	9.55		144.55	165
3030	Impact barrier, UTMCD, barrel type	B-16	30	1.067	"	500	31	23	554	630

34 71 19 – Vehicle Delineators

34 71 19.13 Fixed Vehicle Delineators

		Crew	Daily Output	Labor-Hours	Unit	Material	2014 Bare Costs Labor	Equipment	Total	Total Incl O&P
0010	**FIXED VEHICLE DELINEATORS**									
0020	Crash barriers									
0100	Traffic channelizing pavement markers, layout only	A-7	2000	.012	Ea.		.46	.04	.50	.81
0110	13" x 7-1/2" x 2-1/2" high, non-plowable install	2 Clab	96	.167		24	4.70		28.70	34
0200	8" x 8" x 3-1/4" high, non-plowable, install		96	.167		22.50	4.70		27.20	32.50
0230	4" x 4" x 3/4" high, non-plowable, install		120	.133		1.75	3.76		5.51	8.30
0240	9-1/4" x 5-7/8" x 1/4" high, plowable, concrete pavmt.	A-2A	70	.343		17.85	9.75	6.35	33.95	43
0250	9-1/4" x 5-7/8" x 1/4" high, plowable, asphalt pav't	"	120	.200		3.75	5.70	3.71	13.16	17.75
0300	Barrier and curb delineators, reflectorized, 2" x 4"	2 Clab	150	.107		2	3.01		5.01	7.25
0310	3" x 5"	"	150	.107		3.90	3.01		6.91	9.35
0500	Rumble strip, polycarbonate									
0510	24" x 3-1/2" x 1/2" high	2 Clab	50	.320	Ea.	8.25	9		17.25	24.50

34 72 Railway Construction

34 72 16 – Railway Siding

34 72 16.50 Railroad Sidings	Crew	Daily Output	Labor-Hours	Unit	Material	2014 Bare Costs Labor	Equipment	Total	Total Incl O&P
0010 **RAILROAD SIDINGS** R347216-10									
0800 Siding, yard spur, level grade									
0820 100 lb. new rail	B-14	57	.842	L.F.	129	25	6.40	160.40	190
1020 100 lb. new rail	"	22	2.182	"	179	65	16.60	260.60	325

34 72 16.60 Railroad Turnouts

	Crew	Daily Output	Labor-Hours	Unit	Material	2014 Bare Costs Labor	Equipment	Total	Total Incl O&P
0010 **RAILROAD TURNOUTS**									
2200 Turnout, #8 complete, w/rails, plates, bars, frog, switch point,									
2250 timbers, and ballast to 6" below bottom of ties									
2280 90 lb. rails	B-13	.25	192	Ea.	39,900	5,825	2,975	48,700	57,000
2290 90 lb. relay rails		.25	192		26,800	5,825	2,975	35,600	42,500
2300 100 lb. rails		.25	192		44,500	5,825	2,975	53,300	62,000
2310 100 lb. relay rails		.25	192		29,900	5,825	2,975	38,700	45,900
2320 110 lb. rails		.25	192		49,000	5,825	2,975	57,800	67,000
2330 110 lb. relay rails		.25	192		33,000	5,825	2,975	41,800	49,300
2340 115 lb. rails		.25	192		53,500	5,825	2,975	62,300	72,000
2350 115 lb. relay rails		.25	192		35,800	5,825	2,975	44,600	52,500
2360 132 lb. rails		.25	192		61,500	5,825	2,975	70,300	80,500
2370 132 lb. relay rails		.25	192		40,700	5,825	2,975	49,500	57,500

Estimating Tips

35 01 50 Operation and Maintenance of Marine Construction

Includes unit price lines for pile cleaning and pile wrapping for protection.

35 20 16 Hydraulic Gates

This subdivision includes various types of gates that are commonly used in waterway and canal construction. Various earthwork items and structural support is found in Division 31, and concrete work in Division 3.

35 20 23 Dredging

This subdivision includes barge and shore dredging systems for rivers, canals, and channels.

35 31 00 Shoreline Protection

This subdivision includes breakwaters, bulkheads, and revetments for ocean and river inlets. Additional earthwork may be required from Division 31, and concrete work from Division 3.

35 41 00 Levees

Information on levee construction, including estimated cost of clay cone material.

35 49 00 Waterway Structures

This subdivision includes breakwaters and bulkheads for canals.

35 51 00 Floating Construction

This section includes floating piers, docks, and dock accessories. Fixed Pier Timber Construction is found in 06 13 33. Driven piles are found in Division 31, as well as sheet piling, cofferdams, and riprap.

Reference Numbers

Reference numbers are shown in shaded boxes at the beginning of some major classifications. These numbers refer to related items in the Reference Section. The reference information may be an estimating procedure, an alternate pricing method, or technical information.

Note: Not all subdivisions listed here necessarily appear in this publication.

Division 35 - Waterway and Marine

35 20 Waterway and Marine Construction and Equipment

35 20 23 – Dredging

35 20 23.13 Mechanical Dredging

35 20 23.13 Mechanical Dredging	Crew	Daily Output	Labor-Hours	Unit	Material	2014 Bare Costs Labor	Equipment	Total	Total Incl O&P
0010 **MECHANICAL DREDGING**									
0020 Dredging mobilization and demobilization, add to below, minimum	B-8	.53	105	Total		3,350	6,275	9,625	12,500
0100 Maximum	"	.10	560	"		17,700	33,200	50,900	66,000
0300 Barge mounted clamshell excavation into scows									
0310 Dumped 20 miles at sea, minimum	B-57	310	.129	B.C.Y.		3.96	8	11.96	15.45
0400 Maximum	"	213	.188	"		5.75	11.60	17.35	22.50
0500 Barge mounted dragline or clamshell, hopper dumped,									
0510 pumped 1000' to shore dump, minimum	B-57	340	.118	B.C.Y.		3.61	7.30	10.91	14.05
0525 All pumping uses 2000 gallons of water per cubic yard									
0600 Maximum	B-57	243	.165	B.C.Y.		5.05	10.20	15.25	19.65

35 20 23.23 Hydraulic Dredging

35 20 23.23 Hydraulic Dredging	Crew	Daily Output	Labor-Hours	Unit	Material	Labor	Equipment	Total	Total Incl O&P
0010 **HYDRAULIC DREDGING**									
1000 Hydraulic method, pumped 1000' to shore dump, minimum	B-57	460	.087	B.C.Y.		2.67	5.40	8.07	10.40
1100 Maximum		310	.129			3.96	8	11.96	15.45
1400 Into scows dumped 20 miles, minimum		425	.094			2.89	5.85	8.74	11.25
1500 Maximum		243	.165			5.05	10.20	15.25	19.65
1600 For inland rivers and canals in South, deduct								30%	30%

35 51 Floating Construction

35 51 13 – Floating Piers

35 51 13.23 Floating Wood Piers

35 51 13.23 Floating Wood Piers	Crew	Daily Output	Labor-Hours	Unit	Material	Labor	Equipment	Total	Total Incl O&P
0010 **FLOATING WOOD PIERS**									
0020 Polyethylene encased polystyrene, no pilings included	F-3	330	.121	S.F.	28.50	3.98	2.01	34.49	40
0200 Pile supported, shore constructed, bare, 3" decking		130	.308		27.50	10.10	5.10	42.70	52.50
0250 4" decking		120	.333		28.50	10.95	5.55	45	55.50
0400 Floating, small boat, prefab, no shore facilities, minimum		250	.160		24	5.25	2.65	31.90	38
0500 Maximum		150	.267		51	8.75	4.42	64.17	75.50
0700 Per slip, minimum (180 S.F. each)		1.59	25.157	Ea.	4,900	825	415	6,140	7,200
0800 Maximum		1.40	28.571	"	8,250	935	475	9,660	11,200

Estimating Tips

Products such as conveyors, material handling cranes and hoists, as well as other items specified in this division, require trained installers. The general contractor may not have any choice as to who will perform the installation or when it will be performed. Long lead times are often required for these products, making early decisions in purchasing and scheduling necessary.

The installation of this type of equipment may require the embedment of mounting hardware during construction of floors, structural walls, or interior walls/partitions. Electrical connections will require coordination with the electrical contractor.

Reference Numbers

Reference numbers are shown in shaded boxes at the beginning of some major classifications. These numbers refer to related items in the Reference Section. The reference information may be an estimating procedure, an alternate pricing method, or technical information.

Note: Not all subdivisions listed here necessarily appear in this publication.

41 21 Conveyors

41 21 23 – Piece Material Conveyors

41 21 23.16 Container Piece Material Conveyors	Crew	Daily Output	Labor-Hours	Unit	Material	2014 Bare Costs Labor	2014 Bare Costs Equipment	Total	Total Incl O&P
0010 **CONTAINER PIECE MATERIAL CONVEYORS**									
0020 Gravity fed, 2" rollers, 3" O.C.									
0050 10' sections with 2 supports, 600 lb. capacity, 18" wide				Ea.	450			450	495
0100 24" wide					515			515	570
0150 1400 lb. capacity, 18" wide					415			415	455
0200 24" wide					460			460	505
0350 Horizontal belt, center drive and takeup, 60 fpm									
0400 16" belt, 26.5' length	2 Mill	.50	32	Ea.	3,150	1,200		4,350	5,425
0450 24" belt, 41.5' length		.40	40		4,900	1,500		6,400	7,800
0500 61.5' length		.30	53.333		6,525	2,000		8,525	10,400
0600 Inclined belt, 10' rise with horizontal loader and									
0620 End idler assembly, 27.5' length, 18" belt	2 Mill	.30	53.333	Ea.	7,700	2,000		9,700	11,700
0700 24" belt	"	.15	106	"	8,600	4,000		12,600	15,900
3600 Monorail, overhead, manual, channel type									
3700 125 lb. per L.F.	1 Mill	26	.308	L.F.	14.45	11.55		26	34.50
3900 500 lb. per L.F.	"	21	.381	"	20.50	14.30		34.80	45.50
4000 Trolleys for above, 2 wheel, 125 lb. capacity				Ea.	74			74	81.50
4200 4 wheel, 250 lb. capacity					290			290	320
4300 8 wheel, 500 lb. capacity					675			675	745

41 22 Cranes and Hoists

41 22 13 – Cranes

41 22 13.10 Crane Rail

	Crew	Daily Output	Labor-Hours	Unit	Material	2014 Bare Costs Labor	2014 Bare Costs Equipment	Total	Total Incl O&P
0010 **CRANE RAIL**									
0020 Box beam bridge, no equipment included	E-4	3400	.009	Lb.	1.33	.37	.04	1.74	2.21
0200 Running track only, 104 lb. per yard	"	5600	.006	"	.66	.22	.03	.91	1.18

41 22 13.13 Bridge Cranes

	Crew	Daily Output	Labor-Hours	Unit	Material	2014 Bare Costs Labor	2014 Bare Costs Equipment	Total	Total Incl O&P
0010 **BRIDGE CRANES**									
0100 1 girder, 20' span, 3 ton	M-3	1	34	Ea.	24,100	1,450	140	25,690	29,100
0125 5 ton		1	34		26,400	1,450	140	27,990	31,700
0150 7.5 ton		1	34		31,400	1,450	140	32,990	37,200
0175 10 ton		.80	42.500		41,600	1,825	175	43,600	49,000
0200 15 ton		.80	42.500		53,500	1,825	175	55,500	62,000
0225 30' span, 3 ton		1	34		25,100	1,450	140	26,690	30,200
0250 5 ton		1	34		27,600	1,450	140	29,190	32,900
0275 7.5 ton		1	34		33,000	1,450	140	34,590	38,900
0300 10 ton		.80	42.500		43,000	1,825	175	45,000	50,500
0325 15 ton		.80	42.500		56,000	1,825	175	58,000	64,500
0350 2 girder, 40' span, 3 ton	M-4	.50	72		41,300	3,050	355	44,705	51,000
0375 5 ton		.50	72		43,300	3,050	355	46,705	53,000
0400 7.5 ton		.50	72		47,500	3,050	355	50,905	57,500
0425 10 ton		.40	90		55,500	3,825	445	59,770	68,000
0450 15 ton		.40	90		75,500	3,825	445	79,770	90,000
0475 25 ton		.30	120		89,500	5,100	595	95,195	107,000
0500 50' span, 3 ton		.50	72		47,100	3,050	355	50,505	57,500
0525 5 ton		.50	72		49,000	3,050	355	52,405	59,500
0550 7.5 ton		.50	72		52,500	3,050	355	55,905	63,000
0575 10 ton		.40	90		60,500	3,825	445	64,770	73,500
0600 15 ton		.40	90		79,000	3,825	445	83,270	94,000
0625 25 ton		.30	120		93,500	5,100	595	99,195	112,000

41 22 Cranes and Hoists

41 22 13 – Cranes

41 22 13.19 Jib Cranes		Crew	Daily Output	Labor-Hours	Unit	Material	2014 Bare Costs Labor	Equipment	Total	Total Incl O&P
0010	**JIB CRANES**									
0020	Jib crane, wall cantilever, 500 lb. capacity, 8' span	2 Mill	1	16	Ea.	1,400	600		2,000	2,500
0040	12' span		1	16		1,525	600		2,125	2,650
0060	16' span		1	16		1,700	600		2,300	2,850
0080	20' span		1	16		2,150	600		2,750	3,350
0100	1000 lb. capacity, 8' span		1	16		1,500	600		2,100	2,625
0120	12' span		1	16		1,625	600		2,225	2,775
0130	16' span		1	16		2,150	600		2,750	3,350
0150	20' span		1	16		2,525	600		3,125	3,750

41 22 23 – Hoists

41 22 23.10 Material Handling

41 22 23.10 Material Handling		Crew	Daily Output	Labor-Hours	Unit	Material	2014 Bare Costs Labor	Equipment	Total	Total Incl O&P
0010	**MATERIAL HANDLING**, cranes, hoists and lifts									
1500	Cranes, portable hydraulic, floor type, 2,000 lb. capacity				Ea.	3,500			3,500	3,875
1600	4,000 lb. capacity					4,025			4,025	4,425
1800	Movable gantry type, 12' to 15' range, 2,000 lb. capacity					2,050			2,050	2,250
1900	6,000 lb. capacity					4,825			4,825	5,300
2100	Hoists, electric overhead, chain, hook hung, 15' lift, 1 ton cap.					2,875			2,875	3,175
2200	3 ton capacity					3,375			3,375	3,725
2500	5 ton capacity					7,800			7,800	8,575
2600	For hand-pushed trolley, add					15%				
2700	For geared trolley, add					30%				
2800	For motor trolley, add					75%				
3000	For lifts over 15', 1 ton, add				L.F.	25			25	27.50
3100	5 ton, add				"	52			52	57
3300	Lifts, scissor type, portable, electric, 36" high, 2,000 lb.				Ea.	3,475			3,475	3,825
3400	48" high, 4,000 lb.				"	4,175			4,175	4,600

Division Notes

	CREW	DAILY OUTPUT	LABOR-HOURS	UNIT	BARE COSTS				TOTAL INCL O&P
					MAT.	LABOR	EQUIP.	TOTAL	

Estimating Tips

This division contains information about water and wastewater equipment and systems, which was formerly located in Division 44.

The main areas of focus are total wastewater treatment plants and components of wastewater treatment plants. In addition, there are assemblies such as sewage treatment lagoons that can be found in some publications under G30 Site Mechanical Utilities.

Also included in this section are oil/water separators for wastewater treatment.

Reference Numbers

Reference numbers are shown in shaded boxes at the beginning of some major classifications. These numbers refer to related items in the Reference Section. The reference information may be an estimating procedure, an alternate pricing method, or technical information.

Note: Not all subdivisions listed here necessarily appear in this publication.

46 07 53 – Packaged Wastewater Treatment Equipment

46 07 53.10 Biological Packaged Water Treatment Plants	Crew	Daily Output	Labor-Hours	Unit	Material	2014 Bare Costs Labor	Equipment	Total	Total Incl O&P
0010 **BIOLOGICAL PACKAGED WATER TREATMENT PLANTS**									
0011 Not including fencing or external piping									
0020 Steel packaged, blown air aeration plants									
0100 1,000 GPD				Gal.				55	60.50
0200 5,000 GPD								22	24
0300 15,000 GPD								22	24
0400 30,000 GPD								15.40	16.95
0500 50,000 GPD								11	12.10
0600 100,000 GPD								9.90	10.90
0700 200,000 GPD								8.80	9.70
0800 500,000 GPD				▼				7.70	8.45
1000 Concrete, extended aeration, primary and secondary treatment									
1010 10,000 GPD				Gal.				22	24
1100 30,000 GPD								15.40	16.95
1200 50,000 GPD								11	12.10
1400 100,000 GPD								9.90	10.90
1500 500,000 GPD				▼				7.70	8.45
1700 Municipal wastewater treatment facility									
1720 1.0 MGD				Gal.				11	12.10
1740 1.5 MGD								10.60	11.65
1760 2.0 MGD								10	11
1780 3.0 MGD								7.80	8.60
1800 5.0 MGD				▼				5.80	6.70
2000 Holding tank system, not incl. excavation or backfill									
2010 Recirculating chemical water closet	2 Plum	4	4	Ea.	520	170		690	850
2100 For voltage converter, add	"	16	1		295	42.50		337.50	395
2200 For high level alarm, add	1 Plum	7.80	1.026	▼	114	43.50		157.50	198

46 07 53.20 Wastewater Treatment System

	Crew	Daily Output	Labor-Hours	Unit	Material	2014 Bare Costs Labor	Equipment	Total	Total Incl O&P
0010 **WASTEWATER TREATMENT SYSTEM**									
0020 Fiberglass, 1,000 gallon	B-21	1.29	21.705	Ea.	4,075	655	109	4,839	5,725
0100 1,500 gallon	"	1.03	27.184	"	8,150	825	136	9,111	10,500

Estimating Tips

- When estimating costs for the installation of electrical power generation equipment, factors to review include access to the job site, access and setting at the installation site, required connections, uncrating pads, anchors, leveling, final assembly of the components, and temporary protection from physical damage, including from exposure to the environment.

- Be aware of the cost of equipment supports, concrete pads, and vibration isolators, and cross-reference to other trades' specifications. Also, review site and structural drawings for items that must be included in the estimates.

- It is important to include items that are not documented in the plans and specifications but must be priced. These items include, but are not limited to, testing, dust protection, roof penetration, core drilling concrete floors and walls, patching, cleanup, and final adjustments. Add a contingency or allowance for utility company fees for power hookups, if needed.

- The project size and scope of electrical power generation equipment will have a significant impact on cost. The intent of RSMeans cost data is to provide a benchmark cost so that owners, engineers, and electrical contractors will have a comfortable number with which to start a project. Additionally, there are many websites available to use for research and to obtain a vendor's quote to finalize costs.

Reference Numbers

Reference numbers are shown in shaded boxes at the beginning of some major classifications. These numbers refer to related items in the Reference Section. The reference information may be an estimating procedure, an alternate pricing method, or technical information.

Note: Not all subdivisions listed here necessarily appear in this publication.

48 15 13.50 Wind Turbines and Components		Crew	Daily Output	Labor-Hours	Unit	Material	2014 Bare Costs Labor	Equipment	Total	Total Incl O&P
0010	**WIND TURBINES & COMPONENTS**									
0500	Complete system, grid connected									
1000	20 kW, 31' dia, incl. labor & material, min	G			System					49,900
1010	Maximum	G								92,000
1500	10 kW, 23' dia, incl. labor & material	G								74,000
2000	2.4 kW, 12' dia, incl. labor & material	G								18,000
2900	Component system									
3000	Turbine, 400 watt, 3' dia	G	1 Elec	3.41	2.346	Ea.	755	100		855	995
3100	600 watt, 3' dia	G		2.56	3.125		955	133		1,088	1,275
3200	1000 watt, 9' dia	G		2.05	3.902		3,825	167		3,992	4,500
3400	Mounting hardware									
3500	30' guyed tower kit	G	2 Clab	5.12	3.125	Ea.	455	88		543	650
3505	3' galvanized helical earth screw	G	1 Clab	8	1		53	28		81	106
3510	Attic mount kit	G	1 Rofc	2.56	3.125		133	94		227	320
3520	Roof mount kit	G	1 Clab	3.41	2.346		118	66		184	240
8900	Equipment									
9100	DC to AC inverter for, 48 V, 4,000 watt	G	1 Elec	2	4	Ea.	2,750	171		2,921	3,300

Reference Section

All the reference information is in one section, making it easy to find what you need to know . . . and easy to use the book on a daily basis. This section is visually identified by a vertical gray bar on the page edges.

In this Reference Section, we've included Equipment Rental Costs, a listing of rental and operating costs; Crew Listings, a full listing of all crews and equipment, and their costs; Historical Cost Indexes for cost comparisons over time; City Cost Indexes and Location Factors for adjusting costs to the region you are in; Reference Tables, where you will find explanations, estimating information and procedures, or technical data; Change Orders, information on pricing changes to contract documents; Square Foot Costs that allow you to make a rough estimate for the overall cost of a project; and an explanation of all the Abbreviations in the book.

Table of Contents

Estimating Tips

- This section contains the average costs to rent and operate hundreds of pieces of construction equipment. This is useful information when estimating the time and material requirements of any particular operation in order to establish a unit or total cost. Equipment costs include not only rental, but also operating costs for equipment under normal use.

Rental Costs

- Equipment rental rates are obtained from industry sources throughout North America–contractors, suppliers, dealers, manufacturers, and distributors.
- Rental rates vary throughout the country, with larger cities generally having lower rates. Lease plans for new equipment are available for periods in excess of six months, with a percentage of payments applying toward purchase.
- Monthly rental rates vary from 2% to 5% of the purchase price of the equipment depending on the anticipated life of the equipment and its wearing parts.
- Weekly rental rates are about 1/3 the monthly rates, and daily rental rates are about 1/3 the weekly rate.
- Rental rates can also be treated as reimbursement costs for contractor-owned equipment. Owned equipment costs include depreciation, loan payments, interest, taxes, insurance, storage, and major repairs.

Operating Costs

- The operating costs include parts and labor for routine servicing, such as repair and replacement of pumps, filters and worn lines. Normal operating expendables, such as fuel, lubricants, tires and electricity (where applicable), are also included.
- Extraordinary operating expendables with highly variable wear patterns, such as diamond bits and blades, are excluded. These costs can be found as material costs in the Unit Price section.
- The hourly operating costs listed do not include the operator's wages.

Equipment Cost/Day

- Any power equipment required by a crew is shown in the Crew Listings with a daily cost.
- The daily cost of equipment needed by a crew is based on dividing the weekly rental rate by 5 (number of working days in the week), and then adding the hourly operating cost times 8 (the number of hours in a day). This "Equipment Cost/Day" is shown in the far right column of the Equipment Rental pages.
- If equipment is needed for only one or two days, it is best to develop your own cost by including components for daily rent and hourly operating cost. This is important when the listed Crew for a task does not contain the equipment needed, such as a crane for lifting mechanical heating/cooling equipment up onto a roof.

- If the quantity of work is less than the crew's Daily Output shown for a Unit Price line item that includes a bare unit equipment cost, it is recommended to estimate one day's rental cost and operating cost for equipment shown in the Crew Listing for that line item.

Mobilization/ Demobilization

- The cost to move construction equipment from an equipment yard or rental company to the jobsite and back again is not included in equipment rental costs listed in the Reference section, nor in the bare equipment cost of any Unit Price line item, nor in any equipment costs shown in the Crew listings.
- Mobilization (to the site) and demobilization (from the site) costs can be found in the Unit Price section.
- If a piece of equipment is already at the jobsite, it is not appropriate to utilize mobil./ demob. costs again in an estimate.

01 54 33 | Equipment Rental

			UNIT	HOURLY OPER. COST	RENT PER DAY	RENT PER WEEK	RENT PER MONTH	EQUIPMENT COST/DAY
10	0010	**CONCRETE EQUIPMENT RENTAL** without operators	R015433-10						**10**
	0200	Bucket, concrete lightweight, 1/2 C.Y.		Ea.	.80	23	69	207	20.20
	0300	1 C.Y.			.85	27	81	243	23
	0400	1-1/2 C.Y.			1.10	36.50	110	330	30.80
	0500	2 C.Y.			1.20	43.50	130	390	35.60
	0580	8 C.Y.			5.95	252	755	2,275	198.60
	0600	Cart, concrete, self-propelled, operator walking, 10 C.F.			3.40	55	165	495	60.20
	0700	Operator riding, 18 C.F.			5.65	93.50	280	840	101.20
	0800	Conveyer for concrete, portable, gas, 16" wide, 26' long			13.50	122	365	1,100	181
	0900	46' long			13.90	147	440	1,325	199.20
	1000	56' long			14.05	155	465	1,400	205.40
	1100	Core drill, electric, 2-1/2 H.P., 1" to 8" bit diameter			1.50	57	171	515	46.20
	1150	11 H.P., 8" to 18" cores			5.90	115	345	1,025	116.20
	1200	Finisher, concrete floor, gas, riding trowel, 96" wide			14.05	142	425	1,275	197.40
	1300	Gas, walk-behind, 3 blade, 36" trowel			2.35	20	60	180	30.80
	1400	4 blade, 48" trowel			4.70	26.50	80	240	53.60
	1500	Float, hand-operated (Bull float) 48" wide			.08	13.35	40	120	8.65
	1570	Curb builder, 14 H.P., gas, single screw			14.65	250	750	2,250	267.20
	1590	Double screw			15.30	287	860	2,575	294.40
	1600	Floor grinder, concrete and terrazzo, electric, 22" path			2.19	134	402	1,200	97.90
	1700	Edger, concrete, electric, 7" path			1.02	51.50	155	465	39.15
	1750	Vacuum pick-up system for floor grinders, wet/dry			1.47	81.50	245	735	60.75
	1800	Mixer, powered, mortar and concrete, gas, 6 C.F., 18 H.P.			9.20	117	350	1,050	143.60
	1900	10 C.F., 25 H.P.			11.60	140	420	1,250	176.80
	2000	16 C.F.			11.95	162	485	1,450	192.60
	2100	Concrete, stationary, tilt drum, 2 C.Y.			6.80	228	685	2,050	191.40
	2120	Pump, concrete, truck mounted 4" line 80' boom			24.55	855	2,570	7,700	710.40
	2140	5" line, 110' boom			31.75	1,125	3,400	10,200	934
	2160	Mud jack, 50 C.F. per hr.			7.35	127	380	1,150	134.80
	2180	225 C.F. per hr.			9.65	145	435	1,300	164.20
	2190	Shotcrete pump rig, 12 C.Y./hr.			15.10	220	660	1,975	252.80
	2200	35 C.Y./hr.			17.80	237	710	2,125	284.40
	2600	Saw, concrete, manual, gas, 18 H.P.			7.25	43.50	130	390	84
	2650	Self-propelled, gas, 30 H.P.			14.40	100	300	900	175.20
	2675	V-groove crack chaser, manual, gas, 6 H.P.			2.55	17.35	52	156	30.80
	2700	Vibrators, concrete, electric, 60 cycle, 2 H.P.			.43	8.65	26	78	8.65
	2800	3 H.P.			.61	11.65	35	105	11.90
	2900	Gas engine, 5 H.P.			2.20	16	48	144	27.20
	3000	8 H.P.			3.00	15	45	135	33
	3050	Vibrating screed, gas engine, 8 H.P.			2.78	68.50	205	615	63.25
	3120	Concrete transit mixer, 6 x 4, 250 H.P., 8 C.Y., rear discharge			62.50	565	1,690	5,075	838
	3200	Front discharge			73.60	690	2,065	6,200	1,002
	3300	6 x 6, 285 H.P., 12 C.Y., rear discharge			72.65	650	1,950	5,850	971.20
	3400	Front discharge			75.95	695	2,085	6,250	1,025
20	0010	**EARTHWORK EQUIPMENT RENTAL** without operators	R015433-10						**20**
	0040	Aggregate spreader, push type 8' to 12' wide		Ea.	3.25	25.50	76	228	41.20
	0045	Tailgate type, 8' wide			3.10	32.50	98	294	44.40
	0055	Earth auger, truck-mounted, for fence & sign posts, utility poles			19.75	445	1,335	4,000	425
	0060	For borings and monitoring wells			47.30	680	2,040	6,125	786.40
	0070	Portable, trailer mounted			3.15	32.50	98	294	44.80
	0075	Truck-mounted, for caissons, water wells			100.90	2,900	8,720	26,200	2,551
	0080	Horizontal boring machine, 12" to 36" diameter, 45 H.P.			24.60	193	580	1,750	312.80
	0090	12" to 48" diameter, 65 H.P.			34.85	335	1,005	3,025	479.80
	0095	Auger, for fence posts, gas engine, hand held			.55	6	18	54	8
	0100	Excavator, diesel hydraulic, crawler mounted, 1/2 C.Y. cap.			25.00	415	1,240	3,725	448
	0120	5/8 C.Y. capacity			33.05	550	1,650	4,950	594.40
	0140	3/4 C.Y. capacity			36.00	625	1,870	5,600	662
	0150	1 C.Y. capacity			50.60	685	2,050	6,150	814.80

01 54 33 | Equipment Rental

		UNIT	HOURLY OPER. COST	RENT PER DAY	RENT PER WEEK	RENT PER MONTH	EQUIPMENT COST/DAY	
20	0200	1-1/2 C.Y. capacity	Ea.	60.80	910	2,725	8,175	1,031	20
	0300	2 C.Y. capacity		68.50	1,050	3,135	9,400	1,175	
	0320	2-1/2 C.Y. capacity		104.75	1,325	3,995	12,000	1,637	
	0325	3-1/2 C.Y. capacity		147.35	2,100	6,315	18,900	2,442	
	0330	4-1/2 C.Y. capacity		176.65	2,725	8,150	24,500	3,043	
	0335	6 C.Y. capacity		224.40	2,875	8,640	25,900	3,523	
	0340	7 C.Y. capacity		226.60	2,975	8,915	26,700	3,596	
	0342	Excavator attachments, bucket thumbs		3.20	245	735	2,200	172.60	
	0345	Grapples		2.75	193	580	1,750	138	
	0347	Hydraulic hammer for boom mounting, 5000 ft lb.		14.30	425	1,280	3,850	370.40	
	0349	11,000 ft lb.		23.20	750	2,250	6,750	635.60	
	0350	Gradall type, truck mounted, 3 ton @ 15' radius, 5/8 C.Y.		43.45	890	2,670	8,000	881.60	
	0370	1 C.Y. capacity		47.65	1,050	3,120	9,350	1,005	
	0400	Backhoe-loader, 40 to 45 H.P., 5/8 C.Y. capacity		14.95	233	700	2,100	259.60	
	0450	45 H.P. to 60 H.P., 3/4 C.Y. capacity		23.90	290	870	2,600	365.20	
	0460	80 H.P., 1-1/4 C.Y. capacity		26.20	315	940	2,825	397.60	
	0470	112 H.P., 1-1/2 C.Y. capacity		41.65	645	1,935	5,800	720.20	
	0482	Backhoe-loader attachment, compactor, 20,000 lb.		5.75	142	425	1,275	131	
	0485	Hydraulic hammer, 750 ft lb.		3.25	96.50	290	870	84	
	0486	Hydraulic hammer, 1200 ft lb.		6.30	217	650	1,950	180.40	
	0500	Brush chipper, gas engine, 6" cutter head, 35 H.P.		11.95	107	320	960	159.60	
	0550	Diesel engine, 12" cutter head, 130 H.P.		28.20	285	855	2,575	396.60	
	0600	15" cutter head, 165 H.P.		33.90	330	985	2,950	468.20	
	0750	Bucket, clamshell, general purpose, 3/8 C.Y.		1.25	38.50	115	345	33	
	0800	1/2 C.Y.		1.35	45	135	405	37.80	
	0850	3/4 C.Y.		1.50	53.50	160	480	44	
	0900	1 C.Y.		1.55	58.50	175	525	47.40	
	0950	1-1/2 C.Y.		2.55	80	240	720	68.40	
	1000	2 C.Y.		2.65	88.50	265	795	74.20	
	1010	Bucket, dragline, medium duty, 1/2 C.Y.		.75	23.50	70	210	20	
	1020	3/4 C.Y.		.75	24.50	74	222	20.80	
	1030	1 C.Y.		.80	26	78	234	22	
	1040	1-1/2 C.Y.		1.20	40	120	360	33.60	
	1050	2 C.Y.		1.25	45	135	405	37	
	1070	3 C.Y.		1.95	61.50	185	555	52.60	
	1200	Compactor, manually guided 2-drum vibratory smooth roller, 7.5 H.P.		7.35	207	620	1,850	182.80	
	1250	Rammer/tamper, gas, 8"		2.70	46.50	140	420	49.60	
	1260	15"		3.00	53.50	160	480	56	
	1300	Vibratory plate, gas, 18" plate, 3000 lb. blow		2.65	24.50	73	219	35.80	
	1350	21" plate, 5000 lb. blow		3.30	32.50	98	294	46	
	1370	Curb builder/extruder, 14 H.P., gas, single screw		14.65	250	750	2,250	267.20	
	1390	Double screw		15.30	287	860	2,575	294.40	
	1500	Disc harrow attachment, for tractor		.43	72.50	217	650	46.85	
	1810	Feller buncher, shearing & accumulating trees, 100 H.P.		42.50	650	1,945	5,825	729	
	1860	Grader, self-propelled, 25,000 lb.		39.55	595	1,780	5,350	672.40	
	1910	30,000 lb.		43.25	600	1,805	5,425	707	
	1920	40,000 lb.		64.65	1,000	3,015	9,050	1,120	
	1930	55,000 lb.		84.65	1,600	4,800	14,400	1,637	
	1950	Hammer, pavement breaker, self-propelled, diesel, 1000 to 1250 lb.		30.25	355	1,060	3,175	454	
	2000	1300 to 1500 lb.		45.38	705	2,120	6,350	787.05	
	2050	Pile driving hammer, steam or air, 4150 ft lb. @ 225 bpm		10.35	475	1,425	4,275	367.80	
	2100	8750 ft lb. @ 145 bpm		12.35	660	1,980	5,950	494.80	
	2150	15,000 ft lb. @ 60 bpm		13.95	795	2,380	7,150	587.60	
	2200	24,450 ft lb. @ 111 bpm		14.95	880	2,640	7,925	647.60	
	2250	Leads, 60' high for pile driving hammers up to 20,000 ft lb.		3.30	80.50	242	725	74.80	
	2300	90' high for hammers over 20,000 ft lb.		4.95	141	424	1,275	124.40	
	2350	Diesel type hammer, 22,400 ft lb.		26.93	535	1,610	4,825	537.45	
	2400	41,300 ft lb.		36.30	585	1,760	5,275	642.40	

01 54 33 | Equipment Rental

		UNIT	HOURLY OPER. COST	RENT PER DAY	RENT PER WEEK	RENT PER MONTH	EQUIPMENT COST/DAY	
20	2450	141,000 ft lb.	Ea.	55.55	1,050	3,160	9,475	1,076	**20**
	2500	Vib. elec. hammer/extractor, 200 kW diesel generator, 34 H.P.		56.25	635	1,910	5,725	832	
	2550	80 H.P.		103.45	930	2,785	8,350	1,385	
	2600	150 H.P.		196.65	1,775	5,335	16,000	2,640	
	2800	Log chipper, up to 22" diameter, 600 H.P.		64.95	630	1,895	5,675	898.60	
	2850	Logger, for skidding & stacking logs, 150 H.P.		53.45	820	2,460	7,375	919.60	
	2860	Mulcher, diesel powered, trailer mounted		24.70	213	640	1,925	325.60	
	2900	Rake, spring tooth, with tractor		18.31	335	1,007	3,025	347.90	
	3000	Roller, vibratory, tandem, smooth drum, 20 H.P.		8.75	148	445	1,325	159	
	3050	35 H.P.		11.25	253	760	2,275	242	
	3100	Towed type vibratory compactor, smooth drum, 50 H.P.		26.25	335	1,010	3,025	412	
	3150	Sheepsfoot, 50 H.P.		27.60	370	1,115	3,350	443.80	
	3170	Landfill compactor, 220 H.P.		91.85	1,500	4,485	13,500	1,632	
	3200	Pneumatic tire roller, 80 H.P.		17.00	355	1,065	3,200	349	
	3250	120 H.P.		25.45	605	1,815	5,450	566.60	
	3300	Sheepsfoot vibratory roller, 240 H.P.		69.65	1,100	3,305	9,925	1,218	
	3320	340 H.P.		101.85	1,600	4,830	14,500	1,781	
	3350	Smooth drum vibratory roller, 75 H.P.		25.15	595	1,790	5,375	559.20	
	3400	125 H.P.		32.85	715	2,150	6,450	692.80	
	3410	Rotary mower, brush, 60", with tractor		22.65	305	915	2,750	364.20	
	3420	Rototiller, walk-behind, gas, 5 H.P.		2.23	66	198	595	57.45	
	3422	8 H.P.		3.30	91.50	275	825	81.40	
	3440	Scrapers, towed type, 7 C.Y. capacity		5.70	110	330	990	111.60	
	3450	10 C.Y. capacity		6.45	150	450	1,350	141.60	
	3500	15 C.Y. capacity		6.85	173	520	1,550	158.80	
	3525	Self-propelled, single engine, 14 C.Y. capacity		113.60	1,525	4,600	13,800	1,829	
	3550	Dual engine, 21 C.Y. capacity		174.50	2,000	6,015	18,000	2,599	
	3600	31 C.Y. capacity		232.10	2,850	8,545	25,600	3,566	
	3640	44 C.Y. capacity		287.55	3,650	10,960	32,900	4,492	
	3650	Elevating type, single engine, 11 C.Y. capacity		71.20	1,025	3,050	9,150	1,180	
	3700	22 C.Y. capacity		138.15	2,225	6,690	20,100	2,443	
	3710	Screening plant 110 H.P. w/5' x 10' screen		31.63	435	1,300	3,900	513.05	
	3720	5' x 16' screen		34.85	540	1,615	4,850	601.80	
	3850	Shovel, crawler-mounted, front-loading, 7 C.Y. capacity		246.75	2,900	8,700	26,100	3,714	
	3855	12 C.Y. capacity		354.50	3,950	11,840	35,500	5,204	
	3860	Shovel/backhoe bucket, 1/2 C.Y.		2.45	66.50	200	600	59.60	
	3870	3/4 C.Y.		2.50	73.50	220	660	64	
	3880	1 C.Y.		2.60	83.50	250	750	70.80	
	3890	1-1/2 C.Y.		2.75	96.50	290	870	80	
	3910	3 C.Y.		3.10	130	390	1,175	102.80	
	3950	Stump chipper, 18" deep, 30 H.P.		7.06	176	528	1,575	162.10	
	4110	Dozer, crawler, torque converter, diesel 80 H.P.		29.75	405	1,215	3,650	481	
	4150	105 H.P.		36.10	505	1,515	4,550	591.80	
	4200	140 H.P.		52.10	780	2,335	7,000	883.80	
	4260	200 H.P.		77.35	1,175	3,530	10,600	1,325	
	4310	300 H.P.		100.55	1,700	5,065	15,200	1,817	
	4360	410 H.P.		135.65	2,200	6,620	19,900	2,409	
	4370	500 H.P.		174.30	2,875	8,610	25,800	3,116	
	4380	700 H.P.		261.35	4,000	11,970	35,900	4,485	
	4400	Loader, crawler, torque conv., diesel, 1-1/2 C.Y., 80 H.P.		31.35	455	1,360	4,075	522.80	
	4450	1-1/2 to 1-3/4 C.Y., 95 H.P.		34.15	585	1,760	5,275	625.20	
	4510	1-3/4 to 2-1/4 C.Y., 130 H.P.		54.60	870	2,615	7,850	959.80	
	4530	2-1/2 to 3-1/4 C.Y., 190 H.P.		67.00	1,100	3,275	9,825	1,191	
	4560	3-1/2 to 5 C.Y., 275 H.P.		86.10	1,400	4,215	12,600	1,532	
	4610	Front end loader, 4WD, articulated frame, diesel, 1 to 1-1/4 C.Y., 70 H.P.		19.90	227	680	2,050	295.20	
	4620	1-1/2 to 1-3/4 C.Y., 95 H.P.		25.30	285	855	2,575	373.40	
	4650	1-3/4 to 2 C.Y., 130 H.P.		29.45	365	1,100	3,300	455.60	
	4710	2-1/2 to 3-1/2 C.Y., 145 H.P.		33.35	425	1,280	3,850	522.80	

01 54 33 | Equipment Rental

		UNIT	HOURLY OPER. COST	RENT PER DAY	RENT PER WEEK	RENT PER MONTH	EQUIPMENT COST/DAY
20								**20**
4730	3 to 4-1/2 C.Y., 185 H.P.	Ea.	42.85	550	1,655	4,975	673.80
4760	5-1/4 to 5-3/4 C.Y., 270 H.P.		67.80	845	2,535	7,600	1,049
4810	7 to 9 C.Y., 475 H.P.		116.25	1,775	5,295	15,900	1,989
4870	9 - 11 C.Y., 620 H.P.		155.75	2,425	7,285	21,900	2,703
4880	Skid steer loader, wheeled, 10 C.F., 30 H.P. gas		10.90	145	435	1,300	174.20
4890	1 C.Y., 78 H.P., diesel		20.35	243	730	2,200	308.80
4892	Skid-steer attachment, auger		.50	83.50	251	755	54.20
4893	Backhoe		.66	111	332	995	71.70
4894	Broom		.74	124	372	1,125	80.30
4895	Forks		.23	38.50	115	345	24.85
4896	Grapple		.56	92.50	278	835	60.10
4897	Concrete hammer		1.06	177	531	1,600	114.70
4898	Tree spade		1.03	172	515	1,550	111.25
4899	Trencher		.67	112	335	1,000	72.35
4900	Trencher, chain, boom type, gas, operator walking, 12 H.P.		5.40	46.50	140	420	71.20
4910	Operator riding, 40 H.P.		20.55	292	875	2,625	339.40
5000	Wheel type, diesel, 4' deep, 12" wide		87.50	845	2,530	7,600	1,206
5100	6' deep, 20" wide		93.25	1,925	5,760	17,300	1,898
5150	Chain type, diesel, 5' deep, 8" wide		38.85	560	1,685	5,050	647.80
5200	Diesel, 8' deep, 16" wide		156.45	3,550	10,620	31,900	3,376
5202	Rock trencher, wheel type, 6" wide x 18" deep		21.50	330	985	2,950	369
5206	Chain type, 18" wide x 7' deep		112.60	2,825	8,445	25,300	2,590
5210	Tree spade, self-propelled		14.00	267	800	2,400	272
5250	Truck, dump, 2-axle, 12 ton, 8 C.Y. payload, 220 H.P.		35.15	227	680	2,050	417.20
5300	Three axle dump, 16 ton, 12 C.Y. payload, 400 H.P.		62.40	320	965	2,900	692.20
5310	Four axle dump, 25 ton, 18 C.Y. payload, 450 H.P.		73.20	470	1,410	4,225	867.60
5350	Dump trailer only, rear dump, 16-1/2 C.Y.		5.40	138	415	1,250	126.20
5400	20 C.Y.		5.85	157	470	1,400	140.80
5450	Flatbed, single axle, 1-1/2 ton rating		28.65	68.50	205	615	270.20
5500	3 ton rating		34.25	98.50	295	885	333
5550	Off highway rear dump, 25 ton capacity		74.55	1,200	3,590	10,800	1,314
5600	35 ton capacity		83.10	1,350	4,025	12,100	1,470
5610	50 ton capacity		103.40	1,600	4,800	14,400	1,787
5620	65 ton capacity		106.30	1,575	4,735	14,200	1,797
5630	100 ton capacity		154.35	2,775	8,315	24,900	2,898
6000	Vibratory plow, 25 H.P., walking		9.25	60	180	540	110
40								**40**
0010	**GENERAL EQUIPMENT RENTAL** without operators R015433 -10						
0150	Aerial lift, scissor type, to 15' high, 1000 lb. cap., electric	Ea.	3.10	51.50	155	465	55.80
0160	To 25' high, 2000 lb. capacity		3.55	66.50	200	600	68.40
0170	Telescoping boom to 40' high, 500 lb. capacity, diesel		17.00	315	945	2,825	325
0180	To 45' high, 500 lb. capacity		18.85	355	1,070	3,200	364.80
0190	To 60' high, 600 lb. capacity		21.25	475	1,430	4,300	456
0195	Air compressor, portable, 6.5 CFM, electric		.56	12.65	38	114	12.10
0196	Gasoline		.79	19	57	171	17.70
0200	Towed type, gas engine, 60 CFM		13.55	48.50	145	435	137.40
0300	160 CFM		15.80	51.50	155	465	157.40
0400	Diesel engine, rotary screw, 250 CFM		17.05	110	330	990	202.40
0500	365 CFM		23.10	133	400	1,200	264.80
0550	450 CFM		29.35	167	500	1,500	334.80
0600	600 CFM		51.70	232	695	2,075	552.60
0700	750 CFM		51.90	240	720	2,150	559.20
0800	For silenced models, small sizes, add to rent		3%	5%	5%	5%	
0900	Large sizes, add to rent		5%	7%	7%	7%	
0930	Air tools, breaker, pavement, 60 lb.	Ea.	.50	9.65	29	87	9.80
0940	80 lb.		.50	10.35	31	93	10.20
0950	Drills, hand (jackhammer) 65 lb.		.60	17.35	52	156	15.20
0960	Track or wagon, swing boom, 4" drifter		63.45	885	2,660	7,975	1,040
0970	5" drifter		75.50	1,075	3,255	9,775	1,255

01 54 33 | Equipment Rental

		UNIT	HOURLY OPER. COST	RENT PER DAY	RENT PER WEEK	RENT PER MONTH	EQUIPMENT COST/DAY	
40	0975	Track mounted quarry drill, 6" diameter drill	Ea.	129.75	1,600	4,830	14,500	2,004	**40**
	0980	Dust control per drill		.97	24	72	216	22.15	
	0990	Hammer, chipping, 12 lb.		.55	26	78	234	20	
	1000	Hose, air with couplings, 50' long, 3/4" diameter		.03	5	15	45	3.25	
	1100	1" diameter		.04	6.35	19	57	4.10	
	1200	1-1/2" diameter		.05	9	27	81	5.80	
	1300	2" diameter		.07	12	36	108	7.75	
	1400	2-1/2" diameter		.11	19	57	171	12.30	
	1410	3" diameter		.14	23	69	207	14.90	
	1450	Drill, steel, 7/8" x 2'		.05	8.65	26	78	5.60	
	1460	7/8" x 6'		.05	9	27	81	5.80	
	1520	Moil points		.02	3.33	10	30	2.15	
	1525	Pneumatic nailer w/accessories		.47	31	93	279	22.35	
	1530	Sheeting driver for 60 lb. breaker		.03	5.65	17	51	3.65	
	1540	For 90 lb. breaker		.11	7.35	22	66	5.30	
	1550	Spade, 25 lb.		.45	7	21	63	7.80	
	1560	Tamper, single, 35 lb.		.55	36.50	109	325	26.20	
	1570	Triple, 140 lb.		.82	54.50	164	490	39.35	
	1580	Wrenches, impact, air powered, up to 3/4" bolt		.40	12.65	38	114	10.80	
	1590	Up to 1-1/4" bolt		.50	23.50	70	210	18	
	1600	Barricades, barrels, reflectorized, 1 to 99 barrels		.03	4.60	13.80	41.50	3	
	1610	100 to 200 barrels		.02	3.53	10.60	32	2.30	
	1620	Barrels with flashers, 1 to 99 barrels		.03	5.25	15.80	47.50	3.40	
	1630	100 to 200 barrels		.03	4.20	12.60	38	2.75	
	1640	Barrels with steady burn type C lights		.04	7	21	63	4.50	
	1650	Illuminated board, trailer mounted, with generator		3.55	130	390	1,175	106.40	
	1670	Portable barricade, stock, with flashers, 1 to 6 units		.03	5.25	15.80	47.50	3.40	
	1680	25 to 50 units		.03	4.90	14.70	44	3.20	
	1685	Butt fusion machine, wheeled, 1.5 HP electric, 2" - 8" diameter pipe		2.62	167	500	1,500	120.95	
	1690	Tracked, 20 HP diesel, 4"-12" diameter pipe		11.10	490	1,465	4,400	381.80	
	1695	83 HP diesel, 8" - 24" diameter pipe		30.30	975	2,930	8,800	828.40	
	1700	Carts, brick, hand powered, 1000 lb. capacity		.44	72.50	218	655	47.10	
	1800	Gas engine, 1500 lb., 7-1/2' lift		4.10	115	345	1,025	101.80	
	1822	Dehumidifier, medium, 6 lb./hr., 150 CFM		.99	62	186	560	45.10	
	1824	Large, 18 lb./hr., 600 CFM		2.01	126	378	1,125	91.70	
	1830	Distributor, asphalt, trailer mounted, 2000 gal., 38 H.P. diesel		10.15	330	985	2,950	278.20	
	1840	3000 gal., 38 H.P. diesel		11.65	360	1,075	3,225	308.20	
	1850	Drill, rotary hammer, electric		1.00	26.50	80	240	24	
	1860	Carbide bit, 1-1/2" diameter, add to electric rotary hammer		.02	3.61	10.84	32.50	2.35	
	1865	Rotary, crawler, 250 H.P.		150.45	2,100	6,285	18,900	2,461	
	1870	Emulsion sprayer, 65 gal., 5 H.P. gas engine		2.90	98	294	880	82	
	1880	200 gal., 5 H.P. engine		7.85	163	490	1,475	160.80	
	1900	Floor auto-scrubbing machine, walk-behind, 28" path		4.52	293	880	2,650	212.15	
	1930	Floodlight, mercury vapor, or quartz, on tripod, 1000 watt		.41	19.35	58	174	14.90	
	1940	2000 watt		.78	39	117	350	29.65	
	1950	Floodlights, trailer mounted with generator, 1 - 300 watt light		3.65	71.50	215	645	72.20	
	1960	2 - 1000 watt lights		4.90	98.50	295	885	98.20	
	2000	4 - 300 watt lights		4.60	93.50	280	840	92.80	
	2005	Foam spray rig, incl. box trailer, compressor, generator, proportioner		36.53	490	1,465	4,400	585.25	
	2020	Forklift, straight mast, 12' lift, 5000 lb., 2 wheel drive, gas		25.35	203	610	1,825	324.80	
	2040	21' lift, 5000 lb., 4 wheel drive, diesel		21.15	242	725	2,175	314.20	
	2050	For rough terrain, 42' lift, 35' reach, 9000 lb., 110 H.P.		29.95	485	1,460	4,375	531.60	
	2060	For plant, 4 ton capacity, 80 H.P., 2 wheel drive, gas		15.50	93.50	280	840	180	
	2080	10 ton capacity, 120 H.P., 2 wheel drive, diesel		24.30	162	485	1,450	291.40	
	2100	Generator, electric, gas engine, 1.5 kW to 3 kW		3.95	11.35	34	102	38.40	
	2200	5 kW		5.10	15.35	46	138	50	
	2300	10 kW		9.65	36.50	110	330	99.20	
	2400	25 kW		11.00	86.50	260	780	140	

01 54 33 | Equipment Rental

		UNIT	HOURLY OPER. COST	RENT PER DAY	RENT PER WEEK	RENT PER MONTH	EQUIPMENT COST/DAY	
40	2500	Diesel engine, 20 kW	Ea.	12.55	68.50	205	615	141.40	40
	2600	50 kW		24.35	103	310	930	256.80	
	2700	100 kW		45.15	130	390	1,175	439.20	
	2800	250 kW		88.85	237	710	2,125	852.80	
	2850	Hammer, hydraulic, for mounting on boom, to 500 ft lb.		2.55	75	225	675	65.40	
	2860	1000 ft lb.		4.35	127	380	1,150	110.80	
	2900	Heaters, space, oil or electric, 50 MBH		1.93	7.65	23	69	20.05	
	3000	100 MBH		3.61	10.65	32	96	35.30	
	3100	300 MBH		10.58	38.50	115	345	107.65	
	3150	500 MBH		17.40	45	135	405	166.20	
	3200	Hose, water, suction with coupling, 20' long, 2" diameter		.02	3	9	27	1.95	
	3210	3" diameter		.03	4.33	13	39	2.85	
	3220	4" diameter		.03	5	15	45	3.25	
	3230	6" diameter		.11	17.65	53	159	11.50	
	3240	8" diameter		.20	33.50	100	300	21.60	
	3250	Discharge hose with coupling, 50' long, 2" diameter		.01	1.33	4	12	.90	
	3260	3" diameter		.01	2.33	7	21	1.50	
	3270	4" diameter		.02	3.67	11	33	2.35	
	3280	6" diameter		.06	9.35	28	84	6.10	
	3290	8" diameter		.20	33.50	100	300	21.60	
	3295	Insulation blower		.77	6	18	54	9.75	
	3300	Ladders, extension type, 16' to 36' long		.14	22.50	68	204	14.70	
	3400	40' to 60' long		.19	31	93	279	20.10	
	3405	Lance for cutting concrete		2.52	89	267	800	73.55	
	3407	Lawn mower, rotary, 22", 5 H.P.		2.10	59	177	530	52.20	
	3408	48" self propelled		2.92	75	225	675	68.35	
	3410	Level, electronic, automatic, with tripod and leveling rod		1.49	99	297	890	71.30	
	3430	Laser type, for pipe and sewer line and grade		.73	48.50	145	435	34.85	
	3440	Rotating beam for interior control		.97	64	192	575	46.15	
	3460	Builder's optical transit, with tripod and rod		.10	16.65	50	150	10.80	
	3500	Light towers, towable, with diesel generator, 2000 watt		4.60	93.50	280	840	92.80	
	3600	4000 watt		4.90	98.50	295	885	98.20	
	3700	Mixer, powered, plaster and mortar, 6 C.F., 7 H.P.		2.90	19	57	171	34.60	
	3800	10 C.F., 9 H.P.		3.05	30.50	91	273	42.60	
	3850	Nailer, pneumatic		.47	31	93	279	22.35	
	3900	Paint sprayers complete, 8 CFM		.94	62.50	187	560	44.90	
	4000	17 CFM		1.57	104	313	940	75.15	
	4020	Pavers, bituminous, rubber tires, 8' wide, 50 H.P., diesel		31.85	500	1,500	4,500	554.80	
	4030	10' wide, 150 H.P.		107.95	1,825	5,460	16,400	1,956	
	4050	Crawler, 8' wide, 100 H.P., diesel		90.45	1,825	5,500	16,500	1,824	
	4060	10' wide, 150 H.P.		115.10	2,250	6,715	20,100	2,264	
	4070	Concrete paver, 12' to 24' wide, 250 H.P.		102.05	1,525	4,600	13,800	1,736	
	4080	Placer-spreader-trimmer, 24' wide, 300 H.P.		147.05	2,475	7,405	22,200	2,657	
	4100	Pump, centrifugal gas pump, 1-1/2" diam., 65 GPM		3.95	50	150	450	61.60	
	4200	2" diameter, 130 GPM		5.30	55	165	495	75.40	
	4300	3" diameter, 250 GPM		5.60	56.50	170	510	78.80	
	4400	6" diameter, 1500 GPM		29.35	177	530	1,600	340.80	
	4500	Submersible electric pump, 1-1/4" diameter, 55 GPM		.38	16.65	50	150	13.05	
	4600	1-1/2" diameter, 83 GPM		.42	19	57	171	14.75	
	4700	2" diameter, 120 GPM		1.43	23.50	71	213	25.65	
	4800	3" diameter, 300 GPM		2.55	41.50	125	375	45.40	
	4900	4" diameter, 560 GPM		10.65	160	480	1,450	181.20	
	5000	6" diameter, 1590 GPM		15.75	215	645	1,925	255	
	5100	Diaphragm pump, gas, single, 1-1/2" diameter		1.18	50.50	152	455	39.85	
	5200	2" diameter		4.25	63.50	190	570	72	
	5300	3" diameter		4.25	63.50	190	570	72	
	5400	Double, 4" diameter		6.35	108	325	975	115.80	
	5450	Pressure washer 5 GPM, 3000 psi		4.80	51.50	155	465	69.40	

01 54 33 | Equipment Rental

		UNIT	HOURLY OPER. COST	RENT PER DAY	RENT PER WEEK	RENT PER MONTH	EQUIPMENT COST/DAY	
40	5460	7 GPM, 3000 psi	Ea.	6.25	60	180	540	86	40
	5500	Trash pump, self-priming, gas, 2″ diameter		4.50	21.50	64	192	48.80	
	5600	Diesel, 4″ diameter		9.30	90	270	810	128.40	
	5650	Diesel, 6″ diameter		25.55	150	450	1,350	294.40	
	5655	Grout Pump		26.80	260	780	2,350	370.40	
	5700	Salamanders, L.P. gas fired, 100,000 Btu		3.81	13.65	41	123	38.70	
	5705	50,000 Btu		2.39	10.35	31	93	25.30	
	5720	Sandblaster, portable, open top, 3 C.F. capacity		.55	26.50	80	240	20.40	
	5730	6 C.F. capacity		.95	40	120	360	31.60	
	5740	Accessories for above		.13	21.50	64	192	13.85	
	5750	Sander, floor		.71	17	51	153	15.90	
	5760	Edger		.57	18.35	55	165	15.55	
	5800	Saw, chain, gas engine, 18″ long		2.25	22	66	198	31.20	
	5900	Hydraulic powered, 36″ long		.75	65	195	585	45	
	5950	60″ long		.75	66.50	200	600	46	
	6000	Masonry, table mounted, 14″ diameter, 5 H.P.		1.31	56.50	170	510	44.50	
	6050	Portable cut-off, 8 H.P.		2.40	33.50	100	300	39.20	
	6100	Circular, hand held, electric, 7-1/4″ diameter		.22	4.67	14	42	4.55	
	6200	12″ diameter		.22	8	24	72	6.55	
	6250	Wall saw, w/hydraulic power, 10 H.P.		10.45	60	180	540	119.60	
	6275	Shot blaster, walk-behind, 20″ wide		4.80	293	880	2,650	214.40	
	6280	Sidewalk broom, walk-behind		2.32	70	210	630	60.55	
	6300	Steam cleaner, 100 gallons per hour		3.70	76.50	230	690	75.60	
	6310	200 gallons per hour		5.25	95	285	855	99	
	6340	Tar Kettle/Pot, 400 gallons		10.50	76.50	230	690	130	
	6350	Torch, cutting, acetylene-oxygen, 150′ hose, excludes gases		.30	15	45	135	11.40	
	6360	Hourly operating cost includes tips and gas		19.00				152	
	6410	Toilet, portable chemical		.12	20.50	62	186	13.35	
	6420	Recycle flush type		.15	24.50	74	222	16	
	6430	Toilet, fresh water flush, garden hose,		.18	29.50	89	267	19.25	
	6440	Hoisted, non-flush, for high rise		.15	24.50	73	219	15.80	
	6465	Tractor, farm with attachment		21.90	277	830	2,500	341.20	
	6500	Trailers, platform, flush deck, 2 axle, 25 ton capacity		5.45	117	350	1,050	113.60	
	6600	40 ton capacity		7.00	160	480	1,450	152	
	6700	3 axle, 50 ton capacity		7.55	177	530	1,600	166.40	
	6800	75 ton capacity		9.35	232	695	2,075	213.80	
	6810	Trailer mounted cable reel for high voltage line work		5.35	255	764	2,300	195.60	
	6820	Trailer mounted cable tensioning rig		10.64	505	1,520	4,550	389.10	
	6830	Cable pulling rig		71.33	2,825	8,510	25,500	2,273	
	6900	Water tank trailer, engine driven discharge, 5000 gallons		6.95	143	430	1,300	141.60	
	6925	10,000 gallons		9.50	198	595	1,775	195	
	6950	Water truck, off highway, 6000 gallons		89.80	775	2,330	7,000	1,184	
	7010	Tram car for high voltage line work, powered, 2 conductor		6.27	138	415	1,250	133.15	
	7020	Transit (builder's level) with tripod		.10	16.65	50	150	10.80	
	7030	Trench box, 3000 lb., 6′ x 8′		.56	93.50	280	840	60.50	
	7040	7200 lb., 6′ x 20′		.78	130	389	1,175	84.05	
	7050	8000 lb., 8′ x 16′		1.08	180	540	1,625	116.65	
	7060	9500 lb., 8′ x 20′		1.21	201	603	1,800	130.30	
	7065	11,000 lb., 8′ x 24′		1.27	211	633	1,900	136.75	
	7070	12,000 lb., 10′ x 20′		1.36	227	680	2,050	146.90	
	7100	Truck, pickup, 3/4 ton, 2 wheel drive		15.25	58.50	175	525	157	
	7200	4 wheel drive		15.55	73.50	220	660	168.40	
	7250	Crew carrier, 9 passenger		21.60	86.50	260	780	224.80	
	7290	Flat bed truck, 20,000 lb. GVW		22.30	125	375	1,125	253.40	
	7300	Tractor, 4 x 2, 220 H.P.		31.05	197	590	1,775	366.40	
	7410	330 H.P.		46.05	272	815	2,450	531.40	
	7500	6 x 4, 380 H.P.		52.85	315	950	2,850	612.80	
	7600	450 H.P.		64.05	385	1,150	3,450	742.40	

01 54 33 | Equipment Rental

		UNIT	HOURLY OPER. COST	RENT PER DAY	RENT PER WEEK	RENT PER MONTH	EQUIPMENT COST/DAY	
40	7610	Tractor, with A frame, boom and winch, 225 H.P.	Ea.	33.95	272	815	2,450	434.60	**40**
	7620	Vacuum truck, hazardous material, 2500 gallons		12.00	292	875	2,625	271	
	7625	5,000 gallons		14.27	410	1,230	3,700	360.15	
	7650	Vacuum, HEPA, 16 gallon, wet/dry		.83	18	54	162	17.45	
	7655	55 gallon, wet/dry		.77	27	81	243	22.35	
	7660	Water tank, portable		.16	26.50	80	240	17.30	
	7690	Sewer/catch basin vacuum, 14 C.Y., 1500 gallons		18.61	615	1,850	5,550	518.90	
	7700	Welder, electric, 200 amp		3.64	16.35	49	147	38.90	
	7800	300 amp		5.41	20	60	180	55.30	
	7900	Gas engine, 200 amp		13.90	23.50	70	210	125.20	
	8000	300 amp		15.90	24.50	74	222	142	
	8100	Wheelbarrow, any size		.08	13	39	117	8.45	
	8200	Wrecking ball, 4000 lb.		2.30	68.50	205	615	59.40	
50	0010	**HIGHWAY EQUIPMENT RENTAL** without operators [R015433-10]	Ea.						**50**
	0050	Asphalt batch plant, portable drum mixer, 100 ton/hr.		79.15	1,450	4,320	13,000	1,497	
	0060	200 ton/hr.		90.32	1,525	4,590	13,800	1,641	
	0070	300 ton/hr.		107.39	1,800	5,390	16,200	1,937	
	0100	Backhoe attachment, long stick, up to 185 H.P., 10.5' long		.35	23	69	207	16.60	
	0140	Up to 250 H.P., 12' long		.37	24.50	74	222	17.75	
	0180	Over 250 H.P., 15' long		.52	34.50	103	310	24.75	
	0200	Special dipper arm, up to 100 H.P., 32' long		1.06	70.50	211	635	50.70	
	0240	Over 100 H.P., 33' long		1.32	87.50	263	790	63.15	
	0280	Catch basin/sewer cleaning truck, 3 ton, 9 C.Y., 1000 gal.		46.25	390	1,170	3,500	604	
	0300	Concrete batch plant, portable, electric, 200 C.Y./hr.		22.08	510	1,525	4,575	481.65	
	0520	Grader/dozer attachment, ripper/scarifier, rear mounted, up to 135 H.P.		3.45	65	195	585	66.60	
	0540	Up to 180 H.P.		4.05	81.50	245	735	81.40	
	0580	Up to 250 H.P.		4.45	93.50	280	840	91.60	
	0700	Pvmt. removal bucket, for hyd. excavator, up to 90 H.P.		1.90	51.50	155	465	46.20	
	0740	Up to 200 H.P.		2.10	73.50	220	660	60.80	
	0780	Over 200 H.P.		2.25	85	255	765	69	
	0900	Aggregate spreader, self-propelled, 187 H.P.		53.75	685	2,055	6,175	841	
	1000	Chemical spreader, 3 C.Y.		3.40	43.50	130	390	53.20	
	1900	Hammermill, traveling, 250 H.P.		77.73	2,050	6,120	18,400	1,846	
	2000	Horizontal borer, 3" diameter, 13 H.P. gas driven		6.25	55	165	495	83	
	2150	Horizontal directional drill, 20,000 lb. thrust, 78 H.P. diesel		31.55	675	2,030	6,100	658.40	
	2160	30,000 lb. thrust, 115 H.P.		39.40	1,025	3,105	9,325	936.20	
	2170	50,000 lb. thrust, 170 H.P.		56.45	1,325	3,970	11,900	1,246	
	2190	Mud trailer for HDD, 1500 gallons, 175 H.P., gas		35.35	153	460	1,375	374.80	
	2200	Hydromulcher, diesel, 3000 gallon, for truck mounting		24.05	247	740	2,225	340.40	
	2300	Gas, 600 gallon		9.20	98.50	295	885	132.60	
	2400	Joint & crack cleaner, walk behind, 25 H.P.		4.35	50	150	450	64.80	
	2500	Filler, trailer mounted, 400 gallons, 20 H.P.		9.60	212	635	1,900	203.80	
	3000	Paint striper, self-propelled, 40 gallon, 22 H.P.		7.60	157	470	1,400	154.80	
	3100	120 gallon, 120 H.P.		24.80	400	1,195	3,575	437.40	
	3200	Post drivers, 6" I-Beam frame, for truck mounting		19.65	380	1,145	3,425	386.20	
	3400	Road sweeper, self-propelled, 8' wide, 90 H.P.		40.30	570	1,715	5,150	665.40	
	3450	Road sweeper, vacuum assisted, 4 C.Y., 220 gallons		77.55	625	1,870	5,600	994.40	
	4000	Road mixer, self-propelled, 130 H.P.		47.80	775	2,320	6,950	846.40	
	4100	310 H.P.		84.40	2,100	6,335	19,000	1,942	
	4220	Cold mix paver, incl. pug mill and bitumen tank, 165 H.P.		98.80	2,325	6,965	20,900	2,183	
	4240	Pavement brush, towed		3.20	93.50	280	840	81.60	
	4250	Paver, asphalt, wheel or crawler, 130 H.P., diesel		98.45	2,300	6,905	20,700	2,169	
	4300	Paver, road widener, gas 1' to 6', 67 H.P.		49.40	905	2,715	8,150	938.20	
	4400	Diesel, 2' to 14', 88 H.P.		63.70	1,050	3,170	9,500	1,144	
	4600	Slipform pavers, curb and gutter, 2 track, 75 H.P.		52.00	805	2,410	7,225	898	
	4700	4 track, 165 H.P.		41.65	730	2,185	6,550	770.20	
	4800	Median barrier, 215 H.P.		54.00	890	2,670	8,000	966	

01 54 33 | Equipment Rental

			UNIT	HOURLY OPER. COST	RENT PER DAY	RENT PER WEEK	RENT PER MONTH	EQUIPMENT COST/DAY	
50	4901	Trailer, low bed, 75 ton capacity	Ea.	10.10	232	695	2,075	219.80	50
	5000	Road planer, walk behind, 10" cutting width, 10 H.P.		4.00	33.50	100	300	52	
	5100	Self-propelled, 12" cutting width, 64 H.P.		11.45	113	340	1,025	159.60	
	5120	Traffic line remover, metal ball blaster, truck mounted, 115 H.P.		48.75	750	2,245	6,725	839	
	5140	Grinder, truck mounted, 115 H.P.		55.45	810	2,435	7,300	930.60	
	5160	Walk-behind, 11 H.P.		4.55	53.50	160	480	68.40	
	5200	Pavement profiler, 4' to 6' wide, 450 H.P.		258.10	3,350	10,045	30,100	4,074	
	5300	8' to 10' wide, 750 H.P.		405.10	4,400	13,180	39,500	5,877	
	5400	Roadway plate, steel, 1" x 8' x 20'		.08	13	39	117	8.45	
	5600	Stabilizer, self-propelled, 150 H.P.		50.10	610	1,835	5,500	767.80	
	5700	310 H.P.		100.25	1,700	5,125	15,400	1,827	
	5800	Striper, truck mounted, 120 gallon paint, 460 H.P.		71.05	485	1,460	4,375	860.40	
	5900	Thermal paint heating kettle, 115 gallons		5.95	25.50	77	231	63	
	6000	Tar kettle, 330 gallon, trailer mounted		8.70	58.50	175	525	104.60	
	7000	Tunnel locomotive, diesel, 8 to 12 ton		32.40	585	1,760	5,275	611.20	
	7005	Electric, 10 ton		26.55	670	2,010	6,025	614.40	
	7010	Muck cars, 1/2 C.Y. capacity		2.05	24.50	74	222	31.20	
	7020	1 C.Y. capacity		2.30	32.50	98	294	38	
	7030	2 C.Y. capacity		2.45	36.50	110	330	41.60	
	7040	Side dump, 2 C.Y. capacity		2.65	45	135	405	48.20	
	7050	3 C.Y. capacity		3.55	51.50	155	465	59.40	
	7060	5 C.Y. capacity		5.10	65	195	585	79.80	
	7100	Ventilating blower for tunnel, 7-1/2 H.P.		2.05	51.50	155	465	47.40	
	7110	10 H.P.		2.22	53.50	160	480	49.75	
	7120	20 H.P.		3.43	69.50	208	625	69.05	
	7140	40 H.P.		5.59	98.50	295	885	103.70	
	7160	60 H.P.		8.54	152	455	1,375	159.30	
	7175	75 H.P.		11.25	207	620	1,850	214	
	7180	200 H.P.		22.56	305	910	2,725	362.50	
	7800	Windrow loader, elevating		55.95	1,325	3,960	11,900	1,240	
60	0010	**LIFTING AND HOISTING EQUIPMENT RENTAL** without operators [R015433 -10]							60
	0120	Aerial lift truck, 2 person, to 80'	Ea.	26.75	715	2,145	6,425	643	
	0140	Boom work platform, 40' snorkel [R015433 -15]		16.10	277	830	2,500	294.80	
	0150	Crane, flatbed mounted, 3 ton capacity		16.55	193	580	1,750	248.40	
	0200	Crane, climbing, 106' jib, 6000 lb. capacity, 410 fpm [R312316 -45]		37.76	1,625	4,860	14,600	1,274	
	0300	101' jib, 10,250 lb. capacity, 270 fpm		44.26	2,050	6,160	18,500	1,586	
	0500	Tower, static, 130' high, 106' jib, 6200 lb. capacity at 400 fpm		41.56	1,875	5,620	16,900	1,456	
	0600	Crawler mounted, lattice boom, 1/2 C.Y., 15 tons at 12' radius		37.52	640	1,920	5,750	684.15	
	0700	3/4 C.Y., 20 tons at 12' radius		50.03	800	2,400	7,200	880.25	
	0800	1 C.Y., 25 tons at 12' radius		66.70	1,075	3,195	9,575	1,173	
	0900	1-1/2 C.Y., 40 tons at 12' radius		66.70	1,075	3,225	9,675	1,179	
	1000	2 C.Y., 50 tons at 12' radius		70.70	1,250	3,765	11,300	1,319	
	1100	3 C.Y., 75 tons at 12' radius		75.65	1,475	4,435	13,300	1,492	
	1200	100 ton capacity, 60' boom		85.65	1,700	5,090	15,300	1,703	
	1300	165 ton capacity, 60' boom		109.15	2,000	5,980	17,900	2,069	
	1400	200 ton capacity, 70' boom		132.10	2,500	7,480	22,400	2,553	
	1500	350 ton capacity, 80' boom		184.60	3,725	11,210	33,600	3,719	
	1600	Truck mounted, lattice boom, 6 x 4, 20 tons at 10' radius		37.31	1,100	3,310	9,925	960.50	
	1700	25 tons at 10' radius		40.35	1,200	3,610	10,800	1,045	
	1800	8 x 4, 30 tons at 10' radius		43.85	1,275	3,840	11,500	1,119	
	1900	40 tons at 12' radius		46.92	1,325	4,010	12,000	1,177	
	2000	60 tons at 15' radius		53.24	1,425	4,240	12,700	1,274	
	2050	82 tons at 15' radius		60.06	1,525	4,540	13,600	1,388	
	2100	90 tons at 15' radius		67.57	1,650	4,940	14,800	1,529	
	2200	115 tons at 15' radius		76.34	1,850	5,520	16,600	1,715	
	2300	150 tons at 18' radius		84.40	1,950	5,815	17,400	1,838	
	2350	165 tons at 18' radius		90.25	2,050	6,160	18,500	1,954	
	2400	Truck mounted, hydraulic, 12 ton capacity		43.00	530	1,595	4,775	663	

01 54 33 | Equipment Rental

		UNIT	HOURLY OPER. COST	RENT PER DAY	RENT PER WEEK	RENT PER MONTH	EQUIPMENT COST/DAY	
60								**60**
2500	25 ton capacity	Ea.	45.35	640	1,915	5,750	745.80	
2550	33 ton capacity		45.90	655	1,960	5,875	759.20	
2560	40 ton capacity		59.35	765	2,290	6,875	932.80	
2600	55 ton capacity		77.50	860	2,585	7,750	1,137	
2700	80 ton capacity		101.35	1,400	4,205	12,600	1,652	
2720	100 ton capacity		94.95	1,450	4,325	13,000	1,625	
2740	120 ton capacity		109.95	1,550	4,665	14,000	1,813	
2760	150 ton capacity		128.55	2,050	6,135	18,400	2,255	
2800	Self-propelled, 4 x 4, with telescoping boom, 5 ton		17.75	230	690	2,075	280	
2900	12-1/2 ton capacity		32.65	365	1,100	3,300	481.20	
3000	15 ton capacity		33.35	385	1,160	3,475	498.80	
3050	20 ton capacity		36.30	450	1,350	4,050	560.40	
3100	25 ton capacity		37.90	505	1,520	4,550	607.20	
3150	40 ton capacity		46.50	570	1,705	5,125	713	
3200	Derricks, guy, 20 ton capacity, 60' boom, 75' mast		27.18	395	1,190	3,575	455.45	
3300	100' boom, 115' mast		42.63	685	2,050	6,150	751.05	
3400	Stiffleg, 20 ton capacity, 70' boom, 37' mast		29.70	515	1,550	4,650	547.60	
3500	100' boom, 47' mast		45.64	825	2,480	7,450	861.10	
3550	Helicopter, small, lift to 1250 lb. maximum, w/pilot		100.87	3,200	9,610	28,800	2,729	
3600	Hoists, chain type, overhead, manual, 3/4 ton		.10	.33	1	3	1	
3900	10 ton		.75	6	18	54	9.60	
4000	Hoist and tower, 5000 lb. cap., portable electric, 40' high		4.77	228	685	2,050	175.15	
4100	For each added 10' section, add		.11	18	54	162	11.70	
4200	Hoist and single tubular tower, 5000 lb. electric, 100' high		6.47	320	957	2,875	243.15	
4300	For each added 6'-6" section, add		.19	31	93	279	20.10	
4400	Hoist and double tubular tower, 5000 lb., 100' high		6.95	350	1,054	3,150	266.40	
4500	For each added 6'-6" section, add		.21	34.50	103	310	22.30	
4550	Hoist and tower, mast type, 6000 lb., 100' high		7.48	365	1,093	3,275	278.45	
4570	For each added 10' section, add		.13	21.50	64	192	13.85	
4600	Hoist and tower, personnel, electric, 2000 lb., 100' @ 125 fpm		15.90	970	2,910	8,725	709.20	
4700	3000 lb., 100' @ 200 fpm		18.13	1,100	3,290	9,875	803.05	
4800	3000 lb., 150' @ 300 fpm		20.13	1,225	3,690	11,100	899.05	
4900	4000 lb., 100' @ 300 fpm		20.82	1,250	3,760	11,300	918.55	
5000	6000 lb., 100' @ 275 fpm		22.44	1,325	3,950	11,900	969.50	
5100	For added heights up to 500', add	L.F.	.01	1.67	5	15	1.10	
5200	Jacks, hydraulic, 20 ton	Ea.	.05	2	6	18	1.60	
5500	100 ton		.40	11.65	35	105	10.20	
6100	Jacks, hydraulic, climbing w/50' jackrods, control console, 30 ton cap.		1.97	131	394	1,175	94.55	
6150	For each added 10' jackrod section, add		.05	3.33	10	30	2.40	
6300	50 ton capacity		3.17	211	633	1,900	151.95	
6350	For each added 10' jackrod section, add		.06	4	12	36	2.90	
6500	125 ton capacity		8.30	555	1,660	4,975	398.40	
6550	For each added 10' jackrod section, add		.57	37.50	113	340	27.15	
6600	Cable jack, 10 ton capacity with 200' cable		1.65	110	329	985	79	
6650	For each added 50' of cable, add		.20	13	39	117	9.40	
70								**70**
0010	**WELLPOINT EQUIPMENT RENTAL** without operators	R015433 -10						
0020	Based on 2 months rental							
0100	Combination jetting & wellpoint pump, 60 H.P. diesel	Ea.	18.14	325	976	2,925	340.30	
0200	High pressure gas jet pump, 200 H.P., 300 psi	"	43.54	278	834	2,500	515.10	
0300	Discharge pipe, 8" diameter	L.F.	.01	.53	1.59	4.77	.40	
0350	12" diameter		.01	.78	2.33	7	.55	
0400	Header pipe, flows up to 150 GPM, 4" diameter		.01	.48	1.44	4.32	.35	
0500	400 GPM, 6" diameter		.01	.56	1.69	5.05	.40	
0600	800 GPM, 8" diameter		.01	.78	2.33	7	.55	
0700	1500 GPM, 10" diameter		.01	.82	2.46	7.40	.55	
0800	2500 GPM, 12" diameter		.02	1.55	4.65	13.95	1.10	
0900	4500 GPM, 16" diameter		.03	1.98	5.95	17.85	1.45	

01 54 33 | Equipment Rental

			UNIT	HOURLY OPER. COST	RENT PER DAY	RENT PER WEEK	RENT PER MONTH	EQUIPMENT COST/DAY	
70	0950	For quick coupling aluminum and plastic pipe, add	L.F.	.03	2.05	6.16	18.50	1.45	**70**
	1100	Wellpoint, 25' long, with fittings & riser pipe, 1-1/2" or 2" diameter		.06	4.10	12.29	37	2.95	
	1200	Wellpoint pump, diesel powered, 4" suction, 20 H.P.		7.71	188	563	1,700	174.30	
	1300	6" suction, 30 H.P.		10.54	233	698	2,100	223.90	
	1400	8" suction, 40 H.P.		14.24	320	957	2,875	305.30	
	1500	10" suction, 75 H.P.		21.97	375	1,119	3,350	399.55	
	1600	12" suction, 100 H.P.		31.24	590	1,770	5,300	603.90	
	1700	12" suction, 175 H.P.		46.78	655	1,970	5,900	768.25	
80	0010	**MARINE EQUIPMENT RENTAL** without operators							**80**
	0200	Barge, 400 Ton, 30' wide x 90' long	Ea.	17.50	1,075	3,205	9,625	781	
	0240	800 Ton, 45' wide x 90' long		21.20	1,300	3,900	11,700	949.60	
	2000	Tugboat, diesel, 100 H.P.		38.95	217	650	1,950	441.60	
	2040	250 H.P.		81.55	395	1,185	3,550	889.40	
	2080	380 H.P.		160.00	1,175	3,545	10,600	1,989	
	3000	Small work boat, gas, 16-foot, 50 H.P.		19.15	60	180	540	189.20	
	4000	Large, diesel, 48-foot, 200 H.P.		90.80	1,250	3,745	11,200	1,475	

R015433 -10

Crews

Crew A-1	Hr.	Daily	Hr.	Daily	Bare Costs	Incl. O&P
1 Building Laborer	$28.20	$225.60	$47.45	$379.60	$28.20	$47.45
1 Concrete Saw, Gas Manual		84.00		92.40	10.50	11.55
8 L.H., Daily Totals		$309.60		$472.00	$38.70	$59.00

Crew A-1A	Hr.	Daily	Hr.	Daily	Bare Costs	Incl. O&P
1 Skilled Worker	$36.30	$290.40	$61.30	$490.40	$36.30	$61.30
1 Shot Blaster, 20"		214.40		235.84	26.80	29.48
8 L.H., Daily Totals		$504.80		$726.24	$63.10	$90.78

Crew A-1B	Hr.	Daily	Hr.	Daily	Bare Costs	Incl. O&P
1 Building Laborer	$28.20	$225.60	$47.45	$379.60	$28.20	$47.45
1 Concrete Saw		175.20		192.72	21.90	24.09
8 L.H., Daily Totals		$400.80		$572.32	$50.10	$71.54

Crew A-1C	Hr.	Daily	Hr.	Daily	Bare Costs	Incl. O&P
1 Building Laborer	$28.20	$225.60	$47.45	$379.60	$28.20	$47.45
1 Chain Saw, Gas, 18"		31.20		34.32	3.90	4.29
8 L.H., Daily Totals		$256.80		$413.92	$32.10	$51.74

Crew A-1D	Hr.	Daily	Hr.	Daily	Bare Costs	Incl. O&P
1 Building Laborer	$28.20	$225.60	$47.45	$379.60	$28.20	$47.45
1 Vibrating Plate, Gas, 18"		35.80		39.38	4.47	4.92
8 L.H., Daily Totals		$261.40		$418.98	$32.67	$52.37

Crew A-1E	Hr.	Daily	Hr.	Daily	Bare Costs	Incl. O&P
1 Building Laborer	$28.20	$225.60	$47.45	$379.60	$28.20	$47.45
1 Vibrating Plate, Gas, 21"		46.00		50.60	5.75	6.33
8 L.H., Daily Totals		$271.60		$430.20	$33.95	$53.77

Crew A-1F	Hr.	Daily	Hr.	Daily	Bare Costs	Incl. O&P
1 Building Laborer	$28.20	$225.60	$47.45	$379.60	$28.20	$47.45
1 Rammer/Tamper, Gas, 8"		49.60		54.56	6.20	6.82
8 L.H., Daily Totals		$275.20		$434.16	$34.40	$54.27

Crew A-1G	Hr.	Daily	Hr.	Daily	Bare Costs	Incl. O&P
1 Building Laborer	$28.20	$225.60	$47.45	$379.60	$28.20	$47.45
1 Rammer/Tamper, Gas, 15"		56.00		61.60	7.00	7.70
8 L.H., Daily Totals		$281.60		$441.20	$35.20	$55.15

Crew A-1H	Hr.	Daily	Hr.	Daily	Bare Costs	Incl. O&P
1 Building Laborer	$28.20	$225.60	$47.45	$379.60	$28.20	$47.45
1 Exterior Steam Cleaner		75.60		83.16	9.45	10.40
8 L.H., Daily Totals		$301.20		$462.76	$37.65	$57.84

Crew A-1J	Hr.	Daily	Hr.	Daily	Bare Costs	Incl. O&P
1 Building Laborer	$28.20	$225.60	$47.45	$379.60	$28.20	$47.45
1 Cultivator, Walk-Behind, 5 H.P.		57.45		63.20	7.18	7.90
8 L.H., Daily Totals		$283.05		$442.80	$35.38	$55.35

Crew A-1K	Hr.	Daily	Hr.	Daily	Bare Costs	Incl. O&P
1 Building Laborer	$28.20	$225.60	$47.45	$379.60	$28.20	$47.45
1 Cultivator, Walk-Behind, 8 H.P.		81.40		89.54	10.18	11.19
8 L.H., Daily Totals		$307.00		$469.14	$38.38	$58.64

Crew A-1M	Hr.	Daily	Hr.	Daily	Bare Costs	Incl. O&P
1 Building Laborer	$28.20	$225.60	$47.45	$379.60	$28.20	$47.45
1 Snow Blower, Walk-Behind		60.55		66.61	7.57	8.33
8 L.H., Daily Totals		$286.15		$446.20	$35.77	$55.78

Crew A-2	Hr.	Daily	Hr.	Daily	Bare Costs	Incl. O&P
2 Laborers	$28.20	$451.20	$47.45	$759.20	$28.42	$47.65
1 Truck Driver (light)	28.85	230.80	48.05	384.40		
1 Flatbed Truck, Gas, 1.5 Ton		270.20		297.22	11.26	12.38
24 L.H., Daily Totals		$952.20		$1440.82	$39.67	$60.03

Crew A-2A	Hr.	Daily	Hr.	Daily	Bare Costs	Incl. O&P
2 Laborers	$28.20	$451.20	$47.45	$759.20	$28.42	$47.65
1 Truck Driver (light)	28.85	230.80	48.05	384.40		
1 Flatbed Truck, Gas, 1.5 Ton		270.20		297.22		
1 Concrete Saw		175.20		192.72	18.56	20.41
24 L.H., Daily Totals		$1127.40		$1633.54	$46.98	$68.06

Crew A-2B	Hr.	Daily	Hr.	Daily	Bare Costs	Incl. O&P
1 Truck Driver (light)	$28.85	$230.80	$48.05	$384.40	$28.85	$48.05
1 Flatbed Truck, Gas, 1.5 Ton		270.20		297.22	33.77	37.15
8 L.H., Daily Totals		$501.00		$681.62	$62.63	$85.20

Crew A-3A	Hr.	Daily	Hr.	Daily	Bare Costs	Incl. O&P
1 Truck Driver (light)	$28.85	$230.80	$48.05	$384.40	$28.85	$48.05
1 Pickup Truck, 4 x 4, 3/4 Ton		168.40		185.24	21.05	23.16
8 L.H., Daily Totals		$399.20		$569.64	$49.90	$71.20

Crew A-3B	Hr.	Daily	Hr.	Daily	Bare Costs	Incl. O&P
1 Equip. Oper. (medium)	$37.65	$301.20	$62.35	$498.80	$33.65	$55.88
1 Truck Driver (heavy)	29.65	237.20	49.40	395.20		
1 Dump Truck, 12 C.Y., 400 H.P.		692.20		761.42		
1 F.E. Loader, W.M.,2.5 C.Y.		522.80		575.08	75.94	83.53
16 L.H., Daily Totals		$1753.40		$2230.50	$109.59	$139.41

Crew A-3C	Hr.	Daily	Hr.	Daily	Bare Costs	Incl. O&P
1 Equip. Oper. (light)	$36.25	$290.00	$60.05	$480.40	$36.25	$60.05
1 Loader, Skid Steer, 78 H.P.		308.80		339.68	38.60	42.46
8 L.H., Daily Totals		$598.80		$820.08	$74.85	$102.51

Crew A-3D	Hr.	Daily	Hr.	Daily	Bare Costs	Incl. O&P
1 Truck Driver (light)	$28.85	$230.80	$48.05	$384.40	$28.85	$48.05
1 Pickup Truck, 4 x 4, 3/4 Ton		168.40		185.24		
1 Flatbed Trailer, 25 Ton		113.60		124.96	35.25	38.77
8 L.H., Daily Totals		$512.80		$694.60	$64.10	$86.83

Crew A-3E	Hr.	Daily	Hr.	Daily	Bare Costs	Incl. O&P
1 Equip. Oper. (crane)	$38.70	$309.60	$64.10	$512.80	$34.17	$56.75
1 Truck Driver (heavy)	29.65	237.20	49.40	395.20		
1 Pickup Truck, 4 x 4, 3/4 Ton		168.40		185.24	10.53	11.58
16 L.H., Daily Totals		$715.20		$1093.24	$44.70	$68.33

Crew A-3F	Hr.	Daily	Hr.	Daily	Bare Costs	Incl. O&P
1 Equip. Oper. (crane)	$38.70	$309.60	$64.10	$512.80	$34.17	$56.75
1 Truck Driver (heavy)	29.65	237.20	49.40	395.20		
1 Pickup Truck, 4 x 4, 3/4 Ton		168.40		185.24		
1 Truck Tractor, 6x4, 380 H.P.		612.80		674.08		
1 Lowbed Trailer, 75 Ton		219.80		241.78	62.56	68.82
16 L.H., Daily Totals		$1547.80		$2009.10	$96.74	$125.57

Crew A-3G

Crew No.	Bare Costs Hr.	Daily	Incl. Subs O&P Hr.	Daily	Cost Per Labor-Hour Bare Costs	Incl. O&P
1 Equip. Oper. (crane)	$38.70	$309.60	$64.10	$512.80	$34.17	$56.75
1 Truck Driver (heavy)	29.65	237.20	49.40	395.20		
1 Pickup Truck, 4 x 4, 3/4 Ton		168.40		185.24		
1 Truck Tractor, 6x4, 450 H.P.		742.40		816.64		
1 Lowbed Trailer, 75 Ton		219.80		241.78	70.66	77.73
16 L.H., Daily Totals		$1677.40		$2151.66	$104.84	$134.48

Crew A-3H

Crew No.	Bare Costs Hr.	Daily	Incl. Subs O&P Hr.	Daily	Cost Per Labor-Hour Bare Costs	Incl. O&P
1 Equip. Oper. (crane)	$38.70	$309.60	$64.10	$512.80	$38.70	$64.10
1 Hyd. Crane, 12 Ton (Daily)		874.00		961.40	109.25	120.18
8 L.H., Daily Totals		$1183.60		$1474.20	$147.95	$184.28

Crew A-3I

Crew No.	Bare Costs Hr.	Daily	Incl. Subs O&P Hr.	Daily	Cost Per Labor-Hour Bare Costs	Incl. O&P
1 Equip. Oper. (crane)	$38.70	$309.60	$64.10	$512.80	$38.70	$64.10
1 Hyd. Crane, 25 Ton (Daily)		1003.00		1103.30	125.38	137.91
8 L.H., Daily Totals		$1312.60		$1616.10	$164.07	$202.01

Crew A-3J

Crew No.	Bare Costs Hr.	Daily	Incl. Subs O&P Hr.	Daily	Cost Per Labor-Hour Bare Costs	Incl. O&P
1 Equip. Oper. (crane)	$38.70	$309.60	$64.10	$512.80	$38.70	$64.10
1 Hyd. Crane, 40 Ton (Daily)		1240.00		1364.00	155.00	170.50
8 L.H., Daily Totals		$1549.60		$1876.80	$193.70	$234.60

Crew A-3K

Crew No.	Bare Costs Hr.	Daily	Incl. Subs O&P Hr.	Daily	Cost Per Labor-Hour Bare Costs	Incl. O&P
1 Equip. Oper. (crane)	$38.70	$309.60	$64.10	$512.80	$36.13	$59.83
1 Equip. Oper. (oiler)	33.55	268.40	55.55	444.40		
1 Hyd. Crane, 55 Ton (Daily)		1480.00		1628.00		
1 P/U Truck, 3/4 Ton (Daily)		182.00		200.20	103.88	114.26
16 L.H., Daily Totals		$2240.00		$2785.40	$140.00	$174.09

Crew A-3L

Crew No.	Bare Costs Hr.	Daily	Incl. Subs O&P Hr.	Daily	Cost Per Labor-Hour Bare Costs	Incl. O&P
1 Equip. Oper. (crane)	$38.70	$309.60	$64.10	$512.80	$36.13	$59.83
1 Equip. Oper. (oiler)	33.55	268.40	55.55	444.40		
1 Hyd. Crane, 80 Ton (Daily)		2211.00		2432.10		
1 P/U Truck, 3/4 Ton (Daily)		182.00		200.20	149.56	164.52
16 L.H., Daily Totals		$2971.00		$3589.50	$185.69	$224.34

Crew A-3M

Crew No.	Bare Costs Hr.	Daily	Incl. Subs O&P Hr.	Daily	Cost Per Labor-Hour Bare Costs	Incl. O&P
1 Equip. Oper. (crane)	$38.70	$309.60	$64.10	$512.80	$36.13	$59.83
1 Equip. Oper. (oiler)	33.55	268.40	55.55	444.40		
1 Hyd. Crane, 100 Ton (Daily)		2200.00		2420.00		
1 P/U Truck, 3/4 Ton (Daily)		182.00		200.20	148.88	163.76
16 L.H., Daily Totals		$2960.00		$3577.40	$185.00	$223.59

Crew A-3N

Crew No.	Bare Costs Hr.	Daily	Incl. Subs O&P Hr.	Daily	Cost Per Labor-Hour Bare Costs	Incl. O&P
1 Equip. Oper. (crane)	$38.70	$309.60	$64.10	$512.80	$38.70	$64.10
1 Tower Cane (monthly)		1100.00		1210.00	137.50	151.25
8 L.H., Daily Totals		$1409.60		$1722.80	$176.20	$215.35

Crew A-3P

Crew No.	Bare Costs Hr.	Daily	Incl. Subs O&P Hr.	Daily	Cost Per Labor-Hour Bare Costs	Incl. O&P
1 Equip. Oper. (light)	$36.25	$290.00	$60.05	$480.40	$36.25	$60.05
1 A.T. Forklift, 42' lift		531.60		584.76	66.45	73.09
8 L.H., Daily Totals		$821.60		$1065.16	$102.70	$133.15

Crew A-4

Crew No.	Bare Costs Hr.	Daily	Incl. Subs O&P Hr.	Daily	Cost Per Labor-Hour Bare Costs	Incl. O&P
2 Carpenters	$35.75	$572.00	$60.15	$962.40	$34.25	$57.23
1 Painter, Ordinary	31.25	250.00	51.40	411.20		
24 L.H., Daily Totals		$822.00		$1373.60	$34.25	$57.23

Crew A-5

Crew No.	Bare Costs Hr.	Daily	Incl. Subs O&P Hr.	Daily	Cost Per Labor-Hour Bare Costs	Incl. O&P
2 Laborers	$28.20	$451.20	$47.45	$759.20	$28.27	$47.52
.25 Truck Driver (light)	28.85	57.70	48.05	96.10		
.25 Flatbed Truck, Gas, 1.5 Ton		67.55		74.31	3.75	4.13
18 L.H., Daily Totals		$576.45		$929.61	$32.02	$51.64

Crew A-6

Crew No.	Bare Costs Hr.	Daily	Incl. Subs O&P Hr.	Daily	Cost Per Labor-Hour Bare Costs	Incl. O&P
1 Instrument Man	$36.30	$290.40	$61.30	$490.40	$35.55	$59.55
1 Rodman/Chainman	34.80	278.40	57.80	462.40		
1 Level, Electronic		71.30		78.43	4.46	4.90
16 L.H., Daily Totals		$640.10		$1031.23	$40.01	$64.45

Crew A-7

Crew No.	Bare Costs Hr.	Daily	Incl. Subs O&P Hr.	Daily	Cost Per Labor-Hour Bare Costs	Incl. O&P
1 Chief of Party	$44.30	$354.40	$74.35	$594.80	$38.47	$64.48
1 Instrument Man	36.30	290.40	61.30	490.40		
1 Rodman/Chainman	34.80	278.40	57.80	462.40		
1 Level, Electronic		71.30		78.43	2.97	3.27
24 L.H., Daily Totals		$994.50		$1626.03	$41.44	$67.75

Crew A-8

Crew No.	Bare Costs Hr.	Daily	Incl. Subs O&P Hr.	Daily	Cost Per Labor-Hour Bare Costs	Incl. O&P
1 Chief of Party	$44.30	$354.40	$74.35	$594.80	$37.55	$62.81
1 Instrument Man	36.30	290.40	61.30	490.40		
2 Rodmen/Chainmen	34.80	556.80	57.80	924.80		
1 Level, Electronic		71.30		78.43	2.23	2.45
32 L.H., Daily Totals		$1272.90		$2088.43	$39.78	$65.26

Crew A-9

Crew No.	Bare Costs Hr.	Daily	Incl. Subs O&P Hr.	Daily	Cost Per Labor-Hour Bare Costs	Incl. O&P
1 Asbestos Foreman	$38.35	$306.80	$65.05	$520.40	$37.91	$64.31
7 Asbestos Workers	37.85	2119.60	64.20	3595.20		
64 L.H., Daily Totals		$2426.40		$4115.60	$37.91	$64.31

Crew A-10A

Crew No.	Bare Costs Hr.	Daily	Incl. Subs O&P Hr.	Daily	Cost Per Labor-Hour Bare Costs	Incl. O&P
1 Asbestos Foreman	$38.35	$306.80	$65.05	$520.40	$38.02	$64.48
2 Asbestos Workers	37.85	605.60	64.20	1027.20		
24 L.H., Daily Totals		$912.40		$1547.60	$38.02	$64.48

Crew A-10B

Crew No.	Bare Costs Hr.	Daily	Incl. Subs O&P Hr.	Daily	Cost Per Labor-Hour Bare Costs	Incl. O&P
1 Asbestos Foreman	$38.35	$306.80	$65.05	$520.40	$37.98	$64.41
3 Asbestos Workers	37.85	908.40	64.20	1540.80		
32 L.H., Daily Totals		$1215.20		$2061.20	$37.98	$64.41

Crew A-10C

Crew No.	Bare Costs Hr.	Daily	Incl. Subs O&P Hr.	Daily	Cost Per Labor-Hour Bare Costs	Incl. O&P
3 Asbestos Workers	$37.85	$908.40	$64.20	$1540.80	$37.85	$64.20
1 Flatbed Truck, Gas, 1.5 Ton		270.20		297.22	11.26	12.38
24 L.H., Daily Totals		$1178.60		$1838.02	$49.11	$76.58

Crew A-10D

Crew No.	Bare Costs Hr.	Daily	Incl. Subs O&P Hr.	Daily	Cost Per Labor-Hour Bare Costs	Incl. O&P
2 Asbestos Workers	$37.85	$605.60	$64.20	$1027.20	$36.99	$62.01
1 Equip. Oper. (crane)	38.70	309.60	64.10	512.80		
1 Equip. Oper. (oiler)	33.55	268.40	55.55	444.40		
1 Hydraulic Crane, 33 Ton		759.20		835.12	23.73	26.10
32 L.H., Daily Totals		$1942.80		$2819.52	$60.71	$88.11

Crew A-11

Crew No.	Bare Costs Hr.	Daily	Incl. Subs O&P Hr.	Daily	Cost Per Labor-Hour Bare Costs	Incl. O&P
1 Asbestos Foreman	$38.35	$306.80	$65.05	$520.40	$37.91	$64.31
7 Asbestos Workers	37.85	2119.60	64.20	3595.20		
2 Chip Hammers, 12 Lb., Elec.		40.00		44.00	0.63	0.69
64 L.H., Daily Totals		$2466.40		$4159.60	$38.54	$64.99

Crews

Crew No.	Bare Costs Hr.	Daily	Incl. Subs O&P Hr.	Daily	Bare Costs	Incl. O&P
Crew A-12	Hr.	Daily	Hr.	Daily	Bare Costs	Incl. O&P
1 Asbestos Foreman	$38.35	$306.80	$65.05	$520.40	$37.91	$64.31
7 Asbestos Workers	37.85	2119.60	64.20	3595.20		
1 Trk-Mtd Vac, 14 CY, 1500 Gal.		518.90		570.79		
1 Flatbed Truck, 20,000 GVW		253.40		278.74	12.07	13.27
64 L.H., Daily Totals		$3198.70		$4965.13	$49.98	$77.58

Crew A-13	Hr.	Daily	Hr.	Daily	Bare Costs	Incl. O&P
1 Equip. Oper. (light)	$36.25	$290.00	$60.05	$480.40	$36.25	$60.05
1 Trk-Mtd Vac, 14 CY, 1500 Gal.		518.90		570.79		
1 Flatbed Truck, 20,000 GVW		253.40		278.74	96.54	106.19
8 L.H., Daily Totals		$1062.30		$1329.93	$132.79	$166.24

Crew B-1	Hr.	Daily	Hr.	Daily	Bare Costs	Incl. O&P
1 Labor Foreman (outside)	$30.20	$241.60	$50.85	$406.80	$28.87	$48.58
2 Laborers	28.20	451.20	47.45	759.20		
24 L.H., Daily Totals		$692.80		$1166.00	$28.87	$48.58

Crew B-1A	Hr.	Daily	Hr.	Daily	Bare Costs	Incl. O&P
1 Labor Foreman (outside)	$30.20	$241.60	$50.85	$406.80	$28.87	$48.58
2 Laborers	28.20	451.20	47.45	759.20		
2 Cutting Torches		22.80		25.08		
2 Sets of Gases		304.00		334.40	13.62	14.98
24 L.H., Daily Totals		$1019.60		$1525.48	$42.48	$63.56

Crew B-1B	Hr.	Daily	Hr.	Daily	Bare Costs	Incl. O&P
1 Labor Foreman (outside)	$30.20	$241.60	$50.85	$406.80	$31.32	$52.46
2 Laborers	28.20	451.20	47.45	759.20		
1 Equip. Oper. (crane)	38.70	309.60	64.10	512.80		
2 Cutting Torches		22.80		25.08		
2 Sets of Gases		304.00		334.40		
1 Hyd. Crane, 12 Ton		663.00		729.30	30.93	34.02
32 L.H., Daily Totals		$1992.20		$2767.58	$62.26	$86.49

Crew B-1C	Hr.	Daily	Hr.	Daily	Bare Costs	Incl. O&P
1 Labor Foreman (outside)	$30.20	$241.60	$50.85	$406.80	$28.87	$48.58
2 Laborers	28.20	451.20	47.45	759.20		
1 Aerial Lift Truck, 60' Boom		456.00		501.60	19.00	20.90
24 L.H., Daily Totals		$1148.80		$1667.60	$47.87	$69.48

Crew B-1D	Hr.	Daily	Hr.	Daily	Bare Costs	Incl. O&P
2 Laborers	$28.20	$451.20	$47.45	$759.20	$28.20	$47.45
1 Small Work Boat, Gas, 50 H.P.		189.20		208.12		
1 Pressure Washer, 7 GPM		86.00		94.60	17.20	18.92
16 L.H., Daily Totals		$726.40		$1061.92	$45.40	$66.37

Crew B-1E	Hr.	Daily	Hr.	Daily	Bare Costs	Incl. O&P
1 Labor Foreman (outside)	$30.20	$241.60	$50.85	$406.80	$28.70	$48.30
3 Laborers	28.20	676.80	47.45	1138.80		
1 Work Boat, Diesel, 200 H.P.		1475.00		1622.50		
2 Pressure Washer, 7 GPM		172.00		189.20	51.47	56.62
32 L.H., Daily Totals		$2565.40		$3357.30	$80.17	$104.92

Crew B-1F	Hr.	Daily	Hr.	Daily	Bare Costs	Incl. O&P
2 Skilled Workers	$36.30	$580.80	$61.30	$980.80	$33.60	$56.68
1 Laborer	28.20	225.60	47.45	379.60		
1 Small Work Boat, Gas, 50 H.P.		189.20		208.12		
1 Pressure Washer, 7 GPM		86.00		94.60	11.47	12.61
24 L.H., Daily Totals		$1081.60		$1663.12	$45.07	$69.30

Crew B-1G	Hr.	Daily	Hr.	Daily	Bare Costs	Incl. O&P
2 Laborers	$28.20	$451.20	$47.45	$759.20	$28.20	$47.45
1 Small Work Boat, Gas, 50 H.P.		189.20		208.12	11.82	13.01
16 L.H., Daily Totals		$640.40		$967.32	$40.02	$60.46

Crew B-1H	Hr.	Daily	Hr.	Daily	Bare Costs	Incl. O&P
2 Skilled Workers	$36.30	$580.80	$61.30	$980.80	$33.60	$56.68
1 Laborer	28.20	225.60	47.45	379.60		
1 Small Work Boat, Gas, 50 H.P.		189.20		208.12	7.88	8.67
24 L.H., Daily Totals		$995.60		$1568.52	$41.48	$65.36

Crew B-1J	Hr.	Daily	Hr.	Daily	Bare Costs	Incl. O&P
1 Labor Foreman (inside)	$28.70	$229.60	$48.30	$386.40	$28.45	$47.88
1 Laborer	28.20	225.60	47.45	379.60		
16 L.H., Daily Totals		$455.20		$766.00	$28.45	$47.88

Crew B-1K	Hr.	Daily	Hr.	Daily	Bare Costs	Incl. O&P
1 Carpenter Foreman (inside)	$36.25	$290.00	$61.00	$488.00	$36.00	$60.58
1 Carpenter	35.75	286.00	60.15	481.20		
16 L.H., Daily Totals		$576.00		$969.20	$36.00	$60.58

Crew B-2	Hr.	Daily	Hr.	Daily	Bare Costs	Incl. O&P
1 Labor Foreman (outside)	$30.20	$241.60	$50.85	$406.80	$28.60	$48.13
4 Laborers	28.20	902.40	47.45	1518.40		
40 L.H., Daily Totals		$1144.00		$1925.20	$28.60	$48.13

Crew B-2A	Hr.	Daily	Hr.	Daily	Bare Costs	Incl. O&P
1 Labor Foreman (outside)	$30.20	$241.60	$50.85	$406.80	$28.87	$48.58
2 Laborers	28.20	451.20	47.45	759.20		
1 Aerial Lift Truck, 60' Boom		456.00		501.60	19.00	20.90
24 L.H., Daily Totals		$1148.80		$1667.60	$47.87	$69.48

Crew B-3	Hr.	Daily	Hr.	Daily	Bare Costs	Incl. O&P
1 Labor Foreman (outside)	$30.20	$241.60	$50.85	$406.80	$30.59	$51.15
2 Laborers	28.20	451.20	47.45	759.20		
1 Equip. Oper. (medium)	37.65	301.20	62.35	498.80		
2 Truck Drivers (heavy)	29.65	474.40	49.40	790.40		
1 Crawler Loader, 3 C.Y.		1191.00		1310.10		
2 Dump Trucks, 12 C.Y., 400 H.P.		1384.40		1522.84	53.65	59.02
48 L.H., Daily Totals		$4043.80		$5288.14	$84.25	$110.17

Crew B-3A	Hr.	Daily	Hr.	Daily	Bare Costs	Incl. O&P
4 Laborers	$28.20	$902.40	$47.45	$1518.40	$30.09	$50.43
1 Equip. Oper. (medium)	37.65	301.20	62.35	498.80		
1 Hyd. Excavator, 1.5 C.Y.		1031.00		1134.10	25.77	28.35
40 L.H., Daily Totals		$2234.60		$3151.30	$55.87	$78.78

Crew B-3B	Hr.	Daily	Hr.	Daily	Bare Costs	Incl. O&P
2 Laborers	$28.20	$451.20	$47.45	$759.20	$30.93	$51.66
1 Equip. Oper. (medium)	37.65	301.20	62.35	498.80		
1 Truck Driver (heavy)	29.65	237.20	49.40	395.20		
1 Backhoe Loader, 80 H.P.		397.60		437.36		
1 Dump Truck, 12 C.Y., 400 H.P.		692.20		761.42	34.06	37.46
32 L.H., Daily Totals		$2079.40		$2851.98	$64.98	$89.12

Crew B-3C	Hr.	Daily	Hr.	Daily	Bare Costs	Incl. O&P
3 Laborers	$28.20	$676.80	$47.45	$1138.80	$30.56	$51.17
1 Equip. Oper. (medium)	37.65	301.20	62.35	498.80		
1 Crawler Loader, 4 C.Y.		1532.00		1685.20	47.88	52.66
32 L.H., Daily Totals		$2510.00		$3322.80	$78.44	$103.84

Crew No.		Bare Costs		Incl. Subs O&P		Cost Per Labor-Hour	

Crew B-4	Hr.	Daily	Hr.	Daily	Bare Costs	Incl. O&P
1 Labor Foreman (outside)	$30.20	$241.60	$50.85	$406.80	$28.77	$48.34
4 Laborers	28.20	902.40	47.45	1518.40		
1 Truck Driver (heavy)	29.65	237.20	49.40	395.20		
1 Truck Tractor, 220 H.P.		366.40		403.04		
1 Flatbed Trailer, 40 Ton		152.00		167.20	10.80	11.88
48 L.H., Daily Totals		$1899.60		$2890.64	$39.58	$60.22

Crew B-5	Hr.	Daily	Hr.	Daily	Bare Costs	Incl. O&P
1 Labor Foreman (outside)	$30.20	$241.60	$50.85	$406.80	$30.49	$51.11
3 Laborers	28.20	676.80	47.45	1138.80		
1 Equip. Oper. (medium)	37.65	301.20	62.35	498.80		
1 Air Compressor, 250 cfm		202.40		222.64		
2 Breakers, Pavement, 60 lb.		19.60		21.56		
2 -50' Air Hoses, 1.5"		11.60		12.76		
1 Crawler Loader, 3 C.Y.		1191.00		1310.10	35.62	39.18
40 L.H., Daily Totals		$2644.20		$3611.46	$66.11	$90.29

Crew B-5A	Hr.	Daily	Hr.	Daily	Bare Costs	Incl. O&P
1 Labor Foreman (outside)	$30.20	$241.60	$50.85	$406.80	$30.85	$51.59
6 Laborers	28.20	1353.60	47.45	2277.60		
2 Equip. Oper. (medium)	37.65	602.40	62.35	997.60		
1 Equip. Oper. (light)	36.25	290.00	60.05	480.40		
2 Truck Drivers (heavy)	29.65	474.40	49.40	790.40		
1 Air Compressor, 365 cfm		264.80		291.28		
2 Breakers, Pavement, 60 lb.		19.60		21.56		
8 -50' Air Hoses, 1"		32.80		36.08		
2 Dump Trucks, 8 C.Y., 220 H.P.		834.40		917.84	12.00	13.20
96 L.H., Daily Totals		$4113.60		$6219.56	$42.85	$64.79

Crew B-5B	Hr.	Daily	Hr.	Daily	Bare Costs	Incl. O&P
1 Powderman	$36.30	$290.40	$61.30	$490.40	$33.42	$55.70
2 Equip. Oper. (medium)	37.65	602.40	62.35	997.60		
3 Truck Drivers (heavy)	29.65	711.60	49.40	1185.60		
1 F.E. Loader, W.M.,2.5 C.Y.		522.80		575.08		
3 Dump Trucks, 12 C.Y., 400 H.P.		2076.60		2284.26		
1 Air Compressor, 365 CFM		264.80		291.28	59.67	65.64
48 L.H., Daily Totals		$4468.60		$5824.22	$93.10	$121.34

Crew B-5C	Hr.	Daily	Hr.	Daily	Bare Costs	Incl. O&P
3 Laborers	$28.20	$676.80	$47.45	$1138.80	$31.73	$52.89
1 Equip. Oper. (medium)	37.65	301.20	62.35	498.80		
2 Truck Drivers (heavy)	29.65	474.40	49.40	790.40		
1 Equip. Oper. (crane)	38.70	309.60	64.10	512.80		
1 Equip. Oper. (oiler)	33.55	268.40	55.55	444.40		
2 Dump Trucks, 12 C.Y., 400 H.P.		1384.40		1522.84		
1 Crawler Loader, 4 C.Y.		1532.00		1685.20		
1 S.P. Crane, 4x4, 25 Ton		607.20		667.92	55.06	60.56
64 L.H., Daily Totals		$5554.00		$7261.16	$86.78	$113.46

Crew B-5D	Hr.	Daily	Hr.	Daily	Bare Costs	Incl. O&P
1 Labor Foreman (outside)	$30.20	$241.60	$50.85	$406.80	$30.35	$50.83
3 Laborers	28.20	676.80	47.45	1138.80		
1 Equip. Oper. (medium)	37.65	301.20	62.35	498.80		
1 Truck Driver (heavy)	29.65	237.20	49.40	395.20		
1 Air Compressor, 250 cfm		202.40		222.64		
2 Breakers, Pavement, 60 lb.		19.60		21.56		
2 -50' Air Hoses, 1.5"		11.60		12.76		
1 Crawler Loader, 3 C.Y.		1191.00		1310.10		
1 Dump Truck, 12 C.Y., 400 H.P.		692.20		761.42	44.10	48.51
48 L.H., Daily Totals		$3573.60		$4768.08	$74.45	$99.33

Crew B-6	Hr.	Daily	Hr.	Daily	Bare Costs	Incl. O&P
2 Laborers	$28.20	$451.20	$47.45	$759.20	$30.88	$51.65
1 Equip. Oper. (light)	36.25	290.00	60.05	480.40		
1 Backhoe Loader, 48 H.P.		365.20		401.72	15.22	16.74
24 L.H., Daily Totals		$1106.40		$1641.32	$46.10	$68.39

Crew B-6B	Hr.	Daily	Hr.	Daily	Bare Costs	Incl. O&P
2 Labor Foremen (outside)	$30.20	$483.20	$50.85	$813.60	$28.87	$48.58
4 Laborers	28.20	902.40	47.45	1518.40		
1 S.P. Crane, 4x4, 5 Ton		280.00		308.00		
1 Flatbed Truck, Gas, 1.5 Ton		270.20		297.22		
1 Butt Fusion Mach., 4"-12" diam.		381.80		419.98	19.42	21.36
48 L.H., Daily Totals		$2317.60		$3357.20	$48.28	$69.94

Crew B-6C	Hr.	Daily	Hr.	Daily	Bare Costs	Incl. O&P
2 Labor Foremen (outside)	$30.20	$483.20	$50.85	$813.60	$28.87	$48.58
4 Laborers	28.20	902.40	47.45	1518.40		
1 S.P. Crane, 4x4, 12 Ton		481.20		529.32		
1 Flatbed Truck, Gas, 3 Ton		333.00		366.30		
1 Butt Fusion Mach., 8"-24" diam.		828.40		911.24	34.22	37.64
48 L.H., Daily Totals		$3028.20		$4138.86	$63.09	$86.23

Crew B-7	Hr.	Daily	Hr.	Daily	Bare Costs	Incl. O&P
1 Labor Foreman (outside)	$30.20	$241.60	$50.85	$406.80	$30.11	$50.50
4 Laborers	28.20	902.40	47.45	1518.40		
1 Equip. Oper. (medium)	37.65	301.20	62.35	498.80		
1 Brush Chipper, 12", 130 H.P.		396.60		436.26		
1 Crawler Loader, 3 C.Y.		1191.00		1310.10		
2 Chain Saws, Gas, 36" Long		90.00		99.00	34.95	38.45
48 L.H., Daily Totals		$3122.80		$4269.36	$65.06	$88.94

Crew B-7A	Hr.	Daily	Hr.	Daily	Bare Costs	Incl. O&P
2 Laborers	$28.20	$451.20	$47.45	$759.20	$30.88	$51.65
1 Equip. Oper. (light)	36.25	290.00	60.05	480.40		
1 Rake w/Tractor		347.90		382.69		
2 Chain Saw, Gas, 18"		62.40		68.64	17.10	18.81
24 L.H., Daily Totals		$1151.50		$1690.93	$47.98	$70.46

Crew B-7B	Hr.	Daily	Hr.	Daily	Bare Costs	Incl. O&P
1 Labor Foreman (outside)	$30.20	$241.60	$50.85	$406.80	$30.04	$50.34
4 Laborers	28.20	902.40	47.45	1518.40		
1 Equip. Oper. (medium)	37.65	301.20	62.35	498.80		
1 Truck Driver (heavy)	29.65	237.20	49.40	395.20		
1 Brush Chipper, 12", 130 H.P.		396.60		436.26		
1 Crawler Loader, 3 C.Y.		1191.00		1310.10		
2 Chain Saws, Gas, 36" Long		90.00		99.00		
1 Dump Truck, 8 C.Y., 220 H.P.		417.20		458.92	37.41	41.15
56 L.H., Daily Totals		$3777.20		$5123.48	$67.45	$91.49

Crew B-7C	Hr.	Daily	Hr.	Daily	Bare Costs	Incl. O&P
1 Labor Foreman (outside)	$30.20	$241.60	$50.85	$406.80	$30.04	$50.34
4 Laborers	28.20	902.40	47.45	1518.40		
1 Equip. Oper. (medium)	37.65	301.20	62.35	498.80		
1 Truck Driver (heavy)	29.65	237.20	49.40	395.20		
1 Brush Chipper, 12", 130 H.P.		396.60		436.26		
1 Crawler Loader, 3 C.Y.		1191.00		1310.10		
2 Chain Saws, Gas, 36" Long		90.00		99.00		
1 Dump Truck, 12 C.Y., 400 H.P.		692.20		761.42	42.32	46.55
56 L.H., Daily Totals		$4052.20		$5425.98	$72.36	$96.89

Crew No.	Bare Costs		Incl. Subs O&P		Cost Per Labor-Hour	

Crew B-8

	Hr.	Daily	Hr.	Daily	Bare Costs	Incl. O&P
1 Labor Foreman (outside)	$30.20	$241.60	$50.85	$406.80	$31.60	$52.75
2 Laborers	28.20	451.20	47.45	759.20		
2 Equip. Oper. (medium)	37.65	602.40	62.35	997.60		
2 Truck Drivers (heavy)	29.65	474.40	49.40	790.40		
1 Hyd. Crane, 25 Ton		745.80		820.38		
1 Crawler Loader, 3 C.Y.		1191.00		1310.10		
2 Dump Trucks, 12 C.Y., 400 H.P.		1384.40		1522.84	59.31	65.24
56 L.H., Daily Totals		$5090.80		$6607.32	$90.91	$117.99

Crew B-9

	Hr.	Daily	Hr.	Daily	Bare Costs	Incl. O&P
1 Labor Foreman (outside)	$30.20	$241.60	$50.85	$406.80	$28.60	$48.13
4 Laborers	28.20	902.40	47.45	1518.40		
1 Air Compressor, 250 cfm		202.40		222.64		
2 Breakers, Pavement, 60 lb.		19.60		21.56		
2 -50' Air Hoses, 1.5"		11.60		12.76	5.84	6.42
40 L.H., Daily Totals		$1377.60		$2182.16	$34.44	$54.55

Crew B-9A

	Hr.	Daily	Hr.	Daily	Bare Costs	Incl. O&P
2 Laborers	$28.20	$451.20	$47.45	$759.20	$28.68	$48.10
1 Truck Driver (heavy)	29.65	237.20	49.40	395.20		
1 Water Tank Trailer, 5000 Gal.		141.60		155.76		
1 Truck Tractor, 220 H.P.		366.40		403.04		
2 -50' Discharge Hoses, 3"		3.00		3.30	21.29	23.42
24 L.H., Daily Totals		$1199.40		$1716.50	$49.98	$71.52

Crew B-9B

	Hr.	Daily	Hr.	Daily	Bare Costs	Incl. O&P
2 Laborers	$28.20	$451.20	$47.45	$759.20	$28.68	$48.10
1 Truck Driver (heavy)	29.65	237.20	49.40	395.20		
2 -50' Discharge Hoses, 3"		3.00		3.30		
1 Water Tank Trailer, 5000 Gal.		141.60		155.76		
1 Truck Tractor, 220 H.P.		366.40		403.04		
1 Pressure Washer		69.40		76.34	24.18	26.60
24 L.H., Daily Totals		$1268.80		$1792.84	$52.87	$74.70

Crew B-9D

	Hr.	Daily	Hr.	Daily	Bare Costs	Incl. O&P
1 Labor Foreman (outside)	$30.20	$241.60	$50.85	$406.80	$28.60	$48.13
4 Common Laborers	28.20	902.40	47.45	1518.40		
1 Air Compressor, 250 cfm		202.40		222.64		
2 -50' Air Hoses, 1.5"		11.60		12.76		
2 Air Powered Tampers		52.40		57.64	6.66	7.33
40 L.H., Daily Totals		$1410.40		$2218.24	$35.26	$55.46

Crew B-10

	Hr.	Daily	Hr.	Daily	Bare Costs	Incl. O&P
1 Equip. Oper. (medium)	$37.65	$301.20	$62.35	$498.80	$37.65	$62.35
8 L.H., Daily Totals		$301.20		$498.80	$37.65	$62.35

Crew B-10A

	Hr.	Daily	Hr.	Daily	Bare Costs	Incl. O&P
1 Equip. Oper. (medium)	$37.65	$301.20	$62.35	$498.80	$37.65	$62.35
1 Roller, 2-Drum, W.B., 7.5 H.P.		182.80		201.08	22.85	25.14
8 L.H., Daily Totals		$484.00		$699.88	$60.50	$87.48

Crew B-10B

	Hr.	Daily	Hr.	Daily	Bare Costs	Incl. O&P
1 Equip. Oper. (medium)	$37.65	$301.20	$62.35	$498.80	$37.65	$62.35
1 Dozer, 200 H.P.		1325.00		1457.50	165.63	182.19
8 L.H., Daily Totals		$1626.20		$1956.30	$203.28	$244.54

Crew B-10C

	Hr.	Daily	Hr.	Daily	Bare Costs	Incl. O&P
1 Equip. Oper. (medium)	$37.65	$301.20	$62.35	$498.80	$37.65	$62.35
1 Dozer, 200 H.P.		1325.00		1457.50		
1 Vibratory Roller, Towed, 23 Ton		412.00		453.20	217.13	238.84
8 L.H., Daily Totals		$2038.20		$2409.50	$254.78	$301.19

Crew B-10D

	Hr.	Daily	Hr.	Daily	Bare Costs	Incl. O&P
1 Equip. Oper. (medium)	$37.65	$301.20	$62.35	$498.80	$37.65	$62.35
1 Dozer, 200 H.P.		1325.00		1457.50		
1 Sheepsft. Roller, Towed		443.80		488.18	221.10	243.21
8 L.H., Daily Totals		$2070.00		$2444.48	$258.75	$305.56

Crew B-10E

	Hr.	Daily	Hr.	Daily	Bare Costs	Incl. O&P
1 Equip. Oper. (medium)	$37.65	$301.20	$62.35	$498.80	$37.65	$62.35
1 Tandem Roller, 5 Ton		159.00		174.90	19.88	21.86
8 L.H., Daily Totals		$460.20		$673.70	$57.52	$84.21

Crew B-10F

	Hr.	Daily	Hr.	Daily	Bare Costs	Incl. O&P
1 Equip. Oper. (medium)	$37.65	$301.20	$62.35	$498.80	$37.65	$62.35
1 Tandem Roller, 10 Ton		242.00		266.20	30.25	33.27
8 L.H., Daily Totals		$543.20		$765.00	$67.90	$95.63

Crew B-10G

	Hr.	Daily	Hr.	Daily	Bare Costs	Incl. O&P
1 Equip. Oper. (medium)	$37.65	$301.20	$62.35	$498.80	$37.65	$62.35
1 Sheepsfoot Roller, 240 H.P.		1218.00		1339.80	152.25	167.47
8 L.H., Daily Totals		$1519.20		$1838.60	$189.90	$229.82

Crew B-10H

	Hr.	Daily	Hr.	Daily	Bare Costs	Incl. O&P
1 Equip. Oper. (medium)	$37.65	$301.20	$62.35	$498.80	$37.65	$62.35
1 Diaphragm Water Pump, 2"		72.00		79.20		
1 -20' Suction Hose, 2"		1.95		2.15		
2 -50' Discharge Hoses, 2"		1.80		1.98	9.47	10.42
8 L.H., Daily Totals		$376.95		$582.13	$47.12	$72.77

Crew B-10I

	Hr.	Daily	Hr.	Daily	Bare Costs	Incl. O&P
1 Equip. Oper. (medium)	$37.65	$301.20	$62.35	$498.80	$37.65	$62.35
1 Diaphragm Water Pump, 4"		115.80		127.38		
1 -20' Suction Hose, 4"		3.25		3.58		
2 -50' Discharge Hoses, 4"		4.70		5.17	15.47	17.02
8 L.H., Daily Totals		$424.95		$634.92	$53.12	$79.37

Crew B-10J

	Hr.	Daily	Hr.	Daily	Bare Costs	Incl. O&P
1 Equip. Oper. (medium)	$37.65	$301.20	$62.35	$498.80	$37.65	$62.35
1 Centrifugal Water Pump, 3"		78.80		86.68		
1 -20' Suction Hose, 3"		2.85		3.13		
2 -50' Discharge Hoses, 3"		3.00		3.30	10.58	11.64
8 L.H., Daily Totals		$385.85		$591.91	$48.23	$73.99

Crew B-10K

	Hr.	Daily	Hr.	Daily	Bare Costs	Incl. O&P
1 Equip. Oper. (medium)	$37.65	$301.20	$62.35	$498.80	$37.65	$62.35
1 Centr. Water Pump, 6"		340.80		374.88		
1 -20' Suction Hose, 6"		11.50		12.65		
2 -50' Discharge Hoses, 6"		12.20		13.42	45.56	50.12
8 L.H., Daily Totals		$665.70		$899.75	$83.21	$112.47

Crew B-10L

	Hr.	Daily	Hr.	Daily	Bare Costs	Incl. O&P
1 Equip. Oper. (medium)	$37.65	$301.20	$62.35	$498.80	$37.65	$62.35
1 Dozer, 80 H.P.		481.00		529.10	60.13	66.14
8 L.H., Daily Totals		$782.20		$1027.90	$97.78	$128.49

Crew No.	Bare Costs		Incl. Subs O&P		Cost Per Labor-Hour	

Crew B-10M	Hr.	Daily	Hr.	Daily	Bare Costs	Incl. O&P
1 Equip. Oper. (medium)	$37.65	$301.20	$62.35	$498.80	$37.65	$62.35
1 Dozer, 300 H.P.		1817.00		1998.70	227.13	249.84
8 L.H., Daily Totals		$2118.20		$2497.50	$264.77	$312.19

Crew B-10N	Hr.	Daily	Hr.	Daily	Bare Costs	Incl. O&P
1 Equip. Oper. (medium)	$37.65	$301.20	$62.35	$498.80	$37.65	$62.35
1 F.E. Loader, T.M., 1.5 C.Y		522.80		575.08	65.35	71.89
8 L.H., Daily Totals		$824.00		$1073.88	$103.00	$134.24

Crew B-10O	Hr.	Daily	Hr.	Daily	Bare Costs	Incl. O&P
1 Equip. Oper. (medium)	$37.65	$301.20	$62.35	$498.80	$37.65	$62.35
1 F.E. Loader, T.M., 2.25 C.Y.		959.80		1055.78	119.97	131.97
8 L.H., Daily Totals		$1261.00		$1554.58	$157.63	$194.32

Crew B-10P	Hr.	Daily	Hr.	Daily	Bare Costs	Incl. O&P
1 Equip. Oper. (medium)	$37.65	$301.20	$62.35	$498.80	$37.65	$62.35
1 Crawler Loader, 3 C.Y.		1191.00		1310.10	148.88	163.76
8 L.H., Daily Totals		$1492.20		$1808.90	$186.53	$226.11

Crew B-10Q	Hr.	Daily	Hr.	Daily	Bare Costs	Incl. O&P
1 Equip. Oper. (medium)	$37.65	$301.20	$62.35	$498.80	$37.65	$62.35
1 Crawler Loader, 4 C.Y.		1532.00		1685.20	191.50	210.65
8 L.H., Daily Totals		$1833.20		$2184.00	$229.15	$273.00

Crew B-10R	Hr.	Daily	Hr.	Daily	Bare Costs	Incl. O&P
1 Equip. Oper. (medium)	$37.65	$301.20	$62.35	$498.80	$37.65	$62.35
1 F.E. Loader, W.M., 1 C.Y.		295.20		324.72	36.90	40.59
8 L.H., Daily Totals		$596.40		$823.52	$74.55	$102.94

Crew B-10S	Hr.	Daily	Hr.	Daily	Bare Costs	Incl. O&P
1 Equip. Oper. (medium)	$37.65	$301.20	$62.35	$498.80	$37.65	$62.35
1 F.E. Loader, W.M., 1.5 C.Y.		373.40		410.74	46.67	51.34
8 L.H., Daily Totals		$674.60		$909.54	$84.33	$113.69

Crew B-10T	Hr.	Daily	Hr.	Daily	Bare Costs	Incl. O&P
1 Equip. Oper. (medium)	$37.65	$301.20	$62.35	$498.80	$37.65	$62.35
1 F.E. Loader, W.M.,2.5 C.Y.		522.80		575.08	65.35	71.89
8 L.H., Daily Totals		$824.00		$1073.88	$103.00	$134.24

Crew B-10U	Hr.	Daily	Hr.	Daily	Bare Costs	Incl. O&P
1 Equip. Oper. (medium)	$37.65	$301.20	$62.35	$498.80	$37.65	$62.35
1 F.E. Loader, W.M., 5.5 C.Y.		1049.00		1153.90	131.13	144.24
8 L.H., Daily Totals		$1350.20		$1652.70	$168.78	$206.59

Crew B-10V	Hr.	Daily	Hr.	Daily	Bare Costs	Incl. O&P
1 Equip. Oper. (medium)	$37.65	$301.20	$62.35	$498.80	$37.65	$62.35
1 Dozer, 700 H.P.		4485.00		4933.50	560.63	616.69
8 L.H., Daily Totals		$4786.20		$5432.30	$598.27	$679.04

Crew B-10W	Hr.	Daily	Hr.	Daily	Bare Costs	Incl. O&P
1 Equip. Oper. (medium)	$37.65	$301.20	$62.35	$498.80	$37.65	$62.35
1 Dozer, 105 H.P.		591.80		650.98	73.97	81.37
8 L.H., Daily Totals		$893.00		$1149.78	$111.63	$143.72

Crew B-10X	Hr.	Daily	Hr.	Daily	Bare Costs	Incl. O&P
1 Equip. Oper. (medium)	$37.65	$301.20	$62.35	$498.80	$37.65	$62.35
1 Dozer, 410 H.P.		2409.00		2649.90	301.13	331.24
8 L.H., Daily Totals		$2710.20		$3148.70	$338.77	$393.59

Crew No.	Bare Costs		Incl. Subs O&P		Cost Per Labor-Hour	

Crew B-10Y	Hr.	Daily	Hr.	Daily	Bare Costs	Incl. O&P
1 Equip. Oper. (medium)	$37.65	$301.20	$62.35	$498.80	$37.65	$62.35
1 Vibr. Roller, Towed, 12 Ton		559.20		615.12	69.90	76.89
8 L.H., Daily Totals		$860.40		$1113.92	$107.55	$139.24

Crew B-11A	Hr.	Daily	Hr.	Daily	Bare Costs	Incl. O&P
1 Equipment Oper. (med.)	$37.65	$301.20	$62.35	$498.80	$32.92	$54.90
1 Laborer	28.20	225.60	47.45	379.60		
1 Dozer, 200 H.P.		1325.00		1457.50	82.81	91.09
16 L.H., Daily Totals		$1851.80		$2335.90	$115.74	$145.99

Crew B-11B	Hr.	Daily	Hr.	Daily	Bare Costs	Incl. O&P
1 Equipment Oper. (light)	$36.25	$290.00	$60.05	$480.40	$32.23	$53.75
1 Laborer	28.20	225.60	47.45	379.60		
1 Air Powered Tamper		26.20		28.82		
1 Air Compressor, 365 cfm		264.80		291.28		
2 -50' Air Hoses, 1.5"		11.60		12.76	18.91	20.80
16 L.H., Daily Totals		$818.20		$1192.86	$51.14	$74.55

Crew B-11C	Hr.	Daily	Hr.	Daily	Bare Costs	Incl. O&P
1 Equipment Oper. (med.)	$37.65	$301.20	$62.35	$498.80	$32.92	$54.90
1 Laborer	28.20	225.60	47.45	379.60		
1 Backhoe Loader, 48 H.P.		365.20		401.72	22.82	25.11
16 L.H., Daily Totals		$892.00		$1280.12	$55.75	$80.01

Crew B-11K	Hr.	Daily	Hr.	Daily	Bare Costs	Incl. O&P
1 Equipment Oper. (med.)	$37.65	$301.20	$62.35	$498.80	$32.92	$54.90
1 Laborer	28.20	225.60	47.45	379.60		
1 Trencher, Chain Type, 8' D		3376.00		3713.60	211.00	232.10
16 L.H., Daily Totals		$3902.80		$4592.00	$243.93	$287.00

Crew B-11L	Hr.	Daily	Hr.	Daily	Bare Costs	Incl. O&P
1 Equipment Oper. (med.)	$37.65	$301.20	$62.35	$498.80	$32.92	$54.90
1 Laborer	28.20	225.60	47.45	379.60		
1 Grader, 30,000 Lbs.		707.00		777.70	44.19	48.61
16 L.H., Daily Totals		$1233.80		$1656.10	$77.11	$103.51

Crew B-11M	Hr.	Daily	Hr.	Daily	Bare Costs	Incl. O&P
1 Equipment Oper. (med.)	$37.65	$301.20	$62.35	$498.80	$32.92	$54.90
1 Laborer	28.20	225.60	47.45	379.60		
1 Backhoe Loader, 80 H.P.		397.60		437.36	24.85	27.34
16 L.H., Daily Totals		$924.40		$1315.76	$57.77	$82.23

Crew B-11W	Hr.	Daily	Hr.	Daily	Bare Costs	Incl. O&P
1 Equipment Operator (med.)	$37.65	$301.20	$62.35	$498.80	$30.20	$50.32
1 Common Laborer	28.20	225.60	47.45	379.60		
10 Truck Drivers (heavy)	29.65	2372.00	49.40	3952.00		
1 Dozer, 200 H.P.		1325.00		1457.50		
1 Vibratory Roller, Towed, 23 Ton		412.00		453.20		
10 Dump Trucks, 8 C.Y., 220 H.P.		4172.00		4589.20	61.55	67.71
96 L.H., Daily Totals		$8807.80		$11330.30	$91.75	$118.02

Crew B-11Y	Hr.	Daily	Hr.	Daily	Bare Costs	Incl. O&P
1 Labor Foreman (outside)	$30.20	$241.60	$50.85	$406.80	$31.57	$52.79
5 Common Laborers	28.20	1128.00	47.45	1898.00		
3 Equipment Operators (med.)	37.65	903.60	62.35	1496.40		
1 Dozer, 80 H.P.		481.00		529.10		
2 Roller, 2-Drum, W.B., 7.5 H.P.		365.60		402.16		
4 Vibrating Plate, Gas, 21"		184.00		202.40	14.31	15.75
72 L.H., Daily Totals		$3303.80		$4934.86	$45.89	$68.54

Crew No.	Bare Costs Hr.	Bare Costs Daily	Incl. Subs O&P Hr.	Incl. Subs O&P Daily	Cost Per Labor-Hour Bare Costs	Cost Per Labor-Hour Incl. O&P
Crew B-12A	Hr.	Daily	Hr.	Daily	Bare Costs	Incl. O&P
1 Equip. Oper. (crane)	$38.70	$309.60	$64.10	$512.80	$33.45	$55.77
1 Laborer	28.20	225.60	47.45	379.60		
1 Hyd. Excavator, 1 C.Y.		814.80		896.28	50.92	56.02
16 L.H., Daily Totals		$1350.00		$1788.68	$84.38	$111.79
Crew B-12B	Hr.	Daily	Hr.	Daily	Bare Costs	Incl. O&P
1 Equip. Oper. (crane)	$38.70	$309.60	$64.10	$512.80	$33.45	$55.77
1 Laborer	28.20	225.60	47.45	379.60		
1 Hyd. Excavator, 1.5 C.Y.		1031.00		1134.10	64.44	70.88
16 L.H., Daily Totals		$1566.20		$2026.50	$97.89	$126.66
Crew B-12C	Hr.	Daily	Hr.	Daily	Bare Costs	Incl. O&P
1 Equip. Oper. (crane)	$38.70	$309.60	$64.10	$512.80	$33.45	$55.77
1 Laborer	28.20	225.60	47.45	379.60		
1 Hyd. Excavator, 2 C.Y.		1175.00		1292.50	73.44	80.78
16 L.H., Daily Totals		$1710.20		$2184.90	$106.89	$136.56
Crew B-12D	Hr.	Daily	Hr.	Daily	Bare Costs	Incl. O&P
1 Equip. Oper. (crane)	$38.70	$309.60	$64.10	$512.80	$33.45	$55.77
1 Laborer	28.20	225.60	47.45	379.60		
1 Hyd. Excavator, 3.5 C.Y.		2442.00		2686.20	152.63	167.89
16 L.H., Daily Totals		$2977.20		$3578.60	$186.07	$223.66
Crew B-12E	Hr.	Daily	Hr.	Daily	Bare Costs	Incl. O&P
1 Equip. Oper. (crane)	$38.70	$309.60	$64.10	$512.80	$33.45	$55.77
1 Laborer	28.20	225.60	47.45	379.60		
1 Hyd. Excavator, .5 C.Y.		448.00		492.80	28.00	30.80
16 L.H., Daily Totals		$983.20		$1385.20	$61.45	$86.58
Crew B-12F	Hr.	Daily	Hr.	Daily	Bare Costs	Incl. O&P
1 Equip. Oper. (crane)	$38.70	$309.60	$64.10	$512.80	$33.45	$55.77
1 Laborer	28.20	225.60	47.45	379.60		
1 Hyd. Excavator, .75 C.Y.		662.00		728.20	41.38	45.51
16 L.H., Daily Totals		$1197.20		$1620.60	$74.83	$101.29
Crew B-12G	Hr.	Daily	Hr.	Daily	Bare Costs	Incl. O&P
1 Equip. Oper. (crane)	$38.70	$309.60	$64.10	$512.80	$33.45	$55.77
1 Laborer	28.20	225.60	47.45	379.60		
1 Crawler Crane, 15 Ton		684.15		752.57		
1 Clamshell Bucket, .5 C.Y.		37.80		41.58	45.12	49.63
16 L.H., Daily Totals		$1257.15		$1686.55	$78.57	$105.41
Crew B-12H	Hr.	Daily	Hr.	Daily	Bare Costs	Incl. O&P
1 Equip. Oper. (crane)	$38.70	$309.60	$64.10	$512.80	$33.45	$55.77
1 Laborer	28.20	225.60	47.45	379.60		
1 Crawler Crane, 25 Ton		1173.00		1290.30		
1 Clamshell Bucket, 1 C.Y.		47.40		52.14	76.28	83.90
16 L.H., Daily Totals		$1755.60		$2234.84	$109.72	$139.68
Crew B-12I	Hr.	Daily	Hr.	Daily	Bare Costs	Incl. O&P
1 Equip. Oper. (crane)	$38.70	$309.60	$64.10	$512.80	$33.45	$55.77
1 Laborer	28.20	225.60	47.45	379.60		
1 Crawler Crane, 20 Ton		880.25		968.27		
1 Dragline Bucket, .75 C.Y.		20.80		22.88	56.32	61.95
16 L.H., Daily Totals		$1436.25		$1883.56	$89.77	$117.72
Crew B-12J	Hr.	Daily	Hr.	Daily	Bare Costs	Incl. O&P
1 Equip. Oper. (crane)	$38.70	$309.60	$64.10	$512.80	$33.45	$55.77
1 Laborer	28.20	225.60	47.45	379.60		
1 Gradall, 5/8 C.Y.		881.60		969.76	55.10	60.61
16 L.H., Daily Totals		$1416.80		$1862.16	$88.55	$116.39
Crew B-12K	Hr.	Daily	Hr.	Daily	Bare Costs	Incl. O&P
1 Equip. Oper. (crane)	$38.70	$309.60	$64.10	$512.80	$33.45	$55.77
1 Laborer	28.20	225.60	47.45	379.60		
1 Gradall, 3 Ton, 1 C.Y.		1005.00		1105.50	62.81	69.09
16 L.H., Daily Totals		$1540.20		$1997.90	$96.26	$124.87
Crew B-12L	Hr.	Daily	Hr.	Daily	Bare Costs	Incl. O&P
1 Equip. Oper. (crane)	$38.70	$309.60	$64.10	$512.80	$33.45	$55.77
1 Laborer	28.20	225.60	47.45	379.60		
1 Crawler Crane, 15 Ton		684.15		752.57		
1 F.E. Attachment, .5 C.Y.		59.60		65.56	46.48	51.13
16 L.H., Daily Totals		$1278.95		$1710.53	$79.93	$106.91
Crew B-12M	Hr.	Daily	Hr.	Daily	Bare Costs	Incl. O&P
1 Equip. Oper. (crane)	$38.70	$309.60	$64.10	$512.80	$33.45	$55.77
1 Laborer	28.20	225.60	47.45	379.60		
1 Crawler Crane, 20 Ton		880.25		968.27		
1 F.E. Attachment, .75 C.Y.		64.00		70.40	59.02	64.92
16 L.H., Daily Totals		$1479.45		$1931.08	$92.47	$120.69
Crew B-12N	Hr.	Daily	Hr.	Daily	Bare Costs	Incl. O&P
1 Equip. Oper. (crane)	$38.70	$309.60	$64.10	$512.80	$33.45	$55.77
1 Laborer	28.20	225.60	47.45	379.60		
1 Crawler Crane, 25 Ton		1173.00		1290.30		
1 F.E. Attachment, 1 C.Y.		70.80		77.88	77.74	85.51
16 L.H., Daily Totals		$1779.00		$2260.58	$111.19	$141.29
Crew B-12O	Hr.	Daily	Hr.	Daily	Bare Costs	Incl. O&P
1 Equip. Oper. (crane)	$38.70	$309.60	$64.10	$512.80	$33.45	$55.77
1 Laborer	28.20	225.60	47.45	379.60		
1 Crawler Crane, 40 Ton		1179.00		1296.90		
1 F.E. Attachment, 1.5 C.Y.		80.00		88.00	78.69	86.56
16 L.H., Daily Totals		$1794.20		$2277.30	$112.14	$142.33
Crew B-12P	Hr.	Daily	Hr.	Daily	Bare Costs	Incl. O&P
1 Equip. Oper. (crane)	$38.70	$309.60	$64.10	$512.80	$33.45	$55.77
1 Laborer	28.20	225.60	47.45	379.60		
1 Crawler Crane, 40 Ton		1179.00		1296.90		
1 Dragline Bucket, 1.5 C.Y.		33.60		36.96	75.79	83.37
16 L.H., Daily Totals		$1747.80		$2226.26	$109.24	$139.14
Crew B-12Q	Hr.	Daily	Hr.	Daily	Bare Costs	Incl. O&P
1 Equip. Oper. (crane)	$38.70	$309.60	$64.10	$512.80	$33.45	$55.77
1 Laborer	28.20	225.60	47.45	379.60		
1 Hyd. Excavator, 5/8 C.Y.		594.40		653.84	37.15	40.87
16 L.H., Daily Totals		$1129.60		$1546.24	$70.60	$96.64
Crew B-12S	Hr.	Daily	Hr.	Daily	Bare Costs	Incl. O&P
1 Equip. Oper. (crane)	$38.70	$309.60	$64.10	$512.80	$33.45	$55.77
1 Laborer	28.20	225.60	47.45	379.60		
1 Hyd. Excavator, 2.5 C.Y.		1637.00		1800.70	102.31	112.54
16 L.H., Daily Totals		$2172.20		$2693.10	$135.76	$168.32

Crew No.	Bare Costs		Incl. Subs O&P		Cost Per Labor-Hour	

Crew B-12T

Crew B-12T	Hr.	Daily	Hr.	Daily	Bare Costs	Incl. O&P
1 Equip. Oper. (crane)	$38.70	$309.60	$64.10	$512.80	$33.45	$55.77
1 Laborer	28.20	225.60	47.45	379.60		
1 Crawler Crane, 75 Ton		1492.00		1641.20		
1 F.E. Attachment, 3 C.Y.		102.80		113.08	99.67	109.64
16 L.H., Daily Totals		$2130.00		$2646.68	$133.13	$165.42

Crew B-12V	Hr.	Daily	Hr.	Daily	Bare Costs	Incl. O&P
1 Equip. Oper. (crane)	$38.70	$309.60	$64.10	$512.80	$33.45	$55.77
1 Laborer	28.20	225.60	47.45	379.60		
1 Crawler Crane, 75 Ton		1492.00		1641.20		
1 Dragline Bucket, 3 C.Y.		52.60		57.86	96.54	106.19
16 L.H., Daily Totals		$2079.80		$2591.46	$129.99	$161.97

Crew B-12Y	Hr.	Daily	Hr.	Daily	Bare Costs	Incl. O&P
1 Equip. Oper. (crane)	$38.70	$309.60	$64.10	$512.80	$31.70	$53.00
2 Laborers	28.20	451.20	47.45	759.20		
1 Hyd. Excavator, 3.5 C.Y.		2442.00		2686.20	101.75	111.93
24 L.H., Daily Totals		$3202.80		$3958.20	$133.45	$164.93

Crew B-12Z	Hr.	Daily	Hr.	Daily	Bare Costs	Incl. O&P
1 Equip. Oper. (crane)	$38.70	$309.60	$64.10	$512.80	$31.70	$53.00
2 Laborers	28.20	451.20	47.45	759.20		
1 Hyd. Excavator, 2.5 C.Y.		1637.00		1800.70	68.21	75.03
24 L.H., Daily Totals		$2397.80		$3072.70	$99.91	$128.03

Crew B-13	Hr.	Daily	Hr.	Daily	Bare Costs	Incl. O&P
1 Labor Foreman (outside)	$30.20	$241.60	$50.85	$406.80	$30.28	$50.79
4 Laborers	28.20	902.40	47.45	1518.40		
1 Equip. Oper. (crane)	38.70	309.60	64.10	512.80		
1 Hyd. Crane, 25 Ton		745.80		820.38	15.54	17.09
48 L.H., Daily Totals		$2199.40		$3258.38	$45.82	$67.88

Crew B-13A	Hr.	Daily	Hr.	Daily	Bare Costs	Incl. O&P
1 Labor Foreman (outside)	$30.20	$241.60	$50.85	$406.80	$31.60	$52.75
2 Laborers	28.20	451.20	47.45	759.20		
2 Equipment Operators (med.)	37.65	602.40	62.35	997.60		
2 Truck Drivers (heavy)	29.65	474.40	49.40	790.40		
1 Crawler Crane, 75 Ton		1492.00		1641.20		
1 Crawler Loader, 4 C.Y.		1532.00		1685.20		
2 Dump Trucks, 8 C.Y., 220 H.P.		834.40		917.84	68.90	75.79
56 L.H., Daily Totals		$5628.00		$7198.24	$100.50	$128.54

Crew B-13B	Hr.	Daily	Hr.	Daily	Bare Costs	Incl. O&P
1 Labor Foreman (outside)	$30.20	$241.60	$50.85	$406.80	$30.75	$51.47
4 Laborers	28.20	902.40	47.45	1518.40		
1 Equip. Oper. (crane)	38.70	309.60	64.10	512.80		
1 Equip. Oper. (oiler)	33.55	268.40	55.55	444.40		
1 Hyd. Crane, 55 Ton		1137.00		1250.70	20.30	22.33
56 L.H., Daily Totals		$2859.00		$4133.10	$51.05	$73.81

Crew B-13C	Hr.	Daily	Hr.	Daily	Bare Costs	Incl. O&P
1 Labor Foreman (outside)	$30.20	$241.60	$50.85	$406.80	$30.75	$51.47
4 Laborers	28.20	902.40	47.45	1518.40		
1 Equip. Oper. (crane)	38.70	309.60	64.10	512.80		
1 Equip. Oper. (oiler)	33.55	268.40	55.55	444.40		
1 Crawler Crane, 100 Ton		1703.00		1873.30	30.41	33.45
56 L.H., Daily Totals		$3425.00		$4755.70	$61.16	$84.92

Crew B-13D	Hr.	Daily	Hr.	Daily	Bare Costs	Incl. O&P
1 Laborer	$28.20	$225.60	$47.45	$379.60	$33.45	$55.77
1 Equip. Oper. (crane)	38.70	309.60	64.10	512.80		
1 Hyd. Excavator, 1 C.Y.		814.80		896.28		
1 Trench Box		84.05		92.45	56.18	61.80
16 L.H., Daily Totals		$1434.05		$1881.14	$89.63	$117.57

Crew B-13E	Hr.	Daily	Hr.	Daily	Bare Costs	Incl. O&P
1 Laborer	$28.20	$225.60	$47.45	$379.60	$33.45	$55.77
1 Equip. Oper. (crane)	38.70	309.60	64.10	512.80		
1 Hyd. Excavator, 1.5 C.Y.		1031.00		1134.10		
1 Trench Box		84.05		92.45	69.69	76.66
16 L.H., Daily Totals		$1650.25		$2118.95	$103.14	$132.43

Crew B-13F	Hr.	Daily	Hr.	Daily	Bare Costs	Incl. O&P
1 Laborer	$28.20	$225.60	$47.45	$379.60	$33.45	$55.77
1 Equip. Oper. (crane)	38.70	309.60	64.10	512.80		
1 Hyd. Excavator, 3.5 C.Y.		2442.00		2686.20		
1 Trench Box		84.05		92.45	157.88	173.67
16 L.H., Daily Totals		$3061.25		$3671.05	$191.33	$229.44

Crew B-13G	Hr.	Daily	Hr.	Daily	Bare Costs	Incl. O&P
1 Laborer	$28.20	$225.60	$47.45	$379.60	$33.45	$55.77
1 Equip. Oper. (crane)	38.70	309.60	64.10	512.80		
1 Hyd. Excavator, .75 C.Y.		662.00		728.20		
1 Trench Box		84.05		92.45	46.63	51.29
16 L.H., Daily Totals		$1281.25		$1713.06	$80.08	$107.07

Crew B-13H	Hr.	Daily	Hr.	Daily	Bare Costs	Incl. O&P
1 Laborer	$28.20	$225.60	$47.45	$379.60	$33.45	$55.77
1 Equip. Oper. (crane)	38.70	309.60	64.10	512.80		
1 Gradall, 5/8 C.Y.		881.60		969.76		
1 Trench Box		84.05		92.45	60.35	66.39
16 L.H., Daily Totals		$1500.85		$1954.62	$93.80	$122.16

Crew B-13I	Hr.	Daily	Hr.	Daily	Bare Costs	Incl. O&P
1 Laborer	$28.20	$225.60	$47.45	$379.60	$33.45	$55.77
1 Equip. Oper. (crane)	38.70	309.60	64.10	512.80		
1 Gradall, 3 Ton, 1 C.Y.		1005.00		1105.50		
1 Trench Box		84.05		92.45	68.07	74.87
16 L.H., Daily Totals		$1624.25		$2090.36	$101.52	$130.65

Crew B-13J	Hr.	Daily	Hr.	Daily	Bare Costs	Incl. O&P
1 Laborer	$28.20	$225.60	$47.45	$379.60	$33.45	$55.77
1 Equip. Oper. (crane)	38.70	309.60	64.10	512.80		
1 Hyd. Excavator, 2.5 C.Y.		1637.00		1800.70		
1 Trench Box		84.05		92.45	107.57	118.32
16 L.H., Daily Totals		$2256.25		$2785.55	$141.02	$174.10

Crew B-14	Hr.	Daily	Hr.	Daily	Bare Costs	Incl. O&P
1 Labor Foreman (outside)	$30.20	$241.60	$50.85	$406.80	$29.88	$50.12
4 Laborers	28.20	902.40	47.45	1518.40		
1 Equip. Oper. (light)	36.25	290.00	60.05	480.40		
1 Backhoe Loader, 48 H.P.		365.20		401.72	7.61	8.37
48 L.H., Daily Totals		$1799.20		$2807.32	$37.48	$58.49

Crew B-14A	Hr.	Daily	Hr.	Daily	Bare Costs	Incl. O&P
1 Equip. Oper. (crane)	$38.70	$309.60	$64.10	$512.80	$35.20	$58.55
.5 Laborer	28.20	112.80	47.45	189.80		
1 Hyd. Excavator, 4.5 C.Y.		3043.00		3347.30	253.58	278.94
12 L.H., Daily Totals		$3465.40		$4049.90	$288.78	$337.49

Crew B-14B

Crew No.	Bare Costs Hr.	Daily	Incl. Subs O&P Hr.	Daily	Cost Per L.H. Bare Costs	Incl. O&P
1 Equip. Oper. (crane)	$38.70	$309.60	$64.10	$512.80	$35.20	$58.55
.5 Laborer	28.20	112.80	47.45	189.80		
1 Hyd. Excavator, 6 C.Y.		3523.00		3875.30	293.58	322.94
12 L.H., Daily Totals		$3945.40		$4577.90	$328.78	$381.49

Crew B-14C

Crew No.	Bare Costs Hr.	Daily	Incl. Subs O&P Hr.	Daily	Cost Per L.H. Bare Costs	Incl. O&P
1 Equip. Oper. (crane)	$38.70	$309.60	$64.10	$512.80	$35.20	$58.55
.5 Laborer	28.20	112.80	47.45	189.80		
1 Hyd. Excavator, 7 C.Y.		3596.00		3955.60	299.67	329.63
12 L.H., Daily Totals		$4018.40		$4658.20	$334.87	$388.18

Crew B-14F

Crew No.	Bare Costs Hr.	Daily	Incl. Subs O&P Hr.	Daily	Cost Per L.H. Bare Costs	Incl. O&P
1 Equip. Oper. (crane)	$38.70	$309.60	$64.10	$512.80	$35.20	$58.55
.5 Laborer	28.20	112.80	47.45	189.80		
1 Hyd. Shovel, 7 C.Y.		3714.00		4085.40	309.50	340.45
12 L.H., Daily Totals		$4136.40		$4788.00	$344.70	$399.00

Crew B-14G

Crew No.	Bare Costs Hr.	Daily	Incl. Subs O&P Hr.	Daily	Cost Per L.H. Bare Costs	Incl. O&P
1 Equip. Oper. (crane)	$38.70	$309.60	$64.10	$512.80	$35.20	$58.55
.5 Laborer	28.20	112.80	47.45	189.80		
1 Hyd. Shovel, 12 C.Y.		5204.00		5724.40	433.67	477.03
12 L.H., Daily Totals		$5626.40		$6427.00	$468.87	$535.58

Crew B-14J

Crew No.	Bare Costs Hr.	Daily	Incl. Subs O&P Hr.	Daily	Cost Per L.H. Bare Costs	Incl. O&P
1 Equip. Oper. (medium)	$37.65	$301.20	$62.35	$498.80	$34.50	$57.38
.5 Laborer	28.20	112.80	47.45	189.80		
1 F.E. Loader, 8 C.Y.		1989.00		2187.90	165.75	182.32
12 L.H., Daily Totals		$2403.00		$2876.50	$200.25	$239.71

Crew B-14K

Crew No.	Bare Costs Hr.	Daily	Incl. Subs O&P Hr.	Daily	Cost Per L.H. Bare Costs	Incl. O&P
1 Equip. Oper. (medium)	$37.65	$301.20	$62.35	$498.80	$34.50	$57.38
.5 Laborer	28.20	112.80	47.45	189.80		
1 F.E. Loader, 10 C.Y.		2703.00		2973.30	225.25	247.78
12 L.H., Daily Totals		$3117.00		$3661.90	$259.75	$305.16

Crew B-15

Crew No.	Bare Costs Hr.	Daily	Incl. Subs O&P Hr.	Daily	Cost Per L.H. Bare Costs	Incl. O&P
1 Equipment Oper. (med.)	$37.65	$301.20	$62.35	$498.80	$31.73	$52.82
.5 Laborer	28.20	112.80	47.45	189.80		
2 Truck Drivers (heavy)	29.65	474.40	49.40	790.40		
2 Dump Trucks, 12 C.Y., 400 H.P.		1384.40		1522.84		
1 Dozer, 200 H.P.		1325.00		1457.50	96.76	106.44
28 L.H., Daily Totals		$3597.80		$4459.34	$128.49	$159.26

Crew B-16

Crew No.	Bare Costs Hr.	Daily	Incl. Subs O&P Hr.	Daily	Cost Per L.H. Bare Costs	Incl. O&P
1 Labor Foreman (outside)	$30.20	$241.60	$50.85	$406.80	$29.06	$48.79
2 Laborers	28.20	451.20	47.45	759.20		
1 Truck Driver (heavy)	29.65	237.20	49.40	395.20		
1 Dump Truck, 12 C.Y., 400 H.P.		692.20		761.42	21.63	23.79
32 L.H., Daily Totals		$1622.20		$2322.62	$50.69	$72.58

Crew B-17

Crew No.	Bare Costs Hr.	Daily	Incl. Subs O&P Hr.	Daily	Cost Per L.H. Bare Costs	Incl. O&P
2 Laborers	$28.20	$451.20	$47.45	$759.20	$30.57	$51.09
1 Equip. Oper. (light)	36.25	290.00	60.05	480.40		
1 Truck Driver (heavy)	29.65	237.20	49.40	395.20		
1 Backhoe Loader, 48 H.P.		365.20		401.72		
1 Dump Truck, 8 C.Y., 220 H.P.		417.20		458.92	24.45	26.90
32 L.H., Daily Totals		$1760.80		$2495.44	$55.02	$77.98

Crew B-17A

Crew No.	Bare Costs Hr.	Daily	Incl. Subs O&P Hr.	Daily	Cost Per L.H. Bare Costs	Incl. O&P
2 Labor Foremen (outside)	$30.20	$483.20	$50.85	$813.60	$30.42	$51.24
6 Laborers	28.20	1353.60	47.45	2277.60		
1 Skilled Worker Foreman (out)	38.30	306.40	64.70	517.60		
1 Skilled Worker	36.30	290.40	61.30	490.40		
80 L.H., Daily Totals		$2433.60		$4099.20	$30.42	$51.24

Crew B-17B

Crew No.	Bare Costs Hr.	Daily	Incl. Subs O&P Hr.	Daily	Cost Per L.H. Bare Costs	Incl. O&P
2 Laborers	$28.20	$451.20	$47.45	$759.20	$30.57	$51.09
1 Equip. Oper. (light)	36.25	290.00	60.05	480.40		
1 Truck Driver (heavy)	29.65	237.20	49.40	395.20		
1 Backhoe Loader, 48 H.P.		365.20		401.72		
1 Dump Truck, 12 C.Y., 400 H.P.		692.20		761.42	33.04	36.35
32 L.H., Daily Totals		$2035.80		$2797.94	$63.62	$87.44

Crew B-18

Crew No.	Bare Costs Hr.	Daily	Incl. Subs O&P Hr.	Daily	Cost Per L.H. Bare Costs	Incl. O&P
1 Labor Foreman (outside)	$30.20	$241.60	$50.85	$406.80	$28.87	$48.58
2 Laborers	28.20	451.20	47.45	759.20		
1 Vibrating Plate, Gas, 21"		46.00		50.60	1.92	2.11
24 L.H., Daily Totals		$738.80		$1216.60	$30.78	$50.69

Crew B-19

Crew No.	Bare Costs Hr.	Daily	Incl. Subs O&P Hr.	Daily	Cost Per L.H. Bare Costs	Incl. O&P
1 Pile Driver Foreman (outside)	$36.60	$292.80	$63.15	$505.20	$34.56	$59.07
4 Pile Drivers	34.60	1107.20	59.70	1910.40		
1 Equip. Oper. (crane)	38.70	309.60	64.10	512.80		
1 Building Laborer	28.20	225.60	47.45	379.60		
1 Crawler Crane, 40 Ton		1179.00		1296.90		
1 Lead, 90' High		124.40		136.84		
1 Hammer, Diesel, 22k ft-lb		537.45		591.20	32.87	36.16
56 L.H., Daily Totals		$3776.05		$5332.94	$67.43	$95.23

Crew B-19A

Crew No.	Bare Costs Hr.	Daily	Incl. Subs O&P Hr.	Daily	Cost Per L.H. Bare Costs	Incl. O&P
1 Pile Driver Foreman (outside)	$36.60	$292.80	$63.15	$505.20	$34.56	$59.07
4 Pile Drivers	34.60	1107.20	59.70	1910.40		
1 Equip. Oper. (crane)	38.70	309.60	64.10	512.80		
1 Common Laborer	28.20	225.60	47.45	379.60		
1 Crawler Crane, 75 Ton		1492.00		1641.20		
1 Lead, 90' high		124.40		136.84		
1 Hammer, Diesel, 41k ft-lb		642.40		706.64	40.34	44.37
56 L.H., Daily Totals		$4194.00		$5792.68	$74.89	$103.44

Crew B-19B

Crew No.	Bare Costs Hr.	Daily	Incl. Subs O&P Hr.	Daily	Cost Per L.H. Bare Costs	Incl. O&P
1 Pile Driver Foreman (outside)	$36.60	$292.80	$63.15	$505.20	$34.56	$59.07
4 Pile Drivers	34.60	1107.20	59.70	1910.40		
1 Equip. Oper. (crane)	38.70	309.60	64.10	512.80		
1 Common Laborer	28.20	225.60	47.45	379.60		
1 Crawler Crane, 40 Ton		1179.00		1296.90		
1 Lead, 90' High		124.40		136.84		
1 Hammer, Diesel, 22k ft-lb		537.45		591.20		
1 Barge, 400 Ton		781.00		859.10	46.82	51.50
56 L.H., Daily Totals		$4557.05		$6192.03	$81.38	$110.57

Crew B-19C

Crew No.	Bare Costs Hr.	Daily	Incl. Subs O&P Hr.	Daily	Cost Per L.H. Bare Costs	Incl. O&P
1 Pile Driver Foreman (outside)	$36.60	$292.80	$63.15	$505.20	$34.56	$59.07
4 Pile Drivers	34.60	1107.20	59.70	1910.40		
1 Equip. Oper. (crane)	38.70	309.60	64.10	512.80		
1 Common Laborer	28.20	225.60	47.45	379.60		
1 Crawler Crane, 75 Ton		1492.00		1641.20		
1 Lead, 90' High		124.40		136.84		
1 Hammer, Diesel, 41k ft-lb		642.40		706.64		
1 Barge, 400 Ton		781.00		859.10	54.28	59.71
56 L.H., Daily Totals		$4975.00		$6651.78	$88.84	$118.78

Crew B-20

Crew No.	Bare Costs Hr.	Bare Costs Daily	Incl. Subs O&P Hr.	Incl. Subs O&P Daily	Cost Per Labor-Hour Bare Costs	Cost Per Labor-Hour Incl. O&P
1 Labor Foreman (outside)	$30.20	$241.60	$50.85	$406.80	$28.87	$48.58
2 Laborers	28.20	451.20	47.45	759.20		
24 L.H., Daily Totals		$692.80		$1166.00	$28.87	$48.58

Crew B-20A

Crew No.	Bare Costs Hr.	Bare Costs Daily	Incl. Subs O&P Hr.	Incl. Subs O&P Daily	Cost Per Labor-Hour Bare Costs	Cost Per Labor-Hour Incl. O&P
1 Labor Foreman (outside)	$30.20	$241.60	$50.85	$406.80	$33.77	$56.21
1 Laborer	28.20	225.60	47.45	379.60		
1 Plumber	42.60	340.80	70.30	562.40		
1 Plumber Apprentice	34.10	272.80	56.25	450.00		
32 L.H., Daily Totals		$1080.80		$1798.80	$33.77	$56.21

Crew B-21

Crew No.	Bare Costs Hr.	Bare Costs Daily	Incl. Subs O&P Hr.	Incl. Subs O&P Daily	Cost Per Labor-Hour Bare Costs	Cost Per Labor-Hour Incl. O&P
1 Labor Foreman (outside)	$30.20	$241.60	$50.85	$406.80	$30.27	$50.80
2 Laborers	28.20	451.20	47.45	759.20		
.5 Equip. Oper. (crane)	38.70	154.80	64.10	256.40		
.5 S.P. Crane, 4x4, 5 Ton		140.00		154.00	5.00	5.50
28 L.H., Daily Totals		$987.60		$1576.40	$35.27	$56.30

Crew B-21A

Crew No.	Bare Costs Hr.	Bare Costs Daily	Incl. Subs O&P Hr.	Incl. Subs O&P Daily	Cost Per Labor-Hour Bare Costs	Cost Per Labor-Hour Incl. O&P
1 Labor Foreman (outside)	$30.20	$241.60	$50.85	$406.80	$34.76	$57.79
1 Laborer	28.20	225.60	47.45	379.60		
1 Plumber	42.60	340.80	70.30	562.40		
1 Plumber Apprentice	34.10	272.80	56.25	450.00		
1 Equip. Oper. (crane)	38.70	309.60	64.10	512.80		
1 S.P. Crane, 4x4, 12 Ton		481.20		529.32	12.03	13.23
40 L.H., Daily Totals		$1871.60		$2840.92	$46.79	$71.02

Crew B-21B

Crew No.	Bare Costs Hr.	Bare Costs Daily	Incl. Subs O&P Hr.	Incl. Subs O&P Daily	Cost Per Labor-Hour Bare Costs	Cost Per Labor-Hour Incl. O&P
1 Labor Foreman (outside)	$30.20	$241.60	$50.85	$406.80	$30.70	$51.46
3 Laborers	28.20	676.80	47.45	1138.80		
1 Equip. Oper. (crane)	38.70	309.60	64.10	512.80		
1 Hyd. Crane, 12 Ton		663.00		729.30	16.57	18.23
40 L.H., Daily Totals		$1891.00		$2787.70	$47.27	$69.69

Crew B-21C

Crew No.	Bare Costs Hr.	Bare Costs Daily	Incl. Subs O&P Hr.	Incl. Subs O&P Daily	Cost Per Labor-Hour Bare Costs	Cost Per Labor-Hour Incl. O&P
1 Labor Foreman (outside)	$30.20	$241.60	$50.85	$406.80	$30.75	$51.47
4 Laborers	28.20	902.40	47.45	1518.40		
1 Equip. Oper. (crane)	38.70	309.60	64.10	512.80		
1 Equip. Oper. (oiler)	33.55	268.40	55.55	444.40		
2 Cutting Torches		22.80		25.08		
2 Sets of Gases		304.00		334.40		
1 Lattice Boom Crane, 90 Ton		1529.00		1681.90	33.14	36.45
56 L.H., Daily Totals		$3577.80		$4923.78	$63.89	$87.92

Crew B-22

Crew No.	Bare Costs Hr.	Bare Costs Daily	Incl. Subs O&P Hr.	Incl. Subs O&P Daily	Cost Per Labor-Hour Bare Costs	Cost Per Labor-Hour Incl. O&P
1 Labor Foreman (outside)	$30.20	$241.60	$50.85	$406.80	$30.83	$51.69
2 Laborers	28.20	451.20	47.45	759.20		
.75 Equip. Oper. (crane)	38.70	232.20	64.10	384.60		
.75 S.P. Crane, 4x4, 5 Ton		210.00		231.00	7.00	7.70
30 L.H., Daily Totals		$1135.00		$1781.60	$37.83	$59.39

Crew B-22A

Crew No.	Bare Costs Hr.	Bare Costs Daily	Incl. Subs O&P Hr.	Incl. Subs O&P Daily	Cost Per Labor-Hour Bare Costs	Cost Per Labor-Hour Incl. O&P
1 Labor Foreman (outside)	$30.20	$241.60	$50.85	$406.80	$32.32	$54.23
1 Skilled Worker	36.30	290.40	61.30	490.40		
2 Laborers	28.20	451.20	47.45	759.20		
1 Equipment Operator, Crane	38.70	309.60	64.10	512.80		
1 S.P. Crane, 4x4, 5 Ton		280.00		308.00		
1 Butt Fusion Mach., 4"-12" diam.		381.80		419.98	16.55	18.20
40 L.H., Daily Totals		$1954.60		$2897.18	$48.87	$72.43

Crew B-22B

Crew No.	Bare Costs Hr.	Bare Costs Daily	Incl. Subs O&P Hr.	Incl. Subs O&P Daily	Cost Per Labor-Hour Bare Costs	Cost Per Labor-Hour Incl. O&P
1 Labor Foreman (outside)	$30.20	$241.60	$50.85	$406.80	$32.32	$54.23
1 Skilled Worker	36.30	290.40	61.30	490.40		
2 Laborers	28.20	451.20	47.45	759.20		
1 Equip. Oper. (crane)	38.70	309.60	64.10	512.80		
1 S.P. Crane, 4x4, 5 Ton		280.00		308.00		
1 Butt Fusion Mach., 8"-24" diam.		828.40		911.24	27.71	30.48
40 L.H., Daily Totals		$2401.20		$3388.44	$60.03	$84.71

Crew B-22C

Crew No.	Bare Costs Hr.	Bare Costs Daily	Incl. Subs O&P Hr.	Incl. Subs O&P Daily	Cost Per Labor-Hour Bare Costs	Cost Per Labor-Hour Incl. O&P
1 Skilled Worker	$36.30	$290.40	$61.30	$490.40	$32.25	$54.38
1 Laborer	28.20	225.60	47.45	379.60		
1 Butt Fusion Mach., 2"-8" diam.		120.95		133.04	7.56	8.32
16 L.H., Daily Totals		$636.95		$1003.05	$39.81	$62.69

Crew B-23

Crew No.	Bare Costs Hr.	Bare Costs Daily	Incl. Subs O&P Hr.	Incl. Subs O&P Daily	Cost Per Labor-Hour Bare Costs	Cost Per Labor-Hour Incl. O&P
1 Labor Foreman (outside)	$30.20	$241.60	$50.85	$406.80	$28.60	$48.13
4 Laborers	28.20	902.40	47.45	1518.40		
1 Drill Rig, Truck-Mounted		2551.00		2806.10		
1 Flatbed Truck, Gas, 3 Ton		333.00		366.30	72.10	79.31
40 L.H., Daily Totals		$4028.00		$5097.60	$100.70	$127.44

Crew B-23A

Crew No.	Bare Costs Hr.	Bare Costs Daily	Incl. Subs O&P Hr.	Incl. Subs O&P Daily	Cost Per Labor-Hour Bare Costs	Cost Per Labor-Hour Incl. O&P
1 Labor Foreman (outside)	$30.20	$241.60	$50.85	$406.80	$32.02	$53.55
1 Laborer	28.20	225.60	47.45	379.60		
1 Equip. Oper. (medium)	37.65	301.20	62.35	498.80		
1 Drill Rig, Truck-Mounted		2551.00		2806.10		
1 Pickup Truck, 3/4 Ton		157.00		172.70	112.83	124.12
24 L.H., Daily Totals		$3476.40		$4264.00	$144.85	$177.67

Crew B-23B

Crew No.	Bare Costs Hr.	Bare Costs Daily	Incl. Subs O&P Hr.	Incl. Subs O&P Daily	Cost Per Labor-Hour Bare Costs	Cost Per Labor-Hour Incl. O&P
1 Labor Foreman (outside)	$30.20	$241.60	$50.85	$406.80	$32.02	$53.55
1 Laborer	28.20	225.60	47.45	379.60		
1 Equip. Oper. (medium)	37.65	301.20	62.35	498.80		
1 Drill Rig, Truck-Mounted		2551.00		2806.10		
1 Pickup Truck, 3/4 Ton		157.00		172.70		
1 Centr. Water Pump, 6"		340.80		374.88	127.03	139.74
24 L.H., Daily Totals		$3817.20		$4638.88	$159.05	$193.29

Crew B-24

Crew No.	Bare Costs Hr.	Bare Costs Daily	Incl. Subs O&P Hr.	Incl. Subs O&P Daily	Cost Per Labor-Hour Bare Costs	Cost Per Labor-Hour Incl. O&P
1 Cement Finisher	$34.35	$274.80	$55.60	$444.80	$32.77	$54.40
1 Laborer	28.20	225.60	47.45	379.60		
1 Carpenter	35.75	286.00	60.15	481.20		
24 L.H., Daily Totals		$786.40		$1305.60	$32.77	$54.40

Crew B-25

Crew No.	Bare Costs Hr.	Bare Costs Daily	Incl. Subs O&P Hr.	Incl. Subs O&P Daily	Cost Per Labor-Hour Bare Costs	Cost Per Labor-Hour Incl. O&P
1 Labor Foreman (outside)	$30.20	$241.60	$50.85	$406.80	$30.96	$51.82
7 Laborers	28.20	1579.20	47.45	2657.20		
3 Equip. Oper. (medium)	37.65	903.60	62.35	1496.40		
1 Asphalt Paver, 130 H.P.		2169.00		2385.90		
1 Tandem Roller, 10 Ton		242.00		266.20		
1 Roller, Pneum. Whl., 12 Ton		349.00		383.90	31.36	34.50
88 L.H., Daily Totals		$5484.40		$7596.40	$62.32	$86.32

Crew B-25B

Crew No.	Bare Costs Hr.	Bare Costs Daily	Incl. Subs O&P Hr.	Incl. Subs O&P Daily	Cost Per Labor-Hour Bare Costs	Cost Per Labor-Hour Incl. O&P
1 Labor Foreman (outside)	$30.20	$241.60	$50.85	$406.80	$31.52	$52.70
7 Laborers	28.20	1579.20	47.45	2657.20		
4 Equip. Oper. (medium)	37.65	1204.80	62.35	1995.20		
1 Asphalt Paver, 130 H.P.		2169.00		2385.90		
2 Tandem Rollers, 10 Ton		484.00		532.40		
1 Roller, Pneum. Whl., 12 Ton		349.00		383.90	31.27	34.40
96 L.H., Daily Totals		$6027.60		$8361.40	$62.79	$87.10

Crew No.	Bare Costs		Incl. Subs O&P		Cost Per Labor-Hour	

Crew B-25C

Crew B-25C	Hr.	Daily	Hr.	Daily	Bare Costs	Incl. O&P
1 Labor Foreman (outside)	$30.20	$241.60	$50.85	$406.80	$31.68	$52.98
3 Laborers	28.20	676.80	47.45	1138.80		
2 Equip. Oper. (medium)	37.65	602.40	62.35	997.60		
1 Asphalt Paver, 130 H.P.		2169.00		2385.90		
1 Tandem Roller, 10 Ton		242.00		266.20	50.23	55.25
48 L.H., Daily Totals		$3931.80		$5195.30	$81.91	$108.24

Crew B-25D

Crew B-25D	Hr.	Daily	Hr.	Daily	Bare Costs	Incl. O&P
1 Labor Foreman (outside)	$30.20	$241.60	$50.85	$406.80	$31.76	$53.10
3 Laborers	28.20	676.80	47.45	1138.80		
2.125 Equip. Oper. (medium)	37.65	640.05	62.35	1059.95		
.125 Truck Driver (heavy)	29.65	29.65	49.40	49.40		
.125 Truck Tractor, 6x4, 380 H.P.		76.60		84.26		
.125 Dist. Tanker, 3000 Gallon		38.52		42.38		
1 Asphalt Paver, 130 H.P.		2169.00		2385.90		
1 Tandem Roller, 10 Ton		242.00		266.20	50.52	55.57
50 L.H., Daily Totals		$4114.23		$5433.69	$82.28	$108.67

Crew B-25E

Crew B-25E	Hr.	Daily	Hr.	Daily	Bare Costs	Incl. O&P
1 Labor Foreman (outside)	$30.20	$241.60	$50.85	$406.80	$31.83	$53.21
3 Laborers	28.20	676.80	47.45	1138.80		
2.250 Equip. Oper. (medium)	37.65	677.70	62.35	1122.30		
.25 Truck Driver (heavy)	29.65	59.30	49.40	98.80		
.25 Truck Tractor, 6x4, 380 H.P.		153.20		168.52		
.25 Dist. Tanker, 3000 Gallon		77.05		84.75		
1 Asphalt Paver, 130 H.P.		2169.00		2385.90		
1 Tandem Roller, 10 Ton		242.00		266.20	50.79	55.87
52 L.H., Daily Totals		$4296.65		$5672.07	$82.63	$109.08

Crew B-26

Crew B-26	Hr.	Daily	Hr.	Daily	Bare Costs	Incl. O&P
1 Labor Foreman (outside)	$30.20	$241.60	$50.85	$406.80	$31.55	$52.80
6 Laborers	28.20	1353.60	47.45	2277.60		
2 Equip. Oper. (medium)	37.65	602.40	62.35	997.60		
1 Rodman (reinf.)	38.00	304.00	65.00	520.00		
1 Cement Finisher	34.35	274.80	55.60	444.80		
1 Grader, 30,000 Lbs.		707.00		777.70		
1 Paving Mach. & Equip.		2657.00		2922.70	38.23	42.05
88 L.H., Daily Totals		$6140.40		$8347.20	$69.78	$94.85

Crew B-26A

Crew B-26A	Hr.	Daily	Hr.	Daily	Bare Costs	Incl. O&P
1 Labor Foreman (outside)	$30.20	$241.60	$50.85	$406.80	$31.55	$52.80
6 Laborers	28.20	1353.60	47.45	2277.60		
2 Equip. Oper. (medium)	37.65	602.40	62.35	997.60		
1 Rodman (reinf.)	38.00	304.00	65.00	520.00		
1 Cement Finisher	34.35	274.80	55.60	444.80		
1 Grader, 30,000 Lbs.		707.00		777.70		
1 Paving Mach. & Equip.		2657.00		2922.70		
1 Concrete Saw		175.20		192.72	40.22	44.24
88 L.H., Daily Totals		$6315.60		$8539.92	$71.77	$97.04

Crew B-26B

Crew B-26B	Hr.	Daily	Hr.	Daily	Bare Costs	Incl. O&P
1 Labor Foreman (outside)	$30.20	$241.60	$50.85	$406.80	$32.06	$53.60
6 Laborers	28.20	1353.60	47.45	2277.60		
3 Equip. Oper. (medium)	37.65	903.60	62.35	1496.40		
1 Rodman (reinf.)	38.00	304.00	65.00	520.00		
1 Cement Finisher	34.35	274.80	55.60	444.80		
1 Grader, 30,000 Lbs.		707.00		777.70		
1 Paving Mach. & Equip.		2657.00		2922.70		
1 Concrete Pump, 110' Boom		934.00		1027.40	44.77	49.25
96 L.H., Daily Totals		$7375.60		$9873.40	$76.83	$102.85

Crew B-26C

Crew B-26C	Hr.	Daily	Hr.	Daily	Bare Costs	Incl. O&P
1 Labor Foreman (outside)	$30.20	$241.60	$50.85	$406.80	$30.94	$51.85
6 Laborers	28.20	1353.60	47.45	2277.60		
1 Equip. Oper. (medium)	37.65	301.20	62.35	498.80		
1 Rodman (reinf.)	38.00	304.00	65.00	520.00		
1 Cement Finisher	34.35	274.80	55.60	444.80		
1 Paving Mach. & Equip.		2657.00		2922.70		
1 Concrete Saw		175.20		192.72	35.40	38.94
80 L.H., Daily Totals		$5307.40		$7263.42	$66.34	$90.79

Crew B-27

Crew B-27	Hr.	Daily	Hr.	Daily	Bare Costs	Incl. O&P
1 Labor Foreman (outside)	$30.20	$241.60	$50.85	$406.80	$28.70	$48.30
3 Laborers	28.20	676.80	47.45	1138.80		
1 Berm Machine		294.40		323.84	9.20	10.12
32 L.H., Daily Totals		$1212.80		$1869.44	$37.90	$58.42

Crew B-28

Crew B-28	Hr.	Daily	Hr.	Daily	Bare Costs	Incl. O&P
2 Carpenters	$35.75	$572.00	$60.15	$962.40	$33.23	$55.92
1 Laborer	28.20	225.60	47.45	379.60		
24 L.H., Daily Totals		$797.60		$1342.00	$33.23	$55.92

Crew B-29

Crew B-29	Hr.	Daily	Hr.	Daily	Bare Costs	Incl. O&P
1 Labor Foreman (outside)	$30.20	$241.60	$50.85	$406.80	$30.28	$50.79
4 Laborers	28.20	902.40	47.45	1518.40		
1 Equip. Oper. (crane)	38.70	309.60	64.10	512.80		
1 Gradall, 5/8 C.Y.		881.60		969.76	18.37	20.20
48 L.H., Daily Totals		$2335.20		$3407.76	$48.65	$71.00

Crew B-30

Crew B-30	Hr.	Daily	Hr.	Daily	Bare Costs	Incl. O&P
1 Equip. Oper. (medium)	$37.65	$301.20	$62.35	$498.80	$32.32	$53.72
2 Truck Drivers (heavy)	29.65	474.40	49.40	790.40		
1 Hyd. Excavator, 1.5 C.Y.		1031.00		1134.10		
2 Dump Trucks, 12 C.Y., 400 H.P.		1384.40		1522.84	100.64	110.71
24 L.H., Daily Totals		$3191.00		$3946.14	$132.96	$164.42

Crew B-31

Crew B-31	Hr.	Daily	Hr.	Daily	Bare Costs	Incl. O&P
1 Labor Foreman (outside)	$30.20	$241.60	$50.85	$406.80	$28.60	$48.13
4 Laborers	28.20	902.40	47.45	1518.40		
1 Air Compressor, 250 cfm		202.40		222.64		
1 Sheeting Driver		5.30		5.83		
2 -50' Air Hoses, 1.5"		11.60		12.76	5.48	6.03
40 L.H., Daily Totals		$1363.30		$2166.43	$34.08	$54.16

Crew B-32

Crew B-32	Hr.	Daily	Hr.	Daily	Bare Costs	Incl. O&P
1 Laborer	$28.20	$225.60	$47.45	$379.60	$35.29	$58.63
3 Equip. Oper. (medium)	37.65	903.60	62.35	1496.40		
1 Grader, 30,000 Lbs.		707.00		777.70		
1 Tandem Roller, 10 Ton		242.00		266.20		
1 Dozer, 200 H.P.		1325.00		1457.50	71.06	78.17
32 L.H., Daily Totals		$3403.20		$4377.40	$106.35	$136.79

Crew B-32A

Crew B-32A	Hr.	Daily	Hr.	Daily	Bare Costs	Incl. O&P
1 Laborer	$28.20	$225.60	$47.45	$379.60	$34.50	$57.38
2 Equip. Oper. (medium)	37.65	602.40	62.35	997.60		
1 Grader, 30,000 Lbs.		707.00		777.70		
1 Roller, Vibratory, 25 Ton		692.80		762.08	58.33	64.16
24 L.H., Daily Totals		$2227.80		$2916.98	$92.83	$121.54

Crew No.	Bare Costs Hr.	Daily	Incl. Subs O&P Hr.	Daily	Cost Per Labor-Hour Bare Costs	Incl. O&P
Crew B-32B	Hr.	Daily	Hr.	Daily	Bare Costs	Incl. O&P
1 Laborer	$28.20	$225.60	$47.45	$379.60	$34.50	$57.38
2 Equip. Oper. (medium)	37.65	602.40	62.35	997.60		
1 Dozer, 200 H.P.		1325.00		1457.50		
1 Roller, Vibratory, 25 Ton		692.80		762.08	84.08	92.48
24 L.H., Daily Totals		$2845.80		$3596.78	$118.58	$149.87

Crew B-32C	Hr.	Daily	Hr.	Daily	Bare Costs	Incl. O&P
1 Labor Foreman (outside)	$30.20	$241.60	$50.85	$406.80	$33.26	$55.47
2 Laborers	28.20	451.20	47.45	759.20		
3 Equip. Oper. (medium)	37.65	903.60	62.35	1496.40		
1 Grader, 30,000 Lbs.		707.00		777.70		
1 Tandem Roller, 10 Ton		242.00		266.20		
1 Dozer, 200 H.P.		1325.00		1457.50	47.38	52.11
48 L.H., Daily Totals		$3870.40		$5163.80	$80.63	$107.58

Crew B-33A	Hr.	Daily	Hr.	Daily	Bare Costs	Incl. O&P
1 Equip. Oper. (medium)	$37.65	$301.20	$62.35	$498.80	$37.65	$62.35
.25 Equip. Oper. (medium)	37.65	75.30	62.35	124.70		
1 Scraper, Towed, 7 C.Y.		111.60		122.76		
1.250 Dozers, 300 H.P.		2271.25		2498.38	238.29	262.11
10 L.H., Daily Totals		$2759.35		$3244.64	$275.94	$324.46

Crew B-33B	Hr.	Daily	Hr.	Daily	Bare Costs	Incl. O&P
1 Equip. Oper. (medium)	$37.65	$301.20	$62.35	$498.80	$37.65	$62.35
.25 Equip. Oper. (medium)	37.65	75.30	62.35	124.70		
1 Scraper, Towed, 10 C.Y.		141.60		155.76		
1.250 Dozers, 300 H.P.		2271.25		2498.38	241.29	265.41
10 L.H., Daily Totals		$2789.35		$3277.64	$278.94	$327.76

Crew B-33C	Hr.	Daily	Hr.	Daily	Bare Costs	Incl. O&P
1 Equip. Oper. (medium)	$37.65	$301.20	$62.35	$498.80	$37.65	$62.35
.25 Equip. Oper. (medium)	37.65	75.30	62.35	124.70		
1 Scraper, Towed, 15 C.Y.		158.80		174.68		
1.250 Dozers, 300 H.P.		2271.25		2498.38	243.01	267.31
10 L.H., Daily Totals		$2806.55		$3296.55	$280.65	$329.66

Crew B-33D	Hr.	Daily	Hr.	Daily	Bare Costs	Incl. O&P
1 Equip. Oper. (medium)	$37.65	$301.20	$62.35	$498.80	$37.65	$62.35
.25 Equip. Oper. (medium)	37.65	75.30	62.35	124.70		
1 S.P. Scraper, 14 C.Y.		1829.00		2011.90		
.25 Dozer, 300 H.P.		454.25		499.68	228.32	251.16
10 L.H., Daily Totals		$2659.75		$3135.07	$265.98	$313.51

Crew B-33E	Hr.	Daily	Hr.	Daily	Bare Costs	Incl. O&P
1 Equip. Oper. (medium)	$37.65	$301.20	$62.35	$498.80	$37.65	$62.35
.25 Equip. Oper. (medium)	37.65	75.30	62.35	124.70		
1 S.P. Scraper, 21 C.Y.		2599.00		2858.90		
.25 Dozer, 300 H.P.		454.25		499.68	305.32	335.86
10 L.H., Daily Totals		$3429.75		$3982.07	$342.98	$398.21

Crew B-33F	Hr.	Daily	Hr.	Daily	Bare Costs	Incl. O&P
1 Equip. Oper. (medium)	$37.65	$301.20	$62.35	$498.80	$37.65	$62.35
.25 Equip. Oper. (medium)	37.65	75.30	62.35	124.70		
1 Elev. Scraper, 11 C.Y.		1180.00		1298.00		
.25 Dozer, 300 H.P.		454.25		499.68	163.43	179.77
10 L.H., Daily Totals		$2010.75		$2421.18	$201.07	$242.12

Crew B-33G	Hr.	Daily	Hr.	Daily	Bare Costs	Incl. O&P
1 Equip. Oper. (medium)	$37.65	$301.20	$62.35	$498.80	$37.65	$62.35
.25 Equip. Oper. (medium)	37.65	75.30	62.35	124.70		
1 Elev. Scraper, 22 C.Y.		2443.00		2687.30		
.25 Dozer, 300 H.P.		454.25		499.68	289.73	318.70
10 L.H., Daily Totals		$3273.75		$3810.47	$327.38	$381.05

Crew B-33K	Hr.	Daily	Hr.	Daily	Bare Costs	Incl. O&P
1 Equipment Operator (med.)	$37.65	$301.20	$62.35	$498.80	$34.95	$58.09
.25 Equipment Operator (med.)	37.65	75.30	62.35	124.70		
.5 Laborer	28.20	112.80	47.45	189.80		
1 S.P. Scraper, 31 C.Y.		3566.00		3922.60		
.25 Dozer, 410 H.P.		602.25		662.48	297.73	327.51
14 L.H., Daily Totals		$4657.55		$5398.38	$332.68	$385.60

Crew B-34A	Hr.	Daily	Hr.	Daily	Bare Costs	Incl. O&P
1 Truck Driver (heavy)	$29.65	$237.20	$49.40	$395.20	$29.65	$49.40
1 Dump Truck, 8 C.Y., 220 H.P.		417.20		458.92	52.15	57.37
8 L.H., Daily Totals		$654.40		$854.12	$81.80	$106.77

Crew B-34B	Hr.	Daily	Hr.	Daily	Bare Costs	Incl. O&P
1 Truck Driver (heavy)	$29.65	$237.20	$49.40	$395.20	$29.65	$49.40
1 Dump Truck, 12 C.Y., 400 H.P.		692.20		761.42	86.53	95.18
8 L.H., Daily Totals		$929.40		$1156.62	$116.18	$144.58

Crew B-34C	Hr.	Daily	Hr.	Daily	Bare Costs	Incl. O&P
1 Truck Driver (heavy)	$29.65	$237.20	$49.40	$395.20	$29.65	$49.40
1 Truck Tractor, 6x4, 380 H.P.		612.80		674.08		
1 Dump Trailer, 16.5 C.Y.		126.20		138.82	92.38	101.61
8 L.H., Daily Totals		$976.20		$1208.10	$122.03	$151.01

Crew B-34D	Hr.	Daily	Hr.	Daily	Bare Costs	Incl. O&P
1 Truck Driver (heavy)	$29.65	$237.20	$49.40	$395.20	$29.65	$49.40
1 Truck Tractor, 6x4, 380 H.P.		612.80		674.08		
1 Dump Trailer, 20 C.Y.		140.80		154.88	94.20	103.62
8 L.H., Daily Totals		$990.80		$1224.16	$123.85	$153.02

Crew B-34E	Hr.	Daily	Hr.	Daily	Bare Costs	Incl. O&P
1 Truck Driver (heavy)	$29.65	$237.20	$49.40	$395.20	$29.65	$49.40
1 Dump Truck, Off Hwy., 25 Ton		1314.00		1445.40	164.25	180.68
8 L.H., Daily Totals		$1551.20		$1840.60	$193.90	$230.07

Crew B-34F	Hr.	Daily	Hr.	Daily	Bare Costs	Incl. O&P
1 Truck Driver (heavy)	$29.65	$237.20	$49.40	$395.20	$29.65	$49.40
1 Dump Truck, Off Hwy., 35 Ton		1470.00		1617.00	183.75	202.13
8 L.H., Daily Totals		$1707.20		$2012.20	$213.40	$251.53

Crew B-34G	Hr.	Daily	Hr.	Daily	Bare Costs	Incl. O&P
1 Truck Driver (heavy)	$29.65	$237.20	$49.40	$395.20	$29.65	$49.40
1 Dump Truck, Off Hwy., 50 Ton		1787.00		1965.70	223.38	245.71
8 L.H., Daily Totals		$2024.20		$2360.90	$253.03	$295.11

Crew B-34H	Hr.	Daily	Hr.	Daily	Bare Costs	Incl. O&P
1 Truck Driver (heavy)	$29.65	$237.20	$49.40	$395.20	$29.65	$49.40
1 Dump Truck, Off Hwy., 65 Ton		1797.00		1976.70	224.63	247.09
8 L.H., Daily Totals		$2034.20		$2371.90	$254.28	$296.49

Crews

Crew No.	Bare Costs Hr.	Daily	Incl. Subs O&P Hr.	Daily	Cost Per LH Bare Costs	Incl. O&P

Crew B-34I

	Hr.	Daily	Hr.	Daily	Bare Costs	Incl. O&P
1 Truck Driver (heavy)	$29.65	$237.20	$49.40	$395.20	$29.65	$49.40
1 Dump Truck, 18 C.Y., 450 H.P.		867.60		954.36	108.45	119.30
8 L.H., Daily Totals		$1104.80		$1349.56	$138.10	$168.69

Crew B-34J

	Hr.	Daily	Hr.	Daily	Bare Costs	Incl. O&P
1 Truck Driver (heavy)	$29.65	$237.20	$49.40	$395.20	$29.65	$49.40
1 Dump Truck, Off Hwy., 100 Ton		2898.00		3187.80	362.25	398.48
8 L.H., Daily Totals		$3135.20		$3583.00	$391.90	$447.88

Crew B-34K

	Hr.	Daily	Hr.	Daily	Bare Costs	Incl. O&P
1 Truck Driver (heavy)	$29.65	$237.20	$49.40	$395.20	$29.65	$49.40
1 Truck Tractor, 6x4, 450 H.P.		742.40		816.64		
1 Lowbed Trailer, 75 Ton		219.80		241.78	120.28	132.30
8 L.H., Daily Totals		$1199.40		$1453.62	$149.93	$181.70

Crew B-34L

	Hr.	Daily	Hr.	Daily	Bare Costs	Incl. O&P
1 Equip. Oper. (light)	$36.25	$290.00	$60.05	$480.40	$36.25	$60.05
1 Flatbed Truck, Gas, 1.5 Ton		270.20		297.22	33.77	37.15
8 L.H., Daily Totals		$560.20		$777.62	$70.03	$97.20

Crew B-34M

	Hr.	Daily	Hr.	Daily	Bare Costs	Incl. O&P
1 Equip. Oper. (light)	$36.25	$290.00	$60.05	$480.40	$36.25	$60.05
1 Flatbed Truck, Gas, 3 Ton		333.00		366.30	41.63	45.79
8 L.H., Daily Totals		$623.00		$846.70	$77.88	$105.84

Crew B-34N

	Hr.	Daily	Hr.	Daily	Bare Costs	Incl. O&P
1 Truck Driver (heavy)	$29.65	$237.20	$49.40	$395.20	$29.65	$49.40
1 Dump Truck, 8 C.Y., 220 H.P.		417.20		458.92		
1 Flatbed Trailer, 40 Ton		152.00		167.20	71.15	78.27
8 L.H., Daily Totals		$806.40		$1021.32	$100.80	$127.67

Crew B-34P

	Hr.	Daily	Hr.	Daily	Bare Costs	Incl. O&P
1 Pipe Fitter	$43.30	$346.40	$71.45	$571.60	$36.60	$60.62
1 Truck Driver (light)	28.85	230.80	48.05	384.40		
1 Equip. Oper. (medium)	37.65	301.20	62.35	498.80		
1 Flatbed Truck, Gas, 3 Ton		333.00		366.30		
1 Backhoe Loader, 48 H.P.		365.20		401.72	29.09	32.00
24 L.H., Daily Totals		$1576.60		$2222.82	$65.69	$92.62

Crew B-34Q

	Hr.	Daily	Hr.	Daily	Bare Costs	Incl. O&P
1 Pipe Fitter	$43.30	$346.40	$71.45	$571.60	$36.95	$61.20
1 Truck Driver (light)	28.85	230.80	48.05	384.40		
1 Equip. Oper. (crane)	38.70	309.60	64.10	512.80		
1 Flatbed Trailer, 25 Ton		113.60		124.96		
1 Dump Truck, 8 C.Y., 220 H.P.		417.20		458.92		
1 Hyd. Crane, 25 Ton		745.80		820.38	53.19	58.51
24 L.H., Daily Totals		$2163.40		$2873.06	$90.14	$119.71

Crew B-34R

	Hr.	Daily	Hr.	Daily	Bare Costs	Incl. O&P
1 Pipe Fitter	$43.30	$346.40	$71.45	$571.60	$36.95	$61.20
1 Truck Driver (light)	28.85	230.80	48.05	384.40		
1 Equip. Oper. (crane)	38.70	309.60	64.10	512.80		
1 Flatbed Trailer, 25 Ton		113.60		124.96		
1 Dump Truck, 8 C.Y., 220 H.P.		417.20		458.92		
1 Hyd. Crane, 25 Ton		745.80		820.38		
1 Hyd. Excavator, 1 C.Y.		814.80		896.28	87.14	95.86
24 L.H., Daily Totals		$2978.20		$3769.34	$124.09	$157.06

Crew B-34S

	Hr.	Daily	Hr.	Daily	Bare Costs	Incl. O&P
2 Pipe Fitters	$43.30	$692.80	$71.45	$1143.20	$38.74	$64.10
1 Truck Driver (heavy)	29.65	237.20	49.40	395.20		
1 Equip. Oper. (crane)	38.70	309.60	64.10	512.80		
1 Flatbed Trailer, 40 Ton		152.00		167.20		
1 Truck Tractor, 6x4, 380 H.P.		612.80		674.08		
1 Hyd. Crane, 80 Ton		1652.00		1817.20		
1 Hyd. Excavator, 2 C.Y.		1175.00		1292.50	112.24	123.47
32 L.H., Daily Totals		$4831.40		$6002.18	$150.98	$187.57

Crew B-34T

	Hr.	Daily	Hr.	Daily	Bare Costs	Incl. O&P
2 Pipe Fitters	$43.30	$692.80	$71.45	$1143.20	$38.74	$64.10
1 Truck Driver (heavy)	29.65	237.20	49.40	395.20		
1 Equip. Oper. (crane)	38.70	309.60	64.10	512.80		
1 Flatbed Trailer, 40 Ton		152.00		167.20		
1 Truck Tractor, 6x4, 380 H.P.		612.80		674.08		
1 Hyd. Crane, 80 Ton		1652.00		1817.20	75.53	83.08
32 L.H., Daily Totals		$3656.40		$4709.68	$114.26	$147.18

Crew B-35

	Hr.	Daily	Hr.	Daily	Bare Costs	Incl. O&P
1 Labor Foreman (outside)	$30.20	$241.60	$50.85	$406.80	$35.20	$58.80
1 Skilled Worker	36.30	290.40	61.30	490.40		
1 Welder (plumber)	42.60	340.80	70.30	562.40		
1 Laborer	28.20	225.60	47.45	379.60		
1 Equip. Oper. (crane)	38.70	309.60	64.10	512.80		
1 Welder, Electric, 300 amp		55.30		60.83		
1 Hyd. Excavator, .75 C.Y.		662.00		728.20	17.93	19.73
40 L.H., Daily Totals		$2125.30		$3141.03	$53.13	$78.53

Crew B-35A

	Hr.	Daily	Hr.	Daily	Bare Costs	Incl. O&P
1 Labor Foreman (outside)	$30.20	$241.60	$50.85	$406.80	$33.96	$56.71
2 Laborers	28.20	451.20	47.45	759.20		
1 Skilled Worker	36.30	290.40	61.30	490.40		
1 Welder (plumber)	42.60	340.80	70.30	562.40		
1 Equip. Oper. (crane)	38.70	309.60	64.10	512.80		
1 Equip. Oper. (oiler)	33.55	268.40	55.55	444.40		
1 Welder, Gas Engine, 300 amp		142.00		156.20		
1 Crawler Crane, 75 Ton		1492.00		1641.20	29.18	32.10
56 L.H., Daily Totals		$3536.00		$4973.40	$63.14	$88.81

Crew B-36

	Hr.	Daily	Hr.	Daily	Bare Costs	Incl. O&P
1 Labor Foreman (outside)	$30.20	$241.60	$50.85	$406.80	$32.38	$54.09
2 Laborers	28.20	451.20	47.45	759.20		
2 Equip. Oper. (medium)	37.65	602.40	62.35	997.60		
1 Dozer, 200 H.P.		1325.00		1457.50		
1 Aggregate Spreader		41.20		45.32		
1 Tandem Roller, 10 Ton		242.00		266.20	40.20	44.23
40 L.H., Daily Totals		$2903.40		$3932.62	$72.58	$98.32

Crew B-36A

	Hr.	Daily	Hr.	Daily	Bare Costs	Incl. O&P
1 Labor Foreman (outside)	$30.20	$241.60	$50.85	$406.80	$33.89	$56.45
2 Laborers	28.20	451.20	47.45	759.20		
4 Equip. Oper. (medium)	37.65	1204.80	62.35	1995.20		
1 Dozer, 200 H.P.		1325.00		1457.50		
1 Aggregate Spreader		41.20		45.32		
1 Tandem Roller, 10 Ton		242.00		266.20		
1 Roller, Pneum. Whl., 12 Ton		349.00		383.90	34.95	38.45
56 L.H., Daily Totals		$3854.80		$5314.12	$68.84	$94.89

| Crew No. | Bare Costs | | Incl. Subs O&P | | Cost Per Labor-Hour | |

Crew B-36B	Hr.	Daily	Hr.	Daily	Bare Costs	Incl. O&P
1 Labor Foreman (outside)	$30.20	$241.60	$50.85	$406.80	$33.36	$55.57
2 Laborers	28.20	451.20	47.45	759.20		
4 Equip. Oper. (medium)	37.65	1204.80	62.35	1995.20		
1 Truck Driver (heavy)	29.65	237.20	49.40	395.20		
1 Grader, 30,000 Lbs.		707.00		777.70		
1 F.E. Loader, Crl. 1.5 C.Y.		625.20		687.72		
1 Dozer, 300 H.P.		1817.00		1998.70		
1 Roller, Vibratory, 25 Ton		692.80		762.08		
1 Truck Tractor, 6x4, 450 H.P.		742.40		816.64		
1 Water Tank Trailer, 5000 Gal.		141.60		155.76	73.84	81.23
64 L.H., Daily Totals		$6860.80		$8755.00	$107.20	$136.80

Crew B-36C	Hr.	Daily	Hr.	Daily	Bare Costs	Incl. O&P
1 Labor Foreman (outside)	$30.20	$241.60	$50.85	$406.80	$34.56	$57.46
3 Equip. Oper. (medium)	37.65	903.60	62.35	1496.40		
1 Truck Driver (heavy)	29.65	237.20	49.40	395.20		
1 Grader, 30,000 Lbs.		707.00		777.70		
1 Dozer, 300 H.P.		1817.00		1998.70		
1 Roller, Vibratory, 25 Ton		692.80		762.08		
1 Truck Tractor, 6x4, 450 H.P.		742.40		816.64		
1 Water Tank Trailer, 5000 Gal.		141.60		155.76	102.52	112.77
40 L.H., Daily Totals		$5483.20		$6809.28	$137.08	$170.23

Crew B-36E	Hr.	Daily	Hr.	Daily	Bare Costs	Incl. O&P
1 Labor Foreman (outside)	$30.20	$241.60	$50.85	$406.80	$35.08	$58.27
4 Equip. Oper. (medium)	37.65	1204.80	62.35	1995.20		
1 Truck Driver (heavy)	29.65	237.20	49.40	395.20		
1 Grader, 30,000 Lbs.		707.00		777.70		
1 Dozer, 300 H.P.		1817.00		1998.70		
1 Roller, Vibratory, 25 Ton		692.80		762.08		
1 Truck Tractor, 6x4, 380 H.P.		612.80		674.08		
1 Dist. Tanker, 3000 Gallon		308.20		339.02	86.20	94.82
48 L.H., Daily Totals		$5821.40		$7348.78	$121.28	$153.10

Crew B-37	Hr.	Daily	Hr.	Daily	Bare Costs	Incl. O&P
1 Labor Foreman (outside)	$30.20	$241.60	$50.85	$406.80	$29.88	$50.12
4 Laborers	28.20	902.40	47.45	1518.40		
1 Equip. Oper. (light)	36.25	290.00	60.05	480.40		
1 Tandem Roller, 5 Ton		159.00		174.90	3.31	3.64
48 L.H., Daily Totals		$1593.00		$2580.50	$33.19	$53.76

Crew B-37A	Hr.	Daily	Hr.	Daily	Bare Costs	Incl. O&P
2 Laborers	$28.20	$451.20	$47.45	$759.20	$28.42	$47.65
1 Truck Driver (light)	28.85	230.80	48.05	384.40		
1 Flatbed Truck, Gas, 1.5 Ton		270.20		297.22		
1 Tar Kettle, T.M.		104.60		115.06	15.62	17.18
24 L.H., Daily Totals		$1056.80		$1555.88	$44.03	$64.83

Crew B-37B	Hr.	Daily	Hr.	Daily	Bare Costs	Incl. O&P
3 Laborers	$28.20	$676.80	$47.45	$1138.80	$28.36	$47.60
1 Truck Driver (light)	28.85	230.80	48.05	384.40		
1 Flatbed Truck, Gas, 1.5 Ton		270.20		297.22		
1 Tar Kettle, T.M.		104.60		115.06	11.71	12.88
32 L.H., Daily Totals		$1282.40		$1935.48	$40.08	$60.48

Crew B-37C	Hr.	Daily	Hr.	Daily	Bare Costs	Incl. O&P
2 Laborers	$28.20	$451.20	$47.45	$759.20	$28.52	$47.75
2 Truck Drivers (light)	28.85	461.60	48.05	768.80		
2 Flatbed Trucks, Gas, 1.5 Ton		540.40		594.44		
1 Tar Kettle, T.M.		104.60		115.06	20.16	22.17
32 L.H., Daily Totals		$1557.80		$2237.50	$48.68	$69.92

Crew B-37D	Hr.	Daily	Hr.	Daily	Bare Costs	Incl. O&P
1 Laborer	$28.20	$225.60	$47.45	$379.60	$28.52	$47.75
1 Truck Driver (light)	28.85	230.80	48.05	384.40		
1 Pickup Truck, 3/4 Ton		157.00		172.70	9.81	10.79
16 L.H., Daily Totals		$613.40		$936.70	$38.34	$58.54

Crew B-37E	Hr.	Daily	Hr.	Daily	Bare Costs	Incl. O&P
3 Laborers	$28.20	$676.80	$47.45	$1138.80	$30.89	$51.55
1 Equip. Oper. (light)	36.25	290.00	60.05	480.40		
1 Equip. Oper. (medium)	37.65	301.20	62.35	498.80		
2 Truck Drivers (light)	28.85	461.60	48.05	768.80		
4 Barrels w/ Flasher		13.60		14.96		
1 Concrete Saw		175.20		192.72		
1 Rotary Hammer Drill		24.00		26.40		
1 Hammer Drill Bit		2.35		2.59		
1 Loader, Skid Steer, 30 H.P.		174.20		191.62		
1 Conc. Hammer Attach.		114.70		126.17		
1 Vibrating Plate, Gas, 18"		35.80		39.38		
2 Flatbed Trucks, Gas, 1.5 Ton		540.40		594.44	19.29	21.22
56 L.H., Daily Totals		$2809.85		$4075.07	$50.18	$72.77

Crew B-37F	Hr.	Daily	Hr.	Daily	Bare Costs	Incl. O&P
3 Laborers	$28.20	$676.80	$47.45	$1138.80	$28.36	$47.60
1 Truck Driver (light)	28.85	230.80	48.05	384.40		
4 Barrels w/ Flasher		13.60		14.96		
1 Concrete Mixer, 10 C.F.		176.80		194.48		
1 Air Compressor, 60 cfm		137.40		151.14		
1 -50' Air Hose, 3/4"		3.25		3.58		
1 Spade (Chipper)		7.80		8.58		
1 Flatbed Truck, Gas, 1.5 Ton		270.20		297.22	19.03	20.94
32 L.H., Daily Totals		$1516.65		$2193.16	$47.40	$68.54

Crew B-37G	Hr.	Daily	Hr.	Daily	Bare Costs	Incl. O&P
1 Labor Foreman (outside)	$30.20	$241.60	$50.85	$406.80	$29.88	$50.12
4 Laborers	28.20	902.40	47.45	1518.40		
1 Equip. Oper. (light)	36.25	290.00	60.05	480.40		
1 Berm Machine		294.40		323.84		
1 Tandem Roller, 5 Ton		159.00		174.90	9.45	10.39
48 L.H., Daily Totals		$1887.40		$2904.34	$39.32	$60.51

Crew B-37H	Hr.	Daily	Hr.	Daily	Bare Costs	Incl. O&P
1 Labor Foreman (outside)	$30.20	$241.60	$50.85	$406.80	$29.88	$50.12
4 Laborers	28.20	902.40	47.45	1518.40		
1 Equip. Oper. (light)	36.25	290.00	60.05	480.40		
1 Tandem Roller, 5 Ton		159.00		174.90		
1 Flatbed Trucks, Gas, 1.5 Ton		270.20		297.22		
1 Tar Kettle, T.M.		104.60		115.06	11.12	12.23
48 L.H., Daily Totals		$1967.80		$2992.78	$41.00	$62.35

Crew B-37I

Crew No.	Bare Costs Hr.	Bare Costs Daily	Incl. Subs O&P Hr.	Incl. Subs O&P Daily	Cost Per Labor-Hour Bare Costs	Cost Per Labor-Hour Incl. O&P
3 Laborers	$28.20	$676.80	$47.45	$1138.80	$30.89	$51.55
1 Equip. Oper. (light)	36.25	290.00	60.05	480.40		
1 Equip. Oper. (medium)	37.65	301.20	62.35	498.80		
2 Truck Drivers (light)	28.85	461.60	48.05	768.80		
4 Barrels w/ Flasher		13.60		14.96		
1 Concrete Saw		175.20		192.72		
1 Rotary Hammer Drill		24.00		26.40		
1 Hammer Drill Bit		2.35		2.59		
1 Air Compressor, 60 cfm		137.40		151.14		
1 -50' Air Hose, 3/4"		3.25		3.58		
1 Spade (Chipper)		7.80		8.58		
1 Loader, Skid Steer, 30 H.P.		174.20		191.62		
1 Conc. Hammer Attach.		114.70		126.17		
1 Concrete Mixer, 10 C.F.		176.80		194.48		
1 Vibrating Plate, Gas, 18"		35.80		39.38		
2 Flatbed Trucks, Gas, 1.5 Ton		540.40		594.44	25.10	27.61
56 L.H., Daily Totals		$3135.10		$4432.85	$55.98	$79.16

Crew B-37J

Crew No.	Bare Costs Hr.	Bare Costs Daily	Incl. Subs O&P Hr.	Incl. Subs O&P Daily	Bare Costs	Incl. O&P
1 Labor Foreman (outside)	$30.20	$241.60	$50.85	$406.80	$29.88	$50.12
4 Laborers	28.20	902.40	47.45	1518.40		
1 Equip. Oper. (light)	36.25	290.00	60.05	480.40		
1 Air Compressor, 60 cfm		137.40		151.14		
1 -50' Air Hose, 3/4"		3.25		3.58		
2 Concrete Mixer, 10 C.F.		353.60		388.96		
2 Flatbed Trucks, Gas, 1.5 Ton		540.40		594.44		
1 Shot Blaster, 20"		214.40		235.84	26.02	28.62
48 L.H., Daily Totals		$2683.05		$3779.55	$55.90	$78.74

Crew B-37K

Crew No.	Bare Costs Hr.	Bare Costs Daily	Incl. Subs O&P Hr.	Incl. Subs O&P Daily	Bare Costs	Incl. O&P
1 Labor Foreman (outside)	$30.20	$241.60	$50.85	$406.80	$29.88	$50.12
4 Laborers	28.20	902.40	47.45	1518.40		
1 Equip. Oper. (light)	36.25	290.00	60.05	480.40		
1 Air Compressor, 60 cfm		137.40		151.14		
1 -50' Air Hose, 3/4"		3.25		3.58		
2 Flatbed Trucks, Gas, 1.5 Ton		540.40		594.44		
1 Shot Blaster, 20"		214.40		235.84	18.66	20.52
48 L.H., Daily Totals		$2329.45		$3390.59	$48.53	$70.64

Crew B-38

Crew No.	Bare Costs Hr.	Bare Costs Daily	Incl. Subs O&P Hr.	Incl. Subs O&P Daily	Bare Costs	Incl. O&P
2 Laborers	$28.20	$451.20	$47.45	$759.20	$30.88	$51.65
1 Equip. Oper. (light)	36.25	290.00	60.05	480.40		
1 Backhoe Loader, 48 H.P.		365.20		401.72		
1 Hyd. Hammer, (1200 lb.)		180.40		198.44	22.73	25.01
24 L.H., Daily Totals		$1286.80		$1839.76	$53.62	$76.66

Crew B-39

Crew No.	Bare Costs Hr.	Bare Costs Daily	Incl. Subs O&P Hr.	Incl. Subs O&P Daily	Bare Costs	Incl. O&P
1 Labor Foreman (outside)	$30.20	$241.60	$50.85	$406.80	$28.53	$48.02
5 Laborers	28.20	1128.00	47.45	1898.00		
1 Air Compressor, 250 cfm		202.40		222.64		
2 Breakers, Pavement, 60 lb.		19.60		21.56		
2 -50' Air Hoses, 1.5"		11.60		12.76	4.87	5.35
48 L.H., Daily Totals		$1603.20		$2561.76	$33.40	$53.37

Crew B-40

Crew No.	Bare Costs Hr.	Bare Costs Daily	Incl. Subs O&P Hr.	Incl. Subs O&P Daily	Bare Costs	Incl. O&P
1 Pile Driver Foreman (outside)	$36.60	$292.80	$63.15	$505.20	$34.56	$59.07
4 Pile Drivers	34.60	1107.20	59.70	1910.40		
1 Building Laborer	28.20	225.60	47.45	379.60		
1 Equip. Oper. (crane)	38.70	309.60	64.10	512.80		
1 Crawler Crane, 40 Ton		1179.00		1296.90		
1 Vibratory Hammer & Gen.		2640.00		2904.00	68.20	75.02
56 L.H., Daily Totals		$5754.20		$7508.90	$102.75	$134.09

Crew B-40B

Crew No.	Bare Costs Hr.	Bare Costs Daily	Incl. Subs O&P Hr.	Incl. Subs O&P Daily	Bare Costs	Incl. O&P
1 Labor Foreman (outside)	$30.20	$241.60	$50.85	$406.80	$31.18	$52.14
3 Laborers	28.20	676.80	47.45	1138.80		
1 Equip. Oper. (crane)	38.70	309.60	64.10	512.80		
1 Equip. Oper. (oiler)	33.55	268.40	55.55	444.40		
1 Lattice Boom Crane, 40 Ton		1177.00		1294.70	24.52	26.97
48 L.H., Daily Totals		$2673.40		$3797.50	$55.70	$79.11

Crew B-41

Crew No.	Bare Costs Hr.	Bare Costs Daily	Incl. Subs O&P Hr.	Incl. Subs O&P Daily	Bare Costs	Incl. O&P
1 Labor Foreman (outside)	$30.20	$241.60	$50.85	$406.80	$29.28	$49.19
4 Laborers	28.20	902.40	47.45	1518.40		
.25 Equip. Oper. (crane)	38.70	77.40	64.10	128.20		
.25 Equip. Oper. (oiler)	33.55	67.10	55.55	111.10		
.25 Crawler Crane, 40 Ton		294.75		324.23	6.70	7.37
44 L.H., Daily Totals		$1583.25		$2488.72	$35.98	$56.56

Crew B-42

Crew No.	Bare Costs Hr.	Bare Costs Daily	Incl. Subs O&P Hr.	Incl. Subs O&P Daily	Bare Costs	Incl. O&P
1 Labor Foreman (outside)	$30.20	$241.60	$50.85	$406.80	$32.04	$53.58
4 Laborers	28.20	902.40	47.45	1518.40		
1 Equip. Oper. (crane)	38.70	309.60	64.10	512.80		
1 Welder	42.60	340.80	70.30	562.40		
1 Hyd. Crane, 25 Ton		745.80		820.38		
1 Welder, Gas Engine, 300 amp		142.00		156.20		
1 Horz. Boring Csg. Mch.		479.80		527.78	24.42	26.86
56 L.H., Daily Totals		$3162.00		$4504.76	$56.46	$80.44

Crew B-43

Crew No.	Bare Costs Hr.	Bare Costs Daily	Incl. Subs O&P Hr.	Incl. Subs O&P Daily	Bare Costs	Incl. O&P
1 Labor Foreman (outside)	$30.20	$241.60	$50.85	$406.80	$28.60	$48.13
4 Laborers	28.20	902.40	47.45	1518.40		
1 Drill Rig, Truck-Mounted		2551.00		2806.10	63.77	70.15
40 L.H., Daily Totals		$3695.00		$4731.30	$92.38	$118.28

Crew B-44

Crew No.	Bare Costs Hr.	Bare Costs Daily	Incl. Subs O&P Hr.	Incl. Subs O&P Daily	Bare Costs	Incl. O&P
1 Pile Driver Foreman (outside)	$36.60	$292.80	$63.15	$505.20	$33.76	$57.62
4 Pile Drivers	34.60	1107.20	59.70	1910.40		
1 Equip. Oper. (crane)	38.70	309.60	64.10	512.80		
2 Laborers	28.20	451.20	47.45	759.20		
1 Crawler Crane, 40 Ton		1179.00		1296.90		
1 Lead, 60' High		74.80		82.28		
1 Hammer, Diesel, 15K ft.-lbs.		587.60		646.36	28.77	31.65
64 L.H., Daily Totals		$4002.20		$5713.14	$62.53	$89.27

Crew B-45

Crew No.	Bare Costs Hr.	Bare Costs Daily	Incl. Subs O&P Hr.	Incl. Subs O&P Daily	Bare Costs	Incl. O&P
1 Building Laborer	$28.20	$225.60	$47.45	$379.60	$28.93	$48.42
1 Truck Driver (heavy)	29.65	237.20	49.40	395.20		
1 Dist. Tanker, 3000 Gallon		308.20		339.02	19.26	21.19
16 L.H., Daily Totals		$771.00		$1113.82	$48.19	$69.61

Crew B-46

Crew No.	Bare Costs Hr.	Bare Costs Daily	Incl. Subs O&P Hr.	Incl. Subs O&P Daily	Bare Costs	Incl. O&P
1 Pile Driver Foreman (outside)	$36.60	$292.80	$63.15	$505.20	$31.73	$54.15
2 Pile Drivers	34.60	553.60	59.70	955.20		
3 Laborers	28.20	676.80	47.45	1138.80		
1 Chain Saw, Gas, 36" Long		45.00		49.50	0.94	1.03
48 L.H., Daily Totals		$1568.20		$2648.70	$32.67	$55.18

Crew B-47

Crew No.	Bare Costs Hr.	Bare Costs Daily	Incl. Subs O&P Hr.	Incl. Subs O&P Daily	Bare Costs	Incl. O&P
1 Blast Foreman (outside)	$30.20	$241.60	$50.85	$406.80	$29.20	$49.15
1 Driller	28.20	225.60	47.45	379.60		
1 Air Track Drill, 4"		1040.00		1144.00		
1 Air Compressor, 600 cfm		552.60		607.86		
2 -50' Air Hoses, 3"		29.80		32.78	101.40	111.54
16 L.H., Daily Totals		$2089.60		$2571.04	$130.60	$160.69

Crew No.	Bare Costs Hr.	Daily	Incl. Subs O&P Hr.	Daily	Cost Per Labor-Hour Bare Costs	Incl. O&P
Crew B-47A	**Hr.**	**Daily**	**Hr.**	**Daily**	**Bare Costs**	**Incl. O&P**
1 Drilling Foreman (outside)	$30.20	$241.60	$50.85	$406.80	$34.15	$56.83
1 Equip. Oper. (heavy)	38.70	309.60	64.10	512.80		
1 Equip. Oper. (oiler)	33.55	268.40	55.55	444.40		
1 Air Track Drill, 5"		1255.00		1380.50	52.29	57.52
24 L.H., Daily Totals		$2074.60		$2744.50	$86.44	$114.35
Crew B-47C	**Hr.**	**Daily**	**Hr.**	**Daily**	**Bare Costs**	**Incl. O&P**
1 Laborer	$28.20	$225.60	$47.45	$379.60	$32.23	$53.75
1 Equip. Oper. (light)	36.25	290.00	60.05	480.40		
1 Air Compressor, 750 cfm		559.20		615.12		
2 -50' Air Hoses, 3"		29.80		32.78		
1 Air Track Drill, 4"		1040.00		1144.00	101.81	111.99
16 L.H., Daily Totals		$2144.60		$2651.90	$134.04	$165.74
Crew B-47E	**Hr.**	**Daily**	**Hr.**	**Daily**	**Bare Costs**	**Incl. O&P**
1 Labor Foreman (outside)	$30.20	$241.60	$50.85	$406.80	$28.70	$48.30
3 Laborers	28.20	676.80	47.45	1138.80		
1 Flatbed Truck, Gas, 3 Ton		333.00		366.30	10.41	11.45
32 L.H., Daily Totals		$1251.40		$1911.90	$39.11	$59.75
Crew B-47G	**Hr.**	**Daily**	**Hr.**	**Daily**	**Bare Costs**	**Incl. O&P**
1 Labor Foreman (outside)	$30.20	$241.60	$50.85	$406.80	$28.87	$48.58
2 Laborers	28.20	451.20	47.45	759.20		
1 Air Track Drill, 4"		1040.00		1144.00		
1 Air Compressor, 600 cfm		552.60		607.86		
2 -50' Air Hoses, 3"		29.80		32.78		
1 Gunite Pump Rig		370.40		407.44	83.03	91.34
24 L.H., Daily Totals		$2685.60		$3358.08	$111.90	$139.92
Crew B-47H	**Hr.**	**Daily**	**Hr.**	**Daily**	**Bare Costs**	**Incl. O&P**
1 Skilled Worker Foreman (out)	$38.30	$306.40	$64.70	$517.60	$36.80	$62.15
3 Skilled Workers	36.30	871.20	61.30	1471.20		
1 Flatbed Truck, Gas, 3 Ton		333.00		366.30	10.41	11.45
32 L.H., Daily Totals		$1510.60		$2355.10	$47.21	$73.60
Crew B-48	**Hr.**	**Daily**	**Hr.**	**Daily**	**Bare Costs**	**Incl. O&P**
1 Labor Foreman (outside)	$30.20	$241.60	$50.85	$406.80	$30.28	$50.79
4 Laborers	28.20	902.40	47.45	1518.40		
1 Equip. Oper. (crane)	38.70	309.60	64.10	512.80		
1 Centr. Water Pump, 6"		340.80		374.88		
1 -20' Suction Hose, 6"		11.50		12.65		
1 -50' Discharge Hose, 6"		6.10		6.71		
1 Drill Rig, Truck-Mounted		2551.00		2806.10	60.61	66.67
48 L.H., Daily Totals		$4363.00		$5638.34	$90.90	$117.47
Crew B-49	**Hr.**	**Daily**	**Hr.**	**Daily**	**Bare Costs**	**Incl. O&P**
1 Labor Foreman (outside)	$30.20	$241.60	$50.85	$406.80	$31.01	$52.40
5 Laborers	28.20	1128.00	47.45	1898.00		
1 Equip. Oper. (crane)	38.70	309.60	64.10	512.80		
2 Pile Drivers	34.60	553.60	59.70	955.20		
1 Hyd. Crane, 25 Ton		745.80		820.38		
1 Centr. Water Pump, 6"		340.80		374.88		
1 -20' Suction Hose, 6"		11.50		12.65		
1 -50' Discharge Hose, 6"		6.10		6.71		
1 Drill Rig, Truck-Mounted		2551.00		2806.10	50.77	55.84
72 L.H., Daily Totals		$5888.00		$7793.52	$81.78	$108.24

Crew No.	Bare Costs Hr.	Daily	Incl. Subs O&P Hr.	Daily	Cost Per Labor-Hour Bare Costs	Incl. O&P
Crew B-50	**Hr.**	**Daily**	**Hr.**	**Daily**	**Bare Costs**	**Incl. O&P**
1 Pile Driver Foreman (outside)	$36.60	$292.80	$63.15	$505.20	$32.61	$55.59
6 Pile Drivers	34.60	1660.80	59.70	2865.60		
1 Equip. Oper. (crane)	38.70	309.60	64.10	512.80		
5 Laborers	28.20	1128.00	47.45	1898.00		
1 Crawler Crane, 40 Ton		1179.00		1296.90		
1 Lead, 60' High		74.80		82.28		
1 Hammer, Diesel, 15K ft.-lbs.		587.60		646.36		
1 Air Compressor, 600 cfm		552.60		607.86		
2 -50' Air Hoses, 3"		29.80		32.78		
1 Chain Saw, Gas, 36" Long		45.00		49.50	23.74	26.11
104 L.H., Daily Totals		$5860.00		$8497.28	$56.35	$81.70
Crew B-51	**Hr.**	**Daily**	**Hr.**	**Daily**	**Bare Costs**	**Incl. O&P**
1 Labor Foreman (outside)	$30.20	$241.60	$50.85	$406.80	$28.64	$48.12
4 Laborers	28.20	902.40	47.45	1518.40		
1 Truck Driver (light)	28.85	230.80	48.05	384.40		
1 Flatbed Truck, Gas, 1.5 Ton		270.20		297.22	5.63	6.19
48 L.H., Daily Totals		$1645.00		$2606.82	$34.27	$54.31
Crew B-52	**Hr.**	**Daily**	**Hr.**	**Daily**	**Bare Costs**	**Incl. O&P**
1 Labor Foreman (outside)	$30.20	$241.60	$50.85	$406.80	$30.94	$52.07
1 Carpenter	35.75	286.00	60.15	481.20		
4 Laborers	28.20	902.40	47.45	1518.40		
.5 Rodman (reinf.)	38.00	152.00	65.00	260.00		
.5 Equip. Oper. (medium)	37.65	150.60	62.35	249.40		
.5 Crawler Loader, 3 C.Y.		595.50		655.05	10.63	11.70
56 L.H., Daily Totals		$2328.10		$3570.85	$41.57	$63.77
Crew B-53	**Hr.**	**Daily**	**Hr.**	**Daily**	**Bare Costs**	**Incl. O&P**
1 Building Laborer	$28.20	$225.60	$47.45	$379.60	$28.20	$47.45
1 Trencher, Chain, 12 H.P.		71.20		78.32	8.90	9.79
8 L.H., Daily Totals		$296.80		$457.92	$37.10	$57.24
Crew B-54	**Hr.**	**Daily**	**Hr.**	**Daily**	**Bare Costs**	**Incl. O&P**
1 Equip. Oper. (light)	$36.25	$290.00	$60.05	$480.40	$36.25	$60.05
1 Trencher, Chain, 40 H.P.		339.40		373.34	42.42	46.67
8 L.H., Daily Totals		$629.40		$853.74	$78.67	$106.72
Crew B-54A	**Hr.**	**Daily**	**Hr.**	**Daily**	**Bare Costs**	**Incl. O&P**
.17 Labor Foreman (outside)	$30.20	$41.07	$50.85	$69.16	$36.57	$60.68
1 Equipment Operator (med.)	37.65	301.20	62.35	498.80		
1 Wheel Trencher, 67 H.P.		1206.00		1326.60	128.85	141.73
9.36 L.H., Daily Totals		$1548.27		$1894.56	$165.41	$202.41
Crew B-54B	**Hr.**	**Daily**	**Hr.**	**Daily**	**Bare Costs**	**Incl. O&P**
.25 Labor Foreman (outside)	$30.20	$60.40	$50.85	$101.70	$36.16	$60.05
1 Equipment Operator (med.)	37.65	301.20	62.35	498.80		
1 Wheel Trencher, 150 H.P.		1898.00		2087.80	189.80	208.78
10 L.H., Daily Totals		$2259.60		$2688.30	$225.96	$268.83
Crew B-54D	**Hr.**	**Daily**	**Hr.**	**Daily**	**Bare Costs**	**Incl. O&P**
1 Laborer	$28.20	$225.60	$47.45	$379.60	$32.92	$54.90
1 Equipment Operator (med.)	37.65	301.20	62.35	498.80		
1 Rock Trencher, 6" Width		369.00		405.90	23.06	25.37
16 L.H., Daily Totals		$895.80		$1284.30	$55.99	$80.27

Crew B-54E

Crew B-54E	Bare Costs Hr.	Daily	Incl. Subs O&P Hr.	Daily	Bare Costs	Incl. O&P
1 Laborer	$28.20	$225.60	$47.45	$379.60	$32.92	$54.90
1 Equipment Operator (med.)	37.65	301.20	62.35	498.80		
1 Rock Trencher, 18" Width		2590.00		2849.00	161.88	178.06
16 L.H., Daily Totals		$3116.80		$3727.40	$194.80	$232.96

Crew B-55

Crew B-55	Bare Costs Hr.	Daily	Incl. Subs O&P Hr.	Daily	Bare Costs	Incl. O&P
1 Laborer	$28.20	$225.60	$47.45	$379.60	$28.52	$47.75
1 Truck Driver (light)	28.85	230.80	48.05	384.40		
1 Truck-Mounted Earth Auger		786.40		865.04		
1 Flatbed Truck, Gas, 3 Ton		333.00		366.30	69.96	76.96
16 L.H., Daily Totals		$1575.80		$1995.34	$98.49	$124.71

Crew B-56

Crew B-56	Bare Costs Hr.	Daily	Incl. Subs O&P Hr.	Daily	Bare Costs	Incl. O&P
2 Laborers	$28.20	$451.20	$47.45	$759.20	$28.20	$47.45
1 Air Track Drill, 4"		1040.00		1144.00		
1 Air Compressor, 600 cfm		552.60		607.86		
1 -50' Air Hose, 3"		14.90		16.39	100.47	110.52
16 L.H., Daily Totals		$2058.70		$2527.45	$128.67	$157.97

Crew B-57

Crew B-57	Bare Costs Hr.	Daily	Incl. Subs O&P Hr.	Daily	Bare Costs	Incl. O&P
1 Labor Foreman (outside)	$30.20	$241.60	$50.85	$406.80	$30.70	$51.46
3 Laborers	28.20	676.80	47.45	1138.80		
1 Equip. Oper. (crane)	38.70	309.60	64.10	512.80		
1 Barge, 400 Ton		781.00		859.10		
1 Crawler Crane, 25 Ton		1173.00		1290.30		
1 Clamshell Bucket, 1 C.Y.		47.40		52.14		
1 Centr. Water Pump, 6"		340.80		374.88		
1 -20' Suction Hose, 6"		11.50		12.65		
20 -50' Discharge Hoses, 6"		122.00		134.20	61.89	68.08
40 L.H., Daily Totals		$3703.70		$4781.67	$92.59	$119.54

Crew B-58

Crew B-58	Bare Costs Hr.	Daily	Incl. Subs O&P Hr.	Daily	Bare Costs	Incl. O&P
2 Laborers	$28.20	$451.20	$47.45	$759.20	$30.88	$51.65
1 Equip. Oper. (light)	36.25	290.00	60.05	480.40		
1 Backhoe Loader, 48 H.P.		365.20		401.72		
1 Small Helicopter, w/ Pilot		2729.00		3001.90	128.93	141.82
24 L.H., Daily Totals		$3835.40		$4643.22	$159.81	$193.47

Crew B-59

Crew B-59	Bare Costs Hr.	Daily	Incl. Subs O&P Hr.	Daily	Bare Costs	Incl. O&P
1 Truck Driver (heavy)	$29.65	$237.20	$49.40	$395.20	$29.65	$49.40
1 Truck Tractor, 220 H.P.		366.40		403.04		
1 Water Tank Trailer, 5000 Gal.		141.60		155.76	63.50	69.85
8 L.H., Daily Totals		$745.20		$954.00	$93.15	$119.25

Crew B-60

Crew B-60	Bare Costs Hr.	Daily	Incl. Subs O&P Hr.	Daily	Bare Costs	Incl. O&P
1 Labor Foreman (outside)	$30.20	$241.60	$50.85	$406.80	$31.63	$52.89
3 Laborers	28.20	676.80	47.45	1138.80		
1 Equip. Oper. (crane)	38.70	309.60	64.10	512.80		
1 Equip. Oper. (light)	36.25	290.00	60.05	480.40		
1 Crawler Crane, 40 Ton		1179.00		1296.90		
1 Lead, 60' High		74.80		82.28		
1 Hammer, Diesel, 15K ft.-lbs.		587.60		646.36		
1 Backhoe Loader, 48 H.P.		365.20		401.72	45.97	50.57
48 L.H., Daily Totals		$3724.60		$4966.06	$77.60	$103.46

Crew B-61

Crew B-61	Bare Costs Hr.	Daily	Incl. Subs O&P Hr.	Daily	Bare Costs	Incl. O&P
1 Labor Foreman (outside)	$30.20	$241.60	$50.85	$406.80	$28.60	$48.13
4 Laborers	28.20	902.40	47.45	1518.40		
1 Cement Mixer, 2 C.Y.		191.40		210.54		
1 Air Compressor, 160 cfm		157.40		173.14	8.72	9.59
40 L.H., Daily Totals		$1492.80		$2308.88	$37.32	$57.72

Crew B-62

Crew B-62	Bare Costs Hr.	Daily	Incl. Subs O&P Hr.	Daily	Bare Costs	Incl. O&P
2 Laborers	$28.20	$451.20	$47.45	$759.20	$30.88	$51.65
1 Equip. Oper. (light)	36.25	290.00	60.05	480.40		
1 Loader, Skid Steer, 30 H.P.		174.20		191.62	7.26	7.98
24 L.H., Daily Totals		$915.40		$1431.22	$38.14	$59.63

Crew B-63

Crew B-63	Bare Costs Hr.	Daily	Incl. Subs O&P Hr.	Daily	Bare Costs	Incl. O&P
5 Laborers	$28.20	$1128.00	$47.45	$1898.00	$28.20	$47.45
1 Loader, Skid Steer, 30 H.P.		174.20		191.62	4.36	4.79
40 L.H., Daily Totals		$1302.20		$2089.62	$32.56	$52.24

Crew B-63B

Crew B-63B	Bare Costs Hr.	Daily	Incl. Subs O&P Hr.	Daily	Bare Costs	Incl. O&P
1 Labor Foreman (inside)	$28.70	$229.60	$48.30	$386.40	$30.34	$50.81
2 Laborers	28.20	451.20	47.45	759.20		
1 Equip. Oper. (light)	36.25	290.00	60.05	480.40		
1 Loader, Skid Steer, 78 H.P.		308.80		339.68	9.65	10.62
32 L.H., Daily Totals		$1279.60		$1965.68	$39.99	$61.43

Crew B-64

Crew B-64	Bare Costs Hr.	Daily	Incl. Subs O&P Hr.	Daily	Bare Costs	Incl. O&P
1 Laborer	$28.20	$225.60	$47.45	$379.60	$28.52	$47.75
1 Truck Driver (light)	28.85	230.80	48.05	384.40		
1 Power Mulcher (small)		159.60		175.56		
1 Flatbed Truck, Gas, 1.5 Ton		270.20		297.22	26.86	29.55
16 L.H., Daily Totals		$886.20		$1236.78	$55.39	$77.30

Crew B-65

Crew B-65	Bare Costs Hr.	Daily	Incl. Subs O&P Hr.	Daily	Bare Costs	Incl. O&P
1 Laborer	$28.20	$225.60	$47.45	$379.60	$28.52	$47.75
1 Truck Driver (light)	28.85	230.80	48.05	384.40		
1 Power Mulcher (Large)		325.60		358.16		
1 Flatbed Truck, Gas, 1.5 Ton		270.20		297.22	37.24	40.96
16 L.H., Daily Totals		$1052.20		$1419.38	$65.76	$88.71

Crew B-66

Crew B-66	Bare Costs Hr.	Daily	Incl. Subs O&P Hr.	Daily	Bare Costs	Incl. O&P
1 Equip. Oper. (light)	$36.25	$290.00	$60.05	$480.40	$36.25	$60.05
1 Loader-Backhoe, 40 H.P.		259.60		285.56	32.45	35.70
8 L.H., Daily Totals		$549.60		$765.96	$68.70	$95.75

Crew B-67

Crew B-67	Bare Costs Hr.	Daily	Incl. Subs O&P Hr.	Daily	Bare Costs	Incl. O&P
1 Millwright	$37.55	$300.40	$60.55	$484.40	$36.90	$60.30
1 Equip. Oper. (light)	36.25	290.00	60.05	480.40		
1 Forklift, R/T, 4,000 Lb.		314.20		345.62	19.64	21.60
16 L.H., Daily Totals		$904.60		$1310.42	$56.54	$81.90

Crew B-67B

Crew B-67B	Bare Costs Hr.	Daily	Incl. Subs O&P Hr.	Daily	Bare Costs	Incl. O&P
1 Millwright Foreman (inside)	$38.05	$304.40	$61.35	$490.80	$37.80	$60.95
1 Millwright	37.55	300.40	60.55	484.40		
16 L.H., Daily Totals		$604.80		$975.20	$37.80	$60.95

Crew B-68

Crew B-68	Bare Costs Hr.	Daily	Incl. Subs O&P Hr.	Daily	Bare Costs	Incl. O&P
2 Millwrights	$37.55	$600.80	$60.55	$968.80	$37.12	$60.38
1 Equip. Oper. (light)	36.25	290.00	60.05	480.40		
1 Forklift, R/T, 4,000 Lb.		314.20		345.62	13.09	14.40
24 L.H., Daily Totals		$1205.00		$1794.82	$50.21	$74.78

Crew B-68A

Crew B-68A	Bare Costs Hr.	Daily	Incl. Subs O&P Hr.	Daily	Bare Costs	Incl. O&P
1 Millwright Foreman (inside)	$38.05	$304.40	$61.35	$490.80	$37.72	$60.82
2 Millwrights	37.55	600.80	60.55	968.80		
1 Forklift, 8,000 Lb.		180.00		198.00	7.50	8.25
24 L.H., Daily Totals		$1085.20		$1657.60	$45.22	$69.07

Crew No.	Bare Costs Hr.	Daily	Incl. Subs O&P Hr.	Daily	Cost Per L.H. Bare Costs	Incl. O&P
Crew B-68B	Hr.	Daily	Hr.	Daily	Bare Costs	Incl. O&P
1 Millwright Foreman (inside)	$38.05	$304.40	$61.35	$490.80	$40.54	$66.12
2 Millwrights	37.55	600.80	60.55	968.80		
2 Electricians	42.70	683.20	69.90	1118.40		
2 Plumbers	42.60	681.60	70.30	1124.80		
1 Forklift, 5,000 Lb.		324.80		357.28	5.80	6.38
56 L.H., Daily Totals		$2594.80		$4060.08	$46.34	$72.50

Crew No.	Bare Costs Hr.	Daily	Incl. Subs O&P Hr.	Daily	Bare Costs	Incl. O&P
Crew B-68C	Hr.	Daily	Hr.	Daily	Bare Costs	Incl. O&P
1 Millwright Foreman (inside)	$38.05	$304.40	$61.35	$490.80	$40.23	$65.53
1 Millwright	37.55	300.40	60.55	484.40		
1 Electrician	42.70	341.60	69.90	559.20		
1 Plumber	42.60	340.80	70.30	562.40		
1 Forklift, 5,000 Lb.		324.80		357.28	10.15	11.16
32 L.H., Daily Totals		$1612.00		$2454.08	$50.38	$76.69

Crew B-68D	Hr.	Daily	Hr.	Daily	Bare Costs	Incl. O&P
1 Labor Foreman (inside)	$28.70	$229.60	$48.30	$386.40	$31.05	$51.93
1 Laborer	28.20	225.60	47.45	379.60		
1 Equip. Oper. (light)	36.25	290.00	60.05	480.40		
1 Forklift, 5,000 Lb.		324.80		357.28	13.53	14.89
24 L.H., Daily Totals		$1070.00		$1603.68	$44.58	$66.82

Crew B-68E	Hr.	Daily	Hr.	Daily	Bare Costs	Incl. O&P
1 Struc. Steel Foreman (inside)	$38.85	$310.80	$74.00	$592.00	$38.45	$73.24
3 Struc. Steel Workers	38.35	920.40	73.05	1753.20		
1 Welder	38.35	306.80	73.05	584.40		
1 Forklift, 8,000 Lb.		180.00		198.00	4.50	4.95
40 L.H., Daily Totals		$1718.00		$3127.60	$42.95	$78.19

Crew B-68F	Hr.	Daily	Hr.	Daily	Bare Costs	Incl. O&P
1 Skilled Worker Foreman (out)	$38.30	$306.40	$64.70	$517.60	$36.97	$62.43
2 Skilled Workers	36.30	580.80	61.30	980.80		
1 Forklift, 5,000 Lb.		324.80		357.28	13.53	14.89
24 L.H., Daily Totals		$1212.00		$1855.68	$50.50	$77.32

Crew B-69	Hr.	Daily	Hr.	Daily	Bare Costs	Incl. O&P
1 Labor Foreman (outside)	$30.20	$241.60	$50.85	$406.80	$31.18	$52.14
3 Laborers	28.20	676.80	47.45	1138.80		
1 Equip. Oper. (crane)	38.70	309.60	64.10	512.80		
1 Equip. Oper. (oiler)	33.55	268.40	55.55	444.40		
1 Hyd. Crane, 80 Ton		1652.00		1817.20	34.42	37.86
48 L.H., Daily Totals		$3148.40		$4320.00	$65.59	$90.00

Crew B-69A	Hr.	Daily	Hr.	Daily	Bare Costs	Incl. O&P
1 Labor Foreman (outside)	$30.20	$241.60	$50.85	$406.80	$31.13	$51.86
3 Laborers	28.20	676.80	47.45	1138.80		
1 Equip. Oper. (medium)	37.65	301.20	62.35	498.80		
1 Concrete Finisher	34.35	274.80	55.60	444.80		
1 Curb/Gutter Paver, 2-Track		898.00		987.80	18.71	20.58
48 L.H., Daily Totals		$2392.40		$3477.00	$49.84	$72.44

Crew B-69B	Hr.	Daily	Hr.	Daily	Bare Costs	Incl. O&P
1 Labor Foreman (outside)	$30.20	$241.60	$50.85	$406.80	$31.13	$51.86
3 Laborers	28.20	676.80	47.45	1138.80		
1 Equip. Oper. (medium)	37.65	301.20	62.35	498.80		
1 Cement Finisher	34.35	274.80	55.60	444.80		
1 Curb/Gutter Paver, 4-Track		770.20		847.22	16.05	17.65
48 L.H., Daily Totals		$2264.60		$3336.42	$47.18	$69.51

Crew No.	Bare Costs Hr.	Daily	Incl. Subs O&P Hr.	Daily	Cost Per L.H. Bare Costs	Incl. O&P
Crew B-70	Hr.	Daily	Hr.	Daily	Bare Costs	Incl. O&P
1 Labor Foreman (outside)	$30.20	$241.60	$50.85	$406.80	$32.54	$54.32
3 Laborers	28.20	676.80	47.45	1138.80		
3 Equip. Oper. (medium)	37.65	903.60	62.35	1496.40		
1 Grader, 30,000 Lbs.		707.00		777.70		
1 Ripper, Beam & 1 Shank		81.40		89.54		
1 Road Sweeper, S.P., 8' wide		665.40		731.94		
1 F.E. Loader, W.M., 1.5 C.Y.		373.40		410.74	32.63	35.89
56 L.H., Daily Totals		$3649.20		$5051.92	$65.16	$90.21

Crew B-71	Hr.	Daily	Hr.	Daily	Bare Costs	Incl. O&P
1 Labor Foreman (outside)	$30.20	$241.60	$50.85	$406.80	$32.54	$54.32
3 Laborers	28.20	676.80	47.45	1138.80		
3 Equip. Oper. (medium)	37.65	903.60	62.35	1496.40		
1 Pvmt. Profiler, 750 H.P.		5877.00		6464.70		
1 Road Sweeper, S.P., 8' wide		665.40		731.94		
1 F.E. Loader, W.M., 1.5 C.Y.		373.40		410.74	123.50	135.85
56 L.H., Daily Totals		$8737.80		$10649.38	$156.03	$190.17

Crew B-72	Hr.	Daily	Hr.	Daily	Bare Costs	Incl. O&P
1 Labor Foreman (outside)	$30.20	$241.60	$50.85	$406.80	$33.17	$55.33
3 Laborers	28.20	676.80	47.45	1138.80		
4 Equip. Oper. (medium)	37.65	1204.80	62.35	1995.20		
1 Pvmt. Profiler, 750 H.P.		5877.00		6464.70		
1 Hammermill, 250 H.P.		1846.00		2030.60		
1 Windrow Loader		1240.00		1364.00		
1 Mix Paver 165 H.P.		2183.00		2401.30		
1 Roller, Pneum. Whl., 12 Ton		349.00		383.90	179.61	197.57
64 L.H., Daily Totals		$13618.20		$16185.30	$212.78	$252.90

Crew B-73	Hr.	Daily	Hr.	Daily	Bare Costs	Incl. O&P
1 Labor Foreman (outside)	$30.20	$241.60	$50.85	$406.80	$34.36	$57.19
2 Laborers	28.20	451.20	47.45	759.20		
5 Equip. Oper. (medium)	37.65	1506.00	62.35	2494.00		
1 Road Mixer, 310 H.P.		1942.00		2136.20		
1 Tandem Roller, 10 Ton		242.00		266.20		
1 Hammermill, 250 H.P.		1846.00		2030.60		
1 Grader, 30,000 Lbs.		707.00		777.70		
.5 F.E. Loader, W.M., 1.5 C.Y.		186.70		205.37		
.5 Truck Tractor, 220 H.P.		183.20		201.52		
.5 Water Tank Trailer, 5000 Gal.		70.80		77.88	80.90	88.99
64 L.H., Daily Totals		$7376.50		$9355.47	$115.26	$146.18

Crew B-74	Hr.	Daily	Hr.	Daily	Bare Costs	Incl. O&P
1 Labor Foreman (outside)	$30.20	$241.60	$50.85	$406.80	$33.54	$55.81
1 Laborer	28.20	225.60	47.45	379.60		
4 Equip. Oper. (medium)	37.65	1204.80	62.35	1995.20		
2 Truck Drivers (heavy)	29.65	474.40	49.40	790.40		
1 Grader, 30,000 Lbs.		707.00		777.70		
1 Ripper, Beam & 1 Shank		81.40		89.54		
2 Stabilizers, 310 H.P.		3654.00		4019.40		
1 Flatbed Truck, Gas, 3 Ton		333.00		366.30		
1 Chem. Spreader, Towed		53.20		58.52		
1 Roller, Vibratory, 25 Ton		692.80		762.08		
1 Water Tank Trailer, 5000 Gal.		141.60		155.76		
1 Truck Tractor, 220 H.P.		366.40		403.04	94.21	103.63
64 L.H., Daily Totals		$8175.80		$10204.34	$127.75	$159.44

Crews

Crew B-75	Hr.	Daily	Hr.	Daily	Bare Costs	Incl. O&P
1 Labor Foreman (outside)	$30.20	$241.60	$50.85	$406.80	$34.09	$56.73
1 Laborer	28.20	225.60	47.45	379.60		
4 Equip. Oper. (medium)	37.65	1204.80	62.35	1995.20		
1 Truck Driver (heavy)	29.65	237.20	49.40	395.20		
1 Grader, 30,000 Lbs.		707.00		777.70		
1 Ripper, Beam & 1 Shank		81.40		89.54		
2 Stabilizers, 310 H.P.		3654.00		4019.40		
1 Dist. Tanker, 3000 Gallon		308.20		339.02		
1 Truck Tractor, 6x4, 380 H.P.		612.80		674.08		
1 Roller, Vibratory, 25 Ton		692.80		762.08	108.15	118.96
56 L.H., Daily Totals		$7965.40		$9838.62	$142.24	$175.69

Crew B-76	Hr.	Daily	Hr.	Daily	Bare Costs	Incl. O&P
1 Dock Builder Foreman (outside)	$36.60	$292.80	$63.15	$505.20	$35.62	$60.60
5 Dock Builders	34.60	1384.00	59.70	2388.00		
2 Equip. Oper. (crane)	38.70	619.20	64.10	1025.60		
1 Equip. Oper. (oiler)	33.55	268.40	55.55	444.40		
1 Crawler Crane, 50 Ton		1319.00		1450.90		
1 Barge, 400 Ton		781.00		859.10		
1 Hammer, Diesel, 15K ft.-lbs.		587.60		646.36		
1 Lead, 60' High		74.80		82.28		
1 Air Compressor, 600 cfm		552.60		607.86		
2 -50' Air Hoses, 3"		29.80		32.78	46.46	51.10
72 L.H., Daily Totals		$5909.20		$8042.48	$82.07	$111.70

Crew B-76A	Hr.	Daily	Hr.	Daily	Bare Costs	Incl. O&P
1 Labor Foreman (outside)	$30.20	$241.60	$50.85	$406.80	$30.43	$50.97
5 Laborers	28.20	1128.00	47.45	1898.00		
1 Equip. Oper. (crane)	38.70	309.60	64.10	512.80		
1 Equip. Oper. (oiler)	33.55	268.40	55.55	444.40		
1 Crawler Crane, 50 Ton		1319.00		1450.90		
1 Barge, 400 Ton		781.00		859.10	32.81	36.09
64 L.H., Daily Totals		$4047.60		$5572.00	$63.24	$87.06

Crew B-77	Hr.	Daily	Hr.	Daily	Bare Costs	Incl. O&P
1 Labor Foreman (outside)	$30.20	$241.60	$50.85	$406.80	$28.73	$48.25
3 Laborers	28.20	676.80	47.45	1138.80		
1 Truck Driver (light)	28.85	230.80	48.05	384.40		
1 Crack Cleaner, 25 H.P.		64.80		71.28		
1 Crack Filler, Trailer Mtd.		203.80		224.18		
1 Flatbed Truck, Gas, 3 Ton		333.00		366.30	15.04	16.54
40 L.H., Daily Totals		$1750.80		$2591.76	$43.77	$64.79

Crew B-78	Hr.	Daily	Hr.	Daily	Bare Costs	Incl. O&P
1 Labor Foreman (outside)	$30.20	$241.60	$50.85	$406.80	$28.60	$48.13
4 Laborers	28.20	902.40	47.45	1518.40		
1 Paint Striper, S.P., 40 Gallon		154.80		170.28		
1 Flatbed Truck, Gas, 3 Ton		333.00		366.30		
1 Pickup Truck, 3/4 Ton		157.00		172.70	16.12	17.73
40 L.H., Daily Totals		$1788.80		$2634.48	$44.72	$65.86

Crew B-78B	Hr.	Daily	Hr.	Daily	Bare Costs	Incl. O&P
2 Laborers	$28.20	$451.20	$47.45	$759.20	$29.09	$48.85
.25 Equip. Oper. (light)	36.25	72.50	60.05	120.10		
1 Pickup Truck, 3/4 Ton		157.00		172.70		
1 Line Rem.,11 H.P.,Walk Behind		68.40		75.24		
.25 Road Sweeper, S.P., 8' wide		166.35		182.99	21.76	23.94
18 L.H., Daily Totals		$915.45		$1310.22	$50.86	$72.79

Crew B-78C	Hr.	Daily	Hr.	Daily	Bare Costs	Incl. O&P
1 Labor Foreman (outside)	$30.20	$241.60	$50.85	$406.80	$28.64	$48.12
4 Laborers	28.20	902.40	47.45	1518.40		
1 Truck Driver (light)	28.85	230.80	48.05	384.40		
1 Paint Striper, T.M., 120 Gal.		860.40		946.44		
1 Flatbed Truck, Gas, 3 Ton		333.00		366.30		
1 Pickup Truck, 3/4 Ton		157.00		172.70	28.13	30.95
48 L.H., Daily Totals		$2725.20		$3795.04	$56.77	$79.06

Crew B-78D	Hr.	Daily	Hr.	Daily	Bare Costs	Incl. O&P
2 Labor Foremen (outside)	$30.20	$483.20	$50.85	$813.60	$28.66	$48.19
7 Laborers	28.20	1579.20	47.45	2657.20		
1 Truck Driver (light)	28.85	230.80	48.05	384.40		
1 Paint Striper, T.M., 120 Gal.		860.40		946.44		
1 Flatbed Truck, Gas, 3 Ton		333.00		366.30		
3 Pickup Trucks, 3/4 Ton		471.00		518.10		
1 Air Compressor, 60 cfm		137.40		151.14		
1 -50' Air Hose, 3/4"		3.25		3.58		
1 Breakers, Pavement, 60 lb.		9.80		10.78	22.69	24.95
80 L.H., Daily Totals		$4108.05		$5851.53	$51.35	$73.14

Crew B-78E	Hr.	Daily	Hr.	Daily	Bare Costs	Incl. O&P
2 Labor Foremen (outside)	$30.20	$483.20	$50.85	$813.60	$28.59	$48.07
9 Laborers	28.20	2030.40	47.45	3416.40		
1 Truck Driver (light)	28.85	230.80	48.05	384.40		
1 Paint Striper, T.M., 120 Gal.		860.40		946.44		
1 Flatbed Truck, Gas, 3 Ton		333.00		366.30		
4 Pickup Trucks, 3/4 Ton		628.00		690.80		
2 Air Compressor, 60 cfm		274.80		302.28		
2 -50' Air Hose, 3/4"		6.50		7.15		
2 Breakers, Pavement, 60 lb.		19.60		21.56	22.11	24.32
96 L.H., Daily Totals		$4866.70		$6948.93	$50.69	$72.38

Crew B-78F	Hr.	Daily	Hr.	Daily	Bare Costs	Incl. O&P
2 Labor Foremen (outside)	$30.20	$483.20	$50.85	$813.60	$28.53	$47.98
11 Laborers	28.20	2481.60	47.45	4175.60		
1 Truck Driver (light)	28.85	230.80	48.05	384.40		
1 Paint Striper, T.M., 120 Gal.		860.40		946.44		
1 Flatbed Truck, Gas, 3 Ton		333.00		366.30		
7 Pickup Trucks, 3/4 Ton		1099.00		1208.90		
3 Air Compressor, 60 cfm		412.20		453.42		
3 -50' Air Hose, 3/4"		9.75		10.73		
3 Breakers, Pavement, 60 lb.		29.40		32.34	24.50	26.95
112 L.H., Daily Totals		$5939.35		$8391.73	$53.03	$74.93

Crew B-79	Hr.	Daily	Hr.	Daily	Bare Costs	Incl. O&P
1 Labor Foreman (outside)	$30.20	$241.60	$50.85	$406.80	$28.73	$48.25
3 Laborers	28.20	676.80	47.45	1138.80		
1 Truck Driver (light)	28.85	230.80	48.05	384.40		
1 Paint Striper, T.M., 120 Gal.		860.40		946.44		
1 Heating Kettle, 115 Gallon		63.00		69.30		
1 Flatbed Truck, Gas, 3 Ton		333.00		366.30		
2 Pickup Trucks, 3/4 Ton		314.00		345.40	39.26	43.19
40 L.H., Daily Totals		$2719.60		$3657.44	$67.99	$91.44

Crew B-79B	Hr.	Daily	Hr.	Daily	Bare Costs	Incl. O&P
1 Laborer	$28.20	$225.60	$47.45	$379.60	$28.20	$47.45
1 Set of Gases		152.00		167.20	19.00	20.90
8 L.H., Daily Totals		$377.60		$546.80	$47.20	$68.35

Crew No.	Bare Costs		Incl. Subs O&P		Cost Per Labor-Hour	

Crew B-79C	Hr.	Daily	Hr.	Daily	Bare Costs	Incl. O&P
1 Labor Foreman (outside)	$30.20	$241.60	$50.85	$406.80	$28.58	$48.02
5 Laborers	28.20	1128.00	47.45	1898.00		
1 Truck Driver (light)	28.85	230.80	48.05	384.40		
1 Paint Striper, T.M., 120 Gal.		860.40		946.44		
1 Heating Kettle, 115 Gallon		63.00		69.30		
1 Flatbed Truck, Gas, 3 Ton		333.00		366.30		
3 Pickup Trucks, 3/4 Ton		471.00		518.10		
1 Air Compressor, 60 cfm		137.40		151.14		
1 -50' Air Hose, 3/4"		3.25		3.58		
1 Breakers, Pavement, 60 lb.		9.80		10.78	33.53	36.89
56 L.H., Daily Totals		$3478.25		$4754.84	$62.11	$84.91

Crew B-79D	Hr.	Daily	Hr.	Daily	Bare Costs	Incl. O&P
2 Labor Foremen (outside)	$30.20	$483.20	$50.85	$813.60	$28.78	$48.38
5 Laborers	28.20	1128.00	47.45	1898.00		
1 Truck Driver (light)	28.85	230.80	48.05	384.40		
1 Paint Striper, T.M., 120 Gal.		860.40		946.44		
1 Heating Kettle, 115 Gallon		63.00		69.30		
1 Flatbed Truck, Gas, 3 Ton		333.00		366.30		
4 Pickup Trucks, 3/4 Ton		628.00		690.80		
1 Air Compressor, 60 cfm		137.40		151.14		
1 -50' Air Hose, 3/4"		3.25		3.58		
1 Breakers, Pavement, 60 lb.		9.80		10.78	31.79	34.97
64 L.H., Daily Totals		$3876.85		$5334.34	$60.58	$83.35

Crew B-79E	Hr.	Daily	Hr.	Daily	Bare Costs	Incl. O&P
2 Labor Foremen (outside)	$30.20	$483.20	$50.85	$813.60	$28.66	$48.19
7 Laborers	28.20	1579.20	47.45	2657.20		
1 Truck Driver (light)	28.85	230.80	48.05	384.40		
1 Paint Striper, T.M., 120 Gal.		860.40		946.44		
1 Heating Kettle, 115 Gallon		63.00		69.30		
1 Flatbed Truck, Gas, 3 Ton		333.00		366.30		
5 Pickup Trucks, 3/4 Ton		785.00		863.50		
2 Air Compressors, 60 cfm		274.80		302.28		
2 -50' Air Hoses, 3/4"		6.50		7.15		
2 Breakers, Pavement, 60 lb.		19.60		21.56	29.28	32.21
80 L.H., Daily Totals		$4635.50		$6431.73	$57.94	$80.40

Crew B-80	Hr.	Daily	Hr.	Daily	Bare Costs	Incl. O&P
1 Labor Foreman (outside)	$30.20	$241.60	$50.85	$406.80	$28.87	$48.58
2 Laborers	28.20	451.20	47.45	759.20		
1 Flatbed Truck, Gas, 3 Ton		333.00		366.30		
1 Earth Auger, Truck-Mtd.		425.00		467.50	31.58	34.74
24 L.H., Daily Totals		$1450.80		$1999.80	$60.45	$83.33

Crew B-80A	Hr.	Daily	Hr.	Daily	Bare Costs	Incl. O&P
3 Laborers	$28.20	$676.80	$47.45	$1138.80	$28.20	$47.45
1 Flatbed Truck, Gas, 3 Ton		333.00		366.30	13.88	15.26
24 L.H., Daily Totals		$1009.80		$1505.10	$42.08	$62.71

Crew B-80B	Hr.	Daily	Hr.	Daily	Bare Costs	Incl. O&P
3 Laborers	$28.20	$676.80	$47.45	$1138.80	$30.21	$50.60
1 Equip. Oper. (light)	36.25	290.00	60.05	480.40		
1 Crane, Flatbed Mounted, 3 Ton		248.40		273.24	7.76	8.54
32 L.H., Daily Totals		$1215.20		$1892.44	$37.98	$59.14

Crew B-80C	Hr.	Daily	Hr.	Daily	Bare Costs	Incl. O&P
2 Laborers	$28.20	$451.20	$47.45	$759.20	$28.42	$47.65
1 Truck Driver (light)	28.85	230.80	48.05	384.40		
1 Flatbed Truck, Gas, 1.5 Ton		270.20		297.22		
1 Manual Fence Post Auger, Gas		8.00		8.80	11.59	12.75
24 L.H., Daily Totals		$960.20		$1449.62	$40.01	$60.40

Crew B-81	Hr.	Daily	Hr.	Daily	Bare Costs	Incl. O&P
1 Laborer	$28.20	$225.60	$47.45	$379.60	$28.93	$48.42
1 Truck Driver (heavy)	29.65	237.20	49.40	395.20		
1 Hydromulcher, T.M., 3000 Gal.		340.40		374.44		
1 Truck Tractor, 220 H.P.		366.40		403.04	44.17	48.59
16 L.H., Daily Totals		$1169.60		$1552.28	$73.10	$97.02

Crew B-81A	Hr.	Daily	Hr.	Daily	Bare Costs	Incl. O&P
1 Laborer	$28.20	$225.60	$47.45	$379.60	$28.52	$47.75
1 Truck Driver (light)	28.85	230.80	48.05	384.40		
1 Hydromulcher, T.M., 600 Gal.		132.60		145.86		
1 Flatbed Truck, Gas, 3 Ton		333.00		366.30	29.10	32.01
16 L.H., Daily Totals		$922.00		$1276.16	$57.63	$79.76

Crew B-82	Hr.	Daily	Hr.	Daily	Bare Costs	Incl. O&P
1 Laborer	$28.20	$225.60	$47.45	$379.60	$32.23	$53.75
1 Equip. Oper. (light)	36.25	290.00	60.05	480.40		
1 Horiz. Borer, 6 H.P.		83.00		91.30	5.19	5.71
16 L.H., Daily Totals		$598.60		$951.30	$37.41	$59.46

Crew B-82A	Hr.	Daily	Hr.	Daily	Bare Costs	Incl. O&P
1 Laborer	$28.20	$225.60	$47.45	$379.60	$32.23	$53.75
1 Equip. Oper. (light)	36.25	290.00	60.05	480.40		
1 Flatbed Truck, Gas, 3 Ton		333.00		366.30		
1 Flatbed Trailer, 25 Ton		113.60		124.96		
1 Horiz. Dir. Drill, 20k lb. Thrust		658.40		724.24	69.06	75.97
16 L.H., Daily Totals		$1620.60		$2075.50	$101.29	$129.72

Crew B-82B	Hr.	Daily	Hr.	Daily	Bare Costs	Incl. O&P
2 Laborers	$28.20	$451.20	$47.45	$759.20	$30.88	$51.65
1 Equip. Oper. (light)	36.25	290.00	60.05	480.40		
1 Flatbed Truck, Gas, 3 Ton		333.00		366.30		
1 Flatbed Trailer, 25 Ton		113.60		124.96		
1 Horiz. Dir. Drill, 30k lb. Thrust		936.20		1029.82	57.62	63.38
24 L.H., Daily Totals		$2124.00		$2760.68	$88.50	$115.03

Crew B-82C	Hr.	Daily	Hr.	Daily	Bare Costs	Incl. O&P
2 Laborers	$28.20	$451.20	$47.45	$759.20	$30.88	$51.65
1 Equip. Oper. (light)	36.25	290.00	60.05	480.40		
1 Flatbed Truck, Gas, 3 Ton		333.00		366.30		
1 Flatbed Trailer, 25 Ton		113.60		124.96		
1 Horiz. Dir. Drill, 50k lb. Thrust		1246.00		1370.60	70.53	77.58
24 L.H., Daily Totals		$2433.80		$3101.46	$101.41	$129.23

Crew B-82D	Hr.	Daily	Hr.	Daily	Bare Costs	Incl. O&P
1 Equip. Oper. (light)	$36.25	$290.00	$60.05	$480.40	$36.25	$60.05
1 Mud Trailer for HDD, 1500 Gal.		374.80		412.28	46.85	51.53
8 L.H., Daily Totals		$664.80		$892.68	$83.10	$111.58

Crew B-83	Hr.	Daily	Hr.	Daily	Bare Costs	Incl. O&P
1 Tugboat Captain	$37.65	$301.20	$62.35	$498.80	$32.92	$54.90
1 Tugboat Hand	28.20	225.60	47.45	379.60		
1 Tugboat, 250 H.P.		889.40		978.34	55.59	61.15
16 L.H., Daily Totals		$1416.20		$1856.74	$88.51	$116.05

Crews

Crew B-84	Bare Costs Hr.	Bare Costs Daily	Incl. Subs O&P Hr.	Incl. Subs O&P Daily	Cost Per Labor-Hour Bare Costs	Cost Per Labor-Hour Incl. O&P
1 Equip. Oper. (medium)	$37.65	$301.20	$62.35	$498.80	$37.65	$62.35
1 Rotary Mower/Tractor		364.20		400.62	45.52	50.08
8 L.H., Daily Totals		$665.40		$899.42	$83.17	$112.43

Crew B-85	Bare Costs Hr.	Bare Costs Daily	Incl. Subs O&P Hr.	Incl. Subs O&P Daily	Cost Per Labor-Hour Bare Costs	Cost Per Labor-Hour Incl. O&P
3 Laborers	$28.20	$676.80	$47.45	$1138.80	$30.38	$50.82
1 Equip. Oper. (medium)	37.65	301.20	62.35	498.80		
1 Truck Driver (heavy)	29.65	237.20	49.40	395.20		
1 Aerial Lift Truck, 80'		643.00		707.30		
1 Brush Chipper, 12", 130 H.P.		396.60		436.26		
1 Pruning Saw, Rotary		6.55		7.21	26.15	28.77
40 L.H., Daily Totals		$2261.35		$3183.57	$56.53	$79.59

Crew B-86	Bare Costs Hr.	Bare Costs Daily	Incl. Subs O&P Hr.	Incl. Subs O&P Daily	Cost Per Labor-Hour Bare Costs	Cost Per Labor-Hour Incl. O&P
1 Equip. Oper. (medium)	$37.65	$301.20	$62.35	$498.80	$37.65	$62.35
1 Stump Chipper, S.P.		162.10		178.31	20.26	22.29
8 L.H., Daily Totals		$463.30		$677.11	$57.91	$84.64

Crew B-86A	Bare Costs Hr.	Bare Costs Daily	Incl. Subs O&P Hr.	Incl. Subs O&P Daily	Cost Per Labor-Hour Bare Costs	Cost Per Labor-Hour Incl. O&P
1 Equip. Oper. (medium)	$37.65	$301.20	$62.35	$498.80	$37.65	$62.35
1 Grader, 30,000 Lbs.		707.00		777.70	88.38	97.21
8 L.H., Daily Totals		$1008.20		$1276.50	$126.03	$159.56

Crew B-86B	Bare Costs Hr.	Bare Costs Daily	Incl. Subs O&P Hr.	Incl. Subs O&P Daily	Cost Per Labor-Hour Bare Costs	Cost Per Labor-Hour Incl. O&P
1 Equip. Oper. (medium)	$37.65	$301.20	$62.35	$498.80	$37.65	$62.35
1 Dozer, 200 H.P.		1325.00		1457.50	165.63	182.19
8 L.H., Daily Totals		$1626.20		$1956.30	$203.28	$244.54

Crew B-87	Bare Costs Hr.	Bare Costs Daily	Incl. Subs O&P Hr.	Incl. Subs O&P Daily	Cost Per Labor-Hour Bare Costs	Cost Per Labor-Hour Incl. O&P
1 Laborer	$28.20	$225.60	$47.45	$379.60	$35.76	$59.37
4 Equip. Oper. (medium)	37.65	1204.80	62.35	1995.20		
2 Feller Bunchers, 100 H.P.		1458.00		1603.80		
1 Log Chipper, 22" Tree		898.60		988.46		
1 Dozer, 105 H.P.		591.80		650.98		
1 Chain Saw, Gas, 36" Long		45.00		49.50	74.83	82.32
40 L.H., Daily Totals		$4423.80		$5667.54	$110.60	$141.69

Crew B-88	Bare Costs Hr.	Bare Costs Daily	Incl. Subs O&P Hr.	Incl. Subs O&P Daily	Cost Per Labor-Hour Bare Costs	Cost Per Labor-Hour Incl. O&P
1 Laborer	$28.20	$225.60	$47.45	$379.60	$36.30	$60.22
6 Equip. Oper. (medium)	37.65	1807.20	62.35	2992.80		
2 Feller Bunchers, 100 H.P.		1458.00		1603.80		
1 Log Chipper, 22" Tree		898.60		988.46		
2 Log Skidders, 50 H.P.		1839.20		2023.12		
1 Dozer, 105 H.P.		591.80		650.98		
1 Chain Saw, Gas, 36" Long		45.00		49.50	86.30	94.93
56 L.H., Daily Totals		$6865.40		$8688.26	$122.60	$155.15

Crew B-89	Bare Costs Hr.	Bare Costs Daily	Incl. Subs O&P Hr.	Incl. Subs O&P Daily	Cost Per Labor-Hour Bare Costs	Cost Per Labor-Hour Incl. O&P
1 Skilled Worker	$36.30	$290.40	$61.30	$490.40	$32.25	$54.38
1 Building Laborer	28.20	225.60	47.45	379.60		
1 Flatbed Truck, Gas, 3 Ton		333.00		366.30		
1 Concrete Saw		175.20		192.72		
1 Water Tank, 65 Gal.		17.30		19.03	32.84	36.13
16 L.H., Daily Totals		$1041.50		$1448.05	$65.09	$90.50

Crew B-89A	Bare Costs Hr.	Bare Costs Daily	Incl. Subs O&P Hr.	Incl. Subs O&P Daily	Cost Per Labor-Hour Bare Costs	Cost Per Labor-Hour Incl. O&P
1 Skilled Worker	$36.30	$290.40	$61.30	$490.40	$32.25	$54.38
1 Laborer	28.20	225.60	47.45	379.60		
1 Core Drill (Large)		116.20		127.82	7.26	7.99
16 L.H., Daily Totals		$632.20		$997.82	$39.51	$62.36

Crew B-89B	Bare Costs Hr.	Bare Costs Daily	Incl. Subs O&P Hr.	Incl. Subs O&P Daily	Cost Per Labor-Hour Bare Costs	Cost Per Labor-Hour Incl. O&P
1 Equip. Oper. (light)	$36.25	$290.00	$60.05	$480.40	$32.55	$54.05
1 Truck Driver (light)	28.85	230.80	48.05	384.40		
1 Wall Saw, Hydraulic, 10 H.P.		119.60		131.56		
1 Generator, Diesel, 100 kW		439.20		483.12		
1 Water Tank, 65 Gal.		17.30		19.03		
1 Flatbed Truck, Gas, 3 Ton		333.00		366.30	56.82	62.50
16 L.H., Daily Totals		$1429.90		$1864.81	$89.37	$116.55

Crew B-90	Bare Costs Hr.	Bare Costs Daily	Incl. Subs O&P Hr.	Incl. Subs O&P Daily	Cost Per Labor-Hour Bare Costs	Cost Per Labor-Hour Incl. O&P
1 Labor Foreman (outside)	$30.20	$241.60	$50.85	$406.80	$30.82	$51.51
3 Laborers	28.20	676.80	47.45	1138.80		
2 Equip. Oper. (light)	36.25	580.00	60.05	960.80		
2 Truck Drivers (heavy)	29.65	474.40	49.40	790.40		
1 Road Mixer, 310 H.P.		1942.00		2136.20		
1 Dist. Truck, 2000 Gal.		278.20		306.02	34.69	38.16
64 L.H., Daily Totals		$4193.00		$5739.02	$65.52	$89.67

Crew B-90A	Bare Costs Hr.	Bare Costs Daily	Incl. Subs O&P Hr.	Incl. Subs O&P Daily	Cost Per Labor-Hour Bare Costs	Cost Per Labor-Hour Incl. O&P
1 Labor Foreman (outside)	$30.20	$241.60	$50.85	$406.80	$33.89	$56.45
2 Laborers	28.20	451.20	47.45	759.20		
4 Equip. Oper. (medium)	37.65	1204.80	62.35	1995.20		
2 Graders, 30,000 Lbs.		1414.00		1555.40		
1 Tandem Roller, 10 Ton		242.00		266.20		
1 Roller, Pneum. Whl., 12 Ton		349.00		383.90	35.80	39.38
56 L.H., Daily Totals		$3902.60		$5366.70	$69.69	$95.83

Crew B-90B	Bare Costs Hr.	Bare Costs Daily	Incl. Subs O&P Hr.	Incl. Subs O&P Daily	Cost Per Labor-Hour Bare Costs	Cost Per Labor-Hour Incl. O&P
1 Labor Foreman (outside)	$30.20	$241.60	$50.85	$406.80	$33.26	$55.47
2 Laborers	28.20	451.20	47.45	759.20		
3 Equip. Oper. (medium)	37.65	903.60	62.35	1496.40		
1 Roller, Pneum. Whl., 12 Ton		349.00		383.90		
1 Road Mixer, 310 H.P.		1942.00		2136.20	47.73	52.50
48 L.H., Daily Totals		$3887.40		$5182.50	$80.99	$107.97

Crew B-90C	Bare Costs Hr.	Bare Costs Daily	Incl. Subs O&P Hr.	Incl. Subs O&P Daily	Cost Per Labor-Hour Bare Costs	Cost Per Labor-Hour Incl. O&P
1 Labor Foreman (outside)	$30.20	$241.60	$50.85	$406.80	$31.35	$52.35
4 Laborers	28.20	902.40	47.45	1518.40		
3 Equip. Oper. (medium)	37.65	903.60	62.35	1496.40		
3 Truck Drivers (heavy)	29.65	711.60	49.40	1185.60		
3 Road Mixers, 310 H.P.		5826.00		6408.60	66.20	72.83
88 L.H., Daily Totals		$8585.20		$11015.80	$97.56	$125.18

Crew B-90D	Bare Costs Hr.	Bare Costs Daily	Incl. Subs O&P Hr.	Incl. Subs O&P Daily	Cost Per Labor-Hour Bare Costs	Cost Per Labor-Hour Incl. O&P
1 Labor Foreman (outside)	$30.20	$241.60	$50.85	$406.80	$30.87	$51.60
6 Laborers	28.20	1353.60	47.45	2277.60		
3 Equip. Oper. (medium)	37.65	903.60	62.35	1496.40		
3 Truck Drivers (heavy)	29.65	711.60	49.40	1185.60		
3 Road Mixers, 310 H.P.		5826.00		6408.60	56.02	61.62
104 L.H., Daily Totals		$9036.40		$11775.00	$86.89	$113.22

Crew B-90E	Bare Costs Hr.	Bare Costs Daily	Incl. Subs O&P Hr.	Incl. Subs O&P Daily	Cost Per Labor-Hour Bare Costs	Cost Per Labor-Hour Incl. O&P
1 Labor Foreman (outside)	$30.20	$241.60	$50.85	$406.80	$31.73	$53.01
4 Laborers	28.20	902.40	47.45	1518.40		
3 Equip. Oper. (medium)	37.65	903.60	62.35	1496.40		
1 Truck Driver (heavy)	29.65	237.20	49.40	395.20		
1 Road Mixers, 310 H.P.		1942.00		2136.20	26.97	29.67
72 L.H., Daily Totals		$4226.80		$5953.00	$58.71	$82.68

Crew No.	Bare Costs		Incl. Subs O&P		Cost Per Labor-Hour	
	Hr.	Daily	Hr.	Daily	Bare Costs	Incl. O&P
Crew B-91	Hr.	Daily	Hr.	Daily	Bare Costs	Incl. O&P
1 Labor Foreman (outside)	$30.20	$241.60	$50.85	$406.80	$33.36	$55.57
2 Laborers	28.20	451.20	47.45	759.20		
4 Equip. Oper. (medium)	37.65	1204.80	62.35	1995.20		
1 Truck Driver (heavy)	29.65	237.20	49.40	395.20		
1 Dist. Tanker, 3000 Gallon		308.20		339.02		
1 Truck Tractor, 6x4, 380 H.P.		612.80		674.08		
1 Aggreg. Spreader, S.P.		841.00		925.10		
1 Roller, Pneum. Whl., 12 Ton		349.00		383.90		
1 Tandem Roller, 10 Ton		242.00		266.20	36.77	40.44
64 L.H., Daily Totals		$4487.80		$6144.70	$70.12	$96.01
Crew B-91B	Hr.	Daily	Hr.	Daily	Bare Costs	Incl. O&P
1 Laborer	$28.20	$225.60	$47.45	$379.60	$32.92	$54.90
1 Equipment Oper. (med.)	37.65	301.20	62.35	498.80		
1 Road Sweeper, Vac. Assist.		994.40		1093.84	62.15	68.36
16 L.H., Daily Totals		$1521.20		$1972.24	$95.08	$123.27
Crew B-91C	Hr.	Daily	Hr.	Daily	Bare Costs	Incl. O&P
1 Laborer	$28.20	$225.60	$47.45	$379.60	$28.52	$47.75
1 Truck Driver (light)	28.85	230.80	48.05	384.40		
1 Catch Basin Cleaning Truck		604.00		664.40	37.75	41.52
16 L.H., Daily Totals		$1060.40		$1428.40	$66.28	$89.28
Crew B-91D	Hr.	Daily	Hr.	Daily	Bare Costs	Incl. O&P
1 Labor Foreman (outside)	$30.20	$241.60	$50.85	$406.80	$32.21	$53.74
5 Laborers	28.20	1128.00	47.45	1898.00		
5 Equip. Oper. (medium)	37.65	1506.00	62.35	2494.00		
2 Truck Drivers (heavy)	29.65	474.40	49.40	790.40		
1 Aggreg. Spreader, S.P.		841.00		925.10		
2 Truck Tractor, 6x4, 380 H.P.		1225.60		1348.16		
2 Dist. Tanker, 3000 Gallon		616.40		678.04		
2 Pavement Brush, Towed		163.20		179.52		
2 Roller, Pneum. Whl., 12 Ton		698.00		767.80	34.08	37.49
104 L.H., Daily Totals		$6894.20		$9487.82	$66.29	$91.23
Crew B-92	Hr.	Daily	Hr.	Daily	Bare Costs	Incl. O&P
1 Labor Foreman (outside)	$30.20	$241.60	$50.85	$406.80	$28.70	$48.30
3 Laborers	28.20	676.80	47.45	1138.80		
1 Crack Cleaner, 25 H.P.		64.80		71.28		
1 Air Compressor, 60 cfm		137.40		151.14		
1 Tar Kettle, T.M.		104.60		115.06		
1 Flatbed Truck, Gas, 3 Ton		333.00		366.30	19.99	21.99
32 L.H., Daily Totals		$1558.20		$2249.38	$48.69	$70.29
Crew B-93	Hr.	Daily	Hr.	Daily	Bare Costs	Incl. O&P
1 Equip. Oper. (medium)	$37.65	$301.20	$62.35	$498.80	$37.65	$62.35
1 Feller Buncher, 100 H.P.		729.00		801.90	91.13	100.24
8 L.H., Daily Totals		$1030.20		$1300.70	$128.78	$162.59
Crew B-94A	Hr.	Daily	Hr.	Daily	Bare Costs	Incl. O&P
1 Laborer	$28.20	$225.60	$47.45	$379.60	$28.20	$47.45
1 Diaphragm Water Pump, 2"		72.00		79.20		
1 -20' Suction Hose, 2"		1.95		2.15		
2 -50' Discharge Hoses, 2"		1.80		1.98	9.47	10.42
8 L.H., Daily Totals		$301.35		$462.93	$37.67	$57.87

Crew No.	Bare Costs		Incl. Subs O&P		Cost Per Labor-Hour	
	Hr.	Daily	Hr.	Daily	Bare Costs	Incl. O&P
Crew B-94B	Hr.	Daily	Hr.	Daily	Bare Costs	Incl. O&P
1 Laborer	$28.20	$225.60	$47.45	$379.60	$28.20	$47.45
1 Diaphragm Water Pump, 4"		115.80		127.38		
1 -20' Suction Hose, 4"		3.25		3.58		
2 -50' Discharge Hoses, 4"		4.70		5.17	15.47	17.02
8 L.H., Daily Totals		$349.35		$515.73	$43.67	$64.47
Crew B-94C	Hr.	Daily	Hr.	Daily	Bare Costs	Incl. O&P
1 Laborer	$28.20	$225.60	$47.45	$379.60	$28.20	$47.45
1 Centrifugal Water Pump, 3"		78.80		86.68		
1 -20' Suction Hose, 3"		2.85		3.13		
2 -50' Discharge Hoses, 3"		3.00		3.30	10.58	11.64
8 L.H., Daily Totals		$310.25		$472.71	$38.78	$59.09
Crew B-94D	Hr.	Daily	Hr.	Daily	Bare Costs	Incl. O&P
1 Laborer	$28.20	$225.60	$47.45	$379.60	$28.20	$47.45
1 Centr. Water Pump, 6"		340.80		374.88		
1 -20' Suction Hose, 6"		11.50		12.65		
2 -50' Discharge Hoses, 6"		12.20		13.42	45.56	50.12
8 L.H., Daily Totals		$590.10		$780.55	$73.76	$97.57
Crew C-1	Hr.	Daily	Hr.	Daily	Bare Costs	Incl. O&P
2 Carpenters	$35.75	$572.00	$60.15	$962.40	$31.65	$53.30
1 Carpenter Helper	26.90	215.20	45.45	363.60		
1 Laborer	28.20	225.60	47.45	379.60		
32 L.H., Daily Totals		$1012.80		$1705.60	$31.65	$53.30
Crew C-2	Hr.	Daily	Hr.	Daily	Bare Costs	Incl. O&P
1 Carpenter Foreman (outside)	$37.75	$302.00	$63.55	$508.40	$31.88	$53.70
2 Carpenters	35.75	572.00	60.15	962.40		
2 Carpenter Helpers	26.90	430.40	45.45	727.20		
1 Laborer	28.20	225.60	47.45	379.60		
48 L.H., Daily Totals		$1530.00		$2577.60	$31.88	$53.70
Crew C-2A	Hr.	Daily	Hr.	Daily	Bare Costs	Incl. O&P
1 Carpenter Foreman (outside)	$37.75	$302.00	$63.55	$508.40	$34.59	$57.84
3 Carpenters	35.75	858.00	60.15	1443.60		
1 Cement Finisher	34.35	274.80	55.60	444.80		
1 Laborer	28.20	225.60	47.45	379.60		
48 L.H., Daily Totals		$1660.40		$2776.40	$34.59	$57.84
Crew C-3	Hr.	Daily	Hr.	Daily	Bare Costs	Incl. O&P
1 Rodman Foreman (outside)	$40.00	$320.00	$68.45	$547.60	$34.36	$58.23
3 Rodmen (reinf.)	38.00	912.00	65.00	1560.00		
1 Equip. Oper. (light)	36.25	290.00	60.05	480.40		
3 Laborers	28.20	676.80	47.45	1138.80		
3 Stressing Equipment		30.60		33.66		
.5 Grouting Equipment		82.10		90.31	1.76	1.94
64 L.H., Daily Totals		$2311.50		$3850.77	$36.12	$60.17
Crew C-4	Hr.	Daily	Hr.	Daily	Bare Costs	Incl. O&P
1 Rodman Foreman (outside)	$40.00	$320.00	$68.45	$547.60	$36.05	$61.48
2 Rodmen (reinf.)	38.00	608.00	65.00	1040.00		
1 Building Laborer	28.20	225.60	47.45	379.60		
3 Stressing Equipment		30.60		33.66	0.96	1.05
32 L.H., Daily Totals		$1184.20		$2000.86	$37.01	$62.53
Crew C-4A	Hr.	Daily	Hr.	Daily	Bare Costs	Incl. O&P
2 Rodmen (reinf.)	$38.00	$608.00	$65.00	$1040.00	$38.00	$65.00
4 Stressing Equipment		40.80		44.88	2.55	2.81
16 L.H., Daily Totals		$648.80		$1084.88	$40.55	$67.81

Crew No.	Bare Costs Hr.	Daily	Incl. Subs O&P Hr.	Daily	Cost Per Labor-Hour Bare Costs	Incl. O&P
Crew C-5	Hr.	Daily	Hr.	Daily	Bare Costs	Incl. O&P
1 Rodman Foreman (outside)	$40.00	$320.00	$68.45	$547.60	$35.18	$59.58
2 Rodmen (reinf.)	38.00	608.00	65.00	1040.00		
1 Equip. Oper. (crane)	38.70	309.60	64.10	512.80		
2 Building Laborers	28.20	451.20	47.45	759.20		
1 Hyd. Crane, 25 Ton		745.80		820.38	15.54	17.09
48 L.H., Daily Totals		$2434.60		$3679.98	$50.72	$76.67

Crew C-6	Hr.	Daily	Hr.	Daily	Bare Costs	Incl. O&P
1 Labor Foreman (outside)	$30.20	$241.60	$50.85	$406.80	$29.56	$49.38
4 Laborers	28.20	902.40	47.45	1518.40		
1 Cement Finisher	34.35	274.80	55.60	444.80		
2 Gas Engine Vibrators		66.00		72.60	1.38	1.51
48 L.H., Daily Totals		$1484.80		$2442.60	$30.93	$50.89

Crew C-7	Hr.	Daily	Hr.	Daily	Bare Costs	Incl. O&P
1 Labor Foreman (outside)	$30.20	$241.60	$50.85	$406.80	$30.75	$51.29
5 Laborers	28.20	1128.00	47.45	1898.00		
1 Cement Finisher	34.35	274.80	55.60	444.80		
1 Equip. Oper. (medium)	37.65	301.20	62.35	498.80		
1 Equip. Oper. (oiler)	33.55	268.40	55.55	444.40		
2 Gas Engine Vibrators		66.00		72.60		
1 Concrete Bucket, 1 C.Y.		23.00		25.30		
1 Hyd. Crane, 55 Ton		1137.00		1250.70	17.03	18.73
72 L.H., Daily Totals		$3440.00		$5041.40	$47.78	$70.02

Crew C-8	Hr.	Daily	Hr.	Daily	Bare Costs	Incl. O&P
1 Labor Foreman (outside)	$30.20	$241.60	$50.85	$406.80	$31.59	$52.39
3 Laborers	28.20	676.80	47.45	1138.80		
2 Cement Finishers	34.35	549.60	55.60	889.60		
1 Equip. Oper. (medium)	37.65	301.20	62.35	498.80		
1 Concrete Pump (Small)		710.40		781.44	12.69	13.95
56 L.H., Daily Totals		$2479.60		$3715.44	$44.28	$66.35

Crew C-8A	Hr.	Daily	Hr.	Daily	Bare Costs	Incl. O&P
1 Labor Foreman (outside)	$30.20	$241.60	$50.85	$406.80	$30.58	$50.73
3 Laborers	28.20	676.80	47.45	1138.80		
2 Cement Finishers	34.35	549.60	55.60	889.60		
48 L.H., Daily Totals		$1468.00		$2435.20	$30.58	$50.73

Crew C-8B	Hr.	Daily	Hr.	Daily	Bare Costs	Incl. O&P
1 Labor Foreman (outside)	$30.20	$241.60	$50.85	$406.80	$30.49	$51.11
3 Laborers	28.20	676.80	47.45	1138.80		
1 Equip. Oper. (medium)	37.65	301.20	62.35	498.80		
1 Vibrating Power Screed		63.25		69.58		
1 Roller, Vibratory, 25 Ton		692.80		762.08		
1 Dozer, 200 H.P.		1325.00		1457.50	52.03	57.23
40 L.H., Daily Totals		$3300.65		$4333.56	$82.52	$108.34

Crew C-8C	Hr.	Daily	Hr.	Daily	Bare Costs	Incl. O&P
1 Labor Foreman (outside)	$30.20	$241.60	$50.85	$406.80	$31.13	$51.86
3 Laborers	28.20	676.80	47.45	1138.80		
1 Cement Finisher	34.35	274.80	55.60	444.80		
1 Equip. Oper. (medium)	37.65	301.20	62.35	498.80		
1 Shotcrete Rig, 12 C.Y./hr		252.80		278.08		
1 Air Compressor, 160 cfm		157.40		173.14		
4 -50' Air Hoses, 1"		16.40		18.04		
4 -50' Air Hoses, 2"		31.00		34.10	9.53	10.49
48 L.H., Daily Totals		$1952.00		$2992.56	$40.67	$62.34

Crew C-8D	Hr.	Daily	Hr.	Daily	Bare Costs	Incl. O&P
1 Labor Foreman (outside)	$30.20	$241.60	$50.85	$406.80	$32.25	$53.49
1 Laborer	28.20	225.60	47.45	379.60		
1 Cement Finisher	34.35	274.80	55.60	444.80		
1 Equipment Oper. (light)	36.25	290.00	60.05	480.40		
1 Air Compressor, 250 cfm		202.40		222.64		
2 -50' Air Hoses, 1"		8.20		9.02	6.58	7.24
32 L.H., Daily Totals		$1242.60		$1943.26	$38.83	$60.73

Crew C-8E	Hr.	Daily	Hr.	Daily	Bare Costs	Incl. O&P
1 Labor Foreman (outside)	$30.20	$241.60	$50.85	$406.80	$30.90	$51.48
3 Laborers	28.20	676.80	47.45	1138.80		
1 Cement Finisher	34.35	274.80	55.60	444.80		
1 Equipment Oper. (light)	36.25	290.00	60.05	480.40		
1 Shotcrete Rig, 35 C.Y./hr		284.40		312.84		
1 Air Compressor, 250 cfm		202.40		222.64		
4 -50' Air Hoses, 1"		16.40		18.04		
4 -50' Air Hoses, 2"		31.00		34.10	11.13	12.24
48 L.H., Daily Totals		$2017.40		$3058.42	$42.03	$63.72

Crew C-10	Hr.	Daily	Hr.	Daily	Bare Costs	Incl. O&P
1 Laborer	$28.20	$225.60	$47.45	$379.60	$32.30	$52.88
2 Cement Finishers	34.35	549.60	55.60	889.60		
24 L.H., Daily Totals		$775.20		$1269.20	$32.30	$52.88

Crew C-10B	Hr.	Daily	Hr.	Daily	Bare Costs	Incl. O&P
3 Laborers	$28.20	$676.80	$47.45	$1138.80	$30.66	$50.71
2 Cement Finishers	34.35	549.60	55.60	889.60		
1 Concrete Mixer, 10 C.F.		176.80		194.48		
2 Trowels, 48" Walk-Behind		107.20		117.92	7.10	7.81
40 L.H., Daily Totals		$1510.40		$2340.80	$37.76	$58.52

Crew C-10C	Hr.	Daily	Hr.	Daily	Bare Costs	Incl. O&P
1 Laborer	$28.20	$225.60	$47.45	$379.60	$32.30	$52.88
2 Cement Finishers	34.35	549.60	55.60	889.60		
1 Trowel, 48" Walk-Behind		53.60		58.96	2.23	2.46
24 L.H., Daily Totals		$828.80		$1328.16	$34.53	$55.34

Crew C-10D	Hr.	Daily	Hr.	Daily	Bare Costs	Incl. O&P
1 Laborer	$28.20	$225.60	$47.45	$379.60	$32.30	$52.88
2 Cement Finishers	34.35	549.60	55.60	889.60		
1 Vibrating Power Screed		63.25		69.58		
1 Trowel, 48" Walk-Behind		53.60		58.96	4.87	5.36
24 L.H., Daily Totals		$892.05		$1397.73	$37.17	$58.24

Crew C-10E	Hr.	Daily	Hr.	Daily	Bare Costs	Incl. O&P
1 Laborer	$28.20	$225.60	$47.45	$379.60	$32.30	$52.88
2 Cement Finishers	34.35	549.60	55.60	889.60		
1 Vibrating Power Screed		63.25		69.58		
1 Cement Trowel, 96" Ride-On		197.40		217.14	10.86	11.95
24 L.H., Daily Totals		$1035.85		$1555.92	$43.16	$64.83

Crew C-10F	Hr.	Daily	Hr.	Daily	Bare Costs	Incl. O&P
1 Laborer	$28.20	$225.60	$47.45	$379.60	$32.30	$52.88
2 Cement Finishers	34.35	549.60	55.60	889.60		
1 Aerial Lift Truck, 60' Boom		456.00		501.60	19.00	20.90
24 L.H., Daily Totals		$1231.20		$1770.80	$51.30	$73.78

Crew C-11

Crew No.	Bare Costs Hr.	Bare Costs Daily	Incl. Subs O&P Hr.	Incl. Subs O&P Daily	Cost Per Labor-Hour Bare Costs	Cost Per Labor-Hour Incl. O&P
1 Skilled Worker Foreman	$38.30	$306.40	$64.70	$517.60	$36.93	$62.19
5 Skilled Workers	36.30	1452.00	61.30	2452.00		
1 Equip. Oper. (crane)	38.70	309.60	64.10	512.80		
1 Lattice Boom Crane, 150 Ton		1838.00		2021.80	32.82	36.10
56 L.H., Daily Totals		$3906.00		$5504.20	$69.75	$98.29

Crew C-12

Crew No.	Bare Costs Hr.	Bare Costs Daily	Incl. Subs O&P Hr.	Incl. Subs O&P Daily	Cost Per Labor-Hour Bare Costs	Cost Per Labor-Hour Incl. O&P
1 Carpenter Foreman (outside)	$37.75	$302.00	$63.55	$508.40	$35.32	$59.26
3 Carpenters	35.75	858.00	60.15	1443.60		
1 Laborer	28.20	225.60	47.45	379.60		
1 Equip. Oper. (crane)	38.70	309.60	64.10	512.80		
1 Hyd. Crane, 12 Ton		663.00		729.30	13.81	15.19
48 L.H., Daily Totals		$2358.20		$3573.70	$49.13	$74.45

Crew C-13

Crew No.	Bare Costs Hr.	Bare Costs Daily	Incl. Subs O&P Hr.	Incl. Subs O&P Daily	Cost Per Labor-Hour Bare Costs	Cost Per Labor-Hour Incl. O&P
2 Struc. Steel Workers	$38.35	$613.60	$73.05	$1168.80	$37.48	$68.75
1 Carpenter	35.75	286.00	60.15	481.20		
1 Welder, Gas Engine, 300 amp		142.00		156.20	5.92	6.51
24 L.H., Daily Totals		$1041.60		$1806.20	$43.40	$75.26

Crew C-14

Crew No.	Bare Costs Hr.	Bare Costs Daily	Incl. Subs O&P Hr.	Incl. Subs O&P Daily	Cost Per Labor-Hour Bare Costs	Cost Per Labor-Hour Incl. O&P
1 Carpenter Foreman (outside)	$37.75	$302.00	$63.55	$508.40	$32.28	$54.17
3 Carpenters	35.75	858.00	60.15	1443.60		
2 Carpenter Helpers	26.90	430.40	45.45	727.20		
4 Laborers	28.20	902.40	47.45	1518.40		
2 Rodmen (reinf.)	38.00	608.00	65.00	1040.00		
2 Rodman Helpers	26.90	430.40	45.45	727.20		
2 Cement Finishers	34.35	549.60	55.60	889.60		
1 Equip. Oper. (crane)	38.70	309.60	64.10	512.80		
1 Hyd. Crane, 80 Ton		1652.00		1817.20	12.15	13.36
136 L.H., Daily Totals		$6042.40		$9184.40	$44.43	$67.53

Crew C-14A

Crew No.	Bare Costs Hr.	Bare Costs Daily	Incl. Subs O&P Hr.	Incl. Subs O&P Daily	Cost Per Labor-Hour Bare Costs	Cost Per Labor-Hour Incl. O&P
1 Carpenter Foreman (outside)	$37.75	$302.00	$63.55	$508.40	$35.61	$59.95
16 Carpenters	35.75	4576.00	60.15	7699.20		
4 Rodmen (reinf.)	38.00	1216.00	65.00	2080.00		
2 Laborers	28.20	451.20	47.45	759.20		
1 Cement Finisher	34.35	274.80	55.60	444.80		
1 Equip. Oper. (medium)	37.65	301.20	62.35	498.80		
1 Gas Engine Vibrator		33.00		36.30		
1 Concrete Pump (Small)		710.40		781.44	3.72	4.09
200 L.H., Daily Totals		$7864.60		$12808.14	$39.32	$64.04

Crew C-14B

Crew No.	Bare Costs Hr.	Bare Costs Daily	Incl. Subs O&P Hr.	Incl. Subs O&P Daily	Cost Per Labor-Hour Bare Costs	Cost Per Labor-Hour Incl. O&P
1 Carpenter Foreman (outside)	$37.75	$302.00	$63.55	$508.40	$35.56	$59.78
16 Carpenters	35.75	4576.00	60.15	7699.20		
4 Rodmen (reinf.)	38.00	1216.00	65.00	2080.00		
2 Laborers	28.20	451.20	47.45	759.20		
2 Cement Finishers	34.35	549.60	55.60	889.60		
1 Equip. Oper. (medium)	37.65	301.20	62.35	498.80		
1 Gas Engine Vibrator		33.00		36.30		
1 Concrete Pump (Small)		710.40		781.44	3.57	3.93
208 L.H., Daily Totals		$8139.40		$13252.94	$39.13	$63.72

Crew C-14C

Crew No.	Bare Costs Hr.	Bare Costs Daily	Incl. Subs O&P Hr.	Incl. Subs O&P Daily	Cost Per Labor-Hour Bare Costs	Cost Per Labor-Hour Incl. O&P
1 Carpenter Foreman (outside)	$37.75	$302.00	$63.55	$508.40	$33.96	$57.13
6 Carpenters	35.75	1716.00	60.15	2887.20		
2 Rodmen (reinf.)	38.00	608.00	65.00	1040.00		
4 Laborers	28.20	902.40	47.45	1518.40		
1 Cement Finisher	34.35	274.80	55.60	444.80		
1 Gas Engine Vibrator		33.00		36.30	0.29	0.32
112 L.H., Daily Totals		$3836.20		$6435.10	$34.25	$57.46

Crew C-14D

Crew No.	Bare Costs Hr.	Bare Costs Daily	Incl. Subs O&P Hr.	Incl. Subs O&P Daily	Cost Per Labor-Hour Bare Costs	Cost Per Labor-Hour Incl. O&P
1 Carpenter Foreman (outside)	$37.75	$302.00	$63.55	$508.40	$35.43	$59.56
18 Carpenters	35.75	5148.00	60.15	8661.60		
2 Rodmen (reinf.)	38.00	608.00	65.00	1040.00		
2 Laborers	28.20	451.20	47.45	759.20		
1 Cement Finisher	34.35	274.80	55.60	444.80		
1 Equip. Oper. (medium)	37.65	301.20	62.35	498.80		
1 Gas Engine Vibrator		33.00		36.30		
1 Concrete Pump (Small)		710.40		781.44	3.72	4.09
200 L.H., Daily Totals		$7828.60		$12730.54	$39.14	$63.65

Crew C-14E

Crew No.	Bare Costs Hr.	Bare Costs Daily	Incl. Subs O&P Hr.	Incl. Subs O&P Daily	Cost Per Labor-Hour Bare Costs	Cost Per Labor-Hour Incl. O&P
1 Carpenter Foreman (outside)	$37.75	$302.00	$63.55	$508.40	$34.56	$58.35
2 Carpenters	35.75	572.00	60.15	962.40		
4 Rodmen (reinf.)	38.00	1216.00	65.00	2080.00		
3 Laborers	28.20	676.80	47.45	1138.80		
1 Cement Finisher	34.35	274.80	55.60	444.80		
1 Gas Engine Vibrator		33.00		36.30	0.38	0.41
88 L.H., Daily Totals		$3074.60		$5170.70	$34.94	$58.76

Crew C-14F

Crew No.	Bare Costs Hr.	Bare Costs Daily	Incl. Subs O&P Hr.	Incl. Subs O&P Daily	Cost Per Labor-Hour Bare Costs	Cost Per Labor-Hour Incl. O&P
1 Labor Foreman (outside)	$30.20	$241.60	$50.85	$406.80	$32.52	$53.26
2 Laborers	28.20	451.20	47.45	759.20		
6 Cement Finishers	34.35	1648.80	55.60	2668.80		
1 Gas Engine Vibrator		33.00		36.30	0.46	0.50
72 L.H., Daily Totals		$2374.60		$3871.10	$32.98	$53.77

Crew C-14G

Crew No.	Bare Costs Hr.	Bare Costs Daily	Incl. Subs O&P Hr.	Incl. Subs O&P Daily	Cost Per Labor-Hour Bare Costs	Cost Per Labor-Hour Incl. O&P
1 Labor Foreman (outside)	$30.20	$241.60	$50.85	$406.80	$32.00	$52.59
2 Laborers	28.20	451.20	47.45	759.20		
4 Cement Finishers	34.35	1099.20	55.60	1779.20		
1 Gas Engine Vibrator		33.00		36.30	0.59	0.65
56 L.H., Daily Totals		$1825.00		$2981.50	$32.59	$53.24

Crew C-14H

Crew No.	Bare Costs Hr.	Bare Costs Daily	Incl. Subs O&P Hr.	Incl. Subs O&P Daily	Cost Per Labor-Hour Bare Costs	Cost Per Labor-Hour Incl. O&P
1 Carpenter Foreman (outside)	$37.75	$302.00	$63.55	$508.40	$34.97	$58.65
2 Carpenters	35.75	572.00	60.15	962.40		
1 Rodman (reinf.)	38.00	304.00	65.00	520.00		
1 Laborer	28.20	225.60	47.45	379.60		
1 Cement Finisher	34.35	274.80	55.60	444.80		
1 Gas Engine Vibrator		33.00		36.30	0.69	0.76
48 L.H., Daily Totals		$1711.40		$2851.50	$35.65	$59.41

Crew C-14L

Crew No.	Bare Costs Hr.	Bare Costs Daily	Incl. Subs O&P Hr.	Incl. Subs O&P Daily	Cost Per Labor-Hour Bare Costs	Cost Per Labor-Hour Incl. O&P
1 Carpenter Foreman (outside)	$37.75	$302.00	$63.55	$508.40	$33.28	$55.82
6 Carpenters	35.75	1716.00	60.15	2887.20		
4 Laborers	28.20	902.40	47.45	1518.40		
1 Cement Finisher	34.35	274.80	55.60	444.80		
1 Gas Engine Vibrator		33.00		36.30	0.34	0.38
96 L.H., Daily Totals		$3228.20		$5395.10	$33.63	$56.20

Crew No.	Bare Costs Hr.	Daily	Incl. Subs O&P Hr.	Daily	Cost Per Labor-Hour Bare Costs	Incl. O&P
Crew C-14M	Hr.	Daily	Hr.	Daily	Bare Costs	Incl. O&P
1 Carpenter Foreman (outside)	$37.75	$302.00	$63.55	$508.40	$34.46	$57.71
2 Carpenters	35.75	572.00	60.15	962.40		
1 Rodman (reinf.)	38.00	304.00	65.00	520.00		
2 Laborers	28.20	451.20	47.45	759.20		
1 Cement Finisher	34.35	274.80	55.60	444.80		
1 Equip. Oper. (medium)	37.65	301.20	62.35	498.80		
1 Gas Engine Vibrator		33.00		36.30		
1 Concrete Pump (Small)		710.40		781.44	11.62	12.78
64 L.H., Daily Totals		$2948.60		$4511.34	$46.07	$70.49
Crew C-15	Hr.	Daily	Hr.	Daily	Bare Costs	Incl. O&P
1 Carpenter Foreman (outside)	$37.75	$302.00	$63.55	$508.40	$33.39	$55.82
2 Carpenters	35.75	572.00	60.15	962.40		
3 Laborers	28.20	676.80	47.45	1138.80		
2 Cement Finishers	34.35	549.60	55.60	889.60		
1 Rodman (reinf.)	38.00	304.00	65.00	520.00		
72 L.H., Daily Totals		$2404.40		$4019.20	$33.39	$55.82
Crew C-16	Hr.	Daily	Hr.	Daily	Bare Costs	Incl. O&P
1 Labor Foreman (outside)	$30.20	$241.60	$50.85	$406.80	$31.59	$52.39
3 Laborers	28.20	676.80	47.45	1138.80		
2 Cement Finishers	34.35	549.60	55.60	889.60		
1 Equip. Oper. (medium)	37.65	301.20	62.35	498.80		
1 Gunite Pump Rig		370.40		407.44		
2 -50' Air Hoses, 3/4"		6.50		7.15		
2 -50' Air Hoses, 2"		15.50		17.05	7.01	7.71
56 L.H., Daily Totals		$2161.60		$3365.64	$38.60	$60.10
Crew C-16A	Hr.	Daily	Hr.	Daily	Bare Costs	Incl. O&P
1 Laborer	$28.20	$225.60	$47.45	$379.60	$33.64	$55.25
2 Cement Finishers	34.35	549.60	55.60	889.60		
1 Equip. Oper. (medium)	37.65	301.20	62.35	498.80		
1 Gunite Pump Rig		370.40		407.44		
2 -50' Air Hoses, 3/4"		6.50		7.15		
2 -50' Air Hoses, 2"		15.50		17.05		
1 Aerial Lift Truck, 60' Boom		456.00		501.60	26.51	29.16
32 L.H., Daily Totals		$1924.80		$2701.24	$60.15	$84.41
Crew C-17	Hr.	Daily	Hr.	Daily	Bare Costs	Incl. O&P
2 Skilled Worker Foremen (out)	$38.30	$612.80	$64.70	$1035.20	$36.70	$61.98
8 Skilled Workers	36.30	2323.20	61.30	3923.20		
80 L.H., Daily Totals		$2936.00		$4958.40	$36.70	$61.98
Crew C-17A	Hr.	Daily	Hr.	Daily	Bare Costs	Incl. O&P
2 Skilled Worker Foremen (out)	$38.30	$612.80	$64.70	$1035.20	$36.72	$62.01
8 Skilled Workers	36.30	2323.20	61.30	3923.20		
.125 Equip. Oper. (crane)	38.70	38.70	64.10	64.10		
.125 Hyd. Crane, 80 Ton		206.50		227.15	2.55	2.80
81 L.H., Daily Totals		$3181.20		$5249.65	$39.27	$64.81
Crew C-17B	Hr.	Daily	Hr.	Daily	Bare Costs	Incl. O&P
2 Skilled Worker Foremen (out)	$38.30	$612.80	$64.70	$1035.20	$36.75	$62.03
8 Skilled Workers	36.30	2323.20	61.30	3923.20		
.25 Equip. Oper. (crane)	38.70	77.40	64.10	128.20		
.25 Hyd. Crane, 80 Ton		413.00		454.30		
.25 Trowel, 48" Walk-Behind		13.40		14.74	5.20	5.72
82 L.H., Daily Totals		$3439.80		$5555.64	$41.95	$67.75

Crew No.	Bare Costs Hr.	Daily	Incl. Subs O&P Hr.	Daily	Cost Per Labor-Hour Bare Costs	Incl. O&P
Crew C-17C	Hr.	Daily	Hr.	Daily	Bare Costs	Incl. O&P
2 Skilled Worker Foremen (out)	$38.30	$612.80	$64.70	$1035.20	$36.77	$62.06
8 Skilled Workers	36.30	2323.20	61.30	3923.20		
.375 Equip. Oper. (crane)	38.70	116.10	64.10	192.30		
.375 Hyd. Crane, 80 Ton		619.50		681.45	7.46	8.21
83 L.H., Daily Totals		$3671.60		$5832.15	$44.24	$70.27
Crew C-17D	Hr.	Daily	Hr.	Daily	Bare Costs	Incl. O&P
2 Skilled Worker Foremen (out)	$38.30	$612.80	$64.70	$1035.20	$36.80	$62.08
8 Skilled Workers	36.30	2323.20	61.30	3923.20		
.5 Equip. Oper. (crane)	38.70	154.80	64.10	256.40		
.5 Hyd. Crane, 80 Ton		826.00		908.60	9.83	10.82
84 L.H., Daily Totals		$3916.80		$6123.40	$46.63	$72.90
Crew C-17E	Hr.	Daily	Hr.	Daily	Bare Costs	Incl. O&P
2 Skilled Worker Foremen (out)	$38.30	$612.80	$64.70	$1035.20	$36.70	$61.98
8 Skilled Workers	36.30	2323.20	61.30	3923.20		
1 Hyd. Jack with Rods		94.55		104.01	1.18	1.30
80 L.H., Daily Totals		$3030.55		$5062.40	$37.88	$63.28
Crew C-18	Hr.	Daily	Hr.	Daily	Bare Costs	Incl. O&P
.125 Labor Foreman (outside)	$30.20	$30.20	$50.85	$50.85	$28.42	$47.83
1 Laborer	28.20	225.60	47.45	379.60		
1 Concrete Cart, 10 C.F.		60.20		66.22	6.69	7.36
9 L.H., Daily Totals		$316.00		$496.67	$35.11	$55.19
Crew C-19	Hr.	Daily	Hr.	Daily	Bare Costs	Incl. O&P
.125 Labor Foreman (outside)	$30.20	$30.20	$50.85	$50.85	$28.42	$47.83
1 Laborer	28.20	225.60	47.45	379.60		
1 Concrete Cart, 18 C.F.		101.20		111.32	11.24	12.37
9 L.H., Daily Totals		$357.00		$541.77	$39.67	$60.20
Crew C-20	Hr.	Daily	Hr.	Daily	Bare Costs	Incl. O&P
1 Labor Foreman (outside)	$30.20	$241.60	$50.85	$406.80	$30.40	$50.76
5 Laborers	28.20	1128.00	47.45	1898.00		
1 Cement Finisher	34.35	274.80	55.60	444.80		
1 Equip. Oper. (medium)	37.65	301.20	62.35	498.80		
2 Gas Engine Vibrators		66.00		72.60		
1 Concrete Pump (Small)		710.40		781.44	12.13	13.34
64 L.H., Daily Totals		$2722.00		$4102.44	$42.53	$64.10
Crew C-21	Hr.	Daily	Hr.	Daily	Bare Costs	Incl. O&P
1 Labor Foreman (outside)	$30.20	$241.60	$50.85	$406.80	$30.40	$50.76
5 Laborers	28.20	1128.00	47.45	1898.00		
1 Cement Finisher	34.35	274.80	55.60	444.80		
1 Equip. Oper. (medium)	37.65	301.20	62.35	498.80		
2 Gas Engine Vibrators		66.00		72.60		
1 Concrete Conveyer		205.40		225.94	4.24	4.66
64 L.H., Daily Totals		$2217.00		$3546.94	$34.64	$55.42
Crew C-22	Hr.	Daily	Hr.	Daily	Bare Costs	Incl. O&P
1 Rodman Foreman (outside)	$40.00	$320.00	$68.45	$547.60	$38.29	$65.41
4 Rodmen (reinf.)	38.00	1216.00	65.00	2080.00		
.125 Equip. Oper. (crane)	38.70	38.70	64.10	64.10		
.125 Equip. Oper. (oiler)	33.55	33.55	55.55	55.55		
.125 Hyd. Crane, 25 Ton		93.22		102.55	2.22	2.44
42 L.H., Daily Totals		$1701.47		$2849.80	$40.51	$67.85

Crew No.	Bare Costs Hr.	Daily	Incl. Subs O&P Hr.	Daily	Cost Per Labor-Hour Bare Costs	Incl. O&P
Crew C-23	**Hr.**	**Daily**	**Hr.**	**Daily**	**Bare Costs**	**Incl. O&P**
2 Skilled Worker Foremen (out)	$38.30	$612.80	$64.70	$1035.20	$36.66	$61.69
6 Skilled Workers	36.30	1742.40	61.30	2942.40		
1 Equip. Oper. (crane)	38.70	309.60	64.10	512.80		
1 Equip. Oper. (oiler)	33.55	268.40	55.55	444.40		
1 Lattice Boom Crane, 90 Ton		1529.00		1681.90	19.11	21.02
80 L.H., Daily Totals		$4462.20		$6616.70	$55.78	$82.71
Crew C-24	**Hr.**	**Daily**	**Hr.**	**Daily**	**Bare Costs**	**Incl. O&P**
2 Skilled Worker Foremen (out)	$38.30	$612.80	$64.70	$1035.20	$36.66	$61.69
6 Skilled Workers	36.30	1742.40	61.30	2942.40		
1 Equip. Oper. (crane)	38.70	309.60	64.10	512.80		
1 Equip. Oper. (oiler)	33.55	268.40	55.55	444.40		
1 Lattice Boom Crane, 150 Ton		1838.00		2021.80	22.98	25.27
80 L.H., Daily Totals		$4771.20		$6956.60	$59.64	$86.96
Crew C-25	**Hr.**	**Daily**	**Hr.**	**Daily**	**Bare Costs**	**Incl. O&P**
2 Rodmen (reinf.)	$38.00	$608.00	$65.00	$1040.00	$30.23	$53.17
2 Rodmen Helpers	22.45	359.20	41.35	661.60		
32 L.H., Daily Totals		$967.20		$1701.60	$30.23	$53.17
Crew C-27	**Hr.**	**Daily**	**Hr.**	**Daily**	**Bare Costs**	**Incl. O&P**
2 Cement Finishers	$34.35	$549.60	$55.60	$889.60	$34.35	$55.60
1 Concrete Saw		175.20		192.72	10.95	12.05
16 L.H., Daily Totals		$724.80		$1082.32	$45.30	$67.64
Crew C-28	**Hr.**	**Daily**	**Hr.**	**Daily**	**Bare Costs**	**Incl. O&P**
1 Cement Finisher	$34.35	$274.80	$55.60	$444.80	$34.35	$55.60
1 Portable Air Compressor, Gas		17.70		19.47	2.21	2.43
8 L.H., Daily Totals		$292.50		$464.27	$36.56	$58.03
Crew C-29	**Hr.**	**Daily**	**Hr.**	**Daily**	**Bare Costs**	**Incl. O&P**
1 Laborer	$28.20	$225.60	$47.45	$379.60	$28.20	$47.45
1 Pressure Washer		69.40		76.34	8.68	9.54
8 L.H., Daily Totals		$295.00		$455.94	$36.88	$56.99
Crew C-30	**Hr.**	**Daily**	**Hr.**	**Daily**	**Bare Costs**	**Incl. O&P**
1 Laborer	$28.20	$225.60	$47.45	$379.60	$28.20	$47.45
1 Concrete Mixer, 10 C.F.		176.80		194.48	22.10	24.31
8 L.H., Daily Totals		$402.40		$574.08	$50.30	$71.76
Crew C-31	**Hr.**	**Daily**	**Hr.**	**Daily**	**Bare Costs**	**Incl. O&P**
1 Cement Finisher	$34.35	$274.80	$55.60	$444.80	$34.35	$55.60
1 Grout Pump		370.40		407.44	46.30	50.93
8 L.H., Daily Totals		$645.20		$852.24	$80.65	$106.53
Crew C-32	**Hr.**	**Daily**	**Hr.**	**Daily**	**Bare Costs**	**Incl. O&P**
1 Cement Finisher	$34.35	$274.80	$55.60	$444.80	$31.27	$51.52
1 Laborer	28.20	225.60	47.45	379.60		
1 Crack Chaser Saw, Gas, 6 H.P.		30.80		33.88		
1 Vacuum Pick-Up System		60.75		66.83	5.72	6.29
16 L.H., Daily Totals		$591.95		$925.11	$37.00	$57.82
Crew D-1	**Hr.**	**Daily**	**Hr.**	**Daily**	**Bare Costs**	**Incl. O&P**
1 Bricklayer	$35.60	$284.80	$59.25	$474.00	$32.23	$53.63
1 Bricklayer Helper	28.85	230.80	48.00	384.00		
16 L.H., Daily Totals		$515.60		$858.00	$32.23	$53.63

Crew No.	Bare Costs Hr.	Daily	Incl. Subs O&P Hr.	Daily	Cost Per Labor-Hour Bare Costs	Incl. O&P
Crew D-2	**Hr.**	**Daily**	**Hr.**	**Daily**	**Bare Costs**	**Incl. O&P**
3 Bricklayers	$35.60	$854.40	$59.25	$1422.00	$32.90	$54.75
2 Bricklayer Helpers	28.85	461.60	48.00	768.00		
40 L.H., Daily Totals		$1316.00		$2190.00	$32.90	$54.75
Crew D-3	**Hr.**	**Daily**	**Hr.**	**Daily**	**Bare Costs**	**Incl. O&P**
3 Bricklayers	$35.60	$854.40	$59.25	$1422.00	$33.04	$55.01
2 Bricklayer Helpers	28.85	461.60	48.00	768.00		
.25 Carpenter	35.75	71.50	60.15	120.30		
42 L.H., Daily Totals		$1387.50		$2310.30	$33.04	$55.01
Crew D-4	**Hr.**	**Daily**	**Hr.**	**Daily**	**Bare Costs**	**Incl. O&P**
1 Bricklayer	$35.60	$284.80	$59.25	$474.00	$30.07	$50.14
3 Bricklayer Helpers	28.85	692.40	48.00	1152.00		
1 Building Laborer	28.20	225.60	47.45	379.60		
1 Grout Pump, 50 C.F./hr.		134.80		148.28	3.37	3.71
40 L.H., Daily Totals		$1337.60		$2153.88	$33.44	$53.85
Crew D-5	**Hr.**	**Daily**	**Hr.**	**Daily**	**Bare Costs**	**Incl. O&P**
1 Block Mason Helper	$28.85	$230.80	$48.00	$384.00	$28.85	$48.00
8 L.H., Daily Totals		$230.80		$384.00	$28.85	$48.00
Crew D-6	**Hr.**	**Daily**	**Hr.**	**Daily**	**Bare Costs**	**Incl. O&P**
3 Bricklayers	$35.60	$854.40	$59.25	$1422.00	$32.23	$53.63
3 Bricklayer Helpers	28.85	692.40	48.00	1152.00		
48 L.H., Daily Totals		$1546.80		$2574.00	$32.23	$53.63
Crew D-7	**Hr.**	**Daily**	**Hr.**	**Daily**	**Bare Costs**	**Incl. O&P**
1 Tile Layer	$32.75	$262.00	$52.85	$422.80	$29.35	$47.38
1 Tile Layer Helper	25.95	207.60	41.90	335.20		
16 L.H., Daily Totals		$469.60		$758.00	$29.35	$47.38
Crew D-8	**Hr.**	**Daily**	**Hr.**	**Daily**	**Bare Costs**	**Incl. O&P**
3 Bricklayers	$35.60	$854.40	$59.25	$1422.00	$32.90	$54.75
2 Bricklayer Helpers	28.85	461.60	48.00	768.00		
40 L.H., Daily Totals		$1316.00		$2190.00	$32.90	$54.75
Crew D-9	**Hr.**	**Daily**	**Hr.**	**Daily**	**Bare Costs**	**Incl. O&P**
3 Bricklayers	$35.60	$854.40	$59.25	$1422.00	$32.23	$53.63
3 Bricklayer Helpers	28.85	692.40	48.00	1152.00		
48 L.H., Daily Totals		$1546.80		$2574.00	$32.23	$53.63
Crew D-10	**Hr.**	**Daily**	**Hr.**	**Daily**	**Bare Costs**	**Incl. O&P**
1 Bricklayer Foreman (outside)	$37.60	$300.80	$62.55	$500.40	$35.19	$58.48
1 Bricklayer	35.60	284.80	59.25	474.00		
1 Bricklayer Helper	28.85	230.80	48.00	384.00		
1 Equip. Oper. (crane)	38.70	309.60	64.10	512.80		
1 S.P. Crane, 4x4, 12 Ton		481.20		529.32	15.04	16.54
32 L.H., Daily Totals		$1607.20		$2400.52	$50.23	$75.02
Crew D-11	**Hr.**	**Daily**	**Hr.**	**Daily**	**Bare Costs**	**Incl. O&P**
2 Bricklayers	$35.60	$569.60	$59.25	$948.00	$33.35	$55.50
1 Bricklayer Helper	28.85	230.80	48.00	384.00		
24 L.H., Daily Totals		$800.40		$1332.00	$33.35	$55.50
Crew D-12	**Hr.**	**Daily**	**Hr.**	**Daily**	**Bare Costs**	**Incl. O&P**
2 Bricklayers	$35.60	$569.60	$59.25	$948.00	$32.23	$53.63
2 Bricklayer Helpers	28.85	461.60	48.00	768.00		
32 L.H., Daily Totals		$1031.20		$1716.00	$32.23	$53.63

Crew No.	Bare Costs		Incl. Subs O&P		Cost Per Labor-Hour	
Crew D-13	Hr.	Daily	Hr.	Daily	Bare Costs	Incl. O&P
1 Bricklayer Foreman (outside)	$37.60	$300.80	$62.55	$500.40	$34.20	$56.86
2 Bricklayers	35.60	569.60	59.25	948.00		
2 Bricklayer Helpers	28.85	461.60	48.00	768.00		
1 Equip. Oper. (crane)	38.70	309.60	64.10	512.80		
1 S.P. Crane, 4x4, 12 Ton		481.20		529.32	10.03	11.03
48 L.H., Daily Totals		$2122.80		$3258.52	$44.23	$67.89
Crew E-1	Hr.	Daily	Hr.	Daily	Bare Costs	Incl. O&P
2 Struc. Steel Workers	$38.35	$613.60	$73.05	$1168.80	$38.35	$73.05
1 Welder, Gas Engine, 300 amp		142.00		156.20	8.88	9.76
16 L.H., Daily Totals		$755.60		$1325.00	$47.23	$82.81
Crew E-2	Hr.	Daily	Hr.	Daily	Bare Costs	Incl. O&P
1 Struc. Steel Foreman (outside)	$40.35	$322.80	$76.85	$614.80	$38.74	$72.19
4 Struc. Steel Workers	38.35	1227.20	73.05	2337.60		
1 Equip. Oper. (crane)	38.70	309.60	64.10	512.80		
1 Lattice Boom Crane, 90 Ton		1529.00		1681.90	31.85	35.04
48 L.H., Daily Totals		$3388.60		$5147.10	$70.60	$107.23
Crew E-3	Hr.	Daily	Hr.	Daily	Bare Costs	Incl. O&P
1 Struc. Steel Foreman (outside)	$40.35	$322.80	$76.85	$614.80	$39.02	$74.32
2 Struc. Steel Workers	38.35	613.60	73.05	1168.80		
1 Welder, Gas Engine, 300 amp		142.00		156.20	5.92	6.51
24 L.H., Daily Totals		$1078.40		$1939.80	$44.93	$80.83
Crew E-3A	Hr.	Daily	Hr.	Daily	Bare Costs	Incl. O&P
1 Struc. Steel Foreman (outside)	$40.35	$322.80	$76.85	$614.80	$39.02	$74.32
2 Struc. Steel Workers	38.35	613.60	73.05	1168.80		
1 Welder, Gas Engine, 300 amp		142.00		156.20		
1 Aerial Lift Truck, 40' Boom		325.00		357.50	19.46	21.40
24 L.H., Daily Totals		$1403.40		$2297.30	$58.48	$95.72
Crew E-4	Hr.	Daily	Hr.	Daily	Bare Costs	Incl. O&P
1 Struc. Steel Foreman (outside)	$40.35	$322.80	$76.85	$614.80	$38.85	$74.00
3 Struc. Steel Workers	38.35	920.40	73.05	1753.20		
1 Welder, Gas Engine, 300 amp		142.00		156.20	4.44	4.88
32 L.H., Daily Totals		$1385.20		$2524.20	$43.29	$78.88
Crew E-5	Hr.	Daily	Hr.	Daily	Bare Costs	Incl. O&P
1 Struc. Steel Foreman (outside)	$40.35	$322.80	$76.85	$614.80	$38.61	$72.48
7 Struc. Steel Workers	38.35	2147.60	73.05	4090.80		
1 Equip. Oper. (crane)	38.70	309.60	64.10	512.80		
1 Lattice Boom Crane, 90 Ton		1529.00		1681.90		
1 Welder, Gas Engine, 300 amp		142.00		156.20	23.21	25.53
72 L.H., Daily Totals		$4451.00		$7056.50	$61.82	$98.01
Crew E-6	Hr.	Daily	Hr.	Daily	Bare Costs	Incl. O&P
1 Struc. Steel Foreman (outside)	$40.35	$322.80	$76.85	$614.80	$38.37	$71.84
12 Struc. Steel Workers	38.35	3681.60	73.05	7012.80		
1 Equip. Oper. (crane)	38.70	309.60	64.10	512.80		
1 Equip. Oper. (light)	36.25	290.00	60.05	480.40		
1 Lattice Boom Crane, 90 Ton		1529.00		1681.90		
1 Welder, Gas Engine, 300 amp		142.00		156.20		
1 Air Compressor, 160 cfm		157.40		173.14		
2 Impact Wrenches		36.00		39.60	15.54	17.09
120 L.H., Daily Totals		$6468.40		$10671.64	$53.90	$88.93

Crew No.	Bare Costs		Incl. Subs O&P		Cost Per Labor-Hour	
Crew E-7	Hr.	Daily	Hr.	Daily	Bare Costs	Incl. O&P
1 Struc. Steel Foreman (outside)	$40.35	$322.80	$76.85	$614.80	$38.61	$72.48
7 Struc. Steel Workers	38.35	2147.60	73.05	4090.80		
1 Equip. Oper. (crane)	38.70	309.60	64.10	512.80		
1 Lattice Boom Crane, 90 Ton		1529.00		1681.90		
2 Welder, Gas Engine, 300 amp		284.00		312.40	25.18	27.70
72 L.H., Daily Totals		$4593.00		$7212.70	$63.79	$100.18
Crew E-8	Hr.	Daily	Hr.	Daily	Bare Costs	Incl. O&P
1 Struc. Steel Foreman (outside)	$40.35	$322.80	$76.85	$614.80	$38.56	$72.58
9 Struc. Steel Workers	38.35	2761.20	73.05	5259.60		
1 Equip. Oper. (crane)	38.70	309.60	64.10	512.80		
1 Lattice Boom Crane, 90 Ton		1529.00		1681.90		
4 Welder, Gas Engine, 300 amp		568.00		624.80	23.83	26.21
88 L.H., Daily Totals		$5490.60		$8693.90	$62.39	$98.79
Crew E-9	Hr.	Daily	Hr.	Daily	Bare Costs	Incl. O&P
2 Struc. Steel Foremen (outside)	$40.35	$645.60	$76.85	$1229.60	$38.32	$71.30
5 Struc. Steel Workers	38.35	1534.00	73.05	2922.00		
1 Welder Foreman (outside)	40.35	322.80	76.85	614.80		
5 Welders	38.35	1534.00	73.05	2922.00		
1 Equip. Oper. (crane)	38.70	309.60	64.10	512.80		
1 Equip. Oper. (oiler)	33.55	268.40	55.55	444.40		
1 Equip. Oper. (light)	36.25	290.00	60.05	480.40		
1 Lattice Boom Crane, 90 Ton		1529.00		1681.90		
5 Welder, Gas Engine, 300 amp		710.00		781.00	17.49	19.24
128 L.H., Daily Totals		$7143.40		$11588.90	$55.81	$90.54
Crew E-10	Hr.	Daily	Hr.	Daily	Bare Costs	Incl. O&P
1 Struc. Steel Foreman (outside)	$40.35	$322.80	$76.85	$614.80	$39.02	$74.32
2 Struc. Steel Workers	38.35	613.60	73.05	1168.80		
1 Welder, Gas Engine, 300 amp		142.00		156.20		
1 Flatbed Truck, Gas, 3 Ton		333.00		366.30	19.79	21.77
24 L.H., Daily Totals		$1411.40		$2306.10	$58.81	$96.09
Crew E-11	Hr.	Daily	Hr.	Daily	Bare Costs	Incl. O&P
2 Painters, Struc. Steel	$32.00	$512.00	$62.20	$995.20	$32.11	$57.98
1 Building Laborer	28.20	225.60	47.45	379.60		
1 Equip. Oper. (light)	36.25	290.00	60.05	480.40		
1 Air Compressor, 250 cfm		202.40		222.64		
1 Sandblaster, Portable, 3 C.F.		20.40		22.44		
1 Set Sand Blasting Accessories		13.85		15.23	7.40	8.13
32 L.H., Daily Totals		$1264.25		$2115.51	$39.51	$66.11
Crew E-11A	Hr.	Daily	Hr.	Daily	Bare Costs	Incl. O&P
2 Painters, Struc. Steel	$32.00	$512.00	$62.20	$995.20	$32.11	$57.98
1 Building Laborer	28.20	225.60	47.45	379.60		
1 Equip. Oper. (light)	36.25	290.00	60.05	480.40		
1 Air Compressor, 250 cfm		202.40		222.64		
1 Sandblaster, Portable, 3 C.F.		20.40		22.44		
1 Set Sand Blasting Accessories		13.85		15.23		
1 Aerial Lift Truck, 60' Boom		456.00		501.60	21.65	23.81
32 L.H., Daily Totals		$1720.25		$2617.11	$53.76	$81.78
Crew E-11B	Hr.	Daily	Hr.	Daily	Bare Costs	Incl. O&P
2 Painters, Struc. Steel	$32.00	$512.00	$62.20	$995.20	$30.73	$57.28
1 Building Laborer	28.20	225.60	47.45	379.60		
2 Paint Sprayer, 8 C.F.M.		89.80		98.78		
1 Aerial Lift Truck, 60' Boom		456.00		501.60	22.74	25.02
24 L.H., Daily Totals		$1283.40		$1975.18	$53.48	$82.30

Crew No.	Bare Costs		Incl. Subs O&P		Cost Per Labor-Hour	
	Hr.	Daily	Hr.	Daily	Bare Costs	Incl. O&P
Crew E-12	Hr.	Daily	Hr.	Daily	Bare Costs	Incl. O&P
1 Welder Foreman (outside)	$40.35	$322.80	$76.85	$614.80	$38.30	$68.45
1 Equip. Oper. (light)	36.25	290.00	60.05	480.40		
1 Welder, Gas Engine, 300 amp		142.00		156.20	8.88	9.76
16 L.H., Daily Totals		$754.80		$1251.40	$47.17	$78.21
Crew E-13	Hr.	Daily	Hr.	Daily	Bare Costs	Incl. O&P
1 Welder Foreman (outside)	$40.35	$322.80	$76.85	$614.80	$38.98	$71.25
.5 Equip. Oper. (light)	36.25	145.00	60.05	240.20		
1 Welder, Gas Engine, 300 amp		142.00		156.20	11.83	13.02
12 L.H., Daily Totals		$609.80		$1011.20	$50.82	$84.27
Crew E-14	Hr.	Daily	Hr.	Daily	Bare Costs	Incl. O&P
1 Struc. Steel Worker	$38.35	$306.80	$73.05	$584.40	$38.35	$73.05
1 Welder, Gas Engine, 300 amp		142.00		156.20	17.75	19.52
8 L.H., Daily Totals		$448.80		$740.60	$56.10	$92.58
Crew E-16	Hr.	Daily	Hr.	Daily	Bare Costs	Incl. O&P
1 Welder Foreman (outside)	$40.35	$322.80	$76.85	$614.80	$39.35	$74.95
1 Welder	38.35	306.80	73.05	584.40		
1 Welder, Gas Engine, 300 amp		142.00		156.20	8.88	9.76
16 L.H., Daily Totals		$771.60		$1355.40	$48.23	$84.71
Crew E-17	Hr.	Daily	Hr.	Daily	Bare Costs	Incl. O&P
1 Struc. Steel Foreman (outside)	$40.35	$322.80	$76.85	$614.80	$39.35	$74.95
1 Structural Steel Worker	38.35	306.80	73.05	584.40		
16 L.H., Daily Totals		$629.60		$1199.20	$39.35	$74.95
Crew E-18	Hr.	Daily	Hr.	Daily	Bare Costs	Incl. O&P
1 Struc. Steel Foreman (outside)	$40.35	$322.80	$76.85	$614.80	$38.61	$71.67
3 Structural Steel Workers	38.35	920.40	73.05	1753.20		
1 Equipment Operator (med.)	37.65	301.20	62.35	498.80		
1 Lattice Boom Crane, 20 Ton		960.50		1056.55	24.01	26.41
40 L.H., Daily Totals		$2504.90		$3923.35	$62.62	$98.08
Crew E-19	Hr.	Daily	Hr.	Daily	Bare Costs	Incl. O&P
1 Struc. Steel Foreman (outside)	$40.35	$322.80	$76.85	$614.80	$38.32	$69.98
1 Structural Steel Worker	38.35	306.80	73.05	584.40		
1 Equip. Oper. (light)	36.25	290.00	60.05	480.40		
1 Lattice Boom Crane, 20 Ton		960.50		1056.55	40.02	44.02
24 L.H., Daily Totals		$1880.10		$2736.15	$78.34	$114.01
Crew E-20	Hr.	Daily	Hr.	Daily	Bare Costs	Incl. O&P
1 Struc. Steel Foreman (outside)	$40.35	$322.80	$76.85	$614.80	$38.04	$70.22
5 Structural Steel Workers	38.35	1534.00	73.05	2922.00		
1 Equip. Oper. (crane)	38.70	309.60	64.10	512.80		
1 Equip. Oper. (oiler)	33.55	268.40	55.55	444.40		
1 Lattice Boom Crane, 40 Ton		1177.00		1294.70	18.39	20.23
64 L.H., Daily Totals		$3611.80		$5788.70	$56.43	$90.45
Crew E-22	Hr.	Daily	Hr.	Daily	Bare Costs	Incl. O&P
1 Skilled Worker Foreman (out)	$38.30	$306.40	$64.70	$517.60	$36.97	$62.43
2 Skilled Workers	36.30	580.80	61.30	980.80		
24 L.H., Daily Totals		$887.20		$1498.40	$36.97	$62.43
Crew E-24	Hr.	Daily	Hr.	Daily	Bare Costs	Incl. O&P
3 Structural Steel Workers	$38.35	$920.40	$73.05	$1753.20	$38.17	$70.38
1 Equipment Operator (med.)	37.65	301.20	62.35	498.80		
1 Hyd. Crane, 25 Ton		745.80		820.38	23.31	25.64
32 L.H., Daily Totals		$1967.40		$3072.38	$61.48	$96.01

Crew No.	Bare Costs		Incl. Subs O&P		Cost Per Labor-Hour	
Crew E-25	Hr.	Daily	Hr.	Daily	Bare Costs	Incl. O&P
1 Welder	$38.35	$306.80	$73.05	$584.40	$38.35	$73.05
1 Cutting Torch		11.40		12.54	1.43	1.57
8 L.H., Daily Totals		$318.20		$596.94	$39.77	$74.62
Crew F-3	Hr.	Daily	Hr.	Daily	Bare Costs	Incl. O&P
2 Carpenters	$35.75	$572.00	$60.15	$962.40	$32.80	$55.06
2 Carpenter Helpers	26.90	430.40	45.45	727.20		
1 Equip. Oper. (crane)	38.70	309.60	64.10	512.80		
1 Hyd. Crane, 12 Ton		663.00		729.30	16.57	18.23
40 L.H., Daily Totals		$1975.00		$2931.70	$49.38	$73.29
Crew F-4	Hr.	Daily	Hr.	Daily	Bare Costs	Incl. O&P
2 Carpenters	$35.75	$572.00	$60.15	$962.40	$32.80	$55.06
2 Carpenter Helpers	26.90	430.40	45.45	727.20		
1 Equip. Oper. (crane)	38.70	309.60	64.10	512.80		
1 Hyd. Crane, 55 Ton		1137.00		1250.70	28.43	31.27
40 L.H., Daily Totals		$2449.00		$3453.10	$61.23	$86.33
Crew F-5	Hr.	Daily	Hr.	Daily	Bare Costs	Incl. O&P
2 Carpenters	$35.75	$572.00	$60.15	$962.40	$31.32	$52.80
2 Carpenter Helpers	26.90	430.40	45.45	727.20		
32 L.H., Daily Totals		$1002.40		$1689.60	$31.32	$52.80
Crew F-6	Hr.	Daily	Hr.	Daily	Bare Costs	Incl. O&P
2 Carpenters	$35.75	$572.00	$60.15	$962.40	$33.32	$55.86
2 Building Laborers	28.20	451.20	47.45	759.20		
1 Equip. Oper. (crane)	38.70	309.60	64.10	512.80		
1 Hyd. Crane, 12 Ton		663.00		729.30	16.57	18.23
40 L.H., Daily Totals		$1995.80		$2963.70	$49.90	$74.09
Crew F-7	Hr.	Daily	Hr.	Daily	Bare Costs	Incl. O&P
2 Carpenters	$35.75	$572.00	$60.15	$962.40	$31.98	$53.80
2 Building Laborers	28.20	451.20	47.45	759.20		
32 L.H., Daily Totals		$1023.20		$1721.60	$31.98	$53.80
Crew G-1	Hr.	Daily	Hr.	Daily	Bare Costs	Incl. O&P
1 Roofer Foreman (outside)	$32.15	$257.20	$59.20	$473.60	$28.24	$52.01
4 Roofers Composition	30.15	964.80	55.55	1777.60		
2 Roofer Helpers	22.45	359.20	41.35	661.60		
1 Application Equipment		199.20		219.12		
1 Tar Kettle/Pot		130.00		143.00		
1 Crew Truck		224.80		247.28	9.89	10.88
56 L.H., Daily Totals		$2135.20		$3522.20	$38.13	$62.90
Crew G-2	Hr.	Daily	Hr.	Daily	Bare Costs	Incl. O&P
1 Plasterer	$32.70	$261.60	$53.80	$430.40	$29.97	$49.65
1 Plasterer Helper	29.00	232.00	47.70	381.60		
1 Building Laborer	28.20	225.60	47.45	379.60		
1 Grout Pump, 50 C.F./hr.		134.80		148.28	5.62	6.18
24 L.H., Daily Totals		$854.00		$1339.88	$35.58	$55.83
Crew G-2A	Hr.	Daily	Hr.	Daily	Bare Costs	Incl. O&P
1 Roofer Composition	$30.15	$241.20	$55.55	$444.40	$26.93	$48.12
1 Roofer Helper	22.45	179.60	41.35	330.80		
1 Building Laborer	28.20	225.60	47.45	379.60		
1 Foam Spray Rig, Trailer-Mtd.		585.25		643.77		
1 Pickup Truck, 3/4 Ton		157.00		172.70	30.93	34.02
24 L.H., Daily Totals		$1388.65		$1971.28	$57.86	$82.14

Crew No.	Bare Costs		Incl. Subs O&P		Cost Per Labor-Hour	
Crew G-3	Hr.	Daily	Hr.	Daily	Bare Costs	Incl. O&P
2 Sheet Metal Workers	$40.45	$647.20	$67.45	$1079.20	$34.33	$57.45
2 Building Laborers	28.20	451.20	47.45	759.20		
32 L.H., Daily Totals		$1098.40		$1838.40	$34.33	$57.45
Crew G-4	Hr.	Daily	Hr.	Daily	Bare Costs	Incl. O&P
1 Labor Foreman (outside)	$30.20	$241.60	$50.85	$406.80	$28.87	$48.58
2 Building Laborers	28.20	451.20	47.45	759.20		
1 Flatbed Truck, Gas, 1.5 Ton		270.20		297.22		
1 Air Compressor, 160 cfm		157.40		173.14	17.82	19.60
24 L.H., Daily Totals		$1120.40		$1636.36	$46.68	$68.18
Crew G-5	Hr.	Daily	Hr.	Daily	Bare Costs	Incl. O&P
1 Roofer Foreman (outside)	$32.15	$257.20	$59.20	$473.60	$27.47	$50.60
2 Roofers Composition	30.15	482.40	55.55	888.80		
2 Roofer Helpers	22.45	359.20	41.35	661.60		
1 Application Equipment		199.20		219.12	4.98	5.48
40 L.H., Daily Totals		$1298.00		$2243.12	$32.45	$56.08
Crew G-6A	Hr.	Daily	Hr.	Daily	Bare Costs	Incl. O&P
2 Roofers Composition	$30.15	$482.40	$55.55	$888.80	$30.15	$55.55
1 Small Compressor, Electric		12.10		13.31		
2 Pneumatic Nailers		44.70		49.17	3.55	3.90
16 L.H., Daily Totals		$539.20		$951.28	$33.70	$59.45
Crew G-7	Hr.	Daily	Hr.	Daily	Bare Costs	Incl. O&P
1 Carpenter	$35.75	$286.00	$60.15	$481.20	$35.75	$60.15
1 Small Compressor, Electric		12.10		13.31		
1 Pneumatic Nailer		22.35		24.59	4.31	4.74
8 L.H., Daily Totals		$320.45		$519.10	$40.06	$64.89
Crew H-1	Hr.	Daily	Hr.	Daily	Bare Costs	Incl. O&P
2 Glaziers	$34.80	$556.80	$57.80	$924.80	$36.58	$65.42
2 Struc. Steel Workers	38.35	613.60	73.05	1168.80		
32 L.H., Daily Totals		$1170.40		$2093.60	$36.58	$65.42
Crew H-2	Hr.	Daily	Hr.	Daily	Bare Costs	Incl. O&P
2 Glaziers	$34.80	$556.80	$57.80	$924.80	$32.60	$54.35
1 Building Laborer	28.20	225.60	47.45	379.60		
24 L.H., Daily Totals		$782.40		$1304.40	$32.60	$54.35
Crew H-3	Hr.	Daily	Hr.	Daily	Bare Costs	Incl. O&P
1 Glazier	$34.80	$278.40	$57.80	$462.40	$30.85	$51.63
1 Helper	26.90	215.20	45.45	363.60		
16 L.H., Daily Totals		$493.60		$826.00	$30.85	$51.63
Crew H-4	Hr.	Daily	Hr.	Daily	Bare Costs	Incl. O&P
1 Carpenter	$35.75	$286.00	$60.15	$481.20	$33.60	$56.22
1 Carpenter Helper	26.90	215.20	45.45	363.60		
.5 Electrician	42.70	170.80	69.90	279.60		
20 L.H., Daily Totals		$672.00		$1124.40	$33.60	$56.22
Crew J-1	Hr.	Daily	Hr.	Daily	Bare Costs	Incl. O&P
3 Plasterers	$32.70	$784.80	$53.80	$1291.20	$31.22	$51.36
2 Plasterer Helpers	29.00	464.00	47.70	763.20		
1 Mixing Machine, 6 C.F.		143.60		157.96	3.59	3.95
40 L.H., Daily Totals		$1392.40		$2212.36	$34.81	$55.31

Crew No.	Bare Costs		Incl. Subs O&P		Cost Per Labor-Hour	
Crew J-2	Hr.	Daily	Hr.	Daily	Bare Costs	Incl. O&P
3 Plasterers	$32.70	$784.80	$53.80	$1291.20	$31.29	$51.29
2 Plasterer Helpers	29.00	464.00	47.70	763.20		
1 Lather	31.65	253.20	50.95	407.60		
1 Mixing Machine, 6 C.F.		143.60		157.96	2.99	3.29
48 L.H., Daily Totals		$1645.60		$2619.96	$34.28	$54.58
Crew J-3	Hr.	Daily	Hr.	Daily	Bare Costs	Incl. O&P
1 Terrazzo Worker	$32.50	$260.00	$52.45	$419.60	$29.82	$48.13
1 Terrazzo Helper	27.15	217.20	43.80	350.40		
1 Floor Grinder, 22" Path		97.90		107.69		
1 Terrazzo Mixer		192.60		211.86	18.16	19.97
16 L.H., Daily Totals		$767.70		$1089.55	$47.98	$68.10
Crew J-4	Hr.	Daily	Hr.	Daily	Bare Costs	Incl. O&P
2 Cement Finishers	$34.35	$549.60	$55.60	$889.60	$32.30	$52.88
1 Laborer	28.20	225.60	47.45	379.60		
1 Floor Grinder, 22" Path		97.90		107.69		
1 Floor Edger, 7" Path		39.15		43.06		
1 Vacuum Pick-Up System		60.75		66.83	8.24	9.07
24 L.H., Daily Totals		$973.00		$1486.78	$40.54	$61.95
Crew J-4A	Hr.	Daily	Hr.	Daily	Bare Costs	Incl. O&P
2 Cement Finishers	$34.35	$549.60	$55.60	$889.60	$31.27	$51.52
2 Laborers	28.20	451.20	47.45	759.20		
1 Floor Grinder, 22" Path		97.90		107.69		
1 Floor Edger, 7" Path		39.15		43.06		
1 Vacuum Pick-Up System		60.75		66.83		
1 Floor Auto Scrubber		212.15		233.37	12.81	14.09
32 L.H., Daily Totals		$1410.75		$2099.74	$44.09	$65.62
Crew J-4B	Hr.	Daily	Hr.	Daily	Bare Costs	Incl. O&P
1 Laborer	$28.20	$225.60	$47.45	$379.60	$28.20	$47.45
1 Floor Auto Scrubber		212.15		233.37	26.52	29.17
8 L.H., Daily Totals		$437.75		$612.97	$54.72	$76.62
Crew J-6	Hr.	Daily	Hr.	Daily	Bare Costs	Incl. O&P
2 Painters	$31.25	$500.00	$51.40	$822.40	$31.74	$52.58
1 Building Laborer	28.20	225.60	47.45	379.60		
1 Equip. Oper. (light)	36.25	290.00	60.05	480.40		
1 Air Compressor, 250 cfm		202.40		222.64		
1 Sandblaster, Portable, 3 C.F.		20.40		22.44		
1 Set Sand Blasting Accessories		13.85		15.23	7.40	8.13
32 L.H., Daily Totals		$1252.25		$1942.71	$39.13	$60.71
Crew J-7	Hr.	Daily	Hr.	Daily	Bare Costs	Incl. O&P
2 Painters	$31.25	$500.00	$51.40	$822.40	$31.25	$51.40
1 Floor Belt Sander		15.90		17.49		
1 Floor Sanding Edger		15.55		17.11	1.97	2.16
16 L.H., Daily Totals		$531.45		$857.00	$33.22	$53.56
Crew K-1	Hr.	Daily	Hr.	Daily	Bare Costs	Incl. O&P
1 Carpenter	$35.75	$286.00	$60.15	$481.20	$32.30	$54.10
1 Truck Driver (light)	28.85	230.80	48.05	384.40		
1 Flatbed Truck, Gas, 3 Ton		333.00		366.30	20.81	22.89
16 L.H., Daily Totals		$849.80		$1231.90	$53.11	$76.99

Crew No.	Bare Costs Hr.	Daily	Incl. Subs O&P Hr.	Daily	Cost Per Labor-Hour Bare Costs	Incl. O&P
Crew K-2	Hr.	Daily	Hr.	Daily	Bare Costs	Incl. O&P
1 Struc. Steel Foreman (outside)	$40.35	$322.80	$76.85	$614.80	$35.85	$65.98
1 Struc. Steel Worker	38.35	306.80	73.05	584.40		
1 Truck Driver (light)	28.85	230.80	48.05	384.40		
1 Flatbed Truck, Gas, 3 Ton		333.00		366.30	13.88	15.26
24 L.H., Daily Totals		$1193.40		$1949.90	$49.73	$81.25
Crew L-1	Hr.	Daily	Hr.	Daily	Bare Costs	Incl. O&P
.25 Electrician	$42.70	$85.40	$69.90	$139.80	$42.62	$70.22
1 Plumber	42.60	340.80	70.30	562.40		
10 L.H., Daily Totals		$426.20		$702.20	$42.62	$70.22
Crew L-2	Hr.	Daily	Hr.	Daily	Bare Costs	Incl. O&P
1 Carpenter	$35.75	$286.00	$60.15	$481.20	$31.32	$52.80
1 Carpenter Helper	26.90	215.20	45.45	363.60		
16 L.H., Daily Totals		$501.20		$844.80	$31.32	$52.80
Crew L-3	Hr.	Daily	Hr.	Daily	Bare Costs	Incl. O&P
1 Carpenter	$35.75	$286.00	$60.15	$481.20	$37.14	$62.10
.25 Electrician	42.70	85.40	69.90	139.80		
10 L.H., Daily Totals		$371.40		$621.00	$37.14	$62.10
Crew L-3A	Hr.	Daily	Hr.	Daily	Bare Costs	Incl. O&P
1 Carpenter Foreman (outside)	$37.75	$302.00	$63.55	$508.40	$38.65	$64.85
.5 Sheet Metal Worker	40.45	161.80	67.45	269.80		
12 L.H., Daily Totals		$463.80		$778.20	$38.65	$64.85
Crew L-4	Hr.	Daily	Hr.	Daily	Bare Costs	Incl. O&P
1 Skilled Worker	$36.30	$290.40	$61.30	$490.40	$31.60	$53.38
1 Helper	26.90	215.20	45.45	363.60		
16 L.H., Daily Totals		$505.60		$854.00	$31.60	$53.38
Crew L-5	Hr.	Daily	Hr.	Daily	Bare Costs	Incl. O&P
1 Struc. Steel Foreman (outside)	$40.35	$322.80	$76.85	$614.80	$38.69	$72.31
5 Struc. Steel Workers	38.35	1534.00	73.05	2922.00		
1 Equip. Oper. (crane)	38.70	309.60	64.10	512.80		
1 Hyd. Crane, 25 Ton		745.80		820.38	13.32	14.65
56 L.H., Daily Totals		$2912.20		$4869.98	$52.00	$86.96
Crew L-5A	Hr.	Daily	Hr.	Daily	Bare Costs	Incl. O&P
1 Struc. Steel Foreman (outside)	$40.35	$322.80	$76.85	$614.80	$38.94	$71.76
2 Structural Steel Workers	38.35	613.60	73.05	1168.80		
1 Equip. Oper. (crane)	38.70	309.60	64.10	512.80		
1 S.P. Crane, 4x4, 25 Ton		607.20		667.92	18.98	20.87
32 L.H., Daily Totals		$1853.20		$2964.32	$57.91	$92.64
Crew L-5B	Hr.	Daily	Hr.	Daily	Bare Costs	Incl. O&P
1 Struc. Steel Foreman (outside)	$40.35	$322.80	$76.85	$614.80	$39.55	$68.58
2 Structural Steel Workers	38.35	613.60	73.05	1168.80		
2 Electricians	42.70	683.20	69.90	1118.40		
2 Steamfitters/Pipefitters	43.30	692.80	71.45	1143.20		
1 Equip. Oper. (crane)	38.70	309.60	64.10	512.80		
1 Common Laborer	28.20	225.60	47.45	379.60		
1 Hyd. Crane, 80 Ton		1652.00		1817.20	22.94	25.24
72 L.H., Daily Totals		$4499.60		$6754.80	$62.49	$93.82
Crew L-6	Hr.	Daily	Hr.	Daily	Bare Costs	Incl. O&P
1 Plumber	$42.60	$340.80	$70.30	$562.40	$42.63	$70.17
.5 Electrician	42.70	170.80	69.90	279.60		
12 L.H., Daily Totals		$511.60		$842.00	$42.63	$70.17

Crew No.	Bare Costs Hr.	Daily	Incl. Subs O&P Hr.	Daily	Cost Per Labor-Hour Bare Costs	Incl. O&P
Crew L-7	Hr.	Daily	Hr.	Daily	Bare Costs	Incl. O&P
1 Carpenter	$35.75	$286.00	$60.15	$481.20	$30.84	$51.85
2 Carpenter Helpers	26.90	430.40	45.45	727.20		
.25 Electrician	42.70	85.40	69.90	139.80		
26 L.H., Daily Totals		$801.80		$1348.20	$30.84	$51.85
Crew L-8	Hr.	Daily	Hr.	Daily	Bare Costs	Incl. O&P
1 Carpenter	$35.75	$286.00	$60.15	$481.20	$33.58	$56.30
1 Carpenter Helper	26.90	215.20	45.45	363.60		
.5 Plumber	42.60	170.40	70.30	281.20		
20 L.H., Daily Totals		$671.60		$1126.00	$33.58	$56.30
Crew L-9	Hr.	Daily	Hr.	Daily	Bare Costs	Incl. O&P
1 Skilled Worker Foreman	$38.30	$306.40	$64.70	$517.60	$33.28	$55.97
1 Skilled Worker	36.30	290.40	61.30	490.40		
2 Helpers	26.90	430.40	45.45	727.20		
.5 Electrician	42.70	170.80	69.90	279.60		
36 L.H., Daily Totals		$1198.00		$2014.80	$33.28	$55.97
Crew L-10	Hr.	Daily	Hr.	Daily	Bare Costs	Incl. O&P
1 Struc. Steel Foreman (outside)	$40.35	$322.80	$76.85	$614.80	$39.13	$71.33
1 Structural Steel Worker	38.35	306.80	73.05	584.40		
1 Equip. Oper. (crane)	38.70	309.60	64.10	512.80		
1 Hyd. Crane, 12 Ton		663.00		729.30	27.63	30.39
24 L.H., Daily Totals		$1602.20		$2441.30	$66.76	$101.72
Crew L-11	Hr.	Daily	Hr.	Daily	Bare Costs	Incl. O&P
2 Wreckers	$28.20	$451.20	$51.35	$821.60	$32.84	$56.71
1 Equip. Oper. (crane)	38.70	309.60	64.10	512.80		
1 Equip. Oper. (light)	36.25	290.00	60.05	480.40		
1 Hyd. Excavator, 2.5 C.Y.		1637.00		1800.70		
1 Loader, Skid Steer, 78 H.P.		308.80		339.68	60.81	66.89
32 L.H., Daily Totals		$2996.60		$3955.18	$93.64	$123.60
Crew M-1	Hr.	Daily	Hr.	Daily	Bare Costs	Incl. O&P
3 Elevator Constructors	$55.65	$1335.60	$91.05	$2185.20	$52.86	$86.49
1 Elevator Apprentice	44.50	356.00	72.80	582.40		
5 Hand Tools		48.00		52.80	1.50	1.65
32 L.H., Daily Totals		$1739.60		$2820.40	$54.36	$88.14
Crew M-3	Hr.	Daily	Hr.	Daily	Bare Costs	Incl. O&P
1 Electrician Foreman (outside)	$44.70	$357.60	$73.15	$585.20	$42.93	$70.60
1 Common Laborer	28.20	225.60	47.45	379.60		
.25 Equipment Operator (med.)	37.65	75.30	62.35	124.70		
1 Elevator Constructor	55.65	445.20	91.05	728.40		
1 Elevator Apprentice	44.50	356.00	72.80	582.40		
.25 S.P. Crane, 4x4, 20 Ton		140.10		154.11	4.12	4.53
34 L.H., Daily Totals		$1599.80		$2554.41	$47.05	$75.13
Crew M-4	Hr.	Daily	Hr.	Daily	Bare Costs	Incl. O&P
1 Electrician Foreman (outside)	$44.70	$357.60	$73.15	$585.20	$42.47	$69.86
1 Common Laborer	28.20	225.60	47.45	379.60		
.25 Equipment Operator, Crane	38.70	77.40	64.10	128.20		
.25 Equip. Oper. (oiler)	33.55	67.10	55.55	111.10		
1 Elevator Constructor	55.65	445.20	91.05	728.40		
1 Elevator Apprentice	44.50	356.00	72.80	582.40		
.25 S.P. Crane, 4x4, 40 Ton		178.25		196.07	4.95	5.45
36 L.H., Daily Totals		$1707.15		$2710.97	$47.42	$75.30

Crew No.	Bare Costs		Incl. Subs O&P		Cost Per Labor-Hour	

Crew Q-1	Hr.	Daily	Hr.	Daily	Bare Costs	Incl. O&P
1 Plumber	$42.60	$340.80	$70.30	$562.40	$38.35	$63.27
1 Plumber Apprentice	34.10	272.80	56.25	450.00		
16 L.H., Daily Totals		$613.60		$1012.40	$38.35	$63.27

Crew Q-1A	Hr.	Daily	Hr.	Daily	Bare Costs	Incl. O&P
.25 Plumber Foreman (outside)	$44.60	$89.20	$73.60	$147.20	$43.00	$70.96
1 Plumber	42.60	340.80	70.30	562.40		
10 L.H., Daily Totals		$430.00		$709.60	$43.00	$70.96

Crew Q-1C	Hr.	Daily	Hr.	Daily	Bare Costs	Incl. O&P
1 Plumber	$42.60	$340.80	$70.30	$562.40	$38.12	$62.97
1 Plumber Apprentice	34.10	272.80	56.25	450.00		
1 Equip. Oper. (medium)	37.65	301.20	62.35	498.80		
1 Trencher, Chain Type, 8' D		3376.00		3713.60	140.67	154.73
24 L.H., Daily Totals		$4290.80		$5224.80	$178.78	$217.70

Crew Q-2	Hr.	Daily	Hr.	Daily	Bare Costs	Incl. O&P
1 Plumber	$42.60	$340.80	$70.30	$562.40	$36.93	$60.93
2 Plumber Apprentices	34.10	545.60	56.25	900.00		
24 L.H., Daily Totals		$886.40		$1462.40	$36.93	$60.93

Crew Q-3	Hr.	Daily	Hr.	Daily	Bare Costs	Incl. O&P
2 Plumbers	$42.60	$681.60	$70.30	$1124.80	$38.35	$63.27
2 Plumber Apprentices	34.10	545.60	56.25	900.00		
32 L.H., Daily Totals		$1227.20		$2024.80	$38.35	$63.27

Crew Q-4	Hr.	Daily	Hr.	Daily	Bare Costs	Incl. O&P
2 Plumbers	$42.60	$681.60	$70.30	$1124.80	$40.48	$66.79
1 Welder (plumber)	42.60	340.80	70.30	562.40		
1 Plumber Apprentice	34.10	272.80	56.25	450.00		
1 Welder, Electric, 300 amp		55.30		60.83	1.73	1.90
32 L.H., Daily Totals		$1350.50		$2198.03	$42.20	$68.69

Crew Q-5	Hr.	Daily	Hr.	Daily	Bare Costs	Incl. O&P
1 Steamfitter	$43.30	$346.40	$71.45	$571.60	$38.98	$64.30
1 Steamfitter Apprentice	34.65	277.20	57.15	457.20		
16 L.H., Daily Totals		$623.60		$1028.80	$38.98	$64.30

Crew Q-6	Hr.	Daily	Hr.	Daily	Bare Costs	Incl. O&P
1 Steamfitter	$43.30	$346.40	$71.45	$571.60	$37.53	$61.92
2 Steamfitter Apprentices	34.65	554.40	57.15	914.40		
24 L.H., Daily Totals		$900.80		$1486.00	$37.53	$61.92

Crew Q-7	Hr.	Daily	Hr.	Daily	Bare Costs	Incl. O&P
2 Steamfitters	$43.30	$692.80	$71.45	$1143.20	$38.98	$64.30
2 Steamfitter Apprentices	34.65	554.40	57.15	914.40		
32 L.H., Daily Totals		$1247.20		$2057.60	$38.98	$64.30

Crew Q-8	Hr.	Daily	Hr.	Daily	Bare Costs	Incl. O&P
2 Steamfitters	$43.30	$692.80	$71.45	$1143.20	$41.14	$67.88
1 Welder (steamfitter)	43.30	346.40	71.45	571.60		
1 Steamfitter Apprentice	34.65	277.20	57.15	457.20		
1 Welder, Electric, 300 amp		55.30		60.83	1.73	1.90
32 L.H., Daily Totals		$1371.70		$2232.83	$42.87	$69.78

Crew Q-9	Hr.	Daily	Hr.	Daily	Bare Costs	Incl. O&P
1 Sheet Metal Worker	$40.45	$323.60	$67.45	$539.60	$36.40	$60.70
1 Sheet Metal Apprentice	32.35	258.80	53.95	431.60		
16 L.H., Daily Totals		$582.40		$971.20	$36.40	$60.70

Crew Q-10	Hr.	Daily	Hr.	Daily	Bare Costs	Incl. O&P
2 Sheet Metal Workers	$40.45	$647.20	$67.45	$1079.20	$37.75	$62.95
1 Sheet Metal Apprentice	32.35	258.80	53.95	431.60		
24 L.H., Daily Totals		$906.00		$1510.80	$37.75	$62.95

Crew Q-11	Hr.	Daily	Hr.	Daily	Bare Costs	Incl. O&P
2 Sheet Metal Workers	$40.45	$647.20	$67.45	$1079.20	$36.40	$60.70
2 Sheet Metal Apprentices	32.35	517.60	53.95	863.20		
32 L.H., Daily Totals		$1164.80		$1942.40	$36.40	$60.70

Crew Q-12	Hr.	Daily	Hr.	Daily	Bare Costs	Incl. O&P
1 Sprinkler Installer	$41.00	$328.00	$67.70	$541.60	$36.90	$60.92
1 Sprinkler Apprentice	32.80	262.40	54.15	433.20		
16 L.H., Daily Totals		$590.40		$974.80	$36.90	$60.92

Crew Q-13	Hr.	Daily	Hr.	Daily	Bare Costs	Incl. O&P
2 Sprinkler Installers	$41.00	$656.00	$67.70	$1083.20	$36.90	$60.92
2 Sprinkler Apprentices	32.80	524.80	54.15	866.40		
32 L.H., Daily Totals		$1180.80		$1949.60	$36.90	$60.92

Crew Q-14	Hr.	Daily	Hr.	Daily	Bare Costs	Incl. O&P
1 Asbestos Worker	$37.85	$302.80	$64.20	$513.60	$34.08	$57.80
1 Asbestos Apprentice	30.30	242.40	51.40	411.20		
16 L.H., Daily Totals		$545.20		$924.80	$34.08	$57.80

Crew Q-15	Hr.	Daily	Hr.	Daily	Bare Costs	Incl. O&P
1 Plumber	$42.60	$340.80	$70.30	$562.40	$38.35	$63.27
1 Plumber Apprentice	34.10	272.80	56.25	450.00		
1 Welder, Electric, 300 amp		55.30		60.83	3.46	3.80
16 L.H., Daily Totals		$668.90		$1073.23	$41.81	$67.08

Crew Q-16	Hr.	Daily	Hr.	Daily	Bare Costs	Incl. O&P
2 Plumbers	$42.60	$681.60	$70.30	$1124.80	$39.77	$65.62
1 Plumber Apprentice	34.10	272.80	56.25	450.00		
1 Welder, Electric, 300 amp		55.30		60.83	2.30	2.53
24 L.H., Daily Totals		$1009.70		$1635.63	$42.07	$68.15

Crew Q-17	Hr.	Daily	Hr.	Daily	Bare Costs	Incl. O&P
1 Steamfitter	$43.30	$346.40	$71.45	$571.60	$38.98	$64.30
1 Steamfitter Apprentice	34.65	277.20	57.15	457.20		
1 Welder, Electric, 300 amp		55.30		60.83	3.46	3.80
16 L.H., Daily Totals		$678.90		$1089.63	$42.43	$68.10

Crew Q-17A	Hr.	Daily	Hr.	Daily	Bare Costs	Incl. O&P
1 Steamfitter	$43.30	$346.40	$71.45	$571.60	$38.88	$64.23
1 Steamfitter Apprentice	34.65	277.20	57.15	457.20		
1 Equip. Oper. (crane)	38.70	309.60	64.10	512.80		
1 Hyd. Crane, 12 Ton		663.00		729.30		
1 Welder, Electric, 300 amp		55.30		60.83	29.93	32.92
24 L.H., Daily Totals		$1651.50		$2331.73	$68.81	$97.16

Crew Q-18	Hr.	Daily	Hr.	Daily	Bare Costs	Incl. O&P
2 Steamfitters	$43.30	$692.80	$71.45	$1143.20	$40.42	$66.68
1 Steamfitter Apprentice	34.65	277.20	57.15	457.20		
1 Welder, Electric, 300 amp		55.30		60.83	2.30	2.53
24 L.H., Daily Totals		$1025.30		$1661.23	$42.72	$69.22

Crew Q-19	Hr.	Daily	Hr.	Daily	Bare Costs	Incl. O&P
1 Steamfitter	$43.30	$346.40	$71.45	$571.60	$40.22	$66.17
1 Steamfitter Apprentice	34.65	277.20	57.15	457.20		
1 Electrician	42.70	341.60	69.90	559.20		
24 L.H., Daily Totals		$965.20		$1588.00	$40.22	$66.17

Crew Q-20	Hr.	Daily	Hr.	Daily	Bare Costs	Incl. O&P
1 Sheet Metal Worker	$40.45	$323.60	$67.45	$539.60	$37.66	$62.54
1 Sheet Metal Apprentice	32.35	258.80	53.95	431.60		
.5 Electrician	42.70	170.80	69.90	279.60		
20 L.H., Daily Totals		$753.20		$1250.80	$37.66	$62.54

Crew Q-21	Hr.	Daily	Hr.	Daily	Bare Costs	Incl. O&P
2 Steamfitters	$43.30	$692.80	$71.45	$1143.20	$40.99	$67.49
1 Steamfitter Apprentice	34.65	277.20	57.15	457.20		
1 Electrician	42.70	341.60	69.90	559.20		
32 L.H., Daily Totals		$1311.60		$2159.60	$40.99	$67.49

Crew Q-22	Hr.	Daily	Hr.	Daily	Bare Costs	Incl. O&P
1 Plumber	$42.60	$340.80	$70.30	$562.40	$38.35	$63.27
1 Plumber Apprentice	34.10	272.80	56.25	450.00		
1 Hyd. Crane, 12 Ton		663.00		729.30	41.44	45.58
16 L.H., Daily Totals		$1276.60		$1741.70	$79.79	$108.86

Crew Q-22A	Hr.	Daily	Hr.	Daily	Bare Costs	Incl. O&P
1 Plumber	$42.60	$340.80	$70.30	$562.40	$35.90	$59.52
1 Plumber Apprentice	34.10	272.80	56.25	450.00		
1 Laborer	28.20	225.60	47.45	379.60		
1 Equip. Oper. (crane)	38.70	309.60	64.10	512.80		
1 Hyd. Crane, 12 Ton		663.00		729.30	20.72	22.79
32 L.H., Daily Totals		$1811.80		$2634.10	$56.62	$82.32

Crew Q-23	Hr.	Daily	Hr.	Daily	Bare Costs	Incl. O&P
1 Plumber Foreman (outside)	$44.60	$356.80	$73.60	$588.80	$41.62	$68.75
1 Plumber	42.60	340.80	70.30	562.40		
1 Equip. Oper. (medium)	37.65	301.20	62.35	498.80		
1 Lattice Boom Crane, 20 Ton		960.50		1056.55	40.02	44.02
24 L.H., Daily Totals		$1959.30		$2706.55	$81.64	$112.77

Crew R-1	Hr.	Daily	Hr.	Daily	Bare Costs	Incl. O&P
1 Electrician Foreman	$43.20	$345.60	$70.70	$565.60	$37.52	$61.88
3 Electricians	42.70	1024.80	69.90	1677.60		
2 Helpers	26.90	430.40	45.45	727.20		
48 L.H., Daily Totals		$1800.80		$2970.40	$37.52	$61.88

Crew R-1A	Hr.	Daily	Hr.	Daily	Bare Costs	Incl. O&P
1 Electrician	$42.70	$341.60	$69.90	$559.20	$34.80	$57.67
1 Helper	26.90	215.20	45.45	363.60		
16 L.H., Daily Totals		$556.80		$922.80	$34.80	$57.67

Crew R-2	Hr.	Daily	Hr.	Daily	Bare Costs	Incl. O&P
1 Electrician Foreman	$43.20	$345.60	$70.70	$565.60	$37.69	$62.20
3 Electricians	42.70	1024.80	69.90	1677.60		
2 Helpers	26.90	430.40	45.45	727.20		
1 Equip. Oper. (crane)	38.70	309.60	64.10	512.80		
1 S.P. Crane, 4x4, 5 Ton		280.00		308.00	5.00	5.50
56 L.H., Daily Totals		$2390.40		$3791.20	$42.69	$67.70

Crew R-3	Hr.	Daily	Hr.	Daily	Bare Costs	Incl. O&P
1 Electrician Foreman	$43.20	$345.60	$70.70	$565.60	$42.10	$69.06
1 Electrician	42.70	341.60	69.90	559.20		
.5 Equip. Oper. (crane)	38.70	154.80	64.10	256.40		
.5 S.P. Crane, 4x4, 5 Ton		140.00		154.00	7.00	7.70
20 L.H., Daily Totals		$982.00		$1535.20	$49.10	$76.76

Crew R-4	Hr.	Daily	Hr.	Daily	Bare Costs	Incl. O&P
1 Struc. Steel Foreman (outside)	$40.35	$322.80	$76.85	$614.80	$39.62	$73.18
3 Struc. Steel Workers	38.35	920.40	73.05	1753.20		
1 Electrician	42.70	341.60	69.90	559.20		
1 Welder, Gas Engine, 300 amp		142.00		156.20	3.55	3.90
40 L.H., Daily Totals		$1726.80		$3083.40	$43.17	$77.08

Crew R-5	Hr.	Daily	Hr.	Daily	Bare Costs	Incl. O&P
1 Electrician Foreman	$43.20	$345.60	$70.70	$565.60	$37.00	$61.08
4 Electrician Linemen	42.70	1366.40	69.90	2236.80		
2 Electrician Operators	42.70	683.20	69.90	1118.40		
4 Electrician Groundmen	26.90	860.80	45.45	1454.40		
1 Crew Truck		224.80		247.28		
1 Flatbed Truck, 20,000 GVW		253.40		278.74		
1 Pickup Truck, 3/4 Ton		157.00		172.70		
.2 Hyd. Crane, 55 Ton		227.40		250.14		
.2 Hyd. Crane, 12 Ton		132.60		145.86		
.2 Earth Auger, Truck-Mtd.		85.00		93.50		
1 Tractor w/Winch		434.60		478.06	17.21	18.93
88 L.H., Daily Totals		$4770.80		$7041.48	$54.21	$80.02

Crew R-6	Hr.	Daily	Hr.	Daily	Bare Costs	Incl. O&P
1 Electrician Foreman	$43.20	$345.60	$70.70	$565.60	$37.00	$61.08
4 Electrician Linemen	42.70	1366.40	69.90	2236.80		
2 Electrician Operators	42.70	683.20	69.90	1118.40		
4 Electrician Groundmen	26.90	860.80	45.45	1454.40		
1 Crew Truck		224.80		247.28		
1 Flatbed Truck, 20,000 GVW		253.40		278.74		
1 Pickup Truck, 3/4 Ton		157.00		172.70		
.2 Hyd. Crane, 55 Ton		227.40		250.14		
.2 Hyd. Crane, 12 Ton		132.60		145.86		
.2 Earth Auger, Truck-Mtd.		85.00		93.50		
1 Tractor w/Winch		434.60		478.06		
3 Cable Trailers		586.80		645.48		
.5 Tensioning Rig		194.55		214.01		
.5 Cable Pulling Rig		1136.50		1250.15	39.01	42.91
88 L.H., Daily Totals		$6688.65		$9151.11	$76.01	$103.99

Crew R-7	Hr.	Daily	Hr.	Daily	Bare Costs	Incl. O&P
1 Electrician Foreman	$43.20	$345.60	$70.70	$565.60	$29.62	$49.66
5 Electrician Groundmen	26.90	1076.00	45.45	1818.00		
1 Crew Truck		224.80		247.28	4.68	5.15
48 L.H., Daily Totals		$1646.40		$2630.88	$34.30	$54.81

Crew R-8	Hr.	Daily	Hr.	Daily	Bare Costs	Incl. O&P
1 Electrician Foreman	$43.20	$345.60	$70.70	$565.60	$37.52	$61.88
3 Electrician Linemen	42.70	1024.80	69.90	1677.60		
2 Electrician Groundmen	26.90	430.40	45.45	727.20		
1 Pickup Truck, 3/4 Ton		157.00		172.70		
1 Crew Truck		224.80		247.28	7.95	8.75
48 L.H., Daily Totals		$2182.60		$3390.38	$45.47	$70.63

Crew No.	Bare Costs		Incl. Subs O&P		Cost Per Labor-Hour	
Crew R-9	Hr.	Daily	Hr.	Daily	Bare Costs	Incl. O&P
1 Electrician Foreman	$43.20	$345.60	$70.70	$565.60	$34.86	$57.77
1 Electrician Lineman	42.70	341.60	69.90	559.20		
2 Electrician Operators	42.70	683.20	69.90	1118.40		
4 Electrician Groundmen	26.90	860.80	45.45	1454.40		
1 Pickup Truck, 3/4 Ton		157.00		172.70		
1 Crew Truck		224.80		247.28	5.97	6.56
64 L.H., Daily Totals		$2613.00		$4117.58	$40.83	$64.34
Crew R-10	Hr.	Daily	Hr.	Daily	Bare Costs	Incl. O&P
1 Electrician Foreman	$43.20	$345.60	$70.70	$565.60	$40.15	$65.96
4 Electrician Linemen	42.70	1366.40	69.90	2236.80		
1 Electrician Groundman	26.90	215.20	45.45	363.60		
1 Crew Truck		224.80		247.28		
3 Tram Cars		399.45		439.39	13.01	14.31
48 L.H., Daily Totals		$2551.45		$3852.68	$53.16	$80.26
Crew R-11	Hr.	Daily	Hr.	Daily	Bare Costs	Incl. O&P
1 Electrician Foreman	$43.20	$345.60	$70.70	$565.60	$40.13	$65.98
4 Electricians	42.70	1366.40	69.90	2236.80		
1 Equip. Oper. (crane)	38.70	309.60	64.10	512.80		
1 Common Laborer	28.20	225.60	47.45	379.60		
1 Crew Truck		224.80		247.28		
1 Hyd. Crane, 12 Ton		663.00		729.30	15.85	17.44
56 L.H., Daily Totals		$3135.00		$4671.38	$55.98	$83.42
Crew R-12	Hr.	Daily	Hr.	Daily	Bare Costs	Incl. O&P
1 Carpenter Foreman (inside)	$36.25	$290.00	$61.00	$488.00	$33.46	$56.98
4 Carpenters	35.75	1144.00	60.15	1924.80		
4 Common Laborers	28.20	902.40	47.45	1518.40		
1 Equip. Oper. (medium)	37.65	301.20	62.35	498.80		
1 Steel Worker	38.35	306.80	73.05	584.40		
1 Dozer, 200 H.P.		1325.00		1457.50		
1 Pickup Truck, 3/4 Ton		157.00		172.70	16.84	18.52
88 L.H., Daily Totals		$4426.40		$6644.60	$50.30	$75.51
Crew R-15	Hr.	Daily	Hr.	Daily	Bare Costs	Incl. O&P
1 Electrician Foreman	$43.20	$345.60	$70.70	$565.60	$41.71	$68.39
4 Electricians	42.70	1366.40	69.90	2236.80		
1 Equipment Oper. (light)	36.25	290.00	60.05	480.40		
1 Aerial Lift Truck, 40' Boom		325.00		357.50	6.77	7.45
48 L.H., Daily Totals		$2327.00		$3640.30	$48.48	$75.84
Crew R-15A	Hr.	Daily	Hr.	Daily	Bare Costs	Incl. O&P
1 Electrician Foreman	$43.20	$345.60	$70.70	$565.60	$36.88	$60.91
2 Electricians	42.70	683.20	69.90	1118.40		
2 Common Laborers	28.20	451.20	47.45	759.20		
1 Equip. Oper. (light)	36.25	290.00	60.05	480.40		
1 Aerial Lift Truck, 40' Boom		325.00		357.50	6.77	7.45
48 L.H., Daily Totals		$2095.00		$3281.10	$43.65	$68.36
Crew R-18	Hr.	Daily	Hr.	Daily	Bare Costs	Incl. O&P
.25 Electrician Foreman	$43.20	$86.40	$70.70	$141.40	$33.02	$54.92
1 Electrician	42.70	341.60	69.90	559.20		
2 Helpers	26.90	430.40	45.45	727.20		
26 L.H., Daily Totals		$858.40		$1427.80	$33.02	$54.92
Crew R-19	Hr.	Daily	Hr.	Daily	Bare Costs	Incl. O&P
.5 Electrician Foreman	$43.20	$172.80	$70.70	$282.80	$42.80	$70.06
2 Electricians	42.70	683.20	69.90	1118.40		
20 L.H., Daily Totals		$856.00		$1401.20	$42.80	$70.06

Crew No.	Bare Costs		Incl. Subs O&P		Cost Per Labor-Hour	
Crew R-21	Hr.	Daily	Hr.	Daily	Bare Costs	Incl. O&P
1 Electrician Foreman	$43.20	$345.60	$70.70	$565.60	$42.70	$69.91
3 Electricians	42.70	1024.80	69.90	1677.60		
.1 Equip. Oper. (medium)	37.65	30.12	62.35	49.88		
.1 S.P. Crane, 4x4, 25 Ton		60.72		66.79	1.85	2.04
32.8 L.H., Daily Totals		$1461.24		$2359.87	$44.55	$71.95
Crew R-22	Hr.	Daily	Hr.	Daily	Bare Costs	Incl. O&P
.66 Electrician Foreman	$43.20	$228.10	$70.70	$373.30	$35.99	$59.52
2 Electricians	42.70	683.20	69.90	1118.40		
2 Helpers	26.90	430.40	45.45	727.20		
37.28 L.H., Daily Totals		$1341.70		$2218.90	$35.99	$59.52
Crew R-30	Hr.	Daily	Hr.	Daily	Bare Costs	Incl. O&P
.25 Electrician Foreman (outside)	$44.70	$89.40	$73.15	$146.30	$33.93	$56.33
1 Electrician	42.70	341.60	69.90	559.20		
2 Laborers, (Semi-Skilled)	28.20	451.20	47.45	759.20		
26 L.H., Daily Totals		$882.20		$1464.70	$33.93	$56.33

Historical Cost Indexes

The table below lists both the RSMeans® historical cost index based on Jan. 1, 1993 = 100 as well as the computed value of an index based on Jan. 1, 2014 costs. Since the Jan. 1, 2014 figure is estimated, space is left to write in the actual index figures as they become available through either the quarterly *RSMeans Construction Cost Indexes* or as printed in the *Engineering News-Record*. To compute the actual index based on Jan. 1, 2014 = 100, divide the historical cost index for a particular year by the actual Jan. 1, 2014 construction cost index. Space has been left to advance the index figures as the year progresses.

Year	Historical Cost Index Jan. 1, 1993 = 100		Current Index Based on Jan. 1, 2014 = 100		Year	Historical Cost Index Jan. 1, 1993 = 100	Current Index Based on Jan. 1, 2014 = 100		Year	Historical Cost Index Jan. 1, 1993 = 100	Current Index Based on Jan. 1, 2014 = 100	
	Est.	Actual	Est.	Actual		Actual	Est.	Actual		Actual	Est.	Actual
Oct 2014*					July 1999	117.6	58.0		July 1981	70.0	34.5	
July 2014*					1998	115.1	56.8		1980	62.9	31.0	
April 2014*					1997	112.8	55.6		1979	57.8	28.5	
Jan 2014*	202.7		100.0	100.0	1996	110.2	54.4		1978	53.5	26.4	
July 2013		201.2	99.3		1995	107.6	53.1		1977	49.5	24.4	
2012		194.6	96.0		1994	104.4	51.5		1976	46.9	23.1	
2011		191.2	94.3		1993	101.7	50.2		1975	44.8	22.1	
2010		183.5	90.5		1992	99.4	49.1		1974	41.4	20.4	
2009		180.1	88.9		1991	96.8	47.8		1973	37.7	18.6	
2008		180.4	89.0		1990	94.3	46.5		1972	34.8	17.2	
2007		169.4	83.6		1989	92.1	45.5		1971	32.1	15.8	
2006		162.0	79.9		1988	89.9	44.3		1970	28.7	14.2	
2005		151.6	74.8		1987	87.7	43.3		1969	26.9	13.3	
2004		143.7	70.9		1986	84.2	41.6		1968	24.9	12.3	
2003		132.0	65.1		1985	82.6	40.8		1967	23.5	11.6	
2002		128.7	63.5		1984	82.0	40.4		1966	22.7	11.2	
2001		125.1	61.7		1983	80.2	39.5		1965	21.7	10.7	
2000		120.9	59.6		1982	76.1	37.6		1964	21.2	10.5	

Adjustments to Costs

The "Historical Cost Index" can be used to convert national average building costs at a particular time to the approximate building costs for some other time.

Example:

Estimate and compare construction costs for different years in the same city.

To estimate the national average construction cost of a building in 1970, knowing that it cost $900,000 in 2014:

INDEX in 1970 = 28.7

INDEX in 2014 = 202.7

Note: The city cost indexes for Canada can be used to convert U.S. national averages to local costs in Canadian dollars.

Time Adjustment Using the Historical Cost Indexes:

$$\frac{\text{Index for Year A}}{\text{Index for Year B}} \times \text{Cost in Year B} = \text{Cost in Year A}$$

$$\frac{\text{INDEX } 1970}{\text{INDEX } 2014} \times \text{Cost } 2014 = \text{Cost } 1970$$

$$\frac{28.7}{202.7} \times \$900,000 = .142 \times \$900,000 = \$128,000$$

The construction cost of the building in 1970 is $128,000.

*Historical Cost Index updates and other resources are provided on the following website.
http://www.reedconstructiondata.com/rsmeans/chgnotice/456321

How to Use the City Cost Indexes

What you should know before you begin

RSMeans City Cost Indexes (CCI) are an extremely useful tool to use when you want to compare costs from city to city and region to region.

This publication contains average construction cost indexes for 731 U.S. and Canadian cities covering over 930 three-digit zip code locations, as listed directly under each city.

Keep in mind that a City Cost Index number is a percentage ratio of a specific city's cost to the national average cost of the same item at a stated time period.

In other words, these index figures represent relative construction factors (or, if you prefer, multipliers) for Material and Installation costs, as well as the weighted average for Total In Place costs for each CSI MasterFormat division. Installation costs include both labor and equipment rental costs. When estimating equipment rental rates only, for a specific location, use 01 54 33 EQUIPMENT RENTAL COSTS in the Reference Section at the back of the book.

The 30 City Average Index is the average of 30 major U.S. cities and serves as a National Average.

Index figures for both material and installation are based on the 30 major city average of 100 and represent the cost relationship as of July 1, 2013. The index for each division is computed from representative material and labor quantities for that division. The weighted average for each city is a weighted total of the components listed above it, but does not include relative productivity between trades or cities.

As changes occur in local material prices, labor rates, and equipment rental rates (including fuel costs), the impact of these changes should be accurately measured by the change in the City Cost Index for each particular city (as compared to the 30 City Average).

Therefore, if you know (or have estimated) building costs in one city today, you can easily convert those costs to expected building costs in another city.

In addition, by using the Historical Cost Index, you can easily convert National Average building costs at a particular time to the approximate building costs for some other time. The City Cost Indexes can then be applied to calculate the costs for a particular city.

Quick Calculations

Location Adjustment Using the City Cost Indexes:

$$\frac{\text{Index for City A}}{\text{Index for City B}} \times \text{Cost in City B} = \text{Cost in City A}$$

Time Adjustment for the National Average Using the Historical Cost Index:

$$\frac{\text{Index for Year A}}{\text{Index for Year B}} \times \text{Cost in Year B} = \text{Cost in Year A}$$

Adjustment from the National Average:

$$\frac{\text{Index for City A}}{100} \times \text{National Average Cost} = \text{Cost in City A}$$

Since each of the other RSMeans publications contains many different items, any *one* item multiplied by the particular city index may give incorrect results. However, the larger the number of items compiled, the closer the results should be to actual costs for that particular city.

The City Cost Indexes for Canadian cities are calculated using Canadian material and equipment prices and labor rates, in Canadian dollars. Therefore, indexes for Canadian cities can be used to convert U.S. National Average prices to local costs in Canadian dollars.

How to use this section

1. Compare costs from city to city.

In using the RSMeans Indexes, remember that an index number is not a fixed number but a ratio: It's a percentage ratio of a building component's cost at any stated time to the National Average cost of that same component at the same time period. Put in the form of an equation:

$$\frac{\text{Specific City Cost}}{\text{National Average Cost}} \times 100 = \text{City Index Number}$$

Therefore, when making cost comparisons between cities, do not subtract one city's index number from the index number of another city and read the result as a percentage difference. Instead, divide one city's index number by that of the other city. The resulting number may then be used as a multiplier to calculate cost differences from city to city.

The formula used to find cost differences between cities for the purpose of comparison is as follows:

$$\frac{\text{City A Index}}{\text{City B Index}} \times \text{City B Cost (Known)} = \text{City A Cost (Unknown)}$$

In addition, you can use RSMeans CCI to calculate and compare costs division by division between cities using the same basic formula. (Just be sure that you're comparing similar divisions.)

2. Compare a specific city's construction costs with the National Average.

When you're studying construction location feasibility, it's advisable to compare a prospective project's cost index with an index of the National Average cost.

For example, divide the weighted average index of construction costs of a specific city by that of the 30 City Average, which = 100.

$$\frac{\text{City Index}}{100} = \% \text{ of National Average}$$

As a result, you get a ratio that indicates the relative cost of construction in that city in comparison with the National Average.

3. Convert U.S. National Average to actual costs in Canadian City.

$$\frac{\text{Index for Canadian City}}{100} \times \text{National Average Cost} = \text{Cost in Canadian City in \$ CAN}$$

4. Adjust construction cost data based on a National Average.

When you use a source of construction cost data which is based on a National Average (such as RSMeans cost data publications), it is necessary to adjust those costs to a specific location.

$$\frac{\text{City Index}}{100} \times \begin{array}{c}\text{"Book" Cost Based on} \\ \text{National Average Costs}\end{array} = \begin{array}{c}\text{City Cost} \\ \text{(Unknown)}\end{array}$$

5. When applying the City Cost Indexes to demolition projects, use the appropriate division installation index. For example, for removal of existing doors and windows, use Division 8 (Openings) index.

What you might like to know about how we developed the Indexes

The information presented in the CCI is organized according to the Construction Specifications Institute (CSI) MasterFormat 2012 classification system.

To create a reliable index, RSMeans researched the building type most often constructed in the United States and Canada. Because it was concluded that no one type of building completely represented the building construction industry, nine different types of buildings were combined to create a composite model.

The exact material, labor, and equipment quantities are based on detailed analyses of these nine building types, and then each quantity is weighted in proportion to expected usage. These various material items, labor hours, and equipment rental rates are thus combined to form a composite building representing as closely as possible the actual usage of materials, labor, and equipment used in the North American building construction industry.

The following structures were chosen to make up that composite model:

1. Factory, 1 story
2. Office, 2–4 story
3. Store, Retail
4. Town Hall, 2–3 story
5. High School, 2–3 story
6. Hospital, 4–8 story
7. Garage, Parking
8. Apartment, 1–3 story
9. Hotel/Motel, 2–3 story

For the purposes of ensuring the timeliness of the data, the components of the index for the composite model have been streamlined. They currently consist of:

- specific quantities of 66 commonly used construction materials;
- specific labor-hours for 21 building construction trades; and
- specific days of equipment rental for 6 types of construction equipment (normally used to install the 66 material items by the 21 trades.) Fuel costs and routine maintenance costs are included in the equipment cost.

A sophisticated computer program handles the updating of all costs for each city on a quarterly basis. Material and equipment price quotations are gathered quarterly from 731 cities in the United States and Canada. These prices and the latest negotiated labor wage rates for 21 different building trades are used to compile the quarterly update of the City Cost Index.

The 30 major U.S. cities used to calculate the National Average are:

Atlanta, GA	Memphis, TN
Baltimore, MD	Milwaukee, WI
Boston, MA	Minneapolis, MN
Buffalo, NY	Nashville, TN
Chicago, IL	New Orleans, LA
Cincinnati, OH	New York, NY
Cleveland, OH	Philadelphia, PA
Columbus, OH	Phoenix, AZ
Dallas, TX	Pittsburgh, PA
Denver, CO	St. Louis, MO
Detroit, MI	San Antonio, TX
Houston, TX	San Diego, CA
Indianapolis, IN	San Francisco, CA
Kansas City, MO	Seattle, WA
Los Angeles, CA	Washington, DC

What the CCI does not indicate

The weighted average for each city is a total of the divisional components weighted to reflect typical usage, but it does not include the productivity variations between trades or cities.

In addition, the CCI does not take into consideration factors such as the following:

- managerial efficiency
- competitive conditions
- automation
- restrictive union practices
- unique local requirements
- regional variations due to specific building codes

DIVISION		UNITED STATES 30 CITY AVERAGE			ALABAMA ANNISTON 362			BIRMINGHAM 350 - 352			BUTLER 369			DECATUR 356			DOTHAN 363		
		MAT.	INST.	TOTAL	MAT.	INST.	TOTAL	MAT.	INST.	TOTAL	MAT.	INST.	TOTAL	MAT.	INST.	TOTAL	MAT.	INST.	TOTAL
015433	CONTRACTOR EQUIPMENT		100.0	100.0		101.6	101.6		101.7	101.7		98.8	98.8		101.6	101.6		98.8	98.8
0241, 31 - 34	SITE & INFRASTRUCTURE, DEMOLITION	100.0	100.0	100.0	87.7	94.3	92.3	88.8	94.9	93.1	101.0	88.3	92.1	81.3	92.8	89.3	98.7	88.3	91.4
0310	Concrete Forming & Accessories	100.0	100.0	100.0	92.7	48.2	54.3	93.3	70.2	73.4	89.0	43.6	49.8	94.7	46.4	53.0	97.9	43.0	50.5
0320	Concrete Reinforcing	100.0	100.0	100.0	87.0	87.4	87.2	92.9	87.8	90.4	92.0	47.4	69.7	87.0	79.5	83.3	92.0	46.8	69.4
0330	Cast-in-Place Concrete	100.0	100.0	100.0	102.0	50.5	80.6	99.7	74.7	89.3	99.4	55.7	81.3	93.7	65.1	81.9	99.4	47.0	77.7
03	CONCRETE	100.0	100.0	100.0	99.8	57.9	79.1	95.1	76.1	85.7	100.6	54.0	75.8	91.4	60.7	76.3	100.0	47.0	73.9
04	MASONRY	100.0	100.0	100.0	90.5	67.9	76.5	89.9	76.2	81.4	95.3	49.4	66.9	88.4	52.1	66.0	96.6	40.4	61.8
05	METALS	100.0	100.0	100.0	96.9	92.5	95.5	97.0	94.7	96.3	95.8	78.1	90.4	99.0	87.7	95.5	95.9	76.9	90.0
06	WOOD, PLASTICS & COMPOSITES	100.0	100.0	100.0	92.7	43.7	65.1	96.3	68.3	80.5	87.3	43.4	62.5	98.0	43.9	67.5	99.6	43.4	67.9
07	THERMAL & MOISTURE PROTECTION	100.0	100.0	100.0	100.1	53.8	81.3	95.9	81.4	90.0	100.1	57.6	82.9	93.1	59.3	79.4	100.1	49.9	79.7
08	OPENINGS	100.0	100.0	100.0	93.9	50.9	83.8	95.8	72.3	90.3	94.0	45.2	82.4	98.8	51.6	87.6	94.0	45.2	82.5
0920	Plaster & Gypsum Board	100.0	100.0	100.0	87.5	42.4	56.8	97.0	67.8	77.1	84.9	42.0	55.7	98.1	42.6	60.4	95.3	42.0	59.1
0950, 0980	Ceilings & Acoustic Treatment	100.0	100.0	100.0	87.8	42.4	57.6	98.4	67.8	78.0	87.8	42.0	57.3	95.7	42.6	60.4	87.8	42.0	57.3
0960	Flooring	100.0	100.0	100.0	104.1	41.0	85.2	109.0	76.2	99.2	109.2	57.0	93.6	106.0	51.5	89.7	114.9	28.0	88.9
0970, 0990	Wall Finishes & Painting/Coating	100.0	100.0	100.0	91.4	32.1	55.8	93.5	56.8	71.4	91.4	54.5	69.2	89.3	68.2	76.7	91.4	54.5	69.2
09	FINISHES	100.0	100.0	100.0	92.7	44.0	65.6	99.4	69.3	82.6	95.9	46.7	68.5	95.9	48.8	69.7	98.7	41.0	66.6
COVERS	DIVS. 10 - 14, 25, 28, 41, 43, 44, 46	100.0	100.0	100.0	100.0	70.1	94.0	100.0	87.4	97.5	100.0	42.5	88.5	100.0	44.4	88.9	100.0	42.6	88.5
21, 22, 23	FIRE SUPPRESSION, PLUMBING & HVAC	100.0	100.0	100.0	99.9	56.6	82.6	100.0	62.8	85.1	97.3	34.0	71.9	100.0	41.7	76.6	97.3	33.9	71.9
26, 27, 3370	ELECTRICAL, COMMUNICATIONS & UTIL.	100.0	100.0	100.0	90.7	58.7	74.0	99.7	62.8	80.4	92.6	41.2	65.7	94.5	66.5	79.9	91.5	58.8	74.4
MF2010	WEIGHTED AVERAGE	100.0	100.0	100.0	96.5	63.0	81.9	97.5	74.1	87.3	96.8	50.5	76.6	96.6	59.1	80.3	96.9	50.5	76.7

DIVISION		ALABAMA EVERGREEN 364			GADSDEN 359			HUNTSVILLE 357 - 358			JASPER 355			MOBILE 365 - 366			MONTGOMERY 360 - 361		
		MAT.	INST.	TOTAL	MAT.	INST.	TOTAL	MAT.	INST.	TOTAL	MAT.	INST.	TOTAL	MAT.	INST.	TOTAL	MAT.	INST.	TOTAL
015433	CONTRACTOR EQUIPMENT		98.8	98.8		101.6	101.6		101.6	101.6		101.6	101.6		98.8	98.8		98.8	98.8
0241, 31 - 34	SITE & INFRASTRUCTURE, DEMOLITION	101.5	88.6	92.4	86.7	93.8	91.7	81.1	93.8	90.0	86.3	93.6	91.4	94.0	89.3	90.7	94.0	89.2	90.6
0310	Concrete Forming & Accessories	85.6	45.2	50.8	87.0	43.3	49.3	94.7	71.1	74.3	92.2	35.3	43.0	97.1	55.0	60.7	96.9	45.0	52.1
0320	Concrete Reinforcing	92.0	47.4	69.7	92.2	87.7	90.0	87.0	80.5	83.8	87.0	86.5	86.8	89.8	79.4	84.6	94.9	87.1	91.0
0330	Cast-in-Place Concrete	99.5	58.3	82.4	93.8	66.7	82.5	91.3	69.6	82.3	103.9	44.8	79.3	104.3	67.4	88.9	105.4	57.4	85.5
03	CONCRETE	100.9	52.0	76.8	95.7	61.4	78.8	90.3	73.3	81.9	98.9	50.1	74.8	97.0	65.3	81.4	98.3	58.9	78.8
04	MASONRY	95.4	54.1	69.8	86.7	62.3	71.6	89.7	67.7	76.1	84.2	42.0	58.1	93.8	55.1	69.9	90.4	50.5	65.7
05	METALS	95.9	78.1	90.4	96.9	94.0	96.0	99.0	90.5	96.4	96.9	91.1	95.1	97.9	90.6	95.6	97.0	92.8	95.7
06	WOOD, PLASTICS & COMPOSITES	83.6	43.4	60.0	87.8	39.6	60.6	98.0	74.3	84.6	94.8	32.3	59.6	98.2	54.1	73.3	97.7	43.4	67.0
07	THERMAL & MOISTURE PROTECTION	100.1	57.9	83.0	93.1	72.4	84.7	93.0	78.5	87.1	93.2	46.1	74.1	99.8	71.3	88.2	100.2	67.8	87.0
08	OPENINGS	94.0	45.2	82.4	95.4	49.8	84.6	98.8	68.2	91.5	95.3	48.7	84.3	97.2	58.6	88.1	98.3	54.0	87.8
0920	Plaster & Gypsum Board	84.2	42.0	55.5	89.8	38.2	54.7	98.1	73.9	81.7	94.2	30.7	51.0	92.1	53.1	65.5	91.5	42.0	57.8
0950, 0980	Ceilings & Acoustic Treatment	87.8	42.0	57.3	92.1	38.2	56.2	97.6	73.9	81.9	92.1	30.7	51.2	93.3	53.1	66.5	95.9	42.0	60.0
0960	Flooring	107.0	57.0	92.1	102.0	76.2	94.3	106.0	76.2	97.1	104.3	41.0	85.3	114.6	59.5	98.1	110.8	59.5	95.5
0970, 0990	Wall Finishes & Painting/Coating	91.4	54.5	69.2	89.3	62.0	72.9	89.3	59.7	71.5	89.3	39.4	59.3	95.0	55.4	71.2	91.2	54.5	69.1
09	FINISHES	95.3	47.9	68.9	93.3	49.4	68.8	96.4	71.1	82.3	94.5	35.2	61.5	99.0	54.7	74.3	99.0	47.1	70.1
COVERS	DIVS. 10 - 14, 25, 28, 41, 43, 44, 46	100.0	44.1	88.8	100.0	79.5	95.9	100.0	85.3	97.0	100.0	40.8	88.1	100.0	83.9	96.8	100.0	79.4	95.9
21, 22, 23	FIRE SUPPRESSION, PLUMBING & HVAC	97.3	36.3	72.9	102.0	36.9	75.9	100.0	52.9	81.1	102.0	53.8	82.6	100.0	61.5	84.5	100.1	34.8	73.9
26, 27, 3370	ELECTRICAL, COMMUNICATIONS & UTIL.	90.1	41.2	64.6	94.5	62.8	78.0	95.7	66.5	80.4	94.1	62.8	77.7	93.4	58.5	75.2	93.9	62.3	77.4
MF2010	WEIGHTED AVERAGE	96.5	51.9	77.1	96.7	60.8	81.1	96.7	70.8	85.4	97.0	56.7	79.4	97.8	65.9	83.9	97.9	58.1	80.5

DIVISION		ALABAMA PHENIX CITY 368			SELMA 367			TUSCALOOSA 354			ALASKA ANCHORAGE 995 - 996			FAIRBANKS 997			JUNEAU 998		
		MAT.	INST.	TOTAL	MAT.	INST.	TOTAL	MAT.	INST.	TOTAL	MAT.	INST.	TOTAL	MAT.	INST.	TOTAL	MAT.	INST.	TOTAL
015433	CONTRACTOR EQUIPMENT		98.8	98.8		98.8	98.8		101.6	101.6		113.5	113.5		113.5	113.5		113.5	113.5
0241, 31 - 34	SITE & INFRASTRUCTURE, DEMOLITION	105.2	89.3	94.0	98.6	89.1	92.0	81.6	94.0	90.3	125.5	128.8	127.8	116.4	128.8	125.1	132.0	128.8	129.8
0310	Concrete Forming & Accessories	92.6	39.9	47.1	90.3	43.5	49.9	94.6	48.8	55.1	127.8	119.0	120.2	133.0	118.7	120.7	129.2	118.9	120.3
0320	Concrete Reinforcing	91.9	63.3	77.7	92.0	86.2	89.1	87.0	87.7	87.3	148.0	111.5	129.8	142.1	111.5	126.8	122.7	111.5	117.1
0330	Cast-in-Place Concrete	99.5	57.9	82.2	99.4	47.2	77.8	95.1	68.5	84.1	131.0	117.4	125.3	129.2	117.7	124.4	136.1	117.4	128.3
03	CONCRETE	103.6	52.4	78.3	99.4	54.5	77.3	92.1	64.5	78.5	143.0	116.3	129.8	126.5	116.3	121.4	139.9	116.2	128.2
04	MASONRY	95.3	41.8	62.2	98.7	39.3	62.0	88.6	65.5	74.3	180.9	122.2	144.6	182.2	122.2	145.1	167.6	122.2	139.5
05	METALS	95.8	83.5	92.0	95.8	90.3	94.1	98.2	94.1	96.9	114.6	102.5	110.9	118.8	102.6	113.8	117.6	102.4	112.9
06	WOOD, PLASTICS & COMPOSITES	92.5	36.3	60.8	89.3	43.4	63.4	98.0	45.4	68.3	117.1	117.9	117.6	125.0	117.4	120.7	119.8	117.9	118.7
07	THERMAL & MOISTURE PROTECTION	100.4	64.9	86.0	100.0	53.0	80.9	93.1	74.4	85.5	169.9	115.5	147.8	169.2	116.6	147.9	163.4	115.5	143.9
08	OPENINGS	93.9	44.6	82.3	93.9	54.0	84.5	98.8	59.8	89.6	119.7	115.2	118.7	116.2	115.2	116.0	116.6	115.2	116.3
0920	Plaster & Gypsum Board	89.0	34.7	52.1	86.8	42.0	56.3	98.1	44.2	61.4	126.3	118.3	120.9	148.9	117.8	127.7	131.2	118.3	122.4
0950, 0980	Ceilings & Acoustic Treatment	87.8	34.7	52.5	87.8	42.0	57.3	97.6	44.2	62.1	126.5	118.3	121.0	121.7	117.8	119.1	123.5	118.3	120.0
0960	Flooring	111.3	59.5	95.8	109.8	29.0	85.6	106.0	76.2	97.1	150.1	128.3	143.6	140.7	128.3	137.0	142.1	128.3	138.0
0970, 0990	Wall Finishes & Painting/Coating	91.4	54.5	69.2	91.4	54.5	69.2	89.3	46.9	63.8	146.5	113.3	126.5	143.9	121.9	130.7	143.3	113.3	125.2
09	FINISHES	97.5	43.2	67.2	96.0	41.2	65.5	96.3	52.0	71.6	143.1	120.5	130.5	139.4	121.2	129.2	139.6	120.5	129.0
COVERS	DIVS. 10 - 14, 25, 28, 41, 43, 44, 46	100.0	79.0	95.8	100.0	42.5	88.5	100.0	81.3	96.2	100.0	112.5	102.5	100.0	112.5	102.5	100.0	112.5	102.5
21, 22, 23	FIRE SUPPRESSION, PLUMBING & HVAC	97.3	35.1	72.4	97.3	34.3	72.1	100.0	34.6	73.8	100.2	104.3	101.9	100.2	106.7	102.8	100.1	100.6	100.3
26, 27, 3370	ELECTRICAL, COMMUNICATIONS & UTIL.	92.1	71.2	81.2	91.2	41.2	65.1	95.1	62.8	78.2	120.5	115.6	117.9	134.7	115.6	124.7	125.5	115.6	120.3
MF2010	WEIGHTED AVERAGE	97.3	55.7	79.2	96.7	50.8	76.7	96.7	62.0	81.6	121.3	114.3	118.3	120.7	115.0	118.2	120.6	113.5	117.5

Table 1

DIVISION		ALASKA			ARIZONA														
		KETCHIKAN			CHAMBERS			FLAGSTAFF			GLOBE			KINGMAN			MESA/TEMPE		
		999			865			860			855			864			852		
		MAT.	INST.	TOTAL	MAT.	INST.	TOTAL	MAT.	INST.	TOTAL	MAT.	INST.	TOTAL	MAT.	INST.	TOTAL	MAT.	INST.	TOTAL
015433	CONTRACTOR EQUIPMENT		113.5	113.5		92.6	92.6		92.6	92.6		94.2	94.2		92.6	92.6		94.2	94.2
0241, 31 - 34	SITE & INFRASTRUCTURE, DEMOLITION	170.9	128.8	141.3	67.2	96.6	87.9	84.8	96.8	93.3	100.7	98.4	99.1	67.2	96.8	88.0	91.4	98.6	96.4
0310	Concrete Forming & Accessories	124.5	118.9	119.7	98.2	59.2	64.5	103.7	66.4	71.5	96.3	59.3	64.3	96.5	66.4	70.5	99.3	69.6	73.6
0320	Concrete Reinforcing	111.6	111.5	111.5	100.0	83.5	91.7	99.8	83.5	91.7	110.1	83.5	96.8	100.1	83.5	91.8	110.8	83.5	97.2
0330	Cast-in-Place Concrete	261.0	117.4	201.4	90.3	73.5	83.3	90.4	73.8	83.5	93.8	73.6	85.4	90.0	73.8	83.3	94.6	73.9	86.0
03	CONCRETE	214.6	116.2	166.0	96.5	68.9	82.8	116.1	72.2	94.4	109.8	68.9	89.7	96.1	72.2	84.3	101.7	73.7	87.8
04	MASONRY	191.0	122.2	148.4	90.6	62.7	73.3	90.7	62.8	73.4	110.3	62.7	80.9	90.6	62.8	73.4	110.6	62.8	81.0
05	METALS	119.0	102.4	113.9	95.1	75.0	88.9	95.6	75.7	89.5	92.4	75.5	87.2	95.7	75.8	89.6	92.7	76.4	87.7
06	WOOD, PLASTICS & COMPOSITES	115.7	117.9	117.0	96.1	56.3	73.6	102.2	65.7	81.6	90.0	56.4	71.0	91.6	65.7	77.0	93.4	69.9	80.2
07	THERMAL & MOISTURE PROTECTION	172.3	115.5	149.2	95.1	65.1	82.9	96.7	68.2	85.1	99.3	64.6	85.2	95.0	65.7	83.1	98.6	66.6	85.6
08	OPENINGS	118.1	115.2	117.4	108.1	65.7	98.1	108.2	70.8	99.4	102.2	65.8	93.6	108.3	70.8	99.4	102.3	73.2	95.4
0920	Plaster & Gypsum Board	137.4	118.3	124.4	85.6	55.0	64.8	89.1	64.7	72.5	94.2	55.0	67.5	79.1	64.7	69.3	96.4	69.0	77.7
0950, 0980	Ceilings & Acoustic Treatment	114.7	118.3	117.1	107.8	55.0	72.7	108.7	64.7	79.4	96.4	55.0	68.8	108.7	64.7	79.4	96.4	69.0	78.1
0960	Flooring	140.7	128.3	137.0	92.1	40.3	76.6	94.1	40.4	78.1	100.0	40.3	82.1	91.1	54.7	80.2	101.1	50.4	86.0
0970, 0990	Wall Finishes & Painting/Coating	143.9	113.3	125.5	97.8	56.3	72.9	97.8	56.3	72.9	108.9	56.3	77.3	97.8	56.3	72.9	108.9	56.3	77.3
09	FINISHES	140.7	120.5	129.5	95.7	54.0	72.4	98.8	59.6	76.9	97.6	54.1	73.4	94.7	62.0	76.5	97.1	64.0	78.7
COVERS	DIVS. 10 - 14, 25, 28, 41, 43, 44, 46	100.0	112.5	102.5	100.0	82.3	96.5	100.0	83.3	96.7	100.0	82.5	96.5	100.0	83.3	96.7	100.0	84.0	96.8
21, 22, 23	FIRE SUPPRESSION, PLUMBING & HVAC	98.4	100.6	99.3	97.0	78.9	89.7	100.2	80.0	92.1	95.2	78.9	88.7	97.0	80.0	90.2	100.1	79.0	91.6
26, 27, 3370	ELECTRICAL, COMMUNICATIONS & UTIL.	134.6	115.6	124.7	102.2	72.6	86.7	101.1	65.8	82.7	98.7	65.8	81.6	102.2	65.8	83.2	95.3	65.8	79.9
MF2010	WEIGHTED AVERAGE	132.0	113.5	124.0	97.3	71.9	86.3	101.0	72.9	88.8	99.0	71.2	86.9	97.3	73.2	86.8	98.8	73.8	87.9

Table 2

DIVISION		ARIZONA												ARKANSAS					
		PHOENIX			PRESCOTT			SHOW LOW			TUCSON			BATESVILLE			CAMDEN		
		850,853			863			859			856 - 857			725			717		
		MAT.	INST.	TOTAL	MAT.	INST.	TOTAL	MAT.	INST.	TOTAL	MAT.	INST.	TOTAL	MAT.	INST.	TOTAL	MAT.	INST.	TOTAL
015433	CONTRACTOR EQUIPMENT		94.7	94.7		92.6	92.6		94.2	94.2		94.2	94.2		89.0	89.0		89.0	89.0
0241, 31 - 34	SITE & INFRASTRUCTURE, DEMOLITION	91.9	98.8	96.7	73.5	96.6	89.7	102.8	98.4	99.7	87.1	98.6	95.1	73.4	84.9	81.5	73.3	84.5	81.2
0310	Concrete Forming & Accessories	100.2	69.7	73.9	99.8	53.5	59.8	103.2	69.3	74.0	99.8	69.5	73.6	85.2	45.9	51.3	83.9	31.4	38.6
0320	Concrete Reinforcing	109.0	83.7	96.3	99.8	83.5	91.6	110.8	83.5	97.2	91.8	83.5	87.6	86.7	65.8	76.3	88.2	65.7	76.9
0330	Cast-in-Place Concrete	94.7	74.0	86.1	90.3	73.5	83.3	93.9	73.6	85.5	97.4	73.9	87.6	81.1	46.1	66.6	81.2	39.0	63.7
03	CONCRETE	101.3	73.8	87.7	101.7	66.3	84.2	112.1	73.4	93.0	99.7	73.6	86.8	85.2	50.5	68.0	86.9	41.5	64.5
04	MASONRY	98.0	64.6	77.3	90.7	62.7	73.4	110.4	62.7	80.9	95.9	62.8	75.4	98.7	41.5	63.3	111.6	31.9	62.3
05	METALS	94.2	77.2	88.9	95.6	74.7	89.2	92.2	75.7	87.1	93.5	76.3	88.2	98.0	66.9	88.4	97.3	66.5	87.8
06	WOOD, PLASTICS & COMPOSITES	94.4	69.9	80.6	97.5	48.5	69.9	98.0	69.9	82.1	93.7	69.9	80.3	86.3	46.5	63.9	89.8	30.4	56.3
07	THERMAL & MOISTURE PROTECTION	98.2	68.7	86.2	95.5	64.2	82.8	99.5	66.5	86.1	99.6	65.8	85.9	100.2	44.8	77.7	96.1	36.4	71.9
08	OPENINGS	104.2	73.2	96.9	108.2	61.5	97.2	101.3	73.2	94.7	98.3	73.2	92.4	94.6	46.0	83.1	93.5	40.6	81.0
0920	Plaster & Gypsum Board	98.5	69.0	78.4	85.7	47.0	59.4	98.6	69.0	78.4	101.9	69.0	79.5	81.0	45.4	56.7	80.2	28.7	45.2
0950, 0980	Ceilings & Acoustic Treatment	103.5	69.0	80.5	106.9	47.0	67.1	96.4	69.0	78.1	97.3	69.0	78.4	90.6	45.4	60.5	86.2	28.7	47.9
0960	Flooring	101.4	52.7	86.8	92.9	40.3	77.1	102.5	45.9	85.5	91.9	45.0	77.9	104.6	60.1	91.3	111.2	40.3	90.0
0970, 0990	Wall Finishes & Painting/Coating	108.9	62.0	80.7	97.8	56.3	72.9	108.9	56.3	77.3	110.1	56.3	77.8	99.8	42.0	65.1	99.5	50.8	70.2
09	FINISHES	99.1	65.0	80.1	96.2	49.4	70.1	99.2	63.0	79.0	95.4	62.9	77.3	89.8	47.8	66.4	92.1	34.2	59.8
COVERS	DIVS. 10 - 14, 25, 28, 41, 43, 44, 46	100.0	84.0	96.8	100.0	81.4	96.3	100.0	84.0	96.8	100.0	84.0	96.8	100.0	40.6	88.1	100.0	36.5	87.3
21, 22, 23	FIRE SUPPRESSION, PLUMBING & HVAC	100.0	80.0	92.0	100.2	78.9	91.7	95.2	79.0	88.7	100.1	79.0	91.6	95.3	52.1	77.9	95.3	53.5	78.5
26, 27, 3370	ELECTRICAL, COMMUNICATIONS & UTIL.	102.2	68.3	84.5	100.7	65.8	82.5	95.7	65.8	80.1	97.6	65.8	81.0	95.0	64.0	78.8	91.5	62.0	76.1
MF2010	WEIGHTED AVERAGE	99.4	74.8	88.7	98.9	69.7	86.2	99.1	73.5	88.0	97.6	73.6	87.1	94.2	55.1	77.2	94.5	50.4	75.3

Table 3

DIVISION		ARKANSAS																	
		FAYETTEVILLE			FORT SMITH			HARRISON			HOT SPRINGS			JONESBORO			LITTLE ROCK		
		727			729			726			719			724			720 - 722		
		MAT.	INST.	TOTAL	MAT.	INST.	TOTAL	MAT.	INST.	TOTAL	MAT.	INST.	TOTAL	MAT.	INST.	TOTAL	MAT.	INST.	TOTAL
015433	CONTRACTOR EQUIPMENT		89.0	89.0		89.0	89.0		89.0	89.0		89.0	89.0		107.5	107.5		89.0	89.0
0241, 31 - 34	SITE & INFRASTRUCTURE, DEMOLITION	72.8	86.4	82.4	77.7	86.3	83.8	77.9	84.9	82.8	76.4	85.9	83.0	96.9	100.3	99.3	87.9	86.3	86.8
0310	Concrete Forming & Accessories	80.6	39.4	45.1	100.2	57.7	63.5	89.7	45.8	51.8	81.2	36.5	42.6	88.7	49.2	54.6	95.3	60.4	65.2
0320	Concrete Reinforcing	86.7	71.6	79.2	87.7	72.3	80.0	86.3	65.7	76.0	86.5	65.8	76.2	83.9	64.8	74.4	92.7	66.5	79.6
0330	Cast-in-Place Concrete	81.1	50.2	68.3	92.8	70.4	83.5	90.0	44.2	71.0	83.0	39.5	64.9	88.3	55.9	74.9	91.5	70.5	82.8
03	CONCRETE	84.9	50.1	67.7	93.1	65.3	79.4	92.6	49.8	71.4	90.7	44.0	67.6	89.8	55.9	73.1	94.7	65.4	80.2
04	MASONRY	89.1	42.1	60.0	94.1	50.0	66.8	99.0	39.7	62.3	83.9	34.1	53.1	90.5	42.6	60.9	93.9	50.0	66.7
05	METALS	98.0	69.3	89.1	100.3	71.1	91.3	99.1	66.6	89.1	97.3	66.9	87.9	94.6	78.8	89.7	100.5	69.2	90.8
06	WOOD, PLASTICS & COMPOSITES	81.9	36.3	56.2	103.9	60.4	79.4	92.3	46.5	66.5	86.8	36.5	58.4	90.1	49.4	67.1	96.3	63.9	78.1
07	THERMAL & MOISTURE PROTECTION	101.0	46.2	78.8	101.4	54.5	82.4	100.5	43.5	77.4	96.3	38.6	72.9	105.2	50.0	82.8	97.7	54.9	80.3
08	OPENINGS	94.6	45.8	83.0	95.4	57.1	86.4	95.4	46.7	83.9	93.5	42.4	81.4	97.4	53.5	87.0	96.2	58.9	87.4
0920	Plaster & Gypsum Board	78.7	34.9	48.9	86.6	59.7	68.3	85.5	45.4	58.2	78.8	35.1	49.0	95.4	48.0	63.1	92.1	63.3	72.5
0950, 0980	Ceilings & Acoustic Treatment	90.6	34.9	53.5	92.4	59.7	70.6	92.4	45.4	61.1	86.2	35.1	52.2	93.8	48.0	63.3	95.8	63.3	74.2
0960	Flooring	102.0	60.1	89.5	111.0	61.9	96.3	106.9	60.1	92.9	110.0	60.1	95.1	74.5	54.4	68.5	109.1	61.9	95.0
0970, 0990	Wall Finishes & Painting/Coating	99.8	30.0	57.8	99.8	55.0	72.8	99.8	42.0	65.1	99.5	50.8	70.2	88.3	49.4	64.9	100.9	56.4	74.2
09	FINISHES	88.9	40.9	62.2	93.0	58.4	73.8	91.8	47.8	67.3	91.8	41.3	63.7	86.5	49.6	66.0	95.9	60.7	76.3
COVERS	DIVS. 10 - 14, 25, 28, 41, 43, 44, 46	100.0	50.0	90.0	100.0	76.8	95.4	100.0	50.5	90.1	100.0	37.5	87.5	100.0	46.3	89.3	100.0	77.2	95.4
21, 22, 23	FIRE SUPPRESSION, PLUMBING & HVAC	95.3	50.6	77.4	100.2	50.1	80.1	95.3	49.8	77.0	95.3	49.1	76.8	100.4	52.9	81.4	100.0	56.4	82.5
26, 27, 3370	ELECTRICAL, COMMUNICATIONS & UTIL.	88.8	52.4	69.8	92.3	66.1	78.6	93.5	38.0	64.5	93.5	69.4	81.0	99.0	64.0	80.7	99.3	69.5	83.7
MF2010	WEIGHTED AVERAGE	93.0	52.9	75.6	96.8	61.7	81.5	95.5	51.1	76.1	93.8	52.3	75.8	96.3	59.4	80.2	98.0	63.8	83.1

City Cost Indexes

ARKANSAS / CALIFORNIA

DIVISION		PINE BLUFF 716 MAT.	INST.	TOTAL	RUSSELLVILLE 728 MAT.	INST.	TOTAL	TEXARKANA 718 MAT.	INST.	TOTAL	WEST MEMPHIS 723 MAT.	INST.	TOTAL	ALHAMBRA 917-918 MAT.	INST.	TOTAL	ANAHEIM 928 MAT.	INST.	TOTAL
015433	CONTRACTOR EQUIPMENT		89.0	89.0		89.0	89.0		89.7	89.7		107.5	107.5		98.9	98.9		100.0	100.0
0241, 31 - 34	SITE & INFRASTRUCTURE, DEMOLITION	78.5	86.3	84.0	74.5	84.9	81.8	90.2	86.9	87.9	103.2	100.3	101.2	96.4	109.7	105.7	96.5	107.7	104.4
0310	Concrete Forming & Accessories	80.9	60.3	63.2	85.9	56.0	60.1	87.6	41.0	47.4	94.4	49.5	55.6	115.1	116.9	116.6	105.5	123.1	120.7
0320	Concrete Reinforcing	88.1	66.5	77.3	87.3	65.6	76.5	87.7	65.8	76.8	83.9	64.9	74.4	107.4	114.9	111.1	93.2	114.8	103.9
0330	Cast-in-Place Concrete	83.0	70.4	77.8	85.0	46.0	68.8	90.5	44.0	71.2	92.6	56.0	77.4	94.7	119.1	104.8	91.3	121.7	104.0
03	CONCRETE	91.5	65.4	78.6	88.4	54.9	71.9	89.1	47.6	68.6	97.3	56.0	76.9	104.0	116.4	110.1	103.1	120.0	111.4
04	MASONRY	120.2	50.0	76.8	93.3	38.0	59.1	98.1	33.7	58.2	76.8	42.6	55.7	122.3	118.6	120.0	77.4	116.2	101.4
05	METALS	98.0	69.1	89.1	98.0	66.5	88.3	90.8	67.0	83.5	93.6	79.1	89.2	84.0	99.9	88.9	103.1	100.2	102.2
06	WOOD, PLASTICS & COMPOSITES	86.3	63.9	73.7	87.7	60.4	72.3	95.2	43.0	65.7	96.3	49.4	69.9	96.6	113.1	105.9	98.5	121.4	111.4
07	THERMAL & MOISTURE PROTECTION	96.4	54.9	79.6	101.2	44.7	78.3	97.1	45.3	76.1	105.6	50.0	83.1	95.2	117.2	104.2	97.9	121.3	107.4
08	OPENINGS	93.5	58.9	85.3	94.6	56.2	85.5	98.3	46.7	86.1	97.4	53.5	87.0	89.8	115.5	95.9	100.3	120.2	105.0
0920	Plaster & Gypsum Board	78.4	63.3	68.1	81.0	59.7	66.5	82.2	41.7	54.6	98.0	48.0	64.0	102.1	113.7	110.0	100.6	122.0	115.2
0950, 0980	Ceilings & Acoustic Treatment	86.2	63.3	71.0	90.6	59.7	70.0	89.7	41.7	57.8	91.8	48.0	62.7	102.5	113.7	109.9	106.7	122.0	116.9
0960	Flooring	109.7	61.9	95.4	104.3	60.1	91.1	111.9	51.9	94.0	76.7	54.4	70.0	93.0	109.2	97.8	105.1	114.1	107.8
0970, 0990	Wall Finishes & Painting/Coating	99.5	56.4	73.6	99.8	35.7	61.3	99.5	31.0	58.3	88.3	50.8	65.8	101.7	108.4	105.7	100.4	106.2	103.9
09	FINISHES	91.8	60.7	74.5	90.0	55.3	70.7	94.3	41.3	64.7	87.7	49.8	66.6	98.0	114.0	106.9	102.0	119.6	111.8
COVERS	DIVS. 10 - 14, 25, 28, 41, 43, 44, 46	100.0	77.2	95.4	100.0	42.1	88.4	100.0	33.5	86.7	100.0	46.4	89.3	100.0	110.1	102.0	100.0	111.3	102.3
21, 22, 23	FIRE SUPPRESSION, PLUMBING & HVAC	100.2	52.4	81.1	95.3	51.9	77.9	100.2	54.6	81.9	95.5	66.5	83.9	95.1	113.7	102.6	100.0	118.0	107.2
26, 27, 3370	ELECTRICAL, COMMUNICATIONS & UTIL.	91.6	69.5	80.1	92.2	45.7	68.0	93.4	36.8	63.9	100.6	65.8	82.4	120.2	119.9	120.0	91.4	105.9	99.0
MF2010	WEIGHTED AVERAGE	96.9	62.9	82.1	94.1	54.4	76.8	95.7	49.9	75.7	95.6	62.7	81.2	98.2	113.9	105.0	98.9	114.1	105.6

CALIFORNIA

DIVISION		BAKERSFIELD 932-933 MAT.	INST.	TOTAL	BERKELEY 947 MAT.	INST.	TOTAL	EUREKA 955 MAT.	INST.	TOTAL	FRESNO 936-938 MAT.	INST.	TOTAL	INGLEWOOD 903-905 MAT.	INST.	TOTAL	LONG BEACH 906-908 MAT.	INST.	TOTAL
015433	CONTRACTOR EQUIPMENT		97.9	97.9		98.5	98.5		97.6	97.6		97.9	97.9		95.7	95.7		95.7	95.7
0241, 31 - 34	SITE & INFRASTRUCTURE, DEMOLITION	97.5	105.3	103.0	119.7	106.0	110.1	108.5	101.6	103.7	99.4	104.8	103.2	92.6	102.2	99.3	99.8	102.2	101.5
0310	Concrete Forming & Accessories	104.6	122.7	120.2	118.3	148.0	143.9	114.9	130.6	128.4	103.9	131.7	127.9	113.1	116.9	116.4	108.0	116.9	115.7
0320	Concrete Reinforcing	108.4	114.7	111.5	92.5	116.2	104.3	101.9	115.4	108.6	84.7	115.4	100.0	108.6	114.9	111.7	107.6	114.9	111.2
0330	Cast-in-Place Concrete	92.1	120.7	104.0	127.8	122.0	125.4	99.1	116.3	106.2	97.5	117.3	105.7	87.6	120.2	101.1	99.7	120.2	108.2
03	CONCRETE	101.1	119.4	110.1	110.4	131.2	120.6	114.4	121.4	117.8	101.5	122.4	111.8	95.7	116.8	106.1	105.0	116.8	110.8
04	MASONRY	93.2	115.7	107.1	119.2	131.9	127.0	99.4	123.4	114.3	96.3	121.3	111.7	75.8	118.7	102.4	84.5	118.7	105.7
05	METALS	105.8	99.4	103.8	106.5	100.3	104.6	102.9	97.8	101.3	105.9	100.4	104.2	93.8	100.6	95.9	93.7	100.6	95.8
06	WOOD, PLASTICS & COMPOSITES	93.8	121.5	109.4	110.4	154.0	135.0	112.3	135.9	125.6	105.3	135.9	122.5	106.0	113.2	110.1	99.5	113.2	107.2
07	THERMAL & MOISTURE PROTECTION	104.0	111.9	107.2	103.2	135.9	116.5	101.9	116.0	107.6	94.0	113.6	101.9	100.9	118.5	108.1	101.1	118.5	108.2
08	OPENINGS	96.5	116.2	101.2	96.8	140.5	107.1	99.8	112.7	102.8	96.7	124.0	103.1	91.0	115.5	96.8	91.0	115.5	96.8
0920	Plaster & Gypsum Board	98.9	122.0	114.7	102.8	155.2	138.4	106.0	136.9	127.0	97.5	136.9	124.3	103.9	113.7	110.5	99.8	113.7	109.2
0950, 0980	Ceilings & Acoustic Treatment	109.6	122.0	117.9	104.1	155.2	138.1	112.1	136.9	128.6	106.0	136.9	126.5	101.7	113.7	109.7	101.7	113.7	109.7
0960	Flooring	104.9	109.2	106.2	108.7	126.4	114.0	109.3	118.7	112.1	110.4	135.9	118.0	98.9	109.2	102.0	96.5	109.2	100.3
0970, 0990	Wall Finishes & Painting/Coating	100.8	104.2	102.8	102.7	142.1	126.4	102.0	47.2	69.1	115.0	108.6	111.1	102.1	108.4	105.9	102.1	108.4	105.9
09	FINISHES	102.9	118.7	111.7	103.9	145.5	127.1	107.9	122.2	115.9	104.3	131.9	119.7	101.4	114.1	108.4	100.6	114.1	108.1
COVERS	DIVS. 10 - 14, 25, 28, 41, 43, 44, 46	100.0	111.3	102.5	100.0	125.1	105.0	100.0	121.4	104.3	100.0	121.4	104.3	100.0	110.2	102.0	100.0	110.2	102.0
21, 22, 23	FIRE SUPPRESSION, PLUMBING & HVAC	100.1	108.3	103.4	95.2	144.7	115.0	95.1	99.1	96.7	100.2	109.6	104.0	94.7	113.7	102.3	94.7	113.7	102.4
26, 27, 3370	ELECTRICAL, COMMUNICATIONS & UTIL.	102.0	102.3	102.2	109.2	142.6	126.6	98.8	112.6	106.0	91.7	102.9	97.6	105.5	119.9	113.0	105.2	119.9	112.9
MF2010	WEIGHTED AVERAGE	100.8	110.6	105.1	103.4	133.1	116.4	101.6	111.6	106.0	100.0	114.5	106.3	95.7	113.4	103.4	97.1	113.4	104.2

CALIFORNIA

DIVISION		LOS ANGELES 900-902 MAT.	INST.	TOTAL	MARYSVILLE 959 MAT.	INST.	TOTAL	MODESTO 953 MAT.	INST.	TOTAL	MOJAVE 935 MAT.	INST.	TOTAL	OAKLAND 946 MAT.	INST.	TOTAL	OXNARD 930 MAT.	INST.	TOTAL
015433	CONTRACTOR EQUIPMENT		99.2	99.2		97.6	97.6		97.6	97.6		97.9	97.9		98.5	98.5		96.8	96.8
0241, 31 - 34	SITE & INFRASTRUCTURE, DEMOLITION	100.3	105.7	104.1	104.8	104.5	104.6	99.6	104.5	103.0	93.1	105.3	101.7	126.2	106.0	112.0	99.7	103.4	102.3
0310	Concrete Forming & Accessories	109.9	123.2	121.4	105.0	131.8	128.2	101.3	131.8	127.7	116.3	113.5	113.9	107.2	148.0	142.4	107.7	123.1	121.0
0320	Concrete Reinforcing	109.4	115.0	112.2	101.9	115.3	108.6	105.5	115.5	110.5	102.0	114.6	108.3	94.6	116.2	105.4	100.1	114.8	107.4
0330	Cast-in-Place Concrete	94.6	120.9	105.5	110.7	117.6	113.6	99.1	117.6	106.8	84.4	120.7	99.4	121.2	122.0	121.5	98.2	121.0	107.6
03	CONCRETE	100.9	119.4	110.3	115.1	122.6	118.8	105.9	122.6	114.1	93.9	115.4	104.5	109.9	131.2	120.4	102.1	119.8	110.8
04	MASONRY	90.0	119.9	108.5	100.3	118.2	111.4	99.3	122.3	113.5	94.7	115.7	107.7	126.6	131.9	129.9	97.5	116.5	109.3
05	METALS	100.6	102.0	101.0	102.4	101.1	102.0	99.6	101.4	100.2	102.6	99.3	101.6	100.8	100.3	100.7	100.7	100.0	100.5
06	WOOD, PLASTICS & COMPOSITES	105.7	121.4	114.5	99.5	135.9	120.0	95.3	135.9	118.2	105.0	109.2	107.4	98.4	154.0	129.8	99.6	121.5	111.9
07	THERMAL & MOISTURE PROTECTION	100.3	121.1	108.7	101.4	119.3	108.6	101.0	118.5	108.1	100.1	110.2	104.2	101.2	135.9	115.3	103.3	119.4	109.8
08	OPENINGS	97.8	120.2	103.1	99.1	124.7	105.2	98.0	124.7	104.3	92.1	109.5	96.2	96.8	140.5	107.2	94.5	120.2	100.6
0920	Plaster & Gypsum Board	103.5	122.0	116.1	98.3	136.9	124.5	101.0	136.9	125.4	108.9	109.4	109.2	97.4	155.2	136.7	101.8	122.0	115.6
0950, 0980	Ceilings & Acoustic Treatment	111.6	122.0	118.5	111.2	136.9	128.3	106.7	136.9	126.8	107.4	109.4	108.7	107.0	155.2	139.1	109.9	122.0	118.0
0960	Flooring	96.8	114.1	101.9	105.2	111.3	107.0	105.6	113.5	107.9	110.4	109.2	110.0	104.4	126.4	111.0	102.9	114.1	106.2
0970, 0990	Wall Finishes & Painting/Coating	101.1	108.4	105.5	102.0	118.3	111.8	102.0	118.3	111.8	100.5	104.2	102.7	102.7	142.1	126.4	100.5	101.2	100.9
09	FINISHES	102.9	119.8	112.3	105.0	128.9	118.3	104.0	129.2	118.1	104.6	111.3	108.3	103.1	145.5	126.7	102.3	119.1	111.6
COVERS	DIVS. 10 - 14, 25, 28, 41, 43, 44, 46	100.0	111.3	102.3	100.0	121.4	104.3	100.0	121.4	104.3	100.0	110.0	102.0	100.0	125.1	105.0	100.0	111.5	102.3
21, 22, 23	FIRE SUPPRESSION, PLUMBING & HVAC	100.0	118.0	107.2	95.1	109.8	101.0	100.0	108.8	103.5	95.2	108.3	100.4	100.1	144.7	118.0	100.1	118.0	107.3
26, 27, 3370	ELECTRICAL, COMMUNICATIONS & UTIL.	103.6	120.6	112.5	95.4	109.9	103.0	97.9	106.5	102.4	90.5	102.3	96.6	108.3	142.6	126.2	96.2	109.9	103.3
MF2010	WEIGHTED AVERAGE	100.1	116.5	107.3	100.8	115.1	107.0	100.4	114.9	106.7	96.8	108.6	101.9	103.9	133.1	116.6	99.6	114.2	105.9

CALIFORNIA

	DIVISION	PALM SPRINGS 922			PALO ALTO 943			PASADENA 910 - 912			REDDING 960			RICHMOND 948			RIVERSIDE 925		
		MAT.	INST.	TOTAL	MAT.	INST.	TOTAL	MAT.	INST.	TOTAL	MAT.	INST.	TOTAL	MAT.	INST.	TOTAL	MAT.	INST.	TOTAL
015433	CONTRACTOR EQUIPMENT		98.8	98.8		98.5	98.5		98.9	98.9		97.6	97.6		98.5	98.5		98.8	98.8
0241, 31 - 34	SITE & INFRASTRUCTURE, DEMOLITION	88.2	105.7	100.5	115.6	106.0	108.8	93.4	109.7	104.8	109.5	104.5	106.0	125.4	106.0	111.8	95.0	105.7	102.5
0310	Concrete Forming & Accessories	102.1	116.9	114.9	105.4	144.5	139.2	104.9	116.9	115.2	105.0	129.6	126.2	120.9	147.8	144.2	105.8	123.1	120.7
0320	Concrete Reinforcing	107.1	114.7	110.9	92.5	115.9	104.2	108.3	114.9	111.6	104.7	115.3	110.0	92.5	116.0	104.2	104.1	114.7	109.4
0330	Cast-in-Place Concrete	87.1	121.6	101.4	108.1	122.0	113.8	89.9	119.1	102.0	110.9	117.6	113.7	124.3	122.0	123.4	94.7	121.7	105.9
03	CONCRETE	97.7	117.2	107.3	99.3	129.6	114.2	99.4	116.4	107.8	115.2	121.5	118.3	112.0	131.0	121.4	103.8	120.0	111.8
04	MASONRY	74.9	115.9	100.3	101.7	127.8	117.8	106.8	118.6	114.1	110.3	118.2	115.2	119.0	127.8	124.4	75.9	115.9	100.3
05	METALS	103.8	99.9	102.6	98.3	99.8	98.8	84.1	99.9	88.9	100.5	101.1	100.7	98.4	99.8	98.8	103.4	100.1	102.4
06	WOOD, PLASTICS & COMPOSITES	93.2	113.3	104.5	95.8	149.6	126.1	83.3	113.1	100.1	97.8	132.8	117.5	114.4	154.0	136.7	98.5	121.4	111.4
07	THERMAL & MOISTURE PROTECTION	97.6	119.0	106.3	100.8	133.4	114.0	95.0	117.2	104.0	108.6	118.9	112.8	101.4	134.2	114.7	98.1	121.2	107.5
08	OPENINGS	96.6	115.5	101.1	96.8	137.5	106.5	89.8	115.5	95.9	102.0	123.0	107.0	96.9	139.9	107.1	99.1	120.2	104.1
0920	Plaster & Gypsum Board	95.5	113.7	107.9	95.6	150.6	133.0	95.0	113.7	107.7	104.5	133.7	124.4	104.9	155.2	139.1	99.9	122.0	115.0
0950, 0980	Ceilings & Acoustic Treatment	104.1	113.7	110.5	105.0	150.6	135.4	102.5	113.7	109.9	131.8	133.7	133.1	105.0	155.2	138.4	111.0	122.0	118.4
0960	Flooring	107.7	109.2	108.1	103.4	126.4	110.3	88.9	109.2	95.0	105.4	111.3	107.2	110.3	126.4	115.1	109.1	114.1	110.6
0970, 0990	Wall Finishes & Painting/Coating	98.7	113.7	107.7	102.7	142.1	126.4	101.7	108.4	105.7	104.1	118.3	112.6	102.7	142.1	126.4	98.7	106.2	103.2
09	FINISHES	100.7	114.7	108.5	101.4	142.9	124.5	95.7	114.0	105.9	110.9	127.1	119.9	105.4	145.5	127.7	103.5	119.6	112.5
COVERS	DIVS. 10 - 14, 25, 28, 41, 43, 44, 46	100.0	110.4	102.1	100.0	124.7	104.9	100.0	110.1	102.0	100.0	121.1	104.2	100.0	125.1	105.0	100.0	111.3	102.3
21, 22, 23	FIRE SUPPRESSION, PLUMBING & HVAC	95.1	113.6	102.5	95.2	143.3	114.5	95.1	113.7	102.6	100.1	109.8	104.0	95.2	144.7	115.0	100.0	118.0	107.2
26, 27, 3370	ELECTRICAL, COMMUNICATIONS & UTIL.	95.0	106.0	100.8	108.1	153.8	132.0	116.8	119.9	118.4	97.8	109.9	104.1	108.8	132.4	121.1	91.6	106.0	99.1
MF2010	WEIGHTED AVERAGE	96.7	111.6	103.2	99.5	133.1	114.2	96.3	113.9	104.0	103.6	114.6	108.4	102.5	131.2	115.0	98.9	114.0	105.5

CALIFORNIA

	DIVISION	SACRAMENTO 942,956 - 958			SALINAS 939			SAN BERNARDINO 923 - 924			SAN DIEGO 919 - 921			SAN FRANCISCO 940 - 941			SAN JOSE 951		
		MAT.	INST.	TOTAL	MAT.	INST.	TOTAL	MAT.	INST.	TOTAL	MAT.	INST.	TOTAL	MAT.	INST.	TOTAL	MAT.	INST.	TOTAL
015433	CONTRACTOR EQUIPMENT		98.0	98.0		97.9	97.9		98.8	98.8		99.0	99.0		108.8	108.8		98.5	98.5
0241, 31 - 34	SITE & INFRASTRUCTURE, DEMOLITION	101.0	111.5	108.3	112.3	105.1	107.2	75.1	105.7	96.6	99.7	103.3	102.2	128.6	111.8	116.8	132.0	99.7	109.3
0310	Concrete Forming & Accessories	105.6	132.4	128.7	110.9	132.8	129.8	109.5	116.9	115.9	103.8	112.0	110.9	106.9	149.0	143.2	107.4	147.9	142.3
0320	Concrete Reinforcing	87.6	115.6	101.6	100.6	115.9	108.3	104.1	114.7	109.4	104.9	114.7	109.8	107.8	116.6	112.2	92.8	116.2	104.5
0330	Cast-in-Place Concrete	102.5	118.4	109.1	97.0	117.9	105.7	65.5	121.6	88.8	98.5	108.7	102.7	124.3	123.5	124.0	115.1	121.6	117.8
03	CONCRETE	99.8	122.7	111.1	112.4	123.2	117.7	77.7	117.2	97.2	104.6	110.7	107.6	113.5	132.7	123.0	111.8	131.4	121.5
04	MASONRY	103.4	122.3	115.1	94.4	127.4	114.8	82.4	115.9	103.1	97.1	114.2	107.7	127.2	136.2	132.8	126.8	131.9	130.0
05	METALS	96.4	95.7	96.2	105.3	102.5	104.4	103.3	99.9	102.3	99.6	101.3	100.1	107.1	110.1	108.0	97.8	107.1	100.6
06	WOOD, PLASTICS & COMPOSITES	92.3	136.1	117.0	104.4	136.1	122.3	102.3	113.3	108.5	97.0	108.8	103.6	98.4	154.2	129.9	107.5	153.8	133.6
07	THERMAL & MOISTURE PROTECTION	108.5	121.1	113.6	100.6	125.9	110.9	96.2	119.0	105.8	99.7	106.6	102.5	102.9	139.0	117.6	97.4	138.4	114.1
08	OPENINGS	110.7	124.8	114.1	95.6	130.7	103.9	96.6	115.5	101.1	96.8	111.4	100.3	101.4	140.6	110.7	89.5	140.3	101.5
0920	Plaster & Gypsum Board	92.5	136.9	122.7	102.9	137.1	126.2	101.7	113.7	109.9	102.3	108.9	106.8	99.8	155.2	137.5	96.2	155.2	136.3
0950, 0980	Ceilings & Acoustic Treatment	105.0	136.9	126.2	107.4	137.1	127.2	106.7	113.7	111.4	109.6	108.9	109.1	114.8	155.2	141.7	104.8	155.2	138.3
0960	Flooring	103.3	119.7	108.2	105.1	123.3	110.6	111.0	109.2	110.4	96.2	114.1	101.5	104.4	126.4	111.0	98.7	126.4	107.0
0970, 0990	Wall Finishes & Painting/Coating	100.3	118.3	111.1	101.6	142.1	126.0	98.7	106.2	103.2	98.3	106.4	103.2	102.7	152.6	132.7	102.3	142.1	126.2
09	FINISHES	99.8	130.4	116.9	104.2	133.7	120.6	101.8	113.9	108.6	101.0	111.3	106.7	105.2	146.8	128.4	102.7	145.3	126.4
COVERS	DIVS. 10 - 14, 25, 28, 41, 43, 44, 46	100.0	121.9	104.4	100.0	121.5	104.3	100.0	102.2	102.1	100.0	109.1	101.8	100.0	125.6	105.1	100.0	124.7	105.0
21, 22, 23	FIRE SUPPRESSION, PLUMBING & HVAC	100.0	121.9	108.7	95.2	115.3	103.2	95.1	113.8	102.6	100.0	116.3	106.5	100.0	171.6	128.7	100.0	143.3	117.3
26, 27, 3370	ELECTRICAL, COMMUNICATIONS & UTIL.	103.4	111.3	107.5	91.7	122.8	107.9	95.0	103.7	99.6	102.2	98.9	100.5	108.3	161.4	136.1	101.0	153.8	128.6
MF2010	WEIGHTED AVERAGE	101.2	118.6	108.8	100.2	120.3	108.9	94.6	111.2	101.9	100.2	109.1	104.1	106.1	143.8	122.5	102.2	134.6	116.3

CALIFORNIA

	DIVISION	SAN LUIS OBISPO 934			SAN MATEO 944			SAN RAFAEL 949			SANTA ANA 926 - 927			SANTA BARBARA 931			SANTA CRUZ 950		
		MAT.	INST.	TOTAL	MAT.	INST.	TOTAL	MAT.	INST.	TOTAL	MAT.	INST.	TOTAL	MAT.	INST.	TOTAL	MAT.	INST.	TOTAL
015433	CONTRACTOR EQUIPMENT		97.9	97.9		98.5	98.5		98.5	98.5		98.8	98.8		97.9	97.9		98.5	98.5
0241, 31 - 34	SITE & INFRASTRUCTURE, DEMOLITION	104.7	105.3	105.1	122.8	106.0	111.0	113.7	111.6	112.2	86.7	105.7	100.0	99.6	105.3	103.6	131.6	99.5	109.0
0310	Concrete Forming & Accessories	118.0	116.9	117.0	111.2	147.9	142.9	115.2	147.8	143.4	109.7	116.9	115.9	108.6	123.1	121.1	107.5	133.0	129.5
0320	Concrete Reinforcing	102.0	114.8	108.4	92.5	116.1	104.3	93.1	116.1	104.6	107.6	114.7	111.2	100.1	114.8	107.4	115.0	115.9	115.5
0330	Cast-in-Place Concrete	104.2	120.8	111.1	120.4	122.0	121.0	140.1	121.2	132.2	83.6	121.6	99.4	97.8	120.9	107.4	114.3	119.8	116.6
03	CONCRETE	110.1	116.9	113.4	108.4	131.1	119.6	129.7	130.6	130.2	95.2	117.2	106.1	102.0	119.7	110.7	115.0	124.1	119.5
04	MASONRY	96.1	117.4	109.3	118.7	130.8	126.2	98.0	130.8	118.3	72.6	116.2	99.6	94.9	117.4	108.8	130.4	127.5	128.6
05	METALS	103.2	99.7	102.1	98.2	100.1	98.8	99.6	97.8	99.1	103.4	99.9	102.3	101.1	100.0	100.8	105.1	105.8	105.3
06	WOOD, PLASTICS & COMPOSITES	107.5	113.4	110.8	103.5	154.0	132.0	100.4	153.8	130.5	103.9	113.3	109.2	99.6	121.5	111.9	107.5	136.2	123.7
07	THERMAL & MOISTURE PROTECTION	100.8	117.5	107.6	101.2	136.2	115.4	105.2	132.9	116.5	97.9	119.1	106.5	100.2	119.0	107.9	97.4	128.5	110.0
08	OPENINGS	93.9	111.8	98.1	96.8	139.9	107.0	108.2	139.8	115.7	96.0	115.5	100.6	95.2	120.2	101.1	90.7	130.8	100.2
0920	Plaster & Gypsum Board	110.4	113.7	112.6	100.8	155.2	137.8	102.5	155.2	138.4	102.4	113.7	110.1	101.8	122.0	115.6	103.7	137.1	126.4
0950, 0980	Ceilings & Acoustic Treatment	107.4	113.7	111.6	105.0	155.2	138.4	113.0	155.2	141.1	106.7	113.7	111.4	109.9	122.0	118.0	108.5	137.1	127.5
0960	Flooring	111.3	109.2	110.7	106.0	126.4	112.1	115.1	121.3	117.0	111.5	109.2	110.8	104.4	109.2	105.8	102.8	123.3	108.9
0970, 0990	Wall Finishes & Painting/Coating	100.5	101.1	100.9	102.7	142.1	126.4	99.0	142.1	124.9	98.7	106.2	103.2	100.5	101.2	100.9	102.5	142.1	126.3
09	FINISHES	106.1	112.6	109.7	103.4	145.5	126.8	105.8	144.4	127.3	103.3	113.9	109.2	102.9	118.2	111.4	105.7	133.8	121.3
COVERS	DIVS. 10 - 14, 25, 28, 41, 43, 44, 46	100.0	120.4	104.1	100.0	125.2	105.0	100.0	124.5	104.9	100.0	110.4	102.1	100.0	111.5	102.3	100.0	121.8	104.4
21, 22, 23	FIRE SUPPRESSION, PLUMBING & HVAC	95.2	113.8	102.6	95.2	142.8	114.3	95.1	164.7	123.0	95.1	113.8	102.6	100.1	118.0	107.3	100.0	115.3	106.1
26, 27, 3370	ELECTRICAL, COMMUNICATIONS & UTIL.	90.5	106.0	98.6	108.1	143.6	126.7	105.1	116.4	111.0	95.0	105.9	100.7	89.4	111.8	101.1	99.9	122.8	111.9
MF2010	WEIGHTED AVERAGE	99.3	111.6	104.7	101.7	132.7	115.2	104.2	133.6	117.0	96.5	111.6	103.1	98.9	114.6	105.7	104.1	120.4	111.2

CALIFORNIA / COLORADO

DIVISION		SANTA ROSA 954 MAT.	INST.	TOTAL	STOCKTON 952 MAT.	INST.	TOTAL	SUSANVILLE 961 MAT.	INST.	TOTAL	VALLEJO 945 MAT.	INST.	TOTAL	VAN NUYS 913-916 MAT.	INST.	TOTAL	ALAMOSA 811 MAT.	INST.	TOTAL
015433	CONTRACTOR EQUIPMENT		98.2	98.2		97.6	97.6		97.6	97.6		98.5	98.5		98.9	98.9		93.8	93.8
0241, 31-34	SITE & INFRASTRUCTURE, DEMOLITION	100.1	104.5	103.2	99.4	104.5	103.0	115.9	104.5	107.9	100.5	111.4	108.2	109.9	109.7	109.7	132.1	89.0	101.9
0310	Concrete Forming & Accessories	103.1	146.8	140.8	105.3	131.8	128.2	106.2	129.6	126.4	105.6	146.5	140.9	110.9	116.9	116.1	105.2	69.0	73.9
0320	Concrete Reinforcing	102.7	116.4	109.6	105.5	115.5	110.5	104.7	115.3	110.0	94.3	116.3	105.3	108.3	114.9	111.6	108.0	78.4	93.2
0330	Cast-in-Place Concrete	108.7	119.2	113.1	96.6	117.6	105.3	100.9	117.6	107.8	111.6	119.6	114.9	94.8	119.1	104.9	100.6	79.3	91.8
03	CONCRETE	114.9	130.0	122.4	104.9	122.6	113.6	117.6	121.5	119.5	105.2	129.5	117.2	113.8	116.4	115.1	115.5	74.6	95.3
04	MASONRY	98.6	133.7	120.3	99.2	122.3	113.5	108.3	118.2	114.4	74.6	132.4	110.4	122.3	118.6	120.0	123.2	72.7	92.0
05	METALS	103.7	104.3	103.9	99.8	101.4	100.3	99.6	101.1	100.1	99.6	97.6	99.0	83.2	99.9	88.3	97.2	81.1	92.2
06	WOOD, PLASTICS & COMPOSITES	94.6	153.6	127.9	100.8	135.9	120.6	99.5	132.8	118.3	89.8	153.8	125.9	91.6	113.1	103.8	93.8	69.0	79.8
07	THERMAL & MOISTURE PROTECTION	98.3	134.5	113.0	101.1	118.5	108.2	109.2	118.9	113.2	103.0	134.0	115.6	95.8	117.2	104.5	105.1	78.4	94.2
08	OPENINGS	97.4	140.2	107.6	98.0	124.7	104.3	101.9	123.0	106.9	110.0	140.3	117.2	89.7	115.5	95.8	98.4	75.3	92.9
0920	Plaster & Gypsum Board	97.2	155.2	136.7	101.0	136.9	125.4	105.4	133.7	124.7	97.3	155.2	136.7	99.9	113.7	109.3	75.8	67.9	70.4
0950, 0980	Ceilings & Acoustic Treatment	106.7	155.2	139.0	113.7	136.9	129.1	123.9	133.7	130.4	115.5	155.2	141.8	99.8	113.7	109.1	104.2	67.9	80.1
0960	Flooring	108.1	117.0	110.8	105.6	113.5	107.9	105.9	111.3	107.5	111.2	126.4	115.7	91.1	109.2	96.5	112.4	55.8	95.5
0970, 0990	Wall Finishes & Painting/Coating	98.7	142.1	124.8	102.0	118.3	111.8	104.1	118.3	112.6	99.9	142.1	125.3	101.7	108.4	105.7	113.0	24.1	59.6
09	FINISHES	102.6	143.0	125.1	105.5	129.2	118.7	110.4	127.1	119.7	102.8	144.7	126.1	97.7	114.0	106.8	104.9	61.2	80.5
COVERS	DIVS. 10 - 14, 25, 28, 41, 43, 44, 46	100.0	123.2	104.7	100.0	121.4	104.3	100.0	121.1	104.2	100.0	123.7	104.7	100.0	110.1	102.0	100.0	89.1	97.8
21, 22, 23	FIRE SUPPRESSION, PLUMBING & HVAC	95.1	163.4	122.5	100.0	108.8	103.5	95.2	109.8	101.0	100.0	128.8	111.6	95.1	113.7	102.6	95.2	72.6	86.1
26, 27, 3370	ELECTRICAL, COMMUNICATIONS & UTIL.	95.4	116.6	106.4	97.9	110.9	104.7	98.1	109.9	104.3	100.6	125.1	113.4	116.8	119.9	118.4	96.8	74.2	85.0
MF2010	WEIGHTED AVERAGE	100.3	133.4	114.7	100.5	115.5	107.0	102.6	114.6	107.9	100.6	127.2	112.2	99.1	113.9	105.5	102.0	74.6	90.1

COLORADO

DIVISION		BOULDER 803 MAT.	INST.	TOTAL	COLORADO SPRINGS 808-809 MAT.	INST.	TOTAL	DENVER 800-802 MAT.	INST.	TOTAL	DURANGO 813 MAT.	INST.	TOTAL	FORT COLLINS 805 MAT.	INST.	TOTAL	FORT MORGAN 807 MAT.	INST.	TOTAL
015433	CONTRACTOR EQUIPMENT		94.9	94.9		93.4	93.4		97.7	97.7		93.8	93.8		94.9	94.9		94.9	94.9
0241, 31-34	SITE & INFRASTRUCTURE, DEMOLITION	92.4	95.1	94.3	94.5	93.1	93.5	93.7	101.2	99.0	125.8	89.0	100.0	104.3	94.7	97.5	95.3	94.6	94.8
0310	Concrete Forming & Accessories	102.0	81.7	84.4	92.9	77.4	79.5	98.5	77.7	80.5	111.4	69.2	74.9	99.3	76.4	79.5	102.5	76.6	80.2
0320	Concrete Reinforcing	102.0	78.5	90.3	101.2	82.7	92.0	101.2	82.7	92.0	108.0	78.4	93.2	102.1	78.6	90.3	102.2	78.4	90.3
0330	Cast-in-Place Concrete	102.4	79.8	93.0	105.2	82.9	95.9	99.6	82.6	92.5	115.7	79.4	100.6	115.6	78.6	100.2	100.5	78.6	91.4
03	CONCRETE	104.7	80.6	92.8	108.1	80.6	94.6	102.4	80.6	91.7	117.8	74.8	96.5	115.3	77.8	96.8	103.2	77.8	90.7
04	MASONRY	93.1	73.2	80.8	94.1	73.0	81.0	96.1	73.3	82.0	110.9	72.4	87.1	110.4	76.9	89.7	107.5	72.9	86.1
05	METALS	97.7	84.4	93.6	100.8	86.5	96.4	103.4	86.7	98.2	97.2	81.2	92.2	98.9	81.3	93.5	97.5	81.1	92.4
06	WOOD, PLASTICS & COMPOSITES	93.3	84.9	88.6	83.8	79.1	81.2	91.0	79.0	84.3	102.6	69.0	83.7	90.8	79.0	84.1	93.3	79.0	85.2
07	THERMAL & MOISTURE PROTECTION	104.4	80.5	94.7	105.3	80.3	95.1	103.7	74.6	91.9	105.0	78.3	94.2	104.8	72.2	91.6	104.4	79.9	94.4
08	OPENINGS	101.5	83.9	97.3	105.8	82.0	100.2	106.5	81.9	100.7	105.3	75.3	98.2	101.4	80.7	96.5	101.4	80.7	96.5
0920	Plaster & Gypsum Board	104.0	84.6	90.8	86.1	78.6	81.0	99.6	78.6	85.3	88.1	67.9	74.3	98.0	78.6	84.8	104.0	78.6	86.7
0950, 0980	Ceilings & Acoustic Treatment	98.0	84.6	89.1	105.1	78.6	87.4	108.2	78.6	88.5	104.2	67.9	80.1	98.0	78.6	85.0	98.0	78.6	85.0
0960	Flooring	103.7	85.3	98.2	95.8	69.5	87.9	100.5	86.3	96.3	116.8	55.8	98.5	100.4	55.8	87.1	104.1	55.8	89.7
0970, 0990	Wall Finishes & Painting/Coating	100.8	68.0	81.1	100.5	41.4	65.0	100.8	77.3	86.7	113.0	24.1	59.6	100.8	41.1	64.9	100.8	54.7	73.1
09	FINISHES	102.6	81.2	90.7	99.4	72.0	84.2	103.1	79.0	89.7	106.9	61.2	81.5	101.4	68.9	83.3	102.6	70.4	84.7
COVERS	DIVS. 10 - 14, 25, 28, 41, 43, 44, 46	100.0	90.0	98.0	100.0	89.7	97.9	100.0	89.4	97.9	100.0	89.1	97.8	100.0	89.4	97.9	100.0	89.4	97.9
21, 22, 23	FIRE SUPPRESSION, PLUMBING & HVAC	95.2	77.6	88.1	100.2	72.7	89.2	100.0	79.9	91.9	95.2	84.9	91.0	100.1	77.5	91.0	95.2	77.5	88.1
26, 27, 3370	ELECTRICAL, COMMUNICATIONS & UTIL.	96.9	85.2	90.8	100.5	83.0	91.4	102.1	85.2	93.3	96.2	71.1	83.1	96.9	85.1	90.7	97.2	85.1	90.9
MF2010	WEIGHTED AVERAGE	98.6	82.0	91.3	101.3	79.3	91.7	101.6	82.6	93.3	102.4	76.8	91.2	102.1	79.6	92.3	99.1	79.6	90.6

COLORADO

DIVISION		GLENWOOD SPRINGS 816 MAT.	INST.	TOTAL	GOLDEN 804 MAT.	INST.	TOTAL	GRAND JUNCTION 815 MAT.	INST.	TOTAL	GREELEY 806 MAT.	INST.	TOTAL	MONTROSE 814 MAT.	INST.	TOTAL	PUEBLO 810 MAT.	INST.	TOTAL
015433	CONTRACTOR EQUIPMENT		96.5	96.5		94.9	94.9		96.5	96.5		94.9	94.9		95.1	95.1		93.8	93.8
0241, 31-34	SITE & INFRASTRUCTURE, DEMOLITION	140.8	95.9	109.3	104.4	94.9	97.7	125.5	95.5	104.5	91.7	94.1	93.4	134.6	92.1	104.8	117.7	91.5	99.3
0310	Concrete Forming & Accessories	102.3	76.7	80.2	95.2	76.5	79.1	110.1	76.2	80.8	97.5	80.2	82.5	101.8	76.4	79.9	107.3	77.8	81.8
0320	Concrete Reinforcing	106.9	78.4	92.7	102.2	78.4	90.3	107.3	78.3	92.8	102.0	77.0	89.5	106.8	78.3	92.6	103.3	82.7	93.1
0330	Cast-in-Place Concrete	100.6	78.8	91.5	100.5	78.6	91.4	111.4	78.1	97.5	96.6	58.5	80.8	100.6	78.7	91.5	99.9	83.7	93.2
03	CONCRETE	120.6	77.9	99.6	113.8	77.8	96.0	114.1	77.4	96.0	99.9	72.2	86.3	111.6	77.7	94.9	104.3	81.1	92.8
04	MASONRY	97.5	72.9	82.3	110.3	72.9	87.2	129.6	72.7	94.4	104.6	49.7	70.6	103.9	72.7	84.6	94.1	73.2	81.2
05	METALS	96.9	81.8	92.2	97.7	81.2	92.6	98.4	80.5	92.9	98.9	78.5	92.6	96.0	80.8	91.3	100.0	87.4	96.1
06	WOOD, PLASTICS & COMPOSITES	89.1	79.1	83.4	86.2	79.0	82.1	100.4	79.1	88.4	88.4	84.9	86.4	90.2	79.2	84.0	96.3	79.4	86.8
07	THERMAL & MOISTURE PROTECTION	105.0	79.5	94.6	105.3	74.2	92.7	104.1	68.8	89.8	104.3	65.0	88.3	105.1	79.5	94.7	103.6	80.0	94.0
08	OPENINGS	104.3	80.8	98.7	101.4	80.7	96.5	105.0	80.8	99.3	101.4	83.9	97.3	105.5	80.8	99.7	100.1	82.1	95.9
0920	Plaster & Gypsum Board	111.5	78.6	89.1	95.8	78.6	84.1	123.4	78.6	92.9	96.5	84.6	88.4	75.0	78.6	77.4	80.2	78.6	79.1
0950, 0980	Ceilings & Acoustic Treatment	103.4	78.6	86.9	98.0	78.6	85.0	103.4	78.6	86.9	98.0	84.6	89.1	104.2	78.6	87.2	113.1	78.6	90.1
0960	Flooring	111.7	51.4	93.7	98.3	55.8	85.6	116.2	55.8	98.1	99.5	55.8	86.4	114.6	46.2	94.2	113.4	86.3	105.3
0970, 0990	Wall Finishes & Painting/Coating	112.9	54.7	77.9	100.8	68.0	81.1	112.9	68.0	85.9	100.8	25.6	55.6	113.0	24.1	59.6	113.0	38.4	68.1
09	FINISHES	109.9	69.8	87.5	101.3	72.6	85.3	110.8	72.0	89.2	100.1	70.7	83.7	105.4	65.3	83.1	105.8	74.9	88.6
COVERS	DIVS. 10 - 14, 25, 28, 41, 43, 44, 46	100.0	89.5	97.9	100.0	89.4	97.9	100.0	89.5	97.9	100.0	90.0	98.0	100.0	89.8	98.0	100.0	90.3	98.1
21, 22, 23	FIRE SUPPRESSION, PLUMBING & HVAC	95.2	84.8	91.0	95.2	77.0	87.9	100.0	84.3	93.7	100.1	77.5	91.0	95.2	84.8	91.0	100.0	72.8	89.1
26, 27, 3370	ELECTRICAL, COMMUNICATIONS & UTIL.	93.5	71.1	81.8	97.2	85.1	90.9	95.9	55.1	74.6	96.9	85.1	90.7	95.9	57.7	76.0	96.9	74.3	85.1
MF2010	WEIGHTED AVERAGE	102.2	79.3	92.2	100.6	79.6	91.4	104.4	76.7	92.4	99.7	76.1	89.4	101.2	76.5	90.5	100.9	78.6	91.2

COLORADO / CONNECTICUT

DIVISION		COLORADO SALIDA 812			CONNECTICUT BRIDGEPORT 066			BRISTOL 060			HARTFORD 061			MERIDEN 064			NEW BRITAIN 060		
		MAT.	INST.	TOTAL	MAT.	INST.	TOTAL	MAT.	INST.	TOTAL	MAT.	INST.	TOTAL	MAT.	INST.	TOTAL	MAT.	INST.	TOTAL
015433	CONTRACTOR EQUIPMENT		95.1	95.1		100.6	100.6		100.6	100.6		100.6	100.6		101.1	101.1		100.6	100.6
0241, 31 - 34	SITE & INFRASTRUCTURE, DEMOLITION	125.5	92.4	102.3	111.7	104.0	106.3	110.9	104.0	106.1	106.0	104.0	104.6	108.9	104.7	105.9	111.1	104.0	106.1
0310	Concrete Forming & Accessories	110.0	76.4	81.0	98.2	123.8	120.3	98.2	123.7	120.3	95.1	123.7	119.8	97.9	123.7	120.2	98.6	123.7	120.3
0320	Concrete Reinforcing	106.6	78.3	92.5	110.0	129.3	119.7	110.0	129.3	119.7	109.5	129.3	119.4	110.0	129.3	119.7	110.0	129.3	119.7
0330	Cast-in-Place Concrete	115.2	78.7	100.1	103.7	127.5	113.6	97.2	127.4	109.8	99.0	127.4	110.8	93.5	127.4	107.6	98.8	127.4	110.7
03	CONCRETE	112.8	77.7	95.5	105.3	125.8	115.4	102.2	125.7	113.8	102.8	125.8	114.1	100.5	125.7	112.9	103.0	125.7	114.2
04	MASONRY	131.2	72.7	95.0	98.1	134.8	120.8	90.8	134.8	118.0	94.7	134.8	119.5	90.4	134.8	117.9	92.1	134.8	118.6
05	METALS	95.7	80.8	91.1	102.0	125.1	109.1	102.0	125.1	109.1	107.8	125.1	113.1	99.5	125.1	107.4	98.6	125.1	106.6
06	WOOD, PLASTICS & COMPOSITES	97.4	79.2	87.2	99.1	122.9	112.5	99.1	122.9	112.5	92.6	122.9	109.7	99.1	122.9	112.5	99.1	122.9	112.5
07	THERMAL & MOISTURE PROTECTION	104.1	79.5	94.1	100.3	129.2	112.0	100.4	126.9	111.2	104.8	126.9	113.8	100.4	126.9	111.2	100.4	126.9	111.2
08	OPENINGS	98.5	80.8	94.3	107.0	132.2	113.0	107.0	132.2	113.0	106.1	132.2	112.2	109.4	132.2	114.8	107.0	132.2	113.0
0920	Plaster & Gypsum Board	75.4	78.6	77.5	99.9	123.0	115.6	99.9	123.0	115.6	95.4	123.0	114.2	101.5	123.0	116.1	99.9	123.0	115.6
0950, 0980	Ceilings & Acoustic Treatment	104.2	78.6	87.2	97.9	123.0	114.6	97.9	123.0	114.6	101.3	123.0	115.7	102.1	123.0	116.0	97.9	123.0	114.6
0960	Flooring	119.1	46.2	97.3	99.3	133.6	109.6	99.3	133.6	109.6	97.8	133.6	108.5	99.3	133.6	109.6	99.3	133.6	109.6
0970, 0990	Wall Finishes & Painting/Coating	113.0	24.1	59.6	96.4	122.3	112.0	96.4	122.3	112.0	97.3	122.3	112.3	96.4	122.3	112.0	96.4	122.3	112.0
09	FINISHES	105.6	65.3	83.2	100.8	125.1	114.3	100.8	125.1	114.3	99.7	125.1	113.8	101.9	125.1	114.8	100.8	125.1	114.3
COVERS	DIVS. 10 - 14, 25, 28, 41, 43, 44, 46	100.0	89.9	98.0	100.0	110.4	102.1	100.0	110.5	102.1	100.0	110.5	102.1	100.0	110.5	102.1	100.0	110.5	102.1
21, 22, 23	FIRE SUPPRESSION, PLUMBING & HVAC	95.2	72.6	86.1	100.0	116.0	106.4	100.0	116.0	106.4	100.0	116.0	106.4	95.1	116.0	103.5	100.0	116.0	106.4
26, 27, 3370	ELECTRICAL, COMMUNICATIONS & UTIL.	96.1	74.2	84.7	99.2	108.7	104.2	99.2	111.3	105.5	98.6	112.3	105.7	99.2	111.3	105.5	99.3	111.3	105.6
MF2010	WEIGHTED AVERAGE	101.7	76.2	90.6	101.8	120.2	109.8	101.1	120.4	109.5	102.0	120.6	110.1	99.6	120.5	108.7	100.8	120.4	109.3

CONNECTICUT

DIVISION		NEW HAVEN 065			NEW LONDON 063			NORWALK 068			STAMFORD 069			WATERBURY 067			WILLIMANTIC 062		
		MAT.	INST.	TOTAL	MAT.	INST.	TOTAL	MAT.	INST.	TOTAL	MAT.	INST.	TOTAL	MAT.	INST.	TOTAL	MAT.	INST.	TOTAL
015433	CONTRACTOR EQUIPMENT		101.1	101.1		101.1	101.1		100.6	100.6		100.6	100.6		100.6	100.6		100.6	100.6
0241, 31 - 34	SITE & INFRASTRUCTURE, DEMOLITION	110.9	104.7	106.5	103.1	104.7	104.2	111.5	104.0	106.2	112.2	104.0	106.4	111.4	104.0	106.2	111.6	104.0	106.3
0310	Concrete Forming & Accessories	98.0	123.7	120.2	97.9	123.7	120.2	98.2	124.2	120.6	98.2	124.2	120.7	98.2	123.7	120.2	98.2	123.7	120.2
0320	Concrete Reinforcing	110.0	129.3	119.7	86.3	129.3	107.7	110.0	129.4	119.7	110.0	129.4	119.7	110.0	129.3	119.7	110.0	129.3	119.7
0330	Cast-in-Place Concrete	100.5	127.4	111.7	85.7	127.4	103.0	102.0	128.9	113.2	103.7	128.9	114.2	103.7	127.4	113.6	96.9	127.4	109.6
03	CONCRETE	117.2	125.7	121.4	90.2	125.7	107.7	104.5	126.5	115.3	105.3	126.5	115.8	105.3	125.7	115.4	102.1	125.7	113.7
04	MASONRY	91.0	134.8	118.1	89.4	134.8	117.5	90.6	134.8	118.0	91.3	134.8	118.2	91.3	134.8	118.2	90.6	134.8	118.0
05	METALS	98.8	125.1	106.9	98.5	125.1	106.7	102.0	125.5	109.3	102.0	125.6	109.3	102.0	125.0	109.1	101.8	125.0	108.9
06	WOOD, PLASTICS & COMPOSITES	99.1	122.9	112.5	99.1	122.9	112.5	99.1	122.9	112.5	99.1	122.9	112.5	99.1	122.9	112.5	99.1	122.9	112.5
07	THERMAL & MOISTURE PROTECTION	100.5	126.7	111.1	100.4	126.9	111.1	100.4	129.4	112.2	100.4	129.4	112.2	100.4	126.7	111.1	100.6	125.7	110.8
08	OPENINGS	107.0	132.2	113.0	109.9	132.2	115.2	107.0	132.2	113.0	107.0	132.2	113.0	107.0	132.2	113.0	110.0	132.2	115.2
0920	Plaster & Gypsum Board	99.9	123.0	115.6	99.9	123.0	115.6	99.9	123.0	115.6	99.9	123.0	115.6	99.9	123.0	115.6	99.9	123.0	115.6
0950, 0980	Ceilings & Acoustic Treatment	97.9	123.0	114.6	95.9	123.0	113.9	97.9	123.0	114.6	97.9	123.0	114.6	97.9	123.0	114.6	95.9	123.0	113.9
0960	Flooring	99.3	133.6	109.6	99.3	133.6	109.6	99.3	133.6	109.6	99.3	133.6	109.6	99.3	133.6	109.6	99.3	135.7	110.2
0970, 0990	Wall Finishes & Painting/Coating	96.4	122.3	112.0	96.4	122.3	112.0	96.4	122.3	112.0	96.4	122.3	112.0	96.4	122.3	112.0	96.4	122.3	112.0
09	FINISHES	100.8	125.1	114.4	99.8	125.1	113.9	100.8	125.1	114.4	100.9	125.1	114.4	100.7	125.1	114.3	100.5	125.4	114.4
COVERS	DIVS. 10 - 14, 25, 28, 41, 43, 44, 46	100.0	110.5	102.1	100.0	110.5	102.1	100.0	110.6	102.1	100.0	110.7	102.1	100.0	110.4	102.1	100.0	110.5	102.1
21, 22, 23	FIRE SUPPRESSION, PLUMBING & HVAC	100.0	116.0	106.4	95.1	116.0	103.5	100.0	116.1	106.4	100.0	116.1	106.4	100.0	116.0	106.4	100.0	116.0	106.4
26, 27, 3370	ELECTRICAL, COMMUNICATIONS & UTIL.	99.2	111.3	105.5	95.9	111.3	103.9	99.2	156.4	129.1	99.2	163.8	132.9	98.7	108.7	103.9	99.2	112.2	106.0
MF2010	WEIGHTED AVERAGE	102.2	120.5	110.2	97.7	120.5	107.6	101.4	126.9	112.5	101.5	127.9	113.0	101.4	120.1	109.6	101.4	120.6	109.7

D.C. / DELAWARE / FLORIDA

DIVISION		D.C. WASHINGTON 200 - 205			DELAWARE DOVER 199			NEWARK 197			WILMINGTON 198			FLORIDA DAYTONA BEACH 321			FORT LAUDERDALE 333		
		MAT.	INST.	TOTAL	MAT.	INST.	TOTAL	MAT.	INST.	TOTAL	MAT.	INST.	TOTAL	MAT.	INST.	TOTAL	MAT.	INST.	TOTAL
015433	CONTRACTOR EQUIPMENT		104.4	104.4		117.0	117.0		117.0	117.0		117.2	117.2		98.8	98.8		91.7	91.7
0241, 31 - 34	SITE & INFRASTRUCTURE, DEMOLITION	106.8	94.0	97.8	99.7	112.3	108.6	99.1	112.3	108.4	92.4	112.6	106.6	107.0	90.4	95.4	93.6	78.3	82.9
0310	Concrete Forming & Accessories	99.5	79.2	81.9	97.1	101.5	100.9	97.2	101.5	100.9	98.3	101.5	101.1	97.3	69.7	73.5	95.5	70.1	73.6
0320	Concrete Reinforcing	109.0	91.3	100.2	98.5	105.2	101.9	93.8	105.2	99.5	96.4	105.2	100.8	92.8	79.0	85.9	89.8	74.4	82.1
0330	Cast-in-Place Concrete	121.4	88.1	107.5	99.1	100.6	99.7	84.4	100.6	91.1	88.9	100.6	93.8	86.6	72.0	80.5	90.9	78.4	85.7
03	CONCRETE	109.6	85.8	97.9	99.9	102.8	101.3	92.1	102.8	97.4	94.8	102.8	98.7	88.2	73.4	80.9	90.7	75.0	82.9
04	MASONRY	95.9	80.0	86.1	103.3	97.2	99.5	99.9	97.2	98.2	103.6	97.2	99.6	92.3	66.8	76.5	89.9	69.4	77.3
05	METALS	100.1	107.3	102.3	103.1	117.0	107.4	103.7	117.0	107.8	102.9	117.0	107.3	96.4	92.8	95.3	95.5	91.5	94.2
06	WOOD, PLASTICS & COMPOSITES	103.5	77.2	88.7	95.0	101.1	98.4	97.6	101.1	99.6	98.2	101.1	99.8	99.7	70.8	83.4	96.0	68.7	80.6
07	THERMAL & MOISTURE PROTECTION	102.4	86.0	95.8	101.9	110.2	105.3	104.2	110.2	106.7	102.2	110.2	105.5	99.6	74.9	89.6	96.9	82.3	91.0
08	OPENINGS	100.3	87.6	97.3	94.3	110.5	98.1	93.4	110.5	97.4	96.6	110.5	99.9	98.9	69.1	91.8	96.9	67.1	89.9
0920	Plaster & Gypsum Board	105.8	76.5	85.9	105.9	101.0	102.6	103.4	101.0	101.8	104.8	101.0	102.2	95.1	70.3	78.3	98.5	68.2	77.9
0950, 0980	Ceilings & Acoustic Treatment	107.8	76.5	87.0	104.2	101.0	102.0	95.0	101.0	99.0	102.2	101.0	101.4	90.7	70.3	77.2	91.3	68.2	75.9
0960	Flooring	104.7	95.3	101.9	99.1	109.0	102.1	95.5	109.0	99.6	101.4	109.0	103.7	115.2	74.9	103.2	115.4	70.6	102.0
0970, 0990	Wall Finishes & Painting/Coating	104.6	84.0	92.2	97.3	105.3	102.1	99.5	105.3	103.0	97.3	105.3	102.1	99.4	75.7	85.2	96.5	71.7	81.6
09	FINISHES	101.6	81.7	90.5	101.4	102.8	102.2	97.4	102.8	100.4	102.0	102.8	102.4	100.8	70.9	84.1	99.4	69.6	82.8
COVERS	DIVS. 10 - 14, 25, 28, 41, 43, 44, 46	100.0	98.4	99.7	100.0	89.7	97.9	100.0	89.7	97.9	100.0	89.7	97.9	100.0	83.5	96.7	100.0	86.5	97.3
21, 22, 23	FIRE SUPPRESSION, PLUMBING & HVAC	100.1	92.9	97.2	100.0	115.8	106.3	100.2	115.8	106.5	100.2	115.8	106.4	100.0	77.8	91.1	100.0	68.0	87.2
26, 27, 3370	ELECTRICAL, COMMUNICATIONS & UTIL.	102.7	102.6	102.6	95.2	109.0	102.4	97.7	109.0	103.6	96.6	109.0	103.1	94.4	56.2	74.5	92.6	72.7	82.2
MF2010	WEIGHTED AVERAGE	101.6	91.6	97.2	99.7	108.1	103.3	98.8	108.1	102.8	99.4	108.1	103.2	97.4	74.4	87.3	96.4	73.9	86.6

City Cost Indexes

FLORIDA

DIVISION		FORT MYERS 339,341			GAINESVILLE 326,344			JACKSONVILLE 320,322			LAKELAND 338			MELBOURNE 329			MIAMI 330 - 332,340		
		MAT.	INST.	TOTAL	MAT.	INST.	TOTAL	MAT.	INST.	TOTAL	MAT.	INST.	TOTAL	MAT.	INST.	TOTAL	MAT.	INST.	TOTAL
015433	CONTRACTOR EQUIPMENT		98.8	98.8		98.8	98.8		98.8	98.8		98.8	98.8		98.8	98.8		91.7	91.7
0241, 31 - 34	SITE & INFRASTRUCTURE, DEMOLITION	104.3	89.5	93.9	115.4	89.5	97.2	107.0	89.8	94.9	106.2	89.9	94.7	113.9	89.7	96.9	96.7	78.1	83.6
0310	Concrete Forming & Accessories	91.1	76.6	78.6	92.3	55.5	60.5	97.1	55.9	61.5	87.4	77.1	78.5	93.5	71.4	74.4	100.7	70.5	74.6
0320	Concrete Reinforcing	90.8	95.7	93.3	98.5	66.9	82.7	92.8	67.0	79.9	93.1	96.6	94.8	93.9	79.0	86.5	95.9	74.5	85.2
0330	Cast-in-Place Concrete	94.8	69.4	84.3	99.4	63.6	84.5	87.4	69.5	80.0	97.0	70.8	86.1	104.3	74.3	91.9	91.7	79.4	86.6
03	CONCRETE	91.3	78.6	85.1	98.7	62.0	80.6	88.6	64.2	76.6	93.0	79.5	86.3	99.0	75.0	87.1	92.4	75.5	84.0
04	MASONRY	84.1	62.9	71.0	106.7	62.3	79.2	92.3	62.3	73.7	100.3	77.1	85.9	91.2	71.0	78.7	90.3	73.2	79.7
05	METALS	97.6	98.6	97.9	95.3	86.6	92.7	95.0	87.0	92.5	97.5	99.5	98.1	104.4	93.0	100.9	95.9	90.3	94.1
06	WOOD, PLASTICS & COMPOSITES	92.5	79.2	85.0	93.2	53.0	70.5	99.7	53.0	73.4	87.5	79.2	82.8	94.9	70.8	81.3	103.4	68.7	83.8
07	THERMAL & MOISTURE PROTECTION	96.8	81.3	90.5	99.9	62.5	84.7	99.8	63.1	84.9	96.7	86.0	92.4	100.0	77.3	90.8	98.1	76.5	89.4
08	OPENINGS	97.9	76.2	92.8	97.1	54.0	86.9	98.9	57.2	89.0	97.9	76.9	92.9	98.1	72.4	92.0	99.1	67.0	91.5
0920	Plaster & Gypsum Board	93.9	79.0	83.8	90.8	51.9	64.4	95.1	51.9	65.8	90.5	79.0	82.7	90.8	70.3	76.9	96.2	68.2	77.1
0950, 0980	Ceilings & Acoustic Treatment	85.8	79.0	81.3	86.1	51.9	63.4	90.7	51.9	64.9	85.8	79.0	81.3	88.1	70.3	76.3	95.9	68.2	77.4
0960	Flooring	112.1	56.1	95.4	112.6	43.9	92.1	115.2	65.7	100.4	109.8	57.6	94.2	112.8	74.9	101.5	118.5	74.3	105.3
0970, 0990	Wall Finishes & Painting/Coating	101.6	62.1	77.8	99.4	62.1	77.0	99.4	66.3	79.5	101.6	62.1	77.8	99.4	93.9	96.1	93.5	71.7	80.4
09	FINISHES	98.9	71.5	83.6	99.4	52.9	73.5	100.9	57.7	76.8	97.9	71.8	83.3	99.6	73.9	85.3	101.9	70.8	84.5
COVERS	DIVS. 10 - 14, 25, 28, 41, 43, 44, 46	100.0	74.6	94.9	100.0	81.9	96.4	100.0	81.4	96.3	100.0	74.6	94.9	100.0	84.9	97.0	100.0	87.1	97.4
21, 22, 23	FIRE SUPPRESSION, PLUMBING & HVAC	97.4	65.7	84.7	98.8	65.5	85.5	100.0	65.5	86.2	97.4	82.5	91.5	100.0	79.9	92.0	100.0	67.9	87.1
26, 27, 3370	ELECTRICAL, COMMUNICATIONS & UTIL.	94.7	64.3	78.9	94.7	73.5	83.6	94.1	63.7	78.2	92.8	63.1	77.3	95.7	69.5	82.0	96.6	75.5	85.6
MF2010	WEIGHTED AVERAGE	96.4	74.1	86.7	98.7	68.0	85.3	97.2	67.7	84.3	97.1	79.3	89.4	99.9	77.9	90.3	97.7	74.6	87.6

FLORIDA

DIVISION		ORLANDO 327 - 328,347			PANAMA CITY 324			PENSACOLA 325			SARASOTA 342			ST. PETERSBURG 337			TALLAHASSEE 323		
		MAT.	INST.	TOTAL	MAT.	INST.	TOTAL	MAT.	INST.	TOTAL	MAT.	INST.	TOTAL	MAT.	INST.	TOTAL	MAT.	INST.	TOTAL
015433	CONTRACTOR EQUIPMENT		98.8	98.8		98.8	98.8		98.8	98.8		98.8	98.8		98.8	98.8		98.8	98.8
0241, 31 - 34	SITE & INFRASTRUCTURE, DEMOLITION	108.9	89.6	95.4	119.4	88.6	97.8	118.9	89.1	98.0	111.3	89.6	96.1	107.8	89.3	94.8	105.5	88.9	93.8
0310	Concrete Forming & Accessories	99.8	73.7	77.3	96.4	44.9	52.0	94.4	53.0	58.6	96.2	76.7	79.4	95.0	52.2	58.1	100.4	45.1	52.7
0320	Concrete Reinforcing	95.9	76.2	86.1	97.0	74.9	85.9	98.4	75.4	87.4	92.8	96.5	94.6	93.1	88.8	91.0	102.5	66.8	84.6
0330	Cast-in-Place Concrete	107.4	71.8	92.6	91.9	57.7	77.7	113.4	67.0	94.2	104.0	70.6	90.1	98.0	65.5	84.5	93.5	57.3	78.5
03	CONCRETE	99.0	74.6	86.9	96.8	56.7	77.0	106.3	63.6	85.2	97.2	79.2	88.3	94.6	65.2	80.1	94.3	55.2	75.0
04	MASONRY	97.1	66.8	78.4	97.0	48.1	66.7	114.9	55.4	78.1	92.6	77.1	83.0	138.8	49.9	83.8	93.8	54.8	69.6
05	METALS	95.2	91.3	94.0	96.2	88.2	93.7	97.3	89.6	94.9	99.8	99.1	99.6	98.4	94.6	97.2	93.2	86.2	91.1
06	WOOD, PLASTICS & COMPOSITES	99.3	76.9	86.7	98.5	42.7	67.0	96.1	52.7	71.6	99.4	79.2	88.0	97.4	51.3	71.4	98.3	42.3	66.7
07	THERMAL & MOISTURE PROTECTION	98.9	75.5	89.4	100.1	57.5	82.8	100.0	63.4	85.1	98.4	86.0	93.4	96.9	58.7	81.4	105.5	72.7	92.2
08	OPENINGS	100.0	70.9	93.1	96.8	47.6	85.1	96.7	58.3	87.6	99.6	76.0	94.0	97.9	62.4	89.5	102.0	48.5	89.3
0920	Plaster & Gypsum Board	99.8	76.7	84.0	93.7	41.4	58.1	94.8	51.7	65.5	95.7	79.0	84.3	96.5	50.2	65.0	105.5	40.9	61.6
0950, 0980	Ceilings & Acoustic Treatment	99.6	76.7	84.3	88.1	41.4	57.0	88.1	51.7	63.9	91.3	79.0	83.1	87.8	50.2	62.7	99.5	40.9	60.5
0960	Flooring	112.1	74.9	101.0	114.8	43.8	93.5	110.4	64.1	96.6	117.1	58.9	99.7	114.2	56.2	96.8	112.1	63.1	97.4
0970, 0990	Wall Finishes & Painting/Coating	96.2	71.7	81.5	99.4	66.3	79.5	99.4	66.3	79.5	102.2	62.1	78.1	101.6	62.1	77.8	96.4	66.3	78.3
09	FINISHES	103.1	74.1	86.9	101.3	45.9	73.3	99.8	55.7	75.3	102.6	72.0	85.6	100.4	52.9	74.0	103.5	49.3	73.3
COVERS	DIVS. 10 - 14, 25, 28, 41, 43, 44, 46	100.0	84.2	96.8	100.0	47.4	89.5	100.0	47.5	89.5	100.0	74.6	94.9	100.0	57.3	91.4	100.0	67.6	93.5
21, 22, 23	FIRE SUPPRESSION, PLUMBING & HVAC	100.0	57.8	83.1	100.0	53.4	81.3	100.0	53.6	81.4	99.9	64.1	85.5	100.0	59.7	83.9	100.0	39.8	75.9
26, 27, 3370	ELECTRICAL, COMMUNICATIONS & UTIL.	98.9	61.4	79.3	93.1	60.7	76.2	97.0	56.8	76.0	95.7	63.0	78.6	92.8	63.0	77.3	99.2	60.8	79.1
MF2010	WEIGHTED AVERAGE	99.3	71.4	87.1	98.5	59.1	81.3	100.8	62.4	84.1	99.3	75.3	88.8	100.2	64.7	84.7	98.7	58.0	81.0

FLORIDA / GEORGIA

DIVISION		TAMPA 335 - 336,346			WEST PALM BEACH 334,349			ALBANY 317,398			ATHENS 306			ATLANTA 300 - 303,399			AUGUSTA 308 - 309		
		MAT.	INST.	TOTAL	MAT.	INST.	TOTAL	MAT.	INST.	TOTAL	MAT.	INST.	TOTAL	MAT.	INST.	TOTAL	MAT.	INST.	TOTAL
015433	CONTRACTOR EQUIPMENT		98.8	98.8		91.7	91.7		92.5	92.5		93.8	93.8		94.3	94.3		93.8	93.8
0241, 31 - 34	SITE & INFRASTRUCTURE, DEMOLITION	108.3	89.8	95.3	90.5	78.4	82.0	96.0	79.8	84.6	93.9	93.2	93.4	90.8	94.7	93.5	87.9	92.9	91.4
0310	Concrete Forming & Accessories	98.0	77.3	80.1	99.2	69.7	73.7	90.9	44.5	50.9	90.6	47.0	52.9	94.1	75.0	77.6	91.6	67.0	70.4
0320	Concrete Reinforcing	89.8	96.6	93.2	92.3	74.2	83.3	89.6	81.4	85.5	98.6	80.4	89.5	97.9	82.4	90.2	99.0	74.1	86.6
0330	Cast-in-Place Concrete	95.8	70.9	85.5	86.4	75.5	81.9	92.4	55.3	77.0	107.4	56.5	86.3	107.4	71.1	92.3	101.4	50.6	80.3
03	CONCRETE	93.2	79.6	86.5	87.8	73.7	80.9	91.0	56.7	74.1	103.8	57.3	80.8	101.3	75.1	88.4	96.8	63.0	80.1
04	MASONRY	90.9	77.1	82.4	89.5	77.6	76.0	93.8	49.9	66.6	77.7	54.7	63.5	90.9	66.9	76.1	91.2	44.0	62.0
05	METALS	97.4	99.7	98.1	94.6	90.9	93.5	96.6	86.4	93.5	90.8	74.6	85.8	91.6	77.9	87.4	90.5	72.7	85.0
06	WOOD, PLASTICS & COMPOSITES	101.7	79.2	89.0	101.3	68.7	82.9	93.0	38.9	62.5	90.3	41.9	63.0	94.4	77.5	84.9	91.7	72.6	80.9
07	THERMAL & MOISTURE PROTECTION	97.1	86.0	92.6	96.7	71.4	86.4	96.5	61.4	82.3	93.6	53.8	77.5	93.5	73.0	85.2	93.3	58.1	79.0
08	OPENINGS	99.1	79.2	94.4	96.2	67.1	89.3	98.8	45.0	86.0	90.4	46.9	80.1	95.8	73.4	90.5	90.4	63.7	84.1
0920	Plaster & Gypsum Board	99.2	79.0	85.5	103.2	68.2	79.4	100.1	37.4	57.5	96.9	40.4	58.4	99.1	77.2	84.2	98.0	72.1	80.4
0950, 0980	Ceilings & Acoustic Treatment	91.3	79.0	83.1	85.8	68.2	74.1	93.5	37.4	56.2	94.1	40.4	58.4	94.1	77.2	82.8	95.1	72.1	79.8
0960	Flooring	115.4	57.6	98.1	117.4	67.7	102.5	116.2	48.7	96.0	94.5	54.9	82.7	95.8	66.4	87.0	94.8	47.4	80.6
0970, 0990	Wall Finishes & Painting/Coating	101.6	62.1	77.8	96.5	71.7	81.6	97.6	53.9	71.3	96.1	46.9	66.6	96.1	85.9	89.9	96.1	46.9	66.6
09	FINISHES	102.0	71.8	85.2	99.1	69.0	82.4	101.6	44.2	69.6	93.5	46.8	67.5	93.8	74.8	83.2	93.3	61.9	75.8
COVERS	DIVS. 10 - 14, 25, 28, 41, 43, 44, 46	100.0	84.9	97.0	100.0	86.5	97.3	100.0	80.3	96.1	100.0	79.4	95.9	100.0	85.7	97.1	100.0	80.6	96.1
21, 22, 23	FIRE SUPPRESSION, PLUMBING & HVAC	100.0	82.6	93.0	97.4	64.0	84.0	100.0	69.5	87.7	95.1	71.1	85.5	100.0	71.9	88.7	100.0	62.6	85.0
26, 27, 3370	ELECTRICAL, COMMUNICATIONS & UTIL.	92.6	63.1	77.2	93.8	72.7	82.8	96.1	60.1	77.3	99.5	71.2	84.7	98.8	72.7	85.2	100.1	63.2	80.9
MF2010	WEIGHTED AVERAGE	97.9	79.8	90.0	95.3	72.3	85.3	97.5	62.5	82.3	94.7	65.1	81.8	96.8	75.3	87.5	95.6	64.8	82.2

GEORGIA

DIVISION		COLUMBUS 318 - 319			DALTON 307			GAINESVILLE 305			MACON 310 - 312			SAVANNAH 313 - 314			STATESBORO 304		
		MAT.	INST.	TOTAL	MAT.	INST.	TOTAL	MAT.	INST.	TOTAL	MAT.	INST.	TOTAL	MAT.	INST.	TOTAL	MAT.	INST.	TOTAL
015433	CONTRACTOR EQUIPMENT		92.5	92.5		105.5	105.5		93.8	93.8		102.8	102.8		93.5	93.5		93.2	93.2
0241, 31 - 34	SITE & INFRASTRUCTURE, DEMOLITION	95.9	79.9	84.6	94.2	97.5	96.5	93.7	93.2	93.3	96.6	94.8	95.3	97.6	81.2	86.1	95.0	77.6	82.7
0310	Concrete Forming & Accessories	90.8	55.6	60.4	83.8	47.8	52.7	93.8	43.9	50.7	90.3	53.1	58.2	92.5	51.0	56.7	78.7	52.6	56.2
0320	Concrete Reinforcing	89.8	81.8	85.8	98.1	76.3	87.2	98.4	80.3	89.4	91.0	81.5	86.2	96.8	74.2	85.5	97.7	43.1	70.4
0330	Cast-in-Place Concrete	92.1	54.8	76.6	104.3	51.0	82.2	112.8	53.8	88.3	90.9	66.7	80.8	100.2	55.8	81.8	107.1	60.7	87.9
03	CONCRETE	90.8	61.5	76.4	102.9	55.8	79.7	105.7	54.9	80.6	90.4	64.4	77.6	95.9	58.4	77.4	103.2	55.3	79.5
04	MASONRY	93.7	56.2	70.5	78.8	37.3	53.2	86.3	55.1	67.0	105.6	45.3	68.3	90.3	51.4	66.2	80.2	41.3	56.1
05	METALS	96.1	87.5	93.5	91.6	84.3	89.3	90.0	73.8	85.0	92.2	87.1	90.6	93.3	83.8	90.3	95.0	74.0	88.5
06	WOOD, PLASTICS & COMPOSITES	93.0	53.3	70.6	74.1	48.5	59.7	94.2	38.8	62.9	101.2	52.4	73.7	105.9	47.0	72.7	67.6	55.1	60.6
07	THERMAL & MOISTURE PROTECTION	96.5	64.6	83.5	95.6	52.5	78.1	93.6	55.8	78.2	94.9	63.2	82.1	95.6	57.4	80.1	94.2	52.1	77.1
08	OPENINGS	98.8	60.2	89.6	91.2	50.7	81.6	90.4	40.9	78.7	97.6	53.7	87.2	103.0	49.6	90.4	92.2	41.6	80.2
0920	Plaster & Gypsum Board	100.1	52.3	67.6	84.0	47.3	59.0	99.1	37.2	57.0	105.5	51.3	68.6	98.1	45.8	62.5	84.1	54.1	63.7
0950, 0980	Ceilings & Acoustic Treatment	93.5	52.3	66.1	106.9	47.3	67.2	94.1	37.2	56.2	88.4	51.3	63.7	101.5	45.8	64.4	102.2	54.1	70.2
0960	Flooring	116.2	51.3	96.8	94.7	47.8	80.7	95.7	47.4	81.3	91.7	48.7	78.8	113.7	47.2	93.8	112.7	45.7	92.7
0970, 0990	Wall Finishes & Painting/Coating	97.6	67.9	79.7	87.3	61.1	71.5	96.1	46.9	66.6	99.8	53.9	72.2	96.0	59.5	74.1	94.0	40.1	61.6
09	FINISHES	101.5	54.7	75.4	101.7	48.1	71.9	94.0	42.6	65.3	89.7	51.0	68.2	101.7	49.9	72.9	104.7	50.1	74.3
COVERS	DIVS. 10 - 14, 25, 28, 41, 43, 44, 46	100.0	81.9	96.4	100.0	23.4	84.6	100.0	40.5	88.1	100.0	80.3	96.1	100.0	80.0	96.0	100.0	44.7	88.9
21, 22, 23	FIRE SUPPRESSION, PLUMBING & HVAC	100.0	64.7	85.8	95.2	58.2	80.4	95.1	71.0	85.5	100.0	68.2	87.2	100.0	62.9	85.2	95.7	58.0	80.5
26, 27, 3370	ELECTRICAL, COMMUNICATIONS & UTIL.	96.2	71.3	83.2	109.8	69.3	88.7	99.5	71.2	84.7	95.2	62.7	78.2	101.0	58.7	78.9	99.6	58.7	78.3
MF2010	WEIGHTED AVERAGE	97.4	66.6	84.0	96.4	60.1	80.6	95.2	62.8	81.1	96.2	65.9	83.0	98.4	62.0	82.6	96.5	56.9	79.2

GEORGIA / HAWAII / IDAHO

DIVISION		VALDOSTA 316			WAYCROSS 315			HILO 967			HONOLULU 968			STATES & POSS., GUAM 969			BOISE 836 - 837		
		MAT.	INST.	TOTAL	MAT.	INST.	TOTAL	MAT.	INST.	TOTAL	MAT.	INST.	TOTAL	MAT.	INST.	TOTAL	MAT.	INST.	TOTAL
015433	CONTRACTOR EQUIPMENT		92.5	92.5		92.5	92.5		98.6	98.6		98.6	98.6		162.1	162.1		97.9	97.9
0241, 31 - 34	SITE & INFRASTRUCTURE, DEMOLITION	104.6	79.9	87.3	101.5	78.6	85.4	126.9	106.4	112.5	136.4	106.4	115.3	165.7	103.6	122.1	82.4	97.1	92.7
0310	Concrete Forming & Accessories	81.4	45.0	50.0	83.1	66.3	68.6	108.1	135.3	131.5	119.2	135.3	133.1	110.3	64.7	70.9	100.7	79.2	82.2
0320	Concrete Reinforcing	91.7	78.8	85.3	91.7	75.0	83.3	109.0	121.6	115.3	116.9	121.6	119.2	188.7	31.1	110.0	101.9	81.2	91.6
0330	Cast-in-Place Concrete	90.5	56.5	76.4	102.2	49.0	80.1	186.3	126.3	161.4	153.8	126.3	142.4	161.5	106.6	138.7	91.1	89.4	90.4
03	CONCRETE	95.4	56.9	76.4	98.7	62.8	81.0	148.2	128.4	138.4	141.5	128.4	135.0	149.6	73.5	112.0	100.7	83.2	92.1
04	MASONRY	99.3	51.0	69.4	100.0	39.9	62.8	127.9	128.5	128.3	128.1	128.5	128.4	182.7	44.3	97.1	118.9	82.4	96.3
05	METALS	95.7	85.4	92.5	94.8	79.3	90.0	107.6	107.9	107.7	120.8	107.9	116.8	138.8	76.3	119.5	101.1	81.2	95.0
06	WOOD, PLASTICS & COMPOSITES	81.0	38.5	57.0	82.8	74.1	77.9	101.3	137.9	122.0	119.2	137.9	129.7	113.8	68.6	88.3	88.9	77.7	82.6
07	THERMAL & MOISTURE PROTECTION	96.7	63.3	83.1	96.5	51.2	78.1	108.0	124.8	114.8	123.3	124.8	123.9	124.5	67.7	101.5	95.0	81.2	89.4
08	OPENINGS	94.7	43.5	82.6	94.7	59.2	86.3	99.7	132.7	107.5	108.8	132.7	114.4	104.3	55.2	92.6	99.1	72.5	92.8
0920	Plaster & Gypsum Board	92.0	37.1	54.6	92.4	73.7	79.7	107.7	138.9	128.9	143.9	138.9	140.5	213.3	56.8	106.8	84.9	76.9	79.5
0950, 0980	Ceilings & Acoustic Treatment	90.8	37.1	55.1	88.9	73.7	78.8	121.3	138.9	133.0	132.4	138.9	136.7	240.6	56.8	118.3	107.2	76.9	87.0
0960	Flooring	110.1	48.7	91.7	111.2	30.4	87.1	125.5	138.2	129.3	144.2	138.2	142.4	147.9	47.2	117.8	95.5	85.2	92.4
0970, 0990	Wall Finishes & Painting/Coating	97.6	53.3	70.9	97.6	46.9	67.1	99.1	145.5	127.0	107.4	145.5	130.3	104.1	36.7	63.6	102.9	40.3	65.3
09	FINISHES	99.0	44.5	68.7	98.6	58.7	76.4	115.6	138.1	128.1	130.3	138.1	134.6	192.9	60.0	118.8	97.8	76.5	85.9
COVERS	DIVS. 10 - 14, 25, 28, 41, 43, 44, 46	100.0	79.1	95.8	100.0	52.9	90.6	100.0	116.4	103.3	100.0	116.4	103.3	100.0	76.3	95.3	100.0	89.8	98.0
21, 22, 23	FIRE SUPPRESSION, PLUMBING & HVAC	100.0	71.4	88.5	96.8	58.3	81.4	100.1	109.4	103.8	100.2	109.4	103.8	102.1	38.1	76.4	100.0	72.5	89.0
26, 27, 3370	ELECTRICAL, COMMUNICATIONS & UTIL.	94.2	57.6	75.1	98.7	58.7	77.8	105.2	124.0	115.0	106.5	124.0	115.7	151.3	42.2	94.3	96.6	74.6	85.1
MF2010	WEIGHTED AVERAGE	97.5	62.6	82.3	97.3	60.7	81.3	110.4	121.0	115.0	114.9	121.0	117.6	131.2	58.9	99.7	99.8	79.4	90.9

IDAHO / ILLINOIS

DIVISION		COEUR D'ALENE 838			IDAHO FALLS 834			LEWISTON 835			POCATELLO 832			TWIN FALLS 833			BLOOMINGTON 617		
		MAT.	INST.	TOTAL	MAT.	INST.	TOTAL	MAT.	INST.	TOTAL	MAT.	INST.	TOTAL	MAT.	INST.	TOTAL	MAT.	INST.	TOTAL
015433	CONTRACTOR EQUIPMENT		92.5	92.5		97.9	97.9		92.5	92.5		97.9	97.9		97.9	97.9		101.4	101.4
0241, 31 - 34	SITE & INFRASTRUCTURE, DEMOLITION	79.9	92.3	88.6	80.3	96.9	91.9	86.3	93.1	91.1	83.1	97.1	92.9	89.4	98.0	95.5	96.3	97.8	97.3
0310	Concrete Forming & Accessories	113.8	82.2	86.5	94.9	79.0	81.1	118.9	83.1	88.0	100.9	78.9	81.9	101.8	56.0	62.3	85.5	119.2	114.6
0320	Concrete Reinforcing	109.5	96.9	103.2	103.9	81.0	92.4	109.5	97.1	103.3	102.3	81.2	91.8	104.2	81.0	92.6	95.8	111.2	103.5
0330	Cast-in-Place Concrete	98.5	86.4	93.5	86.8	75.0	81.9	102.3	86.8	95.9	93.7	89.2	91.8	96.1	64.4	82.9	98.7	113.8	104.9
03	CONCRETE	107.5	86.3	97.1	92.9	78.0	85.6	111.1	86.9	99.2	99.9	83.0	91.5	107.5	64.2	86.1	97.2	115.8	106.4
04	MASONRY	120.4	85.3	98.7	114.1	82.4	94.5	120.8	85.3	98.8	116.6	82.4	95.4	119.0	82.4	96.4	113.4	118.3	116.4
05	METALS	95.2	87.1	92.7	108.9	79.6	99.9	94.6	82.0	90.6	109.0	80.9	100.3	109.0	79.5	99.9	97.3	113.3	102.2
06	WOOD, PLASTICS & COMPOSITES	92.7	81.8	86.5	83.0	79.4	80.9	97.9	81.8	88.8	88.9	77.7	82.6	89.8	48.3	66.4	88.1	118.1	105.0
07	THERMAL & MOISTURE PROTECTION	147.5	81.5	120.7	94.6	71.7	85.3	147.7	81.5	120.8	95.0	73.9	86.4	95.7	75.2	87.4	100.3	113.3	105.6
08	OPENINGS	117.8	73.5	107.4	102.8	68.6	94.7	117.8	76.1	107.9	99.8	67.5	92.1	102.8	49.6	90.2	93.1	106.6	96.3
0920	Plaster & Gypsum Board	152.1	81.2	103.9	75.3	78.7	77.6	153.2	81.2	104.3	77.6	76.9	77.1	78.5	46.7	56.8	90.3	118.6	109.5
0950, 0980	Ceilings & Acoustic Treatment	138.9	81.2	100.5	105.1	78.7	87.5	138.9	81.2	100.5	113.1	76.9	89.0	107.8	46.7	67.1	94.3	118.6	110.5
0960	Flooring	137.5	46.7	110.3	95.7	43.9	80.2	140.2	92.5	126.0	98.7	85.2	94.6	99.7	43.9	83.0	98.0	120.9	104.8
0970, 0990	Wall Finishes & Painting/Coating	122.3	66.3	88.7	102.9	41.2	65.8	122.3	66.3	88.7	102.8	42.0	66.2	102.9	38.1	63.9	95.3	127.8	114.8
09	FINISHES	166.2	74.0	114.8	95.5	69.5	81.0	167.3	83.0	120.4	98.9	76.7	86.5	98.9	50.8	72.1	97.4	121.1	110.6
COVERS	DIVS. 10 - 14, 25, 28, 41, 43, 44, 46	100.0	89.7	97.9	100.0	48.9	89.8	100.0	89.7	97.9	100.0	89.8	98.0	100.0	45.4	89.1	100.0	103.9	100.8
21, 22, 23	FIRE SUPPRESSION, PLUMBING & HVAC	99.5	84.3	93.4	101.0	72.3	89.5	100.7	87.2	95.3	100.0	72.4	88.9	100.0	70.8	88.3	95.0	107.8	100.1
26, 27, 3370	ELECTRICAL, COMMUNICATIONS & UTIL.	88.7	79.4	83.9	88.7	70.9	79.4	86.7	80.8	83.6	94.1	70.9	82.0	90.2	61.6	75.2	93.5	96.8	95.3
MF2010	WEIGHTED AVERAGE	107.6	83.3	97.0	99.6	75.5	89.1	108.3	85.5	98.4	100.8	78.4	91.1	101.9	68.5	87.4	96.9	109.9	102.6

ILLINOIS

DIVISION		CARBONDALE 629			CENTRALIA 628			CHAMPAIGN 618 - 619			CHICAGO 606 - 608			DECATUR 625			EAST ST. LOUIS 620 - 622		
		MAT.	INST.	TOTAL	MAT.	INST.	TOTAL	MAT.	INST.	TOTAL	MAT.	INST.	TOTAL	MAT.	INST.	TOTAL	MAT.	INST.	TOTAL
015433	CONTRACTOR EQUIPMENT		107.7	107.7		107.7	107.7		102.1	102.1		93.9	93.9		102.1	102.1		107.7	107.7
0241, 31 - 34	SITE & INFRASTRUCTURE, DEMOLITION	100.2	98.6	99.0	100.5	99.2	99.6	105.2	98.4	100.4	105.3	95.4	98.4	92.2	98.6	96.7	102.6	99.2	100.2
0310	Concrete Forming & Accessories	95.5	107.9	106.2	97.4	114.8	112.4	91.6	117.1	113.7	96.6	159.8	151.1	97.7	116.9	114.2	92.8	115.0	112.0
0320	Concrete Reinforcing	89.8	100.4	95.1	89.8	113.3	101.5	95.8	105.1	100.5	95.5	163.2	129.3	87.9	105.9	96.9	89.7	113.4	101.5
0330	Cast-in-Place Concrete	91.8	101.1	95.7	92.3	118.5	103.2	114.4	109.2	112.2	103.4	149.6	122.6	100.2	111.9	105.1	93.8	118.5	104.1
03	CONCRETE	87.0	104.8	95.8	87.5	116.3	101.7	109.6	112.1	110.8	99.2	155.5	127.0	97.5	113.1	105.2	88.4	116.5	102.3
04	MASONRY	79.4	107.7	96.9	79.5	117.4	102.5	136.2	118.4	125.2	101.8	158.0	136.6	75.9	115.5	100.4	79.7	117.4	103.0
05	METALS	94.3	113.7	100.3	94.4	120.8	102.5	97.3	108.7	100.8	95.0	135.9	107.6	97.9	109.6	101.5	95.4	121.0	103.3
06	WOOD, PLASTICS & COMPOSITES	106.0	106.1	106.1	108.7	112.3	110.7	95.0	116.5	107.1	98.2	159.6	132.8	106.2	116.5	112.0	103.2	112.3	108.3
07	THERMAL & MOISTURE PROTECTION	98.0	101.6	99.5	98.0	112.3	103.8	100.9	114.5	106.5	99.2	147.5	118.8	104.0	109.6	106.3	98.0	111.9	103.6
08	OPENINGS	88.3	110.5	93.6	88.4	117.3	95.2	93.7	112.1	98.1	101.3	162.6	115.8	99.3	112.4	102.4	88.4	117.3	95.3
0920	Plaster & Gypsum Board	95.7	106.2	102.9	96.8	112.6	107.6	92.5	116.9	109.1	89.7	161.3	138.4	98.4	116.9	111.0	94.6	112.6	106.9
0950, 0980	Ceilings & Acoustic Treatment	96.2	106.2	102.9	96.2	112.6	107.1	94.3	116.9	109.4	101.5	161.3	141.3	96.2	116.9	112.1	96.2	112.6	107.1
0960	Flooring	121.3	122.4	121.6	122.3	117.9	120.9	100.7	122.4	107.1	93.1	150.7	110.3	108.6	118.8	111.7	120.2	117.9	119.5
0970, 0990	Wall Finishes & Painting/Coating	104.5	99.5	101.5	104.5	105.2	104.9	95.3	111.1	104.8	93.8	156.1	131.2	96.1	108.4	103.5	104.5	105.2	104.9
09	FINISHES	102.4	108.9	106.0	102.8	114.4	109.3	99.3	118.0	109.7	98.7	158.7	132.1	102.9	117.3	110.9	102.0	114.5	109.0
COVERS	DIVS. 10 - 14, 25, 28, 41, 43, 44, 46	100.0	104.1	100.8	100.0	106.5	101.3	100.0	103.1	100.6	100.0	125.0	105.0	100.0	103.0	100.6	100.0	106.5	101.3
21, 22, 23	FIRE SUPPRESSION, PLUMBING & HVAC	95.0	104.3	98.7	95.0	94.4	94.8	95.0	105.3	99.1	99.9	136.1	114.4	100.0	98.9	99.5	99.9	98.4	99.3
26, 27, 3370	ELECTRICAL, COMMUNICATIONS & UTIL.	94.0	106.7	100.6	95.5	104.3	100.1	96.8	94.5	95.6	96.1	137.1	117.5	98.4	91.3	94.7	95.0	104.3	99.9
MF2010	WEIGHTED AVERAGE	93.9	106.2	99.2	94.1	108.4	100.4	100.2	108.0	103.6	98.9	141.9	117.6	98.2	105.9	101.6	95.5	109.3	101.5

ILLINOIS

DIVISION		EFFINGHAM 624			GALESBURG 614			JOLIET 604			KANKAKEE 609			LA SALLE 613			NORTH SUBURBAN 600 - 603		
		MAT.	INST.	TOTAL	MAT.	INST.	TOTAL	MAT.	INST.	TOTAL	MAT.	INST.	TOTAL	MAT.	INST.	TOTAL	MAT.	INST.	TOTAL
015433	CONTRACTOR EQUIPMENT		102.1	102.1		101.4	101.4		92.0	92.0		92.0	92.0		101.4	101.4		92.0	92.0
0241, 31 - 34	SITE & INFRASTRUCTURE, DEMOLITION	97.5	98.2	98.0	98.7	97.7	98.0	105.2	94.7	97.8	98.9	93.9	95.4	98.1	98.4	98.3	104.4	93.7	96.8
0310	Concrete Forming & Accessories	102.2	115.5	113.7	91.5	119.0	115.3	98.4	163.3	154.4	92.4	141.3	134.6	105.1	125.1	122.4	97.8	153.4	145.8
0320	Concrete Reinforcing	90.7	101.0	95.9	95.4	111.1	103.2	95.5	155.7	125.6	96.3	146.5	121.4	95.5	143.7	119.6	95.5	157.3	126.4
0330	Cast-in-Place Concrete	99.9	107.3	103.0	101.6	107.9	104.2	103.3	149.4	122.4	96.4	132.5	111.4	101.5	123.6	110.7	103.4	143.5	120.0
03	CONCRETE	98.4	109.9	104.1	100.1	113.7	106.8	99.3	155.5	127.1	93.7	138.2	115.6	100.9	127.9	114.3	99.3	149.4	124.0
04	MASONRY	83.8	107.6	98.5	113.5	119.7	117.4	105.0	151.1	133.5	101.3	139.8	125.1	113.5	125.6	121.0	101.8	146.6	129.5
05	METALS	95.1	106.1	98.5	97.3	112.8	102.1	92.9	130.6	104.6	92.9	124.7	102.7	97.4	130.3	107.5	94.1	130.1	105.2
06	WOOD, PLASTICS & COMPOSITES	108.8	116.5	113.1	94.8	118.2	108.0	99.7	164.8	136.4	92.8	140.7	119.8	110.0	123.5	117.6	98.2	154.1	129.7
07	THERMAL & MOISTURE PROTECTION	103.6	107.6	105.2	100.5	109.9	104.3	99.1	144.5	117.5	98.4	135.6	113.5	100.6	119.4	108.2	99.5	140.8	116.3
08	OPENINGS	93.8	111.2	97.9	93.1	112.2	97.6	99.0	163.5	114.2	91.9	147.0	105.0	93.1	128.3	101.5	99.0	157.1	112.8
0920	Plaster & Gypsum Board	98.3	116.9	111.0	92.5	118.7	110.3	86.7	166.8	141.2	84.1	142.0	123.5	99.2	124.2	116.2	89.7	155.8	134.6
0950, 0980	Ceilings & Acoustic Treatment	96.2	116.9	110.0	94.3	118.7	110.5	101.5	166.8	144.9	101.5	142.0	128.4	94.3	124.2	114.2	101.5	155.8	137.6
0960	Flooring	109.7	122.4	113.5	100.6	120.9	106.7	92.7	142.9	107.7	90.1	134.3	103.3	106.5	124.8	112.0	93.1	142.9	108.0
0970, 0990	Wall Finishes & Painting/Coating	96.1	104.2	101.0	95.3	96.0	95.7	92.0	151.4	127.7	92.0	127.8	113.5	95.3	127.8	114.8	93.8	151.4	128.4
09	FINISHES	101.9	116.8	110.2	98.6	117.8	109.3	98.1	160.0	132.6	96.6	137.1	119.2	101.2	124.7	114.3	98.7	152.5	128.7
COVERS	DIVS. 10 - 14, 25, 28, 41, 43, 44, 46	100.0	71.7	94.3	100.0	103.8	100.8	100.0	125.4	105.1	100.0	117.6	103.5	100.0	104.4	100.9	100.0	120.4	104.1
21, 22, 23	FIRE SUPPRESSION, PLUMBING & HVAC	95.1	103.5	98.4	95.0	105.7	99.3	100.0	132.7	113.1	95.1	126.6	107.7	95.0	124.8	107.0	99.9	130.9	112.3
26, 27, 3370	ELECTRICAL, COMMUNICATIONS & UTIL.	96.0	106.6	101.6	94.5	87.3	90.7	95.4	141.2	119.3	90.1	140.4	116.4	91.6	140.4	117.1	95.2	131.5	114.2
MF2010	WEIGHTED AVERAGE	96.3	106.3	100.6	97.6	107.6	102.0	98.4	140.7	116.8	94.8	130.8	110.5	97.7	125.1	109.6	98.5	135.9	114.8

ILLINOIS

DIVISION		PEORIA 615 - 616			QUINCY 623			ROCK ISLAND 612			ROCKFORD 610 - 611			SOUTH SUBURBAN 605			SPRINGFIELD 626 - 627		
		MAT.	INST.	TOTAL	MAT.	INST.	TOTAL	MAT.	INST.	TOTAL	MAT.	INST.	TOTAL	MAT.	INST.	TOTAL	MAT.	INST.	TOTAL
015433	CONTRACTOR EQUIPMENT		101.4	101.4		102.1	102.1		101.4	101.4		101.4	101.4		92.0	92.0		102.1	102.1
0241, 31 - 34	SITE & INFRASTRUCTURE, DEMOLITION	99.2	97.8	98.2	96.3	98.1	97.6	96.8	96.8	96.8	98.5	98.8	98.7	104.4	93.7	96.8	99.2	98.6	98.8
0310	Concrete Forming & Accessories	94.5	119.9	116.4	100.0	113.8	111.9	93.2	101.3	100.2	98.9	130.1	125.8	97.8	153.4	145.8	98.1	117.3	114.6
0320	Concrete Reinforcing	92.9	111.2	102.0	90.4	105.6	98.0	95.4	104.2	99.8	87.8	138.2	113.0	95.5	157.3	126.4	92.8	106.1	99.4
0330	Cast-in-Place Concrete	98.5	116.0	105.8	100.0	104.2	101.8	99.4	98.4	99.0	100.9	126.4	111.5	103.4	143.5	120.0	95.2	108.5	100.7
03	CONCRETE	97.3	116.9	106.9	98.0	109.0	103.4	98.1	101.2	99.6	97.8	130.1	113.7	99.3	149.4	124.0	95.6	112.1	103.7
04	MASONRY	113.5	120.0	117.5	104.2	104.6	104.4	113.4	96.2	102.7	88.8	134.3	117.0	101.8	146.6	129.5	86.1	119.0	106.5
05	METALS	100.0	113.6	104.2	95.1	108.4	99.2	97.3	108.3	100.7	100.0	127.8	108.6	94.1	130.1	105.2	95.5	109.7	99.9
06	WOOD, PLASTICS & COMPOSITES	102.5	118.2	111.4	106.1	116.5	112.0	96.4	100.6	98.8	102.5	127.8	116.8	98.2	154.1	129.7	103.0	116.5	110.6
07	THERMAL & MOISTURE PROTECTION	101.2	113.8	106.3	103.6	104.1	103.8	100.4	98.5	99.7	103.5	128.4	113.6	99.5	140.8	116.3	105.2	112.8	108.3
08	OPENINGS	99.2	116.7	103.4	94.6	112.4	98.8	93.1	101.0	95.0	99.2	132.5	107.1	99.0	157.1	112.8	101.3	112.4	103.9
0920	Plaster & Gypsum Board	96.3	118.7	111.5	96.8	116.9	110.5	92.5	100.5	97.9	96.3	128.5	118.2	89.7	155.8	134.6	97.1	116.9	110.6
0950, 0980	Ceilings & Acoustic Treatment	100.5	118.7	112.6	96.2	116.9	110.0	94.3	100.5	98.4	100.5	128.5	119.2	101.5	155.8	137.6	106.6	116.9	113.5
0960	Flooring	103.8	120.9	108.9	108.6	110.1	109.1	101.7	107.5	103.4	103.8	124.8	110.1	93.1	142.9	108.0	113.1	109.8	112.1
0970, 0990	Wall Finishes & Painting/Coating	95.3	127.8	114.8	96.1	105.1	101.5	95.3	96.0	95.7	95.3	135.3	119.3	93.8	151.4	128.4	94.6	105.1	100.9
09	FINISHES	101.4	121.4	112.6	101.3	113.6	108.2	98.8	101.9	100.6	101.4	129.8	117.2	98.7	152.5	128.7	106.1	115.4	111.3
COVERS	DIVS. 10 - 14, 25, 28, 41, 43, 44, 46	100.0	104.3	100.9	100.0	72.7	94.5	100.0	97.2	99.4	100.0	111.6	102.3	100.0	120.4	104.1	100.0	103.3	100.7
21, 22, 23	FIRE SUPPRESSION, PLUMBING & HVAC	99.9	105.8	102.3	95.1	100.8	97.4	95.0	99.8	96.9	100.0	114.9	106.0	99.9	130.9	112.3	99.9	103.4	101.3
26, 27, 3370	ELECTRICAL, COMMUNICATIONS & UTIL.	95.5	97.4	96.5	93.2	81.3	87.0	86.5	95.7	91.3	95.8	127.0	112.1	95.2	131.5	114.2	101.0	92.8	96.8
MF2010	WEIGHTED AVERAGE	99.9	110.4	104.5	96.9	101.6	99.0	96.6	99.8	98.0	98.9	123.5	109.6	98.5	135.9	114.8	99.0	107.2	102.5

INDIANA

DIVISION		ANDERSON 460 MAT.	INST.	TOTAL	BLOOMINGTON 474 MAT.	INST.	TOTAL	COLUMBUS 472 MAT.	INST.	TOTAL	EVANSVILLE 476 - 477 MAT.	INST.	TOTAL	FORT WAYNE 467 - 468 MAT.	INST.	TOTAL	GARY 463 - 464 MAT.	INST.	TOTAL
015433	CONTRACTOR EQUIPMENT		96.7	96.7		87.2	87.2		87.2	87.2		116.1	116.1		96.7	96.7		96.7	96.7
0241, 31 - 34	SITE & INFRASTRUCTURE, DEMOLITION	90.5	96.0	94.4	82.7	94.8	91.2	79.4	94.6	90.1	87.8	123.5	112.9	91.5	96.0	94.6	91.0	99.2	96.8
0310	Concrete Forming & Accessories	98.8	80.8	83.3	101.9	81.1	83.9	95.9	78.9	81.2	95.4	81.9	83.7	97.1	75.4	78.3	98.9	115.2	113.0
0320	Concrete Reinforcing	98.0	83.7	90.9	87.1	83.4	85.2	87.5	83.4	85.4	95.4	76.7	86.1	98.0	76.8	87.4	98.0	110.1	104.0
0330	Cast-in-Place Concrete	104.8	78.1	93.7	100.8	78.0	91.3	100.4	72.5	88.8	96.3	87.7	92.8	111.3	83.7	99.9	109.5	112.4	110.7
03	CONCRETE	96.3	80.9	88.7	102.3	80.3	91.4	101.6	77.3	89.6	102.7	83.1	93.0	99.3	79.1	89.3	98.5	113.1	105.7
04	MASONRY	84.8	79.7	81.7	90.5	76.4	81.8	90.4	76.2	81.6	86.4	83.3	84.5	88.2	77.3	81.4	86.1	112.8	102.7
05	METALS	92.9	89.8	92.0	95.9	78.7	90.6	95.9	78.0	90.4	89.2	84.4	87.8	92.9	86.4	90.9	92.9	108.0	97.6
06	WOOD, PLASTICS & COMPOSITES	108.2	80.8	92.8	118.0	81.1	97.2	112.5	78.3	93.2	97.4	80.8	88.0	107.9	74.8	89.2	105.7	115.0	110.9
07	THERMAL & MOISTURE PROTECTION	105.4	77.1	93.9	95.3	79.7	88.9	94.9	79.4	88.6	99.3	84.7	93.4	105.2	79.0	94.6	104.0	109.0	106.0
08	OPENINGS	95.0	81.9	91.9	105.0	82.0	99.6	100.8	80.5	96.0	98.3	79.8	93.9	95.0	74.7	90.2	95.0	119.4	100.8
0920	Plaster & Gypsum Board	94.3	80.6	85.0	98.1	81.2	86.6	94.7	78.3	83.6	93.1	79.6	83.9	93.5	74.4	80.5	87.6	115.8	106.8
0950, 0980	Ceilings & Acoustic Treatment	89.6	80.6	83.7	83.9	81.2	82.1	83.9	78.3	80.2	88.8	79.6	82.7	89.6	74.4	79.5	89.6	115.8	107.1
0960	Flooring	99.9	86.6	96.0	105.8	76.4	97.0	101.4	76.4	93.9	100.8	82.2	95.2	99.9	80.2	94.0	99.9	123.6	107.0
0970, 0990	Wall Finishes & Painting/Coating	97.3	70.9	81.4	89.6	83.0	85.7	89.6	83.0	85.7	94.7	86.7	89.9	97.3	74.4	83.5	97.3	126.6	114.9
09	FINISHES	95.0	80.9	87.1	96.2	80.4	87.4	94.5	78.7	85.7	95.2	82.4	88.1	94.8	76.1	84.4	94.0	118.3	107.5
COVERS	DIVS. 10 - 14, 25, 28, 41, 43, 44, 46	100.0	91.5	98.3	100.0	89.1	97.8	100.0	88.7	97.7	100.0	94.1	98.8	100.0	89.5	97.9	100.0	105.3	101.1
21, 22, 23	FIRE SUPPRESSION, PLUMBING & HVAC	100.0	75.8	90.3	99.8	79.0	91.4	94.9	79.0	88.5	100.0	80.2	92.0	100.0	72.4	88.9	100.0	105.9	102.3
26, 27, 3370	ELECTRICAL, COMMUNICATIONS & UTIL.	85.9	88.4	87.2	98.2	83.5	90.5	97.3	85.2	91.0	94.5	86.3	90.2	86.6	78.4	82.3	97.7	110.2	104.2
MF2010	WEIGHTED AVERAGE	95.5	83.1	90.1	98.7	81.5	91.2	96.6	80.9	89.7	96.5	86.6	92.1	96.0	79.2	88.7	96.8	110.1	102.6

INDIANA

DIVISION		INDIANAPOLIS 461 - 462 MAT.	INST.	TOTAL	KOKOMO 469 MAT.	INST.	TOTAL	LAFAYETTE 479 MAT.	INST.	TOTAL	LAWRENCEBURG 470 MAT.	INST.	TOTAL	MUNCIE 473 MAT.	INST.	TOTAL	NEW ALBANY 471 MAT.	INST.	TOTAL
015433	CONTRACTOR EQUIPMENT		93.3	93.3		96.7	96.7		87.2	87.2		105.0	105.0		95.7	95.7		95.1	95.1
0241, 31 - 34	SITE & INFRASTRUCTURE, DEMOLITION	90.3	99.3	96.6	87.1	95.8	93.2	80.2	94.5	90.3	78.0	111.0	101.2	82.5	95.0	91.3	75.3	97.4	90.8
0310	Concrete Forming & Accessories	98.0	85.1	86.9	102.4	77.8	81.2	93.5	82.8	84.3	92.4	77.2	79.3	93.5	80.5	82.3	90.2	75.1	77.2
0320	Concrete Reinforcing	100.0	85.4	92.7	88.7	83.7	86.2	87.1	83.6	85.4	86.3	76.6	81.5	96.3	83.6	90.0	87.7	79.6	83.6
0330	Cast-in-Place Concrete	103.3	84.7	95.6	103.7	81.0	94.3	100.9	80.7	92.5	94.4	76.6	87.0	105.9	77.7	94.2	97.4	75.7	88.5
03	CONCRETE	99.5	84.8	92.3	93.1	80.5	86.9	101.8	81.9	92.0	95.0	77.4	86.3	101.1	80.6	91.0	100.2	76.5	88.5
04	MASONRY	90.3	81.3	84.7	84.4	80.0	81.7	95.5	79.8	85.8	75.6	76.0	75.9	92.4	79.8	84.6	82.3	69.5	74.4
05	METALS	93.6	81.7	89.9	89.5	89.3	89.4	94.3	78.6	89.5	91.1	85.2	89.3	97.7	89.9	95.3	93.0	82.7	89.8
06	WOOD, PLASTICS & COMPOSITES	105.3	85.3	94.0	111.6	76.6	91.9	109.5	83.2	94.7	95.8	77.0	85.2	111.4	80.6	94.0	97.9	76.0	85.5
07	THERMAL & MOISTURE PROTECTION	100.9	82.6	93.5	105.0	77.1	93.7	94.9	81.5	89.5	99.2	78.3	90.7	97.9	78.0	89.8	86.8	71.4	80.6
08	OPENINGS	103.1	84.8	98.8	90.0	79.6	87.5	99.2	83.1	95.4	100.4	76.8	94.8	98.5	81.7	94.5	97.9	78.2	93.2
0920	Plaster & Gypsum Board	88.5	85.1	86.2	99.8	76.3	83.8	91.8	83.3	86.0	72.6	76.8	75.5	93.1	80.6	84.6	91.2	75.6	80.6
0950, 0980	Ceilings & Acoustic Treatment	91.3	85.1	87.2	89.6	76.3	80.8	79.4	83.3	82.0	93.2	76.8	82.3	84.8	80.6	82.0	88.8	75.6	80.0
0960	Flooring	101.7	86.6	97.2	103.6	89.9	99.5	100.4	88.1	96.8	74.8	86.6	78.3	100.7	86.6	96.5	98.3	64.0	88.1
0970, 0990	Wall Finishes & Painting/Coating	99.5	83.0	89.6	97.3	73.3	82.9	89.6	95.1	92.9	90.6	73.2	80.1	89.6	70.9	78.4	94.7	84.5	88.6
09	FINISHES	95.4	85.4	89.8	96.6	79.3	87.0	92.9	85.2	88.6	85.8	78.9	82.0	94.0	80.7	86.6	94.5	74.3	83.2
COVERS	DIVS. 10 - 14, 25, 28, 41, 43, 44, 46	100.0	93.0	98.6	100.0	89.1	97.8	100.0	91.3	98.3	100.0	44.9	89.0	100.0	90.9	98.2	100.0	44.3	88.8
21, 22, 23	FIRE SUPPRESSION, PLUMBING & HVAC	99.9	80.1	92.0	95.1	79.2	88.7	94.9	80.2	89.0	95.6	75.7	87.6	99.8	75.8	90.2	95.1	76.9	87.8
26, 27, 3370	ELECTRICAL, COMMUNICATIONS & UTIL.	100.7	88.3	94.2	90.4	78.8	84.4	96.8	82.6	89.4	92.3	75.3	83.4	90.2	80.3	85.0	92.8	77.6	84.9
MF2010	WEIGHTED AVERAGE	98.3	85.1	92.6	93.3	82.0	88.4	96.3	82.9	90.5	93.3	79.3	87.2	97.3	81.8	90.6	94.4	77.0	86.8

INDIANA / IOWA

DIVISION		SOUTH BEND 465 - 466 MAT.	INST.	TOTAL	TERRE HAUTE 478 MAT.	INST.	TOTAL	WASHINGTON 475 MAT.	INST.	TOTAL	BURLINGTON 526 MAT.	INST.	TOTAL	CARROLL 514 MAT.	INST.	TOTAL	CEDAR RAPIDS 522 - 524 MAT.	INST.	TOTAL
015433	CONTRACTOR EQUIPMENT		105.0	105.0		116.1	116.1		116.1	116.1		100.2	100.2		100.2	100.2		96.8	96.8
0241, 31 - 34	SITE & INFRASTRUCTURE, DEMOLITION	92.9	95.9	95.0	89.7	124.2	113.9	89.2	121.5	111.9	96.5	97.3	97.1	85.8	97.3	93.9	98.5	96.0	96.8
0310	Concrete Forming & Accessories	102.6	79.8	82.9	96.3	78.1	80.6	97.1	80.6	82.9	97.3	77.3	80.1	85.2	51.6	56.2	103.2	81.0	84.1
0320	Concrete Reinforcing	101.1	79.1	90.1	95.4	83.8	89.6	88.2	50.3	69.3	94.3	85.4	89.9	95.1	81.1	88.1	95.1	86.8	90.9
0330	Cast-in-Place Concrete	96.3	80.7	89.8	93.3	87.0	90.7	101.5	86.6	95.3	109.6	56.3	87.5	109.6	61.0	89.4	109.9	81.3	98.0
03	CONCRETE	90.8	81.3	86.1	105.6	82.6	94.2	111.1	77.1	94.3	101.7	72.5	87.3	100.5	61.7	81.3	101.8	82.8	92.4
04	MASONRY	90.7	79.1	83.5	93.6	80.5	85.5	86.4	82.3	83.9	97.2	66.0	77.9	99.0	73.5	83.2	102.8	77.5	87.1
05	METALS	93.0	99.8	95.1	89.9	88.1	89.4	84.7	69.6	80.0	87.0	94.9	89.4	87.0	90.4	88.1	89.3	93.8	90.7
06	WOOD, PLASTICS & COMPOSITES	105.0	79.2	90.4	99.5	76.4	86.5	100.0	80.7	89.1	95.3	78.4	85.7	81.8	45.9	61.6	101.8	80.5	89.8
07	THERMAL & MOISTURE PROTECTION	97.5	81.9	91.2	99.4	81.9	92.3	99.5	84.4	93.4	103.8	75.6	92.4	104.1	70.5	90.5	104.7	79.9	94.6
08	OPENINGS	91.0	78.9	88.1	98.9	79.4	94.3	95.6	69.2	89.3	92.4	72.1	87.6	96.6	54.7	86.7	97.6	81.7	93.8
0920	Plaster & Gypsum Board	87.0	78.9	81.5	93.1	75.0	80.8	93.0	79.5	83.8	100.7	77.7	85.1	95.9	44.3	60.8	105.3	80.1	88.2
0950, 0980	Ceilings & Acoustic Treatment	93.4	78.9	83.8	88.8	75.0	79.6	82.5	79.5	80.5	110.6	77.7	88.7	110.6	44.3	66.5	114.1	80.1	91.5
0960	Flooring	97.4	89.9	95.1	100.8	86.6	96.6	101.7	77.8	94.6	111.2	38.5	89.5	105.6	33.8	84.2	127.9	79.7	113.5
0970, 0990	Wall Finishes & Painting/Coating	87.6	87.4	87.5	94.7	83.7	88.1	94.7	85.2	89.0	99.0	80.2	87.7	99.0	79.9	87.5	100.4	73.7	84.3
09	FINISHES	95.3	82.4	88.1	95.2	79.9	86.6	94.3	81.4	87.1	107.2	70.4	86.7	103.3	49.4	73.3	113.2	80.0	94.7
COVERS	DIVS. 10 - 14, 25, 28, 41, 43, 44, 46	100.0	90.7	98.1	100.0	93.2	98.6	100.0	94.0	98.8	100.0	89.2	97.8	100.0	66.9	93.4	100.0	90.2	98.0
21, 22, 23	FIRE SUPPRESSION, PLUMBING & HVAC	99.9	77.4	90.9	100.0	80.4	92.1	95.1	79.3	88.7	95.3	76.9	87.9	95.3	74.2	86.8	100.2	80.7	92.4
26, 27, 3370	ELECTRICAL, COMMUNICATIONS & UTIL.	97.6	86.6	91.9	92.6	83.6	87.9	93.1	86.3	89.5	100.7	69.3	84.3	101.4	81.3	90.9	98.2	81.3	89.3
MF2010	WEIGHTED AVERAGE	95.7	84.2	90.7	97.2	85.8	92.2	95.0	83.3	89.9	96.6	76.9	88.0	96.4	72.2	85.9	99.4	83.4	92.4

City Cost Indexes

IOWA

DIVISION		COUNCIL BLUFFS 515			CRESTON 508			DAVENPORT 527 - 528			DECORAH 521			DES MOINES 500 - 503,509			DUBUQUE 520		
		MAT.	INST.	TOTAL	MAT.	INST.	TOTAL	MAT.	INST.	TOTAL	MAT.	INST.	TOTAL	MAT.	INST.	TOTAL	MAT.	INST.	TOTAL
015433	CONTRACTOR EQUIPMENT		96.3	96.3		100.2	100.2		100.2	100.2		100.2	100.2		101.8	101.8		95.7	95.7
0241, 31 - 34	SITE & INFRASTRUCTURE, DEMOLITION	103.6	92.3	95.7	86.7	96.4	93.5	96.8	99.3	98.6	95.1	96.3	95.9	95.5	99.7	98.5	96.4	93.3	94.2
0310	Concrete Forming & Accessories	84.6	70.7	72.6	84.5	67.2	69.6	102.5	91.2	92.7	94.9	46.5	53.1	103.2	78.9	82.2	85.9	73.8	75.4
0320	Concrete Reinforcing	97.0	79.3	88.2	93.3	81.2	87.3	95.1	100.0	97.5	94.3	79.0	86.7	102.7	81.4	92.0	93.7	86.6	90.2
0330	Cast-in-Place Concrete	114.3	75.1	98.0	102.1	65.4	86.9	105.9	91.7	100.0	106.7	59.3	87.0	89.8	88.0	89.1	107.6	100.4	104.6
03	CONCRETE	104.1	74.7	89.6	96.9	70.2	83.7	99.9	93.5	96.7	99.6	58.4	79.3	95.0	83.2	89.2	98.6	86.2	92.4
04	MASONRY	104.5	75.9	86.8	96.9	81.4	87.3	100.0	85.5	91.1	117.7	72.7	89.8	90.7	80.4	84.3	103.7	73.7	85.1
05	METALS	94.3	90.2	93.1	89.4	90.6	89.8	89.3	103.9	93.8	87.1	87.7	87.3	95.2	92.9	94.5	88.0	93.5	89.7
06	WOOD, PLASTICS & COMPOSITES	80.6	69.7	74.4	79.1	63.1	70.1	101.9	90.3	95.3	92.3	37.9	61.6	98.8	77.4	86.8	82.2	71.7	76.3
07	THERMAL & MOISTURE PROTECTION	104.2	68.4	89.6	106.2	78.8	95.1	104.2	87.4	97.4	104.0	54.7	84.0	100.6	79.5	92.0	104.4	71.3	91.0
08	OPENINGS	96.6	75.5	91.6	106.6	64.4	96.6	97.6	91.4	96.1	95.2	49.8	84.5	101.9	82.8	97.4	96.6	79.3	92.5
0920	Plaster & Gypsum Board	95.9	69.0	77.6	94.1	62.0	72.2	105.3	90.0	94.9	99.6	36.0	56.4	91.9	76.8	81.6	95.9	71.1	79.0
0950, 0980	Ceilings & Acoustic Treatment	110.6	69.0	82.9	111.5	62.0	78.5	114.1	90.0	98.1	110.6	36.0	61.0	115.0	76.8	89.6	110.6	71.1	84.3
0960	Flooring	104.3	82.1	97.6	104.2	33.8	83.2	113.5	98.7	109.1	111.1	48.0	92.2	109.4	87.6	102.9	118.8	77.6	106.5
0970, 0990	Wall Finishes & Painting/Coating	95.3	66.9	78.2	95.8	79.9	86.3	99.0	97.6	98.1	99.0	33.6	59.7	91.2	79.9	84.4	99.4	65.1	78.8
09	FINISHES	104.1	72.0	86.2	102.4	61.5	79.6	109.1	93.2	100.2	106.9	43.6	71.6	105.5	80.4	91.5	108.4	72.9	88.6
COVERS	DIVS. 10 - 14, 25, 28, 41, 43, 44, 46	100.0	88.9	97.8	100.0	71.4	94.3	100.0	93.1	98.6	100.0	85.2	97.0	100.0	90.3	98.1	100.0	88.6	97.7
21, 22, 23	FIRE SUPPRESSION, PLUMBING & HVAC	100.2	75.8	90.4	95.3	80.3	89.2	100.2	93.2	97.4	95.3	74.5	86.9	100.0	79.8	91.9	100.2	75.4	90.2
26, 27, 3370	ELECTRICAL, COMMUNICATIONS & UTIL.	103.7	81.6	92.1	94.8	81.3	87.8	95.5	91.2	93.2	98.1	45.4	70.6	106.9	81.3	93.6	102.2	78.4	89.8
MF2010	WEIGHTED AVERAGE	100.2	78.8	90.9	96.7	77.9	88.5	98.4	93.4	96.2	97.4	65.6	83.5	99.4	83.9	92.7	98.5	80.4	90.6

IOWA

DIVISION		FORT DODGE 505			MASON CITY 504			OTTUMWA 525			SHENANDOAH 516			SIBLEY 512			SIOUX CITY 510 - 511		
		MAT.	INST.	TOTAL	MAT.	INST.	TOTAL	MAT.	INST.	TOTAL	MAT.	INST.	TOTAL	MAT.	INST.	TOTAL	MAT.	INST.	TOTAL
015433	CONTRACTOR EQUIPMENT		100.2	100.2		100.2	100.2		95.7	95.7		96.3	96.3		100.2	100.2		100.2	100.2
0241, 31 - 34	SITE & INFRASTRUCTURE, DEMOLITION	94.6	95.0	94.9	94.6	96.2	95.8	96.8	91.4	93.0	102.0	91.4	94.6	106.0	95.0	98.3	107.6	95.8	99.3
0310	Concrete Forming & Accessories	85.1	46.0	51.3	89.6	46.4	52.3	92.9	71.9	74.8	86.2	57.8	61.7	86.6	38.7	45.3	103.2	67.9	72.7
0320	Concrete Reinforcing	93.3	67.4	80.4	93.2	80.6	86.9	94.3	85.6	90.0	97.0	68.6	82.8	97.0	67.3	82.2	95.1	78.2	86.7
0330	Cast-in-Place Concrete	95.8	45.0	74.7	95.8	58.7	80.4	110.3	54.8	87.3	110.5	61.1	90.0	109.0	56.7	87.3	109.0	56.7	87.3
03	CONCRETE	92.6	51.1	72.1	92.9	58.5	75.9	101.2	69.4	85.5	101.5	62.1	82.1	100.5	48.1	74.6	101.2	66.9	84.3
04	MASONRY	95.9	38.5	60.4	108.7	69.4	84.4	100.3	57.1	73.6	104.0	75.9	86.6	122.1	38.8	70.6	97.2	55.6	71.4
05	METALS	89.5	81.9	87.2	89.5	88.8	89.3	86.9	92.0	88.5	93.3	84.3	90.5	87.2	81.4	85.4	89.3	88.2	89.0
06	WOOD, PLASTICS & COMPOSITES	79.6	46.2	60.8	83.9	37.9	58.0	89.4	78.2	83.1	82.2	54.0	66.3	83.1	36.7	56.9	101.8	68.2	82.9
07	THERMAL & MOISTURE PROTECTION	105.6	58.5	86.5	105.2	64.6	88.7	104.6	65.2	88.6	103.5	66.6	88.5	103.8	49.2	81.6	104.3	64.9	88.3
08	OPENINGS	100.8	50.1	88.8	93.3	50.2	83.1	96.6	76.2	91.8	88.1	55.5	80.4	93.4	44.9	81.9	97.6	66.9	90.3
0920	Plaster & Gypsum Board	94.1	44.6	60.4	94.1	36.0	54.6	97.0	77.7	83.9	95.9	52.8	66.6	95.9	34.7	54.3	105.3	67.2	79.4
0950, 0980	Ceilings & Acoustic Treatment	111.5	44.6	67.0	111.5	36.0	61.3	110.6	77.7	88.7	110.6	52.8	72.1	110.6	34.7	60.1	114.1	67.2	82.9
0960	Flooring	105.8	48.0	88.5	107.9	48.0	90.0	121.8	51.1	100.6	104.9	34.9	84.0	106.4	34.6	85.0	113.6	54.7	96.0
0970, 0990	Wall Finishes & Painting/Coating	95.8	63.1	76.1	95.8	30.7	56.7	99.4	79.9	87.7	95.3	66.9	78.2	99.0	63.1	77.4	99.0	63.1	77.4
09	FINISHES	104.4	47.1	72.5	105.0	42.9	70.4	109.5	69.2	87.0	104.2	53.4	75.9	106.7	38.9	68.9	110.7	64.8	85.1
COVERS	DIVS. 10 - 14, 25, 28, 41, 43, 44, 46	100.0	79.8	96.0	100.0	84.8	97.0	100.0	84.2	96.8	100.0	67.9	93.6	100.0	78.9	95.8	100.0	86.9	97.4
21, 22, 23	FIRE SUPPRESSION, PLUMBING & HVAC	95.3	65.8	83.4	95.3	71.9	85.9	95.3	71.3	85.7	95.3	75.1	87.2	95.3	69.5	84.9	100.2	76.3	90.6
26, 27, 3370	ELECTRICAL, COMMUNICATIONS & UTIL.	101.9	42.9	71.1	100.9	57.0	77.9	100.5	67.8	83.4	98.1	80.6	89.0	98.1	42.4	69.1	98.2	74.7	85.9
MF2010	WEIGHTED AVERAGE	96.6	58.8	80.2	96.5	66.6	83.5	97.3	73.0	86.7	97.1	72.1	86.2	97.7	57.5	80.2	99.1	73.6	88.0

IOWA / KANSAS

DIVISION		SPENCER 513			WATERLOO 506 - 507			BELLEVILLE 669			COLBY 677			DODGE CITY 678			EMPORIA 668		
		MAT.	INST.	TOTAL	MAT.	INST.	TOTAL	MAT.	INST.	TOTAL	MAT.	INST.	TOTAL	MAT.	INST.	TOTAL	MAT.	INST.	TOTAL
015433	CONTRACTOR EQUIPMENT		100.2	100.2		100.2	100.2		103.1	103.1		103.1	103.1		103.1	103.1		101.4	101.4
0241, 31 - 34	SITE & INFRASTRUCTURE, DEMOLITION	106.1	95.0	98.3	99.5	96.1	97.1	111.0	94.7	99.5	109.4	94.8	99.1	111.9	94.5	99.1	102.8	92.2	95.3
0310	Concrete Forming & Accessories	92.8	38.7	46.1	101.6	48.1	55.4	95.0	55.3	60.7	102.2	59.6	65.4	95.3	59.5	64.4	86.5	66.7	69.4
0320	Concrete Reinforcing	97.0	67.3	82.2	94.0	86.5	90.2	99.6	56.1	77.9	101.2	56.1	78.7	98.8	56.1	77.5	98.2	56.7	77.5
0330	Cast-in-Place Concrete	108.3	45.7	82.3	102.6	55.0	82.9	118.9	56.9	93.2	114.3	57.0	90.6	116.4	56.7	91.6	114.9	54.8	90.0
03	CONCRETE	100.9	48.1	74.9	98.4	59.1	79.0	117.7	57.4	88.0	114.9	59.3	87.5	116.2	59.1	88.0	110.0	61.8	86.2
04	MASONRY	122.1	38.8	70.6	96.6	73.0	82.0	94.9	59.8	73.2	96.9	59.8	73.9	104.4	60.0	76.9	100.5	68.4	80.7
05	METALS	87.1	81.4	85.4	91.8	92.8	92.1	97.8	78.4	91.9	98.2	78.7	92.2	99.7	77.8	92.9	97.6	79.9	92.1
06	WOOD, PLASTICS & COMPOSITES	89.3	36.7	59.6	98.6	37.9	64.4	96.4	53.3	72.1	103.9	59.2	78.7	95.3	59.2	74.9	87.7	68.2	76.7
07	THERMAL & MOISTURE PROTECTION	104.6	49.2	82.1	105.4	71.4	91.6	98.4	62.3	83.7	101.9	62.9	86.1	101.9	62.3	85.8	97.0	77.4	89.1
08	OPENINGS	104.3	44.9	90.2	94.2	53.5	84.5	96.4	49.4	85.3	99.5	52.6	88.4	99.5	52.6	88.4	94.4	57.5	85.6
0920	Plaster & Gypsum Board	97.0	34.7	54.7	103.9	36.0	57.7	98.0	51.8	66.6	100.7	57.9	71.6	94.8	57.9	69.7	95.1	67.1	76.0
0950, 0980	Ceilings & Acoustic Treatment	110.6	34.7	60.1	115.0	36.0	62.5	91.6	51.8	65.1	94.3	57.9	70.1	94.3	57.9	70.1	91.6	67.1	75.3
0960	Flooring	109.1	34.6	86.8	113.3	76.9	102.4	106.4	39.9	86.5	105.7	39.9	86.0	102.2	39.9	83.6	101.8	37.1	82.4
0970, 0990	Wall Finishes & Painting/Coating	99.0	63.1	77.4	95.8	79.4	86.0	97.4	39.8	62.8	97.4	39.8	62.8	97.4	39.8	62.8	97.4	39.8	62.8
09	FINISHES	107.6	38.9	69.3	108.8	54.4	78.5	101.3	50.4	72.9	101.5	53.9	75.0	99.8	53.9	74.2	98.6	58.6	76.3
COVERS	DIVS. 10 - 14, 25, 28, 41, 43, 44, 46	100.0	78.9	95.8	100.0	85.3	97.1	100.0	41.8	88.3	100.0	42.5	88.5	100.0	42.5	88.5	100.0	41.5	88.3
21, 22, 23	FIRE SUPPRESSION, PLUMBING & HVAC	95.3	69.5	84.9	100.2	80.0	92.1	95.1	73.1	86.3	95.1	68.7	84.5	100.0	68.7	87.4	95.1	73.4	86.4
26, 27, 3370	ELECTRICAL, COMMUNICATIONS & UTIL.	99.9	42.4	69.9	97.0	57.0	76.1	93.3	66.0	79.1	97.9	66.0	81.3	94.7	73.4	83.6	90.8	73.1	81.5
MF2010	WEIGHTED AVERAGE	99.2	57.5	81.0	98.3	70.9	86.4	99.4	65.6	84.7	100.2	65.6	85.1	101.7	66.5	86.4	97.8	70.0	85.7

City Cost Indexes

KANSAS

DIVISION		FORT SCOTT 667			HAYS 676			HUTCHINSON 675			INDEPENDENCE 673			KANSAS CITY 660 - 662			LIBERAL 679		
		MAT.	INST.	TOTAL	MAT.	INST.	TOTAL	MAT.	INST.	TOTAL	MAT.	INST.	TOTAL	MAT.	INST.	TOTAL	MAT.	INST.	TOTAL
015433	CONTRACTOR EQUIPMENT		102.3	102.3		103.1	103.1		103.1	103.1		103.1	103.1		103.1	103.1		103.1	103.1
0241, 31 - 34	SITE & INFRASTRUCTURE, DEMOLITION	99.4	93.0	94.9	115.5	94.8	100.9	93.4	94.6	94.3	113.1	94.6	100.1	93.5	92.9	93.1	115.2	94.6	100.7
0310	Concrete Forming & Accessories	102.6	78.6	81.9	99.7	59.6	65.1	89.9	59.5	63.6	110.8	67.8	73.7	99.3	96.3	96.7	95.8	59.5	64.5
0320	Concrete Reinforcing	97.5	96.3	96.9	98.8	56.1	77.5	98.8	56.1	77.5	98.2	63.0	80.6	94.6	97.8	96.2	100.2	56.1	78.2
0330	Cast-in-Place Concrete	106.6	55.7	85.5	90.2	57.0	76.5	83.6	54.2	71.4	116.8	54.5	91.0	91.4	99.3	94.7	90.3	54.2	75.3
03	CONCRETE	105.2	74.6	90.1	106.7	59.3	83.3	89.1	58.3	73.9	117.4	63.3	90.7	97.3	97.9	97.6	108.9	58.3	83.9
04	MASONRY	101.0	61.4	76.5	104.3	59.8	76.8	96.4	59.6	73.6	94.0	65.7	76.5	103.6	99.5	101.1	102.4	59.6	75.9
05	METALS	97.5	94.4	96.5	97.8	78.7	91.9	97.6	77.7	91.5	97.5	81.3	92.5	104.9	100.6	103.5	98.1	77.7	91.8
06	WOOD, PLASTICS & COMPOSITES	106.5	85.4	94.6	100.6	59.2	77.2	89.9	59.2	72.6	114.7	69.6	89.3	102.4	96.7	99.1	95.9	59.2	75.2
07	THERMAL & MOISTURE PROTECTION	97.8	82.8	91.7	102.1	62.9	86.2	100.9	62.2	85.2	101.9	82.4	94.0	97.5	99.8	98.4	102.3	62.2	86.0
08	OPENINGS	94.4	80.1	91.0	99.4	52.6	88.3	99.4	52.6	88.3	97.2	59.8	88.4	95.6	90.5	94.4	99.5	52.6	88.4
0920	Plaster & Gypsum Board	100.6	84.9	89.9	98.1	57.9	70.7	93.6	57.9	69.3	107.8	68.6	81.1	93.5	96.5	95.5	95.5	57.9	69.9
0950, 0980	Ceilings & Acoustic Treatment	91.6	84.9	87.2	94.3	57.9	70.1	94.3	57.9	70.1	94.3	68.6	77.2	91.6	96.5	94.9	94.3	57.9	70.1
0960	Flooring	117.6	40.1	94.4	104.7	39.9	85.3	99.5	39.9	81.7	109.9	39.9	89.0	93.5	100.5	95.6	102.4	39.9	83.7
0970, 0990	Wall Finishes & Painting/Coating	99.2	39.8	63.5	97.4	39.8	62.8	97.4	39.8	62.8	97.4	39.8	62.8	105.6	69.2	83.7	97.4	39.8	62.8
09	FINISHES	104.0	68.4	84.2	101.4	53.9	74.9	97.3	53.9	73.1	103.8	60.0	79.4	98.5	93.1	95.4	100.7	53.9	74.6
COVERS	DIVS. 10 - 14, 25, 28, 41, 43, 44, 46	100.0	47.4	89.5	100.0	42.5	88.5	100.0	42.5	88.5	100.0	43.7	88.7	100.0	63.5	92.7	100.0	42.5	88.5
21, 22, 23	FIRE SUPPRESSION, PLUMBING & HVAC	95.1	69.3	84.7	95.1	68.7	84.5	95.1	68.7	84.5	95.1	71.1	85.5	99.9	96.8	98.6	95.1	68.7	84.5
26, 27, 3370	ELECTRICAL, COMMUNICATIONS & UTIL.	90.1	73.1	81.2	96.8	66.0	80.7	91.7	66.0	78.3	94.0	73.1	83.0	95.5	97.3	96.4	94.7	73.4	83.6
MF2010	WEIGHTED AVERAGE	97.7	74.3	87.5	99.6	65.6	84.8	95.8	65.4	82.5	99.9	70.3	87.0	99.4	95.7	97.7	99.5	66.4	85.1

KANSAS / KENTUCKY

DIVISION		SALINA 674			TOPEKA 664 - 666			WICHITA 670 - 672			ASHLAND 411 - 412			BOWLING GREEN 421 - 422			CAMPTON 413 - 414		
		MAT.	INST.	TOTAL	MAT.	INST.	TOTAL	MAT.	INST.	TOTAL	MAT.	INST.	TOTAL	MAT.	INST.	TOTAL	MAT.	INST.	TOTAL
015433	CONTRACTOR EQUIPMENT		103.1	103.1		101.4	101.4		103.1	103.1		98.0	98.0		95.1	95.1		101.5	101.5
0241, 31 - 34	SITE & INFRASTRUCTURE, DEMOLITION	102.2	94.8	97.0	97.9	91.2	93.2	98.7	93.3	94.9	108.9	87.0	93.5	75.6	97.7	91.1	83.8	98.8	94.3
0310	Concrete Forming & Accessories	91.8	55.7	60.6	97.2	41.8	49.4	97.8	51.7	58.0	89.0	105.7	103.4	86.5	84.0	84.4	90.4	84.6	85.4
0320	Concrete Reinforcing	98.2	62.6	80.4	97.7	97.2	97.5	97.5	75.8	86.7	89.1	106.1	97.6	86.4	89.5	88.0	87.3	105.0	96.1
0330	Cast-in-Place Concrete	101.0	54.7	81.8	96.1	46.5	75.6	94.7	52.7	77.3	88.7	102.9	94.6	88.0	97.5	91.9	98.1	75.2	88.6
03	CONCRETE	103.0	58.0	80.8	98.3	55.4	77.1	97.6	57.8	78.0	96.1	105.2	100.6	94.4	89.7	92.1	98.2	85.2	91.8
04	MASONRY	118.4	59.8	82.1	97.6	56.9	72.4	94.9	51.1	67.8	92.2	105.1	100.2	94.0	81.6	86.3	91.6	70.2	78.4
05	METALS	99.5	81.5	93.9	101.6	96.4	100.0	101.6	83.7	96.1	92.1	109.8	97.6	93.7	86.9	91.6	93.0	93.7	93.2
06	WOOD, PLASTICS & COMPOSITES	91.5	53.3	70.0	95.4	38.1	63.1	95.3	52.5	71.2	79.0	105.4	93.9	92.3	83.9	87.5	90.8	91.1	90.9
07	THERMAL & MOISTURE PROTECTION	101.4	62.6	85.7	100.6	69.1	87.8	100.0	57.6	82.8	91.3	99.3	94.5	86.7	82.1	84.8	99.6	69.4	87.3
08	OPENINGS	99.4	49.7	87.6	98.6	55.3	88.4	101.6	56.6	91.0	97.9	99.3	97.5	93.7	79.4	90.5	99.3	89.8	97.1
0920	Plaster & Gypsum Board	93.6	51.8	65.2	97.6	36.1	55.8	92.4	51.0	64.2	61.2	105.6	91.4	86.4	83.7	84.6	86.4	90.2	89.0
0950, 0980	Ceilings & Acoustic Treatment	94.3	51.8	66.0	97.6	36.1	56.7	99.4	51.0	67.2	83.8	105.6	98.3	88.8	83.7	85.4	88.8	90.2	89.7
0960	Flooring	100.7	63.1	89.5	106.9	75.0	97.3	108.3	64.1	95.1	80.1	104.2	87.3	96.5	87.6	93.9	98.6	42.0	81.7
0970, 0990	Wall Finishes & Painting/Coating	97.4	39.8	62.8	99.2	53.7	71.9	96.3	49.0	67.9	96.9	103.4	100.8	94.7	74.3	82.4	94.7	66.8	77.9
09	FINISHES	98.5	54.8	74.2	103.1	47.0	71.8	102.7	53.5	75.3	82.5	105.7	95.4	93.1	84.0	88.0	93.9	75.7	83.8
COVERS	DIVS. 10 - 14, 25, 28, 41, 43, 44, 46	100.0	54.2	90.8	100.0	48.4	89.7	100.0	51.1	90.2	100.0	96.3	99.3	100.0	59.8	91.9	100.0	57.3	91.4
21, 22, 23	FIRE SUPPRESSION, PLUMBING & HVAC	100.0	68.7	87.5	100.0	69.0	87.5	99.8	64.3	85.6	95.0	92.9	94.1	100.0	84.3	93.7	95.1	81.5	89.7
26, 27, 3370	ELECTRICAL, COMMUNICATIONS & UTIL.	94.5	73.3	83.4	94.2	73.1	83.2	99.0	73.3	85.6	90.7	99.6	95.4	93.3	82.1	87.4	90.6	67.7	78.6
MF2010	WEIGHTED AVERAGE	100.4	67.0	85.9	99.4	66.5	85.1	99.9	65.1	84.8	94.0	100.1	96.6	95.5	84.8	90.8	95.1	80.2	88.6

KENTUCKY

DIVISION		CORBIN 407 - 409			COVINGTON 410			ELIZABETHTOWN 427			FRANKFORT 406			HAZARD 417 - 418			HENDERSON 424		
		MAT.	INST.	TOTAL	MAT.	INST.	TOTAL	MAT.	INST.	TOTAL	MAT.	INST.	TOTAL	MAT.	INST.	TOTAL	MAT.	INST.	TOTAL
015433	CONTRACTOR EQUIPMENT		101.5	101.5		105.0	105.0		95.1	95.1		101.5	101.5		101.5	101.5		116.1	116.1
0241, 31 - 34	SITE & INFRASTRUCTURE, DEMOLITION	83.0	98.5	93.9	79.4	112.3	102.5	70.4	97.8	89.6	87.1	99.7	95.9	81.8	100.1	94.6	78.4	124.1	110.5
0310	Concrete Forming & Accessories	88.9	72.3	74.6	86.0	92.9	92.0	81.6	82.4	82.3	99.5	73.4	77.0	87.1	85.4	85.6	93.4	83.5	84.8
0320	Concrete Reinforcing	87.0	72.1	79.5	85.9	94.0	90.0	86.9	93.8	90.3	99.8	93.7	96.8	87.7	105.0	96.3	86.6	87.6	87.1
0330	Cast-in-Place Concrete	92.2	59.9	78.8	93.9	99.6	96.3	79.6	74.6	77.5	87.2	70.6	80.3	94.4	84.2	90.2	77.8	92.5	83.9
03	CONCRETE	92.6	68.4	80.7	96.5	95.5	96.0	86.6	82.0	84.3	93.0	76.6	84.9	95.0	88.7	91.9	91.6	87.4	89.6
04	MASONRY	89.8	63.0	73.2	105.4	103.3	104.1	78.5	76.8	77.4	87.2	80.8	83.3	89.3	72.8	79.1	97.8	94.5	95.8
05	METALS	93.4	79.8	89.2	91.0	91.7	91.2	92.8	88.8	91.6	95.8	89.5	93.9	93.0	93.7	93.2	84.4	88.6	85.7
06	WOOD, PLASTICS & COMPOSITES	88.5	77.7	82.4	88.7	86.0	87.2	87.4	83.9	85.4	105.5	70.3	85.6	87.7	91.1	89.6	95.1	80.8	87.1
07	THERMAL & MOISTURE PROTECTION	98.8	65.6	85.3	99.4	95.4	97.8	86.4	78.8	83.3	98.8	77.1	90.0	99.5	71.3	88.1	99.0	93.6	96.8
08	OPENINGS	99.3	67.2	91.7	101.3	85.7	97.6	97.9	85.3	94.9	102.1	78.2	96.4	99.7	80.3	95.1	96.0	81.8	92.7
0920	Plaster & Gypsum Board	90.6	76.4	80.9	69.4	86.1	80.8	85.6	83.7	84.3	100.9	68.8	79.0	85.6	90.2	88.7	89.7	79.7	82.9
0950, 0980	Ceilings & Acoustic Treatment	86.1	76.4	79.6	92.3	86.1	88.2	88.8	83.7	85.4	96.8	68.8	78.1	88.8	90.2	89.7	82.5	79.7	80.6
0960	Flooring	100.6	42.0	83.1	72.7	86.2	76.7	94.1	87.6	92.2	108.0	55.4	92.3	97.1	42.7	80.9	100.1	87.6	96.4
0970, 0990	Wall Finishes & Painting/Coating	94.2	50.5	67.9	90.6	84.1	86.7	94.7	77.8	84.6	93.9	81.5	86.5	94.7	66.8	77.9	94.7	66.7	77.9
09	FINISHES	93.9	65.0	77.8	84.8	90.5	87.9	92.0	82.5	86.7	101.6	70.3	84.2	93.2	76.5	83.9	92.6	85.7	88.8
COVERS	DIVS. 10 - 14, 25, 28, 41, 43, 44, 46	100.0	49.7	89.9	100.0	102.8	100.6	100.0	86.6	97.3	100.0	67.2	93.4	100.0	58.1	91.6	100.0	67.1	93.4
21, 22, 23	FIRE SUPPRESSION, PLUMBING & HVAC	95.1	72.9	86.2	95.6	90.6	93.6	95.4	81.9	90.0	100.1	84.1	93.7	95.1	82.4	90.0	95.4	79.3	88.9
26, 27, 3370	ELECTRICAL, COMMUNICATIONS & UTIL.	90.5	82.1	86.1	94.6	79.6	86.8	90.4	82.1	86.1	99.0	89.2	93.9	90.6	59.7	74.5	92.7	82.2	87.2
MF2010	WEIGHTED AVERAGE	94.4	73.3	85.2	95.2	93.2	94.3	92.2	83.7	88.5	97.9	82.4	91.1	94.6	79.9	88.2	93.0	87.9	90.8

KENTUCKY

DIVISION		LEXINGTON 403 - 405			LOUISVILLE 400 - 402			OWENSBORO 423			PADUCAH 420			PIKEVILLE 415 - 416			SOMERSET 425 - 426		
		MAT.	INST.	TOTAL	MAT.	INST.	TOTAL	MAT.	INST.	TOTAL	MAT.	INST.	TOTAL	MAT.	INST.	TOTAL	MAT.	INST.	TOTAL
015433	CONTRACTOR EQUIPMENT		101.5	101.5		95.1	95.1		116.1	116.1		116.1	116.1		98.0	98.0		101.5	101.5
0241, 31 - 34	SITE & INFRASTRUCTURE, DEMOLITION	85.0	100.9	96.2	75.7	97.8	91.3	87.9	124.1	113.3	80.9	123.6	110.9	119.6	86.0	96.0	75.1	99.3	92.1
0310	Concrete Forming & Accessories	101.5	74.3	78.0	100.6	83.0	85.4	91.8	83.4	84.5	89.9	81.8	82.9	97.7	90.9	91.9	88.0	77.6	79.0
0320	Concrete Reinforcing	95.5	93.5	94.5	97.1	93.8	95.4	86.6	90.2	88.4	87.1	89.0	88.0	89.6	105.9	97.7	86.9	93.7	90.3
0330	Cast-in-Place Concrete	94.3	93.9	94.2	95.8	75.4	87.4	90.7	96.1	92.9	82.9	88.3	85.1	97.5	98.7	98.0	77.8	100.3	87.1
03	CONCRETE	95.8	84.9	90.5	96.7	82.5	89.7	103.4	89.1	96.4	96.0	85.5	90.8	109.6	97.1	103.5	81.8	88.6	85.2
04	MASONRY	88.4	73.4	79.1	88.9	78.2	82.3	90.5	92.6	91.8	93.5	90.0	91.3	90.0	98.5	95.2	84.7	78.1	80.6
05	METALS	95.8	89.9	93.9	97.6	88.9	94.9	85.9	90.2	87.2	83.0	88.4	84.6	92.0	108.5	97.1	92.9	89.3	91.8
06	WOOD, PLASTICS & COMPOSITES	105.1	70.3	85.5	103.1	83.9	92.3	93.0	80.8	86.1	90.6	80.9	85.2	88.6	90.4	89.6	88.3	77.7	82.3
07	THERMAL & MOISTURE PROTECTION	99.1	85.7	93.6	97.9	79.5	90.4	99.3	93.9	97.1	99.0	80.9	91.7	91.9	81.5	87.7	99.0	71.8	87.9
08	OPENINGS	99.5	75.3	93.8	99.0	85.3	95.8	96.0	83.9	93.1	95.2	79.4	91.5	97.7	88.4	95.5	98.7	79.6	94.2
0920	Plaster & Gypsum Board	100.6	68.8	79.0	93.2	83.7	86.7	88.2	79.7	82.4	87.1	79.8	82.1	64.5	90.2	82.0	85.6	76.4	79.4
0950, 0980	Ceilings & Acoustic Treatment	90.5	68.8	76.1	94.3	83.7	87.2	82.5	79.7	80.6	82.5	79.8	80.7	83.8	90.2	88.0	88.8	76.4	80.5
0960	Flooring	105.0	71.6	95.0	102.9	87.6	98.3	99.5	87.6	96.0	98.5	60.4	87.1	83.8	104.2	89.9	97.4	42.0	81.2
0970, 0990	Wall Finishes & Painting/Coating	94.2	82.8	87.3	93.9	77.8	84.2	94.7	98.1	96.7	94.7	81.4	86.7	96.9	83.0	88.5	94.7	77.8	84.6
09	FINISHES	97.5	73.6	84.2	97.9	83.5	89.9	92.9	85.2	88.6	92.1	77.8	84.1	84.9	93.0	89.4	92.6	70.9	80.5
COVERS	DIVS. 10 - 14, 25, 28, 41, 43, 44, 46	100.0	88.4	97.7	100.0	87.1	97.4	100.0	100.9	100.2	100.0	63.4	92.7	100.0	57.8	91.5	100.0	60.0	92.0
21, 22, 23	FIRE SUPPRESSION, PLUMBING & HVAC	100.0	80.6	92.2	100.0	82.6	93.0	100.0	78.4	91.3	95.4	82.9	90.4	95.0	89.0	92.6	95.4	79.1	88.8
26, 27, 3370	ELECTRICAL, COMMUNICATIONS & UTIL.	93.4	82.1	87.5	100.0	82.1	90.6	92.7	82.2	87.3	95.1	81.8	88.2	93.7	75.1	84.0	91.0	82.1	86.4
MF2010	WEIGHTED AVERAGE	97.0	82.4	90.7	97.8	84.2	91.9	95.6	88.9	92.7	93.2	86.2	90.2	96.2	90.0	93.5	92.7	81.5	87.8

LOUISIANA

DIVISION		ALEXANDRIA 713 - 714			BATON ROUGE 707 - 708			HAMMOND 704			LAFAYETTE 705			LAKE CHARLES 706			MONROE 712		
		MAT.	INST.	TOTAL	MAT.	INST.	TOTAL	MAT.	INST.	TOTAL	MAT.	INST.	TOTAL	MAT.	INST.	TOTAL	MAT.	INST.	TOTAL
015433	CONTRACTOR EQUIPMENT		89.7	89.7		89.3	89.3		89.9	89.9		89.9	89.9		89.3	89.3		89.7	89.7
0241, 31 - 34	SITE & INFRASTRUCTURE, DEMOLITION	96.3	86.7	89.5	96.0	86.0	89.0	99.1	86.9	90.5	100.1	87.0	90.9	100.8	85.9	90.3	96.3	85.9	89.0
0310	Concrete Forming & Accessories	83.0	44.2	49.5	94.1	61.7	66.1	78.1	46.9	51.2	95.2	54.9	60.4	96.1	57.5	62.8	82.5	43.9	49.2
0320	Concrete Reinforcing	89.4	56.0	72.9	95.1	59.0	77.1	93.3	59.4	76.4	94.6	59.0	76.8	94.8	59.2	76.9	88.4	55.6	72.0
0330	Cast-in-Place Concrete	94.6	50.3	76.2	91.8	58.7	78.0	93.9	43.9	73.2	93.5	47.6	74.4	98.4	67.4	85.5	94.6	56.7	78.8
03	CONCRETE	94.7	49.7	72.5	95.9	60.7	78.5	93.3	49.1	71.5	94.4	53.8	74.4	96.7	61.8	79.5	94.5	51.5	73.3
04	MASONRY	116.0	54.2	77.8	97.6	54.7	71.0	99.0	51.8	69.8	99.0	53.0	70.5	98.3	59.5	74.3	110.9	48.4	72.2
05	METALS	89.5	71.1	83.9	106.0	70.1	94.9	97.6	69.5	88.9	96.7	70.0	88.5	96.7	70.5	88.7	89.5	68.5	83.0
06	WOOD, PLASTICS & COMPOSITES	89.8	42.7	63.2	98.5	65.3	79.8	84.8	48.1	64.1	106.3	57.0	78.5	104.4	59.1	78.8	89.1	43.2	63.2
07	THERMAL & MOISTURE PROTECTION	97.5	54.1	79.9	95.8	62.4	82.2	96.9	57.0	80.7	97.4	60.8	82.5	96.5	59.5	81.5	97.5	54.7	80.1
08	OPENINGS	99.8	45.8	87.0	98.6	60.0	89.5	92.7	52.5	83.2	96.3	53.9	86.3	96.3	55.7	86.7	99.7	48.8	87.7
0920	Plaster & Gypsum Board	79.0	41.4	53.4	99.4	64.6	75.7	100.1	46.8	63.8	109.6	56.0	73.2	109.6	58.1	74.6	78.6	41.9	53.6
0950, 0980	Ceilings & Acoustic Treatment	87.1	41.4	56.7	103.1	64.6	77.4	98.7	46.8	64.2	97.0	56.0	69.7	98.0	58.1	71.5	87.1	41.9	57.0
0960	Flooring	110.0	66.9	97.1	106.0	66.9	94.3	98.6	66.9	89.1	106.8	66.9	94.9	106.8	74.3	97.1	109.5	58.1	94.2
0970, 0990	Wall Finishes & Painting/Coating	99.5	65.8	79.2	96.1	47.3	66.8	103.4	49.3	70.9	103.4	59.2	76.8	103.4	51.0	71.9	99.5	49.1	69.2
09	FINISHES	93.2	50.0	69.1	100.6	61.6	78.9	97.8	50.9	71.7	101.1	57.5	76.8	101.3	59.9	78.2	93.0	46.5	67.1
COVERS	DIVS. 10 - 14, 25, 28, 41, 43, 44, 46	100.0	51.4	90.3	100.0	80.9	96.2	100.0	46.6	89.3	100.0	79.4	95.9	100.0	80.4	96.1	100.0	47.0	89.4
21, 22, 23	FIRE SUPPRESSION, PLUMBING & HVAC	100.2	56.5	82.7	100.0	59.5	83.8	95.2	43.7	74.5	100.1	60.7	84.3	100.1	61.7	84.7	100.2	54.1	81.7
26, 27, 3370	ELECTRICAL, COMMUNICATIONS & UTIL.	90.5	58.2	73.6	103.0	60.8	81.0	98.2	57.3	76.8	99.5	66.6	82.3	98.9	66.6	82.0	92.2	59.6	75.2
MF2010	WEIGHTED AVERAGE	96.8	57.8	79.8	100.4	63.6	84.4	96.3	54.9	78.3	98.5	62.7	82.9	98.6	65.0	84.0	96.7	56.4	79.2

LOUISIANA / MAINE

DIVISION		LOUISIANA NEW ORLEANS 700 - 701			SHREVEPORT 710 - 711			THIBODAUX 703			MAINE AUGUSTA 043			BANGOR 044			BATH 045		
		MAT.	INST.	TOTAL	MAT.	INST.	TOTAL	MAT.	INST.	TOTAL	MAT.	INST.	TOTAL	MAT.	INST.	TOTAL	MAT.	INST.	TOTAL
015433	CONTRACTOR EQUIPMENT		90.2	90.2		89.7	89.7		89.9	89.9		100.6	100.6		100.6	100.6		100.6	100.6
0241, 31 - 34	SITE & INFRASTRUCTURE, DEMOLITION	105.2	88.4	93.4	100.8	86.0	90.4	101.4	87.0	91.3	89.2	100.8	97.3	91.0	101.0	98.1	88.9	100.8	97.2
0310	Concrete Forming & Accessories	97.7	66.5	70.8	98.8	44.7	52.2	90.1	64.3	67.8	99.2	97.0	97.3	93.6	98.8	98.1	89.7	97.2	96.2
0320	Concrete Reinforcing	96.7	60.1	78.4	92.6	56.1	74.4	93.3	59.2	76.3	96.4	110.1	103.2	90.1	111.5	100.8	89.2	111.2	100.2
0330	Cast-in-Place Concrete	99.7	70.1	87.4	99.4	53.4	80.3	100.9	51.3	80.3	97.9	60.3	82.3	80.2	113.0	93.8	80.2	60.3	72.0
03	CONCRETE	97.8	67.1	82.6	99.6	50.9	75.6	98.4	59.3	79.1	104.6	86.2	95.5	94.4	105.3	99.8	94.5	86.4	90.5
04	MASONRY	101.8	60.7	76.4	102.0	51.0	70.4	124.8	49.3	78.1	96.8	64.8	77.0	106.0	103.9	104.7	112.3	85.8	95.9
05	METALS	109.5	73.0	98.3	93.3	69.2	85.9	97.6	69.3	88.9	97.8	88.0	94.8	88.7	90.4	89.2	87.2	89.6	87.9
06	WOOD, PLASTICS & COMPOSITES	99.7	67.9	81.8	101.7	43.7	69.0	92.9	69.7	79.8	98.6	107.7	103.7	95.1	98.7	97.1	89.7	107.7	99.9
07	THERMAL & MOISTURE PROTECTION	96.1	69.0	85.1	97.1	52.2	78.9	96.7	54.6	79.6	104.3	66.8	89.1	100.2	86.0	94.5	100.2	73.2	89.2
08	OPENINGS	96.2	66.4	89.2	98.8	46.4	86.4	97.1	64.2	89.3	104.2	90.0	100.8	102.5	85.0	98.4	102.5	90.0	99.5
0920	Plaster & Gypsum Board	108.2	67.2	80.3	90.0	42.5	57.7	102.7	69.1	79.8	100.8	107.4	105.2	98.8	98.0	98.2	95.1	107.4	103.4
0950, 0980	Ceilings & Acoustic Treatment	98.7	67.2	77.8	91.3	42.5	58.8	98.7	69.1	79.0	101.5	107.4	105.4	91.6	98.0	95.9	89.6	107.4	101.4
0960	Flooring	105.3	66.9	93.8	113.4	62.4	98.1	104.3	44.9	86.5	103.1	56.3	89.1	98.9	113.0	103.1	97.3	56.3	85.0
0970, 0990	Wall Finishes & Painting/Coating	108.8	65.5	82.8	95.5	45.5	65.4	104.7	50.6	72.2	101.0	64.7	79.2	95.3	45.1	65.1	95.3	45.1	65.1
09	FINISHES	102.4	66.6	82.4	98.2	47.4	69.9	100.1	60.1	77.8	101.4	87.7	93.8	98.6	96.3	97.3	97.1	85.6	90.7
COVERS	DIVS. 10 - 14, 25, 28, 41, 43, 44, 46	100.0	83.2	96.6	100.0	77.3	95.5	100.0	81.3	96.3	100.0	103.3	100.7	100.0	110.0	102.0	100.0	103.3	100.7
21, 22, 23	FIRE SUPPRESSION, PLUMBING & HVAC	100.0	65.8	86.3	100.0	58.9	83.5	95.2	61.7	81.7	99.9	65.6	86.2	100.1	75.9	90.4	95.2	65.7	83.4
26, 27, 3370	ELECTRICAL, COMMUNICATIONS & UTIL.	103.2	72.9	87.4	97.7	67.2	81.8	96.7	72.8	84.2	99.3	80.0	89.2	98.5	77.2	87.4	96.4	80.0	87.9
MF2010	WEIGHTED AVERAGE	101.5	69.8	87.7	98.4	59.6	81.5	98.7	64.9	84.0	100.3	80.8	91.8	97.6	90.8	94.7	96.1	83.0	90.4

City Cost Indexes

MAINE

DIVISION		HOULTON 047			KITTERY 039			LEWISTON 042			MACHIAS 046			PORTLAND 040 - 041			ROCKLAND 048		
		MAT.	INST.	TOTAL	MAT.	INST.	TOTAL	MAT.	INST.	TOTAL	MAT.	INST.	TOTAL	MAT.	INST.	TOTAL	MAT.	INST.	TOTAL
015433	CONTRACTOR EQUIPMENT		100.6	100.6		100.6	100.6		100.6	100.6		100.6	100.6		100.6	100.6		100.6	100.6
0241, 31 - 34	SITE & INFRASTRUCTURE, DEMOLITION	90.7	101.8	98.5	85.6	100.8	96.3	88.2	101.0	97.2	90.1	101.8	98.3	86.9	101.0	96.8	86.3	101.8	97.2
0310	Concrete Forming & Accessories	97.1	103.6	102.7	90.4	97.7	96.7	98.9	98.9	98.9	94.4	103.5	102.3	95.8	98.9	98.4	95.4	103.5	102.4
0320	Concrete Reinforcing	90.1	109.9	100.0	84.5	111.3	97.8	110.8	111.5	111.1	90.1	109.9	100.0	107.5	111.5	109.5	90.1	109.9	100.0
0330	Cast-in-Place Concrete	80.3	72.6	77.1	81.4	61.2	73.0	81.9	113.0	94.8	80.2	72.0	76.8	95.5	113.0	102.7	81.9	72.0	77.8
03	CONCRETE	95.5	93.3	94.4	90.1	87.0	88.6	95.1	105.3	100.1	94.9	93.1	94.0	100.8	105.3	103.0	92.2	93.1	92.6
04	MASONRY	91.0	76.3	81.9	101.0	86.8	92.2	91.7	103.9	99.2	91.0	76.3	81.9	101.3	103.9	102.9	85.9	76.3	80.0
05	METALS	87.4	87.9	87.5	87.1	89.8	87.9	91.7	90.4	91.3	87.4	87.9	87.6	99.4	90.4	96.6	87.3	87.9	87.5
06	WOOD, PLASTICS & COMPOSITES	99.1	107.7	104.0	88.7	107.7	99.4	101.2	98.7	99.8	96.1	107.7	102.6	96.1	98.7	97.5	96.9	107.7	103.0
07	THERMAL & MOISTURE PROTECTION	100.3	74.0	89.6	103.2	72.5	90.7	100.1	86.0	94.4	100.3	73.0	89.2	101.4	86.0	95.2	100.0	73.0	89.1
08	OPENINGS	102.6	88.2	99.2	102.7	90.0	99.6	105.6	85.0	100.7	102.6	88.2	99.2	105.7	85.0	100.8	102.5	88.2	99.1
0920	Plaster & Gypsum Board	101.0	107.4	105.3	94.7	107.4	103.3	104.5	98.0	100.1	99.5	107.4	104.8	101.0	98.0	99.0	99.5	107.4	104.8
0950, 0980	Ceilings & Acoustic Treatment	89.6	107.4	101.4	90.6	107.4	101.8	101.4	98.0	99.1	89.6	107.4	101.4	104.4	98.0	100.1	89.6	107.4	101.4
0960	Flooring	100.1	52.7	85.9	97.5	58.7	85.9	101.6	113.0	105.0	99.3	52.7	85.4	101.9	113.0	105.2	99.6	52.7	85.6
0970, 0990	Wall Finishes & Painting/Coating	95.3	140.1	122.2	95.4	39.3	61.7	95.3	45.1	65.1	95.3	140.1	122.2	93.4	45.1	64.4	95.3	140.1	122.2
09	FINISHES	98.8	99.7	99.3	96.2	85.6	90.3	101.8	96.3	98.7	98.3	99.7	99.1	102.5	96.3	99.0	98.0	99.7	98.9
COVERS	DIVS. 10 - 14, 25, 28, 41, 43, 44, 46	100.0	108.9	101.8	100.0	103.6	100.7	100.0	110.0	102.0	100.0	108.9	101.8	100.0	110.0	102.0	100.0	108.9	101.8
21, 22, 23	FIRE SUPPRESSION, PLUMBING & HVAC	95.2	74.1	86.8	95.2	77.3	88.0	100.1	75.9	90.4	95.2	74.1	86.8	100.0	75.9	90.3	95.2	74.1	86.8
26, 27, 3370	ELECTRICAL, COMMUNICATIONS & UTIL.	100.6	80.0	89.9	98.0	80.0	88.6	100.6	80.1	89.9	100.6	80.0	89.9	103.3	80.1	91.2	100.5	80.0	89.8
MF2010	WEIGHTED AVERAGE	95.9	86.6	91.8	95.1	85.7	91.0	98.3	91.2	95.2	95.7	86.5	91.7	100.8	91.2	96.6	95.0	86.5	91.3

		MAINE			MARYLAND														
DIVISION		WATERVILLE 049			ANNAPOLIS 214			BALTIMORE 210 - 212			COLLEGE PARK 207 - 208			CUMBERLAND 215			EASTON 216		
		MAT.	INST.	TOTAL	MAT.	INST.	TOTAL	MAT.	INST.	TOTAL	MAT.	INST.	TOTAL	MAT.	INST.	TOTAL	MAT.	INST.	TOTAL
015433	CONTRACTOR EQUIPMENT		100.6	100.6		99.3	99.3		102.8	102.8		104.3	104.3		99.3	99.3		99.3	99.3
0241, 31 - 34	SITE & INFRASTRUCTURE, DEMOLITION	90.8	100.8	97.8	98.2	90.9	93.1	99.8	94.8	96.3	103.7	94.1	96.9	91.4	90.9	91.1	98.2	88.0	91.0
0310	Concrete Forming & Accessories	89.2	97.0	96.0	98.1	70.3	74.1	100.3	72.6	76.4	86.2	71.2	73.2	91.6	80.8	82.3	89.5	71.7	74.2
0320	Concrete Reinforcing	90.1	110.1	100.1	104.0	82.1	93.0	104.5	82.1	93.3	109.0	80.5	94.7	87.7	74.6	81.2	87.0	80.6	83.8
0330	Cast-in-Place Concrete	80.3	60.3	72.0	110.8	77.1	96.8	111.3	77.9	97.4	122.5	78.0	104.0	93.6	85.7	90.3	104.0	49.2	81.2
03	CONCRETE	96.0	86.2	91.1	103.7	75.9	90.0	104.2	77.2	90.9	109.4	76.6	93.2	89.4	82.2	85.9	97.0	66.6	82.0
04	MASONRY	100.7	64.8	78.5	96.1	72.9	81.7	98.4	72.9	82.6	108.4	69.4	84.3	94.6	84.4	88.3	108.1	43.7	68.2
05	METALS	87.3	88.0	87.5	104.7	93.8	101.3	101.5	94.3	99.3	87.0	97.5	90.2	99.2	91.2	96.7	99.4	88.1	95.9
06	WOOD, PLASTICS & COMPOSITES	89.2	107.7	99.6	97.6	70.6	82.4	97.3	73.7	84.0	87.6	70.8	78.1	86.3	79.8	82.6	84.1	79.1	81.3
07	THERMAL & MOISTURE PROTECTION	100.3	66.8	86.7	101.1	79.6	92.4	99.1	80.2	91.4	102.6	78.5	92.9	99.5	80.4	91.7	99.6	60.4	83.7
08	OPENINGS	102.6	90.0	99.6	99.3	78.1	94.3	97.7	79.8	93.5	94.7	75.2	90.1	96.0	78.7	91.9	94.4	72.9	89.3
0920	Plaster & Gypsum Board	95.1	107.4	103.4	100.5	70.0	79.7	103.4	73.0	82.8	97.1	70.0	78.6	100.7	79.5	86.3	100.3	78.8	85.7
0950, 0980	Ceilings & Acoustic Treatment	89.6	107.4	101.4	100.6	70.0	80.2	98.1	73.0	81.4	98.1	70.0	79.4	100.1	79.5	86.4	100.1	78.8	85.9
0960	Flooring	97.0	56.3	84.8	100.7	78.6	94.1	100.0	78.6	93.6	97.9	80.5	92.7	96.2	92.5	95.1	95.4	52.6	82.6
0970, 0990	Wall Finishes & Painting/Coating	95.3	64.7	76.9	91.7	80.9	85.2	94.6	80.9	86.4	104.6	77.5	88.3	94.4	75.0	82.7	94.4	77.5	84.3
09	FINISHES	97.2	87.7	91.9	97.2	72.1	83.2	99.9	73.9	85.4	96.3	72.8	83.2	97.6	82.3	89.1	97.8	70.5	82.6
COVERS	DIVS. 10 - 14, 25, 28, 41, 43, 44, 46	100.0	103.3	100.7	100.0	85.6	97.1	100.0	86.3	97.3	100.0	83.8	96.8	100.0	90.2	98.0	100.0	77.2	95.4
21, 22, 23	FIRE SUPPRESSION, PLUMBING & HVAC	95.2	65.6	83.3	100.0	81.7	92.6	100.0	81.7	92.7	95.3	85.0	91.2	95.1	73.0	86.2	95.1	68.6	84.5
26, 27, 3370	ELECTRICAL, COMMUNICATIONS & UTIL.	100.6	80.0	89.8	96.7	91.7	94.1	101.4	91.7	96.3	102.2	99.8	100.9	96.6	81.6	88.8	96.1	64.4	79.5
MF2010	WEIGHTED AVERAGE	96.2	80.8	89.5	100.3	81.8	92.3	100.5	82.8	92.8	97.6	83.9	91.7	96.0	81.9	89.9	97.4	69.3	85.2

DIVISION		MARYLAND															MASSACHUSETTS		
		ELKTON 219			HAGERSTOWN 217			SALISBURY 218			SILVER SPRING 209			WALDORF 206			BOSTON 020 - 022, 024		
		MAT.	INST.	TOTAL	MAT.	INST.	TOTAL	MAT.	INST.	TOTAL	MAT.	INST.	TOTAL	MAT.	INST.	TOTAL	MAT.	INST.	TOTAL
015433	CONTRACTOR EQUIPMENT		99.3	99.3		99.3	99.3		99.3	99.3		97.2	97.2		97.2	97.2		106.3	106.3
0241, 31 - 34	SITE & INFRASTRUCTURE, DEMOLITION	85.8	88.7	87.8	89.8	91.6	91.0	98.1	88.0	91.0	91.3	87.5	88.6	98.0	87.1	90.3	100.8	108.2	106.0
0310	Concrete Forming & Accessories	95.5	82.6	84.4	90.6	76.3	78.3	103.5	52.9	59.8	94.8	71.4	74.6	102.4	69.6	74.1	100.9	142.0	136.4
0320	Concrete Reinforcing	87.0	101.6	94.3	87.7	74.6	81.2	87.0	65.6	76.3	107.6	80.4	94.0	108.3	80.4	94.4	108.7	157.1	132.8
0330	Cast-in-Place Concrete	84.2	76.5	81.0	89.2	85.7	87.8	104.0	47.9	80.7	125.4	79.8	106.5	140.5	76.9	114.1	104.6	152.2	124.3
03	CONCRETE	82.6	84.7	83.7	86.0	80.2	83.1	97.9	55.0	76.7	108.0	77.1	92.7	118.7	75.3	97.3	108.3	147.2	127.5
04	MASONRY	94.1	59.9	73.0	100.3	84.4	90.4	107.7	48.1	70.9	107.3	72.7	85.9	92.7	67.6	77.2	108.6	162.1	141.7
05	METALS	99.5	99.2	99.4	99.3	91.3	96.8	99.5	82.4	94.2	91.2	93.9	92.1	91.2	93.8	92.0	100.8	132.1	110.5
06	WOOD, PLASTICS & COMPOSITES	91.3	88.8	89.9	85.4	73.5	78.7	101.5	56.3	76.0	94.5	70.1	80.7	102.3	70.1	84.1	100.3	141.7	123.6
07	THERMAL & MOISTURE PROTECTION	99.2	75.1	89.4	99.2	78.6	90.8	99.8	65.2	85.7	105.6	84.4	97.0	106.1	82.2	96.4	104.0	151.9	123.5
08	OPENINGS	94.4	81.4	91.3	94.4	74.5	89.6	94.6	62.8	87.1	86.8	74.7	84.0	87.5	74.7	84.5	99.2	144.4	109.9
0920	Plaster & Gypsum Board	103.6	88.8	93.6	100.3	73.0	81.8	110.0	55.3	72.8	102.9	70.0	80.5	106.2	70.0	81.6	104.2	142.4	130.2
0950, 0980	Ceilings & Acoustic Treatment	100.1	88.8	92.6	101.0	73.0	82.4	100.1	55.3	70.3	107.8	70.0	82.6	107.8	70.0	82.6	101.8	142.4	128.8
0960	Flooring	97.6	59.5	86.2	95.8	92.5	94.8	101.0	65.9	90.5	104.0	80.5	97.0	107.5	80.5	99.4	98.6	183.1	123.9
0970, 0990	Wall Finishes & Painting/Coating	94.4	77.5	84.3	94.4	77.5	84.3	94.4	77.5	84.3	111.6	77.5	91.1	111.6	77.5	91.1	98.6	150.8	130.0
09	FINISHES	98.0	78.4	87.1	97.5	78.9	87.1	100.7	57.3	76.5	96.8	72.3	83.2	98.5	71.7	83.6	102.1	151.0	129.3
COVERS	DIVS. 10 - 14, 25, 28, 41, 43, 44, 46	100.0	61.4	92.3	100.0	89.5	97.9	100.0	39.7	87.9	100.0	83.1	96.6	100.0	81.4	96.3	100.0	118.6	103.7
21, 22, 23	FIRE SUPPRESSION, PLUMBING & HVAC	95.1	79.3	88.8	100.0	81.4	92.5	95.1	61.2	81.5	95.3	86.3	91.7	95.3	83.7	90.6	100.1	127.0	110.9
26, 27, 3370	ELECTRICAL, COMMUNICATIONS & UTIL.	97.9	91.7	94.6	96.4	81.6	88.7	94.8	68.7	81.2	99.4	99.8	99.6	96.6	99.8	98.3	100.9	138.6	120.6
MF2010	WEIGHTED AVERAGE	95.1	81.9	89.4	96.9	82.8	90.7	97.8	63.3	82.8	96.9	83.8	91.2	97.5	82.2	90.9	101.8	138.1	117.6

City Cost Indexes

		MASSACHUSETTS																
		BROCKTON			BUZZARDS BAY			FALL RIVER			FITCHBURG			FRAMINGHAM			GREENFIELD		
DIVISION		023			025			027			014			017			013		
		MAT.	INST.	TOTAL	MAT.	INST.	TOTAL	MAT.	INST.	TOTAL	MAT.	INST.	TOTAL	MAT.	INST.	TOTAL	MAT.	INST.	TOTAL
015433	CONTRACTOR EQUIPMENT		102.4	102.4		102.4	102.4		103.3	103.3		100.6	100.6		101.8	101.8		100.6	100.6
0241, 31 - 34	SITE & INFRASTRUCTURE, DEMOLITION	95.7	104.8	102.1	85.8	104.8	99.1	94.8	104.9	101.9	85.8	104.7	99.1	82.5	104.5	97.9	89.6	103.2	99.2
0310	Concrete Forming & Accessories	102.6	131.5	127.5	100.2	131.4	127.1	102.6	131.7	127.7	94.8	126.0	121.7	102.0	131.2	127.2	93.2	112.1	109.5
0320	Concrete Reinforcing	106.8	157.0	131.9	85.6	165.2	125.4	106.8	165.2	136.0	85.4	156.0	120.6	85.3	156.7	121.0	88.6	126.0	107.3
0330	Cast-in-Place Concrete	98.6	152.4	120.9	82.0	152.4	111.2	95.4	152.9	119.3	85.7	148.3	111.7	85.8	140.8	108.6	88.2	129.2	105.2
03	CONCRETE	104.8	142.5	123.4	88.7	144.0	115.9	103.3	144.3	123.5	86.8	138.3	112.2	89.7	138.4	113.7	90.6	119.9	105.1
04	MASONRY	102.4	159.6	137.8	95.0	159.6	134.9	103.3	159.5	138.1	93.0	155.2	131.5	98.6	155.3	133.7	96.9	133.2	119.4
05	METALS	99.4	129.7	108.8	94.4	132.9	106.3	99.4	133.3	109.9	95.6	126.2	105.0	95.6	129.0	105.9	97.8	109.2	101.3
06	WOOD, PLASTICS & COMPOSITES	102.0	129.4	117.5	98.9	129.4	116.1	102.0	129.6	117.6	95.7	122.7	111.0	102.2	129.1	117.4	93.5	109.8	102.7
07	THERMAL & MOISTURE PROTECTION	101.7	148.3	120.6	101.0	146.7	119.5	101.6	145.9	119.6	100.8	140.1	116.8	100.9	145.2	118.8	100.9	121.2	109.1
08	OPENINGS	98.1	137.7	107.4	94.0	135.4	103.8	98.1	135.5	106.9	104.5	133.9	111.5	94.7	137.6	104.8	104.5	114.7	106.9
0920	Plaster & Gypsum Board	95.4	129.7	118.7	91.1	129.7	117.3	95.4	129.7	118.7	97.3	122.8	114.6	99.9	129.7	120.1	98.0	109.4	105.8
0950, 0980	Ceilings & Acoustic Treatment	100.9	129.7	120.1	90.0	129.7	116.4	100.9	129.7	120.1	90.6	122.8	112.0	90.6	129.7	116.6	99.5	109.4	106.1
0960	Flooring	100.4	183.1	125.1	98.9	183.1	124.1	99.8	183.1	124.7	98.2	183.1	123.6	99.6	183.1	124.5	97.5	149.9	113.2
0970, 0990	Wall Finishes & Painting/Coating	96.0	135.1	119.5	96.0	135.1	119.5	96.0	135.1	119.5	95.1	135.1	119.2	96.1	135.1	119.6	95.1	108.5	103.1
09	FINISHES	100.0	141.4	123.0	96.0	141.4	121.3	99.9	141.6	123.1	96.1	137.4	119.1	96.7	141.2	121.5	98.3	118.7	109.7
COVERS	DIVS. 10 - 14, 25, 28, 41, 43, 44, 46	100.0	116.4	103.3	100.0	116.4	103.3	100.0	117.0	103.4	100.0	102.5	100.5	100.0	115.9	103.2	100.0	105.1	101.0
21, 22, 23	FIRE SUPPRESSION, PLUMBING & HVAC	100.1	111.2	104.5	95.2	111.2	101.6	100.1	111.3	104.6	95.8	113.6	103.0	95.8	120.4	105.7	95.8	100.8	97.8
26, 27, 3370	ELECTRICAL, COMMUNICATIONS & UTIL.	100.7	100.7	100.7	97.6	100.7	99.2	100.6	100.7	100.6	100.4	104.2	102.4	96.7	129.2	113.7	100.4	92.8	96.4
MF2010	WEIGHTED AVERAGE	100.4	126.3	111.7	94.9	126.7	108.8	100.2	126.8	111.8	96.3	124.6	108.6	95.5	131.0	111.0	97.5	110.2	103.0

		MASSACHUSETTS																
		HYANNIS			LAWRENCE			LOWELL			NEW BEDFORD			PITTSFIELD			SPRINGFIELD		
DIVISION		026			019			018			027			012			010 - 011		
		MAT.	INST.	TOTAL	MAT.	INST.	TOTAL	MAT.	INST.	TOTAL	MAT.	INST.	TOTAL	MAT.	INST.	TOTAL	MAT.	INST.	TOTAL
015433	CONTRACTOR EQUIPMENT		102.4	102.4		102.4	102.4		100.6	100.6		103.3	103.3		100.6	100.6		100.6	100.6
0241, 31 - 34	SITE & INFRASTRUCTURE, DEMOLITION	91.9	104.8	101.0	94.5	104.8	101.7	93.7	104.7	101.5	93.4	104.9	101.5	94.7	103.1	100.6	94.2	103.2	100.5
0310	Concrete Forming & Accessories	94.6	131.4	126.3	103.2	131.7	127.8	100.0	131.5	127.2	102.6	131.7	127.7	99.9	111.5	109.9	100.2	111.7	110.1
0320	Concrete Reinforcing	85.6	165.2	125.4	105.6	146.6	126.0	106.5	146.3	126.4	106.8	165.2	136.0	87.9	126.0	106.9	106.5	126.0	116.2
0330	Cast-in-Place Concrete	90.0	152.4	115.9	99.2	149.8	120.2	90.2	149.7	114.9	84.1	152.9	112.6	98.4	128.3	110.8	93.9	128.5	108.3
03	CONCRETE	95.0	144.0	119.2	104.9	139.8	122.1	96.3	139.5	117.6	97.9	144.3	120.8	97.2	119.3	108.1	98.0	119.4	108.6
04	MASONRY	101.4	159.6	137.4	103.3	159.6	138.1	92.4	155.2	131.3	101.3	159.5	137.3	93.0	131.5	116.8	92.7	131.9	117.0
05	METALS	95.9	132.9	107.3	98.2	125.8	106.7	98.1	123.0	105.8	99.4	133.3	109.9	98.0	109.2	101.4	100.6	109.2	103.2
06	WOOD, PLASTICS & COMPOSITES	91.9	129.4	113.1	102.7	129.4	117.7	101.9	129.4	117.4	102.0	129.6	117.6	101.9	109.8	106.4	101.9	109.8	106.4
07	THERMAL & MOISTURE PROTECTION	101.2	146.7	119.7	101.3	147.9	120.2	101.2	145.8	119.3	101.6	145.9	119.6	101.2	120.4	109.0	101.2	120.6	109.1
08	OPENINGS	94.6	135.4	104.3	98.4	134.9	107.1	105.7	134.9	112.6	98.1	135.5	106.9	105.7	114.7	107.8	105.7	114.7	107.8
0920	Plaster & Gypsum Board	86.7	129.7	115.9	102.8	129.7	121.1	102.8	129.7	121.1	95.4	129.7	118.7	102.8	109.4	107.3	102.8	109.4	107.3
0950, 0980	Ceilings & Acoustic Treatment	92.9	129.7	117.4	101.5	129.7	120.2	101.5	129.7	120.2	100.9	129.7	120.1	101.5	109.4	106.8	101.5	109.4	106.8
0960	Flooring	96.8	183.1	122.6	100.2	183.1	125.0	100.2	183.1	125.0	99.8	183.1	124.7	100.4	149.9	115.2	99.9	149.9	114.8
0970, 0990	Wall Finishes & Painting/Coating	96.0	135.1	119.5	95.2	135.1	119.2	95.1	135.1	119.2	96.0	135.1	119.5	95.1	108.5	103.1	96.5	108.5	103.7
09	FINISHES	95.8	141.4	121.2	100.4	141.4	123.2	100.3	141.4	123.2	99.7	141.6	123.0	100.4	118.3	110.4	100.3	118.4	110.4
COVERS	DIVS. 10 - 14, 25, 28, 41, 43, 44, 46	100.0	116.4	103.3	100.0	116.5	103.3	100.0	116.5	103.3	100.0	117.0	103.4	100.0	104.5	100.9	100.0	104.6	100.9
21, 22, 23	FIRE SUPPRESSION, PLUMBING & HVAC	100.1	111.2	104.5	100.0	120.4	108.2	100.0	118.1	107.3	100.1	111.3	104.6	100.0	100.0	100.0	100.0	100.2	100.1
26, 27, 3370	ELECTRICAL, COMMUNICATIONS & UTIL.	98.1	100.7	99.4	99.4	129.2	115.0	99.9	129.2	115.2	101.5	100.7	101.1	99.9	92.8	96.2	99.9	92.8	96.2
MF2010	WEIGHTED AVERAGE	97.6	126.7	110.3	100.1	131.3	113.7	99.4	130.1	112.8	99.6	126.8	111.4	99.6	109.6	103.9	100.0	109.8	104.3

		MASSACHUSETTS			MICHIGAN														
		WORCESTER			ANN ARBOR			BATTLE CREEK			BAY CITY			DEARBORN			DETROIT		
DIVISION		015 - 016			481			490			487			481			482		
		MAT.	INST.	TOTAL	MAT.	INST.	TOTAL	MAT.	INST.	TOTAL	MAT.	INST.	TOTAL	MAT.	INST.	TOTAL	MAT.	INST.	TOTAL
015433	CONTRACTOR EQUIPMENT		100.6	100.6		110.7	110.7		102.6	102.6		110.7	110.7		110.7	110.7		98.7	98.7
0241, 31 - 34	SITE & INFRASTRUCTURE, DEMOLITION	94.1	104.7	101.5	78.7	97.2	91.6	89.4	87.9	88.4	70.2	96.4	88.6	78.4	97.4	91.7	92.0	99.0	96.9
0310	Concrete Forming & Accessories	100.5	126.1	122.6	97.8	111.4	109.6	97.5	87.1	88.5	97.9	89.0	90.2	97.7	116.2	113.6	99.5	116.2	113.9
0320	Concrete Reinforcing	106.5	155.2	130.8	95.7	123.7	109.7	92.2	96.0	94.1	95.7	122.8	109.3	95.7	123.8	109.8	97.2	123.8	110.5
0330	Cast-in-Place Concrete	93.3	148.3	116.2	86.2	109.5	95.9	95.1	100.0	97.1	82.5	92.0	86.5	84.3	112.5	96.0	91.4	112.5	100.1
03	CONCRETE	97.8	138.2	117.7	92.7	113.2	102.8	96.0	92.6	94.3	91.0	97.0	94.0	91.8	116.4	103.9	95.5	115.2	105.2
04	MASONRY	92.2	155.2	131.2	90.4	118.2	107.6	99.1	86.5	91.3	96.8	87.3	90.9	97.1	113.6	107.3	95.5	113.6	106.7
05	METALS	100.6	126.0	108.4	93.7	118.2	101.2	95.8	88.6	93.6	94.3	115.0	100.7	93.7	118.5	101.4	96.3	101.2	97.8
06	WOOD, PLASTICS & COMPOSITES	102.4	122.7	113.9	94.9	112.4	104.8	100.3	86.3	92.4	94.9	88.7	91.4	94.9	116.9	107.3	97.2	116.9	108.3
07	THERMAL & MOISTURE PROTECTION	101.2	140.1	117.0	100.0	108.5	103.4	96.7	85.5	92.1	97.8	94.2	96.3	98.5	113.5	104.6	97.3	113.5	103.9
08	OPENINGS	105.7	133.7	112.3	97.7	110.0	100.6	94.2	82.7	91.5	97.7	94.8	97.0	97.7	112.4	101.1	100.0	112.1	102.8
0920	Plaster & Gypsum Board	102.8	122.8	116.4	106.2	111.8	110.0	93.0	82.0	85.6	106.2	87.3	93.4	106.2	116.4	113.2	109.0	116.4	114.0
0950, 0980	Ceilings & Acoustic Treatment	101.5	122.8	115.7	93.1	111.8	105.5	96.5	82.0	86.9	94.1	87.3	89.6	93.1	116.4	108.6	96.8	116.4	109.8
0960	Flooring	100.2	183.1	125.0	96.1	117.6	102.5	103.7	93.6	100.7	96.1	81.9	91.8	95.7	116.0	101.8	97.1	116.0	102.7
0970, 0990	Wall Finishes & Painting/Coating	95.1	135.1	119.2	86.5	100.8	95.1	97.2	81.8	87.9	86.5	83.7	84.9	86.5	99.0	94.0	88.5	99.0	94.8
09	FINISHES	100.3	137.4	121.0	94.3	111.7	104.0	97.7	87.5	92.0	94.1	86.5	89.9	94.2	114.8	105.7	96.8	114.8	106.8
COVERS	DIVS. 10 - 14, 25, 28, 41, 43, 44, 46	100.0	108.6	101.7	100.0	106.1	101.2	100.0	98.2	99.6	100.0	92.6	98.5	100.0	107.7	101.5	100.0	107.7	101.5
21, 22, 23	FIRE SUPPRESSION, PLUMBING & HVAC	100.0	113.1	105.3	100.0	99.9	100.0	100.0	87.7	95.1	100.0	84.6	93.8	100.0	108.8	103.5	100.0	109.0	103.6
26, 27, 3370	ELECTRICAL, COMMUNICATIONS & UTIL.	99.9	104.2	102.1	96.0	110.0	103.4	90.3	80.4	85.1	95.0	91.1	92.9	96.0	105.2	100.8	97.2	105.1	101.3
MF2010	WEIGHTED AVERAGE	100.0	124.6	110.7	96.4	107.9	101.4	96.8	87.4	92.7	95.8	92.5	94.4	96.2	110.9	102.6	97.9	109.3	102.8

741

City Cost Indexes

MICHIGAN

DIVISION		FLINT 484 - 485			GAYLORD 497			GRAND RAPIDS 493,495			IRON MOUNTAIN 498 - 499			JACKSON 492			KALAMAZOO 491		
		MAT.	INST.	TOTAL	MAT.	INST.	TOTAL	MAT.	INST.	TOTAL	MAT.	INST.	TOTAL	MAT.	INST.	TOTAL	MAT.	INST.	TOTAL
015433	CONTRACTOR EQUIPMENT		110.7	110.7		105.1	105.1		102.6	102.6		94.2	94.2		105.1	105.1		102.6	102.6
0241, 31 - 34	SITE & INFRASTRUCTURE, DEMOLITION	68.2	96.5	88.1	83.4	85.7	85.0	89.5	88.0	88.4	92.1	94.1	93.5	105.8	88.0	93.3	89.7	87.9	88.4
0310	Concrete Forming & Accessories	100.6	91.4	92.7	95.4	77.7	80.1	97.0	84.7	86.4	87.5	86.1	86.3	92.4	88.3	88.9	97.5	86.8	88.2
0320	Concrete Reinforcing	95.7	123.2	109.5	85.9	109.3	97.6	98.6	95.9	97.2	85.7	95.4	90.6	83.5	123.1	103.3	92.2	93.6	92.9
0330	Cast-in-Place Concrete	86.8	94.7	90.1	94.9	87.8	92.0	100.1	97.6	99.1	112.3	87.2	101.9	94.8	93.8	94.4	97.0	99.8	98.2
03	CONCRETE	93.2	99.1	96.1	92.4	88.2	90.3	99.3	90.7	95.1	101.8	88.4	95.2	87.2	97.3	92.2	99.4	92.0	95.8
04	MASONRY	97.3	96.8	97.0	109.6	80.5	91.6	96.1	86.6	90.2	95.6	87.6	90.7	89.7	92.8	91.7	97.8	86.5	90.8
05	METALS	93.7	115.7	100.5	97.2	111.7	101.6	93.0	88.2	91.5	96.6	91.1	94.9	97.3	113.6	102.4	95.8	87.5	93.3
06	WOOD, PLASTICS & COMPOSITES	98.2	89.9	93.5	92.8	76.9	83.8	101.5	83.1	91.1	87.5	86.1	86.7	91.5	86.6	88.7	100.3	86.3	92.4
07	THERMAL & MOISTURE PROTECTION	97.8	97.9	97.9	95.1	76.2	87.4	99.5	77.4	90.5	98.6	83.1	92.3	94.5	94.5	94.5	96.7	85.5	92.1
08	OPENINGS	97.7	95.5	97.1	94.8	76.0	90.3	100.6	85.6	97.0	101.3	77.3	95.7	93.8	93.9	93.8	94.2	82.1	91.3
0920	Plaster & Gypsum Board	107.7	88.6	94.7	92.8	74.9	80.6	94.9	78.8	83.9	53.7	86.1	75.7	91.0	84.9	86.9	93.0	82.0	85.6
0950, 0980	Ceilings & Acoustic Treatment	93.1	88.6	90.1	95.7	74.9	81.9	105.1	78.8	87.6	94.6	86.1	88.9	95.7	84.9	88.5	96.5	82.0	86.9
0960	Flooring	96.1	94.9	95.7	95.7	93.9	95.1	103.6	84.3	97.8	119.6	95.6	112.4	94.4	84.3	91.4	103.7	77.1	95.8
0970, 0990	Wall Finishes & Painting/Coating	86.5	87.3	87.0	93.1	83.7	87.5	98.9	80.0	87.6	111.4	71.8	87.6	93.1	98.8	96.5	97.2	81.8	87.9
09	FINISHES	93.6	90.7	92.0	97.5	79.8	87.7	101.7	83.8	91.7	99.7	86.4	92.3	98.6	88.0	92.7	97.7	84.2	90.2
COVERS	DIVS. 10 - 14, 25, 28, 41, 43, 44, 46	100.0	93.9	98.8	100.0	90.7	98.1	100.0	98.2	99.6	100.0	89.5	97.9	100.0	93.7	98.7	100.0	98.2	99.6
21, 22, 23	FIRE SUPPRESSION, PLUMBING & HVAC	100.0	90.6	96.2	95.5	80.1	89.3	100.0	83.8	93.5	95.4	86.0	91.6	95.5	88.8	92.8	100.0	81.6	92.6
26, 27, 3370	ELECTRICAL, COMMUNICATIONS & UTIL.	96.0	98.3	97.2	88.4	78.9	83.4	95.2	72.3	83.3	94.5	86.3	90.2	92.2	110.0	101.5	90.2	83.7	86.8
MF2010	WEIGHTED AVERAGE	96.1	96.8	96.4	95.5	84.4	90.7	98.1	84.5	92.2	97.5	87.4	93.1	95.0	95.9	95.4	97.1	85.9	92.2

MICHIGAN / MINNESOTA

DIVISION		LANSING 488 - 489			MUSKEGON 494			ROYAL OAK 480,483			SAGINAW 486			TRAVERSE CITY 496			BEMIDJI 566		
		MAT.	INST.	TOTAL	MAT.	INST.	TOTAL	MAT.	INST.	TOTAL	MAT.	INST.	TOTAL	MAT.	INST.	TOTAL	MAT.	INST.	TOTAL
015433	CONTRACTOR EQUIPMENT		110.7	110.7		102.6	102.6		96.2	96.2		110.7	110.7		94.2	94.2		99.0	99.0
0241, 31 - 34	SITE & INFRASTRUCTURE, DEMOLITION	90.5	96.6	94.8	87.5	87.9	87.8	83.0	96.8	92.7	71.2	96.4	88.9	78.4	93.6	89.0	94.0	98.3	97.0
0310	Concrete Forming & Accessories	98.0	89.2	90.4	97.9	85.6	87.3	93.6	112.7	110.1	97.8	88.8	90.0	87.5	75.7	77.3	88.7	91.4	91.0
0320	Concrete Reinforcing	99.0	123.0	111.0	92.8	96.1	94.5	86.8	123.8	105.2	95.7	122.8	109.3	87.0	92.9	90.0	97.0	108.0	102.5
0330	Cast-in-Place Concrete	100.5	92.9	97.3	94.8	95.8	95.2	75.5	108.3	89.1	85.2	91.9	88.0	87.6	80.0	84.5	104.1	104.2	104.1
03	CONCRETE	100.0	97.4	98.7	94.3	90.6	92.5	79.9	112.2	95.8	92.2	96.9	94.5	83.9	80.8	82.4	96.9	100.0	98.4
04	MASONRY	95.3	93.3	94.1	96.3	89.4	92.0	92.0	112.1	104.5	98.7	87.3	91.6	93.7	82.3	86.7	97.2	104.8	101.9
05	METALS	91.4	115.1	98.7	93.6	88.5	92.0	96.8	99.4	97.6	93.8	114.8	100.3	96.5	89.7	94.4	90.2	121.0	99.7
06	WOOD, PLASTICS & COMPOSITES	96.4	88.0	91.6	96.5	85.2	90.1	90.4	113.1	103.2	91.2	88.7	89.8	87.5	75.2	80.6	71.5	87.5	80.6
07	THERMAL & MOISTURE PROTECTION	98.6	90.6	95.3	95.8	80.4	89.5	96.5	112.3	102.9	98.6	94.2	96.9	97.8	72.8	87.6	105.6	97.1	102.1
08	OPENINGS	98.7	94.4	97.7	93.4	86.5	91.8	96.7	110.4	100.6	95.6	94.8	95.4	101.3	71.4	94.3	97.5	109.2	100.2
0920	Plaster & Gypsum Board	92.2	86.6	88.4	74.3	80.9	78.8	103.2	112.5	109.5	106.2	87.3	93.4	53.7	74.9	68.1	100.6	87.4	91.6
0950, 0980	Ceilings & Acoustic Treatment	96.8	86.6	90.0	97.4	80.9	86.4	92.3	112.5	105.8	93.1	87.3	89.3	94.6	74.9	81.5	137.1	87.4	104.0
0960	Flooring	102.8	84.3	97.2	102.5	84.3	97.1	93.7	116.0	100.4	96.1	81.9	91.8	119.6	93.9	111.9	107.8	123.0	112.3
0970, 0990	Wall Finishes & Painting/Coating	96.3	81.5	87.4	95.6	80.0	86.3	87.9	98.8	94.5	86.5	83.7	84.9	111.4	45.6	71.9	95.3	97.9	96.9
09	FINISHES	98.2	87.0	91.9	94.3	84.0	88.6	93.3	112.2	103.8	93.9	86.5	89.8	98.6	74.3	85.1	111.3	97.1	103.4
COVERS	DIVS. 10 - 14, 25, 28, 41, 43, 44, 46	100.0	93.3	98.7	100.0	98.0	99.6	100.0	104.6	100.9	100.0	92.6	98.5	100.0	86.8	97.4	100.0	99.3	99.9
21, 22, 23	FIRE SUPPRESSION, PLUMBING & HVAC	99.9	88.9	95.5	99.9	83.1	93.1	95.4	108.0	100.5	100.0	84.2	93.7	95.4	79.4	89.0	95.5	84.8	91.2
26, 27, 3370	ELECTRICAL, COMMUNICATIONS & UTIL.	99.2	91.4	95.1	90.7	77.2	83.6	98.3	104.5	101.5	93.5	91.1	92.2	89.9	78.9	84.2	104.4	105.2	104.8
MF2010	WEIGHTED AVERAGE	97.7	94.1	96.1	95.6	85.5	91.2	94.2	107.5	100.0	95.7	92.4	94.2	94.6	81.0	88.6	97.7	99.5	98.5

MINNESOTA

DIVISION		BRAINERD 564			DETROIT LAKES 565			DULUTH 556 - 558			MANKATO 560			MINNEAPOLIS 553 - 555			ROCHESTER 559		
		MAT.	INST.	TOTAL	MAT.	INST.	TOTAL	MAT.	INST.	TOTAL	MAT.	INST.	TOTAL	MAT.	INST.	TOTAL	MAT.	INST.	TOTAL
015433	CONTRACTOR EQUIPMENT		101.6	101.6		99.0	99.0		100.4	100.4		101.6	101.6		103.8	103.8		100.4	100.4
0241, 31 - 34	SITE & INFRASTRUCTURE, DEMOLITION	94.2	103.0	100.4	92.2	98.6	96.7	96.3	100.4	99.2	91.1	103.7	99.9	97.9	105.6	103.3	97.0	100.0	99.1
0310	Concrete Forming & Accessories	90.6	93.6	93.2	85.7	93.5	92.5	100.4	112.2	110.6	98.4	101.1	100.7	101.2	127.4	123.8	102.8	106.6	106.1
0320	Concrete Reinforcing	95.9	108.2	102.0	97.0	108.0	102.5	102.6	108.5	105.5	95.8	118.2	107.0	97.2	118.5	107.8	94.8	118.2	106.5
0330	Cast-in-Place Concrete	113.1	108.2	111.1	101.1	107.5	103.7	107.4	107.0	107.2	104.2	109.0	106.2	110.5	117.3	113.3	109.0	100.9	105.6
03	CONCRETE	100.8	102.4	101.6	94.5	102.1	98.2	101.3	110.3	105.7	96.5	107.9	102.1	103.4	122.6	112.9	100.7	107.7	104.1
04	MASONRY	119.6	113.5	115.8	119.9	110.8	114.2	104.6	117.0	112.3	108.6	110.5	109.8	114.7	125.3	121.3	107.0	112.5	110.4
05	METALS	91.3	121.0	100.5	90.2	120.9	99.7	93.4	123.3	102.6	91.2	126.7	102.1	98.6	130.0	108.3	95.2	128.4	105.4
06	WOOD, PLASTICS & COMPOSITES	89.5	87.3	88.3	68.5	87.5	79.3	103.6	111.9	108.3	99.0	98.7	98.8	109.0	126.0	118.6	109.0	105.2	106.9
07	THERMAL & MOISTURE PROTECTION	104.7	109.9	106.8	105.4	110.1	107.3	100.1	116.9	106.9	105.0	100.6	103.2	102.1	128.6	112.9	103.5	102.0	102.9
08	OPENINGS	84.8	109.0	90.5	97.4	109.2	100.2	98.3	118.2	103.0	89.1	117.7	95.9	94.9	133.8	104.1	93.5	122.5	100.4
0920	Plaster & Gypsum Board	84.6	87.4	86.5	99.5	87.4	91.3	91.1	112.6	105.8	89.5	99.1	96.0	99.3	127.0	118.2	99.5	105.8	103.8
0950, 0980	Ceilings & Acoustic Treatment	66.7	87.4	80.5	137.1	87.4	104.0	98.7	112.6	108.0	66.7	99.1	88.3	98.5	127.0	117.5	95.0	105.8	102.2
0960	Flooring	106.7	123.0	111.6	106.6	123.0	111.5	107.1	124.3	112.3	108.3	123.0	112.7	98.3	123.0	105.7	103.2	123.0	109.1
0970, 0990	Wall Finishes & Painting/Coating	89.6	97.9	94.6	95.3	97.9	96.9	91.0	111.3	103.2	101.0	105.3	103.6	96.5	128.1	115.5	91.3	105.3	99.7
09	FINISHES	93.1	98.5	96.1	110.7	98.6	104.0	101.4	114.7	108.8	94.8	105.3	100.7	100.5	127.2	115.4	99.4	109.5	105.0
COVERS	DIVS. 10 - 14, 25, 28, 41, 43, 44, 46	100.0	100.9	100.2	100.0	101.2	100.2	100.0	100.1	100.0	100.0	101.1	100.2	100.0	109.1	101.8	100.0	102.6	100.5
21, 22, 23	FIRE SUPPRESSION, PLUMBING & HVAC	94.8	87.8	92.0	95.5	87.6	92.3	99.9	97.2	98.8	94.8	88.5	92.3	99.9	116.9	106.7	100.0	96.0	98.4
26, 27, 3370	ELECTRICAL, COMMUNICATIONS & UTIL.	101.9	104.9	103.4	104.1	69.1	85.8	98.4	104.9	101.8	108.8	89.2	98.5	101.8	109.0	105.6	98.2	89.2	93.5
MF2010	WEIGHTED AVERAGE	96.3	102.3	98.9	98.3	96.7	97.6	99.0	108.6	103.2	96.6	102.4	99.1	100.6	119.9	109.0	98.8	104.9	101.5

DIVISION		MINNESOTA																MISSISSIPPI		
		SAINT PAUL			ST. CLOUD			THIEF RIVER FALLS			WILLMAR			WINDOM			BILOXI		
		550 - 551			563			567			562			561			395		
		MAT.	INST.	TOTAL	MAT.	INST.	TOTAL	MAT.	INST.	TOTAL	MAT.	INST.	TOTAL	MAT.	INST.	TOTAL	MAT.	INST.	TOTAL
015433	CONTRACTOR EQUIPMENT		100.4	100.4		101.6	101.6		99.0	99.0		101.6	101.6		101.6	101.6		99.3	99.3
0241, 31 - 34	SITE & INFRASTRUCTURE, DEMOLITION	99.1	101.1	100.5	89.7	105.1	100.5	92.9	98.2	96.7	89.1	102.8	98.7	83.3	101.7	96.3	98.8	89.6	92.3
0310	Concrete Forming & Accessories	102.0	124.9	121.8	87.7	120.4	116.0	89.4	90.8	90.6	87.5	93.1	92.3	92.0	86.8	87.5	95.6	54.1	59.8
0320	Concrete Reinforcing	98.5	118.5	108.5	95.9	118.4	107.1	97.4	107.9	102.7	95.6	118.0	106.8	95.6	117.1	106.4	95.8	58.4	77.1
0330	Cast-in-Place Concrete	120.2	116.7	118.7	99.9	115.8	106.5	103.2	89.5	97.5	101.4	86.9	95.4	87.7	67.8	79.4	108.7	54.8	86.3
03	CONCRETE	110.6	121.3	115.9	92.3	118.9	105.4	95.6	94.6	95.1	92.2	96.7	94.4	83.2	87.2	85.2	100.0	56.8	78.7
04	MASONRY	115.6	125.3	121.6	105.3	122.1	115.7	97.2	104.8	101.9	109.7	113.5	112.0	119.4	91.2	102.0	90.3	45.1	62.4
05	METALS	94.1	129.8	105.1	92.0	128.0	103.1	90.3	120.3	99.6	91.1	125.8	101.8	91.0	123.5	101.0	91.9	82.4	89.0
06	WOOD, PLASTICS & COMPOSITES	102.8	122.7	114.0	86.8	117.6	104.2	72.5	87.5	81.0	86.6	87.5	87.1	90.8	84.8	87.4	102.3	57.4	77.0
07	THERMAL & MOISTURE PROTECTION	101.8	128.1	112.5	104.8	120.1	111.0	106.5	100.0	103.9	104.6	110.8	107.1	104.6	91.0	99.1	97.0	55.4	80.1
08	OPENINGS	97.1	132.0	105.3	89.1	129.2	98.6	97.5	109.2	100.2	86.7	93.5	88.3	90.2	92.0	90.6	97.2	58.6	88.0
0920	Plaster & Gypsum Board	87.3	123.8	112.1	84.6	118.6	107.7	100.2	87.4	91.5	84.6	87.6	86.7	84.6	84.8	84.7	104.4	56.5	71.8
0950, 0980	Ceilings & Acoustic Treatment	98.5	123.8	115.4	66.7	118.6	101.2	137.1	87.4	104.0	66.7	87.6	80.6	66.7	84.8	78.7	95.9	56.5	69.7
0960	Flooring	99.5	123.0	106.5	103.3	123.0	109.2	107.5	123.0	112.1	105.1	123.0	110.4	103.7	123.0	112.0	114.4	56.1	97.0
0970, 0990	Wall Finishes & Painting/Coating	99.9	127.1	116.3	101.0	128.1	117.3	95.3	97.9	96.9	95.3	97.9	96.9	95.3	105.3	101.3	94.7	44.4	64.5
09	FINISHES	99.5	125.1	113.8	92.6	121.9	108.9	111.1	97.1	103.3	92.7	96.2	94.6	92.8	93.2	93.0	100.8	53.6	74.5
COVERS	DIVS. 10 - 14, 25, 28, 41, 43, 44, 46	100.0	108.5	101.7	100.0	107.2	101.4	100.0	99.2	99.8	100.0	100.8	100.2	100.0	95.6	99.1	100.0	56.9	91.4
21, 22, 23	FIRE SUPPRESSION, PLUMBING & HVAC	99.9	114.9	105.9	99.7	116.3	106.3	95.5	84.5	91.1	94.8	108.4	100.2	94.8	85.3	91.0	100.0	50.1	80.0
26, 27, 3370	ELECTRICAL, COMMUNICATIONS & UTIL.	95.2	111.4	103.7	101.9	111.4	106.9	101.4	69.1	84.6	101.9	87.2	94.2	108.8	89.1	98.5	98.5	57.6	77.1
MF2010	WEIGHTED AVERAGE	100.2	118.8	108.3	96.3	117.8	105.7	97.3	93.8	95.7	94.9	103.0	98.4	95.3	93.3	94.4	97.7	59.1	80.9

DIVISION		MISSISSIPPI																		
		CLARKSDALE			COLUMBUS			GREENVILLE			GREENWOOD			JACKSON			LAUREL		
		386			397			387			389			390 - 392			394		
		MAT.	INST.	TOTAL	MAT.	INST.	TOTAL	MAT.	INST.	TOTAL	MAT.	INST.	TOTAL	MAT.	INST.	TOTAL	MAT.	INST.	TOTAL
015433	CONTRACTOR EQUIPMENT		99.3	99.3		99.3	99.3		99.3	99.3		99.3	99.3		99.3	99.3		99.3	99.3
0241, 31 - 34	SITE & INFRASTRUCTURE, DEMOLITION	95.6	89.4	91.2	97.1	89.6	91.9	101.3	89.6	93.1	98.3	89.1	91.8	95.9	89.6	91.5	102.9	89.5	93.5
0310	Concrete Forming & Accessories	85.3	50.4	55.2	84.4	52.4	56.8	82.0	65.2	67.5	94.3	50.4	56.4	94.6	58.9	63.8	84.4	54.2	58.3
0320	Concrete Reinforcing	100.0	42.9	71.5	102.7	43.9	73.3	100.6	62.2	81.4	100.0	54.2	77.1	101.2	57.5	79.4	103.3	40.3	71.9
0330	Cast-in-Place Concrete	103.0	54.4	82.8	110.8	59.5	89.5	106.0	56.5	85.5	110.7	54.1	87.2	98.9	57.8	81.8	108.4	56.1	86.7
03	CONCRETE	95.9	52.1	74.3	101.6	54.9	78.6	101.1	63.0	82.3	102.1	53.9	78.3	96.1	59.7	78.2	104.0	53.9	79.3
04	MASONRY	93.5	45.8	64.0	114.7	52.5	76.2	138.0	50.3	83.8	94.1	45.6	64.1	95.7	50.3	67.6	110.9	49.0	72.6
05	METALS	90.5	74.9	85.7	88.9	75.8	84.9	91.5	84.1	89.3	90.5	76.4	86.2	98.5	82.3	93.5	89.0	74.8	84.6
06	WOOD, PLASTICS & COMPOSITES	85.6	52.4	66.9	87.2	53.4	68.1	82.2	69.7	75.1	98.7	52.4	72.6	99.6	61.0	77.8	88.3	55.9	70.0
07	THERMAL & MOISTURE PROTECTION	95.9	48.0	76.5	97.0	52.3	78.8	96.2	61.0	81.9	96.3	47.9	76.6	97.1	60.3	82.1	97.1	54.0	79.6
08	OPENINGS	96.8	50.6	85.8	96.5	50.7	85.7	96.8	62.9	88.8	96.8	51.9	86.2	101.0	56.8	90.5	93.5	51.5	83.6
0920	Plaster & Gypsum Board	87.7	51.4	63.0	92.7	52.4	65.3	87.3	69.2	75.0	98.9	51.4	66.6	97.4	60.2	72.1	92.7	54.9	67.0
0950, 0980	Ceilings & Acoustic Treatment	87.8	51.4	63.6	90.3	52.4	65.1	89.7	69.2	76.1	87.8	51.4	63.6	98.4	60.2	73.0	90.3	54.9	66.8
0960	Flooring	111.6	53.8	94.3	108.2	60.3	93.9	109.9	53.8	93.1	117.1	53.8	98.2	111.9	56.1	95.2	106.8	53.8	91.0
0970, 0990	Wall Finishes & Painting/Coating	97.4	47.1	67.2	94.7	54.1	70.3	97.4	67.3	79.3	97.4	47.1	67.2	91.7	67.3	77.0	94.7	62.2	75.2
09	FINISHES	96.5	51.0	71.1	96.3	54.4	73.0	97.0	64.3	78.8	99.9	51.0	72.7	100.6	59.6	77.8	96.4	55.5	73.6
COVERS	DIVS. 10 - 14, 25, 28, 41, 43, 44, 46	100.0	57.2	91.4	100.0	58.4	91.7	100.0	60.0	92.0	100.0	57.2	91.4	100.0	59.1	91.8	100.0	38.5	87.7
21, 22, 23	FIRE SUPPRESSION, PLUMBING & HVAC	97.9	42.2	75.6	97.3	38.3	73.7	100.0	48.6	79.4	97.9	40.2	74.7	100.0	58.3	83.3	97.4	46.8	77.1
26, 27, 3370	ELECTRICAL, COMMUNICATIONS & UTIL.	95.6	47.5	70.5	95.7	50.3	72.0	95.6	64.2	79.2	95.6	44.5	68.9	100.1	64.2	81.3	97.3	58.3	77.0
MF2010	WEIGHTED AVERAGE	95.8	53.8	77.5	97.1	55.1	78.8	99.4	63.1	83.6	97.0	53.3	78.0	99.1	63.5	83.6	97.2	57.1	79.7

DIVISION		MISSISSIPPI									MISSOURI								
		MCCOMB			MERIDIAN			TUPELO			BOWLING GREEN			CAPE GIRARDEAU			CHILLICOTHE		
		396			393			388			633			637			646		
		MAT.	INST.	TOTAL	MAT.	INST.	TOTAL	MAT.	INST.	TOTAL	MAT.	INST.	TOTAL	MAT.	INST.	TOTAL	MAT.	INST.	TOTAL
015433	CONTRACTOR EQUIPMENT		99.3	99.3		99.3	99.3		99.3	99.3		106.6	106.6		106.6	106.6		102.1	102.1
0241, 31 - 34	SITE & INFRASTRUCTURE, DEMOLITION	90.3	89.2	89.6	94.3	89.9	91.2	93.1	89.3	90.4	90.1	95.1	93.6	91.7	95.0	94.1	105.0	94.6	97.7
0310	Concrete Forming & Accessories	84.4	52.2	56.6	81.7	64.8	67.1	82.5	52.5	56.6	94.2	88.8	89.5	87.3	75.1	76.8	89.9	95.2	94.5
0320	Concrete Reinforcing	103.9	42.3	73.1	102.7	57.5	80.1	97.9	54.2	76.1	103.2	100.8	102.0	104.5	88.8	96.7	97.4	110.0	103.7
0330	Cast-in-Place Concrete	96.2	53.9	78.7	102.9	60.1	85.2	103.0	55.8	83.4	92.6	85.4	89.6	91.6	87.3	89.8	97.9	87.8	93.7
03	CONCRETE	91.6	52.5	72.3	95.8	63.2	79.7	95.4	55.4	75.7	95.9	91.0	93.5	95.0	83.4	89.3	102.1	95.9	99.1
04	MASONRY	116.2	45.1	72.2	90.0	54.5	68.0	127.9	48.7	78.9	122.1	97.9	107.1	118.5	79.0	94.1	103.6	100.6	101.7
05	METALS	89.1	73.1	84.2	90.0	82.5	87.7	90.4	76.6	86.2	96.1	113.8	101.6	97.2	107.3	100.3	96.9	110.5	101.1
06	WOOD, PLASTICS & COMPOSITES	87.2	55.3	69.2	84.6	66.7	74.5	82.8	53.4	66.2	95.3	88.0	91.2	88.1	71.5	78.7	96.0	95.4	95.7
07	THERMAL & MOISTURE PROTECTION	96.6	47.2	76.6	96.8	62.6	82.9	95.9	53.8	78.8	103.2	98.8	101.4	103.1	83.5	95.1	97.8	97.0	97.4
08	OPENINGS	96.6	52.2	86.1	96.5	65.5	89.2	96.8	51.8	86.1	97.0	98.5	97.3	97.0	75.5	91.9	96.0	98.1	96.5
0920	Plaster & Gypsum Board	92.7	54.3	66.6	92.7	66.1	74.6	87.3	52.4	63.6	97.9	87.6	90.9	96.4	70.6	78.8	97.4	95.1	95.8
0950, 0980	Ceilings & Acoustic Treatment	90.3	54.3	66.4	92.3	66.1	74.8	87.8	52.4	64.2	97.1	87.6	90.8	97.1	70.6	79.5	92.2	95.1	94.1
0960	Flooring	108.2	53.8	91.9	106.7	56.1	91.6	110.1	53.8	93.3	98.4	98.5	98.4	96.5	85.6	92.3	96.0	104.4	98.5
0970, 0990	Wall Finishes & Painting/Coating	94.7	43.2	63.8	94.7	77.8	84.5	97.4	60.0	74.9	102.3	102.8	102.6	102.3	74.8	85.8	96.2	91.3	93.3
09	FINISHES	95.7	52.1	71.4	96.0	65.2	78.8	96.0	53.8	72.5	100.8	91.2	95.4	99.6	75.4	86.1	99.9	96.4	97.9
COVERS	DIVS. 10 - 14, 25, 28, 41, 43, 44, 46	100.0	60.7	92.1	100.0	61.1	92.2	100.0	58.4	91.7	100.0	90.2	98.0	100.0	92.3	98.5	100.0	90.9	98.2
21, 22, 23	FIRE SUPPRESSION, PLUMBING & HVAC	97.3	35.3	72.5	100.0	60.4	84.1	98.1	44.2	76.5	95.0	97.7	96.1	99.9	96.6	98.6	95.2	99.2	96.8
26, 27, 3370	ELECTRICAL, COMMUNICATIONS & UTIL.	94.1	50.6	71.4	97.3	58.2	76.9	95.4	50.4	71.9	98.0	80.8	89.1	98.0	103.9	101.1	93.7	80.5	86.8
MF2010	WEIGHTED AVERAGE	95.7	52.9	77.1	96.2	65.3	82.7	97.3	56.1	79.4	98.1	94.7	96.6	99.1	90.6	95.4	97.7	96.2	97.1

MISSOURI

DIVISION		COLUMBIA 652			FLAT RIVER 636			HANNIBAL 634			HARRISONVILLE 647			JEFFERSON CITY 650 - 651			JOPLIN 648		
		MAT.	INST.	TOTAL	MAT.	INST.	TOTAL	MAT.	INST.	TOTAL	MAT.	INST.	TOTAL	MAT.	INST.	TOTAL	MAT.	INST.	TOTAL
015433	CONTRACTOR EQUIPMENT		107.7	107.7		106.6	106.6		106.6	106.6		102.1	102.1		107.7	107.7		105.8	105.8
0241, 31 - 34	SITE & INFRASTRUCTURE, DEMOLITION	100.0	96.6	97.6	92.8	95.2	94.5	88.0	95.1	93.0	96.1	95.6	95.8	99.2	96.6	97.4	105.6	99.4	101.3
0310	Concrete Forming & Accessories	85.5	80.0	80.7	100.1	86.2	88.1	92.4	79.3	81.1	87.3	100.9	99.1	95.6	80.0	82.1	101.6	73.7	77.5
0320	Concrete Reinforcing	98.1	116.3	107.2	104.5	108.0	106.3	102.7	100.8	101.7	97.0	110.1	103.5	100.4	113.1	106.7	100.6	101.7	101.1
0330	Cast-in-Place Concrete	89.8	87.1	88.7	95.6	94.2	95.0	87.6	85.2	86.6	100.3	106.1	102.7	95.3	87.1	91.9	106.0	79.2	94.9
03	CONCRETE	86.8	90.6	88.7	98.8	94.2	96.6	92.2	86.8	89.5	98.5	104.8	101.6	91.9	90.0	91.0	101.7	81.7	91.8
04	MASONRY	133.2	88.7	105.7	119.0	80.5	95.2	113.5	97.9	103.8	98.3	105.3	102.6	97.0	88.7	91.9	96.6	86.8	90.5
05	METALS	97.1	119.7	104.1	96.0	115.8	102.1	96.1	113.5	101.5	97.3	111.5	101.7	96.6	118.4	103.3	100.0	102.2	100.7
06	WOOD, PLASTICS & COMPOSITES	95.4	76.3	84.6	103.2	84.5	92.7	93.3	75.5	83.2	92.5	99.8	96.6	102.0	76.3	87.5	107.5	71.8	87.4
07	THERMAL & MOISTURE PROTECTION	95.5	88.1	92.5	103.4	93.8	99.5	103.0	96.9	100.5	97.1	105.8	100.6	100.8	88.1	95.7	97.1	79.6	90.0
08	OPENINGS	94.7	93.3	94.4	96.9	98.8	97.4	97.0	84.3	94.0	96.1	102.9	97.7	94.2	92.5	93.8	97.2	78.2	92.7
0920	Plaster & Gypsum Board	85.3	75.5	78.7	103.8	84.1	90.4	96.7	74.7	81.8	92.5	99.6	97.3	89.2	75.5	79.9	103.5	70.7	81.2
0950, 0980	Ceilings & Acoustic Treatment	97.9	75.5	83.0	97.1	84.1	88.4	97.1	74.7	82.2	92.2	99.6	97.1	102.1	75.5	84.4	93.0	70.7	78.2
0960	Flooring	109.7	97.5	106.1	101.3	85.6	96.6	97.7	98.5	98.0	91.7	104.4	95.5	116.0	97.5	110.5	121.0	76.3	107.6
0970, 0990	Wall Finishes & Painting/Coating	102.4	78.8	88.2	102.3	80.0	88.9	102.3	102.8	102.6	101.1	105.3	103.6	99.6	78.8	87.1	95.8	76.5	84.2
09	FINISHES	97.5	81.6	88.6	102.5	84.1	92.3	100.2	83.8	91.1	97.5	101.7	99.9	101.7	81.6	90.5	106.1	74.5	88.4
COVERS	DIVS. 10 - 14, 25, 28, 41, 43, 44, 46	100.0	95.6	99.1	100.0	94.3	98.8	100.0	88.8	97.8	100.0	93.1	98.6	100.0	95.6	99.1	100.0	89.6	97.9
21, 22, 23	FIRE SUPPRESSION, PLUMBING & HVAC	99.9	97.8	99.0	95.0	97.6	96.1	95.0	97.6	96.1	95.1	100.5	97.2	99.9	98.7	99.4	100.1	72.7	89.1
26, 27, 3370	ELECTRICAL, COMMUNICATIONS & UTIL.	98.4	86.6	92.2	102.4	104.0	103.2	96.8	82.9	89.6	100.4	99.7	100.1	104.3	86.6	95.1	91.5	69.7	80.1
MF2010	WEIGHTED AVERAGE	98.6	93.5	96.4	99.0	95.8	97.6	97.1	92.6	95.1	97.3	102.2	99.5	98.4	93.4	96.2	99.5	81.0	91.5

MISSOURI

DIVISION		KANSAS CITY 640 - 641			KIRKSVILLE 635			POPLAR BLUFF 639			ROLLA 654 - 655			SEDALIA 653			SIKESTON 638		
		MAT.	INST.	TOTAL	MAT.	INST.	TOTAL	MAT.	INST.	TOTAL	MAT.	INST.	TOTAL	MAT.	INST.	TOTAL	MAT.	INST.	TOTAL
015433	CONTRACTOR EQUIPMENT		103.4	103.4		99.0	99.0		101.3	101.3		107.7	107.7		99.7	99.7		101.3	101.3
0241, 31 - 34	SITE & INFRASTRUCTURE, DEMOLITION	98.2	98.0	98.0	90.9	91.2	91.1	78.4	95.0	90.1	99.0	96.6	97.3	94.9	92.5	93.2	81.7	95.1	91.1
0310	Concrete Forming & Accessories	100.3	107.8	106.8	85.2	79.3	80.1	85.3	75.0	76.4	92.7	94.0	93.8	90.1	79.3	80.8	86.4	75.0	76.5
0320	Concrete Reinforcing	95.5	117.1	106.3	103.4	101.9	102.6	106.5	97.6	102.0	98.6	97.7	98.2	97.1	109.4	103.2	105.9	101.4	103.6
0330	Cast-in-Place Concrete	98.6	107.8	102.4	95.5	85.1	91.2	73.5	87.8	79.5	91.8	96.4	93.7	95.9	84.5	91.2	78.6	87.8	82.4
03	CONCRETE	97.8	109.7	103.7	110.2	86.4	98.5	86.0	84.6	85.3	88.6	96.5	92.5	101.1	87.6	94.4	89.6	85.3	87.5
04	MASONRY	100.4	109.1	105.8	125.6	88.7	102.8	117.1	79.1	93.6	109.4	89.4	97.0	115.2	86.6	97.5	116.8	79.1	93.5
05	METALS	107.7	114.9	109.9	95.7	105.2	98.6	96.3	102.9	98.3	96.5	111.9	101.3	95.1	109.3	99.5	96.6	104.4	99.0
06	WOOD, PLASTICS & COMPOSITES	106.7	107.5	107.1	81.1	76.3	78.4	80.3	71.5	75.3	103.0	94.9	98.5	95.4	76.3	84.6	81.9	71.5	76.0
07	THERMAL & MOISTURE PROTECTION	97.2	108.6	101.8	109.8	89.1	101.4	108.3	85.3	99.0	95.6	95.5	95.6	101.8	93.7	98.5	108.5	83.9	98.5
08	OPENINGS	103.5	109.8	105.0	102.0	85.6	98.1	103.0	77.9	97.1	94.7	90.4	93.7	99.0	87.3	96.2	103.0	78.9	97.3
0920	Plaster & Gypsum Board	100.2	107.5	105.1	91.8	75.5	80.7	92.3	70.6	77.5	87.2	94.7	92.3	80.4	75.5	77.1	94.1	70.6	78.1
0950, 0980	Ceilings & Acoustic Treatment	99.3	107.5	104.7	95.3	75.5	82.1	97.1	70.6	79.5	97.9	94.7	95.8	97.9	75.5	83.0	97.1	70.6	79.5
0960	Flooring	96.6	109.3	100.4	76.5	97.5	82.8	90.2	83.5	88.2	113.0	97.5	108.3	86.4	97.5	89.7	90.6	83.5	88.5
0970, 0990	Wall Finishes & Painting/Coating	101.1	112.6	108.0	97.6	80.4	87.2	97.1	74.8	83.7	102.4	102.8	102.7	102.4	102.4	102.4	97.1	74.8	83.7
09	FINISHES	101.4	108.5	105.4	100.0	81.7	89.8	99.6	75.1	85.9	98.8	95.5	96.9	95.7	83.7	89.0	100.3	75.1	86.2
COVERS	DIVS. 10 - 14, 25, 28, 41, 43, 44, 46	100.0	101.3	100.3	100.0	89.0	97.8	100.0	92.4	98.5	100.0	91.4	98.3	100.0	91.5	98.3	100.0	92.4	98.5
21, 22, 23	FIRE SUPPRESSION, PLUMBING & HVAC	100.0	106.7	102.7	95.1	97.1	95.9	95.1	96.0	95.4	95.0	98.0	96.2	94.9	93.8	94.5	95.1	96.1	95.5
26, 27, 3370	ELECTRICAL, COMMUNICATIONS & UTIL.	102.0	100.1	101.0	97.0	82.9	89.6	97.2	103.9	100.7	96.6	86.6	91.4	98.2	99.7	99.0	96.3	103.9	100.3
MF2010	WEIGHTED AVERAGE	101.6	106.7	103.8	100.3	90.0	95.8	97.0	90.3	94.1	96.3	95.6	96.0	98.1	92.6	95.7	97.5	90.6	94.5

DIVISION		MISSOURI SPRINGFIELD 656 - 658			ST. JOSEPH 644 - 645			ST. LOUIS 630 - 631			MONTANA BILLINGS 590 - 591			BUTTE 597			GREAT FALLS 594		
		MAT.	INST.	TOTAL	MAT.	INST.	TOTAL	MAT.	INST.	TOTAL	MAT.	INST.	TOTAL	MAT.	INST.	TOTAL	MAT.	INST.	TOTAL
015433	CONTRACTOR EQUIPMENT		102.3	102.3		102.1	102.1		107.6	107.6		99.3	99.3		99.0	99.0		99.0	99.0
0241, 31 - 34	SITE & INFRASTRUCTURE, DEMOLITION	97.2	94.4	95.2	99.8	93.7	95.5	91.9	98.4	96.5	95.9	97.1	96.8	103.3	96.9	98.8	107.1	96.9	100.0
0310	Concrete Forming & Accessories	98.2	74.7	77.9	100.2	91.1	92.3	100.2	103.6	103.1	101.3	71.6	75.7	88.4	73.3	75.4	101.1	71.6	75.6
0320	Concrete Reinforcing	94.3	116.0	105.1	94.4	109.8	102.1	95.5	114.0	104.7	93.9	82.8	88.3	101.9	82.9	92.4	94.0	82.8	88.4
0330	Cast-in-Place Concrete	97.5	78.8	89.7	98.5	103.6	100.6	91.6	105.0	97.2	120.2	68.9	98.9	132.3	70.3	106.6	139.8	65.0	108.7
03	CONCRETE	97.7	84.6	91.2	97.5	99.5	98.5	94.5	106.8	100.5	106.9	73.6	90.5	110.6	74.9	93.0	115.9	72.2	94.3
04	MASONRY	89.5	87.2	88.1	100.1	96.7	98.0	99.7	112.5	107.6	117.9	75.0	91.4	113.3	77.9	91.4	117.5	76.7	92.3
05	METALS	101.2	107.5	103.1	103.7	110.7	105.9	101.9	120.5	107.7	107.5	91.0	102.4	100.6	91.1	97.7	103.8	91.1	99.9
06	WOOD, PLASTICS & COMPOSITES	103.4	72.8	86.1	107.5	89.7	97.4	103.1	100.8	101.8	99.5	70.0	82.8	86.6	72.5	78.6	100.7	70.0	83.4
07	THERMAL & MOISTURE PROTECTION	99.9	81.1	92.2	97.7	97.4	97.5	103.2	107.6	105.0	108.1	71.2	93.1	108.0	72.5	93.6	108.5	69.8	92.8
08	OPENINGS	101.6	81.2	96.8	101.7	98.3	100.9	97.2	110.5	100.4	93.9	68.7	88.0	92.3	71.3	87.3	95.0	68.1	88.6
0920	Plaster & Gypsum Board	88.3	71.9	77.1	104.8	89.1	94.1	104.7	100.8	102.1	99.9	69.3	79.1	100.3	71.9	81.0	109.7	69.3	82.2
0950, 0980	Ceilings & Acoustic Treatment	97.9	71.9	80.6	98.4	89.1	92.2	102.4	100.8	101.3	99.8	69.3	79.5	107.0	71.9	83.6	108.8	69.3	82.5
0960	Flooring	110.5	76.3	100.3	99.8	104.4	101.2	101.1	99.4	100.6	106.0	71.5	95.7	103.9	75.5	95.4	111.0	75.5	100.4
0970, 0990	Wall Finishes & Painting/Coating	96.2	76.5	84.4	96.2	88.6	91.6	102.3	106.5	104.8	99.0	88.5	92.7	97.2	52.3	70.2	97.2	88.5	92.0
09	FINISHES	101.0	75.1	86.6	102.5	92.7	97.0	103.7	102.5	103.0	102.7	73.0	86.2	103.4	71.2	85.5	107.4	73.7	88.6
COVERS	DIVS. 10 - 14, 25, 28, 41, 43, 44, 46	100.0	93.0	98.6	100.0	96.9	99.4	100.0	102.3	100.5	100.0	96.1	99.2	100.0	96.4	99.3	100.0	96.1	99.2
21, 22, 23	FIRE SUPPRESSION, PLUMBING & HVAC	99.9	73.0	89.1	100.1	89.5	95.8	100.0	107.6	103.0	100.1	74.9	90.0	100.2	70.7	88.4	100.2	72.2	89.0
26, 27, 3370	ELECTRICAL, COMMUNICATIONS & UTIL.	102.9	70.3	85.9	100.5	80.5	90.1	100.5	107.1	103.9	96.8	73.9	84.8	104.4	72.2	87.6	96.9	72.2	84.0
MF2010	WEIGHTED AVERAGE	99.9	82.1	92.1	100.7	93.9	97.8	99.6	107.6	103.1	102.2	77.9	91.6	102.0	77.2	91.2	103.4	77.1	92.0

MONTANA

	DIVISION	HAVRE 595			HELENA 596			KALISPELL 599			MILES CITY 593			MISSOULA 598			WOLF POINT 592		
		MAT.	INST.	TOTAL	MAT.	INST.	TOTAL	MAT.	INST.	TOTAL	MAT.	INST.	TOTAL	MAT.	INST.	TOTAL	MAT.	INST.	TOTAL
015433	CONTRACTOR EQUIPMENT		99.0	99.0		99.0	99.0		99.0	99.0		99.0	99.0		99.0	99.0		99.0	99.0
0241, 31 - 34	SITE & INFRASTRUCTURE, DEMOLITION	111.0	96.7	100.9	100.1	96.6	97.7	93.4	96.8	95.8	99.9	96.3	97.4	85.8	96.6	93.4	118.0	96.4	102.9
0310	Concrete Forming & Accessories	81.6	69.1	70.8	104.4	66.7	71.9	91.6	71.5	74.3	99.6	67.6	72.0	91.6	71.5	74.2	92.2	67.8	71.2
0320	Concrete Reinforcing	102.7	82.8	92.8	106.8	82.8	94.8	104.6	83.4	94.0	102.3	82.8	92.6	103.6	83.4	93.5	103.7	82.8	93.3
0330	Cast-in-Place Concrete	142.5	61.8	109.0	106.9	64.3	89.2	114.9	64.0	93.8	125.8	61.6	99.1	97.5	66.2	84.5	140.8	62.0	108.1
03	CONCRETE	119.1	70.0	94.9	104.5	69.8	87.3	100.0	72.0	86.2	107.4	69.3	88.6	88.0	72.7	80.4	123.0	69.6	96.6
04	MASONRY	114.2	71.1	87.5	110.7	77.1	89.9	112.2	78.3	91.2	119.4	66.5	86.7	135.6	77.9	99.9	120.5	67.2	87.5
05	METALS	96.8	90.9	95.0	102.7	90.0	98.7	96.6	91.4	95.0	95.9	91.1	94.4	97.2	91.3	95.4	96.0	91.1	94.5
06	WOOD, PLASTICS & COMPOSITES	78.4	70.0	73.7	103.7	63.8	81.2	89.9	70.0	78.7	97.8	70.0	82.1	89.9	70.0	78.7	89.5	70.0	78.5
07	THERMAL & MOISTURE PROTECTION	108.3	69.4	92.5	105.4	72.2	91.9	107.7	74.3	94.1	108.0	66.8	91.3	107.4	80.6	96.5	108.7	67.1	91.8
08	OPENINGS	92.4	68.1	86.6	96.2	66.3	89.2	92.3	68.3	86.6	91.8	68.0	86.2	92.3	68.0	86.6	91.9	67.8	86.2
0920	Plaster & Gypsum Board	96.2	69.3	77.9	97.9	62.9	74.1	100.3	69.3	79.2	109.0	69.3	82.0	100.3	69.3	79.2	104.2	69.3	80.4
0950, 0980	Ceilings & Acoustic Treatment	107.0	69.3	81.9	109.7	62.9	78.5	107.0	69.3	81.9	106.1	69.3	81.6	107.0	69.3	81.9	106.1	69.3	81.6
0960	Flooring	101.3	75.5	93.6	106.1	60.2	92.4	105.7	75.5	96.7	110.7	71.5	99.0	105.7	75.5	96.7	107.1	71.5	96.5
0970, 0990	Wall Finishes & Painting/Coating	97.2	49.7	68.7	93.5	48.2	66.3	97.2	48.2	67.8	97.2	48.2	67.8	97.2	63.3	76.8	97.2	49.7	68.7
09	FINISHES	102.8	67.9	83.4	104.7	63.0	81.5	103.3	69.4	84.4	106.2	65.9	83.8	102.7	71.0	85.1	105.9	66.2	83.8
COVERS	DIVS. 10 - 14, 25, 28, 41, 43, 44, 46	100.0	72.6	94.5	100.0	95.6	99.1	100.0	96.2	99.2	100.0	92.6	98.5	100.0	96.1	99.2	100.0	92.9	98.6
21, 22, 23	FIRE SUPPRESSION, PLUMBING & HVAC	95.3	69.3	84.9	100.1	70.9	88.4	95.3	70.3	85.3	95.3	69.7	85.0	100.2	69.9	88.0	95.3	70.0	85.2
26, 27, 3370	ELECTRICAL, COMMUNICATIONS & UTIL.	96.9	72.7	84.3	103.8	72.7	87.6	101.2	71.0	85.4	96.9	77.4	86.7	102.2	69.3	85.0	96.9	77.4	86.7
MF2010	WEIGHTED AVERAGE	100.6	74.2	89.1	102.0	75.1	90.2	98.4	76.3	88.8	99.5	74.7	88.7	99.4	76.4	89.4	101.7	74.9	90.0

NEBRASKA

	DIVISION	ALLIANCE 693			COLUMBUS 686			GRAND ISLAND 688			HASTINGS 689			LINCOLN 683 - 685			MCCOOK 690		
		MAT.	INST.	TOTAL	MAT.	INST.	TOTAL	MAT.	INST.	TOTAL	MAT.	INST.	TOTAL	MAT.	INST.	TOTAL	MAT.	INST.	TOTAL
015433	CONTRACTOR EQUIPMENT		97.5	97.5		101.4	101.4		101.4	101.4		101.4	101.4		101.4	101.4		101.4	101.4
0241, 31 - 34	SITE & INFRASTRUCTURE, DEMOLITION	98.8	98.4	98.6	99.1	92.0	94.1	103.8	92.8	96.1	102.6	92.0	95.2	93.6	92.8	93.0	102.1	91.9	95.0
0310	Concrete Forming & Accessories	88.3	57.7	61.9	95.9	68.1	71.9	95.4	74.0	76.9	98.5	73.6	77.0	97.5	68.9	72.8	93.9	57.3	62.3
0320	Concrete Reinforcing	110.1	85.0	97.6	101.7	76.9	89.3	101.1	76.8	89.0	101.1	77.5	89.3	103.1	76.5	89.8	103.1	76.5	89.8
0330	Cast-in-Place Concrete	109.4	61.3	89.4	114.9	61.3	92.6	121.6	68.6	99.6	121.6	64.6	97.9	99.8	71.0	87.9	117.6	60.6	94.0
03	CONCRETE	120.2	64.5	92.7	106.9	68.2	87.8	111.7	73.4	92.8	111.9	71.9	92.1	98.0	71.9	85.1	109.5	63.1	86.6
04	MASONRY	109.7	74.9	88.2	112.6	79.0	91.8	105.7	77.4	88.2	114.2	89.5	98.9	95.9	68.4	78.9	105.5	74.7	86.5
05	METALS	101.2	79.1	94.4	91.9	85.2	89.8	93.6	87.0	91.5	94.4	86.5	91.9	95.6	86.2	92.7	96.0	84.2	92.4
06	WOOD, PLASTICS & COMPOSITES	88.3	53.4	68.6	99.7	67.2	81.4	99.0	73.9	84.8	102.7	73.9	86.4	98.3	67.2	80.7	97.1	53.4	72.5
07	THERMAL & MOISTURE PROTECTION	106.4	69.5	91.4	104.4	70.7	90.7	104.5	74.2	92.2	104.5	85.4	96.8	100.4	70.1	88.1	100.8	67.4	87.2
08	OPENINGS	92.8	59.4	84.9	94.1	66.7	87.6	94.2	70.9	88.7	94.2	70.3	88.5	103.2	63.5	93.8	93.2	57.5	84.7
0920	Plaster & Gypsum Board	81.0	51.9	61.2	88.7	66.1	73.3	88.0	73.0	77.8	89.9	73.0	78.4	90.1	66.1	73.8	92.5	51.9	64.9
0950, 0980	Ceilings & Acoustic Treatment	98.5	51.9	67.5	93.3	66.1	75.2	93.3	73.0	79.8	93.3	73.0	79.8	99.3	66.1	77.2	94.3	51.9	66.1
0960	Flooring	104.5	83.6	98.2	102.5	102.2	102.4	102.3	109.2	104.4	103.4	102.2	103.1	107.6	85.1	100.9	101.6	83.6	96.2
0970, 0990	Wall Finishes & Painting/Coating	174.1	56.0	103.1	91.9	65.1	75.8	91.9	69.1	78.2	91.9	65.1	75.8	100.0	79.6	87.7	95.3	48.8	67.3
09	FINISHES	102.8	60.8	79.4	98.5	72.9	84.3	98.7	78.8	87.6	99.2	76.9	86.8	102.3	72.7	85.8	99.6	59.9	77.5
COVERS	DIVS. 10 - 14, 25, 28, 41, 43, 44, 46	100.0	67.0	93.4	100.0	88.3	97.7	100.0	89.3	97.9	100.0	89.1	97.8	100.0	88.6	97.7	100.0	66.3	93.2
21, 22, 23	FIRE SUPPRESSION, PLUMBING & HVAC	95.3	72.0	85.9	95.1	77.1	87.9	100.0	78.5	91.4	95.1	77.2	87.9	99.9	78.5	91.3	95.0	77.1	87.8
26, 27, 3370	ELECTRICAL, COMMUNICATIONS & UTIL.	91.7	71.0	80.9	92.0	82.4	87.0	90.7	65.9	77.8	90.1	85.6	87.7	103.2	65.9	83.7	93.9	71.0	81.9
MF2010	WEIGHTED AVERAGE	100.4	71.6	87.9	97.5	77.9	88.9	99.1	77.8	89.9	98.5	81.2	90.9	99.5	75.3	89.0	98.1	72.1	86.8

NEBRASKA / NEVADA

	DIVISION	NORFOLK 687			NORTH PLATTE 691			OMAHA 680 - 681			VALENTINE 692			CARSON CITY 897			ELKO 898		
		MAT.	INST.	TOTAL	MAT.	INST.	TOTAL	MAT.	INST.	TOTAL	MAT.	INST.	TOTAL	MAT.	INST.	TOTAL	MAT.	INST.	TOTAL
015433	CONTRACTOR EQUIPMENT		92.7	92.7		101.4	101.4		92.7	92.7		95.6	95.6		97.9	97.9		97.9	97.9
0241, 31 - 34	SITE & INFRASTRUCTURE, DEMOLITION	82.3	91.1	88.5	103.4	92.0	95.4	86.4	91.8	90.2	86.4	95.9	93.1	78.7	99.6	93.4	61.9	98.4	87.5
0310	Concrete Forming & Accessories	82.4	72.7	74.0	96.3	73.1	76.3	93.5	72.9	75.7	84.5	57.1	60.8	105.3	94.6	96.1	111.2	83.2	87.0
0320	Concrete Reinforcing	101.8	66.6	84.3	102.5	77.4	90.0	104.1	76.9	90.5	103.1	66.3	84.8	107.5	118.0	112.7	106.9	113.9	110.4
0330	Cast-in-Place Concrete	116.1	63.8	94.4	117.6	65.9	96.2	92.6	77.1	86.2	104.3	58.6	85.3	104.1	86.2	96.7	98.7	80.9	91.3
03	CONCRETE	105.7	68.7	87.5	109.6	72.1	91.1	94.6	75.4	85.1	107.0	60.0	83.8	104.1	96.0	100.1	98.6	88.3	93.5
04	MASONRY	118.7	78.7	93.9	93.2	89.5	90.9	98.9	79.9	87.1	105.3	74.8	86.4	116.6	89.3	99.7	114.9	73.1	89.0
05	METALS	95.2	74.1	88.7	95.1	86.1	92.3	95.4	79.5	90.5	107.3	74.1	97.1	90.1	104.0	94.4	92.8	99.5	94.8
06	WOOD, PLASTICS & COMPOSITES	82.8	73.4	77.5	99.1	73.9	84.9	91.2	72.1	80.5	82.8	52.9	65.9	91.6	96.6	94.4	99.4	83.7	90.6
07	THERMAL & MOISTURE PROTECTION	104.4	74.9	92.4	100.8	84.1	94.0	100.0	79.8	91.8	101.6	69.1	88.4	102.7	91.2	98.0	99.0	76.6	89.9
08	OPENINGS	95.9	67.7	89.2	92.5	70.3	87.3	101.4	71.9	94.4	95.0	56.5	85.9	99.6	109.4	101.9	100.6	87.3	97.4
0920	Plaster & Gypsum Board	88.7	73.0	78.0	92.5	73.0	79.3	99.5	71.7	80.6	94.7	51.9	65.6	91.3	96.4	94.8	93.3	83.1	86.4
0950, 0980	Ceilings & Acoustic Treatment	106.9	73.0	84.4	94.3	73.0	80.1	112.8	71.7	85.5	113.1	51.9	72.4	101.8	96.4	98.2	102.3	83.1	89.5
0960	Flooring	131.7	102.2	122.9	102.4	102.2	102.3	129.9	83.4	116.0	133.3	81.3	117.7	108.0	109.9	103.6	103.7	52.1	88.2
0970, 0990	Wall Finishes & Painting/Coating	164.9	65.1	104.9	95.3	65.1	77.1	148.8	68.2	100.4	171.4	67.5	108.9	102.7	82.5	90.6	104.2	97.9	100.4
09	FINISHES	120.0	76.9	96.0	99.9	76.9	87.1	119.6	74.0	94.2	123.7	61.1	88.8	100.4	96.2	98.1	99.4	78.9	88.0
COVERS	DIVS. 10 - 14, 25, 28, 41, 43, 44, 46	100.0	87.9	97.6	100.0	68.6	93.7	100.0	88.1	97.6	100.0	64.3	92.8	100.0	92.0	98.4	100.0	64.5	92.9
21, 22, 23	FIRE SUPPRESSION, PLUMBING & HVAC	94.9	76.9	87.7	99.9	77.1	90.8	99.8	78.0	91.1	94.7	76.9	87.6	100.0	81.4	92.6	97.7	81.2	91.1
26, 27, 3370	ELECTRICAL, COMMUNICATIONS & UTIL.	90.9	82.4	86.5	92.0	78.9	85.2	97.9	82.4	89.8	89.0	88.6	88.8	100.4	97.4	98.8	98.1	97.3	97.7
MF2010	WEIGHTED AVERAGE	99.2	77.5	89.8	98.5	79.6	90.2	99.6	79.3	90.7	100.6	73.6	88.9	99.1	93.8	96.8	97.6	86.1	92.6

NEVADA / NEW HAMPSHIRE

DIVISION		ELY 893			LAS VEGAS 889 - 891			RENO 894 - 895			CHARLESTON 036			CLAREMONT 037			CONCORD 032 - 033		
		MAT.	INST.	TOTAL	MAT.	INST.	TOTAL	MAT.	INST.	TOTAL	MAT.	INST.	TOTAL	MAT.	INST.	TOTAL	MAT.	INST.	TOTAL
015433	CONTRACTOR EQUIPMENT		97.9	97.9		97.9	97.9		97.9	97.9		100.6	100.6		100.6	100.6		100.6	100.6
0241, 31 - 34	SITE & INFRASTRUCTURE, DEMOLITION	67.0	99.9	90.1	69.7	101.6	92.1	67.0	99.6	89.9	87.4	99.2	95.7	81.2	99.2	93.9	94.5	101.4	99.3
0310	Concrete Forming & Accessories	104.2	105.9	105.6	105.4	111.0	110.3	100.5	94.5	95.3	88.1	82.9	83.6	93.8	82.9	84.4	95.9	94.3	94.5
0320	Concrete Reinforcing	105.7	115.2	110.4	97.5	121.8	109.6	99.9	121.4	110.6	84.5	95.2	89.8	84.5	95.2	89.8	92.9	95.8	94.4
0330	Cast-in-Place Concrete	105.9	106.7	106.2	102.6	107.5	104.6	112.0	86.2	101.3	97.4	72.1	86.9	89.5	72.1	82.3	111.5	92.2	103.5
03	CONCRETE	106.6	107.6	107.1	101.8	111.4	106.6	106.3	96.6	101.5	99.5	81.6	90.6	91.5	81.6	86.6	106.0	93.7	100.0
04	MASONRY	119.0	104.2	109.9	108.1	102.8	104.8	114.2	89.3	98.8	87.8	82.3	84.4	87.3	82.3	84.2	97.6	102.1	100.4
05	METALS	92.7	104.8	96.4	99.8	109.3	102.7	94.2	105.3	97.6	95.2	90.6	93.8	95.2	90.6	93.8	101.2	94.0	99.0
06	WOOD, PLASTICS & COMPOSITES	90.3	106.3	99.3	89.2	110.4	101.2	85.2	96.6	91.6	86.9	92.3	90.0	93.3	92.3	92.7	94.8	93.3	93.9
07	THERMAL & MOISTURE PROTECTION	99.6	95.9	98.1	112.5	102.0	108.2	99.1	91.2	95.9	102.8	72.0	90.3	102.7	72.0	90.2	104.9	91.4	99.4
08	OPENINGS	100.5	99.6	100.3	99.6	117.9	104.0	98.6	104.2	99.9	102.6	78.0	96.8	103.8	78.0	97.7	104.1	88.4	100.4
0920	Plaster & Gypsum Board	90.0	106.4	101.1	87.8	110.7	103.4	82.0	96.4	91.8	94.7	91.4	92.5	95.8	91.4	92.8	98.4	92.4	94.4
0950, 0980	Ceilings & Acoustic Treatment	102.3	106.4	105.0	111.1	110.7	110.8	107.6	96.4	100.1	90.6	91.4	91.2	90.6	91.4	91.2	95.9	92.4	93.6
0960	Flooring	101.5	58.2	88.6	93.3	109.9	98.3	98.8	109.9	102.1	96.3	32.7	77.3	98.2	32.7	78.6	97.1	112.2	101.6
0970, 0990	Wall Finishes & Painting/Coating	104.2	123.6	115.9	107.2	123.6	117.0	104.2	82.5	91.2	95.4	46.7	66.2	95.4	46.9	66.3	95.1	97.5	96.5
09	FINISHES	98.9	99.4	99.2	98.4	112.2	106.1	98.0	96.2	97.0	94.9	71.3	81.8	95.1	71.3	81.9	95.9	98.0	97.0
COVERS	DIVS. 10 - 14, 25, 28, 41, 43, 44, 46	100.0	65.0	93.0	100.0	106.3	101.3	100.0	92.0	98.4	100.0	90.0	98.0	100.0	90.0	98.0	100.0	104.8	101.0
21, 22, 23	FIRE SUPPRESSION, PLUMBING & HVAC	97.7	106.7	101.3	100.2	105.1	102.1	100.0	81.5	92.6	95.2	40.4	73.2	95.2	40.5	73.3	99.9	86.1	94.4
26, 27, 3370	ELECTRICAL, COMMUNICATIONS & UTIL.	98.4	109.7	104.3	102.7	120.6	112.0	98.8	97.4	98.0	99.6	54.1	75.8	99.6	54.1	75.8	99.6	80.4	89.6
MF2010	WEIGHTED AVERAGE	98.7	103.4	100.8	100.2	109.4	104.2	99.0	93.8	96.7	96.9	70.1	85.2	96.0	70.1	84.7	100.8	92.3	97.1

NEW HAMPSHIRE / NEW JERSEY

DIVISION		KEENE 034			LITTLETON 035			MANCHESTER 031			NASHUA 030			PORTSMOUTH 038			ATLANTIC CITY 082,084		
		MAT.	INST.	TOTAL	MAT.	INST.	TOTAL	MAT.	INST.	TOTAL	MAT.	INST.	TOTAL	MAT.	INST.	TOTAL	MAT.	INST.	TOTAL
015433	CONTRACTOR EQUIPMENT		100.6	100.6		100.6	100.6		100.6	100.6		100.6	100.6		100.6	100.6		98.8	98.8
0241, 31 - 34	SITE & INFRASTRUCTURE, DEMOLITION	95.2	99.5	98.2	81.3	99.5	94.1	93.6	101.4	99.1	96.5	101.4	100.0	90.1	101.5	98.1	98.0	104.4	102.5
0310	Concrete Forming & Accessories	92.6	84.9	85.9	103.4	84.9	87.4	98.4	94.8	95.3	100.3	94.8	95.5	89.4	95.1	94.3	110.1	128.4	125.9
0320	Concrete Reinforcing	84.5	95.3	89.9	85.2	95.3	90.3	106.7	95.8	101.3	105.5	95.8	100.7	84.5	95.9	90.2	79.1	121.6	100.3
0330	Cast-in-Place Concrete	97.9	74.4	88.1	87.9	74.4	82.3	111.9	115.3	113.3	92.6	115.3	102.0	87.9	115.4	99.3	84.2	132.2	104.1
03	CONCRETE	99.2	83.2	91.3	91.0	83.3	87.2	108.6	101.9	105.3	99.5	101.9	100.6	91.0	102.1	96.4	92.9	127.3	109.9
04	MASONRY	91.7	85.9	88.1	96.9	85.9	90.1	94.9	102.1	99.4	91.4	102.1	98.0	87.7	102.1	96.6	99.2	125.4	115.4
05	METALS	95.8	91.2	94.4	95.9	91.2	94.4	103.8	94.5	100.9	100.8	94.5	98.9	97.3	95.1	96.7	95.6	106.5	99.0
06	WOOD, PLASTICS & COMPOSITES	91.6	92.3	92.0	102.9	92.3	96.9	95.1	93.3	94.1	101.4	93.3	96.8	88.2	93.3	91.1	115.5	130.2	123.9
07	THERMAL & MOISTURE PROTECTION	103.2	75.0	91.8	102.8	73.5	90.9	106.9	94.9	102.0	103.6	94.9	100.1	103.3	115.6	108.3	104.6	123.2	112.2
08	OPENINGS	101.1	82.9	96.8	104.8	78.7	98.6	106.9	88.4	102.6	105.8	88.4	101.6	106.5	85.1	101.4	102.3	125.4	107.7
0920	Plaster & Gypsum Board	95.1	91.4	92.6	108.4	91.4	96.9	98.7	92.4	94.4	103.8	92.4	96.1	94.7	92.4	93.2	107.3	130.5	123.1
0950, 0980	Ceilings & Acoustic Treatment	90.6	91.4	91.2	90.6	91.4	91.2	98.6	92.4	94.5	101.4	92.4	95.4	91.6	92.4	92.2	88.9	130.5	116.6
0960	Flooring	97.9	53.6	84.7	106.2	32.7	84.2	98.2	112.2	102.4	100.9	112.2	104.2	96.5	112.2	101.2	102.2	150.6	116.6
0970, 0990	Wall Finishes & Painting/Coating	95.4	46.7	66.2	95.4	61.2	74.9	98.2	97.5	97.8	95.4	97.5	96.7	95.4	97.5	96.7	93.0	117.3	107.6
09	FINISHES	96.7	76.2	85.3	99.0	73.8	85.0	98.5	98.0	98.2	101.0	98.0	99.3	95.9	98.0	97.1	99.4	132.5	117.8
COVERS	DIVS. 10 - 14, 25, 28, 41, 43, 44, 46	100.0	91.2	98.2	100.0	99.2	99.8	100.0	104.8	101.0	100.0	104.8	101.0	100.0	104.8	101.0	100.0	102.1	102.1
21, 22, 23	FIRE SUPPRESSION, PLUMBING & HVAC	95.2	44.2	74.7	95.2	65.2	83.2	99.9	86.2	94.4	100.1	86.2	94.5	100.1	86.2	94.5	99.6	119.6	107.6
26, 27, 3370	ELECTRICAL, COMMUNICATIONS & UTIL.	99.6	64.7	81.4	100.8	57.3	78.1	101.6	80.4	90.6	102.2	80.4	90.8	100.1	80.4	89.8	92.7	141.4	118.1
MF2010	WEIGHTED AVERAGE	97.4	74.0	87.2	97.1	77.2	88.4	102.1	93.6	98.4	100.6	93.6	97.6	98.2	94.2	96.4	98.1	123.5	109.2

NEW JERSEY

DIVISION		CAMDEN 081			DOVER 078			ELIZABETH 072			HACKENSACK 076			JERSEY CITY 073			LONG BRANCH 077		
		MAT.	INST.	TOTAL	MAT.	INST.	TOTAL	MAT.	INST.	TOTAL	MAT.	INST.	TOTAL	MAT.	INST.	TOTAL	MAT.	INST.	TOTAL
015433	CONTRACTOR EQUIPMENT		98.8	98.8		100.6	100.6		100.6	100.6		100.6	100.6		98.8	98.8		98.4	98.4
0241, 31 - 34	SITE & INFRASTRUCTURE, DEMOLITION	99.1	104.7	103.0	108.2	105.4	106.3	112.7	105.4	107.6	108.9	105.5	106.5	98.0	105.4	103.2	102.6	105.3	104.5
0310	Concrete Forming & Accessories	101.7	128.4	124.7	97.4	129.0	124.7	109.3	129.0	126.3	97.4	128.9	124.6	101.1	129.0	125.2	101.7	128.7	125.0
0320	Concrete Reinforcing	103.8	121.8	112.8	80.0	128.6	104.3	80.0	128.6	104.3	80.0	128.6	104.3	103.8	128.6	116.2	80.0	128.6	104.3
0330	Cast-in-Place Concrete	81.6	132.1	102.6	102.2	127.3	112.6	87.8	127.3	104.2	99.9	127.3	111.3	79.8	127.4	99.5	88.7	132.1	106.7
03	CONCRETE	94.1	127.3	110.4	99.7	127.4	113.3	95.3	127.4	111.1	97.8	127.3	112.4	93.2	127.2	110.0	97.1	128.7	112.7
04	MASONRY	89.7	125.4	111.8	87.3	125.9	111.2	101.2	125.9	116.5	90.8	125.9	112.5	80.8	125.9	108.7	94.4	125.4	113.6
05	METALS	100.7	112.6	102.5	95.6	113.6	101.2	97.1	113.6	102.2	95.7	113.4	101.2	100.8	111.2	104.0	95.7	111.1	100.5
06	WOOD, PLASTICS & COMPOSITES	104.2	130.2	118.9	101.5	130.2	117.7	117.1	130.2	124.5	101.5	130.2	117.7	102.3	130.2	118.0	103.4	130.1	118.5
07	THERMAL & MOISTURE PROTECTION	104.5	122.7	111.9	101.5	130.6	113.4	101.7	130.6	113.5	101.3	123.3	110.3	101.1	130.6	113.1	101.2	123.4	110.3
08	OPENINGS	104.6	125.4	109.5	108.8	127.9	113.4	106.9	127.9	111.9	106.2	127.9	111.4	104.5	127.9	110.0	100.7	127.9	107.1
0920	Plaster & Gypsum Board	102.8	130.5	121.6	99.9	130.5	120.7	107.7	130.5	123.2	99.9	130.5	120.7	103.2	130.5	121.8	101.7	130.5	121.3
0950, 0980	Ceilings & Acoustic Treatment	99.7	130.5	120.2	88.6	130.5	116.5	90.6	130.5	117.2	88.6	130.5	116.5	99.5	130.5	120.1	88.6	130.5	116.5
0960	Flooring	98.7	150.6	114.2	96.8	172.3	119.4	101.2	172.3	122.5	96.8	172.3	119.4	97.7	172.3	120.0	97.9	172.3	120.1
0970, 0990	Wall Finishes & Painting/Coating	93.0	117.3	107.6	94.6	119.3	109.4	94.6	119.3	109.4	94.6	119.3	109.4	94.7	119.3	109.5	94.7	117.3	108.3
09	FINISHES	100.0	132.5	118.1	97.1	135.5	118.5	100.4	135.5	119.9	96.9	135.5	118.4	99.8	135.5	119.7	97.9	136.0	119.2
COVERS	DIVS. 10 - 14, 25, 28, 41, 43, 44, 46	100.0	110.5	102.1	100.0	113.6	102.7	100.0	113.6	102.7	100.0	113.6	102.7	100.0	113.6	102.7	100.0	110.4	102.1
21, 22, 23	FIRE SUPPRESSION, PLUMBING & HVAC	100.0	119.7	107.9	99.6	123.4	109.1	100.0	122.8	109.1	99.6	123.3	109.1	100.0	123.4	109.3	99.6	122.6	108.8
26, 27, 3370	ELECTRICAL, COMMUNICATIONS & UTIL.	97.9	141.4	120.6	90.9	137.6	115.3	91.5	137.6	115.6	90.9	139.7	116.4	95.5	139.7	118.6	90.6	131.5	111.9
MF2010	WEIGHTED AVERAGE	99.4	123.6	109.9	98.7	125.4	110.3	99.5	125.3	110.7	98.4	125.5	110.2	98.5	125.5	110.2	97.8	124.1	109.2

NEW JERSEY

DIVISION		NEW BRUNSWICK 088 - 089			NEWARK 070 - 071			PATERSON 074 - 075			POINT PLEASANT 087			SUMMIT 079			TRENTON 085 - 086		
		MAT.	INST.	TOTAL	MAT.	INST.	TOTAL	MAT.	INST.	TOTAL	MAT.	INST.	TOTAL	MAT.	INST.	TOTAL	MAT.	INST.	TOTAL
015433	CONTRACTOR EQUIPMENT		98.4	98.4		100.6	100.6		100.6	100.6		98.4	98.4		100.6	100.6		98.4	98.4
0241, 31 - 34	SITE & INFRASTRUCTURE, DEMOLITION	111.8	105.3	107.3	114.4	105.4	108.1	110.9	105.5	107.1	113.5	105.3	107.7	110.1	105.4	106.8	96.6	105.3	102.7
0310	Concrete Forming & Accessories	104.6	128.9	125.6	97.2	129.0	124.6	99.4	128.9	124.8	99.3	120.3	117.4	100.2	129.0	125.0	99.9	128.6	124.6
0320	Concrete Reinforcing	80.0	128.6	104.3	103.3	128.6	116.0	103.8	128.6	116.2	80.0	128.5	104.2	80.0	128.6	104.3	103.3	115.7	109.5
0330	Cast-in-Place Concrete	103.9	132.3	115.7	109.6	127.3	117.0	101.6	127.3	112.3	103.9	128.4	114.1	84.9	127.3	102.5	99.5	132.0	113.0
03	CONCRETE	109.8	128.9	119.3	106.9	127.4	117.0	103.4	127.3	115.2	109.5	123.7	116.5	92.3	127.4	109.6	102.3	126.3	114.1
04	MASONRY	96.6	125.9	114.7	93.4	125.9	113.5	87.8	125.9	111.4	86.4	124.6	110.0	89.3	125.9	112.0	92.1	125.4	112.7
05	METALS	95.7	111.2	100.4	102.8	113.6	106.1	95.7	113.5	101.2	95.7	110.7	100.3	95.6	113.6	101.1	100.4	105.7	102.0
06	WOOD, PLASTICS & COMPOSITES	108.9	130.1	120.9	99.0	130.2	116.6	104.1	130.2	118.8	101.6	119.1	111.5	105.3	130.2	119.3	101.4	130.1	117.6
07	THERMAL & MOISTURE PROTECTION	104.8	129.9	115.0	102.0	130.6	113.6	101.6	123.3	110.4	104.8	122.1	111.8	101.9	130.6	113.6	104.2	123.1	111.9
08	OPENINGS	97.2	127.9	104.5	107.5	127.9	112.3	111.6	127.9	115.4	99.1	122.2	104.6	113.6	127.9	117.0	106.7	124.4	110.9
0920	Plaster & Gypsum Board	103.9	130.5	122.0	99.9	130.5	120.7	103.2	130.5	121.8	99.4	119.1	112.8	101.7	130.5	121.3	99.9	130.5	120.7
0950, 0980	Ceilings & Acoustic Treatment	88.9	130.5	116.6	102.4	130.5	121.1	99.5	130.5	120.1	88.9	119.1	109.0	88.6	130.5	116.5	101.4	130.5	120.8
0960	Flooring	100.0	172.3	121.6	98.5	172.3	120.6	97.7	172.3	120.0	97.8	150.6	113.6	98.0	172.3	120.2	99.3	172.3	121.1
0970, 0990	Wall Finishes & Painting/Coating	93.0	119.3	108.8	96.0	119.3	110.0	94.6	119.3	109.4	93.0	117.3	107.6	94.6	119.3	109.4	98.3	117.3	109.7
09	FINISHES	99.7	135.4	119.6	98.6	135.5	119.1	100.0	135.5	119.8	98.5	125.9	113.7	98.0	135.5	118.9	100.1	136.0	120.1
COVERS	DIVS. 10 - 14, 25, 28, 41, 43, 44, 46	100.0	113.4	102.7	100.0	113.6	102.7	100.0	113.6	102.7	100.0	104.2	100.8	100.0	113.6	102.7	100.0	110.4	102.1
21, 22, 23	FIRE SUPPRESSION, PLUMBING & HVAC	99.6	122.9	109.1	100.0	122.8	109.1	100.0	123.4	109.4	99.6	122.5	108.7	99.6	122.8	108.9	100.0	122.5	109.0
26, 27, 3370	ELECTRICAL, COMMUNICATIONS & UTIL.	93.4	137.6	116.5	99.2	139.7	120.3	95.5	137.6	117.5	92.7	131.5	112.9	91.5	137.6	115.6	101.4	138.7	120.8
MF2010	WEIGHTED AVERAGE	99.7	125.2	110.8	101.9	125.6	112.2	100.2	125.2	111.1	99.2	121.4	108.8	98.7	125.3	110.3	100.8	124.0	110.9

DIVISION		NEW JERSEY VINELAND 080,083			NEW MEXICO ALBUQUERQUE 870 - 872			CARRIZOZO 883			CLOVIS 881			FARMINGTON 874			GALLUP 873		
		MAT.	INST.	TOTAL	MAT.	INST.	TOTAL	MAT.	INST.	TOTAL	MAT.	INST.	TOTAL	MAT.	INST.	TOTAL	MAT.	INST.	TOTAL
015433	CONTRACTOR EQUIPMENT		98.8	98.8		109.6	109.6		109.6	109.6		109.6	109.6		109.6	109.6		109.6	109.6
0241, 31 - 34	SITE & INFRASTRUCTURE, DEMOLITION	102.7	104.7	104.1	82.2	104.1	97.6	102.9	104.1	103.7	91.2	104.1	100.2	88.4	104.1	99.4	96.0	104.1	101.7
0310	Concrete Forming & Accessories	96.8	128.4	124.1	101.4	65.0	70.0	99.2	65.0	69.7	99.1	64.9	69.6	101.4	65.0	70.0	101.5	65.0	70.0
0320	Concrete Reinforcing	79.1	118.5	98.7	100.5	71.1	85.8	109.9	71.1	90.5	111.2	71.1	91.2	109.9	71.1	90.5	105.2	71.1	88.2
0330	Cast-in-Place Concrete	90.7	132.2	107.9	96.9	71.2	86.2	95.4	71.2	85.3	95.3	71.1	85.3	97.8	71.2	86.8	92.1	71.2	83.4
03	CONCRETE	97.6	126.7	111.9	101.9	69.4	85.9	119.1	69.4	94.6	107.6	69.3	88.7	105.7	69.4	87.8	112.5	69.4	91.2
04	MASONRY	87.9	125.4	111.1	99.5	60.6	75.4	101.6	60.6	76.2	101.7	60.6	76.2	106.3	60.6	78.0	95.4	60.6	73.8
05	METALS	95.6	106.0	98.8	103.8	87.9	98.9	98.4	87.9	95.2	98.1	87.8	94.9	101.4	87.9	97.2	100.6	87.9	96.6
06	WOOD, PLASTICS & COMPOSITES	98.5	130.2	116.4	92.8	65.5	77.4	88.9	65.5	75.7	88.9	65.5	75.7	92.9	65.5	77.4	92.9	65.5	77.4
07	THERMAL & MOISTURE PROTECTION	104.4	123.2	112.1	99.4	71.8	88.2	100.7	71.8	89.0	99.6	71.8	88.3	99.6	71.8	88.3	100.5	71.8	88.8
08	OPENINGS	98.6	125.0	104.9	101.4	68.5	93.6	98.6	68.5	91.5	98.8	68.5	91.6	104.0	68.5	95.6	104.1	68.5	95.7
0920	Plaster & Gypsum Board	98.0	130.5	120.1	88.3	64.1	71.8	75.4	64.1	67.7	75.4	64.1	67.7	81.6	64.1	69.7	81.6	64.1	69.7
0950, 0980	Ceilings & Acoustic Treatment	88.9	130.5	116.6	106.3	64.1	78.2	104.2	64.1	77.5	104.2	64.1	77.5	103.1	64.1	77.2	103.1	64.1	77.2
0960	Flooring	97.1	150.6	113.1	100.2	67.2	90.3	100.2	67.2	90.4	100.2	67.2	90.4	101.7	67.2	91.4	101.7	67.2	91.4
0970, 0990	Wall Finishes & Painting/Coating	93.0	117.3	107.6	109.1	68.1	84.4	102.9	68.1	82.0	102.9	68.1	82.0	102.9	68.1	82.0	102.9	68.1	82.0
09	FINISHES	97.2	132.5	116.8	98.3	65.5	80.0	99.0	65.5	80.3	97.6	65.5	79.7	96.9	65.5	79.4	98.1	65.5	79.9
COVERS	DIVS. 10 - 14, 25, 28, 41, 43, 44, 46	100.0	110.5	102.1	100.0	76.3	95.2	100.0	76.3	95.2	100.0	76.3	95.2	100.0	76.3	95.2	100.0	76.3	95.2
21, 22, 23	FIRE SUPPRESSION, PLUMBING & HVAC	99.6	119.6	107.6	100.2	70.7	88.4	97.2	70.7	86.6	97.2	70.5	86.5	100.1	70.7	88.3	97.1	70.7	86.6
26, 27, 3370	ELECTRICAL, COMMUNICATIONS & UTIL.	92.7	141.4	118.1	88.5	72.9	80.4	90.6	72.9	81.4	88.1	72.9	80.2	86.8	72.9	79.6	86.0	72.9	79.2
MF2010	WEIGHTED AVERAGE	97.5	123.4	108.8	99.2	73.6	88.0	100.1	73.6	88.5	98.1	73.5	87.4	99.7	73.6	88.3	99.3	73.6	88.1

NEW MEXICO

DIVISION		LAS CRUCES 880			LAS VEGAS 877			ROSWELL 882			SANTA FE 875			SOCORRO 878			TRUTH/CONSEQUENCES 879		
		MAT.	INST.	TOTAL	MAT.	INST.	TOTAL	MAT.	INST.	TOTAL	MAT.	INST.	TOTAL	MAT.	INST.	TOTAL	MAT.	INST.	TOTAL
015433	CONTRACTOR EQUIPMENT		86.0	86.0		109.6	109.6		109.6	109.6		109.6	109.6		109.6	109.6		86.1	86.1
0241, 31 - 34	SITE & INFRASTRUCTURE, DEMOLITION	91.6	83.8	86.1	87.8	104.1	99.2	93.3	104.1	100.9	92.9	104.1	100.7	84.3	104.1	98.2	101.9	83.8	89.2
0310	Concrete Forming & Accessories	95.6	63.8	68.2	101.4	65.0	70.0	99.2	65.0	69.7	100.1	65.0	69.8	101.5	65.0	70.0	98.7	63.8	68.6
0320	Concrete Reinforcing	107.3	71.0	89.1	106.9	71.1	89.0	111.2	71.1	91.2	106.0	71.1	88.6	109.1	71.1	90.1	102.8	71.0	86.9
0330	Cast-in-Place Concrete	89.9	63.7	79.0	95.2	71.2	85.2	95.3	71.2	85.3	103.2	71.2	89.9	93.2	71.2	84.1	102.1	63.7	86.1
03	CONCRETE	86.1	65.9	76.1	103.1	69.4	86.4	108.3	69.4	89.1	105.6	69.4	87.7	102.0	69.4	85.9	95.1	65.9	80.7
04	MASONRY	97.5	60.2	74.4	95.6	60.6	73.9	112.2	60.6	80.3	99.5	60.6	75.4	95.5	60.6	73.9	93.1	60.2	72.8
05	METALS	97.1	81.3	92.2	100.3	87.9	96.4	99.3	87.9	95.8	97.7	87.9	94.7	100.6	87.9	96.6	100.1	81.4	94.3
06	WOOD, PLASTICS & COMPOSITES	78.8	64.4	70.7	92.9	65.5	77.4	88.9	65.5	75.7	94.6	65.5	78.2	92.9	65.5	77.4	84.6	64.4	73.2
07	THERMAL & MOISTURE PROTECTION	86.2	67.2	78.5	99.2	71.8	88.1	99.7	71.8	88.4	101.7	71.8	89.5	99.1	71.8	88.0	86.9	67.2	78.9
08	OPENINGS	91.5	67.9	85.9	100.3	68.5	92.8	98.6	68.5	91.5	102.4	68.5	94.4	100.1	68.5	92.7	93.3	67.9	87.3
0920	Plaster & Gypsum Board	74.2	64.1	67.3	81.6	64.1	69.7	75.4	64.1	67.7	91.6	64.1	72.9	81.6	64.1	69.7	83.4	64.1	70.3
0950, 0980	Ceilings & Acoustic Treatment	91.4	64.1	73.2	103.1	64.1	77.2	104.2	64.1	77.5	103.6	64.1	77.3	103.1	64.1	77.2	90.4	64.1	72.9
0960	Flooring	129.3	67.2	110.7	101.7	67.2	91.4	100.2	67.2	90.4	108.8	67.2	96.4	101.7	67.2	91.4	132.2	67.2	112.7
0970, 0990	Wall Finishes & Painting/Coating	90.1	68.1	76.8	102.9	68.1	82.0	102.9	68.1	82.0	107.7	68.1	83.9	102.9	68.1	82.0	93.7	68.1	78.3
09	FINISHES	107.1	64.6	83.4	96.8	65.5	79.3	97.7	65.5	79.8	101.9	65.5	81.6	96.7	65.5	79.3	109.0	64.6	84.3
COVERS	DIVS. 10 - 14, 25, 28, 41, 43, 44, 46	100.0	73.6	94.7	100.0	76.3	95.2	100.0	76.3	95.2	100.0	76.3	95.2	100.0	76.3	95.2	100.0	73.6	94.7
21, 22, 23	FIRE SUPPRESSION, PLUMBING & HVAC	100.4	70.5	88.4	97.1	70.7	86.6	100.0	70.7	88.3	100.1	70.7	88.3	97.1	70.7	86.6	97.0	70.5	86.4
26, 27, 3370	ELECTRICAL, COMMUNICATIONS & UTIL.	89.9	72.9	81.0	88.5	72.9	80.4	89.6	72.9	80.9	100.8	72.9	86.3	86.5	72.9	79.4	90.1	72.9	81.1
MF2010	WEIGHTED AVERAGE	95.8	70.4	84.7	97.7	73.6	87.2	99.8	73.6	88.4	100.5	73.6	88.8	97.3	73.6	87.0	97.0	70.4	85.4

City Cost Indexes

Table 1

DIVISION		NEW MEXICO TUCUMCARI 884			NEW YORK ALBANY 120 - 122			NEW YORK BINGHAMTON 137 - 139			NEW YORK BRONX 104			NEW YORK BROOKLYN 112			NEW YORK BUFFALO 140 - 142		
		MAT.	INST.	TOTAL	MAT.	INST.	TOTAL	MAT.	INST.	TOTAL	MAT.	INST.	TOTAL	MAT.	INST.	TOTAL	MAT.	INST.	TOTAL
015433	CONTRACTOR EQUIPMENT		109.6	109.6		113.5	113.5		114.4	114.4		112.8	112.8		114.1	114.1		97.0	97.0
0241, 31 - 34	SITE & INFRASTRUCTURE, DEMOLITION	90.8	104.1	100.1	75.0	107.1	97.5	92.8	94.3	93.9	110.9	123.1	119.5	117.0	128.4	125.0	98.8	98.3	98.4
0310	Concrete Forming & Accessories	99.1	64.9	69.6	100.7	96.1	96.7	102.2	83.3	85.9	103.3	171.7	162.3	108.6	171.2	162.6	97.4	115.5	113.1
0320	Concrete Reinforcing	109.0	71.1	90.1	105.6	106.3	106.0	93.5	96.4	94.9	96.7	184.6	140.6	94.9	184.6	139.7	102.1	103.0	102.5
0330	Cast-in-Place Concrete	95.3	71.1	85.3	88.1	100.9	93.4	100.9	127.9	112.1	94.6	173.8	127.5	103.0	172.0	131.7	105.5	119.2	111.2
03	CONCRETE	106.7	69.3	88.3	101.0	100.3	100.6	96.2	102.7	99.4	96.5	173.2	134.4	108.3	172.0	139.7	104.6	113.7	109.1
04	MASONRY	112.9	60.6	80.5	90.9	100.3	96.7	105.8	126.6	118.7	94.3	176.4	145.1	116.4	176.4	153.5	107.3	119.6	114.9
05	METALS	98.1	87.8	94.9	101.3	109.5	103.9	96.0	118.2	102.9	100.8	149.3	115.8	104.4	140.3	115.4	99.5	95.6	98.3
06	WOOD, PLASTICS & COMPOSITES	88.9	65.5	75.7	97.7	93.6	95.4	107.3	79.3	91.5	100.1	171.4	140.4	109.3	171.1	144.1	98.7	115.2	108.0
07	THERMAL & MOISTURE PROTECTION	99.5	71.8	88.3	99.4	96.7	98.3	106.9	96.3	102.6	108.5	163.2	130.7	108.9	162.7	130.8	101.5	110.4	105.1
08	OPENINGS	98.5	68.5	91.4	99.9	92.0	98.0	90.7	81.6	88.5	87.0	172.2	107.1	88.0	166.5	106.6	91.8	103.3	94.6
0920	Plaster & Gypsum Board	75.4	64.1	67.7	105.0	93.1	96.9	111.6	78.2	88.9	105.4	173.3	151.6	106.9	173.3	152.1	103.2	115.4	111.5
0950, 0980	Ceilings & Acoustic Treatment	104.2	64.1	77.5	95.9	93.1	94.0	94.6	78.2	83.7	82.8	173.3	143.0	90.2	173.3	145.5	101.6	115.4	110.8
0960	Flooring	100.2	67.2	90.4	97.0	105.2	99.4	106.2	93.1	102.3	96.6	185.6	123.2	113.2	185.6	134.8	101.0	120.1	106.7
0970, 0990	Wall Finishes & Painting/Coating	102.9	68.1	82.0	96.8	89.4	92.4	93.3	95.3	94.5	97.9	148.0	128.0	124.2	148.0	138.5	102.4	112.5	108.5
09	FINISHES	97.6	65.5	79.7	97.8	96.7	97.2	96.7	84.9	90.1	95.3	172.0	138.1	111.3	171.8	145.0	101.0	116.9	109.9
COVERS	DIVS. 10 - 14, 25, 28, 41, 43, 44, 46	100.0	76.3	95.2	100.0	96.0	99.2	100.0	93.5	98.7	100.0	132.7	106.6	100.0	132.0	106.4	100.0	106.1	101.2
21, 22, 23	FIRE SUPPRESSION, PLUMBING & HVAC	97.2	70.5	86.5	100.0	98.8	99.5	100.4	87.3	95.1	100.2	164.7	126.1	99.8	164.4	125.7	100.0	97.1	98.8
26, 27, 3370	ELECTRICAL, COMMUNICATIONS & UTIL.	90.6	72.9	81.4	96.0	99.3	97.7	98.9	107.9	103.6	96.1	175.0	137.3	98.7	175.0	138.5	97.5	101.9	99.8
MF2010	WEIGHTED AVERAGE	98.8	73.5	87.8	98.6	100.2	99.3	98.1	99.4	98.6	98.0	163.9	126.7	102.6	162.9	128.9	99.7	105.8	102.4

Table 2 — NEW YORK

DIVISION		ELMIRA 148 - 149			FAR ROCKAWAY 116			FLUSHING 113			GLENS FALLS 128			HICKSVILLE 115,117,118			JAMAICA 114		
		MAT.	INST.	TOTAL	MAT.	INST.	TOTAL	MAT.	INST.	TOTAL	MAT.	INST.	TOTAL	MAT.	INST.	TOTAL	MAT.	INST.	TOTAL
015433	CONTRACTOR EQUIPMENT		116.0	116.0		114.1	114.1		114.1	114.1		113.5	113.5		114.1	114.1		114.1	114.1
0241, 31 - 34	SITE & INFRASTRUCTURE, DEMOLITION	93.3	94.3	94.0	120.2	128.4	125.9	120.2	128.4	126.0	65.2	106.7	94.3	110.1	127.3	122.2	114.5	128.4	124.3
0310	Concrete Forming & Accessories	83.9	86.3	86.0	94.9	171.2	160.8	98.7	171.2	161.3	87.1	86.9	86.9	91.5	144.5	137.3	98.7	171.2	161.3
0320	Concrete Reinforcing	100.5	90.6	95.6	94.9	184.6	139.7	96.5	184.6	140.5	97.0	94.1	95.5	94.9	184.4	139.6	94.9	184.6	139.7
0330	Cast-in-Place Concrete	94.7	96.4	95.4	111.4	172.0	136.6	111.4	172.0	136.6	81.7	96.9	88.0	94.7	165.6	124.1	103.0	172.0	131.7
03	CONCRETE	95.0	92.3	93.7	114.3	172.0	142.8	114.9	172.0	143.1	89.9	92.6	91.3	100.1	157.8	128.6	107.6	172.0	139.4
04	MASONRY	101.4	93.7	96.6	119.7	176.4	154.8	113.9	176.4	152.6	90.1	93.2	92.0	110.5	166.0	144.9	118.1	176.4	154.2
05	METALS	95.4	114.7	101.3	104.4	140.3	115.5	104.4	140.3	115.5	94.8	105.1	98.0	105.9	138.2	115.8	104.4	140.3	115.5
06	WOOD, PLASTICS & COMPOSITES	86.3	84.9	85.5	92.2	171.1	136.7	97.1	171.1	138.8	86.1	84.9	85.4	88.7	141.5	118.5	97.1	171.1	138.8
07	THERMAL & MOISTURE PROTECTION	102.2	84.1	94.8	108.8	162.7	130.7	108.9	162.7	130.7	93.0	92.8	92.9	108.5	154.3	127.1	108.7	162.7	130.6
08	OPENINGS	92.4	83.8	90.3	86.7	166.5	105.6	86.7	166.5	105.6	91.3	84.5	89.7	86.7	150.3	101.8	86.7	166.5	105.6
0920	Plaster & Gypsum Board	100.2	84.2	89.3	95.1	173.3	148.3	97.8	173.3	149.1	95.2	84.2	87.7	94.8	142.7	127.4	97.8	173.3	149.1
0950, 0980	Ceilings & Acoustic Treatment	93.4	84.2	87.2	78.7	173.3	141.6	78.7	173.3	141.6	85.9	84.2	84.8	77.7	142.7	121.0	78.7	173.3	141.6
0960	Flooring	92.9	93.1	93.0	108.5	185.6	131.6	110.0	185.6	132.6	86.1	105.2	91.8	107.6	145.3	118.9	110.0	185.6	132.6
0970, 0990	Wall Finishes & Painting/Coating	101.7	87.6	93.2	124.2	148.0	138.5	124.2	148.0	138.5	94.1	89.3	91.2	124.2	148.0	138.5	124.2	148.0	138.5
09	FINISHES	96.1	87.4	91.3	106.4	171.8	142.8	107.1	171.8	143.1	89.1	89.8	89.5	104.9	143.7	126.5	106.6	171.8	142.9
COVERS	DIVS. 10 - 14, 25, 28, 41, 43, 44, 46	100.0	93.4	98.7	100.0	132.0	106.4	100.0	132.0	106.4	100.0	92.7	98.5	100.0	125.1	105.0	100.0	132.0	106.4
21, 22, 23	FIRE SUPPRESSION, PLUMBING & HVAC	95.3	87.8	92.3	94.9	164.4	122.8	94.9	164.4	122.8	95.4	92.0	94.0	99.8	151.8	120.6	94.9	164.4	122.8
26, 27, 3370	ELECTRICAL, COMMUNICATIONS & UTIL.	95.5	96.9	96.2	106.1	175.0	142.1	106.1	175.0	142.1	91.1	99.3	95.4	98.0	135.8	117.7	96.9	175.0	137.7
MF2010	WEIGHTED AVERAGE	95.9	93.1	94.7	102.4	162.9	128.7	102.3	162.9	128.7	92.6	95.0	93.6	100.7	146.6	120.7	100.6	162.9	127.7

Table 3 — NEW YORK

DIVISION		JAMESTOWN 147			KINGSTON 124			LONG ISLAND CITY 111			MONTICELLO 127			MOUNT VERNON 105			NEW ROCHELLE 108		
		MAT.	INST.	TOTAL	MAT.	INST.	TOTAL	MAT.	INST.	TOTAL	MAT.	INST.	TOTAL	MAT.	INST.	TOTAL	MAT.	INST.	TOTAL
015433	CONTRACTOR EQUIPMENT		94.0	94.0		114.1	114.1		114.1	114.1		114.1	114.1		112.8	112.8		112.8	112.8
0241, 31 - 34	SITE & INFRASTRUCTURE, DEMOLITION	94.5	93.8	94.0	122.1	124.3	123.7	118.1	128.4	125.3	117.5	124.2	122.2	117.9	118.8	118.6	117.1	118.8	118.3
0310	Concrete Forming & Accessories	83.9	81.2	81.6	88.7	106.0	103.6	103.1	171.2	161.9	95.7	105.0	103.7	93.5	128.5	123.7	108.6	128.5	125.8
0320	Concrete Reinforcing	100.7	98.6	99.6	97.4	140.6	119.0	94.9	184.6	139.7	96.6	140.4	118.5	95.2	183.2	139.2	95.3	183.2	139.2
0330	Cast-in-Place Concrete	98.3	91.3	95.4	110.4	131.3	119.1	106.3	172.0	133.6	103.4	126.8	113.1	105.7	128.9	115.3	105.7	128.9	115.3
03	CONCRETE	98.0	88.0	93.0	112.5	120.8	116.6	110.7	172.0	140.9	107.2	118.8	112.9	105.9	137.8	121.6	105.4	137.8	121.4
04	MASONRY	109.1	91.1	98.0	104.0	136.8	124.3	113.3	176.4	152.3	98.0	131.0	118.4	100.0	126.1	116.2	100.0	126.1	116.2
05	METALS	92.7	90.9	92.2	103.3	116.5	107.4	104.4	140.3	115.4	103.3	116.1	107.2	100.6	134.6	111.1	100.9	134.6	111.3
06	WOOD, PLASTICS & COMPOSITES	84.8	78.6	81.3	87.3	98.6	93.7	103.3	171.1	141.5	95.2	98.6	97.1	89.3	131.7	113.2	107.6	131.7	121.2
07	THERMAL & MOISTURE PROTECTION	101.6	84.0	94.5	114.3	136.3	123.3	108.8	162.7	130.7	114.0	134.0	122.1	109.4	135.8	120.1	109.4	135.8	120.2
08	OPENINGS	92.2	82.5	89.9	92.8	117.5	98.7	86.7	166.5	105.6	88.5	117.5	95.4	87.0	145.0	100.7	87.0	145.0	100.7
0920	Plaster & Gypsum Board	93.2	77.7	82.6	97.2	98.6	98.1	102.6	173.3	150.7	99.5	98.6	98.9	100.1	132.3	122.0	112.8	132.3	126.1
0950, 0980	Ceilings & Acoustic Treatment	90.7	77.7	82.0	74.3	98.6	90.5	78.7	173.3	141.6	74.3	98.6	90.5	81.1	132.3	115.2	81.1	132.3	115.2
0960	Flooring	95.9	89.7	94.1	103.1	73.8	94.4	111.4	185.6	133.6	105.4	73.8	95.9	89.0	180.7	116.4	95.2	180.7	120.8
0970, 0990	Wall Finishes & Painting/Coating	103.0	91.3	96.0	125.9	113.8	121.3	124.2	148.0	138.5	125.9	113.8	118.6	96.1	148.0	127.3	96.1	148.0	127.3
09	FINISHES	95.6	83.0	88.6	103.7	98.4	100.7	107.9	171.8	143.5	104.2	97.8	100.7	92.8	139.7	118.9	96.0	139.7	120.3
COVERS	DIVS. 10 - 14, 25, 28, 41, 43, 44, 46	100.0	94.8	99.0	100.0	109.7	101.9	100.0	132.0	106.4	100.0	108.9	101.8	100.0	117.8	103.6	100.0	117.8	103.6
21, 22, 23	FIRE SUPPRESSION, PLUMBING & HVAC	95.2	84.6	91.0	95.3	121.1	105.6	99.8	164.4	125.7	95.3	117.9	104.4	95.4	118.6	104.7	95.4	118.6	104.7
26, 27, 3370	ELECTRICAL, COMMUNICATIONS & UTIL.	94.3	90.4	92.3	92.7	113.7	103.6	97.5	175.0	137.9	92.7	113.7	103.6	94.4	158.9	128.1	94.4	158.9	128.1
MF2010	WEIGHTED AVERAGE	96.0	87.8	92.4	100.7	118.3	108.4	102.2	162.9	128.6	99.4	116.5	106.8	97.9	133.3	113.3	98.2	133.3	113.5

City Cost Indexes

		NEW YORK																
DIVISION		NEW YORK			NIAGARA FALLS			PLATTSBURGH			POUGHKEEPSIE			QUEENS			RIVERHEAD		
		100 - 102			143			129			125 - 126			110			119		
		MAT.	INST.	TOTAL	MAT.	INST.	TOTAL	MAT.	INST.	TOTAL	MAT.	INST.	TOTAL	MAT.	INST.	TOTAL	MAT.	INST.	TOTAL
015433	CONTRACTOR EQUIPMENT		113.2	113.2		94.0	94.0		99.2	99.2		114.1	114.1		114.1	114.1		114.1	114.1
0241, 31 - 34	SITE & INFRASTRUCTURE, DEMOLITION	119.6	123.8	122.5	96.6	95.4	95.8	89.9	102.7	98.9	118.3	124.0	122.3	113.4	128.4	123.9	111.3	127.3	122.5
0310	Concrete Forming & Accessories	107.7	179.3	169.5	83.9	113.2	109.2	91.9	83.8	84.9	88.7	148.2	140.0	91.7	171.2	160.3	96.0	144.5	137.9
0320	Concrete Reinforcing	102.4	184.7	143.5	99.3	99.3	99.3	101.3	93.6	97.5	97.4	140.9	119.1	96.5	184.6	140.5	96.7	184.4	140.5
0330	Cast-in-Place Concrete	106.4	179.2	136.7	101.6	118.7	108.7	100.1	92.7	97.0	106.9	127.3	115.4	97.9	172.0	128.7	96.3	165.6	125.0
03	CONCRETE	106.7	178.5	142.1	100.2	111.7	105.9	104.1	88.4	96.3	109.6	138.2	123.7	103.3	172.0	137.2	100.8	157.8	128.9
04	MASONRY	104.1	178.4	150.0	117.3	118.8	118.2	85.9	87.3	86.8	97.8	128.1	116.6	107.8	176.4	150.2	115.8	166.0	146.9
05	METALS	114.1	149.5	125.0	95.4	92.3	94.5	99.2	85.5	95.0	103.3	118.5	108.0	104.4	140.3	115.4	106.3	138.2	116.1
06	WOOD, PLASTICS & COMPOSITES	104.6	180.6	147.5	84.7	110.9	99.5	94.1	81.9	87.2	87.3	158.2	127.3	88.8	171.1	135.3	94.0	141.5	120.8
07	THERMAL & MOISTURE PROTECTION	108.5	165.3	131.5	101.7	108.0	104.3	108.4	89.8	100.9	114.3	138.8	124.2	108.5	162.7	130.5	109.2	154.3	127.5
08	OPENINGS	92.6	177.5	112.7	92.2	100.2	94.1	98.8	80.1	94.4	92.8	149.1	106.2	86.7	166.5	105.6	86.7	150.3	101.8
0920	Plaster & Gypsum Board	112.2	182.7	160.2	93.2	111.0	105.3	119.4	80.6	93.0	97.2	160.0	139.9	94.8	173.3	148.2	96.1	142.7	127.8
0950, 0980	Ceilings & Acoustic Treatment	101.5	182.7	155.5	90.7	111.0	104.2	100.8	80.6	87.4	74.3	160.0	131.3	78.7	173.3	141.6	78.5	142.7	121.3
0960	Flooring	97.6	185.6	123.9	95.9	113.8	101.3	109.9	105.2	108.5	103.1	148.0	116.6	105.8	185.6	130.9	108.5	145.3	119.5
0970, 0990	Wall Finishes & Painting/Coating	97.9	156.4	133.1	103.0	109.7	107.0	123.3	76.4	95.1	125.9	113.8	118.6	124.2	148.0	138.5	124.2	148.0	138.5
09	FINISHES	101.2	178.9	144.5	95.7	113.6	105.7	100.9	86.4	92.9	103.5	146.3	127.3	105.3	171.8	142.3	105.5	143.7	126.8
COVERS	DIVS. 10 - 14, 25, 28, 41, 43, 44, 46	100.0	137.1	107.4	100.0	104.7	100.9	100.0	48.9	89.8	100.0	113.3	102.7	100.0	132.0	106.4	100.0	125.1	105.0
21, 22, 23	FIRE SUPPRESSION, PLUMBING & HVAC	100.1	165.7	126.4	95.2	97.1	95.9	95.3	92.0	94.0	95.3	117.9	104.4	99.8	164.4	125.7	100.0	151.8	120.7
26, 27, 3370	ELECTRICAL, COMMUNICATIONS & UTIL.	104.2	175.0	141.1	92.9	99.3	96.3	89.2	90.4	89.8	92.7	113.7	103.6	98.0	175.0	138.2	99.7	135.8	118.5
MF2010	WEIGHTED AVERAGE	103.8	166.4	131.1	96.9	103.9	100.0	97.3	88.4	93.4	100.0	127.5	112.0	100.8	162.9	127.8	101.4	146.6	121.1

		NEW YORK																
DIVISION		ROCHESTER			SCHENECTADY			STATEN ISLAND			SUFFERN			SYRACUSE			UTICA		
		144 - 146			123			103			109			130 - 132			133 - 135		
		MAT.	INST.	TOTAL	MAT.	INST.	TOTAL	MAT.	INST.	TOTAL	MAT.	INST.	TOTAL	MAT.	INST.	TOTAL	MAT.	INST.	TOTAL
015433	CONTRACTOR EQUIPMENT		116.4	116.4		113.5	113.5		112.8	112.8		112.8	112.8		113.5	113.5		113.5	113.5
0241, 31 - 34	SITE & INFRASTRUCTURE, DEMOLITION	77.8	109.6	100.2	74.9	107.1	97.5	122.7	123.1	123.0	113.8	119.1	117.5	91.8	106.6	102.2	70.8	104.5	94.4
0310	Concrete Forming & Accessories	104.8	92.4	94.1	103.1	96.1	97.1	93.0	171.7	160.9	102.1	131.2	127.2	101.1	91.2	92.5	102.4	82.2	85.0
0320	Concrete Reinforcing	101.9	90.7	96.3	96.0	106.3	101.2	96.7	184.6	140.6	95.3	140.9	118.1	94.4	94.8	94.6	94.4	91.9	93.2
0330	Cast-in-Place Concrete	97.6	98.9	98.1	98.6	100.9	99.5	105.7	173.8	134.0	102.5	134.8	115.9	93.8	105.4	98.6	85.8	98.3	91.0
03	CONCRETE	107.3	95.2	101.3	104.5	100.3	102.4	107.6	173.2	140.0	102.4	133.3	117.6	99.5	97.5	98.6	97.8	90.6	94.2
04	MASONRY	100.2	98.6	99.2	88.1	100.3	95.7	106.7	176.4	149.8	99.4	138.2	123.4	98.1	106.3	103.2	90.0	97.7	94.8
05	METALS	101.4	104.5	102.3	98.8	109.5	102.1	98.7	149.3	114.3	98.7	118.1	104.7	99.5	105.0	101.2	97.5	103.8	99.5
06	WOOD, PLASTICS & COMPOSITES	103.8	90.6	96.4	106.0	93.6	99.0	87.8	171.4	135.0	99.7	131.7	117.7	103.7	87.6	94.6	103.7	79.4	90.0
07	THERMAL & MOISTURE PROTECTION	100.5	98.0	99.5	94.2	96.7	95.3	108.8	163.2	130.9	109.3	140.9	122.1	102.5	97.9	100.6	90.9	94.4	92.3
08	OPENINGS	96.7	86.9	94.4	96.9	92.0	95.7	87.0	172.2	107.1	87.0	135.5	98.5	92.5	80.4	89.6	95.2	79.2	91.4
0920	Plaster & Gypsum Board	111.1	90.3	96.9	106.6	93.1	97.4	100.2	173.3	149.9	104.6	132.3	123.5	101.9	89.0	91.7	101.9	78.6	86.0
0950, 0980	Ceilings & Acoustic Treatment	99.4	90.3	93.3	92.0	93.1	92.8	82.8	173.3	143.0	81.1	132.3	115.2	94.6	87.0	89.5	94.6	78.6	83.9
0960	Flooring	92.3	104.9	96.1	92.6	105.2	96.3	92.9	185.6	120.6	92.0	145.3	107.9	93.6	94.9	94.0	90.9	95.0	92.1
0970, 0990	Wall Finishes & Painting/Coating	102.9	97.4	99.6	94.1	89.4	91.3	97.9	148.0	128.0	96.1	121.7	111.5	98.3	97.0	97.5	90.8	97.0	94.5
09	FINISHES	103.1	95.2	98.7	94.5	96.7	95.8	94.7	172.0	137.8	93.8	130.2	114.1	96.0	92.1	93.8	94.1	85.4	89.2
COVERS	DIVS. 10 - 14, 25, 28, 41, 43, 44, 46	100.0	97.0	99.4	100.0	96.0	99.2	100.0	132.7	106.6	100.0	121.8	104.4	100.0	96.3	99.3	100.0	91.9	98.4
21, 22, 23	FIRE SUPPRESSION, PLUMBING & HVAC	100.0	87.9	95.1	100.2	98.8	99.6	100.2	164.7	126.1	95.4	119.6	105.1	100.2	91.2	96.6	100.2	88.8	95.6
26, 27, 3370	ELECTRICAL, COMMUNICATIONS & UTIL.	99.2	94.3	96.7	95.5	99.3	97.5	96.1	175.0	137.3	102.3	121.5	112.3	99.1	97.7	98.4	97.3	97.7	97.5
MF2010	WEIGHTED AVERAGE	100.3	95.6	98.3	97.8	100.2	98.8	99.7	163.9	127.6	98.0	126.2	110.3	98.5	97.0	97.9	96.7	93.2	95.1

		NEW YORK									NORTH CAROLINA								
DIVISION		WATERTOWN			WHITE PLAINS			YONKERS			ASHEVILLE			CHARLOTTE			DURHAM		
		136			106			107			287 - 288			281 - 282			277		
		MAT.	INST.	TOTAL	MAT.	INST.	TOTAL	MAT.	INST.	TOTAL	MAT.	INST.	TOTAL	MAT.	INST.	TOTAL	MAT.	INST.	TOTAL
015433	CONTRACTOR EQUIPMENT		113.5	113.5		112.8	112.8		112.8	112.8		95.6	95.6		95.6	95.6		100.8	100.8
0241, 31 - 34	SITE & INFRASTRUCTURE, DEMOLITION	78.1	106.1	97.8	110.6	118.8	116.4	119.1	118.8	118.9	102.4	76.6	84.3	106.0	76.7	85.4	102.6	85.3	90.4
0310	Concrete Forming & Accessories	87.5	87.4	87.4	107.1	128.5	125.6	107.4	128.5	125.7	95.4	42.1	49.4	98.6	43.7	51.2	100.0	45.1	52.7
0320	Concrete Reinforcing	95.0	94.8	94.9	95.3	183.2	139.2	99.1	183.2	141.1	94.4	63.0	78.7	100.3	58.3	79.3	94.8	57.6	76.2
0330	Cast-in-Place Concrete	99.8	91.8	96.5	93.8	128.9	108.4	105.0	128.9	114.9	110.7	51.9	86.3	115.3	50.4	88.4	104.1	47.6	80.7
03	CONCRETE	110.2	91.2	100.8	96.1	137.8	116.7	105.6	137.9	121.5	102.3	51.2	77.1	104.9	50.5	78.1	98.8	50.1	74.8
04	MASONRY	91.0	100.2	96.7	98.9	126.1	115.7	103.6	126.1	117.5	81.7	44.5	58.7	88.9	52.1	66.1	85.5	38.6	56.4
05	METALS	97.6	104.8	99.8	100.3	134.6	110.9	109.9	134.6	117.5	94.2	82.7	90.7	95.0	81.3	90.8	108.6	80.2	99.9
06	WOOD, PLASTICS & COMPOSITES	85.0	86.3	85.8	105.6	131.7	120.3	105.4	131.7	120.3	96.4	41.2	65.2	101.6	42.8	68.4	99.5	45.7	69.1
07	THERMAL & MOISTURE PROTECTION	91.2	94.9	92.7	109.2	135.8	120.0	109.5	135.8	120.2	103.8	44.5	79.7	98.5	47.5	77.8	106.6	46.6	82.2
08	OPENINGS	95.2	83.2	92.4	87.0	145.0	100.7	90.0	145.3	103.1	94.7	44.6	82.9	99.9	45.5	87.1	97.8	47.7	85.9
0920	Plaster & Gypsum Board	92.2	85.7	87.7	107.6	132.3	124.4	111.8	132.3	125.8	97.5	39.6	57.8	97.8	40.9	59.1	108.8	43.8	64.6
0950, 0980	Ceilings & Acoustic Treatment	94.6	85.7	88.6	81.1	132.3	115.2	99.7	132.3	121.4	91.6	39.2	56.7	96.0	40.9	59.3	95.1	43.8	61.0
0960	Flooring	84.8	95.0	87.9	93.8	180.7	119.8	93.4	180.7	119.5	101.5	43.5	84.1	101.1	44.2	84.1	106.2	43.5	87.4
0970, 0990	Wall Finishes & Painting/Coating	90.8	91.4	91.2	96.1	148.0	127.3	96.1	148.0	127.3	107.1	41.1	67.4	107.3	50.4	73.1	103.4	38.2	64.2
09	FINISHES	91.7	88.8	90.1	94.3	139.7	119.5	99.4	139.7	121.8	96.8	41.5	66.0	97.0	43.8	67.4	100.2	43.8	68.8
COVERS	DIVS. 10 - 14, 25, 28, 41, 43, 44, 46	100.0	93.8	98.8	100.0	117.8	103.6	100.0	120.5	104.1	100.0	78.2	95.6	100.0	78.6	95.7	100.0	73.8	94.8
21, 22, 23	FIRE SUPPRESSION, PLUMBING & HVAC	100.2	81.5	92.7	100.4	118.6	107.7	100.4	118.6	107.7	100.4	53.5	81.6	100.0	55.3	82.1	100.3	53.1	81.4
26, 27, 3370	ELECTRICAL, COMMUNICATIONS & UTIL.	99.1	90.5	94.6	94.4	158.9	128.1	102.4	158.9	131.9	96.8	57.0	76.0	95.7	59.9	77.1	94.4	45.6	68.9
MF2010	WEIGHTED AVERAGE	98.1	91.9	95.4	98.0	133.3	113.4	102.5	133.4	116.0	97.6	55.9	79.4	98.7	57.6	80.8	100.2	54.4	80.2

City Cost Indexes

NORTH CAROLINA

DIVISION		ELIZABETH CITY 279			FAYETTEVILLE 283			GASTONIA 280			GREENSBORO 270,272-274			HICKORY 286			KINSTON 285		
		MAT.	INST.	TOTAL	MAT.	INST.	TOTAL	MAT.	INST.	TOTAL	MAT.	INST.	TOTAL	MAT.	INST.	TOTAL	MAT.	INST.	TOTAL
015433	CONTRACTOR EQUIPMENT		105.0	105.0		100.8	100.8		95.6	95.6		100.8	100.8		100.8	100.8		100.8	100.8
0241, 31 - 34	SITE & INFRASTRUCTURE, DEMOLITION	107.1	87.0	93.0	101.6	85.2	90.1	102.2	76.6	84.3	102.5	85.3	90.4	101.3	85.1	90.0	100.4	85.2	89.7
0310	Concrete Forming & Accessories	85.5	43.0	49.1	95.0	60.4	65.1	101.9	39.5	48.0	99.7	45.4	52.8	91.6	37.9	45.2	87.9	43.0	49.2
0320	Concrete Reinforcing	92.8	47.3	70.1	98.0	57.7	77.9	94.8	58.3	76.6	93.7	57.8	75.8	94.4	57.9	76.1	93.9	47.2	70.6
0330	Cast-in-Place Concrete	104.3	47.4	80.7	116.1	48.9	88.2	108.2	53.4	85.5	103.4	48.2	80.5	110.7	48.7	84.9	106.9	45.4	81.3
03	CONCRETE	98.8	47.3	73.4	104.4	57.3	81.2	100.9	49.7	75.6	98.3	50.4	74.7	102.0	47.3	75.0	98.9	46.4	73.0
04	MASONRY	97.5	48.8	67.4	84.7	39.6	56.8	85.8	51.7	64.7	82.9	42.1	57.6	72.2	44.4	55.0	77.5	49.0	59.8
05	METALS	96.1	76.9	90.2	113.2	80.4	103.1	94.9	81.2	90.7	101.9	80.4	95.3	94.3	79.9	89.9	93.2	76.0	87.9
06	WOOD, PLASTICS & COMPOSITES	82.0	44.5	60.9	95.9	66.6	79.4	105.5	37.4	67.1	99.2	45.9	69.1	90.9	36.0	59.9	87.7	43.9	63.0
07	THERMAL & MOISTURE PROTECTION	105.9	44.1	80.8	103.7	46.6	80.5	104.0	46.0	80.5	106.3	43.7	80.9	104.1	42.5	79.1	103.9	43.7	79.5
08	OPENINGS	95.0	39.3	81.8	94.8	59.1	86.4	98.4	42.0	85.1	97.8	47.8	86.0	94.8	37.6	81.2	94.9	44.2	82.9
0920	Plaster & Gypsum Board	100.1	42.0	60.6	102.8	65.4	77.3	105.1	35.3	57.6	110.5	44.0	65.3	97.5	33.9	54.2	97.6	42.0	59.8
0950, 0980	Ceilings & Acoustic Treatment	95.1	42.0	59.7	92.5	65.4	74.5	95.2	35.3	55.3	95.1	44.0	61.1	91.6	33.9	53.2	95.2	42.0	59.8
0960	Flooring	98.3	23.6	76.0	101.7	43.5	84.3	104.8	43.5	86.5	106.2	40.4	86.5	101.4	33.5	81.1	98.7	23.0	76.1
0970, 0990	Wall Finishes & Painting/Coating	103.4	42.9	67.0	107.1	33.9	63.1	107.1	41.1	67.4	103.4	32.3	60.7	107.1	41.1	67.4	107.1	40.1	66.8
09	FINISHES	97.1	39.5	65.0	97.7	55.5	74.2	99.5	39.4	66.0	100.5	42.8	68.3	96.9	36.2	63.1	96.8	38.8	64.5
COVERS	DIVS. 10 - 14, 25, 28, 41, 43, 44, 46	100.0	72.2	94.4	100.0	76.0	95.2	100.0	77.9	95.6	100.0	77.8	95.6	100.0	77.6	95.5	100.0	73.4	94.7
21, 22, 23	FIRE SUPPRESSION, PLUMBING & HVAC	95.3	52.2	78.0	100.3	52.8	81.3	100.4	53.5	81.6	100.2	53.3	81.4	95.5	53.3	78.6	95.5	52.3	78.2
26, 27, 3370	ELECTRICAL, COMMUNICATIONS & UTIL.	94.1	35.3	63.4	95.6	51.9	72.8	96.2	58.7	76.6	93.4	57.0	74.4	94.2	58.7	75.7	94.0	47.2	69.6
MF2010	WEIGHTED AVERAGE	96.9	52.2	77.4	100.9	58.5	82.5	98.4	56.1	80.0	98.8	56.3	80.3	95.6	54.9	77.9	95.3	53.7	77.2

NORTH CAROLINA / NORTH DAKOTA

DIVISION		MURPHY 289			RALEIGH 275 - 276			ROCKY MOUNT 278			WILMINGTON 284			WINSTON-SALEM 271			BISMARCK 585		
		MAT.	INST.	TOTAL	MAT.	INST.	TOTAL	MAT.	INST.	TOTAL	MAT.	INST.	TOTAL	MAT.	INST.	TOTAL	MAT.	INST.	TOTAL
015433	CONTRACTOR EQUIPMENT		95.6	95.6		100.8	100.8		100.8	100.8		95.6	95.6		100.8	100.8		99.0	99.0
0241, 31 - 34	SITE & INFRASTRUCTURE, DEMOLITION	103.6	76.5	84.5	103.7	85.3	90.8	105.0	85.3	91.2	103.6	76.8	84.8	102.8	85.3	90.5	100.7	97.6	98.5
0310	Concrete Forming & Accessories	102.6	40.2	48.7	98.7	47.6	54.6	92.1	45.2	51.6	96.8	49.9	56.3	101.6	49.0	56.2	103.6	41.3	49.8
0320	Concrete Reinforcing	93.9	46.9	70.4	100.0	57.8	78.9	92.8	57.6	75.2	95.1	57.6	76.4	93.7	57.6	75.7	105.6	83.2	94.4
0330	Cast-in-Place Concrete	114.5	45.0	85.7	109.3	52.0	85.5	102.0	48.3	79.7	110.3	50.2	85.3	105.9	50.6	83.0	109.5	48.4	84.1
03	CONCRETE	105.3	45.0	75.5	102.0	52.8	77.7	99.5	50.3	75.2	102.2	53.1	77.9	99.6	52.8	76.5	103.6	53.0	78.6
04	MASONRY	74.5	41.9	54.4	88.1	42.9	60.2	76.2	40.2	53.9	72.4	42.4	53.9	83.0	39.3	56.0	110.9	57.4	77.8
05	METALS	92.1	75.3	87.0	94.8	80.4	90.4	95.3	79.6	90.5	93.9	80.2	89.7	99.4	80.2	93.5	97.7	85.4	93.9
06	WOOD, PLASTICS & COMPOSITES	106.2	40.5	69.2	97.9	48.6	70.1	89.5	45.7	64.8	98.8	50.1	71.3	99.2	50.4	71.7	87.3	35.6	58.1
07	THERMAL & MOISTURE PROTECTION	104.0	41.6	78.6	100.6	47.9	79.2	106.3	41.6	80.1	103.8	47.9	81.1	106.3	44.3	81.2	109.3	50.8	85.6
08	OPENINGS	94.7	39.8	81.7	97.0	48.5	85.5	94.3	42.9	82.1	94.9	51.7	84.6	97.8	50.3	86.5	100.9	47.9	88.4
0920	Plaster & Gypsum Board	104.2	38.5	59.5	102.5	46.8	64.6	102.1	43.8	62.5	100.3	48.3	65.0	110.5	48.7	68.5	94.3	33.8	53.1
0950, 0980	Ceilings & Acoustic Treatment	91.6	38.5	56.3	95.9	46.8	63.2	92.4	43.8	60.1	92.5	48.3	63.1	95.1	48.7	64.2	136.9	33.8	68.3
0960	Flooring	105.2	24.5	81.1	103.4	43.5	85.4	101.8	22.2	78.0	102.3	45.3	85.2	106.2	43.5	87.4	109.8	73.4	98.9
0970, 0990	Wall Finishes & Painting/Coating	107.1	40.2	66.9	102.1	37.7	63.4	103.4	39.3	64.9	107.1	39.5	66.5	103.4	37.5	63.8	94.1	30.0	55.6
09	FINISHES	99.0	36.8	64.3	99.7	45.7	69.6	97.9	40.2	65.8	97.6	47.8	69.9	100.5	46.7	70.5	111.7	43.8	73.9
COVERS	DIVS. 10 - 14, 25, 28, 41, 43, 44, 46	100.0	77.5	95.5	100.0	74.5	94.9	100.0	74.4	94.9	100.0	75.7	95.1	100.0	79.3	95.9	100.0	84.8	97.0
21, 22, 23	FIRE SUPPRESSION, PLUMBING & HVAC	95.5	52.0	78.0	100.0	53.6	81.4	95.3	53.9	78.7	100.4	55.1	82.2	100.2	53.5	81.5	100.2	61.3	84.6
26, 27, 3370	ELECTRICAL, COMMUNICATIONS & UTIL.	97.8	30.0	62.4	96.5	41.3	67.7	96.1	40.6	67.1	97.0	51.9	73.4	93.4	57.0	74.4	102.2	73.3	87.1
MF2010	WEIGHTED AVERAGE	96.4	49.2	75.8	98.2	55.1	79.4	96.0	53.2	77.4	97.2	56.6	79.5	98.5	57.1	80.5	102.0	64.0	85.5

NORTH DAKOTA

DIVISION		DEVILS LAKE 583			DICKINSON 586			FARGO 580 - 581			GRAND FORKS 582			JAMESTOWN 584			MINOT 587		
		MAT.	INST.	TOTAL	MAT.	INST.	TOTAL	MAT.	INST.	TOTAL	MAT.	INST.	TOTAL	MAT.	INST.	TOTAL	MAT.	INST.	TOTAL
015433	CONTRACTOR EQUIPMENT		99.0	99.0		99.0	99.0		99.0	99.0		99.0	99.0		99.0	99.0		99.0	99.0
0241, 31 - 34	SITE & INFRASTRUCTURE, DEMOLITION	103.3	95.2	97.6	111.5	93.7	99.0	98.4	97.7	97.9	107.3	93.7	97.8	102.3	93.7	96.3	104.8	97.6	99.8
0310	Concrete Forming & Accessories	102.6	36.0	45.1	91.7	34.9	42.7	102.5	42.2	50.5	95.6	34.8	43.1	93.2	34.6	42.6	91.4	66.0	69.5
0320	Concrete Reinforcing	101.9	83.5	92.7	102.8	41.0	71.9	94.5	83.3	88.9	100.3	83.3	91.8	102.5	48.3	75.4	103.8	83.6	93.7
0330	Cast-in-Place Concrete	122.9	47.0	91.4	111.2	45.2	83.8	100.9	50.3	79.9	111.2	45.1	83.8	121.4	45.0	89.7	111.2	47.5	84.7
03	CONCRETE	110.8	50.2	80.9	110.1	41.0	76.0	104.7	54.0	79.7	107.3	48.7	78.4	109.3	42.2	76.2	105.8	63.7	85.0
04	MASONRY	111.7	64.4	82.4	113.4	59.2	79.8	97.9	57.4	72.9	106.2	63.8	80.0	123.8	33.4	67.8	105.6	64.2	80.0
05	METALS	95.1	84.6	91.9	95.1	64.1	85.5	99.0	86.0	95.1	95.1	79.3	90.2	95.1	65.1	85.8	95.4	86.3	92.6
06	WOOD, PLASTICS & COMPOSITES	88.7	32.8	57.1	76.6	32.8	51.9	86.8	36.1	58.2	80.8	32.8	53.7	78.5	32.8	52.7	76.4	68.7	72.0
07	THERMAL & MOISTURE PROTECTION	106.7	49.4	83.4	107.1	47.3	82.8	108.7	51.8	85.6	106.9	49.4	83.5	106.6	41.5	80.1	106.6	56.0	86.1
08	OPENINGS	96.6	40.8	83.4	96.5	30.9	81.0	98.8	48.2	86.8	96.6	40.8	83.4	96.6	33.0	81.5	96.7	66.0	89.4
0920	Plaster & Gypsum Board	115.2	30.9	57.9	105.2	30.9	54.7	91.5	34.3	52.6	106.7	30.9	55.1	106.3	30.9	55.0	105.2	67.9	79.8
0950, 0980	Ceilings & Acoustic Treatment	142.1	30.9	68.1	142.1	30.9	68.1	138.7	34.3	69.2	142.1	30.9	68.1	142.1	30.9	68.1	142.1	67.9	92.7
0960	Flooring	117.0	36.5	92.9	110.5	36.5	88.4	109.8	73.4	98.9	112.4	36.5	89.7	111.2	36.5	88.9	110.3	86.4	103.1
0970, 0990	Wall Finishes & Painting/Coating	94.9	23.0	51.7	94.9	23.0	51.7	91.0	72.2	79.7	94.9	28.9	55.2	94.9	23.0	51.7	94.9	25.2	51.7
09	FINISHES	117.6	32.9	70.4	115.3	32.9	69.4	112.3	48.8	76.9	115.5	33.6	69.9	114.7	32.9	69.1	114.5	65.4	87.1
COVERS	DIVS. 10 - 14, 25, 28, 41, 43, 44, 46	100.0	33.3	86.6	100.0	33.5	86.7	100.0	84.9	97.0	100.0	33.4	86.7	100.0	82.8	96.6	100.0	88.5	97.7
21, 22, 23	FIRE SUPPRESSION, PLUMBING & HVAC	95.5	74.6	87.1	95.5	67.1	84.1	100.1	77.6	91.1	100.4	33.9	73.8	95.5	35.8	71.5	100.4	61.4	84.7
26, 27, 3370	ELECTRICAL, COMMUNICATIONS & UTIL.	99.3	36.7	66.6	109.1	74.2	90.9	104.8	67.7	85.5	103.3	54.8	78.0	99.3	36.6	66.6	106.9	77.5	91.5
MF2010	WEIGHTED AVERAGE	101.0	58.6	82.5	101.9	57.9	82.7	101.7	67.6	86.9	101.8	51.6	79.9	101.0	45.1	76.7	101.8	71.0	88.4

City Cost Indexes

Table 1

DIVISION		NORTH DAKOTA WILLISTON 588			OHIO AKRON 442 - 443			OHIO ATHENS 457			OHIO CANTON 446 - 447			OHIO CHILLICOTHE 456			OHIO CINCINNATI 451 - 452		
		MAT.	INST.	TOTAL	MAT.	INST.	TOTAL	MAT.	INST.	TOTAL	MAT.	INST.	TOTAL	MAT.	INST.	TOTAL	MAT.	INST.	TOTAL
015433	CONTRACTOR EQUIPMENT		99.0	99.0		95.3	95.3		90.7	90.7		95.3	95.3		100.3	100.3		100.0	100.0
0241, 31 - 34	SITE & INFRASTRUCTURE, DEMOLITION	105.3	93.7	97.2	96.8	102.4	100.7	111.6	92.6	98.3	96.9	102.0	100.4	96.5	104.0	101.8	93.6	103.5	100.5
0310	Concrete Forming & Accessories	97.3	34.9	43.5	100.2	92.2	93.3	94.1	85.8	86.9	100.2	82.3	84.7	96.2	92.1	92.6	98.1	80.6	83.0
0320	Concrete Reinforcing	104.8	41.0	72.9	93.9	93.3	93.6	90.1	86.6	88.4	93.9	76.5	85.2	87.0	81.0	84.0	92.2	81.7	87.0
0330	Cast-in-Place Concrete	111.2	45.2	83.8	92.4	97.4	94.5	111.9	92.2	103.7	93.3	95.2	94.1	101.6	96.1	99.3	93.6	93.6	93.6
03	CONCRETE	107.3	41.0	74.6	92.9	93.5	93.2	106.4	87.6	97.2	93.4	85.3	89.4	100.8	91.3	96.1	95.3	85.5	90.4
04	MASONRY	100.0	59.2	74.7	92.1	94.1	93.3	82.7	89.5	87.0	92.8	84.6	87.7	90.1	96.7	94.2	89.8	85.5	87.1
05	METALS	95.2	64.2	85.7	94.8	82.2	90.9	101.6	78.6	94.5	94.8	75.1	88.7	93.7	84.9	91.0	95.9	84.6	92.4
06	WOOD, PLASTICS & COMPOSITES	82.2	32.8	54.3	99.1	91.4	94.7	83.4	86.8	85.3	99.5	80.8	88.9	96.0	90.6	92.9	98.5	78.5	87.2
07	THERMAL & MOISTURE PROTECTION	106.8	47.3	82.7	111.2	95.8	104.9	99.7	91.9	96.6	112.3	91.6	103.9	101.2	94.3	98.4	99.5	89.9	95.6
08	OPENINGS	96.7	30.9	81.1	115.2	92.5	109.8	99.9	83.6	96.1	108.5	77.2	101.1	91.9	84.0	90.0	99.9	78.9	94.9
0920	Plaster & Gypsum Board	106.7	30.9	55.1	102.0	90.8	94.4	93.9	86.1	88.6	103.1	79.9	87.3	96.6	90.5	92.5	98.3	78.1	84.6
0950, 0980	Ceilings & Acoustic Treatment	142.1	30.9	68.1	98.7	90.8	93.5	102.0	86.1	91.5	98.7	79.9	86.2	96.3	90.5	92.5	97.2	78.1	84.5
0960	Flooring	113.2	36.5	90.3	98.6	92.5	96.7	124.5	100.8	117.4	98.7	82.0	93.7	101.5	100.8	101.3	102.5	90.0	98.7
0970, 0990	Wall Finishes & Painting/Coating	94.9	32.2	57.2	97.1	103.9	101.2	104.9	93.1	97.8	97.1	82.8	88.5	102.2	89.8	94.7	102.2	84.8	91.7
09	FINISHES	115.6	34.0	70.1	100.1	93.3	96.4	102.9	90.1	95.8	100.4	81.8	90.0	100.4	93.7	96.6	100.8	82.2	90.4
COVERS	DIVS. 10 - 14, 25, 28, 41, 43, 44, 46	100.0	33.5	86.7	100.0	95.3	99.1	100.0	53.3	90.6	100.0	93.1	98.6	100.0	93.1	98.6	100.0	91.4	98.3
21, 22, 23	FIRE SUPPRESSION, PLUMBING & HVAC	95.5	67.1	84.1	100.0	94.3	97.7	95.2	52.4	78.0	100.0	82.5	93.0	95.6	94.0	94.9	100.0	81.3	92.5
26, 27, 3370	ELECTRICAL, COMMUNICATIONS & UTIL.	103.7	74.2	88.3	99.3	92.8	95.9	97.8	98.9	98.3	98.5	87.8	92.9	97.3	85.4	91.1	96.1	79.7	87.6
MF2010	WEIGHTED AVERAGE	100.3	58.0	81.9	99.8	93.4	97.0	99.1	80.6	91.1	99.2	85.0	93.0	96.4	92.2	94.5	97.8	84.8	92.1

Table 2

DIVISION		OHIO CLEVELAND 441			OHIO COLUMBUS 430 - 432			OHIO DAYTON 453 - 454			OHIO HAMILTON 450			OHIO LIMA 458			OHIO LORAIN 440		
		MAT.	INST.	TOTAL	MAT.	INST.	TOTAL	MAT.	INST.	TOTAL	MAT.	INST.	TOTAL	MAT.	INST.	TOTAL	MAT.	INST.	TOTAL
015433	CONTRACTOR EQUIPMENT		95.6	95.6		94.9	94.9		95.3	95.3		100.3	100.3		93.1	93.1		95.3	95.3
0241, 31 - 34	SITE & INFRASTRUCTURE, DEMOLITION	96.7	102.9	101.1	95.2	99.3	98.1	92.4	103.4	100.1	92.3	103.6	100.2	105.2	92.5	96.3	96.3	101.3	99.8
0310	Concrete Forming & Accessories	100.3	97.9	98.2	99.1	85.9	87.7	98.1	79.0	81.6	98.1	80.1	82.5	94.0	84.3	85.6	100.3	85.3	87.3
0320	Concrete Reinforcing	94.3	93.7	94.0	101.6	81.7	91.7	92.2	80.6	86.4	92.2	81.7	87.0	90.1	79.1	84.6	93.9	93.6	93.7
0330	Cast-in-Place Concrete	90.7	105.5	96.8	90.6	95.9	92.8	87.0	86.0	86.6	93.3	92.8	93.1	102.8	97.2	100.5	88.0	103.5	94.4
03	CONCRETE	92.2	99.0	95.5	95.8	88.3	92.1	92.2	81.5	86.9	95.1	85.0	90.1	99.3	87.6	93.5	90.8	92.6	91.7
04	MASONRY	96.6	105.1	101.9	97.9	94.8	96.0	89.3	81.7	84.6	89.6	84.0	86.1	112.9	81.7	93.6	88.8	98.5	94.8
05	METALS	96.3	85.2	92.9	95.9	80.5	91.2	95.2	77.8	89.9	95.2	85.1	92.1	101.6	80.4	95.1	95.4	83.3	91.6
06	WOOD, PLASTICS & COMPOSITES	98.2	94.8	96.2	97.5	83.7	89.7	99.7	77.3	87.1	98.5	78.5	87.2	83.3	84.0	83.7	99.1	82.0	89.4
07	THERMAL & MOISTURE PROTECTION	109.8	108.1	109.1	101.8	95.7	99.3	104.5	86.4	97.2	101.3	88.7	96.2	99.3	92.5	96.5	112.2	101.1	107.7
08	OPENINGS	104.5	94.3	102.1	103.0	80.4	97.7	99.3	78.0	94.2	96.9	78.9	92.6	99.9	78.3	94.8	108.5	87.4	103.5
0920	Plaster & Gypsum Board	101.2	94.3	96.5	97.6	83.2	87.8	98.3	76.8	83.7	98.3	78.1	84.6	93.9	83.2	86.6	102.0	81.2	87.8
0950, 0980	Ceilings & Acoustic Treatment	97.0	94.3	95.2	100.4	83.2	89.0	98.2	76.8	84.0	97.2	78.1	84.5	101.0	83.2	89.2	98.7	81.2	87.1
0960	Flooring	98.4	105.1	100.4	94.7	87.9	92.6	105.2	80.7	97.9	102.5	90.0	98.7	123.6	88.3	113.1	98.7	105.1	100.6
0970, 0990	Wall Finishes & Painting/Coating	97.1	105.2	102.0	100.9	93.3	96.3	102.2	85.2	92.0	102.2	84.8	91.7	104.9	83.8	92.2	97.1	105.2	102.0
09	FINISHES	99.7	99.6	99.6	97.5	86.6	91.4	101.7	79.5	89.3	100.7	81.9	90.2	101.9	84.7	92.3	100.2	90.4	94.7
COVERS	DIVS. 10 - 14, 25, 28, 41, 43, 44, 46	100.0	102.1	100.4	100.0	93.8	98.8	100.0	90.9	98.2	100.0	90.9	98.2	100.0	94.1	98.8	100.0	98.3	99.7
21, 22, 23	FIRE SUPPRESSION, PLUMBING & HVAC	100.0	99.8	99.9	100.0	92.3	96.9	100.8	81.7	93.1	100.5	80.5	92.5	95.2	84.7	91.0	100.0	85.2	94.0
26, 27, 3370	ELECTRICAL, COMMUNICATIONS & UTIL.	98.8	106.2	102.6	97.1	88.1	92.4	94.7	82.7	88.4	95.1	81.0	87.8	98.1	78.4	87.8	98.7	86.7	92.4
MF2010	WEIGHTED AVERAGE	98.9	100.0	99.4	98.6	89.7	94.7	97.5	83.2	91.3	97.4	84.5	91.8	99.6	84.4	93.0	98.8	90.4	95.2

Table 3

DIVISION		OHIO MANSFIELD 448 - 449			OHIO MARION 433			OHIO SPRINGFIELD 455			OHIO STEUBENVILLE 439			OHIO TOLEDO 434 - 436			OHIO YOUNGSTOWN 444 - 445		
		MAT.	INST.	TOTAL	MAT.	INST.	TOTAL	MAT.	INST.	TOTAL	MAT.	INST.	TOTAL	MAT.	INST.	TOTAL	MAT.	INST.	TOTAL
015433	CONTRACTOR EQUIPMENT		95.3	95.3		94.5	94.5		95.3	95.3		99.3	99.3		97.3	97.3		95.3	95.3
0241, 31 - 34	SITE & INFRASTRUCTURE, DEMOLITION	92.7	102.2	99.3	91.1	97.8	95.8	92.7	102.1	99.3	134.7	107.7	115.8	94.4	99.8	98.2	96.7	103.0	101.1
0310	Concrete Forming & Accessories	90.3	83.5	84.4	95.7	81.3	83.3	98.1	83.3	85.4	97.6	87.9	89.2	99.0	92.5	93.4	100.2	85.9	87.9
0320	Concrete Reinforcing	85.4	75.6	80.5	93.7	81.5	87.6	92.2	78.9	85.6	91.1	85.9	88.5	101.6	87.2	94.4	93.9	86.1	90.0
0330	Cast-in-Place Concrete	85.6	94.5	89.3	82.8	92.9	87.0	89.4	85.9	87.9	89.9	94.7	91.9	90.6	100.2	94.6	91.5	97.1	93.9
03	CONCRETE	85.6	85.4	85.5	88.0	85.1	86.5	93.3	83.1	88.3	91.7	89.3	90.5	95.8	93.9	94.9	92.5	89.3	90.9
04	MASONRY	91.2	93.7	92.7	100.0	92.4	95.3	89.5	81.7	84.6	86.5	93.8	91.0	106.6	96.8	100.6	92.4	91.1	91.6
05	METALS	95.6	75.5	89.4	95.0	78.1	89.8	95.1	77.0	89.5	91.6	79.7	87.9	95.7	86.9	93.0	94.8	79.3	90.0
06	WOOD, PLASTICS & COMPOSITES	86.8	82.0	84.1	93.5	81.7	86.9	101.1	83.4	91.1	89.3	86.1	87.5	97.5	91.5	94.1	99.1	84.1	90.6
07	THERMAL & MOISTURE PROTECTION	111.6	93.6	104.3	101.4	82.0	93.5	104.4	87.0	97.4	113.5	96.6	106.6	103.4	100.9	102.4	112.4	92.8	104.4
08	OPENINGS	108.8	76.7	101.2	97.1	77.6	92.5	97.4	78.6	92.9	97.5	82.9	94.0	100.4	88.8	97.6	108.5	84.2	102.7
0920	Plaster & Gypsum Board	95.2	81.2	85.7	95.4	81.2	85.7	98.3	83.2	88.0	95.5	85.1	88.4	97.6	91.2	93.2	102.0	83.3	89.3
0950, 0980	Ceilings & Acoustic Treatment	99.6	81.2	87.4	100.4	81.2	87.6	98.2	83.2	88.2	97.3	85.1	89.2	100.4	91.2	94.3	98.7	83.3	88.5
0960	Flooring	94.6	104.7	97.6	93.5	71.0	86.8	105.2	80.7	97.9	122.7	99.8	115.9	93.9	101.5	96.2	98.7	92.1	96.7
0970, 0990	Wall Finishes & Painting/Coating	97.1	88.5	91.9	100.9	48.5	69.4	102.2	85.2	92.0	114.2	102.6	107.2	100.9	102.1	101.6	97.1	92.6	94.4
09	FINISHES	98.0	87.7	92.3	96.4	76.1	85.1	101.7	83.1	91.4	114.3	91.2	101.4	97.2	94.8	95.9	100.3	87.3	93.0
COVERS	DIVS. 10 - 14, 25, 28, 41, 43, 44, 46	100.0	93.2	98.6	100.0	54.9	91.0	100.0	91.6	98.3	100.0	95.2	99.0	100.0	96.3	99.3	100.0	94.0	98.8
21, 22, 23	FIRE SUPPRESSION, PLUMBING & HVAC	95.1	83.4	90.4	95.2	89.7	93.0	100.8	81.7	93.1	95.5	91.9	94.0	100.1	99.2	99.7	100.0	88.4	95.3
26, 27, 3370	ELECTRICAL, COMMUNICATIONS & UTIL.	96.2	77.7	86.5	91.2	77.7	84.1	94.7	85.6	90.0	86.4	112.7	100.1	97.2	101.6	99.5	98.7	82.9	90.5
MF2010	WEIGHTED AVERAGE	96.6	85.6	91.8	95.0	83.7	90.1	97.5	84.2	91.7	96.8	94.5	95.8	98.7	96.4	97.7	99.1	88.3	94.4

DIVISION		OHIO ZANESVILLE 437 - 438			OKLAHOMA ARDMORE 734			OKLAHOMA CLINTON 736			OKLAHOMA DURANT 747			OKLAHOMA ENID 737			OKLAHOMA GUYMON 739		
		MAT.	INST.	TOTAL	MAT.	INST.	TOTAL	MAT.	INST.	TOTAL	MAT.	INST.	TOTAL	MAT.	INST.	TOTAL	MAT.	INST.	TOTAL
015433	CONTRACTOR EQUIPMENT		94.5	94.5		82.5	82.5		81.6	81.6		81.6	81.6		81.6	81.6		81.6	81.6
0241, 31 - 34	SITE & INFRASTRUCTURE, DEMOLITION	93.9	99.5	97.9	94.7	91.4	92.4	96.1	90.0	91.8	92.5	89.7	90.6	97.6	90.0	92.2	99.9	89.7	92.7
0310	Concrete Forming & Accessories	92.8	82.6	84.0	94.4	41.3	48.6	92.9	47.7	53.9	85.7	45.1	50.6	96.6	34.8	43.3	100.3	45.9	53.3
0320	Concrete Reinforcing	93.1	85.3	89.2	87.6	80.2	83.9	88.1	80.2	84.2	92.3	80.6	86.4	87.5	80.2	83.9	88.1	80.2	84.1
0330	Cast-in-Place Concrete	87.2	93.3	89.8	99.3	44.2	76.4	95.9	45.9	75.2	92.1	43.5	71.9	95.9	47.2	75.7	96.0	43.9	74.3
03	CONCRETE	91.5	86.5	89.0	97.5	50.0	74.1	97.1	53.5	75.6	92.9	51.5	72.5	97.7	48.2	73.3	100.7	51.9	76.7
04	MASONRY	96.8	83.4	88.5	93.4	58.1	71.5	118.8	58.1	81.2	92.4	63.4	74.5	100.6	58.1	74.3	95.9	54.6	70.3
05	METALS	96.4	80.3	91.4	93.3	70.6	86.3	93.4	70.6	86.4	91.4	71.3	85.2	94.8	70.5	87.3	93.9	70.3	86.6
06	WOOD, PLASTICS & COMPOSITES	89.6	81.7	85.2	100.7	38.7	65.7	99.7	47.3	70.1	89.5	44.0	63.8	103.6	30.0	62.0	107.5	47.0	73.4
07	THERMAL & MOISTURE PROTECTION	101.5	91.1	97.3	106.1	61.0	87.8	106.1	62.0	88.2	99.9	62.3	84.6	106.2	60.3	87.6	106.5	58.4	87.0
08	OPENINGS	97.1	80.2	93.1	93.9	49.6	83.4	93.9	54.0	84.4	93.9	52.7	84.1	93.9	44.4	82.1	94.0	49.8	83.5
0920	Plaster & Gypsum Board	92.8	81.2	84.9	84.3	37.5	52.4	84.0	46.3	58.3	79.1	42.9	54.5	85.1	28.4	46.5	85.7	46.0	58.7
0950, 0980	Ceilings & Acoustic Treatment	100.4	81.2	87.6	86.2	37.5	53.8	86.2	46.3	59.7	85.4	42.9	57.1	86.2	28.4	47.8	88.9	46.0	60.4
0960	Flooring	92.0	86.9	90.5	110.5	43.9	90.6	109.4	41.9	89.2	106.9	63.1	93.8	111.2	41.9	90.5	112.9	24.8	86.5
0970, 0990	Wall Finishes & Painting/Coating	100.9	76.0	85.9	96.5	52.4	70.0	96.5	52.4	70.0	100.1	52.4	71.4	96.5	52.4	70.0	96.5	33.8	58.8
09	FINISHES	95.9	82.2	88.3	93.8	41.0	64.4	93.6	45.8	67.0	91.8	47.7	67.2	94.3	35.4	61.5	95.8	39.7	64.6
COVERS	DIVS. 10 - 14, 25, 28, 41, 43, 44, 46	100.0	90.0	98.0	100.0	78.0	95.6	100.0	79.0	95.8	100.0	78.3	95.7	100.0	77.1	95.4	100.0	77.8	95.5
21, 22, 23	FIRE SUPPRESSION, PLUMBING & HVAC	95.2	89.7	93.0	95.4	66.3	83.7	95.4	66.3	83.7	95.4	65.8	83.5	100.3	66.3	86.6	95.4	64.2	82.9
26, 27, 3370	ELECTRICAL, COMMUNICATIONS & UTIL.	91.5	78.2	84.6	89.7	70.4	79.6	90.7	70.4	80.1	94.7	70.4	82.0	90.7	70.4	80.1	92.3	63.0	77.0
MF2010	WEIGHTED AVERAGE	95.5	85.6	91.2	95.2	62.3	80.9	96.5	63.6	82.2	94.3	64.0	81.1	97.2	60.9	81.4	96.3	60.5	80.7

DIVISION		OKLAHOMA LAWTON 735			MCALESTER 745			MIAMI 743			MUSKOGEE 744			OKLAHOMA CITY 730 - 731			PONCA CITY 746		
		MAT.	INST.	TOTAL	MAT.	INST.	TOTAL	MAT.	INST.	TOTAL	MAT.	INST.	TOTAL	MAT.	INST.	TOTAL	MAT.	INST.	TOTAL
015433	CONTRACTOR EQUIPMENT		82.5	82.5		81.6	81.6		89.7	89.7		89.7	89.7		82.7	82.7		81.6	81.6
0241, 31 - 34	SITE & INFRASTRUCTURE, DEMOLITION	94.3	91.4	92.2	86.3	89.9	88.9	87.8	87.2	87.4	88.0	87.0	87.3	93.7	91.8	92.3	93.0	89.9	90.8
0310	Concrete Forming & Accessories	100.2	45.3	52.8	83.6	44.6	49.9	96.8	67.7	71.7	101.3	34.1	43.3	98.2	55.5	61.3	92.2	47.3	53.4
0320	Concrete Reinforcing	87.7	80.2	84.0	91.9	80.2	86.1	90.5	80.3	85.4	91.3	79.7	85.5	92.8	80.2	86.5	91.3	80.3	85.8
0330	Cast-in-Place Concrete	92.8	47.3	73.9	80.8	46.0	66.3	84.6	48.3	69.6	85.7	46.6	69.4	94.5	47.7	75.1	94.6	45.5	74.2
03	CONCRETE	93.8	52.9	73.6	83.4	52.1	68.0	88.2	64.0	76.2	90.0	48.3	69.4	97.3	57.5	77.7	95.0	53.1	74.3
04	MASONRY	95.9	58.1	72.5	110.7	57.1	77.5	95.2	57.2	71.7	113.0	46.0	71.5	98.7	57.4	73.1	87.8	57.1	68.8
05	METALS	98.5	70.6	89.9	91.3	70.5	84.9	91.3	82.8	88.6	92.7	81.0	89.1	92.0	70.7	85.4	91.3	70.8	84.9
06	WOOD, PLASTICS & COMPOSITES	106.4	44.1	71.3	86.9	44.0	62.7	102.4	74.6	86.7	107.0	31.4	64.3	100.3	58.2	76.5	97.6	47.0	69.1
07	THERMAL & MOISTURE PROTECTION	106.1	61.7	88.1	99.6	61.0	83.9	99.9	64.9	85.7	100.0	49.5	79.5	98.8	62.8	84.2	100.1	66.7	86.5
08	OPENINGS	95.4	52.1	85.1	93.9	52.5	84.1	93.9	69.3	88.1	93.9	42.8	81.8	94.8	59.7	86.5	93.9	53.8	84.4
0920	Plaster & Gypsum Board	87.1	43.0	57.1	77.9	42.9	54.1	85.0	74.3	77.7	87.2	29.7	48.1	92.9	57.5	68.8	83.5	46.0	58.0
0950, 0980	Ceilings & Acoustic Treatment	94.2	43.0	60.1	85.4	42.9	57.1	85.4	74.3	78.0	94.3	29.7	51.3	97.5	57.5	70.9	85.4	46.0	59.2
0960	Flooring	113.1	41.9	91.8	105.8	41.9	86.7	112.8	63.1	97.9	115.3	40.5	92.9	109.5	41.9	89.3	109.9	41.9	89.6
0970, 0990	Wall Finishes & Painting/Coating	96.5	52.4	70.0	100.1	38.6	63.1	100.1	79.1	87.5	100.1	34.9	60.9	97.9	52.4	70.6	100.1	52.4	71.4
09	FINISHES	96.4	43.8	67.1	90.8	42.0	63.6	93.7	68.8	79.8	96.7	33.7	61.6	98.6	52.0	72.6	93.4	45.3	66.6
COVERS	DIVS. 10 - 14, 25, 28, 41, 43, 44, 46	100.0	78.6	95.7	100.0	78.3	95.6	100.0	82.1	96.4	100.0	76.5	95.3	100.0	80.0	96.0	100.0	78.6	95.7
21, 22, 23	FIRE SUPPRESSION, PLUMBING & HVAC	100.3	66.3	86.7	95.4	61.5	81.8	95.4	61.8	81.9	100.3	60.5	84.3	100.0	66.0	86.4	95.4	61.7	81.9
26, 27, 3370	ELECTRICAL, COMMUNICATIONS & UTIL.	92.3	70.4	80.9	93.1	66.1	79.0	94.6	66.1	79.7	92.7	53.7	72.3	97.3	70.4	83.3	92.7	70.0	80.8
MF2010	WEIGHTED AVERAGE	97.5	63.3	82.6	93.7	61.1	79.5	94.0	68.3	82.8	96.6	56.3	79.0	97.3	65.4	83.4	94.3	62.5	80.5

DIVISION		OKLAHOMA POTEAU 749			SHAWNEE 748			TULSA 740 - 741			WOODWARD 738			OREGON BEND 977			EUGENE 974		
		MAT.	INST.	TOTAL	MAT.	INST.	TOTAL	MAT.	INST.	TOTAL	MAT.	INST.	TOTAL	MAT.	INST.	TOTAL	MAT.	INST.	TOTAL
015433	CONTRACTOR EQUIPMENT		89.0	89.0		81.6	81.6		89.7	89.7		81.6	81.6		97.9	97.9		97.9	97.9
0241, 31 - 34	SITE & INFRASTRUCTURE, DEMOLITION	74.3	85.9	82.4	96.0	89.9	91.7	94.2	87.4	89.4	96.3	90.0	91.9	106.8	102.8	103.9	96.9	102.7	101.0
0310	Concrete Forming & Accessories	90.0	41.9	48.5	85.5	44.7	50.3	101.4	41.1	49.4	93.1	47.8	54.0	111.2	100.6	102.0	107.6	100.4	101.4
0320	Concrete Reinforcing	92.4	80.3	86.3	91.3	80.2	85.8	91.6	80.2	85.9	87.5	80.3	83.9	95.7	101.5	98.6	99.7	101.5	100.6
0330	Cast-in-Place Concrete	84.6	45.7	68.5	97.6	43.7	75.2	93.3	47.0	74.1	95.9	46.1	75.2	94.2	104.1	98.3	91.2	104.0	96.5
03	CONCRETE	90.6	51.6	71.3	96.6	51.4	74.3	95.3	51.7	73.8	97.4	53.6	75.8	104.8	101.6	103.2	96.3	101.5	98.9
04	MASONRY	95.5	57.2	71.8	111.9	57.1	78.0	96.1	61.0	74.4	89.5	58.1	70.1	98.7	104.5	102.3	96.0	104.5	101.3
05	METALS	91.3	82.4	88.5	91.2	70.4	84.8	95.9	82.0	91.6	93.5	71.0	86.5	90.7	96.6	92.5	91.4	96.4	93.0
06	WOOD, PLASTICS & COMPOSITES	94.3	40.0	63.7	89.3	44.0	63.7	106.2	37.5	67.4	99.8	47.0	70.0	103.3	100.3	101.6	98.8	100.3	99.6
07	THERMAL & MOISTURE PROTECTION	100.0	61.0	84.2	100.0	60.3	83.9	100.0	62.6	84.8	106.2	67.1	90.3	104.6	96.3	101.2	103.9	93.4	99.6
08	OPENINGS	93.9	50.5	83.6	93.9	52.5	84.1	95.4	48.1	84.2	93.9	53.8	84.4	93.8	103.8	96.2	94.2	103.8	96.5
0920	Plaster & Gypsum Board	82.0	38.7	52.5	79.1	42.9	54.5	87.2	36.0	52.4	84.6	46.0	58.4	103.7	100.2	101.3	101.1	100.2	100.5
0950, 0980	Ceilings & Acoustic Treatment	85.4	38.7	54.3	85.4	42.9	57.1	94.3	36.0	55.5	88.9	46.0	60.4	92.3	100.2	97.5	93.3	100.2	97.9
0960	Flooring	109.3	63.1	95.4	106.9	33.3	84.9	114.0	43.6	92.9	109.4	43.9	89.8	107.6	105.3	106.9	106.1	105.3	105.9
0970, 0990	Wall Finishes & Painting/Coating	100.1	45.3	71.4	100.1	34.9	60.9	100.1	41.4	60.9	96.5	52.4	70.0	104.6	72.3	85.2	104.6	72.3	85.2
09	FINISHES	91.5	45.3	65.8	92.1	40.1	63.1	96.5	39.7	64.9	94.4	45.9	67.4	103.3	98.1	100.4	101.7	98.1	99.7
COVERS	DIVS. 10 - 14, 25, 28, 41, 43, 44, 46	100.0	78.1	95.6	100.0	78.3	95.7	100.0	79.3	95.8	100.0	79.0	95.8	100.0	101.9	100.4	100.0	101.9	100.4
21, 22, 23	FIRE SUPPRESSION, PLUMBING & HVAC	95.4	61.7	81.9	95.4	65.8	83.5	100.3	63.5	85.5	95.4	66.3	83.7	95.1	102.6	98.1	100.0	102.6	101.0
26, 27, 3370	ELECTRICAL, COMMUNICATIONS & UTIL.	92.8	66.1	78.9	94.8	70.4	82.1	94.7	66.1	79.8	92.2	70.4	80.8	95.8	96.3	96.1	94.5	96.3	95.4
MF2010	WEIGHTED AVERAGE	93.5	62.1	79.8	95.7	62.2	81.1	97.4	62.2	82.1	95.3	63.8	81.6	97.3	100.5	98.7	97.1	100.4	98.5

City Cost Indexes

OREGON

DIVISION		KLAMATH FALLS 976			MEDFORD 975			PENDLETON 978			PORTLAND 970-972			SALEM 973			VALE 979		
		MAT.	INST.	TOTAL	MAT.	INST.	TOTAL	MAT.	INST.	TOTAL	MAT.	INST.	TOTAL	MAT.	INST.	TOTAL	MAT.	INST.	TOTAL
015433	CONTRACTOR EQUIPMENT		97.9	97.9		97.9	97.9		95.4	95.4		97.9	97.9		97.9	97.9		95.4	95.4
0241, 31-34	SITE & INFRASTRUCTURE, DEMOLITION	110.8	102.7	105.1	104.5	102.7	103.3	103.2	96.4	98.4	99.4	102.8	101.7	92.9	102.8	99.8	91.4	96.3	94.9
0310	Concrete Forming & Accessories	104.1	100.3	100.9	103.2	100.3	100.7	104.4	100.7	101.2	108.8	100.6	101.7	107.1	100.6	101.5	110.9	99.7	101.2
0320	Concrete Reinforcing	95.7	101.5	98.6	97.3	101.5	99.4	95.1	101.5	98.3	100.5	101.5	101.0	106.1	101.5	103.8	92.7	101.4	97.0
0330	Cast-in-Place Concrete	94.2	104.0	98.3	94.2	104.0	98.3	95.0	105.4	99.3	93.7	104.1	98.0	88.4	104.1	94.9	74.9	105.0	87.4
03	CONCRETE	107.6	101.5	104.6	102.2	101.5	101.8	88.4	102.1	95.2	97.7	101.6	99.7	96.0	101.6	98.8	74.7	101.5	88.0
04	MASONRY	110.8	104.5	106.9	93.1	104.5	100.2	101.7	104.6	103.5	96.5	104.5	101.3	103.3	104.5	104.1	100.2	104.6	102.9
05	METALS	90.7	96.3	92.5	91.0	96.3	92.6	97.1	97.1	97.1	92.4	96.6	93.7	97.8	96.6	97.4	97.0	96.0	96.7
06	WOOD, PLASTICS & COMPOSITES	93.8	100.3	97.5	92.6	100.3	97.0	95.9	100.4	98.4	99.8	100.3	100.1	96.7	100.3	98.7	104.8	100.4	102.3
07	THERMAL & MOISTURE PROTECTION	104.7	94.8	100.7	104.4	94.8	100.5	97.4	95.4	96.6	103.8	98.1	101.5	101.7	96.3	99.5	96.9	94.8	96.1
08	OPENINGS	93.9	103.8	96.2	96.3	103.8	98.1	89.5	103.9	92.9	92.2	103.8	95.0	95.9	103.8	97.8	89.4	95.8	90.9
0920	Plaster & Gypsum Board	98.2	100.2	99.6	97.5	100.2	99.3	85.2	100.2	95.4	100.9	100.2	100.4	97.3	100.2	99.3	91.9	100.2	97.5
0950, 0980	Ceilings & Acoustic Treatment	100.3	100.2	100.2	107.3	100.2	102.6	64.6	100.2	88.3	95.3	100.2	98.5	100.7	100.2	100.4	64.6	100.2	88.3
0960	Flooring	105.0	105.3	105.1	104.4	105.3	104.7	72.5	105.3	82.3	103.6	105.3	104.1	104.3	105.3	104.6	74.2	105.3	83.5
0970, 0990	Wall Finishes & Painting/Coating	104.6	59.4	77.4	104.6	59.4	77.4	96.1	66.9	78.5	104.3	66.9	81.8	102.8	72.3	84.5	96.1	72.3	81.8
09	FINISHES	104.0	96.7	99.9	104.4	96.7	100.1	71.8	97.6	86.2	101.4	97.5	99.2	100.5	98.1	99.2	72.3	98.2	86.7
COVERS	DIVS. 10 - 14, 25, 28, 41, 43, 44, 46	100.0	101.8	100.4	100.0	101.8	100.4	100.0	92.2	98.4	100.0	101.9	100.4	100.0	101.9	100.4	100.0	102.1	100.4
21, 22, 23	FIRE SUPPRESSION, PLUMBING & HVAC	95.1	102.6	98.1	100.0	102.6	101.0	96.9	115.3	104.3	100.0	102.6	101.0	100.0	102.6	101.1	96.9	71.5	86.7
26, 27, 3370	ELECTRICAL, COMMUNICATIONS & UTIL.	94.6	81.3	87.6	97.9	81.3	89.2	87.3	96.5	92.1	94.7	103.2	99.1	102.1	96.3	99.1	87.3	73.9	80.3
MF2010	WEIGHTED AVERAGE	98.2	98.2	98.2	98.4	98.2	98.3	93.1	102.5	97.2	97.2	101.4	99.1	99.0	100.5	99.7	91.3	89.8	90.7

PENNSYLVANIA

DIVISION		ALLENTOWN 181			ALTOONA 166			BEDFORD 155			BRADFORD 167			BUTLER 160			CHAMBERSBURG 172		
		MAT.	INST.	TOTAL	MAT.	INST.	TOTAL	MAT.	INST.	TOTAL	MAT.	INST.	TOTAL	MAT.	INST.	TOTAL	MAT.	INST.	TOTAL
015433	CONTRACTOR EQUIPMENT		113.5	113.5		113.5	113.5		110.5	110.5		113.5	113.5		113.5	113.5		112.7	112.7
0241, 31-34	SITE & INFRASTRUCTURE, DEMOLITION	90.7	105.4	101.0	94.2	105.5	102.1	103.7	102.2	102.7	89.5	104.8	100.3	85.7	106.9	100.6	85.1	102.7	97.4
0310	Concrete Forming & Accessories	100.5	114.2	112.3	85.7	80.4	81.1	85.2	82.7	83.0	87.9	82.5	83.2	87.2	95.7	94.5	89.5	81.8	82.9
0320	Concrete Reinforcing	94.4	111.5	103.0	91.5	106.0	98.7	89.7	83.5	86.6	93.5	106.4	99.9	92.2	112.5	102.3	88.7	106.3	97.5
0330	Cast-in-Place Concrete	85.0	101.5	91.8	94.7	87.5	91.7	109.6	71.2	93.6	90.4	92.9	91.5	83.7	98.1	89.6	94.9	71.0	85.0
03	CONCRETE	94.3	110.0	102.1	89.5	89.1	89.3	103.4	80.2	91.9	96.0	92.0	94.0	81.7	100.8	91.1	103.3	84.1	93.8
04	MASONRY	94.2	102.2	99.2	96.9	65.6	77.5	114.6	88.5	98.5	94.0	88.5	90.6	98.9	98.5	98.7	94.7	88.9	91.1
05	METALS	99.9	123.1	107.0	93.7	118.3	101.3	97.5	105.6	100.0	97.8	118.2	104.1	93.4	123.4	102.7	99.5	116.5	104.7
06	WOOD, PLASTICS & COMPOSITES	103.0	117.3	111.1	81.2	82.7	82.0	83.7	82.6	83.1	87.6	80.3	83.5	82.6	94.8	89.5	92.5	82.7	87.0
07	THERMAL & MOISTURE PROTECTION	102.5	120.4	109.7	101.8	92.0	97.8	104.0	88.6	97.8	102.4	92.3	98.3	101.5	100.5	101.1	102.8	74.0	91.1
08	OPENINGS	92.5	116.3	98.1	86.4	90.1	87.3	92.1	83.6	90.1	92.6	92.3	92.5	86.4	105.7	91.0	89.7	84.8	88.6
0920	Plaster & Gypsum Board	99.7	117.6	111.8	91.1	81.9	84.8	91.6	81.9	85.0	91.9	79.4	83.4	91.1	94.4	93.3	99.4	81.9	87.5
0950, 0980	Ceilings & Acoustic Treatment	85.7	117.6	106.9	90.1	81.9	84.6	95.7	81.9	86.5	88.4	79.4	82.4	91.1	94.4	93.3	90.3	81.9	84.7
0960	Flooring	93.6	97.6	94.8	87.4	99.3	91.0	96.9	89.8	94.7	88.5	105.6	93.6	88.2	82.5	86.5	93.7	47.0	79.7
0970, 0990	Wall Finishes & Painting/Coating	98.3	72.1	82.5	94.6	108.9	103.2	104.7	83.3	91.9	98.3	92.6	94.9	94.6	108.9	103.2	101.9	83.3	90.7
09	FINISHES	93.8	107.1	101.2	92.2	85.9	88.7	98.3	82.6	89.6	91.9	85.7	88.5	92.1	93.5	92.9	93.9	75.4	83.6
COVERS	DIVS. 10 - 14, 25, 28, 41, 43, 44, 46	100.0	104.5	100.9	100.0	95.3	99.1	100.0	98.6	99.7	100.0	99.3	99.9	100.0	102.3	100.5	100.0	95.2	99.0
21, 22, 23	FIRE SUPPRESSION, PLUMBING & HVAC	100.2	110.6	104.4	99.8	84.3	93.6	95.0	89.1	92.7	95.4	90.9	93.6	95.0	93.9	94.5	95.4	89.0	92.8
26, 27, 3370	ELECTRICAL, COMMUNICATIONS & UTIL.	98.2	98.9	98.6	88.3	111.1	100.2	93.7	111.1	102.8	91.7	111.1	101.8	88.9	110.1	100.0	89.4	88.3	88.9
MF2010	WEIGHTED AVERAGE	97.6	108.8	102.4	94.3	92.7	93.6	98.0	92.6	95.7	95.3	96.8	96.0	92.1	102.2	96.5	96.0	89.7	93.2

PENNSYLVANIA

DIVISION		DOYLESTOWN 189			DUBOIS 158			ERIE 164 - 165			GREENSBURG 156			HARRISBURG 170 - 171			HAZLETON 182		
		MAT.	INST.	TOTAL	MAT.	INST.	TOTAL	MAT.	INST.	TOTAL	MAT.	INST.	TOTAL	MAT.	INST.	TOTAL	MAT.	INST.	TOTAL
015433	CONTRACTOR EQUIPMENT		94.6	94.6		110.5	110.5		113.5	113.5		110.5	110.5		112.7	112.7		113.5	113.5
0241, 31-34	SITE & INFRASTRUCTURE, DEMOLITION	103.5	91.4	95.1	108.7	102.5	104.4	91.1	105.9	101.5	99.8	104.7	103.2	85.2	104.5	98.7	84.1	105.7	99.3
0310	Concrete Forming & Accessories	84.7	129.1	123.0	84.7	83.9	84.0	99.9	88.3	89.9	91.5	95.6	95.1	99.8	89.4	90.8	82.3	90.2	89.1
0320	Concrete Reinforcing	91.3	135.0	113.1	89.1	106.7	97.9	93.5	106.5	100.0	89.1	112.5	100.8	98.1	106.7	102.4	91.7	110.5	101.0
0330	Cast-in-Place Concrete	80.3	87.6	83.4	105.7	93.5	100.6	93.1	82.6	88.7	101.7	97.5	100.0	97.1	96.8	97.0	80.3	92.7	85.5
03	CONCRETE	90.0	115.6	102.6	104.8	92.8	98.9	88.6	90.9	89.7	98.4	100.5	99.4	99.2	96.5	97.9	87.0	96.1	91.5
04	MASONRY	97.2	127.9	116.2	114.6	89.6	99.2	86.7	92.8	90.5	125.3	98.5	108.7	95.0	90.6	92.3	106.2	96.5	100.2
05	METALS	97.4	125.6	106.1	97.5	117.6	103.7	93.9	117.0	101.0	97.5	121.9	105.0	106.1	120.3	110.5	99.6	121.4	106.3
06	WOOD, PLASTICS & COMPOSITES	83.1	131.5	110.4	82.6	82.4	82.5	99.2	86.7	92.1	90.5	94.7	92.9	100.1	88.7	93.7	81.6	88.6	85.6
07	THERMAL & MOISTURE PROTECTION	100.6	132.8	113.7	104.3	95.5	100.7	102.3	93.4	98.7	103.9	100.1	102.4	106.2	112.2	108.6	102.0	107.6	104.2
08	OPENINGS	94.7	140.0	105.4	92.1	93.5	92.4	86.6	93.0	88.1	92.1	105.7	95.3	95.8	95.4	95.7	93.0	94.5	93.4
0920	Plaster & Gypsum Board	89.6	132.2	118.6	90.5	81.7	84.5	99.7	86.0	90.4	92.9	94.4	93.9	103.4	88.1	93.0	90.0	88.0	88.7
0950, 0980	Ceilings & Acoustic Treatment	84.9	132.2	116.4	95.7	81.7	86.4	85.7	86.0	85.9	94.8	94.4	94.5	99.4	88.1	91.9	86.7	88.0	87.6
0960	Flooring	78.6	136.8	96.0	96.7	105.8	99.4	92.3	93.5	92.7	99.8	69.3	90.7	98.7	93.4	97.1	86.2	96.3	89.2
0970, 0990	Wall Finishes & Painting/Coating	97.8	70.5	81.4	104.7	108.9	107.2	103.3	92.6	96.9	104.7	108.9	107.2	102.3	91.5	95.8	98.3	105.6	102.7
09	FINISHES	85.1	123.5	106.5	98.6	89.3	93.4	94.3	89.2	91.5	98.7	91.9	94.9	98.8	89.9	93.8	90.2	91.0	90.6
COVERS	DIVS. 10 - 14, 25, 28, 41, 43, 44, 46	100.0	71.9	94.4	100.0	98.6	99.7	100.0	100.9	100.2	100.0	102.1	100.4	100.0	96.4	99.3	100.0	99.1	99.8
21, 22, 23	FIRE SUPPRESSION, PLUMBING & HVAC	95.0	125.4	107.2	95.0	89.5	92.8	99.8	93.1	97.1	95.0	92.8	94.1	100.0	90.7	96.3	95.4	98.8	96.7
26, 27, 3370	ELECTRICAL, COMMUNICATIONS & UTIL.	91.1	126.9	109.8	94.3	111.1	103.1	90.1	87.4	88.7	94.3	111.1	103.1	96.8	88.4	92.4	92.6	91.5	92.0
MF2010	WEIGHTED AVERAGE	94.6	120.8	106.0	98.4	97.1	97.8	94.1	95.0	94.5	98.0	101.6	99.5	99.6	95.9	98.0	95.0	98.8	96.7

753

PENNSYLVANIA

DIVISION		INDIANA 157			JOHNSTOWN 159			KITTANNING 162			LANCASTER 175 - 176			LEHIGH VALLEY 180			MONTROSE 188		
		MAT.	INST.	TOTAL	MAT.	INST.	TOTAL	MAT.	INST.	TOTAL	MAT.	INST.	TOTAL	MAT.	INST.	TOTAL	MAT.	INST.	TOTAL
015433	CONTRACTOR EQUIPMENT		110.5	110.5		110.5	110.5		113.5	113.5		112.7	112.7		113.5	113.5		113.5	113.5
0241, 31 - 34	SITE & INFRASTRUCTURE, DEMOLITION	97.9	103.3	101.7	104.2	103.9	104.0	88.2	106.8	101.3	77.7	104.4	96.5	87.9	105.1	99.9	86.6	103.4	98.4
0310	Concrete Forming & Accessories	85.8	86.3	86.2	84.7	84.2	84.3	87.2	95.8	94.6	91.6	88.9	89.3	94.2	113.6	110.9	83.3	88.5	87.8
0320	Concrete Reinforcing	88.4	112.6	100.5	89.7	112.2	100.9	92.2	112.6	102.4	88.4	106.6	97.5	91.7	111.4	101.5	96.0	108.4	102.2
0330	Cast-in-Place Concrete	99.7	97.3	98.7	110.6	92.9	103.2	86.9	98.0	91.5	80.8	97.7	87.8	86.9	100.9	92.7	85.2	90.9	87.6
03	CONCRETE	95.9	96.3	96.1	104.2	93.7	99.0	84.1	100.8	92.4	90.9	96.5	93.7	93.3	109.4	101.2	92.0	94.1	93.1
04	MASONRY	110.3	100.2	104.1	111.1	88.0	96.8	101.7	100.2	100.8	99.9	90.8	94.3	94.2	101.7	98.8	94.1	96.0	95.3
05	METALS	97.6	121.5	105.0	97.5	120.1	104.5	93.5	123.4	102.7	99.5	119.7	105.7	99.5	121.7	106.4	97.9	115.3	103.2
06	WOOD, PLASTICS & COMPOSITES	84.5	82.4	83.3	82.6	82.6	82.6	82.6	94.8	89.5	95.2	88.7	91.5	94.4	117.3	107.3	82.4	88.3	85.8
07	THERMAL & MOISTURE PROTECTION	103.8	97.9	101.4	104.0	93.7	99.8	101.6	100.9	101.3	102.4	98.5	100.8	102.3	103.6	102.8	102.0	92.4	98.1
08	OPENINGS	92.1	95.2	92.8	92.1	91.8	92.0	86.4	102.0	90.1	89.7	99.3	92.0	93.0	116.3	98.5	89.8	93.8	90.8
0920	Plaster & Gypsum Board	92.0	81.7	85.0	90.3	81.9	84.6	91.1	94.4	93.3	101.3	88.1	92.3	93.0	117.6	109.7	90.4	87.7	88.6
0950, 0980	Ceilings & Acoustic Treatment	95.7	81.7	86.4	94.8	81.9	86.2	91.1	94.4	93.3	90.3	88.1	88.8	86.7	117.6	107.2	88.4	87.7	88.0
0960	Flooring	97.4	105.8	99.9	96.7	100.0	97.7	88.2	105.8	93.5	94.5	93.4	94.2	90.9	97.6	92.9	86.7	58.9	78.4
0970, 0990	Wall Finishes & Painting/Coating	104.7	108.9	107.2	104.7	108.9	107.2	94.6	108.9	103.2	101.9	58.4	75.7	98.3	67.9	80.0	98.3	105.6	102.7
09	FINISHES	98.0	90.2	93.7	97.9	88.7	92.8	92.3	97.5	95.2	93.9	86.2	89.6	92.2	105.5	99.6	91.0	84.8	87.5
COVERS	DIVS. 10 - 14, 25, 28, 41, 43, 44, 46	100.0	100.7	100.1	100.0	98.8	99.8	100.0	102.3	100.5	100.0	96.3	99.3	100.0	104.1	100.8	100.0	99.1	99.8
21, 22, 23	FIRE SUPPRESSION, PLUMBING & HVAC	95.0	92.7	94.1	95.0	89.8	92.9	95.0	96.1	95.4	95.4	90.8	93.5	95.4	110.3	101.4	95.4	98.0	96.4
26, 27, 3370	ELECTRICAL, COMMUNICATIONS & UTIL.	94.3	111.1	103.1	94.3	111.1	103.1	88.3	111.1	100.2	90.9	45.1	67.0	92.6	133.5	113.9	91.7	97.2	94.5
MF2010	WEIGHTED AVERAGE	96.9	100.1	98.3	97.9	97.3	97.7	92.5	103.4	97.3	94.8	89.3	92.4	95.4	112.5	102.9	94.4	97.1	95.6

PENNSYLVANIA

DIVISION		NEW CASTLE 161			NORRISTOWN 194			OIL CITY 163			PHILADELPHIA 190 - 191			PITTSBURGH 150 - 152			POTTSVILLE 179		
		MAT.	INST.	TOTAL	MAT.	INST.	TOTAL	MAT.	INST.	TOTAL	MAT.	INST.	TOTAL	MAT.	INST.	TOTAL	MAT.	INST.	TOTAL
015433	CONTRACTOR EQUIPMENT		113.5	113.5		98.0	98.0		113.5	113.5		97.5	97.5		111.8	111.8		112.7	112.7
0241, 31 - 34	SITE & INFRASTRUCTURE, DEMOLITION	86.1	106.9	100.7	92.4	99.8	97.6	84.7	105.0	99.0	99.9	99.2	99.4	103.4	106.7	105.7	80.4	104.6	97.4
0310	Concrete Forming & Accessories	87.2	97.4	96.0	83.5	130.8	124.3	87.2	83.5	84.0	98.7	139.9	134.3	99.0	98.7	98.7	83.2	90.0	89.1
0320	Concrete Reinforcing	91.0	93.3	92.2	92.5	142.2	117.3	92.2	93.1	92.6	100.5	142.2	121.3	90.1	112.9	101.5	87.7	103.8	95.7
0330	Cast-in-Place Concrete	84.4	96.9	89.6	79.7	127.5	99.6	82.0	96.5	88.1	94.8	131.7	110.1	105.7	97.7	102.4	86.0	97.9	91.0
03	CONCRETE	82.0	97.6	89.7	86.9	131.4	108.9	80.5	91.2	85.7	98.2	136.9	117.3	101.7	102.0	101.9	94.6	96.6	95.6
04	MASONRY	98.1	98.5	98.4	106.5	125.7	118.4	98.2	95.2	96.3	95.5	130.2	117.0	103.3	103.3	103.3	94.5	92.9	93.5
05	METALS	93.5	114.0	99.8	99.4	130.9	109.1	93.5	112.1	99.2	100.7	131.2	110.1	98.9	122.9	106.3	99.7	118.9	105.6
06	WOOD, PLASTICS & COMPOSITES	82.6	98.1	91.4	81.5	131.4	109.7	82.6	80.3	81.3	97.2	141.5	122.2	100.5	98.0	99.1	84.9	88.6	87.0
07	THERMAL & MOISTURE PROTECTION	101.5	97.0	99.7	103.9	132.6	115.6	101.4	94.9	98.8	102.7	135.7	116.1	104.1	102.0	103.3	102.5	107.1	104.3
08	OPENINGS	86.4	98.0	89.2	88.6	142.0	101.2	86.4	80.7	85.1	94.4	147.5	106.9	95.5	107.5	98.3	89.8	92.5	90.4
0920	Plaster & Gypsum Board	91.1	97.8	95.7	88.2	132.2	118.1	91.1	79.4	83.2	97.2	142.6	128.1	99.8	97.8	98.5	95.7	88.0	90.5
0950, 0980	Ceilings & Acoustic Treatment	91.1	97.8	95.6	90.5	132.2	118.3	91.1	79.4	83.3	91.6	142.6	125.6	95.7	97.8	97.1	90.3	88.0	88.8
0960	Flooring	88.2	58.5	79.4	91.6	139.5	105.9	88.2	105.8	93.5	98.5	139.5	110.7	102.8	108.0	104.3	91.1	93.4	91.8
0970, 0990	Wall Finishes & Painting/Coating	94.6	108.9	103.2	100.8	147.4	128.8	94.6	108.9	103.2	105.9	154.0	134.8	104.7	121.2	114.6	101.9	105.6	104.1
09	FINISHES	92.1	91.2	91.6	92.9	133.9	115.7	92.0	88.3	89.9	98.2	141.6	122.4	100.9	102.1	101.6	92.4	91.9	92.1
COVERS	DIVS. 10 - 14, 25, 28, 41, 43, 44, 46	100.0	102.6	100.5	100.0	111.7	102.3	100.0	100.4	100.1	100.0	120.5	104.1	100.0	102.5	100.5	100.0	96.7	99.3
21, 22, 23	FIRE SUPPRESSION, PLUMBING & HVAC	95.0	93.5	94.4	95.2	125.8	107.4	95.0	92.6	94.0	100.0	130.5	112.2	99.9	101.2	100.4	95.4	98.2	96.5
26, 27, 3370	ELECTRICAL, COMMUNICATIONS & UTIL.	88.9	88.7	88.8	92.0	148.7	121.6	90.8	110.1	100.9	98.6	148.7	124.7	96.7	111.1	104.2	89.0	91.1	90.1
MF2010	WEIGHTED AVERAGE	92.1	97.2	94.4	94.9	129.5	110.0	92.1	97.0	94.3	98.9	133.4	113.9	99.7	105.8	102.3	94.7	98.0	96.1

PENNSYLVANIA

DIVISION		READING 195 - 196			SCRANTON 184 - 185			STATE COLLEGE 168			STROUDSBURG 183			SUNBURY 178			UNIONTOWN 154		
		MAT.	INST.	TOTAL	MAT.	INST.	TOTAL	MAT.	INST.	TOTAL	MAT.	INST.	TOTAL	MAT.	INST.	TOTAL	MAT.	INST.	TOTAL
015433	CONTRACTOR EQUIPMENT		117.0	117.0		113.5	113.5		112.7	112.7		113.5	113.5		113.5	113.5		110.5	110.5
0241, 31 - 34	SITE & INFRASTRUCTURE, DEMOLITION	96.9	111.5	107.1	91.1	105.9	101.5	81.6	104.2	97.5	85.6	103.5	98.2	90.9	105.6	101.2	98.5	104.7	102.8
0310	Concrete Forming & Accessories	99.0	90.5	91.7	100.7	90.1	91.5	85.4	80.1	80.9	88.7	89.5	89.4	95.8	88.9	89.9	79.0	95.7	93.4
0320	Concrete Reinforcing	93.8	103.9	98.8	94.4	108.7	101.6	92.7	106.7	99.7	94.7	115.2	104.9	90.1	106.7	98.4	89.1	112.5	100.8
0330	Cast-in-Place Concrete	71.5	98.2	82.6	88.7	92.9	90.5	85.6	66.6	77.7	83.6	73.4	79.4	94.0	96.5	95.0	99.7	97.5	98.8
03	CONCRETE	86.2	96.9	91.5	96.1	95.8	96.0	96.3	81.9	89.2	90.8	89.8	90.3	98.2	96.2	97.2	95.5	100.6	98.0
04	MASONRY	96.3	94.0	94.9	94.6	96.5	95.8	99.5	79.2	87.0	91.8	101.3	97.7	93.9	90.4	91.7	127.7	98.5	109.6
05	METALS	99.7	119.2	105.7	101.9	121.2	107.9	97.6	119.0	104.2	99.6	117.8	105.2	99.4	120.0	105.8	97.3	122.0	104.9
06	WOOD, PLASTICS & COMPOSITES	100.3	88.5	93.7	103.0	88.2	94.7	89.7	82.7	85.7	88.6	88.3	88.4	93.2	88.6	90.6	76.4	94.7	86.7
07	THERMAL & MOISTURE PROTECTION	104.3	113.6	108.1	102.4	96.3	99.9	101.6	92.1	97.7	102.1	85.8	95.5	103.5	105.8	104.4	103.7	100.2	102.3
08	OPENINGS	93.1	98.3	94.3	92.5	93.7	92.8	89.6	90.1	89.7	93.0	89.1	92.1	89.9	93.4	90.7	92.0	105.7	95.3
0920	Plaster & Gypsum Board	100.4	88.0	92.0	101.9	87.6	92.2	93.1	81.9	85.5	91.4	87.7	88.9	95.2	88.0	90.3	88.4	94.4	92.5
0950, 0980	Ceilings & Acoustic Treatment	81.5	88.0	85.8	94.6	87.6	89.9	85.8	81.9	83.2	84.9	87.7	86.8	86.8	88.0	87.6	94.8	94.4	94.5
0960	Flooring	95.5	93.4	94.9	93.6	108.9	98.2	91.4	99.3	93.8	89.0	52.3	78.0	91.8	89.3	91.0	94.4	105.8	97.8
0970, 0990	Wall Finishes & Painting/Coating	99.5	105.6	103.1	98.3	105.6	102.7	98.3	108.9	104.7	98.3	66.0	78.9	101.9	105.6	104.1	104.7	108.9	107.2
09	FINISHES	94.0	91.5	92.6	96.0	94.6	95.2	91.2	85.9	88.3	90.9	80.3	85.0	93.1	90.6	91.7	96.5	97.3	96.9
COVERS	DIVS. 10 - 14, 25, 28, 41, 43, 44, 46	100.0	99.0	99.8	100.0	99.1	99.8	100.0	91.8	98.4	100.0	63.5	92.7	100.0	95.9	99.2	100.0	102.1	100.4
21, 22, 23	FIRE SUPPRESSION, PLUMBING & HVAC	100.2	107.3	103.0	100.2	98.8	99.6	95.4	84.6	91.1	95.4	100.5	97.4	95.4	90.4	93.4	95.0	92.8	94.1
26, 27, 3370	ELECTRICAL, COMMUNICATIONS & UTIL.	98.7	91.1	94.7	98.2	97.2	97.7	90.8	111.1	101.4	92.6	142.5	118.6	89.3	93.0	91.2	91.3	111.1	101.6
MF2010	WEIGHTED AVERAGE	97.1	101.1	98.8	98.3	99.7	98.9	94.9	93.0	94.1	94.9	102.0	98.0	95.5	96.3	95.8	97.1	102.2	99.4

City Cost Indexes

TEXAS

DIVISION		BEAUMONT 776 - 777			BROWNWOOD 768			BRYAN 778			CHILDRESS 792			CORPUS CHRISTI 783 - 784			DALLAS 752 - 753		
		MAT.	INST.	TOTAL	MAT.	INST.	TOTAL	MAT.	INST.	TOTAL	MAT.	INST.	TOTAL	MAT.	INST.	TOTAL	MAT.	INST.	TOTAL
015433	CONTRACTOR EQUIPMENT		91.2	91.2		89.7	89.7		91.2	91.2		89.7	89.7		96.2	96.2		99.1	99.1
0241, 31 - 34	SITE & INFRASTRUCTURE, DEMOLITION	89.0	87.6	88.0	100.5	86.1	90.4	80.7	90.3	87.5	103.1	87.0	91.8	138.3	82.8	99.3	107.7	88.2	94.0
0310	Concrete Forming & Accessories	106.7	48.4	56.4	97.7	33.0	41.8	84.5	45.5	50.8	98.7	61.9	66.9	98.8	39.8	47.9	97.5	64.1	68.7
0320	Concrete Reinforcing	89.0	41.5	65.3	91.7	50.7	71.3	91.3	49.5	70.4	89.5	51.0	70.3	84.6	47.2	65.9	99.1	52.8	76.0
0330	Cast-in-Place Concrete	86.8	51.7	72.2	105.3	42.7	79.3	69.6	65.7	68.0	102.7	49.4	80.6	109.1	46.9	83.3	96.4	54.8	79.1
03	CONCRETE	96.2	49.3	73.1	105.2	40.8	73.4	80.7	54.5	67.8	107.8	56.2	82.3	99.0	45.5	72.6	99.6	60.1	80.1
04	MASONRY	99.8	57.3	73.5	130.0	48.3	79.5	137.2	56.3	87.2	102.9	49.8	70.0	88.6	51.4	65.6	101.9	56.5	73.8
05	METALS	95.2	64.6	85.8	97.3	62.8	86.6	94.8	70.5	87.3	98.1	65.7	88.1	92.7	75.0	87.2	100.6	79.6	94.1
06	WOOD, PLASTICS & COMPOSITES	114.0	48.4	77.0	101.5	29.2	60.7	79.0	39.6	56.8	103.5	67.5	83.2	116.8	38.2	72.4	102.3	67.6	82.7
07	THERMAL & MOISTURE PROTECTION	103.5	55.5	84.0	100.1	44.1	77.4	95.4	56.2	79.5	101.7	48.8	80.3	102.3	48.4	80.4	92.1	62.5	80.1
08	OPENINGS	94.4	45.2	82.8	91.6	37.0	78.7	97.4	45.9	85.2	90.0	56.6	82.1	106.7	39.5	90.8	103.9	58.4	93.2
0920	Plaster & Gypsum Board	97.4	47.3	63.4	87.8	27.5	46.8	84.7	38.3	53.1	85.8	66.9	73.0	93.9	36.7	54.9	96.7	66.9	76.4
0950, 0980	Ceilings & Acoustic Treatment	95.5	47.3	63.5	91.7	27.5	49.0	89.0	38.3	55.3	91.5	66.9	75.2	91.5	36.7	55.0	103.4	66.9	79.1
0960	Flooring	109.1	74.3	98.7	109.2	45.5	90.1	84.2	62.9	77.9	111.6	41.6	90.7	115.4	64.2	100.1	107.8	48.6	90.1
0970, 0990	Wall Finishes & Painting/Coating	96.1	48.6	67.6	96.3	29.8	56.3	92.6	62.5	74.5	98.8	38.6	62.7	115.0	57.7	80.6	105.5	51.5	73.1
09	FINISHES	90.2	52.7	69.4	95.3	34.0	61.2	79.5	48.8	62.4	96.4	56.8	74.4	103.7	45.6	71.3	100.4	60.4	78.1
COVERS	DIVS. 10 - 14, 25, 28, 41, 43, 44, 46	100.0	79.4	95.9	100.0	37.3	87.4	100.0	79.8	96.0	100.0	70.0	94.0	100.0	78.3	95.7	100.0	82.0	96.4
21, 22, 23	FIRE SUPPRESSION, PLUMBING & HVAC	100.2	59.7	83.9	95.3	49.1	76.8	95.3	65.9	83.5	95.4	52.3	78.1	100.2	40.0	76.0	100.0	62.1	84.8
26, 27, 3370	ELECTRICAL, COMMUNICATIONS & UTIL.	92.1	70.8	81.0	93.2	43.7	67.4	90.2	67.7	78.4	94.9	43.4	68.0	91.8	61.4	76.0	95.7	65.2	79.7
MF2010	WEIGHTED AVERAGE	96.7	61.2	81.2	98.5	48.4	76.7	94.1	63.0	80.5	97.9	56.9	80.0	99.7	53.7	79.6	100.1	65.8	85.2

TEXAS

DIVISION		DEL RIO 788			DENTON 762			EASTLAND 764			EL PASO 798 - 799,885			FORT WORTH 760 - 761			GALVESTON 775		
		MAT.	INST.	TOTAL	MAT.	INST.	TOTAL	MAT.	INST.	TOTAL	MAT.	INST.	TOTAL	MAT.	INST.	TOTAL	MAT.	INST.	TOTAL
015433	CONTRACTOR EQUIPMENT		89.0	89.0		95.7	95.7		89.7	89.7		89.8	89.8		89.7	89.7		100.1	100.1
0241, 31 - 34	SITE & INFRASTRUCTURE, DEMOLITION	119.1	85.4	95.4	100.5	79.3	85.6	103.1	86.0	91.1	95.1	86.1	88.8	97.4	87.1	90.1	108.0	88.1	94.1
0310	Concrete Forming & Accessories	95.3	36.5	44.6	104.6	32.3	42.2	98.5	35.8	44.4	97.2	43.8	51.1	96.9	63.5	68.1	94.2	65.6	69.5
0320	Concrete Reinforcing	85.2	46.7	66.0	93.0	51.0	72.1	92.0	50.7	71.3	97.5	45.8	71.7	97.3	52.7	75.0	90.8	62.8	76.8
0330	Cast-in-Place Concrete	117.4	42.8	86.4	81.5	44.4	66.1	111.3	43.3	83.1	96.6	41.3	73.7	98.6	50.7	78.7	92.3	66.9	81.8
03	CONCRETE	119.8	41.7	81.3	82.8	42.0	62.7	110.0	42.4	76.6	99.9	44.3	72.5	100.7	57.7	79.5	97.2	67.1	82.3
04	MASONRY	103.6	50.0	70.4	138.8	47.1	82.1	99.9	48.2	67.9	96.5	46.9	65.8	98.4	56.4	72.4	95.9	56.4	71.5
05	METALS	92.5	60.8	82.7	96.9	75.5	90.3	97.1	63.2	86.6	95.3	62.6	85.2	98.8	68.5	89.5	96.3	88.8	94.0
06	WOOD, PLASTICS & COMPOSITES	97.0	34.6	61.8	112.9	31.9	67.2	108.3	32.8	65.7	99.9	45.8	69.4	99.5	67.5	81.4	96.4	66.4	79.4
07	THERMAL & MOISTURE PROTECTION	99.2	43.6	76.6	98.3	44.1	76.3	100.5	44.2	77.6	98.9	54.5	80.9	98.4	52.6	79.8	94.5	65.3	82.6
08	OPENINGS	99.3	33.9	83.9	107.8	37.5	91.1	72.9	39.0	64.9	91.2	43.9	80.0	98.7	58.3	89.2	101.8	64.0	92.9
0920	Plaster & Gypsum Board	89.7	33.0	51.2	92.3	30.2	50.0	87.8	31.2	49.3	93.7	44.6	60.3	99.0	66.9	74.9	92.0	65.7	74.1
0950, 0980	Ceilings & Acoustic Treatment	87.8	33.0	51.4	96.2	30.2	52.2	91.7	31.2	51.4	95.9	44.6	61.7	102.3	66.9	78.8	91.6	65.7	74.4
0960	Flooring	97.3	34.7	78.6	102.5	43.5	84.8	141.2	45.5	112.6	114.0	63.5	98.9	137.1	41.4	108.5	98.1	62.9	87.6
0970, 0990	Wall Finishes & Painting/Coating	101.3	38.4	63.5	106.2	29.6	60.2	97.8	30.5	57.4	93.2	34.9	58.2	95.2	51.1	68.7	104.3	47.0	69.9
09	FINISHES	95.8	36.0	62.5	92.0	33.5	59.4	104.8	36.3	66.6	99.2	46.5	69.9	107.4	58.8	80.3	88.8	63.0	74.4
COVERS	DIVS. 10 - 14, 25, 28, 41, 43, 44, 46	100.0	37.1	87.4	100.0	36.0	87.2	100.0	38.4	87.7	100.0	77.3	95.4	100.0	81.7	96.3	100.0	84.3	96.9
21, 22, 23	FIRE SUPPRESSION, PLUMBING & HVAC	95.2	46.9	75.8	95.3	37.9	72.3	95.3	49.4	76.9	100.0	34.2	73.6	100.0	57.7	83.1	95.2	66.0	83.5
26, 27, 3370	ELECTRICAL, COMMUNICATIONS & UTIL.	94.0	30.1	60.6	95.6	43.8	68.6	93.1	43.8	67.3	92.7	54.9	73.0	94.5	62.4	77.8	91.7	69.5	80.1
MF2010	WEIGHTED AVERAGE	99.4	46.2	76.3	98.2	46.6	75.7	96.5	49.1	75.9	97.2	50.6	76.9	99.6	62.5	83.5	96.3	69.7	84.7

TEXAS

DIVISION		GIDDINGS 789			GREENVILLE 754			HOUSTON 770 - 772			HUNTSVILLE 773			LAREDO 780			LONGVIEW 756		
		MAT.	INST.	TOTAL	MAT.	INST.	TOTAL	MAT.	INST.	TOTAL	MAT.	INST.	TOTAL	MAT.	INST.	TOTAL	MAT.	INST.	TOTAL
015433	CONTRACTOR EQUIPMENT		89.0	89.0		96.7	96.7		100.0	100.0		91.2	91.2		89.0	89.0		91.5	91.5
0241, 31 - 34	SITE & INFRASTRUCTURE, DEMOLITION	105.0	85.4	91.3	101.0	83.5	88.7	106.7	87.9	93.5	95.8	87.9	90.3	99.1	86.8	90.5	97.3	90.3	92.4
0310	Concrete Forming & Accessories	93.0	55.5	60.7	89.1	27.3	35.7	96.3	65.8	69.9	91.8	55.4	60.4	95.3	40.0	47.5	85.5	28.1	35.9
0320	Concrete Reinforcing	85.8	46.8	66.3	99.6	24.9	62.3	90.6	63.3	77.0	91.5	50.5	71.0	85.2	47.6	66.4	98.4	22.7	60.6
0330	Cast-in-Place Concrete	99.5	42.9	76.0	87.8	37.7	67.0	89.5	66.9	80.1	95.6	48.2	75.9	84.1	59.3	73.8	102.1	35.0	74.2
03	CONCRETE	96.5	50.2	73.7	92.2	32.6	62.8	94.9	67.2	81.3	103.8	52.8	78.7	91.4	49.1	70.6	108.4	30.8	70.1
04	MASONRY	111.8	50.0	73.5	159.0	46.1	89.1	95.8	66.6	77.7	135.8	51.6	83.7	97.3	58.6	73.3	154.6	42.0	85.0
05	METALS	92.0	61.8	82.6	97.9	63.6	87.3	99.2	89.7	96.3	94.7	66.3	85.9	95.0	64.0	85.5	91.2	50.5	78.7
06	WOOD, PLASTICS & COMPOSITES	96.0	59.4	75.4	92.3	26.3	55.1	98.8	66.4	80.5	88.3	58.2	71.3	97.0	38.1	63.7	86.2	28.4	53.6
07	THERMAL & MOISTURE PROTECTION	99.9	47.7	78.7	92.2	39.5	70.8	94.1	68.1	83.6	96.3	48.2	76.8	98.2	51.9	79.4	93.5	34.9	69.7
08	OPENINGS	98.5	49.9	86.7	102.1	26.0	84.1	104.4	64.0	94.8	97.4	48.5	85.8	99.2	39.4	85.0	91.7	26.0	76.1
0920	Plaster & Gypsum Board	88.6	58.7	68.3	90.4	24.5	45.5	94.5	65.7	74.9	89.5	57.4	67.7	90.8	36.7	54.0	88.7	26.8	46.6
0950, 0980	Ceilings & Acoustic Treatment	87.8	58.7	68.4	99.0	24.5	49.4	97.0	65.7	76.2	89.0	57.4	67.9	92.2	36.7	55.2	95.4	26.8	49.7
0960	Flooring	97.8	34.7	79.0	103.7	47.8	87.0	99.1	62.9	88.3	87.4	34.7	71.7	97.1	64.2	87.3	108.1	35.1	86.2
0970, 0990	Wall Finishes & Painting/Coating	101.3	30.5	58.8	105.5	25.1	57.2	104.3	62.5	79.2	92.6	31.3	55.8	101.3	54.4	73.1	95.1	29.3	55.6
09	FINISHES	94.7	50.2	69.9	96.9	30.4	59.8	96.0	64.7	78.5	81.9	49.9	64.1	95.2	45.1	67.3	101.0	29.4	61.1
COVERS	DIVS. 10 - 14, 25, 28, 41, 43, 44, 46	100.0	42.9	88.6	100.0	34.4	86.9	100.0	84.3	96.9	100.0	43.3	88.6	100.0	76.3	95.2	100.0	21.9	84.4
21, 22, 23	FIRE SUPPRESSION, PLUMBING & HVAC	95.3	62.5	82.1	95.2	43.5	74.4	100.0	66.1	86.4	95.3	63.3	82.5	100.1	38.8	75.5	95.1	27.5	68.0
26, 27, 3370	ELECTRICAL, COMMUNICATIONS & UTIL.	90.8	43.4	66.1	92.3	27.1	58.3	93.7	67.8	80.2	90.2	43.4	65.8	94.2	59.9	76.3	92.7	53.2	72.0
MF2010	WEIGHTED AVERAGE	96.4	55.6	78.6	99.4	42.2	74.5	98.7	70.9	86.6	97.2	56.9	79.6	97.1	53.7	78.2	99.0	40.5	73.5

		TEXAS																
	DIVISION	LUBBOCK			LUFKIN			MCALLEN			MCKINNEY			MIDLAND			ODESSA		
		793 - 794			759			785			750			797			797		
		MAT.	INST.	TOTAL	MAT.	INST.	TOTAL	MAT.	INST.	TOTAL	MAT.	INST.	TOTAL	MAT.	INST.	TOTAL	MAT.	INST.	TOTAL
015433	CONTRACTOR EQUIPMENT		98.2	98.2		91.5	91.5		96.4	96.4		96.7	96.7		98.2	98.2		89.7	89.7
0241, 31 - 34	SITE & INFRASTRUCTURE, DEMOLITION	116.1	85.0	94.3	92.5	91.8	92.0	142.5	82.9	100.6	97.4	83.6	87.7	118.7	85.0	95.1	94.2	87.0	89.1
0310	Concrete Forming & Accessories	99.1	51.0	57.6	88.6	56.8	61.2	99.9	35.8	44.6	88.2	36.3	43.4	103.0	51.0	58.2	100.2	50.9	57.7
0320	Concrete Reinforcing	90.5	51.7	71.1	100.2	62.4	81.3	84.8	47.1	66.0	99.6	51.1	75.4	91.4	50.9	71.2	89.4	50.9	70.2
0330	Cast-in-Place Concrete	100.3	48.4	78.8	91.3	44.7	72.0	118.5	45.3	88.1	82.4	45.2	66.9	106.6	48.6	82.5	100.1	47.5	78.3
03	CONCRETE	96.9	52.0	74.7	100.8	54.3	77.8	106.6	43.1	75.3	87.6	44.0	66.0	101.6	51.9	77.1	98.3	50.7	74.8
04	MASONRY	98.1	55.7	71.8	118.7	52.3	77.6	103.2	51.4	71.1	171.0	48.4	95.1	114.8	42.0	69.7	98.7	42.0	63.6
05	METALS	104.1	80.1	96.7	98.0	69.1	89.1	92.4	74.5	86.9	97.8	74.4	90.6	102.4	79.0	95.2	99.9	67.1	89.8
06	WOOD, PLASTICS & COMPOSITES	104.1	54.9	76.3	94.3	59.4	74.6	115.4	33.6	69.2	91.0	36.4	60.2	109.1	54.9	78.5	104.2	54.7	76.3
07	THERMAL & MOISTURE PROTECTION	90.8	52.7	75.3	93.3	48.0	74.9	102.6	45.0	79.2	92.0	45.9	73.3	91.0	47.4	73.3	101.2	46.6	79.0
08	OPENINGS	103.6	49.4	90.8	69.6	53.4	65.8	103.4	36.8	87.6	102.0	39.8	87.3	102.5	49.1	89.9	92.8	49.0	82.4
0920	Plaster & Gypsum Board	86.7	53.8	64.3	87.7	58.7	68.0	94.9	31.9	52.0	89.6	34.8	52.4	88.3	53.8	64.8	86.2	53.8	64.2
0950, 0980	Ceilings & Acoustic Treatment	95.1	53.8	67.6	88.3	58.7	68.6	92.2	31.9	52.1	99.0	34.8	56.3	92.4	53.8	66.7	93.3	53.8	67.0
0960	Flooring	107.0	39.3	86.7	143.4	38.2	112.0	114.9	65.0	100.0	103.3	35.6	83.1	108.2	48.6	90.4	113.4	48.6	94.0
0970, 0990	Wall Finishes & Painting/Coating	110.2	49.5	73.7	95.1	37.8	60.6	115.0	28.9	63.2	105.5	41.2	66.9	110.2	49.5	73.7	98.8	49.5	69.2
09	FINISHES	98.8	48.8	70.9	109.1	52.0	77.3	104.3	39.8	68.4	96.4	36.7	63.1	99.2	50.7	72.1	96.2	50.6	70.8
COVERS	DIVS. 10 - 14, 25, 28, 41, 43, 44, 46	100.0	77.8	95.6	100.0	70.8	94.2	100.0	76.0	95.2	100.0	39.7	87.9	100.0	78.6	95.7	100.0	78.3	95.6
21, 22, 23	FIRE SUPPRESSION, PLUMBING & HVAC	99.8	45.2	77.9	95.1	63.5	82.4	95.3	30.8	69.4	95.2	41.4	73.6	94.9	45.3	75.0	100.3	45.3	78.2
26, 27, 3370	ELECTRICAL, COMMUNICATIONS & UTIL.	93.6	49.6	70.6	94.0	43.4	67.6	91.6	34.2	61.6	92.4	45.2	67.8	93.5	40.4	65.8	95.0	40.3	66.4
MF2010	WEIGHTED AVERAGE	100.0	56.3	81.0	95.9	59.1	79.9	99.7	46.6	76.6	99.3	48.9	77.3	99.9	53.6	79.7	98.2	52.5	78.3

		TEXAS																
	DIVISION	PALESTINE			SAN ANGELO			SAN ANTONIO			TEMPLE			TEXARKANA			TYLER		
		758			769			781 - 782			765			755			757		
		MAT.	INST.	TOTAL	MAT.	INST.	TOTAL	MAT.	INST.	TOTAL	MAT.	INST.	TOTAL	MAT.	INST.	TOTAL	MAT.	INST.	TOTAL
015433	CONTRACTOR EQUIPMENT		91.5	91.5		89.7	89.7		91.5	91.5		89.7	89.7		91.5	91.5		91.5	91.5
0241, 31 - 34	SITE & INFRASTRUCTURE, DEMOLITION	98.6	91.1	93.3	97.0	88.1	90.8	101.8	91.4	94.5	86.0	85.9	85.9	87.0	91.1	89.9	96.6	91.5	93.1
0310	Concrete Forming & Accessories	80.1	55.8	59.1	98.0	36.5	44.9	94.5	54.8	60.3	101.3	39.7	48.1	95.4	34.0	42.4	90.3	33.1	40.9
0320	Concrete Reinforcing	97.7	50.7	74.2	91.6	50.9	71.3	91.8	49.1	70.5	91.8	47.4	69.6	97.6	52.4	75.0	98.4	53.0	75.7
0330	Cast-in-Place Concrete	83.5	42.6	66.5	99.3	46.6	77.4	84.5	65.4	76.6	81.4	48.4	67.7	84.1	43.4	67.2	100.2	42.5	76.3
03	CONCRETE	102.9	50.9	77.2	100.4	43.9	72.5	92.6	58.3	75.7	86.0	45.2	65.9	93.6	42.0	68.1	108.0	41.4	75.1
04	MASONRY	113.5	48.5	73.3	126.6	41.6	74.0	98.9	66.5	78.8	137.9	48.4	82.5	175.4	44.7	94.5	164.8	54.4	96.5
05	METALS	97.7	62.7	86.9	97.4	66.5	87.9	96.1	68.7	87.6	97.1	62.8	86.5	91.1	66.9	83.6	97.6	68.0	88.5
06	WOOD, PLASTICS & COMPOSITES	84.7	59.4	70.4	101.8	36.1	64.7	96.7	52.8	71.9	111.0	39.4	70.6	98.1	32.3	61.0	96.0	30.5	59.0
07	THERMAL & MOISTURE PROTECTION	93.7	46.4	74.5	100.0	42.1	76.5	95.9	64.3	83.1	99.6	45.0	77.4	93.2	47.2	74.5	93.6	53.2	77.2
08	OPENINGS	69.5	50.7	65.1	91.7	38.8	79.2	99.9	51.7	88.5	69.6	41.8	63.0	91.7	37.9	78.9	69.5	36.9	61.8
0920	Plaster & Gypsum Board	84.4	58.7	66.9	87.8	34.6	51.6	88.8	51.8	63.6	87.8	38.0	53.9	93.2	30.7	50.7	87.7	28.9	47.7
0950, 0980	Ceilings & Acoustic Treatment	88.3	58.7	68.6	91.7	34.6	53.7	91.2	51.8	65.0	91.7	38.0	56.0	95.4	30.7	52.4	88.3	28.9	48.7
0960	Flooring	135.3	58.9	112.5	109.2	34.7	86.9	97.6	64.3	87.6	143.4	41.7	113.0	115.6	59.4	98.7	145.3	37.0	112.9
0970, 0990	Wall Finishes & Painting/Coating	95.1	30.5	56.3	96.3	49.5	68.2	98.5	54.4	72.0	97.8	38.5	62.2	95.1	39.4	61.6	95.1	39.4	61.6
09	FINISHES	106.9	54.4	77.7	95.0	36.4	62.4	94.8	55.4	72.8	104.1	39.6	68.2	103.1	38.1	66.9	109.9	32.6	66.9
COVERS	DIVS. 10 - 14, 25, 28, 41, 43, 44, 46	100.0	40.7	88.1	100.0	75.0	95.0	100.0	80.6	96.1	100.0	36.8	87.3	100.0	74.9	95.0	100.0	74.7	94.9
21, 22, 23	FIRE SUPPRESSION, PLUMBING & HVAC	95.1	58.5	80.4	95.3	44.6	75.0	100.0	64.5	85.8	95.3	48.2	76.4	95.1	32.9	70.2	95.1	57.7	80.1
26, 27, 3370	ELECTRICAL, COMMUNICATIONS & UTIL.	90.1	43.4	65.7	97.2	45.8	70.4	94.3	60.0	76.4	94.3	64.9	79.0	93.8	61.1	76.8	92.7	55.0	73.0
MF2010	WEIGHTED AVERAGE	95.4	55.8	78.2	98.2	49.5	77.0	97.5	64.5	83.1	95.0	52.7	76.6	98.4	49.7	77.2	98.9	54.6	79.6

		TEXAS															UTAH		
	DIVISION	VICTORIA			WACO			WAXAHACHIE			WHARTON			WICHITA FALLS			LOGAN		
		779			766 - 767			751			774			763			843		
		MAT.	INST.	TOTAL	MAT.	INST.	TOTAL	MAT.	INST.	TOTAL	MAT.	INST.	TOTAL	MAT.	INST.	TOTAL	MAT.	INST.	TOTAL
015433	CONTRACTOR EQUIPMENT		99.0	99.0		89.7	89.7		96.7	96.7		100.1	100.1		89.7	89.7		97.2	97.2
0241, 31 - 34	SITE & INFRASTRUCTURE, DEMOLITION	112.7	82.3	91.4	94.2	87.0	89.2	99.0	84.4	88.8	118.4	85.5	95.3	94.9	86.7	89.1	93.4	96.2	95.4
0310	Concrete Forming & Accessories	94.0	35.1	43.2	99.9	39.6	47.9	88.2	59.5	63.5	88.7	36.7	43.9	99.9	37.2	45.8	104.8	58.1	64.5
0320	Concrete Reinforcing	87.2	30.3	58.8	91.5	49.4	70.5	99.6	51.1	75.4	90.7	50.2	70.5	91.5	51.7	71.6	102.3	80.2	91.3
0330	Cast-in-Place Concrete	103.6	41.0	77.7	88.1	65.8	78.8	86.9	41.7	68.1	106.5	51.2	83.5	94.1	44.7	73.6	86.9	72.8	81.0
03	CONCRETE	104.5	38.5	71.9	93.0	51.7	72.6	91.3	53.2	72.5	108.8	46.4	78.0	95.8	43.8	70.1	107.9	67.9	88.2
04	MASONRY	112.4	34.1	64.0	98.3	53.7	70.7	159.7	48.5	90.9	97.0	44.6	64.6	98.8	56.9	72.9	103.9	59.7	76.5
05	METALS	94.9	70.3	87.3	99.4	67.0	89.4	97.9	77.0	91.4	96.3	78.5	90.8	99.4	68.5	89.8	101.0	78.2	94.0
06	WOOD, PLASTICS & COMPOSITES	99.9	35.9	63.8	109.2	35.1	67.4	91.0	67.5	77.8	89.4	32.6	57.3	109.2	35.0	67.3	81.5	56.2	67.2
07	THERMAL & MOISTURE PROTECTION	98.4	39.5	74.5	100.5	46.9	78.8	92.1	46.3	73.5	94.8	49.3	76.3	100.5	50.5	80.2	97.9	61.8	83.3
08	OPENINGS	101.7	35.2	85.9	81.5	42.5	72.2	102.1	56.8	91.3	101.8	37.4	86.6	81.5	40.3	71.7	94.3	57.1	85.5
0920	Plaster & Gypsum Board	89.3	34.3	51.9	88.3	33.6	51.1	90.1	66.9	74.3	86.8	30.9	48.8	88.3	33.4	51.0	75.6	54.8	61.4
0950, 0980	Ceilings & Acoustic Treatment	92.5	34.3	53.8	93.5	33.6	53.6	100.7	66.9	78.2	91.6	30.9	51.2	93.5	33.4	53.5	105.1	54.8	71.6
0960	Flooring	97.8	38.2	80.0	142.3	45.1	113.3	103.3	38.2	83.8	96.1	45.5	80.9	143.5	77.9	123.9	100.2	48.6	84.8
0970, 0990	Wall Finishes & Painting/Coating	104.5	37.8	64.4	97.8	49.8	69.0	105.5	37.8	64.8	104.3	31.3	60.5	100.5	49.5	69.9	102.9	62.0	78.3
09	FINISHES	87.0	36.0	58.6	104.7	40.2	68.8	97.1	54.8	73.5	88.3	36.7	59.5	105.3	45.0	71.7	98.5	56.0	74.8
COVERS	DIVS. 10 - 14, 25, 28, 41, 43, 44, 46	100.0	36.6	87.3	100.0	78.2	95.6	100.0	40.6	88.1	100.0	38.7	87.7	100.0	65.2	93.0	100.0	54.1	90.8
21, 22, 23	FIRE SUPPRESSION, PLUMBING & HVAC	95.3	31.2	69.6	100.2	54.2	81.8	95.2	40.5	73.2	95.2	63.4	82.5	100.2	48.4	79.5	100.0	69.0	87.6
26, 27, 3370	ELECTRICAL, COMMUNICATIONS & UTIL.	96.5	39.7	66.9	97.4	65.1	80.5	92.4	65.2	78.2	95.3	43.8	68.4	99.1	61.0	79.2	95.4	74.3	84.4
MF2010	WEIGHTED AVERAGE	98.2	42.7	74.1	97.2	57.3	79.8	99.3	56.4	80.6	98.1	53.8	78.8	97.8	55.0	79.2	99.7	68.8	86.2

DIVISION		UTAH										VERMONT					
		OGDEN 842,844			PRICE 845			PROVO 846-847			SALT LAKE CITY 840-841			BELLOWS FALLS 051			BENNINGTON 052	
		MAT.	INST.	TOTAL	MAT.	INST.	TOTAL	MAT.	INST.	TOTAL	MAT.	INST.	TOTAL	MAT.	INST.	TOTAL	MAT.	INST.	TOTAL
015433	CONTRACTOR EQUIPMENT		97.2	97.2		96.3	96.3		96.3	96.3		97.2	97.2		100.6	100.6		100.6	100.6
0241, 31 - 34	SITE & INFRASTRUCTURE, DEMOLITION	82.2	96.2	92.1	90.8	94.6	93.5	89.8	94.6	93.2	81.8	96.2	91.9	82.6	100.1	94.9	82.0	100.1	94.7
0310	Concrete Forming & Accessories	104.8	58.1	64.5	107.1	49.4	57.3	106.3	58.0	64.6	107.3	58.0	64.7	100.2	87.5	89.3	97.8	109.1	107.6
0320	Concrete Reinforcing	102.0	80.2	91.1	109.8	80.1	95.0	110.7	80.2	95.5	104.3	80.2	92.3	83.0	87.3	85.2	83.0	87.3	85.2
0330	Cast-in-Place Concrete	88.2	72.8	81.8	87.0	60.0	75.8	87.0	72.7	81.1	96.4	72.7	86.6	89.5	113.1	99.3	89.5	113.1	99.3
03	CONCRETE	97.5	67.9	82.9	109.3	59.6	84.8	107.8	67.8	88.1	116.9	67.8	92.6	93.5	96.2	94.8	93.3	105.8	99.5
04	MASONRY	97.8	59.7	74.2	109.1	59.7	78.5	109.3	59.7	78.6	111.0	59.7	79.3	94.6	96.9	96.0	102.1	96.9	98.9
05	METALS	101.5	78.2	94.3	98.3	77.6	91.9	99.3	78.0	92.7	106.1	78.0	97.4	95.5	89.3	93.6	95.5	89.2	93.4
06	WOOD, PLASTICS & COMPOSITES	81.5	56.2	67.2	84.4	45.3	62.3	82.9	56.2	67.8	83.2	56.2	68.0	102.2	85.5	92.8	99.2	115.1	108.1
07	THERMAL & MOISTURE PROTECTION	96.9	61.8	82.6	99.5	59.4	83.3	99.5	61.8	84.2	103.8	61.8	86.8	98.0	84.8	92.7	98.0	83.1	92.0
08	OPENINGS	94.3	57.1	85.5	98.3	50.1	86.9	98.3	57.1	88.5	96.1	57.1	86.9	103.5	88.1	99.9	103.5	104.2	103.7
0920	Plaster & Gypsum Board	75.6	54.8	61.4	77.9	43.5	54.5	76.0	54.8	61.6	83.0	54.8	63.8	99.8	84.4	89.3	97.9	114.9	109.5
0950, 0980	Ceilings & Acoustic Treatment	105.1	54.8	71.6	105.1	43.5	64.2	105.1	54.8	71.6	99.2	54.8	69.6	92.3	84.4	87.1	92.3	114.9	107.3
0960	Flooring	98.0	48.6	83.3	101.2	36.1	81.8	100.9	48.6	85.3	102.2	48.6	86.2	101.6	106.5	103.1	100.8	106.5	102.5
0970, 0990	Wall Finishes & Painting/Coating	102.9	62.0	78.3	102.9	38.3	64.1	102.9	49.0	70.5	106.5	49.0	71.9	95.7	106.8	102.3	95.7	106.8	102.3
09	FINISHES	96.5	56.0	74.0	99.5	44.5	68.9	99.1	54.6	74.3	98.2	54.6	73.9	97.2	92.6	94.6	96.7	110.1	104.2
COVERS	DIVS. 10 - 14, 25, 28, 41, 43, 44, 46	100.0	54.1	90.8	100.0	47.0	89.4	100.0	54.0	90.8	100.0	54.0	90.8	100.0	100.3	100.1	100.0	103.5	100.7
21, 22, 23	FIRE SUPPRESSION, PLUMBING & HVAC	100.0	69.0	87.6	97.5	68.6	85.9	100.0	69.0	87.6	100.1	69.0	87.6	95.2	98.5	96.5	95.2	98.4	96.5
26, 27, 3370	ELECTRICAL, COMMUNICATIONS & UTIL.	95.7	74.3	84.5	101.2	74.3	87.1	96.2	61.2	77.9	98.6	61.2	79.1	98.6	91.5	94.9	98.6	62.6	79.8
MF2010	WEIGHTED AVERAGE	97.9	68.8	85.2	100.1	65.3	84.9	100.1	66.7	85.6	102.2	66.8	86.8	96.6	94.7	95.8	96.9	95.3	96.2

DIVISION		VERMONT																
		BRATTLEBORO 053			BURLINGTON 054			GUILDHALL 059			MONTPELIER 056			RUTLAND 057			ST. JOHNSBURY 058	
		MAT.	INST.	TOTAL	MAT.	INST.	TOTAL	MAT.	INST.	TOTAL	MAT.	INST.	TOTAL	MAT.	INST.	TOTAL	MAT.	INST.	TOTAL
015433	CONTRACTOR EQUIPMENT		100.6	100.6		100.6	100.6		100.6	100.6		100.6	100.6		100.6	100.6		100.6	100.6
0241, 31 - 34	SITE & INFRASTRUCTURE, DEMOLITION	83.4	100.1	95.1	86.2	100.0	95.9	81.7	98.7	93.6	86.6	99.8	95.8	85.9	99.8	95.6	81.7	98.7	93.6
0310	Concrete Forming & Accessories	100.5	87.4	89.2	98.0	89.6	90.8	98.1	80.1	82.6	101.8	86.1	88.2	100.8	89.6	91.1	96.5	80.1	82.4
0320	Concrete Reinforcing	82.2	87.3	84.7	105.7	87.2	96.4	83.8	87.2	85.5	89.0	87.2	88.1	103.7	87.2	95.5	82.2	87.2	84.7
0330	Cast-in-Place Concrete	92.3	113.1	100.9	102.6	112.0	106.5	86.8	103.2	93.6	105.0	111.9	107.9	87.7	111.9	97.8	86.8	103.2	93.6
03	CONCRETE	95.5	96.2	95.9	104.0	96.7	100.4	91.0	89.5	90.3	102.8	95.2	99.0	96.9	96.7	96.8	90.7	89.5	90.1
04	MASONRY	101.1	96.9	98.5	104.8	95.4	99.0	101.3	79.6	87.8	100.1	95.4	97.2	85.8	95.4	91.7	124.9	79.6	96.9
05	METALS	95.5	89.2	93.6	104.0	88.4	99.2	95.6	88.3	93.3	100.2	88.3	96.5	101.0	88.4	97.1	95.6	88.3	93.3
06	WOOD, PLASTICS & COMPOSITES	102.6	85.5	92.9	98.3	90.3	93.8	98.5	85.5	91.2	96.4	85.5	90.3	102.7	90.3	95.7	93.6	85.5	89.0
07	THERMAL & MOISTURE PROTECTION	98.1	80.0	90.8	104.3	82.5	95.4	97.9	72.6	87.6	105.0	82.0	95.6	98.2	82.5	91.8	97.8	72.6	87.6
08	OPENINGS	103.5	88.1	99.9	107.5	86.4	102.5	103.5	83.8	98.8	103.8	83.8	99.1	106.6	86.4	101.8	103.5	83.8	98.8
0920	Plaster & Gypsum Board	99.8	84.4	89.3	100.5	89.3	92.9	106.1	84.4	91.3	105.4	84.4	91.1	100.5	89.3	92.9	108.0	84.4	91.9
0950, 0980	Ceilings & Acoustic Treatment	92.3	84.4	87.1	96.0	89.3	91.6	92.3	84.4	87.1	102.5	84.4	90.5	97.0	89.3	91.9	92.3	84.4	87.1
0960	Flooring	101.7	106.5	103.2	103.1	106.5	104.1	104.6	106.5	105.2	104.0	106.5	104.8	101.6	106.5	103.1	107.7	106.5	107.3
0970, 0990	Wall Finishes & Painting/Coating	95.7	106.8	102.3	100.4	85.3	91.4	95.7	85.3	89.4	100.5	85.3	91.4	95.7	85.3	89.4	95.7	85.3	89.4
09	FINISHES	97.3	92.6	94.7	99.1	92.7	95.5	98.8	85.9	91.6	101.0	89.8	94.8	98.4	92.7	95.2	99.9	85.9	92.1
COVERS	DIVS. 10 - 14, 25, 28, 41, 43, 44, 46	100.0	100.3	100.1	100.0	100.2	100.0	100.0	94.3	98.9	100.0	99.7	99.9	100.0	100.2	100.0	100.0	94.3	98.9
21, 22, 23	FIRE SUPPRESSION, PLUMBING & HVAC	95.2	98.4	96.5	99.9	73.3	89.3	95.2	65.3	83.2	95.0	73.3	86.3	100.1	73.3	89.3	95.2	65.3	83.2
26, 27, 3370	ELECTRICAL, COMMUNICATIONS & UTIL.	98.6	91.5	94.9	98.0	62.6	79.5	98.6	62.6	79.8	98.0	62.6	79.5	98.6	62.6	79.8	98.6	62.6	79.8
MF2010	WEIGHTED AVERAGE	97.2	94.5	96.0	101.5	85.1	94.4	96.8	79.2	89.1	99.2	84.3	92.7	99.2	85.1	93.0	97.9	79.2	89.8

DIVISION		VERMONT			VIRGINIA													
		WHITE RIVER JCT. 050			ALEXANDRIA 223			ARLINGTON 222			BRISTOL 242			CHARLOTTESVILLE 229			CULPEPER 227	
		MAT.	INST.	TOTAL	MAT.	INST.	TOTAL	MAT.	INST.	TOTAL	MAT.	INST.	TOTAL	MAT.	INST.	TOTAL	MAT.	INST.	TOTAL
015433	CONTRACTOR EQUIPMENT		100.6	100.6		102.1	102.1		100.8	100.8		100.8	100.8		105.1	105.1		100.8	100.8
0241, 31 - 34	SITE & INFRASTRUCTURE, DEMOLITION	85.7	98.8	94.9	113.5	89.3	96.5	123.7	87.3	98.2	107.8	85.7	92.3	112.6	87.7	95.1	111.2	87.2	94.3
0310	Concrete Forming & Accessories	95.0	80.7	82.7	93.3	73.6	76.3	92.5	73.0	75.7	88.4	43.4	49.6	86.8	49.6	54.7	83.9	72.3	73.9
0320	Concrete Reinforcing	83.0	87.2	85.1	85.0	87.0	86.0	95.9	87.0	91.5	95.9	67.3	81.6	95.3	73.0	84.2	95.9	86.9	91.4
0330	Cast-in-Place Concrete	92.3	104.1	97.2	107.5	82.2	97.0	104.6	81.4	95.0	104.1	49.1	81.3	108.3	56.1	86.6	107.1	68.8	91.2
03	CONCRETE	97.3	90.1	93.7	101.2	80.1	90.8	105.6	79.6	92.8	102.1	51.7	77.2	102.8	57.9	80.7	100.1	74.9	87.6
04	MASONRY	112.6	81.2	93.1	86.0	72.9	77.8	99.1	71.3	81.9	89.1	52.3	66.3	112.3	54.2	76.3	100.9	71.2	82.5
05	METALS	95.6	88.3	93.3	102.5	97.0	100.8	101.1	97.4	99.9	99.9	85.8	95.6	100.2	90.6	97.2	100.3	95.4	98.8
06	WOOD, PLASTICS & COMPOSITES	95.9	85.5	90.0	98.1	71.9	83.3	94.4	71.9	81.7	86.6	40.9	60.8	85.1	46.6	63.4	83.7	71.9	77.1
07	THERMAL & MOISTURE PROTECTION	98.2	73.3	88.1	103.2	82.4	94.7	105.1	81.2	95.4	104.1	63.1	87.1	104.3	69.0	90.0	104.5	78.7	94.0
08	OPENINGS	103.5	83.8	98.8	96.4	75.6	91.5	94.6	75.6	90.1	97.4	46.8	85.5	95.7	52.7	85.5	96.0	75.6	91.2
0920	Plaster & Gypsum Board	96.5	84.4	88.3	108.4	70.9	82.9	104.4	70.9	81.6	100.1	38.9	58.4	100.1	44.1	62.0	100.3	70.9	80.3
0950, 0980	Ceilings & Acoustic Treatment	92.3	84.4	87.1	97.7	70.9	79.9	95.1	70.9	79.0	94.2	38.9	57.4	94.2	44.1	60.8	95.1	70.9	79.0
0960	Flooring	99.7	106.5	101.8	106.7	84.5	100.0	105.2	82.7	98.5	101.9	67.7	91.7	100.6	67.7	90.7	100.6	82.7	95.2
0970, 0990	Wall Finishes & Painting/Coating	95.7	85.3	89.4	120.5	79.9	96.1	120.5	79.9	96.1	106.3	55.5	75.7	106.3	77.7	89.1	120.5	77.7	94.8
09	FINISHES	96.5	86.3	90.8	102.9	75.5	87.6	102.6	74.7	87.0	99.2	48.2	70.8	98.8	54.6	74.2	99.6	74.3	85.5
COVERS	DIVS. 10 - 14, 25, 28, 41, 43, 44, 46	100.0	94.9	99.0	100.0	88.5	97.7	100.0	86.0	97.2	100.0	69.5	93.9	100.0	78.0	95.6	100.0	86.0	97.2
21, 22, 23	FIRE SUPPRESSION, PLUMBING & HVAC	95.2	66.1	83.5	100.3	87.7	95.2	100.3	86.8	94.9	95.4	51.6	77.8	95.4	68.7	84.7	95.4	73.2	86.5
26, 27, 3370	ELECTRICAL, COMMUNICATIONS & UTIL.	98.6	62.6	79.8	95.8	99.2	97.6	93.4	99.2	96.5	95.5	36.2	64.6	95.4	70.8	82.6	98.0	99.2	98.6
MF2010	WEIGHTED AVERAGE	97.9	79.7	90.0	99.8	85.4	93.5	100.6	84.7	93.6	98.1	55.6	79.6	99.2	67.3	85.3	98.6	80.8	90.9

VIRGINIA

DIVISION		FAIRFAX 220 - 221			FARMVILLE 239			FREDERICKSBURG 224 - 225			GRUNDY 246			HARRISONBURG 228			LYNCHBURG 245		
		MAT.	INST.	TOTAL	MAT.	INST.	TOTAL	MAT.	INST.	TOTAL	MAT.	INST.	TOTAL	MAT.	INST.	TOTAL	MAT.	INST.	TOTAL
015433	CONTRACTOR EQUIPMENT		100.8	100.8		105.1	105.1		100.8	100.8		100.8	100.8		100.8	100.8		100.8	100.8
0241, 31 - 34	SITE & INFRASTRUCTURE, DEMOLITION	122.4	87.3	97.8	107.2	87.2	93.2	110.8	87.2	94.2	105.6	84.4	90.7	119.4	85.9	95.9	106.5	85.9	92.1
0310	Concrete Forming & Accessories	86.8	72.8	74.7	100.4	44.6	52.3	86.8	70.8	73.0	91.5	37.2	44.6	82.9	43.5	48.9	88.4	61.6	65.3
0320	Concrete Reinforcing	95.9	87.0	91.5	94.7	51.5	73.1	96.7	86.9	91.8	94.6	52.0	73.3	95.9	66.9	81.5	95.3	67.3	81.3
0330	Cast-in-Place Concrete	104.6	81.3	94.9	106.8	54.1	85.0	106.2	64.7	89.0	104.1	48.1	80.9	104.6	58.8	85.6	104.1	58.4	85.2
03	CONCRETE	105.3	79.4	92.5	101.4	50.9	76.5	99.8	72.8	86.5	100.9	45.3	73.5	103.2	54.9	79.3	100.8	63.0	82.1
04	MASONRY	99.0	71.3	81.8	95.6	45.6	64.7	99.9	71.2	82.1	90.9	48.1	64.4	97.4	51.2	68.8	104.9	54.1	73.5
05	METALS	100.4	97.0	99.3	100.0	78.2	93.3	100.3	96.2	99.0	99.9	71.0	91.0	100.2	85.1	95.6	100.1	86.3	95.9
06	WOOD, PLASTICS & COMPOSITES	86.6	71.9	78.3	101.9	45.0	69.8	86.6	69.6	77.0	89.6	35.8	59.3	82.7	39.8	58.5	86.6	64.0	73.9
07	THERMAL & MOISTURE PROTECTION	105.0	73.9	92.4	105.3	50.2	83.0	104.5	79.1	94.2	104.7	46.1	80.9	104.9	64.5	88.5	104.5	65.1	88.5
08	OPENINGS	94.6	75.6	90.1	94.9	44.0	82.9	95.7	74.0	90.6	97.4	35.2	82.7	96.0	50.6	85.3	96.0	59.4	87.3
0920	Plaster & Gypsum Board	100.3	70.9	80.3	109.3	42.5	63.8	100.3	68.5	78.7	100.1	33.7	54.9	100.1	37.8	57.7	100.1	62.7	74.7
0950, 0980	Ceilings & Acoustic Treatment	95.1	70.9	79.0	92.5	42.5	59.2	95.1	68.5	77.4	94.2	33.7	53.9	94.2	37.8	56.7	94.2	62.7	73.3
0960	Flooring	102.2	82.7	96.4	108.6	61.4	94.5	102.2	82.7	96.4	103.2	34.3	82.6	100.3	75.3	92.9	101.9	67.7	91.7
0970, 0990	Wall Finishes & Painting/Coating	120.5	79.9	96.1	107.7	39.6	66.7	120.5	77.7	94.8	106.3	35.9	64.0	120.5	55.5	81.4	106.3	55.5	75.7
09	FINISHES	101.2	74.7	86.4	101.8	47.0	71.3	100.1	72.9	85.0	99.3	35.9	64.0	100.0	48.9	71.5	99.0	61.5	78.1
COVERS	DIVS. 10 - 14, 25, 28, 41, 43, 44, 46	100.0	86.0	97.2	100.0	46.8	89.3	100.0	81.9	96.4	100.0	44.8	88.9	100.0	69.3	93.8	100.0	72.7	94.5
21, 22, 23	FIRE SUPPRESSION, PLUMBING & HVAC	95.4	86.8	91.9	95.3	44.3	74.9	95.4	86.5	91.8	95.4	63.5	82.6	95.4	67.1	84.1	95.4	68.4	84.6
26, 27, 3370	ELECTRICAL, COMMUNICATIONS & UTIL.	96.6	99.2	98.0	90.4	49.4	69.0	93.6	99.2	96.6	95.5	45.7	69.5	95.7	98.7	97.3	96.6	53.9	74.3
MF2010	WEIGHTED AVERAGE	99.3	84.4	92.8	97.8	53.3	78.5	98.2	83.0	91.6	98.0	53.4	78.6	98.8	68.1	85.5	98.6	66.1	84.5

VIRGINIA

DIVISION		NEWPORT NEWS 236			NORFOLK 233 - 235			PETERSBURG 238			PORTSMOUTH 237			PULASKI 243			RICHMOND 230 - 232		
		MAT.	INST.	TOTAL	MAT.	INST.	TOTAL	MAT.	INST.	TOTAL	MAT.	INST.	TOTAL	MAT.	INST.	TOTAL	MAT.	INST.	TOTAL
015433	CONTRACTOR EQUIPMENT		105.1	105.1		105.7	105.7		105.1	105.1		105.0	105.0		100.8	100.8		105.0	105.0
0241, 31 - 34	SITE & INFRASTRUCTURE, DEMOLITION	106.2	88.4	93.7	105.7	89.4	94.3	109.7	88.6	94.9	104.7	88.2	93.1	104.9	85.1	91.0	103.5	88.6	93.0
0310	Concrete Forming & Accessories	99.7	65.4	70.1	99.5	65.6	70.2	93.0	58.3	63.1	88.9	54.2	58.9	91.5	39.5	46.6	100.7	58.3	64.1
0320	Concrete Reinforcing	94.4	72.8	83.6	99.5	72.8	86.2	94.1	73.2	83.6	94.1	72.8	83.4	94.6	66.7	80.7	100.7	73.2	87.0
0330	Cast-in-Place Concrete	103.8	66.8	88.5	111.9	66.9	93.2	110.3	54.2	87.0	102.8	66.7	87.8	104.1	48.9	81.2	98.8	54.2	80.3
03	CONCRETE	98.6	68.6	83.8	103.3	68.7	86.2	103.6	61.2	82.7	97.3	63.5	80.7	100.9	49.6	75.6	97.3	61.2	79.5
04	MASONRY	90.6	54.9	68.5	99.1	54.9	71.7	103.3	53.6	72.5	96.0	54.9	70.6	85.9	49.1	63.1	92.1	53.5	68.2
05	METALS	102.2	90.4	98.6	102.0	90.5	98.4	100.1	91.1	97.3	101.2	89.7	97.7	100.0	83.8	95.0	106.2	91.1	101.5
06	WOOD, PLASTICS & COMPOSITES	100.6	67.7	82.0	97.0	67.7	80.5	91.4	59.8	73.6	87.6	52.6	67.8	89.6	37.6	60.3	101.6	59.8	78.0
07	THERMAL & MOISTURE PROTECTION	105.3	69.7	90.8	101.9	69.7	88.8	105.3	69.6	90.8	105.3	67.0	89.7	104.7	51.0	82.9	103.7	69.6	89.8
08	OPENINGS	95.3	63.3	87.7	94.2	63.3	86.9	94.6	59.9	86.4	95.4	55.0	85.8	97.5	43.2	84.6	99.0	59.9	89.8
0920	Plaster & Gypsum Board	110.2	65.8	80.0	106.3	65.8	78.8	101.7	57.7	71.8	102.0	50.2	66.8	100.1	35.5	56.1	104.7	57.7	72.8
0950, 0980	Ceilings & Acoustic Treatment	96.1	65.8	75.9	97.7	65.8	76.5	93.4	57.7	69.7	96.1	50.2	65.6	94.2	35.5	55.1	100.4	57.7	72.0
0960	Flooring	108.6	67.7	96.4	103.5	67.7	92.8	104.7	72.5	95.1	101.7	67.7	91.5	103.2	67.7	92.6	109.4	72.5	98.4
0970, 0990	Wall Finishes & Painting/Coating	107.7	42.9	68.8	105.8	77.7	88.9	107.7	77.7	89.7	107.7	77.7	89.7	106.3	55.5	75.7	107.0	77.7	89.4
09	FINISHES	102.5	63.5	80.8	100.7	67.4	82.2	100.1	62.5	79.1	99.5	57.9	76.3	99.3	44.7	68.9	104.4	62.5	81.1
COVERS	DIVS. 10 - 14, 25, 28, 41, 43, 44, 46	100.0	75.4	95.1	100.0	75.4	95.1	100.0	78.2	95.6	100.0	73.7	94.7	100.0	45.0	89.0	100.0	78.2	95.6
21, 22, 23	FIRE SUPPRESSION, PLUMBING & HVAC	100.2	64.1	85.7	100.0	64.7	85.8	95.3	66.9	83.9	100.2	64.7	86.0	95.4	63.4	82.5	100.0	66.9	86.7
26, 27, 3370	ELECTRICAL, COMMUNICATIONS & UTIL.	93.1	60.3	76.0	96.9	59.7	77.4	93.3	70.8	81.5	91.4	59.7	74.9	95.5	55.7	74.7	96.2	70.8	83.0
MF2010	WEIGHTED AVERAGE	99.2	68.2	85.7	100.0	68.8	86.4	98.6	68.9	85.6	98.6	66.1	84.5	97.7	58.3	80.6	100.4	68.9	86.7

VIRGINIA / WASHINGTON

DIVISION		ROANOKE 240 - 241			STAUNTON 244			WINCHESTER 226			CLARKSTON 994			EVERETT 982			OLYMPIA 985		
		MAT.	INST.	TOTAL	MAT.	INST.	TOTAL	MAT.	INST.	TOTAL	MAT.	INST.	TOTAL	MAT.	INST.	TOTAL	MAT.	INST.	TOTAL
015433	CONTRACTOR EQUIPMENT		100.8	100.8		105.1	105.1		100.8	100.8		90.4	90.4		102.1	102.1		102.1	102.1
0241, 31 - 34	SITE & INFRASTRUCTURE, DEMOLITION	105.2	85.9	91.7	109.1	87.3	93.8	118.1	87.2	96.4	97.1	90.0	92.1	89.4	110.3	104.1	90.2	110.4	104.4
0310	Concrete Forming & Accessories	97.9	61.8	66.8	91.1	51.1	56.6	85.2	70.8	72.8	114.8	68.8	75.1	114.9	99.6	101.7	103.1	99.8	100.2
0320	Concrete Reinforcing	95.6	67.4	81.5	95.3	50.5	72.9	95.3	86.3	90.8	105.7	87.4	96.6	110.2	100.2	105.2	116.1	100.2	105.2
0330	Cast-in-Place Concrete	118.3	58.5	93.5	108.3	52.0	84.9	104.6	64.7	88.1	97.0	83.2	91.3	99.8	103.8	101.5	89.2	105.4	96.0
03	CONCRETE	105.5	63.1	84.6	102.3	53.0	78.0	102.6	72.7	87.9	110.7	77.4	94.3	98.7	100.7	99.7	96.9	101.3	99.1
04	MASONRY	92.1	54.1	68.6	100.6	52.3	70.7	95.1	60.0	73.3	97.2	80.7	87.0	111.9	99.0	103.9	103.1	99.9	101.1
05	METALS	102.2	86.5	97.4	100.2	81.7	94.5	100.3	94.8	98.6	88.1	81.2	86.0	104.3	91.7	100.4	104.2	91.6	100.3
06	WOOD, PLASTICS & COMPOSITES	99.0	64.0	79.3	89.6	51.0	67.8	85.1	69.6	76.4	103.3	65.2	81.8	112.1	99.3	104.9	94.6	99.3	97.2
07	THERMAL & MOISTURE PROTECTION	104.3	67.2	89.3	104.3	53.0	83.5	105.0	76.2	93.3	142.7	76.9	116.0	100.5	100.5	100.5	101.6	97.8	100.1
08	OPENINGS	96.4	59.4	87.6	96.0	49.2	84.9	97.5	74.7	92.1	106.7	69.7	98.0	101.9	99.8	101.4	103.5	99.8	102.6
0920	Plaster & Gypsum Board	108.4	62.7	77.3	100.1	48.6	65.1	100.3	68.5	78.7	130.6	64.0	85.3	110.7	99.2	102.9	103.1	99.2	100.5
0950, 0980	Ceilings & Acoustic Treatment	97.7	62.7	74.5	94.2	48.6	63.9	95.1	68.5	77.4	97.9	64.0	75.3	99.9	99.2	99.5	106.3	99.2	101.6
0960	Flooring	106.7	67.7	95.0	102.7	40.2	84.0	101.6	82.7	96.0	98.3	48.0	83.2	117.9	93.3	110.6	109.2	93.4	104.5
0970, 0990	Wall Finishes & Painting/Coating	106.3	55.5	75.7	106.3	35.3	63.6	120.5	89.1	101.6	106.4	59.8	78.4	104.8	90.1	96.0	110.3	90.1	98.1
09	FINISHES	101.8	62.4	79.8	99.2	47.6	70.4	100.5	74.2	85.9	114.8	62.6	85.7	109.0	97.1	102.4	104.6	97.4	100.6
COVERS	DIVS. 10 - 14, 25, 28, 41, 43, 44, 46	100.0	72.7	94.5	100.0	72.6	94.5	100.0	85.7	97.1	100.0	77.3	95.5	100.0	99.6	99.9	100.0	100.1	100.0
21, 22, 23	FIRE SUPPRESSION, PLUMBING & HVAC	100.3	65.8	86.5	95.4	60.1	81.2	95.4	86.8	91.9	95.4	84.7	91.1	100.1	100.3	100.2	100.0	100.8	100.3
26, 27, 3370	ELECTRICAL, COMMUNICATIONS & UTIL.	95.5	55.7	74.7	94.3	74.6	84.0	94.1	99.2	96.8	94.9	94.4	94.6	103.0	98.5	100.7	101.0	99.7	100.3
MF2010	WEIGHTED AVERAGE	100.2	66.0	85.3	98.4	62.7	82.9	98.7	82.1	91.5	100.6	80.7	92.0	102.1	99.6	101.0	101.0	100.0	100.6

City Cost Indexes

WASHINGTON

DIVISION		RICHLAND 993 MAT.	INST.	TOTAL	SEATTLE 980-981,987 MAT.	INST.	TOTAL	SPOKANE 990-992 MAT.	INST.	TOTAL	TACOMA 983-984 MAT.	INST.	TOTAL	VANCOUVER 986 MAT.	INST.	TOTAL	WENATCHEE 988 MAT.	INST.	TOTAL
015433	CONTRACTOR EQUIPMENT		90.4	90.4		102.0	102.0		90.4	90.4		102.1	102.1		97.1	97.1		102.1	102.1
0241, 31 - 34	SITE & INFRASTRUCTURE, DEMOLITION	99.6	90.8	93.4	94.5	108.6	104.4	98.7	90.8	93.2	92.4	110.4	105.0	102.3	98.1	99.3	101.4	109.2	106.9
0310	Concrete Forming & Accessories	114.9	78.4	83.4	106.9	100.3	101.2	119.8	78.0	83.7	105.5	99.8	100.6	106.2	92.1	94.0	107.2	77.5	81.6
0320	Concrete Reinforcing	101.4	87.6	94.5	112.2	100.3	106.3	102.1	87.6	94.9	109.0	100.2	104.6	109.9	100.0	104.9	109.8	89.3	99.6
0330	Cast-in-Place Concrete	97.2	85.5	92.4	103.6	105.6	104.5	101.0	85.3	94.5	102.6	105.4	103.8	114.6	99.5	108.3	104.8	77.4	93.4
03	CONCRETE	110.3	82.6	96.6	102.0	101.7	101.8	112.6	82.3	97.6	100.5	101.3	100.9	110.5	95.9	103.3	108.4	79.8	94.3
04	MASONRY	99.3	83.2	89.3	109.2	99.9	103.4	99.9	83.8	89.9	106.7	99.9	102.5	107.3	96.7	100.7	109.1	91.5	98.2
05	METALS	88.5	84.1	87.1	104.5	93.4	101.1	90.8	83.7	88.6	106.0	91.6	101.6	103.4	92.1	99.9	103.5	86.1	98.1
06	WOOD, PLASTICS & COMPOSITES	103.4	75.7	87.8	102.2	99.3	100.6	112.1	75.7	91.6	101.3	99.3	100.2	93.1	91.9	92.5	102.9	75.9	87.6
07	THERMAL & MOISTURE PROTECTION	144.1	79.7	117.9	97.6	100.9	99.0	140.6	79.1	115.6	100.2	98.7	99.6	100.6	92.5	97.3	100.8	82.2	93.3
08	OPENINGS	109.2	71.2	100.2	105.2	99.8	103.9	109.7	71.7	100.7	102.7	99.8	102.0	98.5	94.4	97.5	102.2	71.5	94.9
0920	Plaster & Gypsum Board	130.6	74.8	92.6	106.9	99.2	101.7	121.5	74.8	89.7	111.5	99.2	103.1	109.4	91.9	97.5	114.0	75.1	87.5
0950, 0980	Ceilings & Acoustic Treatment	104.8	74.8	84.8	101.8	99.2	100.1	99.8	74.8	83.2	103.5	99.2	100.6	98.4	91.9	94.1	95.3	75.1	81.8
0960	Flooring	98.7	81.6	93.5	110.9	101.0	108.0	98.2	86.9	94.8	111.4	93.4	106.0	118.1	104.0	113.9	114.1	63.8	99.1
0970, 0990	Wall Finishes & Painting/Coating	106.4	66.2	82.2	104.2	90.1	95.7	106.6	72.4	86.0	104.8	90.1	96.0	107.2	68.4	83.9	104.8	66.2	81.6
09	FINISHES	116.6	76.7	94.4	108.1	98.9	102.9	114.3	78.5	94.3	108.2	97.4	102.2	105.6	91.9	98.0	108.5	72.9	88.7
COVERS	DIVS. 10 - 14, 25, 28, 41, 43, 44, 46	100.0	87.2	97.4	100.0	100.1	100.0	100.0	87.1	97.4	100.0	100.1	100.0	100.0	62.0	92.4	100.0	78.5	95.7
21, 22, 23	FIRE SUPPRESSION, PLUMBING & HVAC	100.3	109.7	104.1	100.0	117.1	106.8	100.2	85.9	94.5	100.1	100.8	100.4	100.2	88.6	95.5	95.2	87.9	92.3
26, 27, 3370	ELECTRICAL, COMMUNICATIONS & UTIL.	92.1	94.4	93.3	102.4	107.0	104.8	90.5	79.1	84.5	102.8	99.7	101.2	107.5	101.0	104.1	103.7	98.5	101.0
MF2010	WEIGHTED AVERAGE	102.2	89.6	96.7	102.5	104.8	103.5	102.5	82.7	93.8	102.3	100.0	101.3	103.1	93.2	98.8	102.0	87.1	95.5

WASHINGTON / WEST VIRGINIA

DIVISION		YAKIMA 989 MAT.	INST.	TOTAL	BECKLEY 258-259 MAT.	INST.	TOTAL	BLUEFIELD 247-248 MAT.	INST.	TOTAL	BUCKHANNON 262 MAT.	INST.	TOTAL	CHARLESTON 250-253 MAT.	INST.	TOTAL	CLARKSBURG 263-264 MAT.	INST.	TOTAL
015433	CONTRACTOR EQUIPMENT		102.1	102.1		100.8	100.8		100.8	100.8		100.8	100.8		100.8	100.8		100.8	100.8
0241, 31 - 34	SITE & INFRASTRUCTURE, DEMOLITION	94.7	109.8	105.3	97.9	89.2	91.8	99.6	89.2	92.3	105.8	89.2	94.1	99.0	90.0	92.7	106.3	89.2	94.3
0310	Concrete Forming & Accessories	106.0	95.3	96.8	86.3	92.0	91.2	88.3	91.9	91.4	87.7	92.2	91.6	99.6	93.4	94.2	85.3	92.1	91.1
0320	Concrete Reinforcing	109.5	88.8	99.2	92.3	89.4	90.9	94.2	84.9	89.6	94.8	85.0	89.9	100.6	89.5	95.1	94.8	84.4	89.6
0330	Cast-in-Place Concrete	109.6	84.4	99.2	102.0	102.1	102.0	101.9	102.1	102.0	101.6	100.3	101.0	106.0	102.7	101.4	111.3	98.4	105.9
03	CONCRETE	105.1	90.0	97.7	96.5	95.5	96.0	96.9	94.7	95.8	99.7	94.2	97.0	98.1	96.4	97.2	103.7	93.4	98.6
04	MASONRY	100.4	81.6	88.8	90.8	93.4	92.4	87.5	93.4	91.1	97.4	92.3	94.2	89.2	95.3	93.0	100.7	92.3	95.5
05	METALS	104.2	85.7	98.5	101.2	98.2	100.3	100.2	96.5	99.1	100.4	97.3	99.4	99.8	98.9	99.5	100.4	96.9	99.3
06	WOOD, PLASTICS & COMPOSITES	101.7	99.3	100.4	85.1	92.8	89.4	88.6	92.8	91.0	87.9	92.8	90.6	101.1	92.8	96.4	84.4	92.8	89.1
07	THERMAL & MOISTURE PROTECTION	100.3	81.6	92.7	107.1	89.4	99.9	104.4	89.4	98.4	104.7	90.0	98.7	103.6	90.2	98.2	104.6	88.9	98.3
08	OPENINGS	102.2	81.0	97.2	96.1	85.0	93.5	97.9	83.9	94.6	97.9	83.9	94.6	98.1	85.0	95.0	97.9	85.1	94.9
0920	Plaster & Gypsum Board	111.1	99.2	103.0	93.3	92.4	92.7	99.3	92.4	94.6	99.7	92.4	94.7	97.5	92.4	94.0	97.5	92.4	94.0
0950, 0980	Ceilings & Acoustic Treatment	97.3	99.2	98.6	93.4	92.4	92.7	92.4	92.4	92.4	94.2	92.4	93.0	102.2	92.4	95.7	94.2	92.4	93.0
0960	Flooring	112.4	59.1	96.4	100.5	114.1	104.6	99.8	114.1	104.1	99.5	114.1	103.9	104.4	114.1	107.3	98.6	114.1	103.2
0970, 0990	Wall Finishes & Painting/Coating	104.8	72.4	85.3	107.1	93.5	98.9	106.3	93.5	98.6	106.3	93.8	98.8	106.6	93.5	98.7	106.3	93.8	98.8
09	FINISHES	107.2	86.5	95.7	97.8	96.9	97.3	97.5	96.9	97.2	98.4	96.7	97.4	102.4	97.4	99.6	97.7	96.7	97.1
COVERS	DIVS. 10 - 14, 25, 28, 41, 43, 44, 46	100.0	97.3	99.5	100.0	56.6	91.3	100.0	56.6	91.3	100.0	96.7	99.3	100.0	97.7	99.5	100.0	96.7	99.3
21, 22, 23	FIRE SUPPRESSION, PLUMBING & HVAC	100.1	109.1	103.7	95.5	91.5	93.9	95.4	91.5	93.8	95.4	92.3	94.2	100.1	92.9	97.2	95.4	92.2	94.1
26, 27, 3370	ELECTRICAL, COMMUNICATIONS & UTIL.	105.9	94.4	99.9	91.2	91.9	91.6	94.4	91.9	93.1	95.8	96.8	96.3	96.3	91.9	94.0	95.8	96.8	96.3
MF2010	WEIGHTED AVERAGE	102.5	94.4	99.0	96.9	92.0	94.8	97.1	91.7	94.7	98.2	93.6	96.2	99.0	94.1	96.9	98.8	93.5	96.5

WEST VIRGINIA

DIVISION		GASSAWAY 266 MAT.	INST.	TOTAL	HUNTINGTON 255-257 MAT.	INST.	TOTAL	LEWISBURG 249 MAT.	INST.	TOTAL	MARTINSBURG 254 MAT.	INST.	TOTAL	MORGANTOWN 265 MAT.	INST.	TOTAL	PARKERSBURG 261 MAT.	INST.	TOTAL
015433	CONTRACTOR EQUIPMENT		100.8	100.8		100.8	100.8		100.8	100.8		100.8	100.8		100.8	100.8		100.8	100.8
0241, 31 - 34	SITE & INFRASTRUCTURE, DEMOLITION	103.2	89.2	93.3	102.4	90.4	94.0	115.3	89.2	97.0	101.4	89.7	93.2	100.6	89.8	93.0	108.8	89.9	95.5
0310	Concrete Forming & Accessories	87.2	92.2	91.5	98.2	96.0	96.3	85.6	91.8	91.0	86.3	82.4	83.0	85.6	91.8	91.0	89.8	90.0	90.0
0320	Concrete Reinforcing	94.8	85.0	89.9	93.7	90.6	92.2	94.8	84.9	89.9	92.3	83.0	87.6	94.8	84.3	89.6	94.2	84.8	89.5
0330	Cast-in-Place Concrete	106.3	101.0	104.1	111.1	103.5	108.0	101.9	102.1	102.0	106.8	96.0	102.3	101.5	100.1	101.0	103.8	97.1	101.0
03	CONCRETE	100.2	94.4	97.3	101.8	98.0	99.9	105.8	94.6	100.3	99.9	88.0	94.1	96.6	93.8	95.3	101.6	92.1	96.9
04	MASONRY	101.5	92.3	95.8	89.8	99.9	96.0	90.3	93.4	92.2	91.7	85.6	87.9	117.9	92.3	102.0	78.3	90.7	86.0
05	METALS	100.3	97.2	99.4	103.6	99.5	102.3	100.3	96.5	99.1	101.6	94.9	99.5	100.4	96.7	99.3	101.0	96.8	99.7
06	WOOD, PLASTICS & COMPOSITES	87.0	92.8	90.2	97.2	95.4	96.2	84.7	92.8	89.3	85.1	81.3	82.9	84.7	92.8	89.3	88.0	88.8	88.4
07	THERMAL & MOISTURE PROTECTION	104.4	90.0	98.6	107.3	91.4	100.8	105.2	89.4	98.8	107.4	78.2	95.5	104.5	88.9	98.2	104.4	89.6	98.4
08	OPENINGS	96.1	83.9	93.2	95.4	86.6	93.4	97.9	83.9	94.6	98.1	73.9	92.4	99.1	85.1	95.8	96.9	81.8	93.3
0920	Plaster & Gypsum Board	99.0	92.4	94.5	102.1	95.1	97.4	97.5	92.4	94.0	93.9	80.5	84.8	97.5	92.4	94.0	100.1	88.3	92.0
0950, 0980	Ceilings & Acoustic Treatment	94.2	92.4	93.0	96.1	95.1	95.4	94.2	92.4	93.0	96.1	80.5	85.7	94.2	92.4	93.0	94.2	88.3	90.3
0960	Flooring	99.3	114.1	103.8	107.9	120.3	111.6	98.7	114.1	103.3	100.5	114.1	104.6	98.7	114.1	103.3	102.4	114.1	105.9
0970, 0990	Wall Finishes & Painting/Coating	106.3	93.5	98.6	107.1	93.5	98.9	106.3	77.0	88.7	107.1	42.2	68.1	106.3	93.8	98.8	106.3	93.5	98.6
09	FINISHES	97.9	96.6	97.2	101.7	100.5	101.0	98.8	95.1	96.7	98.7	82.3	89.6	97.3	96.7	96.9	99.3	94.8	96.8
COVERS	DIVS. 10 - 14, 25, 28, 41, 43, 44, 46	100.0	96.7	99.3	100.0	98.6	99.7	100.0	56.6	91.3	100.0	95.4	99.1	100.0	65.4	93.1	100.0	97.1	99.4
21, 22, 23	FIRE SUPPRESSION, PLUMBING & HVAC	95.4	91.4	93.8	100.4	89.3	95.9	95.4	91.5	93.8	95.5	86.7	91.9	95.4	92.2	94.1	100.2	88.1	95.4
26, 27, 3370	ELECTRICAL, COMMUNICATIONS & UTIL.	95.8	91.9	93.8	94.9	96.1	95.5	91.8	91.9	91.8	96.9	82.8	89.6	96.0	96.8	96.4	96.0	92.8	94.3
MF2010	WEIGHTED AVERAGE	98.2	92.8	95.8	99.8	95.2	97.8	98.4	91.4	95.4	98.3	86.1	93.0	98.8	92.6	96.1	98.9	91.4	95.6

DIVISION		WEST VIRGINIA									WISCONSIN								
		PETERSBURG			ROMNEY			WHEELING			BELOIT			EAU CLAIRE			GREEN BAY		
		268			267			260			535			547			541 - 543		
		MAT.	INST.	TOTAL	MAT.	INST.	TOTAL	MAT.	INST.	TOTAL	MAT.	INST.	TOTAL	MAT.	INST.	TOTAL	MAT.	INST.	TOTAL
015433	CONTRACTOR EQUIPMENT		100.8	100.8		100.8	100.8		100.8	100.8		102.6	102.6		101.2	101.2		99.0	99.0
0241, 31 - 34	SITE & INFRASTRUCTURE, DEMOLITION	99.9	89.8	92.8	102.6	89.8	93.6	109.5	89.9	95.7	95.8	108.6	104.8	94.6	103.6	100.9	98.2	99.6	99.2
0310	Concrete Forming & Accessories	88.7	91.6	91.2	84.8	91.6	90.7	91.5	92.6	92.4	100.1	102.1	101.9	99.7	101.3	101.1	107.8	100.5	101.5
0320	Concrete Reinforcing	94.2	84.9	89.6	94.8	76.3	85.6	93.6	84.3	89.0	96.6	117.1	106.9	93.7	100.9	97.3	91.9	93.2	92.6
0330	Cast-in-Place Concrete	101.5	96.3	99.4	106.3	96.3	102.1	103.8	100.9	102.6	103.7	101.9	102.9	102.1	99.5	101.0	105.6	100.9	103.7
03	CONCRETE	96.8	92.5	94.7	100.0	91.0	95.5	101.6	94.4	98.1	99.9	104.9	102.3	98.8	100.7	99.7	101.9	99.5	100.7
04	MASONRY	92.9	92.3	92.5	90.7	92.3	91.7	100.2	91.7	94.9	98.5	104.8	102.4	89.8	102.7	97.8	120.3	101.9	108.9
05	METALS	100.5	96.6	99.3	100.5	93.7	98.4	101.2	96.9	99.9	94.2	108.4	98.6	93.1	102.7	96.5	95.4	99.1	96.5
06	WOOD, PLASTICS & COMPOSITES	88.9	92.8	91.1	83.8	92.8	88.9	89.6	92.8	91.4	98.2	101.6	100.1	105.2	101.6	103.2	110.0	101.6	105.3
07	THERMAL & MOISTURE PROTECTION	104.5	84.5	96.4	104.6	81.2	95.1	104.7	89.5	98.5	103.4	97.9	101.2	103.2	88.1	97.1	105.0	87.1	97.7
08	OPENINGS	99.1	83.9	95.5	99.0	82.0	95.0	97.6	85.1	94.7	103.6	110.2	105.1	101.0	98.1	100.3	97.4	97.8	97.5
0920	Plaster & Gypsum Board	99.7	92.4	94.7	97.1	92.4	93.9	100.1	92.4	94.8	92.8	101.9	99.0	101.4	101.9	101.8	96.6	101.9	100.2
0950, 0980	Ceilings & Acoustic Treatment	94.2	92.4	93.0	94.2	92.4	93.0	94.2	92.4	93.0	92.5	101.9	98.8	101.7	101.9	101.9	92.7	101.9	98.9
0960	Flooring	100.3	114.1	104.5	98.5	114.1	103.2	103.2	114.1	106.4	101.9	120.3	107.4	94.2	116.2	100.8	113.3	116.2	114.2
0970, 0990	Wall Finishes & Painting/Coating	106.3	93.8	98.8	106.3	93.8	98.8	106.3	93.8	98.8	91.8	99.3	96.3	88.0	88.3	88.2	98.1	85.0	90.2
09	FINISHES	98.1	96.7	97.3	97.4	96.7	97.0	99.5	96.9	98.1	99.7	105.1	102.7	99.2	103.2	101.4	103.3	102.6	102.9
COVERS	DIVS. 10 - 14, 25, 28, 41, 43, 44, 46	100.0	65.3	93.1	100.0	96.7	99.3	100.0	97.1	99.4	100.0	98.2	99.6	100.0	98.5	99.7	100.0	98.1	99.6
21, 22, 23	FIRE SUPPRESSION, PLUMBING & HVAC	95.4	91.2	93.7	95.4	90.8	93.6	100.3	92.8	97.3	100.0	100.0	100.0	100.1	87.5	95.1	100.4	84.3	93.9
26, 27, 3370	ELECTRICAL, COMMUNICATIONS & UTIL.	99.2	82.9	90.7	98.5	82.9	90.3	93.1	96.8	95.0	102.8	87.3	94.7	103.9	86.9	95.0	98.2	82.9	90.2
MF2010	WEIGHTED AVERAGE	98.0	90.1	94.6	98.2	90.4	94.8	99.8	93.8	97.2	99.6	101.9	100.6	98.7	96.4	97.7	100.5	94.1	97.7

DIVISION		WISCONSIN																	
		KENOSHA			LA CROSSE			LANCASTER			MADISON			MILWAUKEE			NEW RICHMOND		
		531			546			538			537			530,532			540		
		MAT.	INST.	TOTAL	MAT.	INST.	TOTAL	MAT.	INST.	TOTAL	MAT.	INST.	TOTAL	MAT.	INST.	TOTAL	MAT.	INST.	TOTAL
015433	CONTRACTOR EQUIPMENT		100.5	100.5		101.2	101.2		102.6	102.6		102.6	102.6		90.8	90.8		101.6	101.6
0241, 31 - 34	SITE & INFRASTRUCTURE, DEMOLITION	101.8	105.5	104.4	88.5	103.6	99.1	95.0	108.5	104.4	91.3	108.6	103.4	98.0	98.7	98.5	91.7	104.0	100.3
0310	Concrete Forming & Accessories	106.8	102.5	103.1	86.7	100.8	98.9	99.5	99.7	99.7	103.7	101.7	102.0	102.2	120.1	117.6	95.2	102.8	101.8
0320	Concrete Reinforcing	96.4	98.6	97.5	93.4	92.9	93.1	97.9	92.8	95.4	102.3	93.1	97.7	100.5	98.9	99.7	91.0	100.7	95.9
0330	Cast-in-Place Concrete	112.8	106.0	109.9	91.8	97.0	94.0	103.0	101.0	102.2	94.3	101.8	97.4	102.3	110.6	105.7	106.3	83.6	96.9
03	CONCRETE	104.6	103.0	103.8	90.1	98.1	94.1	99.6	98.9	99.2	97.1	100.1	98.6	100.3	111.9	106.0	96.6	95.9	96.3
04	MASONRY	95.9	115.5	108.1	89.0	102.7	97.5	98.6	104.9	102.5	99.4	104.8	102.8	102.2	120.5	113.5	115.4	102.8	107.6
05	METALS	95.0	101.6	97.0	93.0	98.9	94.8	91.8	96.1	93.1	93.5	98.1	94.9	98.1	94.9	97.1	93.2	101.5	95.8
06	WOOD, PLASTICS & COMPOSITES	101.8	98.7	100.1	90.2	101.6	96.7	97.5	101.6	99.8	97.0	101.6	99.6	101.1	121.3	112.5	94.0	104.9	100.2
07	THERMAL & MOISTURE PROTECTION	103.4	108.4	105.4	102.7	87.2	96.4	103.1	83.5	95.2	106.5	94.0	101.4	99.9	113.0	105.2	104.9	93.8	100.4
08	OPENINGS	97.6	102.8	98.9	101.0	86.7	97.6	99.2	87.5	96.4	105.1	101.6	104.3	106.2	115.1	108.3	86.9	99.9	90.0
0920	Plaster & Gypsum Board	83.2	99.0	93.9	95.9	101.9	100.0	91.5	101.9	98.6	94.2	101.9	99.5	99.9	122.1	115.0	85.5	105.5	99.1
0950, 0980	Ceilings & Acoustic Treatment	92.5	99.0	96.8	100.8	101.9	101.6	87.2	101.9	97.0	102.4	101.9	102.1	96.1	122.1	113.4	65.8	105.5	92.2
0960	Flooring	120.9	112.4	118.4	88.3	116.2	96.7	101.6	112.6	104.9	103.5	112.6	106.2	101.6	116.1	105.9	106.5	116.2	109.4
0970, 0990	Wall Finishes & Painting/Coating	101.5	115.2	109.7	88.0	75.5	80.5	91.8	67.8	77.4	89.8	99.3	95.5	93.2	125.6	112.7	101.0	88.3	93.4
09	FINISHES	104.6	105.5	105.1	96.1	101.8	99.3	98.3	98.4	98.3	101.0	103.9	102.6	102.5	121.0	112.8	93.7	103.3	99.0
COVERS	DIVS. 10 - 14, 25, 28, 41, 43, 44, 46	100.0	101.6	100.3	100.0	98.5	99.7	100.0	50.6	90.1	100.0	98.2	99.6	100.0	104.8	101.0	100.0	98.4	99.7
21, 22, 23	FIRE SUPPRESSION, PLUMBING & HVAC	100.2	96.9	98.9	100.1	87.4	95.0	95.1	87.2	92.0	100.0	96.3	98.5	100.0	102.5	101.0	94.8	86.8	91.6
26, 27, 3370	ELECTRICAL, COMMUNICATIONS & UTIL.	103.4	99.6	101.4	104.2	87.1	95.3	102.6	87.1	94.5	103.6	94.3	98.8	102.9	101.9	102.4	102.0	87.1	94.3
MF2010	WEIGHTED AVERAGE	100.2	102.9	101.4	97.2	96.3	96.3	97.4	93.5	95.4	99.5	99.8	99.6	100.9	107.9	104.0	96.2	95.9	96.1

DIVISION		WISCONSIN																	
		OSHKOSH			PORTAGE			RACINE			RHINELANDER			SUPERIOR			WAUSAU		
		549			539			534			545			548			544		
		MAT.	INST.	TOTAL	MAT.	INST.	TOTAL	MAT.	INST.	TOTAL	MAT.	INST.	TOTAL	MAT.	INST.	TOTAL	MAT.	INST.	TOTAL
015433	CONTRACTOR EQUIPMENT		99.0	99.0		102.6	102.6		102.6	102.6		99.0	99.0		101.6	101.6		99.0	99.0
0241, 31 - 34	SITE & INFRASTRUCTURE, DEMOLITION	90.0	99.6	96.7	85.8	108.4	101.6	95.6	109.3	105.2	102.1	99.6	100.3	88.6	104.0	99.4	85.9	99.6	95.5
0310	Concrete Forming & Accessories	91.0	99.9	98.7	92.1	100.7	99.5	100.4	102.5	102.2	88.4	99.9	98.3	93.4	94.0	94.0	90.3	100.5	99.1
0320	Concrete Reinforcing	92.0	93.1	92.6	98.0	93.0	95.5	96.6	98.6	97.6	92.2	92.2	92.2	91.0	92.7	91.8	92.2	92.9	92.5
0330	Cast-in-Place Concrete	97.9	100.8	99.1	88.5	103.0	94.5	101.7	105.7	103.3	111.0	101.0	106.9	100.1	100.0	100.1	91.3	99.3	95.3
03	CONCRETE	91.7	99.1	95.3	87.5	100.1	93.7	98.9	102.9	100.9	103.6	99.0	101.3	91.2	96.1	93.6	86.8	99.4	93.0
04	MASONRY	102.5	102.2	102.3	97.5	104.8	102.1	98.6	115.5	109.0	118.7	102.7	108.8	114.7	106.3	109.5	102.1	101.9	102.0
05	METALS	93.4	98.4	94.9	92.5	97.1	93.9	95.9	101.5	97.6	93.3	97.8	94.7	94.1	99.4	95.7	93.2	98.9	94.9
06	WOOD, PLASTICS & COMPOSITES	89.8	101.6	96.5	88.4	101.6	95.8	98.4	98.7	98.6	87.4	101.6	95.4	92.4	92.2	92.3	89.3	101.6	96.3
07	THERMAL & MOISTURE PROTECTION	104.2	87.2	97.3	102.6	93.8	99.0	103.4	107.9	105.2	105.0	85.2	96.9	104.5	94.3	100.4	104.1	85.8	96.6
08	OPENINGS	93.4	97.8	94.5	99.3	94.2	98.1	103.6	102.8	103.4	93.5	88.8	92.4	86.4	92.5	87.8	93.6	97.7	94.6
0920	Plaster & Gypsum Board	83.9	101.9	96.2	85.4	101.9	96.7	92.8	99.0	97.0	83.9	101.9	96.2	85.4	92.4	90.2	83.9	101.9	96.2
0950, 0980	Ceilings & Acoustic Treatment	92.7	101.9	98.9	89.9	101.9	97.9	92.5	99.0	96.8	92.7	101.9	98.9	66.7	92.4	83.8	92.7	101.9	98.9
0960	Flooring	105.1	116.2	108.4	98.2	120.3	104.8	101.9	112.4	105.0	104.3	116.2	107.9	107.8	124.7	112.9	104.9	116.2	108.3
0970, 0990	Wall Finishes & Painting/Coating	95.3	85.0	89.1	91.8	67.8	77.4	91.8	115.3	105.9	95.3	61.7	75.1	89.6	103.7	98.1	95.3	85.0	89.1
09	FINISHES	98.4	100.9	99.8	96.4	100.5	98.7	99.7	105.5	103.0	99.3	99.1	99.2	93.1	100.7	97.3	98.1	102.6	100.6
COVERS	DIVS. 10 - 14, 25, 28, 41, 43, 44, 46	100.0	66.1	93.2	100.0	64.8	92.9	100.0	101.6	100.3	100.0	56.4	91.3	100.0	96.7	99.3	100.0	98.1	99.6
21, 22, 23	FIRE SUPPRESSION, PLUMBING & HVAC	95.5	83.4	90.6	95.1	96.1	95.5	100.0	96.9	98.7	95.5	87.0	92.1	94.8	90.4	93.0	95.5	86.3	91.8
26, 27, 3370	ELECTRICAL, COMMUNICATIONS & UTIL.	102.6	81.0	91.3	106.8	94.3	100.3	102.6	95.2	98.7	101.9	82.6	91.8	107.2	99.3	103.1	103.8	82.6	92.7
MF2010	WEIGHTED AVERAGE	96.3	92.4	94.6	96.1	97.9	96.9	99.7	102.6	101.0	98.7	92.4	95.9	96.1	97.6	96.7	95.7	94.4	95.2

City Cost Indexes

WYOMING

DIVISION		CASPER 826			CHEYENNE 820			NEWCASTLE 827			RAWLINS 823			RIVERTON 825			ROCK SPRINGS 829 - 831		
		MAT.	INST.	TOTAL	MAT.	INST.	TOTAL	MAT.	INST.	TOTAL	MAT.	INST.	TOTAL	MAT.	INST.	TOTAL	MAT.	INST.	TOTAL
015433	CONTRACTOR EQUIPMENT		97.9	97.9		97.9	97.9		97.9	97.9		97.9	97.9		97.9	97.9		97.9	97.9
0241, 31 - 34	SITE & INFRASTRUCTURE, DEMOLITION	97.2	95.2	95.8	90.1	95.2	93.7	82.0	94.8	91.0	95.8	94.8	95.1	89.3	94.8	93.2	85.8	94.7	92.1
0310	Concrete Forming & Accessories	104.4	43.5	51.9	106.6	54.7	61.8	97.1	63.5	68.1	101.3	63.5	68.6	96.0	63.0	67.5	103.5	62.9	68.4
0320	Concrete Reinforcing	108.6	70.5	89.6	100.8	71.3	86.1	108.4	71.7	90.1	108.1	71.7	89.9	109.1	71.4	90.2	109.1	71.4	90.3
0330	Cast-in-Place Concrete	98.6	72.6	87.8	91.1	72.7	83.5	92.0	62.1	79.6	92.1	62.1	79.6	92.0	52.6	75.7	92.0	52.3	75.5
03	CONCRETE	103.0	59.4	81.5	100.1	64.6	82.6	100.6	64.8	82.9	114.3	64.8	89.9	108.9	61.3	85.4	101.1	61.2	81.4
04	MASONRY	100.0	34.5	59.5	95.8	47.6	65.9	92.6	55.7	69.7	92.6	55.7	69.7	92.6	49.9	66.1	147.5	48.7	86.4
05	METALS	98.1	71.0	89.7	101.5	72.4	92.5	96.6	72.4	89.2	96.7	72.4	89.2	96.8	71.6	89.0	97.5	71.9	89.6
06	WOOD, PLASTICS & COMPOSITES	96.3	41.0	65.1	95.6	55.6	73.0	85.6	68.4	75.9	89.6	68.4	77.6	84.5	68.4	75.5	93.6	68.4	79.4
07	THERMAL & MOISTURE PROTECTION	105.2	49.4	82.5	99.7	54.4	81.3	101.2	55.9	82.8	102.7	55.9	83.7	102.1	59.7	84.9	101.3	59.3	84.2
08	OPENINGS	102.1	48.9	89.5	102.3	56.9	91.6	106.2	60.8	95.5	105.9	60.8	95.2	106.1	60.8	95.3	106.5	60.8	95.7
0920	Plaster & Gypsum Board	93.1	39.1	56.3	84.6	54.2	63.9	80.3	67.4	71.5	80.7	67.4	71.6	80.3	67.4	71.5	90.0	67.4	74.6
0950, 0980	Ceilings & Acoustic Treatment	108.9	39.1	62.4	100.3	54.2	69.6	102.3	67.4	79.0	102.3	67.4	79.0	102.3	67.4	79.0	102.3	67.4	79.0
0960	Flooring	109.6	33.6	86.8	107.4	54.0	91.5	101.0	52.6	86.5	103.8	52.6	88.5	100.6	52.6	86.2	105.9	52.6	89.9
0970, 0990	Wall Finishes & Painting/Coating	100.0	44.0	66.3	106.9	44.0	69.1	102.6	56.6	74.9	102.6	56.6	74.9	102.6	56.6	74.9	102.6	56.6	74.9
09	FINISHES	106.4	40.1	69.5	103.2	52.8	75.1	97.9	60.6	77.1	100.2	60.6	78.2	98.7	60.6	77.5	100.6	60.3	78.2
COVERS	DIVS. 10 - 14, 25, 28, 41, 43, 44, 46	100.0	88.9	97.8	100.0	90.6	98.1	100.0	91.5	98.3	100.0	91.5	98.3	100.0	58.0	91.6	100.0	82.7	96.5
21, 22, 23	FIRE SUPPRESSION, PLUMBING & HVAC	100.0	65.4	86.1	100.0	65.5	86.2	97.5	64.8	84.3	97.5	64.8	84.3	97.5	64.7	84.3	100.0	64.2	85.6
26, 27, 3370	ELECTRICAL, COMMUNICATIONS & UTIL.	96.0	65.6	80.1	99.1	70.2	84.0	96.8	70.6	83.2	96.8	70.6	83.2	96.8	64.4	79.9	95.0	64.4	79.0
MF2010	WEIGHTED AVERAGE	100.4	60.7	83.1	100.1	65.7	85.2	98.2	67.8	84.9	100.2	67.8	86.1	99.3	64.9	84.3	101.8	65.4	85.9

WYOMING / CANADA

DIVISION		SHERIDAN 828			WHEATLAND 822			WORLAND 824			YELLOWSTONE NAT'L PA 821			BARRIE, ONTARIO			BATHURST, NEW BRUNSWICK		
		MAT.	INST.	TOTAL	MAT.	INST.	TOTAL	MAT.	INST.	TOTAL	MAT.	INST.	TOTAL	MAT.	INST.	TOTAL	MAT.	INST.	TOTAL
015433	CONTRACTOR EQUIPMENT		97.9	97.9		97.9	97.9		97.9	97.9		97.9	97.9		101.6	101.6		101.9	101.9
0241, 31 - 34	SITE & INFRASTRUCTURE, DEMOLITION	89.8	95.2	93.6	86.4	94.8	92.3	83.9	94.7	91.5	84.0	94.9	91.7	115.3	101.0	105.3	98.4	97.3	97.6
0310	Concrete Forming & Accessories	104.3	51.6	58.8	99.1	51.1	57.7	99.2	62.7	67.7	99.2	64.0	68.8	125.1	91.5	96.1	103.7	65.1	70.4
0320	Concrete Reinforcing	109.1	71.8	90.4	108.4	71.7	90.1	109.1	71.1	90.1	111.0	71.1	91.1	174.2	86.5	130.4	139.2	58.3	98.8
0330	Cast-in-Place Concrete	95.1	72.7	85.8	96.0	61.8	81.8	92.0	52.2	75.5	92.0	54.2	76.3	166.0	90.4	134.6	136.1	62.8	105.7
03	CONCRETE	108.8	63.3	86.3	105.4	59.2	82.6	100.8	61.0	81.2	101.1	62.3	81.9	151.0	90.3	121.1	130.9	63.7	97.7
04	MASONRY	92.8	57.2	70.8	92.9	55.2	69.6	92.6	44.9	63.1	92.6	48.5	65.3	165.2	99.8	124.7	165.6	66.1	104.0
05	METALS	100.3	72.9	91.9	96.6	72.2	89.1	96.8	71.2	88.9	97.4	71.2	89.3	108.2	91.4	103.0	104.4	72.6	94.6
06	WOOD, PLASTICS & COMPOSITES	97.0	51.6	71.4	87.5	52.1	67.5	87.5	68.4	76.8	87.5	68.4	76.8	120.6	90.1	103.4	97.8	65.4	79.5
07	THERMAL & MOISTURE PROTECTION	102.4	56.5	83.7	101.5	55.0	82.6	101.3	56.0	82.9	100.8	57.5	83.2	112.4	91.0	103.7	104.6	63.6	87.9
08	OPENINGS	106.8	52.5	93.9	104.8	54.7	93.0	106.4	60.8	95.6	99.8	60.8	90.6	92.5	88.6	91.5	89.2	57.2	81.6
0920	Plaster & Gypsum Board	105.6	50.0	67.8	80.3	50.5	60.0	80.3	67.4	71.5	80.5	67.4	71.6	151.2	89.8	109.4	151.8	64.2	92.2
0950, 0980	Ceilings & Acoustic Treatment	105.2	50.0	68.5	102.3	50.5	67.8	102.3	67.4	79.0	103.1	67.4	79.3	95.2	89.8	91.6	100.9	64.2	76.5
0960	Flooring	105.0	52.6	89.3	102.5	51.7	87.3	102.5	52.6	87.6	102.5	52.6	87.6	130.7	100.7	121.7	117.8	48.0	96.9
0970, 0990	Wall Finishes & Painting/Coating	105.1	44.0	68.4	102.6	35.2	62.1	102.6	56.6	74.9	102.6	56.6	74.9	111.9	91.8	99.8	108.4	52.7	74.9
09	FINISHES	106.2	49.7	74.7	98.6	48.3	70.6	98.3	60.5	77.2	98.5	61.4	77.8	117.3	93.5	104.0	113.4	60.9	84.2
COVERS	DIVS. 10 - 14, 25, 28, 41, 43, 44, 46	100.0	90.1	98.0	100.0	82.0	96.4	100.0	57.8	91.5	100.0	59.0	91.8	139.2	76.2	126.6	131.1	66.9	118.3
21, 22, 23	FIRE SUPPRESSION, PLUMBING & HVAC	97.5	65.5	84.6	97.5	64.5	84.2	97.5	64.4	84.2	97.5	66.2	84.9	102.2	101.5	101.9	102.5	71.3	90.0
26, 27, 3370	ELECTRICAL, COMMUNICATIONS & UTIL.	99.5	64.5	81.2	96.8	70.2	82.9	96.8	64.4	79.9	95.7	64.4	79.4	116.5	92.6	104.0	114.2	63.3	87.6
MF2010	WEIGHTED AVERAGE	100.9	65.2	85.4	98.7	64.6	83.9	98.3	64.1	83.4	97.7	65.2	83.5	117.3	94.9	107.5	112.1	68.6	93.1

CANADA

DIVISION		BRANDON, MANITOBA			BRANTFORD, ONTARIO			BRIDGEWATER, NOVA SCOTIA			CALGARY, ALBERTA			CAP-DE-LA-MADELEINE, QUEBEC			CHARLESBOURG, QUEBEC		
		MAT.	INST.	TOTAL	MAT.	INST.	TOTAL	MAT.	INST.	TOTAL	MAT.	INST.	TOTAL	MAT.	INST.	TOTAL	MAT.	INST.	TOTAL
015433	CONTRACTOR EQUIPMENT		103.9	103.9		101.6	101.6		101.5	101.5		106.4	106.4		102.5	102.5		102.5	102.5
0241, 31 - 34	SITE & INFRASTRUCTURE, DEMOLITION	117.9	99.9	105.3	114.9	101.3	105.4	99.9	98.9	99.2	124.6	105.7	111.3	95.9	100.6	99.2	95.9	100.6	99.2
0310	Concrete Forming & Accessories	126.8	74.1	81.3	124.9	99.1	102.6	97.1	73.2	76.5	127.7	96.8	101.0	130.3	90.0	95.5	130.3	90.0	95.5
0320	Concrete Reinforcing	189.5	54.9	122.3	167.9	85.2	126.6	142.9	48.2	95.6	130.9	74.1	102.5	142.9	81.4	112.2	142.9	81.4	112.2
0330	Cast-in-Place Concrete	146.1	77.7	117.7	162.0	112.0	141.3	166.5	73.2	127.8	201.5	106.2	162.0	130.8	99.3	117.7	130.8	99.3	117.7
03	CONCRETE	138.9	72.4	106.1	147.1	100.9	124.3	144.7	69.3	107.5	167.1	95.9	132.0	128.7	91.7	110.5	128.7	91.7	110.5
04	MASONRY	186.5	68.8	113.7	167.9	104.4	128.6	163.2	73.2	107.5	203.4	90.7	133.7	163.7	88.6	117.2	163.7	88.6	117.2
05	METALS	117.8	77.8	105.5	105.5	92.2	101.4	104.6	75.3	95.6	130.4	89.2	117.7	103.8	88.8	99.2	103.8	88.8	99.2
06	WOOD, PLASTICS & COMPOSITES	124.4	75.1	96.6	119.8	97.9	107.4	89.2	72.6	79.9	107.8	96.5	101.4	131.6	89.9	108.1	131.6	89.9	108.1
07	THERMAL & MOISTURE PROTECTION	109.1	73.3	94.6	112.6	96.6	106.1	107.5	71.4	92.9	121.9	94.1	110.6	106.2	91.8	100.3	106.2	91.8	100.3
08	OPENINGS	97.0	66.3	89.7	93.6	94.9	93.9	86.6	66.4	81.8	94.2	86.1	92.3	94.7	83.0	91.9	94.7	83.0	91.9
0920	Plaster & Gypsum Board	129.5	73.9	91.7	142.7	97.8	112.1	141.8	71.7	94.1	140.9	95.9	110.3	172.3	89.4	115.9	172.3	89.4	115.9
0950, 0980	Ceilings & Acoustic Treatment	102.5	73.9	83.5	97.4	97.8	97.6	97.4	71.7	80.3	145.9	95.9	112.6	97.4	89.4	92.1	97.4	89.4	92.1
0960	Flooring	136.3	71.5	116.9	130.5	100.7	121.6	113.1	68.5	99.8	133.3	94.3	121.7	130.5	101.4	121.8	130.5	101.4	121.8
0970, 0990	Wall Finishes & Painting/Coating	113.1	60.0	81.2	109.0	100.8	104.1	109.0	65.5	82.9	114.2	112.4	113.1	109.0	93.7	99.8	109.0	93.7	99.8
09	FINISHES	118.8	72.5	93.0	115.6	100.1	107.0	109.9	71.8	88.7	129.1	98.5	112.0	118.9	92.8	104.4	118.9	92.8	104.4
COVERS	DIVS. 10 - 14, 25, 28, 41, 43, 44, 46	131.1	69.1	118.7	131.1	78.4	120.6	131.1	68.2	118.5	131.1	98.4	124.6	131.1	87.3	122.4	131.1	87.3	122.4
21, 22, 23	FIRE SUPPRESSION, PLUMBING & HVAC	102.5	85.9	95.9	102.5	104.5	103.3	102.5	86.3	96.0	101.3	92.2	97.6	102.9	93.0	98.9	102.9	93.0	98.9
26, 27, 3370	ELECTRICAL, COMMUNICATIONS & UTIL.	120.0	71.3	94.6	112.9	92.1	102.0	118.7	65.9	91.1	114.2	100.8	107.2	112.6	74.3	92.6	112.6	74.3	92.6
MF2010	WEIGHTED AVERAGE	118.7	77.3	100.7	115.5	98.8	108.2	113.4	76.1	97.2	124.7	95.4	111.9	112.8	89.4	102.6	112.8	89.4	102.6

CANADA

DIVISION		CHARLOTTETOWN, PRINCE EDWARD ISLAND			CHICOUTIMI, QUEBEC			CORNER BROOK, NEWFOUNDLAND			CORNWALL, ONTARIO			DALHOUSIE, NEW BRUNSWICK			DARTMOUTH, NOVA SCOTIA		
		MAT.	INST.	TOTAL	MAT.	INST.	TOTAL	MAT.	INST.	TOTAL	MAT.	INST.	TOTAL	MAT.	INST.	TOTAL	MAT.	INST.	TOTAL
015433	CONTRACTOR EQUIPMENT		101.5	101.5		102.5	102.5		103.1	103.1		101.6	101.6		101.9	101.9		101.5	101.5
0241, 31 - 34	SITE & INFRASTRUCTURE, DEMOLITION	115.8	96.4	102.2	96.1	99.7	98.6	120.7	97.9	104.7	113.0	100.8	104.5	97.6	97.3	97.4	111.0	98.9	102.5
0310	Concrete Forming & Accessories	105.6	59.5	65.8	131.4	92.8	98.1	106.9	63.0	69.0	122.8	91.6	95.9	103.2	65.3	70.5	98.9	73.2	76.8
0320	Concrete Reinforcing	146.3	48.3	97.3	105.0	96.4	100.7	173.8	50.1	112.0	167.9	84.9	126.5	144.1	58.4	101.3	181.7	48.2	115.0
0330	Cast-in-Place Concrete	164.6	62.0	122.0	128.2	99.2	116.1	170.1	71.7	129.2	145.7	102.2	127.7	137.6	62.8	106.6	164.2	73.2	126.4
03	CONCRETE	153.1	59.1	106.7	120.1	95.6	108.0	167.6	64.5	116.8	139.3	94.1	117.0	135.2	63.8	100.0	152.9	69.3	111.6
04	MASONRY	182.6	63.7	109.0	167.4	94.1	122.0	183.2	65.3	110.2	166.7	95.7	122.7	158.4	66.1	101.3	196.5	73.2	120.2
05	METALS	127.0	68.6	108.9	104.2	92.3	100.6	118.3	74.0	104.6	105.5	90.8	101.0	101.7	72.8	92.8	118.3	75.3	105.0
06	WOOD, PLASTICS & COMPOSITES	88.5	59.1	71.9	132.6	93.2	110.4	104.3	62.1	80.5	118.6	91.0	103.0	97.7	65.4	79.5	94.6	72.6	82.2
07	THERMAL & MOISTURE PROTECTION	119.5	61.7	96.1	105.0	95.9	101.3	112.7	63.2	92.6	112.4	91.1	103.8	110.8	63.6	91.6	110.4	71.4	94.6
08	OPENINGS	93.4	51.1	83.4	93.8	80.5	90.6	102.9	58.5	92.4	94.7	88.2	93.1	90.3	57.2	82.4	88.3	66.4	83.1
0920	Plaster & Gypsum Board	144.0	57.7	85.3	176.1	92.8	119.4	160.5	60.8	92.7	208.0	90.7	128.2	148.2	64.2	91.1	156.0	71.7	98.6
0950, 0980	Ceilings & Acoustic Treatment	121.3	57.7	79.0	100.1	92.8	95.2	103.4	60.8	75.0	100.9	90.7	94.1	100.2	64.2	76.3	110.5	71.7	84.7
0960	Flooring	116.1	64.0	100.5	132.3	101.4	123.0	122.1	58.3	103.0	130.5	99.2	121.1	116.3	73.4	103.5	118.0	68.5	103.2
0970, 0990	Wall Finishes & Painting/Coating	112.9	43.9	71.4	108.4	105.7	106.7	113.0	63.1	83.0	109.0	93.9	99.9	109.9	52.7	75.5	113.0	65.5	84.4
09	FINISHES	118.9	59.1	85.6	120.3	96.5	107.0	119.5	62.2	87.6	125.3	93.6	107.6	112.7	65.9	86.6	118.0	71.8	92.3
COVERS	DIVS. 10 - 14, 25, 28, 41, 43, 44, 46	131.1	66.4	118.2	131.1	88.0	122.5	131.1	67.2	118.3	131.1	75.8	120.1	131.1	66.9	118.3	131.1	68.2	118.5
21, 22, 23	FIRE SUPPRESSION, PLUMBING & HVAC	102.7	65.2	87.7	102.5	93.7	99.0	102.5	73.4	90.8	102.9	102.3	102.6	102.5	71.3	90.0	102.5	86.3	96.0
26, 27, 3370	ELECTRICAL, COMMUNICATIONS & UTIL.	111.9	53.6	81.5	111.0	86.5	98.2	117.4	59.7	87.2	113.9	93.1	103.0	115.3	59.8	86.3	122.2	65.9	92.8
MF2010	WEIGHTED AVERAGE	120.5	64.0	95.9	111.9	93.1	103.7	122.2	69.0	99.0	115.5	95.1	106.7	112.1	68.8	93.2	119.7	76.1	100.7

CANADA

DIVISION		EDMONTON, ALBERTA			FORT MCMURRAY, ALBERTA			FREDERICTON, NEW BRUNSWICK			GATINEAU, QUEBEC			GRANBY, QUEBEC			HALIFAX, NOVA SCOTIA		
		MAT.	INST.	TOTAL	MAT.	INST.	TOTAL	MAT.	INST.	TOTAL	MAT.	INST.	TOTAL	MAT.	INST.	TOTAL	MAT.	INST.	TOTAL
015433	CONTRACTOR EQUIPMENT		106.4	106.4		103.7	103.7		101.9	101.9		102.5	102.5		102.5	102.5		101.5	101.5
0241, 31 - 34	SITE & INFRASTRUCTURE, DEMOLITION	146.0	105.7	117.7	120.4	101.9	107.4	100.8	97.3	98.3	95.7	100.5	99.1	96.2	100.5	99.2	105.2	98.8	100.7
0310	Concrete Forming & Accessories	127.2	96.8	101.0	123.0	94.3	98.2	122.7	65.6	73.5	130.3	89.8	95.4	130.3	89.8	95.3	104.9	78.3	81.9
0320	Concrete Reinforcing	140.3	74.1	107.2	155.3	74.1	114.7	136.1	58.5	97.4	151.1	81.3	116.3	151.1	81.3	116.3	147.6	62.8	105.3
0330	Cast-in-Place Concrete	201.0	106.2	161.7	215.2	104.8	169.4	134.8	62.9	104.9	129.0	99.3	116.7	133.3	99.2	119.2	165.6	81.0	130.5
03	CONCRETE	168.4	95.9	132.6	170.0	94.3	132.7	133.1	64.0	99.0	129.2	91.7	110.7	131.2	91.6	111.7	146.0	76.9	111.9
04	MASONRY	193.2	90.7	129.8	207.6	89.6	134.6	192.4	67.6	115.2	163.6	88.6	117.2	163.9	88.6	117.3	193.7	83.4	125.5
05	METALS	130.4	89.2	117.7	130.8	89.0	117.9	123.0	73.3	107.7	103.8	88.7	99.2	103.8	88.6	99.1	130.3	81.6	115.3
06	WOOD, PLASTICS & COMPOSITES	108.6	96.5	101.8	113.7	93.8	102.5	112.9	65.4	86.1	131.6	89.9	108.1	131.6	89.9	108.1	88.7	77.4	82.3
07	THERMAL & MOISTURE PROTECTION	127.2	94.1	113.8	120.1	92.6	108.9	117.3	64.6	95.9	106.2	91.8	100.3	106.2	90.2	99.7	118.6	77.9	102.1
08	OPENINGS	94.4	86.1	92.4	94.7	84.6	92.3	89.3	56.1	81.5	94.7	78.2	90.8	94.7	78.2	90.8	86.5	72.0	83.1
0920	Plaster & Gypsum Board	145.5	95.9	111.8	140.9	93.3	108.5	153.7	64.2	92.8	140.5	89.4	105.8	143.0	89.4	106.6	140.8	76.6	97.1
0950, 0980	Ceilings & Acoustic Treatment	150.5	95.9	114.2	107.2	93.3	97.9	113.3	64.2	80.6	97.4	89.4	92.1	97.4	89.4	92.1	116.1	76.6	89.8
0960	Flooring	135.0	94.3	122.8	130.5	94.3	119.7	128.5	76.7	113.0	130.5	101.4	121.8	130.5	101.4	121.8	118.2	90.0	109.8
0970, 0990	Wall Finishes & Painting/Coating	114.6	112.4	113.3	109.1	97.5	102.2	112.6	67.2	85.3	109.0	93.7	99.8	109.0	93.7	99.8	113.9	82.0	94.7
09	FINISHES	133.3	98.5	113.9	118.9	95.0	105.6	121.4	68.1	91.7	114.5	92.8	102.4	114.9	92.8	102.6	117.2	81.2	97.2
COVERS	DIVS. 10 - 14, 25, 28, 41, 43, 44, 46	131.1	98.4	124.6	131.1	97.5	124.4	131.1	66.9	118.3	131.1	87.3	122.4	131.1	87.3	122.4	131.1	69.6	118.8
21, 22, 23	FIRE SUPPRESSION, PLUMBING & HVAC	101.2	92.2	97.6	102.9	101.0	102.2	102.6	81.1	94.0	102.9	93.0	98.9	102.5	93.0	98.7	100.7	77.7	91.5
26, 27, 3370	ELECTRICAL, COMMUNICATIONS & UTIL.	110.3	100.8	105.4	107.1	87.5	96.8	117.2	78.9	97.2	112.6	74.3	92.6	113.2	74.3	92.9	120.1	80.5	99.4
MF2010	WEIGHTED AVERAGE	125.0	95.4	112.1	124.1	94.2	111.1	118.1	74.0	99.0	118.8	89.2	102.3	112.8	89.1	102.4	119.9	80.6	102.8

CANADA

DIVISION		HAMILTON, ONTARIO			HULL, QUEBEC			JOLIETTE, QUEBEC			KAMLOOPS, BRITISH COLUMBIA			KINGSTON, ONTARIO			KITCHENER, ONTARIO		
		MAT.	INST.	TOTAL	MAT.	INST.	TOTAL	MAT.	INST.	TOTAL	MAT.	INST.	TOTAL	MAT.	INST.	TOTAL	MAT.	INST.	TOTAL
015433	CONTRACTOR EQUIPMENT		108.3	108.3		102.5	102.5		102.5	102.5		105.6	105.6		103.9	103.9		103.8	103.8
0241, 31 - 34	SITE & INFRASTRUCTURE, DEMOLITION	117.0	112.7	114.0	95.7	100.5	99.1	96.3	100.6	99.3	118.4	104.0	108.3	113.0	104.5	107.1	101.2	105.1	104.0
0310	Concrete Forming & Accessories	127.9	94.2	98.8	130.3	89.8	95.4	130.3	90.0	95.5	123.5	92.8	97.0	122.9	91.7	96.0	118.0	86.6	90.9
0320	Concrete Reinforcing	153.0	93.1	123.1	151.1	81.3	116.3	142.9	81.4	112.2	112.0	79.2	95.6	167.9	84.9	126.5	103.3	93.0	98.2
0330	Cast-in-Place Concrete	151.7	100.2	130.3	129.0	99.3	116.7	134.4	99.3	119.8	116.3	103.1	110.8	145.7	102.2	127.6	140.7	90.1	119.7
03	CONCRETE	140.5	96.0	118.6	129.2	91.7	110.7	130.4	91.7	111.3	136.9	93.9	115.7	141.2	94.1	118.0	118.8	89.2	104.2
04	MASONRY	193.0	99.7	135.3	163.6	88.6	117.2	164.0	88.6	117.2	170.7	96.6	124.9	173.6	95.7	125.4	159.0	95.3	119.6
05	METALS	121.5	92.7	112.6	103.8	88.7	99.2	103.8	88.8	99.2	106.2	88.7	100.8	107.2	90.7	102.1	113.9	92.5	107.3
06	WOOD, PLASTICS & COMPOSITES	105.6	93.7	98.9	131.6	89.9	108.1	131.6	89.9	108.1	101.3	91.3	95.7	118.6	91.1	103.1	109.7	85.3	96.0
07	THERMAL & MOISTURE PROTECTION	124.3	95.0	112.4	106.2	91.8	100.3	106.2	91.8	100.3	121.2	88.6	108.0	112.4	92.2	104.2	112.1	91.6	103.8
08	OPENINGS	91.9	92.1	91.9	94.7	78.2	90.8	94.7	83.0	91.9	91.0	87.7	90.2	94.7	87.9	93.1	85.7	85.8	85.7
0920	Plaster & Gypsum Board	172.8	93.5	118.9	140.5	89.4	105.8	172.3	89.4	115.9	124.3	90.6	101.4	211.3	90.8	129.4	141.4	84.9	102.9
0950, 0980	Ceilings & Acoustic Treatment	130.0	93.5	105.7	97.4	89.4	92.1	97.4	89.4	92.1	97.4	90.6	92.9	114.3	90.8	98.7	105.3	84.9	91.7
0960	Flooring	132.6	104.1	124.1	130.5	101.4	121.8	130.5	101.4	121.8	129.8	56.6	107.9	130.5	99.2	121.1	124.4	104.1	118.3
0970, 0990	Wall Finishes & Painting/Coating	114.2	102.5	107.2	109.0	93.7	99.8	109.0	93.7	99.8	109.0	85.8	95.0	109.0	86.8	95.6	107.9	92.5	98.6
09	FINISHES	129.3	97.1	111.3	114.5	92.8	102.4	118.9	92.8	104.4	115.0	86.0	98.9	128.7	92.9	108.7	114.3	90.1	100.8
COVERS	DIVS. 10 - 14, 25, 28, 41, 43, 44, 46	131.1	100.4	125.0	131.1	87.3	122.4	131.1	87.3	122.4	131.1	97.9	124.5	131.1	75.8	120.1	131.1	98.3	124.6
21, 22, 23	FIRE SUPPRESSION, PLUMBING & HVAC	101.4	85.5	95.1	102.5	93.0	98.7	102.5	93.0	98.7	102.5	96.5	100.1	102.9	102.5	102.7	100.5	87.6	95.3
26, 27, 3370	ELECTRICAL, COMMUNICATIONS & UTIL.	111.6	96.0	103.5	114.5	74.3	93.5	113.2	74.3	92.9	116.7	83.9	99.6	113.9	91.7	102.3	114.4	93.6	103.6
MF2010	WEIGHTED AVERAGE	119.3	95.3	108.8	112.6	89.2	102.4	113.0	89.4	102.7	114.9	92.4	105.1	116.6	95.2	107.3	111.6	92.0	103.1

City Cost Indexes

CANADA

DIVISION		LAVAL, QUEBEC			LETHBRIDGE, ALBERTA			LLOYDMINSTER, ALBERTA			LONDON, ONTARIO			MEDICINE HAT, ALBERTA			MONCTON, NEW BRUNSWICK		
		MAT.	INST.	TOTAL	MAT.	INST.	TOTAL	MAT.	INST.	TOTAL	MAT.	INST.	TOTAL	MAT.	INST.	TOTAL	MAT.	INST.	TOTAL
015433	CONTRACTOR EQUIPMENT		102.5	102.5		103.7	103.7		103.7	103.7		103.9	103.9		103.7	103.7		101.9	101.9
0241, 31 - 34	SITE & INFRASTRUCTURE, DEMOLITION	96.1	100.5	99.2	113.0	102.5	105.6	112.9	101.9	105.2	116.2	105.3	108.5	111.6	101.9	104.8	97.8	97.5	97.6
0310	Concrete Forming & Accessories	130.5	89.8	95.4	124.2	94.4	98.5	122.4	84.4	89.6	126.1	88.0	93.2	124.1	84.3	89.8	103.7	65.9	71.0
0320	Concrete Reinforcing	151.1	81.3	116.3	155.3	74.1	114.8	155.3	74.0	114.7	130.9	93.0	112.0	155.3	74.0	114.7	139.2	61.5	100.4
0330	Cast-in-Place Concrete	133.3	99.3	119.2	161.4	104.8	137.9	149.7	101.0	129.5	161.6	98.1	135.2	149.7	101.0	129.5	131.1	79.8	109.8
03	CONCRETE	131.2	91.7	111.7	144.7	94.4	119.9	139.1	88.6	114.2	141.5	92.5	117.3	139.2	88.6	114.2	128.5	70.8	100.1
04	MASONRY	163.8	88.6	117.3	181.6	89.6	124.7	163.2	82.9	113.5	196.0	97.0	134.7	163.2	82.9	113.5	165.2	66.2	103.9
05	METALS	103.9	88.7	99.2	124.2	89.0	113.4	106.4	88.9	101.0	122.9	92.0	113.4	106.4	88.8	100.9	104.4	81.5	97.4
06	WOOD, PLASTICS & COMPOSITES	131.8	89.9	108.2	117.3	93.8	104.1	113.7	83.8	96.9	108.5	86.4	96.0	117.3	83.8	98.4	97.8	65.4	79.5
07	THERMAL & MOISTURE PROTECTION	106.8	91.8	100.7	117.4	92.6	107.3	114.3	88.0	103.7	125.2	92.8	112.0	120.9	88.0	107.6	108.9	65.8	91.4
08	OPENINGS	94.7	78.2	90.8	94.7	84.6	92.3	94.7	79.2	91.0	91.1	87.0	90.1	94.7	79.2	91.0	89.2	62.4	82.8
0920	Plaster & Gypsum Board	143.3	89.4	106.7	131.4	93.3	105.5	126.2	83.0	96.8	173.0	86.0	113.8	129.2	83.0	97.7	151.8	64.2	92.2
0950, 0980	Ceilings & Acoustic Treatment	97.4	89.4	92.1	106.3	93.3	97.6	97.4	83.0	87.8	130.1	86.0	100.7	97.4	83.0	87.8	100.9	64.2	76.5
0960	Flooring	130.5	101.4	121.8	130.5	94.3	119.7	130.5	94.3	119.7	132.6	104.1	124.1	130.5	94.3	119.7	117.8	73.4	104.5
0970, 0990	Wall Finishes & Painting/Coating	109.0	93.7	99.8	109.0	106.5	107.5	109.1	83.0	93.4	112.6	99.3	104.6	109.0	83.0	93.4	108.4	52.7	74.9
09	FINISHES	114.9	92.8	102.6	116.5	95.9	105.0	113.9	85.7	98.2	129.0	91.9	108.3	114.2	85.7	98.3	113.4	65.9	86.9
COVERS	DIVS. 10 - 14, 25, 28, 41, 43, 44, 46	131.1	87.3	122.4	131.1	97.5	124.4	131.1	94.1	123.7	131.1	99.0	124.7	131.1	94.1	123.7	131.1	66.9	118.3
21, 22, 23	FIRE SUPPRESSION, PLUMBING & HVAC	100.5	93.0	97.5	102.7	97.6	100.8	102.9	97.6	100.8	101.5	82.8	94.0	102.5	94.2	99.2	102.5	71.6	90.1
26, 27, 3370	ELECTRICAL, COMMUNICATIONS & UTIL.	114.4	74.3	93.5	108.4	87.5	97.5	106.1	87.5	96.4	109.7	93.6	101.3	106.1	87.5	96.4	118.8	63.3	89.8
MF2010	WEIGHTED AVERAGE	112.4	89.2	102.3	118.7	93.7	107.8	113.9	90.3	103.6	119.5	91.9	107.5	114.0	89.6	103.4	112.3	71.4	94.5

CANADA

DIVISION		MONTREAL, QUEBEC			MOOSE JAW, SASKATCHEWAN			NEW GLASGOW, NOVA SCOTIA			NEWCASTLE, NEW BRUNSWICK			NORTH BAY, ONTARIO			OSHAWA, ONTARIO		
		MAT.	INST.	TOTAL	MAT.	INST.	TOTAL	MAT.	INST.	TOTAL	MAT.	INST.	TOTAL	MAT.	INST.	TOTAL	MAT.	INST.	TOTAL
015433	CONTRACTOR EQUIPMENT		104.0	104.0		100.2	100.2		101.5	101.5		101.9	101.9		101.6	101.6		103.8	103.8
0241, 31 - 34	SITE & INFRASTRUCTURE, DEMOLITION	107.7	100.0	102.3	112.7	96.5	101.3	104.4	98.9	100.5	98.4	97.3	97.6	119.5	100.4	106.1	112.9	104.5	107.0
0310	Concrete Forming & Accessories	131.4	93.1	98.4	107.3	61.9	68.1	98.8	73.2	76.8	103.7	65.3	70.6	127.4	89.0	94.3	123.8	91.1	95.6
0320	Concrete Reinforcing	135.8	96.4	116.1	109.6	63.8	86.7	173.8	48.2	111.1	139.2	58.4	98.8	205.4	84.4	145.0	163.7	87.1	125.4
0330	Cast-in-Place Concrete	174.5	100.5	143.8	145.3	72.1	114.9	164.2	73.2	126.4	136.1	62.9	105.7	158.1	88.4	129.1	162.7	89.2	132.2
03	CONCRETE	148.7	96.2	122.8	122.3	66.5	94.8	151.6	69.3	111.0	130.9	63.8	97.8	154.2	88.1	121.6	145.4	89.9	118.0
04	MASONRY	172.0	94.1	123.8	161.7	65.5	102.2	182.8	73.2	115.0	165.6	66.1	104.0	188.0	91.5	128.3	162.1	96.0	121.2
05	METALS	124.5	92.8	114.7	102.7	74.9	94.1	116.0	75.3	103.4	104.4	72.8	94.7	117.0	90.4	108.8	105.5	92.6	101.5
06	WOOD, PLASTICS & COMPOSITES	120.2	93.5	105.1	99.0	60.4	77.2	94.6	72.6	82.2	97.8	65.4	79.5	127.3	89.6	106.0	117.2	90.1	101.9
07	THERMAL & MOISTURE PROTECTION	118.4	96.5	109.5	105.6	65.5	89.3	110.4	71.4	94.6	108.9	63.6	90.5	115.7	87.4	104.2	113.1	89.2	103.4
08	OPENINGS	92.8	82.4	90.3	90.1	58.1	82.5	88.3	66.4	83.1	89.2	57.2	81.6	95.9	85.7	93.5	92.2	89.9	91.7
0920	Plaster & Gypsum Board	144.9	92.8	109.5	121.3	59.1	79.0	154.0	71.7	98.0	151.8	64.2	92.2	151.5	89.2	109.1	146.6	89.8	108.0
0950, 0980	Ceilings & Acoustic Treatment	115.8	92.8	100.5	97.4	59.1	71.9	102.5	71.7	82.0	100.9	64.2	76.5	102.5	89.2	93.6	100.8	89.8	93.5
0960	Flooring	138.7	101.4	127.5	120.8	64.4	104.0	118.0	68.5	103.2	117.8	73.4	104.5	136.3	99.2	125.2	127.7	106.8	121.5
0970, 0990	Wall Finishes & Painting/Coating	112.9	105.7	108.6	109.0	68.2	84.5	113.0	65.5	84.4	108.4	52.7	74.9	113.0	93.1	101.1	107.9	106.6	107.1
09	FINISHES	123.1	96.7	108.4	110.3	62.7	83.8	116.0	71.8	91.4	113.4	65.9	86.9	121.6	91.8	105.0	115.7	95.7	104.5
COVERS	DIVS. 10 - 14, 25, 28, 41, 43, 44, 46	131.1	88.6	122.6	131.1	66.1	118.1	131.1	68.2	118.5	131.1	66.9	118.3	131.1	74.5	119.8	131.1	99.7	124.8
21, 22, 23	FIRE SUPPRESSION, PLUMBING & HVAC	101.3	93.8	98.3	102.9	77.8	92.8	102.5	86.3	96.0	102.5	71.3	90.0	102.5	100.3	101.6	100.5	102.9	101.5
26, 27, 3370	ELECTRICAL, COMMUNICATIONS & UTIL.	113.8	86.5	99.6	115.4	64.3	88.7	117.7	65.9	90.7	113.4	63.3	87.3	117.7	93.0	104.8	115.6	92.6	103.6
MF2010	WEIGHTED AVERAGE	119.2	93.4	107.9	111.2	70.8	93.6	117.7	76.1	99.6	112.1	69.3	93.5	120.5	92.9	108.5	114.6	96.1	106.5

CANADA

DIVISION		OTTAWA, ONTARIO			OWEN SOUND, ONTARIO			PETERBOROUGH, ONTARIO			PORTAGE LA PRAIRIE, MANITOBA			PRINCE ALBERT, SASKATCHEWAN			PRINCE GEORGE, BRITISH COLUMBIA		
		MAT.	INST.	TOTAL	MAT.	INST.	TOTAL	MAT.	INST.	TOTAL	MAT.	INST.	TOTAL	MAT.	INST.	TOTAL	MAT.	INST.	TOTAL
015433	CONTRACTOR EQUIPMENT		103.8	103.8		101.6	101.6		101.6	101.6		103.9	103.9		100.2	100.2		105.6	105.6
0241, 31 - 34	SITE & INFRASTRUCTURE, DEMOLITION	110.8	105.0	106.7	115.3	100.9	105.2	114.9	100.8	105.0	113.7	99.9	104.0	107.8	96.7	100.0	121.8	104.0	109.3
0310	Concrete Forming & Accessories	126.4	90.9	95.8	125.1	87.5	92.6	124.9	90.1	94.9	124.3	73.6	80.6	107.3	61.7	67.9	113.0	87.5	91.0
0320	Concrete Reinforcing	144.0	93.0	118.5	174.2	86.5	130.4	167.9	84.9	126.5	155.3	54.9	105.2	114.6	63.8	89.2	112.0	79.2	95.6
0330	Cast-in-Place Concrete	161.6	99.0	135.6	166.0	84.3	132.1	162.0	90.1	132.2	149.7	77.1	119.6	131.6	72.0	106.9	145.8	103.1	128.0
03	CONCRETE	143.6	94.1	119.2	151.0	86.4	119.2	147.1	89.3	118.6	132.7	72.0	102.7	116.7	66.3	91.9	150.0	91.5	121.2
04	MASONRY	175.1	97.0	126.8	165.2	97.3	123.2	167.9	98.4	124.9	166.3	67.7	105.3	160.8	65.5	101.8	172.9	96.6	125.7
05	METALS	123.6	91.9	113.8	108.2	91.2	103.0	105.5	90.9	101.0	106.4	77.7	97.5	102.8	74.7	94.1	106.2	88.8	100.8
06	WOOD, PLASTICS & COMPOSITES	108.8	90.5	98.5	120.6	86.2	101.2	119.8	88.2	102.0	117.1	75.1	93.4	99.0	60.4	77.2	101.3	83.9	91.5
07	THERMAL & MOISTURE PROTECTION	127.5	92.7	113.4	112.4	88.2	102.6	112.6	93.1	104.7	106.1	72.8	92.6	105.5	64.4	88.8	115.3	87.9	104.1
08	OPENINGS	93.8	89.2	92.7	92.5	85.0	90.7	93.6	87.5	92.2	94.7	66.3	88.0	88.9	58.1	81.6	91.0	83.7	89.3
0920	Plaster & Gypsum Board	192.8	90.2	123.0	151.2	85.7	106.7	142.7	87.8	105.4	123.6	73.9	89.8	121.3	59.1	79.0	124.3	83.0	96.2
0950, 0980	Ceilings & Acoustic Treatment	134.7	90.2	105.1	95.3	85.7	88.9	97.4	87.8	91.0	97.4	73.9	81.8	97.4	59.1	71.9	97.4	83.0	87.8
0960	Flooring	126.9	99.2	118.6	130.7	100.7	121.7	130.5	99.2	121.1	130.5	71.5	112.8	120.8	64.4	104.0	126.1	77.6	111.6
0970, 0990	Wall Finishes & Painting/Coating	112.4	94.1	101.4	111.9	91.8	99.8	109.0	95.5	100.9	109.1	60.0	79.6	109.0	58.2	78.5	109.0	85.8	95.0
09	FINISHES	130.7	92.9	109.7	117.3	90.6	102.4	115.6	92.5	102.7	113.4	72.3	90.5	110.3	61.6	83.2	113.9	85.1	97.9
COVERS	DIVS. 10 - 14, 25, 28, 41, 43, 44, 46	131.1	97.1	124.3	139.2	75.0	126.4	131.1	76.0	120.1	131.1	68.7	118.6	131.1	66.1	118.1	131.1	97.1	124.3
21, 22, 23	FIRE SUPPRESSION, PLUMBING & HVAC	101.5	83.2	94.2	102.2	100.2	101.4	102.5	103.9	103.1	102.5	85.4	95.6	102.9	70.1	89.7	102.5	96.5	100.1
26, 27, 3370	ELECTRICAL, COMMUNICATIONS & UTIL.	109.0	94.4	101.4	117.9	91.7	104.2	112.9	92.6	102.3	115.1	61.5	87.1	115.4	64.3	88.7	113.1	83.9	97.8
MF2010	WEIGHTED AVERAGE	119.2	92.5	107.5	117.4	93.0	106.8	115.5	94.9	106.5	113.9	75.6	97.2	110.3	69.0	92.3	115.9	91.7	105.3

765

CANADA

DIVISION		QUEBEC, QUEBEC			RED DEER, ALBERTA			REGINA, SASKATCHEWAN			RIMOUSKI, QUEBEC			ROUYN-NORANDA, QUEBEC			SAINT HYACINTHE, QUEBEC		
		MAT.	INST.	TOTAL	MAT.	INST.	TOTAL	MAT.	INST.	TOTAL	MAT.	INST.	TOTAL	MAT.	INST.	TOTAL	MAT.	INST.	TOTAL
015433	CONTRACTOR EQUIPMENT		104.4	104.4		103.7	103.7		100.2	100.2		102.5	102.5		102.5	102.5		102.5	102.5
0241, 31 - 34	SITE & INFRASTRUCTURE, DEMOLITION	103.7	100.0	101.1	111.6	101.9	104.8	123.5	98.4	105.9	96.1	99.7	98.6	95.7	100.5	99.1	96.1	100.5	99.2
0310	Concrete Forming & Accessories	131.8	93.4	98.6	139.3	84.3	91.9	114.1	90.4	93.7	130.3	92.8	98.0	130.3	89.8	95.4	130.3	89.8	95.4
0320	Concrete Reinforcing	136.6	96.4	116.5	155.3	74.0	114.7	132.1	83.4	107.8	107.7	96.4	102.1	151.1	81.3	116.3	151.1	81.3	116.3
0330	Cast-in-Place Concrete	142.8	100.9	125.4	149.7	101.0	129.5	173.6	94.9	140.9	135.7	99.2	120.5	129.0	99.3	116.7	133.3	99.3	119.2
03	CONCRETE	133.9	96.4	115.4	140.3	88.6	114.8	150.3	90.6	120.9	125.3	95.6	110.7	129.2	91.7	110.7	131.2	91.7	111.7
04	MASONRY	172.0	94.1	123.8	163.2	82.9	113.5	184.7	94.4	128.8	163.4	94.1	120.5	163.6	88.6	117.2	163.8	88.6	117.3
05	METALS	124.4	93.0	114.7	106.4	88.8	100.9	125.6	85.7	113.3	103.4	92.3	100.0	103.8	88.7	99.2	103.8	88.7	99.2
06	WOOD, PLASTICS & COMPOSITES	119.9	93.5	105.0	117.3	83.8	98.4	98.3	91.3	94.4	131.6	93.2	110.0	131.6	89.9	108.1	131.6	89.9	108.1
07	THERMAL & MOISTURE PROTECTION	118.9	96.6	109.9	130.7	88.0	113.4	117.9	85.6	104.8	106.2	95.9	102.0	106.2	91.8	100.3	106.6	91.8	100.6
08	OPENINGS	94.0	90.3	93.1	94.7	79.2	91.0	90.8	80.2	88.3	94.2	80.5	91.0	94.7	78.2	90.8	94.7	78.2	90.8
0920	Plaster & Gypsum Board	164.8	92.8	115.8	129.2	83.0	97.7	147.8	91.0	109.2	172.1	92.8	118.1	140.3	89.4	105.7	142.7	89.4	106.5
0950, 0980	Ceilings & Acoustic Treatment	122.8	92.8	102.8	97.4	83.0	87.8	123.9	91.0	102.0	96.5	92.8	94.0	96.5	89.4	91.8	96.5	89.4	91.8
0960	Flooring	134.3	101.4	124.5	133.2	94.3	121.6	132.5	66.7	112.8	130.5	101.4	121.8	130.5	101.4	121.8	130.5	101.4	121.8
0970, 0990	Wall Finishes & Painting/Coating	115.4	105.7	109.5	109.0	83.0	93.4	112.9	90.9	99.7	109.0	105.7	107.0	109.0	93.7	99.8	109.0	93.7	99.8
09	FINISHES	126.3	96.7	109.8	115.0	85.7	98.7	125.5	86.8	103.9	118.7	96.5	106.3	114.3	92.8	102.3	114.6	92.8	102.5
COVERS	DIVS. 10 - 14, 25, 28, 41, 43, 44, 46	131.1	88.7	122.6	131.1	94.1	123.7	131.1	73.5	119.6	131.1	88.0	122.5	131.1	87.3	122.4	131.1	87.3	122.4
21, 22, 23	FIRE SUPPRESSION, PLUMBING & HVAC	101.2	93.8	98.3	102.5	94.2	99.2	100.7	84.2	94.1	102.5	93.7	99.0	102.5	93.0	98.3	98.9	93.0	96.5
26, 27, 3370	ELECTRICAL, COMMUNICATIONS & UTIL.	110.9	86.5	98.2	106.1	87.5	96.4	115.4	91.4	102.9	113.2	86.5	99.3	113.2	74.3	92.9	114.0	74.3	93.3
MF2010	WEIGHTED AVERAGE	117.5	93.8	107.2	114.5	89.6	103.6	120.3	88.4	106.4	112.3	93.1	103.9	112.5	89.2	102.3	111.9	89.2	102.0

CANADA

DIVISION		SAINT JOHN, NEW BRUNSWICK			SARNIA, ONTARIO			SASKATOON, SASKATCHEWAN			SAULT STE MARIE, ONTARIO			SHERBROOKE, QUEBEC			SOREL, QUEBEC		
		MAT.	INST.	TOTAL	MAT.	INST.	TOTAL	MAT.	INST.	TOTAL	MAT.	INST.	TOTAL	MAT.	INST.	TOTAL	MAT.	INST.	TOTAL
015433	CONTRACTOR EQUIPMENT		101.9	101.9		101.6	101.6		100.2	100.2		101.6	101.6		102.5	102.5		102.5	102.5
0241, 31 - 34	SITE & INFRASTRUCTURE, DEMOLITION	98.5	98.5	98.5	113.4	100.9	104.6	108.7	98.4	101.5	103.7	100.4	101.4	96.2	100.5	99.2	96.3	100.6	99.3
0310	Concrete Forming & Accessories	123.2	66.3	74.1	123.7	97.4	101.0	107.4	90.4	92.7	113.0	87.0	90.6	130.3	89.8	95.4	130.3	90.0	95.5
0320	Concrete Reinforcing	139.2	61.9	100.6	119.4	86.3	102.9	115.5	83.4	99.5	107.8	84.6	96.2	151.1	81.3	116.3	142.9	81.4	112.2
0330	Cast-in-Place Concrete	134.1	80.7	111.9	149.5	103.7	130.5	141.4	94.9	122.1	134.3	88.5	115.3	133.3	99.3	119.2	134.4	99.3	119.8
03	CONCRETE	131.4	71.4	101.8	133.3	97.4	115.6	122.5	90.6	106.7	117.3	87.3	102.5	131.2	91.7	111.7	130.4	91.7	111.3
04	MASONRY	185.8	72.2	115.5	179.3	101.2	131.0	167.2	94.4	122.2	164.3	94.5	121.1	163.9	88.6	117.3	164.0	88.6	117.3
05	METALS	104.3	82.6	97.6	105.5	91.3	101.1	101.9	85.7	96.9	104.7	90.8	100.4	103.8	88.7	99.2	103.8	88.8	99.2
06	WOOD, PLASTICS & COMPOSITES	121.4	64.5	89.3	118.9	96.8	106.4	98.0	91.3	94.3	106.0	86.5	95.0	131.6	89.9	108.1	131.6	89.9	108.1
07	THERMAL & MOISTURE PROTECTION	109.2	69.6	93.1	112.6	96.7	106.2	106.6	85.6	98.2	111.5	89.4	102.5	106.2	91.8	100.3	106.2	91.8	100.3
08	OPENINGS	89.1	60.8	82.4	95.7	91.5	94.7	90.1	80.2	87.7	87.2	85.3	86.8	94.7	78.2	90.8	94.7	83.0	91.9
0920	Plaster & Gypsum Board	169.4	63.3	97.2	164.7	96.7	118.4	129.7	91.0	103.4	131.7	86.0	100.6	142.7	89.4	106.5	172.1	89.4	115.9
0950, 0980	Ceilings & Acoustic Treatment	107.2	63.3	78.0	102.7	96.7	98.7	119.7	91.0	100.6	97.4	86.0	89.8	96.5	89.4	91.8	96.5	89.4	91.8
0960	Flooring	128.4	73.4	112.0	130.5	108.5	123.9	120.7	66.7	104.6	123.6	102.7	117.3	130.5	101.4	121.8	130.5	101.4	121.8
0970, 0990	Wall Finishes & Painting/Coating	108.4	78.8	90.6	109.0	108.0	108.4	109.9	90.9	98.5	109.0	100.0	103.6	109.0	93.7	99.8	109.0	93.7	99.8
09	FINISHES	120.2	68.5	91.4	119.8	101.1	109.4	116.5	86.8	99.9	111.4	91.3	100.2	114.6	92.8	102.5	118.7	92.8	104.3
COVERS	DIVS. 10 - 14, 25, 28, 41, 43, 44, 46	131.1	67.3	118.3	131.1	77.5	120.4	131.1	73.5	119.6	131.1	98.4	124.6	131.1	87.3	122.4	131.1	87.3	122.4
21, 22, 23	FIRE SUPPRESSION, PLUMBING & HVAC	102.5	81.0	93.9	102.5	110.2	105.6	100.6	84.2	94.0	102.5	96.8	100.2	102.9	93.0	98.9	102.5	93.0	98.7
26, 27, 3370	ELECTRICAL, COMMUNICATIONS & UTIL.	121.9	90.3	105.4	115.7	94.9	104.8	117.1	91.4	103.7	114.4	93.0	103.2	113.2	74.3	92.9	113.2	74.3	92.9
MF2010	WEIGHTED AVERAGE	114.6	78.3	98.8	115.3	99.5	108.4	111.3	88.4	101.3	110.7	93.1	103.0	112.8	89.2	102.5	113.0	89.4	102.7

CANADA

DIVISION		ST CATHARINES, ONTARIO			ST JEROME, QUEBEC			ST JOHNS, NEWFOUNDLAND			SUDBURY, ONTARIO			SUMMERSIDE, PRINCE EDWARD ISLAND			SYDNEY, NOVA SCOTIA		
		MAT.	INST.	TOTAL	MAT.	INST.	TOTAL	MAT.	INST.	TOTAL	MAT.	INST.	TOTAL	MAT.	INST.	TOTAL	MAT.	INST.	TOTAL
015433	CONTRACTOR EQUIPMENT		101.6	101.6		102.5	102.5		103.1	103.1		101.6	101.6		101.5	101.5		101.5	101.5
0241, 31 - 34	SITE & INFRASTRUCTURE, DEMOLITION	101.8	101.8	101.8	95.7	100.5	99.1	116.4	99.9	104.8	101.9	101.3	101.5	112.2	96.4	101.1	100.1	98.9	99.2
0310	Concrete Forming & Accessories	115.9	93.9	96.9	130.3	89.8	95.4	113.8	82.4	86.7	111.9	87.4	90.7	99.1	59.6	65.0	98.8	73.2	76.8
0320	Concrete Reinforcing	104.3	93.0	98.7	151.1	81.3	116.3	161.9	74.4	118.2	105.1	93.0	99.0	171.5	48.3	110.0	173.8	48.2	111.1
0330	Cast-in-Place Concrete	134.4	100.1	120.1	129.0	99.3	116.7	166.6	87.6	133.8	135.5	96.2	119.2	155.8	62.0	116.9	126.6	73.2	104.5
03	CONCRETE	115.8	95.8	105.9	129.2	91.7	110.7	159.3	83.0	121.6	116.2	91.6	104.0	156.5	59.1	108.5	133.8	69.3	102.0
04	MASONRY	158.6	99.7	122.1	163.8	88.6	117.2	187.1	89.8	126.9	158.6	94.9	119.2	181.9	63.7	108.8	180.0	73.2	113.9
05	METALS	104.6	92.4	100.8	103.8	88.7	99.2	126.2	83.4	113.0	104.6	91.9	100.7	116.0	68.6	101.4	116.0	75.3	103.4
06	WOOD, PLASTICS & COMPOSITES	107.4	93.6	99.6	131.6	89.9	108.1	101.4	80.9	89.8	103.5	86.5	93.9	94.9	59.1	74.7	94.6	72.6	82.2
07	THERMAL & MOISTURE PROTECTION	112.1	95.9	105.5	106.2	91.8	100.3	118.6	84.9	105.0	111.5	90.3	102.9	109.9	62.5	90.7	110.4	71.4	94.6
08	OPENINGS	85.2	90.7	86.5	94.7	78.2	90.8	99.3	73.4	93.2	86.0	85.3	85.8	99.1	51.1	87.8	88.3	66.4	83.1
0920	Plaster & Gypsum Board	129.0	93.4	104.8	140.3	89.4	105.7	154.5	80.1	103.9	133.6	86.0	101.2	154.4	57.7	88.6	154.0	71.7	98.0
0950, 0980	Ceilings & Acoustic Treatment	100.8	93.4	95.9	96.5	89.4	91.8	116.8	80.1	92.4	95.5	86.0	89.2	102.5	57.7	72.7	102.5	71.7	82.3
0960	Flooring	123.0	100.7	116.3	130.5	101.4	121.8	122.3	60.3	103.8	120.9	102.7	115.4	118.1	64.0	101.9	118.0	68.5	103.2
0970, 0990	Wall Finishes & Painting/Coating	107.9	102.5	104.7	109.0	93.7	99.8	112.8	75.8	90.6	107.9	93.5	99.3	113.0	43.9	71.4	113.0	65.5	84.4
09	FINISHES	111.2	96.4	103.0	114.3	92.8	102.3	121.1	78.0	97.1	110.1	90.7	99.3	117.0	59.1	84.7	116.0	71.8	91.4
COVERS	DIVS. 10 - 14, 25, 28, 41, 43, 44, 46	131.1	76.3	120.1	131.1	87.3	122.4	131.1	73.2	119.5	131.1	98.5	124.6	131.1	66.4	118.2	131.1	68.2	118.5
21, 22, 23	FIRE SUPPRESSION, PLUMBING & HVAC	100.5	84.4	94.1	102.5	93.0	98.7	100.8	73.9	90.0	102.5	85.8	95.8	102.5	65.2	87.6	102.5	86.3	96.0
26, 27, 3370	ELECTRICAL, COMMUNICATIONS & UTIL.	116.0	94.5	104.7	113.8	74.3	93.2	115.9	72.4	93.2	113.1	94.8	103.6	116.7	53.6	83.7	117.7	65.9	90.7
MF2010	WEIGHTED AVERAGE	109.7	93.0	102.4	112.5	89.2	102.3	122.0	80.4	103.9	109.9	91.7	101.9	119.5	64.1	95.4	115.6	76.1	98.4

City Cost Indexes

CANADA

DIVISION		THUNDER BAY, ONTARIO			TIMMINS, ONTARIO			TORONTO, ONTARIO			TROIS RIVIERES, QUEBEC			TRURO, NOVA SCOTIA			VANCOUVER, BRITISH COLUMBIA		
		MAT.	INST.	TOTAL	MAT.	INST.	TOTAL	MAT.	INST.	TOTAL	MAT.	INST.	TOTAL	MAT.	INST.	TOTAL	MAT.	INST.	TOTAL
015433	CONTRACTOR EQUIPMENT		101.6	101.6		101.6	101.6		103.9	103.9		102.5	102.5		101.5	101.5		112.1	112.1
0241, 31 - 34	SITE & INFRASTRUCTURE, DEMOLITION	106.8	101.7	103.2	114.9	100.4	104.7	137.0	105.8	115.1	100.9	100.6	100.7	100.1	98.9	99.2	120.3	108.2	111.8
0310	Concrete Forming & Accessories	123.7	90.8	95.3	124.9	89.0	93.9	128.5	99.5	103.4	133.2	90.0	95.9	97.1	73.3	76.5	122.0	91.6	95.8
0320	Concrete Reinforcing	93.2	91.9	92.5	167.9	84.4	126.2	151.3	93.2	122.3	173.8	81.4	127.6	142.9	48.2	95.6	142.2	81.7	112.0
0330	Cast-in-Place Concrete	147.9	98.5	127.4	162.0	88.4	131.5	150.7	108.2	133.1	131.1	99.3	117.9	168.3	73.3	128.8	157.7	99.2	133.4
03	CONCRETE	124.2	93.7	109.2	147.1	88.1	118.0	139.8	101.1	120.7	136.8	91.7	114.6	145.5	69.3	107.9	148.1	92.7	120.8
04	MASONRY	159.3	99.0	122.0	167.9	91.5	120.6	194.2	104.1	138.4	183.8	88.6	124.9	163.4	73.2	107.6	182.3	93.0	127.0
05	METALS	104.4	91.3	100.4	105.5	90.4	100.9	125.1	93.1	115.2	115.1	88.8	107.0	104.6	75.3	95.6	141.4	91.4	126.0
06	WOOD, PLASTICS & COMPOSITES	117.2	89.5	101.6	119.8	89.6	102.7	111.5	98.7	104.3	139.8	89.9	111.7	89.2	72.6	79.9	104.1	91.7	97.1
07	THERMAL & MOISTURE PROTECTION	112.4	93.0	104.5	112.6	87.4	102.4	124.3	99.6	114.2	109.3	91.8	102.2	107.5	71.4	92.9	130.0	88.5	113.2
08	OPENINGS	84.3	87.8	85.1	93.6	85.7	91.7	91.8	96.8	93.0	97.0	83.0	93.7	86.6	66.4	81.8	94.5	87.9	93.0
0920	Plaster & Gypsum Board	162.4	89.2	112.6	142.7	89.2	106.3	155.3	98.6	116.7	186.1	89.4	120.3	141.8	71.7	94.1	140.0	90.9	106.6
0950, 0980	Ceilings & Acoustic Treatment	95.5	89.2	91.3	97.4	89.2	91.9	125.4	98.6	107.6	101.6	89.4	93.5	97.4	71.7	80.3	150.0	90.9	110.7
0960	Flooring	127.7	107.8	121.7	130.5	99.2	121.1	132.8	110.4	126.1	136.3	101.4	125.8	113.1	68.5	99.8	129.2	97.7	119.8
0970, 0990	Wall Finishes & Painting/Coating	107.9	92.1	98.4	109.0	93.1	99.5	114.8	106.6	109.9	113.0	93.7	101.4	109.0	65.5	82.9	114.0	97.7	104.2
09	FINISHES	116.4	94.2	104.0	115.6	91.8	102.4	127.3	102.5	113.5	125.3	92.8	107.2	109.9	71.8	88.7	129.1	93.6	109.3
COVERS	DIVS. 10 - 14, 25, 28, 41, 43, 44, 46	131.1	76.0	120.1	131.1	74.5	119.8	131.1	102.1	125.3	131.1	87.3	122.4	131.1	68.2	118.5	131.1	96.9	124.3
21, 22, 23	FIRE SUPPRESSION, PLUMBING & HVAC	100.5	84.3	94.0	102.5	100.3	101.6	101.2	94.6	98.6	102.5	93.0	98.7	102.5	86.3	96.0	101.3	82.3	93.7
26, 27, 3370	ELECTRICAL, COMMUNICATIONS & UTIL.	114.4	93.0	103.2	114.4	93.0	103.2	111.5	96.6	103.7	118.0	74.3	95.2	112.9	65.9	88.4	111.3	81.3	95.6
MF2010	WEIGHTED AVERAGE	110.9	91.7	102.6	115.6	92.9	105.7	120.2	99.0	111.0	117.9	89.4	105.5	113.0	76.1	96.9	123.3	90.0	108.8

CANADA

DIVISION		VICTORIA, BRITISH COLUMBIA			WHITEHORSE, YUKON			WINDSOR, ONTARIO			WINNIPEG, MANITOBA			YARMOUTH, NOVA SCOTIA			YELLOWKNIFE, NWT		
		MAT.	INST.	TOTAL	MAT.	INST.	TOTAL	MAT.	INST.	TOTAL	MAT.	INST.	TOTAL	MAT.	INST.	TOTAL	MAT.	INST.	TOTAL
015433	CONTRACTOR EQUIPMENT		108.7	108.7		101.7	101.7		101.6	101.6		105.9	105.9		101.5	101.5		101.6	101.6
0241, 31 - 34	SITE & INFRASTRUCTURE, DEMOLITION	121.5	107.7	111.8	123.0	97.4	105.0	97.3	101.6	100.3	119.5	101.3	106.7	104.2	98.9	100.5	138.7	101.7	112.8
0310	Concrete Forming & Accessories	112.9	91.0	94.0	117.7	60.9	68.7	123.7	90.0	94.6	131.5	68.1	76.8	98.8	73.2	76.8	116.1	82.0	86.7
0320	Concrete Reinforcing	113.0	81.6	97.3	153.9	61.9	107.9	102.2	93.0	97.6	141.0	57.4	99.3	173.8	48.2	111.1	154.5	64.7	109.6
0330	Cast-in-Place Concrete	146.4	98.6	126.6	191.7	71.3	141.7	137.7	100.3	122.1	181.5	73.8	136.8	162.4	73.2	125.4	231.5	89.4	172.5
03	CONCRETE	152.5	91.9	122.6	158.2	65.4	112.4	117.6	94.1	106.0	153.4	68.7	111.6	150.8	69.3	110.6	176.9	81.7	129.9
04	MASONRY	170.1	93.0	122.4	205.6	63.9	117.9	158.7	97.8	121.0	179.6	69.3	111.4	182.6	73.2	114.9	209.1	76.2	126.8
05	METALS	104.3	87.4	99.1	129.3	74.6	112.5	104.5	91.8	100.6	143.3	74.6	122.1	116.0	75.3	103.4	129.3	79.8	114.0
06	WOOD, PLASTICS & COMPOSITES	101.6	91.6	96.0	100.8	59.6	77.5	117.2	89.1	101.4	111.1	69.0	87.3	94.6	72.6	82.2	100.3	83.7	90.9
07	THERMAL & MOISTURE PROTECTION	115.8	88.3	104.7	125.8	63.4	100.5	112.2	92.2	104.0	118.7	70.7	99.2	110.4	71.4	94.6	122.1	80.0	105.0
08	OPENINGS	91.8	84.1	90.0	95.4	56.8	86.3	84.1	88.1	85.0	93.1	61.6	85.6	88.3	66.4	83.1	94.3	70.5	88.7
0920	Plaster & Gypsum Board	121.7	90.9	100.7	146.1	58.2	86.3	147.7	88.8	107.6	139.7	67.5	90.6	154.0	71.7	98.0	176.0	83.1	112.8
0950, 0980	Ceilings & Acoustic Treatment	99.3	90.9	93.7	127.7	58.2	81.4	95.5	88.8	91.0	143.6	67.5	93.0	102.5	71.7	82.0	133.5	83.1	99.9
0960	Flooring	125.9	77.6	111.5	140.3	62.5	117.0	127.7	105.0	120.9	131.3	74.0	114.1	118.0	68.5	103.2	134.7	94.2	122.6
0970, 0990	Wall Finishes & Painting/Coating	109.9	97.7	102.6	124.2	57.2	83.9	107.9	95.4	100.4	112.9	55.4	78.4	113.0	65.5	84.4	121.6	82.0	97.8
09	FINISHES	114.1	90.1	100.7	130.9	60.6	91.7	114.0	93.5	102.6	127.8	68.3	94.6	116.0	71.8	91.4	134.9	83.7	106.4
COVERS	DIVS. 10 - 14, 25, 28, 41, 43, 44, 46	131.1	72.9	119.5	131.1	65.4	118.0	131.1	75.4	120.0	131.1	67.9	118.5	131.1	68.2	118.5	131.1	68.7	118.6
21, 22, 23	FIRE SUPPRESSION, PLUMBING & HVAC	102.5	82.2	94.4	102.9	76.4	92.3	100.5	83.9	93.9	101.2	65.7	87.0	102.5	86.3	96.0	103.0	96.0	100.2
26, 27, 3370	ELECTRICAL, COMMUNICATIONS & UTIL.	113.8	81.3	96.8	134.3	63.7	97.5	119.3	94.5	106.4	112.9	66.9	88.9	117.7	65.9	90.7	132.1	87.2	108.7
MF2010	WEIGHTED AVERAGE	115.9	88.1	103.8	126.3	69.8	101.7	110.2	91.7	102.2	123.6	70.8	100.6	117.6	76.1	99.6	128.8	85.8	110.1

Location Factors

Costs shown in RSMeans cost data publications are based on national averages for materials and installation. To adjust these costs to a specific location, simply multiply the base cost by the factor and divide by 100 for that city. The data is arranged alphabetically by state and postal zip code numbers. For a city not listed, use the factor for a nearby city with similar economic characteristics.

STATE/ZIP	CITY	MAT.	INST.	TOTAL
ALABAMA				
350-352	Birmingham	97.5	74.1	87.3
354	Tuscaloosa	96.7	62.0	81.6
355	Jasper	97.0	56.7	79.4
356	Decatur	96.6	59.1	80.3
357-358	Huntsville	96.7	70.8	85.4
359	Gadsden	96.7	60.8	81.1
360-361	Montgomery	97.9	58.1	80.5
362	Anniston	96.5	63.0	81.9
363	Dothan	96.9	50.5	76.7
364	Evergreen	96.5	51.9	77.1
365-366	Mobile	97.8	65.9	83.9
367	Selma	96.7	50.8	76.7
368	Phenix City	97.3	55.7	79.2
369	Butler	96.8	50.5	76.6
ALASKA				
995-996	Anchorage	121.3	114.3	118.3
997	Fairbanks	120.7	115.0	118.2
998	Juneau	120.6	113.5	117.5
999	Ketchikan	132.0	113.5	124.0
ARIZONA				
850,853	Phoenix	99.4	74.8	88.7
851,852	Mesa/Tempe	98.8	73.8	87.9
855	Globe	99.0	71.2	86.9
856-857	Tucson	97.6	73.6	87.1
859	Show Low	99.1	73.5	88.0
860	Flagstaff	101.0	72.9	88.8
863	Prescott	98.9	69.7	86.2
864	Kingman	97.3	73.2	86.8
865	Chambers	97.3	71.9	86.3
ARKANSAS				
716	Pine Bluff	96.9	62.9	82.1
717	Camden	94.5	50.4	75.3
718	Texarkana	95.7	49.9	75.7
719	Hot Springs	93.8	52.3	75.8
720-722	Little Rock	98.0	63.8	83.1
723	West Memphis	95.6	62.7	81.2
724	Jonesboro	96.3	59.4	80.2
725	Batesville	94.2	55.1	77.2
726	Harrison	95.5	51.1	76.1
727	Fayetteville	93.0	52.9	75.6
728	Russellville	94.1	54.4	76.8
729	Fort Smith	96.8	61.7	81.5
CALIFORNIA				
900-902	Los Angeles	100.1	116.5	107.3
903-905	Inglewood	95.7	113.4	103.4
906-908	Long Beach	97.1	113.4	104.2
910-912	Pasadena	96.3	113.9	104.0
913-916	Van Nuys	99.1	113.9	105.5
917-918	Alhambra	98.2	113.9	105.0
919-921	San Diego	100.2	109.1	104.1
922	Palm Springs	96.7	111.6	103.2
923-924	San Bernardino	94.6	111.2	101.9
925	Riverside	98.9	114.0	105.5
926-927	Santa Ana	96.5	111.6	103.1
928	Anaheim	98.9	114.1	105.6
930	Oxnard	99.6	114.2	105.9
931	Santa Barbara	98.9	114.6	105.7
932-933	Bakersfield	100.8	110.6	105.1
934	San Luis Obispo	99.3	111.6	104.7
935	Mojave	96.8	108.6	101.9
936-938	Fresno	100.0	114.5	106.3
939	Salinas	100.2	120.3	108.9
940-941	San Francisco	106.1	143.8	122.5
942,956-958	Sacramento	101.2	118.6	108.8
943	Palo Alto	99.5	133.1	114.2
944	San Mateo	101.7	132.7	115.2
945	Vallejo	100.6	127.2	112.2
946	Oakland	103.9	133.1	116.6
947	Berkeley	103.4	133.1	116.4
948	Richmond	102.5	131.2	115.0
949	San Rafael	104.2	133.6	117.0
950	Santa Cruz	104.1	120.4	111.2
CALIFORNIA (CONT'D)				
951	San Jose	102.2	134.6	116.3
952	Stockton	100.5	115.5	107.0
953	Modesto	100.4	114.9	106.7
954	Santa Rosa	100.3	133.4	114.7
955	Eureka	101.6	111.6	106.0
959	Marysville	100.8	115.1	107.0
960	Redding	103.6	114.6	108.4
961	Susanville	102.6	114.6	107.8
COLORADO				
800-802	Denver	101.6	82.6	93.3
803	Boulder	98.6	82.0	91.3
804	Golden	100.6	79.6	91.4
805	Fort Collins	102.1	79.6	92.3
806	Greeley	99.7	76.1	89.4
807	Fort Morgan	99.1	79.6	90.6
808-809	Colorado Springs	101.3	79.3	91.7
810	Pueblo	100.9	78.6	91.2
811	Alamosa	102.0	74.6	90.1
812	Salida	101.7	76.2	90.6
813	Durango	102.4	76.8	91.2
814	Montrose	101.2	76.5	90.5
815	Grand Junction	104.4	76.7	92.4
816	Glenwood Springs	102.2	79.3	92.2
CONNECTICUT				
060	New Britain	100.8	120.4	109.3
061	Hartford	102.0	120.6	110.1
062	Willimantic	101.4	120.6	109.7
063	New London	97.7	120.5	107.6
064	Meriden	99.6	120.5	108.7
065	New Haven	102.2	120.5	110.2
066	Bridgeport	101.8	120.2	109.8
067	Waterbury	101.4	120.1	109.6
068	Norwalk	101.4	126.9	112.5
069	Stamford	101.5	127.9	113.0
D.C.				
200-205	Washington	101.6	91.6	97.2
DELAWARE				
197	Newark	98.8	108.1	102.8
198	Wilmington	99.4	108.1	103.2
199	Dover	99.7	108.1	103.3
FLORIDA				
320,322	Jacksonville	97.2	67.7	84.3
321	Daytona Beach	97.4	74.4	87.3
323	Tallahassee	98.7	58.0	81.0
324	Panama City	98.5	59.1	81.3
325	Pensacola	100.8	62.4	84.1
326,344	Gainesville	98.7	68.0	85.3
327-328,347	Orlando	99.3	71.4	87.1
329	Melbourne	99.9	77.9	90.3
330-332,340	Miami	97.7	74.6	87.6
333	Fort Lauderdale	96.4	73.9	86.6
334,349	West Palm Beach	95.3	72.3	85.3
335-336,346	Tampa	97.9	79.8	90.0
337	St. Petersburg	100.2	64.7	84.7
338	Lakeland	97.1	79.3	89.4
339,341	Fort Myers	96.4	74.1	86.7
342	Sarasota	99.3	75.3	88.8
GEORGIA				
300-303,399	Atlanta	96.8	75.3	87.5
304	Statesboro	96.5	56.9	79.2
305	Gainesville	95.2	62.8	81.1
306	Athens	94.7	65.1	81.8
307	Dalton	96.4	60.1	80.6
308-309	Augusta	95.6	64.8	82.2
310-312	Macon	96.2	65.9	83.0
313-314	Savannah	98.4	62.0	82.6
315	Waycross	97.3	60.7	81.3
316	Valdosta	97.5	62.6	82.3
317,398	Albany	97.5	62.5	82.3
318-319	Columbus	97.4	66.6	84.0

Location Factors

STATE/ZIP	CITY	MAT.	INST.	TOTAL
HAWAII				
967	Hilo	110.4	121.0	115.0
968	Honolulu	114.9	121.0	117.6
STATES & POSS.				
969	Guam	131.2	58.9	99.7
IDAHO				
832	Pocatello	100.8	78.4	91.1
833	Twin Falls	101.9	68.5	87.4
834	Idaho Falls	99.6	75.5	89.1
835	Lewiston	108.3	85.5	98.4
836-837	Boise	99.8	79.4	90.9
838	Coeur d'Alene	107.6	83.3	97.0
ILLINOIS				
600-603	North Suburban	98.5	135.9	114.8
604	Joliet	98.4	140.7	116.8
605	South Suburban	98.5	135.9	114.8
606-608	Chicago	98.9	141.9	117.6
609	Kankakee	94.8	130.8	110.5
610-611	Rockford	98.9	123.5	109.6
612	Rock Island	96.6	99.8	98.0
613	La Salle	97.7	125.1	109.6
614	Galesburg	97.6	107.6	102.0
615-616	Peoria	99.9	110.4	104.5
617	Bloomington	96.9	109.9	102.6
618-619	Champaign	100.2	108.0	103.6
620-622	East St. Louis	95.5	109.3	101.5
623	Quincy	96.9	101.6	99.0
624	Effingham	96.3	106.3	100.6
625	Decatur	98.2	105.9	101.6
626-627	Springfield	99.0	107.2	102.5
628	Centralia	94.1	108.4	100.4
629	Carbondale	93.9	106.2	99.2
INDIANA				
460	Anderson	95.5	83.1	90.1
461-462	Indianapolis	98.3	85.1	92.6
463-464	Gary	96.8	110.1	102.6
465-466	South Bend	95.7	84.2	90.7
467-468	Fort Wayne	96.0	79.2	88.7
469	Kokomo	93.3	82.0	88.4
470	Lawrenceburg	93.3	79.3	87.2
471	New Albany	94.4	77.0	86.8
472	Columbus	96.6	80.9	89.7
473	Muncie	97.3	81.8	90.6
474	Bloomington	98.7	81.5	91.2
475	Washington	95.0	83.3	89.9
476-477	Evansville	96.5	86.6	92.1
478	Terre Haute	97.2	85.8	92.2
479	Lafayette	96.3	82.9	90.5
IOWA				
500-503,509	Des Moines	99.4	83.9	92.7
504	Mason City	96.5	66.6	83.5
505	Fort Dodge	96.6	58.8	80.2
506-507	Waterloo	98.3	70.9	86.4
508	Creston	96.7	77.9	88.5
510-511	Sioux City	99.1	73.6	88.0
512	Sibley	97.7	57.5	80.2
513	Spencer	99.2	57.5	81.0
514	Carroll	96.4	72.2	85.9
515	Council Bluffs	100.2	78.8	90.9
516	Shenandoah	97.1	72.1	86.2
520	Dubuque	98.5	80.4	90.6
521	Decorah	97.4	65.6	83.5
522-524	Cedar Rapids	99.4	83.4	92.4
525	Ottumwa	97.3	73.0	86.7
526	Burlington	96.6	76.9	88.0
527-528	Davenport	98.4	93.4	96.2
KANSAS				
660-662	Kansas City	99.4	95.7	97.7
664-666	Topeka	99.4	66.5	85.1
667	Fort Scott	97.7	74.3	87.5
668	Emporia	97.8	70.0	85.7
669	Belleville	99.4	65.6	84.7
670-672	Wichita	99.9	65.1	84.8
673	Independence	99.9	70.3	87.0
674	Salina	100.4	67.0	85.9
675	Hutchinson	95.8	65.4	82.5
676	Hays	99.6	65.6	84.8
677	Colby	100.2	65.6	85.1

STATE/ZIP	CITY	MAT.	INST.	TOTAL
KANSAS (CONT'D)				
678	Dodge City	101.7	66.5	86.4
679	Liberal	99.5	66.4	85.1
KENTUCKY				
400-402	Louisville	97.8	84.2	91.9
403-405	Lexington	97.0	82.4	90.7
406	Frankfort	97.9	82.4	91.1
407-409	Corbin	94.4	73.3	85.2
410	Covington	95.2	93.2	94.3
411-412	Ashland	94.0	100.1	96.6
413-414	Campton	95.1	80.2	88.6
415-416	Pikeville	96.2	90.0	93.5
417-418	Hazard	94.6	79.9	88.2
420	Paducah	93.2	86.2	90.2
421-422	Bowling Green	95.5	84.8	90.8
423	Owensboro	95.6	88.9	92.7
424	Henderson	93.0	87.9	90.8
425-426	Somerset	92.7	81.5	87.8
427	Elizabethtown	92.2	83.7	88.5
LOUISIANA				
700-701	New Orleans	101.5	69.8	87.7
703	Thibodaux	98.7	64.9	84.0
704	Hammond	96.3	54.9	78.3
705	Lafayette	98.5	62.7	82.9
706	Lake Charles	98.6	65.0	84.0
707-708	Baton Rouge	100.4	63.6	84.4
710-711	Shreveport	98.4	59.6	81.5
712	Monroe	96.7	56.4	79.2
713-714	Alexandria	96.8	57.8	79.8
MAINE				
039	Kittery	95.1	85.7	91.0
040-041	Portland	100.8	91.2	96.6
042	Lewiston	98.3	91.2	95.2
043	Augusta	100.3	80.8	91.8
044	Bangor	97.6	90.8	94.7
045	Bath	96.1	83.0	90.4
046	Machias	95.7	86.5	91.7
047	Houlton	95.9	86.6	91.8
048	Rockland	95.0	86.5	91.3
049	Waterville	96.2	80.8	89.5
MARYLAND				
206	Waldorf	97.5	82.2	90.9
207-208	College Park	97.6	83.9	91.7
209	Silver Spring	96.9	83.8	91.2
210-212	Baltimore	100.5	82.8	92.8
214	Annapolis	100.3	81.8	92.3
215	Cumberland	96.0	81.9	89.9
216	Easton	97.4	69.3	85.2
217	Hagerstown	96.9	82.8	90.7
218	Salisbury	97.8	63.3	82.8
219	Elkton	95.1	81.9	89.4
MASSACHUSETTS				
010-011	Springfield	100.0	109.8	104.3
012	Pittsfield	99.6	109.6	103.9
013	Greenfield	97.5	110.2	103.0
014	Fitchburg	96.3	124.6	108.6
015-016	Worcester	100.0	124.6	110.7
017	Framingham	95.5	131.0	111.0
018	Lowell	99.4	130.1	112.8
019	Lawrence	100.1	131.3	113.7
020-022, 024	Boston	101.8	138.1	117.6
023	Brockton	100.4	126.3	111.7
025	Buzzards Bay	94.9	126.7	108.8
026	Hyannis	97.6	126.7	110.3
027	New Bedford	99.6	126.8	111.4
MICHIGAN				
480,483	Royal Oak	94.2	107.5	100.0
481	Ann Arbor	96.4	107.9	101.4
482	Detroit	97.9	109.3	102.8
484-485	Flint	96.1	96.8	96.4
486	Saginaw	95.7	92.4	94.2
487	Bay City	95.8	92.5	94.4
488-489	Lansing	97.7	94.1	96.1
490	Battle Creek	96.8	87.4	92.7
491	Kalamazoo	97.1	85.9	92.2
492	Jackson	95.0	95.9	95.4
493,495	Grand Rapids	98.1	84.5	92.2
494	Muskegon	95.6	85.5	91.2

STATE/ZIP	CITY	MAT.	INST.	TOTAL
MICHIGAN (CONT'D)				
496	Traverse City	94.6	81.0	88.6
497	Gaylord	95.5	84.4	90.7
498-499	Iron mountain	97.5	87.4	93.1
MINNESOTA				
550-551	Saint Paul	100.2	118.8	108.3
553-555	Minneapolis	100.6	119.9	109.0
556-558	Duluth	99.0	108.6	103.2
559	Rochester	98.8	104.9	101.5
560	Mankato	96.6	102.4	99.1
561	Windom	95.3	93.3	94.4
562	Willmar	94.9	103.0	98.4
563	St. Cloud	96.3	117.8	105.7
564	Brainerd	96.3	102.3	98.9
565	Detroit Lakes	98.3	96.7	97.6
566	Bemidji	97.7	99.5	98.5
567	Thief River Falls	97.3	93.8	95.7
MISSISSIPPI				
386	Clarksdale	95.8	53.8	77.5
387	Greenville	99.4	63.1	83.6
388	Tupelo	97.3	56.1	79.4
389	Greenwood	97.0	53.3	78.0
390-392	Jackson	99.1	63.5	83.6
393	Meridian	96.2	65.3	82.7
394	Laurel	97.2	57.1	79.7
395	Biloxi	97.7	59.1	80.9
396	Mccomb	95.7	52.9	77.1
397	Columbus	97.1	55.1	78.8
MISSOURI				
630-631	St. Louis	99.6	107.6	103.1
633	Bowling Green	98.1	94.7	96.6
634	Hannibal	97.1	92.6	95.1
635	Kirksville	100.3	90.0	95.8
636	Flat River	99.0	95.8	97.6
637	Cape Girardeau	99.1	90.6	95.4
638	Sikeston	97.5	90.6	94.5
639	Poplar Bluff	97.0	90.3	94.1
640-641	Kansas City	101.6	106.7	103.8
644-645	St. Joseph	100.7	93.9	97.8
646	Chillicothe	97.7	96.2	97.1
647	Harrisonville	97.3	102.2	99.5
648	Joplin	99.5	81.0	91.5
650-651	Jefferson City	98.4	93.4	96.2
652	Columbia	98.6	93.5	96.4
653	Sedalia	98.1	92.6	95.7
654-655	Rolla	96.3	95.6	96.0
656-658	Springfield	99.9	82.1	92.1
MONTANA				
590-591	Billings	102.2	77.9	91.6
592	Wolf Point	101.7	74.9	90.0
593	Miles City	99.5	74.7	88.7
594	Great Falls	103.4	77.1	92.0
595	Havre	100.6	74.2	89.1
596	Helena	102.0	75.1	90.2
597	Butte	102.0	77.2	91.2
598	Missoula	99.4	76.4	89.4
599	Kalispell	98.4	76.3	88.8
NEBRASKA				
680-681	Omaha	99.6	79.3	90.7
683-685	Lincoln	99.5	75.3	89.0
686	Columbus	97.5	77.9	88.9
687	Norfolk	99.2	77.5	89.8
688	Grand Island	99.1	77.8	89.9
689	Hastings	98.5	81.2	90.9
690	Mccook	98.1	72.1	86.8
691	North Platte	98.5	79.6	90.2
692	Valentine	100.6	73.6	88.9
693	Alliance	100.4	71.6	87.9
NEVADA				
889-891	Las Vegas	100.2	109.4	104.2
893	Ely	98.7	103.4	100.8
894-895	Reno	99.0	93.8	96.7
897	Carson City	99.1	93.8	96.8
898	Elko	97.6	86.1	92.6
NEW HAMPSHIRE				
030	Nashua	100.6	93.6	97.6
031	Manchester	102.1	93.6	98.4

STATE/ZIP	CITY	MAT.	INST.	TOTAL
NEW HAMPSHIRE (CONT'D)				
032-033	Concord	100.8	92.3	97.1
034	Keene	97.4	74.0	87.2
035	Littleton	97.1	77.2	88.4
036	Charleston	96.9	70.1	85.2
037	Claremont	96.0	70.1	84.7
038	Portsmouth	98.2	94.2	96.4
NEW JERSEY				
070-071	Newark	101.9	125.6	112.2
072	Elizabeth	99.5	125.3	110.7
073	Jersey City	98.5	125.5	110.2
074-075	Paterson	100.2	125.2	111.1
076	Hackensack	98.4	125.5	110.2
077	Long Branch	97.8	124.1	109.2
078	Dover	98.7	125.4	110.3
079	Summit	98.7	125.3	110.3
080,083	Vineland	97.5	123.4	108.8
081	Camden	99.4	123.6	109.9
082,084	Atlantic City	98.1	123.5	109.2
085-086	Trenton	100.8	124.0	110.9
087	Point Pleasant	99.2	121.4	108.8
088-089	New Brunswick	99.7	125.2	110.8
NEW MEXICO				
870-872	Albuquerque	99.2	73.6	88.0
873	Gallup	99.3	73.6	88.1
874	Farmington	99.7	73.6	88.3
875	Santa Fe	100.5	73.6	88.8
877	Las Vegas	97.7	73.6	87.2
878	Socorro	97.3	73.6	87.0
879	Truth/Consequences	97.0	70.4	85.4
880	Las Cruces	95.8	70.4	84.7
881	Clovis	98.1	73.5	87.4
882	Roswell	99.8	73.6	88.4
883	Carrizozo	100.1	73.6	88.5
884	Tucumcari	98.8	73.5	87.8
NEW YORK				
100-102	New York	103.8	166.4	131.1
103	Staten Island	99.7	163.9	127.6
104	Bronx	98.0	163.9	126.7
105	Mount Vernon	97.9	133.3	113.3
106	White Plains	98.0	133.3	113.4
107	Yonkers	102.5	133.4	116.0
108	New Rochelle	98.2	133.3	113.5
109	Suffern	98.0	126.2	110.3
110	Queens	100.8	162.9	127.8
111	Long Island City	102.2	162.9	128.6
112	Brooklyn	102.6	162.9	128.9
113	Flushing	102.3	162.9	128.7
114	Jamaica	100.6	162.9	127.7
115,117,118	Hicksville	100.7	146.6	120.7
116	Far Rockaway	102.4	162.9	128.7
119	Riverhead	101.4	146.6	121.1
120-122	Albany	98.6	100.2	99.3
123	Schenectady	97.8	100.2	98.8
124	Kingston	100.7	118.3	108.4
125-126	Poughkeepsie	100.0	127.5	112.0
127	Monticello	99.4	116.5	106.8
128	Glens Falls	92.6	95.0	93.6
129	Plattsburgh	97.3	88.4	93.4
130-132	Syracuse	98.5	97.0	97.9
133-135	Utica	96.7	93.2	95.1
136	Watertown	98.1	91.9	95.4
137-139	Binghamton	98.1	99.4	98.6
140-142	Buffalo	99.7	105.8	102.4
143	Niagara Falls	96.9	103.9	100.0
144-146	Rochester	100.3	95.6	98.3
147	Jamestown	96.0	87.8	92.4
148-149	Elmira	95.9	93.1	94.7
NORTH CAROLINA				
270,272-274	Greensboro	98.8	56.3	80.3
271	Winston-Salem	98.5	57.1	80.5
275-276	Raleigh	98.2	55.1	79.4
277	Durham	100.2	54.4	80.2
278	Rocky Mount	96.0	53.2	77.4
279	Elizabeth City	96.9	52.2	77.4
280	Gastonia	98.4	56.1	80.0
281-282	Charlotte	98.7	57.6	80.8
283	Fayetteville	100.9	58.5	82.5
284	Wilmington	97.2	56.6	79.5
285	Kinston	95.3	53.7	77.2

STATE/ZIP	CITY	MAT.	INST.	TOTAL	STATE/ZIP	CITY	MAT.	INST.	TOTAL
NORTH CAROLINA (CONT'D)					**PENNSYLVANIA (CONT'D)**				
286	Hickory	95.6	54.9	77.9	177	Williamsport	93.6	79.3	87.4
287-288	Asheville	97.6	55.9	79.4	178	Sunbury	95.5	96.3	95.8
289	Murphy	96.4	49.2	75.8	179	Pottsville	94.7	98.0	96.1
					180	Lehigh Valley	95.4	112.5	102.9
NORTH DAKOTA					181	Allentown	97.6	108.8	102.4
580-581	Fargo	101.7	67.6	86.9	182	Hazleton	95.0	98.8	96.7
582	Grand Forks	101.8	51.6	79.9	183	Stroudsburg	94.9	102.0	98.0
583	Devils Lake	101.0	58.6	82.5	184-185	Scranton	98.3	99.7	98.9
584	Jamestown	101.0	45.1	76.7	186-187	Wilkes-Barre	94.7	99.2	96.7
585	Bismarck	102.0	64.0	85.5	188	Montrose	94.4	97.1	95.6
586	Dickinson	101.9	57.9	82.7	189	Doylestown	94.6	120.8	106.0
587	Minot	101.8	71.0	88.4	190-191	Philadelphia	98.9	133.4	113.9
588	Williston	100.3	58.0	81.9	193	Westchester	95.8	121.7	107.1
					194	Norristown	94.9	129.5	110.0
OHIO					195-196	Reading	97.1	101.1	98.8
430-432	Columbus	98.6	89.7	94.7					
433	Marion	95.0	83.7	90.1	**PUERTO RICO**				
434-436	Toledo	98.7	96.4	97.7	009	San Juan	122.1	24.6	79.7
437-438	Zanesville	95.5	85.6	91.2					
439	Steubenville	96.8	94.5	95.8	**RHODE ISLAND**				
440	Lorain	98.8	90.4	95.2	028	Newport	99.0	116.6	106.6
441	Cleveland	98.9	100.0	99.4	029	Providence	101.5	116.6	108.1
442-443	Akron	99.8	93.4	97.0					
444-445	Youngstown	99.1	88.3	94.4	**SOUTH CAROLINA**				
446-447	Canton	99.2	85.0	93.0	290-292	Columbia	97.2	57.3	79.8
448-449	Mansfield	96.6	85.6	91.8	293	Spartanburg	96.4	57.4	79.5
450	Hamilton	97.4	84.5	91.8	294	Charleston	97.7	66.4	84.1
451-452	Cincinnati	97.8	84.8	92.1	295	Florence	96.2	57.8	79.4
453-454	Dayton	97.5	83.2	91.3	296	Greenville	96.2	56.5	78.9
455	Springfield	97.5	84.2	91.7	297	Rock Hill	95.6	51.2	76.3
456	Chillicothe	96.4	92.2	94.5	298	Aiken	96.4	70.4	85.1
457	Athens	99.1	80.6	91.1	299	Beaufort	97.1	45.7	74.7
458	Lima	99.6	84.4	93.0					
					SOUTH DAKOTA				
OKLAHOMA					570-571	Sioux Falls	100.0	58.8	82.1
730-731	Oklahoma City	97.3	65.4	83.4	572	Watertown	98.5	50.2	77.5
734	Ardmore	95.2	62.3	80.9	573	Mitchell	97.5	49.5	76.6
735	Lawton	97.5	63.3	82.6	574	Aberdeen	100.1	50.6	78.6
736	Clinton	96.5	63.6	82.2	575	Pierre	100.8	59.2	82.7
737	Enid	97.2	60.9	81.4	576	Mobridge	98.1	49.8	77.1
738	Woodward	95.3	63.8	81.6	577	Rapid City	100.0	60.3	82.7
739	Guymon	96.3	60.5	80.7					
740-741	Tulsa	97.4	62.2	82.1	**TENNESSEE**				
743	Miami	94.0	68.3	82.8	370-372	Nashville	97.9	74.1	87.5
744	Muskogee	96.6	56.3	79.0	373-374	Chattanooga	99.5	65.5	84.7
745	Mcalester	93.7	61.1	79.5	375,380-381	Memphis	98.5	71.3	86.7
746	Ponca City	94.3	62.5	80.5	376	Johnson City	99.2	56.7	80.7
747	Durant	94.3	64.0	81.1	377-379	Knoxville	96.2	60.5	80.6
748	Shawnee	95.7	62.2	81.1	382	Mckenzie	96.6	60.4	80.9
749	Poteau	93.5	62.1	79.8	383	Jackson	98.3	62.5	82.7
					384	Columbia	95.3	67.5	83.2
OREGON					385	Cookeville	96.4	60.4	80.7
970-972	Portland	97.2	101.4	99.1					
973	Salem	99.0	100.5	99.7	**TEXAS**				
974	Eugene	97.1	100.4	98.5	750	Mckinney	99.3	48.9	77.3
975	Medford	98.4	98.2	98.3	751	Waxahackie	99.3	56.4	80.6
976	Klamath Falls	98.2	98.2	98.2	752-753	Dallas	100.1	65.8	85.2
977	Bend	97.3	100.5	98.7	754	Greenville	99.4	42.2	74.5
978	Pendleton	93.1	102.5	97.2	755	Texarkana	98.4	49.7	77.2
979	Vale	91.3	89.8	90.7	756	Longview	99.0	40.5	73.5
					757	Tyler	98.9	54.6	79.6
PENNSYLVANIA					758	Palestine	95.4	55.8	78.2
150-152	Pittsburgh	99.7	105.8	102.3	759	Lufkin	95.9	59.1	79.9
153	Washington	96.7	103.2	99.5	760-761	Fort Worth	99.6	62.5	83.5
154	Uniontown	97.1	102.2	99.4	762	Denton	98.2	46.6	75.7
155	Bedford	98.0	92.6	95.7	763	Wichita Falls	97.8	55.0	79.2
156	Greensburg	98.0	101.6	99.5	764	Eastland	96.5	49.1	75.9
157	Indiana	96.9	100.1	98.3	765	Temple	95.0	52.7	76.6
158	Dubois	98.4	97.1	97.8	766-767	Waco	97.2	57.3	79.8
159	Johnstown	97.9	97.3	97.7	768	Brownwood	98.5	48.4	76.7
160	Butler	92.1	102.2	96.5	769	San Angelo	98.2	49.5	77.0
161	New Castle	92.1	97.2	94.4	770-772	Houston	98.7	70.9	86.6
162	Kittanning	92.5	103.4	97.3	773	Huntsville	97.2	56.9	79.6
163	Oil City	92.1	97.0	94.3	774	Wharton	98.1	53.8	78.8
164-165	Erie	94.1	95.0	94.5	775	Galveston	96.3	69.7	84.7
166	Altoona	94.3	92.7	93.6	776-777	Beaumont	96.7	61.2	81.2
167	Bradford	95.3	96.8	96.0	778	Bryan	94.1	63.0	80.5
168	State College	94.9	93.0	94.1	779	Victoria	98.2	42.7	74.1
169	Wellsboro	95.9	92.3	94.3	780	Laredo	97.1	53.7	78.2
170-171	Harrisburg	99.6	95.9	98.0	781-782	San Antonio	97.5	64.5	83.1
172	Chambersburg	96.0	89.7	93.2	783-784	Corpus Christi	99.7	53.7	79.6
173-174	York	96.5	96.0	96.3	785	Mc Allen	99.7	46.6	76.6
175-176	Lancaster	94.8	89.3	92.4	786-787	Austin	98.6	59.1	81.4

STATE/ZIP	CITY	MAT.	INST.	TOTAL
TEXAS (CONT'D)				
788	Del Rio	99.4	46.2	76.3
789	Giddings	96.4	55.6	78.6
790-791	Amarillo	98.2	60.0	81.6
792	Childress	97.9	56.9	80.0
793-794	Lubbock	100.0	56.3	81.0
795-796	Abilene	98.3	53.6	78.8
797	Midland	99.9	53.6	79.7
798-799,885	El Paso	97.2	50.6	76.9
UTAH				
840-841	Salt Lake City	102.2	66.8	86.8
842,844	Ogden	97.9	68.8	85.2
843	Logan	99.7	68.8	86.2
845	Price	100.1	65.3	84.9
846-847	Provo	100.1	66.7	85.6
VERMONT				
050	White River Jct.	97.9	79.7	90.0
051	Bellows Falls	96.6	94.7	95.8
052	Bennington	96.9	95.3	96.2
053	Brattleboro	97.2	94.5	96.0
054	Burlington	101.5	85.1	94.4
056	Montpelier	99.2	84.3	92.7
057	Rutland	99.2	85.1	93.0
058	St. Johnsbury	97.9	79.2	89.8
059	Guildhall	96.8	79.2	89.1
VIRGINIA				
220-221	Fairfax	99.3	84.4	92.8
222	Arlington	100.6	84.7	93.6
223	Alexandria	99.8	85.4	93.5
224-225	Fredericksburg	98.2	83.0	91.6
226	Winchester	98.7	82.1	91.5
227	Culpeper	98.6	80.8	90.9
228	Harrisonburg	98.8	68.1	85.5
229	Charlottesville	99.2	67.3	85.3
230-232	Richmond	100.4	68.9	86.7
233-235	Norfolk	100.0	68.8	86.4
236	Newport News	99.2	68.2	85.7
237	Portsmouth	98.6	66.1	84.5
238	Petersburg	98.6	68.9	85.6
239	Farmville	97.8	53.3	78.5
240-241	Roanoke	100.2	66.0	85.3
242	Bristol	98.1	55.6	79.6
243	Pulaski	97.7	58.3	80.6
244	Staunton	98.4	62.7	82.9
245	Lynchburg	98.6	66.1	84.5
246	Grundy	98.0	53.4	78.6
WASHINGTON				
980-981,987	Seattle	102.5	104.8	103.5
982	Everett	102.1	99.6	101.0
983-984	Tacoma	102.3	100.0	101.3
985	Olympia	101.0	100.0	100.6
986	Vancouver	103.1	93.2	98.8
988	Wenatchee	102.0	87.1	95.5
989	Yakima	102.5	94.4	99.0
990-992	Spokane	102.5	82.7	93.8
993	Richland	102.2	89.6	96.7
994	Clarkston	100.6	80.7	92.0
WEST VIRGINIA				
247-248	Bluefield	97.1	91.7	94.7
249	Lewisburg	98.4	91.4	95.4
250-253	Charleston	99.0	94.1	96.9
254	Martinsburg	98.3	86.1	93.0
255-257	Huntington	99.8	95.2	97.8
258-259	Beckley	96.9	92.0	94.8
260	Wheeling	99.8	93.8	97.2
261	Parkersburg	98.9	91.4	95.6
262	Buckhannon	98.2	93.6	96.2
263-264	Clarksburg	98.8	93.5	96.5
265	Morgantown	98.8	92.6	96.1
266	Gassaway	98.2	92.8	95.8
267	Romney	98.2	90.4	94.8
268	Petersburg	98.0	90.1	94.6
WISCONSIN				
530,532	Milwaukee	100.9	107.9	104.0
531	Kenosha	100.2	102.9	101.4
534	Racine	99.7	102.6	101.0
535	Beloit	99.6	101.9	100.6
537	Madison	99.5	99.8	99.6

STATE/ZIP	CITY	MAT.	INST.	TOTAL
WISCONSIN (CONT'D)				
538	Lancaster	97.4	93.5	95.7
539	Portage	96.1	97.9	96.9
540	New Richmond	96.2	95.9	96.1
541-543	Green Bay	100.5	94.1	97.7
544	Wausau	95.7	94.4	95.2
545	Rhinelander	98.7	92.4	95.9
546	La Crosse	97.2	95.0	96.3
547	Eau Claire	98.7	96.4	97.7
548	Superior	96.1	97.6	96.7
549	Oshkosh	96.3	92.4	94.6
WYOMING				
820	Cheyenne	100.1	65.7	85.2
821	Yellowstone Nat'l Park	97.7	65.2	83.5
822	Wheatland	98.7	64.6	83.9
823	Rawlins	100.2	67.8	86.1
824	Worland	98.3	64.1	83.4
825	Riverton	99.3	64.9	84.3
826	Casper	100.4	60.7	83.1
827	Newcastle	98.2	67.8	84.9
828	Sheridan	100.9	65.2	85.4
829-831	Rock Springs	101.8	65.4	85.9
CANADIAN FACTORS (reflect Canadian currency)				
ALBERTA				
	Calgary	124.7	95.4	111.9
	Edmonton	125.0	95.4	112.1
	Fort McMurray	124.1	94.2	111.1
	Lethbridge	118.7	93.7	107.8
	Lloydminster	113.9	90.3	103.6
	Medicine Hat	114.0	89.6	103.4
	Red Deer	114.5	89.6	103.6
BRITISH COLUMBIA				
	Kamloops	114.9	92.4	105.1
	Prince George	115.9	91.7	105.3
	Vancouver	123.3	90.0	108.8
	Victoria	115.9	88.1	103.8
MANITOBA				
	Brandon	118.7	77.3	100.7
	Portage la Prairie	113.9	75.6	97.2
	Winnipeg	123.6	70.8	100.6
NEW BRUNSWICK				
	Bathurst	112.1	68.6	93.1
	Dalhousie	112.1	68.8	93.2
	Fredericton	118.1	74.0	98.9
	Moncton	112.3	71.4	94.5
	Newcastle	112.1	69.3	93.5
	St. John	114.6	78.3	98.8
NEWFOUNDLAND				
	Corner Brook	122.2	69.0	99.0
	St Johns	122.0	80.4	103.9
NORTHWEST TERRITORIES				
	Yellowknife	128.8	85.8	110.1
NOVA SCOTIA				
	Bridgewater	113.4	76.1	97.2
	Dartmouth	119.7	76.1	100.7
	Halifax	119.9	80.6	102.8
	New Glasgow	117.7	76.1	99.6
	Sydney	115.6	76.1	98.4
	Truro	113.0	76.1	96.9
	Yarmouth	117.6	76.1	99.6
ONTARIO				
	Barrie	117.3	94.9	107.5
	Brantford	115.5	98.8	108.2
	Cornwall	115.5	95.1	106.7
	Hamilton	119.3	95.3	108.8
	Kingston	116.6	95.2	107.3
	Kitchener	111.6	92.0	103.1
	London	119.5	91.9	107.5
	North Bay	120.5	92.9	108.5
	Oshawa	114.6	96.1	106.5
	Ottawa	119.2	92.5	107.5
	Owen Sound	117.4	93.0	106.8
	Peterborough	115.5	94.9	106.5
	Sarnia	115.3	99.5	108.4

Location Factors

STATE/ZIP	CITY	MAT.	INST.	TOTAL
ONTARIO (CONT'D)				
	Sault Ste Marie	110.7	93.1	103.0
	St. Catharines	109.7	93.0	102.4
	Sudbury	109.9	91.7	101.9
	Thunder Bay	110.9	91.7	102.6
	Timmins	115.6	92.9	105.7
	Toronto	120.2	99.0	111.0
	Windsor	110.2	91.7	102.2
PRINCE EDWARD ISLAND				
	Charlottetown	120.5	64.0	95.9
	Summerside	119.5	64.1	95.4
QUEBEC				
	Cap-de-la-Madeleine	112.8	89.4	102.6
	Charlesbourg	112.8	89.4	102.6
	Chicoutimi	111.9	93.1	103.7
	Gatineau	112.5	89.2	102.3
	Granby	112.8	89.1	102.4
	Hull	112.6	89.2	102.4
	Joliette	113.0	89.4	102.7
	Laval	112.4	89.2	102.3
	Montreal	119.2	93.4	107.9
	Quebec	117.5	93.8	107.2
	Rimouski	112.3	93.1	103.9
	Rouyn-Noranda	112.5	89.2	102.3
	Saint Hyacinthe	111.9	89.2	102.0
	Sherbrooke	112.8	89.2	102.5
	Sorel	113.0	89.4	102.7
	St Jerome	112.5	89.2	102.3
	Trois Rivieres	117.9	89.4	105.5
SASKATCHEWAN				
	Moose Jaw	111.2	70.8	93.6
	Prince Albert	110.3	69.0	92.3
	Regina	120.3	88.4	106.4
	Saskatoon	111.3	88.4	101.3
YUKON				
	Whitehorse	126.3	69.8	101.7

R011105-05   Tips for Accurate Estimating

1. Use pre-printed or columnar forms for orderly sequence of dimensions and locations and for recording telephone quotations.

2. Use only the front side of each paper or form except for certain pre-printed summary forms.

3. Be consistent in listing dimensions: For example, length x width x height. This helps in rechecking to ensure that, the total length of partitions is appropriate for the building area.

4. Use printed (rather than measured) dimensions where given.

5. Add up multiple printed dimensions for a single entry where possible.

6. Measure all other dimensions carefully.

7. Use each set of dimensions to calculate multiple related quantities.

8. Convert foot and inch measurements to decimal feet when listing. Memorize decimal equivalents to .01 parts of a foot (1/8″ equals approximately .01′).

9. Do not "round off" quantities until the final summary.

10. Mark drawings with different colors as items are taken off.

11. Keep similar items together, different items separate.

12. Identify location and drawing numbers to aid in future checking for completeness.

13. Measure or list everything on the drawings or mentioned in the specifications.

14. It may be necessary to list items not called for to make the job complete.

15. Be alert for: Notes on plans such as N.T.S. (not to scale); changes in scale throughout the drawings; reduced size drawings; discrepancies between the specifications and the drawings.

16. Develop a consistent pattern of performing an estimate. For example:
    a. Start the quantity takeoff at the lower floor and move to the next higher floor.
    b. Proceed from the main section of the building to the wings.
    c. Proceed from south to north or vice versa, clockwise or counterclockwise.
    d. Take off floor plan quantities first, elevations next, then detail drawings.

17. List all gross dimensions that can be either used again for different quantities, or used as a rough check of other quantities for verification (exterior perimeter, gross floor area, individual floor areas, etc.).

18. Utilize design symmetry or repetition (repetitive floors, repetitive wings, symmetrical design around a center line, similar room layouts, etc.). Note: Extreme caution is needed here so as not to omit or duplicate an area.

19. Do not convert units until the final total is obtained. For instance, when estimating concrete work, keep all units to the nearest cubic foot, then summarize and convert to cubic yards.

20. When figuring alternatives, it is best to total all items involved in the basic system, then total all items involved in the alternates. Therefore you work with positive numbers in all cases. When adds and deducts are used, it is often confusing whether to add or subtract a portion of an item; especially on a complicated or involved alternate.

R011105-50 Metric Conversion Factors

Description: This table is primarily for converting customary U.S. units in the left hand column to SI metric units in the right hand column. In addition, conversion factors for some commonly encountered Canadian and non-SI metric units are included.

If You Know		Multiply By		To Find
Length	Inches	x 25.4[a]	=	Millimeters
	Feet	x 0.3048[a]	=	Meters
	Yards	x 0.9144[a]	=	Meters
	Miles (statute)	x 1.609	=	Kilometers
Area	Square inches	x 645.2	=	Square millimeters
	Square feet	x 0.0929	=	Square meters
	Square yards	x 0.8361	=	Square meters
Volume (Capacity)	Cubic inches	x 16,387	=	Cubic millimeters
	Cubic feet	x 0.02832	=	Cubic meters
	Cubic yards	x 0.7646	=	Cubic meters
	Gallons (U.S. liquids)[b]	x 0.003785	=	Cubic meters[c]
	Gallons (Canadian liquid)[b]	x 0.004546	=	Cubic meters[c]
	Ounces (U.S. liquid)[b]	x 29.57	=	Milliliters[c, d]
	Quarts (U.S. liquid)[b]	x 0.9464	=	Liters[c, d]
	Gallons (U.S. liquid)[b]	x 3.785	=	Liters[c, d]
Force	Kilograms force[d]	x 9.807	=	Newtons
	Pounds force	x 4.448	=	Newtons
	Pounds force	x 0.4536	=	Kilograms force[d]
	Kips	x 4448	=	Newtons
	Kips	x 453.6	=	Kilograms force[d]
Pressure, Stress, Strength (Force per unit area)	Kilograms force per square centimeter[d]	x 0.09807	=	Megapascals
	Pounds force per square inch (psi)	x 0.006895	=	Megapascals
	Kips per square inch	x 6.895	=	Megapascals
	Pounds force per square inch (psi)	x 0.07031	=	Kilograms force per square centimeter[d]
	Pounds force per square foot	x 47.88	=	Pascals
	Pounds force per square foot	x 4.882	=	Kilograms force per square meter[d]
Bending Moment Or Torque	Inch-pounds force	x 0.01152	=	Meter-kilograms force[d]
	Inch-pounds force	x 0.1130	=	Newton-meters
	Foot-pounds force	x 0.1383	=	Meter-kilograms force[d]
	Foot-pounds force	x 1.356	=	Newton-meters
	Meter-kilograms force[d]	x 9.807	=	Newton-meters
Mass	Ounces (avoirdupois)	x 28.35	=	Grams
	Pounds (avoirdupois)	x 0.4536	=	Kilograms
	Tons (metric)	x 1000	=	Kilograms
	Tons, short (2000 pounds)	x 907.2	=	Kilograms
	Tons, short (2000 pounds)	x 0.9072	=	Megagrams[e]
Mass per Unit Volume	Pounds mass per cubic foot	x 16.02	=	Kilograms per cubic meter
	Pounds mass per cubic yard	x 0.5933	=	Kilograms per cubic meter
	Pounds mass per gallon (U.S. liquid)[b]	x 119.8	=	Kilograms per cubic meter
	Pounds mass per gallon (Canadian liquid)[b]	x 99.78	=	Kilograms per cubic meter
Temperature	Degrees Fahrenheit	(F-32)/1.8	=	Degrees Celsius
	Degrees Fahrenheit	(F+459.67)/1.8	=	Degrees Kelvin
	Degrees Celsius	C+273.15	=	Degrees Kelvin

[a]The factor given is exact
[b]One U.S. gallon = 0.8327 Canadian gallon
[c]1 liter = 1000 milliliters = 1000 cubic centimeters
  1 cubic decimeter = 0.001 cubic meter

[d]Metric but not SI unit
[e]Called "tonne" in England and "metric ton" in other metric countries

R011105-60   Weights and Measures

Measures of Length
1 Mile = 1760 Yards = 5280 Feet
1 Yard = 3 Feet = 36 inches
1 Foot = 12 Inches
1 Mil = 0.001 Inch
1 Fathom = 2 Yards = 6 Feet
1 Rod = 5.5 Yards = 16.5 Feet
1 Hand = 4 Inches
1 Span = 9 Inches
1 Micro-inch = One Millionth Inch or 0.000001 Inch
1 Micron = One Millionth Meter + 0.00003937 Inch

Surveyor's Measure
1 Mile = 8 Furlongs = 80 Chains
1 Furlong = 10 Chains = 220 Yards
1 Chain = 4 Rods = 22 Yards = 66 Feet = 100 Links
1 Link = 7.92 Inches

Square Measure
1 Square Mile = 640 Acres = 6400 Square Chains
1 Acre = 10 Square Chains = 4840 Square Yards =
43,560 Sq. Ft.
1 Square Chain = 16 Square Rods = 484 Square Yards =
4356 Sq. Ft.
1 Square Rod = 30.25 Square Yards = 272.25 Square Feet = 625 Square
Lines
1 Square Yard = 9 Square Feet
1 Square Foot = 144 Square Inches
An Acre equals a Square 208.7 Feet per Side

Cubic Measure
1 Cubic Yard = 27 Cubic Feet
1 Cubic Foot = 1728 Cubic Inches
1 Cord of Wood = 4 x 4 x 8 Feet = 128 Cubic Feet
1 Perch of Masonry = 16½ x 1½ x 1 Foot = 24.75 Cubic Feet

Avoirdupois or Commercial Weight
1 Gross or Long Ton = 2240 Pounds
1 Net or Short ton = 2000 Pounds
1 Pound = 16 Ounces = 7000 Grains
1 Ounce = 16 Drachms = 437.5 Grains
1 Stone = 14 Pounds

Shipping Measure
For Measuring Internal Capacity of a Vessel:
1 Register Ton = 100 Cubic Feet

For Measurement of Cargo:
Approximately 40 Cubic Feet of Merchandise is considered a Shipping Ton, unless that bulk would weigh more than 2000 Pounds, in which case Freight Charge may be based upon weight.

40 Cubic Feet = 32.143 U.S. Bushels = 31.16 Imp. Bushels

Liquid Measure
1 Imperial Gallon = 1.2009 U.S. Gallon = 277.42 Cu. In.
1 Cubic Foot = 7.48 U.S. Gallons

R011110-10   Architectural Fees

Tabulated below are typical percentage fees by project size, for good professional architectural service. Fees may vary from those listed depending upon degree of design difficulty and economic conditions in any particular area.

Rates can be interpolated horizontally and vertically. Various portions of the same project requiring different rates should be adjusted proportionally. For alterations, add 50% to the fee for the first $500,000 of project cost and add 25% to the fee for project cost over $500,000.

Architectural fees tabulated below include Structural, Mechanical and Electrical Engineering Fees. They do not include the fees for special consultants such as kitchen planning, security, acoustical, interior design, etc.

Civil Engineering fees are included in the Architectural fee for project sites requiring minimal design such as city sites. However, separate Civil Engineering fees must be added when utility connections require design, drainage calculations are needed, stepped foundations are required, or provisions are required to protect adjacent wetlands.

Building Types	Total Project Size in Thousands of Dollars						
	100	250	500	1,000	5,000	10,000	50,000
Factories, garages, warehouses, repetitive housing	9.0%	8.0%	7.0%	6.2%	5.3%	4.9%	4.5%
Apartments, banks, schools, libraries, offices, municipal buildings	12.2	12.3	9.2	8.0	7.0	6.6	6.2
Churches, hospitals, homes, laboratories, museums, research	15.0	13.6	12.7	11.9	9.5	8.8	8.0
Memorials, monumental work, decorative furnishings	—	16.0	14.5	13.1	10.0	9.0	8.3

R011110-30   Engineering Fees

Typical **Structural Engineering Fees** based on type of construction and total project size. These fees are included in Architectural Fees.

Type of Construction	Total Project Size (in thousands of dollars)			
	$500	$500-$1,000	$1,000-$5,000	Over $5000
Industrial buildings, factories & warehouses	Technical payroll times 2.0 to 2.5	1.60%	1.25%	1.00%
Hotels, apartments, offices, dormitories, hospitals, public buildings, food stores		2.00%	1.70%	1.20%
Museums, banks, churches and cathedrals		2.00%	1.75%	1.25%
Thin shells, prestressed concrete, earthquake resistive		2.00%	1.75%	1.50%
Parking ramps, auditoriums, stadiums, convention halls, hangars & boiler houses		2.50%	2.00%	1.75%
Special buildings, major alterations, underpinning & future expansion		Add to above 0.5%	Add to above 0.5%	Add to above 0.5%

For complex reinforced concrete or unusually complicated structures, add 20% to 50%.

Typical **Mechanical and Electrical Engineering Fees** are based on the size of the subcontract. The fee structure for both are shown below. These fees are included in Architectural Fees.

Type of Construction	Subcontract Size							
	$25,000	$50,000	$100,000	$225,000	$350,000	$500,000	$750,000	$1,000,000
Simple structures	6.4%	5.7%	4.8%	4.5%	4.4%	4.3%	4.2%	4.1%
Intermediate structures	8.0	7.3	6.5	5.6	5.1	5.0	4.9	4.8
Complex structures	10.1	9.0	9.0	8.0	7.5	7.5	7.0	7.0

For renovations, add 15% to 25% to applicable fee.

General Requirements   **R0121 Allowances**

R012157-20   Construction Time Requirements

Table at left is average construction time in months for different types of building projects. Table at right is the construction time in months for different size projects. Design time runs 25% to 40% of construction time.

Type Building	Construction Time	Project Value	Construction Time
Industrial Buildings	12 Months	Under $1,400,000	10 Months
Commercial Buildings	15 Months	Up to $3,800,000	15 Months
Research & Development	18 Months	Up to $19,000,000	21 Months
Institutional Buildings	20 Months	over $19,000,000	28 Months

R012909-80 Sales Tax by State

State sales tax on materials is tabulated below (5 states have no sales tax). Many states allow local jurisdictions, such as a county or city, to levy additional sales tax.

Some projects may be sales tax exempt, particularly those constructed with public funds.

State	Tax (%)	State	Tax (%)	State	Tax (%)	State	Tax (%)
Alabama	4	Illinois	6.25	Montana	0	Rhode Island	7
Alaska	0	Indiana	7	Nebraska	5.5	South Carolina	6
Arizona	5.6	Iowa	6	Nevada	6.85	South Dakota	4
Arkansas	6	Kansas	6.3	New Hampshire	0	Tennessee	7
California	7.25	Kentucky	6	New Jersey	7	Texas	6.25
Colorado	2.9	Louisiana	4	New Mexico	5.13	Utah	5.95
Connecticut	6.35	Maine	5	New York	4	Vermont	6
Delaware	0	Maryland	6	North Carolina	4.75	Virginia	5
District of Columbia	6	Massachusetts	6.25	North Dakota	5	Washington	6.5
Florida	6	Michigan	6	Ohio	5.5	West Virginia	6
Georgia	4	Minnesota	6.88	Oklahoma	4.5	Wisconsin	5
Hawaii	4	Mississippi	7	Oregon	0	Wyoming	4
Idaho	6	Missouri	4.23	Pennsylvania	6	Average	5.06 %

Sales Tax by Province (Canada)

GST - a value-added tax, which the government imposes on most goods and services provided in or imported into Canada. PST - a retail sales tax, which three of the provinces impose on the price of most goods and some services. QST - a value-added tax, similar to the federal GST, which Quebec imposes. HST - Five provinces have combined their retail sales tax with the federal GST into one harmonized tax.

Province	PST (%)	QST (%)	GST(%)	HST(%)
Alberta	0	0	5	0
British Columbia	7	0	5	0
Manitoba	7	0	5	0
New Brunswick	0	0	0	13
Newfoundland	0	0	0	13
Northwest Territories	0	0	5	0
Nova Scotia	0	0	0	15
Ontario	0	0	0	13
Prince Edward Island	0	0	5	14
Quebec	0	9.975	5	0
Saskatchewan	5	0	5	0
Yukon	0	0	5	0

R012909-85   Unemployment Taxes and Social Security Taxes

State unemployment tax rates vary not only from state to state, but also with the experience rating of the contractor. The federal unemployment tax rate is 6.0% of the first $7,000 of wages. This is reduced by a credit of up to 5.4% for timely payment to the state. The minimum federal unemployment tax is 0.6% after all credits.

Social security (FICA) for 2014 is estimated at time of publication to be 7.65% of wages up to $115,800.

R012909-90   Overtime

One way to improve the completion date of a project or eliminate negative float from a schedule is to compress activity duration times. This can be achieved by increasing the crew size or working overtime with the proposed crew.

To determine the costs of working overtime to compress activity duration times, consider the following examples. Below is an overtime efficiency and cost chart based on a five, six, or seven day week with an eight through twelve hour day. Payroll percentage increases for time and one half and double time are shown for the various working days.

| Days per Week | Hours per Day | Production Efficiency | | | | | Payroll Cost Factors | |
		1st Week	2nd Week	3rd Week	4th Week	Average 4 Weeks	@ 1-1/2 Times	@ 2 Times
	8	100%	100%	100%	100%	100 %	100 %	100 %
	9	100	100	95	90	96.25	105.6	111.1
5	10	100	95	90	85	91.25	110.0	120.0
	11	95	90	75	65	81.25	113.6	127.3
	12	90	85	70	60	76.25	116.7	133.3
	8	100	100	95	90	96.25	108.3	116.7
	9	100	95	90	85	92.50	113.0	125.9
6	10	95	90	85	80	87.50	116.7	133.3
	11	95	85	70	65	78.75	119.7	139.4
	12	90	80	65	60	73.75	122.2	144.4
	8	100	95	85	75	88.75	114.3	128.6
	9	95	90	80	70	83.75	118.3	136.5
7	10	90	85	75	65	78.75	121.4	142.9
	11	85	80	65	60	72.50	124.0	148.1
	12	85	75	60	55	68.75	126.2	152.4

R013113-40   Builder's Risk Insurance

Builder's Risk Insurance is insurance on a building during construction. Premiums are paid by the owner or the contractor. Blasting, collapse and underground insurance would raise total insurance costs above those listed. Floater policy for materials delivered to the job runs $.75 to $1.25 per $100 value. Contractor equipment insurance runs $.50 to $1.50 per $100 value. Insurance for miscellaneous tools to $1,500 value runs from $3.00 to $7.50 per $100 value.

Tabulated below are New England Builder's Risk insurance rates in dollars per $100 value for $1,000 deductible. For $25,000 deductible, rates can be reduced 13% to 34%. On contracts over $1,000,000, rates may be lower than those tabulated. Policies are written annually for the total completed value in place. For "all risk" insurance (excluding flood, earthquake and certain other perils) add $.025 to total rates below.

| Coverage | Frame Construction (Class 1) | | | Brick Construction (Class 4) | | | Fire Resistive (Class 6) | | |
	Range		Average	Range		Average	Range		Average
Fire Insurance	$.350 to	$ .850	$.600	$.158 to	$.189	$.174	$.052 to	$.080	$.070
Extended Coverage	.115 to	.200	.158	.080 to	.105	.101	.081 to	.105	.100
Vandalism	.012 to	.016	.014	.008 to	.011	.011	.008 to	.011	.010
Total Annual Rate	$.477 to	$1.066	$.772	$.246 to	$.305	$.286	$.141 to	$.196	$.180

R013113-50   General Contractor's Overhead

There are two distinct types of overhead on a construction project: Project Overhead and Main Office Overhead. Project Overhead includes those costs at a construction site not directly associated with the installation of construction materials. Examples of Project Overhead costs include the following:

1. Superintendent
2. Construction office and storage trailers
3. Temporary sanitary facilities
4. Temporary utilities
5. Security fencing
6. Photographs
7. Clean up
8. Performance and payment bonds

The above Project Overhead items are also referred to as General Requirements and therefore are estimated in Division 1. Division 1 is the first division listed in the CSI MasterFormat but it is usually the last division estimated. The sum of the costs in Divisions 1 through 49 is referred to as the sum of the direct costs.

All construction projects also include indirect costs. The primary components of indirect costs are the contractor's Main Office Overhead and profit. The amount of the Main Office Overhead expense varies depending on the the following:

1. Owner's compensation
2. Project managers and estimator's wages
3. Clerical support wages
4. Office rent and utilities
5. Corporate legal and accounting costs
6. Advertising
7. Automobile expenses
8. Association dues
9. Travel and entertainment expenses

These costs are usually calculated as a percentage of annual sales volume. This percentage can range from 35% for a small contractor doing less than $500,000 to 5% for a large contractor with sales in excess of $100 million.

R013113-60   Workers' Compensation Insurance Rates by Trade

The table below tabulates the national averages for workers' compensation insurance rates by trade and type of building. The average "Insurance Rate" is multiplied by the "% of Building Cost" for each trade. This produces the "Workers' Compensation" cost by % of total labor cost, to be added for each trade by building type to determine the weighted average workers' compensation rate for the building types analyzed.

Trade	Insurance Rate (% Labor Cost)			% of Building Cost			Workers' Compensation		
	Range		Average	Office Bldgs.	Schools & Apts.	Mfg.	Office Bldgs.	Schools & Apts.	Mfg.
Excavation, Grading, etc.	3.9 % to	18.7%	9.7%	4.8%	4.9%	4.5%	0.47%	0.48%	0.44%
Piles & Foundations	5.8 to	37	14.7	7.1	5.2	8.7	1.04	0.76	1.28
Concrete	4.6 to	38.6	13.1	5.0	14.8	3.7	0.66	1.94	0.48
Masonry	5.1 to	35	13.5	6.9	7.5	1.9	0.93	1.01	0.26
Structural Steel	5.8 to	108.2	34.6	10.7	3.9	17.6	3.70	1.35	6.09
Miscellaneous & Ornamental Metals	5.3 to	31.2	12.0	2.8	4.0	3.6	0.34	0.48	0.43
Carpentry & Millwork	5.5 to	34.9	15.4	3.7	4.0	0.5	0.57	0.62	0.08
Metal or Composition Siding	5.8 to	68.3	18.2	2.3	0.3	4.3	0.42	0.05	0.78
Roofing	5.8 to	93.3	31.3	2.3	2.6	3.1	0.72	0.81	0.97
Doors & Hardware	4.2 to	34.8	11.1	0.9	1.4	0.4	0.10	0.16	0.04
Sash & Glazing	5.3 to	36.8	13.1	3.5	4.0	1.0	0.46	0.52	0.13
Lath & Plaster	3.7 to	35	11.6	3.3	6.9	0.8	0.38	0.80	0.09
Tile, Marble & Floors	3.3 to	27.1	8.5	2.6	3.0	0.5	0.22	0.26	0.04
Acoustical Ceilings	3.4 to	36.7	8.1	2.4	0.2	0.3	0.19	0.02	0.02
Painting	5 to	33	11.5	1.5	1.6	1.6	0.17	0.18	0.18
Interior Partitions	5.5 to	34.9	15.4	3.9	4.3	4.4	0.60	0.66	0.68
Miscellaneous Items	2.5 to	150	14.4	5.2	3.7	9.7	0.75	0.53	1.40
Elevators	1.6 to	14.4	5.7	2.1	1.1	2.2	0.12	0.06	0.13
Sprinklers	3.2 to	18.3	7.2	0.5	—	2.0	0.04	—	0.14
Plumbing	2.6 to	17.5	7.1	4.9	7.2	5.2	0.35	0.51	0.37
Heat., Vent., Air Conditioning	4 to	18.8	8.8	13.5	11.0	12.9	1.19	0.97	1.14
Electrical	2.8 to	13.2	5.8	10.1	8.4	11.1	0.59	0.49	0.64
Total	1.6 % to	150%	—	100.0%	100.0%	100.0%	14.01%	12.66%	15.81%
						Overall Weighted Average	14.16%		

Workers' Compensation Insurance Rates by States

The table below lists the weighted average workers' compensation base rate for each state with a factor comparing this with the national average of 14%.

State	Weighted Average	Factor	State	Weighted Average	Factor	State	Weighted Average	Factor
Alabama	20.3%	145	Kentucky	14.9%	106	North Dakota	9.6%	69
Alaska	14.3	102	Louisiana	19.3	138	Ohio	8.6	61
Arizona	13.1	94	Maine	12.7	91	Oklahoma	12.9	92
Arkansas	8.6	61	Maryland	14.6	104	Oregon	12.3	88
California	26.8	191	Massachusetts	12.0	86	Pennsylvania	18.1	129
Colorado	7.5	54	Michigan	16.9	121	Rhode Island	12.6	90
Connecticut	24.6	176	Minnesota	23.5	168	South Carolina	19.6	140
Delaware	12.4	89	Mississippi	13.8	99	South Dakota	15.5	111
District of Columbia	11.5	82	Missouri	15.4	110	Tennessee	12.5	89
Florida	11.1	79	Montana	8.9	64	Texas	9.5	68
Georgia	29.2	209	Nebraska	18.3	131	Utah	9.1	65
Hawaii	8.4	60	Nevada	9.0	64	Vermont	13.6	97
Idaho	10.7	76	New Hampshire	20.8	149	Virginia	9.9	71
Illinois	28.1	201	New Jersey	15.0	107	Washington	10.9	78
Indiana	5.7	41	New Mexico	15.0	107	West Virginia	8.3	59
Iowa	15.1	108	New York	17.9	128	Wisconsin	13.6	97
Kansas	8.7	62	North Carolina	17.4	124	Wyoming	6.3	45
			Weighted Average for U.S. is	14.2% of payroll = 100%				

Rates in the following table are the base or manual costs per $100 of payroll for workers' compensation in each state. Rates are usually applied to straight time wages only and not to premium time wages and bonuses.

The weighted average skilled worker rate for 35 trades is 14%. For bidding purposes, apply the full value of workers' compensation directly to total labor costs, or if labor is 38%, materials 42% and overhead and profit 20% of total cost, carry 38/80 × 14% =6.6% of cost (before overhead and profit) into overhead. Rates vary not only from state to state but also with the experience rating of the contractor.

Rates are the most current available at the time of publication.

R013113-60 Workers' Compensation Insurance Rates by Trade and State (cont.)

State	Carpentry — 3 stories or less	Carpentry — interior cab. work	Carpentry — general	Concrete Work — NOC	Concrete Work — flat (flr., sdwk.)	Electrical Wiring — inside	Excavation — earth NOC	Excavation — rock	Glaziers	Insulation Work	Lathing	Masonry	Painting & Decorating	Pile Driving	Plastering	Plumbing
	5651	5437	5403	5213	5221	5190	6217	6217	5462	5479	5443	5022	5474	6003	5480	5183
AL	34.03	17.01	24.59	13.79	10.37	8.87	16.42	16.42	19.75	19.84	9.24	23.79	15.91	18.57	15.88	8.73
AK	17.14	9.44	11.58	10.41	9.44	5.63	8.23	8.23	32.03	14.36	11.73	10.86	10.79	21.68	11.31	6.20
AZ	21.40	9.27	20.28	10.31	6.93	6.08	7.07	7.07	10.80	14.99	5.47	13.01	12.78	10.80	8.64	6.84
AR	12.80	4.77	9.18	6.63	5.16	4.03	6.82	6.82	8.14	7.67	3.99	8.30	7.08	8.10	13.00	4.55
CA	34.87	34.83	34.86	16.55	16.55	13.24	18.65	18.65	24.16	16.48	17.83	25.13	23.59	23.18	35.04	17.48
CO	8.95	4.93	6.07	6.68	4.75	2.92	5.49	5.49	6.00	7.27	3.95	8.29	6.56	6.51	5.69	4.16
CT	30.95	18.48	31.07	26.49	14.43	7.89	16.02	16.02	20.24	20.60	9.92	31.53	18.60	20.17	18.75	11.28
DE	12.46	12.46	9.93	10.07	8.80	4.53	7.70	7.70	10.90	9.93	6.60	11.53	13.39	15.03	10.90	6.60
DC	8.92	7.25	6.94	12.65	7.38	4.69	8.02	8.02	9.61	6.63	9.83	9.32	5.82	17.36	8.00	7.80
FL	11.32	8.62	11.92	12.51	6.20	6.17	7.30	7.30	10.56	10.45	5.53	10.92	10.23	17.84	9.68	5.63
GA	68.34	20.32	28.40	21.36	15.09	12.05	17.32	17.32	19.39	18.80	11.94	35.11	33.04	26.44	19.65	12.76
HI	8.51	6.92	12.69	7.05	4.02	4.47	5.40	5.40	8.22	5.20	6.26	7.01	6.19	7.32	8.33	5.31
ID	14.63	6.84	12.43	11.48	5.28	4.43	7.25	7.25	8.81	9.06	4.46	10.55	9.38	7.65	8.43	5.10
IL	33.34	21.75	28.57	38.59	16.83	10.03	14.53	14.53	25.55	21.41	14.32	28.94	18.57	24.53	32.84	12.51
IN	8.36	4.21	6.98	4.56	4.15	2.83	3.92	3.92	5.29	6.15	3.85	5.14	4.97	7.23	3.71	2.56
IA	15.46	11.35	19.21	14.85	11.16	5.20	11.01	11.01	15.76	9.89	6.48	14.30	10.13	11.38	21.73	7.80
KS	14.92	7.39	9.74	8.07	5.70	4.46	5.55	5.55	7.54	8.17	4.09	8.38	7.75	7.56	6.20	5.23
KY	18.75	13.00	20.00	8.50	6.50	6.00	14.00	14.00	22.12	11.15	7.60	7.50	9.00	16.03	12.93	5.00
LA	31.05	16.86	25.02	13.35	12.37	7.85	14.11	14.11	19.19	15.06	7.99	17.31	17.64	18.85	14.84	7.10
ME	12.24	8.87	16.18	16.43	8.70	4.74	12.34	12.34	14.82	12.79	5.09	10.88	12.44	9.00	9.99	5.90
MD	11.40	15.89	15.00	19.22	6.00	5.23	8.11	8.11	13.77	12.42	6.15	10.11	6.40	15.19	9.17	6.65
MA	8.68	5.23	9.61	18.85	6.24	2.84	4.35	4.35	9.58	7.78	5.27	10.55	5.09	12.92	4.68	3.50
MI	18.41	10.45	18.41	18.27	12.58	5.82	13.28	13.28	11.67	10.92	10.45	18.82	13.49	37.00	10.88	7.18
MN	20.27	20.82	34.13	11.58	13.15	5.83	11.00	11.00	36.85	18.37	11.55	15.59	17.55	27.58	11.58	8.09
MS	22.76	9.99	13.34	9.60	6.67	6.18	9.49	9.49	14.94	10.15	5.94	13.12	11.01	13.14	10.43	8.17
MO	19.66	11.10	12.81	12.38	10.34	6.15	9.96	9.96	9.47	11.55	7.44	15.13	11.42	13.38	12.15	9.00
MT	9.67	6.59	10.80	6.22	5.67	3.71	7.41	7.41	7.50	8.67	4.15	7.62	8.22	7.95	6.80	4.79
NE	21.80	13.15	21.48	18.23	11.20	8.03	17.38	17.38	12.05	21.53	8.35	18.73	13.00	13.93	13.68	8.73
NV	10.41	6.82	12.39	10.83	5.26	4.33	8.75	8.75	6.55	7.55	3.41	6.63	7.10	8.43	6.21	6.76
NH	24.24	11.06	19.63	28.40	16.47	5.63	12.61	12.61	14.12	12.63	7.30	16.19	20.93	18.53	11.20	9.49
NJ	18.69	13.18	18.69	15.51	11.69	5.13	10.83	10.83	11.21	12.63	15.13	18.71	11.28	15.79	15.13	6.96
NM	25.01	9.56	18.92	11.73	9.43	6.05	7.22	7.22	10.95	10.56	6.11	15.74	12.91	12.66	14.20	6.70
NY	12.54	10.74	19.18	23.71	17.15	7.85	12.16	12.16	18.72	10.88	12.86	21.24	14.99	20.13	10.02	10.83
NC	30.12	9.54	15.76	16.11	9.31	10.56	15.41	15.41	14.28	13.03	8.11	13.05	14.08	16.61	14.12	10.73
ND	9.54	4.31	9.54	5.43	5.43	3.75	4.13	4.13	10.50	10.50	9.93	6.52	6.00	10.59	9.93	6.11
OH	7.73	4.31	5.52	4.67	4.92	3.43	4.79	4.79	8.83	11.38	36.65	6.93	8.15	6.99	7.80	3.52
OK	18.82	10.32	12.49	13.50	7.66	6.82	9.48	9.48	11.79	11.31	5.13	14.63	10.66	11.24	14.01	6.82
OR	22.30	8.52	11.92	10.51	10.42	5.35	9.08	9.08	12.64	10.88	6.09	14.37	11.81	11.44	10.81	6.35
PA	19.22	19.22	15.60	19.54	13.58	7.39	11.11	11.11	14.34	15.60	14.34	16.04	17.13	19.44	14.34	9.19
RI	9.84	11.55	13.75	12.56	9.68	4.58	8.16	8.16	10.61	12.48	5.17	10.07	8.82	19.30	8.69	6.75
SC	29.32	13.80	17.10	12.84	8.21	9.82	12.01	12.01	12.92	14.13	9.57	15.39	16.10	15.67	14.47	9.40
SD	20.86	17.96	20.35	16.10	10.49	5.08	9.75	9.75	10.84	14.71	6.95	14.65	11.22	12.63	10.35	10.02
TN	22.71	10.14	11.54	10.75	7.08	5.49	10.05	10.05	11.07	10.34	6.60	11.69	8.27	12.08	11.04	5.17
TX	10.12	7.33	10.12	8.08	5.99	5.98	7.60	7.60	8.25	9.27	4.15	8.69	7.28	10.26	7.28	5.27
UT	14.72	6.59	7.50	7.34	6.57	3.56	6.79	6.79	7.45	7.15	6.41	8.96	7.73	6.72	5.56	4.17
VT	15.69	10.21	13.77	13.60	11.57	4.37	11.83	11.83	12.40	15.34	5.79	11.92	8.78	10.43	9.35	7.38
VA	12.38	8.14	8.89	10.51	5.76	4.50	7.40	7.40	8.02	7.27	5.45	7.98	8.93	8.31	6.69	5.07
WA	9.18	9.18	9.18	8.55	8.55	3.18	6.68	6.68	13.99	6.79	9.18	13.26	12.26	21.68	10.43	4.33
WV	14.85	5.54	8.34	7.68	4.51	3.53	6.46	6.46	6.74	6.29	4.33	8.39	6.03	8.09	6.54	3.52
WI	12.52	13.14	17.06	11.98	7.59	5.08	7.84	7.84	13.88	11.22	4.00	13.69	12.43	28.24	10.16	5.95
WY	5.82	5.82	5.82	5.82	5.82	5.82	5.82	5.82	5.82	5.82	5.82	5.82	5.82	5.82	5.82	5.82
AVG.	18.19	11.07	15.38	13.15	8.92	5.83	9.69	9.69	13.15	11.67	8.12	13.49	11.54	14.65	11.55	7.08

R013113-60 Workers' Compensation Insurance Rates by Trade and State (cont.)

State	Roofing 5551	Sheet Metal Work (HVAC) 5538	Steel Erection — door & sash 5102	Steel Erection — inter., ornam. 5102	Steel Erection — structure 5040	Steel Erection — NOC 5057	Tile Work — (interior ceramic) 5348	Waterproofing 9014	Wrecking 5701	Boiler- making 3726	Mill- wrights 3724	Structural Painters 5037	Elevator Constructor 5160	Truck Drivers 7219	Sprinkler Installer 5188
AL	54.71	10.34	12.52	12.52	40.75	21.56	12.35	9.27	40.75	11.93	12.83	55.64	10.09	23.31	8.40
AK	25.49	8.05	7.82	7.82	29.28	26.40	5.33	5.77	29.28	8.56	8.24	31.37	4.06	11.75	5.13
AZ	29.22	10.31	13.61	13.61	26.91	12.89	4.50	6.21	26.91	9.07	7.41	59.76	5.09	8.01	5.48
AR	16.03	4.74	8.34	8.34	15.40	11.28	6.69	2.58	15.40	4.94	5.76	25.69	2.73	10.96	5.72
CA	71.13	18.78	18.41	18.41	35.28	19.69	14.59	23.59	19.69	8.98	13.58	35.28	5.07	27.13	18.32
CO	15.60	4.16	5.36	5.36	23.64	10.59	4.10	3.23	18.40	4.37	3.87	22.88	2.78	7.22	3.85
CT	58.74	12.93	21.24	21.24	65.13	29.83	15.63	6.43	65.13	19.44	14.12	66.07	11.07	22.67	10.49
DE	26.71	5.55	13.16	13.16	23.27	13.16	8.00	11.53	23.27	6.17	6.19	23.27	6.19	11.13	6.60
DC	17.05	6.45	23.33	23.33	26.02	7.91	6.08	4.38	26.02	15.31	7.62	35.16	9.65	14.34	4.00
FL	18.17	7.69	9.91	9.91	23.04	12.59	5.63	5.26	23.04	9.07	6.05	39.44	3.54	9.24	6.41
GA	93.33	16.61	22.17	22.17	60.89	25.88	13.50	11.64	60.89	19.54	14.79	72.60	7.53	19.39	15.17
HI	17.24	4.93	7.60	7.60	21.77	6.88	6.52	5.40	21.77	4.82	7.71	24.83	2.28	10.54	3.49
ID	24.73	7.46	12.31	12.31	25.42	10.44	6.15	4.84	25.42	5.30	5.61	29.98	3.26	9.46	4.65
IL	47.55	15.21	31.16	31.16	84.68	19.36	27.09	7.88	84.68	23.23	15.10	101.23	14.42	19.73	16.65
IN	11.57	4.32	5.32	5.32	11.59	4.80	3.26	2.77	11.59	3.85	3.70	13.20	1.58	5.75	3.20
IA	28.01	8.53	9.15	9.15	52.79	14.30	9.38	6.15	25.61	14.19	8.59	87.69	6.14	13.60	7.75
KS	16.26	5.64	6.71	6.71	18.97	11.93	5.23	4.63	11.96	6.01	7.60	26.96	3.22	7.88	5.30
KY	34.00	12.00	11.72	11.72	36.00	11.02	16.73	3.50	36.00	12.15	8.35	150.00	9.56	10.00	10.32
LA	43.53	14.84	20.14	20.14	44.26	12.79	9.99	7.91	44.20	15.48	10.94	55.57	6.11	23.25	11.22
ME	22.72	6.77	8.92	8.92	37.18	12.21	5.76	4.64	37.18	8.08	6.58	54.29	4.39	8.15	6.70
MD	29.05	11.90	11.92	11.92	59.02	17.92	6.49	5.84	32.91	14.58	9.95	43.60	4.46	16.02	11.88
MA	30.99	5.72	6.89	6.89	54.08	33.00	5.81	2.48	23.75	15.42	5.98	23.51	4.21	8.28	4.13
MI	41.18	9.83	12.28	12.28	37.00	11.27	11.73	6.46	37.00	9.41	8.67	11.27	5.13	9.09	8.21
MN	67.71	17.30	9.82	9.82	108.16	7.70	14.69	7.95	7.70	10.92	12.24	36.60	6.41	11.39	7.62
MS	31.61	7.46	15.08	15.08	38.45	7.53	8.45	5.85	38.45	7.77	9.97	38.74	4.78	52.03	7.53
MO	36.73	8.64	12.33	12.33	47.55	24.29	10.41	5.92	47.55	14.45	9.66	60.85	6.20	12.44	8.43
MT	29.42	4.80	6.98	6.98	18.72	5.89	5.47	4.64	5.89	5.03	5.91	28.63	3.01	6.06	3.67
NE	35.08	12.88	14.80	14.80	59.03	14.13	8.68	6.73	67.83	16.33	11.35	66.18	7.13	15.98	10.30
NV	16.59	7.34	7.06	7.06	19.32	12.20	4.42	4.23	12.20	4.79	6.15	28.67	4.30	10.30	5.47
NH	36.82	8.93	14.28	14.28	95.03	28.57	12.35	7.17	95.03	8.91	9.04	54.18	6.29	36.82	10.68
NJ	40.10	7.22	12.87	12.87	17.25	13.36	9.55	6.63	16.86	4.18	9.20	23.37	7.00	15.75	5.89
NM	35.07	9.63	11.79	11.79	45.52	16.76	7.73	7.53	45.52	8.00	8.00	42.38	8.41	14.60	7.75
NY	35.96	13.56	19.25	19.25	35.26	19.08	10.35	7.49	18.10	21.41	10.22	42.40	12.20	14.37	6.45
NC	35.39	11.87	14.43	14.43	45.05	22.54	7.62	6.10	45.05	18.41	9.71	78.32	8.90	17.84	10.60
ND	17.63	6.11	10.59	10.59	10.90	10.59	10.50	17.63	8.18	3.33	10.50	10.59	3.33	8.79	6.11
OH	14.89	4.00	6.58	6.58	11.33	5.84	4.85	4.58	5.84	2.76	4.52	24.79	2.13	10.02	3.68
OK	22.44	9.62	10.98	10.98	29.21	15.15	6.69	6.41	32.94	9.25	6.21	52.38	3.88	11.26	6.40
OR	27.22	6.85	7.08	7.08	22.04	13.44	9.10	6.73	22.04	9.10	9.28	11.81	3.70	14.41	6.02
PA	38.35	8.92	19.10	19.10	30.01	19.10	11.69	16.04	30.01	7.95	8.85	30.01	8.85	16.69	9.19
RI	23.59	8.48	7.37	7.37	35.11	24.46	5.33	4.98	22.15	11.33	6.32	39.60	4.85	10.13	5.85
SC	46.45	10.88	15.24	15.24	31.33	24.73	7.98	5.42	31.33	11.24	10.59	66.07	8.64	15.07	10.12
SD	34.39	7.29	14.74	14.74	33.52	23.05	6.19	5.30	33.52	22.67	11.38	66.74	6.69	10.62	8.14
TN	29.78	8.13	13.42	13.42	16.07	18.88	7.46	4.09	16.07	8.10	7.46	40.34	4.92	10.23	6.10
TX	16.22	11.69	7.60	7.60	22.99	9.48	4.68	5.57	7.13	4.30	5.95	7.34	3.34	12.75	5.27
UT	23.93	5.78	5.71	5.71	24.61	11.81	5.75	4.31	20.14	5.91	4.77	21.36	3.71	7.05	4.16
VT	27.01	7.30	12.01	12.01	34.39	18.99	7.01	7.90	34.39	8.67	7.28	48.29	6.07	13.40	6.27
VA	25.97	5.47	7.46	7.46	29.39	10.80	5.76	3.30	29.39	4.92	7.38	27.90	5.39	9.03	5.30
WA	21.14	4.47	8.09	8.09	8.09	8.09	7.86	21.14	8.09	2.77	6.15	12.26	2.46	8.52	4.70
WV	19.62	5.62	7.13	7.13	19.39	9.55	4.86	3.11	20.70	5.62	6.64	35.86	4.23	8.93	3.76
WI	28.04	9.43	12.08	12.08	20.72	16.12	13.78	5.07	20.72	9.68	8.34	24.08	4.11	10.15	4.64
WY	5.82	5.82	5.82	5.82	5.82	5.82	5.82	5.82	5.82	5.82	5.82	5.82	5.82	5.82	5.82
AVG.	31.29	8.79	11.95	11.95	34.64	15.21	8.54	6.86	29.21	9.87	8.39	41.47	5.67	13.67	7.24

R013113-60 Workers' Compensation (cont.) (Canada in Canadian dollars)

Province		Alberta	British Columbia	Manitoba	Ontario	New Brunswick	Newfndld. & Labrador	Northwest Territories	Nova Scotia	Prince Edward Island	Quebec	Saskatchewan	Yukon
Carpentry—3 stories or less	Rate	5.71	3.27	3.98	4.55	3.17	7.81	4.99	6.85	6.42	12.03	3.43	6.63
	Code	42143	721028	40102	723	238130	4226	4-41	4226	403	80110	B1226	202
Carpentry—interior cab. work	Rate	1.89	2.80	3.98	4.55	3.17	4.07	4.99	5.87	3.94	12.03	3.43	6.63
	Code	42133	721021	40102	723	238350	4279	4-41	4274	402	80110	B1127	202
CARPENTRY—general	Rate	5.71	3.27	3.98	4.55	3.17	4.07	4.99	6.85	6.42	12.03	3.43	6.63
	Code	42143	721028	40102	723	238130	4299	4-41	4226	403	80110	B1202	202
CONCRETE WORK—NOC	Rate	3.88	3.57	6.50	18.31	3.17	7.81	4.99	5.75	3.94	1.92	2.99	6.63
	Code	42104	721010	40110	748	238110	4224	4-41	4224	402	80100	B1314	203
CONCRETE WORK—flat (flr. sidewalk)	Rate	3.88	3.57	6.50	18.31	3.17	7.81	4.99	5.75	3.94	11.92	2.99	6.63
	Code	42104	721010	40110	748	238110	4224	4-41	4224	402	80100	B1314	203
ELECTRICAL Wiring—inside	Rate	1.56	1.18	1.65	3.69	1.28	2.29	2.44	1.97	3.94	5.04	1.83	3.89
	Code	42124	721019	40203	704	238210	4261	4-46	4261	402	80170	B1105	206
EXCAVATION—earth NOC	Rate	1.86	3.79	4.00	5.29	3.17	2.93	3.88	3.89	3.94	6.40	2.19	3.89
	Code	40604	721031	40706	711	238190	4214	4-43	4214	402	80030	R1106	207
EXCAVATION—rock	Rate	1.86	3.79	4.00	5.29	3.17	2.93	3.88	3.89	3.94	6.40	2.19	3.89
	Code	40604	721031	40706	711	238190	4214	4-43	4214	402	80030	R1106	207
GLAZIERS	Rate	2.23	3.79	3.98	10.25	3.17	5.10	4.99	5.22	3.94	15.02	2.99	3.89
	Code	42121	715020	40109	751	238150	4233	4-41	4233	402	80150	B1304	212
INSULATION WORK	Rate	1.62	9.87	3.98	10.25	3.17	5.10	4.99	5.22	3.94	12.03	3.43	6.63
	Code	42184	721029	40102	751	238310	4234	4-41	4234	402	80110	B1207	202
LATHING	Rate	4.20	7.84	3.98	4.55	3.17	4.07	4.99	5.87	3.94	12.03	2.99	6.63
	Code	42135	721042	40102	723	238390	4279	4-41	4271	402	80110	B1316	202
MASONRY	Rate	3.88	3.30	3.98	12.70	3.17	5.10	4.99	5.22	3.94	11.92	2.99	6.63
	Code	42102	721037	40102	741	238140	4231	4-41	4231	402	80100	B1318	202
PAINTING & DECORATING	Rate	3.16	3.62	3.11	7.51	3.17	4.07	4.99	5.87	3.94	12.03	3.43	6.63
	Code	42111	721041	40105	719	238320	4275	4-41	4275	402	80110	B1201	202
PILE DRIVING	Rate	3.88	3.42	4.00	7.03	3.17	2.93	3.88	5.75	6.42	6.40	2.99	6.63
	Code	42159	722004	40706	732	238190	4129	4-43	4221	403	80030	B1310	202
PLASTERING	Rate	4.20	7.84	4.45	7.51	3.17	4.07	4.99	5.87	3.94	12.03	3.43	6.63
	Code	42135	721042	40108	719	238390	4271	4-41	4271	402	80110	B1221	202
PLUMBING	Rate	1.56	2.55	2.78	4.16	1.28	2.47	2.44	2.81	3.94	5.89	1.83	3.89
	Code	42122	721043	40204	707	238220	4241	4-46	4241	401	80160	B1101	214
ROOFING	Rate	4.71	5.42	7.22	14.80	3.17	7.81	4.99	9.43	3.94	18.52	2.99	6.63
	Code	42118	721036	40403	728	238160	4236	4-41	4236	402	80130	B1320	202
SHEET METAL WORK (HVAC)	Rate	1.56	2.55	7.22	4.16	1.28	2.47	2.44	2.81	3.94	5.89	1.83	3.89
	Code	42117	721043	40402	707	238220	4244	4-46	4244	401	80160	B1107	208
STEEL ERECTION—door & sash	Rate	1.62	10.62	6.82	18.31	3.17	7.81	4.99	5.22	3.94	16.70	2.99	6.63
	Code	42106	722005	40502	748	238120	4227	-37	4227	402	80080	B1322	202
STEEL ERECTION—inter., ornam.	Rate	1.62	10.62	6.82	18.31	3.17	7.81	4.99	5.22	3.94	16.70	2.99	6.63
	Code	42106	722005	40502	748	238120	4227	4-41	4227	402	80080	B1322	202
STEEL ERECTION—structure	Rate	1.62	10.62	6.82	18.31	3.17	7.81	4.99	5.22	3.94	16.70	2.99	6.63
	Code	42106	722005	40502	748	238120	4227	4-41	4227	402	80080	B1322	202
STEEL ERECTION—NOC	Rate	1.62	10.62	6.82	18.31	3.17	7.81	4.99	5.22	3.94	16.70	2.99	6.63
	Code	42106	722005	40502	748	238120	4227	4-41	4227	402	80080	B1322	202
TILE WORK—inter. (ceramic)	Rate	3.02	3.65	1.86	7.51	3.17	4.07	4.99	5.87	3.94	12.03	2.99	6.63
	Code	42113	721054	40103	719	238340	4276	4-41	4276	402	80110	B1301	202
WATERPROOFING	Rate	3.16	3.62	3.98	4.55	3.17	4.07	4.99	5.22	3.94	18.52	3.13	6.63
	Code	42139	721016	40102	723	238190	4299	4-41	4239	402	80130	B1217	202
WRECKING	Rate	1.86	5.64	6.90	18.31	3.17	2.93	3.88	3.89	3.94	12.03	2.19	6.63
	Code	40604	721005	40106	748	238190	4211	4-43	4211	402	80110	R1125	202

General Requirements | R0131 Project Management & Coordination

R013113-80   Performance Bond

This table shows the cost of a Performance Bond for a construction job scheduled to be completed in 12 months. Add 1% of the premium cost per month for jobs requiring more than 12 months to complete. The rates are "standard" rates offered to contractors that the bonding company considers financially sound and capable of doing the work. Preferred rates are offered by some bonding companies based upon financial strength of the contractor. Actual rates vary from contractor to contractor and from bonding company to bonding company. Contractors should prequalify through a bonding agency before submitting a bid on a contract that requires a bond.

Contract Amount	Building Construction Class B Projects			Highways & Bridges					
				Class A New Construction			Class A-1 Highway Resurfacing		
First $ 100,000 bid	$25.00 per M			$15.00 per M			$9.40 per M		
Next 400,000 bid	$ 2,500	plus	$15.00 per M	$ 1,500	plus	$10.00 per M	$ 940	plus	$7.20 per M
Next 2,000,000 bid	8,500	plus	10.00 per M	5,500	plus	7.00 per M	3,820	plus	5.00 per M
Next 2,500,000 bid	28,500	plus	7.50 per M	19,500	plus	5.50 per M	15,820	plus	4.50 per M
Next 2,500,000 bid	47,250	plus	7.00 per M	33,250	plus	5.00 per M	28,320	plus	4.50 per M
Over 7,500,000 bid	64,750	plus	6.00 per M	45,750	plus	4.50 per M	39,570	plus	4.00 per M

General Requirements | R0151 Temporary Utilities

R015113-65   Temporary Power Equipment

Cost data for the temporary equipment was developed utilizing the following information.

1) Re-usable material-services, transformers, equipment and cords are based on new purchase and prorated to three projects.	4) Labor units include an allowance for removal.
	5) No utility company charges or fees are included.
2) PVC feeder includes trench and backfill.	6) Concrete pads or vaults are not included.
3) Connections include disconnects and fuses.	7) Utility company conduits not included.

R015423-10   Steel Tubular Scaffolding

On new construction, tubular scaffolding is efficient up to 60' high or five stories. Above this it is usually better to use a hung scaffolding if construction permits. Swing scaffolding operations may interfere with tenants. In this case, the tubular is more practical at all heights.

In repairing or cleaning the front of an existing building the cost of tubular scaffolding per S.F. of building front increases as the height increases above the first tier. The first tier cost is relatively high due to leveling and alignment.

The minimum efficient crew for erecting and dismantling is three workers. They can set up and remove 18 frame sections per day up to 5 stories high. For 6 to 12 stories high, a crew of four is most efficient. Use two or more on top and two on the bottom for handing up or hoisting. They can

also set up and remove 18 frame sections per day. At 7' horizontal spacing, this will run about 800 S.F. per day of erecting and dismantling. Time for placing and removing planks must be added to the above. A crew of three can place and remove 72 planks per day up to 5 stories. For over 5 stories, a crew of four can place and remove 80 planks per day.

The table below shows the number of pieces required to erect tubular steel scaffolding for 1000 S.F. of building frontage. This area is made up of a scaffolding system that is 12 frames (11 bays) long by 2 frames high.

For jobs under twenty-five frames, add 50% to rental cost. Rental rates will be lower for jobs over three months duration. Large quantities for long periods can reduce rental rates by 20%.

Description of Component	Number of Pieces for 1000 S.F. of Building Front	Unit
5' Wide Standard Frame, 6'-4" High	24	Ea.
Leveling Jack & Plate	24	
Cross Brace	44	
Side Arm Bracket, 21"	12	
Guardrail Post	12	
Guardrail, 7' section	22	
Stairway Section	2	
Stairway Starter Bar	1	
Stairway Inside Handrail	2	
Stairway Outside Handrail	2	
Walk-Thru Frame Guardrail	2	

Scaffolding is often used as falsework over 15' high during construction of cast-in-place concrete beams and slabs. Two foot wide scaffolding is generally used for heavy beam construction. The span between frames depends upon the load to be carried with a maximum span of 5'.

Heavy duty shoring frames with a capacity of 10,000#/leg can be spaced up to 10' O.C. depending upon form support design and loading.

Scaffolding used as horizontal shoring requires less than half the material required with conventional shoring.

On new construction, erection is done by carpenters.

Rolling towers supporting horizontal shores can reduce labor and speed the job. For maintenance work, catwalks with spans up to 70' can be supported by the rolling towers.

R015423-20   Pump Staging

Pump staging is generally not available for rent. The table below shows the number of pieces required to erect pump staging for 2400 S.F. of building frontage. This area is made up of a pump jack system that is 3 poles (2 bays) wide by 2 poles high.

Item	Number of Pieces for 2400 S.F. of Building Front	Unit
Aluminum pole section, 24' long	6	Ea.
Aluminum splice joint, 6' long	3	
Aluminum foldable brace	3	
Aluminum pump jack	3	
Aluminum support for workbench/back safety rail	3	
Aluminum scaffold plank/workbench, 14" wide x 24' long	4	
Safety net, 22' long	2	
Aluminum plank end safety rail	2	

The cost in place for this 2400 S.F. will depend on how many uses are realized during the life of the equipment.

R015433-10   Contractor Equipment

Rental Rates shown elsewhere in the book pertain to late model high quality machines in excellent working condition, rented from equipment dealers. Rental rates from contractors may be substantially lower than the rental rates from equipment dealers depending upon economic conditions; for older, less productive machines, reduce rates by a maximum of 15%. Any overtime must be added to the base rates. For shift work, rates are lower. Usual rule of thumb is 150% of one shift rate for two shifts; 200% for three shifts.

For periods of less than one week, operated equipment is usually more economical to rent than renting bare equipment and hiring an operator.

Costs to move equipment to a job site (mobilization) or from a job site (demobilization) are not included in rental rates, nor in any Equipment costs on any Unit Price line items or crew listings. These costs can be found elsewhere. If a piece of equipment is already at a job site, it is not appropriate to utilize mob/demob costs in an estimate again.

Rental rates vary throughout the country with larger cities generally having lower rates. Lease plans for new equipment are available for periods in excess of six months with a percentage of payments applying toward purchase.

Rental rates can also be treated as reimbursement costs for contractor-owned equipment. Owned equipment costs include depreciation, loan payments, interest, taxes, insurance, storage, and major repairs.

Monthly rental rates vary from 2% to 5% of the cost of the equipment depending on the anticipated life of the equipment and its wearing parts. Weekly rates are about 1/3 the monthly rates and daily rental rates about 1/3 the weekly rate.

The hourly operating costs for each piece of equipment include costs to the user such as fuel, oil, lubrication, normal expendables for the equipment, and a percentage of mechanic's wages chargeable to maintenance. The hourly operating costs listed do not include the operator's wages.

The daily cost for equipment used in the standard crews is figured by dividing the weekly rate by five, then adding eight times the hourly operating cost to give the total daily equipment cost, not including the operator. This figure is in the right hand column of the Equipment listings under Equipment Cost/Day.

Pile Driving rates shown for pile hammer and extractor do not include leads, crane, boiler or compressor. Vibratory pile driving requires an added field specialist during set-up and pile driving operation for the electric model. The hydraulic model requires a field specialist for set-up only. Up to 125 reuses of sheet piling are possible using vibratory drivers. For normal conditions, crane capacity for hammer type and size are as follows.

Crane Capacity	Hammer Type and Size		
	Air or Steam	Diesel	Vibratory
25 ton	to 8,750 ft.-lb.		70 H.P.
40 ton	15,000 ft.-lb.	to 32,000 ft.-lb.	170 H.P.
60 ton	25,000 ft.-lb.		300 H.P.
100 ton		112,000 ft.-lb.	

Cranes should be specified for the job by size, building and site characteristics, availability, performance characteristics, and duration of time required.

Backhoes & Shovels rent for about the same as equivalent size cranes but maintenance and operating expense is higher. Crane operators rate must be adjusted for high boom heights. Average adjustments: for 150' boom add 2% per hour; over 185', add 4% per hour; over 210', add 6% per hour; over 250', add 8% per hour and over 295', add 12% per hour.

Tower Cranes of the climbing or static type have jibs from 50' to 200' and capacities at maximum reach range from 4,000 to 14,000 pounds. Lifting capacities increase up to maximum load as the hook radius decreases.

Typical rental rates, based on purchase price are about 2% to 3% per month.

Erection and dismantling runs between 500 and 2000 labor hours. Climbing operation takes 10 labor hours per 20' climb. Crane dead time is about 5 hours per 40' climb. If crane is bolted to side of the building add cost of ties and extra mast sections. Climbing cranes have from 80' to 180' of mast while static cranes have 80' to 800' of mast.

Truck Cranes can be converted to tower cranes by using tower attachments. Mast heights over 400' have been used.

A single 100' high material **Hoist and Tower** can be erected and dismantled in about 400 labor hours; a double 100' high hoist and tower in about 600 labor hours. Erection times for additional heights are 3 and 4 labor hours per vertical foot respectively up to 150', and 4 to 5 labor hours per vertical foot over 150' high. A 40' high portable Buck hoist takes about 160 labor hours to erect and dismantle. Additional heights take 2 labor hours per vertical foot to 80' and 3 labor hours per vertical foot for the next 100'. Most material hoists do not meet local code requirements for carrying personnel.

A 150' high **Personnel Hoist** requires about 500 to 800 labor hours to erect and dismantle. Budget erection time at 5 labor hours per vertical foot for all trades. Local code requirements or labor scarcity requiring overtime can add up to 50% to any of the above erection costs.

Earthmoving Equipment: The selection of earthmoving equipment depends upon the type and quantity of material, moisture content, haul distance, haul road, time available, and equipment available. Short haul cut and fill operations may require dozers only, while another operation may require excavators, a fleet of trucks, and spreading and compaction equipment. Stockpiled material and granular material are easily excavated with front end loaders. Scrapers are most economically used with hauls between 300' and 1-1/2 miles if adequate haul roads can be maintained. Shovels are often used for blasted rock and any material where a vertical face of 8' or more can be excavated. Special conditions may dictate the use of draglines, clamshells, or backhoes. Spreading and compaction equipment must be matched to the soil characteristics, the compaction required and the rate the fill is being supplied.

R015433-15   Heavy Lifting

Hydraulic Climbing Jacks

The use of hydraulic heavy lift systems is an alternative to conventional type crane equipment. The lifting, lowering, pushing, or pulling mechanism is a hydraulic climbing jack moving on a square steel jackrod from 1-5/8" to 4" square, or a steel cable. The jackrod or cable can be vertical or horizontal, stationary or movable, depending on the individual application. When the jackrod is stationary, the climbing jack will climb the rod and push or pull the load along with itself. When the climbing jack is stationary, the jackrod is movable with the load attached to the end and the climbing jack will lift or lower the jackrod with the attached load. The heavy lift system is normally operated by a single control lever located at the hydraulic pump.

The system is flexible in that one or more climbing jacks can be applied wherever a load support point is required, and the rate of lift synchronized.

Economic benefits have been demonstrated on projects such as: erection of ground assembled roofs and floors, complete bridge spans, girders and trusses, towers, chimney liners and steel vessels, storage tanks, and heavy machinery. Other uses are raising and lowering offshore work platforms, caissons, tunnel sections and pipelines.

R024119-10   Demolition Defined

Whole Building Demolition - Demolition of the whole building with no concern for any particular building element, component, or material type being demolished. This type of demolition is accomplished with large pieces of construction equipment that break up the structure, load it into trucks and haul it to a disposal site, but disposal or dump fees are not included. Demolition of below-grade foundation elements, such as footings, foundation walls, grade beams, slabs on grade, etc., is not included. Certain mechanical equipment containing flammable liquids or ozone-depleting refrigerants, electric lighting elements, communication equipment components, and other building elements may contain hazardous waste, and must be removed, either selectively or carefully, as hazardous waste before the building can be demolished.

Foundation Demolition - Demolition of below-grade foundation footings, foundation walls, grade beams, and slabs on grade. This type of demolition is accomplished by hand or pneumatic hand tools, and does not include saw cutting, or handling, loading, hauling, or disposal of the debris.

Gutting - Removal of building interior finishes and electrical/mechanical systems down to the load-bearing and sub-floor elements of the rough building frame, with no concern for any particular building element, component, or material type being demolished. This type of demolition is accomplished by hand or pneumatic hand tools, and includes loading into trucks, but not hauling, disposal or dump fees, scaffolding, or shoring. Certain mechanical equipment containing flammable liquids or ozone-depleting refrigerants, electric lighting elements, communication equipment components, and other building elements may contain hazardous waste, and must be removed, either selectively or carefully, as hazardous waste, before the building is gutted.

Selective Demolition - Demolition of a selected building element, component, or finish, with some concern for surrounding or adjacent elements, components, or finishes (see the first Subdivision(s) at the beginning of appropriate Divisions). This type of demolition is accomplished by hand or pneumatic hand tools, and does not include handling, loading, storing, hauling, or disposal of the debris, scaffolding, or shoring. "Gutting" methods may be used in order to save time, but damage that is caused to surrounding or adjacent elements, components, or finishes may have to be repaired at a later time.

Careful Removal - Removal of a piece of service equipment, building element or component, or material type, with great concern for both the removed item and surrounding or adjacent elements, components or finishes. The purpose of careful removal may be to protect the removed item for later re-use, preserve a higher salvage value of the removed item, or replace an item while taking care to protect surrounding or adjacent elements, components, or finishes from cosmetic and/or structural damage. An approximation of the time required to perform this type of removal is 1/3 to 1/2 the time it would take to install a new item of like kind (see Reference Number R220105-10). This type of removal is accomplished by hand or pneumatic hand tools, and does not include loading, hauling, or storing the removed item, scaffolding, shoring, or lifting equipment.

Cutout Demolition - Demolition of a small quantity of floor, wall, roof, or other assembly, with concern for the appearance and structural integrity of the surrounding materials. This type of demolition is accomplished by hand or pneumatic hand tools, and does not include saw cutting, handling, loading, hauling, or disposal of debris, scaffolding, or shoring.

Rubbish Handling - Work activities that involve handling, loading or hauling of debris. Generally, the cost of rubbish handling must be added to the cost of all types of demolition, with the exception of whole building demolition.

Minor Site Demolition - Demolition of site elements outside the footprint of a building. This type of demolition is accomplished by hand or pneumatic hand tools, or with larger pieces of construction equipment, and may include loading a removed item onto a truck (check the Crew for equipment used). It does not include saw cutting, hauling or disposal of debris, and, sometimes, handling or loading.

R024119-20   Dumpsters

Dumpster rental costs on construction sites are presented in two ways.

The cost per week rental includes the delivery of the Dumpster; its pulling or emptying once per week, and its final removal. The assumption is made that the dumpster contractor could choose to empty a Dumpster by simply bringing in an empty unit and removing the full one. These costs also include the disposal of the materials in the dumpster.

The Alternate Pricing can be used when actual planned conditions are not approximated by the weekly numbers. For example, these lines can be used when a Dumpster is needed for 4 weeks and will need to be emptied 2 or 3 times per week. Conversely the Alternate Pricing lines can be used when a dumpster will be rented for several weeks or months but needs to be emptied only a few times over this period.

R024119-30   Rubbish Handling Chutes

To correctly estimate the cost of rubbish handling chute systems, the individual components must be priced separately. First choose the size of the system; a 30-inch diameter chute is quite common, but the sizes range from 18 to 36 inches in diameter. The 30-inch chute comes in a standard weight and two thinner weights. The thinner weight chutes are sometimes chosen for cost savings, but they are more easily damaged.

There are several types of major chute pieces that make up the chute system. The first component to consider is the top chute section (top intake hopper) where the material is dropped into the chute at the highest point. After determining the top chute, the intermediate chute pieces called the regular chute sections are priced. Next, the number of chute control door sections (intermediate intake hoppers) must be determined. In the more complex systems, a chute control door section is provided at each floor level. The last major component to consider is bolt down frames; these are usually provided at every other floor level.

There are a number of accessories to consider for safe operation and control. There are covers for the top chute and the chute door sections. The top chute can have a trough that allows for better loading of the chute. For the safest operation, a chute warning light system can be added that will warn the other chute intake locations not to load while another is being used. There are dust control devices that spray a water mist to keep down the dust as the debris is loaded into a Dumpster. There are special breakaway cords that are used to prevent damage to the chute if the Dumpster is removed without disconnecting from the chute. There are chute liners that can be installed to protect the chute structure from physical damage from rough abrasive materials. Warning signs can be posted at each floor level that is provided with a chute control door section.

In summary, a complete rubbish handling chute system will include one top section, several intermediate regular sections, several intermediate control door (intake hopper) sections and bolt down frames at every other floor level starting with the top floor. If so desired, the system can also include covers and a light warning system for a safer operation. The bottom of the chute should always be above the Dumpster and should be tied off with a breakaway cord to the Dumpster.

R026510-20   Underground Storage Tank Removal

Underground Storage Tank Removal can be divided into two categories: Non-Leaking and Leaking. Prior to removing an underground storage tank, tests should be made, with the proper authorities present, to determine whether a tank has been leaking or the surrounding soil has been contaminated.

To safely remove Liquid Underground Storage Tanks:
1. Excavate to the top of the tank.
2. Disconnect all piping.
3. Open all tank vents and access ports.
4. Remove all liquids and/or sludge.
5. Purge the tank with an inert gas.
6. Provide access to the inside of the tank and clean out the interior using proper personal protective equipment (PPE).
7. Excavate soil surrounding the tank using proper PPE for on-site personnel.
8. Pull and properly dispose of the tank.
9. Clean up the site of all contaminated material.
10. Install new tanks or close the excavation.

R028213-20 Asbestos Removal Process

Asbestos removal is accomplished by a specialty contractor who understands the federal and state regulations regarding the handling and disposal of the material. The process of asbestos removal is divided into many individual steps. An accurate estimate can be calculated only after all the steps have been priced.

The steps are generally as follows:

1. Obtain an asbestos abatement plan from an industrial hygienist.
2. Monitor the air quality in and around the removal area and along the path of travel between the removal area and transport area. This establishes the background contamination.
3. Construct a two part decontamination chamber at entrance to removal area.
4. Install a HEPA filter to create a negative pressure in the removal area.
5. Install wall, floor and ceiling protection as required by the plan, usually 2 layers of fireproof 6 mil polyethylene.

6. Industrial hygienist visually inspects work area to verify compliance with plan.
7. Provide temporary supports for conduit and piping affected by the removal process.
8. Proceed with asbestos removal and bagging process. Monitor air quality as described in Step #2. Discontinue operations when contaminate levels exceed applicable standards.
9. Document the legal disposal of materials in accordance with EPA standards.
10. Thoroughly clean removal area including all ledges, crevices and surfaces.
11. Post abatement inspection by industrial hygienist to verify plan compliance.
12. Provide a certificate from a licensed industrial hygienist attesting that contaminate levels are within acceptable standards before returning area to regular use.

| **Existing Conditions** | **R0283 Lead Remediation** |

R028319-60 Lead Paint Remediation Methods

Lead paint remediation can be accomplished by the following methods.

1. Abrasive blast
2. Chemical stripping
3. Power tool cleaning with vacuum collection system
4. Encapsulation
5. Remove and replace
6. Enclosure

Each of these methods has strengths and weakness depending on the specific circumstances of the project. The following is an overview of each method.

1. **Abrasive blasting** is usually accomplished with sand or recyclable metallic blast. Before work can begin, the area must be contained to ensure the blast material with lead does not escape to the atmosphere. The use of vacuum blast greatly reduces the containment requirements. Lead abatement equipment that may be associated with this work includes a negative air machine. In addition, it is necessary to have an industrial hygienist monitor the project on a continual basis. When the work is complete, the spent blast sand with lead must be disposed of as a hazardous material. If metallic shot was used, the lead is separated from the shot and disposed of as hazardous material. Worker protection includes disposable clothing and respiratory protection.

2. **Chemical stripping** requires strong chemicals be applied to the surface to remove the lead paint. Before the work can begin, the area under/adjacent to the work area must be covered to catch the chemical and removed lead. After the chemical is applied to the painted surface it is usually covered with paper. The chemical is left in place for the specified period, then the paper with lead paint is pulled or scraped off. The process may require several chemical applications. The paper with chemicals and lead paint adhered to it, plus the containment and loose scrapings collected by a HEPA (High Efficiency Particulate Air Filter) vac, must be disposed of as a hazardous material. The chemical stripping process usually requires a neutralizing agent and several wash downs after the paint is removed. Worker protection includes a neoprene or other compatible protective clothing and respiratory protection with face shield. An industrial hygienist is required intermittently during the process.

3. **Power tool cleaning** is accomplished using shrouded needle blasting guns. The shrouding with different end configurations is held up against the surface to be cleaned. The area is blasted with hardened needles and the shroud captures the lead with a HEPA vac and deposits it in a holding tank. An industrial hygienist monitors the project, protective clothing and a respirator is required until air samples prove otherwise. When the work is complete the lead must be disposed of as a hazardous material.

4. **Encapsulation** is a method that leaves the well bonded lead paint in place after the peeling paint has been removed. Before the work can begin, the area under/adjacent to the work must be covered to catch the scrapings. The scraped surface is then washed with a detergent and rinsed. The prepared surface is covered with approximately 10 mils of paint. A reinforcing fabric can also be embedded in the paint covering. The scraped paint and containment must be disposed of as a hazardous material. Workers must wear protective clothing and respirators.

5. **Remove and replace** is an effective way to remove lead paint from windows, gypsum walls and concrete masonry surfaces. The painted materials are removed and new materials are installed. Workers should wear a respirator and tyvek suit. The demolished materials must be disposed of as hazardous waste if it fails the TCLP (Toxicity Characteristic Leachate Process) test.

6. **Enclosure** is the process that permanently seals lead painted materials in place. This process has many applications such as covering lead painted drywall with new drywall, covering exterior construction with tyvek paper then residing, or covering lead painted structural members with aluminum or plastic. The seams on all enclosing materials must be securely sealed. An industrial hygienist monitors the project, and protective clothing and a respirator is required until air samples prove otherwise.

All the processes require clearance monitoring and wipe testing as required by the hygienist.

R031113-10   Wall Form Materials

Aluminum Forms

Approximate weight is 3 lbs. per S.F.C.A. Standard widths are available from 4" to 36" with 36" most common. Standard lengths of 2', 4', 6' to 8' are available. Forms are lightweight and fewer ties are needed with the wider widths. The form face is either smooth or textured.

Metal Framed Plywood Forms

Manufacturers claim over 75 reuses of plywood and over 300 reuses of steel frames. Many specials such as corners, fillers, pilasters, etc. are available. Monthly rental is generally about 15% of purchase price for first month and 9% per month thereafter with 90% of rental applied to purchase for the first month and decreasing percentages thereafter. Aluminum framed forms cost 25% to 30% more than steel framed.

After the first month, extra days may be prorated from the monthly charge. Rental rates do not include ties, accessories, cleaning, loss of hardware or freight in and out. Approximate weight is 5 lbs. per S.F. for steel; 3 lbs. per S.F. for aluminum.

Forms can be rented with option to buy.

Plywood Forms, Job Fabricated

There are two types of plywood used for concrete forms.
1. Exterior plyform which is completely waterproof. This is face oiled to facilitate stripping. Ten reuses can be expected with this type with 25 reuses possible.
2. An overlaid type consists of a resin fiber fused to exterior plyform. No oiling is required except to facilitate cleaning. This is available in both high density (HDO) and medium density overlaid (MDO). Using HDO, 50 reuses can be expected with 200 possible.

Plyform is available in 5/8" and 3/4" thickness. High density overlaid is available in 3/8", 1/2", 5/8" and 3/4" thickness.

5/8" thick is sufficient for most building forms, while 3/4" is best on heavy construction.

Plywood Forms, Modular, Prefabricated

There are many plywood forming systems without frames. Most of these are manufactured from 1-1/8" (HDO) plywood and have some hardware attached. These are used principally for foundation walls 8' or less high. With care and maintenance, 100 reuses can be attained with decreasing quality of surface finish.

Steel Forms

Approximate weight is 6-1/2 lbs. per S.F.C.A. including accessories. Standard widths are available from 2" to 24", with 24" most common. Standard lengths are from 2' to 8', with 4' the most common. Forms are easily ganged into modular units.

Forms are usually leased for 15% of the purchase price per month prorated daily over 30 days.

Rental may be applied to sale price, and usually rental forms are bought. With careful handling and cleaning 200 to 400 reuses are possible.

Straight wall gang forms up to 12' x 20' or 8' x 30' can be fabricated. These crane handled forms usually lease for approx. 9% per month.

Individual job analysis is available from the manufacturer at no charge.

R031113-30   Slipforms

The slipform method of forming may be used for forming circular silo and multi-celled storage bin type structures over 30' high, and building core shear walls over eight stories high. The shear walls, usually enclose elevator shafts, stairwells, mechanical spaces, and toilet rooms. Reuse of the form on duplicate structures will reduce the height necessary and spread the cost of building the form. Slipform systems can be used to cast chimneys, towers, piers, dams, underground shafts or other structures capable of being extruded.

Slipforms are usually 4' high and are raised semi-continuously by jacks climbing on rods which are embedded in the concrete. The jacks are powered by a hydraulic, pneumatic, or electric source and are available in 3, 6, and 22 ton capacities. Interior work decks and exterior scaffolds must be provided for placing inserts, embedded items, reinforcing steel, and

concrete. Scaffolds below the form for finishers may be required. The interior work decks are often used as roof slab forms on silos and bin work. Form raising rates will range from 6" to 20" per hour for silos; 6" to 30" per hour for buildings; and 6" to 48" per hour for shaft work.

Reinforcing bars and stressing strands are usually hoisted by crane or gin pole, and the concrete material can be hoisted by crane, winch-powered skip, or pumps. The slipform system is operated on a continuous 24-hour day when a monolithic structure is desired. For least cost, the system is operated only during normal working hours.

Placing concrete will range from 0.5 to 1.5 labor-hours per C.Y. Bucks, blockouts, keyways, weldplates, etc. are extra.

R031113-40   Forms for Reinforced Concrete

Design Economy

Avoid many sizes in proportioning beams and columns.

From story to story avoid changing column dimensions. Gain strength by adding steel or using a richer mix. If a change in size of column is necessary, vary one dimension only to minimize form alterations. Keep beams and columns the same width.

From floor to floor in a multi-story building vary beam depth, not width, as that will leave slab panel form unchanged. It is cheaper to vary the strength of a beam from floor to floor by means of steel area than by 2″ changes in either width or depth.

Cost Factors

Material includes the cost of lumber, cost of rent for metal pans or forms if used, nails, form ties, form oil, bolts and accessories.

Labor includes the cost of carpenters to make up, erect, remove and repair, plus common labor to clean and move. Having carpenters remove forms minimizes repairs.

Improper alignment and condition of forms will increase finishing cost. When forms are heavily oiled, concrete surfaces must be neutralized before finishing. Special curing compounds will cause spillages to spall off in first frost. Gang forming methods will reduce costs on large projects.

Materials Used

Boards are seldom used unless their architectural finish is required. Generally, steel, fiberglass and plywood are used for contact surfaces. Labor on plywood is 10% less than with boards. The plywood is backed up with 2 x 4′s at 12″ to 32″ O.C. Walers are generally 2 - 2 x 4′s. Column forms are held together with steel yokes or bands. Shoring is with adjustable shoring or scaffolding for high ceilings.

Reuse

Floor and column forms can be reused four or possibly five times without excessive repair. Remember to allow for 10% waste on each reuse.

When modular sized wall forms are made, up to twenty uses can be expected with exterior plyform.

When forms are reused, the cost to erect, strip, clean and move will not be affected. 10% replacement of lumber should be included and about one hour of carpenter time for repairs on each reuse per 100 S.F.

The reuse cost for certain accessory items normally rented on a monthly basis will be lower than the cost for the first use.

After fifth use, new material required plus time needed for repair prevent form cost from dropping further and it may go up. Much depends on care in stripping, the number of special bays, changes in beam or column sizes and other factors.

Costs for multiple use of formwork may be developed as follows:

2 Uses	3 Uses	4 Uses
$\dfrac{(\text{1st Use} + \text{Reuse})}{2} = \text{avg. cost/2 uses}$	$\dfrac{(\text{1st Use} + 2\ \text{Reuse})}{3} = \text{avg. cost/3 uses}$	$\dfrac{(\text{1st use} + 3\ \text{Reuse})}{4} = \text{avg. cost/4 uses}$

R031113-60 Formwork Labor-Hours

Item	Unit	Hours Required			Total Hours	Multiple Use		
		Fabricate	Erect & Strip	Clean & Move	1 Use	2 Use	3 Use	4 Use
Beam and Girder, interior beams, 12" wide	100 S.F.	6.4	8.3	1.3	16.0	13.3	12.4	12.0
Hung from steel beams		5.8	7.7	1.3	14.8	12.4	11.6	11.2
Beam sides only, 36" high		5.8	7.2	1.3	14.3	11.9	11.1	10.7
Beam bottoms only, 24" wide		6.6	13.0	1.3	20.9	18.1	17.2	16.7
Box out for openings		9.9	10.0	1.1	21.0	16.6	15.1	14.3
Buttress forms, to 8' high		6.0	6.5	1.2	13.7	11.2	10.4	10.0
Centering, steel, 3/4" rib lath			1.0		1.0			
3/8" rib lath or slab form			0.9		0.9			
Chamfer strip or keyway	100 L.F.		1.5		1.5	1.5	1.5	1.5
Columns, fiber tube 8" diameter			20.6		20.6			
12"			21.3		21.3			
16"			22.9		22.9			
20"			23.7		23.7			
24"			24.6		24.6			
30"			25.6		25.6			
Columns, round steel, 12" diameter			22.0		22.0	22.0	22.0	22.0
16"			25.6		25.6	25.6	25.6	25.6
20"			30.5		30.5	30.5	30.5	30.5
24"			37.7		37.7	37.7	37.7	37.7
Columns, plywood 8" x 8"	100 S.F.	7.0	11.0	1.2	19.2	16.2	15.2	14.7
12" x 12"		6.0	10.5	1.2	17.7	15.2	14.4	14.0
16" x 16"		5.9	10.0	1.2	17.1	14.7	13.8	13.4
24" x 24"		5.8	9.8	1.2	16.8	14.4	13.6	13.2
Columns, steel framed plywood 8" x 8"			10.0	1.0	11.0	11.0	11.0	11.0
12" x 12"			9.3	1.0	10.3	10.3	10.3	10.3
16" x 16"			8.5	1.0	9.5	9.5	9.5	9.5
24" x 24"			7.8	1.0	8.8	8.8	8.8	8.8
Drop head forms, plywood		9.0	12.5	1.5	23.0	19.0	17.7	17.0
Coping forms		8.5	15.0	1.5	25.0	21.3	20.0	19.4
Culvert, box			14.5	4.3	18.8	18.8	18.8	18.8
Curb forms, 6" to 12" high, on grade		5.0	8.5	1.2	14.7	12.7	12.1	11.7
On elevated slabs		6.0	10.8	1.2	18.0	15.5	14.7	14.3
Edge forms to 6" high, on grade	100 L.F.	2.0	3.5	0.6	6.1	5.6	5.4	5.3
7" to 12" high	100 S.F.	2.5	5.0	1.0	8.5	7.8	7.5	7.4
Equipment foundations		10.0	18.0	2.0	30.0	25.5	24.0	23.3
Flat slabs, including drops		3.5	6.0	1.2	10.7	9.5	9.0	8.8
Hung from steel		3.0	5.5	1.2	9.7	8.7	8.4	8.2
Closed deck for domes		3.0	5.8	1.2	10.0	9.0	8.7	8.5
Open deck for pans		2.2	5.3	1.0	8.5	7.9	7.7	7.6
Footings, continuous, 12" high		3.5	3.5	1.5	8.5	7.3	6.8	6.6
Spread, 12" high		4.7	4.2	1.6	10.5	8.7	8.0	7.7
Pile caps, square or rectangular		4.5	5.0	1.5	11.0	9.3	8.7	8.4
Grade beams, 24" deep		2.5	5.3	1.2	9.0	8.3	8.0	7.9
Lintel or Sill forms		8.0	17.0	2.0	27.0	23.5	22.3	21.8
Spandrel beams, 12" wide		9.0	11.2	1.3	21.5	17.5	16.2	15.5
Stairs			25.0	4.0	29.0	29.0	29.0	29.0
Trench forms in floor		4.5	14.0	1.5	20.0	18.3	17.7	17.4
Walls, Plywood, at grade, to 8' high		5.0	6.5	1.5	13.0	11.0	9.7	9.5
8' to 16'		7.5	8.0	1.5	17.0	13.8	12.7	12.1
16' to 20'		9.0	10.0	1.5	20.5	16.5	15.2	14.5
Foundation walls, to 8' high		4.5	6.5	1.0	12.0	10.3	9.7	9.4
8' to 16' high		5.5	7.5	1.0	14.0	11.8	11.0	10.6
Retaining wall to 12' high, battered		6.0	8.5	1.5	16.0	13.5	12.7	12.3
Radial walls to 12' high, smooth		8.0	9.5	2.0	19.5	16.0	14.8	14.3
2' chords		7.0	8.0	1.5	16.5	13.5	12.5	12.0
Prefabricated modular, to 8' high		—	4.3	1.0	5.3	5.3	5.3	5.3
Steel, to 8' high		—	6.8	1.2	8.0	8.0	8.0	8.0
8' to 16' high		—	9.1	1.5	10.6	10.3	10.2	10.2
Steel framed plywood to 8' high		—	6.8	1.2	8.0	7.5	7.3	7.2
8' to 16' high		—	9.3	1.2	10.5	9.5	9.2	9.0

R032110-10   Reinforcing Steel Weights and Measures

Bar Designation No.**	Nominal Weight Lb./Ft.	U.S. Customary Units Nominal Dimensions*			SI Units Nominal Dimensions*			
		Diameter in.	Cross Sectional Area, in.²	Perimeter in.	Nominal Weight kg/m	Diameter mm	Cross Sectional Area, cm²	Perimeter mm
3	.376	.375	.11	1.178	.560	9.52	.71	29.9
4	.668	.500	.20	1.571	.994	12.70	1.29	39.9
5	1.043	.625	.31	1.963	1.552	15.88	2.00	49.9
6	1.502	.750	.44	2.356	2.235	19.05	2.84	59.8
7	2.044	.875	.60	2.749	3.042	22.22	3.87	69.8
8	2.670	1.000	.79	3.142	3.973	25.40	5.10	79.8
9	3.400	1.128	1.00	3.544	5.059	28.65	6.45	90.0
10	4.303	1.270	1.27	3.990	6.403	32.26	8.19	101.4
11	5.313	1.410	1.56	4.430	7.906	35.81	10.06	112.5
14	7.650	1.693	2.25	5.320	11.384	43.00	14.52	135.1
18	13.600	2.257	4.00	7.090	20.238	57.33	25.81	180.1

* The nominal dimensions of a deformed bar are equivalent to those of a plain round bar having the same weight per foot as the deformed bar.
** Bar numbers are based on the number of eighths of an inch included in the nominal diameter of the bars.

R032110-20   Metric Rebar Specification - ASTM A615-81

Grade 300 (300 MPa* = 43,560 psi; +8.7% vs. Grade 40)				
Grade 400 (400 MPa* = 58,000 psi; −3.4% vs. Grade 60)				
Bar No.	Diameter mm	Area mm²	Equivalent in.²	Comparison with U.S. Customary Bars
10M	11.3	100	.16	Between #3 & #4
15M	16.0	200	.31	#5 (.31 in.²)
20M	19.5	300	.47	#6 (.44 in.²)
25M	25.2	500	.78	#8 (.79 in.²)
30M	29.9	700	1.09	#9 (1.00 in.²)
35M	35.7	1000	1.55	#11 (1.56 in.²)
45M	43.7	1500	2.33	#14 (2.25 in.²)
55M	56.4	2500	3.88	#18 (4.00 in.²)

* MPa = megapascals

R032110-40   Weight of Steel Reinforcing Per Square Foot of Wall (PSF)

Reinforced Weights: The table below suggests the weights per square foot for reinforcing steel in walls. Weights are approximate and will be the same for all grades of steel bars. For bars in two directions, add weights for each size and spacing.

C/C Spacing in Inches	Bar Size								
	#3 Wt. (PSF)	#4 Wt. (PSF)	#5 Wt. (PSF)	#6 Wt. (PSF)	#7 Wt. (PSF)	#8 Wt. (PSF)	#9 Wt. (PSF)	#10 Wt. (PSF)	#11 Wt. (PSF)
2″	2.26	4.01	6.26	9.01	12.27				
3″	1.50	2.67	4.17	6.01	8.18	10.68	13.60	17.21	21.25
4″	1.13	2.01	3.13	4.51	6.13	8.10	10.20	12.91	15.94
5″	.90	1.60	2.50	3.60	4.91	6.41	8.16	10.33	12.75
6″	.752	1.34	2.09	3.00	4.09	5.34	6.80	8.61	10.63
8″	.564	1.00	1.57	2.25	3.07	4.01	5.10	6.46	7.97
10″	.451	.802	1.25	1.80	2.45	3.20	4.08	5.16	6.38
12″	.376	.668	1.04	1.50	2.04	2.67	3.40	4.30	5.31
18″	.251	.445	.695	1.00	1.32	1.78	2.27	2.86	3.54
24″	.188	.334	.522	.751	1.02	1.34	1.70	2.15	2.66
30″	.150	.267	.417	.600	.817	1.07	1.36	1.72	2.13
36″	.125	.223	.348	.501	.681	.890	1.13	1.43	1.77
42″	.107	.191	.298	.429	.584	.753	.97	1.17	1.52
48″	.094	.167	.261	.376	.511	.668	.85	1.08	1.33

R032110-50   Minimum Wall Reinforcement Weight (PSF)

This table lists the approximate minimum wall reinforcement weights per S.F. according to the specification of .12% of gross area for vertical bars and .20% of gross area for horizontal bars.

Location	Wall Thickness	Bar Size	Horizontal Steel Spacing C/C	Sq. In. Req'd per S.F.	Total Wt. per S.F.	Bar Size	Vertical Steel Spacing C/C	Sq. In. Req'd per S.F.	Total Wt. per S.F.	Horizontal & Vertical Steel Total Weight per S.F.
	10″	#4	18″	.24	.89#	#3	18″	.14	.50#	1.39#
	12″	#4	16″	.29	1.00	#3	16″	.17	.60	1.60
Both Faces	14″	#4	14″	.34	1.14	#3	13″	.20	.69	1.84
	16″	#4	12″	.38	1.34	#3	11″	.23	.82	2.16
	18″	#5	17″	.43	1.47	#4	18″	.26	.89	2.36
	6″	#3	9″	.15	.50	#3	18″	.09	.25	.75
One Face	8″	#4	12″	.19	.67	#3	11″	.12	.41	1.08
	10″	#5	15″	.24	.83	#4	16″	.14	.50	1.34

R032110-70   Bend, Place and Tie Reinforcing

Placing and tying by rodmen for footings and slabs runs from nine hrs. per ton for heavy bars to fifteen hrs. per ton for light bars. For beams, columns, and walls, production runs from eight hrs. per ton for heavy bars to twenty hrs. per ton for light bars. Overall average for typical reinforced concrete buildings is about fourteen hrs. per ton. These production figures include the time for placing of accessories and usual inserts, but not their material cost (allow 15% of the cost of delivered bent rods). Equipment handling is necessary for the larger-sized bars so that installation costs for the very heavy bars will not decrease proportionately.

Installation costs for splicing reinforcing bars include allowance for equipment to hold the bars in place while splicing as well as necessary scaffolding for iron workers.

R032110-80   Shop-Fabricated Reinforcing Steel

The material prices for reinforcing, shown in the unit cost sections of the book, are for 50 tons or more of shop-fabricated reinforcing steel and include:
1. Mill base price of reinforcing steel
2. Mill grade/size/length extras
3. Mill delivery to the fabrication shop
4. Shop storage and handling
5. Shop drafting/detailing
6. Shop shearing and bending
7. Shop listing
8. Shop delivery to the job site

Both material and installation costs can be considerably higher for small jobs consisting primarily of smaller bars, while material costs may be slightly lower for larger jobs.

Concrete R0322 Welded Wire Fabric Reinforcing

R032205-30 Common Stock Styles of Welded Wire Fabric

This table provides some of the basic specifications, sizes, and weights of welded wire fabric used for reinforcing concrete.

	New Designation	Old Designation		Steel Area per Foot				Approximate Weight per 100 S.F.	
	Spacing — Cross Sectional Area (in.) — (Sq. in. 100)	Spacing — Wire Gauge (in.) — (AS & W)		Longitudinal		Transverse			
				in.	cm	in.	cm	lbs	kg
Rolls	6 x 6 — W1.4 x W1.4	6 x 6 — 10 x 10		.028	.071	.028	.071	21	9.53
	6 x 6 — W2.0 x W2.0	6 x 6 — 8 x 8	1	.040	.102	.040	.102	29	13.15
	6 x 6 — W2.9 x W2.9	6 x 6 — 6 x 6		.058	.147	.058	.147	42	19.05
	6 x 6 — W4.0 x W4.0	6 x 6 — 4 x 4		.080	.203	.080	.203	58	26.91
	4 x 4 — W1.4 x W1.4	4 x 4 — 10 x 10		.042	.107	.042	.107	31	14.06
	4 x 4 — W2.0 x W2.0	4 x 4 — 8 x 8	1	.060	.152	.060	.152	43	19.50
	4 x 4 — W2.9 x W2.9	4 x 4 — 6 x 6		.087	.227	.087	.227	62	28.12
	4 x 4 — W4.0 x W4.0	4 x 4 — 4 x 4		.120	.305	.120	.305	85	38.56
Sheets	6 x 6 — W2.9 x W2.9	6 x 6 — 6 x 6		.058	.147	.058	.147	42	19.05
	6 x 6 — W4.0 x W4.0	6 x 6 — 4 x 4		.080	.203	.080	.203	58	26.31
	6 x 6 — W5.5 x W5.5	6 x 6 — 2 x 2	2	.110	.279	.110	.279	80	36.29
	4 x 4 — W1.4 x W1.4	4 x 4 — 4 x 4		.120	.305	.120	.305	85	38.56

NOTES: 1. Exact W—number size for 8 gauge is W2.1
2. Exact W—number size for 2 gauge is W5.4

Concrete R0330 Cast-In-Place Concrete

R033053-50 Industrial Chimneys

Foundation requirements in C.Y. of concrete for various sized chimneys.

Size Chimney	2 Ton Soil		3 Ton Soil		Size Chimney	2 Ton Soil		3 Ton Soil		Size Chimney	2 Ton Soil		3 Ton Soil	
75' x 3'-0"	13	C.Y.	11	C.Y.	160' x 6'-6"	86	C.Y.	76	C.Y.	300' x 10'-0"	325	C.Y.	245	C.Y.
85' x 5'-6"	19		16		175' x 7'-0"	108		95		350' x 12'-0"	422		320	
100' x 5'-0"	24		20		200' x 6'-0"	125		105		400' x 14'-0"	520		400	
125' x 5'-6"	43		36		250' x 8'-0"	230		175		500' x 18'-0"	725		575	

R033105-10 Proportionate Quantities

The tables below show both quantities per S.F. of floor areas as well as form and reinforcing quantities per C.Y. Unusual structural requirements would increase the ratios below. High strength reinforcing would reduce the steel weights. Figures are for 3000 psi concrete and 60,000 psi reinforcing unless specified otherwise.

Type of Construction	Live Load	Span	Per S.F. of Floor Area				Per C.Y. of Concrete		
			Concrete	Forms	Reinf.	Pans	Forms	Reinf.	Pans
Flat Plate	50 psf	15 Ft.	.46 C.F.	1.06 S.F.	1.71 lb.		62 S.F.	101 lb.	
		20	.63	1.02	2.40		44	104	
		25	.79	1.02	3.03		35	104	
	100	15	.46	1.04	2.14		61	126	
		20	.71	1.02	2.72		39	104	
		25	.83	1.01	3.47		33	113	
Flat Plate (waffle construction) 20" domes	50	20	.43	1.00	2.10	.84 S.F.	63	135	53 S.F.
		25	.52	1.00	2.90	.89	52	150	46
		30	.64	1.00	3.70	.87	42	155	37
	100	20	.51	1.00	2.30	.84	53	125	45
		25	.64	1.00	3.20	.83	42	135	35
		30	.76	1.00	4.40	.81	36	160	29
Waffle Construction 30" domes	50	25	.69	1.06	1.83	.68	42	72	40
		30	.74	1.06	2.39	.69	39	87	39
		35	.86	1.05	2.71	.69	33	85	39
		40	.78	1.00	4.80	.68	35	165	40
Flat Slab (two way with drop panels)	50	20	.62	1.03	2.34		45	102	
		25	.77	1.03	2.99		36	105	
		30	.95	1.03	4.09		29	116	
	100	20	.64	1.03	2.83		43	119	
		25	.79	1.03	3.88		35	133	
		30	.96	1.03	4.66		29	131	
	200	20	.73	1.03	3.03		38	112	
		25	.86	1.03	4.23		32	133	
		30	1.06	1.03	5.30		26	135	
One Way Joists 20" Pans	50	15	.36	1.04	1.40	.93	78	105	70
		20	.42	1.05	1.80	.94	67	120	60
		25	.47	1.05	2.60	.94	60	150	54
	100	15	.38	1.07	1.90	.93	77	140	66
		20	.44	1.08	2.40	.94	67	150	58
		25	.52	1.07	3.50	.94	55	185	49
One Way Joists 8" x 16" filler blocks	50	15	.34	1.06	1.80	.81 Ea.	84	145	64 Ea.
		20	.40	1.08	2.20	.82	73	145	55
		25	.46	1.07	3.20	.83	63	190	49
	100	15	.39	1.07	1.90	.81	74	130	56
		20	.46	1.09	2.80	.82	64	160	48
		25	.53	1.10	3.60	.83	56	190	42
One Way Beam & Slab	50	15	.42	1.30	1.73		84	111	
		20	.51	1.28	2.61		68	138	
		25	.64	1.25	2.78		53	117	
	100	15	.42	1.30	1.90		84	122	
		20	.54	1.35	2.69		68	154	
		25	.69	1.37	3.93		54	145	
	200	15	.44	1.31	2.24		80	137	
		20	.58	1.40	3.30		65	163	
		25	.69	1.42	4.89		53	183	
Two Way Beam & Slab	100	15	.47	1.20	2.26		69	130	
		20	.63	1.29	3.06		55	131	
		25	.83	1.33	3.79		43	123	
	200	15	.49	1.25	2.70		41	149	
		20	.66	1.32	4.04		54	165	
		25	.88	1.32	6.08		41	187	

R033105-10 Proportionate Quantities (cont.)

4000 psi Concrete and 60,000 psi Reinforcing—Form and Reinforcing Quantities per C.Y.

Item	Size	Forms	Reinforcing	Minimum	Maximum
	10" x 10"	130 S.F.C.A.	#5 to #11	220 lbs.	875 lbs.
	12" x 12"	108	#6 to #14	200	955
	14" x 14"	92	#7 to #14	190	900
	16" x 16"	81	#6 to #14	187	1082
	18" x 18"	72	#6 to #14	170	906
	20" x 20"	65	#7 to #18	150	1080
Columns	22" x 22"	59	#8 to #18	153	902
(square tied)	24" x 24"	54	#8 to #18	164	884
	26" x 26"	50	#9 to #18	169	994
	28" x 28"	46	#9 to #18	147	864
	30" x 30"	43	#10 to #18	146	983
	32" x 32"	40	#10 to #18	175	866
	34" x 34"	38	#10 to #18	157	772
	36" x 36"	36	#10 to #18	175	852
	38" x 38"	34	#10 to #18	158	765
	40" x 40"	32	#10 to #18	143	692

Item	Size	Form	Spiral	Reinforcing	Minimum	Maximum
	12" diameter	34.5 L.F.	190 lbs.	#4 to #11	165 lbs.	1505 lb.
		34.5	190	#14 & #18	—	1100
	14"	25	170	#4 to #11	150	970
		25	170	#14 & #18	800	1000
	16"	19	160	#4 to #11	160	950
		19	160	#14 & #18	605	1080
	18"	15	150	#4 to #11	160	915
		15	150	#14 & #18	480	1075
	20"	12	130	#4 to #11	155	865
		12	130	#14 & #18	385	1020
	22"	10	125	#4 to #11	165	775
		10	125	#14 & #18	320	995
	24"	9	120	#4 to #11	195	800
		9	120	#14 & #18	290	1150
Columns	26"	7.3	100	#4 to #11	200	729
(spirally reinforced)		7.3	100	#14 & #18	235	1035
	28"	6.3	95	#4 to #11	175	700
		6.3	95	#14 & #18	200	1075
	30"	5.5	90	#4 to #11	180	670
		5.5	90	#14 & #18	175	1015
	32"	4.8	85	#4 to #11	185	615
		4.8	85	#14 & #18	155	955
	34"	4.3	80	#4 to #11	180	600
		4.3	80	#14 & #18	170	855
	36"	3.8	75	#4 to #11	165	570
		3.8	75	#14 & #18	155	865
	40"	3.0	70	#4 to #11	165	500
		3.0	70	#14 & #18	145	765

R033105-10   Proportionate Quantities (cont.)

3000 psi Concrete and 60,000 psi Reinforcing—Form and Reinforcing Quantities per C.Y.						
Item	Type	Loading	Height	C.Y./L.F.	Forms/C.Y.	Reinf./C.Y.
Retaining Walls	Cantilever	Level Backfill	4 Ft.	0.2 C.Y.	49 S.F.	35 lbs.
			8	0.5	42	45
			12	0.8	35	70
			16	1.1	32	85
			20	1.6	28	105
		Highway Surcharge	4	0.3	41	35
			8	0.5	36	55
			12	0.8	33	90
			16	1.2	30	120
			20	1.7	27	155
		Railroad Surcharge	4	0.4	28	45
			8	0.8	25	65
			12	1.3	22	90
			16	1.9	20	100
			20	2.6	18	120
	Gravity, with Vertical Face	Level Backfill	4	0.4	37	None
			7	0.6	27	
			10	1.2	20	
		Sloping Backfill	4	0.3	31	
			7	0.8	21	
			10	1.6	15	↓

		Live Load in Kips per Linear Foot							
	Span	Under 1 Kip		2 to 3 Kips		4 to 5 Kips		6 to 7 Kips	
		Forms	Reinf.	Forms	Reinf.	Forms	Reinf.	Forms	Reinf.
Beams	10 Ft.	—	—	90 S.F.	170 #	85 S.F.	175 #	75 S.F.	185 #
	16	130 S.F.	165 #	85	180	75	180	65	225
	20	110	170	75	185	62	200	51	200
	26	90	170	65	215	62	215	—	—
	30	85	175	60	200	—	—	—	—

Item	Size	Type	Forms per C.Y.	Reinforcing per C.Y.
Spread Footings	Under 1 C.Y.	1,000 psf soil	24 S.F.	44 lbs.
		5,000	24	42
		10,000	24	52
	1 C.Y. to 5 C.Y.	1,000	14	49
		5,000	14	50
		10,000	14	50
	Over 5 C.Y.	1,000	9	54
		5,000	9	52
		10,000	9	56
Pile Caps (30 Ton Concrete Piles)	Under 5 C.Y.	shallow caps	20	65
		medium	20	50
		deep	20	40
	5 C.Y. to 10 C.Y.	shallow	14	55
		medium	15	45
		deep	15	40
	10 C.Y. to 20 C.Y.	shallow	11	60
		medium	11	45
		deep	12	35
	Over 20 C.Y.	shallow	9	60
		medium	9	45
		deep	10	40

R033105-10 Proportionate Quantities (cont.)

			3000 psi Concrete and 60,000 psi Reinforcing — Form and Reinforcing Quantities per C.Y.			
Item	Size	Pile Spacing	50 T Pile	100 T Pile	50 T Pile	100 T Pile
Pile Caps (Steel H Piles)	Under 5 C.Y.	24" O.C.	24 S.F.	24 S.F.	75 lbs.	90 lbs.
		30"	25	25	80	100
		36"	24	24	80	110
	5 C.Y. to 10 C.Y.	24"	15	15	80	110
		30"	15	15	85	110
		36"	15	15	75	90
	Over 10 C.Y.	24"	13	13	85	90
		30"	11	11	85	95
		36"	10	10	85	90

		8" Thick		10" Thick		12" Thick		15" Thick	
	Height	Forms	Reinf.	Forms	Reinf.	Forms	Reinf.	Forms	Reinf.
Basement Walls	7 Ft.	81 S.F.	44 lbs.	65 S.F.	45 lbs.	54 S.F.	44 lbs.	41 S.F.	43 lbs.
	8		44		45		44		43
	9		46		45		44		43
	10		57		45		44		43
	12		83		50		52		43
	14		116		65		64		51
	16				86		90		65
	18						106		70

R033105-20   Materials for One C.Y. of Concrete

This is an approximate method of figuring quantities of cement, sand and coarse aggregate for a field mix with waste allowance included.

With crushed gravel as coarse aggregate, to determine barrels of cement required, divide 10 by total mix; that is, for 1:2:4 mix, 10 divided by 7 = 1-3/7 barrels.

If the coarse aggregate is crushed stone, use 10-1/2 instead of 10 as given for gravel.

To determine tons of sand required, multiply barrels of cement by parts of sand and then by 0.2; that is, for the 1:2:4 mix, as above, 1-3/7 x 2 x .2 = .57 tons.

Tons of crushed gravel are in the same ratio to tons of sand as parts in the mix, or 4/2 x .57 = 1.14 tons.

1 bag cement = 94#	1 C.Y. sand or crushed gravel = 2700#	1 C.Y. crushed stone = 2575#
4 bags = 1 barrel	1 ton sand or crushed gravel = 20 C.F.	1 ton crushed stone = 21 C.F.

Average carload of cement is 692 bags; of sand or gravel is 56 tons.

Do not stack stored cement over 10 bags high.

R033105-30   Metric Equivalents of Cement Content for Concrete Mixes

94 Pound Bags per Cubic Yard	Kilograms per Cubic Meter	94 Pound Bags per Cubic Yard	Kilograms per Cubic Meter
1.0	55.77	7.0	390.4
1.5	83.65	7.5	418.3
2.0	111.5	8.0	446.2
2.5	139.4	8.5	474.0
3.0	167.3	9.0	501.9
3.5	195.2	9.5	529.8
4.0	223.1	10.0	557.7
4.5	251.0	10.5	585.6
5.0	278.8	11.0	613.5
5.5	306.7	11.5	641.3
6.0	334.6	12.0	669.2
6.5	362.5	12.5	697.1

a. If you know the cement content in pounds per cubic yard,
   multiply by .5933 to obtain kilograms per cubic meter.

b. If you know the cement content in 94 pound bags per cubic yard,
   multiply by 55.77 to obtain kilograms per cubic meter.

R033105-40 Metric Equivalents of Common Concrete Strengths
(to convert other psi values to megapascals, multiply by 0.006895)

U.S. Values psi	SI Value Megapascals	Non-SI Metric Value kgf/cm²*
2000	14	140
2500	17	175
3000	21	210
3500	24	245
4000	28	280
4500	31	315
5000	34	350
6000	41	420
7000	48	490
8000	55	560
9000	62	630
10,000	69	705

* kilograms force per square centimeter

R033105-50 Quantities of Cement, Sand and Stone for One C.Y. of Concrete per Various Mixes

This table can be used to determine the quantities of the ingredients for smaller quantities of site mixed concrete.

Concrete (C.Y.)	Mix = 1:1:1-3/4			Mix = 1:2:2.25			Mix = 1:2.25:3			Mix = 1:3:4		
	Cement (sacks)	Sand (C.Y.)	Stone (C.Y.)	Cement (sacks)	Sand (C.Y.)	Stone (C.Y.)	Cement (sacks)	Sand (C.Y.)	Stone (C.Y.)	Cement (sacks)	Sand (C.Y.)	Stone (C.Y.)
1	10	.37	.63	7.75	.56	.65	6.25	.52	.70	5	.56	.74
2	20	.74	1.26	15.50	1.12	1.30	12.50	1.04	1.40	10	1.12	1.48
3	30	1.11	1.89	23.25	1.68	1.95	18.75	1.56	2.10	15	1.68	2.22
4	40	1.48	2.52	31.00	2.24	2.60	25.00	2.08	2.80	20	2.24	2.96
5	50	1.85	3.15	38.75	2.80	3.25	31.25	2.60	3.50	25	2.80	3.70
6	60	2.22	3.78	46.50	3.36	3.90	37.50	3.12	4.20	30	3.36	4.44
7	70	2.59	4.41	54.25	3.92	4.55	43.75	3.64	4.90	35	3.92	5.18
8	80	2.96	5.04	62.00	4.48	5.20	50.00	4.16	5.60	40	4.48	5.92
9	90	3.33	5.67	69.75	5.04	5.85	56.25	4.68	6.30	45	5.04	6.66
10	100	3.70	6.30	77.50	5.60	6.50	62.50	5.20	7.00	50	5.60	7.40
11	110	4.07	6.93	85.25	6.16	7.15	68.75	5.72	7.70	55	6.16	8.14
12	120	4.44	7.56	93.00	6.72	7.80	75.00	6.24	8.40	60	6.72	8.88
13	130	4.82	8.20	100.76	7.28	8.46	81.26	6.76	9.10	65	7.28	9.62
14	140	5.18	8.82	108.50	7.84	9.10	87.50	7.28	9.80	70	7.84	10.36
15	150	5.56	9.46	116.26	8.40	9.76	93.76	7.80	10.50	75	8.40	11.10
16	160	5.92	10.08	124.00	8.96	10.40	100.00	8.32	11.20	80	8.96	11.84
17	170	6.30	10.72	131.76	9.52	11.06	106.26	8.84	11.90	85	9.52	12.58
18	180	6.66	11.34	139.50	10.08	11.70	112.50	9.36	12.60	90	10.08	13.32
19	190	7.04	11.98	147.26	10.64	12.36	118.76	9.84	13.30	95	10.64	14.06
20	200	7.40	12.60	155.00	11.20	13.00	125.00	10.40	14.00	100	11.20	14.80
21	210	7.77	13.23	162.75	11.76	13.65	131.25	10.92	14.70	105	11.76	15.54
22	220	8.14	13.86	170.05	12.32	14.30	137.50	11.44	15.40	110	12.32	16.28
23	230	8.51	14.49	178.25	12.88	14.95	143.75	11.96	16.10	115	12.88	17.02
24	240	8.88	15.12	186.00	13.44	15.60	150.00	12.48	16.80	120	13.44	17.76
25	250	9.25	15.75	193.75	14.00	16.25	156.25	13.00	17.50	125	14.00	18.50
26	260	9.64	16.40	201.52	14.56	16.92	162.52	13.52	18.20	130	14.56	19.24
27	270	10.00	17.00	209.26	15.12	17.56	168.76	14.04	18.90	135	15.02	20.00
28	280	10.36	17.64	217.00	15.68	18.20	175.00	14.56	19.60	140	15.68	20.72
29	290	10.74	18.28	224.76	16.24	18.86	181.26	15.08	20.30	145	16.24	21.46

R033105-65   Field-Mix Concrete

Presently most building jobs are built with ready-mixed concrete except at isolated locations and some larger jobs requiring over 10,000 C.Y. where land is readily available for setting up a temporary batch plant.

The most economical mix is a controlled mix using local aggregate proportioned by trial to give the required strength with the least cost of material.

R033105-70   Placing Ready-Mixed Concrete

For ground pours allow for 5% waste when figuring quantities.

Prices in the front of the book assume normal deliveries. If deliveries are made before 8 A.M. or after 5 P.M. or on Saturday afternoons add 30%. Negotiated discounts for large volumes are not included in prices in front of book.

For the lower floors without truck access, concrete may be wheeled in rubber-tired buggies, conveyer handled, crane handled or pumped. Pumping is economical if there is top steel. Conveyers are more efficient for thick slabs.

At higher floors the rubber-tired buggies may be hoisted by a hoisting tower and wheeled to location. Placement by a conveyer is limited to three floors

and is best for high-volume pours. Pumped concrete is best when building has no crane access. Concrete may be pumped directly as high as thirty-six stories using special pumping techniques. Normal maximum height is about fifteen stories.

Best pumping aggregate is screened and graded bank gravel rather than crushed stone.

Pumping downward is more difficult than pumping upward. Horizontal distance from pump to pour may increase preparation time prior to pour. Placing by cranes, either mobile, climbing or tower types, continues as the most efficient method for high-rise concrete buildings.

R033105-85   Lift Slabs

The cost advantage of the lift slab method is due to placing all concrete, reinforcing steel, inserts and electrical conduit at ground level and in reduction of formwork. Minimum economical project size is about 30,000 S.F. Slabs may be tilted for parking garage ramps.

It is now used in all types of buildings and has gone up to 22 stories high in apartment buildings. Current trend is to use post-tensioned flat plate slabs with spans from 22' to 35'. Cylindrical void forms are used when deep slabs are required. One pound of prestressing steel is about equal to seven pounds of conventional reinforcing.

To be considered cured for stressing and lifting, a slab must have attained 75% of design strength. Seven days are usually sufficient with four to five days possible if high early strength cement is used. Slabs can be stacked using two coats of a non-bonding agent to insure that slabs do not stick to each other. Lifting is done by companies specializing in this work. Lift rate is 5' to 15' per hour with an average of 10' per hour. Total areas up to 33,000 S.F. have been lifted at one time. 24 to 36 jacking columns are common. Most economical bay sizes are 24' to 28' with four to fourteen stories most efficient. Continuous design reduces reinforcing steel cost. Use of post-tensioned slabs allows larger bay sizes.

R033543-10   Polished Concrete Floors

A polished concrete floor has a glossy mirror-like appearance and is created by grinding the concrete floor with finer and finer diamond grits, similar to sanding wood, until the desired level of reflective clarity and sheen are achieved. The technical term for this type of polished concrete is bonded abrasive polished concrete. The basic piece of equipment used in the polishing process is a walk-behind planetary grinder for working large floor areas. This grinder drives diamond-impregnated abrasive discs, which progress from coarse- to fine-grit discs.

The process begins with the use of very coarse diamond segments or discs bonded in a metallic matrix. These segments are coarse enough to allow the removal of pits, blemishes, stains, and light coatings from the floor surface in preparation for final smoothing. The condition of the original concrete surface will dictate the grit coarsness of the initial grinding step which will generally end up being a three- to four-step process using ever finer grits. The purpose of this initial grinding step is to remove surface coatings and blemishes and to cut down into the cream for very fine aggregate exposure, or deeper into the fine aggregate layer just below the cream layer, or even deeper into the coarse aggregate layer. These initial grinding steps will progress up to the 100/120 grit. If wet grinding is done, a waste slurry is produced that must be removed between grit changes and disposed of properly. If dry grinding is done, a high performance vacuum will pick up the dust during grinding and collect it in bags which must be disposed of properly.

The process continues with honing the floor in a series of steps that progress from 100-grit to 400-grit diamond abrasive discs embedded in a plastic or resin matrix. At some point during, or just prior to, the honing step, one or two coats of stain or dye can be sprayed onto the surface to give color to the concrete, and two coats of densifier/hardener must be applied to the floor surface and allowed to dry. This sprayed-on densifier/hardener will penetrate about 1/8" into the concrete to make the surface harder, denser and more abrasion-resistant.

The process ends with polishing the floor surface in a series of steps that progress from resin-impregnated 800-grit (medium polish) to 1500-grit (high polish) to 3000-grit (very high polish), depending on the desired level of reflective clarity and sheen.

The Concrete Polishing Association of America (CPAA) has defined the flooring options available when processing concrete to a desired finish. The first category is aggregate exposure, the grinding of a concrete surface with bonded abrasives, in as many abrasive grits necessary, to achieve one of the following classes:

A. Cream – very little surface cut depth; little aggregate exposure

B. Fine aggregate (salt and pepper) – surface cut depth of 1/16"; fine aggregate exposure with little or no medium aggregate exposure at random locations

C. Medium aggregate – surface cut depth of 1/8"; medium aggregate exposure with little or no large aggregate exposure at random locations

D. Large aggregate – surface cut depth of 1/4"; large aggregate exposure with little or no fine aggregate exposure at random locations

The second CPAA defined category is reflective clarity and sheen, the polishing of a concrete surface with the minimum number of bonded abrasives as indicated to achieve one of the following levels:

1. Ground – flat appearance with none to very slight diffused reflection; none to very low reflective sheen; using a minimum total of 4 grit levels up 100-grit

2. Honed – matte appearance with or without slight diffused reflection; low to medium reflective sheen; using a minimum total of 5 grit levels up to 400-grit

3. Semi-polished – objects being reflected are not quite sharp and crisp but can be easily identified; medium to high reflective sheen; using a minimum total of 6 grit levels up to 800-grit

4. Highly-polished – objects being reflected are sharp and crisp as would be seen in a mirror-like reflection; high to highest reflective sheen; using a minimum total of up to 8 grit levels up to 1500-grit or 3000-grit

The CPAA defines reflective clarity as the degree of sharpness and crispness of the reflection of overhead objects when viewed 5' above and perpendicular to the floor surface; and reflective sheen as the degree of gloss reflected from a surface when viewed at least 20' from and at an angle to the floor surface. These terms are relatively subjective. The final outcome depends on the internal makeup and surface condition of the original concrete floor, the experience of the floor polishing crew, and expectations of the owner. Before the grinding, honing, and polishing work commences on the main floor area, it might be beneficial to do a mock-up panel in the same floor but in an out of the way place to demonstrate the sequence of steps with increasingly fine abrasive grits and to demonstrate the final reflective clarity and reflective sheen. This mock-up panel will be within the area of, and part of, the final work.

R034105-30　Prestressed Precast Concrete Structural Units

Type	Location	Depth	Span in Ft.		Live Load Lb. per S.F.
Double Tee 8' to 10'	Floor	28" to 34"	60 to 80		50 to 80
	Roof	12" to 24"	30 to 50		40
	Wall	Width 8'	Up to 55' high		Wind
Multiple Tee 8'	Roof	8" to 12"	15 to 40		40
	Floor	8" to 12"	15 to 30		100
Plank	Roof		Roof	Floor	
		4"	13	12	40 for Roof
		6"	22	18	
or	or	8"	26	25	
		10"	33	29	100 for Floor
	Floor	12"	42	32	
Single Tee 8' to 10'	Roof	28"	40		
		32"	80		
		36"	100		40
		48"	120		
AASHO Girder	Bridges	Type 4	100		
		5	110		Highway
		6	125		
Box Beam 4'	Bridges	15"	40		
		27"	to		Highway
		33"	100		

The majority of precast projects today utilize double tees rather than single tees because of speed and ease of installation. As a result casting beds at manufacturing plants are normally formed for double tees. Single tee projects will therefore require an initial set up charge to be spread over the individual single tee costs.

For floors, a 2" to 3" topping is field cast over the shapes. For roofs, insulating concrete or rigid insulation is placed over the shapes.

Member lengths up to 40' are standard haul, 40' to 60' require special permits and lengths over 60' must be escorted. Over width and/or over length can add up to 100% on hauling costs.

Large heavy members may require two cranes for lifting which would increase erection costs by about 45%. An eight man crew can install 12 to 20 double tees, or 45 to 70 quad tees or planks per day.

Grouting of connections must also be included.

Several system buildings utilizing precast members are available. Heights can go up to 22 stories for apartment buildings. Optimum design ratio is 3 S.F. of surface to 1 S.F. of floor area.

R034136-90   Prestressed Concrete, Post-Tensioned

In post-tensioned concrete the steel tendons are tensioned after the concrete has reached about 3/4 of its ultimate strength. The cableways are grouted after tensioning to provide bond between the steel and concrete. If bond is to be prevented, the tendons are coated with a corrosion-preventative grease and wrapped with waterproofed paper or plastic. Bonded tendons are usually used when ultimate strength (beams & girders) are controlling factors.

High strength concrete is used to fully utilize the steel, thereby reducing the size and weight of the member. A plasticizing agent may be added to reduce water content. Maximum size aggregate ranges from 1/2" to 1-1/2" depending on the spacing of the tendons.

The types of steel commonly used are bars and strands. Job conditions determine which is best suited. Bars are best for vertical prestresses since they are easy to support. The trend is for steel manufacturers to supply a finished package, cut to length, which reduces field preparation to a minimum.

Bars vary from 3/4" to 1-3/8" diameter. Table below gives time in labor-hours per tendon for placing, tensioning and grouting (if required) a 75' beam. Tendons used in buildings are not usually grouted; tendons for bridges usually are grouted. For strands the table indicates the labor-hours per pound for typical prestressed units 100' long. Simple span beams usually require one-end stressing regardless of lengths. Continuous beams are usually stressed from two ends. Long slabs are poured from the center outward and stressed in 75' increments after the initial 150' center pour.

Labor Hours per Tendon and per Pound of Prestressed Steel						
Length	100' Beam		75' Beam		100' Slab	
Type Steel	Strand		Bars		Strand	
Diameter	0.5"		3/4"	1-3/8"	0.5"	0.6"
Number	4	12	1	1	1	1
Force in Kips	100	300	42	143	25	35
Preparation & Placing Cables	3.6	7.4	0.9	2.9	0.9	1.1
Stressing Cables	2.0	2.4	0.8	1.6	0.5	0.5
Grouting, if required	2.5	3.0	0.6	1.3		
Total Labor Hours	8.1	12.8	2.3	5.8	1.4	1.6
Prestressing Steel Weights (Lbs.)	215	640	115	380	53	74
Labor-hours per Lb. Bonded	0.038	0.020	0.020	0.015		
Non-bonded					0.026	0.022

Flat Slab construction — 4000 psi concrete with span-to-depth ratio between 36 and 44. Two way post-tensioned steel averages 1.0 lb. per S.F. for 24' to 28' bays (usually strand) and additional reinforcing steel averages .5 lb. per S.F.

Pan and Joist construction — 4000 psi concrete with span-to-depth ratio 28 to 30. Post-tensioned steel averages .8 lb. per S.F. and reinforcing steel about 1.0 lb. per S.F. Placing and stressing averages 40 hours per ton of total material.

Beam construction — 4000 to 5000 psi concrete. Steel weights vary greatly.

Labor cost per pound goes down as the size and length of the tendon increase. The primary economic consideration is the cost per kip for the member.

Post-tensioning becomes feasible for beams and girders over 30' long; for continuous two-way slabs over 20' clear; also in transferring upper building loads over longer spans at lower levels. Post-tension suppliers will provide engineering services at no cost to the user. Substantial economies are possible by using post-tensioned Lift Slabs.

R034513-10   Precast Concrete Wall Panels

Panels are either solid or insulated with plain, colored or textured finishes. Transportation is an important cost factor. Prices shown in the unit cost section of the book are based on delivery within 50 miles of a plant including fabricators' overhead and profit. Engineering data is available from fabricators to assist with construction details. Usual minimum job size for economical use of panels is about 5000 S.F. Small jobs can double the prices shown. For large, highly repetitive jobs, deduct up to 15% from the prices shown.

2″ thick panels cost about the same as 3″ thick panels, and maximum panel size is less. For building panels faced with granite, marble or stone, add the material prices from those unit cost sections to the plain panel price shown. There is a growing trend toward aggregate facings and broken rib finish rather than plain gray concrete panels.

No allowance has been made in the unit cost section for supporting steel framework. On one story buildings, panels may rest on grade beams and require only wind bracing and fasteners. On multi-story buildings panels can span from column to column and floor to floor. Plastic-designed steel-framed structures may have large deflections which slow down erection and raise costs.

Large panels are more economical than small panels on a S.F. basis. When figuring areas include all protrusions, returns, etc. Overhangs can triple erection costs. Panels over 45′ have been produced. Larger flat units should be prestressed. Vacuum lifting of smooth finish panels eliminates inserts and can speed erection.

Concrete | **R0347 Site-Cast Concrete**

R034713-20   Tilt Up Concrete Panels

The advantage of tilt up construction is in the low cost of forms and the placing of concrete and reinforcing. Panels up to 75′ high and 5-1/2″ thick have been tilted using strongbacks. Tilt up has been used for one to five story buildings and is well-suited for warehouses, stores, offices, schools and residences.

The panels are cast in forms on the floor slab. Most jobs use 5-1/2″ thick solid reinforced concrete panels. Sandwich panels with a layer of insulating materials are also used. Where dampness is a factor, lightweight aggregate is used. Optimum panel size is 300 to 500 S.F.

Slabs are usually poured with 3000 psi concrete which permits tilting seven days after pouring. Slabs may be stacked on top of each other and are separated from each other by either two coats of bond breaker or a film of polyethylene. Use of high early-strength cement allows tilting two days after a pour. Tilting up is done with a roller outrigger crane with a capacity of at least 1-1/2 times the weight of the panel at the required reach. Exterior precast columns can be set at the same time as the panels; interior precast columns can be set first and the panels clipped directly to them. The use of cast-in-place concrete columns is diminishing due to shrinkage problems. Structural steel columns are sometimes used if crane rails are planned. Panels can be clipped to the columns or lowered between the flanges. Steel channels with anchors may be used as edge forms for the slab. When the panels are lifted the channels form an integral steel column to take structural loads. Roof loads can be carried directly by the panels for wall heights to 14′.

Requirements of local building codes may be a limiting factor and should be checked. Building floor slabs should be poured first and should be a minimum of 5″ thick with 100% compaction of soil or 6″ thick with less than 100% compaction.

Setting times as fast as nine minutes per panel have been observed, but a safer expectation would be four panels per hour with a crane and a four-man setting crew. If crane erects from inside building, some provision must be made to get crane out after walls are erected. Good yarding procedure is important to minimize delays. Equalizing three-point lifting beams and self-releasing pick-up hooks speed erection. If panels must be carried to their final location, setting time per panel will be increased and erection costs may approach the erection cost range of architectural precast wall panels. Placing panels into slots formed in continuous footers will speed erection.

Reinforcing should be with #5 bars with vertical bars on the bottom. If surface is to be sandblasted, stainless steel chairs should be used to prevent rust staining.

Use of a broom finish is popular since the unavoidable surface blemishes are concealed.

Precast columns run from three to five times the C.Y. price of the panels only.

Concrete | **R0352 Lightweight Concrete Roof Insulation**

R035216-10   Lightweight Concrete

Lightweight aggregate concrete is usually purchased ready mixed, but it can also be field mixed.

Vermiculite or Perlite comes in bags of 4 C.F. under various trade names. Weight is about 8 lbs. per C.F. For insulating roof fill use 1:6 mix. For structural deck use 1:4 mix over gypsum boards, steeltex, steel centering, etc., supported by closely spaced joists or bulb trees. For structural slabs use 1:3:2 vermiculite sand concrete over steeltex, metal lath, steel centering, etc., on joists spaced 2′-0″ O.C. for maximum L.L. of 80 P.S.F. Use same mix

for slab base fill over steel flooring or regular reinforced concrete slab when tile, terrazzo or other finish is to be laid over.

For slabs on grade use 1:3:2 mix when tile, etc., finish is to be laid over. If radiant heating units are installed use a 1:6 mix for a base. After coils are in place, cover with a regular granolithic finish (mix 1:3:2) to a minimum depth of 1-1/2″ over top of units.

Reinforce all slabs with 6 x 6 or 10 x 10 welded wire mesh.

R040130-10   Cleaning Face Brick

On smooth brick a person can clean 70 S.F. an hour; on rough brick 50 S.F. per hour. Use one gallon muriatic acid to 20 gallons of water for 1000

S.F. Do not use acid solution until wall is at least seven days old, but a mild soap solution may be used after two days.

Time has been allowed for clean-up in brick prices.

R040513-10   Cement Mortar (material only)

Type N - 1:1:6 mix by volume. Use everywhere above grade except as noted below. - 1:3 mix using conventional masonry cement which saves handling two separate bagged materials.

Type M - 1:1/4:3 mix by volume, or 1 part cement, 1/4 (10% by wt.) lime, 3 parts sand. Use for heavy loads and where earthquakes or hurricanes may occur. Also for reinforced brick, sewers, manholes and everywhere below grade.

Mix Proportions by Volume and Compressive Strength of Mortar

Where Used	Mortar Type	Allowable Proportions by Volume				Compressive Strength @ 28 days
		Portland Cement	Masonry Cement	Hydrated Lime	Masonry Sand	
Plain Masonry	M	1	1	—	6	
		1	—	1/4	3	2500 psi
	S	1/2	1	—	4	
		1	—	1/4 to 1/2	4	1800 psi
	N	—	1	—	3	
		1	—	1/2 to 1-1/4	6	750 psi
	O	—	1	—	3	
		1	—	1-1/4 to 2-1/2	9	350 psi
	K	1	—	2-1/2 to 4	12	75 psi
Reinforced Masonry	PM	1	1	—	6	2500 psi
	PL	1	—	1/4 to 1/2	4	2500 psi

Note: The total aggregate should be between 2.25 to 3 times the sum of the cement and lime used.

The labor cost to mix the mortar is included in the productivity and labor cost of unit price lines in unit cost sections for brickwork, blockwork and stonework.

The material cost of mixed mortar is included in the material cost of those same unit price lines and includes the cost of renting and operating a 10 C.F. mixer at the rate of 200 C.F. per day.

There are two types of mortar color used. One type is the inert additive type with about 100 lbs. per M brick as the typical quantity required. These colors are also available in smaller-batch-sized bags (1 lb. to 15 lb.) which can be placed directly into the mixer without measuring. The other type is premixed and replaces the masonry cement. Dark green color has the highest cost.

R040519-50   Masonry Reinforcing

Horizontal joint reinforcing helps prevent wall cracks where wall movement may occur and in many locations is required by code. Horizontal joint reinforcing is generally not considered to be structural reinforcing and an unreinforced wall may still contain joint reinforcing.

Reinforcing strips come in 10' and 12' lengths and in truss and ladder shapes, with and without drips. Field labor runs between 2.7 to 5.3 hours per 1000 L.F. for wall thicknesses up to 12".

The wire meets ASTM A82 for cold drawn steel wire and the typical size is 9 ga. sides and ties with 3/16" diameter also available. Typical finish is mill galvanized with zinc coating at .10 oz. per S.F. Class I (.40 oz. per S.F.) and Class III (.80 oz per S.F.) are also available, as is hot dipped galvanizing at 1.50 oz. per S.F.

R042110-10   Economy in Bricklaying

Have adequate supervision. Be sure bricklayers are always supplied with materials so there is no waiting. Place best bricklayers at corners and openings.

Use only screened sand for mortar. Otherwise, labor time will be wasted picking out pebbles. Use seamless metal tubs for mortar as they do not leak or catch the trowel. Locate stack and mortar for easy wheeling.

Have brick delivered for stacking. This makes for faster handling, reduces chipping and breakage, and requires less storage space. Many dealers will deliver select common in 2' x 3' x 4' pallets or face brick packaged. This affords quick handling with a crane or forklift and easy tonging in units of ten, which reduces waste.

Use wider bricks for one wythe wall construction. Keep scaffolding away from wall to allow mortar to fall clear and not stain wall.

On large jobs develop specialized crews for each type of masonry unit.

Consider designing for prefabricated panel construction on high rise projects.

Avoid excessive corners or openings. Each opening adds about 50% to labor cost for area of opening.

Bolting stone panels and using window frames as stops reduces labor costs and speeds up erection.

R042110-20   Common and Face Brick

Common building brick manufactured according to ASTM C62 and facing brick manufactured according to ASTM C216 are the two standard bricks available for general building use.

Building brick is made in three grades; SW, where high resistance to damage caused by cyclic freezing is required; MW, where moderate resistance to cyclic freezing is needed; and NW, where little resistance to cyclic freezing is needed. Facing brick is made in only the two grades SW and MW. Additionally, facing brick is available in three types; FBS, for general use; FBX, for general use where a higher degree of precision and lower permissible variation in size than FBS is needed; and FBA, for general use to produce characteristic architectural effects resulting from non-uniformity in size and texture of the units.

In figuring the material cost of brickwork, an allowance of 25% mortar waste and 3% brick breakage was included. If bricks are delivered palletized

with 280 to 300 per pallet, or packaged, allow only 1-1/2% for breakage. Packaged or palletized delivery is practical when a job is big enough to have a crane or other equipment available to handle a package of brick. This is so on all industrial work but not always true on small commercial buildings.

The use of buff and gray face is increasing, and there is a continuing trend to the Norman, Roman, Jumbo and SCR brick.

Common red clay brick for backup is not used that often. Concrete block is the most usual backup material with occasional use of sand lime or cement brick. Building brick is commonly used in solid walls for strength and as a fire stop.

Brick panels built on the ground and then crane erected to the upper floors have proven to be economical. This allows the work to be done under cover and without scaffolding.

R042110-50   Brick, Block & Mortar Quantities

Running Bond						For Other Bonds Standard Size Add to S.F. Quantities in Table to Left		
Number of Brick per S.F. of Wall - Single Wythe with 3/8" Joints				C.F. of Mortar per M Bricks, Waste Included				
Type Brick	Nominal Size (incl. mortar) L H W	Modular Coursing	Number of Brick per S.F.	3/8" Joint	1/2" Joint	Bond Type	Description	Factor
Standard	8 x 2-2/3 x 4	3C=8"	6.75	10.3	12.9	Common	full header every fifth course	+20%
Economy	8 x 4 x 4	1C=4"	4.50	11.4	14.6		full header every sixth course	+16.7%
Engineer	8 x 3-1/5 x 4	5C=16"	5.63	10.6	13.6	English	full header every second course	+50%
Fire	9 x 2-1/2 x 4-1/2	2C=5"	6.40	550 # Fireclay	—	Flemish	alternate headers every course	+33.3%
Jumbo	12 x 4 x 6 or 8	1C=4"	3.00	23.8	30.8		every sixth course	+5.6%
Norman	12 x 2-2/3 x 4	3C=8"	4.50	14.0	17.9	Header = W x H exposed		+100%
Norwegian	12 x 3-1/5 x 4	5C=16"	3.75	14.6	18.6	Rowlock = H x W exposed		+100%
Roman	12 x 2 x 4	2C=4"	6.00	13.4	17.0	Rowlock stretcher = L x W exposed		+33.3%
SCR	12 x 2-2/3 x 6	3C=8"	4.50	21.8	28.0	Soldier = H x L exposed		—
Utility	12 x 4 x 4	1C=4"	3.00	15.4	19.6	Sailor = W x L exposed		-33.3%

Concrete Blocks Nominal Size		Approximate Weight per S.F.		Blocks per 100 S.F.	Mortar per M block, waste included	
		Standard	Lightweight		Partitions	Back up
2"	x 8" x 16"	20 PSF	15 PSF	113	27 C.F.	36 C.F.
4"		30	20		41	51
6"		42	30		56	66
8"		55	38		72	82
10"		70	47		87	97
12"		85	55		102	112

Masonry — R0422 Concrete Unit Masonry

R042210-20   Concrete Block

The material cost of special block such as corner, jamb and head block can be figured at the same price as ordinary block of same size. Labor on specials is about the same as equal-sized regular block.

Bond beam and 16″ high lintel blocks are more expensive than regular units of equal size. Lintel blocks are 8″ long and either 8″ or 16″ high.

Use of motorized mortar spreader box will speed construction of continuous walls.

Hollow non-load-bearing units are made according to ASTM C129 and hollow load-bearing units according to ASTM C90.

Metals — R0505 Common Work Results for Metals

R050516-30   Coating Structural Steel

On field-welded jobs, the shop-applied primer coat is necessarily omitted. All painting must be done in the field and usually consists of red oxide rust inhibitive paint or an aluminum paint. The table below shows paint coverage and daily production for field painting.

See Division 05 05 13.50 for hot-dipped galvanizing and Division 09 97 13.23 for field-applied cold galvanizing and other paints and protective coatings.

See Division 05 01 10.51 for steel surface preparation treatments such as wire brushing, pressure washing and sand blasting.

Type Construction	Surface Area per Ton	Coat	One Gallon Covers		In 8 Hrs. Person Covers		Average per Ton Spray	
			Brush	Spray	Brush	Spray	Gallons	Labor-hours
Light Structural	300 S.F. to 500 S.F.	1st	500 S.F.	455 S.F.	640 S.F.	2000 S.F.	0.9 gals.	1.6 L.H.
		2nd	450	410	800	2400	1.0	1.3
		3rd	450	410	960	3200	1.0	1.0
Medium	150 S.F. to 300 S.F.	All	400	365	1600	3200	0.6	0.6
Heavy Structural	50 S.F. to 150 S.F.	1st	400	365	1920	4000	0.2	0.2
		2nd	400	365	2000	4000	0.2	0.2
		3rd	400	365	2000	4000	0.2	0.2
Weighted Average	225 S.F.	All	400	365	1350	3000	0.6	0.6

R050521-20   Welded Structural Steel

Usual weight reductions with welded design run 10% to 20% compared with bolted or riveted connections. This amounts to about the same total cost compared with bolted structures since field welding is more expensive than bolts. For normal spans of 18′ to 24′ figure 6 to 7 connections per ton.

Trusses — For welded trusses add 4% to weight of main members for connections. Up to 15% less steel can be expected in a welded truss compared to one that is shop bolted. Cost of erection is the same whether shop bolted or welded.

General — Typical electrodes for structural steel welding are E6010, E6011, E60T and E70T. Typical buildings vary between 2# to 8# of weld rod per

ton of steel. Buildings utilizing continuous design require about three times as much welding as conventional welded structures. In estimating field erection by welding, it is best to use the average linear feet of weld per ton to arrive at the welding cost per ton. The type, size and position of the weld will have a direct bearing on the cost per linear foot. A typical field welder will deposit 1.8# to 2# of weld rod per hour manually. Using semiautomatic methods can increase production by as much as 50% to 75%.

R050523-10   High Strength Bolts

Common bolts (A307) are usually used in secondary connections (see Division 05 05 23.10).

High strength bolts (A325 and A490) are usually specified for primary connections such as column splices, beam and girder connections to columns, column bracing, connections for supports of operating equipment or of other live loads which produce impact or reversal of stress, and in structures carrying cranes of over 5-ton capacity.

Allow 20 field bolts per ton of steel for a 6 story office building, apartment house or light industrial building. For 6 to 12 stories allow 25 bolts per ton, and above 12 stories, 30 bolts per ton. On power stations, 20 to 25 bolts per ton are needed.

R051223-10   Structural Steel

The bare material prices for structural steel, shown in the unit cost sections of the book, are for 100 tons of shop-fabricated structural steel and include:

1. Mill base price of structural steel
2. Mill scrap/grade/size/length extras
3. Mill delivery to a metals service center (warehouse)
4. Service center storage and handling
5. Service center delivery to a fabrication shop
6. Shop storage and handling
7. Shop drafting/detailing
8. Shop fabrication

9. Shop coat of primer paint
10. Shop listing
11. Shop delivery to the job site

In unit cost sections of the book that contain items for field fabrication of steel components, the bare material cost of steel includes:

1. Mill base price of structural steel
2. Mill scrap/grade/size/length extras
3. Mill delivery to a metals service center (warehouse)
4. Service center storage and handling
5. Service center delivery to the job site

R051223-20   Steel Estimating Quantities

One estimate on erection is that a crane can handle 35 to 60 pieces per day. Say the average is 45. With usual sizes of beams, girders, and columns, this would amount to about 20 tons per day. The type of connection greatly affects the speed of erection. Moment connections for continuous design slow down production and increase erection costs.

Short open web bar joists can be set at the rate of 75 to 80 per day, with 50 per day being the average for setting long span joists.

After main members are calculated, add the following for usual allowances: base plates 2% to 3%; column splices 4% to 5%; and miscellaneous details 4% to 5%, for a total of 10% to 13% in addition to main members.

The ratio of column to beam tonnage varies depending on type of steels used, typical spans, story heights and live loads.

It is more economical to keep the column size constant and to vary the strength of the column by using high strength steels. This also saves floor space. Buildings have recently gone as high as ten stories with 8" high strength columns. For light columns under W8X31 lb. sections, concrete filled steel columns are economical.

High strength steels may be used in columns and beams to save floor space and to meet head room requirements. High strength steels in some sizes sometimes require long lead times.

Round, square and rectangular columns, both plain and concrete filled, are readily available and save floor area, but are higher in cost per pound than rolled columns. For high unbraced columns, tube columns may be less expensive.

Below are average minimum figures for the weights of the structural steel frame for different types of buildings using A36 steel, rolled shapes and simple joints. For economy in domes, rise to span ratio = .13. Open web joist framing systems will reduce weights by 10% to 40%. Composite design can reduce steel weight by up to 25% but additional concrete floor slab thickness may be required. Continuous design can reduce the weights up to 20%. There are many building codes with different live load requirements and different structural requirements, such as hurricane and earthquake loadings which can alter the figures.

Structural Steel Weights per S.F. of Floor Area

Type of Building	No. of Stories	Avg. Spans	L.L. #/S.F.	Lbs. Per S.F.	Type of Building	No. of Stories	Avg. Spans	L.L. #/S.F.	Lbs. Per S.F.
Steel Frame Mfg.	1	20'x20'	40	8	Apartments	2-8	20'x20'	40	8
		30'x30'		13		9-25			14
		40'x40'		18	Office	to 10	Various	80	10
Parking garage	4	Various	80	8.5		20			18
Domes (Schwedler)*	1	200'	30	10		30			26
		300'		15		over 50			35

R051223-25 Common Structural Steel Specifications

ASTM A992 (formerly A36, then A572 Grade 50) is the all-purpose carbon grade steel widely used in building and bridge construction.

The other high-strength steels listed below may each have certain advantages over ASTM A992 stuctural carbon steel, depending on the application. They have proven to be economical choices where, due to lighter members, the reduction of dead load and the associated savings in shipping cost can be significant.

ASTM A588 atmospheric weathering, high-strength low-alloy steels can be used in the bare (uncoated) condition, where exposure to normal atmosphere causes a tightly adherant oxide to form on the surface protecting the steel from further oxidation. ASTM A242 corrosion-resistant, high-strength low-alloy steels have enhanced atmospheric corrosion resistance of at least two times that of carbon structural steels with copper, or four times that of carbon structural steels without copper. The reduction or elimination of maintenance resulting from the use of these steels often offsets their higher initial cost.

Steel Type	ASTM Designation	Minimum Yield Stress in KSI	Shapes Available
Carbon	A36	36	All structural shape groups, and plates & bars up thru 8" thick
	A529	50	Structural shape group 1, and plates & bars up thru 2" thick
High-Strength Low-Alloy Quenched & Self-Tempered	A913	50	All structural shape groups
		60	
		65	
		70	
High-Strength Low-Alloy Columbium-Vanadium	A572	42	All structural shape groups, and plates & bars up thru 6" thick
		50	All structural shape groups, and plates & bars up thru 4" thick
		55	Structural shape groups 1 & 2, and plates & bars up thru 2" thick
		60	Structural shape groups 1 & 2, and plates & bars up thru 1-1/4" thick
		65	Structural shape group 1, and plates & bars up thru 1-1/4" thick
High-Strength Low-Alloy Columbium-Vanadium	A992	50	All structural shape groups
Weathering High-Strength Low-Alloy	A242	42	Structural shape groups 4 & 5, and plates & bars over 1-1/2" up thru 4" thick
		46	Structural shape group 3, and plates & bars over 3/4" up thru 1-1/2" thick
Weathering High-Strength Low-Alloy	A588	50	Structural shape groups 1 & 2, and plates & bars up thru 3/4" thick
		42	Plates & bars over 5" up thru 8" thick
		46	Plates & bars over 4" up thru 5" thick
Quenched and Tempered	A852	50	All structural shape groups, and plates & bars up thru 4" thick
		70	Plates & bars up thru 4" thick
Low-Alloy Quenched and Tempered Alloy	A514	90	Plates & bars over 2-1/2" up thru 6" thick
		100	Plates & bars up thru 2-1/2" thick

R051223-30 High Strength Steels

The mill price of high strength steels may be higher than A992 carbon steel but their proper use can achieve overall savings thru total reduced weights. For columns with L/r over 100, A992 steel is best; under 100, high strength steels are economical. For heavy columns, high strength steels are economical when cover plates are eliminated. There is no economy using high strength steels for clip angles or supports or for beams where deflection governs. Thinner members are more economical than thick.

The per ton erection and fabricating costs of the high strength steels will be higher than for A992 since the same number of pieces, but less weight, will be installed.

R051223-35 Common Steel Sections

The upper portion of this table shows the name, shape, common designation and basic characteristics of commonly used steel sections. The lower portion explains how to read the designations used for the above illustrated common sections.

Shape & Designation	Name & Characteristics	Shape & Designation	Name & Characteristics
W	W Shape — Parallel flange surfaces	MC	Miscellaneous Channel — Infrequently rolled by some producers
S	American Standard Beam (I Beam) — Sloped inner flange	L	Angle — Equal or unequal legs, constant thickness
M	Miscellaneous Beams — Cannot be classified as W, HP or S; infrequently rolled by some producers	T	Structural Tee — Cut from W, M or S on center of web
C	American Standard Channel — Sloped inner flange	HP	Bearing Pile — Parallel flanges and equal flange and web thickness

Common drawing designations follow:

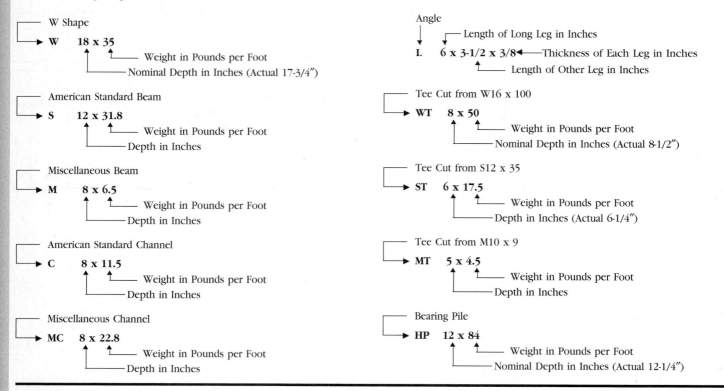

W Shape: **W 18 x 35** — Weight in Pounds per Foot; Nominal Depth in Inches (Actual 17-3/4")

American Standard Beam: **S 12 x 31.8** — Weight in Pounds per Foot; Depth in Inches

Miscellaneous Beam: **M 8 x 6.5** — Weight in Pounds per Foot; Depth in Inches

American Standard Channel: **C 8 x 11.5** — Weight in Pounds per Foot; Depth in Inches

Miscellaneous Channel: **MC 8 x 22.8** — Weight in Pounds per Foot; Depth in Inches

Angle: **L 6 x 3-1/2 x 3/8** — Length of Long Leg in Inches; Thickness of Each Leg in Inches; Length of Other Leg in Inches

Tee Cut from W16 x 100: **WT 8 x 50** — Weight in Pounds per Foot; Nominal Depth in Inches (Actual 8-1/2")

Tee Cut from S12 x 35: **ST 6 x 17.5** — Weight in Pounds per Foot; Depth in Inches (Actual 6-1/4")

Tee Cut from M10 x 9: **MT 5 x 4.5** — Weight in Pounds per Foot; Depth in Inches

Bearing Pile: **HP 12 x 84** — Weight in Pounds per Foot; Nominal Depth in Inches (Actual 12-1/4")

R051223-45   Installation Time for Structural Steel Building Components

The following tables show the expected average installation times for various structural steel shapes. Table A presents installation times for columns, Table B for beams, Table C for light framing and bolts, and Table D for structural steel for various project types.

Table A		
Description	Labor-Hours	Unit
Columns		
Steel, Concrete Filled		
3-1/2" Diameter	.933	Ea.
6-5/8" Diameter	1.120	Ea.
Steel Pipe		
3" Diameter	.933	Ea.
8" Diameter	1.120	Ea.
12" Diameter	1.244	Ea.
Structural Tubing		
4" x 4"	.966	Ea.
8" x 8"	1.120	Ea.
12" x 8"	1.167	Ea.
W Shape 2 Tier		
W8 x 31	.052	L.F.
W8 x 67	.057	L.F.
W10 x 45	.054	L.F.
W10 x 112	.058	L.F.
W12 x 50	.054	L.F.
W12 x 190	.061	L.F.
W14 x 74	.057	L.F.
W14 x 176	.061	L.F.

Table B				
Description	Labor-Hours	Unit	Labor-Hours	Unit
Beams, W Shape				
W6 x 9	.949	Ea.	.093	L.F.
W10 x 22	1.037	Ea.	.085	L.F.
W12 x 26	1.037	Ea.	.064	L.F.
W14 x 34	1.333	Ea.	.069	L.F.
W16 x 31	1.333	Ea.	.062	L.F.
W18 x 50	2.162	Ea.	.088	L.F.
W21 x 62	2.222	Ea.	.077	L.F.
W24 x 76	2.353	Ea.	.072	L.F.
W27 x 94	2.581	Ea.	.067	L.F.
W30 x 108	2.857	Ea.	.067	L.F.
W33 x 130	3.200	Ea.	.071	L.F.
W36 x 300	3.810	Ea.	.077	L.F.

Table C		
Description	Labor-Hours	Unit
Light Framing		
Angles 4" and Larger	.055	lbs.
Less than 4"	.091	lbs.
Channels 8" and Larger	.048	lbs.
Less than 8"	.072	lbs.
Cross Bracing Angles	.055	lbs.
Rods	.034	lbs.
Hanging Lintels	.069	lbs.
High Strength Bolts in Place		
3/4" Bolts	.070	Ea.
7/8" Bolts	.076	Ea.

Table D				
Description	Labor-Hours	Unit	Labor-Hours	Unit
Apartments, Nursing Homes, etc.				
1-2 Stories	4.211	Piece	7.767	Ton
3-6 Stories	4.444	Piece	7.921	Ton
7-15 Stories	4.923	Piece	9.014	Ton
Over 15 Stories	5.333	Piece	9.209	Ton
Offices, Hospitals, etc.				
1-2 Stories	4.211	Piece	7.767	Ton
3-6 Stories	4.741	Piece	8.889	Ton
7-15 Stories	4.923	Piece	9.014	Ton
Over 15 Stories	5.120	Piece	9.209	Ton
Industrial Buildings				
1 Story	3.478	Piece	6.202	Ton

R051223-50   Subpurlins

Bulb tee subpurlins are structural members designed to support and reinforce a variety of roof deck systems such as precast cement fiber roof deck tiles, monolithic roof deck systems, and gypsum or lightweight concrete over formboard. Other uses include interstitial service ceiling systems, wall panel systems, and joist anchoring in bond beams. See Unit Price section for pricing on a square foot basis at 32-5/8" O.C. Maximum span is based on a 3-span condition with a total allowable vertical load of 40 psf.

R051223-80   Dimensions and Weights of Sheet Steel

| Gauge No. | Approximate Thickness | | | | | Weight | | |
| | Inches (in fractions) | Inches (in decimal parts) | | Millimeters | | | | per Square Meter in Kg. |
	Wrought Iron	Wrought Iron	Steel	Steel		per S.F. in Ounces	per S.F. in Lbs.	
0000000	1/2"	.5	.4782	12.146		320	20.000	97.650
000000	15/32"	.46875	.4484	11.389		300	18.750	91.550
00000	7/16"	.4375	.4185	10.630		280	17.500	85.440
0000	13/32"	.40625	.3886	9.870		260	16.250	79.330
000	3/8"	.375	.3587	9.111		240	15.000	73.240
00	11/32"	.34375	.3288	8.352		220	13.750	67.130
0	5/16"	.3125	.2989	7.592		200	12.500	61.030
1	9/32"	.28125	.2690	6.833		180	11.250	54.930
2	17/64"	.265625	.2541	6.454		170	10.625	51.880
3	1/4"	.25	.2391	6.073		160	10.000	48.820
4	15/64"	.234375	.2242	5.695		150	9.375	45.770
5	7/32"	.21875	.2092	5.314		140	8.750	42.720
6	13/64"	.203125	.1943	4.935		130	8.125	39.670
7	3/16"	.1875	.1793	4.554		120	7.500	36.320
8	11/64"	.171875	.1644	4.176		110	6.875	33.570
9	5/32"	.15625	.1495	3.797		100	6.250	30.520
10	9/64"	.140625	.1345	3.416		90	5.625	27.460
11	1/8"	.125	.1196	3.038		80	5.000	24.410
12	7/64"	.109375	.1046	2.657		70	4.375	21.360
13	3/32"	.09375	.0897	2.278		60	3.750	18.310
14	5/64"	.078125	.0747	1.897		50	3.125	15.260
15	9/128"	.0713125	.0673	1.709		45	2.813	13.730
16	1/16"	.0625	.0598	1.519		40	2.500	12.210
17	9/160"	.05625	.0538	1.367		36	2.250	10.990
18	1/20"	.05	.0478	1.214		32	2.000	9.765
19	7/160"	.04375	.0418	1.062		28	1.750	8.544
20	3/80"	.0375	.0359	.912		24	1.500	7.324
21	11/320"	.034375	.0329	.836		22	1.375	6.713
22	1/32"	.03125	.0299	.759		20	1.250	6.103
23	9/320"	.028125	.0269	.683		18	1.125	5.490
24	1/40"	.025	.0239	.607		16	1.000	4.882
25	7/320"	.021875	.0209	.531		14	.875	4.272
26	3/160"	.01875	.0179	.455		12	.750	3.662
27	11/640"	.0171875	.0164	.417		11	.688	3.357
28	1/64"	.015625	.0149	.378		10	.625	3.052

R053100-10   Decking Descriptions

General - All Deck Products

Steel deck is made by cold forming structural grade sheet steel into a repeating pattern of parallel ribs. The strength and stiffness of the panels are the result of the ribs and the material properties of the steel. Deck lengths can be varied to suit job conditions, but because of shipping considerations, are usually less than 40 feet. Standard deck width varies with the product used but full sheets are usually 12″, 18″, 24″, 30″, or 36″. Deck is typically furnished in a standard width with the ends cut square. Any cutting for width, such as at openings or for angular fit, is done at the job site.

Deck is typically attached to the building frame with arc puddle welds, self-drilling screws, or powder or pneumatically driven pins. Sheet to sheet fastening is done with screws, button punching (crimping), or welds.

Composite Floor Deck

After installation and adequate fastening, floor deck serves several purposes. It (a) acts as a working platform, (b) stabilizes the frame, (c) serves as a concrete form for the slab, and (d) reinforces the slab to carry the design loads applied during the life of the building. Composite decks are distinguished by the presence of shear connector devices as part of the deck. These devices are designed to mechanically lock the concrete and deck together so that the concrete and the deck work together to carry subsequent floor loads. These shear connector devices can be rolled-in embossments, lugs, holes, or wires welded to the panels. The deck profile can also be used to interlock concrete and steel.

Composite deck finishes are either galvanized (zinc coated) or phosphatized/painted. Galvanized deck has a zinc coating on both the top and bottom surfaces. The phosphatized/painted deck has a bare (phosphatized) top surface that will come into contact with the concrete. This bare top surface can be expected to develop rust before the concrete is placed. The bottom side of the deck has a primer coat of paint.

Composite floor deck is normally installed so the panel ends do not overlap on the supporting beams. Shear lugs or panel profile shape often prevent a tight metal to metal fit if the panel ends overlap; the air gap caused by overlapping will prevent proper fusion with the structural steel supports when the panel end laps are shear stud welded.

Adequate end bearing of the deck must be obtained as shown on the drawings. If bearing is actually less in the field than shown on the drawings, further investigation is required.

Roof Deck

Roof deck is not designed to act compositely with other materials. Roof deck acts alone in transferring horizontal and vertical loads into the building frame. Roof deck rib openings are usually narrower than floor deck rib openings. This provides adequate support of rigid thermal insulation board.

Roof deck is typically installed to endlap approximately 2″ over supports. However, it can be butted (or lapped more than 2″) to solve field fit problems. Since designers frequently use the installed deck system as part of the horizontal bracing system (the deck as a diaphragm), any fastening substitution or change should be approved by the designer. Continuous perimeter support of the deck is necessary to limit edge deflection in the finished roof and may be required for diaphragm shear transfer.

Standard roof deck finishes are galvanized or primer painted. The standard factory applied paint for roof deck is a primer paint and is not intended to weather for extended periods of time. Field painting or touching up of abrasions and deterioration of the primer coat or other protective finishes is the responsibility of the contractor.

Cellular Deck

Cellular deck is made by attaching a bottom steel sheet to a roof deck or composite floor deck panel. Cellular deck can be used in the same manner as floor deck. Electrical, telephone, and data wires are easily run through the chase created between the deck panel and the bottom sheet.

When used as part of the electrical distribution system, the cellular deck must be installed so that the ribs line up and create a smooth cell transition at abutting ends. The joint that occurs at butting cell ends must be taped or otherwise sealed to prevent wet concrete from seeping into the cell. Cell interiors must be free of welding burrs, or other sharp intrusions, to prevent damage to wires.

When used as a roof deck, the bottom flat plate is usually left exposed to view. Care must be maintained during erection to keep good alignment and prevent damage.

Cellular deck is sometimes used with the flat plate on the top side to provide a flat working surface. Installation of the deck for this purpose requires special methods for attachment to the frame because the flat plate, now on the top, can prevent direct access to the deck material that is bearing on the structural steel. It may be advisable to treat the flat top surface to prevent slipping.

Cellular deck is always furnished galvanized or painted over galvanized.

Form Deck

Form deck can be any floor or roof deck product used as a concrete form. Connections to the frame are by the same methods used to anchor floor and roof deck. Welding washers are recommended when welding deck that is less than 20 gauge thickness.

Form deck is furnished galvanized, prime painted, or uncoated. Galvanized deck must be used for those roof deck systems where form deck is used to carry a lightweight insulating concrete fill.

Wood, Plastics & Comp. R0611 Wood Framing

R061110-30 Lumber Product Material Prices

The price of forest products fluctuates widely from location to location and from season to season depending upon economic conditions. The bare material prices in the unit cost sections of the book show the National Average material prices in effect Jan. 1 of this book year. It must be noted that lumber prices in general may change significantly during the year.

Availability of certain items depends upon geographic location and must be checked prior to firm-price bidding.

Wood, Plastics & Comp. R0616 Sheathing

R061636-20 Plywood

There are two types of plywood used in construction: interior, which is moisture-resistant but not waterproofed, and exterior, which is waterproofed.

The grade of the exterior surface of the plywood sheets is designated by the first letter: A, for smooth surface with patches allowed; B, for solid surface with patches and plugs allowed; C, which may be surface plugged or may have knot holes up to 1″ wide; and D, which is used only for interior type plywood and may have knot holes up to 2-1/2″ wide. "Structural Grade" is specifically designed for engineered applications such as box beams. All CC & DD grades have roof and floor spans marked on them.

Underlayment-grade plywood runs from 1/4″ to 1-1/4″ thick. Thicknesses 5/8″ and over have optional tongue and groove joints which eliminate the need for blocking the edges. Underlayment 19/32″ and over may be referred to as Sturd-i-Floor.

The price of plywood can fluctuate widely due to geographic and economic conditions.

Typical uses for various plywood grades are as follows:

AA-AD Interior — cupboards, shelving, paneling, furniture

BB Plyform — concrete form plywood

CDX — wall and roof sheathing

Structural — box beams, girders, stressed skin panels

AA-AC Exterior — fences, signs, siding, soffits, etc.

Underlayment — base for resilient floor coverings

Overlaid HDO — high density for concrete forms & highway signs

Overlaid MDO — medium density for painting, siding, soffits & signs

303 Siding — exterior siding, textured, striated, embossed, etc.

Thermal & Moist. Protec. R0731 Shingles & Shakes

R073126-20 Roof Slate

16″, 18″ and 20″ are standard lengths, and slate usually comes in random widths. For standard 3/16″ thickness use 1-1/2″ copper nails. Allow for 3% breakage.

Thermal & Moist. Protec. R0751 Built-Up Bituminous Roofing

R075113-20 Built-Up Roofing

Asphalt is available in kegs of 100 lbs. each; coal tar pitch in 560 lb. kegs. Prepared roofing felts are available in a wide range of sizes, weights and characteristics. However, the most commonly used are #15 (432 S.F. per roll, 13 lbs. per square) and #30 (216 S.F. per roll, 27 lbs. per square).

Inter-ply bitumen varies from 24 lbs. per sq. (asphalt) to 30 lbs. per sq. (coal tar) per ply, MF4@ 25%. Flood coat bitumen also varies from 60 lbs. per sq. (asphalt) to 75 lbs. per sq. (coal tar), MF4@ 25%. Expendable equipment (mops, brooms, screeds, etc.) runs about 16% of the bitumen cost. For new, inexperienced crews this factor may be much higher.

Rigid insulation board is typically applied in two layers. The first is mechanically attached to nailable decks or spot or solid mopped to non-nailable decks; the second layer is then spot or solid mopped to the first layer. Membrane application follows the insulation, except in protected membrane roofs, where the membrane goes down first and the insulation on top, followed with ballast (stone or concrete pavers). Insulation and related labor costs are NOT included in prices for built-up roofing.

Thermal & Moist. Protec. | **R0752 Modified Bituminous Membrane Roofing**

Reference Tables

R075213-30   Modified Bitumen Roofing

The cost of modified bitumen roofing is highly dependent on the type of installation that is planned. Installation is based on the type of modifier used in the bitumen. The two most popular modifiers are atactic polypropylene (APP) and styrene butadiene styrene (SBS). The modifiers are added to heated bitumen during the manufacturing process to change its characteristics. A polyethylene, polyester or fiberglass reinforcing sheet is then sandwiched between layers of this bitumen. When completed, the result is a pre-assembled, built-up roof that has increased elasticity and weatherablility. Some manufacturers include a surfacing material such as ceramic or mineral granules, metal particles or sand.

The preferred method of adhering SBS-modified bitumen roofing to the substrate is with hot-mopped asphalt (much the same as built-up roofing). This installation method requires a tar kettle/pot to heat the asphalt, as well as the labor, tools and equipment necessary to distribute and spread the hot asphalt.

The alternative method for applying APP and SBS modified bitumen is as follows. A skilled installer uses a torch to melt a small pool of bitumen off the membrane. This pool must form across the entire roll for proper adhesion. The installer must unroll the roofing at a pace slow enough to melt the bitumen, but fast enough to prevent damage to the rest of the membrane.

Modified bitumen roofing provides the advantages of both built-up and single-ply roofing. Labor costs are reduced over those of built-up roofing because only a single ply is necessary. The elasticity of single-ply roofing is attained with the reinforcing sheet and polymer modifiers. Modifieds have some self-healing characteristics and because of their multi-layer construction, they offer the reliability and safety of built-up roofing.

R078413-30   Firestopping

Firestopping is the sealing of structural, mechanical, electrical and other penetrations through fire-rated assemblies. The basic components of firestop systems are safing insulation and firestop sealant on both sides of wall penetrations and the top side of floor penetrations.

Pipe penetrations are assumed to be through concrete, grout, or joint compound and can be sleeved or unsleeved. Costs for the penetrations and sleeves are not included. An annular space of 1″ is assumed. Escutcheons are not included.

Metallic pipe is assumed to be copper, aluminum, cast iron or similar metallic material. Insulated metallic pipe is assumed to be covered with a thermal insulating jacket of varying thickness and materials.

Non-metallic pipe is assumed to be PVC, CPVC, FR Polypropylene or similar plastic piping material. Intumescent firestop sealant or wrap strips are included. Collars on both sides of wall penetrations and a sheet metal plate on the underside of floor penetrations are included.

Ductwork is assumed to be sheet metal, stainless steel or similar metallic material. Duct penetrations are assumed to be through concrete, grout or joint compound. Costs for penetrations and sleeves are not included. An annular space of 1/2″ is assumed.

Multi-trade openings include costs for sheet metal forms, firestop mortar, wrap strips, collars and sealants as necessary.

Structural penetrations joints are assumed to be 1/2″ or less. CMU walls are assumed to be within 1-1/2″ of metal deck. Drywall walls are assumed to be tight to the underside of metal decking.

Metal panel, glass or curtain wall systems include a spandrel area of 5′ filled with mineral wool foil-faced insulation. Fasteners and stiffeners are included.

Openings — R0813 Metal Doors

R081313-20 Steel Door Selection Guide

Standard steel doors are classified into four levels, as recommended by the Steel Door Institute in the chart below. Each of the four levels offers a range of construction models and designs, to meet architectural requirements for preference and appearance, including full flush, seamless, and stile & rail. Recommended minimum gauge requirements are also included.

For complete standard steel door construction specifications and available sizes, refer to the Steel Door Institute Technical Data Series, ANSI A250.8-98 (SDI-100), and ANSI A250.4-94 Test Procedure and Acceptance Criteria for Physical Endurance of Steel Door and Hardware Reinforcements.

Level		Model	Construction	For Full Flush or Seamless		
				Min. Gauge	Thickness (in)	Thickness (mm)
I	Standard Duty	1	Full Flush	20	0.032	0.8
		2	Seamless			
II	Heavy Duty	1	Full Flush	18	0.042	1.0
		2	Seamless			
III	Extra Heavy Duty	1	Full Flush	16	0.053	1.3
		2	Seamless			
		3	*Stile & Rail			
IV	Maximum Duty	1	Full Flush	14	0.067	1.6
		2	Seamless			

*Stiles & rails are 16 gauge; flush panels, when specified, are 18 gauge

Openings — R0851 Metal Windows

R085123-10 Steel Sash

Ironworker crew will erect 25 S.F. or 1.3 sash unit per hour, whichever is less.

Mechanic will point 30 L.F. per hour.

Painter will paint 90 S.F. per coat per hour.

Glazier production depends on light size.

Allow 1 lb. special steel sash putty per 16" x 20" light.

Openings — R0852 Wood Windows

R085216-10 Window Estimates

To ensure a complete window estimate, be sure to include the material and labor costs for each window, as well as the material and labor costs for an interior wood trim set.

R087110-10   Hardware Finishes

This table describes hardware finishes used throughout the industry. It also shows the base metal and the respective symbols in the three predominate systems of identification. Many of these are used in pricing descriptions in Division Eight.

US″	BMHA*	CDN^	Base	Description
US P	600	CP	Steel	Primed for Painting
US 1B	601	C1B	Steel	Bright Black Japanned
US 2C	602	C2C	Steel	Zinc Plated
US 2G	603	C2G	Steel	Zinc Plated
US 3	605	C3	Brass	Bright Brass, Clear Coated
US 4	606	C4	Brass	Satin Brass, Clear Coated
US 5	609	C5	Brass	Satin Brass, Blackened, Satin Relieved, Clear Coated
US 7	610	C7	Brass	Satin Brass, Blackened, Bright Relived, Clear Coated
US 9	611	C9	Bronze	Bright Bronze, Clear Coated
US 10	612	C10	Bronze	Satin Bronze, Clear Coated
US 10A	641	C10A	Steel	Antiqued Bronze, Oiled and Lacquered
US 10B	613	C10B	Bronze	Antiqued Bronze, Oiled
US 11	616	C11	Bronze	Satin Bronze, Blackened, Satin Relieved, Clear Coated
US 14	618	C14	Brass/Bronze	Bright Nickel Plated, Clear Coated
US 15	619	C15	Brass/Bronze	Satin Nickel, Clear Coated
US 15A	620	C15A	Brass/Bronze	Satin Nickel Plated, Blackened, Satin Relieved, Clear Coated
US 17A	621	C17A	Brass/Bronze	Nickel Plated, Blackened, Relieved, Clear Coated
US 19	622	C19	Brass/Bronze	Flat Black Coated
US 20	623	C20	Brass/Bronze	Statuary Bronze, Light
US 20A	624	C20A	Brass/Bronze	Statuary Bronze, Dark
US 26	625	C26	Brass/Bronze	Bright Chromium
US 26D	626	C26D	Brass/Bronze	Satin Chromium
US 20	627	C27	Aluminum	Satin Aluminum Clear
US 28	628	C28	Aluminum	Anodized Dull Aluminum
US 32	629	C32	Stainless Steel	Bright Stainless Steel
US 32D	630	C32D	Stainless Steel	Stainless Steel
US 3	632	C3	Steel	Bright Brass Plated, Clear Coated
US 4	633	C4	Steel	Satin Brass, Clear Coated
US 7	636	C7	Steel	Satin Brass Plated, Blackened, Bright Relieved, Clear Coated
US 9	637	C9	Steel	Bright Bronze Plated, Clear Coated
US 5	638	C5	Steel	Satin Brass Plated, Blackened, Bright Relieved, Clear Coated
US 10	639	C10	Steel	Satin Bronze Plated, Clear Coated
US 10B	640	C10B	Steel	Antique Bronze, Oiled
US 10A	641	C10A	Steel	Antiqued Bronze, Oiled and Lacquered
US 11	643	C11	Steel	Satin Bronze Plated, Blackened, Bright Relieved, Clear Coated
US 14	645	C14	Steel	Bright Nickel Plated, Clear Coated
US 15	646	C15	Steel	Satin Nickel Plated, Clear Coated
US 15A	647	C15A	Steel	Nickel Plated, Blackened, Bright Relieved, Clear Coated
US 17A	648	C17A	Steel	Nickel Plated, Blackened, Relieved, Clear Coated
US 20	649	C20	Steel	Statuary Bronze, Light
US 20A	650	C20A	Steel	Statuary Bronze, Dark
US 26	651	C26	Steel	Bright Chromium Plated
US 26D	652	C26D	Steel	Satin Chromium Plated

* - BMHA Builders Hardware Manufacturing Association
″ - US Equivalent
^ - Canadian Equivalent
Japanning is imitating Asian lacquer work

R087120-10 Hinges

All closer equipped doors should have ball bearing hinges. Lead lined or extremely heavy doors require special strength hinges. Usually 1-1/2 pair of hinges are used per door up to 7'-6" high openings. Table below shows typical hinge requirements.

Use Frequency	Type Hinge Required	Type of Opening	Type of Structure
High	Heavy weight ball bearing	Entrances	Banks, Office buildings, Schools, Stores & Theaters
		Toilet Rooms	Office buildings and Schools
Average	Standard weight ball bearing	Entrances	Dwellings
		Corridors	Office buildings and Schools
		Toilet Rooms	Stores
Low	Plain bearing	Interior	Dwellings

Door Thickness	Weight of Doors in Pounds per Square Foot				
	White Pine	Oak	Hollow Core	Solid Core	Hollow Metal
1-3/8"	3psf	6psf	1-1/2psf	3-1/2 — 4psf	6-1/2psf
1-3/4"	3-1/2	7	2-1/2	4-1/2 — 5-1/4	6-1/2
2-1/4"	4-1/2	9	—	5-1/2 — 6-3/4	6-1/2

R088110-10 Glazing Productivity

Some glass sizes are estimated by the "united inch" (height + width). The table below shows the number of lights glazed in an eight-hour period by the crew size indicated, for glass up to 1/4" thick. Square or nearly square lights are more economical on a S.F. basis. Long slender lights will have a high S.F. installation cost. For insulated glass reduce production by 33%. For 1/2" float glass reduce production by 50%. Production time for glazing with two glaziers per day averages: 1/4" float glass 120 S.F.; 1/2" float glass 55 S.F.; 1/2" insulated glass 95 S.F.; 3/4" insulated glass 75 S.F.

Glazing Method	United Inches per Light							
	40"	60"	80"	100"	135"	165"	200"	240"
Number of Men in Crew	1	1	1	1	2	3	3	4
Industrial sash, putty	60	45	24	15	18	—	—	—
With stops, putty bed	50	36	21	12	16	8	4	3
Wood stops, rubber	40	27	15	9	11	6	3	2
Metal stops, rubber	30	24	14	9	9	6	3	2
Structural glass	10	7	4	3	—	—	—	—
Corrugated glass	12	9	7	4	4	4	3	—
Storefronts	16	15	13	11	7	6	4	4
Skylights, putty glass	60	36	21	12	16	—	—	—
Thiokol set	15	15	11	9	9	6	3	2
Vinyl set, snap on	18	18	13	12	12	7	5	4
Maximum area per light	2.8 S.F.	6.3 S.F.	11.1 S.F.	17.4 S.F.	31.6 S.F.	47 S.F.	69 S.F.	100 S.F.

R092000-50 Lath, Plaster and Gypsum Board

Gypsum board lath is available in 3/8″ thick x 16″ wide x 4′ long sheets as a base material for multi-layer plaster applications. It is also available as a base for either multi-layer or veneer plaster applications in 1/2″ and 5/8″ thick–4′ wide x 8′, 10′ or 12′ long sheets. Fasteners are screws or blued ring shank nails for wood framing and screws for metal framing.

Metal lath is available in diamond mesh pattern with flat or self-furring profiles. Paper backing is available for applications where excessive plaster waste needs to be avoided. A slotted mesh ribbed lath should be used in areas where the span between structural supports is greater than normal. Most metal lath comes in 27″ x 96″ sheets. Diamond mesh weighs 1.75, 2.5 or 3.4 pounds per square yard, slotted mesh lath weighs 2.75 or 3.4 pounds per square yard. Metal lath can be nailed, screwed or tied in place.

Many **accessories** are available. Corner beads, flat reinforcing strips, casing beads, control and expansion joints, furring brackets and channels are some examples. Note that accessories are not included in plaster or stucco line items.

Plaster is defined as a material or combination of materials that when mixed with a suitable amount of water, forms a plastic mass or paste. When applied to a surface, the paste adheres to it and subsequently hardens, preserving in a rigid state the form or texture imposed during the period of elasticity.

Gypsum plaster is made from ground calcined gypsum. It is mixed with aggregates and water for use as a base coat plaster.

Vermiculite plaster is a fire-retardant plaster covering used on steel beams, concrete slabs and other heavy construction materials. Vermiculite is a group name for certain clay minerals, hydrous silicates or aluminum, magnesium and iron that have been expanded by heat.

Perlite plaster is a plaster using perlite as an aggregate instead of sand. Perlite is a volcanic glass that has been expanded by heat.

Gauging plaster is a mix of gypsum plaster and lime putty that when applied produces a quick drying finish coat.

Veneer plaster is a one or two component gypsum plaster used as a thin finish coat over special gypsum board.

Keenes cement is a white cementitious material manufactured from gypsum that has been burned at a high temperature and ground to a fine powder. Alum is added to accelerate the set. The resulting plaster is hard and strong and accepts and maintains a high polish, hence it is used as a finishing plaster.

Stucco is a Portland cement based plaster used primarily as an exterior finish.

Plaster is used on both interior and exterior surfaces. Generally it is applied in multiple-coat systems. A three-coat system uses the terms scratch, brown and finish to identify each coat. A two-coat system uses base and finish to describe each coat. Each type of plaster and application system has attributes that are chosen by the designer to best fit the intended use.

Gypsum Plaster	2 Coat, 5/8″ Thick		3 Coat, 3/4″ Thick		
	Base	Finish	Scratch	Brown	Finish
Quantities for 100 S.Y.	1:3 Mix	2:1 Mix	1:2 Mix	1:3 Mix	2:1 Mix
Gypsum plaster	1,300 lb.		1,350 lb.	650 lb.	
Sand	1.75 C.Y.		1.85 C.Y.	1.35 C.Y.	
Finish hydrated lime		340 lb.			340 lb.
Gauging plaster		170 lb.			170 lb.

Vermiculite or Perlite Plaster	2 Coat, 5/8″ Thick		3 Coat, 3/4″ Thick		
Quantities for 100 S.Y.	Base	Finish	Scratch	Brown	Finish
Gypsum plaster	1,250 lb.		1,450 lb.	800 lb.	
Vermiculite or perlite	7.8 bags		8.0 bags	3.3 bags	
Finish hydrated lime		340 lb.			340 lb.
Gauging plaster		170 lb.			170 lb.

Stucco–Three-Coat System Quantities for 100 S.Y.	On Wood Frame	On Masonry
Portland cement	29 bags	21 bags
Sand	2.6 C.Y.	2.0 C.Y.
Hydrated lime	180 lb.	120 lb.

R092910-10 Levels of Gypsum Drywall Finish

In the past, contract documents often used phrases such as "industry standard" and "workmanlike finish" to specify the expected quality of gypsum board wall and ceiling installations. The vagueness of these descriptions led to unacceptable work and disputes.

In order to resolve this problem, four major trade associations concerned with the manufacture, erection, finish, and decoration of gypsum board wall and ceiling systems have developed an industry-wide *Recommended Levels of Gypsum Board Finish*.

The finish of gypsum board walls and ceilings for specific final decoration is dependent on a number of factors. A primary consideration is the location of the surface and the degree of decorative treatment desired. Painted and unpainted surfaces in warehouses and other areas where appearance is normally not critical may simply require the taping of wallboard joints and 'spotting' of fastener heads. Blemish-free, smooth, monolithic surfaces often intended for painted and decorated walls and ceilings in habitated structures, ranging from single-family dwellings through monumental buildings, require additional finishing prior to the application of the final decoration.

Other factors to be considered in determining the level of finish of the gypsum board surface are (1) the type of angle of surface illumination (both natural and artificial lighting), and (2) the paint and method of application or the type and finish of wallcovering specified as the final decoration. Critical lighting conditions, gloss paints, and thin wall coverings require a higher level of gypsum board finish than do heavily textured surfaces which are subsequently painted or surfaces which are to be decorated with heavy grade wall coverings.

The following descriptions were developed jointly by the Association of the Wall and Ceiling Industries-International (AWCI), Ceiling & Interior Systems Construction Association (CISCA), Gypsum Association (GA), and Painting and Decorating Contractors of America (PDCA) as a guide.

Level 0: Used in temporary construction or wherever the final decoration has not been determined. Unfinished. No taping, finishing or corner beads are required. Also could be used where non-predecorated panels will be used in demountable-type partitions that are to be painted as a final finish.

Level 1: Frequently used in plenum areas above ceilings, in attics, in areas where the assembly would generally be concealed, or in building service corridors and other areas not normally open to public view. Some degree of sound and smoke control is provided; in some geographic areas, this level is referred to as "fire-taping," although this level of finish does not typically meet fire-resistant assembly requirements. Where a fire resistance rating is required for the gypsum board assembly, details of construction should be in accordance with reports of fire tests of assemblies that have met the requirements of the fire rating acceptable.

All joints and interior angles shall have tape embedded in joint compound. Accessories are optional at specifier discretion in corridors and other areas with pedestrian traffic. Tape and fastener heads need not be covered with joint compound. Surface shall be free of excess joint compound. Tool marks and ridges are acceptable.

Level 2: It may be specified for standard gypsum board surfaces in garages, warehouse storage, or other similar areas where surface appearance is not of primary importance.

All joints and interior angles shall have tape embedded in joint compound and shall be immediately wiped with a joint knife or trowel, leaving a thin coating of joint compound over all joints and interior angles. Fastener heads and accessories shall be covered with a coat of joint compound. Surface shall be free of excess joint compound. Tool marks and ridges are acceptable.

Level 3: Typically used in areas that are to receive heavy texture (spray or hand applied) finishes before final painting, or where commercial-grade (heavy duty) wall coverings are to be applied as the final decoration. This level of finish should not be used where smooth painted surfaces or where lighter weight wall coverings are specified. The prepared surface shall be coated with a drywall primer prior to the application of final finishes.

All joints and interior angles shall have tape embedded in joint compound and shall be immediately wiped with a joint knife or trowel, leaving a thin coating of joint compound over all joints and interior angles. One additional coat of joint compound shall be applied over all joints and interior angles. Fastener heads and accessories shall be covered with two separate coats of joint compound. All joint compounds shall be smooth and free of tool marks and ridges. The prepared surface shall be covered with a drywall primer prior to the application of the final decoration.

Level 4: This level should be used where residential grade (light duty) wall coverings, flat paints, or light textures are to be applied. The prepared surface shall be coated with a drywall primer prior to the application of final finishes. Release agents for wall coverings are specifically formulated to minimize damage if coverings are subsequently removed.

The weight, texture, and sheen level of the wall covering material selected should be taken into consideration when specifying wall coverings over this level of drywall treatment. Joints and fasteners must be sufficiently concealed if the wall covering material is lightweight, contains limited pattern, has a glossy finish, or has any combination of these features. In critical lighting areas, flat paints applied over light textures tend to reduce joint photographing. Gloss, semi-gloss, and enamel paints are not recommended over this level of finish.

All joints and interior angles shall have tape embedded in joint compound and shall be immediately wiped with a joint knife or trowel, leaving a thin coating of joint compound over all joints and interior angles. In addition, two separate coats of joint compound shall be applied over all flat joints and one separate coat of joint compound applied over interior angles. Fastener heads and accessories shall be covered with three separate coats of joint compound. All joint compounds shall be smooth and free of tool marks and ridges. The prepared surface shall be covered with a drywall primer like Sheetrock® First Coat prior to the application of the final decoration.

Level 5: The highest quality finish is the most effective method to provide a uniform surface and minimize the possibility of joint photographing and of fasteners showing through the final decoration. This level of finish is required where gloss, semi-gloss, or enamel is specified; when flat joints are specified over an untextured surface; or where critical lighting conditions occur. The prepared surface shall be coated with a drywall primer prior to the application of final decoration.

All joints and interior angles shall have tape embedded in joint compound and be immediately wiped with a joint knife or trowel, leaving a thin coating of joint compound over all joints and interior angles. Two separate coats of joint compound shall be applied over all flat joints and one separate coat of joint compound applied over interior angles. Fastener heads and accessories shall be covered with three separate coats of joint compound.

A thin skim coat of joint compound shall be trowel applied to the entire surface. Excess compound is immediately troweled off, leaving a film or skim coating of compound completely covering the paper. As an alternative to a skim coat, a material manufactured especially for this purpose may be applied such as Sheetrock® Tuff-Hide primer surfacer. The surface must be smooth and free of tool marks and ridges. The prepared surface shall be covered with a drywall primer prior to the application of the final decoration.

Finishes — R0966 Terrazzo Flooring

R096613-10   Terrazzo Floor

The table below lists quantities required for 100 S.F. of 5/8″ terrazzo topping, either bonded or not bonded.

Description	Bonded to Concrete 1-1/8″ Bed, 1:4 Mix	Not Bonded 2-1/8″ Bed and 1/4″ Sand
Portland cement, 94 lb. Bag	6 bags	8 bags
Sand	10 C.F.	20 C.F.
Divider strips, 4′ squares	50 L.F.	50 L.F.
Terrazzo fill, 50 lb. Bag	12 bags	12 bags
15 Lb. tarred felt		1 C.S.F.
Mesh 2 x 2 #14 galvanized		1 C.S.F.
Crew J-3	0.77 days	0.87 days

2′ x 2′ panels require 1.00 L.F. divider strip per S.F.

3′ x 3′ panels require 0.67 L.F. divider strip per S.F.

4′ x 4′ panels require 0.50 L.F. divider strip per S.F.

5′ x 5′ panels require 0.40 L.F. divider strip per S.F.

6′ x 6′ panels require 0.33 L.F. divider strip per S.F.

Finishes — R0972 Wall Coverings

R097223-10   Wall Covering

The table below lists the quantities required for 100 S.F. of wall covering.

Description	Medium-Priced Paper	Expensive Paper
Paper	1.6 dbl. rolls	1.6 dbl. rolls
Wall sizing	0.25 gallon	0.25 gallon
Vinyl wall paste	0.6 gallon	0.6 gallon
Apply sizing	0.3 hour	0.3 hour
Apply paper	1.2 hours	1.5 hours

Most wallpapers now come in double rolls only.
To remove old paper, allow 1.3 hours per 100 S.F.

R099100-10 Painting Estimating Techniques

Proper estimating methodology is needed to obtain an accurate painting estimate. There is no known reliable shortcut or square foot method. The following steps should be followed:

- List all surfaces to be painted, with an accurate quantity (area) of each. Items having similar surface condition, finish, application method and accessibility may be grouped together.

- List all the tasks required for each surface to be painted, including surface preparation, masking, and protection of adjacent surfaces. Surface preparation may include minor repairs, washing, sanding and puttying.

- Select the proper Means line for each task. Review and consider all adjustments to labor and materials for type of paint and location of work. Apply the height adjustment carefully. For instance, when applying the adjustment for work over 8' high to a wall that is 12' high, apply the adjustment only to the area between 8' and 12' high, and not to the entire wall.

When applying more than one percent (%) adjustment, apply each to the base cost of the data, rather than applying one percentage adjustment on top of the other.

When estimating the cost of painting walls and ceilings remember to add the brushwork for all cut-ins at inside corners and around windows and doors as a LF measure. One linear foot of cut-in with brush equals one square foot of painting.

All items for spray painting include the labor for roll-back.

Deduct for openings greater than 100 SF, or openings that extend from floor to ceiling and are greater than 5' wide. Do not deduct small openings.

The cost of brushes, rollers, ladders and spray equipment are considered to be part of a painting contractor's overhead, and should not be added to the estimate. The cost of rented equipment such as scaffolding and swing staging should be added to the estimate.

R099100-20 Painting

Item	Coat	One Gallon Covers			In 8 Hours a Laborer Covers			Labor-Hours per 100 S.F.		
		Brush	Roller	Spray	Brush	Roller	Spray	Brush	Roller	Spray
Paint wood siding	prime	250 S.F.	225 S.F.	290 S.F.	1150 S.F.	1300 S.F.	2275 S.F.	.695	.615	.351
	others	270	250	290	1300	1625	2600	.615	.492	.307
Paint exterior trim	prime	400	—	—	650	—	—	1.230	—	—
	1st	475	—	—	800	—	—	1.000	—	—
	2nd	520	—	—	975	—	—	.820	—	—
Paint shingle siding	prime	270	255	300	650	975	1950	1.230	.820	.410
	others	360	340	380	800	1150	2275	1.000	.695	.351
Stain shingle siding	1st	180	170	200	750	1125	2250	1.068	.711	.355
	2nd	270	250	290	900	1325	2600	.888	.603	.307
Paint brick masonry	prime	180	135	160	750	800	1800	1.066	1.000	.444
	1st	270	225	290	815	975	2275	.981	.820	.351
	2nd	340	305	360	815	1150	2925	.981	.695	.273
Paint interior plaster or drywall	prime	400	380	495	1150	2000	3250	.695	.400	.246
	others	450	425	495	1300	2300	4000	.615	.347	.200
Paint interior doors and windows	prime	400	—	—	650	—	—	1.230	—	—
	1st	425	—	—	800	—	—	1.000	—	—
	2nd	450	—	—	975	—	—	.820	—	—

R131113-20 Swimming Pools

Pool prices given per square foot of surface area include pool structure, filter and chlorination equipment, pumps, related piping, ladders/steps, maintenance kit, skimmer and vacuum system. Decks and electrical service to equipment are not included.

Residential in-ground pool construction can be divided into two categories: vinyl lined and gunite. Vinyl lined pool walls are constructed of different materials including wood, concrete, plastic or metal. The bottom is often graded with sand over which the vinyl liner is installed. Vermiculite or soil cement bottoms may be substituted for an added cost.

Gunite pool construction is used both in residential and municipal installations. These structures are steel reinforced for strength and finished with a white cement limestone plaster.

Municipal pools will have a higher cost because plumbing codes require more expensive materials, chlorination equipment and higher filtration rates.

Municipal pools greater than 1,800 S.F. require gutter systems to control waves. This gutter may be formed into the concrete wall. Often a vinyl/stainless steel gutter or gutter/wall system is specified, which will raise the pool cost.

Competition pools usually require tile bottoms and sides with contrasting lane striping, which will also raise the pool cost.

R133113-10 Air Supported Structures

Air supported structures are made from fabrics that can be classified into two groups: temporary and permanent. Temporary fabrics include nylon, woven polyethylene, vinyl film, and vinyl coated dacron. These have lifespans that range from five to fifteen plus years. The cost per square foot includes a fabric shell, tension cables, primary and back-up inflation systems and doors. The lower cost structures are used for construction shelters, bulk storage and pond covers. The more expensive are used for recreational structures and warehouses.

Permanent fabrics are teflon coated fiberglass. The life of this structure is twenty plus years. The high cost limits its application to architectural designed structures which call for a clear span covered area, such as stadiums and convention centers. Both temporary and permanent structures are available in translucent fabrics which eliminates the need for daytime lighting.

Areas to be covered vary from 10,000 S.F. to any area up to 1000 foot wide by any length. Height restrictions range from a maximum of 1/2 of

width to a minimum of 1/6 of the width. Erection of even the largest of the temporary structures requires no more than a week.

Centrifugal fans provide the inflation necessary to support the structure during application of live loads. Airlocks are usually used at large entrances to prevent loss of static pressure. Some manufacturers employ propeller fans which generate sufficient airflow (30,000 CFM) to eliminate the need for airlocks. These fans may also be automatically controlled to resist high wind conditions, regulate humidity (air changes), and provide cooling and heat.

Insulation can be provided with the addition of a second or even third interior liner, creating a dead air space with an "R" value of four to nine. Some structures allow for the liner to be collapsed into the outer shell to enable the internal heat to melt accumulated snow. For cooling or air conditioning, the exterior face of the liner can be aluminized to reflect the sun's heat.

R133113-90 Seismic Bracing

Sometimes referred to as anti-sway bracing, this support system is required in earthquake areas. The individual components must be assembled to

make a required system.

Example	C-Clamp 3/8″ rod	2 ea.
	Rod, continuous thread 3/8″	10 L.F.
	Field, weld 1″	2 ea.

Additionally, height factors must be taken into account. Add the following percentages to labor for elevated installations:

Height	Percentage
15′ to 20′ high	10%
21′ to 25′ high	20%
26′ to 30′ high	30%
31′ to 35′ high	40%
36′ to 40′ high	50%
41′ to 50′ high	60%

Special Construction · R1334 Fabricated Engineered Structures

R133419-10 Pre-Engineered Steel Buildings

These buildings are manufactured by many companies and normally erected by franchised dealers throughout the U.S. The four basic types are: Rigid Frames, Truss type, Post and Beam and the Sloped Beam type. Most popular roof slope is low pitch of 1″ in 12″. The minimum economical area of these buildings is about 3000 S.F. of floor area. Bay sizes are usually 20′ to 24′ but can go as high as 30′ with heavier girts and purlins. Eave heights are usually 12′ to 24′ with 18′ to 20′ most typical.

Material prices shown in the Unit Price section are bare costs for the building shell only and do not include floors, foundations, anchor bolts, interior finishes or utilities. Costs assume at least three bays of 24′ each, a 1″ in 12″ roof slope, and they are based on 30 psf roof load and 20 psf wind load

(wind load is a function of wind speed, building height, and terrain characteristics; this should be determined by a Registered Structural Engineer) and no unusual requirements. Costs include the structural frame, 26 ga. non-insulated colored corrugated or ribbed roofing and siding panels, fasteners, closures, trim and flashing but no allowance for insulation, doors, windows, skylights, gutters or downspouts. Very large projects would generally cost less for materials than the prices shown. For roof panel substitutions and wall panel substitutions, see appropriate Unit Price sections.

Conditions at the site, weather, shape and size of the building, and labor availability will affect the erection cost of the building.

R133423-30 Dome Structures

Steel — The four types are Lamella, Schwedler, Arch and Geodesic. For maximum economy, rise should be about 15 to 20% of diameter. Most common diameters are in the 200′ to 300′ range. Lamella domes weigh about 5 P.S.F. of floor area less than Schwedler domes. Schwedler dome weight in lbs. per S.F. approaches .046 times the diameter. Domes below 125′ diameter weigh .07 times diameter and the cost per ton of steel is higher. See R051223-20 for estimating weight.

Wood — Small domes are of sawn lumber, larger ones are laminated. In larger sizes, triaxial and triangular cost about the same; radial domes cost more. Radial domes are economical in the 60′ to 70′ diameter range. Most economical range of all types is 80′ to 200′ diameters. Diameters can

run over 400′. All costs are quoted above the foundation. Prices include 2″ decking and a tension tie ring in place.

Plywood — Stock prefab geodesic domes are available with diameters from 24′ to 60′.

Fiberglass — Aluminum framed translucent sandwich panels with spans from 5′ to 45′ are commercially available.

Aluminum — Stressed skin aluminum panels form geodesic domes with spans ranging from 82′ to 232′. An aluminum space truss, triangulated or nontriangulated, with aluminum or clear acrylic closure panels can be used for clear spans of 40′ to 415′.

R142000-10 Freight Elevators

Capacities run from 2,000 lbs. to over 100,000 lbs. with 3,000 lbs. to 10,000 lbs. most common. Travel speeds are generally lower and control less intricate than on passenger elevators. Costs in the Unit Price Section are for hydraulic and geared elevators.

R142000-20 Elevator Selective Costs See R142000-40 for cost development.

A. Base Unit	Passenger		Freight		Hospital	
	Hydraulic	**Electric**	**Hydraulic**	**Electric**	**Hydraulic**	**Electric**
Capacity	1,500 lb.	2,000 lb.	2,000 lb.	4,000 lb.	4,000 lb.	4,000 lb.
Speed	100 F.P.M.	200 F.P.M.	100 F.P.M.	200 F.P.M.	100 F.P.M.	200 F.P.M.
#Stops/Travel Ft.	2/12	4/40	2/20	4/40	2/20	4/40
Push Button Oper.	Yes	Yes	Yes	Yes	Yes	Yes
Telephone Box & Wire	"	"	"	"	"	"
Emergency Lighting	"	"	No	No	"	"
Cab	Plastic Lam. Walls	Plastic Lam. Walls	Painted Steel	Painted Steel	Plastic Lam. Walls	Plastic Lam. Walls
Cove Lighting	Yes	Yes	No	No	Yes	Yes
Floor	V.C.T.	V.C.T.	Wood w/Safety Treads	Wood w/Safety Treads	V.C.T.	V.C.T.
Doors, & Speedside Slide	Yes	Yes	Yes	Yes	Yes	Yes
Gates, Manual	No	No	No	No	No	No
Signals, Lighted Buttons	Car and Hall	Car and Hall	Car and Hall	Car and Hall	Car and Hall	Car and Hall
O.H. Geared Machine	N.A.	Yes	N.A.	Yes	N.A.	Yes
Variable Voltage Contr.	"	"	N.A.	"	"	"
Emergency Alarm	Yes	"	Yes	"	Yes	"
Class "A" Loading	N.A.	N.A.	"	"	N.A.	N.A.

R142000-30 Passenger Elevators

Electric elevators are used generally but hydraulic elevators can be used for lifts up to 70' and where large capacities are required. Hydraulic speeds are limited to 200 F.P.M. but cars are self leveling at the stops. On low rises, hydraulic installation runs about 15% less than standard electric types but on higher rises this installation cost advantage is reduced. Maintenance of hydraulic elevators is about the same as electric type but underground portion is not included in the maintenance contract.

In electric elevators there are several control systems available, the choice of which will be based upon elevator use, size, speed and cost criteria. The two types of drives are geared for low speeds and gearless for 450 F.P.M. and over.

The tables on the preceding pages illustrate typical installed costs of the various types of elevators available.

R142000-40 Elevator Cost Development

To price a new car or truck from the factory, you must start with the manufacturer's basic model, then add or exchange optional equipment and features. The same is true for pricing elevators.

Requirement: One-passenger elevator, five-story hydraulic, 2,500 lb. capacity, 12' floor to floor, speed 150 F.P.M., emergency power switching and maintenance contract.

Example:

Description	Adjustment
A. Base Elevator: Hydraulic Passenger, 1500 lb. Capacity, 100 fpm, 2 Stops, Standard Finish	1 Ea.
B. Capacity Adjustment (2,500 lb.)	1 Ea.
C. Excess Travel Adjustment: 48' Total Travel (4 x 12') minus 12' Base Unit Travel =	36 V.L.F.
D. Stops Adjustment: 5 Total Stops minus 2 Stops (Base Unit) =	3 Stops
E. Speed Adjustment (150 F.P.M.)	1 Ea.
F. Options:	
1. Intercom Service	1 Ea.
2. Emergency Power Switching, Automatic	1 Ea.
3. Stainless Steel Entrance Doors	5 Ea.
4. Maintenance Contract (12 Months)	1 Ea.
5. Position Indicator for main floor level (none indicated in Base Unit)	1 Ea.

Conveying Equipment   R1431 Escalators

R143110-10   Escalators

Moving stairs can be used for buildings where 600 or more people are to be carried to the second floor or beyond. Freight cannot be carried on escalators and at least one elevator must be available for this function.

Carrying capacity is 5,000 to 8,000 people per hour. Power requirement is 2 to 3 KW per hour and incline angle is 30°.

Conveying Equipment   R1432 Moving Walks

R143210-20   Moving Ramps and Walks

These are a specialized form of conveyor 3' to 6' wide with capacities of 3,600 to 18,000 persons per hour. Maximum speed is 140 F.P.M. and normal incline is 0° to 15°.

Local codes will determine the maximum angle. Outdoor units would require additional weather protection.

Plumbing   R2201 Operation & Maintenance of Plumbing

R220102-20   Labor Adjustment Factors

Labor Adjustment Factors are provided for Divisions 21, 22, and 23 to assist the mechanical estimator account for the various complexities and special conditions of any particular project. While a single percentage has been entered on each line of Division 22 01 02.20, it should be understood that these are just suggested midpoints of ranges of values commonly used by mechanical estimators. They may be increased or decreased depending on the severity of the special conditions.

The group for "existing occupied buildings", has been the subject of requests for explanation. Actually there are two stages to this group: buildings that are existing and "finished" but unoccupied, and those that also are occupied. Buildings that are "finished" may result in higher labor costs due to the workers having to be more careful not to damage finished walls, ceilings, floors, etc. and may necessitate special protective coverings and barriers. Also corridor bends and doorways may not accommodate long pieces of pipe or larger pieces of equipment. Work above an already hung ceiling can be very time consuming. The addition of occupants may force the work to be done on premium time (nights and/or weekends), eliminate the possible use of some preferred tools such as pneumatic drivers, powder charged drivers etc. The estimator should evaluate the access to the work area and just how the work is going to be accomplished to arrive at an increase in labor costs over "normal" new construction productivity.

R220105-10   Demolition (Selective vs. Removal for Replacement)

Demolition can be divided into two basic categories.

One type of demolition involves the removal of material with no concern for its replacement. The labor-hours to estimate this work are found under "Selective Demolition" in the Fire Protection, Plumbing and HVAC Divisions. It is selective in that individual items or all the material installed as a system or trade grouping such as plumbing or heating systems are removed. This may be accomplished by the easiest way possible, such as sawing, torch cutting, or sledge hammer as well as simple unbolting.

The second type of demolition is the removal of some item for repair or replacement. This removal may involve careful draining, opening of unions, disconnecting and tagging of electrical connections, capping of pipes/ducts to prevent entry of debris or leakage of the material contained as well as transport of the item away from its in-place location to a truck/dumpster. An approximation of the time required to accomplish this type of demolition is to use half of the time indicated as necessary to install a new unit. For example; installation of a new pump might be listed as requiring 6 labor-hours so if we had to estimate the removal of the old pump we would allow an additional 3 hours for a total of 9 hours. That is, the complete replacement of a defective pump with a new pump would be estimated to take 9 labor-hours.

827

R221113-50   Pipe Material Considerations

1. Malleable fittings should be used for gas service.
2. Malleable fittings are used where there are stresses/strains due to expansion and vibration.
3. Cast fittings may be broken as an aid to disassembling of heating lines frozen by long use, temperature and minerals.
4. Cast iron pipe is extensively used for underground and submerged service.
5. Type M (light wall) copper tubing is available in hard temper only and is used for nonpressure and less severe applications than K and L.

6. Type L (medium wall) copper tubing, available hard or soft for interior service.
7. Type K (heavy wall) copper tubing, available in hard or soft temper for use where conditions are severe. For underground and interior service.
8. Hard drawn tubing requires fewer hangers or supports but should not be bent. Silver brazed fittings are recommended, however soft solder is normally used.
9. Type DMV (very light wall) copper tubing designed for drainage, waste and vent plus other non-critical pressure services.

Domestic/Imported Pipe and Fittings Cost

The prices shown in this publication for steel/cast iron pipe and steel, cast iron, malleable iron fittings are based on domestic production sold at the normal trade discounts. The above listed items of foreign manufacture may be available at prices of 1/3 to 1/2 those shown. Some imported items after minor machining or finishing operations are being sold as domestic to further complicate the system.

Caution: Most pipe prices in this book also include a coupling and pipe hangers which for the larger sizes can add significantly to the per foot cost and should be taken into account when comparing "book cost" with quoted supplier's cost.

Plumbing   **R2240 Plumbing Fixtures**

R224000-40   Plumbing Fixture Installation Time

Item	Rough-In	Set	Total Hours	Item	Rough-In	Set	Total Hours
Bathtub	5	5	10	Shower head only	2	1	3
Bathtub and shower, cast iron	6	6	12	Shower drain	3	1	4
Fire hose reel and cabinet	4	2	6	Shower stall, slate		15	15
Floor drain to 4 inch diameter	3	1	4	Slop sink	5	3	8
Grease trap, single, cast iron	5	3	8	Test 6 fixtures			14
Kitchen gas range		4	4	Urinal, wall	6	2	8
Kitchen sink, single	4	4	8	Urinal, pedestal or floor	6	4	10
Kitchen sink, double	6	6	12	Water closet and tank	4	3	7
Laundry tubs	4	2	6	Water closet and tank, wall hung	5	3	8
Lavatory wall hung	5	3	8	Water heater, 45 gals. gas, automatic	5	2	7
Lavatory pedestal	5	3	8	Water heaters, 65 gals. gas, automatic	5	2	7
Shower and stall	6	4	10	Water heaters, electric, plumbing only	4	2	6

Fixture prices in front of book are based on the cost per fixture set in place. The rough-in cost, which must be added for each fixture, includes carrier, if required, some supply, waste and vent pipe connecting fittings and stops. The lengths of rough-in pipe are nominal runs which would connect to the larger runs and stacks. The supply runs and DWV runs and stacks must be accounted for in separate entries. In the eastern half of the United States it is common for the plumber to carry these to a point 5' outside the building.

R224000-50   Water Cooler Application

Type of Service	Requirement
Office, School or Hospital	12 persons per gallon per hour
Office, Lobby or Department Store	4 or 5 gallons per hour per fountain
Light manufacturing	7 persons per gallon per hour
Heavy manufacturing	5 persons per gallon per hour
Hot heavy manufacturing	4 persons per gallon per hour
Hotel	.08 gallons per hour per room
Theatre	1 gallon per hour per 100 seats

Heating, Ventilating & A.C. | R2331 HVAC Ducts & Casings

R233100-20 Ductwork

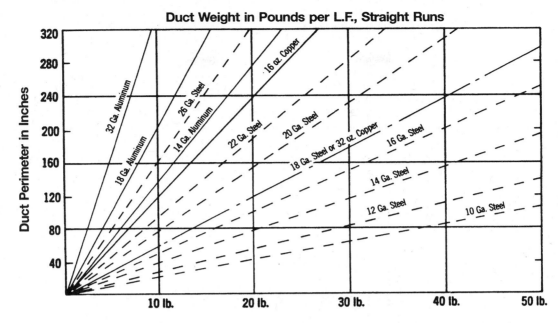

Duct Weight in Pounds per L.F., Straight Runs

Add to the above for fittings; 90° elbow is 3 L.F.; 45° elbow is 2.5 L.F.; offset is 4 L.F.; transition offset is 6 L.F.; square-to-round transition is 4 L.F.; 90° reducing elbow is 5 L.F. For bracing and waste, add 20% to aluminum and copper, 15% to steel.

Heating, Ventilating & A.C. | R2334 HVAC Fans

R233400-10 Recommended Ventilation Air Changes

Table below lists range of time in minutes per change for various types of facilities.

Assembly Halls	2-10	Dance Halls	2-10	Laundries	1-3
Auditoriums	2-10	Dining Rooms	3-10	Markets	2-10
Bakeries	2-3	Dry Cleaners	1-5	Offices	2-10
Banks	3-10	Factories	2-5	Pool Rooms	2-5
Bars	2-5	Garages	2-10	Recreation Rooms	2-10
Beauty Parlors	2-5	Generator Rooms	2-5	Sales Rooms	2-10
Boiler Rooms	1-5	Gymnasiums	2-10	Theaters	2-8
Bowling Alleys	2-10	Kitchens-Hospitals	2-5	Toilets	2-5
Churches	5-10	Kitchens-Restaurant	1-3	Transformer Rooms	1-5

CFM air required for changes = Volume of room in cubic feet ÷ Minutes per change.

Heating, Ventilating & A.C. | R2350 Central Heating Equipment

R235000-35 Heating (42° degrees latitude)

$$\text{Approximate S.F. radiation} = \frac{\text{S.F. sash}}{2} + \frac{\text{S.F. wall} + \text{roof} - \text{sash}}{20} + \frac{\text{C.F. building}}{200}$$

R235000-50 Factor for Determining Heat Loss for Various Types of Buildings

General: While the most accurate estimates of heating requirements would naturally be based on detailed information about the building being considered, it is possible to arrive at a reasonable approximation using the following procedure:

1. Calculate the cubic volume of the room or building.
2. Select the appropriate factor from Table 1 below. Note that the factors apply only to inside temperatures listed in the first column and to 0° F outside temperature.

3. If the building has bad north and west exposures, multiply the heat loss factor by 1.1.
4. If the outside design temperature is other than 0° F, multiply the factor from Table 1 by the factor from Table 2.
5. Multiply the cubic volume by the factor selected from Table 1. This will give the estimated BTUH heat loss which must be made up to maintain inside temperature.

Table 1 — Building Type	Conditions	Qualifications	Loss Factor*
Factories & Industrial Plants General Office Areas at 70° F	One Story	Skylight in Roof	6.2
		No Skylight in Roof	5.7
	Multiple Story	Two Story	4.6
		Three Story	4.3
		Four Story	4.1
		Five Story	3.9
		Six Story	3.6
	All Walls Exposed	Flat Roof	6.9
		Heated Space Above	5.2
	One Long Warm Common Wall	Flat Roof	6.3
		Heated Space Above	4.7
	Warm Common Walls on Both Long Sides	Flat Roof	5.8
		Heated Space Above	4.1
Warehouses at 60° F	All Walls Exposed	Skylights in Roof	5.5
		No Skylight in Roof	5.1
		Heated Space Above	4.0
	One Long Warm Common Wall	Skylight in Roof	5.0
		No Skylight in Roof	4.9
		Heated Space Above	3.4
	Warm Common Walls on Both Long Sides	Skylight in Roof	4.7
		No Skylight in Roof	4.4
		Heated Space Above	3.0

*Note: This table tends to be conservative particularly for new buildings designed for minimum energy consumption.

Table 2 — Outside Design Temperature Correction Factor (for Degrees Fahrenheit)									
Outside Design Temperature	50	40	30	20	10	0	-10	-20	-30
Correction Factor	.29	.43	.57	.72	.86	1.00	1.14	1.28	1.43

R235616-60 Solar Heating (Space and Hot Water)

Collectors should face as close to due South as possible, however, variations of up to 20 degrees on either side of true South are acceptable. Local climate and collector type may influence the choice between east or west deviations. Obviously they should be located so they are not shaded from the sun's rays. Incline collectors at a slope of latitude minus 5 degrees for domestic hot water and latitude plus 15 degrees for space heating.

Flat plate collectors consist of a number of components as follows: Insulation to reduce heat loss through the bottom and sides of the collector. The enclosure which contains all the components in this assembly is usually weatherproof and prevents dust, wind and water from coming in contact with the absorber plate. The cover plate usually consists of one or more layers of a variety of glass or plastic and reduces the reradiation by creating an air space which traps the heat between the cover and the absorber plates.

The absorber plate must have a good thermal bond with the fluid passages. The absorber plate is usually metallic and treated with a surface coating which improves absorptivity. Black or dark paints or selective coatings are used for this purpose, and the design of this passage and plate combination helps determine a solar system's effectiveness.

Heat transfer fluid passage tubes are attached above and below or integral with an absorber plate for the purpose of transferring thermal energy from the absorber plate to a heat transfer medium. The heat exchanger is a device for transferring thermal energy from one fluid to another.

Piping and storage tanks should be well insulated to minimize heat losses.

Size domestic water heating storage tanks to hold 20 gallons of water per user, minimum, plus 10 gallons per dishwasher or washing machine. For domestic water heating an optimum collector size is approximately 3/4 square foot of area per gallon of water storage. For space heating of residences and small commercial applications the collector is commonly sized between 30% and 50% of the internal floor area. For space heating of large commercial applications, collector areas less than 30% of the internal floor area can still provide significant heat reductions.

A supplementary heat source is recommended for Northern states for December through February.

The solar energy transmission per square foot of collector surface varies greatly with the material used. Initial cost, heat transmittance and useful life are obviously interrelated.

Heating, Ventilating & A.C. R2360 Central Cooling Equipment

R236000-20 Air Conditioning Requirements

BTU's per hour per S.F. of floor area and S.F. per ton of air conditioning.

Type of Building	BTU/Hr. per S.F.	S.F. per Ton	Type of Building	BTU/Hr per S.F.	S.F. per Ton	Type of Building	BTU/Hr per S.F.	S.F. per Ton
Apartments, Individual	26	450	Dormitory, Rooms	40	300	Libraries	50	240
Corridors	22	550	Corridors	30	400	Low Rise Office, Exterior	38	320
Auditoriums & Theaters	40	300/18*	Dress Shops	43	280	Interior	33	360
Banks	50	240	Drug Stores	80	150	Medical Centers	28	425
Barber Shops	48	250	Factories	40	300	Motels	28	425
Bars & Taverns	133	90	High Rise Office—Ext. Rms.	46	263	Office (small suite)	43	280
Beauty Parlors	66	180	Interior Rooms	37	325	Post Office, Individual Office	42	285
Bowling Alleys	68	175	Hospitals, Core	43	280	Central Area	46	260
Churches	36	330/20*	Perimeter	46	260	Residences	20	600
Cocktail Lounges	68	175	Hotel, Guest Rooms	44	275	Restaurants	60	200
Computer Rooms	141	85	Corridors	30	400	Schools & Colleges	46	260
Dental Offices	52	230	Public Spaces	55	220	Shoe Stores	55	220
Dept. Stores, Basement	34	350	Industrial Plants, Offices	38	320	Shop'g. Ctrs., Supermarkets	34	350
Main Floor	40	300	General Offices	34	350	Retail Stores	48	250
Upper Floor	30	400	Plant Areas	40	300	Specialty	60	200

*Persons per ton
12,000 BTU = 1 ton of air conditioning

R260519-91　Maximum Circuit Length (approximate) for Various Power Requirements Assuming THW, Copper Wire @ 75°C, Based Upon a 4% Voltage Drop

Maximum Circuit Length: Table R260519-91 indicates typical maximum installed length a circuit can have and still maintain an adequate voltage level at the point of use. The circuit length is similar to the conduit length.

If the circuit length for an ampere load and a copper wire size exceeds the length obtained from Table R260519-91, use the next largest wire size to compensate voltage drop.

Example: A 130 ampere load at 480 volts, 3 phase, 3 wire with No. 1 wire can be run a maximum of 555 L.F. and provide satisfactory operation. If the same load is to be wired at the end of a 625 L.F. circuit, then a larger wire must be used.

Amperes	Wire Size	Maximum Circuit Length in Feet				
		2 Wire, 1 Phase		3 Wire, 3 Phase		
		120V	240V	240V	480V	600V
15	14*	50	105	120	240	300
	14	50	100	120	235	295
20	12*	60	125	145	290	360
	12	60	120	140	280	350
30	10*	65	130	155	305	380
	10	65	130	150	300	375
50	8	60	125	145	285	355
65	6	75	150	175	345	435
85	4	90	185	210	425	530
115	2	110	215	250	500	620
130	1	120	240	275	555	690
150	1/0	130	260	305	605	760
175	2/0	140	285	330	655	820
200	3/0	155	315	360	725	904
230	4/0	170	345	395	795	990
255	250	185	365	420	845	1055
285	300	195	395	455	910	1140
310	350	210	420	485	975	1220
380	500	245	490	565	1130	1415

*Solid Conductor

Note: The circuit length is the one-way distance between the origin and the load.

R260519-92   Minimum Copper and Aluminum Wire Size Allowed for Various Types of Insulation

Minimum Wire Sizes

Amperes	Copper THW THWN or XHHW	Copper THHN XHHW*	Aluminum THW XHHW	Aluminum THHN XHHW*	Amperes	Copper THW THWN or XHHW	Copper THHN XHHW*	Aluminum THW XHHW	Aluminum THHN XHHW*
15A	#14	#14	#12	#12	195	3/0	2/0	250kcmil	4/0
20	#12	#12	#10	#10	200	3/0	3/0	250kcmil	4/0
25	#10	#10	#10	#10	205	4/0	3/0	250kcmil	4/0
30	#10	#10	#8	#8	225	4/0	3/0	300kcmil	250kcmil
40	#8	#8	#8	#8	230	4/0	4/0	300kcmil	250kcmil
45	#8	#8	#6	#8	250	250kcmil	4/0	350kcmil	300kcmil
50	#8	#8	#6	#6	255	250kcmil	4/0	400kcmil	300kcmil
55	#6	#8	#4	#6	260	300kcmil	4/0	400kcmil	350kcmil
60	#6	#6	#4	#6	270	300kcmil	250kcmil	400kcmil	350kcmil
65	#6	#6	#4	#4	280	300kcmil	250kcmil	500kcmil	350kcmil
75	#4	#6	#3	#4	285	300kcmil	250kcmil	500kcmil	400kcmil
85	#4	#4	#2	#3	290	350kcmil	250kcmil	500kcmil	400kcmil
90	#3	#4	#2	#2	305	350kcmil	300kcmil	500kcmil	400kcmil
95	#3	#4	#1	#2	310	350kcmil	300kcmil	500kcmil	500kcmil
100	#3	#3	#1	#2	320	400kcmil	300kcmil	600kcmil	500kcmil
110	#2	#3	1/0	#1	335	400kcmil	350kcmil	600kcmil	500kcmil
115	#2	#2	1/0	#1	340	500kcmil	350kcmil	600kcmil	500kcmil
120	#1	#2	1/0	1/0	350	500kcmil	350kcmil	700kcmil	500kcmil
130	#1	#2	2/0	1/0	375	500kcmil	400kcmil	700kcmil	600kcmil
135	1/0	#1	2/0	1/0	380	500kcmil	400kcmil	750kcmil	600kcmil
150	1/0	#1	3/0	2/0	385	600kcmil	500kcmil	750kcmil	600kcmil
155	2/0	1/0	3/0	3/0	420	600kcmil	500kcmil		700kcmil
170	2/0	1/0	4/0	3/0	430		500kcmil		750kcmil
175	2/0	2/0	4/0	3/0	435		600kcmil		750kcmil
180	3/0	2/0	4/0	4/0	475		600kcmil		

*Dry Locations Only

Notes:
1. Size #14 to 4/0 is in AWG units (American Wire Gauge).
2. Size 250 to 750 is in kcmil units (Thousand Circular Mils).
3. Use next higher ampere value if exact value is not listed in table.
4. For loads that operate continuously increase ampere value by 25% to obtain proper wire size.
5. Refer to Table R260519-91 for the maximum circuit length for the various size wires.
6. Table R260519-92 has been written for estimating purpose only, based on ambient temperature of 30°C (86° F); for ambient temperature other than 30°C (86° F), ampacity correction factors will be applied.

R260533-22　Conductors in Conduit

Table below lists maximum number of conductors for various sized conduit using THW, TW or THWN insulations.

Copper Wire Size	1/2"			3/4"			1"			1-1/4"			1-1/2"			2"			2-1/2"			3"		3-1/2"		4"	
	TW	THW	THWN	TW	THW	THWN	TW	THW	THWN	TW	THW	THWN	TW	THW	THWN	TW	THW	THWN	TW	THW	THWN	THW	THWN	THW	THWN	THW	THWN
#14	9	6	13	15	10	24	25	16	39	44	29	69	60	40	94	99	65	154	142	93		143		192			
#12	7	4	10	12	8	18	19	13	29	35	24	51	47	32	70	78	53	114	111	76	164	117		157			
#10	5	4	6	9	6	11	15	11	18	26	19	32	36	26	44	60	43	73	85	61	104	95	160	127		163	
#8	2	1	3	4	3	5	7	5	9	12	10	16	17	13	22	28	22	36	40	32	51	49	79	66	106	85	136
#6		1	1		2	4		4	6		7	11		10	15		16	26		23	37	36	57	48	76	62	98
#4		1	1		1	2		3	4		5	7		7	9		12	16		17	22	27	35	36	47	47	60
#3		1	1		1	1		2	3		4	6		6	8		10	13		15	19	23	29	31	39	40	51
#2		1	1		1	1		2	3		4	5		5	7		9	11		13	16	20	25	27	33	34	43
#1					1	1		1	1		3	3		4	5		6	8		9	12	14	18	19	25	25	32
1/0					1	1		1	1		2	3		3	4		5	7		8	10	12	15	16	21	21	27
2/0					1	1		1	1		1	2		3	3		5	6		7	8	10	13	14	17	18	22
3/0					1	1		1	1		1	1		2	3		4	5		6	7	9	11	12	14	15	18
4/0						1		1	1		1	1		1	2		3	4		5	6	7	9	10	12	13	15
250 kcmil								1	1		1	1		1	1		2	3		4	4	6	7	8	10	10	12
300								1	1		1	1		1	1		2	3		3	4	5	6	7	8	9	11
350									1		1	1		1	1		1	2		3	3	4	5	6	7	8	9
400											1	1		1	1		1	1		2	3	4	5	5	6	7	8
500											1	1		1	1		1	1		1	2	3	4	4	5	6	7
600												1		1	1		1	1		1	1	3	3	4	4	5	5
700														1	1		1	1		1	1	2	3	3	4	4	5
750														1	1		1	1		1	1	2	2	3	3	4	4

R312316-40 Excavating

The selection of equipment used for structural excavation and bulk excavation or for grading is determined by the following factors.
1. Quantity of material
2. Type of material
3. Depth or height of cut
4. Length of haul
5. Condition of haul road
6. Accessibility of site
7. Moisture content and dewatering requirements
8. Availability of excavating and hauling equipment

Some additional costs must be allowed for hand trimming the sides and bottom of concrete pours and other excavation below the general excavation.

Number of B.C.Y. per truck = 1.5 C.Y. bucket x 8 passes = 12 loose C.Y.

$$= 12 \times \frac{100}{118} = 10.2 \text{ B.C.Y. per truck}$$

Truck Haul Cycle:

Load truck, 8 passes	=	4 minutes
Haul distance, 1 mile	=	9 minutes
Dump time	=	2 minutes
Return, 1 mile	=	7 minutes
Spot under machine	=	1 minute
		23 minute cycle

Add the mobilization and demobilization costs to the total excavation costs. When equipment is rented for more than three days, there is often no mobilization charge by the equipment dealer. On larger jobs outside of urban areas, scrapers can move earth economically provided a dump site or fill area and adequate haul roads are available. Excavation within sheeting bracing or cofferdam bracing is usually done with a clamshell and production

When planning excavation and fill, the following should also be considered.
1. Swell factor
2. Compaction factor
3. Moisture content
4. Density requirements

A typical example for scheduling and estimating the cost of excavation of a 15' deep basement on a dry site when the material must be hauled off the site is outlined below.

Assumptions:
1. Swell factor, 18%
2. No mobilization or demobilization
3. Allowance included for idle time and moving on job
4. No dewatering, sheeting, or bracing
5. No truck spotter or hand trimming

Fleet Haul Production per day in B.C.Y.

$$4 \text{ trucks} \times \frac{50 \text{ min. hour}}{23 \text{ min. haul cycle}} \times 8 \text{ hrs.} \times 10.2 \text{ B.C.Y.}$$

$$= 4 \times 2.2 \times 8 \times 10.2 = 718 \text{ B.C.Y./day}$$

is low, since the clamshell may have to be guided by hand between the bracing. When excavating or filling an area enclosed with a wellpoint system, add 10% to 15% to the cost to allow for restricted access. When estimating earth excavation quantities for structures, allow work space outside the building footprint for construction of the foundation and a slope of 1:1 unless sheeting is used.

R312316-45 Excavating Equipment

The table below lists THEORETICAL hourly production in C.Y./hr. bank measure for some typical excavation equipment. Figures assume 50 minute hours, 83% job efficiency, 100% operator efficiency, 90° swing and properly sized hauling units, which must be modified for adverse digging and loading conditions. Actual production costs in the front of the book average about 50% of the theoretical values listed here.

Equipment	Soil Type	B.C.Y. Weight	% Swell	1 C.Y.	1-1/2 C.Y.	2 C.Y.	2-1/2 C.Y.	3 C.Y.	3-1/2 C.Y.	4 C.Y.
Hydraulic Excavator	Moist loam, sandy clay	3400 lb.	40%	85	125	175	220	275	330	380
"Backhoe"	Sand and gravel	3100	18	80	120	160	205	260	310	365
15' Deep Cut	Common earth	2800	30	70	105	150	190	240	280	330
	Clay, hard, dense	3000	33	65	100	130	170	210	255	300
	Moist loam, sandy clay	3400	40	170 (6.0)	245 (7.0)	295 (7.8)	335 (8.4)	385 (8.8)	435 (9.1)	475 (9.4)
Power Shovel	Sand and gravel	3100	18	165 (6.0)	225 (7.0)	275 (7.8)	325 (8.4)	375 (8.8)	420 (9.1)	460 (9.4)
Optimum Cut (Ft.)	Common earth	2800	30	145 (7.8)	200 (9.2)	250 (10.2)	295 (11.2)	335 (12.1)	375 (13.0)	425 (13.8)
	Clay, hard, dense	3000	33	120 (9.0)	175 (10.7)	220 (12.2)	255 (13.3)	300 (14.2)	335 (15.1)	375 (16.0)
	Moist loam, sandy clay	3400	40	130 (6.6)	180 (7.4)	220 (8.0)	250 (8.5)	290 (9.0)	325 (9.5)	385 (10.0)
Drag Line	Sand and gravel	3100	18	130 (6.6)	175 (7.4)	210 (8.0)	245 (8.5)	280 (9.0)	315 (9.5)	375 (10.0)
Optimum Cut (Ft.)	Common earth	2800	30	110 (8.0)	160 (9.0)	190 (9.9)	220 (10.5)	250 (11.0)	280 (11.5)	310 (12.0)
	Clay, hard, dense	3000	33	90 (9.3)	130 (10.7)	160 (11.8)	190 (12.3)	225 (12.8)	250 (13.3)	280 (12.0)

Equipment	Soil Type	B.C.Y. Weight	% Swell	Wheel Loaders				Track Loaders		
				3 C.Y.	4 C.Y.	6 C.Y.	8 C.Y.	2-1/4 C.Y.	3 C.Y.	4 C.Y.
	Moist loam, sandy clay	3400	40	260	340	510	690	135	180	250
	Sand and gravel	3100	18	245	320	480	650	130	170	235
Loading Tractors	Common earth	2800	30	230	300	460	620	120	155	220
	Clay, hard, dense	3000	33	200	270	415	560	110	145	200
	Rock, well-blasted	4000	50	180	245	380	520	100	130	180

R312319-90   Wellpoints

A single stage wellpoint system is usually limited to dewatering an average 15' depth below normal ground water level. Multi-stage systems are employed for greater depth with the pumping equipment installed only at the lowest header level. Ejectors with unlimited lift capacity can be economical when two or more stages of wellpoints can be replaced or when horizontal clearance is restricted, such as in deep trenches or tunneling projects, and where low water flows are expected. Wellpoints are usually spaced on 2-1/2' to 10' centers along a header pipe. Wellpoint spacing, header size, and pump size are all determined by the expected flow as dictated by soil conditions.

In almost all soils encountered in wellpoint dewatering, the wellpoints may be jetted into place. Cemented soils and stiff clays may require sand wicks about 12" in diameter around each wellpoint to increase efficiency and eliminate weeping into the excavation. These sand wicks require 1/2 to 3 C.Y. of washed filter sand and are installed by using a 12" diameter steel casing and hole puncher jetted into the ground 2' deeper than the wellpoint. Rock may require predrilled holes.

Labor required for the complete installation and removal of a single stage wellpoint system is in the range of 3/4 to 2 labor-hours per linear foot of header, depending upon jetting conditions, wellpoint spacing, etc.

Continuous pumping is necessary except in some free draining soil where temporary flooding is permissible (as in trenches which are backfilled after each day's work). Good practice requires provision of a stand-by pump during the continuous pumping operation.

Systems for continuous trenching below the water table should be installed three to four times the length of expected daily progress to ensure uninterrupted digging, and header pipe size should not be changed during the job.

For pervious free draining soils, deep wells in place of wellpoints may be economical because of lower installation and maintenance costs. Daily production ranges between two to three wells per day, for 25' to 40' depths, to one well per day for depths over 50'.

Detailed analysis and estimating for any dewatering problem is available at no cost from wellpoint manufacturers. Major firms will quote "sufficient equipment" quotes or their affiliates offer lump sum proposals to cover complete dewatering responsibility.

Description for 200' System with 8" Header		Quantities
Equipment & Material	Wellpoints 25' long, 2" diameter @ 5' O.C.	40 Each
	Header pipe, 8" diameter	200 L.F.
	Discharge pipe, 8" diameter	100 L.F.
	8" valves	3 Each
	Combination jetting & wellpoint pump (standby)	1 Each
	Wellpoint pump, 8" diameter	1 Each
	Transportation to and from site	1 Day
	Fuel for 30 days x 60 gal./day	1800 Gallons
	Lubricants for 30 days x 16 lbs./day	480 Lbs.
	Sand for points	40 C.Y.
Labor	Technician to supervise installation	1 Week
	Labor for installation and removal of system	300 Labor-hours
	4 Operators straight time 40 hrs./wk. for 4.33 wks.	693 Hrs.
	4 Operators overtime 2 hrs./wk. for 4.33 wks.	35 Hrs.

R312323-30   Compacting Backfill

Compaction of fill in embankments, around structures, in trenches, and under slabs is important to control settlement. Factors affecting compaction are:

1. Soil gradation
2. Moisture content
3. Equipment used
4. Depth of fill per lift
5. Density required

Production Rate:

$$\frac{1.75' \text{ plate width x 50 F.P.M. x 50 min./hr. x .67' lift}}{27 \text{ C.F. per C.Y.}} = 108.5 \text{ C.Y./hr.}$$

Production Rate for 4 Passes:

$$\frac{108.5 \text{ C.Y.}}{4 \text{ passes}} = 27.125 \text{ C.Y./hr. x 8 hrs.} = 217 \text{ C.Y./day}$$

Example:

Compact granular fill around a building foundation using a 21" wide x 24" vibratory plate in 8" lifts. Operator moves at 50 F.P.M. working a 50 minute hour to develop 95% Modified Proctor Density with 4 passes.

R314116-40   Wood Sheet Piling

Wood sheet piling may be used for depths to 20' where there is no ground water. If moderate ground water is encountered Tongue & Groove sheeting will help to keep it out. When considerable ground water is present, steel sheeting must be used.

For estimating purposes on trench excavation, sizes are as follows:

Depth	Sheeting	Wales	Braces	B.F. per S.F.
To 8'	3 x 12's	6 x 8's, 2 line	6 x 8's, @ 10'	4.0 @ 8'
8' x 12'	3 x 12's	10 x 10's, 2 line	10 x 10's, @ 9'	5.0 average
12' to 20'	3 x 12's	12 x 12's, 3 line	12 x 12's, @ 8'	7.0 average

Sheeting to be toed in at least 2' depending upon soil conditions. A five person crew with an air compressor and sheeting driver can drive and brace 440 SF/day at 8' deep, 360 SF/day at 12' deep, and 320 SF/day at 16' deep.

For normal soils, piling can be pulled in 1/3 the time to install. Pulling difficulty increases with the time in the ground. Production can be increased by high pressure jetting.

R314116-45   Steel Sheet Piling

Limiting weights are 22 to 38#/S.F. of wall surface with 27#/S.F. average for usual types and sizes. (Weights of piles themselves are from 30.7#/L.F. to 57#/L.F. but they are 15" to 21" wide.) Lightweight sections 12" to 28" wide from 3 ga. to 12 ga. thick are also available for shallow excavations. Piles may be driven two at a time with an impact or vibratory hammer (use vibratory to pull) hung from a crane without leads. A reasonable estimate of the life of steel sheet piling is 10 uses with up to 125 uses possible if a vibratory hammer is used. Used piling costs from 50% to 80% of new piling depending on location and market conditions. Sheet piling and H piles can be rented for about 30% of the delivered mill price for the first month and 5% per month thereafter. Allow 1 labor-hour per pile for cleaning and trimming after driving. These costs increase with depth and hydrostatic head. Vibratory drivers are faster in wet granular soils and are excellent for pile extraction. Pulling difficulty increases with the time in the ground and may cost more than driving. It is often economical to abandon the sheet piling, especially if it can be used as the outer wall form. Allow about 1/3 additional length or more for toeing into ground. Add bracing, waler and strut costs. Waler costs can equal the cost per ton of sheeting.

R314513-90   Vibroflotation and Vibro Replacement Soil Compaction

Vibroflotation is a proprietary system of compacting sandy soils in place to increase relative density to about 70%. Typical bearing capacities attained will be 6000 psf for saturated sand and 12,000 psf for dry sand. Usual range is 4000 to 8000 psf capacity. Costs in the front of the book are for a vertical foot of compacted cylinder 6' to 10' in diameter.

Vibro replacement is a proprietary system of improving cohesive soils in place to increase bearing capacity. Most silts and clays above or below the water table can be strengthened by installation of stone columns.

The process consists of radial displacement of the soil by vibration. The created hole is then backfilled in stages with coarse granular fill which is thoroughly compacted and displaced into the surrounding soil in the form of a column.

The total project cost would depend on the number and depth of the compacted cylinders. The installing company guarantees relative soil density of the sand cylinders after compaction and the bearing capacity of the soil after the replacement process. Detailed estimating information is available from the installer at no cost.

R316326-60   Caissons

The three principal types of cassions are:

(1) Belled Caissons, which except for shallow depths and poor soil conditions, are generally recommended. They provide more bearing than shaft area. Because of its conical shape, no horizontal reinforcement of the bell is required.

(2) Straight Shaft Caissons are used where relatively light loads are to be supported by caissons that rest on high value bearing strata. While the shaft is larger in diameter than for belled types this is more than offset by the saving in time and labor.

(3) Keyed Caissons are used when extremely heavy loads are to be carried. A keyed or socketed caisson transfers its load into rock by a combination of end-bearing and shear reinforcing of the shaft. The most economical shaft often consists of a steel casing, a steel wide flange core and concrete. Allowable compressive stresses of .225 f'c for concrete, 16,000 psi for the wide flange core, and 9,000 psi for the steel casing are commonly used. The usual range of shaft diameter is 18″ to 84″. The number of sizes specified for any one project should be limited due to the problems of casing and auger storage. When hand work is to be performed, shaft diameters should not be less than 32″. When inspection of borings is required a minimum shaft diameter of 30″ is recommended. Concrete caissons are intended to be poured against earth excavation so permanent forms which add to cost should not be used if the excavation is clean and the earth sufficiently impervious to prevent excessive loss of concrete.

Soil Conditions for Belling		
Good	Requires Handwork	Not Recommended
Clay	Hard Shale	Silt
Sandy Clay	Limestone	Sand
Silty Clay	Sandstone	Gravel
Clayey Silt	Weathered Mica	Igneous Rock
Hard-pan		
Soft Shale		
Decomposed Rock		

R329219-50   Seeding

The type of grass is determined by light, shade and moisture content of soil plus intended use. Fertilizer should be disked 4″ before seeding. For steep slopes disk five tons of mulch and lay two tons of hay or straw on surface per acre after seeding. Surface mulch can be staked, lightly disked or tar emulsion sprayed. Material for mulch can be wood chips, peat moss, partially rotted hay or straw, wood fibers and sprayed emulsions. Hemp seed blankets with fertilizer are also available. For spring seeding, watering is necessary. Late fall seeding may have to be reseeded in the spring. Hydraulic seeding, power mulching, and aerial seeding can be used on large areas.

Utilities   R3311 Water Utility Distribution Piping

R331113-80   Piping Designations

There are several systems currently in use to describe pipe and fittings. The following paragraphs will help to identify and clarify classifications of piping systems used for water distribution.

Piping may be classified by schedule. Piping schedules include 5S, 10S, 10, 20, 30, Standard, 40, 60, Extra Strong, 80, 100, 120, 140, 160 and Double Extra Strong. These schedules are dependent upon the pipe wall thickness. The wall thickness of a particular schedule may vary with pipe size.

Ductile iron pipe for water distribution is classified by Pressure Classes such as Class 150, 200, 250, 300 and 350. These classes are actually the rated water working pressure of the pipe in pounds per square inch (psi). The pipe in these pressure classes is designed to withstand the rated water working pressure plus a surge allowance of 100 psi.

The American Water Works Association (AWWA) provides standards for various types of **plastic pipe.** C-900 is the specification for polyvinyl chloride (PVC) piping used for water distribution in sizes ranging from 4″ through 12″. C-901 is the specification for polyethylene (PE) pressure pipe, tubing and fittings used for water distribution in sizes ranging from 1/2″ through 3″. C-905 is the specification for PVC piping sizes 14″ and greater.

PVC pressure-rated pipe is identified using the standard dimensional ratio (SDR) method. This method is defined by the American Society for Testing and Materials (ASTM) Standard D 2241. This pipe is available in SDR numbers 64, 41, 32.5, 26, 21, 17, and 13.5. Pipe with an SDR of 64 will have the thinnest wall while pipe with an SDR of 13.5 will have the thickest wall. When the pressure rating (PR) of a pipe is given in psi, it is based on a line supplying water at 73 degrees F.

The National Sanitation Foundation (NSF) seal of approval is applied to products that can be used with potable water. These products have been tested to ANSI/NSF Standard 14.

Valves and strainers are classified by American National Standards Institute (ANSI) Classes. These Classes are 125, 150, 200, 250, 300, 400, 600, 900, 1500 and 2500. Within each class there is an operating pressure range dependent upon temperature. Design parameters should be compared to the appropriate material dependent, pressure-temperature rating chart for accurate valve selection.

Transportation   R3472 Railway Construction

R347216-10   Single Track R.R. Siding

The costs for a single track RR siding in the Unit Price section include the components shown in the table below.

Description of Component	Qty. per L.F. of Track	Unit
Ballast, 1-1/2″ crushed stone	.667	C.Y.
6″ x 8″ x 8′-6″ Treated timber ties, 22″ O.C.	.545	Ea.
Tie plates, 2 per tie	1.091	Ea.
Track rail	2.000	L.F.
Spikes, 6″, 4 per tie	2.182	Ea.
Splice bars w/ bolts, lock washers & nuts, @ 33′ O.C.	.061	Pair
Crew B-14 @ 57 L.F./Day	.018	Day

R347216-20   Single Track, Steel Ties, Concrete Bed

The costs for a R.R. siding with steel ties and a concrete bed in the Unit Price section include the components shown in the table below.

Description of Component	Qty. per L.F. of Track	Unit
Concrete bed, 9′ wide, 10″ thick	.278	C.Y.
Ties, W6x16 x 6′-6″ long, @ 30″ O.C.	.400	Ea.
Tie plates, 4 per tie	1.600	Ea.
Track rail	2.000	L.F.
Tie plate bolts, 1″, 8 per tie	3.200	Ea.
Splice bars w/bolts, lock washers & nuts, @ 33′ O.C.	.061	Pair
Crew B-14 @ 22 L.F./Day	.045	Day

Change Orders

Change Order Considerations

A change order is a written document, usually prepared by the design professional, and signed by the owner, the architect/engineer, and the contractor. A change order states the agreement of the parties to: an addition, deletion, or revision in the work; an adjustment in the contract sum, if any; or an adjustment in the contract time, if any. Change orders, or "extras" in the construction process occur after execution of the construction contract and impact architects/engineers, contractors, and owners.

Change orders that are properly recognized and managed can ensure orderly, professional, and profitable progress for all who are involved in the project. There are many causes for change orders and change order requests. In all cases, change orders or change order requests should be addressed promptly and in a precise and prescribed manner. The following paragraphs include information regarding change order pricing and procedures.

The Causes of Change Orders

Reasons for issuing change orders include:

- Unforeseen field conditions that require a change in the work
- Correction of design discrepancies, errors, or omissions in the contract documents
- Owner-requested changes, either by design criteria, scope of work, or project objectives
- Completion date changes for reasons unrelated to the construction process
- Changes in building code interpretations, or other public authority requirements that require a change in the work
- Changes in availability of existing or new materials and products

Procedures

Properly written contract documents must include the correct change order procedures for all parties—owners, design professionals and contractors—to follow in order to avoid costly delays and litigation.

Being "in the right" is not always a sufficient or acceptable defense. The contract provisions requiring notification and documentation must be adhered to within a defined or reasonable time frame.

The appropriate method of handling change orders is by a written proposal and acceptance by all parties involved. Prior to starting work on a project, all parties should identify their authorized agents who may sign and accept change orders, as well as any limits placed on their authority.

Time may be a critical factor when the need for a change arises. For such cases, the contractor might be directed to proceed on a "time and materials" basis, rather than wait for all paperwork to be processed—a delay that could impede progress. In this situation, the contractor must still follow the prescribed change order procedures including, but not limited to, notification and documentation.

All forms used for change orders should be dated and signed by the proper authority. Lack of documentation can be very costly, especially if legal judgments are to be made, and if certain field personnel are no longer available. For time and material change orders, the contractor should keep accurate daily records of all labor and material allocated to the change.

Owners or awarding authorities who do considerable and continual building construction (such as the federal government) realize the inevitability of change orders for numerous reasons, both predictable and unpredictable. As a result, the federal government, the American Institute of Architects (AIA), the Engineers Joint Contract Documents Committee (EJCDC) and other contractor, legal, and technical organizations have developed standards and procedures to be followed by all parties to achieve contract continuance and timely completion, while being financially fair to all concerned.

In addition to the change order standards put forth by industry associations, there are also many books available on the subject.

Pricing Change Orders

When pricing change orders, regardless of their cause, the most significant factor is when the change occurs. The need for a change may be perceived in the field or requested by the architect/engineer *before* any of the actual installation has begun, or may evolve or appear *during* construction when the item of work in question is partially installed. In the latter cases, the original sequence of construction is disrupted, along with all contiguous and supporting systems. Change orders cause the greatest impact when they occur *after* the installation has been completed and must be uncovered, or even replaced. Post-completion changes may be caused by necessary design changes, product failure, or changes in the owner's requirements that are not discovered until the building or the systems begin to function.

Specified procedures of notification and record keeping must be adhered to and enforced regardless of the stage of construction: *before, during,* or *after* installation. Some bidding documents anticipate change orders by requiring that unit prices including overhead and profit percentages—for additional as well as deductible changes—be listed. Generally these unit prices do not fully take into account the ripple effect, or impact on other trades, and should be used for general guidance only.

When pricing change orders, it is important to classify the time frame in which the change occurs. There are two basic time frames for change orders: *pre-installation change orders,* which occur before the start of construction, and *post-installation change orders,* which involve reworking after the original installation. Change orders that occur between these stages may be priced according to the extent of work completed using a combination of techniques developed for pricing *pre-* and *post-installation* changes.

The following factors are the basis for a check list to use when preparing a change order estimate.

Factors To Consider When Pricing Change Orders

As an estimator begins to prepare a change order, the following questions should be reviewed to determine their impact on the final price.

General

- *Is the change order work* pre-installation *or* post-installation?

  Change order work costs vary according to how much of the installation has been completed. Once workers have the project scoped in their minds, even though they have not started, it can be difficult to refocus.

Consequently they may spend more than the normal amount of time understanding the change. Also, modifications to work in place, such as trimming or refitting, usually take more time than was initially estimated. The greater the amount of work in place, the more reluctant workers are to change it. Psychologically they may resent the change and as a result the rework takes longer than normal. Post-installation change order estimates must include demolition of existing work as required to accomplish the change. If the work is performed at a later time, additional obstacles, such as building finishes, may be present which must be protected. Regardless of whether the change

occurs pre-installation or post-installation, attempt to isolate the identifiable factors and price them separately. For example, add shipping costs that may be required pre-installation or any demolition required post-installation. Then analyze the potential impact on productivity of psychological and/or learning curve factors and adjust the output rates accordingly. One approach is to break down the typical workday into segments and quantify the impact on each segment. The following chart may be useful as a guide:

Task	Activities (Productivity) Expressed as Percentages of a Workday		
	Means Mechanical Cost Data (for New Construction)	Pre-Installation Change Orders	Post-Installation Change Orders
1. Study plans	3%	6%	6%
2. Material procurement	3%	3%	3%
3. Receiving and storing	3%	3%	3%
4. Mobilization	5%	5%	5%
5. Site movement	5%	5%	8%
6. Layout and marking	8%	10%	12%
7. Actual installation	64%	59%	54%
8. Clean-up	3%	3%	3%
9. Breaks—non-productive	6%	6%	6%
Total	100%	100%	100%

Change Order Installation Efficiency

The labor-hours expressed (for new construction) are based on average installation time, using an efficiency level of approximately 60%–65%. For change order situations, adjustments to this efficiency level should reflect the daily labor-hour allocation for that particular occurrence.

If any of the specific percentages expressed in the above chart do not apply to a particular project situation, then those percentage points should be reallocated to the appropriate task(s). Example: Using data for new construction, assume there is no new material being utilized. The percentages for Tasks 2 and 3 would therefore be reallocated to other tasks. If the time required for Tasks 2 and 3 can now be applied to installation, we can add the time allocated for *Material Procurement* and *Receiving and Storing* to the *Actual Installation* time for new construction, thereby increasing the Actual Installation percentage.

This chart shows that, due to reduced productivity, labor costs will be higher than those for new construction by 5%–15% for pre-installation change orders and by 15%–25% for post-installation change orders. Each job and change order is unique and must be examined individually. Many factors, covered elsewhere in this section, can each have a significant impact on productivity and change order costs. All such factors should be considered in every case.

- *Will the change substantially delay the original completion date?*

  A significant change in the project may cause the original completion date to be extended. The extended schedule may subject the contractor to new wage rates dictated by relevant labor contracts. Project supervision and other project overhead must also be extended beyond the original completion date. The schedule extension may also put installation into a new weather season. For example, underground piping scheduled for October installation was delayed until January. As a result, frost penetrated the trench area, thereby changing the degree of difficulty of the task. Changes and delays may have a ripple effect throughout the project. This effect must be analyzed and negotiated with the owner.

- *What is the net effect of a deduct change order?*

  In most cases, change orders resulting in a deduction or credit reflect only bare costs. The contractor may retain the overhead and profit based on the original bid.

Materials

- *Will you have to pay more or less for the new material, required by the change order, than you paid for the original purchase?*

  The same material prices or discounts will usually apply to materials purchased for change orders as new construction. In some instances, however, the contractor may forfeit the advantages of competitive pricing for change orders. Consider the following example:

  A contractor purchased over $20,000 worth of fan coil units for an installation, and obtained the maximum discount. Some time later it was determined the project required an additional matching unit. The contractor has to purchase this unit from the original supplier to ensure a match. The supplier at this time may not discount the unit because of the small quantity, and the fact that he is no longer in a competitive situation. The impact of quantity on purchase can add between 0% and 25% to material prices and/or subcontractor quotes.

- *If materials have been ordered or delivered to the job site, will they be subject to a cancellation charge or restocking fee?*

  Check with the supplier to determine if ordered materials are subject to a cancellation charge. Delivered materials not used as result of a change order may be subject to a restocking fee if returned to the supplier. Common restocking charges run between 20% and 40%. Also, delivery charges to return the goods to the supplier must be added.

Labor

- *How efficient is the existing crew at the actual installation?*

  Is the same crew that performed the initial work going to do the change order? Possibly the change consists of the installation of a unit identical to one already installed; therefore, the change should take less time. Be sure to consider this potential productivity increase and modify the productivity rates accordingly.

- *If the crew size is increased, what impact will that have on supervision requirements?*

  Under most bargaining agreements or management practices, there is a point at which a working foreman is replaced by a nonworking foreman. This replacement increases project overhead by adding a nonproductive worker. If additional workers are added to accelerate the project or to perform changes while maintaining the schedule, be sure to add additional supervision time if warranted. Calculate the hours involved and the additional cost directly if possible.

- *What are the other impacts of increased crew size?*

  The larger the crew, the greater the potential for productivity to decrease. Some of the factors that cause this productivity loss are: overcrowding (producing restrictive conditions in the working space), and possibly a shortage of any special tools and equipment required. Such factors affect not only the crew working on the elements directly involved in the change order, but other crews whose movement may also be hampered.

  As the crew increases, check its basic composition for changes by the addition or deletion of apprentices or nonworking foreman, and quantify the potential effects of equipment shortages or other logistical factors.

- *As new crews, unfamiliar with the project, are brought onto the site, how long will it take them to become oriented to the project requirements?*

  The orientation time for a new crew to become 100% effective varies with the site and type of project. Orientation is easiest at a new construction site, and most difficult at existing, very restrictive renovation sites. The type of work also affects orientation time. When all elements of the work are exposed, such as concrete or masonry work, orientation is decreased. When the work is concealed or less visible, such as existing electrical systems, orientation takes longer. Usually orientation can be accomplished in one day or less. Costs for added orientation should be itemized and added to the total estimated cost.

- *How much actual production can be gained by working overtime?*

  Short term overtime can be used effectively to accomplish more work in a day. However, as overtime is scheduled to run beyond several weeks, studies have shown marked decreases in output. The following chart shows the effect of long term overtime on worker efficiency. If the anticipated change requires extended overtime to keep the job on schedule, these factors can be used as a guide to predict the impact on time and cost. Add project overhead, particularly supervision, that may also be incurred.

Days per Week	Hours per Day	Production Efficiency					Payroll Cost Factors	
		1 Week	2 Weeks	3 Weeks	4 Weeks	Average 4 Weeks	@ 1-1/2 Times	@ 2 Times
5	8	100%	100%	100%	100%	100%	100%	100%
	9	100	100	95	90	96.25	105.6	111.1
	10	100	95	90	85	91.25	110.0	120.0
	11	95	90	75	65	81.25	113.6	127.3
	12	90	85	70	60	76.25	116.7	133.3
6	8	100	100	95	90	96.25	108.3	116.7
	9	100	95	90	85	92.50	113.0	125.9
	10	95	90	85	80	87.50	116.7	133.3
	11	95	85	70	65	78.75	119.7	139.4
	12	90	80	65	60	73.75	122.2	144.4
7	8	100	95	85	75	88.75	114.3	128.6
	9	95	90	80	70	83.75	118.3	136.5
	10	90	85	75	65	78.75	121.4	142.9
	11	85	80	65	60	72.50	124.0	148.1
	12	85	75	60	55	68.75	126.2	152.4

Effects of Overtime

Caution: Under many labor agreements, Sundays and holidays are paid at a higher premium than the normal overtime rate.

The use of long-term overtime is counterproductive on almost any construction job; that is, the longer the period of overtime, the lower the actual production rate. Numerous studies have been conducted, and while they have resulted in slightly different numbers, all reach the same conclusion. The figure above tabulates the effects of overtime work on efficiency.

As illustrated, there can be a difference between the *actual* payroll cost per hour and the *effective* cost per hour for overtime work. This is due to the reduced production efficiency with the increase in weekly hours beyond 40. This difference between actual and effective cost results from overtime work over a prolonged period. Short-term overtime work does not result in as great a reduction in efficiency and, in such cases, effective cost may not vary significantly from the actual payroll cost. As the total hours per week are increased on a regular basis, more time is lost due to fatigue, lowered morale, and an increased accident rate.

As an example, assume a project where workers are working 6 days a week, 10 hours per day. From the figure above (based on productivity studies), the average effective productive hours over a 4-week period are:

$$0.875 \times 60 = 52.5$$

Depending upon the locale and day of week, overtime hours may be paid at time and a half or double time. For time and a half, the overall (average) *actual* payroll cost (including regular and overtime hours) is determined as follows:

$$\frac{40 \text{ reg. hrs.} + (20 \text{ overtime hrs.} \times 1.5)}{60 \text{ hrs.}} = 1.167$$

Based on 60 hours, the payroll cost per hour will be 116.7% of the normal rate at 40 hours per week. However, because the effective production (efficiency) for 60 hours is reduced to the equivalent of 52.5 hours, the effective cost of overtime is calculated as follows:

For time and a half:

$$\frac{40 \text{ reg. hrs.} + (20 \text{ overtime hrs.} \times 1.5)}{52.5 \text{ hrs.}} = 1.33$$

Installed cost will be 133% of the normal rate (for labor).

Thus, when figuring overtime, the actual cost per unit of work will be higher than the apparent overtime payroll dollar increase, due to the reduced productivity of the longer workweek. These efficiency calculations are true only for those cost factors determined by hours worked. Costs that are applied weekly or monthly, such as equipment rentals, will not be similarly affected.

Equipment

- *What equipment is required to complete the change order?*

Change orders may require extending the rental period of equipment already on the job site, or the addition of special equipment brought in to accomplish the change work. In either case, the additional rental charges and operator labor charges must be added.

Summary

The preceding considerations and others you deem appropriate should be analyzed and applied to a change order estimate. The impact of each should be quantified and listed on the estimate to form an audit trail.

Change orders that are properly identified, documented, and managed help to ensure the orderly, professional and profitable progress of the work. They also minimize potential claims or disputes at the end of the project.

Estimating Tips

- The cost figures in this Square Foot Cost section were derived from approximately 11,000 projects contained in the RSMeans database of completed construction projects. They include the contractor's overhead and profit, but do not generally include architectural fees or land costs. The figures have been adjusted to January of the current year. New projects are added to our files each year, and outdated projects are discarded. For this reason, certain costs may not show a uniform annual progression. In no case are all subdivisions of a project listed.

- These projects were located throughout the U.S. and reflect a tremendous variation in square foot (S.F.) and cubic foot (C.F.) costs. This is due to differences, not only in labor and material costs, but also in individual owners' requirements. For instance, a bank in a large city would have different features than one in a rural area. This is true of all the different types of buildings analyzed. Therefore, caution should be exercised when using these square foot costs. For example, for courthouses, costs in the database are local courthouse costs and will not apply to the larger, more elaborate federal courthouses. As a general rule, the projects in the 1/4 column do not include any site work or equipment, while the projects in the 3/4 column may include both equipment and site work. The median figures do not generally include site work.

- None of the figures "go with" any others. All individual cost items were computed and tabulated separately. Thus, the sum of the median figures for plumbing, HVAC and electrical will not normally total up to the total mechanical and electrical costs arrived at by separate analysis and tabulation of the projects.

- Each building was analyzed as to total and component costs and percentages. The figures were arranged in ascending order with the results tabulated as shown. The 1/4 column shows that 25% of the projects had lower costs and 75% had higher. The 3/4 column shows that 75% of the projects had lower costs and 25% had higher. The median column shows that 50% of the projects had lower costs and 50% had higher.

- There are two times when square foot costs are useful. The first is in the conceptual stage when no details are available. Then square foot costs make a useful starting point. The second is after the bids are in and the costs can be worked back into their appropriate categories for information purposes. As soon as details become available in the project design, the square foot approach should be discontinued and the project priced as to its particular components. When more precision is required, or for estimating the replacement cost of specific buildings, the current edition of *RSMeans Square Foot Costs* should be used.

- In using the figures in this section, it is recommended that the median column be used for preliminary figures if no additional information is available. The median figures, when multiplied by the total city construction cost index figures (see city cost indexes) and then multiplied by the project size modifier at the end of this section, should present a fairly accurate base figure, which would then have to be adjusted in view of the estimator's experience, local economic conditions, code requirements, and the owner's particular requirements. There is no need to factor the percentage figures, as these should remain constant from city to city. All tabulations mentioning air conditioning had at least partial air conditioning.

- The editors of this book would greatly appreciate receiving cost figures on one or more of your recent projects, which would then be included in the averages for next year. All cost figures received will be kept confidential, except that they will be averaged with other similar projects to arrive at square foot cost figures for next year's book. See the last page of the book for details and the discount available for submitting one or more of your projects.

50 17 00 | S.F. Costs

		UNIT	UNIT COSTS			% OF TOTAL			
			1/4	MEDIAN	3/4	1/4	MEDIAN	3/4	
01	**0010**	**APARTMENTS Low Rise (1 to 3 story)**	S.F.	73	92.50	123				**01**
	0020	Total project cost	C.F.	6.55	8.70	10.75				
	0100	Site work	S.F.	5.35	8.55	15	6.05%	10.55%	13.95%	
	0500	Masonry		1.44	3.55	5.80	1.54%	3.92%	6.50%	
	1500	Finishes		7.75	10.65	13.15	9.05%	10.75%	12.85%	
	1800	Equipment		2.40	3.63	5.40	2.71%	3.99%	5.95%	
	2720	Plumbing		5.70	7.30	9.30	6.65%	8.95%	10.05%	
	2770	Heating, ventilating, air conditioning		3.63	4.47	6.55	4.20%	5.60%	7.60%	
	2900	Electrical		4.25	5.65	7.65	5.20%	6.65%	8.35%	
	3100	Total: Mechanical & Electrical		15.10	19.60	24	16.05%	18.20%	23%	
	9000	Per apartment unit, total cost	Apt.	68,000	104,000	153,500				
	9500	Total: Mechanical & Electrical	"	12,900	20,300	26,500				
02	**0010**	**APARTMENTS Mid Rise (4 to 7 story)**	S.F.	97	117	144				**02**
	0020	Total project costs	C.F.	7.55	10.45	14.30				
	0100	Site work	S.F.	3.88	7.85	15.15	5.25%	6.70%	9.20%	
	0500	Masonry		4.05	8.90	12.15	5.10%	7.25%	10.50%	
	1500	Finishes		12.70	17	20	10.70%	13.50%	17.70%	
	1800	Equipment		2.71	4.22	5.55	2.54%	3.47%	4.31%	
	2500	Conveying equipment		2.20	2.70	3.26	2.05%	2.27%	2.69%	
	2720	Plumbing		5.70	9.10	9.65	5.70%	7.20%	8.95%	
	2900	Electrical		6.40	8.70	10.55	6.35%	7.20%	8.95%	
	3100	Total: Mechanical & Electrical		20.50	25.50	31	18.25%	21%	23%	
	9000	Per apartment unit, total cost	Apt.	109,500	129,500	214,000				
	9500	Total: Mechanical & Electrical	"	20,700	24,000	25,100				
03	**0010**	**APARTMENTS High Rise (8 to 24 story)**	S.F.	110	127	152				**03**
	0020	Total project costs	C.F.	10.70	12.45	14.65				
	0100	Site work	S.F.	3.99	6.45	9	2.58%	4.84%	6.15%	
	0500	Masonry		6.35	11.55	14.40	4.74%	9.65%	11.05%	
	1500	Finishes		12.20	15.25	18	9.75%	11.80%	13.70%	
	1800	Equipment		3.54	4.35	5.75	2.78%	3.49%	4.35%	
	2500	Conveying equipment		2.50	3.79	5.15	2.23%	2.78%	3.37%	
	2720	Plumbing		7.05	9.55	11.70	6.80%	7.20%	10.45%	
	2900	Electrical		7.55	9.55	12.90	6.45%	7.65%	8.80%	
	3100	Total: Mechanical & Electrical		22.50	29	35	17.95%	22.50%	24.50%	
	9000	Per apartment unit, total cost	Apt.	114,000	126,000	174,500				
	9500	Total: Mechanical & Electrical	"	22,700	28,200	29,900				
04	**0010**	**AUDITORIUMS**	S.F.	115	158	230				**04**
	0020	Total project costs	C.F.	7.15	9.95	14.30				
	2720	Plumbing	S.F.	6.80	10	11.95	5.85%	7.20%	8.70%	
	2900	Electrical		9.20	13.30	22	6.85%	9.50%	11.40%	
	3100	Total: Mechanical & Electrical		61	81.50	99	24.50%	27.50%	31%	
05	**0010**	**AUTOMOTIVE SALES**	S.F.	84.50	115	143				**05**
	0020	Total project costs	C.F.	5.55	6.70	8.65				
	2720	Plumbing	S.F.	3.86	6.70	7.30	2.89%	6.05%	6.50%	
	2770	Heating, ventilating, air conditioning		5.95	9.10	9.80	4.61%	10%	10.35%	
	2900	Electrical		6.80	10.70	15.70	7.25%	8.80%	12.15%	
	3100	Total: Mechanical & Electrical		19	30.50	36.50	17.30%	20.50%	22%	
06	**0010**	**BANKS**	S.F.	166	207	263				**06**
	0020	Total project costs	C.F.	11.85	16.10	21				
	0100	Site work	S.F.	19	30	42.50	7.90%	12.95%	17%	
	0500	Masonry		7.55	16.15	29	3.36%	6.90%	10.05%	
	1500	Finishes		14.85	22.50	28	5.85%	8.65%	11.70%	
	1800	Equipment		6.25	13.75	28	1.34%	5.55%	10.50%	
	2720	Plumbing		5.20	7.45	10.85	2.82%	3.90%	4.93%	
	2770	Heating, ventilating, air conditioning		9.85	13.20	17.60	4.86%	7.15%	8.50%	
	2900	Electrical		15.75	21	27.50	8.25%	10.20%	12.20%	
	3100	Total: Mechanical & Electrical		38	50.50	61	16.55%	19.45%	24%	
	3500	See also division 11020 & 11030 (MF2004 11 16 00 & 11 17 00)								

		50 17 00 | S.F. Costs	UNIT	UNIT COSTS			% OF TOTAL			
				1/4	MEDIAN	3/4	1/4	MEDIAN	3/4	
13	0010	**CHURCHES**	S.F.	112	143	185				13
	0020	Total project costs	C.F.	6.90	8.75	11.50				
	1800	Equipment	S.F.	1.21	3.17	6.80	.93%	2.11%	4.31%	
	2720	Plumbing		4.35	6.10	8.95	3.51%	4.96%	6.25%	
	2770	Heating, ventilating, air conditioning		10.15	13.25	18.75	7.50%	10%	12%	
	2900	Electrical		9.55	12.95	17.65	7.30%	8.80%	10.90%	
	3100	Total: Mechanical & Electrical	↓	29.50	39	51.50	18.30%	22%	24.50%	
	3500	See also division 11040 (MF2004 11 91 00)								
15	0010	**CLUBS, COUNTRY**	S.F.	120	144	182				15
	0020	Total project costs	C.F.	9.65	11.75	16.25				
	2720	Plumbing	S.F.	7.25	10.75	24.50	5.60%	7.90%	10%	
	2900	Electrical		9.40	12.90	16.80	7%	8.95%	11%	
	3100	Total: Mechanical & Electrical	↓	50	62.50	66	19%	26.50%	29.50%	
17	0010	**CLUBS, SOCIAL Fraternal**	S.F.	101	138	184				17
	0020	Total project costs	C.F.	5.95	9.05	10.80				
	2720	Plumbing	S.F.	6	7.50	11.30	5.60%	6.90%	8.55%	
	2770	Heating, ventilating, air conditioning		7.05	10.50	13.45	8.20%	9.25%	14.40%	
	2900	Electrical		6.85	11.80	13.55	5.95%	9.30%	10.55%	
	3100	Total: Mechanical & Electrical	↓	37	40	51	21%	23%	23.50%	
18	0010	**CLUBS, Y.M.C.A.**	S.F.	132	164	247				18
	0020	Total project costs	C.F.	5.55	9.25	13.80				
	2720	Plumbing	S.F.	7.60	15.10	16.95	5.65%	7.60%	10.85%	
	2900	Electrical		9.85	12.75	22	6.45%	8%	9.20%	
	3100	Total: Mechanical & Electrical	↓	40	45.50	74.50	20.50%	21.50%	28.50%	
19	0010	**COLLEGES Classrooms & Administration**	S.F.	116	164	212				19
	0020	Total project costs	C.F.	6.95	12.35	19.85				
	0500	Masonry	S.F.	9.15	16.85	20.50	5.10%	8.05%	10.50%	
	2720	Plumbing		5.20	12.65	23.50	5.10%	6.60%	8.95%	
	2900	Electrical		9.85	15.55	21.50	7.70%	9.85%	12%	
	3100	Total: Mechanical & Electrical	↓	41.50	57	76	23%	28%	31.50%	
21	0010	**COLLEGES Science, Engineering, Laboratories**	S.F.	225	264	305				21
	0020	Total project costs	C.F.	12.95	18.85	21.50				
	1800	Equipment	S.F.	6.10	28.50	31	2%	6.45%	12.65%	
	2900	Electrical		18.60	26.50	40.50	7.10%	9.40%	12.10%	
	3100	Total: Mechanical & Electrical	↓	69	82	127	28.50%	31.50%	41%	
	3500	See also division 11600 (MF2004 11 53 00)								
23	0010	**COLLEGES Student Unions**	S.F.	144	195	236				23
	0020	Total project costs	C.F.	8	10.50	13				
	3100	Total: Mechanical & Electrical	S.F.	54	58.50	69	23.50%	26%	29%	
25	0010	**COMMUNITY CENTERS**	S.F.	120	147	199				25
	0020	Total project costs	C.F.	7.75	11.05	14.35				
	1800	Equipment	S.F.	2.40	4.70	7.75	1.47%	3.01%	5.30%	
	2720	Plumbing		5.60	9.85	13.45	4.85%	7%	8.95%	
	2770	Heating, ventilating, air conditioning		8.45	13.10	18.80	6.80%	10.35%	12.90%	
	2900	Electrical		10.05	13.25	19.50	7.15%	8.90%	10.40%	
	3100	Total: Mechanical & Electrical	↓	33	42	60	18.80%	23%	30%	
28	0010	**COURT HOUSES**	S.F.	171	202	278				28
	0020	Total project costs	C.F.	13.15	15.70	19.80				
	2720	Plumbing	S.F.	8.15	11.35	12.90	5.95%	7.45%	8.20%	
	2900	Electrical		18.20	20.50	30	9.05%	10.65%	12.15%	
	3100	Total: Mechanical & Electrical	↓	51	66.50	73	22.50%	26.50%	30%	
30	0010	**DEPARTMENT STORES**	S.F.	63.50	85.50	108				30
	0020	Total project costs	C.F.	3.39	4.40	5.95				
	2720	Plumbing	S.F.	1.97	2.49	3.78	1.82%	4.21%	5.90%	
	2770	Heating, ventilating, air conditioning	↓	4.79	8.90	13.35	8.20%	9.10%	14.80%	

		50 17 00 | S.F. Costs	UNIT	UNIT COSTS			% OF TOTAL		
				1/4	MEDIAN	3/4	1/4	MEDIAN	3/4
30	2900	Electrical	S.F.	7.25	9.95	11.75	9.05%	12.15%	14.95%
	3100	Total: Mechanical & Electrical	↓	12.80	16.35	28.50	13.20%	21.50%	50%
31	0010	**DORMITORIES Low Rise (1 to 3 story)**	S.F.	120	166	208			
	0020	Total project costs	C.F.	6.80	10.95	16.45			
	2720	Plumbing	S.F.	7.20	9.65	12.20	8.05%	9%	9.65%
	2770	Heating, ventilating, air conditioning		7.65	9.15	12.20	4.61%	8.05%	10%
	2900	Electrical		7.95	12.10	16.55	6.40%	8.65%	9.50%
	3100	Total: Mechanical & Electrical	↓	41.50	44.50	69	22%	25%	27%
	9000	Per bed, total cost	Bed	51,000	56,500	121,000			
32	0010	**DORMITORIES Mid Rise (4 to 8 story)**	S.F.	147	192	237			
	0020	Total project costs	C.F.	16.25	17.85	21.50			
	2900	Electrical	S.F.	15.65	17.80	24	8.20%	10.20%	11.95%
	3100	Total: Mechanical & Electrical	"	44	87.50	88.50	25%	30.50%	35.50%
	9000	Per bed, total cost	Bed	21,000	47,900	277,000			
34	0010	**FACTORIES**	S.F.	55.50	83	128			
	0020	Total project costs	C.F.	3.58	5.35	8.85			
	0100	Site work	S.F.	6.35	11.60	18.40	6.95%	11.45%	17.95%
	2720	Plumbing		3.01	5.60	9.25	3.73%	6.05%	8.10%
	2770	Heating, ventilating, air conditioning		5.85	8.40	11.35	5.25%	8.45%	11.35%
	2900	Electrical		6.95	10.95	16.75	8.10%	10.50%	14.20%
	3100	Total: Mechanical & Electrical	↓	19.80	30.50	40	21%	28.50%	35.50%
36	0010	**FIRE STATIONS**	S.F.	111	153	209			
	0020	Total project costs	C.F.	6.45	8.90	11.85			
	0500	Masonry	S.F.	15.10	29	37.50	7.50%	10.95%	15.55%
	1140	Roofing		3.61	9.75	11.10	1.90%	4.94%	5.05%
	1580	Painting		2.80	4.18	4.28	1.37%	1.57%	2.07%
	1800	Equipment		1.38	2.64	4.87	.62%	1.63%	3.42%
	2720	Plumbing		6.20	9.85	13.95	5.85%	7.35%	9.45%
	2770	Heating, ventilating, air conditioning		6.15	9.95	15.35	5.15%	7.40%	9.40%
	2900	Electrical		7.95	14.10	19	6.90%	8.60%	10.60%
	3100	Total: Mechanical & Electrical	↓	40.50	52	59	18.40%	23%	27%
37	0010	**FRATERNITY HOUSES & Sorority Houses**	S.F.	111	142	195			
	0020	Total project costs	C.F.	11	11.50	13.85			
	2720	Plumbing	S.F.	8.35	9.60	17.55	6.80%	8%	10.85%
	2900	Electrical	↓	7.30	15.80	19.35	6.60%	9.90%	10.65%
38	0010	**FUNERAL HOMES**	S.F.	117	159	289			
	0020	Total project costs	C.F.	11.90	13.25	25.50			
	2900	Electrical	S.F.	5.15	9.45	10.35	3.58%	4.44%	5.95%
39	0010	**GARAGES, COMMERCIAL (Service)**	S.F.	66	102	141			
	0020	Total project costs	C.F.	4.35	6.40	9.35			
	1800	Equipment	S.F.	3.73	8.40	13.05	2.21%	4.62%	6.80%
	2720	Plumbing		4.58	7.05	12.85	5.45%	7.85%	10.65%
	2730	Heating & ventilating		4.51	7.80	9.95	5.25%	6.85%	8.20%
	2900	Electrical		6.30	9.60	13.80	7.15%	9.25%	10.85%
	3100	Total: Mechanical & Electrical	↓	11.85	26.50	39	12.35%	17.40%	26%
40	0010	**GARAGES, MUNICIPAL (Repair)**	S.F.	97	129	182			
	0020	Total project costs	C.F.	6.05	7.70	13.25			
	0500	Masonry	S.F.	5.10	17.85	27.50	4.03%	9.15%	12.50%
	2720	Plumbing		4.36	8.35	15.75	3.59%	6.70%	7.95%
	2730	Heating & ventilating		7.45	10.80	21	6.15%	7.45%	13.50%
	2900	Electrical		7.15	11.30	16.40	6.65%	8.15%	11.15%
	3100	Total: Mechanical & Electrical	↓	33	46	66.50	21.50%	23%	28.50%
41	0010	**GARAGES, PARKING**	S.F.	38.50	55	95			
	0020	Total project costs	C.F.	3.55	4.82	7			

		**50 17 00	S.F. Costs**	UNIT	UNIT COSTS			% OF TOTAL			
				1/4	MEDIAN	3/4	1/4	MEDIAN	3/4	
41	2720	Plumbing	S.F.	.65	1.66	2.56	1.72%	2.70%	3.85%	**41**
	2900	Electrical		2.08	2.74	4	4.52%	5.40%	6.35%	
	3100	Total: Mechanical & Electrical	↓	4.03	5.90	7.35	7%	8.90%	11.05%	
	3200									
	9000	Per car, total cost	Car	16,000	20,000	25,500				
43	0010	**GYMNASIUMS**	S.F.	105	140	193				**43**
	0020	Total project costs	C.F.	5.25	7.10	8.75				
	1800	Equipment	S.F.	2.50	4.68	8.45	1.76%	3.26%	6.70%	
	2720	Plumbing		5.75	7.75	10.20	4.65%	6.40%	7.75%	
	2770	Heating, ventilating, air conditioning		6.25	10.90	22	5.15%	9.05%	11.10%	
	2900	Electrical		8.35	11	14.65	6.75%	8.50%	10.30%	
	3100	Total: Mechanical & Electrical	↓	28.50	40	48.50	19.75%	23.50%	29%	
	3500	See also division 11480 (MF2004 11 67 00)								
46	0010	**HOSPITALS**	S.F.	202	253	350				**46**
	0020	Total project costs	C.F.	15.30	19.05	27				
	1800	Equipment	S.F.	5.10	9.85	17	.80%	2.53%	4.80%	
	2720	Plumbing		17.40	24.50	31.50	7.60%	9.10%	10.85%	
	2770	Heating, ventilating, air conditioning		25.50	32.50	45.50	7.80%	12.95%	16.65%	
	2900	Electrical		22.50	30	44.50	10%	11.75%	14.10%	
	3100	Total: Mechanical & Electrical	↓	65	90.50	134	28%	33.50%	37%	
	9000	Per bed or person, total cost	Bed	233,500	322,000	371,000				
	9900	See also division 11700 (MF2004 11 71 00)								
48	0010	**HOUSING For the Elderly**	S.F.	99	126	154				**48**
	0020	Total project costs	C.F.	7.10	9.85	12.55				
	0100	Site work	S.F.	6.90	10.75	15.75	5.05%	7.90%	12.10%	
	0500	Masonry		1.87	11.30	16.50	1.30%	6.05%	11%	
	1800	Equipment		2.40	3.30	5.25	1.88%	3.23%	4.43%	
	2510	Conveying systems		2.24	3.24	4.40	1.78%	2.20%	2.81%	
	2720	Plumbing		7.40	9.40	11.85	8.15%	9.55%	10.50%	
	2730	Heating, ventilating, air conditioning		3.78	5.35	8	3.30%	5.60%	7.25%	
	2900	Electrical		7.40	10.05	12.85	7.30%	8.50%	10.25%	
	3100	Total: Mechanical & Electrical	↓	25.50	31.50	40.50	18.10%	22.50%	29%	
	9000	Per rental unit, total cost	Unit	92,500	108,000	120,000				
	9500	Total: Mechanical & Electrical	"	20,600	23,600	27,600				
50	0010	**HOUSING Public (Low Rise)**	S.F.	83.50	116	151				**50**
	0020	Total project costs	C.F.	6.60	9.25	11.50				
	0100	Site work	S.F.	10.60	15.30	25	8.35%	11.75%	16.50%	
	1800	Equipment		2.27	3.70	5.65	2.26%	3.03%	4.24%	
	2720	Plumbing		6	7.95	10.05	7.15%	9.05%	11.60%	
	2730	Heating, ventilating, air conditioning		3.02	5.85	6.40	4.26%	6.05%	6.45%	
	2900	Electrical		5.05	7.50	10.45	5.10%	6.55%	8.25%	
	3100	Total: Mechanical & Electrical	↓	24	31	34.50	14.50%	17.55%	26.50%	
	9000	Per apartment, total cost	Apt.	91,500	104,000	131,000				
	9500	Total: Mechanical & Electrical	"	19,500	24,100	26,700				
51	0010	**ICE SKATING RINKS**	S.F.	71.50	167	183				**51**
	0020	Total project costs	C.F.	5.25	5.35	6.20				
	2720	Plumbing	S.F.	2.66	5	5.10	3.12%	3.23%	5.65%	
	2900	Electrical	↓	7.65	11.70	12.40	6.30%	10.15%	15.05%	
52	0010	**JAILS**	S.F.	185	280	360				**52**
	0020	Total project costs	C.F.	19.60	27.50	32				
	1800	Equipment	S.F.	8.45	25	42.50	2.80%	6.95%	9.80%	
	2720	Plumbing		21	28	37	7%	8.90%	13.35%	
	2770	Heating, ventilating, air conditioning		19.60	26	50.50	7.50%	9.45%	17.75%	
	2900	Electrical		23	31	39	9.40%	11.70%	15.25%	
	3100	Total: Mechanical & Electrical	↓	61	108	128	28%	30%	34%	
53	0010	**LIBRARIES**	S.F.	140	186	243				**53**
	0020	Total project costs	C.F.	9.40	11.75	15				

50 17 00 | S.F. Costs

			UNIT	UNIT COSTS			% OF TOTAL			
				1/4	MEDIAN	3/4	1/4	MEDIAN	3/4	
53	0500	Masonry	S.F.	9.30	19	31.50	5.60%	7.15%	10.95%	53
	1800	Equipment		1.88	5.05	7.60	.28%	1.39%	4.07%	
	2720	Plumbing		5.05	7.20	10	3.38%	4.60%	5.70%	
	2770	Heating, ventilating, air conditioning		11.20	19	23	7.80%	10.95%	12.80%	
	2900	Electrical		14.10	18.65	25	8.40%	10.55%	12%	
	3100	Total: Mechanical & Electrical	↓	46	56	65.50	21%	24%	28%	
54	0010	**LIVING, ASSISTED**	S.F.	127	151	176				54
	0020	Total project costs	C.F.	10.70	12.50	14.20				
	0500	Masonry	S.F.	3.68	4.44	5.45	2.36%	3.16%	3.86%	
	1800	Equipment		2.81	3.35	4.30	2.12%	2.45%	2.87%	
	2720	Plumbing		10.65	14.25	14.75	6.05%	8.15%	10.60%	
	2770	Heating, ventilating, air conditioning		12.65	13.20	14.45	7.95%	9.35%	9.70%	
	2900	Electrical		12.45	14	16.15	9%	9.95%	10.65%	
	3100	Total: Mechanical & Electrical	↓	34	40.50	47	24%	28.50%	31.50%	
55	0010	**MEDICAL CLINICS**	S.F.	129	159	203				55
	0020	Total project costs	C.F.	9.45	12.25	16.30				
	1800	Equipment	S.F.	1.65	7.35	11.40	1.05%	2.94%	6.35%	
	2720	Plumbing		8.60	12.10	16.15	6.15%	8.40%	10.10%	
	2770	Heating, ventilating, air conditioning		10.25	13.40	19.70	6.65%	8.85%	11.35%	
	2900	Electrical		11.10	15.75	20.50	8.10%	10%	12.20%	
	3100	Total: Mechanical & Electrical	↓	35.50	48	66	22%	27%	33.50%	
	3500	See also division 11700 (MF2004 11 71 00)								
57	0010	**MEDICAL OFFICES**	S.F.	121	151	185				57
	0020	Total project costs	C.F.	9.05	12.30	16.60				
	1800	Equipment	S.F.	4.01	7.95	11.15	.66%	4.87%	6.50%	
	2720	Plumbing		6.70	10.35	13.95	5.60%	6.80%	8.50%	
	2770	Heating, ventilating, air conditioning		8.10	11.70	15.45	6.10%	8%	9.70%	
	2900	Electrical		9.70	14.20	19.75	7.50%	9.80%	11.70%	
	3100	Total: Mechanical & Electrical	↓	26.50	38.50	55	19.30%	23%	28.50%	
59	0010	**MOTELS**	S.F.	76.50	111	145				59
	0020	Total project costs	C.F.	6.80	9.15	14.95				
	2720	Plumbing	S.F.	7.75	9.90	11.80	9.45%	10.60%	12.55%	
	2770	Heating, ventilating, air conditioning		4.74	7.05	12.65	5.60%	5.60%	10%	
	2900	Electrical		7.25	9.15	11.40	7.45%	9.05%	10.45%	
	3100	Total: Mechanical & Electrical	↓	21.50	31	53	18.50%	24%	25.50%	
	5000									
	9000	Per rental unit, total cost	Unit	39,000	74,000	80,000				
	9500	Total: Mechanical & Electrical	"	7,600	11,500	13,400				
60	0010	**NURSING HOMES**	S.F.	120	155	193				60
	0020	Total project costs	C.F.	9.45	11.80	16.15				
	1800	Equipment	S.F.	3.28	5	8.40	2%	3.62%	4.99%	
	2720	Plumbing		10.30	15.60	18.80	8.75%	10.10%	12.70%	
	2770	Heating, ventilating, air conditioning		10.85	16.45	22	9.70%	11.45%	11.80%	
	2900	Electrical		11.90	14.95	20.50	9.40%	10.60%	12.50%	
	3100	Total: Mechanical & Electrical	↓	28.50	39.50	66.50	26%	28%	30%	
	9000	Per bed or person, total cost	Bed	53,500	67,000	86,000				
61	0010	**OFFICES Low Rise (1 to 4 story)**	S.F.	101	132	172				61
	0020	Total project costs	C.F.	7.25	9.95	13.10				
	0100	Site work	S.F.	8.15	14.20	21	5.95%	9.70%	13.55%	
	0500	Masonry		3.92	7.90	14.40	2.61%	5.40%	8.45%	
	1800	Equipment		.91	2.11	5.75	.57%	1.50%	3.42%	
	2720	Plumbing		3.62	5.60	8.20	3.66%	4.50%	6.10%	
	2770	Heating, ventilating, air conditioning		8	11.15	16.35	7.20%	10.30%	11.70%	
	2900	Electrical		8.30	11.85	16.85	7.45%	9.65%	11.40%	
	3100	Total: Mechanical & Electrical	↓	23	31.50	48	18.20%	22%	27%	
62	0010	**OFFICES Mid Rise (5 to 10 story)**	S.F.	107	130	176				62
	0020	Total project costs	C.F.	7.60	9.70	13.75				

50 17 00 | S.F. Costs		UNIT	UNIT COSTS			% OF TOTAL			
			1/4	MEDIAN	3/4	1/4	MEDIAN	3/4	
62 2720	Plumbing	S.F.	3.24	5	7.20	2.83%	3.74%	4.50%	**62**
2770	Heating, ventilating, air conditioning		8.15	11.65	18.60	7.65%	9.40%	11%	
2900	Electrical		7.95	10.20	15.40	6.35%	7.80%	10%	
3100	Total: Mechanical & Electrical	↓	20.50	26.50	50.50	18.95%	21%	27.50%	
63 0010	**OFFICES High Rise (11 to 20 story)**	S.F.	132	166	204				**63**
0020	Total project costs	C.F.	9.20	11.50	16.50				
2900	Electrical	S.F.	8	9.75	14.50	5.80%	7.85%	10.50%	
3100	Total: Mechanical & Electrical	↓	26	34.50	58.50	16.90%	23.50%	34%	
64 0010	**POLICE STATIONS**	S.F.	158	208	265				**64**
0020	Total project costs	C.F.	12.60	15.40	21				
0500	Masonry	S.F.	15.80	26	33	7.80%	9.10%	11.35%	
1800	Equipment		2.27	11.05	17.50	.98%	3.35%	6.70%	
2720	Plumbing		8.85	17.60	22	5.65%	6.90%	10.75%	
2770	Heating, ventilating, air conditioning		12.95	18.35	26	5.85%	10.55%	11.70%	
2900	Electrical		17.25	25	32.50	9.80%	11.70%	14.50%	
3100	Total: Mechanical & Electrical	↓	65.50	69	92	28.50%	31.50%	32.50%	
65 0010	**POST OFFICES**	S.F.	125	154	196				**65**
0020	Total project costs	C.F.	7.50	9.50	10.80				
2720	Plumbing	S.F.	5.05	6.95	8.80	4.24%	5.30%	5.60%	
2770	Heating, ventilating, air conditioning		7.85	10.85	12.05	6.65%	7.15%	9.35%	
2900	Electrical		10.30	14.50	17.20	7.25%	9%	11%	
3100	Total: Mechanical & Electrical	↓	29.50	39	44	16.25%	18.80%	22%	
66 0010	**POWER PLANTS**	S.F.	865	1,150	2,100				**66**
0020	Total project costs	C.F.	24	52	111				
2900	Electrical	S.F.	61	130	193	9.30%	12.75%	21.50%	
8100	Total: Mechanical & Electrical	↓	152	495	1,100	32.50%	32.50%	52.50%	
67 0010	**RELIGIOUS EDUCATION**	S.F.	101	131	161				**67**
0020	Total project costs	C.F.	5.60	8	10				
2720	Plumbing	S.F.	4.20	5.95	8.40	4.40%	5.30%	7.10%	
2770	Heating, ventilating, air conditioning		10.60	12	16.95	10.05%	11.45%	12.35%	
2900	Electrical		7.40	11.25	14.85	7.60%	9.05%	10.35%	
3100	Total: Mechanical & Electrical	↓	32.50	42.50	52	22%	23%	27%	
69 0010	**RESEARCH Laboratories & Facilities**	S.F.	154	217	315				**69**
0020	Total project costs	C.F.	11.20	22	26.50				
1800	Equipment	S.F.	6.70	13.15	32	.94%	4.58%	9.10%	
2720	Plumbing		10.95	19.30	31	6.15%	8.30%	10.80%	
2770	Heating, ventilating, air conditioning		13.55	45.50	54	7.25%	16.50%	17.50%	
2900	Electrical		18.10	29	47.50	9.55%	11.15%	14.60%	
3100	Total: Mechanical & Electrical	↓	57.50	102	144	29.50%	37%	41%	
70 0010	**RESTAURANTS**	S.F.	146	188	245				**70**
0020	Total project costs	C.F.	12.25	16.10	21				
1800	Equipment	S.F.	8.65	23	35	6.10%	13%	15.65%	
2720	Plumbing		11.55	14	18.40	6.10%	8.15%	9%	
2770	Heating, ventilating, air conditioning		14.70	20.50	24.50	9.20%	12%	12.40%	
2900	Electrical		15.40	19	24.50	8.35%	10.55%	11.55%	
3100	Total: Mechanical & Electrical	↓	47.50	51	66	21%	25%	29.50%	
9000	Per seat unit, total cost	Seat	5,350	7,125	8,450				
9500	Total: Mechanical & Electrical	"	1,350	1,775	2,100				
72 0010	**RETAIL STORES**	S.F.	68	91.50	121				**72**
0020	Total project costs	C.F.	4.62	6.60	9.15				
2720	Plumbing	S.F.	2.47	4.12	7.05	3.26%	4.60%	6.80%	
2770	Heating, ventilating, air conditioning		5.35	7.30	10.95	6.75%	8.75%	10.15%	
2900	Electrical		6.15	8.40	12.10	7.25%	9.90%	11.60%	
3100	Total: Mechanical & Electrical	↓	16.30	21	28	17.05%	21%	23.50%	
74 0010	**SCHOOLS Elementary**	S.F.	111	138	169				**74**
0020	Total project costs	C.F.	7.25	9.30	12.05				
0500	Masonry	S.F.	7.85	16.95	25	4.89%	10.50%	14%	
1800	Equipment	↓	2.58	4.93	9.30	1.83%	3.13%	4.61%	

50 17 00 | S.F. Costs

			UNIT	UNIT COSTS			% OF TOTAL			
				1/4	MEDIAN	3/4	1/4	MEDIAN	3/4	
74	2720	Plumbing	S.F.	6.40	9.05	12.05	5.70%	7.15%	9.35%	74
	2730	Heating, ventilating, air conditioning		9.60	15.25	21.50	8.15%	10.80%	14.90%	
	2900	Electrical		10.50	14	17.85	8.45%	10.05%	11.85%	
	3100	Total: Mechanical & Electrical	↓	38	46.50	59	25%	27.50%	30%	
	9000	Per pupil, total cost	Ea.	12,800	19,000	42,500				
	9500	Total: Mechanical & Electrical	"	3,600	4,550	11,500				
76	0010	**SCHOOLS Junior High & Middle**	S.F.	115	142	173				76
	0020	Total project costs	C.F.	7.30	9.40	10.55				
	0500	Masonry	S.F.	12.30	18.40	22.50	7.55%	11.10%	14.30%	
	1800	Equipment		3.14	5.90	8.65	1.80%	3.03%	4.80%	
	2720	Plumbing		6.70	8.25	10.20	5.30%	6.80%	7.25%	
	2770	Heating, ventilating, air conditioning		13.35	16.20	28.50	8.90%	11.55%	14.20%	
	2900	Electrical		11.70	14.45	18.25	8.05%	9.55%	10.60%	
	3100	Total: Mechanical & Electrical	↓	36.50	47	58.50	23%	25.50%	29.50%	
	9000	Per pupil, total cost	Ea.	14,500	19,100	25,600				
78	0010	**SCHOOLS Senior High**	S.F.	120	147	184				78
	0020	Total project costs	C.F.	7.20	10.10	17.05				
	1800	Equipment	S.F.	3.17	7.40	10.25	1.88%	2.67%	4.30%	
	2720	Plumbing		6.70	10.05	18.35	5.60%	6.90%	8.30%	
	2770	Heating, ventilating, air conditioning		11.50	15.65	24	8.95%	11.60%	15%	
	2900	Electrical		12.05	16.05	23.50	8.70%	10.35%	12.50%	
	3100	Total: Mechanical & Electrical	↓	39.50	47	76	24%	26.50%	28.50%	
	9000	Per pupil, total cost	Ea.	11,200	22,900	28,600				
80	0010	**SCHOOLS Vocational**	S.F.	96.50	140	173				80
	0020	Total project costs	C.F.	6	8.60	11.90				
	0500	Masonry	S.F.	4.24	14	21.50	3.20%	4.61%	10.95%	
	1800	Equipment		3.02	7.50	10.35	1.24%	3.10%	4.26%	
	2720	Plumbing		6.15	9.20	13.55	5.40%	6.90%	8.55%	
	2770	Heating, ventilating, air conditioning		8.65	16.05	27	8.60%	11.90%	14.65%	
	2900	Electrical		10.05	13.75	18.80	8.45%	11%	13.20%	
	3100	Total: Mechanical & Electrical	↓	38	66.50	85	27.50%	29.50%	31%	
	9000	Per pupil, total cost	Ea.	13,400	36,000	53,500				
83	0010	**SPORTS ARENAS**	S.F.	84.50	113	174				83
	0020	Total project costs	C.F.	4.58	8.20	10.60				
	2720	Plumbing	S.F.	4.22	7.40	15.65	4.35%	6.35%	9.40%	
	2770	Heating, ventilating, air conditioning		10.55	12.45	17.30	8.80%	10.20%	13.55%	
	2900	Electrical	↓	7.80	11.90	15.40	7.65%	9.75%	11.90%	
85	0010	**SUPERMARKETS**	S.F.	78	90	106				85
	0020	Total project costs	C.F.	4.34	5.25	7.95				
	2720	Plumbing	S.F.	4.35	5.50	6.40	5.40%	6%	7.45%	
	2770	Heating, ventilating, air conditioning		6.40	8.50	10.35	8.60%	8.65%	9.60%	
	2900	Electrical		9.15	11.15	13.25	10.40%	12.45%	13.60%	
	3100	Total: Mechanical & Electrical	↓	25	26.50	35.50	23.50%	27.50%	28.50%	
86	0010	**SWIMMING POOLS**	S.F.	126	295	450				86
	0020	Total project costs	C.F.	10.10	12.60	13.75				
	2720	Plumbing	S.F.	11.65	13.35	17.90	4.80%	9.70%	20.50%	
	2900	Electrical		9.60	15.35	34	6.05%	6.95%	7.60%	
	3100	Total: Mechanical & Electrical	↓	60	79	104	11.15%	14.10%	23.50%	
87	0010	**TELEPHONE EXCHANGES**	S.F.	157	238	310				87
	0020	Total project costs	C.F.	10.40	16.75	23				
	2720	Plumbing	S.F.	7.05	10.90	16	4.52%	5.80%	6.90%	
	2770	Heating, ventilating, air conditioning		16.40	33	41	11.80%	16.05%	18.40%	
	2900	Electrical		17.05	27	48	10.90%	14%	17.85%	
	3100	Total: Mechanical & Electrical	↓	50.50	95.50	135	29.50%	33.50%	44.50%	
91	0010	**THEATERS**	S.F.	99.50	135	199				91
	0020	Total project costs	C.F.	4.87	7.20	10.55				

50 17 00 | S.F. Costs		UNIT	UNIT COSTS			% OF TOTAL			
			1/4	MEDIAN	3/4	1/4	MEDIAN	3/4	
91	2720	Plumbing	S.F.	3.28	3.80	15.55	2.92%	4.70%	6.80%	**91**
	2770	Heating, ventilating, air conditioning		10.25	12.40	15.35	8%	12.25%	13.40%	
	2900	Electrical		9.20	12.45	25.50	8.05%	9.35%	12.25%	
	3100	Total: Mechanical & Electrical		23.50	32	37.50	21.50%	25.50%	27.50%	
94	0010	**TOWN HALLS City Halls & Municipal Buildings**	S.F.	110	149	195				**94**
	0020	Total project costs	C.F.	7.95	12.40	18.10				
	2720	Plumbing	S.F.	4.91	9.20	16.10	4.31%	5.95%	7.95%	
	2770	Heating, ventilating, air conditioning		8.85	17.60	26	7.05%	9.05%	13.45%	
	2900	Electrical		11.15	15.40	21	8.05%	9.45%	11.65%	
	3100	Total: Mechanical & Electrical		38.50	49	75	22%	26.50%	31%	
97	0010	**WAREHOUSES & Storage Buildings**	S.F.	44	63	93				**97**
	0020	Total project costs	C.F.	2.30	3.60	5.95				
	0100	Site work	S.F.	4.53	9	13.55	6.05%	12.95%	19.55%	
	0500	Masonry		2.49	6.25	13.45	3.60%	7.35%	12%	
	1800	Equipment		.67	1.52	8.55	.72%	1.69%	5.55%	
	2720	Plumbing		1.46	2.62	4.91	2.90%	4.80%	6.55%	
	2730	Heating, ventilating, air conditioning		1.67	4.71	6.30	2.41%	5%	8.90%	
	2900	Electrical		2.60	4.89	8	5.15%	7.20%	10.05%	
	3100	Total: Mechanical & Electrical		7.25	11.10	22	13.30%	18.90%	26%	
99	0010	**WAREHOUSE & OFFICES Combination**	S.F.	54	72	99				**99**
	0020	Total project costs	C.F.	2.76	4.01	5.90				
	1800	Equipment	S.F.	.93	1.81	2.69	.42%	1.19%	2.40%	
	2720	Plumbing		2.08	3.63	5.40	3.74%	4.76%	6.30%	
	2770	Heating, ventilating, air conditioning		3.29	5.15	7.20	5%	5.65%	10.05%	
	2900	Electrical		3.68	5.45	8.50	5.85%	8%	10%	
	3100	Total: Mechanical & Electrical		10.25	15.55	24.50	14.55%	19.95%	24.50%	

Square Foot Project Size Modifier

One factor that affects the S.F. cost of a particular building is the size. In general, for buildings built to the same specifications in the same locality, the larger building will have the lower S.F. cost. This is due mainly to the decreasing contribution of the exterior walls, plus the economy of scale usually achievable in larger buildings. The area conversion scale shown below will give a factor to convert costs for the typical size building to an adjusted cost for the particular project.

The square foot base size table lists the median costs, most typical project size in our accumulated data, and the range in size of the projects.

The size factor for your project is determined by dividing your project area in S.F. by the typical project size for the particular building type. With this factor, enter the area conversion scale at the appropriate size factor and determine the appropriate cost multiplier for your building size.

Example: Determine the cost per S.F. for a 100,000 S.F. Mid-rise apartment building.

$$\frac{\text{Proposed building area} = 100,000 \text{ S.F.}}{\text{Typical size from below} = 50,000 \text{ S.F.}} = 2.00$$

Enter area conversion scale at 2.0, intersect curve, read horizontally the appropriate cost multiplier of .94. Size adjusted cost becomes .94 × $117.00 = $110.00 based on national average costs.

Note: For size factors less than .50, the cost multiplier is 1.1
For size factors greater than 3.5, the cost multiplier is .90

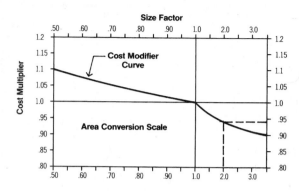

Square Foot Base Size

Building Type	Median Cost per S.F.	Typical Size Gross S.F.	Typical Range Gross S.F.	Building Type	Median Cost per S.F.	Typical Size Gross S.F.	Typical Range Gross S.F.
Apartments, Low Rise	$ 92.50	21,000	9,700 - 37,200	Jails	$ 280.00	40,000	5,500 - 145,000
Apartments, Mid Rise	117.00	50,000	32,000 - 100,000	Libraries	186.00	12,000	7,000 - 31,000
Apartments, High Rise	127.00	145,000	95,000 - 600,000	Living, Assisted	151.00	32,300	23,500 - 50,300
Auditoriums	158.00	25,000	7,600 - 39,000	Medical Clinics	159.00	7,200	4,200 - 15,700
Auto Sales	115.00	20,000	10,800 - 28,600	Medical Offices	151.00	6,000	4,000 - 15,000
Banks	207.00	4,200	2,500 - 7,500	Motels	111.00	40,000	15,800 - 120,000
Churches	143.00	17,000	2,000 - 42,000	Nursing Homes	155.00	23,000	15,000 - 37,000
Clubs, Country	144.00	6,500	4,500 - 15,000	Offices, Low Rise	132.00	20,000	5,000 - 80,000
Clubs, Social	138.00	10,000	6,000 - 13,500	Offices, Mid Rise	130.00	120,000	20,000 - 300,000
Clubs, YMCA	164.00	28,300	12,800 - 39,400	Offices, High Rise	166.00	260,000	120,000 - 800,000
Colleges (Class)	164.00	50,000	15,000 - 150,000	Police Stations	208.00	10,500	4,000 - 19,000
Colleges (Science Lab)	264.00	45,600	16,600 - 80,000	Post Offices	154.00	12,400	6,800 - 30,000
College (Student Union)	195.00	33,400	16,000 - 85,000	Power Plants	1150.00	7,500	1,000 - 20,000
Community Center	147.00	9,400	5,300 - 16,700	Religious Education	131.00	9,000	6,000 - 12,000
Court Houses	202.00	32,400	17,800 - 106,000	Research	217.00	19,000	6,300 - 45,000
Dept. Stores	85.50	90,000	44,000 - 122,000	Restaurants	188.00	4,400	2,800 - 6,000
Dormitories, Low Rise	166.00	25,000	10,000 - 95,000	Retail Stores	91.50	7,200	4,000 - 17,600
Dormitories, Mid Rise	192.00	85,000	20,000 - 200,000	Schools, Elementary	138.00	41,000	24,500 - 55,000
Factories	83.00	26,400	12,900 - 50,000	Schools, Jr. High	142.00	92,000	52,000 - 119,000
Fire Stations	153.00	5,800	4,000 - 8,700	Schools, Sr. High	147.00	101,000	50,500 - 175,000
Fraternity Houses	142.00	12,500	8,200 - 14,800	Schools, Vocational	140.00	37,000	20,500 - 82,000
Funeral Homes	159.00	10,000	4,000 - 20,000	Sports Arenas	113.00	15,000	5,000 - 40,000
Garages, Commercial	102.00	9,300	5,000 - 13,600	Supermarkets	90.00	44,000	12,000 - 60,000
Garages, Municipal	129.00	8,300	4,500 - 12,600	Swimming Pools	295.00	20,000	10,000 - 32,000
Garages, Parking	55.00	163,000	76,400 - 225,300	Telephone Exchange	238.00	4,500	1,200 - 10,600
Gymnasiums	140.00	19,200	11,600 - 41,000	Theaters	135.00	10,500	8,800 - 17,500
Hospitals	253.00	55,000	27,200 - 125,000	Town Halls	149.00	10,800	4,800 - 23,400
House (Elderly)	126.00	37,000	21,000 - 66,000	Warehouses	63.00	25,000	8,000 - 72,000
Housing (Public)	116.00	36,000	14,400 - 74,400	Warehouse & Office	72.00	25,000	8,000 - 72,000
Ice Rinks	167.00	29,000	27,200 - 33,600				

A	Area Square Feet; Ampere	Brk., brk	Brick	Csc	Cosecant
AAFES	Army and Air Force Exchange Service	brkt	Bracket	C.S.F.	Hundred Square Feet
		Brng.	Bearing	CSI	Construction Specifications Institute
ABS	Acrylonitrile Butadiene Stryrene; Asbestos Bonded Steel	Brs.	Brass		
		Brz.	Bronze	CT	Current Transformer
A.C., AC	Alternating Current; Air-Conditioning; Asbestos Cement; Plywood Grade A & C	Bsn.	Basin	CTS	Copper Tube Size
		Btr.	Better	Cu	Copper, Cubic
		Btu	British Thermal Unit	Cu. Ft.	Cubic Foot
		BTUH	BTU per Hour	cw	Continuous Wave
ACI	American Concrete Institute	Bu.	bushels	C.W.	Cool White; Cold Water
ACR	Air Conditioning Refrigeration	BUR	Built-up Roofing	Cwt.	100 Pounds
ADA	Americans with Disabilities Act	BX	Interlocked Armored Cable	C.W.X.	Cool White Deluxe
AD	Plywood, Grade A & D	°C	degree centegrade	C.Y.	Cubic Yard (27 cubic feet)
Addit.	Additional	c	Conductivity, Copper Sweat	C.Y./Hr.	Cubic Yard per Hour
Adj.	Adjustable	C	Hundred; Centigrade	Cyl.	Cylinder
af	Audio-frequency	C/C	Center to Center, Cedar on Cedar	d	Penny (nail size)
AFUE	Annual Fuel Utilization Efficiency	C-C	Center to Center	D	Deep; Depth; Discharge
AGA	American Gas Association	Cab	Cabinet	Dis., Disch.	Discharge
Agg.	Aggregate	Cair.	Air Tool Laborer	Db	Decibel
A.H., Ah	Ampere Hours	Cal.	caliper	Dbl.	Double
A hr.	Ampere-hour	Calc	Calculated	DC	Direct Current
A.H.U., AHU	Air Handling Unit	Cap.	Capacity	DDC	Direct Digital Control
A.I.A.	American Institute of Architects	Carp.	Carpenter	Demob.	Demobilization
AIC	Ampere Interrupting Capacity	C.B.	Circuit Breaker	d.f.t.	Dry Film Thickness
Allow.	Allowance	C.C.A.	Chromate Copper Arsenate	d.f.u.	Drainage Fixture Units
alt., alt	Alternate	C.C.F.	Hundred Cubic Feet	D.H.	Double Hung
Alum.	Aluminum	cd	Candela	DHW	Domestic Hot Water
a.m.	Ante Meridiem	cd/sf	Candela per Square Foot	DI	Ductile Iron
Amp.	Ampere	CD	Grade of Plywood Face & Back	Diag.	Diagonal
Anod.	Anodized	CDX	Plywood, Grade C & D, exterior glue	Diam., Dia	Diameter
ANSI	American National Standards Institute			Distrib.	Distribution
		Cefi.	Cement Finisher	Div.	Division
APA	American Plywood Association	Cem.	Cement	Dk.	Deck
Approx.	Approximate	CF	Hundred Feet	D.L.	Dead Load; Diesel
Apt.	Apartment	C.F.	Cubic Feet	DLH	Deep Long Span Bar Joist
Asb.	Asbestos	CFM	Cubic Feet per Minute	dlx	Deluxe
A.S.B.C.	American Standard Building Code	CFRP	Carbon Fiber Reinforced Plastic	Do.	Ditto
Asbe.	Asbestos Worker	c.g.	Center of Gravity	DOP	Dioctyl Phthalate Penetration Test (Air Filters)
ASCE	American Society of Civil Engineers	CHW	Chilled Water; Commercial Hot Water		
A.S.H.R.A.E.	American Society of Heating, Refrig. & AC Engineers			Dp., dp	Depth
		C.I., CI	Cast Iron	D.P.S.T.	Double Pole, Single Throw
ASME	American Society of Mechanical Engineers	C.I.P., CIP	Cast in Place	Dr.	Drive
		Circ.	Circuit	DR	Dimension Ratio
ASTM	American Society for Testing and Materials	C.L.	Carload Lot	Drink.	Drinking
		CL	Chain Link	D.S.	Double Strength
Attchmt.	Attachment	Clab.	Common Laborer	D.S.A.	Double Strength A Grade
Avg., Ave.	Average	Clam	Common maintenance laborer	D.S.B.	Double Strength B Grade
AWG	American Wire Gauge	C.L.F.	Hundred Linear Feet	Dty.	Duty
AWWA	American Water Works Assoc.	CLF	Current Limiting Fuse	DWV	Drain Waste Vent
Bbl.	Barrel	CLP	Cross Linked Polyethylene	DX	Deluxe White, Direct Expansion
B&B, BB	Grade B and Better; Balled & Burlapped	cm	Centimeter	dyn	Dyne
		CMP	Corr. Metal Pipe	e	Eccentricity
B&S	Bell and Spigot	CMU	Concrete Masonry Unit	E	Equipment Only; East; emissivity
B.&W.	Black and White	CN	Change Notice	Ea.	Each
b.c.c.	Body-centered Cubic	Col.	Column	EB	Encased Burial
B.C.Y.	Bank Cubic Yards	CO₂	Carbon Dioxide	Econ.	Economy
BE	Bevel End	Comb.	Combination	E.C.Y	Embankment Cubic Yards
B.F.	Board Feet	comm.	Commercial, Communication	EDP	Electronic Data Processing
Bg. cem.	Bag of Cement	Compr.	Compressor	EIFS	Exterior Insulation Finish System
BHP	Boiler Horsepower; Brake Horsepower	Conc.	Concrete	E.D.R.	Equiv. Direct Radiation
		Cont., cont	Continuous; Continued, Container	Eq.	Equation
B.I.	Black Iron	Corr.	Corrugated	EL	elevation
bidir.	bidirectional	Cos	Cosine	Elec.	Electrician; Electrical
Bit., Bitum.	Bituminous	Cot	Cotangent	Elev.	Elevator; Elevating
Bit., Conc.	Bituminous Concrete	Cov.	Cover	EMT	Electrical Metallic Conduit; Thin Wall Conduit
Bk.	Backed	C/P	Cedar on Paneling		
Bkrs.	Breakers	CPA	Control Point Adjustment	Eng.	Engine, Engineered
Bldg., bldg	Building	Cplg.	Coupling	EPDM	Ethylene Propylene Diene Monomer
Blk.	Block	CPM	Critical Path Method		
Bm.	Beam	CPVC	Chlorinated Polyvinyl Chloride	EPS	Expanded Polystyrene
Boil.	Boilermaker	C.Pr.	Hundred Pair	Eqhv.	Equip. Oper., Heavy
bpm	Blows per Minute	CRC	Cold Rolled Channel	Eqlt.	Equip. Oper., Light
BR	Bedroom	Creos.	Creosote	Eqmd.	Equip. Oper., Medium
Brg.	Bearing	Crpt.	Carpet & Linoleum Layer	Eqmm.	Equip. Oper., Master Mechanic
Brhe.	Bricklayer Helper	CRT	Cathode-ray Tube	Eqol.	Equip. Oper., Oilers
Bric.	Bricklayer	CS	Carbon Steel, Constant Shear Bar Joist	Equip.	Equipment
				ERW	Electric Resistance Welded

E.S.	Energy Saver	H	High Henry	Lath.	Lather
Est.	Estimated	HC	High Capacity	Lav.	Lavatory
esu	Electrostatic Units	H.D., HD	Heavy Duty; High Density	lb.; #	Pound
E.W.	Each Way	H.D.O.	High Density Overlaid	L.B., LB	Load Bearing; L Conduit Body
EWT	Entering Water Temperature	HDPE	High density polyethelene plastic	L. & E.	Labor & Equipment
Excav.	Excavation	Hdr.	Header	lb./hr.	Pounds per Hour
excl	Excluding	Hdwe.	Hardware	lb./L.F.	Pounds per Linear Foot
Exp., exp	Expansion, Exposure	H.I.D., HID	High Intensity Discharge	lbf/sq.in.	Pound-force per Square Inch
Ext., ext	Exterior; Extension	Help.	Helper Average	L.C.L.	Less than Carload Lot
Extru.	Extrusion	HEPA	High Efficiency Particulate Air	L.C.Y.	Loose Cubic Yard
f.	Fiber stress		Filter	Ld.	Load
F	Fahrenheit; Female; Fill	Hg	Mercury	LE	Lead Equivalent
Fab., fab	Fabricated; fabric	HIC	High Interrupting Capacity	LED	Light Emitting Diode
FBGS	Fiberglass	HM	Hollow Metal	L.F.	Linear Foot
F.C.	Footcandles	HMWPE	high molecular weight	L.F. Nose	Linear Foot of Stair Nosing
f.c.c.	Face-centered Cubic		polyethylene	L.F. Rsr	Linear Foot of Stair Riser
f'c.	Compressive Stress in Concrete;	HO	High Output	Lg.	Long; Length; Large
	Extreme Compressive Stress	Horiz.	Horizontal	L & H	Light and Heat
F.E.	Front End	H.P., HP	Horsepower; High Pressure	LH	Long Span Bar Joist
FEP	Fluorinated Ethylene Propylene	H.P.F.	High Power Factor	L.H.	Labor Hours
	(Teflon)	Hr.	Hour	L.L., LL	Live Load
F.G.	Flat Grain	Hrs./Day	Hours per Day	L.L.D.	Lamp Lumen Depreciation
F.H.A.	Federal Housing Administration	HSC	High Short Circuit	lm	Lumen
Fig.	Figure	Ht.	Height	lm/sf	Lumen per Square Foot
Fin.	Finished	Htg.	Heating	lm/W	Lumen per Watt
FIPS	Female Iron Pipe Size	Htrs.	Heaters	LOA	Length Over All
Fixt.	Fixture	HVAC	Heating, Ventilation & Air-	log	Logarithm
FJP	Finger jointed and primed		Conditioning	L-O-L	Lateralolet
Fl. Oz.	Fluid Ounces	Hvy.	Heavy	long.	longitude
Flr.	Floor	HW	Hot Water	L.P., LP	Liquefied Petroleum; Low Pressure
FM	Frequency Modulation;	Hyd.; Hydr.	Hydraulic	L.P.F.	Low Power Factor
	Factory Mutual	Hz	Hertz (cycles)	LR	Long Radius
Fmg.	Framing	I.	Moment of Inertia	L.S.	Lump Sum
FM/UL	Factory Mutual/Underwriters Labs	IBC	International Building Code	Lt.	Light
Fdn.	Foundation	I.C.	Interrupting Capacity	Lt. Ga.	Light Gauge
FNPT	Female National Pipe Thread	ID	Inside Diameter	L.T.L.	Less than Truckload Lot
Fori.	Foreman, Inside	I.D.	Inside Dimension; Identification	Lt. Wt.	Lightweight
Foro.	Foreman, Outside	I.F.	Inside Frosted	L.V.	Low Voltage
Fount.	Fountain	I.M.C.	Intermediate Metal Conduit	M	Thousand; Material; Male;
fpm	Feet per Minute	In.	Inch		Light Wall Copper Tubing
FPT	Female Pipe Thread	Incan.	Incandescent	M²CA	Meters Squared Contact Area
Fr	Frame	Incl.	Included; Including	m/hr.; M.H.	Man-hour
F.R.	Fire Rating	Int.	Interior	mA	Milliampere
FRK	Foil Reinforced Kraft	Inst.	Installation	Mach.	Machine
FSK	Foil/scrim/kraft	Insul., insul	Insulation/Insulated	Mag. Str.	Magnetic Starter
FRP	Fiberglass Reinforced Plastic	I.P.	Iron Pipe	Maint.	Maintenance
FS	Forged Steel	I.P.S., IPS	Iron Pipe Size	Marb.	Marble Setter
FSC	Cast Body; Cast Switch Box	IPT	Iron Pipe Threaded	Mat; Mat'l.	Material
Ft., ft	Foot; Feet	I.W.	Indirect Waste	Max.	Maximum
Ftng.	Fitting	J	Joule	MBF	Thousand Board Feet
Ftg.	Footing	J.I.C.	Joint Industrial Council	MBH	Thousand BTU's per hr.
Ft lb.	Foot Pound	K	Thousand; Thousand Pounds;	MC	Metal Clad Cable
Furn.	Furniture		Heavy Wall Copper Tubing, Kelvin	MCC	Motor Control Center
FVNR	Full Voltage Non-Reversing	K.A.H.	Thousand Amp. Hours	M.C.F.	Thousand Cubic Feet
FVR	Full Voltage Reversing	kcmil	Thousand Circular Mils	MCFM	Thousand Cubic Feet per Minute
FXM	Female by Male	KD	Knock Down	M.C.M.	Thousand Circular Mils
Fy.	Minimum Yield Stress of Steel	K.D.A.T.	Kiln Dried After Treatment	MCP	Motor Circuit Protector
g	Gram	kg	Kilogram	MD	Medium Duty
G	Gauss	kG	Kilogauss	MDF	Medium-density fibreboard
Ga.	Gauge	kgf	Kilogram Force	M.D.O.	Medium Density Overlaid
Gal., gal.	Gallon	kHz	Kilohertz	Med.	Medium
gpm, GPM	Gallon per Minute	Kip	1000 Pounds	MF	Thousand Feet
Galv., galv	Galvanized	KJ	Kiljoule	M.F.B.M.	Thousand Feet Board Measure
GC/MS	Gas Chromatograph/Mass	K.L.	Effective Length Factor	Mfg.	Manufacturing
	Spectrometer	K.L.F.	Kips per Linear Foot	Mfrs.	Manufacturers
Gen.	General	Km	Kilometer	mg	Milligram
GFI	Ground Fault Interrupter	KO	Knock Out	MGD	Million Gallons per Day
GFRC	Glass Fiber Reinforced Concrete	K.S.F.	Kips per Square Foot	MGPH	Thousand Gallons per Hour
Glaz.	Glazier	K.S.I.	Kips per Square Inch	MH, M.H.	Manhole; Metal Halide; Man-Hour
GPD	Gallons per Day	kV	Kilovolt	MHz	Megahertz
gpf	Gallon per flush	kVA	Kilovolt Ampere	Mi.	Mile
GPH	Gallons per Hour	kVAR	Kilovar (Reactance)	MI	Malleable Iron; Mineral Insulated
GPM	Gallons per Minute	KW	Kilowatt	MIPS	Male Iron Pipe Size
GR	Grade	KWh	Kilowatt-hour	mj	Mechanical Joint
Gran.	Granular	L	Labor Only; Length; Long;	m	Meter
Grnd.	Ground		Medium Wall Copper Tubing	mm	Millimeter
GVW	Gross Vehicle Weight	Lab.	Labor	Mill.	Millwright
GWB	Gypsum wall board	lat	Latitude	Min., min.	Minimum, minute

Misc.	Miscellaneous
ml	Milliliter, Mainline
M.L.F.	Thousand Linear Feet
Mo.	Month
Mobil.	Mobilization
Mog.	Mogul Base
MPH	Miles per Hour
MPT	Male Pipe Thread
MRGWB	Moisture Resistant Gypsum Wallboard
MRT	Mile Round Trip
ms	Millisecond
M.S.F.	Thousand Square Feet
Mstz.	Mosaic & Terrazzo Worker
M.S.Y.	Thousand Square Yards
Mtd., mtd., mtd	Mounted
Mthe.	Mosaic & Terrazzo Helper
Mtng.	Mounting
Mult.	Multi; Multiply
M.V.A.	Million Volt Amperes
M.V.A.R.	Million Volt Amperes Reactance
MV	Megavolt
MW	Megawatt
MXM	Male by Male
MYD	Thousand Yards
N	Natural; North
nA	Nanoampere
NA	Not Available; Not Applicable
N.B.C.	National Building Code
NC	Normally Closed
NEMA	National Electrical Manufacturers Assoc.
NEHB	Bolted Circuit Breaker to 600V.
NFPA	National Fire Protection Association
NLB	Non-Load-Bearing
NM	Non-Metallic Cable
nm	Nanometer
No.	Number
NO	Normally Open
N.O.C.	Not Otherwise Classified
Nose.	Nosing
NPT	National Pipe Thread
NQOD	Combination Plug-on/Bolt on Circuit Breaker to 240V.
N.R.C., NRC	Noise Reduction Coefficient/ Nuclear Regulator Commission
N.R.S.	Non Rising Stem
ns	Nanosecond
nW	Nanowatt
OB	Opposing Blade
OC	On Center
OD	Outside Diameter
O.D.	Outside Dimension
ODS	Overhead Distribution System
O.G.	Ogee
O.H.	Overhead
O&P	Overhead and Profit
Oper.	Operator
Opng.	Opening
Orna.	Ornamental
OSB	Oriented Strand Board
OS&Y	Outside Screw and Yoke
OSHA	Occupational Safety and Health Act
Ovhd.	Overhead
OWG	Oil, Water or Gas
Oz.	Ounce
P.	Pole; Applied Load; Projection
p.	Page
Pape.	Paperhanger
P.A.P.R.	Powered Air Purifying Respirator
PAR	Parabolic Reflector
P.B., PB	Push Button
Pc., Pcs.	Piece, Pieces
P.C.	Portland Cement; Power Connector
P.C.F.	Pounds per Cubic Foot
PCM	Phase Contrast Microscopy

PDCA	Painting and Decorating Contractors of America
P.E., PE	Professional Engineer; Porcelain Enamel; Polyethylene; Plain End
P.E.C.I.	Porcelain Enamel on Cast Iron
Perf.	Perforated
PEX	Cross linked polyethylene
Ph.	Phase
P.I.	Pressure Injected
Pile.	Pile Driver
Pkg.	Package
Pl.	Plate
Plah.	Plasterer Helper
Plas.	Plasterer
plf	Pounds Per Linear Foot
Pluh.	Plumbers Helper
Plum.	Plumber
Ply.	Plywood
p.m.	Post Meridiem
Pntd.	Painted
Pord.	Painter, Ordinary
pp	Pages
PP, PPL	Polypropylene
P.P.M.	Parts per Million
Pr.	Pair
P.E.S.B.	Pre-engineered Steel Building
Prefab.	Prefabricated
Prefin.	Prefinished
Prop.	Propelled
PSF, psf	Pounds per Square Foot
PSI, psi	Pounds per Square Inch
PSIG	Pounds per Square Inch Gauge
PSP	Plastic Sewer Pipe
Pspr.	Painter, Spray
Psst.	Painter, Structural Steel
P.T.	Potential Transformer
P. & T.	Pressure & Temperature
Ptd.	Painted
Ptns.	Partitions
Pu	Ultimate Load
PVC	Polyvinyl Chloride
Pvmt.	Pavement
PRV	Pressure Relief Valve
Pwr.	Power
Q	Quantity Heat Flow
Qt.	Quart
Quan., Qty.	Quantity
Q.C.	Quick Coupling
r	Radius of Gyration
R	Resistance
R.C.P.	Reinforced Concrete Pipe
Rect.	Rectangle
recpt.	receptacle
Reg.	Regular
Reinf.	Reinforced
Req'd.	Required
Res.	Resistant
Resi.	Residential
RF	Radio Frequency
RFID	Radio-frequency identification
Rgh.	Rough
RGS	Rigid Galvanized Steel
RHW	Rubber, Heat & Water Resistant; Residential Hot Water
rms	Root Mean Square
Rnd.	Round
Rodm.	Rodman
Rofc.	Roofer, Composition
Rofp.	Roofer, Precast
Rohe.	Roofer Helpers (Composition)
Rots.	Roofer, Tile & Slate
R.O.W.	Right of Way
RPM	Revolutions per Minute
R.S.	Rapid Start
Rsr	Riser
RT	Round Trip
S.	Suction; Single Entrance; South
SBS	Styrene Butadiere Styrene

SC	Screw Cover
SCFM	Standard Cubic Feet per Minute
Scaf.	Scaffold
Sch., Sched.	Schedule
S.C.R.	Modular Brick
S.D.	Sound Deadening
SDR	Standard Dimension Ratio
S.E.	Surfaced Edge
Sel.	Select
SER, SEU	Service Entrance Cable
S.F.	Square Foot
S.F.C.A.	Square Foot Contact Area
S.F. Flr.	Square Foot of Floor
S.F.G.	Square Foot of Ground
S.F. Hor.	Square Foot Horizontal
SFR	Square Feet of Radiation
S.F. Shlf.	Square Foot of Shelf
S4S	Surface 4 Sides
Shee.	Sheet Metal Worker
Sin.	Sine
Skwk.	Skilled Worker
SL	Saran Lined
S.L.	Slimline
Sldr.	Solder
SLH	Super Long Span Bar Joist
S.N.	Solid Neutral
SO	Stranded with oil resistant inside insulation
S-O-L	Socketolet
sp	Standpipe
S.P.	Static Pressure; Single Pole; Self-Propelled
Spri.	Sprinkler Installer
spwg	Static Pressure Water Gauge
S.P.D.T.	Single Pole, Double Throw
SPF	Spruce Pine Fir; Sprayed Polyurethane Foam
S.P.S.T.	Single Pole, Single Throw
SPT	Standard Pipe Thread
Sq.	Square; 100 Square Feet
Sq. Hd.	Square Head
Sq. In.	Square Inch
S.S.	Single Strength; Stainless Steel
S.S.B.	Single Strength B Grade
sst, ss	Stainless Steel
Sswk.	Structural Steel Worker
Sswl.	Structural Steel Welder
St.; Stl.	Steel
STC	Sound Transmission Coefficient
Std.	Standard
Stg.	Staging
STK	Select Tight Knot
STP	Standard Temperature & Pressure
Stpi.	Steamfitter, Pipefitter
Str.	Strength; Starter; Straight
Strd.	Stranded
Struct.	Structural
Sty.	Story
Subj.	Subject
Subs.	Subcontractors
Surf.	Surface
Sw.	Switch
Swbd.	Switchboard
S.Y.	Square Yard
Syn.	Synthetic
S.Y.P.	Southern Yellow Pine
Sys.	System
t.	Thickness
T	Temperature; Ton
Tan	Tangent
T.C.	Terra Cotta
T & C	Threaded and Coupled
T.D.	Temperature Difference
Tdd	Telecommunications Device for the Deaf
T.E.M.	Transmission Electron Microscopy
temp	Temperature, Tempered, Temporary
TFFN	Nylon Jacketed Wire

TFE	Tetrafluoroethylene (Teflon)	U.L., UL	Underwriters Laboratory	w/	With
T. & G.	Tongue & Groove;	Uld.	unloading	W.C., WC	Water Column; Water Closet
	Tar & Gravel	Unfin.	Unfinished	W.F.	Wide Flange
Th., Thk.	Thick	UPS	Uninterruptible Power Supply	W.G.	Water Gauge
Thn.	Thin	URD	Underground Residential	Wldg.	Welding
Thrded	Threaded		Distribution	W. Mile	Wire Mile
Tilf.	Tile Layer, Floor	US	United States	W-O-L	Weldolet
Tilh.	Tile Layer, Helper	USGBC	U.S. Green Building Council	W.R.	Water Resistant
THHN	Nylon Jacketed Wire	USP	United States Primed	Wrck.	Wrecker
THW.	Insulated Strand Wire	UTMCD	Uniform Traffic Manual For Control	W.S.P.	Water, Steam, Petroleum
THWN	Nylon Jacketed Wire		Devices	WT., Wt.	Weight
T.L., TL	Truckload	UTP	Unshielded Twisted Pair	WWF	Welded Wire Fabric
T.M.	Track Mounted	V	Volt	XFER	Transfer
Tot.	Total	VA	Volt Amperes	XFMR	Transformer
T-O-L	Threadolet	V.C.T.	Vinyl Composition Tile	XHD	Extra Heavy Duty
tmpd	Tempered	VAV	Variable Air Volume	XHHW,	Cross-Linked Polyethylene Wire
TPO	Thermoplastic Polyolefin	VC	Veneer Core	XLPE	Insulation
T.S.	Trigger Start	VDC	Volts Direct Current	XLP	Cross-linked Polyethylene
Tr.	Trade	Vent.	Ventilation	Xport	Transport
Transf.	Transformer	Vert.	Vertical	Y	Wye
Trhv.	Truck Driver, Heavy	V.F.	Vinyl Faced	yd	Yard
Trlr	Trailer	V.G.	Vertical Grain	yr	Year
Trlt.	Truck Driver, Light	VHF	Very High Frequency	Δ	Delta
TTY	Teletypewriter	VHO	Very High Output	%	Percent
TV	Television	Vib.	Vibrating	~	Approximately
T.W.	Thermoplastic Water Resistant	VLF	Vertical Linear Foot	Ø	Phase; diameter
	Wire	VOC	Volitile Organic Compound	@	At
UCI	Uniform Construction Index	Vol.	Volume	#	Pound; Number
UF	Underground Feeder	VRP	Vinyl Reinforced Polyester	<	Less Than
UGND	Underground Feeder	W	Wire; Watt; Wide; West	>	Greater Than
UHF	Ultra High Frequency			Z	zone
U.I.	United Inch				

Index

Index

Index

Index

Division Notes

		CREW	DAILY OUTPUT	LABOR-HOURS	UNIT	BARE COSTS				TOTAL INCL O&P
						MAT.	LABOR	EQUIP.	TOTAL	

Division Notes

	CREW	DAILY OUTPUT	LABOR-HOURS	UNIT	BARE COSTS				TOTAL INCL O&P
					MAT.	LABOR	EQUIP.	TOTAL	

Division Notes

		CREW	DAILY OUTPUT	LABOR-HOURS	UNIT	BARE COSTS				TOTAL INCL O&P
						MAT.	LABOR	EQUIP.	TOTAL	

Division Notes

	CREW	DAILY OUTPUT	LABOR-HOURS	UNIT	BARE COSTS				TOTAL INCL O&P
					MAT.	LABOR	EQUIP.	TOTAL	

Reed Construction Data/RSMeans— a tradition of excellence in construction cost information and services since 1942

Table of Contents
Annual Cost Guides
Seminars
New Titles
Reference Books
Order Form

For more information visit the RSMeans website at **www.rsmeans.com**

Unit prices according to the latest MasterFormat!

Book Selection Guide

The following table provides definitive information on the content of each cost data publication. The number of lines of data provided in each unit price or assemblies division, as well as the number of reference tables and crews, is listed for each book. The presence of other elements such as equipment rental costs, historical cost indexes, city cost indexes, square foot models, or cross-referenced indexes is also indicated. You can use the table to help select the RSMeans book that has the quantity and type of information you most need in your work.

Unit Cost Divisions	Building Construction	Mechanical	Electrical	Commercial Renovation	Square Foot	Site Work Landsc.	Green Building	Interior	Concrete Masonry	Open Shop	Heavy Construction	Light Commercial	Facilities Construction	Plumbing	Residential
1	582	395	411	508		521	196	319	463	581	511	244	1054	411	180
2	789	279	85	741		1005	180	399	222	788	746	481	1233	289	257
3	1689	347	231	1087		1477	995	329	2040	1688	1685	479	1787	317	385
4	963	21	0	932		729	179	620	1159	931	621	521	1176	0	435
5	1873	158	155	1068		811	1779	1073	716	1873	1034	954	1874	204	723
6	2404	18	18	2062		110	560	1523	278	2400	126	2085	2076	22	2612
7	1531	215	128	1569		584	747	516	509	1528	26	1282	1633	227	1018
8	2107	81	45	2530		268	1140	1768	112	2093	0	2109	2842	0	1511
9	1929	72	26	1726		313	449	2014	387	1870	15	1644	2179	54	1430
10	1006	17	10	623		215	27	818	158	1006	29	511	1098	235	224
11	1026	208	165	489		126	54	878	28	1010	0	230	1046	169	110
12	557	0	2	327		248	151	1669	12	545	19	364	1718	23	317
13	729	117	114	246		347	128	253	66	728	253	82	756	71	80
14	277	36	0	224		0	0	261	0	277	0	12	297	16	6
21	90	0	16	37		0	0	250	0	87	0	68	427	432	220
22	1159	7329	156	1170		1578	1099	849	20	1123	1687	861	7171	9082	712
23	1182	6901	586	886		160	898	741	38	1106	111	759	5013	1830	434
26	1379	499	10134	1039		816	661	1142	55	1351	562	1305	10083	444	621
27	72	0	298	34		13	0	60	0	72	39	52	280	0	4
28	97	58	137	72		0	21	79	0	100	0	41	152	44	26
31	1498	735	610	803		3206	289	7	1208	1443	3285	600	1560	660	611
32	782	54	8	859		4396	352	362	286	753	1824	407	1660	166	455
33	509	1020	542	209		2036	41	0	231	508	2024	120	1585	1211	118
34	109	0	47	4		192	0	0	31	64	195	0	130	0	0
35	18	0	0	0		327	0	0	0	18	442	0	83	0	0
41	60	0	0	32		0	0	22	0	60	30	0	67	14	0
44	75	83	0	0		0	0	0	0	0	0	0	75	75	0
46	23	16	0	0		274	151	0	0	23	264	0	33	33	0
48	12	0	27	0		0	27	0	0	12	19	12	12	0	12
Totals	**24527**	**18659**	**13951**	**19277**		**19752**	**10124**	**15952**	**8019**	**24038**	**15547**	**15223**	**49100**	**16029**	**12501**

Assem Div	Building Construction	Mechanical	Electrical	Commercial Renovation	Square Foot	Site Work Landscape	Assemblies	Green Building	Interior	Concrete Masonry	Heavy Construction	Light Commercial	Facilities Construction	Plumbing	Asm Div	Residential
A		15	0	188	150	577	598	0	0	536	571	154	24	0	1	368
B		0	0	848	2498	0	5658	56	329	1975	368	2089	174	0	2	211
C		0	0	647	872	0	1251	0	1576	146	0	762	249	0	3	588
D		1067	943	712	1856	72	2532	330	822	0	0	1342	1106	1081	4	851
E		0	0	86	260	0	300	0	5	0	0	257	5	0	5	392
F		0	0	0	114	0	114	0	0	0	0	114	3	0	6	357
G		522	442	318	262	3740	663	0	0	534	1558	199	288	758	7	307
															8	760
															9	80
															10	0
															11	0
															12	0
Totals		**1604**	**1385**	**2799**	**6012**	**4389**	**11116**	**386**	**2732**	**3191**	**2497**	**4917**	**1849**	**1839**		**3914**

Reference Section	Building Construction Costs	Mechanical	Electrical	Commercial Renovation	Square Foot	Site Work Landscape	Assem.	Green Building	Interior	Concrete Masonry	Open Shop	Heavy Construction	Light Commercial	Facilities Construction	Plumbing	Resi.
Reference Tables	yes	yes	yes	yes	no	yes	yes	yes	yes	yes	yes	yes	yes	yes	yes	yes
Models					111			25					50			28
Crews	561	561	561	540		561		558	561	561	538	561	538	540	561	538
Equipment Rental Costs	yes	yes	yes	yes		yes		yes	yes	yes	yes	yes	yes	yes	yes	yes
Historical Cost Indexes	yes	yes	yes	yes	yes	yes	yes	yes	yes	yes	yes	yes	yes	yes	yes	no
City Cost Indexes	yes	yes	yes	yes	yes	yes	yes	yes	yes	yes	yes	yes	yes	yes	yes	yes

901

RSMeans Building Construction Cost Data 2014

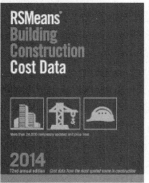

Offers you unchallenged unit price reliability in an easy-to-use format. Whether used for verifying complete, finished estimates or for periodic checks, it supplies more cost facts better and faster than any comparable source. More than 24,000 unit prices have been updated for 2014. The City Cost Indexes and Location Factors cover more than 930 areas, for indexing to any project location in North America. Order and get *RSMeans Quarterly Update Service* FREE.

$194.95 | Available Sept. 2013 | Catalog no. 60014

RSMeans Mechanical Cost Data 2014

Total unit and systems price guidance for mechanical construction . . . materials, parts, fittings, and complete labor cost information. Includes prices for piping, heating, air conditioning, ventilation, and all related construction.

Plus new 2014 unit costs for:

- Thousands of installed HVAC/controls assemblies components
- "On-site" Location Factors for more than 930 cities and towns in the U.S. and Canada
- Crews, labor, and equipment

$191.95 | Available Oct. 2013 | Catalog no. 60024

RSMeans Square Foot Costs 2014
Accurate and Easy-to-Use

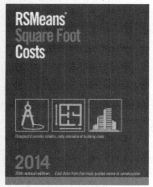

- **Updated price information** based on nationwide figures from suppliers, estimators, labor experts, and contractors
- New green building models
- Realistic graphics, offering true-to-life illustrations of building projects
- Extensive information on using square foot cost data, including sample estimates and alternate pricing methods

$205.95 | Available Oct. 2013 | Catalog no. 60054

RSMeans Green Building Cost Data 2014

Estimate, plan, and budget the costs of green building for both new commercial construction and renovation work with this fourth edition of *RSMeans Green Building Cost Data*. More than 10,000 unit costs for a wide array of green building products plus assemblies costs. Easily identified cross references to LEED and Green Globes building rating systems criteria.

$160.95 | Available Nov. 2013 | Catalog no. 60554

RSMeans Facilities Construction Cost Data 2014

For the maintenance and construction of commercial, industrial, municipal, and institutional properties. Costs are shown for new and remodeling construction and are broken down into materials, labor, equipment, and overhead and profit. Special emphasis is given to sections on mechanical, electrical, furnishings, site work, building maintenance, finish work, and demolition.

More than 49,000 unit costs, plus assemblies costs and a comprehensive Reference Section are included.

$496.95 | Available Nov. 2013 | Catalog no. 60204

RSMeans Commercial Renovation Cost Data 2014
Commercial/Multifamily Residential

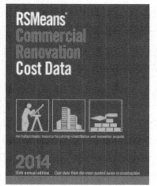

Use this valuable tool to estimate commercial and multifamily residential renovation and remodeling.

Includes: New costs for hundreds of unique methods, materials, and conditions that only come up in repair and remodeling, PLUS:

- Unit costs for more than 19,000 construction components
- Installed costs for more than 2,000 assemblies
- More than 930 "on-site" localization factors for the U.S. and Canada

$156.95 | Available Oct. 2013 | Catalog no. 60044

RSMeans Electrical Cost Data 2014

Pricing information for every part of electrical cost planning. More than 13,000 unit and systems costs with design tables; clear specifications and drawings; engineering guides; illustrated estimating procedures; complete labor-hour and materials costs for better scheduling and procurement; and the latest electrical products and construction methods.

- A variety of special electrical systems, including cathodic protection
- Costs for maintenance, demolition, HVAC/mechanical, specialties, equipment, and more

$196.95 | Available Oct. 2013 | Catalog no. 60034

RSMeans Assemblies Cost Data 2014

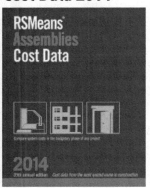

RSMeans Assemblies Cost Data takes the guesswork out of preliminary or conceptual estimates. Now you don't have to try to calculate the assembled cost by working up individual component costs. We've done all the work for you.

Presents detailed illustrations, descriptions, specifications, and costs for every conceivable building assembly—over 350 types in all—arranged in the easy-to-use UNIFORMAT II system. Each illustrated "assembled" cost includes a complete grouping of materials and associated installation costs, including the installing contractor's overhead and profit.

$315.95 | Available Sept. 2013 | Catalog no. 60064

RSMeans Residential Cost Data 2014

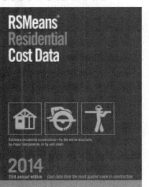

Contains square foot costs for 28 basic home models with the look of today, plus hundreds of custom additions and modifications you can quote right off the page. Includes costs for more than 700 residential systems. Complete with blank estimating forms, sample estimates, and step-by-step instructions.

Contains line items for cultured stone and brick, PVC trim lumber, and TPO roofing.

$139.95 | Available Oct. 2013 | Catalog no. 60174

RSMeans Electrical Change Order Cost Data 2014

RSMeans Electrical Change Order Cost Data provides you with electrical unit prices exclusively for pricing change orders—based on the recent, direct experience of contractors and suppliers. Analyze and check your own change order estimates against the experience others have had doing the same work. It also covers productivity analysis and change order cost justifications. With useful information for calculating the effects of change orders and dealing with their administration.

$187.95 | Available Dec. 2013 | Catalog no. 60234

RSMeans Open Shop Building Construction Cost Data 2014

The latest costs for accurate budgeting and estimating of new commercial and residential construction . . . renovation work . . . change orders . . . cost engineering.

RSMeans Open Shop "BCCD" will assist you to:

- Develop benchmark prices for change orders
- Plug gaps in preliminary estimates and budgets
- Estimate complex projects
- Substantiate invoices on contracts
- Price ADA-related renovations

$165.95 | Available Dec. 2013 | Catalog no. 60154

RSMeans Site Work & Landscape Cost Data 2014

Includes unit and assemblies costs for earthwork, sewerage, piped utilities, site improvements, drainage, paving, trees and shrubs, street openings/repairs, underground tanks, and more. Contains 78 types of assemblies costs for accurate conceptual estimates.

Includes:

- Estimating for infrastructure improvements
- Environmentally-oriented construction
- ADA-mandated handicapped access
- Hazardous waste line items

$187.95 | Available Dec. 2013 | Catalog no. 60284

RSMeans Facilities Maintenance & Repair Cost Data 2014

RSMeans Facilities Maintenance & Repair Cost Data gives you a complete system to manage and plan your facility repair and maintenance costs and budget efficiently. Guidelines for auditing a facility and developing an annual maintenance plan. Budgeting is included, along with reference tables on cost and management, and information on frequency and productivity of maintenance operations.

The only nationally recognized source of maintenance and repair costs. Developed in cooperation with the Civil Engineering Research Laboratory (CERL) of the Army Corps of Engineers.

$434.95 | Available Nov. 2013 | Catalog no. 60304

RSMeans Concrete & Masonry Cost Data 2014

Provides you with cost facts for virtually all concrete/masonry estimating needs, from complicated formwork to various sizes and face finishes of brick and block—all in great detail. The comprehensive Unit Price Section contains more than 8,000 selected entries. Also contains an Assemblies [Cost] Section, and a detailed Reference Section that supplements the cost data.

$177.95 | Available Dec. 2013 | Catalog no. 60114

RSMeans Construction Cost Indexes 2014

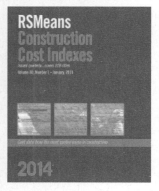

What materials and labor costs will change unexpectedly this year? By how much?

- Breakdowns for 318 major cities
- National averages for 30 key cities
- Expanded five major city indexes
- Historical construction cost indexes

$362.00 per year (subscription) | Catalog no. 50144
$93.50 individual quarters | Catalog no. 60144 A,B,C,D

RSMeans Light Commercial Cost Data 2014

Specifically addresses the light commercial market, which is a specialized niche in the construction industry. Aids you, the owner/designer/contractor, in preparing all types of estimates—from budgets to detailed bids. Includes new advances in methods and materials.

Assemblies Section allows you to evaluate alternatives in the early stages of design/planning.

More than 15,000 unit costs ensure that you have the prices you need . . . when you need them.

$144.95 | Available Nov. 2013 | Catalog no. 60184

RSMeans Labor Rates for the Construction Industry 2014

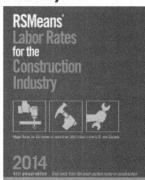

Complete information for estimating labor costs, making comparisons, and negotiating wage rates by trade for more than 300 U.S. and Canadian cities. With 46 construction trades listed by local union number in each city, and historical wage rates included for comparison. Each city chart lists the county and is alphabetically arranged with handy visual flip tabs for quick reference.

$424.95 | Available Dec. 2013 | Catalog no. 60124

RSMeans Interior Cost Data 2014

Provides you with prices and guidance needed to make accurate interior work estimates. Contains costs on materials, equipment, hardware, custom installations, furnishings, and labor costs . . . for new and remodel commercial and industrial interior construction, including updated information on office furnishings, and reference information.

$196.95 | Available Nov. 2013 | Catalog no. 60094

For more information visit the RSMeans website at **www.rsmeans.com**

Unit prices according to the latest MasterFormat!

RSMeans Heavy Construction Cost Data 2014

A comprehensive guide to heavy construction costs. Includes costs for highly specialized projects such as tunnels, dams, highways, airports, and waterways. Information on labor rates, equipment, and materials costs is included. Features unit price costs, systems costs, and numerous reference tables for costs and design.

$192.95 | Available Dec. 2013 | Catalog no. 60164

RSMeans Plumbing Cost Data 2014

Comprehensive unit prices and assemblies for plumbing, irrigation systems, commercial and residential fire protection, point-of-use water heaters, and the latest approved materials. This publication and its companion, *RSMeans Mechanical Cost Data*, provide full-range cost estimating coverage for all the mechanical trades.

Now contains updated costs for potable water and radiant heat systems and high efficiency fixtures.

$194.95 | Available Oct. 2013 | Catalog no. 60214

2014 RSMeans Seminar Schedule

Note: call for exact dates and details.

Location	Dates	Location	Dates
Seattle, WA	January and August	Jacksonville FL	September
Dallas/Ft. Worth, TX	January	Dallas, TX	September
Austin, TX	February	Charleston, SC	October
Anchorage, AK	March and September	Houston, TX	October
Las Vegas, NV	March and October	Atlanta, GA	November
Washington, DC	April and September	Baltimore, MD	November
Phoenix, AZ	April	Orlando, FL	November
Kansas City, MO	April	San Diego, CA	December
Toronto	May	San Antonio, TX	December
Denver, CO	May	Raleigh, NC	December
San Francisco, CA	June		
Bethesda, MD	June		
Columbus, GA	June		
El Segundo, CA	August		

1-800-334-3509, Press 1

Professional Development

For more information visit the RSMeans website at **www.rsmeans.com**

eLearning Training Sessions

Learn how to use *RSMeans Online™* or *RSMeans CostWorks®* CD from the convenience of your home or office. Our eLearning training sessions let you join a training conference call and share the instructors' desktops, so you can view the presentation and step-by-step instructions on your own computer screen. The live webinars are held from 9 a.m. to 4 p.m. eastern standard time, with a one-hour break for lunch.

For these sessions, you must have a computer with high speed Internet access and a compatible Web browser. Learn more at www.rsmeansonline.com or call for a schedule: 1-800-334-3509 and press 1. Webinars are generally held on selected Wednesdays each month.

RSMeans Online™
$299 per person

RSMeans CostWorks® CD
$299 per person

Professional Development

RSMeans Online™ Training

Construction estimating is vital to the decision-making process at each state of every project. RSMeansOnline works the way you do. It's systematic, flexible and intuitive. In this one day class you will see how you can estimate any phase of any project faster and better.

Some of what you'll learn:

- Customizing RSMeansOnline
- Making the most of RSMeans "Circle Reference" numbers
- How to integrate your cost data
- Generate reports, exporting estimates to MS Excel, sharing, collaborating and more

Also available: RSMeans Online™ training webinar

Facilities Construction Estimating

In this *two-day* course, professionals working in facilities management can get help with their daily challenges to establish budgets for all phases of a project.

Some of what you'll learn:

- Determining the full scope of a project
- Identifying the scope of risks and opportunities
- Creative solutions to estimating issues
- Organizing estimates for presentation and discussion
- Special techniques for repair/remodel and maintenance projects
- Negotiating project change orders

Who should attend: facility managers, engineers, contractors, facility tradespeople, planners, and project managers.

Scheduling with Microsoft Project

Two days of hands-on training gives you a look at the basics to putting it all together with MS Project to create a complete project schedule. Learn to work better and faster, manage changes and updates, enhance tracking, generate actionable reports, and boost control of your time and budget.

Some of what you'll learn:

- Defining task/activity relationships: link tasks, establish predecessor/successor relationships and create logs
- Baseline scheduling: the essential what/when
- Using MS Project to determine the critical path
- Integrate RSMeans data with MS Project
- The dollar-loaded schedule: enhance the reliability of this "must-know" technique for scheduling public projects.

Who should attend: contractors' project-management teams, architects and engineers, project owners and their representatives, and those interested in improving their project planning and scheduling and management skills.

Maintenance & Repair Estimating for Facilities

This *two-day* course teaches attendees how to plan, budget, and estimate the cost of ongoing and preventive maintenance and repair for existing buildings and grounds.

Some of what you'll learn:

- The most financially favorable maintenance, repair, and replacement scheduling and estimating
- Auditing and value engineering facilities
- Preventive planning and facilities upgrading
- Determining both in-house and contract-out service costs
- Annual, asset-protecting M&R plan

Who should attend: facility managers, maintenance supervisors, buildings and grounds superintendents, plant managers, planners, estimators, and others involved in facilities planning and budgeting.

Practical Project Management for Construction Professionals

In this *two-day* course, acquire the essential knowledge and develop the skills to effectively and efficiently execute the day-to-day responsibilities of the construction project manager.

Covers:

- General conditions of the construction contract
- Contract modifications: change orders and construction change directives
- Negotiations with subcontractors and vendors
- Effective writing: notification and communications
- Dispute resolution: claims and liens

Who should attend: architects, engineers, owner's representatives, project managers.

Mechanical & Electrical Estimating

This *two-day* course teaches attendees how to prepare more accurate and complete mechanical/electrical estimates, avoiding the pitfalls of omission and double-counting, while understanding the composition and rationale within the RSMeans mechanical/electrical database.

Some of what you'll learn:

- The unique way mechanical and electrical systems are interrelated
- M&E estimates—conceptual, planning, budgeting, and bidding stages
- Order of magnitude, square foot, assemblies, and unit price estimating
- Comparative cost analysis of equipment and design alternatives

Who should attend: architects, engineers, facilities managers, mechanical and electrical contractors, and others who need a highly reliable method for developing, understanding, and evaluating mechanical and electrical contracts.

Unit Price Estimating

This interactive *two-day* seminar teaches attendees how to interpret project information and process it into final, detailed estimates with the greatest accuracy level.

The most important credential an estimator can take to the job is the ability to visualize construction and estimate accurately.

Some of what you'll learn:
- Interpreting the design in terms of cost
- The most detailed, time-tested methodology for accurate pricing
- Key cost drivers—material, labor, equipment, staging, and subcontracts
- Understanding direct and indirect costs for accurate job cost accounting and change order management

Who should attend: corporate and government estimators and purchasers, architects, engineers, and others who need to produce accurate project estimates.

RSMeans CostWorks® CD Training

This one-day course helps users become more familiar with the functionality of *RSMeans CostWork*s program. Each menu, icon, screen, and function found in the program is explained in depth. Time is devoted to hands-on estimating exercises.

Some of what you'll learn:
- Searching the database using all navigation methods
- Exporting RSMeans data to your preferred spreadsheet format
- Viewing crews, assembly components, and much more
- Automatically regionalizing the database

This training session requires you to bring a laptop computer to class.

When you register for this course you will receive an outline for your laptop requirements.

Also offering web training for CostWorks CD!

Facilities Est. Using RSMeans CostWorks® CD

Combines hands-on skill building with best estimating practices and real-life problems. Brings you up-to-date with key concepts, and provides tips, pointers, and guidelines to save time and avoid cost oversights and errors.

Some of what you'll learn:
- Estimating process concepts
- Customizing and adapting RSMeans cost data
- Establishing scope of work to account for all known variables
- Budget estimating: when, why, and how
- Site visits: what to look for—what you can't afford to overlook
- How to estimate repair and remodeling variables

This training session requires you to bring a laptop computer to class.

Who should attend: facility managers, architects, engineers, contractors, facility tradespeople, planners, project managers and anyone involved with JOC, SABRE, or IDIQ.

Conceptual Estimating Using RSMeans CostWorks® CD

This *two day* class uses the leading industry data and a powerful software package to develop highly accurate conceptual estimates for your construction projects. All attendees must bring a laptop computer loaded with the current year *Square Foot Model Costs* and the *Assemblies Cost Data* CostWorks titles.

Some of what you'll learn:
- Introduction to conceptual estimating
- Types of conceptual estimates
- Helpful hints
- Order of magnitude estimating
- Square foot estimating
- Assemblies estimating

Who should attend: architects, engineers, contractors, construction estimators, owner's representatives, and anyone looking for an electronic method for performing square foot estimating.

Assessing Scope of Work for Facility Construction Estimating

This *two-day* practical training program addresses the vital importance of understanding the SCOPE of projects in order to produce accurate cost estimates for facility repair and remodeling.

Some of what you'll learn:
- Discussions of site visits, plans/specs, record drawings of facilities, and site-specific lists
- Review of CSI divisions, including means, methods, materials, and the challenges of scoping each topic
- Exercises in SCOPE identification and SCOPE writing for accurate estimating of projects
- Hands-on exercises that require SCOPE, take-off, and pricing

Who should attend: corporate and government estimators, planners, facility managers, and others who need to produce accurate project estimates.

Unit Price Est. Using RSMeans CostWorks® CD

Step-by-step instruction and practice problems to identify and track key cost drivers—material, labor, equipment, staging, and subcontractors—for each specific task. Learn the most detailed, time-tested methodology for accurately "pricing" these variables, their impact on each other and on total cost.

Some of what you'll learn:
- Unit price cost estimating
- Order of magnitude, square foot, and assemblies estimating
- Quantity takeoff
- Direct and indirect construction costs
- Development of contractor's bill rates
- How to use *RSMeans Building Construction Cost Data*

This training session requires you to bring a laptop computer to class.

Who should attend: architects, engineers, corporate and government estimators, facility managers, and government procurement staff.

Registration Information

Register early . . . Save up to $100! Register 30 days before the start date of a seminar and save $100 off your total fee. *Note: This discount can be applied only once per order. It cannot be applied to team discount registrations or any other special offer.*

How to register Register by phone today! The RSMeans toll-free number for making reservations is **1-800-334-3509, Press 1.**

Two day seminar registration fee - $935. One-day *RSMeans CostWorks*® training registration fee - $375. To register by mail, complete the registration form and return, with your full fee, to: RSMeans Seminars, 700 Longwater Drive, Norwell, MA 02061.

Government pricing All federal government employees save off the regular seminar price. Other promotional discounts cannot be combined with the government discount.

Team discount program for two to four seminar registrations. Call for pricing: 1-800-334-3509, Press 1

Multiple course discounts When signing up for two or more courses, call for pricing.

Refund policy Cancellations will be accepted up to ten business days prior to the seminar start. There are no refunds for cancellations received later than ten working days prior to the first day of the seminar. A $150 processing fee will be applied for all cancellations. Written notice of cancellation is required. Substitutions can be made at any time before the session starts. **No-shows are subject to the full seminar fee.**

AACE approved courses Many seminars described and offered here have been approved for 14 hours (1.4 recertification credits) of credit by the AACE International Certification Board toward meeting the continuing education requirements for recertification as a Certified Cost Engineer/Certified Cost Consultant.

AIA Continuing Education We are registered with the AIA Continuing Education System (AIA/CES) and are committed to developing quality learning activities in accordance with the CES criteria. Many seminars meet the AIA/CES criteria for Quality Level 2. AIA members may receive (14) learning units (LUs) for each two-day RSMeans course.

Daily course schedule The first day of each seminar session begins at 8:30 a.m. and ends at 4:30 p.m. The second day begins at 8:00 a.m. and ends at 4:00 p.m. Participants are urged to bring a hand-held calculator, since many actual problems will be worked out in each session.

Continental breakfast Your registration includes the cost of a continental breakfast, and a morning and afternoon refreshment break. These informal segments allow you to discuss topics of mutual interest with other seminar attendees. (You are free to make your own lunch and dinner arrangements.)

Hotel/transportation arrangements RSMeans arranges to hold a block of rooms at most host hotels. To take advantage of special group rates when making your reservation, be sure to mention that you are attending the RSMeans seminar. You are, of course, free to stay at the lodging place of your choice. **(Hotel reservations and transportation arrangements should be made directly by seminar attendees.)**

Important Class sizes are limited, so please register as soon as possible.

Note: Pricing subject to change.

Registration Form   **ADDS-1000**

Call 1-800-334-3509, Press 1 to register or FAX this form 1-800-632-6732. Visit our website: www.rsmeans.com

Please register the following people for the RSMeans construction seminars as shown here. We understand that we must make our own hotel reservations if overnight stays are necessary.

☐ Full payment of $_____enclosed.

☐ Bill me.

Please print name of registrant(s).

(To appear on certificate of completion)

_____

_____

_____

_____

P.O. #: _____
  GOVERNMENT AGENCIES MUST SUPPLY PURCHASE ORDER NUMBER OR
  TRAINING FORM.

Firm name_____

Address_____

City/State/Zip_____

Telephone no._____ Fax no._____

E-mail address_____

Charge registration(s) to: ☐ MasterCard ☐ VISA ☐ American Express

Account no._____Exp. date_____

Cardholder's signature_____

Seminar name_____

Seminar City _____

Please mail check to: RSMeans Seminars, 700 Longwater Drive, Norwell, MA 02061 USA

Solar Energy: Technologies & Project Delivery for Buildings

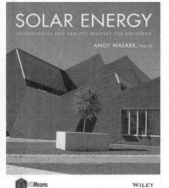

by Andy Walker

An authoritative reference on the design of solar energy systems in building projects, with applications, operating principles, and simple tools for the construction, engineering, and design professionals, the book simplifies the solar design and engineering process and provides sample documentation for the complete design of a solar energy system for buildings.

$85.00 | 320 pages, hardover | Catalog no. 67365

Project Control: Integrating Cost & Schedule in Construction

by Wayne J. Del Pico

Written by a seasoned professional in the field, *Project Control: Integrating Cost and Schedule in Construction* fills a void in the area of project control as applied in the construction industry today. It demonstrates how productivity models for an individual project are created, monitored, and controlled, and how corrective actions are implemented as deviations from the baseline occur.

$95.00 | 240 pages, softcover | Catalog no. 67366

Project Scheduling & Management for Construction, 4th Edition

by David R. Pierce

First published in 1988 by RSMeans, the new edition of *Project Scheduling and Management for Construction* has been substantially revised for both professionals and students enrolled in construction management and civil engineering programs. While retaining its emphasis on developing practical, professional-level scheduling skills, the new edition is a relatable, real world case study.

$95.00 | 272 pages, softcover | Catalog no. 67367

How to Estimate with Means Data & CostWorks, 4th Edition

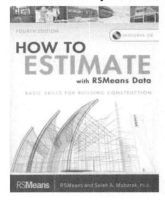

by RSMeans and Saleh A. Mubarak, Ph.D.

This step-by-step guide takes you through all the major construction items with extensive coverage of site work, concrete and masonry, wood and metal framing, doors and windows, and other divisions. The only construction cost estimating handbook that uses the most popular source of construction data, RSMeans, this indispensible guide features access to the instructional version of CostWorks in electronic form, enabling you to practice techniques to solve real-world estimating problems.

$75.00 | 292 pages, softcover | Includes CostWorks CD
Catalog no. 67324C

Estimating Building Costs, 2nd Edition
For the Residential & Light Commercial Construction Professional

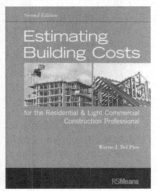

by Wayne J. Del Pico

This book guides readers through the entire estimating process, explaining in detail how to put together a reliable estimate that can be used not only for budgeting, but also for developing a schedule, managing a project, dealing with contingencies, and ultimately making a profit.

Completely revised and updated to reflect the CSI MasterFormat 2010 system, this practical guide describes estimating techniques for each building system and how to apply them according to the latest industry standards.

$75.00 | 398 pages, softcover | Catalog no. 67343A

RSMeans Cost Data, Student Edition

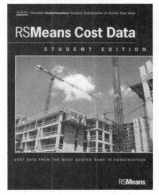

This book provides a thorough introduction to cost estimating in a self-contained print and online package. With clear explanations and a hands-on, example-driven approach, it is the ideal reference for students and new professionals.

Features include:

- Commercial and residential construction cost data in print and online formats
- Complete how-to guidance on the essentials of cost estimating
- A supplemental website with plans, problem sets, and a full sample estimate

$99.00 | 512 pages, softcover | Catalog no. 67363

Value Engineering: Practical Applications

For Design, Construction, Maintenance & Operations

by Alphonse Dell'Isola, PE

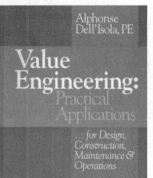

A tool for immediate application—for engineers, architects, facility managers, owners, and contractors. Includes making the case for VE—the management briefing; integrating VE into planning, budgeting, and design; conducting life cycle costing; using VE methodology in design review and consultant selection; case studies; VE workbook; and a life cycle costing program on disk.

$85.00 | Over 450 pages, illustrated, softcover | Catalog no. 67319A

Risk Management for Design & Construction

Introduces risk as a central pillar of project management and shows how a project manager can prepare to deal with uncertainty. Experts in the field use clear, straightforward terminology to demystify the concepts of project uncertainty and risk. Includes:

- Integrated cost and schedule risk analysis
- An introduction to a ready-to-use system of analyzing a project's risks and tools to proactively manage risks
- A methodology that was developed and used by the Washington State Department of Transportation

- Case studies and examples on the proper application of principles
- Information about combining value analysis with risk analysis

$125.00 | Over 250 pages, softcover | Catalog no. 67359

How Your House Works, 2nd Edition

by Charlie Wing

Knowledge of your home's systems helps you control repair and construction costs and makes sure the correct elements are being installed or replaced. This book uncovers the mysteries behind just about every major appliance and building element in your house. See-through, cross-section drawings in full color show you exactly how these things should be put together and how they function, including what to check if they don't work. It just might save you having to call in a professional.

$22.95 | 192 pages, softcover | Catalog no. 67351A

Complete Book of Framing, 2nd Edition

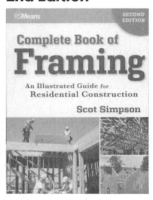

by Scot Simpson

This updated, easy-to-learn guide to rough carpentry and framing is written by an expert with more than thirty years of framing experience. Starting with the basics, this book begins with types of lumber, nails, and what tools are needed, followed by detailed, fully illustrated steps for framing each building element. Framer-Friendly Tips throughout the book show how to get a task done right—and more easily.

$29.95 | 352 pages, softcover | Catalog no. 67353A

Green Home Improvement

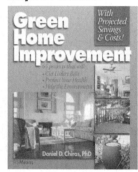

by Daniel D. Chiras, PhD

With energy costs rising and environmental awareness increasing, people are looking to make their homes greener. This book, with 65 projects and actual costs and projected savings help homeowners prioritize their green improvements.

Projects range from simple water savers that cost only a few dollars, to bigger-ticket items such as HVAC systems. With color photos and cost estimates, each project compares options and describes the work involved, the benefits, and the savings.

$34.95 | 320 pages, illustrated, softcover | Catalog no. 67355

Life Cycle Costing for Facilities

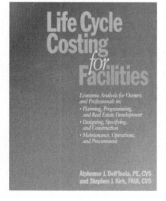

by Alphonse Dell'Isola and Dr. Steven Kirk

Guidance for achieving higher quality design and construction projects at lower costs! Cost-cutting efforts often sacrifice quality to yield the cheapest product. Life cycle costing enables building designers and owners to achieve both. The authors of this book show how LCC can work for a variety of projects — from roads to HVAC upgrades to different types of buildings.

$99.95 | 396 pages, hardcover | Catalog no. 67341

Builder's Essentials: Plan Reading & Material Takeoff
For Residential and Light Commercial Construction

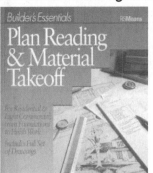

by Wayne J. DelPico

A valuable tool for understanding plans and specs, and accurately calculating material quantities. Step-by-step instructions and takeoff procedures based on a full set of working drawings.

$45.00 | Over 420 pages, softcover | Catalog no. 67307

Concrete Repair & Maintenance Illustrated

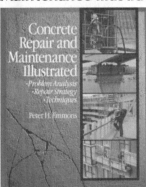

by Peter Emmons

Hundreds of illustrations show users how to analyze, repair, clean, and maintain concrete structures for optimal performance and cost effectiveness. From parking garages to roads and bridges to structural concrete, this comprehensive book describes the causes, effects, and remedies for concrete wear and failure. Invaluable for planning jobs, selecting materials, and training employees, this book is a must-have for concrete specialists, general contractors, facility managers, civil and structural engineers, and architects.

$75.00 | 300 pages, illustrated, softcover | Catalog no. 67146

Electrical Estimating Methods, 3rd Edition

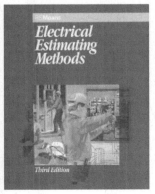

Expanded edition includes sample estimates and cost information in keeping with the latest version of the CSI MasterFormat and UNIFORMAT II. Complete coverage of fiber optic and uninterruptible power supply electrical systems, broken down by components, and explained in detail. Includes a new chapter on computerized estimating methods. A practical companion to *RSMeans Electrical Cost Data.*

$75.00 | Over 325 pages, hardcover | Catalog no. 67230B

Means Unit Price Estimating Methods, 4th Edition

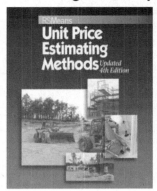

Includes cost data and estimating examples, updated to reflect changes to the CSI numbering system and new features of RSMeans cost data. It describes the most productive, universally accepted ways to estimate, and uses checklists and forms to illustrate shortcuts and timesavers. A model estimate demonstrates procedures. A new chapter explores computer estimating alternatives.

$75.00 | Over 350 pages, illustrated, softcover | Catalog no. 67303B

Square Foot & UNIFORMAT Assemblies Estimating Methods, 3rd Edition

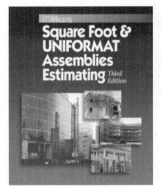

Develop realistic square foot and assemblies costs for budgeting and construction funding. The new edition features updated guidance on square foot and assemblies estimating using UNIFORMAT II. An essential reference for anyone who performs conceptual estimates.

$75.00 | Over 300 pages, illustrated, softcover | Catalog no. 67145B

Residential & Light Commercial Construction Standards, 3rd Edition

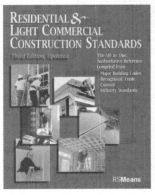

Updated by RSMeans and contributing authors

This book provides authoritative requirements and recommendations compiled from leading professional associations, industry publications, and building code organizations. This all-in-one reference helps establish a standard for workmanship, quickly resolve disputes, and avoid defect claims. Updated third edition includes new coverage of green building, seismic, hurricane, and mold-resistant construction.

$65.00 | Over 550 pages, illustrated, softcover | Catalog no. 67322B

Construction Business Management

by Nick Ganaway

Only 43% of construction firms stay in business after four years. Make sure your company thrives with valuable guidance from a pro with 25 years of success as a commercial contractor. Find out what it takes to build all aspects of a business that is profitable, enjoyable, and enduring. With a bonus chapter on retail construction.

$55.00 | 200 pages, softcover | Catalog no. 67352

Project Scheduling & Management for Construction, 3rd Edition

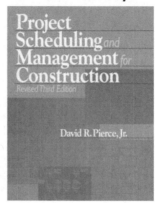

by David R. Pierce, Jr.

A comprehensive yet easy-to-follow guide to construction project scheduling and control—from vital project management principles through the latest scheduling, tracking, and controlling techniques. The author is a leading authority on scheduling, with years of field and teaching experience at leading academic institutions. Spend a few hours with this book and come away with a solid understanding of this essential management topic.

$64.95 | Over 300 pages, illustrated, hardcover | Catalog no. 67247B

The Practice of Cost Segregation Analysis

by Bruce A. Desrosiers and Wayne J. DelPico

This expert guide walks you through the practice of cost segregation analysis, which enables property owners to defer taxes and benefit from "accelerated cost recovery" through depreciation deductions on assets that are properly identified and classified.

With a glossary of terms, sample cost segregation estimates for various building types, key information resources, and updates via a dedicated website, this book is a critical resource for anyone involved in cost segregation analysis.

$105.00 | Over 225 pages | Catalog no. 67345

Preventive Maintenance for Multi-Family Housing

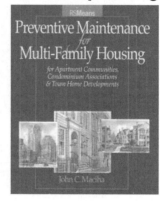

by John C. Maciha

Prepared by one of the nation's leading experts on multi-family housing.

This complete PM system for apartment and condominium communities features expert guidance, checklists for buildings and grounds maintenance tasks and their frequencies, a reusable wall chart to track maintenance, and a dedicated website featuring customizable electronic forms. A must-have for anyone involved with multi-family housing maintenance and upkeep.

$95.00 | 225 pages | Catalog no. 67346

Green Building: Project Planning & Cost Estimating, 3rd Edition

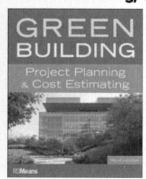

Since the widely read first edition of this book, green building has gone from a growing trend to a major force in design and construction.

This new edition has been updated with the latest in green building technologies, design concepts, standards, and costs. Full-color with all new case studies—plus a new chapter on commercial real estate.

$110.00 | Over 450 pages, softcover | Catalog no. 67338B

Job Order Contracting: Expediting Construction Project Delivery

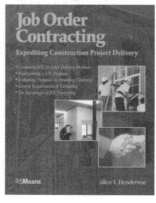

by Allen L. Henderson

Expert guidance to help you implement JOC—fast becoming the preferred project delivery method for repair and renovation, minor new construction, and maintenance projects in the public sector and in many states and municipalities. The author, a leading JOC expert and practitioner, shows how to:

- Establish a JOC program
- Evaluate proposals & award contracts
- Handle general requirements and estimating
- Partner for maximum benefits

$89.95 | 192 pages, illustrated, hardcover | Catalog no. 67348

Construction Supervision

This brand new title inspires supervisory excellence with proven tactics and techniques applied by thousands of construction supervisors over the past decade. Recognizing the unique and critical role the supervisor plays in project success, the book's leadership guidelines carve out a practical blueprint for motivating work performance and increasing productivity through effective communication.

Features:

- A unique focus on field supervision and crew management
- Coverage of supervision from the foreman to the superintendent level
- An overview of technical skills whose mastery will build confidence and success for the supervisor
- A detailed view of "soft" management and communication skills

$95.00 | Over 450 pages, softcover | Catalog no. 67358

The Homeowner's Guide to Mold

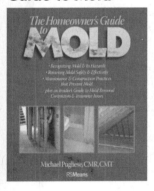

By Michael Pugliese

Expert guidance to protect your health and your home.

Mold, whether caused by leaks, humidity or flooding, is a real health and financial issue—for homeowners and contractors.

This full-color book explains:

- Construction and maintenance practices to prevent mold
- How to inspect for and remove mold
- Mold remediation procedures and costs
- What to do after a flood
- How to deal with insurance companies

$21.95 | 144 pages, softcover | Catalog no. 67344

Landscape Estimating Methods, 5th Edition

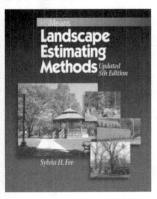

Answers questions about preparing competitive landscape construction estimates, with up-to-date cost estimates and the new MasterFormat classification system. Expanded and revised to address the latest materials and methods, including new coverage on approaches to green building. Includes:

- Step-by-step explanation of the estimating process
- Sample forms and worksheets that save time and prevent errors

$75.00 | Over 350 pages, softcover | Catalog no. 67295C

Building & Renovating Schools

This all-inclusive guide covers every step of the school construction process—from initial planning, needs assessment, and design, right through moving into the new facility. A must-have resource for anyone concerned with new school construction or renovation. With square foot cost models for elementary, middle, and high school facilities, and real-life case studies of recently completed school projects.

The contributors to this book—architects, construction project managers, contractors, and estimators who specialize in school construction—provide start-to-finish, expert guidance on the process.

$99.95 | Over 425 pages, hardcover | Catalog no. 67342

Universal Design Ideas for Style, Comfort & Safety

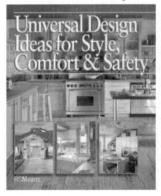

by RSMeans and Lexicon Consulting, Inc.

Incorporating universal design when building or remodeling helps people of any age and physical ability more fully and safely enjoy their living spaces. This book shows how universal design can be artfully blended into the most attractive homes. It discusses specialized products like adjustable countertops and chair lifts, as well as simple ways to enhance a home's safety and comfort. With color photos and expert guidance, every area of the home is covered. Includes budget estimates that give an idea how much projects will cost.

$21.95 | 160 pages, illustrated, softcover | Catalog no. 67354

Plumbing Estimating Methods, 3rd Edition

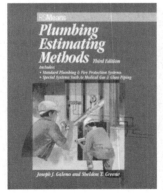

by Joseph J. Galeno and Sheldon T. Greene

Updated and revised! This practical guide walks you through a plumbing estimate, from basic materials and installation methods through change order analysis. *Plumbing Estimating Methods* covers residential, commercial, industrial, and medical systems, and features sample takeoff and estimate forms and detailed illustrations of systems and components.

$65.00 | 330+ pages, softcover | Catalog no. 67283B

Understanding & Negotiating Construction Contracts

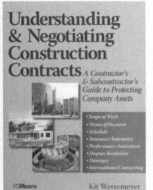

by Kit Werremeyer

Take advantage of the author's 30 years' experience in small-to-large (including international) construction projects. Learn how to identify, understand, and evaluate high risk terms and conditions typically found in all construction contracts—then negotiate to lower or eliminate the risk, improve terms of payment, and reduce exposure to claims and disputes. The author avoids "legalese" and gives real-life examples from actual projects.

$80.00 | 300 pages, softcover | Catalog no. 67350

The Gypsum Construction Handbook

by USG

An invaluable reference of construction procedures for gypsum drywall, cement board, veneer plaster, and conventional plaster. This new edition includes the newest product developments, installation methods, fire- and sound-rated construction information, illustrated framing-to-finish application instructions, estimating and planning information, and more. Great for architects and engineers; contractors, builders, and dealers; apprentices and training programs; building inspectors and code officials; and anyone interested in gypsum construction. Features information on tools and safety practices, a glossary of construction terms, and a list of important agencies and associations. Also available in Spanish.

$40.00 | Over 575 pages, illustrated, softcover | Catalog no. 67357A

Mechanical Estimating Methods, 4th Edition

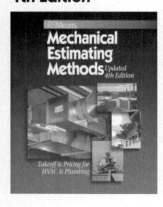

Completely updated, this guide assists you in making a review of plans, specs, and bid packages, with suggestions for takeoff procedures, listings, substitutions, and pre-bid scheduling for all components of HVAC. Includes suggestions for budgeting labor and equipment usage. Compares materials and construction methods to allow you to select the best option.

$70.00 per copy | Over 350 pages, illustrated, softcover | Catalog no. 67294B

Means Illustrated Construction Dictionary

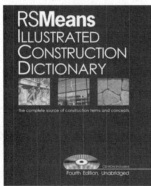

Unabridged 4th Edition, with CD-ROM

Long regarded as the industry's finest, *Means Illustrated Construction Dictionary* is now even better. With nearly 20,000 terms and more than 1,400 illustrations and photos, it is the clear choice for the most comprehensive and current information. The companion CD-ROM that comes with this new edition adds extra features such as: larger graphics and expanded definitions.

$99.95 | Over 790 pages, illust., hardcover | Catalog no. 67292B

RSMeans Estimating Handbook, 3rd Edition

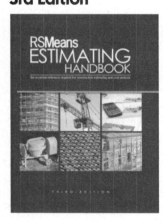

Widely used in the industry for tasks ranging from routine estimates to special cost analysis projects, this handbook has been completely updated and reorganized with new and expanded technical information.

RSMeans Estimating Handbook will help construction professionals:

- Evaluate architectural plans and specifications
- Prepare accurate quantity takeoffs
- Compare design alternatives and costs
- Perform value engineering
- Double-check estimates and quotes
- Estimate change orders

$110.00 | Over 900 pages, hardcover | Catalog No. 67276B

Qty.	Book no.	COST ESTIMATING BOOKS	Unit Price	Total	Qty.	Book no.	REFERENCE BOOKS (Cont.)	Unit Price	Total
	60064	Assemblies Cost Data 2014	$315.95			67344	Homeowner's Guide to Mold	21.95	
	60014	Building Construction Cost Data 2014	194.95			67324C	How to Est.w/Means Data & CostWorks, 4th Ed.	75.00	
	60044	Commercial Renovaion Cost Data 2014	156.95			67351A	How Your House Works, 2nd Ed.	22.95	
	60114	Concrete & Masonry Cost Data 2014	177.95			67282A	Illustrated Const. Dictionary, Condensed, 2nd Ed.	65.00	
	50144	Construction Cost Indexes 2014 (subscription)	362.00			67292B	Illustrated Const. Dictionary, w/CD-ROM, 4th Ed.	99.95	
	60144A	Construction Cost Index–January 2014	93.50			67362	Illustrated Const. Dictionary, Student Ed.	55.00	
	60144B	Construction Cost Index–April 2014	93.50			67348	Job Order Contracting	89.95	
	60144C	Construction Cost Index–July 2014	93.50			67295C	Landscape Estimating Methods, 5th Ed.	75.00	
	60144D	Construction Cost Index–October 2014	93.50			67341	Life Cycle Costing for Facilities	99.95	
	60344	Contr. Pricing Guide: Resid. R & R Costs 2014	39.95			67294B	Mechanical Estimating Methods, 4th Ed.	70.00	
	60234	Electrical Change Order Cost Data 2014	187.95			67283B	Plumbing Estimating Methods, 3rd Ed.	65.00	
	60034	Electrical Cost Data 2014	196.95			67345	Practice of Cost Segregation Analysis	105.00	
	60204	Facilities Construction Cost Data 2014	496.95			67366	Project Control: Integrating Cost & Sched.	95.00	
	60304	Facilities Maintenance & Repair Cost Data 2014	434.95			67346	Preventive Maint. for Multi-Family Housing	95.00	
	60554	Green Building Cost Data 2014	160.95			67367	Project Scheduling & Manag. for Constr., 4th Ed.	95.00	
	60164	Heavy Construction Cost Data 2014	192.95			67322B	Resi. & Light Commercial Const. Stds., 3rd Ed.	65.00	
	60094	Interior Cost Data 2014	196.95			67359	Risk Management for Design & Construction	125.00	
	60124	Labor Rates for the Const. Industry 2014	424.95			67365	Solar Energy: Technology & Project Delivery	85.00	
	60184	Light Commercial Cost Data 2014	144.95			67145B	Sq. Ft. & Assem. Estimating Methods, 3rd Ed.	75.00	
	60024	Mechanical Cost Data 2014	191.95			67321	Total Productive Facilities Management	85.00	
	60154	Open Shop Building Const. Cost Data 2014	165.95			67350	Understanding and Negotiating Const. Contracts	80.00	
	60214	Plumbing Cost Data 2014	194.95			67303B	Unit Price Estimating Methods, 4th Ed.	75.00	
	60174	Residential Cost Data 2014	139.95			67354	Universal Design	21.95	
	60284	Site Work & Landscape Cost Data 2014	187.95			67319A	Value Engineering: Practical Applications	85.00	
	60054	Square Foot Costs 2014	205.95						
	62013	Yardsticks for Costing (2013)	185.95						
	62014	Yardsticks for Costing (2014)	189.95						
		REFERENCE BOOKS							
	67329	Bldrs Essentials: Best Bus. Practices for Bldrs	40.00						
	67307	Bldrs Essentials: Plan Reading & Takeoff	35.95						
	67342	Building & Renovating Schools	99.95						
	67261A	The Building Prof. Guide to Contract Documents	75.00						
	67339	Building Security: Strategies & Costs	95.00						
	67353A	Complete Book of Framing, 2nd Ed.	29.95						
	67146	Concrete Repair & Maintenance Illustrated	75.00						
	67352	Construction Business Management	55.00						
	67364	Construction Law	110.00						
	67358	Construction Supervision	95.00						
	67363	Cost Data Student Edition	99.00						
	67314	Cost Planning & Est. for Facil. Maint.	95.00						
	67230B	Electrical Estimating Methods, 3rd Ed.	75.00						
	67343A	Est. Bldg. Costs for Resi. & Lt. Comm., 2nd Ed.	75.00						
	67276B	Estimating Handbook, 3rd Ed.	110.00						
	67318	Facilities Operations & Engineering Reference	115.00						
	67301	Facilities Planning & Relocation	89.95						
	67338B	Green Building: Proj. Planning & Cost Est., 3rd Ed.	110.00						
	67355	Green Home Improvement	34.95						
	67357A	The Gypsum Construction Handbook	40.00						
	67148	Heavy Construction Handbook	110.00						
	67308E	Home Improvement Costs–Int. Projects, 9th Ed.	24.95						
	67309E	Home Improvement Costs–Ext. Projects, 9th Ed.	24.95						

MA residents add 6.25% state sales tax

Shipping & Handling**

Total (U.S. Funds)*

Prices are subject to change and are for U.S. delivery only. *Canadian customers may call for current prices. **Shipping & handling charges: Add 7% of total order for check and credit card payments. Add 9% of total order for invoiced orders.

Send order to: ADDV-1000

Name (please print) _____

Company _____

☐ Company

☐ Home Address _____

_____

City/State/Zip _____

Phone # _____ P.O. # _____

(Must accompany all orders being billed)

RSMeans Project Cost Report

By filling out this report, your project data will contribute to the database that supports the RSMeans® Project Cost Square Foot Data. When you fill out this form, RSMeans will provide a $50 discount off one of the RSMeans products advertised in the preceding pages. Please complete the form including all items where you have cost data, and all the items marked (☑).

$50.00 Discount per product for each report you submit

Project Description (NEW construction only, please)

☑ Building Use (Office School . . .) _____

☑ Address (City, State)_____

_____

☑ Total Building Area (SF) _____

☑ Ground Floor (SF) _____

☑ Frame (Wood, Steel . . .) _____

☑ Exterior Wall (Brick, Tilt-up . . .) _____

☑ Basement: (check one) ☐ Full ☐ Partial ☐ None

☑ Number of Stories _____

☑ Floor-to-Floor Height_____

☑ Volume (C.F.) _____

% Air Conditioned _____ Tons_____

Total Project Cost $ _____

Owner _____

Architect_____

General Contractor _____

☑ Bid Date _____

☑ Typical Bay Size _____

☑ Occupant Capacity_____

☑ Labor Force: ____ % Union ____ % Non-Union

☑ Project Description (Circle one number in each line.)

  1. Economy 2. Average 3. Custom 4. Luxury

  1. Square 2. Rectangular 3. Irregular 4. Very Irregular

Comments _____

_____

A	☑	General Conditions	$
B	☑	Site Work	$
C	☑	Concrete	$
D	☑	Masonry	$
E	☑	Metals	$
F	☑	Wood & Plastics	$
G	☑	Thermal &Moisture Protection	$
GR		Roofing & Flashing	$
H	☑	Doors and Windows	$
J	☑	Finishes	$
JP		Painting & Wall Covering	$

K	☑	Specialties	$
L	☑	Equipment	$
M	☑	Furnishings	$
N	☑	SpecialConstruction	$
P	☑	ConveyingSystems	$
Q	☑	Mechanical	$
QP		Plumbing	$
QB		HVAC	$
R	☑	Electrical	$
S	☑	Mech./Elec. Combined	$

Please specify the RSMeans product you wish to receive. Complete the address information.

Product Name _____

Product Number _____

Your Name _____

Title _____

Company_____

 ☐ Company

 ☐ Home Street Address_____

City, State, Zip _____

Email Address _____

Return by mail or fax 888-492-6770.

Method of Payment:

Credit Card # _____

Expiration Date _____

Check_____

Purchase Order _____

Phone Number _____
(if you would prefer a sales call)

RSMeans
a division of Reed Construction Data
Square Foot Costs Department
700 Longwater Drive
Norwell, MA 02061
www.RSMeans.com